Sullivan's Guide to Putting It Together

P9-ECR-898

Putting It Together Sections	Objective	Page(s)
5.6 Putting It Together: Which Method Do I Use?	Determine the appropriate probability rule to use	315–317
	Determine the appropriate counting technique to use	317–319
9.5 Putting It Together: Which Method Do I Use?	Determine the appropriate confidence interval to construct	503–504
10.6 Putting It Together: Which Method Do I Use?	Determine the appropriate hypothesis test to perform (one sample)	567
11.5 Putting It Together: Which Method Do I Use?	Determine the appropriate hypothesis test to perform (two samples)	632

Putting It Together Exercises	Skills Utilized	Section(s) Covered	Page(s)
1.2.23 Passive Smoke	Variables, observational studies, designed experiments	1.1, 1.2	22
1.4.37 Comparing Sampling Methods	Simple random sampling and other sampling techniques	1.3, 1.4	38
1.4.38 Thinking about Randomness	Random sampling	1.3, 1.4	38
1.5.43 Speed Limit	Population, variables, level of measurement, sampling, bias	1.1–1.5	45
1.6.37 Mosquito Control	Population, variables, design of experiments	1.1, 1.6	57–58
2.1.32 Online Homework	Variables, designed experiments, bar graphs	1.1, 1.2, 1.6, 2.1	79–80
2.2.51 Time Viewing a Webpage	Graphing data	2.2	100
2.3.27 Shark!	Graphing data	2.3	109
3.1.47 Shape, Mean, and Median	Discrete vs. continuous data, histograms, shape of a distribution, mean, median, mode, bias	1.1, 1.4, 2.2, 3.1	142
3.5.17 Paternal Smoking	Observational studies, designed experiments, lurking variables, mean, median, standard deviation, quartiles, boxplots	1.2, 1.6, 3.1, 3.2, 3.4, 3.5	183
4.2.31 Housing Prices	Scatter diagrams, correlation, linear regression	4.1, 4.2	222
4.2.32 Smoking and Birth Weight	Observational study vs. designed experiment, prospective studies, scatter diagrams, linear regression, correlation vs. causation, lurking variables	1.2, 4.1, 4.2	222–223
4.3.37 Building a Financial Model	Scatter diagrams, correlation, linear regression, residual analysis	4.1, 4.2, 4.3	236–237
5.1.58 Drug Side Effects	Variables, graphical summaries of data, experiments, probability	1.1, 1.6, 2.1, 5.1	273
5.2.47 Red Light Cameras	Variables, relative frequency distributions, bar graphs, mean, standard deviation, probability, Simpson's Paradox	1.1, 2.1, 3.1, 3.2, 4.4, 5.1, 5.2	285
7.3.30 Birth Weights	Relative frequency distribution, histograms, mean and standard deviation from grouped data, normal probabilities	2.1, 2.2, 3.3, 7.3	403–404
8.1.39 Playing Roulette	Probability distributions, mean and standard deviation of a random variable, sampling distributions	6.1, 8.1	442
9.1.59 Smoking Cessation Study	Experimental design, confidence intervals	1.6, 9.1	474–475
9.3.36 Hand Washing	Observational studies, bias, confidence intervals	1.2, 1.5, 9.3	495–496
10.2.40 Analyzing a Study	Statistical process, confidence intervals, hypothesis testing, Case-control studies	1.1, 1.2, 9.1, 10.1, 10.2	539–540
10.4.27 Lupus	Observational studies, retrospective vs. prospective studies, bar graphs, confidence intervals, hypothesis testing	1.2, 2.1, 9.3, 10.4	560
10.6.23 Ideal Number of Children	Relative frequency histogram, mode, mean, standard deviation, Central Limit Theorem, hypothesis testing	2.2, 3.1, 3.2, 8.1, 10.3	569
11.1.24 Glide Testing	Matched-pairs design, hypothesis testing	1.6, 11.1	594
11.2.23 Online Homework	Completely randomized design, confounding, hypothesis testing	1.6, 11.2	606
11.3.33 Salk Vaccine	Completely randomized design, hypothesis testing	1.6, 11.3	621
12.1.29 The V-2 Rocket in London	Mean of discrete data; expected value; Poisson probability distribution; goodness-of-fit	6.1, 6.3, 12.1	655

Putting It Together Exercises	Skills Utilized	Section(s) Covered	Page(s)
12.2.19 Women, Aspirin, and Heart Attacks	Population; sample; variables; observational study vs. designed experiment; experimental design; compare two proportions; chi-square test of homogeneity	1.1, 1.2, 1.6, 11.3, 12.2	670
13.1.23 Psychological Profiles	Standard deviation; sampling methods; Two-sample t-test; Central Limit Theorem; One-way Analysis of Variance	1.4, 3.2, 8.1, 11.2, 13.1	693
13.2.19 Time to Complete a Degree	Observational studies; sample mean; sample standard deviation; Confidence intervals for a mean; One-way Analysis of Variance; Tukey's test	1.2, 3.1, 3.2, 9.2, 13.1, 13.2	702
13.4.22 Students at Ease	Population; Designed experiments versus observational studies, Variables; sample means; sample standard deviation; Two sample t-tests; One-way ANOVA, Interaction effects; Non-sampling error	1.1, 1.2, 3.1, 3.2, 11.2, 13.1, 13.4	727
14.2.17 Plasma Television Prices	Scatter diagrams; correlation coefficient; linear relations; least-squares regression; residual analysis; confidence and prediction intervals; lurking variables	4.1, 4.2, 4.3, 14.1, 14.2	757–758
14.3.26 Purchasing Diamonds	Level of measurement; correlation matrix; multiple regression; confidence and prediction intervals	1.1, 14.3	779–780

Applet ▲	Section	Activity/Problem
Sample from a population	1.3	Use this applet to help students visualize how samples are obtained from populations. Can also be used to show variability from sampling.
Mean versus median	3.1	Problems 19, 20
Standard deviation	3.2	Use this applet to help students visualize this measure of spread
Correlation by eye	4.1	Problems 44–46
Regression by eye	4.2	Problem 30
Regression by eye	4.3	Problem 36
Simulating the probability of flipping a head with a fair coin	5.1	Problem 57(a)–(d)
Simulating the probability of flipping a head with an unfair coin	5.1	Problem 57(e)
Binomial distribution	6.2	Problem 54
Sampling distributions	8.1	Problems 36–38
	8.2	Problem 25
Confidence intervals for a mean (the impact of confidence level)	9.1	Problems 56–58
Confidence intervals for a mean (the impact of not knowing the standard deviation)	9.2	Problem 33
Confidence intervals for a proportion	9.3	Problems 34 and 35
Hypothesis tests for a mean	10.2	Use this applet to illustrate the concepts of a hypothesis test, P-values, and the consequences of not meeting model requirements
Hypothesis tests for a proportion	10.4	Use this applet to illustrate the concepts of a hypothesis test, P-values, and the consequences of not meeting model requirements

STATISTICS
Informed Decisions Using Data
Third Edition

Michael Sullivan, III

Joliet Junior College

Prentice Hall
is an imprint of

Upper Saddle River, New Jersey 07458

Editor in Chief, Mathematics and Statistics: Deirdre Lynch
Acquisitions Editor: Christopher Cummings
Senior Project Editor: Joanne Dill
Assistant Editor: Christina Lepre
Editorial Assistant: Dana Jones
Production Management: Bob Walters, Prepress Management, Inc.
Project Manager: Barbara Mack
Senior Managing Editor: Linda Mihatov Behrens
Senior Operations Supervisor: Diane Peirano
Marketing Manager: Alex Gay
Marketing Assistant: Kathleen DeChavez
Art Director: Heather Scott
Interior Designer: Michael Fruhbeis/Fruhbilicious Design

AV Project Manager: Thomas Benfatti
Executive Manager, Course Production: Peter Silvia
Media Producers: Audra Walsh and Richard Bretan
Associate Producer: Jean Choe
MyStatLab Project Supervisor: Edward Chappell
QA Manager: Marty Wright
Photo Research Development Manager: Elaine Soares
Photo Researcher: Rachel Lucas
Image Permissions Coordinator: Joanne Dippel
Manager, Cover Visual Research and Permissions: Karen Sanatar
Cover Image: Cloki/Shutterstock
Compositor: Macmillan Publishing Solutions
Art Studio: Precision Graphics

Prentice Hall
is an imprint of

© 2010, 2007, 2004 Pearson Education, Inc.
Pearson Prentice Hall
Pearson Education, Inc.
Upper Saddle River, New Jersey 07458

Printed in the United States of America.
10 9 8 7 6 5 4 3 2 1

ISBN-13: 978-0-321-57527-2 (Annotated Instructor's Edition)
ISBN-10: 0-321-57527-X

ISBN-13: 978-0-321-56802-1 (Student Edition)
ISBN-10: 0-321-56802-8

Pearson Education Ltd., *London*
Pearson Education Singapore, Pte. Ltd.
Pearson Education Canada, Inc.
Pearson Education—*Japan*
Pearson Education Australia PTY, Limited
Pearson Education North Asia, Ltd., *Hong Kong*
Pearson Educación de Mexico, S.A. de C.V.
Pearson Education Malaysia, Pte. Ltd.
Pearson Education *Upper Saddle River, New Jersey*

To My Wife Yolanda

and

My Children
Michael, Kevin, and Marissa

Contents

Preface to the Instructor   x
Supplements   xv
Technology Resources   xvi
An Introduction to the Applets   xvii
Applications Index   xix

Part 1: Getting the Information You Need   1

Chapter 1 Data Collection   2

1.1 Introduction to the Practice of Statistics   3
1.2 Observational Studies versus Designed Experiments   15
1.3 Simple Random Sampling   22
1.4 Other Effective Sampling Methods   30
1.5 Bias in Sampling   38
1.6 The Design of Experiments   45
Chapter 1 Review   *58*
Chapter Test   *61*
Making an Informed Decision: What Movie Should I Go To?   *62*
Case Study: Chrysalises for Cash   *63*

Part 2: Descriptive Statistics   65

Chapter 2 Organizing and Summarizing Data   66

2.1 Organizing Qualitative Data   67
2.2 Organizing Quantitative Data: The Popular Displays   82
2.3 Additional Displays of Quantitative Data   102
2.4 Graphical Misrepresentations of Data   110
Chapter 2 Review   *119*
Chapter Test   *123*
Making an Informed Decision: Tables or Graphs?   *125*
Case Study: The Day the Sky Roared   *126*

Chapter 3 Numerically Summarizing Data   128

3.1 Measures of Central Tendency   129
3.2 Measures of Dispersion   143
3.3 Measures of Central Tendency and Dispersion
     from Grouped Data   160
3.4 Measures of Position and Outliers   167
3.5 The Five-Number Summary and Boxplots   175
Chapter 3 Review   *184*
Chapter Test   *187*
Making an Informed Decision: What Car Should I Buy?   *189*
Case Study: Who Was "A Mourner"?   *190*

Chapter 4 **Describing the Relation between Two Variables 192**

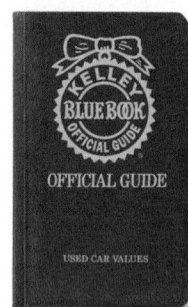

4.1   Scatter Diagrams and Correlation   193
4.2   Least-Squares Regression   209
4.3   Diagnostics on the Least-Squares Regression Line   223
4.4   Contingency Tables and Association   238
4.5   Nonlinear Regression: Transformations (on CD)   4–1
        Chapter 4 Review   *248*
        Chapter Test   *253*
        Making an Informed Decision: What Car Should I Buy?   *254*
        Case Study: Thomas Malthus, Population, and Subsistence   *255*

Part 3: Probability and Probability Distributions   257

Chapter 5 **Probability 258**

5.1   Probability Rules   259
5.2   The Addition Rule and Complements   274
5.3   Independence and the Multiplication Rule   286
5.4   Conditional Probability and the General Multiplication Rule   292
5.5   Counting Techniques   302
5.6   Putting It Together: Which Method Do I Use?   315
5.7   Bayes's Rule (on CD)   5–1
        Chapter 5 Review   *321*
        Chapter Test   *324*
        Making an Informed Decision: Sports Probabilities   *326*
        Case Study: The Case of the Body in the Bag   *327*

Chapter 6 **Discrete Probability Distributions 330**

6.1   Discrete Random Variables   331
6.2   The Binomial Probability Distribution   343
6.3   The Poisson Probability Distribution   358
6.4   The Hypergeometric Probability Distribution (on CD)   6–1
        Chapter 6 Review   *365*
        Chapter Test   *368*
        Making an Informed Decision: Should We Convict?   *369*
        Case Study: The Voyage of the *St. Andrew*   *370*

Chapter 7 **The Normal Probability Distribution 372**

7.1   Properties of the Normal Distribution   373
7.2   The Standard Normal Distribution   385
7.3   Applications of the Normal Distribution   397
7.4   Assessing Normality   405
7.5   The Normal Approximation to the Binomial Probability Distribution   412

Chapter 7 Review   *417*

Chapter Test   *420*

Making an Informed Decision: Join the Club   *421*

Case Study: A Tale of Blood Chemistry and Health   *421*

Part 4: Inference: From Samples to Population   425

Chapter 8   Sampling Distributions   426

8.1   Distribution of the Sample Mean   427

8.2   Distribution of the Sample Proportion   442

Chapter 8 Review   *451*

Chapter Test   *452*

Making an Informed Decision: How Much Time Do You Spend in a Day . . .?   *453*

Case Study: Sampling Distribution of the Median   *454*

Chapter 9   Estimating the Value of a Parameter Using Confidence Intervals   456

9.1   The Logic in Constructing Confidence Intervals for a Population Mean When the Population Standard Deviation Is Known   457

9.2   Confidence Intervals for a Population Mean When the Population Standard Deviation Is Unknown   475

9.3   Confidence Intervals for a Population Proportion   488

9.4   Confidence Intervals for a Population Standard Deviation   496

9.5   Putting It Together: Which Procedure Do I Use?   503

Chapter 9 Review   *507*

Chapter Test   *510*

Making an Informed Decision: What's Your Major?   *511*

Case Study: When Model Requirements Fail   *511*

Chapter 10   Hypothesis Tests Regarding a Parameter   514

10.1   The Language of Hypothesis Testing   515

10.2   Hypothesis Tests for a Population Mean—Population Standard Deviation Known   523

10.3   Hypothesis Tests for a Population Mean—Population Standard Deviation Unknown   541

10.4   Hypothesis Tests for a Population Proportion   552

10.5   Hypothesis Tests for a Population Standard Deviation   561

10.6   Putting It Together: Which Method Do I Use?   567

10.7   The Probability of a Type II Error and the Power of the Test   569

Chapter 10 Review   *575*

Chapter Test   *578*

Making an Informed Decision: What Does It Really Weigh?   *579*

Case Study: How Old Is Stonehenge?   *580*

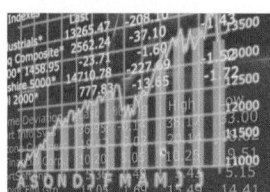

Chapter 11   Inferences on Two Samples   582

11.1 Inference about Two Means: Dependent Samples   583
11.2 Inference about Two Means: Independent Samples   595
11.3 Inference about Two Population Proportions   608
11.4 Inference for Two Population Standard Deviations   621
11.5 Putting It Together: Which Method Do I Use?   632

Chapter 11 Review   636

Chapter Test   639

Making an Informed Decision: Where Should I Invest?   641

Case Study: Control in the Design of an Experiment   642

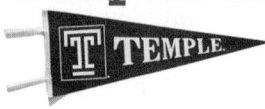

Chapter 12   Inference on Categorical Data   644

12.1 Goodness-of-Fit Test   645
12.2 Tests for Independence and the Homogeneity of Proportions   656

Chapter 12 Review   671

Chapter Test   673

Making an Informed Decision: Benefits of College   674

Case Study: Feeling Lucky? Well, Are You?   675

Chapter 13   Comparing Three or More Means   678

13.1 Comparing Three or More Means (One-Way Analysis of Variance)   679
13.2 Post Hoc Tests on One-Way Analysis of Variance   694
13.3 The Randomized Complete Block Design   704
13.4 Two-Way Analysis of Variance   713

Chapter 13 Review   728

Chapter Test   732

Making an Informed Decision: Where Should I Invest? Part II   733

Case Study: Hat Size and Intelligence   734

Chapter 14   Inference on the Least-Squares Regression Model and Multiple Regression   736

14.1 Testing the Significance of the Least-Squares Regression Model   737
14.2 Confidence and Prediction Intervals   753
14.3 Multiple Regression   758

Chapter 14 Review   781

Chapter Test   784

Making an Informed Decision: Buying a Car   785

Case Study: Housing Boom   786

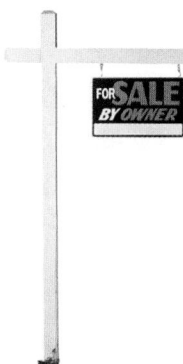

Chapter 15   Nonparametric Statistics (on CD)   15–1

15.1 An Overview of Nonparametric Statistics   15–2

15.2 Runs Test for Randomness   15–4

15.3 Inferences about Measures of Central Tendency   15–11

15.4 Inferences about the Difference between Two Medians: Dependent Samples   15–18

15.5 Inferences about the Difference between Two Medians: Independent Samples   15–29

15.6 Spearman's Rank-Correlation Test   15–39

15.7 Kruskal–Wallis Test   15–45

Chapter 15 Review   15–53

Chapter Test   15–56

Making an Informed Decision: Where Should I Live?   15–57

Case Study: Evaluating Alabama's 1891 House Bill 504   *15–58*

Appendix A   Tables   A–1

Appendix A   Tables (on CD)   A–23

Appendix B   Lines (on CD)   B–1

Photo Credits   PC–1

Answers   ANS–1

Index   I–1

Preface to the Instructor

Capturing a Powerful and Exciting Discipline in a Textbook

Statistics is a powerful subject, and it is one of my passions. Bringing my passion for the subject together with my desire to create a text that would work for me, my students, and my school led me to write the first edition of this textbook. It continues to motivate me as I revise the book to reflect changes in students, in the statistics community, and in the world around us.

When I started writing, I used the manuscript of this text in class. My students provided valuable, insightful feedback, and I made adjustments based on their comments. In many respects, this text was written by students and for students. I also received constructive feedback from a wide range of statistics faculty, which has refined ideas in the book and in my teaching. I continue to receive valuable feedback from both faculty and students, and this text continues to evolve with the goal of providing clear, concise, and readable explanations, while challenging students to think statistically.

In writing the last two editions, I made a special effort to abide by the *Guidelines for Assessment and Instruction in Statistics Education* (GAISE) for the college introductory course endorsed by the American Statistical Association (ASA). The GAISE Report gives six recommendations for the course:

1. Emphasize statistical literacy and develop statistical thinking
2. Use real data in teaching statistics
3. Stress conceptual understanding
4. Foster active learning
5. Use technology for developing conceptual understanding
6. Use assessments to improve and evaluate student learning

You'll see in both changes to this edition and in the hallmark features a strong adherence to these important GAISE guidelines.

Putting It Together

When students are learning statistics, often they struggle with seeing the big picture of how it all fits together. One of my goals is to help students learn not just the important concepts and methods of statistics but also how to put them together.

On the inside front cover, you'll see a pathway that provides a guide for students as they navigate through the process of learning statistics. The features and chapter organization in the third edition reinforce this important process.

New to This Edition
Pedagogical Changes

- **Over 30% New and Updated Exercises** The third edition makes a concerted effort to require students to write a few sentences to explain what the results of their statistical analysis actually mean. In addition, the answers in the back of the text provide recommended explanations of the statistical results.
- **Over 40% New and Updated Examples** The examples continue to be engaging and provide clear, concise explanations for the students and continue to follow the **Problem**, **Approach**, **Solution** presentation. *Problem* lays out the scenario of the example, *Approach* provides insight into the thought process behind the methodology used to solve the problem, and *Solution* goes through the solution utilizing the methodology suggested in the approach.
- **Preparing for This Section** quizzes tie into the Preparing for This Section skills in the textbook. They verify that students have the prerequisite knowledge for

the next section, and include page numbers for reference. These quizzes are available for download at the Instructor's Resource Center.

- **You Explain It!** problems within select Applying the Concepts sections require students to explain the meaning of statistical results in their own words.
- **Putting It Together** problems at the end of most exercise sets represent a synthesis review of many topics already covered in a single problem. A complete list of Putting It Together problems and the concepts tested is available on the front inside cover of the text.
- **Chapter Review** All answers are now available at the back of the book.
- **Chapter Test** After completing the chapter review, students can prepare for the exam by taking the Chapter Test.
- **Technology Answers** When technology answers differ from by-hand answers, both are provided in the back of the text.

Hallmark Features

- Because the use of **Real Data** peaks student interest and helps show the relevance of statistics, great efforts have been made to extensively incorporate Real Data in the exercises and examples.
- **Putting It Together** sections open each chapter to help students put the current material in context with previously studied material.
- **Step-by-Step Annotated Examples** guide a student from problem to solution in 3 easy-to-follow steps.
- **"Now Work"** problems follow most examples so students can practice the concepts shown.
- Multiple types of **Exercises** are used at the end of sections and chapters to test varying skills with progressive levels of difficulty. These exercises include **Concepts and Vocabulary**, **Skill Building**, and **Applying the Concepts**.
- **Chapter Review** sections include:
  - **Chapter Summary**.
  - A list of key chapter **Vocabulary**.
  - A list of **Formulas** used in the chapter.
  - **Chapter Objectives** listed with corresponding review exercises.
  - **Review Exercises** with all answers available in the back of the book.
- Each chapter concludes with **Case Studies** that help students apply their knowledge and promote active learning.
- **Activities** are included in each chapter that foster active learning and group work.

Integration of Technology

This book can be used with or without technology. Should you choose to integrate technology in the course, the following resources are available for your students:

- **Technology Step-by-Step** guides are included in applicable sections that show how to use MINITAB®, Excel®, and the TI-83/84 to complete statistics processes.
- Any problem that has 15 or more observations in the **Data Set** has a CD icon (💿) indicating that data set is included on the companion CD in various formats: MINITAB, TI-83/84, Excel, JMP®, SPSS®, and TXT.
- Where applicable, exercises and examples incorporate output screens from various software including MINITAB, the TI-83/84, and Excel.
- 20 **Applets** are included on the companion CD and connected with certain exercises, allowing students to manipulate data and interact with animations. See the front inside cover for a list of applets.
- Accompanying **Technology Manuals** are available that contain detailed tutorial instructions and worked out examples and exercises for the TI-83/84 and 89, Excel, SPSS, and MINITAB.

Companion CD Contents

- **Data Sets** for MINITAB, Excel, the TI-83/84, JMP, SPSS, and TXT format.
- 20 **Applets** (See description on pages xvii–xviii.)
- **DDXL** Excel add-in to enhance Excel's statistics capabilities
- **Formula Cards and Tables** in PDF format
- **Additional Topics Folder** including:
  - Sections 4.5, 5.7, 6.4
  - Chapter 15
  - Appendix A and Appendix B

Key Chapter Content Changes

Chapter 1 Data Collection

Former Section 1.2 is now divided into two sections. The new Section 1.2 elaborates on the differences between observational studies and designed experiments. The discussion on observational studies was expanded to include the various types of observational studies. The new Section 1.3 presents random sampling and simple random sampling.

Chapter 2 Organizing and Summarizing Data

This chapter now includes an increased emphasis on reading and interpreting graphs.

Chapter 3 Numerically Summarizing Data

Students are asked to interpret percentiles. The presentation of quartiles has changed to help emphasize conceptually what the quartiles represent. The discussion of computing percentiles from a discrete data set has been removed.

Chapter 4 Describing the Relation between Two Variables

Section 4.1 now contains expanded coverage of correlation versus causation. Section 12.2 from the second edition was moved to Section 4.4. Section 4.4 now includes coverage of Simpson's Paradox.

Chapter 5 Probability

More emphasis has been placed on using tree diagrams to determine probabilities and more emphasis on the interpretation of a probability. A new Putting It Together section summarizing the various techniques for computing probabilities is now included. This section includes two flowcharts to help students decide the method to use in determining probabilities.

Chapter 6 Discrete Probability Distributions

This chapter now has additional emphasis on using probabilities to identify unusual results.

Chapter 8 Sampling Distributions

Section 8.1 was rewritten to include more relevant examples that utilize simulation to demonstrate the sampling distribution of the sample mean. A new activity develops the concept of the mean and standard deviation of the sampling distribution of the sample mean. Section 8.1 and 8.2 problems foreshadow the concept of a P-value.

Chapter 9 Estimating the Value of a Parameter Using Confidence Intervals

Example 2 in Section 9.2 was rewritten so that the interpretation of "level of confidence" is clear. New You Explain It! exercises have been added to Sections 9.2 and 9.3. The chapter project now includes a discussion of bootstrapping along with an algorithm for generating bootstrap samples. A discussion of methods for estimating the population proportion when the normality condition is not satisfied was also added to the chapter project.

Chapter 10 Hypothesis Tests Regarding a Parameter

The language of the problems was revamped to eliminate the wording, "test the claim." Now, the problems are written in everyday language that leads to a hypothesis test. In addition, there is more of an emphasis on using confidence intervals to test hypotheses.

Chapter 11 Inferences on Two Samples

A new objective was added to Section 11.3 on McNemar's test for comparing two population proportions from dependent sampling, and a new Section 11.5 Putting It Together asks students to decide on the appropriate test.

Chapter 12 Inference on Categorical Data

Section 12.2 was moved to Section 4.4. Exercises have been updated with more relevant/interesting data sets, and there is more of an emphasis on looking at the conditional distributions to identify the major contributors to the size of the chi-square test statistic.

Chapter 13 Comparing Three or More Means

The discussion of one-way analysis of variance was rewritten to emphasize the logic behind the procedure.

Flexible to Work with Your Syllabus

To meet the varied needs of diverse syllabi, this book has been organized to be flexible. You will notice the "Preparing for This Section" material at the beginning of each section, which will tip you off to dependencies within the course. The two most common variations within an introductory statistics course are the treatment of regression analysis and the treatment of probability.

- **Coverage of Correlation and Regression** The text was written with the descriptive portion of bivariate data (Chapter 4) presented after the descriptive portion of univariate data (Chapter 3). Instructors who prefer to postpone the discussion of bivariate data can skip Chapter 4 and return to it before covering Chapter 14. (Because Section 4.5 on nonlinear regression is covered by a select few instructors, it is located on the CD that accompanies the text in Adobe PDF form, so that it can be easily printed.)
- **Coverage of Probability** The text allows for either light to extensive coverage of probability. Instructors wishing to minimize probability may cover Section 5.1 and skip the remaining sections. A mid-level treatment of probability can be accomplished by covering Sections 5.1 through 5.3. Instructors who will cover the chi-square test for independence will want to cover Sections 5.1 through 5.3. In addition, an instructor who will cover binomial probabilities will want to cover independence in Section 5.3 and combinations in Section 5.5.

Acknowledgments

Textbooks evolve into their final form through the efforts and contributions of many people. First and foremost, I would like to thank my family, whose dedication to this project was just as much as mine: my wife, Yolanda, whose words of encouragement and support were unabashed, and my children, Michael, Kevin, and Marissa, who would come and greet me every morning with smiles that only children can deliver. I owe each of them my sincerest gratitude. I would also like to thank the entire Mathematics Department at Joliet Junior College, my colleagues who provided support, ideas, and encouragement to help me complete this project. From Pearson Education: Deirdre Lynch, who provided many suggestions that clearly demonstrate her experience and knowledge as an editor; Christopher Cummings, who stepped into this project with both feet and provided suggestions that have proven invaluable; Joanne Dill, who provided organizational skills that made this project go so smoothly; Alex Gay, for his marketing savvy and dedication to getting the word out; and the Pearson Arts and Sciences sales team, for their confidence and support of this book. I thank Bob Walters, my Production Editor, for his dedication, enthusiasm, pride, and uncanny knack for attention to detail. Thanks also to the individuals who rigorously accuracy-checked this text: Diane Benner, Harrisburg Area Community College; Dr. Linda M. Myers, Harrisburg Area Community College; and the Pearson math tutors, Alice Armstrong, Dimitrios Fotiadis, Abdellah Dakhama, Joan Saniuk, and Diane Watson. I also wish to thank Brent Griffin, Craig Johnson, Kathleen McLaughlin, Alana Tuckey, and Dorothy Wakefield for help in creating supplements. Many thanks also to all the reviewers, whose insights and ideas form the backbone of this text. I apologize for any omissions.

Finally, I would like to extend my sincerest thanks to Kevin Bodden and Randy Gallaher, of Lewis & Clark Community College. The dedication to education and professionalism of Kevin and Randy were apparent as they helped to develop the manuscript, write exercises, and proofread the text. In addition, my thanks go to Kevin and Randy for writing the solutions manuals and verifying the answers in the back of the text.

CALIFORNIA Charles Biles, *Humboldt State University* • Carol Curtis, *Fresno City College* • Freida Ganter, *California State University-Fresno* • Craig Nance, *Santiago Canyon College* **COLORADO** Roxanne Byrne, *University of Colorado-Denver* **CONNECTICUT** Kathleen McLaughlin, *Manchester Community College* • Dorothy Wakefield, *University of Connecticut* • Cathleen M. Zucco Teveloff, *Trinity College* **DISTRICT OF COLUMBIA** Jill McGowan, *Howard University* **FLORIDA** Randall Allbritton, *Daytona Beach Community College* • Franco Fedele, *University of West Florida* • Laura Heath, *Palm Beach Community College* Perrian Herring, *Okaloosa Walton College* • Marilyn Hixson, *Brevard Community College* • Philip Pina, *Florida Atlantic University* • Mike Rosenthal, *Florida International University* • James Smart, *Tallahassee Community College* **GEORGIA** Virginia Parks, *Georgia Perimeter College* • Chandler Pike, *University of Georgia* • Jill Smith, *University of Georgia* **IDAHO** K. Shane Goodwin, *Brigham Young University* • Craig Johnson, *Brigham Young University* • Brent Timothy, *Brigham Young University* • Kirk Trigsted, *University of Idaho* **ILLINOIS** Grant Alexander, *Joliet Junior College* • Linda Blanco, *Joliet Junior College* • Kevin Bodden, *Lewis & Clark Community College* • Joanne Brunner, *Joliet Junior College* • James Butterbach, *Joliet Junior College* • Elena Catoiu, *Joliet Junior College* • Faye Dang, *Joliet Junior College* • Laura Egner, *Joliet Junior College* • Jason Eltrevoog, *Joliet Junior College* • Erica Egizio, *Joliet Junior College* • Randy Gallaher, *Lewis & Clark Community College* • Iraj Kalantari, *Western Illinois University* • Donna Katula, *Joliet Junior College* • Diane Long, *College of DuPage* • Jean McArthur, *Joliet Junior College* • David McGuire, *Joliet Junior College* • Angela McNulty, *Joliet Junior College* • Linda Padilla, *Joliet Junior College* • David Ruffato, *Joliet Junior College* • Patrick Stevens, *Joliet Junior College* • Robert Tuskey, *Joliet Junior College* • Stephen Zuro, *Joliet Junior College* **INDIANA** Jason Parcon, *Indiana University-Purdue University Ft. Wayne* **KANSAS** Donna Gorton, *Butler Community College* • Ingrid Peterson, *University of Kansas* **MARYLAND** John Climent, *Cecil Community College* • Rita Kolb, *The Community College of Baltimore County* **MASSACHUSETTS** Daniel Weiner, *Boston University* • Pradipta Seal, *Boston University of Public Health* **MICHIGAN** Margaret M. Balachowski, *Michigan Technological University* • Diane Krasnewich, *Muskegon Community College* • Susan Lenker, *Central Michigan University* • Timothy D. Stebbins, *Kalamazoo Valley Community College* • Sharon Stokero, *Michigan Technological University* • Alana Tuckey, *Jackson Community College* **MINNESOTA** Mezbhur Rahman, *Minnesota State University* **MISSOURI** Farroll Tim Wright, *University of Missouri-Columbia* **NEBRASKA** JaneKeller, *Metropolitan Community College* **NEW YORK** Jacob Amidon, *Finger Lakes Community College* • Stella Aminova, *Hunter College* • Pinyuen Chen, *Syracuse University* • Bryan Ingham, *Finger Lakes Community College* • Anne M. Jowsey, *Niagara County Community College* • Maryann E. Justinger, *Erie Community College-South Campus* • Kathleen Miranda, *SUNY at OldWestbury* • Robert Sackett, *Erie Community College-North Campus* **NORTH CAROLINA** Fusan Akman, *Coastal Carolina Community College* • Mohammad Kazemi, *University of North Carolina-Charlotte* •Janet Mays, *Elon University* • Marilyn McCollum, *North Carolina State University* • Claudia McKenzie, *Central Piedmont Community College* • Said E. Said, *East Carolina University* • Karen Spike, *University of North Carolina-Wilmington* • Jeanette Szwec, *Cape Fear Community College* • Richard Einsporn, *The University of Akron* **OHIO** Michael McCraith, *Cuyaghoga Community College* **OREGON** Daniel Kim, *Southern Oregon University* • Jong Sung Kin, *Portland State University* **SOUTH CAROLINA** Diana Asmus, *Greenville Technical College* • Dr. William P. Fox, *Francis Marion University* • Cheryl Hawkins, *Greenville Technical College* • Rose Jenkins, *Midlands Technical College* • Lindsay Packer, *College of Charleston* **TENNESSEE** Nancy Pevey, *Pellissippi State Technical Community College* • David Ray, *University of Tennessee-Martin* **TEXAS** Jada Hill, *Richland College* • David Lane, *Rice University* • Alma F. Lopez, *South Plains College* **UTAH** Joe Gallegos, *Salt Lake City Community College* **VIRGINIA** Kim Jones, *Virginia Commonwealth University* • Vasanth Solomon, *Old Dominion University* **WEST VIRGINIA** Mike Mays, *West Virginia University* **WISCONSIN** William Applebaugh, *University of Wisconsin–Eau Claire* • Carolyn Chapel, *Western Wisconsin Technical College* • Beverly Dretzke, *University of Wisconsin-Eau Claire* • Jolene Hartwick, *Western Wisconsin Technical College* • Thomas Pomykalski, *Madison Area Technical College*

Michael Sullivan, III
Joliet Junior College

SUPPLEMENTS

FOR THE INSTRUCTOR

Annotated Instructor's Edition
(ISBN 13: 978-0-321-57527-2; ISBN 10: 0-321-57527-X)
Margin notes include helpful teaching tips, suggest alternative presentations, and point out common student errors. Exercise answers are included in the exercise sets when space allows. The complete answer section is located in the back of the text.

Instructor's Solutions Manual by Kevin Bodden and Randall Gallaher, *Lewis and Clark Community College*
(ISBN 13: 978-0-321-57578-4; ISBN 10: 0-321-57578-4)
Fully worked solutions to every textbook exercise, including the chapter review and new chapter tests. Case Study Answers are also provided.

Instructor's Resource Center
All instructor resources can be downloaded from *www.pearsonhighered.com/irc.* This is a password-protected site that requires instructors to set up an account or, alternatively, instructor resources can be ordered from your Pearson Higher Education sales representative.

Mini Lectures by Craig Johnson, *Brigham Young University*
(ISBN 13: 978-0-321-57753-5; ISBN 10: 0-321-57753-1)
Mini Lectures are provided to help with lecture preparation by providing learning objectives, classroom examples not found in the text, teaching notes, and the answers to these examples. Mini Lectures are available from the Instructor's Resource Center and MyStatLab™.

TestGen®
TestGen (www.pearsonhighered.com/testgen) enables instructors to build, edit, print, and administer tests using a computerized bank of questions developed to cover all the objectives of the text. TestGen is algorithmically based, allowing instructors to create multiple but equivalent versions of the same question or test with the click of a button. Instructors can also modify test bank questions or add new questions. Tests can be printed or administered online. The software and test bank are available for download from Pearson Education's online catalog.

Online Test Bank
A test bank derived from TestGen is available on the Instructor's Resource Center. There is also a link to the TestGen website within the Instructor Resource area of MyStatLab.

PowerPoint® Lecture Slides
Free to qualified adopters, this classroom lecture presentation software is geared specifically to the sequence and philosophy of *Statistics: Informed Decisions Using Data.* Key graphics from the book are included to help bring the statistical concepts alive in the classroom. Slides are available for download from the Instructor's Resource Center and are available within MyStatLab.

Pearson Math Adjunct Support Center
The **Pearson Math Adjunct Support Center** (http://www.pearsontutorservices.com/math-adjunct.html) is staffed by qualified instructors with more than 50 years of combined experience at both the community college and university levels. Assistance is provided for faculty in the following areas:

- Suggested syllabus consultation
- Tips on using materials packed with your book
- Book-specific content assistance
- Teaching suggestions, including advice on classroom strategies

FOR THE STUDENT

Video Lectures on DVD
(ISBN 13: 978-0-321-57721-4; ISBN 10: 0-321-57721-3)
A comprehensive set of videos, tied to the textbook, in which examples from each chapter are worked out by Michael Sullivan and master statistics teachers. The videos provide excellent support for students who require additional assistance, for distance learning and self-paced programs, or for students who missed class. These videos are also available in MyStatLab.

Camtasia Lecture Videos by Michael Sullivan, III, *Joliet Junior College*
These are actual classroom lectures presented and filmed by the author using Camtasia. Students not only will see additional fully worked-out examples, but also hear and see the development of the material. The videos provide excellent support for students who require additional assistance, for distance learning and self-paced programs, or for students who miss class.

Student's Solutions Manual by Kevin Bodden and Randall Gallaher, *Lewis and Clark Community College*
(ISBN 13: 978-0-321-57751-1; ISBN 10: 0-321-57751-5)
Fully worked solutions to odd-numbered exercises with all solutions to the chapter reviews and chapter tests.

Technology Manuals The following technology manuals contain detailed tutorial instructions and worked-out examples and exercises:

- **Excel Manual (including DDXL)** by Alana Tuckey, *Jackson Community College*
  (ISBN 13: 978-0-321-57747-4; ISBN 10: 0-321-57747-7)
- **Graphing Calculator Manual for the TI-83/84 Plus and TI-89** by Kathleen McLaughlin and Dorothy Wakefield
  (ISBN 13: 978-0-321-57778-8; ISBN 10: 0-321-57778-7)
- **MINITAB Manual** by Kathleen McLaughlin and Dorothy Wakefield
  (ISBN 13: 978-0-321-57779-5; ISBN 10: 0-321-57779-5)
- **SPSS Manual** by Brent Timothy
  Available online only at the Instructor's Resource Center.

TECHNOLOGY RESOURCES

MyStatLab™

MyStatLab (part of the MyMathLab® and MathXL® product family) is a text-specific, easily customizable on-line course that integrates interactive multimedia instruction with textbook content. Powered by CourseCompass™ (Pearson Education's online teaching and learning environment) and MathXL (our online homework, tutorial, and assessment system), MyStatLab gives you the tools you need to deliver all or a portion of your course online, whether your students are in a lab setting or working from home. MyStatLab provides a rich and flexible set of course materials, featuring free-response tutorial exercises for unlimited practice and mastery. Students can also use online tools, such as video lectures, animations, and a multimedia textbook, to independently improve their understanding and performance. Instructors can use MyStatLab's homework and test managers to select and assign online exercises correlated directly to the textbook, and they can also create and assign their own online exercises and import TestGen tests for added flexibility. MyStatLab's online gradebook—designed specifically for mathematics and statistics—automatically tracks students' homework and test results and gives the instructor control over how to calculate final grades. Instructors can also add offline (paper-and-pencil) grades to the gradebook. MyStatLab also includes access to the **Pearson Tutor Center** (www.pearsontutorservices.com). The Tutor Center is staffed by qualified mathematics instructors who provide textbook-specific tutoring for students via toll-free phone, fax, email, and interactive Web.

Active Learning Questions

Prepared in PowerPoint®, these questions are intended for use with classroom response systems. Several multiple-choice questions are available for each chapter of the book, allowing instructors to quickly assess mastery of material in class. The Active Learning Questions are available to download from within MyStatLab and from Pearson Education's online catalog.

MathXL® for Statistics

MathXL® for Statistics is a powerful online homework, tutorial, and assessment system that accompanies Pearson Education textbooks in statistics. With MathXL for Statistics, instructors can create, edit, and assign online homework and tests using algorithmically generated exercises correlated at the objective level to the textbook. They can also create and assign their own online exercises and import TestGen tests for added flexibility. All student work is tracked in MathXL's online gradebook. Students can take chapter tests in MathXL and receive personalized study plans based on their test results. The study plan diagnoses weaknesses and links students directly to tutorial exercises for the objectives they need to study and retest. Students can also access supplemental animations and video clips directly from selected exercises. MathXL for Statistics is available to qualified adopters. For more information, visit our website at *www.mathxl.com*, or contact your sales representative.

ActivStats®

Developed by Paul Velleman and Data Description, Inc., ActivStats is an award-winning multimedia introduction to statistics and a comprehensive learning tool that works in conjunction with the book. It complements this text with interactive features such as videos of real-world stories, teaching applets, and animated expositions of major statistics topics. It also contains tutorials for learning a variety of statistics software, including Data Desk®, Excel®, JMP®, MINITAB®, and SPSS®. ActivStats for Windows and Macintosh ISBN 13: 978-0-321-50014-4; ISBN 10: 0-321-50014-8. Contact your Pearson Arts & Sciences sales representative for details or visit *www.aw-bc.com/activstats*.

The Student Edition of MINITAB

A condensed version of the Professional release of MINITAB statistical software. It offers the full range of statistical methods and graphical capabilities, along with worksheets that can include up to 10,000 data points. ISBN 13: 978-0-321-11313-9. Individual copies of the software can be bundled with the text. ISBN 10: 0-321-11313-6 (CD only).

JMP Student Edition

An easy-to-use, streamlined version of JMP desktop statistical discovery software from SAS Institute Inc., and is available for bundling with the text. (ISBN 13: 978-0-321-51738-8; ISBN 10: 0-321-51738-5)

SPSS

This is a statistical and data management software package, is also available for bundling with the text. (ISBN 13: 978-0-205-56941-0; ISBN 10: 0-205-56941-2)

Instructors can contact local sales representatives for details on purchasing and bundling supplements with the textbook or contact the company at exam@pearson.com for examination copies of many of these items.

StatCrunch

StatCrunch is a powerful online tool that provides an interactive environment for doing statistics. You can use Stat-Crunch for both numerical and graphical data analysis, taking advantage of interactive graphics to help you see the connection between objects selected in a graph and the underlying data. In MyStatLab, the data sets from your textbook are pre-loaded into StatCrunch. Stat-Crunch is also available as a tool from the online homework and practice exercises in MyStatLab and in MathXL for Statistics.

An Introduction to the Applets

The 20 applets on the CD-ROM, bound inside the front of all new copies of this text, are designed to help students understand a wide range of introductory statistics topics. In the Third Edition, the applets have been greatly enhanced by changes to the user interface, and the addition of new capabilities that support better pedagogy. Most notably, the font size has been increased to allow the applets to be projected with great clarity in the classroom.

- The **sample from a population** applet allows the user to select samples of various sizes from a wide range of population shapes including uniform, bell-shaped, skewed and binary (including a range of values for the probability of a 1) populations. Students can alter any of the default populations to create a custom distribution by dragging the mouse over the population. Small samples are drawn in an animated fashion to help students understand the basic idea of sampling. Larger samples are drawn in an unanimated fashion so that characteristics of larger samples can be quickly compared to population characteristics.

- The **sampling distributions** applet bootstraps off the previous applet by adding the values of user-selected statistics for each sample. Students can study the resulting distributions and see how characteristics of the sampling distribution such as center and spread are affected by sample size and population shape. Students can also compare sampling distributions of different statistics such as the sample mean and median.

- The **random numbers** applet allows students to select a random sample from a range of user-defined integer values. Students can use the applet to study basic probability by considering the relative frequency of particular outcomes among the samples. They can also select samples from a list of values for a hands-on sampling activity.

- Six **long run probability demonstration** applets simulate the rolling of a die, flipping of a coin, and the fluctuation of the stock market. Students can select the number of times a simulation occurs, and whether or not they would like it animated. The relative frequency of an event of interest is plotted versus the number of simulations. As the number of simulations increases, the convergence of the relative frequency to the true probability of the event will be evident.

- The **mean versus median** applet allows students to construct a data set interactively by clicking on a graphic that displays the mean and median of the data, allowing students to study the effects of shape and outliers on the mean and the median. The **standard deviation** applet provides a similar type of exploration. In the Third Edition, this applet is also offered in a stacked form so that data sets with different standard deviations can be compared easily.

- Three applets help students better understand confidence intervals. The **confidence intervals for a proportion** applet allows students to simulate 95% and 99% confidence intervals for a population proportion. The confidence intervals are plotted illustrating their relationship in terms of width and their random nature. The sample size and the true underlying proportion are specified by the user, who can then study the effect of these values on the coverage probabilities tabled in the applet. Two applets allow students to study **confidence intervals for a mean** in a similar manner. The first can be used to show how sample size and distributional shape impact the performance of classic t intervals for the mean. The second allows students to compare the performance of z and t intervals for different distributional shapes and sample sizes.

- The applets for **hypothesis tests for a proportion** and **hypothesis tests for a mean** allow students to understand how the underlying assumptions affect the performance of hypothesis tests. These applets plot test statistics and corresponding P-values for data generated under different user-supplied conditions. Tabled rejection proportions allow students to determine how the conditions specified affect the true level of significance for the tests.

- The **correlation by eye** applet allows students to guess the value of the correlation coefficient based on a scatterplot of simulated data. In addition, students can see how adding and deleting points affects the correlation coefficient. Likewise, the **regression by eye** applet allows students to attempt to interactively determine the regression line for simulated data.

- The **binomial distribution** applet generates samples from the binomial distribution at user-specified parameter values. By varying the parameters, students can develop an understanding of how these parameters impact the binomial distribution.

Applications Index

Accounting
client satisfaction, 24–27

Aeronautics
bone length and space travel, 748–49
O-ring failures on *Columbia*, 136
Skylab, 62
space flight and water consumption, 712
Spacelab, 180, 597–600, 602, 627–28

Agriculture
corn production, 118, 689, 700
growing season, 485, 501
optimal level of fertilizer, 48–49, 51–52
orchard damage, 62
yield
of orchard, 37
plowing method vs., 591
soybean, 155, 550, 690, 700

Airline travel. *See under Travel*

Animals/nature
American black bears, weight and length of, 204, 206, 219, 235, 750
shark attacks, 251

Anthropometrics
upper leg length of 20- to 29-year-old males, 439

Appliances
refrigerator life span, 383

Arboriculture
white oak tree diameter, 479–81

Archaeology
Stonehenge, 580–81

Art
body art (tattoos), 494

Astronomy
life on Mars, 324
planetary motion, 751–52
sidereal year, 235

Biology
alcohol effects, 56
blood type, 78, 269, 289, 344, 345–46, 414–15
bone length, 204, 220, 235, 748–49, 756–57
cholesterol level, 38, 367, 378–79, 494, 558, 577, 725, 753, 754, 755–56
age and, 737–39, 741, 744–46, 747, 751, 757
HDL, 679, 680, 715, 717–20, 722–23, 751, 757
saturated fat and, 760–63, 767, 768
cost of biology journals, 140
DNA sequences/structure, 309, 313, 324
fertility rate, 124
gestation period, 383–84, 402, 439, 506
hemoglobin, 714–15
in cats, 174
in rats, 592
kidney weight, 157
lymphocyte count, 62
pulse rates, 139, 155, 175, 199
reaction time, 55–56, 138–39, 154
red blood cell mass, 597–600, 602, 627–28
resting pulse rate, 93
serum HDL, 165
age vs., 204–5
sickle-cell anemia, 296–97
step pulses, 606
systolic blood pressure, 630–31

Biomechanics
grip strength, 784–85

Business. *See also Work*
acceptance of shipment, 295–96, 299, 313, 314, 324
advertising
campaign, 36
humor in, 61
methods of, 56
skin cream, 122
airline customer opinion, 36
bolts manufacturing, 60, 157, 173
butterfly suppliers, 63–64
car dealer profits, 140–41

carpet flaws, 367
car rentals, 593
car sales, 94
civilian labor force, 283
coffee sales, 323
conference members, 299
consumer complaints, 322
copier maintenance, 367
customer satisfaction, 31–32, 61
customer service, 411
defective products, 295–96, 299, 300, 311, 313, 314, 324
Disney World statistics conference, 271
drive-through rate, 332, 359–61, 363, 402, 403
bank, 369
fast-food, 82–84, 92, 123–24, 440, 469, 473, 486, 578, 638, 639
mean waiting time, 549
employee morale, 37
entrepreneurship, 452
Internet, 142, 157
learning time for task, 733
lemonade sales, 759–60
marketing research, 38
new store opening decision, 43
oil change time, 440
packaging error, 299, 313, 323
quality assurance in customer relations, 364
quality control, 36, 37, 62, 173, 289–90, 545–46, 563–64
restaurant
meatloaf recipe, 188
tipping in, 484
waiting time for table, 97, 100, 630
shopping habits of customers, 43
Speedy Lube, 403
stocks on the NASDAQ, 312
stocks on the NYSE, 312
Target demographic information gathering, 38
traveling salesman, 304, 312
unemployment and inflation, 107–8
union membership, 116
waiting in line, 340, 566
Walmart versus Target pricing, 634
worker injury, 117
worker morale, 29

Chemistry
acid rain, 537–38, 565, 639, 640
calcium in rainwater, 537, 565
pH in rain, 692, 700
pH in water, 138, 154
pH meter calibration, 549
reaction time, 382
soil testing, 729–30

Combinatorics
arranging flags, 310, 322
clothing options, 312
combination locks, 312
committee formation, 312
subcommittees, 317, 324
committee structures, 303
license plate numbers, 312, 322
seat choices, 322
seating arrangements, 318
starting lineups, 318

Communication(s)
caller ID, 44
cell phone, 449, 521, 579
bill, 528–29, 532–34
brain tumors and, 16
crime rate and, 207
ownership, 347–48, 351, 353–54
rates, 383
talk time on, 510
use of, 133–34, 137, 154
do-not-call registry, 44
e-mail, 509
fraud detection, 174, 175

high-speed Internet service, 60
language spoken at home, 282
newspaper article analysis, 252
phone call length, 382
teen, 300
text messaging, 449
time spent on phone calls and email, 578
voice-recognition systems, 620

Computer(s). *See also* **Internet**
anxiety over, 775–76
calls to help desk, 362
downloading music, 577
download time, 37
DSL Internet connection speed, 37
fingerprint identification, 291
high-speed Internet connection, 355
hits to a Web site, 362, 364
passwords, 314, 324
phishing, 449
toner cartridges, 188, 568–69
user names, 312

Construction
basement waterproofing, 159
of commuter rail station, 37
new homes, 116–17
quality control, 363

Consumers
Coke or Pepsi preferences, 57
his and hers razors, 301
taste test, 20

Crime(s)
aggravated assault, 505
burglaries, 110–11
conviction for, 369
driving under the influence, 290
fraud, 652–53
identity, 75
larceny theft, 187–88, 270
murder/homicide
clearances, 355, 356
by firearms, 416
victims of, 77
weapons used in, 120, 281
property, 368
rate of, 100
cell phones and, 207
by state, 121
robberies, 116
speeding, 38
stolen credit card, 174–75
victim-offender relationship, 326–28
violent, 98, 100, 174, 207
percent of births to unmarried women and, 253
weapon of choice, 653

Criminology
fraud detection, 174, 175

Demographics
adult children living at home, 355–56
age married, 486
age of death-row inmates, 549
births
distribution of months of, 654
live, 120, 341
proportion born each day of week, 650–51
deaths. *See also* Mortality
airline fatalities, 363
due to cancer, 298, 300
by legal intervention, 106
traffic fatalities, 322, 363
distribution of residents in United States, 645, 646–49
family size, 121, 509, 569
females living at home, 417
fertility rate, 124
household size, 93, 433–34
households speaking foreign language as primary language, 43

life expectancy, 9, 287, 288, 289
living alone, 559, 655
males living at home, 416–17
male teachers in Colorado, 559
marital status, 277–78, 298
    gender and, 292–93
    happiness and, 657–59, 660–64
    number of children for 50- to 54-year-old
        mothers, 436–37
pet ownership, 494–95
population
    age of, 106, 166
    of selected countries, 9
    of smokers, 299
    of United States, 751
population density, 186–87
population growth and subsistence, 255
race and region of residence, 673–74
southpaws, 289
teenage mothers, 521

Dentistry
repair systems for chipped veneer in
    prosthodontics, 681–82, 687–88, 697–99

Drugs. *See also* Pharmaceuticals
alcohol
    abstinence from, 619
    effects on reaction times, 590
marijuana legalization, 668–69
marijuana use, 319, 522

Ecology
mosquito control, eco-friendly, 57–58

Economics
abolishing the penny, 495
retail milk prices, 470–71

Economy
health care expenditures, 118
housing prices, 99, 124, 222, 777
income and birthrate, 203
poverty, 74, 88–90, 165
unemployment and inflation, 107–8

Education. *See also* Test(s)
advanced degrees, 452
age vs. study time, 236
attendance, 220, 653
attitudes toward quality of, 559
bachelor's degree, 297, 357
    elapsed time to earn, 603
    income and, 202–3
boarding school admissions, 173
board work, 299
calculus exam score, 12
class average, 165
college
    alcohol use among students, 12
    algebra courses in self-study format, 578
    benefits of, 674
    bias at University of California,
        Berkeley, 244–45
    campus safety, 30–31
    community college enrollments, 96
    costs, 118
    dropping a course, 669
    enrollment to, 108, 355, 356
    evaluation tool for rating professors, 208
    gender and seating arrangement, feeling at
        ease in classroom and, 727
    gender bias in acceptance to, 244–45, 254
    health-risk behaviors among students in, 76
    hours studied, 420
    literature selection, 27
    major, 511
    mean age of full-time students, 539
    mean time to graduate, 510
    proportion of males and females
        completing, 621
    readiness for, 537, 554–55, 558–59
    SAT reports sent to, 319
    saving for, 125
    seating choice versus GPA, 731
    self-injurious behavior among students, 367
    student union, 450
    success in, 773
    teen birthrates vs. population with bachelor's
        degree by state, 234–35
    test scores on application, 188
    textbook packages required, 43

time spent online by college students, 122
    undergraduate tuition, 96
course grade, 783
course selection, 27
developmental math, 54–55
doctorates, 75, 281
educational TV for toddlers, 14–15
equal opportunity to obtain quality, 668
exam grades/scores, 61, 79–80, 130–31, 136, 144,
    145–46, 147–50, 181
    study time and, 218
faculty opinion poll, 27
foreign language study, 78
gender differences in reaction to
    instruction, 57
GPA, 162, 165, 186
    SAT score and, 194
    seating choice versus, 782
    video games and, 218
high school
    athletics participation, 357
    dropouts, 298
    enrollment, 341
    illegal drug use in, 12
    math and science, 559
    National Honor Society, 319
home schooling, 654–55
illicit drug use among students, 12, 43
learning and testing conditions, 721–22
level of, 123, 357
    of adults 25 years and older, 71–73, 76
    belief in heaven and, 253–54
    distribution of, 673
    employment status and, 238–44
    feelings on abortion and, 246
    gambling and, 674
    health and, 668
    income and, 122, 297, 777
    marital status and, 300
    premature birth and, 672
    smoking and, 640
male teachers in Colorado, 559
mathematics
    teaching techniques, 20
    TIMMS report and Kumon, 634
missing exam grade, 141
music's impact on learning, 50
online homework, 79–80, 174, 606
parental involvement in, 340
political affiliation and, 669–70
poverty
    length of school day and, 252
    school academic performance and, 252
reading rates
    of second-grade students, 439
    of sixth-grade students, 402, 403
    speed reading, 181
school enrollment, 95
school loans, 411
seat location in classroom, influence of, 653
standardized test score performance, 591
student arrangement, 312
student government satisfaction survey, 283
student opinion poll/survey, 27–28, 37
student services fees, 37
teacher evaluations by students
    evaluation tool for rating professors, 208
    influence of distributing chocolate on, 634
teaching reading, 54
visual vs. textual learners, 605

Electricity
average per kilowatt-hour prices of, 117
battery life, 61, 452, 485, 501
Christmas lights, 289
light bulbs, 313, 339, 402, 516, 517
    intensity, 205
    mean life of, 186

Electronics
disposable, 74–75
electric ballast, 60–61
plasma television prices, 757–58
televisions in the household, 97, 100

Employment. *See* Work

Energy
average per kilowatt-hour prices of
    electricity, 117

carbon dioxide emissions and energy
    production, 219, 236
consumption of, 120
gas price hike, 118
household expenditure for, 549
    mean natural gas bill, 141
oil reserves, 117

Engineering
batteries and temperature, 57
bearing failures, 188
bolts manufacturing, 60
catapults, 731
concrete, 234
    mix, 137, 154
    strength, 604, 693, 712, 726, 749, 757, 776–77
engine additives, 522
failure rate of electrical components, 454–55
filling machines, 452, 496–97, 517–18, 538, 561,
    565, 630
grading timber, 730–31
hardness testing equipment, 592
linear rotary bearing, 577
O-ring thickness, 411
pump design, 565
rope strength, 732–33
steel beam yield strength, 568
tensile strength, 484
tire design, 57
valve pressure, 521
wet drilling vs. dry drilling, 779

**Entertainment. *See also* Leisure
    and recreation**
Academy Award winners, 100, 441
cable television subscription, 348–50, 415
CD
    random playback, 299
    songs on, 312, 313
Dateline questionnaire, 34
digital music players, 319
dramas, 471
length of songs of 1970s, 132
media players, 13
movie ratings, 60
neighborhood party, 299
People Meter measurement, 34
raffle, 14
spending on, 175
student survey of spending on, 175
television
    amount of time spent watching, 440, 548
    in bedroom, obesity and, 21
    educational, for toddlers, 14–15
    high-definition (HDTV) ownership, 348–50
    number in household, 452
    plasma television prices, 757–58
    watching hours, 410–11
    widescreen, 13
tickets to concert, 24, 263–64
video games and GPAs, 218

Entomology
beetle distribution, 361–62
mosquito control, eco-friendly, 57–58

Environment
acid rain, 537–38, 565, 639, 640
carbon dioxide emissions
    by country, 139
    energy production and, 219, 236
    per capita, 174, 182
levels of carbon monoxide, 510
pH in rain, 692, 700
Secchi disk, 591–92
U.S. greenhouse emissions, 123
water clarity, 510

Epidemiology
SARS epidemic, 483–84
West Nile virus, 486

Exercise
habits, 484
proportion of men and women participating in,
    620–21
pulse rate during, 506
routines, 319
treadmills, 80

Family
adult children living at home, 355–56
babies' first talk, 513

birth and gender orders of children, 313
employment status of married couples with children, 283
family members in jail, 510
foster care, 282
ideal number of children, 341, 569
infidelity among married men, 559
kids and leisure, 606

Farming. *See also* **Agriculture**
incubation times for hen eggs, 382, 402, 403

Fashion
women's preference for shoes, 122

Finance. *See also* **Investment(s)**
ATM withdrawals, 441, 537, 574
car buying decision, 156, 189, 254, 785–86
charitable contributions, 521
Christmas spending, 472
cost of kids, 117
credit card debt, 495, 576
credit card ownership, 449
depreciation, 783
earnings and educational attainment, 122
estate tax returns, 505
financial worries, 14
health care expenditures, 118
housing prices, 99, 124, 222, 777
income, 777
    annual salaries of married couples, 590
    average, 97
    birthrate and, 203
    FICO credit score and, 548
    household, 33, 43, 279–80, 427
    mean, 427
    median, 116, 117
    by region, 298
    student survey of, 175
income taxes, 620
IRS audits, 290
law grads' pay, 506
lodging prices, 711–12
mortgage rates, 568
net worth, 453
    of all U.S. households, 141
price of gasoline, 157
real estate taxes, 538
retirement and, 505, 558
school loans, 411
tips, 484

Firearms
gun control, 495
gun ownership, 620
muzzle velocity, 185, 505, 591
pistol shooting precision, 776
as weapon of choice, 653

Food. *See also* **Nutrition**
allergies, 453
candy
    mixed chocolates, 165
    M&Ms, 140, 155, 182, 260, 506, 645, 651, 652
    Skittles® Brand, 557
    Snickers, 563–64
cauliflower, 513
cereals
    calories versus sugar, 234
cookies
    Chips Ahoy!, 402, 403, 410
    chips per cookie, 182
    diameter of, 121
    Girl Scout Cookies, 324
fast-food, 785
    fat and calories in cheeseburgers, 249
    serving sizes, 124
ice cream, favorite flavor, 568
insect fragments in, 362, 440
meatloaf contents, 188
milk prices, 125, 470–71
number of possible meals, 302–3
nut mix, 165–66
peanuts, 502
popcorn consumption, 522
salads, 559
Salmonella bacteria outbreaks, 670–71
time spent eating or drinking, 469–70

Forestry
grading timber, 730–31

Gambling. *See also* **Game(s)**
betting on sports, 290–91
casino visits, 290
level of education and, 674
Little Lotto, 313
lotteries, 310–11, 312, 322, 324
    Cash Five Lottery, 342
    instant winner, 319
    Powerball, 342
    state, 279, 289, 323, 675–77
Mega Millions, 313
perfecta, 312
roulette, 269, 282, 286–87, 321, 323, 342, 357, 442
    balance of wheel, 672
trifecta, 306

Game(s). *See also* **Gambling**
card dealing, 313–14
card drawing, 275–76, 277, 282, 297–98, 299, 322, 344
carnival, 367
coin toss, 258–59, 268, 269, 270–72, 286, 289
    cheating at, 515
Deal or No Deal?, 315–16
die/dice, 257, 259, 268, 269
    craps, 323–24
    fair, 268, 673
    loaded, 271, 654
    rolling, 94, 261, 262–63, 271, 289, 292
five-card stud, 323
Jumble, 324
Let's Make a Deal, 300–301
Lingo, 319
poker
    flush, 300
    royal flush, 300
    seven-card stud, 268
    stud, 268, 323
Text Twist, 319
World Championship Punkin Chunkin contest, 690–91
zero-sum, 339

Gardening
planting tulips, 269, 299

Gender
aggression and, 516, 517
bias at University of California, Berkeley, 244–45
lupus and, 560
marital happiness and, 247
marital status and, 292–93
political party affiliation and, 246
recumbent length by, 158

Genetics
Huntington's disease, 270
sickle-cell anemia, 269

Geography
highest elevation for continents, 79
random sample of states, 28
soil testing, 729–30

Geology
age of Stonehenge, 580–81
Calistoga Old Faithful (California) geyser, 140, 155–56, 182
density of Earth, 419
earthquakes, 96
Old Faithful geyser (Calistoga, California), 233–34
Old Faithful geyser (Yellowstone Park), 439
    time between eruptions, 188

Government
civil liberties, 620
fighting terrorism, 616–17, 620
IRS audits, 290
Social Security numbers, 312
Social Security reform, 449
state, 12
supermajority in, 579
trust in, 578
type of, 9

Grains. *See* **Agriculture**

Health. *See also* **Exercise; Medicine; Mental health**
age and height, 187, 188
alcohol dependence treatment, 54
alcohol effects on the brain, 548
allergy sufferers, 355, 356, 453

asthma control, 356
blood chemistry, 421–23
blood pressure, 158
    hypertension, 57, 509–10
    intracellular calcium, 158
body mass index, 619
bone mineral density and cola consumption, 62, 201, 220
brain tumors and cell phones, 16
cancer, 298
    cell phones and brain tumors, 16
    childhood, in relation to distance from high voltage power lines, 540
    cigar smoking and, 283
    death due to, 298, 300
    leukemia and proximity to high-tension wires, 20
    lung, 18
    passive smoke and lung cancer, 22
    power lines and, 21–22
    prostate, tomatoes and, 57
    skin, 404
    skin, coffee consumption and, 20
cholesterol, 38, 367, 378–79, 494, 558, 577, 725, 753, 754, 755–56
    age and, 204–5, 737–39, 741, 744–46, 747, 751, 757
    dieting and, 692–93, 700
    in men vs. women, 638–39
    saturated fat and, 760–63, 767, 768
    serum HDL, 97–98, 165, 204, 472
college students' health-risk behaviors, 270
common cold, 364
doctor visits, 282
education and, 668
effect of Lipitor on cardiovascular disease, 46–47
eliminating syphilis, 122
fertility rate, 124
fitness club member satisfaction, 37
flu shots for seniors, 17
ginkgo and memory, 55
hand-washing behavior, 495–96
happiness and, 246–47, 634, 668
hazardous activities, participation in, 620
health care expenditures, 118
health-risk behaviors among college students, 76
hearing problems, 282, 447–48
HIV test false positives, 289
hospital admissions, 77
hygiene habits, 12
indoor tanning, 450
injuries requiring rehabilitation, 136–37
insomnia, 55
insurance, 97, 116, 298
    age and, 300
life expectancy, 287, 288, 289
live births, 120
Lyme disease versus drownings, 207
male survival rate, 357
marriage/cohabitation and weight gain, 21
migraine sufferers, 355, 356, 416
    massage therapy for, 522
obesity, 43, 207
    in adult men, 291
    artery calcification and, 21
    television in the bedroom and, 21
overweight, 43, 118
    in children, 521
para-nonylphenol effects, 548
paternal smoking habits and birth weight, 183
physical rehabilitation of patient, 67, 68, 69–70
pregnancy
    E.P.T. Pregnancy Tests, 290
    energy needs during, 451–52
St. John's wort and depression, 55
salmonella, 670–71
self-injurious behavior, 367
self-treatment with dietary supplements, 58
skinfold thickness procedure, 187
sleeping habits of students, 43
sleep time for postpartum women, 578–79
smoking, 247, 355, 356, 416, 453, 620
    birth weight and, 222–23
    cigar, 283, 298, 300

cigarettes smoked per day, 543–45
  education level and, 640
  heart rate, 701
  hypnosis and, 640
  lung cancer and, 18
  by mothers, 559
  population of smokers, 299
  profile of smokers, 668
  quitting, 368, 474–75
  tar and nicotine levels in cigarettes, 749, 757
  weight gain after smoking cessation, 640
spina bifida, 364
sunscreens and, 404
television stations and life expectancy, 207
tooth whitener, 54
Tylenol tablets, 182
vision problems, 282
waist circumference of males, 420
water quality, 237
weight gain during pregnancy, 437–38
weight loss, 73
weight of college students, 43
weights of males versus females, 186
West Nile virus, 486
women, aspirin, and heart attacks, 670

Height(s)
arm span vs., 638, 639
average
  of men vs. women, 173
  of women, 537
of baseball players, 236, 566, 752
of boys, 784
  sons vs. fathers, 592
  ten-year-old, 383
of females, 574
  five-year-old, 384
  three-year-old, 376–78, 379–80, 397–401
head circumference vs., 203–4, 219, 235, 756, 777–78
of males, 505–6

Houses and housing
apartments, 249–50, 318
  rents on, 250, 577–78, 782–83
construction of new homes, 116
garage door code, 312
home ownership, 495
home sales, 486
household winter temperature, 164–65
increase in assessments, 442, 449
mortgage rates, 568
number of rooms per unit, 282
paint comparisons, 57
paper towels, 607
price of, 99, 124, 777
  square footage and, 222
rental units, 341
second homes, 471
single-family home price, 521
square footage, 164
vacation homes, 471
valuation of, 786–88
water filtration, 237

Insurance
auto, 568
  collision claims, 169–70, 171, 172, 633
health, 116
life, 341–42, 368
term life policy, 337

Intelligence
brain size and, 205, 220–21, 778–79
head size and, 734–35
IQ scores, 94–95, 141, 143–44, 150, 156, 157, 428–30, 432, 441, 460–61, 473, 486, 508
Mozart effect, 568

Internet
connection time to ISP, 140
content creation by teens, 488–91
frequency of use of, 76
high-speed access to, 355, 495
hits to Web site, 362, 364
online auctions, 76
online homework, 79–80, 606
parents' attitudes toward, 75
problems with spam, 77
searches using Google, 356

time online, 122
  on MySpace.com, 469
time viewing a Web page, 100
users of, 74
time watching television, 548

Investment(s)
beta of a stock, 236–37
diversification, 158, 206–7
dividend yield, 98, 165
earnings predictions, 550
expected profit from, 342
of inheritance, 678, 733
in mutual funds
  risk of, 565
  selection of, 156
P/E ratio, 701
rate of return on, 109, 156, 160–61, 163–64, 440, 497, 516, 517, 691
  choosing based on, 641
  comparing, 635
  of Google, 174
  mean, 639
  standard deviation, 579
in real estate, 342
risk of, 502
in Roth IRA, 84–88, 90–91, 93, 102–4
in second homes, 471
stock price, 104–5, 107, 108
United Technologies vs. S&P 500, 749–50, 757
in vacation home, 471
volatility of stock, 621–22, 625–27
volume of stock
  Altria Group, 98
  Dell Computer, 538
  General Electric and Pfizer, comparing, 634–35
  Google, 538–39
  Harley-Davidson, 484
  PepsiCo, 484–85

Journalism
Americans' perception of, 494

Landscaping
golf course, 313

Language
spoken at home, 282

Law(s)
chief justices, 185–86
death penalty, 495, 619
driver's license, 13
fair packaging and labeling, 521
gun control, 43, 495
jury selection, 313, 356

Law enforcement
age of death-row inmates, 549
catching speeders, 294, 506
jury duty as civic duty, 638
police dispatch, 363
racial profiling, 356, 653–54
sentence length for men vs. women, 639

Leisure and recreation. *See also* **Entertainment**
Boy Scouts merit badge requirements, 27
Boy Scout troop, 341
fishing, 155
kids and, 606
Nielsen ratings, 368
Six Flags over Mid-America, 271
theme park spending, 505
vacation time, dissatisfaction with, 420
waiting in line, 592
  at amusement ride, 382, 408–9, 481–82, 712

Literacy. *See* **Reading**

Manufacturing
ball bearings, 403
copper tubing, 452
potato chips, 523–26
to specifications, 579
steel rods, 403

Marriage
gender and happiness in, 247
infidelity in, 43, 559
number of unemployed and number of, 251
unemployment rate and rate of, 251

Math
Benford's Law of frequency of digits, 274–75

Measurement. *See also* **Height(s); Weight(s)**
anthropometry, 173
mean height of students in class, 141
pH meter calibration, 549

Media
death penalty survey by, 560, 640
president's job approval rating, 559

Medicine. *See also* **Drugs; Health; Pharmaceuticals**
abortion, 246, 640
alcohol dependence treatment, 54
Alzheimer's disease treatment, 60
antibiotics for children, 517–18, 519, 520–21
blood chemistry, 421–23
blood type, 78, 269, 289, 344, 345–46
cancer medication, 20
Cancer Prevention Study II, 60
carpal tunnel syndrome, 20
cholesterol level, 38, 367, 378–79, 494, 558, 577, 725, 753, 754, 755–56
  age and, 737–39, 741, 744–46, 747, 751, 757
  HDL, 97–98, 165, 204–5, 472, 679, 680, 715, 717–20, 722–23
  saturated fat and, 760–63, 767, 768
clinical trials
  of Clarinex allergy medicine, 619
  of treatment of skin disorder, 619–20
coagulants and healing rate, 711
cold treatment, 629–30
cosmetic surgery, 74
depression therapy, 55
effect of Lipitor on cardiovascular disease, 46–47
epidurals, 13–14
flu season, 74
folate and hypertension, 13
gastric bypass, 640
hearing trouble, 447–48
hip arthroplasty, 693
homocysteine levels and cardiac hypertrophy, 642–43
hospitals
  admissions, 77, 141
  bacteria in, 605
  mean length of stay in for-profit, 637
  survival status of surgery patients, 251
kidney stones, treating, 247
Lipitor, 494, 558
live births, 96, 341
lupus, 560
osteoporosis treatment, 638
placebo effect, 283–84
poison ivy ointments, 614–15, 620
Prevnar vaccine, 555–56
Salk vaccine, 621
SARS epidemic, 483–84
sickle-cell anemia, 296–97
survival rate of patients with rare disease, 512
syphilis, 122
ulcers, 494
Viagra side effects, 272
wart treatment, 13, 633
West Nile virus, 486

Mental health
attention deficit-hyperactivity disorder, 449, 700–701
bipolar mania, 603–4, 629
psychological profiles of children, 693
schizophrenia, brain abnormalities and, 591

Meteorology. *See* **Weather**

Military
active-duty personnel, 114–15, 284
atomic bomb, protection from, 568
Iraq War, 620
night vision goggles, 60
peacekeeping missions, 36
Prussian army, 363
satellite defense system, 290
V-2 rocket hits in London, 655

Miscellaneous
aluminum bottles, 606
average height of men vs. women, 173
birthdays, 269, 282, 299–300
clothing options, 312

diameter of Douglas fir trees, 509
fingerprints, 291
fires, 324
gender preference for only child, 417
identity of A MOURNER, 190–91
lying, 417
pierced ears, 316
purchasing diamonds, 779–80
shark attacks, 109
sleeping, 469
tattoos, 316, 494, 568, 619
toilet flushing habits, 113–14

**Money. See also Finance;
    Investment(s)**
abolishing the penny, 495
FICO credit score, 548
income taxes, 620
real estate taxes, 538
retirement and, 558
weights of quarters, 188

Morality
moral values of candidates, 673
state of moral values in United States, 443–45,
    446, 613–14
unwed women having children, 634

Mortality
airline fatalities, 362
bicycle deaths, 654
death due to cancer, 298
motorcycle deaths, 653
pedestrian deaths, 654
Titanic disaster, 672
vehicle-related fatalities. *See under* Motor
    vehicle(s)

**Motor vehicle(s). See also
    Transportation**
accidents
    male vs. female rates, 205, 221
    red-light camera program and, 284
blood alcohol concentration (BAC) for drivers
    involved in, 469
BMWs, 13
braking distance, 593
car buying, 156, 189, 254, 785–86
car color, 77
carpoolers, 181
car rentals, 593
collision coverage claims, 169–70, 171, 172, 633
commuting to work
    via car-pooling, 493
    stress of, 494
Corvette, 3-year-old, 500, 517–18
crash data, 137, 154, 470, 691–92, 711, 732
death rates, 118
defensive driving, 731
dependability survey of, 99
depreciation of, 250, 254, 783
driving age, 367
driving under the influence, 290
    simulator for, 593
emissions test, 60, 569
engine additives, 522
fatalities, 363
    alcohol-related, 95, 322
    driver, 284, 298, 300
fuel catalysts, 538
gas mileage/fuel economy, 99, 384, 440, 504,
    566, 770–73
engine size/ curb weight/ horsepower
    and, 778
    in Ford Mustang, 484
    octane and, 711
    weight vs., 204, 205–6, 219–20, 235–36
gasoline prices, 470
gas price hike, 118
male 16-year-old drivers, 259
miles on a Hummer, 471–73
new Hyundai Elantras, 319
new versus used car satisfaction, 251
octane in fuel, 57, 593–94
oil change, 440, 726–27
Platinum Gassaver, 522
price of cars, 172, 185
production, 107
seatbelt wearing, 270

speeding tickets, 186, 294
speed limits, 45
student car ownership, 5
tires
    testing, 487
    wear on, 418, 704–6
Music
effect on learning, 50
Mozart for unborn babies, IQ and, 568
rhythm & blues vs. alternative, 605
Neurology
brain abnormalities and schizophrenia, 591
Nutrition. See also Food
antioxidants, 702–3
bone mineral density and cola consumption,
    62, 201, 220
breakfast cereal, 783–84
caffeinated sports drinks, 53–54
calcium consumption, 557–58, 618
calories
    burning of, 115
    in cheeseburgers, 249
    sugar vs., 234, 750–51, 757
carbohydrates in smoked turkey, 565
chicken consumption, 670–71
cholesterol in diet
    dieting and, 692–93, 700
daily dietary supplement, 539
diets
    low-carbohydrate, 443
    weight gain and, 707, 708–9
    Zone diet, 579
dissolving rates of vitamins, 182
eating together, 559
energy needs during pregnancy, 451–52
fast-food, 98, 100, 785
fat in, 98, 100
    in cheeseburgers, 249
    saturated, 760–63, 767, 768
nutrient intake of American children, 701–2
overweight, 118
in pregnancy, 726
skim vs. whole milk, 701–2
Obstetrics. See also Pediatrics
birth(s)
    by day of week, 650–51, 690
    ethnicity and delivery method, 246
    gestation period versus weight at, 322
    by month, 654
    multiple, 165, 270, 281–82
    premature, level of education and, 672
prenatal care, 667–68
sleeping patterns of pregnant women, 578
weight gain during pregnancy, 437–38
Optometry
eyeglasses, 551
Pediatrics. See also Obstetrics
age of mother at childbirth, 166
birth weight, 135, 164, 173, 294, 322, 382, 383,
    403–4, 538, 577, 578, 655, 726
    smoking and, 183, 222–23
breast-feeding and obesity, 207
crawling babies, 485, 501
heights
    of five-year-old females, 384
    head circumference vs., 203–4, 219, 235, 748,
        756, 777–78
    of ten-year-old males, 383
    of three-year-old females, 376–77, 379–80,
        397–401
spina bifida, 364
vitamin A supplements in low-birth-weight
    babies, 630
Pets
talking to, 559
**Pharmaceuticals. See also Drugs;
    Medicine**
Accupril, 620
alcohol dependence treatment, 54
Celebrex, 669
cholesterol research, 38
cholestyramine, 664–66
Clarinex, 619
cold medication, 54, 583–84
drug effectiveness, 56

drug regulation of HDL, 715, 717–20, 722–23
experimental drug effects on hemoglobin
    levels, 714–15
hair growth drug, 679, 680
Lipitor, 46–47, 494, 558
memory drug, 55
Nasonex, 608–9, 610–13
Nexium, 558
pain relievers, 568
Pepcid, 494
Prevnar, 619
skin ointment, 62
Tylenol tablets, 182
Zocor, 664–66
Zoloft, 640
Physics
catapults, 731
catching falling meter stick, 584, 585–88, 589,
    590
muzzle velocity, 185, 591
tensile strength, 732–33
Physiology
fat-free mass vs. energy expenditure, 750, 757
flexibility, 606
reaction time, 55–56
step pulses, 606
Politics
civic duty to vote, 638
elections
    county, 37
    presidential, 45, 77, 172, 494, 495
estate taxes, 36
exit polls, 44
Future Government Club, 28, 37
health care and health insurance, 38
mayor and small business owners, 60
moral values of candidates, 673
party affiliation, 120
    education and, 669–70
    gender and, 246
political views, 141
poll of voters, 20
presidents
    age at inauguration, 98, 181, 471
    birthplaces of, 79
    inaugural addresses, 187
    inauguration costs, 115
    job approval rating, 559
    random sample of, 28
public knowledge about, 12
public policy survey, 61
right-to-die battle and political party, 111–12
Senate committee selection, 313
student government satisfaction survey, 283
village poll, 28
voter polls, 39
Polls and surveys
on abortion, 246
alcoholic beverage consumption among high
    school students, 142
of city residents, 37
Current Population Survey, 44
customer satisfaction, 61
election, 39, 45, 60
e-mail survey, 43
exit, 44
faculty opinion, 27
family values, 494
on financial worries, 14
on frequency of having sex, 43
of gender of children in family, 264–65, 266–67
about gun-control laws, 6
on happiness and health, 246–47
on happiness in marriage, 247
on high-speed Internet service, 60
on hour of day or night when personally at
    one's best, 14
on immigration debate, 246
informed opinion, 45
on life satisfaction, 449, 488
on number of drinks, 486
order of the questions in, 44, 45
police department, 43
political, 20
population, 39

random digit dialing, 44
rotating choices, 44
on state of moral values in the country, 613–14
student opinion, 27–28, 37
student sample for, 37
on tattoos, 494
on televisions in the household, 97, 100
traditional journalism, 494
village, 28
wording of questions, 45

Psychiatry
attention deficit-hyperactivity disorder, 700–701
bipolar mania, 603–4, 629

Psychology
depression, 55
gender differences in reaction to instruction, 57
insomnia relief, 55

Psychometrics
IQ scores, 94–95, 141, 143, 150–52, 153, 156, 157, 428–30, 432, 441, 460–61, 473, 486, 508
stimulus response, 591

Race/ethnicity
mothers' method of delivery and, 246

Reading
amount of time devoted to, 472
number of books read, 419, 483
rates, 439, 549

Recreation. *See Leisure and recreation*

Religion
Roman Catholics, 493–94
teen prayer, 578

Residential. *See Houses and housing*

Sex and sexuality
sexual intercourse frequency, 43, 486

Social work
truancy deterrence, 56

Society
abortion issue, 246, 640, 668
affirmative action, 495
charitable contributions, 521
civic duty to vote and serve, 638
day care enrollment, 269
death penalty, 495, 619
divorce rate, 98
dog ownership, 269
family structure and sexual activity, 667
housing prices, 99
marijuana use, 522
poverty, 74, 88–90, 165
Social Security, 449
superstition, 494
unwed women having children, 634
Valentine's Day dread, 494
volunteerism, 269

Sports
baseball
baseballs manufacturing, 419
batting averages, 12, 157, 339, 452
batting champions, 173
Bonds's 756th homerun ball, 61
Boston Red Sox, 324
cold streaks, 290
designated hitter, 605
ERA, 109, 173
heights and weights of players, 236, 566, 752
home runs, 100, 271, 323
most hits in season, 340
on-base percentage, 218–19
predictions, 325
run production, 167–68
salaries by position, 78
starting lineup, 313
winning percentage, 206, 218
World Series, 267, 341, 672
basketball, 141, 269
free throws, 95, 332, 334, 335–36, 344, 357
hot streaks, 290
O'Neal's points per season, 108
performance consistency, 566
betting on, 290–91
bowling, 290

caffeinated sports drinks, 53–54, 509
car racing
Daytona 500, 317–18
INDY 500, 312
5-kilometer race, 176–78
football
completion rate for passes, 60
fans, 495
futsal starting lineups, 318
golf, 193–95, 197–99, 200, 209–17, 223–25, 226, 230, 231–32, 269, 299, 307
balls, 549
club comparisons, 56
disc golf, 485, 501–2
pitching wedge, 384
greyhound races, 406–8
high school students participating in, 269, 357
hockey, 366
human growth hormone (HGH) use among high school athletes, 36
NASCAR, 290
Olympics, 324
soccer, 114, 318
captains in, 27
softball, 566
tennis
men's singles at Wimbledon, 123, 368, 472, 473
prize money at Wimbledon, 108
Wimbledon men's singles championship (1968-2007), 123
Tour de France, 139–40

Surveys. *See Polls and surveys*

Temperature
cricket chirps vs., 253, 784
heat index, 776
household winter, 164–65
of humans, 548–49
predicted, accuracy of, 550
of a probe over time, 228
wind chill, 235, 776

Test(s)
ACT, 537, 554–55, 558–59
scores, 106–7, 117, 158
vs. SAT, 750
essay, 319
exam scores, 144, 145–46, 147–50
IQ scores, 94–95, 141, 143–44, 150–52, 153, 156, 157, 428–30, 432, 441, 460–61, 473, 486, 508
multiple-choice, 61, 324
preparation for, 522
results as related to conditions of, 721–22
SAT, 319
math portion, 157, 521, 522, 537
penalty, 342
reasoning portion, 527–28, 530–32
scores, 107, 112–13, 158, 165, 168, 522, 527–28, 530–32, 539, 574–75, 630
scores on college application, 188
Wechsler Intelligence Scale, 418–19
for Children (WISC), 486

Time
answering or writing email, 578
to change oil, 440
on eating or drinking, 469–70
between eruptions of Old Faithful in Yellowstone National Park, 188
flight, 137, 154
incubation, 382, 402
learning, 733
online, 122, 469
connecting to ISP, 140
downloading, 37
viewing Web page, 100
on phone calls, 510, 578
reaction, 55–56, 138–39, 154, 382, 591, 631, 691, 725–26
alcohol effects on, 590
to catch falling meter stick, 584, 585–88, 589, 590
male vs. female, 604
reading, 472
sleep, for postpartum women, 578–79
to study, 236, 420

temperature of a probe over, 228
travel, 139, 175
to school, 155
to work, 157, 186, 470, 484, 535, 559, 637
waiting, 97, 100, 630
in drive-through, 638, 639
lateness of friend, 373–74

Transportation. *See also Motor vehicle(s)*
alcohol-related traffic fatalities, 95
carpoolers, 181, 493
flight time, 137, 154
highway speeds, 457–58, 463–67
male versus female accident rate, 205, 221
on-time flights, 416
potholes, 362
seatbelt use, 505, 620
streetlight replacement, 569

Travel
air
airport codes, 303
fatalities, 362
fear of flying, 449
flight time, 154
glide testing single-propeller-driven aircraft, 594
on-time flights, 355, 356
satisfaction with, 355
walking in airport, 604
creative thinking during, 419
driving age, 367
fear of flying, 449
lodging prices, 711–12
means of, to work, 261–62
time for, 139, 175
commuting to work, 157, 186, 470, 484, 535, 559, 637
to school, 155
Titanic survivors, 318–19
voyage of the *St. Andrew*, 370–71

Utilities
electric rates, 99

Weapons. *See Firearms*

Weather
daily high temperatures, 156
forecast, 319, 550
heat index, 776
hurricanes, 363
Memphis snowfall, 411
rainfall
April showers, 174
days of, 298
snowfall, 187
tornadoes, 126–27
wind chill, 235, 776

Weight(s)
of baseball players, 236
body mass index, 619
gain after smoking cessation, 640
head circumference and, 777–78
net, 579

Work. *See also Business*
civilian labor force, 283
commuting to, 157, 282–83, 470, 484, 535, 559, 637
car-pooling, 493
stress of, 494
critical job skills, 559
distribution of class of workers in Memphis, Tennessee, 322
employee morale, 29, 37
at home, 559
hours at, 469
income and, 777
marginal distribution of a variable, 238–44
marriage and
children and, 283
unemployment and, 251
means of travel to, 261–62
multiple jobs, 299
teaching profession, 559
unemployment, 107–8, 251
walking to, 513
working students, 140

PART 1

Getting the Information You Need

CHAPTER 1
Data Collection

Statistics is a process—a series of steps that leads to a goal. This text is divided into four parts to help the reader see the process of statistics.

Part 1 focuses on the first step in the process, which is to determine the research objective or question to be answered. Then information is obtained to answer the questions stated in the research objective.

Data Collection

Outline

1.1 Introduction to the Practice of Statistics

1.2 Observational Studies versus Designed Experiments

1.3 Simple Random Sampling

1.4 Other Effective Sampling Methods

1.5 Bias in Sampling

1.6 The Design of Experiments

Note to Instructor

Due to the tremendous number of terms in this chapter, you may want students to create a list of terms, definitions, and their own examples for each term. This will allow students to make a personal connection to the concepts and will lead to a greater understanding of the vocabulary. Remind students that many terms presented in this chapter will be presented again in upcoming chapters, so they should not feel overwhelmed by the number of definitions.

MAKING AN INFORMED DECISION

It is Monday morning and already you are thinking about Friday night—movie night. You don't trust the movie reviews published by professional critics, so you decide to survey "regular" people yourself. You need to design a questionnaire that can be used to help you make an informed decision about whether to attend a particular movie. See the Decisions project on page 62.

PUTTING IT TOGETHER

Statistics plays a major role in many different areas of our lives. For example, it is used in sports to help a general manager decide which player might be the best fit for a team. It is used by politicians to help them understand how the public feels about various governmental policies. Statistics is used to help determine the effectiveness (efficacy) of experimental drugs.

Used appropriately, statistics can provide an understanding of the world around us. Used inappropriately, it can lend support to inaccurate beliefs. Understanding the methodologies of statistics will provide you with the ability to analyze and critique studies. With this ability, you will be an informed consumer of information, which will enable you to distinguish solid analysis from the bogus presentation of numerical "facts."

To help you understand the features of this text, and for hints to help you study, read the Pathway to Success on the front inside cover of the text.

1.1 INTRODUCTION TO THE PRACTICE OF STATISTICS

> **Objectives**
>
> **1** Define statistics and statistical thinking
> **2** Explain the process of statistics
> **3** Distinguish between qualitative and quantitative variables
> **4** Distinguish between discrete and continuous variables
> **5** Determine the level of measurement of a variable

1 Define Statistics and Statistical Thinking

Note to Instructor

This first objective defines what statistics is, but also lists some key elements to solid statistical thinking.

1. *Anecdotal claims can be refuted with statistical analysis.*
2. *Poorly collected data are not useful.*
3. *Watch out for lurking variables in a study.*
4. *Results in statistics are not certain.*

The Guidelines for Assessment and Instruction in Statistics Education (GAISE) report suggests these as major components of statistical thinking.

What is statistics? When asked this question, many people respond that statistics is numbers. After all, we are bombarded by numbers that supposedly represent how we feel and who we are. For example, we hear on the radio that 50% of first marriages, 67% of second marriages, and 74% of third marriages end in divorce (Forest Institute of Professional Psychology, Springfield, MO).

Another interesting consideration about the "facts" we hear or read is that two different sources can report two different results. For example, a July 12–15, 2007, Gallup poll indicated that 66% of Americans disapproved of the job that Congress was doing. However, a July 25–29, 2007, poll conducted by the Pew Research Center indicated that 54% of Americans disapproved of the job that Congress was doing. Is it possible that Congress's disapproval rating could decrease by 12% in less than 2 weeks or is something else going on? Statistics helps to provide the answer.

Certainly, statistics has a lot to do with numbers, but this definition is only partially correct. Statistics is also about where the numbers come from (that is, how they were obtained) and how closely the numbers reflect reality.

Definition   **Statistics** is the science of collecting, organizing, summarizing, and analyzing information to draw conclusions or answer questions. In addition, statistics is about providing a measure of confidence in any conclusions.

It is helpful to consider this definition in four parts. The first part of the definition states that statistics involves the collection of information. The second refers to the organization and summarization of information. The third states that the information is analyzed to draw conclusions or answer specific questions. The fourth part states that results should be reported with some measure that represents how convinced we are that our conclusions reflect reality.

What is the information referred to in the definition? The information is *data*. The *American Heritage Dictionary* defines **data** as "a fact or proposition used to draw a conclusion or make a decision." Data can be numerical, as in height, or nonnumerical, as in gender. In either case, data describe characteristics of an individual. The reason that data are important in statistics can be seen in this definition: data are used to draw a conclusion or make a decision.

In Other Words
Anecdotal means that the information being conveyed is based on casual observation, not scientific research.

Analysis of data can lead to powerful results. Data can be used to offset anecdotal claims, such as the suggestion that cellular telephones cause brain cancer. After carefully collecting, summarizing, and analyzing data regarding this phenomenon, it was determined that there is no link between cell phone usage and brain cancer. See Examples 1 and 2 in Section 1.2.

Because data are powerful, they can be dangerous when misused. The misuse of data usually occurs when data are incorrectly obtained or analyzed. For example, radio or television talk shows regularly ask poll questions for which respondents must call in or use the Internet to supply their vote. Most likely, the individuals who are going to call in are those that have a strong opinion about the topic. This group is not likely to be representative of people in general, so the results of the poll are not meaningful. Whenever we look at data, we should be mindful of where the data come from.

Even when data tell us that a relation exists, we need to investigate. For example, a study showed that breast-fed children have higher IQs than those who were not breast-fed. Does this study mean that mothers should breast-feed their children? Not necessarily. It may be that some other factor contributes to the IQ of the children. In this case, it turns out that mothers who breast-feed generally have higher IQs than those who do not. Therefore, it may be genetics that leads to the higher IQ, not breast-feeding. This illustrates an idea in statistics known as the *lurking variable*. In statistics, we must consider lurking variables, because two variables are often influenced by a third variable. A good statistical study will have a way of dealing with lurking variables.

A key aspect of data is that they vary. To help understand this variability, consider the students in your classroom. Is everyone the same height? No. Does everyone have the same color hair? No. So, among a group of individuals there is variation. Now consider yourself. Do you eat the same amount of food each day? No. Do you sleep the same number of hours each day? No. So, even looking at an individual there is variation. Data vary. One goal of statistics is to describe and understand the sources of variation. Variability in data may help to explain the different results obtained by Gallup and Pew mentioned at the beginning of this section.

Because of this variability, the results that we obtain using data can vary. This is a very different idea than what you may be used to from your mathematics classes. In mathematics, if Bob and Jane are asked to solve $3x + 5 = 11$, they will both obtain $x = 2$ as the solution, if they use the correct procedures. In statistics, if Bob and Jane are asked to estimate the average commute time for workers in Dallas, Texas, they will likely get different answers, even though they both use the correct procedure. The different answers occur because they likely surveyed different individuals, and these individuals have different commute times. Note: The only way Bob and Jane would get the same result is if they both asked *all* commuters or the same commuters how long it takes to get to work, but how likely is this?

So, in mathematics when a problem is solved correctly, the results can be reported with 100% certainty. In statistics, when a problem is solved, the results do not have 100% certainty. In statistics, we might say that we are 95% confident that the average commute time in Dallas, Texas, is between 20 and 23 minutes. While uncertain results may sound disturbing now, it will become more apparent what this means as we proceed through the course.

Without certainty, how can statistics be useful? Statistics can provide an understanding of the world around us because recognizing where variability in data comes from can help us to control it. Understanding the techniques presented in this text will provide you with powerful tools that will give you the ability to analyze and critique media reports, make investment decisions (such as what mutual fund to invest in), or conduct research on major purchases (such as what type of car you should buy). This will help to make you an informed consumer of information and guide you in becoming a critical and statistical thinker.

2 Explain the Process of Statistics

Consider the following scenario.

> You are walking down the street and notice that a person walking in front of you drops $100. Nobody seems to notice the $100 except you. Since you could keep the money without anyone knowing, would you keep the money or return it to the owner?

Note: Certainly, obtaining a truthful response to a question such as this is challenging. In Section 1.5, we present some techniques for obtaining truthful responses to sensitive questions. ◀

Suppose you wanted to use this scenario as a gauge of the morality of students at your school by determining the percent of students who would return the money. How might you go about doing this? Well, you could attempt to present the scenario to every student at the school, but this is likely to be difficult or impossible since the number of enrolled students is likely large. A second possibility is to present the scenario to 50 students and use the results from these 50 students to make a statement about all the students at the school.

Figure 1

Population

Sample

Individual

Definitions

The entire group of individuals to be studied is called the **population**. An **individual** is a person or object that is a member of the population being studied. A **sample** is a subset of the population that is being studied. See Figure 1.

In the scenario presented, the population is all the students at the school. Each student is an individual. The sample is the 50 students selected to participate in the study.

Suppose 39 of the 50 students stated that they would return the money to the owner. We could present this result by saying the percent of students in the survey that stated they would return the money to the owner is 78%. This is an example of a *descriptive statistic* because it describes the results of the sample without making any general conclusions about the population.

Definitions

A **statistic** is a numerical summary of a sample. **Descriptive statistics** consist of organizing and summarizing data. Descriptive statistics describe data through numerical summaries, tables, and graphs.

So 78% is a statistic because it is based on a sample. Descriptive statistics make it easier to get an overview of what the data are telling us.

If we extend the results of our sample to the population and say that the proportion of all students at the school who would return the money is 78%, we are performing *inferential statistics*.

Definition

Inferential statistics uses methods that take a result from a sample, extend it to the population, and measure the reliability of the result.

When generalizing to a population from a sample, there is always uncertainty as to the accuracy of the generalization, because we cannot learn everything about a population by looking at a sample. Therefore, when performing inferential statistics, we always report a measure that quantifies how confident we are in our results. So, rather than saying that 78% of all students would return the money, we might say that we are 95% confident that between 76% and 80% of all students would return the money. Notice how this inferential statement includes a level of confidence (measure of reliability) in our results. It also provides a range of values to account for the variability in our results.

One goal of inferential statistics is to use statistics to estimate *parameters*.

Definition

A **parameter** is a numerical summary of a population.

EXAMPLE 1	**Parameter versus Statistic**

Suppose the percentage of all students on your campus that own a car is 48.2%. This value represents a parameter because it is a numerical summary of a population. Suppose a sample of 100 students is obtained, and from this sample we find that 46% own a car. This value represents a statistic because it is a numerical summary of a sample.

Now Work Problem 13

The methods of statistics follow a process.

> **The Process of Statistics**
>
> **1.** *Identify the research objective.* A researcher must determine the question(s) he or she wants answered. The question(s) must be detailed so that it identifies the population that is to be studied.
>
> **2.** *Collect the data needed to answer the question(s) posed in (1).* Gaining access to an entire population is often difficult and expensive. When conducting research, we typically look at a sample. The collection-of-data step is vital to the statistical process, because if the data are not collected correctly, the conclusions drawn are meaningless. Do not overlook the importance of appropriate data-collection processes. We discuss this step in detail in Sections 1.2 through 1.6.
>
> **3.** *Describe the data.* Obtaining descriptive statistics allows the researcher to obtain an overview of the data and can provide insight as to the type of statistical methods the researcher should use. We discuss this step in detail in Chapters 2 through 4.
>
> **4.** *Perform inference.* Apply the appropriate techniques to extend the results obtained from the sample to the population and report a level of reliability of the results. We discuss techniques for measuring reliability in Chapters 5 through 8 and inferential techniques in Chapters 9 through 15.

◇ **CAUTION** Many nonscientific studies are based on *convenience samples*, such as Internet surveys or phone-in polls. The results of any study performed using this type of sampling method are not reliable.

Note to Instructor
Notice how the parts of the text are divided according to the process of statistics. As you enter a new part of the course, be sure to remind students where they are in the process of statistics.

EXAMPLE 2 **The Process of Statistics: Do You Favor Stricter Gun Laws?**

A poll was conducted by the Gallup Organization on October 4–7, 2007, to learn how Americans feel about existing gun-control laws. The following statistical process allowed the researchers at Gallup to conduct their study.

1. *Identify the research objective.* The researchers wished to determine the percentage of Americans aged 18 years or older who were in favor of more strict gun-control laws. Therefore, the population being studied was Americans aged 18 years or older.

2. *Collect the information needed to answer the question posed in (1).* It is unreasonable to expect to survey the more than 200 million Americans aged 18 years or older to determine how they feel about gun-control laws. So the researchers surveyed a sample of 1,010 Americans aged 18 years or older. Of those surveyed, 515 stated they were in favor of more strict laws covering the sale of firearms.

3. *Describe the data.* Of the 1,010 individuals in the survey, 51% (= 515/1,010) are in favor of more strict laws covering the sale of firearms. This is a descriptive statistic because its value is determined from a sample.

4. *Perform inference.* The researchers at Gallup wanted to extend the results of the survey to all Americans aged 18 years or older. Remember, when generalizing results from a sample to a population, the results are uncertain. To account for this uncertainty, Gallup reported a 3% *margin of error*. This means that Gallup feels fairly certain (in fact, Gallup is 95% certain) that the percentage of *all* Americans aged 18 years or older in favor of more strict laws covering the sale of firearms is somewhere between 48% (51% − 3%) and 54% (51% + 3%).

Now Work Problem 57

Distinguish between Qualitative and Quantitative Variables

Once a research objective is stated, a list of the information the researcher desires about the individuals must be created. **Variables** are the characteristics of the individuals within the population. For example, this past spring my son and I planted a tomato plant in our backyard. We decided to collect some information about the tomatoes harvested from the plant. The individuals we studied were the tomatoes. The variable that interested us was the weight of the tomatoes. My son noted that the tomatoes had different weights even though they all came from the same plant. He discovered that variables such as weight vary.

If variables did not vary, they would be constants, and statistical inference would not be necessary. Think about it this way: If all the tomatoes had the same weight, then knowing the weight of one tomato would be sufficient to determine the weights of all tomatoes. However, the weights vary from one tomato to the next. One goal of research is to learn the causes of the variability so that we can learn to grow plants that yield the best tomatoes.

Variables can be classified into two groups: *qualitative* or *quantitative*.

Definitions

Qualitative, or categorical, variables allow for classification of individuals based on some attribute or characteristic.

Quantitative variables provide numerical measures of individuals. Arithmetic operations such as addition and subtraction can be performed on the values of a quantitative variable and will provide meaningful results.

Many examples in this text will include a suggested **approach**, or a way to look at and organize a problem so that it can be solved. The approach will be a suggested method of *attack* toward solving the problem. This does not mean that the approach given is the only way to solve the problem, because many problems have more than one approach leading to a correct solution. For example, if you turn the key in your car's ignition and it doesn't start, one approach would be to look under the hood to try to determine what is wrong. (Of course, this approach will work only if you know how to fix cars.) A second, equally valid approach would be to call an automobile mechanic to service the car.

In Other Words
Typically, there is more than one correct approach to solving a problem.

EXAMPLE 3   Distinguishing between Qualitative and Quantitative Variables

Problem: Determine whether the following variables are qualitative or quantitative.
(a) Gender
(b) Temperature
(c) Number of days during the past week that a college student aged 21 years or older has had at least one drink
(d) Zip code

Approach: Quantitative variables are numerical measures such that meaningful arithmetic operations can be performed on the values of the variable. Qualitative variables describe an attribute or characteristic of the individual that allows researchers to categorize the individual.

Solution
(a) Gender is a qualitative variable because it allows a researcher to categorize the individual as male or female. Notice that arithmetic operations cannot be performed on these attributes.

(b) Temperature is a quantitative variable because it is numeric, and operations such as addition and subtraction provide meaningful results. For example, 70°F is 10°F warmer than 60°F.

(c) Number of days during the past week that a college student aged 21 years or older had at least one drink is a quantitative variable because it is numeric, and operations such as addition and subtraction provide meaningful results.

(d) Zip code is a qualitative variable because it categorizes a location. Notice that, even though they are numeric, the addition or subtraction of zip codes does not provide meaningful results.

Now Work Problem 21

On the basis of the result of Example 3(d), we conclude that a variable may be qualitative while having values that are numeric. Just because the value of a variable is numeric does not mean that the variable is quantitative.

4 Distinguish between Discrete and Continuous Variables

We can further classify quantitative variables into two types: *discrete* or *continuous*.

Definitions

In Other Words
If you count to get the value of a quantitative variable, it is discrete. If you measure to get the value of a quantitative variable, it is continuous. When deciding whether a variable is discrete or continuous, ask yourself if it is counted or measured.

A **discrete variable** is a quantitative variable that has either a finite number of possible values or a countable number of possible values. The term *countable* means that the values result from counting, such as 0, 1, 2, 3, and so on.

A **continuous variable** is a quantitative variable that has an infinite number of possible values that are not countable.

Figure 2 illustrates the relationship among qualitative, quantitative, discrete, and continuous variables.

Figure 2

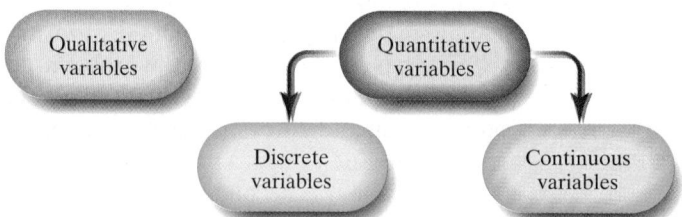

An example should help to clarify the definitions.

EXAMPLE 4 | **Distinguishing between Discrete and Continuous Variables**

Problem: Determine whether the following quantitative variables are discrete or continuous.

(a) The number of heads obtained after flipping a coin five times.

(b) The number of cars that arrive at a McDonald's drive-through between 12:00 P.M. and 1:00 P.M.

(c) The distance a 2007 Toyota Prius can travel in city driving conditions with a full tank of gas.

Approach: A variable is discrete if its value results from counting. A variable is continuous if its value is measured.

Solution

(a) The number of heads obtained by flipping a coin five times would be a discrete variable because we would count the number of heads obtained. The possible values of the discrete variable are 0, 1, 2, 3, 4, 5.

(b) The number of cars that arrive at a McDonald's drive-through between 12:00 P.M. and 1:00 P.M. is a discrete variable because its value would result from counting the cars. The possible values of the discrete variable are 0, 1, 2, 3, 4, and so on. Notice that there is no predetermined upper limit to the number of cars that may arrive.

(c) The distance traveled is a continuous variable because we measure the distance.

Now Work Problem 29

Continuous variables are often rounded. For example, when the miles per gallon (mpg) of gasoline for a certain make of car is given as 24 mpg, it means that the miles per gallon is greater than or equal to 23.5 and less than 24.5, or $23.5 \le \text{mpg} < 24.5$.

The type of variable (qualitative, discrete, or continuous) dictates the methods that can be used to analyze the data.

The list of observed values for a variable is **data**. Gender is a variable; the observations male or female are data. **Qualitative data** are observations corresponding to a qualitative variable. **Quantitative data** are observations corresponding to a quantitative variable. **Discrete data** are observations corresponding to a discrete variable, and **continuous data** are observations corresponding to a continuous variable.

EXAMPLE 5 **Distinguishing between Variables and Data**

Problem: Table 1 presents a group of selected countries and information regarding these countries as of October, 2007. Identify the individuals, variables, and data in Table 1.

Table 1			
Country	**Government Type**	**Life Expectancy (years)**	**Population (in millions)**
Australia	Federal parliamentary democracy	80.62	20.4
Canada	Constitutional monarchy	80.34	33.4
France	Republic	80.59	63.7
Morocco	Constitutional monarchy	71.22	33.8
Poland	Republic	75.19	38.52
Sri Lanka	Republic	74.80	20.93
United States	Federal republic	78.00	301.14

Source: CIA *World Factbook*

Approach: An individual is an object or person for whom we wish to obtain data. The variables are the characteristics of the individuals, and the data are the specific values of the variables.

Solution: The individuals in the study are the countries: Australia, Canada, and so on (in red ink). The variables measured for each country are *government type*, *life expectancy*, and *population* (in blue ink). The variable *government type* is qualitative because it categorizes the individual. The variables *life expectancy* and *population* are quantitative.

The quantitative variable *life expectancy* is continuous because it is measured. The quantitative variable *population* is discrete because we count people. The observations are the data (in green ink). For example, the data corresponding to the variable *life expectancy* are 80.62, 80.34, 80.59, 71.22, 75.19, 74.80, and 78.00. The following data correspond to the individual Poland: a *republic* government with residents whose *life expectancy* is 75.19 years and where *population* is 38.52 million people. Republic is an instance of qualitative data that results from observing the value of the qualitative variable *government type*. The life expectancy of 75.19 years is an instance of quantitative data that results from observing the value of the quantitative variable *life expectancy*.

Now Work Problem 51

Determine the Level of Measurement of a Variable

Rather than classify a variable as qualitative or quantitative, we can assign a level of measurement to the variable.

Definitions

A variable is at the **nominal level of measurement** if the values of the variable name, label, or categorize. In addition, the naming scheme does not allow for the values of the variable to be arranged in a ranked or specific order.

A variable is at the **ordinal level of measurement** if it has the properties of the nominal level of measurement and the naming scheme allows for the values of the variable to be arranged in a ranked or specific order.

A variable is at the **interval level of measurement** if it has the properties of the ordinal level of measurement and the differences in the values of the variable have meaning. A value of zero in the interval level of measurement does not mean the absence of the quantity. Arithmetic operations such as addition and subtraction can be performed on values of the variable.

A variable is at the **ratio level of measurement** if it has the properties of the interval level of measurement and the ratios of the values of the variable have meaning. A value of zero in the ratio level of measurement means the absence of the quantity. Arithmetic operations such as multiplication and division can be performed on the values of the variable.

In Other Words
The word *nominal* comes from the Latin word *nomen*, which means to name. When you see the word *ordinal*, think order.

Variables that are nominal or ordinal are qualitative variables, while variables that are interval or ratio are quantitative variables.

EXAMPLE 6 **Determining the Level of Measurement of a Variable**

Problem: For each of the following variables, determine the level of measurement.
(a) Gender
(b) Temperature
(c) Number of days during the past week that a college student aged 21 years or older has had at least one drink
(d) Letter grade earned in your statistics class

Approach: For each variable, we ask the following: Does the variable simply categorize each individual? If so, the variable is nominal. Does the variable categorize *and* allow ranking of each value of the variable? If so, the variable is ordinal. Do differences in values of the variable have meaning, but a value of zero does not mean the absence of the quantity? If so, the variable is interval. Do ratios of values of the variable have meaning *and* there is a natural zero starting point? If so, the variable is ratio.

Solution
(a) Gender is a variable measured at the nominal level because it only allows for categorization of male or female. Plus, it is not possible to rank gender classifications.
(b) Temperature is a variable measured at the interval level because differences in the value of the variable make sense. For example, 70°F is 10°F warmer than 60°F. Notice that the ratio of temperatures does not represent a meaningful result. For example, 60°F is not twice as warm as 30°F. In addition, 0°F does not represent the absence of heat.
(c) Number of days during the past week that a college student aged 21 years or older has had at least one drink is measured at the ratio level, because the ratio of two values makes sense and a value of zero has meaning. For example, a student who had four drinks had twice as many drinks as a student who had two drinks.

(d) Letter grade is a variable measured at the ordinal level because the values of the variable can be ranked, but differences in values have no meaning. For example, an A is better than a B, but A – B has no meaning.

Now Work Problem 37

When classifying variables according to their level of measurement, it is extremely important to be careful to recognize what the variable is intended to measure. For example, suppose we want to know whether cars with 4-cylinder engines get better gas mileage than cars with 6-cylinder engines. Here, engine size represents a category of data and so the variable is nominal. On the other hand, if we want to know the average number of cylinders in cars in the United States, the variable is classified as ratio (an 8-cylinder engine has twice as many cylinders as a 4-cylinder engine).

IN CLASS ACTIVITY

Validity, Reliability, and Variability

Divide the class into groups of four to six students.

(a) Select one student to be the group leader. Each student in the group measures the length of the right arm of the group leader. As the group leader is being measured, the other students in the group do not look on. Do not share the measurements obtained with others in the group until everyone has obtained a measurement! Record the results.

(b) The group leader measures the length of the right arm of each of the other students in the group. Record the results.

(c) Validity of a variable or measurement represents how close to the true value the measurement is. In other words, a variable is valid if it measures what it is supposed to measure. For example, if a student measured arm length from the shoulder to the wrist and another student measured arm length from the shoulder to the tip of the middle finger, the variable is not valid. How valid are the results obtained from part (a)? What could have been done by the group to increase the validity of the variable?

(d) Reliability of a variable or measurement represents the ability of different measurements of the same individual to yield the same results. How reliable are the measurements obtained in part (b)? Why is it likely that the results from part (b) are valid, but may not be reliable?

(e) Which set of data appears to have more variability, the data from part (a) or the data from part (b)? Why?

(f) Compare the results of all the groups. Which group do you think has the most valid results? Which group has the most reliable results?

Note to Instructor
The purpose of this activity is to expose students to variability in measuring variables. It also allows students to see the importance of defining a variable. It should take about 20 to 30 minutes.

1.1 ASSESS YOUR UNDERSTANDING

Concepts and Vocabulary

1. Define statistics.

2. Explain the difference between a population and a sample.

3. A(n) individual is a person or object that is a member of the population being studied.

4. Descriptive statistics consists of organizing and summarizing information collected, while inferential statistics uses methods that generalize results obtained from a sample to the population and measure the reliability of the results.

5. A(n) statistic is a numerical summary of sample. A(n) parameter is a numerical summary of a population.

6. Variables are the characteristics of the individuals of the population being studied.

7. Contrast the differences between qualitative and quantitative variables.

8. Discuss the differences between discrete and continuous variables.

9. In your own words, define the four levels of measurement of a variable. Give an example of each.

10. Explain what is meant when we say "data vary." How does this variability affect the results of statistical analysis?

11. Explain the process of statistics.

12. The age of a person is commonly considered to be a continuous random variable. Could it be considered a discrete random variable instead? Explain.

Skill Building

In Problems 13–20, determine whether the underlined value is a parameter or a statistic.

13. **State Government** Following the 2006 national midterm **NW** election, 18% of the governors of the 50 United States were female. Parameter

    Source: National Governors Association

14. **Calculus Exam** The average score for a class of 28 students taking a calculus midterm exam was 72%. Parameter

15. **Illegal Drugs** In a national survey of high school students (grades 9 to 12), 25% of respondents reported that someone had offered, sold, or given them an illegal drug on school property. Statistic

    Source: Bureau of Justice Statistics jointly with the U.S. Department of Education, *Indicators of School Crime and Safety, 2006*, December 2006

16. **Alcohol Use** In a national survey on substance abuse, 66.4% of respondents who were full-time college students aged 18 to 22 reported using alcohol within the past month. Statistic

    Source: Substance Abuse and Mental Health Services Administration, *Results from the 2006 National Survey on Drug Use and Health: National Findings*, September 2007

17. **Batting Average** Ty Cobb is one of Major League Baseball's greatest hitters of all time, with a career batting average of 0.366. Parameter

    Source: baseball-almanac.com

18. **Moonwalkers** Only 12 men have walked on the moon. The average age of these men at the time of their moonwalks was 39 years, 11 months, 15 days. Parameter

    Source: Wikipedia.org

19. **Hygiene Habits** A study of 6,076 adults in public rest rooms (in Atlanta, Chicago, New York City, and San Francisco) found that 23% did not wash their hands before exiting. Statistic

    Source: American Society for Microbiology and the Soap and Detergent Association, *Press Release: Hygiene Habits Stall: Public Handwashing Down.* September 17, 2007

20. **Public Knowledge** Telephone interviews of 1,502 adults 18 years of age or older, conducted nationwide February 1–13, 2007, found that only 69% could identify the current vice-president. Statistic

    Source: The Pew Research Center, *Public Knowledge of Current Affairs Little Changed by News and Information Revolutions: What Americans Know: 1989–2007*, April 15, 2007

In Problems 21–28, classify the variable as qualitative or quantitative.

21. Nation of origin Qualitative
    NW

22. Number of siblings Quantitative

23. Grams of carbohydrates in a doughnut Quantitative

24. Number on a football player's jersey Qualitative

25. Number of unpopped kernels in a bag of ACT microwave popcorn Quantitative

26. Assessed value of a house Quantitative

27. Phone number Qualitative

28. Student ID number Qualitative

In Problems 29–36, determine whether the quantitative variable is discrete or continuous. 30. Continuous

29. Runs scored in a season by Albert Pujols Discrete
    NW

30. Volume of water lost each day through a leaky faucet

31. Length (in minutes) of a country song Continuous

32. Number of sequoia trees in a randomly selected acre of Yosemite National Park Discrete

33. Temperature on a randomly selected day in Memphis, Tennessee Continuous

34. Internet connection speed in kilobytes per second Continuous

35. Points scored in an NCAA basketball game Discrete

36. Air pressure in pounds per square inch in an automobile tire Continuous

In Problems 37–44, determine the level of measurement of each variable. 41. Ordinal

37. Nation of origin Nominal
    NW

38. Movie ratings of one star through five stars Ordinal

39. Volume of water used by a household in a day Ratio

40. Year of birth of college students Interval

41. Highest degree conferred (high school, bachelor's, and so on)

42. Eye color Nominal

43. Assessed value of a house Ratio

44. Time of day measured in military time Interval

In Problems 45–50, a research objective is presented. For each research objective, identify the population and sample in the study.

45. The Gallup Organization contacts 1,028 teenagers who are 13 to 17 years of age and live in the United States and asks whether or not they had been prescribed medications for any mental disorders, such as depression or anxiety.

46. A quality-control manager randomly selects 50 bottles of Coca-Cola that were filled on October 15 to assess the calibration of the filling machine.

47. A farmer wanted to learn about the weight of his soybean crop. He randomly sampled 100 plants and weighed the soybeans on each plant.

48. Every year the U.S. Census Bureau releases the *Current Population Report* based on a survey of 50,000 households. The

goal of this report is to learn the demographic characteristics of all households within the United States, such as income.

49. Folate and Hypertension Researcher John P. Forman and co-workers wanted to determine whether or not higher folate intake is associated with a lower risk of hypertension (high blood pressure) in younger women (27 to 44 years of age). To make this determination, they looked at 7,373 cases of hypertension in younger women and found that younger women who consumed at least 1,000 micrograms per day (μg/d) of total folate (dietary plus supplemental) had a decreased risk of hypertension compared with those who consumed less than 200 μg/d.

Source: John P. Forman, MD; Eric B. Rimm, ScD; Meir J. Stampfer, MD; Gary C. Curhan, MD, ScD, "Folate Intake and the Risk of Incident Hypertension among US Women," *Journal of the American Medical Association* 293:320–329, 2005

50. A large community college has noticed that an increasing number of full-time students are working while attending the school. The administration randomly selects 128 students and asks this question: How many hours per week do you work?

In Problems 51–54, identify the individuals, variables, and data corresponding to the variables. Determine whether each variable is qualitative, continuous, or discrete.

51. Widescreen TVs The following data relate to widescreen NW high-definition televisions.

Model	Size (in.)	Screen Type	Price ($)
Hitachi #P50X901	50	Plasma	4,000
Mitsubishi #WD-73833	73	Projection	4,300
Sony #KDF-50E3000	50	Projection	1,500
Panasonic #TH-65PZ750U	65	Plasma	9,000
Phillips #60PP9200D37	60	Projection	1,600
Samsung #FP-T5884	58	Plasma	4,200
LG #52LB5D	52	Plasma	3,500

Source: bestbuy.com

52. BMW Cars The following information relates to the 2008 model year product line of BMW automobiles.

Model	Body Style	Weight (lb)	Number of Seats
3 Series	Coupe	3,351	4
5 Series	Sedan	3,505	5
6 Series	Convertible	4,277	4
7 Series	Sedan	4,486	5
X3	Sport utility	4,012	5
Z4 Roadster	Coupe	3,087	2

Source: www.motortrend.com

53. Driver's License Laws The following data represent driver's license laws for various states.

State	Minimum Age for Driver's License (unrestricted)	Mandatory Belt Use Seating Positions	Maximum Allowable Speed Limit (cars on rural interstate), mph, 2007
Alabama	17	Front	70
Colorado	17	Front	75
Indiana	18	All	70
North Carolina	16	All	70
Wisconsin	18	All	65

Source: Governors Highway Safety Association

54. Media Players The following information concerns various digital media players that can be purchased online at circuitcity.com.

Product	Memory Size (GB)	Weight (oz)	Price ($)
Samsung YP-U3	2	0.8	79.99
SanDisk Sansa c200	2	10.4	74.99
Microsoft Zune	4	8.3	149.99
SanDisk Sansa Connect	4	1.7	129.99
Apple iPod nano	4	1.7	149.99
Apple iPod touch	8	4.2	299.99
Archos 605	30	6.7	299.99

Applying the Concepts

55. A Cure for the Common Wart A study conducted by researchers was designed "to determine if application of duct tape is as effective as cryotherapy in the treatment of common warts." The researchers randomly divided 51 patients into two groups. The 26 patients in group 1 had their warts treated by applying duct tape to the wart for 6.5 days and then removing the tape for 12 hours, at which point the cycle was repeated for a maximum of 2 months. The 25 patients in group 2 had their warts treated by cryotherapy (liquid nitrogen applied to the wart for 10 seconds every 2 to 3 weeks) for a maximum of six treatments. Once the treatments were complete, it was determined that 85% of the patients in group 1 and 60% of the patients in group 2 had complete resolution of their warts. The researchers concluded that duct tape is significantly more effective in treating warts than cryotherapy.

Source: Dean R. Focht III, Carole Spicer, Mary P. Fairchok. "The Efficacy of Duct Tape vs. Cryotherapy in the Treatment of Verruca Vulgaris (The Common Wart)," *Archives of Pediatrics and Adolescent Medicine*, 156(10), 2002

(a) What is the research objective?
(b) What is the population being studied? What is the sample?
(c) What are the descriptive statistics?
(d) What are the conclusions of the study?

56. Early Epidurals A study was conducted at Northwestern University in Chicago to determine if pregnant women in first-time labor could receive early low-dose epidurals, an anesthesis to control pain during childbirth, without raising

55. (a) To determine if duct tape is as effective as cryotherapy in the treatment of warts.   55. (b) People with warts; 51 patients with warts
55. (c) 85% in group 1, 60% in group 2 had resolution of their warts   55. (d) Duct tape is more effective in treating warts.

their chances of a Cesarean section. In the study, reported in the *New England Journal of Medicine*, "728 women in first-time labor were divided into two groups. One group received the spinal shot and then got epidurals when the cervix dilated to about 2 centimeters. The other group initially received pain-relieving medicine directly into their bloodstreams, and put off epidurals until 4 centimeters if they could tolerate the pain." In the end, the C-section rate was 18% in the early epidural group and 21% in the delayed group. The researchers concluded that pregnant women in first-time labor can be given a low-dose epidural early without raising their chances of a C-section.

Source: Associated Press, February, 22, 2005

(a) What is the research objective?

(b) What is the population being studied? What is the sample?

(c) What are the descriptive statistics?

(d) What are the conclusions of the study?

57. When Are You Best? Gallup News Service conducted a survey of 1,019 American adults aged 18 years or older, August 13–16, 2007. The respondents were asked, "Generally speaking, at what hour of the day or night are you personally at your best?" Of the 1,019 adults surveyed, 55% said they were personally at their best in the morning (5 A.M. to 11:59 A.M.). Gallup reported that 55% of all adult Americans felt they were personally at their best in the morning, with a 3% margin of error with 95% confidence.

(a) What is the research objective?

(b) What is the population?

(c) What is the sample?

(d) List the descriptive statistics.

(e) What can be inferred from this survey?

58. Financial Worries? Gallup News Service conducted a survey of 1,006 American adults aged 18 years or older, September 24–27, 2007. The respondents were asked, "What, if anything, worries you most about your personal financial situation in the long term?" Of the 1,006 adults surveyed, 18% said they were most worried about having enough money for retirement. (Ironically, not having enough money for retirement was not a short-term concern.) Gallup reported that 18% of all adult Americans were most worried about not having enough money for retirement, with a 4% margin of error with 95% confidence.

(a) What is the research objective?

(b) What is the population?

(c) What is the sample?

(d) List the descriptive statistics.

(e) What can be inferred from this survey?

59. What Level of Measurement? It is extremely important for a researcher to clearly define the variables in a study because this helps to determine the type of analysis that can be performed on the data. For example, if a researcher wanted to describe baseball players based on jersey number, what level of measurement would the variable *jersey number* be? Now suppose the researcher felt that certain players who were of lower caliber received higher numbers. Does the level of measurement of the variable change? If so, how?

60. Interpreting the Variable Suppose a fundraiser holds a raffle for which each person that enters the room receives a ticket. The tickets are numbered 1 to *N*, where *N* is the number of people at the fundraiser. The first person to arrive receives ticket number 1, the second person receives ticket number 2, and so on. Determine the level of measurement for each of the following interpretations of the variable *ticket number*.

(a) The winning ticket number. Nominal

(b) The winning ticket number was announced as 329. An attendee noted his ticket number was 294 and stated, "I guess I arrived too early." Ordinal

(c) The winning ticket number was announced as 329. An attendee looked around the room and commented, "It doesn't look like there are 329 people in attendance." Ratio

61. Analyze the Article Read the newspaper article and identify (a) the research question the study addresses, (b) the population, (c) the sample, (d) the descriptive statistics, and (e) the inferences of the study.

Study: Educational TV for Toddlers OK

CHICAGO (AP)—*Arthur* and *Barney* are OK for toddler TV-watching, but not *Rugrats* and certainly not *Power Rangers*, reports a new study of early TV-watching and future attention problems.

The research involved children younger than 3, so TV is mostly a no–no anyway, according to the experts. But if TV is allowed, it should be of the educational variety, the researchers said.

Every hour per day that kids under 3 watched violent child-oriented entertainment their risk doubled for attention problems five years later, the study found. Even nonviolent kids' shows like *Rugrats* and *The Flintstones* carried a still substantial risk for attention problems, though slightly lower. On the other hand, educational shows, including *Arthur*, *Barney* and *Sesame Street* had no association with future attention problems.

Interestingly, the risks only occurred in children younger than age 3, perhaps because that is a particularly crucial period of brain development. Those results echo a different study last month that suggested TV-watching has less impact on older children's behavior than on toddlers.

The American Academy of Pediatrics recommends no television for children younger than 2 and limited TV for older children.

The current study by University of Washington researchers was prepared for release Monday in November's issue of the journal *Pediatrics*.

Previous research and news reports on TV's effects have tended to view television as a single entity, without regard to content. But "the reality is that it's not inherently good or bad. It really depends on what they watch," said Dr. Dimitri Christakis, who co-authored the study with researcher Frederick Zimmerman.

Their study was based on parent questionnaires. They acknowledge it's observational data that only suggests a link and isn't proof that TV habits cause attention problems. Still, they think the connection is plausible.

57. (a) To determine the hour of the day adults feel at their best

57. (b) American adults aged 18 years or older

57. (c) 1,019 American adults surveyed

57. (d) 55% felt they were best in the morning

58. (a) To determine what worries adults most about their personal financial situation in the long term

58. (b) American adults aged 18 years or older

58. (c) 1,006 American adults surveyed

58. (d) 18% were most worried about having enough money for retirement

The researchers called a show violent if it involved fighting, hitting people, threats or other violence that was central to the plot or a main character. Shows listed included *Power Rangers, Lion King* and *Scooby Doo.*

These shows, and other kids' shows without violence, also tend to be very fast-paced, which may hamper children's ability to focus attention, Christakis said.

Shows with violence also send a flawed message, namely that "if someone gets bonked on the head with a rolling pin, it just makes a funny sound and someone gets dizzy for a minute and then everything is back to normal," Christakis said.

Dennis Wharton of the National Association of Broadcasters, a trade association for stations and networks including those with entertainment and educational children's TV shows, said he had not had a chance to thoroughly review the research and declined to comment on specifics.

Wharton said his group believes "there are many superb television programs for children, and would acknowledge that it is important for parents to supervise the media consumption habits of young children."

The study involved a nationally representative sample of 967 children whose parents answered government-funded child development questionnaires in 1997 and 2002. Questions involved television viewing habits in 1997. Parents were asked in 2002 about their children's behavior, including inattentiveness, difficulty concentrating and restlessness.

The researchers took into account other factors that might have influenced the results—including cultural differences and parents' education levels—and still found a strong link between the non-educational shows and future attention problems.

Peggy O'Brien, senior vice president for educational programming and services at the Corporation for Public Broadcasting, said violence in ads accompanying shows on commercial TV might contribute to the study results.

She said lots of research about brain development goes into the production of educational TV programming for children, and that the slower pace is intentional.

"We want it to be kind of an extension of play" rather than fantasy, she said.

1.2 OBSERVATIONAL STUDIES VERSUS DESIGNED EXPERIMENTS

| **Objectives** | **1** | Distinguish between an observational study and an experiment |
| | **2** | Explain the various types of observational studies |

 Distinguish between an Observational Study and an Experiment

Once our research question is developed, we must develop methods for obtaining the data that can be used to answer the questions posed in our research objective. There are two methods for collecting data, *observational studies* and *designed experiments*. To help see the difference between these two methods for obtaining data, read the following two studies.

EXAMPLE 1   **Cellular Phones and Brain Tumors**

Researchers Joachim Schüz and associates wanted "to investigate cancer risk among Danish cellular telephone users who were followed for up to 21 years." To do so, they kept track of 420,095 people whose first cellular telephone prescription was between 1982 and 1995. In 2002, they recorded the number of people out of the 420,095 people who had a brain tumor and compared the rate of brain tumors in this group to the rate of brain tumors in the general population. They found no significant difference in the rate of brain tumors between the two groups. The researchers concluded "cellular telephone use was not associated with increased risk for brain tumors." (*Source*: Joachim Schüz et al. "Cellular Telephone Use and Cancer Risk: Update of a Nationwide Danish Cohort," *Journal of the National Cancer Institute* 98(23): 1707–1713, 2006)

| EXAMPLE 2 | Cellular Phones and Brain Tumors |

Researchers Joseph L. Roti Roti and associates examined "whether chronic exposure to radio frequency (RF) radiation at two common cell phone signals—835.62 megahertz, a frequency used by analogue cell phones, and 847.74 megahertz, a frequency used by digital cell phones—caused brain tumors in rats." To do so, the researchers divided 480 rats into three groups. The rats in group 1 were exposed to the analogue cell phone frequency; the rats in group 2 were exposed to the digital frequency; the rats in group 3 served as controls and received no radiation. The exposure was done for 4 hours a day, 5 days a week for 2 years. The rats in all three groups were treated the same, except for the RF exposure.

After 505 days of exposure, the researchers reported the following after analyzing the data. "We found no statistically significant increases in any tumor type, including brain, liver, lung or kidney, compared to the control group." (*Source*: M. La Regina, E. Moros, W. Pickard, W. Straube, J. L. Roti Roti, "The Effect of Chronic Exposure to 835.62 MHz FMCW or 847.7 MHz CDMA on the Incidence of Spontaneous Tumors in Rats," Bioelectromagnetic Society Conference, June 25, 2002.)

In both studies, the goal was to determine if radio frequencies from cell phones increase the risk of contracting brain tumors. Whether or not brain cancer was contracted is the *response variable*. The level of cell phone usage is the *explanatory variable*. In research, we wish to determine how varying the amount of an **explanatory variable** affects the value of a **response variable**.

What are the differences between the study in Example 1 and the study in Example 2? Obviously, in Example 1 the study was conducted on humans, whereas the study in Example 2 was conducted on rats. However, there is a bigger difference. In Example 1, no attempt was made to influence the individuals in the study. The researchers simply let the 420,095 people go through their everyday lives and talk on the phone as much or as little as they wished. In other words, no attempt was made to influence the value of the explanatory variable, radio-frequency exposure (cell phone use). Because the researchers simply observed the behavior of the study participants, we call the study in Example 1 an *observational study*.

Definition | An **observational study** measures the value of the response variable without attempting to influence the value of either the response or explanatory variables. That is, in an observational study, the researcher observes the behavior of the individuals in the study without trying to influence the outcome of the study.

Now let's consider the study in Example 2. In this study, the researchers obtained 480 rats and divided the rats into three groups. Each group was *intentionally* exposed to various levels of radiation. The researchers then compared the number of rats that had brain tumors. Clearly, there was an attempt to influence the individuals in this study because the value of the explanatory variable (exposure to radio frequency) was influenced. Because the researchers controlled the value of the explanatory variable, we call the study in Example 2 a *designed experiment*.

Definition | If a researcher assigns the individuals in a study to a certain group, intentionally changes the value of the explanatory variable, and then records the value of the response variable for each group, the researcher is conducting a **designed experiment**.

Now Work Problem 9

Which Is Better? A Designed Experiment or an Observational Study?

To answer this question, let's consider another study.

| EXAMPLE 3 | **Do Flu Shots Benefit Seniors?** |

Researchers wanted to determine the long-term benefits of the influenza vaccine on seniors aged 65 years and older. The researchers looked at records of over 36,000 seniors for 10 years. The seniors were divided into two groups. Group 1 were seniors who chose to get a flu vaccination shot, and group 2 were seniors who chose not to get a flu vaccination shot. After observing the seniors for 10 years, it was determined that seniors who get flu shots are 27% less likely to be hospitalized for pneumonia or influenza and 48% less likely to die from pneumonia or influenza. (*Source*: Kristin L. Nichol, MD, MPH, MBA, James D. Nordin, MD, MPH, David B. Nelson, PhD, John P. Mullooly, PhD, Eelko Hak, PhD. "Effectiveness of Influenza Vaccine in the Community-Dwelling Elderly," *New England Journal of Medicine* 357:1373–1381, 2007)

Wow! The results of this study sound great! All seniors should go out and get a flu shot. Right? Well, hold on a second. The authors of the study admitted that there may be some flaws in their results. They were concerned with *confounding*. That is, the authors were concerned that there might be a different explanation for lower hospitalization and death rates than the flu shot. Could it be that seniors that get flu shots are more health conscious in the first place? Could it be that seniors who get flu shots are able to get around more easily, so they can get to the clinic to get the flu shot? Does race, income, or gender play a role in whether one might contract (and possibly die from) influenza?

Definition   **Confounding** in a study occurs when the effects of two or more explanatory variables are not separated. Therefore, any relation that may exist between an explanatory variable and the response variable may be due to some other variable or variables not accounted for in the study.

Confounding is potentially a major problem with observational studies. Often, the cause of confounding is a *lurking variable*.

Definition   A **lurking variable** is an explanatory variable that was not considered in a study, but that affects the value of the response variable in the study. In addition, lurking variables are typically related to explanatory variables considered in the study.

In the influenza study, possible lurking variables might be age, health status, or mobility of the senior. How can we manage the effect of lurking variables? One possibility is to look at the individuals in the study to determine if they differ in any significant way. For example, it turns out in the influenza study that the seniors who elected to get a flu shot were actually *less* healthy than those who did not. The researchers also accounted for race and income. Another variable the authors identified as a potential lurking variable was *functional status*, meaning the ability of the seniors to conduct day-to-day activities on their own. The authors were able to adjust their results for this variable as well.

Even after accounting for all the potential lurking variables in the study, the authors were still careful to conclude that getting an influenza shot is *associated* with a lower risk of being hospitalized or dying from influenza. The reason the authors used the term *associated* instead of saying that influenza shots result in (or *cause*) a lower risk of death due to influenza is because the study was observational.

Observational studies do not allow a researcher to claim causation, only association.

Designed experiments, on the other hand, are used whenever control of certain variables is possible and desirable. This type of research allows the researcher to identify certain cause and effect relationships among the variables in the study.

So why ever conduct a study through an observational experiment? Often, it is unethical to conduct an experiment. Consider the link between smoking and lung cancer. Would you want to participate in a designed experiment to determine if smoking causes lung cancer in humans? To do so, a researcher would divide a group of volunteers into two groups. Group 1 would be told to smoke a pack of cigarettes every day for the next 10 years, while group 2 would not. In addition, the researcher would control eating habits, sleeping habits, and exercise so that the only difference between the two groups was smoking. After 10 years the researcher would compare the incidence rate of lung cancer (the response variable) in the smoking group to the nonsmoking group. If the two cancer rates differ significantly, we could say that smoking causes cancer. By approaching the study in this way, we are able to control many of the factors that might affect the incidence rate of lung cancer that were beyond our control in the observational study.

Other reasons exist for conducting observational studies over designed experiments. Kjell Benson and Arthur Hartz wrote an article in the *New England Journal of Medicine* in support of observational studies by stating, "observational studies have several advantages over designed experiments, including lower cost, greater timeliness, and a broader range of patients." (*Source*: Kjell Benson, BA, and Arthur J. Hartz, MD, PhD. "A Comparison of Observational Studies and Randomized, Controlled Trials," *New England Journal of Medicine* 342:1878–1886, 2000)

For the remainder of this section, and in Sections 1.3 through 1.5, we will look at obtaining data through various types of observational studies. We look at designed experiments in Section 1.6.

② Explain the Various Types of Observational Studies

There are three major categories of observational studies: (1) cross-sectional studies, (2) case-control studies, and (3) cohort studies.

Cross-sectional Studies These are observational studies that collect information about individuals at a specific point in time or over a very short period of time.

For example, a researcher might want to assess the risk associated with smoking by looking at a group of people, determining how many are smokers and comparing the incidence rate of lung cancer of the smokers to the nonsmokers.

A clear advantage of cross-sectional studies is that they are cheap and quick to do. However, cross-sectional studies have limitations. For our lung cancer study, it could be that individuals develop cancer after the data are collected, so our study will not give the full picture.

Case-control Studies These studies are **retrospective**, meaning that they require individuals to look back in time or require the researcher to look at existing records. In case-control studies, individuals that have a certain characteristic are matched with those that do not.

For example, we might match individuals that have lung cancer with those that do not. When we say "match" individuals, we mean that we would like the individuals in the study to be as similar (homogeneous) as possible in terms of demographics and other variables that may affect the response variable. Once homogeneous groups are established, we would ask the individuals in each group how much they smoked. The incidence rate of lung cancer between the two groups would then be compared.

Certainly, a disadvantage to this type of study is that it requires individuals to recall information from the past. Plus, it requires the individuals to be truthful in their responses. An advantage of case-control studies is that they are relatively inexpensive to conduct and can be done relatively quickly.

Cohort Studies A cohort study first identifies a group of individuals to participate in the study (the cohort). The cohort is then observed over a period of time (sometimes a long period of time). Over this time period, characteristics about the individuals are recorded and some individuals in the study will be exposed to certain factors (not intentionally) and others will not. At the end of the study the value of the response variable is recorded for the individuals.

The observational study in Example 1 is a cohort study that took over 21 years to complete! The individuals were divided into groups depending on their cell phone usage. A cohort study was done to further advance the link between lung cancer and smoking. Typically, cohort studies require many individuals to participate over long periods of time. Because the data are collected over time, cohort studies are **prospective**. Another problem with cohort studies is that individuals tend to drop out due to the long time frame. This could lead to misleading results. Cohort studies definitely are the most powerful of the observational studies.

One of the largest cohort studies is the Framingham Heart Study. In this study, more than 10,000 individuals have been monitored since 1948. The study continues to this day, with the grandchildren of the original participants taking part in the study. This cohort study is responsible for many of the breakthroughs in understanding heart disease. The cost of this study is in excess of $10 million.

Some Concluding Remarks about Observational Studies versus Designed Experiments

Is a designed experiment superior to an observational study? Not necessarily. Plus, observational studies play a role in the research process. For example, because cross-sectional and case-control observational studies are relatively inexpensive, they provide an opportunity to explore possible associations prior to undertaking large cohort studies or designing experiments.

Also, it is not always possible to conduct an experiment. For example, we could not conduct an experiment to investigate the perceived link between high tension wires and leukemia. Do you see why?

Now Work Problem 19

Existing Sources of Data and Census Data

Have you ever heard this saying? *There is no point in reinventing the wheel.* Well, there is no point in spending energy obtaining data that already exist either. If a researcher wishes to conduct a study and a data set exists that can be used to answer the researcher's questions, then it would be silly to collect the data from scratch. For example, various federal agencies regularly collect data that are available to the public. Some of these agencies include the Centers for Disease Control and Prevention (www.cdc.gov), the Internal Revenue Service (www.irs.gov), and the Department of Justice (http://fjsrc.urban.org/index.cfm). In fact, a great website that lists virtually all the sources of federal data is www.fedstats.gov. Another great source of data is the General Social Survey (GSS) administered by the University of Chicago. This survey regularly asks "demographic and attitudinal questions" of individuals around the country. The website is www.gss.norc.org.

Another source of data is a *census*.

Definition
> A **census** is a list of all individuals in a population along with certain characteristics of each individual.

The United States attempts to conduct a census every 10 years to learn the demographic makeup of the United States. Everyone whose usual residence is within the borders of the United States must fill out a questionnaire packet. There are two different census forms: a short form and a long form. The short form goes to every household in the United States and includes questions on name, gender, age, relationship of individuals living in the household, Hispanic origin, race, and housing tenure (whether the home is owned or rented). About 83% of all households received the short form in 2000, with the remaining households receiving the long form. The cost of obtaining the census in 2000 was approximately $6 billion; about 860,000 temporary workers were hired to assist in collecting the data.

Why is the U.S. Census so important? The results of the census are used to determine the number of representatives in the House of Representatives in each state, congressional districts, distribution of funds for government programs (such as Medicaid), and planning for the construction of schools and roads. The first census of the United States was obtained in 1790 under the direction of Thomas Jefferson. It is a constitutional mandate that a census be conducted every 10 years (Article 1, Section 2, of the U.S. Constitution).

Is the United States successful in obtaining a census? Not entirely. Inevitably, certain individuals in the United States go uncounted. Why? There are a number of reasons, but a few of the common reasons include illiteracy, language issues, and homelessness. Given what is at stake politically based on the results of the census, politicians often debate on how to count these individuals. In fact, statisticians have offered solutions to the counting problem. The interested reader can go to www.census.gov and in the search box type *count homeless*. You will find many articles related to the Census Bureau's attempt to count the homeless. The bottom line is that even census data can have flaws.

1.2 ASSESS YOUR UNDERSTANDING

Concepts and Vocabulary

1. In your own words, define explanatory variable and response variable.

2. What is an observational study? What is a designed experiment? Which allows the researcher to claim causation between an explanatory variable and a response variable?

3. Explain what is meant by confounding. What is a lurking variable?

4. Given a choice, would you conduct a study using an observational study or a designed experiment? Why?

5. What is a cross-sectional study? What is a case-control study? Which is the superior observational study? Why?

6. The data used in the influenza study presented in Example 3 were obtained from a cohort study. What does this mean? Why is a cohort study superior to a case-control study?

7. Explain why it would be unlikely to use a designed experiment to answer the research question posed in Example 3.

8. What does it mean when an observational study is retrospective? What does it mean when an observational study is prospective?

Skill Building

In Problems 9–16, determine whether the study depicts an observational study or an experiment.

9. Researchers wanted to know if there is a link between proximity to high-tension wires and the rate of leukemia in children. To conduct the study, researchers compared the incidence rate of leukemia for children who lived within $\frac{1}{2}$ mile of high-tension wires to the incidence rate of leukemia for children who did not live within $\frac{1}{2}$ mile of high-tension wires. Observational study

10. Rats with cancer are divided into two groups. One group receives 5 milligrams (mg) of a medication that is thought to fight cancer, and the other receives 10 mg. After 2 years, the spread of the cancer is measured. Experiment

11. Seventh-grade students are randomly divided into two groups. One group is taught math using traditional techniques; the other is taught math using a reform method. After 1 year, each group is given an achievement test to compare proficiency. Experiment

12. A poll is conducted in which 500 people are asked whom they plan to vote for in the upcoming election. Observational study

13. A survey is conducted asking 400 people, "Do you prefer Coke or Pepsi?" Observational study

14. While shopping, 200 people are asked to perform a taste test in which they drink from two randomly placed, unmarked cups. They are then asked which drink they prefer. Experiment

15. Sixty patients with carpal tunnel syndrome are randomly divided into two groups. One group is treated weekly with both acupuncture and an exercise regimen. The other is treated weekly with the exact same exercise regimen, but no acupuncture. After 1 year, both groups are questioned about their level of pain due to carpal tunnel syndrome. Experiment

16. Conservation agents netted 250 large-mouth bass in a lake and determined how many were carrying parasites. Observational study

Applying the Concepts

17. **Daily Coffee Consumption** Researchers wanted to determine if there was an association between daily coffee consumption and the occurrence of skin cancer. The researchers looked at 93,676 women enrolled in the Women's Health Initiative Observational Study and asked them to report their coffee-drinking habits. The researchers also determined which of the women had nonmelanoma skin cancer. After their analysis, the researchers concluded that consumption of six or more cups of caffeinated coffee per day was associated with a reduction in nonmelanoma skin cancer.

Source: European Journal of Cancer Prevention, 16(5): 446–452, October 2007

17. (a) Cross-sectional   17. (b) Whether the woman has nonmelanoma skin cancer or not; consumption of caffeinated coffee

(a) What type of observational study was this? Explain.

(b) What is the response variable in the study? What is the explanatory variable?

(c) In their report, the researchers stated that "After adjusting for various demographic and lifestyle variables, daily consumption of six or more cups was associated with a 30% reduced prevalence of nonmelanoma skin cancer." Why was it important to adjust for these variables?

18. **Obesity and Artery Calcification** Scientists were interested in determining if abdominal obesity is related to coronary artery calcification (CAC). The scientists studied 2,951 participants in the Coronary Artery Risk Development in Young Adults Study to investigate a possible link. Waist and hip girths were measured in 1985–1986, 1995–1996 (year 10), and in 2000–2001 (waist girth only). CAC measurements were taken in 2001–2002. The results of the study indicated that abdominal obesity measured by waist girth is associated with early atherosclerosclerosis as measured by the presence of CAC in participants.

Source: *American Journal of Clinical Nutrition*, 86(1): 48–54, 2007   18. (a) Cohort study

(a) What type of observational study was this? Explain.

(b) What is the response variable in the study? What is the explanatory variable? Presence of CAC; waist girth

19. **Television in the Bedroom** Researchers Christelle Delmas
NW and associates wanted to determine if having a television (TV) in the bedroom is associated with obesity. The researchers administered a questionnaire to 379 twelve-year-old French adolescents. After analyzing the results, the researchers determined that the body mass index of the adolescents who had a TV in their bedroom was significantly higher than that of the adolescents who did not have a TV in their bedroom.

Source: Christelle Delmas, Carine Platat, Brigette Schweitzer, Aline Wagner, Mohamed Oujaa, and Chantal Simon. "Association Between Television in Bedroom and Adiposity Throughout Adolescence," *Obesity*, 15:2495–2503, 2007

(a) Why is this an observational study? What type of observational study is this? Cross-sectional

(b) What is the response variable in the study? What is the explanatory variable?

(c) Can you think of any lurking variables that may affect the results of the study?

(d) In the report, the researchers stated, "These results remain significant after adjustment for socioeconomic status." What does this mean?

(e) Does a television in the bedroom cause a higher body mass index? Explain. No

20. **Get Married, Gain Weight** Researcher Penny Gordon-Larson and her associate wanted to determine whether young couples who marry or cohabitate are more likely to gain weight than those who stay single. The researchers followed 8,000 men and women from 1995 through 2002 as they matured from the teens to young adults. When the study began, none of the participants was married or living with a romantic partner. By 2002, 14% of the participants were married and 16% were living with a romantic partner. At the end of the study, married or cohabiting women gained, on average, 9 pounds more than single women, and married or cohabiting men gained, on average, 6 pounds more than single men.

(a) Why is this an observational study? What type of observational study is this? Cohort study

(b) What is the response variable in the study? What is the explanatory variable?

(c) Identify some potential lurking variables in this study.

(d) Does getting married or cohabiting cause one to gain weight? Explain.

21. **Analyze the Article** Write a summary of the following opinion. The opinion is posted at abcnews.com. Include the type of study conducted, possible lurking variables, and conclusions. What is the message of the author of the article?

Power Lines and Cancer—To Move or Not to Move

New Research May Cause More Fear Than Warranted, One Physician Explains

OPINION by JOSEPH MOORE, M.D.

May 30, 2007—

A recent study out of Switzerland indicates there might be an increased risk of certain blood cancers in people with prolonged exposure to electromagnetic fields, like those generated from high-voltage power lines.

If you live in a house near one of these high-voltage power lines, a study like this one might make you wonder whether you should move.

But based on what we know now, I don't think that's necessary. We can never say there is no risk, but we can say that the risk appears to be extremely small.

"Scare Science"

The results of studies like this add a bit more to our knowledge of potential harmful environmental exposures, but they should also be seen in conjunction with the results of hundreds of studies that have gone before. It cannot be seen as a definitive call to action in and of itself.

The current study followed more than 20,000 Swiss railway workers over a period of 30 years. True, that represents a lot of people over a long period of time.

However, the problem with many epidemiological studies, like this one, is that it is difficult to have an absolute control group of people to compare results with. The researchers compared the incidence of different cancers of workers with a high amount of electromagnetic field exposure to those workers with lower exposures.

These studies aren't like those that have identified definitive links between an exposure and a disease—like those involving smoking and lung cancer. In those studies, we can actually measure the damage done to lung tissue as a direct result of smoking. But usually it's very difficult for the conclusions of an epidemiological study to rise to the level of controlled studies in determining public policy.

Remember the recent scare about coffee and increased risk of pancreatic cancer? Or the always-simmering issue of cell phone use and brain tumors?

As far as I can tell, none of us have turned in our cell phones. In our own minds, we've decided that any links to cell phone use and brain cancer have not been proven definitively. While we can't say that there is absolutely no risk in using cell phones, individuals have determined on their own that the potential risks appear to be quite small and are outweighed by the benefits.

Findings Shouldn't Lead to Fear

As a society, we should continue to investigate these and other related exposures to try to prove one way or another whether they are disease-causing. If we don't continue to study, we won't find out. It's that simple.

When findings like these come out, and I'm sure there will be more in the future, I would advise people not to lose their heads. Remain calm. You should take the results as we scientists do—as intriguing pieces of data about a problem we will eventually learn more about, either positively or negatively, in the future. It should not necessarily alter what we do right now.

What we can do is take actions that we know will reduce our chances of developing cancer.

Stop smoking and avoid passive smoke. It is the leading cause of cancer that individuals have control over.

Whenever you go outside, put on sunscreen or cover up.

Eat a healthy diet and stay physically active.

Make sure you get tested or screened. Procedures like colonoscopies, mammograms, pap smears and prostate exams can catch the early signs of cancer, when the chances of successfully treating them are the best.

Taking the actions above will go much farther in reducing your risks for cancer than moving away from power lines or throwing away your cell phone.

Dr. Joseph Moore is a medical oncologist at Duke University Comprehensive Cancer Center.

Source: Reprinted with the permission of the author.

22. Reread the article in Problem 61 from Section 1.1. What type of observational study does this appear to be? Name some lurking variables that the researchers accounted for.

23. Putting It Together: Passive Smoke The following abstract appears in *The New England Journal of Medicine:*

BACKGROUND. The relation between passive smoking and lung cancer is of great public health importance. Some previous studies have suggested that exposure to environmental tobacco smoke in the household can cause lung cancer, but others have found no effect. Smoking by the spouse has been the most commonly used measure of this exposure.

METHODS. In order to determine whether lung cancer is associated with exposure to tobacco smoke within the household, we conducted a case-control study of 191 patients with lung cancer who had never smoked and an equal number of persons without lung cancer who had never smoked. Lifetime residential histories including information on exposure to environmental tobacco smoke were compiled and analyzed. Exposure was measured in terms of "smoker-years," determined by multiplying the number of years in each residence by the number of smokers in the household.

RESULTS. Household exposure to 25 or more smoker-years during childhood and adolescence doubled the risk of lung cancer. Approximately 15 percent of the control subjects who had never smoked reported this level of exposure. Household exposure of less than 25 smoker-years during childhood and adolescence did not increase the risk of lung cancer. Exposure to a spouse's smoking, which constituted less than one third of total household exposure on average, was not associated with an increase in risk.

CONCLUSIONS. The possibility of recall bias and other methodologic problems may influence the results of case-control studies of environmental tobacco smoke. Nonetheless, our findings regarding exposure during early life suggest that approximately 17 percent of lung cancers among non-smokers can be attributed to high levels of exposure to cigarette smoke during childhood and adolescence.

(a) What is the research objective?

(b) What makes this study a case-control study? Why is this a retrospective study?

(c) What is the response variable in the study? Is it qualitative or quantitative?

(d) What is the explanatory variable in the study? Is it qualitative or quantitative?

(e) Can you identify any lurking variables that may have affected this study?

(f) What is the conclusion of the study? Does exposure to smoke in the household cause lung cancer?

(g) Would it be possible to design an experiment to answer the research question in part (a)? Explain.

23. (c) Whether the individual has lung cancer; qualitative

23. (d) Number of smoker-years; quantitative

23. (e) Income; amount of exposure outside the home

1.3 SIMPLE RANDOM SAMPLING

Objective		Obtain a simple random sample

Sampling

Besides the observational studies that we looked at in Section 1.2, observational studies can also be conducted by administering a survey. Whenever administering a survey, the researcher must first identify the population that is to be targeted. For example, the Gallup Organization regularly surveys Americans about various pop-culture and political issues. Often, the population of interest in these surveys is adult Americans aged 18 years or older. Of course, it is unreasonable to expect the Gallup Organization to survey *all* adult Americans (there are over 200 million), so instead the Gallup Organization will typically survey a *random sample* of about 1,000 adult Americans.

Definition

Random sampling is the process of using chance to select individuals from a population to be included in the sample.

Note to Instructor

Spend some time in class talking about the following. Suppose a grocery store manager wants to get a feel for how customers view the store. Why would a sample of the first 100 shoppers leaving a grocery store not be representative of the population? Why is this sampling method not random sampling?

What allows a researcher to be confident the results of a survey accurately reflect the feelings of an entire population? For the results of a survey to be reliable, the characteristics of the individuals in the sample must be representative of the characteristics of the individuals in the population. How can this be accomplished? The key to obtaining a sample representative of a population is to let *chance* or *randomness* play a role in dictating which individuals are in the sample, rather than convenience. If convenience is used to obtain a sample, the results of the survey are meaningless.

For example, suppose that Gallup wants to know the proportion of adult Americans who consider themselves to be baseball fans. If Gallup obtained a sample by standing outside of Fenway Park (home of the Boston Red Sox professional baseball team), the results of the survey are not likely to be reliable. Why? Clearly, the individuals in the sample do not accurately reflect the makeup of the entire population. As another example, suppose you wanted to learn the proportion of students on your campus who work. It might be convenient to survey the students in your statistics class, but do the students in your class represent the overall student body? Is the proportion of freshmen, sophomores, juniors, and seniors in your class close to the proportion of freshmen, sophomores, juniors, and seniors on campus? Is the proportion of males and females in your class close to the proportion of males and females on campus? Probably not. For this reason, the convenient sample is not representative of the population, which means the results of your survey are misleading.

We will discuss four basic sampling techniques: *simple random sampling*, *stratified sampling*, *systematic sampling*, and *cluster sampling*. These sampling methods are designed so that any selection biases introduced (knowingly or unknowingly) by the surveyor during the selection process are eliminated. In other words, the surveyor does not have a choice as to which individuals are in the study. We will discuss simple random sampling now and the remaining three types of sampling in the next section.

① Obtain a Simple Random Sample

The most basic sample survey design is *simple random sampling.*

Definition

A sample of size n from a population of size N is obtained through **simple random sampling** if every possible sample of size n has an equally likely chance of occurring. The sample is then called a **simple random sample**.

In Other Words

Simple random sampling is like selecting names from a hat.

The sample is always a subset of the population, meaning that the number of individuals in the sample is less than the number of individuals in the population.

Note to Instructor

The purpose of this activity is to allow students to visualize simple random sampling. It also helps to foreshadow the idea of a sampling distribution by showing that different samples lead to different individuals in the sample. It should take about 15 to 20 minutes.

 CLASS ACTIVITY

Simple Random Sampling

This activity illustrates the idea of simple random sampling.

(a) Choose 5 students in the class to represent a population. Number the students 1 through 5.

(b) Form all possible samples of size $n = 2$ from the population of size $N = 5$. How many different simple random samples are possible?

(c) Write the numbers 1 through 5 on five pieces of paper and then place the paper in a hat. Select two of the numbers. The two individuals corresponding to these numbers are in the sample.

(d) Put the two numbers back in the hat. Select two of the numbers. The two individuals corresponding to these numbers are in the sample. Are the individuals in the second sample the same as the individuals in the first sample?

Illustrating Simple Random Sampling

Problem: Sophia has four tickets to a concert. Six of her friends, Yolanda, Michael, Kevin, Marissa, Annie, and Katie, have all expressed an interest in going to the concert. Sophia decides to randomly select three of her six friends to attend the concert.

(a) List all possible samples of size $n = 3$ (without replacement) from the population of size $N = 6$.

(b) Comment on the likelihood of the sample containing Michael, Kevin, and Marissa.

Approach: We list all possible combinations of three people chosen from the six. Remember, in simple random sampling, each sample of size 3 is equally likely to occur.

Solution

(a) The possible samples of size 3 are listed in Table 2.

Table 2			
Yolanda, Michael, Kevin	Yolanda, Michael, Marissa	Yolanda, Michael, Annie	Yolanda, Michael, Katie
Yolanda, Kevin, Marissa	Yolanda, Kevin, Annie	Yolanda, Kevin, Katie	Yolanda, Marissa, Annie
Yolanda, Marissa, Katie	Yolanda, Annie, Katie	Michael, Kevin, Marissa	Michael, Kevin, Annie
Michael, Kevin, Katie	Michael, Marissa, Annie	Michael, Marissa, Katie	Michael, Annie, Katie
Kevin, Marissa, Annie	Kevin, Marissa, Katie	Kevin, Annie, Katie	Marissa, Annie, Katie

From Table 2, we see that there are 20 possible samples of size 3 from the population of size 6. We use the term *sample* to mean the individuals in the sample.

(b) There is 1 sample that contains Michael, Kevin, and Marissa and 20 possible samples, so there is a 1 in 20 chance that the simple random sample will contain Michael, Kevin, and Marissa. In fact, all the samples of size 3 have a 1 in 20 chance of occurring.

Now Work Problem 7

Obtaining a Simple Random Sample

The results of Example 1 leave one question unanswered: How do we select the individuals in a simple random sample? To obtain a simple random sample from a population, we could write the names of the individuals in the population on different sheets of paper and then select names from a hat.

Often, however, the size of the population is so large that performing simple random sampling in this fashion is not practical. Typically, random numbers are used by assigning each individual in the population a unique number between 1 and N, where N is the size of the population. Then n random numbers from this list are selected, where n represents the size of the sample. Because we must number the individuals in the population, we must have a list of all the individuals within the population, called a **frame**.

In Other Words

A frame lists all the individuals in a population. For example, a list of all registered voters in a particular precinct might be a frame.

Obtaining a Simple Random Sample

Problem: Senese and Associates has increased their accounting business. To make sure their clients are still satisfied with the services they are receiving, Senese and Associates decides to send a survey out to a simple random sample of 5 of its 30 clients.

Approach

Note to Instructor

In-class discussion: What is meant by sampling "with replacement"? What is meant by sampling "without replacement"?

Step 1: A list of the 30 clients must be obtained (the frame). Each client is then assigned a unique number from 01 to 30.

Step 2: Five unique numbers will be randomly selected. The clients corresponding to the numbers are sent a survey. This process is called *sampling without replacement*. When we **sample without replacement**, once an individual is selected, he or she is removed from the population and cannot be chosen again. Contrast this with **sampling with replacement**, which means the selected individual is placed back into the population and so could be chosen a second time. We use sampling without replacement so that we don't select the same client twice.

Solution

Step 1: Table 3 shows the list of clients. We arrange the clients in alphabetic order (although this is not necessary). Because there are 30 clients, we number the clients from 01 to 30.

Table 3		
01. ABC Electric	11. Fox Studios	21. R&Q Realty
02. Brassil Construction	12. Haynes Hauling	22. Ritter Engineering
03. Bridal Zone	13. House of Hair	23. Simplex Forms
04. Casey's Glass House	14. John's Bakery	24. Spruce Landscaping
05. Chicago Locksmith	15. Logistics Management, Inc.	25. Thors, Robert DDS
06. DeSoto Painting	16. Lucky Larry's Bistro	26. Travel Zone
07. Dino Jump	17. Moe's Exterminating	27. Ultimate Electric
08. Euro Car Care	18. Nick's Tavern	28. Venetian Gardens Restaurant
09. Farrell's Antiques	19. Orion Bowling	29. Walker Insurance
10. First Fifth Bank	20. Precise Plumbing	30. Worldwide Wireless

Step 2: A table of random numbers can be used to select the individuals to be in the sample. See Table 4.* We select a starting place in the table of random numbers. This

Column 4

Table 4									
Column Number									
Row Number	**01–05**	**06–10**	**11–15**	**16–20**	**21–25**	**26–30**	**31–35**	**36–40**	**41–45**	**46–50**
01	89392	**23**212	74483	36590	25956	36544	68518	40805	09980	00467
02	61458	17639	96252	95649	73727	33912	72896	66218	52341	97141
03	11452	74197	81962	48433	90360	26480	73231	37740	26628	44690
04	27575	04429	31308	02241	01698	19191	18948	78871	36030	23980
05	36829	59109	88976	46845	28329	47460	88944	08264	00843	84592
06	81902	93458	42161	26099	09419	89073	82849	09160	61845	40906
07	59761	55212	33360	68751	86737	79743	85262	31887	37879	17525
08	46827	25906	64708	20307	78423	15910	86548	08763	47050	18513
09	24040	66449	32353	83668	13874	86741	81312	54185	78824	00718
10	98144	96372	50277	15571	82261	66628	31457	00377	63423	55141
11	14228	17930	30118	00438	49666	65189	62869	31304	17117	71489
12	55366	51057	90065	14791	62426	02957	85518	28822	30588	32798
13	96**101**	30646	35526	90389	73634	79304	96635	06626	94683	16696
14	38**152**	55474	30153	26525	83647	31988	82182	98377	33802	80471
15	85**007**	18416	24661	95581	45868	15662	28906	36392	07617	50248
16	85**544**	15890	80011	18160	33468	84106	40603	01315	74664	20553
17	10**446**	20699	98370	17684	16932	80449	92654	02084	19985	59321
18	67**237**	45509	17638	65115	29757	80705	82686	48565	72612	61760
19	23**026**	89817	05403	82209	30573	47501	00135	33955	50250	72592
20	67**411**	58542	18678	46491	13219	84084	27783	34508	55158	78742

Row 13

We skip 52 because it is larger than 30.

*Each digit is in its own column. The digits are displayed in groups of five for ease of reading. The digits in row 1 are 893922321274483, and so on. The first digit, 8, is in column 1; the second digit, 9, is in column 2; the ninth digit, 1, is in column 9.

can be done by closing the eyes and placing a finger on the table. This may sound haphazard, but it accomplishes the goal of being random. Suppose we start in column 4, row 13. Because our data have two digits, we select two-digit numbers from the table using columns 4 and 5. We only select numbers greater than or equal to 01 and less than or equal to 30. Anytime we encounter 00, a number greater than 30, or a number already selected, we skip it and continue to the next number.

The first number in the list is 01, so the client corresponding to 01 will receive a survey. Moving down the list, the next number is 52. Because 52 is greater than 30, we skip it. Continuing down the list, the following numbers are selected from the list:

$$01, 07, 26, 11, 23$$

The clients corresponding to these numbers are

ABC Electric, Dino Jump, Travel Zone, Fox Studios, Simplex Forms

Each random number used to select the individuals in the sample is set in boldface type in Table 4 to help you to understand where the numbers come from.

| EXAMPLE 3 | **Obtaining a Simple Random Sample Using Technology** |

Note to Instructor
Many types of statistical software packages and calculators can be used in statistics. Because of the number of statistical packages available, it is impossible for a text to present each of them. Therefore, the three most popular (MINITAB, Excel, and TI83/TI84), as learned from our surveys, are presented in this text. The technology used will vary from example to example. However, the purpose of the examples that use technology is to illustrate how it can obtain the results we need to solve a problem. Once we have the results, work still must be done to determine its meaning. So, just because the software or calculator used in a technology example is not the one used by you, do not feel obligated to skip it.

Problem: Find a simple random sample of five clients for the problem presented in Example 2.

Approach: The approach is similar to that given in Example 2.

Step 1: A list of the 30 clients must be obtained (the frame). The clients are then assigned a number from 01 to 30.

Step 2: Five numbers are randomly selected using a random number generator. The clients corresponding to the numbers are given a survey. We sample without replacement so that we don't select the same client twice. To use a random-number generator using technology, we must first set the *seed*. The **seed** in a random-number generator provides an initial point for the generator to start creating random numbers. It is just like selecting the initial point in the table of random numbers. The seed can be any nonzero number. Statistical software such as MINITAB or Excel can be used to generate random numbers, but we will use a TI-84 Plus graphing calculator. The steps for obtaining random numbers using MINITAB, Excel, and the TI-83/84 graphing calculator can be found in the Technology Step-by-Step on page 29.

Solution

Step 1: Table 3 on page 25 shows the list of clients and numbers corresponding to the clients.

Step 2: See Figure 3(a) for an illustration of setting the seed using a TI-84 Plus graphing calculator, where the seed is set at 34. We are now ready to obtain the list of random numbers. Figure 3(b) shows the results obtained from a TI-84 Plus graphing calculator.

Using Technology
If you are using a different statistical package or type of calculator, the random numbers generated will likely be different. This does not mean you are wrong. There is no such thing as a wrong random sample as long as the correct procedures are followed.

Figure 3

(a) (b)

The following numbers are generated by the calculator:

11, 4, 20, 29, 11, 27

We ignore the second 11 because we are sampling without replacement. The clients corresponding to these numbers are the clients to be surveyed: Fox Studios, Casey's Glass House, Precise Plumbing, Walker Insurance, and Ultimate Electric.

Now Work Problem 11

CAUTION Random-number generators are not truly random, because they are programs, and programs do not act "randomly." The seed dictates the random numbers that are generated.

There is a very important consequence when comparing the by hand and technology solutions from Examples 2 and 3. Because both samples were obtained randomly, they resulted in different individuals in the sample! For this reason, each sample will likely result in different descriptive statistics. Any inference based on each sample *may* result in different conclusions regarding the population. This is the nature of statistics. Inferences based on samples will vary because the individuals in different samples vary.

1.3 ASSESS YOUR UNDERSTANDING

Concepts and Vocabulary

1. Explain why a frame is necessary to obtain a simple random sample.

2. Discuss why sampling is used in statistics.

3. What does it mean when sampling is done without replacement?

4. What is random sampling? Why is it used and how does it compare with convenience sampling?

Skill Building

5. **Literature** As part of a college literature course, students must select three classic works of literature from the provided list and complete critical book reviews for each selected work. Obtain a simple random sample of size 3 from this list. Write a short description of the process you used to generate your sample.

Pride and Prejudice	The Sun Also Rises	The Jungle
As I Lay Dying	A Tale of Two Cities	Huckleberry Finn
Death of a Salesman	Scarlet Letter	Crime and Punishment

6. **Team Captains** A coach must select two players to serve as captains at the beginning of a soccer match. He has 10 players on his team and, to be fair, wants to randomly select 2 players to be the captains. Obtain a simple random sample of size 2 from the following list. Write a short description of the process you used to generate your sample.

Mady	Breanne	Jory
Evin	Tori	Payton
Emily	Claire	Jordyn
Caty		

7. **Course Selection** A student entering a doctoral program in
NW educational psychology is required to select two courses from the list of courses provided as part of his or her program.

EPR 616, Research in Child Development
EPR 630, Educational Research Planning and Interpretation
EPR 631, Nonparametric Statistics

EPR 632, Methods of Multivariate Analysis
EPR 645, Theory of Measurement
EPR 649, Fieldwork Methods in Educational Research
EPR 650, Interpretive Methods in Educational Research

(a) List all possible two-course selections.
(b) Comment on the likelihood that the pair of courses EPR 630 and EPR 645 will be selected.

8. **Merit Badge Requirements** To complete the Citizenship in the World merit badge, one must select TWO of the following organizations and describe their role in the world.
Source: Boy Scouts of America
1. The United Nations
2. The World Court
3. World Organization of the Scout Movement
4. The World Health Organization
5. Amnesty International
6. The International Committee of the Red Cross
7. CARE

(a) List all possible pairs of organizations.
(b) Comment on the likelihood that the pair The United Nations and Amnesty International will be selected.

Applying the Concepts

9. **Sampling the Faculty** A small community college employs 87 full-time faculty members. To gain the faculty's opinions about an upcoming building project, the college president wishes to obtain a simple random sample that will consist of 9 faculty members. He numbers the faculty from 1 to 87.

(a) Using Table I from Appendix A, the president closes his eyes and drops his ink pen on the table. It points to the digit in row 5, column 22. Using this position as the starting point and proceeding downward, determine the numbers for the 9 faculty members who will be included in the sample.
(b) If the president uses technology, determine the numbers for the 9 faculty members who will be included in the sample.

10. **Sampling the Students** The same community college from Problem 9 has 7,656 students currently enrolled in classes.

9. (a) 83, 67, 84, 38, 22, 24, 36, 58, 34

To gain the students' opinions about an upcoming building project, the college president wishes to obtain a simple random sample of 20 students. He numbers the students from 1 to 7,656.

(a) Using Table I from Appendix A, the president closes his eyes and drops his ink pen on the table. It points to the digit in row 11, column 32. Using this position as the starting point and proceeding downward, determine the numbers for the 20 students who will be included in the sample.

(b) If the president uses technology, determine the numbers for the 20 students who will be included in the sample.

11. Obtaining a Simple Random Sample The following table lists the 50 states.

NW (a) Obtain a simple random sample of size 10 using Table I in Appendix A, a graphing calculator, or computer software.

(b) Obtain a second simple random sample of size 10 using Table I in Appendix A, a graphing calculator, or computer software.

1. Alabama	11. Hawaii	21. Massachusetts	31. New Mexico	41. South Dakota
2. Alaska	12. Idaho	22. Michigan	32. New York	42. Tennessee
3. Arizona	13. Illinois	23. Minnesota	33. North Carolina	43. Texas
4. Arkansas	14. Indiana	24. Mississippi	34. North Dakota	44. Utah
5. California	15. Iowa	25. Missouri	35. Ohio	45. Vermont
6. Colorado	16. Kansas	26. Montana	36. Oklahoma	46. Virginia
7. Connecticut	17. Kentucky	27. Nebraska	37. Oregon	47. Washington
8. Delaware	18. Louisiana	28. Nevada	38. Pennsylvania	48. West Virginia
9. Florida	19. Maine	29. New Hampshire	39. Rhode Island	49. Wisconsin
10. Georgia	20. Maryland	30. New Jersey	40. South Carolina	50. Wyoming

12. Obtaining a Simple Random Sample The following table lists the 43 presidents of the United States.

(a) Obtain a simple random sample of size 8 using Table I in Appendix A, a graphing calculator, or computer software.

(b) Obtain a second simple random sample of size 8 using Table I in Appendix A, a graphing calculator, or computer software.

1. Washington	10. Tyler	19. Hayes	28. Wilson	37. Nixon
2. J. Adams	11. Polk	20. Garfield	29. Harding	38. Ford
3. Jefferson	12. Taylor	21. Arthur	30. Coolidge	39. Carter
4. Madison	13. Fillmore	22. Cleveland	31. Hoover	40. Reagan
5. Monroe	14. Pierce	23. B. Harrison	32. F. D. Roosevelt	41. George H. Bush
6. J. Q. Adams	15. Buchanan	24. Cleveland	33. Truman	42. Clinton
7. Jackson	16. Lincoln	25. McKinley	34. Eisenhower	43. George W. Bush
8. Van Buren	17. A. Johnson	26. T. Roosevelt	35. Kennedy	
9. W. H. Harrison	18. Grant	27. Taft	36. L. B. Johnson	

13. Obtaining a Simple Random Sample Suppose you are the president of the student government. You wish to conduct a survey to determine the student body's opinion regarding student services. The administration provides you with a list of the names and phone numbers of the 19,935 registered students.

(a) Discuss the procedure you would follow to obtain a simple random sample of 25 students.

(b) Obtain this sample.

14. Obtaining a Simple Random Sample Suppose the mayor of Justice, Illinois, asks you to poll the residents of the village. The mayor provides you with a list of the names and phone numbers of the 5,832 residents of the village.

(a) Discuss the procedure you would follow to obtain a simple random sample of 20 residents.

(b) Obtain this sample.

15. Future Government Club The Future Government Club wants to sponsor a panel discussion on the upcoming national election. The club wants four of its members to lead the panel discussion. Obtain a simple random sample of size 4 from the table. Write a short description of the process you used to generate your sample.

Blouin	Fallenbuchel	Niemeyer	Rice
Bolden	Grajewski	Nolan	Salihar
Bolt	Haydra	Ochs	Tate
Carter	Keating	Opacian	Thompson
Cooper	Khouri	Pawlak	Trudeau
Debold	Lukens	Pechtold	Washington
De Young	May	Ramirez	Wright
Engler	Motola	Redmond	Zenkel

16. **Worker Morale** The owner of a private food store is concerned about employee morale. She decides to survey the employees to see if she can learn about work environment and job satisfaction. Obtain a simple random sample of size 5 from the names in the given table. Write a short description of the process you used to generate your sample.

Archer	Foushi	Kemp	Oliver
Bolcerek	Gow	Lathus	Orsini
Bryant	Grove	Lindsey	Salazar
Carlisle	Hall	Massie	Ullrich
Cole	Hills	McGuffin	Vaneck
Dimas	Houston	Musa	Weber
Ellison	Kats	Nickas	Zavodny
Everhart			

TECHNOLOGY STEP-BY-STEP   Obtaining a Simple Random Sample

TI-83/84 Plus

1. Enter any nonzero number (the seed) on the HOME screen.
2. Press the STO ▶ button.
3. Press the MATH button.
4. Highlight the PRB menu and select 1: rand.
5. From the HOME screen press ENTER.
6. Press the MATH button. Highlight PRB menu and select 5: randInt(.
7. With randInt(on the HOME screen, enter 1, N, where N is the population size. For example, if N = 500, enter the following:

randInt(1,500)

Press ENTER to obtain the first individual in the sample. Continue pressing ENTER until the desired sample size is obtained.

MINITAB

1. Select the **Calc** menu and highlight **Set Base** ....
2. Enter any seed number you desire. Note that it is not necessary to set the seed, because MINITAB uses the time of day in seconds to set the seed.
3. Select the **Calc** menu, highlight **Random Data**, and select **Integer** ....
4. Fill in the following window with the appropriate values. To obtain a simple random sample for the situation in Example 2, we would enter the following:

The reason we generate 10 rows of data (instead of 5) is in case any of the random numbers repeat. Select OK, and the random numbers will appear in column 1 (C1) in the spreadsheet.

Excel

1. Be sure the Data Analysis Tool Pak is activated. This is done by selecting the **Tools** menu and highlighting **Add – Ins** .... Check the box for the Analysis ToolPak and select OK.
2. Select **Tools** and highlight **Data Analysis** .... Highlight **Random Number Generation** and select OK.
3. Fill in the window with the appropriate values. To obtain a simple random sample for the situation in Example 2, we would fill in the following:

The reason we generate 10 rows of data (instead of 5) is in case any of the random numbers repeat. Notice also that the parameter is between 1 and 31, so any value greater than or equal to 1 and less than or equal to 31 is possible. In the unlikely event that 31 appears, simply ignore it. Select OK and the random numbers will appear in column 1 (A1) in the spreadsheet. Ignore any values to the right of the decimal place.

1.4 OTHER EFFECTIVE SAMPLING METHODS

Objectives **1** Obtain a stratified sample
2 Obtain a systematic sample
3 Obtain a cluster sample

Note to Instructor
The material in this section is optional and can be skipped without loss of continuity.

The goal of sampling is to obtain as much information as possible about the population at the least cost. Remember, we are using the word *cost* in a general sense. Cost includes monetary outlays, time, and other resources. With this goal in mind, we may find it advantageous to use sampling techniques other than simple random sampling.

 Obtain a Stratified Sample

Under certain circumstances, *stratified sampling* provides more information about the population for less cost than simple random sampling.

Definition

A **stratified sample** is obtained by separating the population into nonoverlapping groups called *strata* and then obtaining a simple random sample from each stratum. The individuals within each stratum should be homogeneous (or similar) in some way.

For example, suppose Congress was considering a bill that abolishes estate taxes. In an effort to determine the opinion of her constituency, a senator asks a pollster to conduct a survey within her district. The pollster may divide the population of registered voters within the district into three strata: Republican, Democrat, and Independent. This grouping makes sense because the members within each of the three party affiliations may have the same opinion regarding estate taxes, but opinions between parties may differ. The main criterion in performing a stratified sample is that each group (stratum) must have a common attribute that results in the individuals being similar within the stratum.

In Other Words
Stratum is singular, while strata is plural. The word strata means divisions. So a stratified sample is a simple random sample of different divisions of the population.

An advantage of stratified sampling over simple random sampling is that it may allow fewer individuals to be surveyed while obtaining the same or more information. This result occurs because individuals within each subgroup have similar characteristics, so opinions within the group are not as likely vary much from one individual to the next. In addition, a stratified sample guarantees that each stratum is represented in the sample.

EXAMPLE 1 **Obtaining a Stratified Sample**

Problem: The president of DePaul University wants to conduct a survey to determine the community's opinion regarding campus safety. The president divides the DePaul community into three groups: resident students, nonresident (commuting) students, and staff (including faculty) so that he can obtain a stratified sample. Suppose there are 6,204 resident students, 13,304 nonresident students, and 2,401 staff, for a total of 21,909 individuals in the population. The president wants to obtain a sample of size 100, with the number of individuals selected from each stratum weighted by the population size. So resident students make up $6,204/21,909 = 28\%$ of the sample, nonresident students account for 61% of the sample, and staff constitute 11% of the sample. To obtain a sample of size 100, the president will obtain a stratified sample of $0.28(100) = 28$ resident students, $0.61(100) = 61$ nonresident students, and $0.11(100) = 11$ staff.

Approach: To obtain the stratified sample, conduct a simple random sample within each group. That is, obtain a simple random sample of 28 resident students (from the 6,204 resident students), a simple random sample of 61 nonresident students, and a simple random sample of 11 staff. Be sure to use a different seed for each stratum.

Solution: Using MINITAB, with the seed set to 4032 and the values shown in Figure 4, we obtain the following sample of staff:

240, 630, 847, 190, 2096, 705, 2320, 323, 701, 471, 744

Figure 4

CAUTION Do not use the same seed (or starting point in Table I) for all the groups in a stratified sample, because we want the simple random samples within each stratum to be independent of each other.

Repeat this procedure for the resident and nonresident students using a different seed.

An advantage of stratified sampling over simple random sampling is that the researcher is able to determine characteristics within each stratum. This allows an analysis to be performed on each subgroup to see if any significant differences between the groups exist. For example, we could analyze the data obtained in Example 1 to see if there is a difference in the opinions of students versus staff.

Now Work Problem 25

2 Obtain a Systematic Sample

In both simple random sampling and stratified sampling, it is necessary for a list of the individuals in the population being studied (the frame) to exist. Therefore, these sampling techniques require some preliminary work before the sample is obtained. A sampling technique that does not require a frame is *systematic sampling*.

Definition   A **systematic sample** is obtained by selecting every kth individual from the population. The first individual selected corresponds to a random number between 1 and k.

Because systematic sampling does not require a frame, it is a useful technique when you can't obtain a list of the individuals in the population that you wish to study.

The idea behind obtaining a systematic sample is relatively simple: Select a number k, randomly select a number between 1 and k and survey that individual, then survey every kth individual thereafter. For example, we might decide to survey every $k = 8$th individual. We randomly select a number between 1 and 8 such as 5. This means we survey the 5th, $5 + 8 = 13$th, $13 + 8 = 21$st, $21 + 8 = 29$th, and so on, individuals until we reach the desired sample size.

EXAMPLE 2   ## Obtaining a Systematic Sample without a Frame

Problem: The manager of Kroger Food Stores wants to measure the satisfaction of the store's customers. Design a sampling technique that can be used to obtain a sample of 40 customers.

Approach: A frame of Kroger customers would be difficult, if not impossible, to obtain. Therefore, it is reasonable to use systematic sampling by surveying every kth customer who leaves the store.

Solution: The manager decides to obtain a systematic sample by surveying every 7th customer. He randomly determines a number between 1 and 7, say 5. He then surveys the 5th customer exiting the store and every 7th customer thereafter, until a sample of 40 customers is reached. The survey will include customers 5, 12, 19, ..., 278.[*]

But how do we select the value of k? If the size of the population is unknown, there is no mathematical way to determine k. It must be chosen by determining a value of k that is not so large that we are unable to achieve our desired sample size, but not so small that we do not obtain a sample size that is representative of the population.

To clarify this point, let's revisit Example 2. Suppose we chose a value of k that was too large, say 30. This means that we will survey every 30th shopper, starting with the 5th. To obtain a sample of size 40 would require that 1,175 shoppers visit Kroger on that day. If Kroger does not have 1,175 shoppers, the desired sample size will not be achieved. On the other hand, if k is too small, say 4, we would survey the 5th, 9th, ..., 161st shopper. It may be that the 161st shopper exits the store at 3 P.M., which means our survey did not include any of the evening shoppers. Certainly, this sample is not representative of *all* Kroger patrons! An estimate of the size of the population would certainly help determine an appropriate value for k.

To determine the value of k when the size of the population, N, is known is relatively straightforward. Suppose we wish to survey a population whose size is known to be $N = 20{,}325$ and we desire a sample of size $n = 100$. To guarantee that individuals are selected evenly from both the beginning and the end of the population (such as early and late shoppers), we compute N/n and round down to the nearest integer. For example, $20{,}325/100 = 203.25$, so $k = 203$. Then we randomly select a number between 1 and 203 and select every 203rd individual thereafter. So, if we randomly selected 90 as our starting point, we would survey the 90th, 293rd, 496th, ..., 20,187th individuals.

We summarize the procedure as follows:

Steps in Systematic Sampling

Step 1: If possible, approximate the population size, N.

Step 2: Determine the sample size desired, n.

Step 3: Compute $\frac{N}{n}$ and round down to the nearest integer. This value is k.

Step 4: Randomly select a number between 1 and k. Call this number p.

Step 5: The sample will consist of the following individuals:

$$p, p + k, p + 2k, \ldots, p + (n - 1)k$$

Because systematic sampling does not require a frame, it typically provides more information for a given cost than does simple random sampling. In addition, systematic sampling is easier to employ, so there is less likelihood of interviewer error occurring, such as selecting the wrong individual to be surveyed.

Now Work Problem 27

3 · Obtain a Cluster Sample

A fourth sampling method is called *cluster sampling*. The previous three sampling methods discussed have benefits under certain circumstances. So does cluster sampling.

---

[*]Because we are surveying 40 customers, the first individual surveyed is the 5th, the second is the $5 + 7 = 12$th, the third is the $5 + (2)\,7 = 19$th, and so on, until we reach the 40th, which is the $5 + (39)\,7 = 278$th shopper.

Definition

A **cluster sample** is obtained by selecting all individuals within a randomly selected collection or group of individuals.

In Other Words
Imagine a mall parking lot. Each subsection of the lot could be a cluster (Section F-4, for example).

A school administrator wants to learn the characteristics of students enrolled in online classes. Rather than obtaining a simple random sample based on the frame of all students enrolled in online classes, the administrator could treat each online class as a cluster and then obtain a simple random sample of these clusters. The administrator would then survey *all* the students in the selected clusters.

EXAMPLE 3   **Obtaining a Cluster Sample**

Problem: A sociologist wants to gather data regarding household income within the city of Boston. Obtain a sample using cluster sampling.

Approach: The city of Boston can be set up so that each city block is a cluster. Once the city blocks have been identified, we obtain a simple random sample of the city blocks and survey all households on the blocks selected.

Solution: Suppose there are 10,493 city blocks in Boston. First, we must number the blocks from 1 to 10,493. Suppose the sociologist has enough time and money to survey 20 clusters (city blocks). Therefore, the sociologist should obtain a simple random sample of 20 numbers between 1 and 10,493 and survey all households from the clusters selected. Cluster sampling is a good choice in this example because it reduces the travel time to households that is likely to occur with both simple random sampling and stratified sampling. In addition, there is no need to obtain a detailed frame with cluster sampling. The only frame needed is one that provides information regarding city blocks.

Recall that in systematic sampling we had to determine an appropriate value for k, the number of individuals to skip between individuals selected to be in the sample. We have a similar problem in cluster sampling. The following are a few of the questions that arise:

- How do I cluster the population?
- How many clusters do I sample?
- How many individuals should be in each cluster?

First, it must be determined whether the individuals within the proposed cluster are homogeneous (similar individuals) or heterogeneous (dissimilar individuals). Consider the results of Example 3. City blocks tend to have similar households. Surveying one house on a city block is likely to result in similar responses from another house on the same block. This results in duplicate information. We conclude the following: If the clusters have homogeneous individuals, it is better to have more clusters with fewer individuals in each cluster.

What if the cluster is heterogeneous? Under this circumstance, the heterogeneity of the cluster likely resembles the heterogeneity of the population. In other words, each cluster is a scaled-down representation of the overall population. For example, a quality-control manager might use shipping boxes that contain 100 light bulbs as a cluster, since the rate of defects within the cluster would closely mimic the rate of defects in the population, assuming the bulbs are randomly placed in the box. Thus, when each cluster is heterogeneous, fewer clusters with more individuals in each cluster are appropriate.

The four sampling techniques just presented are sampling techniques in which the individuals are selected randomly. Often, however, sampling methods are used in which the individuals are not randomly selected, such as *convenience sampling*.

CAUTION   Stratified and cluster samples are different. In a stratified sample, we divide the population into two or more homogeneous groups. Then we obtain a simple random sample from each group. In a cluster sample, we divide the population into groups, obtain a simple random sample of some of the groups, and survey *all* individuals in the selected groups.

Now Work Problem 13

Convenience Sampling

Have you ever been stopped in the mall by someone holding a clipboard? These folks are responsible for gathering information, but their methods of data collection are inappropriate, and the results of their analysis are suspect because they obtained their data using a *convenience sample*.

Definition

A **convenience sample** is a sample in which the individuals are easily obtained and not based on randomness.

⬦ CAUTION

Studies that use convenience sampling generally have results that are suspect. The results should be looked on with extreme skepticism.

Note to Instructor

Discuss some problems encountered in obtaining a sample from a nearby mall.

There are many types of convenience samples, but probably the most popular are those in which the individuals in the sample are **self-selected** (the individuals themselves decide to participate in a survey). These are also called **voluntary response** samples. Examples of self-selected sampling include phone-in polling; a radio personality will ask his or her listeners to phone the station to submit their opinions. Another example is the use of the Internet to conduct surveys. For example, *Dateline* will present a story regarding a certain topic and ask its viewers to "tell us what you think" by completing a questionnaire online or phoning in an opinion. Both of these samples are poor designs because the individuals who decide to be in the sample generally have strong opinions about the topic. A more typical individual in the population will not bother phoning or logging on to a computer to complete a survey. Any inference made regarding the population from this type of sample should be made with extreme caution.

The reason convenience samples yield unreliable results is that the individuals chosen to participate in the survey are not chosen using random sampling. Instead, the interviewer or participant selects who is in the survey. Do you think an interviewer would select an ornery individual? Of course not! Therefore, the sample is likely not to be representative of the population.

Multistage Sampling

In practice, most large-scale surveys obtain samples using a combination of the techniques just presented.

As an example of multistage sampling, consider Nielsen Media Research. Nielsen randomly selects households and monitors the television programs these households are watching through a People Meter. The meter is an electronic box placed on each TV within the household. The People Meter measures what program is being watched and who is watching it. Nielsen selects the households with the use of a two-stage sampling process.

Stage 1: Using U.S. Census data, Nielsen divides the country into geographic areas (strata). The strata are typically city blocks in urban areas and geographic regions in rural areas. About 6,000 strata are randomly selected.

Stage 2: Nielsen sends representatives to the selected strata and lists the households within the strata. The households are then randomly selected through a simple random sample.

Nielsen sells the information obtained to television stations and companies. These results are used to help determine prices for commercials.

As another example of multistage sampling, consider the sample used by the Census Bureau for the Current Population Survey. This survey requires five stages of sampling:

Stage 1: Stratified sample

Stage 2: Cluster sample

Stage 3: Stratified sample

Stage 4: Cluster sample

Stage 5: Systematic sample

This survey is very important because it is used to obtain demographic estimates of the United States in noncensus years. A detailed presentation of the sampling method used by the Census Bureau can be found in *The Current Population Survey: Design and Methodology*, Technical Paper No. 40.

Sample Size Considerations

Throughout our discussion of sampling, we did not mention how to determine the sample size. Determining the sample size is key in the overall statistical process. In other words, the researcher must ask this question: "How many individuals must I survey to draw conclusions about the population within some predetermined margin of error?" The researcher must find the correct balance between the reliability of the results and the cost of obtaining these results. The bottom line is that time and money determine the level of confidence a researcher will place on the conclusions drawn from the sample data. The more time and money the researcher has available, the more accurate the results of the statistical inference will be.

Nonetheless, techniques do exist for determining the sample size required to estimate characteristics regarding the population within some margin of error. We will consider some of these techniques in Sections 9.1 and 9.3. (For a detailed discussion of sample size considerations, consult a text on sampling techniques such as *Elements of Sampling Theory and Methods* by Z. Govindarajulu, Prentice Hall, 1999.)

Summary

Figure 5 provides a summary of the four sampling techniques presented.

Figure 5

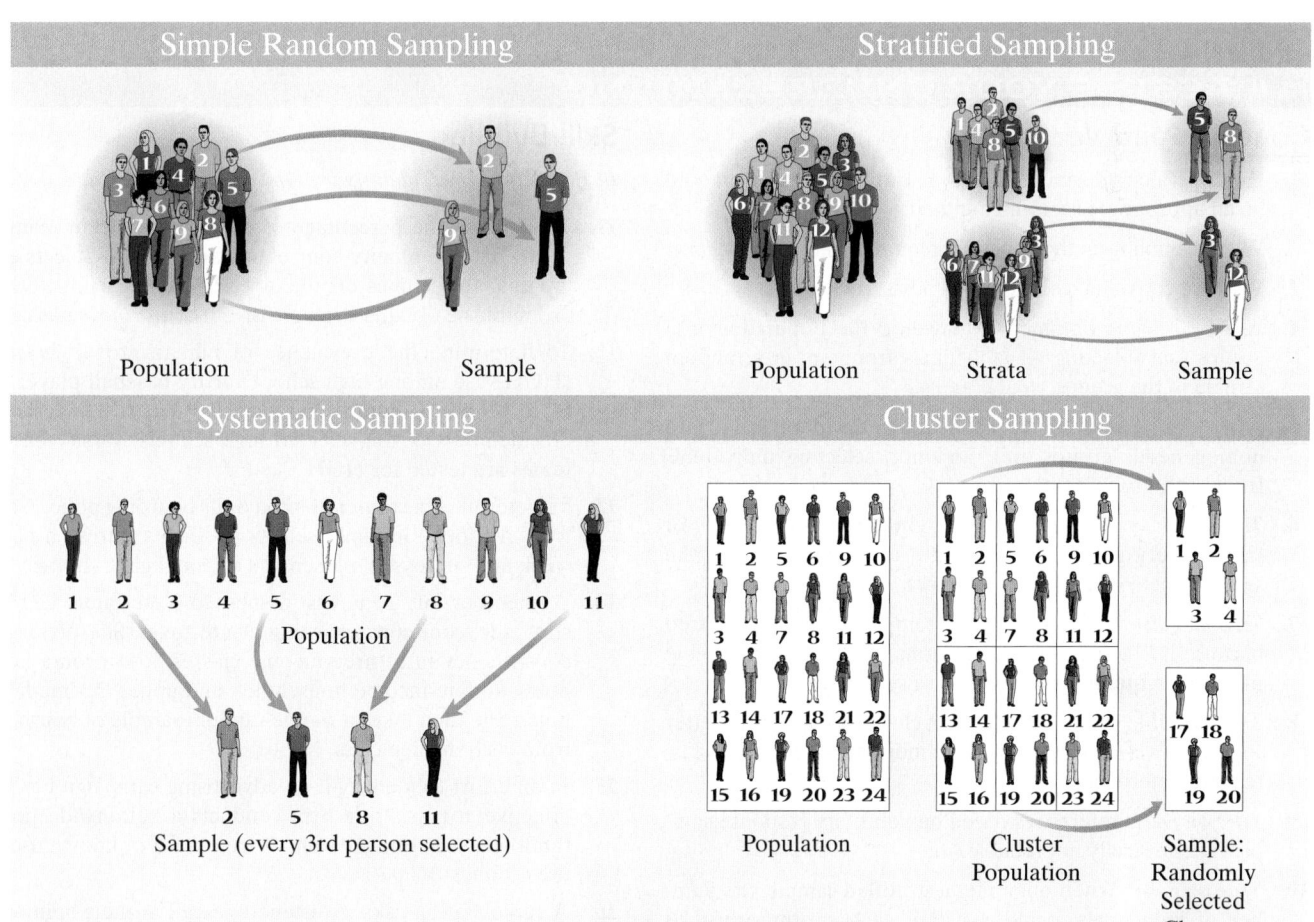

Simple Random Sampling

Population Sample

Stratified Sampling

Population Strata Sample

Systematic Sampling

1 2 3 4 5 6 7 8 9 10 11
Population

2 5 8 11
Sample (every 3rd person selected)

Cluster Sampling

1 2 5 6 9 10
3 4 7 8 11 12
13 14 17 18 21 22
15 16 19 20 23 24
Population

1 2 5 6 9 10
3 4 7 8 11 12
13 14 17 18 21 22
15 16 19 20 23 24
Cluster Population

1 2
3 4

17 18
19 20
Sample: Randomly Selected Clusters

IN CLASS ACTIVITY

Different Sampling Methods

The following question was recently asked by the Gallup Organization: In general, are you satisfied or dissatisfied with the way things are going in the country?

(a) Number the students in the class from 1 to N, where N is the number of students. Obtain a simple random sample and have them answer this question. Record the number of satisfied responses and the number of dissatisfied responses.

(b) Divide the students in the class by gender. Treat each gender as a stratum. Obtain a simple random sample from each stratum and have them answer this question. Record the number of satisfied responses and the number of dissatisfied responses.

(c) Treat each row of desks as a cluster. Obtain a simple random sample of clusters and have each student in the selected clusters answer this question. Record the number of satisfied responses and the number of dissatisfied responses.

(d) Number the students in the class from 1 to N, where N is the number of students. Obtain a systematic sample and have the selected students answer this question. Record the number of satisfied responses and the number of dissatisfied responses.

(e) Were there any differences in the results of the survey? State some reasons for any differences.

1.4 ASSESS YOUR UNDERSTANDING

Concepts and Vocabulary

1. Describe a circumstance in which stratified sampling would be an appropriate sampling method.

2. Which sampling method does not require a frame? Systematic

3. Why are convenience samples ill advised?

4. A(n) _____ is obtained by dividing the population into groups and selecting all individuals from within a random sample of the groups. cluster sample

5. A(n) _____ is obtained by dividing the population into homogeneous groups and randomly selecting individuals from each group. stratified sample

6. *True or False*: When taking a systematic random sample of size n, every group of size n from the population has the same chance of being selected. False

7. *True or False*: A simple random sample is always preferred because it obtains the same information as other sampling plans but requires a smaller sample size. False

8. *True or False*: When conducting a cluster sample, it is better to have fewer clusters with more individuals when the clusters are heterogeneous. True

9. *True or False*: Inferences based on voluntary response samples are generally not reliable. True

10. *True or False*: When obtaining a stratified sample, the number of individuals included within each stratum must be equal. False

Skill Building

In Problems 11–22, identify the type of sampling used.

11. To estimate the percentage of defects in a recent manufacturing batch, a quality-control manager at Intel selects every 8th chip that comes off the assembly line starting with the 3rd until she obtains a sample of 140 chips. Systematic

12. To determine the prevalence of human growth hormone (HGH) use among high school varsity baseball players, the State Athletic Commission randomly selects 50 high schools. All members of the selected high schools' varsity baseball teams are tested for HGH. Cluster

13. To determine customer opinion of its boarding policy, Southwest Airlines randomly selects 60 flights during a certain week and surveys all passengers on the flights. Cluster

14. A member of Congress wishes to determine her constituency's opinion regarding estate taxes. She divides her constituency into three income classes: low-income households, middle-income households, and upper-income households. She then takes a simple random sample of households from each income class. Stratified

15. In an effort to identify if an advertising campaign has been effective, a marketing firm conducts a nationwide poll by randomly selecting individuals from a list of known users of the product. Simple random

16. A radio station asks its listeners to call in their opinion regarding the use of U.S. forces in peacekeeping missions. Convenience

29. SRS: number from 1 to 1,280; randomly select 128 students to survey. Stratified: randomly select 4 students from each section to survey. Cluster: randomly select 4 sections, survey all students in these 4 sections. Answers will vary.

17. A farmer divides his orchard into 50 subsections, randomly selects 4, and samples all the trees within the 4 subsections to approximate the yield of his orchard. Cluster

18. A school official divides the student population into five classes: freshman, sophomore, junior, senior, and graduate student. The official takes a simple random sample from each class and asks the members' opinions regarding student services. Stratified

19. A survey regarding download time on a certain website is administered on the Internet by a market research firm to anyone who would like to take it. Convenience

20. The presider of a guest-lecture series at a university stands outside the auditorium before a lecture begins and hands every fifth person who arrives, beginning with the third, a speaker evaluation survey to be completed and returned at the end of the program. Systematic

21. To determine his DSL Internet connection speed, Shawn divides up the day into four parts: morning, midday, evening, and late night. He then measures his Internet connection speed at 5 randomly selected times during each part of the day. Stratified

22. 24 Hour Fitness wants to administer a satisfaction survey to its current members. Using its membership roster, the club randomly selects 40 club members and asks them about their level of satisfaction with the club. Simple random

23. A salesperson obtained a systematic sample of size 20 from a list of 500 clients. To do so, he randomly selected a number from 1 of 25, obtaining the number 16. He included in the sample the 16th client on the list and every 25th client thereafter. List the numbers that correspond to the 20 clients selected.

24. A quality-control expert wishes to obtain a cluster sample by selecting 10 of 795 clusters. She numbers the clusters from 1 to 795. Using Table I from Appendix A, she closes her eyes and drops a pencil on the table. It points to the digit in row 8, column 38. Using this position as the starting point and proceeding downward, determine the numbers for the 10 clusters selected. 763, 185, 377, 304, 626, 392, 315, 084, 565, 508

23. 16, 41, 66, 91, 116, 141, 166, 191, 216, 241, 266, 291, 316, 341, 366, 391, 416, 441, 466, 491

Applying the Concepts

25. Stratified Sampling The Future Government Club wants to sponsor a panel discussion on the upcoming national election. The club wants to have four of its members lead the panel discussion. To be fair, however, the panel should consist of two Democrats and two Republicans. From the list of current members of the club, obtain a stratified sample of two Democrats and two Republicans to serve on the panel.

Democrats		Republicans	
Bolden	Motola	Blouin	Ochs
Bolt	Nolan	Cooper	Pechtold
Carter	Opacian	De Young	Redmond
Debold	Pawlak	Engler	Rice
Fallenbuchel	Ramirez	Grajewski	Salihar
Haydra	Tate	Keating	Thompson
Khouri	Washington	May	Trudeau
Lukens	Wright	Niemeyer	Zenkel

26. Stratified Sampling The owner of a private food store is concerned about employee morale. She decides to survey the managers and hourly employees to see if she can learn about work environment and job satisfaction. From the list of workers at the store, obtain a stratified sample of two managers and four hourly employees to survey.

Managers		Hourly Employees		
Carlisle	Oliver	Archer	Foushi	Massie
Hills	Orsini	Bolcerek	Gow	Musa
Kats	Ullrich	Bryant	Grove	Nickas
Lindsey	McGuffin	Cole	Hall	Salazar
		Dimas	Houston	Vaneck
		Ellison	Kemp	Weber
		Everhart	Lathus	Zavodny

27. Systematic Sample The human resource department at a certain company wants to conduct a survey regarding worker morale. The department has an alphabetical list of all 4,502 employees at the company and wants to conduct a systematic sample.
   (a) Determine k if the sample size is 50. 90
   (b) Determine the individuals who will be administered the survey. More than one answer is possible.

28. Systematic Sample To predict the outcome of a county election, a newspaper obtains a list of all 945,035 registered voters in the county and wants to conduct a systematic sample.
   (a) Determine k if the sample size is 130. 7269
   (b) Determine the individuals who will be administered the survey. More than one answer is possible.

29. Which Method? The mathematics department at a university wishes to administer a survey to a sample of students taking college algebra. The department is offering 32 sections of college algebra, similar in class size and makeup, with a total of 1,280 students. They would like the sample size to be roughly 10% of the population of college algebra students this semester. How might the department obtain a simple random sample? A stratified sample? A cluster sample? Which method do you think is best in this situation?

30. Good Sampling Method? To obtain students' opinions about proposed changes to course registration procedures, the administration of a small college asked for faculty volunteers who were willing to administer a survey in one of their classes. Twenty-three faculty members volunteered. Each of these faculty members gave the survey to all the students in one course of their choosing. Would this sampling method be considered a cluster sample? Why or why not? No. The "clusters" were not randomly selected.

31. Sample Design The city of Naperville is considering the construction of a new commuter rail station. The city wishes to survey the residents of the city to obtain their opinion regarding the use of tax dollars for this purpose. Design a sampling method to obtain the individuals in the sample. Be sure to support your choice.

32. Sample Design A school board at a local community college is considering raising the student services fees. The board wants to obtain the opinion of the student body before proceeding. Design a sampling method to obtain the individuals in the sample. Be sure to support your choice.

33. Sample Design Target wants to open a new store in the village of Lockport. Before construction, Target's marketers want to obtain some demographic information regarding the area under consideration. Design a sampling method to obtain the individuals in the sample. Be sure to support your choice.

34. Sample Design The county sheriff wishes to determine if a certain highway has a high proportion of speeders traveling on it. Design a sampling method to obtain the individuals in the sample. Be sure to support your choice.

35. Sample Design A pharmaceutical company wants to conduct a survey of 30 individuals who have high cholesterol. The company has obtained a list from doctors throughout the country of 6,600 individuals who are known to have high cholesterol. Design a sampling method to obtain the individuals in the sample. Be sure to support your choice.

36. Sample Design A marketing executive for Coca-Cola, Inc., wants to identify television shows that people in the Boston area who typically drink Coke are watching. The executive has a list of all households in the Boston area. Design a sampling method to obtain the individuals in the sample. Be sure to support your choice.

37. Putting It Together: Comparing Sampling Methods Suppose a political strategist wants to get a sense of how American

37. (a) Registered voters who have voted in the past few elections

adults aged 18 years or older feel about health care and health insurance.

(a) In a political poll, what would be a good frame to use for obtaining a sample?

(b) Explain why simple random sampling may not guarantee that the sample has an accurate representation of registered Democrats, registered Republicans, and registered Independents.

(c) How can stratified sampling guarantee this representation?

38. Putting It Together: Thinking about Randomness What is random sampling? Why is it necessary for a sample to be obtained randomly rather than conveniently? Will randomness guarantee that a sample will provide accurate information about the population? Explain.

39. Research the origins of the Gallup Poll and the current sampling method the organization uses. Report your findings to the class.

40. Research the sampling methods used by a market research firm in your neighborhood. Report your findings to the class. The report should include the types of sampling methods used, number of stages, and sample size.

1.5 BIAS IN SAMPLING

Objective		Explain the sources of bias in sampling

 Explain the Sources of Bias in Sampling

So far we have looked at *how* to obtain samples, but not at some of the problems that inevitably arise in sampling. Remember, the goal of sampling is to obtain information about a population through a sample.

Note to Instructor
If you are pressed for time, this section can be given to the students as a reading assignment with light in-class coverage.

Definition

If the results of the sample are not representative of the population, then the sample has **bias**.

In Other Words
The word *bias* could mean to give preference to selecting some individuals over others. It could also mean that certain responses are more likely to occur in the sample than in the population.

There are three sources of bias in sampling:

1. Sampling bias
2. Nonresponse bias
3. Response bias

Sampling Bias
Sampling bias means that the technique used to obtain the individuals to be in the sample tends to favor one part of the population over another. Any convenience sample has sampling bias because the individuals are not chosen through a random sample. For example, a voluntary response sample will have sampling bias because the opinions of individuals who decide to be in the sample are probably not representative of the population as a whole.

Sampling bias also results due to *undercoverage*. **Undercoverage** occurs when the proportion of one segment of the population is lower in a sample than it is in the population. Undercoverage can result because the frame used to obtain the sample is incomplete or not representative of the population. Recall that the frame is the list of all individuals in the population under study. Sometimes, obtaining the frame would seem to be a relatively easy task, such as obtaining the list of all registered voters for a study regarding voter preference in an upcoming election. Even under this circumstance, however, the frame may be incomplete since people who recently registered to vote may not be on the published list of registered voters.

Sampling bias can result in incorrect predictions. For example, the magazine *Literary Digest* predicted that Alfred M. Landon would defeat Franklin D. Roosevelt in the 1936 presidential election. The *Literary Digest* conducted a poll by mailing questionnaires based on a list of its subscribers, telephone directories, and automobile owners. On the basis of the results, the *Literary Digest* predicted that Landon would win the election with 57% of the popular vote. However, Roosevelt won the election with about 62% of the popular vote. Bear in mind that this election was taking place during the height of the Great Depression. The incorrect prediction by the *Literary Digest* was the result of sampling bias. In 1936, most subscribers to the magazine, households with telephones, and automobile owners were Republican, the party of Landon. Therefore, the choice of the frame used to conduct the survey led to an incorrect prediction. Essentially, there was undercoverage of Democrats.

Often, it is difficult to gain access to a *complete* list of individuals in a population. For example, in public-opinion polls, random telephone surveys are frequently conducted, which implies that the frame is all households with telephones. This method of sampling will exclude any household that does not have a telephone, as well as homeless people. If the individuals without a telephone or homeless people differ in some way from people with a telephone or with homes, then the results of the sample may not be valid.

Nonresponse Bias

Nonresponse bias exists when individuals selected to be in the sample who do not respond to the survey have different opinions from those who do. Nonresponse can occur because individuals selected for the sample do not wish to respond or the interviewer was unable to contact them.

All surveys will suffer from nonresponse. The federal government uses a complex random sample to select individuals to participate in its Current Population Survey. Overall, the response rate is about 92%, but it varies depending on the age of the individual. For example, the response rate for 20- to 29-year-olds is 85%, while the response rate for individuals at least 70 years of age is 99%. Response rates in random digit dialing (RDD) telephone surveys are typically around 70%. Response rates for e-mail surveys typically hover around 40%, and mail surveys can have response rates as high as 60%.

Nonresponse bias can be controlled using callbacks. For example, if nonresponse occurs because a mailed questionnaire was not returned, a callback might mean phoning the individual to conduct the survey. If nonresponse occurs because an individual was not at home, a callback might mean returning to the home at other times in the day or on other days of the week.

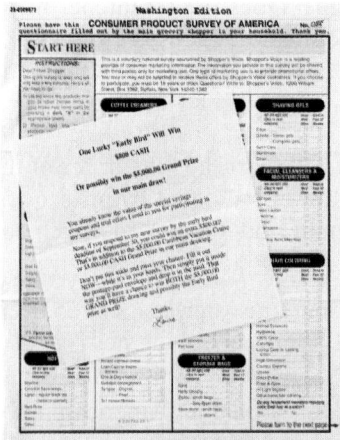

Another method to improve nonresponse is using rewards and incentives. Rewards may include cash payments for completing a questionnaire. Incentives might include a cover letter that states that the responses to the questionnaire will determine future policy. For example, I received $1 with a survey regarding my satisfaction with a recent purchase. The $1 "payment" was meant to make me feel guilty enough to fill out the questionnaire. As another example, a city may send out questionnaires to households and state in a cover letter that the responses to the questionnaire will be used to decide pending issues within the city.

Let's consider the *Literary Digest* poll again. The *Literary Digest* mailed out more than 10 million questionnaires and 2.3 million people responded. The rather low response rate (23%) contributed to the *Literary Digest* making an incorrect prediction. After all, Roosevelt was the incumbent president and only those who were unhappy with his administration were likely to respond. By the way, in the same election, the 35-year-old George Gallup predicted that Roosevelt would win the election. He surveyed only 50,000 people to come to his conclusion.

Response Bias

Response bias exists when the answers on a survey do not reflect the true feelings of the respondent. Response bias can find its way into survey results in a number of ways.

Interviewer Error A trained interviewer is essential to obtain accurate information from a survey. A good interviewer will have the skill necessary to elicit responses from individuals within a sample and be able to make the interviewee feel comfortable enough to give truthful responses. For example, a good interviewer should be able to obtain truthful answers to questions as sensitive as "Have you ever cheated on your taxes?" Do not be quick to trust surveys that are conducted by poorly trained interviewers. Do not trust survey results if the sponsor has a vested interest in the results of the survey. Would you trust a survey conducted by a car dealer that reports 90% of customers say they would buy another car from the dealer?

Misrepresented Answers Some survey questions result in responses that misrepresent facts or are flat-out lies. For example, a survey of recent college graduates may find that self-reported salaries are somewhat inflated. Also, people may overestimate their abilities. For example, ask people how many push-ups they can do in 1 minute, and then ask them to do the push-ups. How accurate were they?

The wording of questions can significantly affect the responses and, therefore, the validity of a study.

Wording of Questions The wording of a question plays a large role in the type of response given to the question. The way a question is worded can lead to response bias in a survey, so questions must always be asked in balanced form. For example, the "yes/no" question

Do you oppose the reduction of estate taxes?

should be written

Do you favor or oppose the reduction of estate taxes?

The second question is balanced. Do you see the difference? Consider the following report based on studies from Schuman and Presser (*Questions and Answers in Attitude Surveys*, 1981, p. 277), who asked the following two questions:

(A) Do you think the United States should forbid public speeches against democracy?

(B) Do you think the United States should allow public speeches against democracy?

For those respondents presented with question A, 21.4% gave "yes" responses, while for those given question B, 47.8% gave "no" responses. The conclusion you may arrive at is that most people are not necessarily willing to forbid something, but more people are willing not to allow something. These results imply that the wording of the question can alter the outcome of a survey.

Another consideration in wording a question is not to be vague. For example, the question "How much do you study?" is too vague. Does the researcher mean how much do I study for all my classes or just for statistics? Does the researcher mean per day or per week? The question should be written "How many hours do you study statistics each week?"

Ordering of Questions or Words Many surveys will rearrange the order of the questions within a questionnaire so that responses are not affected by prior questions. Consider the following example from Schuman and Presser in which the following two questions were asked:

(A) Do you think the United States should let Communist newspaper reporters from other countries come in here and send back to their papers the news as they see it?

(B) Do you think a Communist country such as Russia should let American newspaper reporters come in and send back to America the news as they see it?

For surveys conducted in 1980 in which the questions appeared in the order (A, B), 54.7% of respondents answered "yes" to A and 63.7% answered "yes" to B. If the questions were ordered (B, A), then 74.6% answered "yes" to A and 81.9% answered "yes" to B. When Americans are first asked if U.S. reporters should be allowed to report Communist news, they are more likely to agree that Communists should be allowed to report American news. Questions should be rearranged as much as possible to help reduce effects of this type.

Pollsters will also rearrange words within a question. For example, the Gallup Organization asked the following question of 1,017 adults aged 18 years or older:

Do you [rotated: approve (or) disapprove] of the job George W. Bush is doing as president?

Notice how the words *approve* and *disapprove* were rotated. The purpose of this is to remove the effect that may occur by writing the word *approve* first in the question.

Type of Question One of the first considerations in designing a question is determining whether the question should be *open* or *closed*.

An **open question** is one for which the respondent is free to choose his or her response. For example:

What is the most important problem facing America's youth today?

A **closed question** is one for which the respondent must choose from a list of predetermined responses.

What is the most important problem facing America's youth today?
(a) Drugs
(b) Violence
(c) Single-parent homes
(d) Promiscuity
(e) Peer pressure

Not only should the order of the questions or certain words within the question be rearranged, but in closed questions the possible responses should also be rearranged. The reason is that respondents are likely to choose early choices in a list rather than later choices.

When designing an open question, be sure to phrase the question so that the responses are similar. (You don't want a wide variety of responses.) This allows for easy analysis of the responses. The benefit of closed questions is that they limit the number of respondent choices and, therefore, the results are much easier to analyze. However, this limits the choices and does not always allow the respondent to respond the way he or she might want to. If the desired answer is not provided as a choice, the respondent will be forced to choose a secondary answer or skip the question.

Survey designers recommend conducting pretest surveys with open questions and then using the most popular answers as the choices on closed-question surveys. Another issue to consider in the closed-question design is the number of responses the respondent may choose from. It is recommended that the option "no opinion" be omitted, because this option does not allow for meaningful analysis. The bottom line is to try to limit the number of choices in a closed-question format without forcing respondents to choose an option they otherwise would not. If the respondents choose an option they otherwise would not choose, the survey will have response bias.

Data-entry Error Although not technically a result of response bias, data-entry error will lead to results that are not representative of the population. Once data are collected, the results typically must be entered into a computer, which could result in input errors. For example, 39 may be entered as 93. It is imperative that data be checked for accuracy. In this text, we present some suggestions for checking for data error.

Can a Census Have Bias?

The discussion thus far has focused on bias in samples. This is not to imply that bias cannot occur when conducting a census, however. For example, it is entirely possible that a question on a census form is misunderstood, thereby leading to response bias in the results. We also mentioned that it is often difficult to contact each individual in a population. For example, the U.S. Census Bureau is challenged to count each homeless person in the country, so the census data published by the U.S. government likely suffers from nonresponse bias.

Sampling Error versus Nonsampling Error

Nonresponse bias, response bias, and data-entry errors are types of *nonsampling error*. However, whenever a sample is used to learn information about a population, there will inevitably also be *sampling error*.

Definitions

Nonsampling errors are errors that result from undercoverage, nonresponse bias, response bias, or data-entry error. Such errors could also be present in a complete census of the population. **Sampling error** is the error that results from using a sample to estimate information about a population. This type of error occurs because a sample gives incomplete information about a population.

By incomplete information, we mean that the individuals in the sample cannot reveal all the information about the population. Consider the following: Suppose that we wanted to determine the average age of the students enrolled in an introductory statistics course. To do this, we obtain a simple random sample of four students and ask them to write their age on a sheet of paper and turn it in. The average age of these four students is found to be 23.25 years. Assume that no students lied about their age, nobody misunderstood the question, and the sampling was done appropriately. If the actual average age of all 30 students in the class (the population) is 22.91 years, then the sampling error is $23.25 - 22.91 = 0.34$ year. Now suppose that the same survey is conducted, but this time one individual lies about his age. Then the results of the survey will also have nonsampling error.

In Other Words

We can think of sampling error as error that results from using a subset of the population to describe characteristics of the population. Nonsampling error is error that results from obtaining and recording the information collected.

IN CLASS ACTIVITY

A Classroom Survey

As a class, answer the following questions. Throughout the semester, the results of the survey can be used to illustrate various statistical concepts.

1. What is your gender?
2. What is your age?
3. How many semester hours are you enrolled in this semester?
4. How many minutes did you watch television last night?
5. What is your major? If you don't know, state undeclared.
6. How many hours did you work last week? If you don't work, write 0.
7. How many siblings do you have (include half- and step-siblings)?
8. Do you own your own car? If so, what make (Chevrolet, Honda, etc.)?
9. Do you speak more than one language fluently? If so, what language(s)?
10. How many hours do you study each week?
11. How many hours did you study last night?
12. How long does it take you (in minutes) to get to campus?
13. What is your eye color?

Note to Instructor

The purpose of this activity is to collect data about your class. You can then use the data to illustrate various concepts throughout the semester. To do some of the analysis, you will need to make the assumption that the data are the result of a simple random sample. This activity should only take 5 to 10 minutes.

1.5 ASSESS YOUR UNDERSTANDING

Concepts and Vocabulary

1. Why is it rare for frames to be completely accurate?

2. What are some solutions to nonresponse?

3. What is a closed question? What is an open question? Discuss the advantages and disadvantages of each type of question.

4. What does it mean when a part of the population is under-represented?

5. Discuss the benefits of having trained interviewers.

6. What are the advantages of having a presurvey when constructing a questionnaire that has closed questions?

7. Discuss the pros and cons of telephone interviews that take place during dinner time in the early evening.

8. Why is a high response rate desired? How would a low response rate affect survey results?

9. Discuss why the order of questions or choices within a questionnaire are important in sample surveys.

10. Suppose a survey asks, "Do you own any CDs?" Explain how this could be interpreted in more than one way. Suggest a way in which the question could be improved.

11. What is bias? Name the three sources of bias and provide an example of each. How can a census have bias?

12. Distinguish between nonsampling error and sampling error.

Skill Building

In Problems 13–24, the survey has bias. (a) Determine the type of bias. (b) Suggest a remedy.

13. A retail store manager wants to conduct a study regarding the shopping habits of his customers. He selects the first 60 customers who enter his store on a Saturday morning. Sampling bias

14. The village of Oak Lawn wishes to conduct a study regarding the income level of households within the village. The village manager selects 10 homes in the southwest corner of the village and sends an interviewer to the homes to determine household income. Sampling bias

15. An antigun advocate wants to estimate the percentage of people who favor stricter gun laws. He conducts a nationwide survey of 1,203 randomly selected adults 18 years old and older. The interviewer asks the respondents, "Do you favor harsher penalties for individuals who sell guns illegally?" Response bias; poorly worded question

16. Suppose you are conducting a survey regarding the sleeping habits of students. From a list of registered students, you obtain a simple random sample of 150 students. One survey question is "How much sleep do you get?"

17. A polling organization conducts a study to estimate the percentage of households that speaks a foreign language as the primary language. It mails a questionnaire to 1,023 randomly selected households throughout the United States and asks the head of household if a foreign language is the primary language spoken in the home. Of the 1,023 households selected, 12 responded. Nonresponse

18. Cold Stone Creamery is considering opening a new store in O'Fallon. Before opening the store, the company would like to know the percentage of households in O'Fallon that regularly visit an ice cream shop. The market researcher obtains a list of households in O'Fallon and randomly selects 150 of them. He mails a questionnaire to the 150 households that asks about ice cream eating habits and flavor preferences. Of the 150 questionnaires mailed, 4 are returned. Nonresponse

19. A newspaper article reported, "The *Cosmopolitan* magazine survey of more than 5,000 Australian women aged 18–34 found about 42 percent considered themselves overweight or obese."

Source: *Herald Sun*, September 9, 2007

20. A health teacher wishes to do research on the weight of college students. She obtains the weights for all the students in her 9 A.M. class by looking at their driver's licenses or state IDs. Sampling bias and possible response bias

21. A magazine is conducting a study on the effects of infidelity in a marriage. The editors randomly select 400 women whose husbands were unfaithful and ask, "Do you believe a marriage can survive when the husband destroys the trust that must exist between husband and wife?"

22. A textbook publisher wants to determine what percentage of college professors either require or recommend that their students purchase textbook packages with supplemental materials, such as study guides, digital media, and online tools. The publisher sends out surveys by e-mail to a random sample of 320 faculty members who have registered with its website and have agreed to receive solicitations. The publisher reports that 80% of college professors require or recommend that their students purchase some type of textbook package. Sampling bias; poor choice of a frame

23. Suppose you are conducting a survey regarding illicit drug use among teenagers in the Baltimore school district. You obtain a cluster sample of 12 schools within the district and sample all sophomore students in the randomly selected schools. The survey is administered by the teachers. Response bias

24. To determine the public's opinion of the police department, the police chief obtains a cluster sample of 15 census tracts within his jurisdiction and samples all households in the randomly selected tracts. Uniformed police officers go door to door to conduct the survey. Response bias

Applying the Concepts

25. **Response Rates** Surveys tend to suffer from low response rates. Based on past experience, a researcher determines that the typical response rate for an e-mail survey is 40%. She wishes to obtain a sample of 300 respondents, so she e-mails the survey to 1500 randomly selected e-mail addresses. Assuming the response rate for her survey is 40%, will the respondents form an unbiased sample? Explain.

26. **Delivery Format** The General Social Survey asked, "About how often did you have sex in the past 12 months?" About 47% of respondents indicated they had sex at least once a week. In a Web survey for a marriage and family wellness center, respondents were asked, "How often do you and your partner have sex (on average)?" About 31% of respondents indicated they had sex with their partner at least once a week. Explain how the delivery method for such a question could result in biased responses.

16. Response bias; poorly worded question   19. Sampling bias and possible interviewer error   21. Response bias; poorly worded question
25. No; undercoverage (sampling bias), nonresponse bias, and response bias

27. **Order of the Questions** Consider the following two questions:

    (a) Suppose that a rape is committed in which the woman becomes pregnant. Do you think the criminal should or should not face additional charges if the woman becomes pregnant?

    (b) Do you think abortions should be legal under any circumstances, legal under certain circumstances, or illegal in all circumstances?

    Do you think the order in which the questions are asked will affect the survey results? If so, what can the pollster do to alleviate this response bias?

28. **Order of the Questions** Consider the following two questions:

    (a) Do you believe that the government should or should not be allowed to prohibit individuals from expressing their religious beliefs at their place of employment?

    (b) Do you believe that the government should or should not be allowed to prohibit teachers from expressing their religious beliefs in public school classrooms?

    Do you think the order in which the questions are asked will affect the survey results? If so, what can the pollster do to alleviate this response bias? Discuss the choice of the word *prohibit* in the survey questions.

29. **Improving Response Rates** Suppose you are reading an article at psychcentral.com and the following text appears in a pop-up window:

    What tactic is the company using to increase the response rate for its survey?

30. **Rotating Choices** Consider this question from a recent Gallup poll:

    Which of the following approaches to solving the nation's energy problems do you think the U.S. should follow right now — [ROTATED: emphasize production of more oil, gas and coal supplies (or) emphasize more conservation by consumers of existing energy supplies]?

    Why is it important to rotate the two choices presented in the question?

31. **Random Digit Dialing** Many polls use random digit dialing (RDD) to obtain a sample, which means a computer randomly generates phone numbers. What is the frame for this type of sampling? Who would be excluded from the survey and how might this affect the results of the survey?

32. **Caller ID** How do you think caller ID has affected phone surveys?

33. **Don't Call Me!** The Telephone Consumer Protection Act (TCPA) allows consumers to put themselves on a do-not-call registry. If a number is on the registry, commercial telemarketers are not allowed to call you. Do you believe this has affected the ability of surveyors to obtain accurate polling results? If so, how?

34. **Current Population Survey** In the federal government's Current Population Survey, the response rate for 20- to 29-year-olds is 85%, while response rates for individuals at least 70 years of age is 99%. Why do you think this is?

35. **Analyze an Article** Read the following article from the January 20, 2005 *USA Today*. What types of nonsampling errors led to incorrect exit polls?

Firms Report Flaws That Threw Off Exit Polls
Kerry backers' willingness, pollsters' inexperience cited

By Mark Memmott, USA Today

The exit polls of voters on Election Day so overstated Sen. John Kerry's support that, going back to 1988, they rank as the most inaccurate in a presidential election, the firms that did the work concede.

One reason the surveys were skewed, they say, was because Kerry's supporters were more willing to participate than Bush's. Also, the people they hired to quiz voters were on average too young and too inexperienced and needed more training.

The exit polls, which are supposed to help the TV networks shape their coverage on election night, were sharply criticized. Leaks of preliminary data showed up on the Internet in the early afternoon of Election Day, fueling talk that Kerry was beating President Bush. After the election, some political scientists, pollsters and journalists questioned their value.

In a report to the six media companies that paid them to conduct the voter surveys, pollsters Warren Mitofsky and Joseph Lenski said Wednesday that "on average, the results from each precinct overstated the Kerry-Bush difference by 6.5 (percentage) points. This is the largest (overstatement) we have observed . . . in the last five presidential elections."

Lenski said Wednesday that issuing the report was like "hanging out your dirty underwear. You hope it's cleaner than people expected."

Among the findings:

• They hired too many relatively young adults to conduct the interviews. Half of the 1,400 interviewers were younger than 35. That may explain in part why Kerry voters were more inclined to participate, since he drew more of the youth vote than did Bush. But Mitofsky and Lenski also found younger interviewers were more likely to make mistakes.

• Early results were skewed by a "programming error" that led to including too many female voters. Kerry outpolled Bush among women.

• Some local officials prevented interviewers from getting close to voters.

For future exit polls, Lenski and Mitofsky recommended hiring more experienced polltakers and giving them better training, and working with election officials to ensure access to polling places.

Lenski and Mitofsky noted that none of the media outlets they worked for—ABC, CBS, CNN, Fox News, NBC and the Associated Press—made any wrong "calls" on election night. Representatives of those six are reviewing the report. Many other news media, including *USA Today*, also paid to get some of the data.

Source: USA TODAY. January 20, 2005. Reprinted with Permission.

36. Increasing Response Rates Offering rewards or incentives is one way of attempting to increase response rates. Discuss a possible disadvantage of such a practice.

37. Wording Survey Questions Write a survey question that contains strong wording and a survey question that contains tempered wording. Present the strongly worded question to 10 randomly selected people and the tempered question to 10 different randomly selected people. How does the wording affect the response?

38. Order in Survey Questions Write two questions that could have different responses, depending on the order in which the questions are presented. Randomly select 20 people and present the questions in one order to 10 of the people and in the opposite order to the other 10 people. Did the results differ?

39. Research a survey method used by a company or government branch. Determine the sampling method used, the sample size, the method of collection, and the frame used.

40. Informed Opinions People often respond to survey questions without any knowledge of the subject matter. A common example of this is the discussion on banning dihydrogen monoxide. The Centers for Disease Control (CDC) reports that there were 1,493 deaths due to asbestos in 2002, but over 3,200 deaths were attributed to dihydrogen monoxide in 2000. Articles and Web sites, such as www.dhmo.org tell how this substance is widely used despite the dangers associated with it. Many people have joined the cause to ban this substance without realizing that dihydrogen monoxide is simply water (H_2O). Their eagerness to protect the environment or their fear of seeming uninformed may be part of the problem. Put together a survey that asks individuals whether dihydrogen monoxide should or should not be banned. Give the survey to 20 randomly selected students around campus and report your results to the class. An example survey might look like the following:

Dihydrogen monoxide is colorless, odorless, and kills thousands of people every year. Most of these deaths are caused by accidental inhalation, but the dangers of dihydrogen monoxide do not stop there. Prolonged exposure to its solid form can severely damage skin tissue. Symptoms of ingestion can include excessive sweating and urination and possibly a bloated feeling, nausea, vomiting, and body electrolyte imbalance. Dihydrogen monoxide is a major component of acid rain and can cause corrosion after coming in contact with certain metals.

Do you believe that the government should or should not ban the use of dihydrogen monoxide?

41. Name two biases that led to the *Literary Digest* making an incorrect prediction in the presidential election of 1936.

42. Research on George Gallup Research the polling done by George Gallup in the 1936 presidential election. Write a report on your findings. Be sure to include information about the sampling technique and sample size. Now research the polling done by Gallup for the 1948 presidential election. Did Gallup accurately predict the outcome of the election? What lessons were learned by Gallup?

43. Putting It Together: Speed Limit In the state of California, speed limits are established through traffic engineering surveys. One aspect of the survey is for city officials to measure the speed of vehicles on a particular road.

Source: www.ci.eureka.ca.gov, www.nctimes.com

(a) What is the population of interest for this portion of the engineering survey?

(b) What is the variable of interest for this portion of the engineering survey? *Speed*

(c) Is the variable qualitative or quantitative? *Quantitative*

(d) What is the level of measurement for the variable? *Ratio*

(e) Is a census feasible in this situation? Explain why or why not. *No*

(f) Is a sample feasible in this situation? If so, explain what type of sampling plan could be used? If not, explain why not. *Systematic*

(g) In July 2007, the Temecula City Council refused a request to increase the speed limit on Pechanga Parkway from 40 to 45 mph despite survey results indicating that the prevailing speed on the parkway favored the increase. Opponents were concerned that it was visitors to a nearby casino who were driving at the increased speeds and that city residents actually favored the lower speed limit. Explain how bias might be playing a role in the city council's decision.

1.6 THE DESIGN OF EXPERIMENTS

Objectives	
1	Describe the characteristics of an experiment
2	Explain the steps in designing an experiment
3	Explain the completely randomized design
4	Explain the matched-pairs design
5	Explain the randomized block design

The major theme of this chapter has been data collection. Section 1.2 briefly discussed the idea of an experiment, but the main focus was on observational studies. Sections 1.3 through 1.5 focused on sampling and surveys. In this section, we further develop the idea of collecting data through an experiment.

Describe the Characteristics of an Experiment

Remember, in an observational study, if an association exists between an explanatory variable and response variable, the researcher cannot claim causality. If a researcher is interested in demonstrating how changes in the explanatory variable *cause* changes in the response variable, the researcher needs to conduct an *experiment*.

Definition

An **experiment** is a controlled study conducted to determine the effect varying one or more explanatory variables or **factors** has on a response variable. Any combination of the values of the factors is called a **treatment**.

Historical Note

Sir Ronald Fisher, often called the Father of Modern Statistics, was born in England on February 17, 1890. He received a BA in astronomy from Cambridge University in 1912. In 1914, he took a position teaching mathematics and physics at a high school. He did this to help serve his country during World War I. (He was rejected by the army because of his poor eyesight.) In 1919, Fisher took a job as a statistician at Rothamsted Experimental Station, where he was involved in agricultural research. In 1933, Fisher became Galton Professor of Eugenics at Cambridge University, where he studied Rh blood groups. In 1943 he was appointed to the Balfour Chair of Genetics at Cambridge. He was knighted by Queen Elizabeth in 1952. Fisher retired in 1957 and died in Adelaide, Australia, on July 29, 1962. One of his famous quotations is "To call in the statistician after the experiment is done may be no more than asking him to perform a postmortem examination: he may be able to say what the experiment died of."

In an experiment, the **experimental unit** is a person, object, or some other well-defined item upon which a treatment is applied. We often refer to the experimental unit as a **subject** when he or she is a person. The subject is analogous to the individual in a survey.

The overriding goal in an experiment is to determine the effect various treatments have on the response variable. For example, we might want to determine whether a new treatment is superior to an existing treatment (or no treatment at all). To make this determination, experiments require a *control group*. A **control group** serves as a baseline treatment that can be used to compare to other treatments. For example, a researcher in education might want to determine if students who do their homework using an online homework system do better on an exam than those who do their homework from the text. The students doing the text homework might serve as the control group (since this is the currently accepted practice). The factor is the type of homework. There are two treatments: online homework and text homework. A second method for defining the control group is through the use of a *placebo*. A **placebo** is an innocuous medication, such as a sugar tablet, that looks, tastes, and smells like the experimental medication.

In an experiment, it is important that each group be treated the same way. It is also important that individuals do not adjust their behavior in some way due to the treatment they are receiving. For this reason, many experiments use a technique called *blinding*. **Blinding** refers to nondisclosure of the treatment an experimental unit is receiving. There are two types of blinding: *single blinding* and *double blinding*.

Definitions

A **single-blind** experiment is one in which the experimental unit (or subject) does not know which treatment he or she is receiving. A **double-blind** experiment is one in which neither the experimental unit nor the researcher in contact with the experimental unit knows which treatment the experimental unit is receiving.

EXAMPLE 1   **The Characteristics of an Experiment**

Problem: Lipitor is a cholesterol-lowering drug by Pfizer. In the Collaborative Atorvastatin Diabetes Study (CARDS), the effect of Lipitor on cardiovascular disease was assessed in 2,838 subjects, ages 40 to 75, with type 2 diabetes, without prior history of cardiovascular disease. In this placebo-controlled, double-blind experiment, subjects were randomly allocated to either Lipitor 10 mg daily (1,429) or placebo (1,411) and were followed for 4 years. The response variable was the occurrence of any major cardiovascular event.

Lipitor significantly reduced the rate of major cardiovascular events (83 events in the Lipitor group versus 127 events in the placebo group). There were 61 deaths in the Lipitor group versus 82 deaths in the placebo group.

(a) What does it mean for the experiment to be placebo-controlled?

(b) What does it mean for the experiment to be double-blind?

(c) What is the population for which this study applies? What is the sample?

(d) What are the treatments?

(e) What is the response variable?

Approach: We will apply the definitions just presented.

Solution

(a) The placebo is a medication that looks, smells, and tastes like Lipitor. The purpose of the placebo control group is to serve as a baseline against which to compare the results from the group receiving Lipitor. Another reason for the placebo is to account for the fact that people tend to behave differently when they are in a study. By having a placebo control group, the effect of this is neutralized.

(b) Since the experiment is double-blind, the subjects do not know whether they are receiving Lipitor or the placebo. Plus, the individual monitoring the subjects does not know whether the subject is receiving Lipitor or the placebo. The reason we double-blind is so that the subjects receiving the medication do not behave differently from those receiving the placebo and the individual monitoring the subjects does not treat the folks in the Lipitor group differently from those in the placebo group.

(c) The population is individuals from 40 to 75 years of age with type 2 diabetes without a prior history of cardiovascular disease. The sample is the 2,838 subjects in the study.

(d) The treatments are 10 mg of Lipitor or a placebo daily.

(e) The response variable is whether the subject had any major cardiovascular event, such as a stroke, or not.

Now Work Problem 11

2 Explain the Steps in Designing an Experiment

To **design** an experiment means to describe the overall plan in conducting the experiment. The process of conducting an experiment requires a series of steps.

Step 1: *Identify the Problem to Be Solved.* The statement of the problem should be as explicit as possible. The statement should provide the experimenter with direction. In addition, the statement must identify the response variable and the population to be studied. Often, the statement is referred to as the *claim*.

Step 2: *Determine the Factors That Affect the Response Variable.* The factors are usually identified by an expert in the field of study. In identifying the factors, we must ask, "What things affect the value of the response variable?" Once the factors are identified, it must be determined which factors will be fixed at some predetermined level, which will be manipulated, and which will be uncontrolled.

Step 3: *Determine the Number of Experimental Units.* As a general rule, choose as many experimental units as time and money will allow. Techniques do exist for determining sample size, provided certain information is available. Some of these techniques are discussed later in the text.

Step 4: *Determine the Level of Each Factor.* There are two ways to deal with the factors:

    1. Control: There are two ways to control the factors.

        (a) Fix their level at one predetermined value throughout the experiment. These are factors whose effect on the response variable is not of interest.

(b) Set them at predetermined levels. These are the factors whose effect on the response variable interests us. The combinations of the levels of these factors constitute the treatments in the experiment.

2. **Randomize:** Randomize the experimental units to various treatment groups so that the effect of factors whose levels cannot be controlled is minimized. The idea is that randomization averages out the effects of uncontrolled factors (explanatory variables). It is difficult, if not impossible, to identify all factors in an experiment. This is why randomization is so important. It mutes the effect of variation attributable to factors not controlled.

Step 5: *Conduct the Experiment.*

(a) The experimental units are randomly assigned to the treatments. **Replication** occurs when each treatment is applied to more than one experimental unit. By using more than one experimental unit for each treatment, we can be assured that the effect of a treatment is not due to some characteristic of a single experimental unit. It is a good idea to assign an equal number of experimental units to each treatment.

(b) Collect and process the data. Measure the value of the response variable for each replication. Then organize the results. The idea is that the value of the response variable for each treatment group is the same before the experiment because of randomization. Then any difference in the value of the response variable among the different treatment groups can be attributed to differences in the level of the treatment.

Step 6: *Test the Claim.* This is the subject of inferential statistics. **Inferential statistics** is a process in which generalizations about a population are made on the basis of results obtained from a sample. In addition, a statement regarding our level of confidence in our generalization is provided. We study methods of inferential statistics in Chapters 9 through 15.

3 Explain the Completely Randomized Design

The steps just given apply to any type of designed experiment. We now concentrate on the simplest type of experiment.

Definition
> A **completely randomized design** is one in which each experimental unit is randomly assigned to a treatment.

We illustrate this type of experimental design using the steps just given.

EXAMPLE 2 **A Completely Randomized Design**

Problem: A farmer wishes to determine the optimal level of a new fertilizer on his soybean crop. Design an experiment that will assist him.

Approach: We follow the steps for designing an experiment.

Solution

Step 1: The farmer wants to identify the optimal level of fertilizer for growing soybeans. We define *optimal* as the level that maximizes yield. So the response variable will be crop yield.

Step 2: Some factors that affect crop yield are fertilizer, precipitation, sunlight, method of tilling the soil, type of soil, plant, and temperature.

Step 3: In this experiment, we will plant 60 soybean plants (experimental units).

Step 4: We list the factors and their levels.

- **Fertilizer.** This factor will be set at three levels. We wish to measure the effect of varying the level of this variable on the response variable, yield. We will set the treatments (level of fertilizer) as follows:

  Treatment A: 20 soybean plants receive no fertilizer.

  Treatment B: 20 soybean plants receive 2 teaspoons of fertilizer per gallon of water every 2 weeks.

  Treatment C: 20 soybean plants receive 4 teaspoons of fertilizer per gallon of water every 2 weeks.

  See Figure 6.

Figure 6

- **Precipitation.** Although we cannot control the amount of rainfall, we can control the amount of watering we do. This factor will be controlled so that each plant receives the same amount of precipitation.
- **Sunlight.** This is an uncontrollable factor, but it will be roughly the same for each plant.
- **Method of tilling.** We can control this factor. We agree to use the round-up ready method of tilling for each plant.
- **Type of soil.** We can control certain aspects of the soil such as level of acidity. In addition, each plant will be planted within a 1-acre area, so it is reasonable to assume that the soil conditions for each plant are equivalent.
- **Plant.** There may be variation from plant to plant. To account for this, we randomly assign the plants to a treatment.
- **Temperature.** This factor is not within our control, but will be the same for each plant.

Step 5

(a) We need to assign each plant to a treatment group. To do this, we will number the plants from 1 to 60. To determine which plants get treatment A, we randomly generate 20 numbers. The plants corresponding to these numbers get treatment A. Now number the remaining plants 1 to 40 and randomly generate 20 numbers. The plants corresponding to these numbers get treatment B. The remaining plants get treatment C. Now till the soil, plant the soybean plants, and fertilize according to the schedule prescribed.

(b) At the end of the growing season, determine the crop yield for each plant.

Step 6: Determine whether any differences in yield exist among the three treatment groups.

Figure 7 illustrates the experimental design.

Figure 7

Example 2 is a completely randomized design because the experimental units (the plants) were randomly assigned to the treatments. It is the most popular experimental design because of its simplicity, but it is not always the best. We discuss inferential procedures for the completely randomized design in which there are two treatments in Section 11.2 and in which there are three or more treatments in Section 13.1.

Now Work Problem 13

4 Explain the Matched-Pairs Design

Another type of experimental design is called a *matched-pairs design*.

Definition

A **matched-pairs design** is an experimental design in which the experimental units are paired up. The pairs are matched up so that they are somehow related (that is, the same person before and after a treatment, twins, husband and wife, same geographical location, and so on). There are only two levels of treatment in a matched-pairs design.

In matched-pairs design, one matched individual will receive one treatment and the other matched individual receives a different treatment. The assignment of the matched pair to the treatment is done randomly using a coin flip or a random-number generator. We then look at the difference in the results of each matched pair. One common type of matched-pairs design is to measure a response variable on an experimental unit before a treatment is applied, and then to measure the response variable on the same experimental unit after the treatment is applied. In this way, the individual is matched against itself. These experiments are sometimes called before–after or pretest–posttest experiments.

EXAMPLE 3 | **A Matched-Pairs Design**

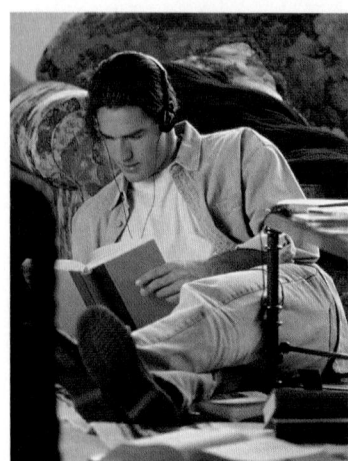

Problem: An educational psychologist wanted to determine whether listening to music has an effect on a student's ability to learn. Design an experiment to help the psychologist answer the question.

Approach: We will use a matched-pairs design by matching students according to IQ and gender (just in case gender plays a role in learning with music).

Solution: We match students according to IQ and gender. For example, a female with an IQ in the 110 to 115 range will be matched with a second female with an IQ in the 110 to 115 range.

For each pair of students, we will flip a coin to determine whether the first student in the pair is assigned the treatment of a quiet room or a room with music playing in the background.

Each student will be given a statistics textbook and asked to study Section 1.1. After 2 hours, the students will enter a testing center and take a short quiz on the material in the section. We compute the difference in the scores of each matched pair. Any differences in scores will be attributed to the treatment. Figure 8 illustrates the design.

Figure 8

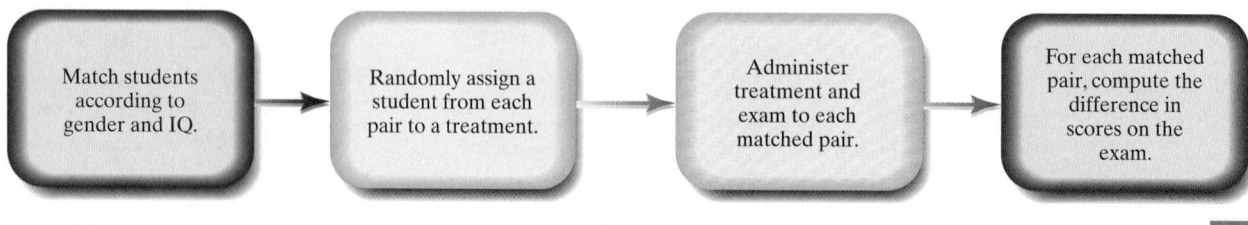

Now Work Problem 15

We discuss statistical inference for the matched-pairs design in Section 11.1.

⑤ Explain the Randomized Block Design

The completely randomized design is the simplest experimental design. However, its simplicity can lead to flaws. Before we introduce a slightly more complicated experimental design, consider the following story.

I coach my son's soccer team, which is comprised of four 10-year-olds, six 9-year-olds, and four 8-year-olds. After each practice, I like to have a 15-minute scrimmage where I randomly assign seven players to each team. I quickly learned that randomly assigning players, without taking age into consideration, would sometimes result in very unequal teams (once I randomly created a team of four 10-year-olds and three 9-year-olds). So I learned that I should randomly assign two 10-year-olds to one team with the other two 10-year-olds going on the other team. I then assigned three 9-year-olds to each team and two 8-year-olds to each team. Using the language of statistics, I was *blocking* by age.

Definition

> Grouping similar (homogeneous) experimental units together and then randomizing the experimental units within each group to a treatment is called **blocking**. Each group of homogeneous individuals is called a **block**.

With the soccer story in mind, let's revisit our crop-yield experiment from Example 2, where we assumed that the soybean plants were the same variety. Suppose we found out that we in fact had two varieties of soybeans: Chemgro and Pioneer. Using the completely randomized design, it is impossible to know whether any differences in yield were due to the differences in fertilizer or to the differences in variety.

It may be that the Chemgro variety naturally has higher yield potential than Pioneer. If a majority of the soybean plants that were randomly assigned to treatment C was Chemgro, we would not know whether to attribute the different crop yields to the level of fertilizer or to the plant variety. This effect is known as *confounding*. **Confounding** occurs when the effect of two factors (explanatory variables) on the response variable cannot be distinguished.

To resolve issues of this type, we introduce a third experimental design.

Definition

> A **randomized block design** is used when the experimental units are divided into homogeneous groups called blocks. Within each block, the experimental units are randomly assigned to treatments.

In a randomized block design, we do not wish to determine whether the differences between blocks result in any difference in the value of the response variable. Our goal is to isolate any variability in the response variable that may be attributable to the block. We discuss this design in the next example.

EXAMPLE 4   **The Randomized Block Design**

Problem: Suppose that the 60 soybean plants were actually two different varieties: 30 Chemgro soybean plants and 30 Pioneer soybean plants. In addition, the Chemgro variety may have a different yield potential than the Pioneer variety. Design an experiment that could be used to measure the effect of level of fertilizer while taking into account the variety of soybean.

Approach: Because the yield of Chemgro may differ from that of Pioneer, we will use a randomized block design to determine which level of fertilizer results in the highest yield. We will block by soybean variety.

Solution: In a randomized block design, we divide 60 plants into two blocks. Block 1 will contain the 30 Chemgro plants and block 2 will contain the 30 Pioneer plants. Within each block, we randomly assign 10 plants to each treatment (A, B, or C). The other factors that may affect yield are controlled as they were in Example 2. See Figure 9.

Figure 9

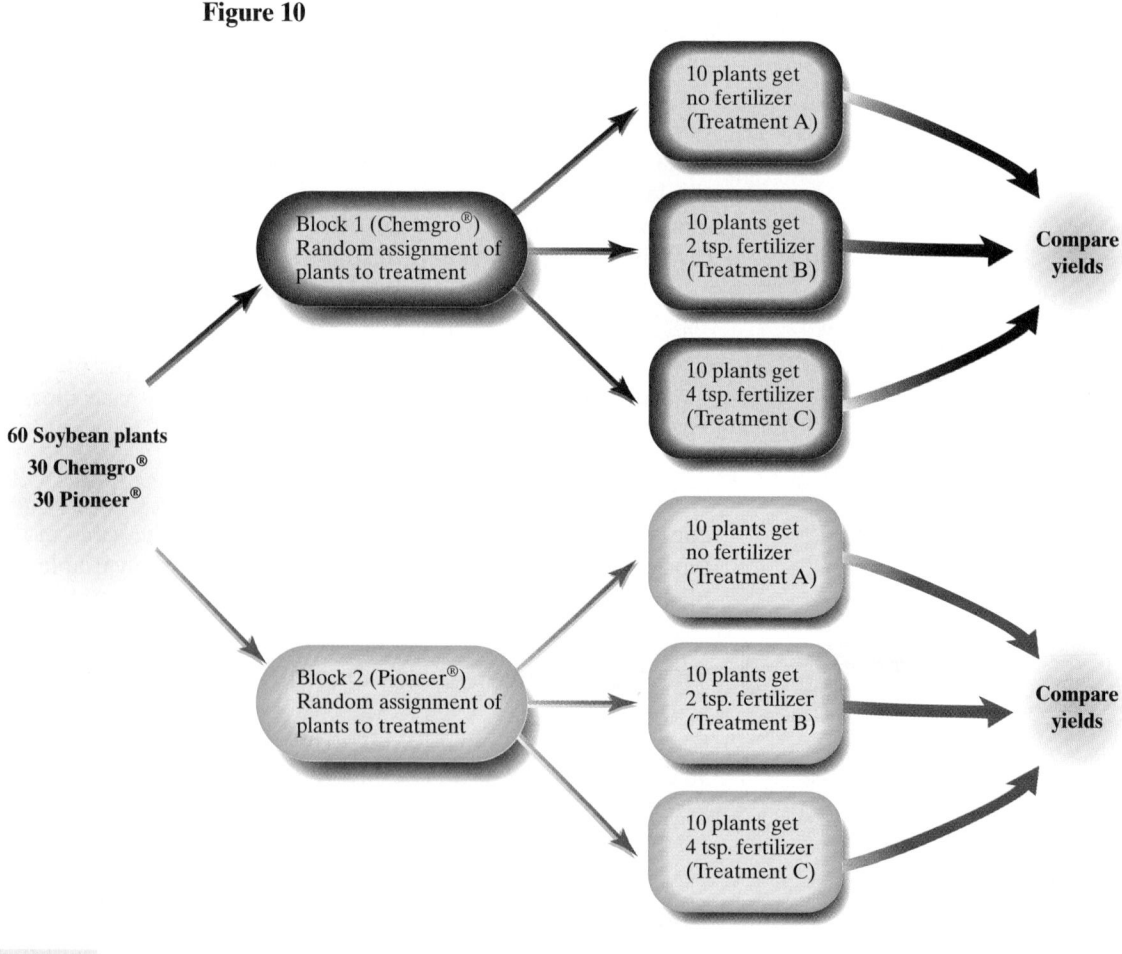

Treatment A
(10 Pioneer plants)

Treatment C
(10 Pioneer plants)

Treatment C
(10 Chemgro plants)

Treatment A
(10 Chemgro plants)

Treatment B
(10 Chemgro plants)

Treatment B
(10 Pioneer plants)

The idea is that in each block the plants are all the same variety of plant, so plant variety does not affect the value of the response variable. Figure 10 illustrates the design. Notice that we do not compare yields across plant variety because this was not our goal—we already know which variety yields more. The reason for blocking is to reduce variability due to plant variety by comparing yields within each variety.

Figure 10

60 Soybean plants
30 Chemgro®
30 Pioneer®

Block 1 (Chemgro®)
Random assignment of
plants to treatment

10 plants get
no fertilizer
(Treatment A)

10 plants get
2 tsp. fertilizer
(Treatment B)

10 plants get
4 tsp. fertilizer
(Treatment C)

Compare
yields

Block 2 (Pioneer®)
Random assignment of
plants to treatment

10 plants get
no fertilizer
(Treatment A)

10 plants get
2 tsp. fertilizer
(Treatment B)

10 plants get
4 tsp. fertilizer
(Treatment C)

Compare
yields

Now Work Problem 23

One note about the relation between a designed experiment and simple random sampling: It is often the case that the experimental units selected to participate in a study are not randomly selected. This is because we often need the experimental units to have some common trait, such as high blood pressure. For this reason, participants in experiments are recruited or volunteer to be in a study. However,

Note to Instructor

The purpose of this activity is to allow students to see why good experiments need control, randomization, and replication. In addition, students recognize how much thought needs to go into an experiment, even for something simple like paper frogs.

There are several possible designs for the frogs (e.g., www.frogsonice.com/froggy/origami/index.s/html or http://origami.ousaan.com/studio/traditional/frog/01/index.html), so choose whichever seems easiest for students to use.

Before the jumping, there should be discussions about why the order of the jumps is randomized, why the same person should jump all the frogs, and so on. In addition, students should decide how they will measure the distance jumped before they start jumping.

A good design might be a matched-pairs design so that the variability due to who is making the frog is eliminated and type of paper is not confounded with the person making the frog.

This activity may be done with paper airplanes as well.

once we have the experimental units, we use simple random sampling to assign them to treatment groups. With random assignment we assume that the participants are similar at the start of the experiment. Because the treatment is the only difference between the groups, we can say the treatment *caused* the difference observed in the response variable.

IN CLASS ACTIVITY

Experimental Design (Hippity-Hop)

You are commissioned by the board of directors of Paper Toys, Inc. to design a new paper frog for their Christmas catalog. The design for the construction of the frog has already been completed and will be provided to you. However, the material with which to make the frogs has not yet been determined. The Materials Department has narrowed the choices down to either newspaper or brown paper (such as that used in grocery bags). You have decided to test both types of paper. Management decided to build the frogs from sheets of paper 9 inches square.

The goal of the experiment is to determine the material that results in frogs that jump farther.

(a) As a class, design an experiment that will answer the research question.

(b) Make the frogs.

(c) Conduct the experiment.

(d) As a class, discuss the strengths and weaknesses of the design. Would you change anything?

1.6 ASSESS YOUR UNDERSTANDING

Concepts and Vocabulary

1. Define the following:
   (a) Experimental unit
   (b) Treatment
   (c) Response variable
   (d) Factor
   (e) Placebo
   (f) Confounding

2. What is replication in an experiment?

3. Explain the difference between a single-blind and a double-blind experiment.

4. List the steps in designing an experiment.

5. A(n) _____ _____ design is one in which each experimental unit is randomly assigned to a treatment. A(n) _____ _____ design is one in which the experimental units are paired up. completely randomized; matched pairs

6. Grouping together similar experimental units and then randomly assigning the experimental units within each group to a treatment is called _____. blocking

7. *True or False*: Generally, the goal of an experiment is to determine the effect that treatments will have on the response variable. True

8. *True or False*: Observational studies can be used to determine causality between explanatory and response variables.

9. Discuss why control groups are needed in experiments.

10. Discuss how a randomized block design is similar to a stratified random sample. What is the purpose of blocking?

8. False

Applying the Concepts

11. **Caffeinated Sports Drinks** Researchers conducted a double-blind, placebo-controlled, repeated-measures experiment to compare the effectiveness of a commercial caffeinated carbohydrate–electrolyte sports drink with a commercial noncaffeinated carbohydrate–electrolyte sports drink and a flavored-water placebo. Sixteen highly trained cyclists each completed three trials of prolonged cycling in a warm environment: one while receiving the placebo, one while receiving the noncaffeinated sports drink, and one while receiving the caffeinated sports drink. For a given trial, one beverage treatment was administered throughout a 2-hour variable-intensity cycling bout followed by a 15-minute performance ride. Total work in kilojoules (kJ) performed during the final 15 minutes was used to measure performance. The beverage order for the individual subjects was randomly assigned. A period of at least 5 days separated the trials. All trials took place at approximately the same time of day in an environmental chamber at 28.5°C and 60% relative humidity with fan airflow of approximately 2.5 meters per second (m/s).

The researchers found that cycling performance, as assessed by the total work completed during the performance ride, was 23% greater for the caffeinated sports drink than for the placebo and 15% greater for the caffeinated sports drink than for the noncaffeinated sports drink. Cycling performances for the noncaffeinated sports drink and the placebo were not significantly different. The researchers

11. (e) *Caffeinated sports drink, noncaffeinated sports drink, or flavored-water placebo*

concluded that the caffeinated carbohydrate–electrolyte sports drink substantially enhanced physical performance during prolonged exercise compared with the noncaffeinated carbohydrate–electrolyte sports drink and the placebo.

Source: Kirk J. Cureton, Gordon L. Warren et al. "Caffeinated Sports Drink: Ergogenic Effects and Possible Mechanisms," *International Journal of Sport Nutrition and Exercise Metabolism*, 17(1):35–55, 2007

(a) What does it mean for the experiment to be placebo-controlled?

(b) What does it mean for the experiment to be double-blind? Why do you think it is necessary for the experiment to be double-blind?

(c) How is randomization used in this experiment?

(d) What is the population for which this study applies? What is the sample? *All athletes; 16 cyclists*

(e) What are the treatments?

(f) What is the response variable? *Total work*

(g) This experiment used a *repeated-measures design*, a design type that has not been directly discussed in this textbook. Using this experiment as a guide, determine what it means for the design of the experiment to be repeated-measures. How does this design relate to the matched-pairs design?

12. **Alcohol Dependence** To determine if topiramate is a safe and effective treatment for alcohol dependence, researchers conducted a 14-week trial of 371 men and women aged 18 to 65 years diagnosed with alcohol dependence. In this double-blind, randomized, placebo-controlled experiment, subjects were randomly given either 300 milligrams (mg) of topiramate (183 subjects) or a placebo (188 subjects) daily, along with a weekly compliance enhancement intervention. The variable used to determine the effectiveness of the treatment was self-reported percentage of heavy drinking days. Results indicated that topiramate was more effective than placebo at reducing the percentage of heavy drinking days. The researchers concluded that topiramate is a promising treatment for alcohol dependence.

Source: Bankole A. Johnson, Norman Rosenthal, et al. "Topiramate for Treating Alcohol Dependence: A Randomized Controlled Trial," *Journal of the American Medical Association*, 298(14):1641–1651, 2007

(a) What does it mean for the experiment to be placebo-controlled?

(b) What does it mean for the experiment to be double-blind? Why do you think it is necessary for the experiment to be double-blind?

(c) What does it mean for the experiment to be randomized?

(d) What is the population for which this study applies? What is the sample?

(e) What are the treatments?

(f) What is the response variable? *Percentage of heavy drinking days*

13. **School Psychology** A school psychologist wants to test the effectiveness of a new method for teaching reading. She recruits 500 first-grade students in District 203 and randomly divides them into two groups. Group 1 is taught by means of the new method, while group 2 is taught via traditional

methods. The same teacher is assigned to teach both groups. At the end of the year, an achievement test is administered and the results of the two groups are compared.

(a) What is the response variable in this experiment?

(b) Think of some of the factors in the study. How are they controlled?

(c) What are the treatments? How many treatments are there? *New teaching method and traditional method; 2*

(d) How are the factors that are not controlled dealt with? *Random assignment*

(e) Which group serves as the control group? *Group 2*

(f) What type of experimental design is this?

(g) Identify the subjects. *500 students*

(h) Draw a diagram similar to Figure 7, 8, or 10 to illustrate the design.

14. **Pharmacy** A pharmaceutical company has developed an experimental drug meant to relieve symptoms associated with the common cold. The company identifies 300 adult males 25 to 29 years old who have a common cold and randomly divides them into two groups. Group 1 is given the experimental drug, while group 2 is given a placebo. After 1 week of treatment, the proportions of each group that still have cold symptoms are compared. 14. (a) *Proportion of subjects with cold*

(a) What is the response variable in this experiment?

(b) Think of some of the factors in the study. How are they controlled?

(c) What are the treatments? How many treatments are there? *Experimental drug and placebo; 2*

(d) How are the factors that are not controlled dealt with? *Random assignment*

(e) What type of experimental design is this?

(f) Identify the subjects. *300 males*

(g) Draw a diagram similar to Figure 7, 8, or 10 to illustrate the design.

15. **Whiter Teeth** An ad for Crest Whitestrips Premium claims
that the strips will whiten teeth in 7 days and the results will last for 12 months. A researcher who wishes to test this claim studies 20 sets of identical twins. Within each set of twins, one is randomly selected to use Crest Whitestrips Premium in addition to regular brushing and flossing, while the other just brushes and flosses. Whiteness of teeth is measured at the beginning of the study, after 7 days, and every month thereafter for 12 months. 15. (b) *Whiteness level*

(a) What type of experimental design is this? *Matched pairs*

(b) What is the response variable in this experiment?

(c) What are the treatments?

(d) What are other factors (controlled or uncontrolled) that could affect the response variable?

(e) What might be an advantage of using identical twins as subjects in this experiment?

16. **Assessment** To help assess student learning in her developmental math courses, a mathematics professor at a community college implemented pre- and posttests for her developmental math students. A knowledge-gained score was obtained by taking the difference of the two test scores.

12. (d) *All 18–65 year olds with alcohol dependence; 371 men and women aged 18 to 65 years of age with alcohol dependence*
12. (e) *300 mg of topiramate or a placebo daily*   13. (a) *Score on achievement test*   13. (b) *Method of teaching, grade level, intelligence, school district, teacher; Fixed: grade level, school district, teacher; Set to a predetermined level: method of teaching*
13. (f) *Completely randomized design*   14. (b) *Gender, age, geographic location, overall health, drug intervention; Fixed: gender, age, location; Set to a predetermined level: drug intervention*   14. (e) *Completely randomized design*   15. (c) *Whitening method; Crest Whitestrips Premium with brushing and flossing versus brushing and flossing alone*

(a) What type of experimental design is this? Matched pair
(b) What is the response variable in this experiment?
(c) What is the treatment? Math course

17. Insomnia Researchers Jack D. Edinger and associates wanted to test the effectiveness of a new cognitive behavioral therapy (CBT) compared with both an older behavioral treatment and a placebo therapy for treating insomnia. They identified 75 adults with chronic insomnia. Patients were randomly assigned to one of three treatment groups. Twenty-five patients were randomly assigned to receive CBT (sleep education, stimulus control, and time-in-bed restrictions), another 25 received muscle relaxation training (RT), and the final 25 received a placebo treatment. Treatment lasted 6 weeks, with follow-up conducted at 6 months. To measure the effectiveness of the treatment, researchers used wake time after sleep onset (WASO). Cognitive behavioral therapy produced larger improvements than did RT or placebo treatment. For example, the CBT-treated patients achieved an average 54% reduction in their WASO, whereas RT-treated and placebo-treated patients, respectively, achieved only 16% and 12% reductions in this measure. Results suggest that CBT treatment leads to significant sleep improvements within 6 weeks, and these improvements appear to endure through 6 months of follow-up. 17. (a) Completely randomized design

Source: Jack D. Edinger, PhD; William K. Wohlgemuth, PhD; Rodney A. Radtke, MD; Gail R. Marsh, PhD; Ruth E. Quillian, PhD. "Cognitive Behavioral Therapy for Treatment of Chronic Primary Insomnia," *Journal of the American Medical Association*, 285:1856–1864, 2001

(a) What type of experimental design is this?
(b) What is the population being studied?
(c) What is the response variable in this study?
(d) What are the treatments?
(e) Identify the experimental units. 75 adults with insomnia
(f) Draw a diagram similar to Figure 7, 8, or 10 to illustrate the design.

18. Depression Researchers wanted to compare the effectiveness and safety of an extract of St. John's wort with placebo in outpatients with major depression. To do this, they recruited 200 adult outpatients diagnosed as having major depression and having a baseline Hamilton Rating Scale for Depression (HAM-D) score of at least 20. Participants were randomly assigned to receive either St. John's wort extract, 900 milligrams per day (mg/d) for 4 weeks, increased to 1200 mg/d in the absence of an adequate response thereafter, or a placebo for 8 weeks. The response variable was the change on the HAM-D over the treatment period. After analysis of the data, it was concluded that St. John's wort was not effective for treatment of major depression.

Source: Richard C. Shelton, MD, et al. "Effectiveness of St. John's Wort in Major Depression," *Journal of the American Medical Association* 285:1978–1986, 2001

(a) What type of experimental design is this?
(b) What is the population that is being studied?
(c) What is the response variable in this study?

(d) What are the treatments?
(e) Identify the experimental units. 200 outpatients
(f) What is the control group in this study? Placebo group
(g) Draw a diagram similar to Figure 7, 8, or 10 to illustrate the design.

19. The Memory Drug? Researchers wanted to evaluate whether ginkgo, an over-the-counter herb marketed as enhancing memory, improves memory in elderly adults as measured by objective tests. To do this, they recruited 98 men and 132 women older than 60 years and in good health. Participants were randomly assigned to receive ginkgo, 40 milligrams (mg) 3 times per day, or a matching placebo. The measure of memory improvement was determined by a standardized test of learning and memory. After 6 weeks of treatment, the data indicated that ginkgo did not increase performance on standard tests of learning, memory, attention, and concentration. These data suggest that, when taken following the manufacturer's instructions, ginkgo provides no measurable increase in memory or related cognitive function to adults with healthy cognitive function.

Source: Paul R. Solomon et al. "Ginkgo for Memory Enhancement," *Journal of the American Medical Association* 288:835–840, 2002

(a) What type of experimental design is this?
(b) What is the population being studied?
(c) What is the response variable in this study?
(d) What is the factor that is set to predetermined levels? What are the treatments?
(e) Identify the experimental units.
(f) What is the control group in this study? Placebo group
(g) Draw a diagram similar to Figure 7, 8, or 10 to illustrate the design.

20. Treating Depression Researchers wanted to test whether a new drug therapy results in a more rapid response in patients with major depression. To do this, they recruited 63 inpatients with a diagnosis of major depression. Patients were randomly assigned to two treatment groups receiving either placebo (31 patients) or the new drug therapy (32 patients). The response variable was the Hamilton Rating Scale for Depression score. After collecting and analyzing the data, it was concluded that the new drug therapy is effective in the treatment of major depression.

Source: Jahn Holger, MD, et al. "Metyrapone as Additive Treatment in Major Depression," *Archives of General Psychiatry*, 61:1235–1244, 2004

(a) What type of experimental design is this?
(b) What is the population that is being studied?
(c) What is the response variable in this study?
(d) What are the treatments? Placebo or new drug therapy
(e) Identify the experimental units.
(f) Draw a diagram similar to Figure 7, 8, or 10 to illustrate the design.

21. Dominant Hand Professor Andy Neill wanted to determine if the reaction time of people differs in their dominant hand versus their nondominant hand. To do this, he recruited

18. (a) Completely randomized design   18. (b) Adult outpatients diagnosed as having major depression and having a baseline Hamilton Rating Scale for Depression (HAM-D) score of at least 20   18. (c) Change in the HAM-D over the treatment period
18. (d) Type of drug: St. John's wort extract or placebo   19. (a) Completely randomized design   19. (b) Adults older than 60 years in good health   19. (c) Standardized test of learning and memory   19. (d) Drug: 40 mg of ginkgo 3 times per day or a matching placebo   19. (e) 98 men and 132 women older than 60 in good health   20. (a) Completely randomized design
20. (b) Inpatients with a diagnosis of major depression   20. (c) Hamilton Rating Scale for Depression score
20. (e) 63 inpatients with a diagnosis of major depression

15 students. Each student was asked to hold a yardstick between the index finger and thumb. The student was asked to open the hand, release the yardstick, and then asked to catch the yardstick between the index finger and thumb. The distance that the yardstick fell served as a measure of reaction time. A coin flip was used to determine whether the student would use their dominant hand first or the nondominant hand. Results indicated that the reaction time in the dominant hand exceeded that of the nondominant hand.

(a) What type of experimental design is this?
(b) What is the response variable in this study?
(c) What is the treatment? Dominant versus nondominant hand
(d) Identify the experimental units. 15 students
(e) Why did Professor Neill use a coin flip to determine whether the student should begin with the dominant hand or the nondominant hand?
(f) Draw a diagram similar to Figure 7, 8, or 10 to illustrate the design.

22. **Golf Anyone?** A local golf pro wanted to compare two styles of golf club. One golf club had a graphite shaft and the other had the latest style of steel shaft. It is a common belief that graphite shafts allow a player to hit the ball farther, but the manufacturer of the new steel shaft said the ball travels just as far with its new technology. To test this belief, the pro recruited 10 golfers from the driving range. Each player was asked to hit one ball with the graphite-shafted club and one ball with the new steel-shafted club. The distance that the ball traveled was determined using a range finder. A coin flip was used to determine whether the player hit with the graphite club or the steel club first. Results indicated that the distance the ball was hit with the graphite club was no different than the distance when using the steel club.

(a) What type of experimental design is this?
(b) What is the response variable in this study?
(c) What is the factor that is set to predetermined levels? What is the treatment?
(d) Identify the experimental units. 10 golfers
(e) Why did the golf pro use a coin flip to determine whether the golfer should hit with the graphite first or the steel first?
(f) Draw a diagram similar to Figure 7, 8, or 10 to illustrate the design.

23. **Marketing** A marketing research firm wishes to determine
NW the most effective method of advertising: print, radio, or television. They recruit 300 volunteers to participate in the study. The chief researcher believes that level of education plays a role in the effectiveness of advertising, so she segments the volunteers by level of education. Of the 300 volunteers, 120 have a high school education, 120 have a college diploma, and 60 have advanced degrees. The 120 volunteers with a high school diploma are randomly assigned to either the print advertising group, the radio group, or the television group. The same procedure is followed for the college graduate and advanced degree volunteers. Each group is exposed to the advertising. After 1 hour, a recall exam is given and the proportion of correct answers recorded.

(a) What type of experimental design is this?
(b) What is the response variable in this experiment?
(c) What are the treatments? Print, radio, television

(d) What variable serves as the block? Level of education
(e) Draw a diagram similar to Figure 7, 8, or 10 to illustrate the design.

24. **Social Work** A social worker wants to examine methods that can be used to deter truancy. Three hundred chronically truant students from District 103 volunteer for the study. Because the social worker believes that socioeconomic class plays a role in truancy, she divides the 300 volunteers according to household income. Of the 300 students, 120 fall in the low-income category, 132 fall in the middle-income category, and the remaining 48 fall in the upper-income category. The students within each income category are randomly divided into three groups. The students in group 1 receive no intervention. The students in group 2 are treated with positive reinforcement in which, for each day the student is not truant, he or she receives a star that can be traded in for rewards. The students in group 3 are treated with negative reinforcement such that each truancy results in a 1-hour detention. However, the hours of detention are cumulative, meaning that the first truancy results in 1 hour of detention, the second truancy results in 2 hours, and so on. After a full school year, the total number of truancies are compared.

(a) What type of experimental design is this?
(b) What is the response variable in this experiment?
(c) What are the treatments?
(d) What variable serves as the block? Income
(e) Draw a diagram similar to Figure 7, 8, or 10 to illustrate the design.

25. **Drug Effectiveness** A pharmaceutical company wants to test the effectiveness of an experimental drug meant to reduce high cholesterol. The researcher at the pharmaceutical company has decided to test the effectiveness of the drug through a completely randomized design. She has obtained 20 volunteers with high cholesterol: Ann, John, Michael, Kevin, Marissa, Christina, Eddie, Shannon, Julia, Randy, Sue, Tom, Wanda, Roger, Laurie, Rick, Kim, Joe, Colleen, and Bill. Number the volunteers from 1 to 20. Use a random-number generator to randomly assign 10 of the volunteers to the experimental group. The remaining volunteers will go into the control group. List the individuals in each group.

26. **Effects of Alcohol** A researcher has recruited 20 volunteers to participate in a study. The researcher wishes to measure the effect of alcohol on an individual's reaction time. The 20 volunteers are randomly divided into two groups. Group 1 will serve as a control group in which participants drink four 1-ounce cups of a liquid that looks, smells, and tastes like alcohol in 15-minute increments. Group 2 will serve as an experimental group in which participants drink four 1-ounce cups of 80-proof alcohol in 15-minute increments. After drinking the last 1-ounce cup, the participants sit for 20 minutes. After the 20-minute resting period, the reaction time to a stimulus is measured.

(a) What type of experimental design is this?
(b) Use Table I in Appendix A or a random-number generator to divide the 20 volunteers into groups 1 and 2 by assigning the volunteers a number between 1 and 20. Then randomly select 10 numbers between 1 and 20. The individuals corresponding to these numbers will go into group 1.

21. (b) Distance yardstick falls   21. (e) To eliminate bias due to starting on dominant or nondominant first for each trial
22. (a) Matched-pairs design   22. (b) Distance ball hit   22. (c) Shaft type: graphite shaft versus steel shaft   22. (e) To eliminate bias due to type of shaft used first   23. (a) Randomized block design   23. (b) Score on recall exam   24. (a) Randomized block design
24. (b) Total number of truancies   24. (c) No intervention, positive reinforcement, negative reinforcement   26. (a) Completely randomized design

27. Tomatoes An oncologist wants to perform a long-term study on the benefits of eating tomatoes. In particular, she wishes to determine whether there is a significant difference in the rate of prostate cancer among adult males after eating one serving of tomatoes per week for 5 years, after eating three servings of tomatoes per week for 5 years, and after eating five servings of tomatoes per week for 5 years. Help the oncologist design the experiment. Include a diagram to illustrate your design. *Completely randomized design*

28. Batteries An engineer wants to determine the effect of temperature on battery voltage. In particular, he is interested in determining if there is a significant difference in the voltage of the batteries when exposed to temperatures of 90°F, 70°F, and 50°F. Help the engineer design the experiment. Include a diagram to illustrate your design. *Completely randomized design*

29. The Better Paint Suppose you are interested in comparing Benjamin Moore's MoorLife Latex house paint with Sherwin Williams' LowTemp 35 Exterior Latex paint. Design an experiment that will answer this question: Which paint is better for painting the exterior of a house? Include a diagram to illustrate your design.

30. Tire Design An engineer has just developed a new tire design. However, before going into production, the tire company wants to determine if the new tire reduces braking distance on a car traveling 60 miles per hour compared with radial tires. Design an experiment to help the engineer determine if the new tire reduces braking distance.

31. Octane Does the level of octane in gasoline affect gas mileage? To answer this question, an automotive engineer obtains 60 cars. Twenty of the cars are considered to be compact, 20 are full size, and 20 are sport utility vehicles (SUVs). Design an experiment for the engineer. Include a diagram to illustrate your design. *Randomized block design*

32. School Psychology The school psychologist first presented in Problem 13 worries that girls and boys may react differently to the two methods of instruction. Design an experiment that will eliminate the variability due to gender on the response variable, the score on the achievement test. Include a diagram to illustrate your design. *Randomized block design*

33. Designing an Experiment Researchers wish to know if there is a link between hypertension (high blood pressure) and consumption of salt. Past studies have indicated that the consumption of fruits and vegetables offsets the negative impact of salt consumption. It is also known that there is quite a bit of person-to-person variability as far as the ability of the body to process and eliminate salt. However, no method exists for identifying individuals who have a higher ability to process salt. The U.S. Department of Agriculture recommends that daily intake of salt should not exceed 2400 milligrams (mg). The researchers want to keep the design simple, so they choose to conduct their study using a completely randomized design.

(a) What is the response variable in the study? *Blood pressure*
(b) Name three factors that have been identified.
(c) For each factor identified, determine whether the variable can be controlled or cannot be controlled. If a factor cannot be controlled, what should be done to reduce variability in the response variable?
(d) How many treatments would you recommend? Why?

34. Search a newspaper, magazine, or other periodical that describes an experiment. Identify the population, experimental unit, response variable, treatment, factors, and their levels.

35. Research the *placebo effect* and the *Hawthorne effect*. Write a paragraph that describes how each affects the outcome of an experiment.

36. Coke or Pepsi Suppose you want to perform an experiment whose goal is to determine whether people prefer Coke or Pepsi. Design an experiment that utilizes the completely randomized design. Design an experiment that utilizes the matched-pairs design. In both designs, be sure to identify the response variable, the role of blinding, and randomization. Which design do you prefer? Why?

37. Putting It Together: Mosquito Control In an attempt to identify ecologically friendly methods for controlling mosquito populations, researchers conducted field experiments in India where aquatic nymphs of the dragonfly *Brachytron pretense* were used against the larvae of mosquitoes. For the experiment, the researchers selected ten 300-liter (L) outdoor, open, concrete water tanks, which were natural breeding places for mosquitoes. Each tank was manually sieved to ensure that it was free of any nonmosquito larvae, nymphs, or fish. Only larvae of mosquitoes were allowed to remain in the tanks. The larval density in each tank was assessed using a 250-milliliter (mL) dipper. For each tank, 30 dips were taken and the mean larval density per dip was calculated. Ten freshly collected nymphs of *Brachytron pretense* were introduced into each of five randomly selected tanks. No nymphs were released into the remaining five tanks, which served as controls. After 15 days, larval densities in all the tanks were assessed again and all the introduced nymphs were removed. After another 15 days, the larval densities in all the tanks were assessed a third time.

In the nymph-treated tanks, the density of larval mosquitoes dropped significantly from 7.34 to 0.83 larvae per dip 15 days after the *Brachytron pretense* nymphs were introduced. Further, the larval density increased significantly to 6.83 larvae per dip 15 days after the nymphs were removed. Over the same time period, the control tanks did not show a significant difference in larval density, with density measurements of 7.12, 6.83, and 6.79 larvae per dip. The researchers concluded that *Brachytron pretense* can be used effectively as a strong, ecologically friendly control of mosquitoes and mosquito borne diseases.

Source: S. N. Chatterjee, A. Ghosh, and G. Chandra. "Eco-Friendly Control of Mosquito Larvae by *Brachytron pretense* Nymph," *Journal of Environmental Health*, 69(8):44–48, 2007

(a) Identify the research objective.
(b) What type of experimental design is this?
(c) What is the response variable? It is quantitative or qualitative? If quantitative, is it discrete or continuous?
(d) What is the factor the researchers controlled and set to predetermined levels? What are the treatments?

33. (b) Daily consumption of salt, daily consumption of fruits and vegetables, body's ability to process salt   33. (c) Salt: controlled; Fruits and vegetables: controlled; Body: cannot be controlled. To deal with variability in body types, randomize experimental units to each treatment group.   33. (d) Answers will vary, but three might be a good choice: one below RDA, one equal to RDA, one above RDA.
37. (a) To determine if nymphs of *Brachytron pretense* will control mosquitoes   37. (b) Completely randomized design
37. (c) Mosquito larvae density; quantitative; discrete

(e) Can you think of other factors that may affect larvae of mosquitoes? How are they controlled or dealt with?

(f) What is the population for which this study applies? What is the sample?

(g) List the descriptive statistics.

(h) How did the researchers control this experiment?

(i) Draw a diagram similar to Figure 7, 8, or 10 to illustrate the design.

(j) State the conclusion made in the study.

Consumer Reports Emotional "Aspirin"

Americans have a long history of altering their moods with chemicals, ranging from alcohol and illicit drugs to prescription medications, such as diazepam (Valium) for anxiety and fluoxetine (Prozac) for depression. Today, there's a new trend: the over-the-counter availability of apparently effective mood modifiers in the form of herbs and other dietary supplements.

One problem is that many people who are treating themselves with these remedies may be sufficiently anxious or depressed to require professional care and monitoring. Self-treatment can be dangerous, particularly with depression, which causes some 20,000 reported suicides a year in the United States. Another major pitfall is that dietary supplements are largely unregulated by the government, so consumers have almost no protection against substandard preparations.

To help consumers and doctors, *Consumer Reports* tested the amounts of key ingredients in representative brands of several major mood-changing pills. To avoid potential bias, we tested samples from different lots of the pills using a randomized statistical design. The table contains a subset of the data from this study.

Each of these pills has a label claim of 200 mg of SAM-E. The column labeled Random Code contains a set of 3-digit random codes that were used so that the laboratory did not know which manufacturer was being tested. The column labeled Mg SAM-E contains the amount of SAM-E measured by the laboratory.

(a) Why is it important to label the pills with random codes?

(b) Why is it important to randomize the order in which the pills are tested instead of testing all of brand A first, followed by all of brand B, and so on?

Run Order	Brand	Random Code	Mg SAM-E
1	B	461	238.9
2	D	992	219.2
3	C	962	227.1
4	A	305	231.2
5	B	835	263.7
6	D	717	251.1
7	A	206	232.9
8	D	649	192.8
9	C	132	213.4
10	B	923	224.6
11	A	823	261.1
12	C	515	207.8

(c) Sort the data by brand. Does it appear that each brand is meeting its label claims?

(d) Design an experiment that follows the steps presented to answer the following research question: "Is there a difference in the amount of SAM-E contained in brands A, B, C, and D?"

Note to Readers: *In many cases, our test protocol and analytical methods are more complicated than described in this example. The data and discussion have been modified to make the material more appropriate for the audience.*

Source: © 2002 by Consumers Union of U.S., Inc., Yonkers, NY 10703-1057, a nonprofit organization. Reprinted with permission from the Dec. 2002 issue of CONSUMER REPORTS® for educational purposes only. No commercial use or photocopying permitted. To learn more about Consumers Union, log onto www.ConsumersReports.org.

CHAPTER 1 REVIEW

Summary

We defined statistics as a science in which data are collected, organized, summarized, and analyzed to infer characteristics regarding a population. Statistics also provides a measure of confidence in the conclusions that are drawn. Descriptive statistics consists of organizing and summarizing information, while inferential statistics consists of drawing conclusions about a population based on results obtained from a sample. The population is a collection of individuals about which information is desired and the sample is a subset of the population.

Data are the observations of a variable. Data can be either qualitative or quantitative. Quantitative data are either discrete or continuous.

Data can be obtained from four sources: a census, existing sources, observational studies, or a designed experiment. A census

will list all the individuals in the population, along with certain characteristics. Due to the cost of obtaining a census, most researchers opt for obtaining a sample. In observational studies, the response variable is measured without attempting to influence its value. In addition, the explanatory variable is not manipulated. Designed experiments are used when control of the individuals in the study is desired to isolate the effect of a certain treatment on a response variable.

We introduced five sampling methods: simple random sampling, stratified sampling, systematic sampling, cluster sampling, and convenience sampling. All the sampling methods, except for convenience sampling, allow for unbiased statistical inference to be made. Convenience sampling typically leads to an unrepresentative sample and biased results.

Vocabulary

Be sure you can define the following:

Statistics (p. 3)
Data (pp. 3, 9)
Population (p. 5)
Individual (p. 5)
Sample (p. 5)
Descriptive statistics (p. 5)
Statistic (p. 5)
Inferential statistics (pp. 5, 48)
Parameter (p. 5)
Variable (p. 7)
Qualitative variable (p. 7)
Quantitative variable (p. 7)
Discrete variable (p. 8)
Continuous variable (p. 8)
Qualitative data (p. 9)
Quantitative data (p. 9)
Discrete data (p. 9)
Continuous data (p. 9)
Nominal level of measurement (p. 10)
Ordinal level of measurement (p. 10)
Interval level of measurement (p. 10)
Ratio level of measurement (p. 10)
Validity (p. 11)
Reliability (p. 11)

Explanatory variable (p. 16)
Response variable (p. 16)
Observational study (p. 16)
Designed experiment (p. 16)
Confounding (pp. 17, 51)
Lurking variable (p. 17)
Retrospective (p. 18)
Prospective (p. 19)
Census (p. 19)
Random sampling (p. 23)
Simple random sampling (p. 23)
Simple random sample (p. 23)
Frame (p. 24)
Sampling without replacement (p. 24)
Sampling with replacement (p. 24)
Seed (p. 26)
Stratified sample (p. 30)
Systematic sample (p. 31)
Cluster sample (p. 33)
Convenience sample (p. 34)
Self-selected (p. 34)
Voluntary response (p. 34)
Bias (p. 38)
Sampling bias (p. 38)

Undercoverage (p. 38)
Nonresponse bias (p. 39)
Response bias (p. 40)
Open question (p. 41)
Closed question (p. 41)
Nonsampling error (p. 42)
Sampling error (p. 42)
Experiment (p. 46)
Factors (p. 46)
Treatment (p. 46)
Experimental unit (p. 46)
Subject (p. 46)
Control group (p. 46)
Placebo (p. 46)
Blinding (p. 46)
Single-blind (p. 46)
Double-blind (p. 46)
Design (p. 47)
Replication (p. 48)
Completely randomized design (p. 48)
Matched-pairs design (p. 50)
Blocking (p. 51)
Block (p. 51)
Randomized block design (p. 51)

Objectives

Section	You should be able to . . .	Example(s)	Review Exercises
1.1	1 Define statistics and statistical thinking (p. 3)	pp. 3–4	1
	2 Explain the process of statistics (p. 4)	1, 2	7, 14, 15
	3 Distinguish between qualitative and quantitative variables (p. 7)	3	11–13
	4 Distinguish between discrete and continuous variables (p. 8)	4, 5	11–13
	5 Determine the level of measurement of a variable (p. 10)	6	16–19
1.2	1 Distinguish between an observational study and an experiment (p. 15)	1–3	20–21
	2 Explain the various types of observational studies (p. 18)	pp. 18–19	6, 22
1.3	1 Obtain a simple random sample (p. 23)	1–3	28, 30
1.4	1 Obtain a stratified sample (p. 30)	1	25
	2 Obtain a systematic sample (p. 31)	2	26, 29
	3 Obtain a cluster sample (p. 32)	3	24
1.5	1 Explain the sources of bias in sampling (p. 38)	pp. 38–42	8, 9, 27
1.6	1 Describe the characteristics of an experiment (p. 46)	1	5
	2 Explain the steps in designing an experiment (p. 47)	pp. 47–48	10
	3 Explain the completely randomized design (p. 48)	2	31, 34(a), 35
	4 Explain the matched-pairs design (p. 50)	3	35
	5 Explain the randomized block design (p. 51)	4	32, 34(b)

Review Exercises

In Problems 1–5, provide a definition using your own words.

1. Statistics
2. Population
3. Sample
4. Observational study
5. Designed experiment
6. List and describe the three major types of observational studies.

7. What is meant by the *process of statistics*?

8. List and explain the three sources of bias in sampling. Provide some methods that might be used to minimize bias in sampling.

9. Distinguish between sampling and nonsampling error.

10. Explain the steps in designing an experiment.

In Problems 11–13, classify the variable as qualitative or quantitative. If the variable is quantitative, state whether it is discrete or continuous.

11. Number of new automobiles sold at a dealership on a given day Quantitative; discrete

12. Weight in carats of an uncut diamond Quantitative; continuous

13. Brand name of a pair of running shoes Qualitative

In Problems 14 and 15, determine whether the underlined value is a parameter or a statistic.

14. In a survey of 1011 people age 50 or older, <u>73%</u> agreed with the statement "I believe in life after death." Statistic

Source: Bill Newcott. "Life after Death," *AARP Magazine*, Sept./Oct. 2007

15. **Completion Rate** In the 2007 NCAA Football Championship Game, quarterback Chris Leak completed <u>69%</u> of his passes for a total of 213 yards and 1 touchdown. Parameter

In Problems 16–19, determine the level of measurement of each variable.

16. Birth year Interval

17. Marital status Nominal

18. Stock rating (strong buy, buy, hold, sell, strong sell) Ordinal

19. Number of siblings Ratio

In Problems 20 and 21, determine whether the study depicts an observational study or a designed experiment.

20. A parent group examines 25 randomly selected PG-13 movies and 25 randomly selected PG movies and records the number of sexual innuendos and curse words that occur in each. They then compare the number of sexual innuendos and curse words between the two movie ratings. Observational study

21. A sample of 504 patients in early stages of Alzheimer's disease is divided into two groups. One group receives an experimental drug; the other receives a placebo. The advance of the disease in the patients from the two groups is tracked at 1-month intervals over the next year. Experiment

22. Read the following description of an observational study and determine whether it is a cross-sectional, a case-control, or a cohort study. Explain your choice.

> The Cancer Prevention Study II (CPS-II) examines the relationship among environmental and lifestyle factors of cancer cases by tracking approximately 1.2 million men and women. Study participants completed an initial study questionnaire in 1982 providing information on a range of lifestyle factors, such as diet, alcohol and tobacco use, occupation, medical history, and family cancer history. These data have been examined extensively in relation to cancer mortality. The vital status of study participants is updated biennially. Cohort study
>
> *Source*: American Cancer Society

In Problems 23–26, determine the type of sampling used.

23. On election day, a pollster for Fox News positions herself outside a polling place near her home. She then asks the first 50 voters leaving the facility to complete a survey.

24. An Internet service provider randomly selects 15 residential blocks from a large city. It then surveys every household in these 15 blocks to determine the number that would use a high-speed Internet service if it were made available.

25. Thirty-five sophomores, 22 juniors, and 35 seniors are randomly selected to participate in a study from 574 sophomores, 462 juniors, and 532 seniors at a certain high school.

26. Officers for the Department of Motor Vehicles pull aside every 40th tractor trailer passing through a weigh station, starting with the 12th, for an emissions test.

27. Each survey has bias. Determine the type of bias and suggest a remedy.

   (a) A politician sends a survey about tax issues to a random sample of subscribers to a literary magazine.

   (b) An interviewer with little foreign language knowledge is sent to an area where her language is not commonly spoken. Response bias; interviewer error

   (c) A data-entry clerk mistypes survey results into his computer. Data-entry error

28. **Obtaining a Simple Random Sample** The mayor of a small town wants to conduct personal interviews with small business owners to determine if there is anything the mayor could to do to help improve business conditions. The following list gives the names of the companies in the town. Obtain a simple random sample of size 5 from the companies in the town.

Allied Tube and Conduit	Lighthouse Financial	Senese's Winery
Bechstien Construction Co.	Mill Creek Animal Clinic	Skyline Laboratory
Cizer Trucking Co.	Nancy's Flowers	Solus, Maria, DDS
D & M Welding	Norm's Jewelry	Trust Lock and Key
Grace Cleaning Service	Papoose Children's Center	Ultimate Carpet
Jiffy Lube	Plaza Inn Motel	Waterfront Tavern
Levin, Thomas, MD	Risky Business Security	WPA Pharmacy

29. **Obtaining a Systematic Sample** A quality-control engineer wants to be sure that bolts coming off an assembly line are within prescribed tolerances. He wants to conduct a systematic sample by selecting every 9th bolt to come off the assembly line. The machine produces 30,000 bolts per day, and the engineer wants a sample of 32 bolts. Which bolts will be sampled?

30. **Obtaining a Simple Random Sample** Based on the Military Standard 105E (ANS1/ASQC Z1.4, ISO 2859) Tables, a lot of 91 to 150 items with an acceptable quality level (AQL) of 1% and a normal inspection plan would require a sample of size 13 to be inspected for defects. If the sample contains no defects, the entire lot is accepted. Otherwise, the entire lot is rejected. A shipment of 100 night-vision goggles is received and must be inspected. Discuss the procedure you would follow to obtain a simple random sample of 13 goggles to inspect.

31. **Ballasts** An electronics company has just developd a new electric ballast to be used in fluorescent bulbs. To determine if the new ballast is more energy efficient than the older ballast, the company randomly divides 200 fluorescent bulbs into two groups. The group 1 bulbs are to be given the new ballast and the group 2 bulbs are to be given the old ballast. The amount of energy required to light each bulb is measured.

  (a) What type of experimental design is this?

  (b) What is the response variable in this experiment?

  (c) What are the treatments? *Old and new ballasts*

  (d) Which group serves as the control group?

  (e) What are the experimental units? *200 fluorescent bulbs*

  (f) What role does randomization play in this experiment?

  (g) Draw a diagram similar to Figure 7, 8, or 10 to illustrate the design.

32. Exam Grades A statistics instructor wants to see if allowing students to use a notecard on exams will affect their overall exam scores. The instructor thinks that the results could be affected by the type of class: traditional, Web-enhanced, or online. He randomly selects half of his students from each type of class to use notecards. At the end of the semester, the average exam grades for those using notecards is compared to the average for those without notecards.

  (a) What type of experimental design is this?

  (b) What is the response variable in this experiment?

  (c) What is the factor that is set to predetermined levels? What are the treatments?

  (d) Identify the experimental units.

  (e) Draw a diagram similar to Figure 7, 8, or 10 to illustrate the design.

33. Multiple Choice A common tip for taking multiple-choice tests is to always pick (b) or (c) if you are unsure. The idea is that instructors tend to feel the answer is more hidden if it is surrounded by distractor answers. An astute statistics instructor is aware of this and decides to use a table of random digits to select which choice will be the correct answer. If each question has five choices, use Table I in Appendix A or a random-number generator to determine the correct answers for a 20-question multiple-choice exam.

34. Humor in Advertising A marketing research firm wants to know whether information presented in a commercial is better recalled when presented using humor or serious commentary by adults between 18 and 35 years of age. They will use an exam that asks questions of 50 subjects about information presented in the ad. The response variable will be percentage of information recalled.

  (a) Create a completely randomized design to answer the question. Be sure to include a diagram to illustrate your design.

  (b) The chief of advertising criticizes your design because she knows that women react differently from men to advertising. Redesign the experiment as a randomized block design assuming that 30 of the subjects in your study are female and the remaining 20 are male. Be sure to include a diagram to illustrate your design.

35. Describe what is meant by a matched-pairs design. Contrast this experimental design with a completely randomized design.

CHAPTER TEST

Full solutions for this chapter test are available on the CD that accompanies this text. *3. Ratio, quantitative, continuous*

1. List the four components that comprise the definition of statistics.

2. What is meant by the *process of statistics*?

In Problems 3–5, determine the level of measurement for the variable and identify if the variable is qualitative or quantitative. If the variable is quantitative, determine if it is discrete or continuous.

3. Time to complete the 500-meter race in speed skating.

4. Video game rating system by the Entertainment Software Rating Board (EC, E, E10+, T, M, AO, RP) *Ordinal, qualitative*

5. The number of surface imperfections on a camera lens. *Ratio, quantitative, discrete*

In Problems 6 and 7, determine whether the study depicts an observational study or a designed experiment. Identify the response variable in each case.

6. A random sample of 30 digital cameras is selected and divided into two groups. One group uses a brand-name battery, while the other uses a generic plain-label battery. All variables besides battery type are controlled. Pictures are taken under identical conditions and the battery life of the two groups is compared. *Experiment, battery life*

7. A sports reporter asks 100 baseball fans if Barry Bonds's 756th homerun ball should be marked with an asterisk when sent to the Baseball Hall of Fame. *Observational study, asterisk or not*

8. Contrast the three major types of observational studies in terms of the time frame when the data are collected.

9. Compare and contrast observational studies and designed experiments. Which study allows a researcher to claim causality? *Experiment*

10. Explain why it is important to use a control group and blinding in an experiment.

11. List the steps required to conduct an experiment.

12. A tanning company is looking for ways to improve customer satisfaction. They want to select a simple random sample of four stores from their 15 franchises in which to conduct customer satisfaction surveys. Discuss the procedure you would use, and then use the procedure to select a simple random sample of size $n = 4$. The locations are as follows:

Afton	Ballwin	Chesterfield	Clayton	Deer Creek
Ellisville	Farmington	Fenton	Ladue	Lake St. Louis
O'Fallon	Pevely	Shrewsbury	Troy	Warrenton

13. A congresswoman wants to survey her constituency regarding public policy. She asks one of her staff members to obtain a sample of residents of the district. The frame she has available lists 9,012 Democrats, 8,302 Republicans, and 3,012 Independents. Obtain a stratified random sample of 8 Democrats, 7 Republicans, and 3 Independents. Be sure to discuss the procedure used.

14. A farmer has a 500-acre orchard in Florida. Each acre is subdivided into blocks of 5. Altogether, there are 2,500 blocks of trees on the farm. After a frost, he wants to get an idea of the extent of the damage. Obtain a sample of 10 blocks of trees using a cluster sample. Be sure to discuss the procedure used.

15. A casino manager wants to inspect a sample of 14 slot machines in his casino for quality-control purposes. There are 600 sequentially numbered slot machines operating in the casino. Obtain a systematic sample of 14 slot machines. Be sure to discuss how you obtained the sample.

16. Describe what is meant by an experiment that is a completely randomized design. Contrast this experimental design with a randomized block design.

17. Each of the following surveys has bias. Identify the type of bias.   17. (a) Sampling bias (voluntary response)

(a) A television survey that gives 900 phone numbers for viewers to call with their vote. Each call costs $2.00.

(b) An employer distributes a survey to her 450 employees asking them how many hours each week, on average, they surf the Internet during business hours. Three of the employees complete the survey. Nonresponse bias

(c) A question on a survey asks, "Do you favor or oppose a minor increase in property tax to ensure fair salaries for teachers and properly equipped school buildings?"

(d) A researcher conducting a poll about national politics sends a survey to a random sample of subscribers to *Time* magazine. Sampling bias (undercoverage)

18. The four members of Skylab had their lymphocyte count per cubic millimeter measured 1 day before lift-off and measured again on their return to Earth.   18. (a) Lymphocyte count

(a) What is the response variable in this experiment?

(b) What is the treatment? Space flight

(c) What type of experimental design is this? Matched pair

(d) Identify the experimental units. 4 members

(e) Draw a diagram similar to Figure 7, 8, or 10 to illustrate the design.

19. Nucryst Pharmaceuticals, Inc., announced the results of its first human trial of NPI 32101, a topical form of its skin ointment. A total of 225 patients diagnosed with skin irritations were randomly divided into three groups as part of a double-blind, placebo-controlled study to test the effectiveness of the new topical cream. The first group received a 0.5% cream, the second group received a 1.0% cream, and the third group received a placebo. Groups were treated twice daily for a 6-week period.

Source: www.nucryst.com

(a) What type of experimental design is this?

(b) What is the response variable in this experiment?

(c) What is the factor that is set to predetermined levels? What are the treatments? Topical cream; 0.5%, 1.0%, 0%

(d) What does it mean for this study to be double-blind?

(e) What is the control group for this study?

(f) Identify the experimental units.

(g) Draw a diagram similar to Figure 7, 8, or 10 to illustrate the design.

20. Researchers Katherine Tucker and associates wanted to determine whether consumption of cola is associated with lower bone mineral density. They looked at 1,125 men and 1,413 women in the Framingham Osteoporosis Study, which is a cohort that began in 1971. The first examination in this study began between 1971 and 1975, with participants returning for an examination every 4 years. Based on results of questionnaires, the researchers were able to determine cola consumption on a weekly basis. Analysis of the results indicated that women who consumed at least one cola per day (on average) had a bone mineral density that was significantly lower at the femoral neck than those who consumed less than one cola per day. The researchers did not find this relation in men.

Source: "Colas, but not other carbonated beverages, are associated with low bone mineral density in older women: The Framingam Osteoporosis Study," *American Journal of Clinical Nutrition* 84:936–942, 2006

(a) Why is this a cohort study?

(b) What is the response variable in this study? What is the explanatory variable?

(c) Is the response variable qualitative or quantitative?

(d) The following appears in the article: "Variables that could potentially confound the relation between carbonated beverage consumption and bone mineral density were obtained from information collected (in the questionnaire)." What does this mean?

(e) Can you think of any lurking variables that should be accounted for?

(f) What are the conclusions of the study? Does increased cola consumption cause a lower bone mineral density? Women who consumed at least one cola per day had a bone mineral density that was significantly lower at femoral neck than those who consumed less than one cola per day. No, they are associated.

MAKING AN INFORMED DECISION

What Movie Should I Go To?

One of the most difficult tasks of surveying is phrasing questions so that they are not misunderstood. In addition, questions must be phrased so that the researcher obtains answers that allow for meaningful analysis. We wish to create a questionnaire that can be used to make an informed decision about whether to attend a certain movie. Select a movie that you wish to see. If the movie is still in theaters, make sure that it has been released for at least a couple of weeks so that it is likely that a number of people have seen it. Design a questionnaire to be filled out by individuals who have seen the movie. You may wish to include questions regarding the demographics of the respondents first (such as age, gender, level of education, and so on). Ask as many questions as you feel are necessary to obtain an opinion regarding the movie. The questions can be open or closed. Administer the survey to at least 20 randomly selected people who have seen the movie. While administering the survey, keep track of those individuals who have not seen the movie. In particular, keep track of their demographic information. After administering the survey, summarize your findings. On the basis of the survey results, do you think that you will enjoy the movie? Why? Now see the movie. Did you like it? Did the survey accurately predict whether you would enjoy the movie? Now answer the following questions:

(a) What sampling method did you use? Why? Did you have a frame for the population?

(b) Did you have any problems with respondents misinterpreting your questions? How could this issue have been resolved?

(c) What role did the demographics of the respondents have in forming your opinion? Why?

(d) Did the demographics of individuals who did not see the movie play a role while you were forming your opinion regarding the movie?

(e) Look up a review of the movie by a professional movie critic. Did the movie critic's opinion agree with yours? What might account for the similarities or differences in your opinions?

(f) Describe the problems that you had in administering the survey. If you had to do this survey over again, would you change anything? Why?

CASE STUDY

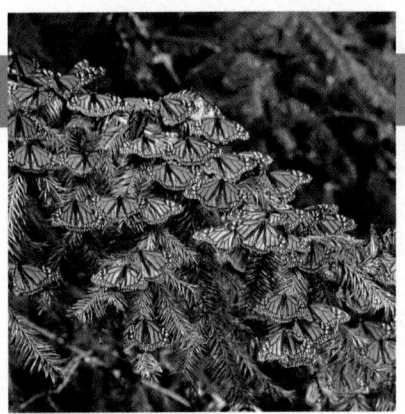

Chrysalises for Cash

The colorful butterfly symbolizes the notion of personal change. Increasingly, people are turning to butterflies to consecrate meaningful events, such as birthdays, weddings, and funerals. To fill this need, a new industry has hatched.

Suppliers of butterflies are closely monitored by governmental agencies to ensure that local environments are not subjected to the introduction of invasive species. In addition to following these regulations, butterfly suppliers need to ensure the quality and quantity of their product, while maintaining a profit. To this end, an individual supplier may hire a number of smaller independent contractors to hatch the varieties needed. These entrepreneurs are paid a small fee for each chrysalis delivered, with a 50% bonus added for each hatched healthy butterfly. This fee structure provides little room for profit. Therefore, it is important that these small contractors deliver a high proportion of healthy butterflies that emerge at a fairly predictable rate.

In Florida, one such entrepreneur specializes in harvesting the black swallowtail butterfly. In the southern United States, the black swallowtail has at least three broods a year. The female flutters through open fields seeking plants of the Apiaceae family, such as carrot and parsley, upon which to lay her eggs. The resulting caterpillars are dark brown with a small white saddle mark. As the caterpillars consume the leaves of their host plant, they increase in size, changing color to a vibrant green with intermittent stripes of yellow and black. Once a caterpillar has eaten enough, it secures itself and sheds its skin, revealing an emerald chrysalis. During this resting phase, environmental factors such as temperature and humidity may affect the transformation process. Typically, the black swallowtail takes about 1 week to complete its metamorphosis and emerge from its chrysalis. The transformation occasionally results in a deformed butterfly. Deformities range from wings that will not fully open to missing limbs.

The Florida contractor believes that there are differences in quality and emergence time among his broods. Not having taken a scientific approach to the problem, he relies on his memory of seasons past. It seems to him that late-season butterflies emerge sooner and with a greater number of deformities than their early-season counterparts. He also speculates that the type and nutritional value of the food consumed by the caterpillar might contribute to any observed differences. This year he is committed to a more formal approach to his butterfly harvest.

Since it takes 2 days to deliver the chrysalises from the contractor to the supplier, it is important that the butterflies do not emerge prematurely. It is equally important that the number of defective butterflies be minimized. With these two goals in mind, the contractor seeks the best combination of food source, fertilizer, and brood season to maximize his profits. To examine the effects of these variables on emergence time and number of deformed butterflies, the entrepreneur designed the following experiment.

Eight identical pots were filled with equal amounts of a particular soil mixture. The watering of all the pots and the plants contained within them was carefully monitored for consistency. Four pots were set outside during the early part of the brood season. Of these, two contained carrot plants, while the remaining pair grew parsley. For the carrot pair, one pot was fed a fixed amount of liquid fertilizer, while the other pot was fed a nutritionally similar amount of solid fertilizer. The two pots containing parsley were similarly fertilized. All four pots were placed next to each other to ensure similar exposures to environmental conditions such as temperature and solar radiation. Five black swallowtail caterpillars of similar age were placed into each container. The caterpillars were allowed to mature and form a chrysalis. The time from chrysalis formation until emergence was reported to the nearest day. The occurrence of any defects was also noted. The same procedure was followed with the four pots that were placed outdoors during the late brood season.

Write a report describing the experimental goals and design for the entrepreneur's experiment. Follow the procedure outlined in the box on the steps in designing and conducting an experiment (pp. 47–48). Step 5(b), *collect and process the data*, of this procedure is provided in the following table and should be included in your report.

Florida Black Swallowtail Chrysalis Experiment Data				
Season	**Food**	**Fertilizer**	**Number Deformed**	**Emergence Time (Days)**
Early	Parsley	Solid	0	6, 6, 7, 7, 7
Early	Parsley	Liquid	0	6, 7, 7, 8, 8
Early	Carrot	Solid	1	3, 6, 6, 7, 8
Early	Carrot	Liquid	0	6, 6, 7, 8, 8
Late	Parsley	Solid	2	2, 3, 4, 4, 5
Late	Parsley	Liquid	1	2, 3, 4, 5, 5
Late	Carrot	Solid	2	3, 3, 3, 4, 5
Late	Carrot	Liquid	0	2, 4, 4, 4, 5

In your report, provide a general descriptive analysis of these data. Be sure to include recommendations for the combination of season, food source, and type of fertilizer that result in the fewest deformed butterflies while achieving a long emergence time.

Conclude your report with recommendations for further experiments. For each proposed experiment, be sure to do the following:

1. State the problem to be solved and define the response variables.
2. Define the factors that affect the response variables.
3. State the number of experimental units.
4. State the treatment.

PART 2

Descriptive Statistics

CHAPTER 2
Organizing and
Summarizing Data

CHAPTER 3
Numerically
Summarizing Data

CHAPTER 4
Describing the
Relation between
Two Variables

Remember, statistics is a process. The first chapter (Part 1) dealt with the first two steps in the statistical process: (1) identify the research objective and (2) collect the information needed to answer the questions in the research objective. The next three chapters deal with organizing, summarizing, and presenting the data collected. This step in the process is called *descriptive statistics*.

2 Organizing and Summarizing Data

Outline

2.1 Organizing Qualitative Data

2.2 Organizing Quantitative Data: The Popular Displays

2.3 Additional Displays of Quantitative Data

2.4 Graphical Misrepresentations of Data

MAKING AN INFORMED DECISION

Suppose that you work for the school newspaper. Your editor approaches you with a special reporting assignment. Your task is to write an article that describes the "typical" student at your school, complete with supporting information. How are you going to do this assignment? See the Decisions project on page 125.

PUTTING IT TOGETHER

Chapter 1 discussed how to identify the research objective and collect data. We learned that data can be obtained from either observational studies or designed experiments. When data are obtained, they are referred to as **raw data**. Raw data must be organized into a meaningful form, so we can get a sense as to what the data are telling us.

The purpose of this chapter is to learn how to organize raw data in tables or graphs, which allow for a quick overview of the information collected. Describing data is the third step in the statistical process. The procedures used in this step depend on whether the data are qualitative, discrete, or continuous.

2.1 ORGANIZING QUALITATIVE DATA

Preparing for This Section   Before getting started, review the following:

• Qualitative data (Section 1.1, p. 7)   • Level of measurement (Section 1.1, pp. 10–11)

Objectives

1 Organize qualitative data in tables

2 Construct bar graphs

3 Construct pie charts

Note to Instructor

If you like, you can print out and distribute the *Preparing for This Section* quiz located in the *Instructor's Resource Center*. The purpose of the quiz is to verify the students have the prerequisite knowledge for the section.

In this section we will concentrate on tabular and graphical summaries of qualitative data. Sections 2.2 and 2.3 discuss methods for summarizing quantitative data.

1   **Organize Qualitative Data in Tables**

Recall that qualitative (or categorical) data provide measures that categorize or classify an individual. When qualitative data are collected, we are often interested in determining the number of individuals observed within each category.

Definition

A **frequency distribution** lists each category of data and the number of occurrences for each category of data.

EXAMPLE 1   **Organizing Qualitative Data into a Frequency Distribution**

Problem: A physical therapist wants to get a sense of the types of rehabilitation required by her patients. To do so, she obtains a simple random sample of 30 of her patients and records the body part requiring rehabilitation. See Table 1. Construct a frequency distribution of location of injury.

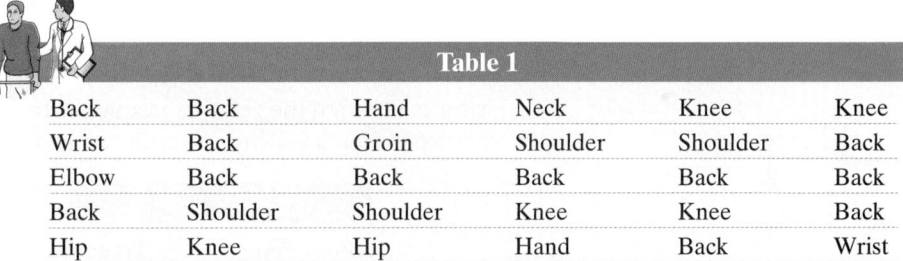

Table 1					
Back	Back	Hand	Neck	Knee	Knee
Wrist	Back	Groin	Shoulder	Shoulder	Back
Elbow	Back	Back	Back	Back	Back
Back	Shoulder	Shoulder	Knee	Knee	Back
Hip	Knee	Hip	Hand	Back	Wrist

Source: Krystal Catton, student at Joliet Junior College

Approach: To construct a frequency distribution, we create a list of the body parts (categories) and tally each occurrence. Finally, we add up the number of tallies to determine the frequency.

Solution: See Table 2. From the table, we can see that the back is the most common body part requiring rehabilitation, with a total of 12.

Table 2		
Body Part	**Tally**	**Frequency**
Back	卌 卌 ‖	12
Wrist	‖	2
Elbow			1
Hip	‖	2
Shoulder	‖‖	4
Knee	卌	5
Hand	‖	2
Groin			1
Neck			1

CAUTION   The data in Table 2 are still qualitative. The frequency simply represents the count of each category.

With frequency distributions, it is a good idea to add up the frequency column to make sure that it sums to the number of observations. In the case of the data in Example 1, the frequency column adds up to 30, as it should.

Often, rather than being concerned with the frequency with which categories of data occur, we want to know the *relative frequency* of the categories.

Definition

In Other Words
A frequency distribution shows the number of observations that belong in each category. A relative frequency distribution shows the proportion of observations that belong in each category.

The **relative frequency** is the proportion (or percent) of observations within a category and is found using the formula

$$\text{Relative frequency} = \frac{\text{frequency}}{\text{sum of all frequencies}} \qquad \textbf{(1)}$$

A **relative frequency distribution** lists each category of data together with the relative frequency.

EXAMPLE 2 **Constructing a Relative Frequency Distribution of Qualitative Data**

Problem: Using the data in Table 2, construct a relative frequency distribution.

Approach: Add all the frequencies, and then use Formula (1) to compute the relative frequency of each category of data.

Solution: We add the values in the frequency column in Table 2:

Sum of all frequencies = 12 + 2 + 1 + 2 + 4 + 5 + 2 + 1 + 1 = 30

We now compute the relative frequency of each category. For example, the relative frequency of the category *Back* is

$$\frac{12}{30} = 0.4$$

After computing the relative frequency for the remaining categories, we obtain the relative frequency distribution shown in Table 3.

Table 3		
Body Part	**Frequency**	**Relative Frequency**
Back	12	$\frac{12}{30} = 0.4$
Wrist	2	$\frac{2}{30} \approx 0.0667$
Elbow	1	0.0333
Hip	2	0.0667
Shoulder	4	0.1333
Knee	5	0.1667
Hand	2	0.0667
Groin	1	0.0333
Neck	1	0.0333

Using Technology
Some statistical spreadsheets such as MINITAB have a `Tally` command. This command will construct a frequency and relative frequency distribution of raw qualitative data.

From the table, we can see that the most common body part for rehabilitation is the back.

Now Work Problems 25(a)–(b)

It is a good idea to add up the relative frequencies to be sure they sum to 1. In fraction form, the sum should be exactly 1. In decimal form, the sum may differ slightly from 1 due to rounding.

2   **Construct Bar Graphs**

Once raw data are organized in a table, we can create graphs. Graphs allow us to see the data and get a sense of what the data are saying about the individuals in the study. The cliché, "A picture is worth a thousand words," has a similar application when dealing with data. In general, pictures of data result in a more powerful message than tables. Try the following exercise for yourself: Open a newspaper and look at a table and a graph. Study each. Now put the paper away and close your eyes. What do you see in your mind's eye? Can you recall information more easily from the table or the graph? In general, people are more likely to recall information obtained from a graph than they are from a table.

One of the most common devices for graphically representing qualitative data is a bar graph. Both nominal and ordinal data can easily be displayed with this type of graph.

Definition   A **bar graph** is constructed by labeling each category of data on either the horizontal or vertical axis and the frequency or relative frequency of the category on the other axis. Rectangles of equal width are drawn for each category. The height of each rectangle represents the category's frequency or relative frequency.

EXAMPLE 3   **Constructing a Frequency and Relative Frequency Bar Graph**

Problem: Use the data summarized in Table 3 to construct the following:

(a) Frequency bar graph

(b) Relative frequency bar graph

Approach: We will use a horizontal axis to indicate the categories of the data (body parts, in this case) and a vertical axis to represent the frequency or relative frequency. Rectangles of equal width are drawn to the height that is the frequency or relative frequency for each category. The bars do not touch each other.

Solution

(a) Figure 1(a) shows the frequency bar graph.

(b) Figure 1(b) shows the relative frequency bar graph.

Figure 1

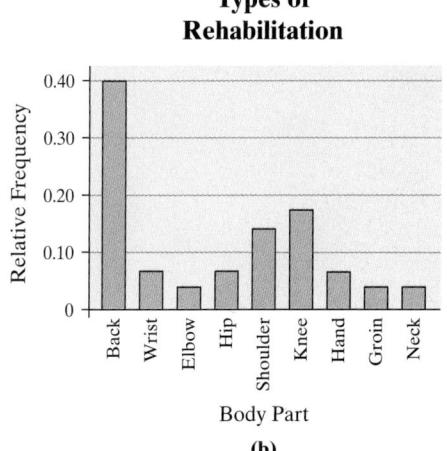

⬥ **CAUTION** Watch out for graphs that start the scale at some value other than 0, have bars with unequal widths, have bars with different colors, or have three-dimensional bars because they can misrepresent the data.

EXAMPLE 4   **Constructing a Frequency or Relative Frequency Bar Graph Using Technology**

Problem: Use a statistical spreadsheet to construct a frequency or relative frequency bar graph.

Using Technology

The graphs obtained from a different statistical package may differ from those in Figure 2. Some packages use the word *count* in place of *frequency* or *percent* in place of *relative frequency*, however.

Approach: We will use Excel to construct the frequency and relative frequency bar graph. The steps for constructing the graphs using MINITAB or Excel are given in the Technology Step-by-Step on page 81. **Note:** The TI-83 and TI-84 Plus graphing calculators cannot draw frequency or relative frequency bar graphs.

Solution: Figure 2(a) shows the frequency bar graph and Figure 2(b) shows the relative frequency bar graph obtained from Excel.

Figure 2

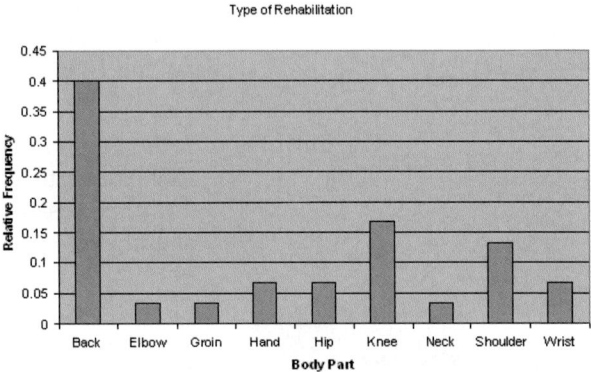

Now Work Problems 25(c)–(d)

Notice the order of the categories differ in Figures 1 and 2. In bar graphs, the order of the categories does not matter, unless one is creating a *Pareto chart*.

Some statisticians prefer to create bar graphs with the categories arranged in decreasing order of frequency. Such graphs help prioritize categories for decision making purposes in areas such as quality control, human resources, and marketing.

Definition

A **Pareto chart** is a bar graph whose bars are drawn in decreasing order of frequency or relative frequency.

Figure 3 illustrates a relative frequency Pareto chart for the data in Table 3.

Figure 3

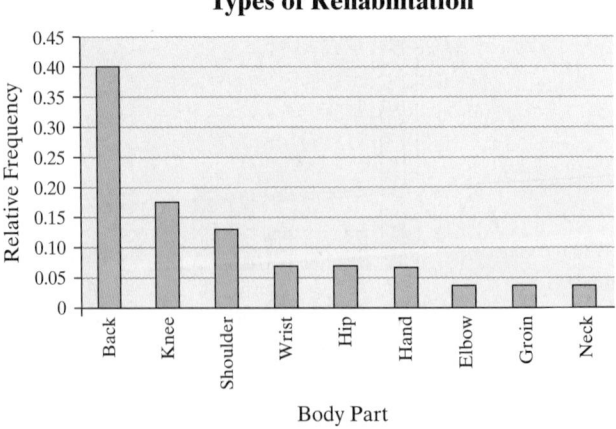

Types of Rehabilitation

Side-by-Side Bar Graphs

Graphics can provide insight when you are comparing two sets of data. For example, suppose we wanted to know if more people are finishing college today than in 1990. We could draw a **side-by-side bar graph** to compare the two data sets. Data sets should be compared by using relative frequencies, because different sample or population sizes make comparisons using frequencies difficult or misleading. However, when making comparisons, relative frequencies alone are not sufficient.

Suppose a researcher reports that 75% of a sample of electrical components have a certain quality. Since 30,000 out of 40,000 (75%) is more convincing than 3 out of 4 (75%), sample size should also be considered. Later in the course, we will see how sample size affects the precision of our results.

EXAMPLE 5   Comparing Two Data Sets

Problem: The data in Table 4 represent the educational attainment in 1990 and 2006 of adults 25 years and older who are residents of the United States. The data are in thousands. So 16,502 represents 16,502,000.

(a) Draw a side-by-side relative frequency bar graph of the data.

(b) Are a greater proportion of Americans dropping out of college before earning a degree?

Table 4		
Educational Attainment	**1990**	**2006**
Less than 9th grade	16,502	11,742
9th to 12th grade, no diploma	22,842	16,154
High school diploma	47,643	60,898
Some college, no degree	29,780	32,611
Associate's degree	9,792	16,760
Bachelor's degree	20,833	35,153
Graduate or professional degree	11,478	18,567
Totals	**158,870**	**191,885**

Source: U.S. Census Bureau

Approach: First, we determine the relative frequencies of each category for each year. To construct the side-by-side bar graphs, we draw two bars for each category of data. One of the bars will represent 1990 and the other will represent 2006.

Solution: Table 5 shows the relative frequency for each category.

(a) The side-by-side bar graph is shown in Figure 4.

Figure 4

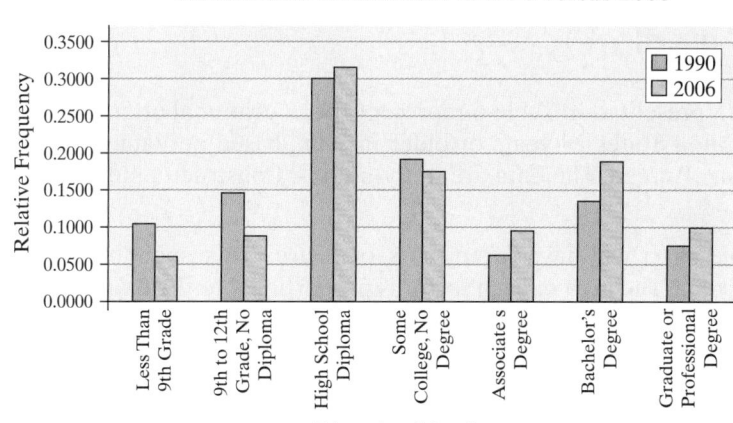

Educational Attainment in 1990 versus 2006

Table 5		
Educational Attainment	**1990**	**2006**
Less than 9th grade	0.1039	0.0612
9th to 12th grade, no diploma	0.1438	0.0842
High school diploma	0.2999	0.3174
Some college, no degree	0.1874	0.1700
Associate's degree	0.0616	0.0873
Bachelor's degree	0.1311	0.1832
Graduate or professional degree	0.0722	0.0968

(b) From the graph, we can see that the proportion of Americans 25 years and older who had some college, but no degree, was higher in 1990. This information is not clear from the frequency table, because the sizes of the populations are different. Increases in the number of Americans who did not complete a degree are due partly to increases in the sizes of the populations.

Now Work Problem 21

Horizontal Bars

So far we have only looked at bar graphs with vertical bars. However, the bars may also be horizontal. Horizontal bars may be preferred when the category names are lengthy. For example, Figure 5 uses horizontal bars to display the same data as in Figure 4.

Figure 5

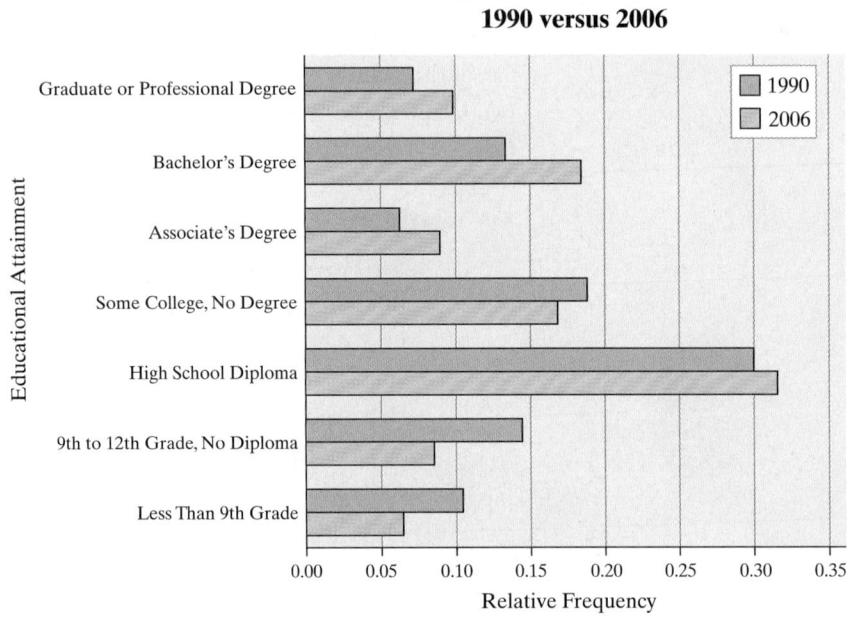

Educational Attainment in 1990 versus 2006

Note to Instructor
The by hand approach to constructing pie charts is given so that students will have a conceptual understanding of the process. Encourage students to construct pie charts using technology.

3 Construct Pie Charts

Pie charts are typically used to present the relative frequency of qualitative data. In most cases the data are nominal, but ordinal data can also be displayed in a pie chart.

Definition

A **pie chart** is a circle divided into sectors. Each sector represents a category of data. The area of each sector is proportional to the frequency of the category.

EXAMPLE 6 Constructing a Pie Chart

Note to Instructor
Ask students to compare and contrast the similarities and differences of pie charts and bar graphs.

Table 6	
Educational Attainment	**2006**
Less than 9th grade	11,742
9th to 12th grade, no diploma	16,154
High school diploma	60,898
Some college, no degree	32,611
Associate's degree	16,760
Bachelor's degree	35,153
Graduate or professional degree	18,567
Totals	**191,885**

Problem: The data presented in Table 6 represent the educational attainment of residents of the United States 25 years or older in 2006, based on data obtained from the U.S. Census Bureau. The data are in thousands. Construct a pie chart of the data.

Approach: The pie chart will have seven parts, or sectors, corresponding to the seven categories of data. The area of each sector is proportional to the frequency of each category. For example,

$$\frac{11,742}{191,885} = 0.0612$$

of all U.S. residents 25 years or older have less than a 9th-grade education. The category "less than 9th grade" will make up 6.12% of the area of the pie chart. Since a circle has 360 degrees, the degree measure of the sector for the category "less than 9th-grade" will be $(0.0612)360° \approx 22°$. Use a protractor to measure each angle.

Solution: We follow the approach presented for the remaining categories of data to obtain Table 7.

Using Technology

Most statistical spreadsheets are capable of drawing pie charts. See the Technology Step-by-Step on page 81 for instructions on drawing pie charts using MINITAB or Excel. The TI-83 and TI-84 Plus graphing calculators do not draw pie charts.

Figure 6

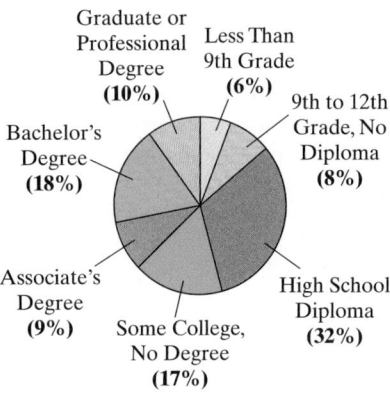

Educational Attainment, 2006

Now Work Problem 25(e)

Table 7			
Educational Attainment	Frequency	Relative Frequency	Degree Measure of Each Sector
Less than 9th grade	11,742	0.0612	22
9th to 12th grade, no diploma	16,154	0.0842	30
High school diploma	60,898	0.3174	114
Some college, no degree	32,611	0.1700	61
Associate's degree	16,760	0.0873	31
Bachelor's degree	35,153	0.1832	66
Graduate or professional degree	18,567	0.0968	35

To construct a pie chart by hand, we use a protractor to approximate the angles for each sector. See Figure 6.

Pie charts can be created only if all the categories of the variable under consideration are represented. For example, from the data given in Example 1, we could create a bar graph that lists the proportion of patients requiring rehabilitation on their back, shoulder or knee only, but it would not make sense to construct a pie chart for this situation. Do you see why? Only 70% of the data would be represented.

When should a bar graph be used to display information? When should a pie chart be used? Pie charts are useful for showing the division of all possible values of a qualitative variable into its parts. However, because angles are often hard to judge in pie charts, they are not as useful in comparing two specific values of the qualitative variable. Instead the emphasis is on comparing the part to the whole. Bar graphs are useful when we want to compare the different parts, not necessarily the parts to the whole. For example, if we wanted to get the "big picture" regarding educational attainment in 2006, then a pie chart is a good visual summary. However, if we want to compare bachelor's degrees to high school diplomas, then a bar graph is a good visual summary. Since bars are easier to draw and compare, some practitioners forego pie charts altogether in favor of Pareto charts when comparing parts to the whole.

2.1 ASSESS YOUR UNDERSTANDING

Concepts and Vocabulary

1. Define raw data in your own words.

2. A frequency distribution lists the __number__ of occurrences of each category of data, while a relative frequency distribution lists the _proportion_ of occurrences of each category of data.

3. When constructing a frequency distribution, why is it a good idea to add up the frequencies?

4. In a relative frequency distribution, what should the relative frequencies add up to? _One_

5. What is a Pareto chart?

6. When should relative frequencies be used when comparing two data sets? When dealing with samples, why is it important to also report the sample sizes along with the relative frequencies?

7. Suppose you need to summarize ordinal data in a bar graph. How would you arrange the categories of data on the axis? Is it possible to make the order of the data apparent in a pie chart?

8. Consider the information in the "Why we can't lose weight" chart shown next, which is in the *USA Today* style of graph. Could the information provided be organized into a pie chart? Why or why not.   No

Skill Building

9. **Flu Season** The pie chart shown, the type we see in *USA Today*, depicts the approaches people use to avoid getting the flu.

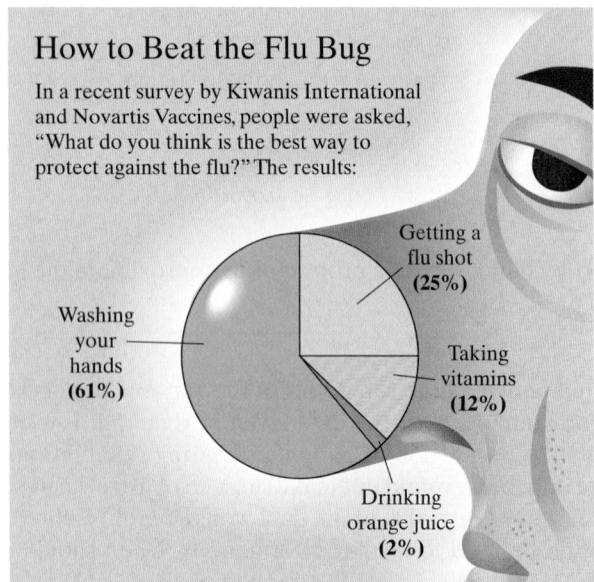

How to Beat the Flu Bug

In a recent survey by Kiwanis International and Novartis Vaccines, people were asked, "What do you think is the best way to protect against the flu?" The results:

Getting a flu shot (25%)
Washing your hands (61%)
Taking vitamins (12%)
Drinking orange juice (2%)

Source: Kiwanis International and Novartis Vaccines

9. (a) Washing your hands; 61%

   (a) What is the most commonly used approach? What percentage of the population chooses this method?
   (b) What is the least used approach? What percentage of the population chooses this method? Drinking orange juice; 2%
   (c) What percentage of the population thinks flu shots are the best way to beat the flu? 25%

10. **Cosmetic Surgery** This *USA Today*-type chart shows the most frequent cosmetic surgeries for women in 2006.

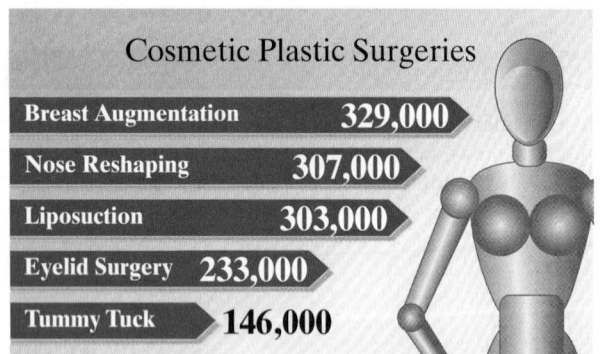

Cosmetic Plastic Surgeries

Breast Augmentation **329,000**
Nose Reshaping **307,000**
Liposuction **303,000**
Eyelid Surgery **233,000**
Tummy Tuck **146,000**

By Anne R. Carey and Suzy Parker, USA Today
Source: American Society of Plastic Surgeons (plasticsurgery.org)

   (a) If women had 1.9 million cosmetic surgeries in 2006, what percent were for tummy tucks? 7.7%
   (b) What percent were for nose reshaping? 16.2%
   (c) How many surgeries are not accounted for in the graph? 582,000

11. **Internet Users** The following Pareto chart represents the top 10 countries in Internet users as of June 2007.
   Source: www.internetworldstats.com

11. (a) United States

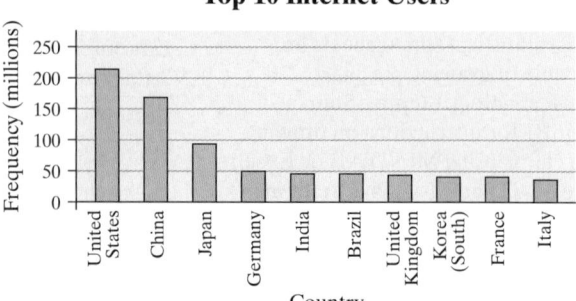

Top 10 Internet Users

   (a) Which country had the most Internet users in 2007?
   (b) Approximately what was the Internet usage in Germany in 2007? 50 million
   (c) Approximately how many more users were in China than in Germany in 2007? 110 million

12. **Poverty** Every year the U.S. Census Bureau counts the number of people living in poverty. The bureau uses money income thresholds as its definition of poverty, so noncash benefits such as Medicaid and food stamps do not count toward poverty thresholds. For example, in 2006 the poverty threshold for a family of four with two children was $20,444. The bar chart represents the number of people living in poverty in the United States in 2006, by ethnicity, based on March 2007 estimates.

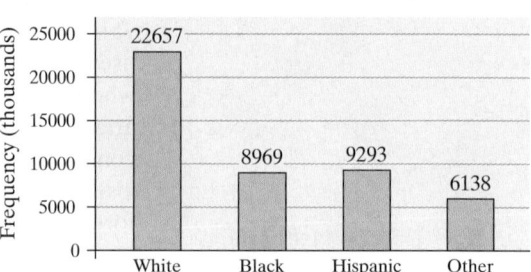

Number in Poverty

12. (a) 22,657,000   12. (b) 19.7%

   Source: The Henry Kaiser Family Foundation (www.statehealthfacts.kff.org)

   (a) How many whites were living in poverty in 2006?
   (b) Of the impoverished, what percent were Hispanic?
   (c) How might this graph be misleading?

13. **Disposable Electronics** The following data represent the percent of owners of an electronic device planning to purchase a replacement device within the next 12 months.
   Source: *Birmingham News*, Nov. 22, 2007

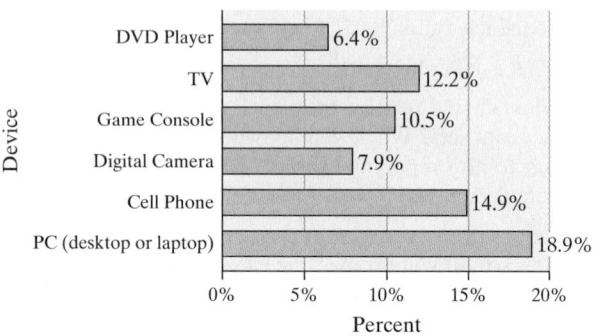

Owners Planning to Replace Electronic Device

13. (d) No; in a relative frequency bar chart, the percents refer to the whole and sum to 100%. In this chart, the percents refer to each category individually.
14. (b) 1.78 million 14. (c) No, the percents do not add to 100%. Add another category such as "Someone Else" to cover the remaining cases.

(a) What percent of game console owners plan to buy a replacement device within the next 12 months? 10.5%

(b) If there were 250 million Americans in 2007 who owned a cell phone, how many expect to replace their phone within the next 12 months? 37.25 million

(c) Is the given chart a Pareto chart? Explain why or why not. No, the bars are not arranged in decreasing order.

(d) Is the given chart a relative frequency bar chart? Explain why or why not.

14. **Identity Fraud** In a study conducted by the Better Business Bureau and Javelin Strategy and Research, victims of identity fraud were asked, "Who was the person who misused your personal information?" The following Pareto chart represents the results for cases in the year 2006 for which the perpetrator's identity was known.

Person Who Misused Personal Information

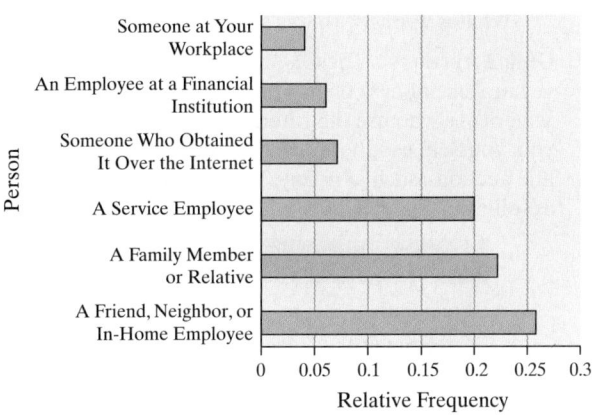

Source: Javelin Strategy & Research, 2006.

(a) Approximately what percentage of identity-fraud victims were victimized by someone who obtained their information on the Internet? 7%

(b) If there were 8.9 million identity-fraud victims in 2006, how many were victimized by a service employee?

(c) Can the data presented be displayed in a pie chart? If not, what could be done so that a pie chart would be possible?

15. **Internet and Parents** The following side-by-side bar graph represents feelings toward the Internet by parents of 12- to 17-year-olds for the years 2000, 2004, and 2006. Participants in a survey were asked, "Overall, would you say that e-mail and the Internet have been a GOOD thing for your child, a BAD thing, or haven't they had much effect one way or the other?"

Parents of Teenagers – Attitudes Towards the Internet

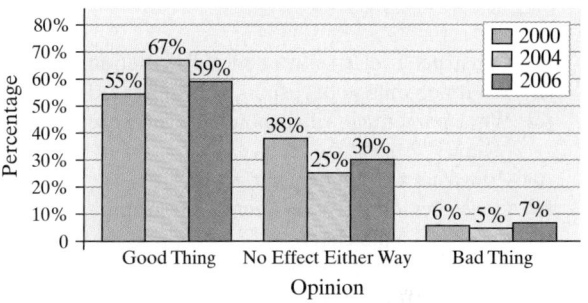

Source: Pew Internet & American Life Project, 2007

15. (c) No, their opinion could change to "no effect."

(a) What proportion of parents felt the Internet was a good thing for their children in 2000? In 2006? 55%; 59%

(b) Which opinion saw the greatest increase between 2004 and 2006? No effect

(c) Does a decrease in the percentage of parents who view the Internet as a good thing necessarily correspond to an equivalent increase in the percentage who view the Internet as a bad thing?

(d) Why might the percentages within each year not add up to 100%? Some participants may not have answered the question (nonresponse).

16. **Doctorate Recipients** The following side-by-side bar graph represents the number of doctorate recipients from U.S. universities within broad fields of study for the years 1998, 2002, and 2006.

Doctorate Recipients from U.S. Universities

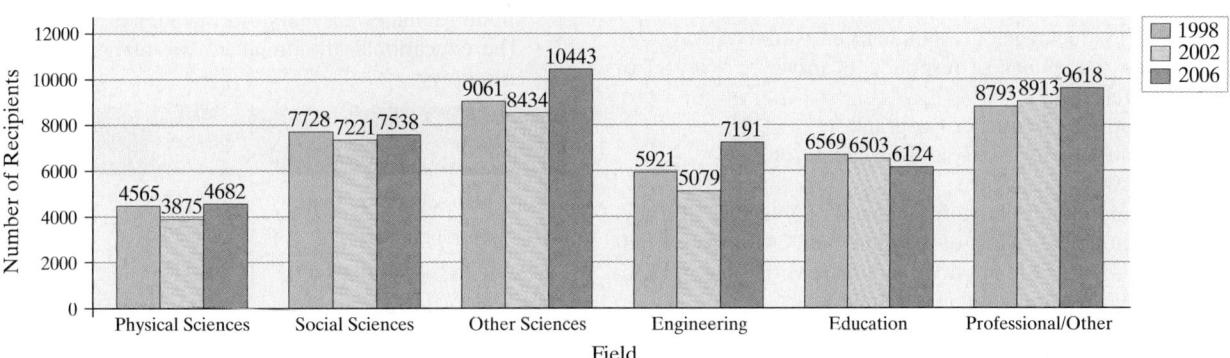

Source: NSF/NIH/USED/NEH/USDA/NASA, 2006 Survey of Earned Doctorates

(a) How many more engineering doctorates were awarded in 2006 than in 2002? 2112

(b) In 2006, what percentage of doctoral recipients received degrees in physical science? In education? About 10.3%; about 13.4%

(c) What field of study consistently decreased in the number of doctoral degree recipients between 1998 and 2006? Which increased? Education; professional/other

(d) Which field of study had the largest increase in the number of doctoral degree recipients in the 3 years of the survey?

(e) What field of study had the largest percent increase in doctoral degree recipients between 1998 and 2006? Engineering

16. (d) Other sciences

17. (b) 52.7%   18. (b) 64.8%

Applying the Concepts

17. College Survey In a national survey conducted by the Centers for Disease Control to determine health-risk behaviors among college students, college students were asked, "How often do you wear a seat belt when riding in a car driven by someone else?" The frequencies were as follows:

Response	Frequency
Never	125
Rarely	324
Sometimes	552
Most of the time	1,257
Always	2,518

(a) Construct a relative frequency distribution.
(b) What percentage of respondents answered "Always"?
(c) What percentage of respondents answered "Never" or "Rarely"? 9.4%
(d) Construct a frequency bar graph.
(e) Construct a relative frequency bar graph.
(f) Construct a pie chart.
(g) Suppose that a representative from the Centers for Disease Control says, "52.7% of all college students always wear a seat belt." Is this a descriptive or inferential statement? Inferential

18. College Survey In a national survey conducted by the Centers for Disease Control to determine health-risk behaviors among college students, college students were asked, "How often do you wear a seat belt when driving a car?" The frequencies were as follows:

Response	Frequency
I do not drive a car	249
Never	118
Rarely	249
Sometimes	345
Most of the time	716
Always	3,093

(a) Construct a relative frequency distribution.
(b) What percentage of respondents answered "Always"?
(c) What percentage of respondents answered "Never" or "Rarely"? 7.7%
(d) Construct a frequency bar graph.
(e) Construct a relative frequency bar graph.
(f) Construct a pie chart.
(g) Compute the relative frequencies of "Never," "Rarely," "Sometimes," "Most of the time," and "Always," excluding those that do not drive. Compare with those in Problem 17. What might you conclude?
(h) Suppose that a representative from the Centers for Disease Control says, "2.5% of the college students in this survey responded that they never wear a seat belt." Is this a descriptive or inferential statement? Descriptive

19. Use the Internet? The Gallup organization conducted a survey in December 2006 in which 1,025 randomly sampled adult Americans were asked, "How much time, if at all, do you personally spend using the Internet—more than 1 hour a day, up to 1 hour a day, a few times a week, a few times a month or less, or never?" The results of the survey were as follows:

Response	Frequency
More than 1 hour a day	377
Up to 1 hour a day	192
A few times a week	132
A few times a month or less	81
Never	243

(a) Construct a relative frequency distribution.
(b) What proportion of those surveyed never use the Internet? 0.2371 (about 24%)
(c) Construct a frequency bar graph.
(d) Construct a relative frequency bar graph.
(e) Construct a pie chart.
(f) A local news broadcast reported that 37% of adult Americans use the Internet more than 1 hour a day. What is wrong with this statement? No level of confidence

20. Online Auctions? The Gallup organization conducted a survey in December 2005 in which 770 randomly selected adult Americans who use the Internet were asked, "How often do you, yourself, use the Internet to buy or sell products in online auctions, such as e-Bay?" The results of the survey were as follows: 20. (b) 0.60, or 60%

Response	Frequency
Frequently	54
Occasionally	123
Rarely	131
Never	462

(a) Construct a relative frequency distribution.
(b) What proportion of those surveyed never use the Internet to buy or sell products in an online auction?
(c) Construct a frequency bar graph.
(d) Construct a relative frequency bar graph.
(e) Construct a pie chart.
(f) What is the population that is being studied by Gallup? Adult Internet users

21. Educational Attainment On the basis of the 2006 Current [NW] Population Survey, there were 92.2 million males and 99.6 million females 25 years old or older in the United States. The educational attainment of the males and females was as follows:

Educational Attainment	Males (in millions)	Females (in millions)
Not a high school graduate	13.8	14.1
High school graduate	29.4	31.5
Some college, but no degree	15.0	17.6
Associate's degree	7.1	9.6
Bachelor's degree	17.1	18.1
Advanced degree	9.8	8.7

Source: U.S. Census Bureau

(a) Construct a relative frequency distribution for males.
(b) Construct a relative frequency distribution for females.
(c) Construct a side-by-side relative frequency bar graph.
(d) Compare each gender's educational attainment. Make a conjecture about the reasons for the differences.

22. Problems with Spam A survey of U.S. adults aged 18 and older in 2003 and 2007 asked, "Which of the following describes how spam affects your life on the Internet?"

Feeling	2003	2007
Big problem	373	269
Annoying, but not a big problem	850	761
No problem at all	239	418
Don't know/refused	15	45

Source: Pew Internet & American Life Project Survey, 2007

(a) Construct a relative frequency distribution for 2003.
(b) Construct a relative frequency distribution for 2007.
(c) Construct a side-by-side relative frequency bar graph.
(d) Compare each year's feelings. Make some conjectures about the reasons for any differences or similarities.

23. Murder Victims A criminologist wanted to know if there was any relation between age and gender of murder victims. The following data represent the number of male and female murder victims by age in 2006.

Age	Number of Males	Number of Females
Less than 17	791	373
17–24	3,762	550
25–34	3,220	599
35–54	2,977	1,102
55 or older	860	465

Source: U.S. Federal Bureau of Investigation

(a) Construct a relative frequency distribution for males.
(b) Construct a relative frequency distribution for females.
(c) Construct a side-by-side relative frequency bar graph.
(d) Compare each gender's age percentages. Make a conjecture about the reasons for the differences or similarities.

24. Car Color DuPont Automotive is a major supplier of paint to the automotive industry. A survey of 100 randomly selected autos in the luxury car segment and 100 randomly selected autos in the sports car segment that were recently purchased yielded the following colors.

Color	Number of Luxury Cars	Number of Sports Cars
White	25	10
Black	22	15
Silver	16	18
Gray	12	15
Blue	7	13
Red	7	15
Gold	6	5
Green	3	2
Brown	2	7

Source: Based on results from www.infoplease.com

(a) Construct a relative frequency distribution for each car type.
(b) Draw a side-by-side relative frequency bar graph.
(c) Compare the colors for the two car types. Make a conjecture about the reasons for the differences.

25. 2008 Democratic Presidential Nomination Early in the 2008 presidential primary, a survey was conducted in which a random sample of 40 voters was asked which candidate they would likely support for the Democratic nomination for president. The results of the survey were as follows:

Obama	Clinton	Clinton	Clinton	Clinton
Clinton	Edwards	Clinton	Obama	Clinton
Kucinich	Obama	Kucinich	Edwards	Obama
Clinton	Clinton	Obama	Clinton	Clinton
Obama	Clinton	Biden	Clinton	Edwards
Clinton	No opinion	Clinton	Clinton	Clinton
Edwards	Clinton	Obama	Biden	No opinion
Edwards	No opinion	Clinton	No opinion	Obama

(a) Construct a frequency distribution.
(b) Construct a relative frequency distribution.
(c) Construct a frequency bar graph.
(d) Construct a relative frequency bar graph.
(e) Construct a pie chart.
(f) On the basis of the data, make a conjecture about who will win the Democratic nomination on the basis of this sample (assume the sample was drawn appropriately). Would your conjecture be descriptive statistics or inferential statistics? Would your confidence in making this conjecture increase if you had a sample of 1,500 voters? Why?   Inferential

26. Hospital Admissions The following data represent the diagnoses of a random sample of 20 patients admitted to a hospital.

Cancer	Motor vehicle accident	Congestive heart failure
Gunshot wound	Fall	Gunshot wound
Gunshot wound	Motor vehicle accident	Gunshot wound
Assault	Motor vehicle accident	Gunshot wound
Motor vehicle accident	Motor vehicle accident	Gunshot wound
Motor vehicle accident	Gunshot wound	Motor vehicle accident
Fall	Gunshot wound	

Source: Tamela Ohm, student at Joliet Junior College

26. (c) Gunshot wound

(a) Construct a frequency distribution.
(b) Construct a relative frequency distribution.
(c) Which diagnosis had the most admissions?
(d) What percentage of diagnoses was motor vehicle accidents?   35%
(e) Construct a frequency bar graph.
(f) Construct a relative frequency bar graph.
(g) Construct a pie chart.
(h) Suppose that an admission specialist at the hospital stated that 40% of all admissions were gunshot wounds. Would this statement be descriptive or inferential? Why?   Inferential

27. **Which Position in Baseball Pays the Most?** You are a prospective baseball agent and are in search of clients. You would like to recruit the highest-paid players as clients, so you perform a study in which you identify the 25 top-paid players for the 2007 season and their positions. The table shows the results of your study.

Player	Position	Player	Position
Jason Giambi	Designated hitter	Carlos Delgado	First base
Alex Rodriguez	Third base	Vladimir Guerrero	Right field
Derek Jeter	Shortstop	Mike Hampton	Pitcher
Manny Ramirez	Left field	Pedro Martinez	Pitcher
Todd Helton	First base	J.D. Drew	Right field
Bartolo Colon	Pitcher	Andruw Jones	Center field
Andy Pettitte	Pitcher	Miguel Tejada	Shortstop
Jason Schmidt	Pitcher	Rafael Furcal	Shortstop
Garret Anderson	Left field	Carlos Beltran	Center field
Richie Sexson	First base	Pat Burrell	Left field
Bobby Abreu	Right field	Derrek Lee	First base
Jim Thome	Designated hitter	David Oritz	Designated hitter
Lance Berkman	First base		

Source: usatoday.com

(a) Construct a frequency distribution of position.
(b) Construct a relative frequency distribution of position.
(c) Which position appears to be the most lucrative? For which position would you recruit? *Pitcher or first base*
(d) Are there any positions that you would avoid recruiting? Why? *Second base or catcher*
(e) Draw a frequency bar graph.
(f) Draw a relative frequency bar graph.
(g) Draw a pie chart.

---

28. **Blood Type** A phlebotomist draws the blood of a random sample of 50 patients and determines their blood types as shown:

O	O	A	A	O
B	O	B	A	O
AB	B	A	B	AB
O	O	A	A	O
AB	O	A	B	A
O	A	A	O	A
O	A	O	AB	A
O	B	A	A	O
O	O	O	A	O
O	A	O	A	O

(a) Construct a frequency distribution.
(b) Construct a relative frequency distribution.
(c) According to the data, which blood type is most common? *O*
(d) According to the data, which blood type is least common? *AB*
(e) Use the results of the sample to conjecture the percentage of the population that has type O blood. Is this an example of descriptive or inferential statistics?
(f) Contact a local hospital and ask them the percentage of the population that is blood type O. Why might the results differ?

(g) Draw a frequency bar graph.
(h) Draw a relative frequency bar graph.
(i) Draw a pie chart.

29. **Foreign Language** According to the Modern Language Association, the number of college students studying foreign language is increasing. The following data represent the foreign language being studied based on a simple random sample of 30 students learning a foreign language.

Spanish	Chinese	Spanish	Spanish	Spanish
Chinese	German	Spanish	Spanish	French
Spanish	Spanish	Japanese	Latin	Spanish
German	German	Spanish	Italian	Spanish
Italian	Japanese	Chinese	Spanish	French
Spanish	Spanish	Russian	Latin	French

Source: Based on data obtained from the Modern Language Association

(a) Construct a frequency distribution.
(b) Construct a relative frequency distribution.
(c) Construct a frequency bar graph.
(d) Construct a relative frequency bar graph.
(e) Construct a pie chart.

28. (e) 44%; inferential

30. President's State of Birth The following table lists the presidents of the United States (as of July, 2008) and their state of birth.

Birthplace of U.S. President					
President	**State of Birth**	**President**	**State of Birth**	**President**	**State of Birth**
Washington	Virginia	Lincoln	Kentucky	Coolidge	Vermont
J. Adams	Massachusetts	A. Johnson	North Carolina	Hoover	Iowa
Jefferson	Virginia	Grant	Ohio	F. D. Roosevelt	New York
Madison	Virginia	Hayes	Ohio	Truman	Missouri
Monroe	Virginia	Garfield	Ohio	Eisenhower	Texas
J. Q. Adams	Massachusetts	Arthur	Vermont	Kennedy	Massachusetts
Jackson	South Carolina	Cleveland	New Jersey	L. B. Johnson	Texas
Van Buren	New York	B. Harrison	Ohio	Nixon	California
W. H. Harrison	Virginia	Cleveland	New Jersey	Ford	Nebraska
Tyler	Virginia	McKinley	Ohio	Carter	Georgia
Polk	North Carolina	T. Roosevelt	New York	Reagan	Illinois
Taylor	Virginia	Taft	Ohio	George H. Bush	Massachusetts
Fillmore	New York	Wilson	Virginia	Clinton	Arkansas
Pierce	New Hampshire	Harding	Ohio	George W. Bush	Connecticut
Buchanan	Pennsylvania				

(a) Construct a frequency bar graph for state of birth.

(b) Which state has yielded the most presidents? Virginia

(c) Explain why the answer obtained in part (b) may be considered to be misleading.

31. Highest Elevation The following data represent the land area and highest elevation for each of the seven continents.

Continent	Land Area (square miles)	Highest Elevation (feet)
Africa	11,608,000	19,340
Antarctica	5,100,000	16,066
Asia	17,212,000	29,035
Australia	3,132,000	7,310
Europe	3,837,000	18,510
North America	9,449,000	20,320
South America	6,879,000	22,834

Source: www.infoplease.com

(a) Would it make sense to draw a pie chart for land area? Why? If so, draw a pie chart. Yes

(b) Would it make sense to draw a pie chart for the highest elevation? Why? If so, draw a pie chart. No

32. Putting It Together: Online Homework Keeping students engaged in the learning process greatly increases their chance of success in a course. Traditional lecture-based math instruction has been giving way to a more student-engaged approach where students interact with the teacher in class and receive immediate feedback to their responses. The teacher presence allows students, when incorrect in a response, to be guided through a solution and then immediately be given a similar problem to attempt.

A researcher conducted a study to investigate whether an online homework system using an attempt–feedback–reattempt approach improved student learning over traditional pencil-and-paper homework. The online homework system was designed to increase student engagement outside class, something commonly missing in traditional pencil-and-paper assignments, ultimately leading to increased learning.

32. (a) To determine if online homework improves student learning

The study was conducted using two first-semester calculus classes taught by the researcher in a single semester. One class was assigned traditional homework and the other was assigned online homework that used the attempt–feedback–reattempt approach. The following data summaries are based on data from the study.

	Prior College Experience		No Prior College Experience	
	Traditional	**Online**	**Traditional**	**Online**
Number of students	10	9	23	18
Average age	22.8	19.4	18.13	18.11
Average exam score	84.52	68.9	79.38	80.61

Grades Earned on Exams (no prior college experience)

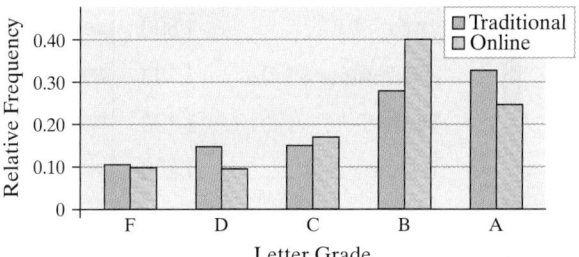

Source: *Journal of Computers in Mathematics and Science Teaching* 26(1):55–73, 2007

(a) What is the research objective?

(b) Is this study an observational study or experiment? Experiment

(c) Give an example of how the researcher attempted to control variables in the study.

(d) Explain why assigning homework type to entirely separate classes can confound the conclusions of the study.

(e) For the data in the table, (i) identify the variables, (ii) indicate whether the variables are qualitative or quantitative, and (iii) for each quantitative variable, indicate whether the variable is discrete or continuous.

(f) What type of variable is letter grade? What level of measurement is letter grade? Do you think presenting

32. (g) Side-by-side relative frequency bar graph

the data in a table from A to F would be a better representation of the data than presenting it in a graph?

(g) What type of graph is displayed?

(h) Could the data in the graph be presented in a pie chart? If so, what is the "whole"? If not, why not?

(i) Considering the students with no prior college experience, how might the table and the graph generate conflicting conclusions?

32. (h) Yes; all students who received a grade in the course

Consumer Reports Rates Treadmills

A study that compared exercisers who worked out equally hard for the same time on several different types of machines found that they generally burned the most calories on treadmills. Our own research has shown that treadmills are less likely than other machines to sit unused. So it should come as no surprise that treadmills are the best-selling home exercise machine in the United States.

In a study by *Consumer Reports*, we tested 11 best-selling brands of treadmills ranging in price from $500 to $3,000. The treadmills were rated on ease of use, ergonomics, exercise factors, construction, and durability. Ease of use is based on how straightforward the treadmill is to use. Ergonomics, including safety factors, belt size, and handrail placement, indicates how well the treadmill fits people of different sizes. Exercise includes evaluations of the minimum incline level, speed control, and heart-rate monitoring. Construction covers factors like the motor's continuous-duty horsepower rating and weld quality.

To help compare the treadmills, the individual attribute scores were combined into an overall score. The figure is a

ratings chart for the 11 treadmills based on our test results. In addition to the performance ratings, other useful information, such as the models' price and belt size, is included.

(a) What type of graph is illustrated to display overall score in the figure?

(b) Which model has the highest construction score? Which models have the lowest ease of use score?

(c) For ease of use, how many treadmills rated excellent? very good? good? fair? poor?

(d) Draw a frequency bar graph for each rating category. In other words, draw a bar graph for ease of use, ergonomics, and so on.

(e) Does there appear to be a relationship between price and overall score? Explain your opinion.

Note to Readers: *In many cases, our test protocol and analytical methods are more complicated than described in these examples. The data and discussions have been modified to make the material more appropriate for the audience.*

Ratings Chart for Treadmills

Overall Ratings — In performance order

Excellent, Very good, Good, Fair, Poor

KEY NO.	BRAND & MODEL; SIMILAR MODELS IN SMALL TYPE	PRICE	OVERALL SCORE	BELT (IN.)	EASE	ERGONOMICS	EXERCISE	CONSTRUCTION	FOLDS
1	**Life Fitness** T3 T3i	$2,200		19x52	Excellent	Excellent	Excellent	Very good	
2	**Reebok** ACD4	1,850		19x61	Very good	Excellent	Excellent	Very good	✔
3	**Precor** M9.33 M9.35	3,000		20x59	Good	Excellent	Excellent	Excellent	
4	**Star Trac** TR901	2,500		19x50	Very good	Very good	Excellent	Very good	
5	**Image** 10.6QL	1,500		20x61	Very good	Very good	Excellent	Good	✔
6	**HealthRider** S500xi	1,100		19x54	Very good	Good	Excellent	Good	✔
7	**Tunturi** J6F J6	2,100		18x55	Fair	Very good	Very good	Very good	✔
8	**Trimline** 2610	1,200		18x48	Very good	Good	Very good	Very good	
9	**ProForm** 785SS	750		20x55	Very good	Very good	Fair	Very good	✔
10	**NordicTrack** EXP 1000i	800		20x55	Very good	Very good	Fair	Fair	✔
11	**ProForm** 525E	500		18x52	Fair	Good	Fair	Fair	✔

TECHNOLOGY STEP-BY-STEP   Drawing Bar Graphs and Pie Charts

TI-83/84 Plus

The TI-83 or TI-84 Plus does not have the ability to draw bar graphs or pie charts.

MINITAB

Frequency or Relative Frequency Distributions from Raw Data

1. Enter the raw data in C1.
2. Select **Stat** and highlight **Tables** and select Tally Individual Variables . . .
3. Fill in the window with appropriate values. In the "Variables" box, enter C1. Check "counts" for a frequency distribution and/or "percents" for a relative frequency distribution. Click OK.

Bar Graphs from Summarized Data

1. Enter the categories in C1 and the frequency or relative frequency in C2.
2. Select **Graph** and highlight **Bar Chart**.
3. In the "Bars represent" pull-down menu, select "Values from a table" and highlight "Simple." Press OK.
4. Fill in the window with the appropriate values. In the "Graph variables" box, enter C2. In the "Categorical variable" box, enter C1. By pressing Labels, you can add a title to the graph. Click OK to obtain the bar graph.

Bar Graphs from Raw Data

1. Enter the raw data in C1.
2. Select **Graph** and highlight **Bar Chart**.
3. In the "Bars represent" pull-down menu, select "Counts of unique values" and highlight "Simple." Press OK.
4. Fill in the window with the appropriate values. In the "Categorical variable" box, enter C1. By pressing Labels, you can add a title to the graph. Click OK to obtain the bar graph.

Pie Chart from Raw or Summarized Data

1. If the data are in a summarized table, enter the categories in C1 and the frequency or

relative frequency in C2. If the data are raw, enter the data in C1.
2. Select **Graph** and highlight **Pie Chart**.
3. Fill in the window with the appropriate values. If the data are summarized, click the "Chart values from a table" radio button; if the data are raw, click the "Chart raw data" radio button. For summarized data, enter C1 in the "Categorical variable" box and C2 in the "Summary variable" box. If the data are raw, enter C1 in the "Categorical variable" box. By pressing Labels, you can add a title to the graph. Click OK to obtain the pie chart.

Excel

Bar Graphs from Summarized Data

1. Enter the categories in column A and the frequency or relative frequency in column B.
2. Select the chart wizard icon. Click the "column" chart type. Select the chart type in the upper-left corner and hit "Next."
3. Click inside the data range cell. Use the mouse to highlight the data to be graphed. Click "Next."
4. Click the "Titles" tab to enter x-axis, y-axis, and chart titles. Click "Finish."

Pie Charts from Summarized Data

1. Enter the categories in column A and the frequencies in column B. Select the chart wizard icon and click the "pie" chart type. Select the pie chart in the upper-left corner.
2. Click inside the data range cell. Use the mouse to highlight the data to be graphed. Click "Next."
3. Click the "Titles" tab to the chart title. Click the "Data Labels" tab and select "Show label and percent." Click "Finish."

2.2 ORGANIZING QUANTITATIVE DATA: THE POPULAR DISPLAYS

Preparing for This Section Before getting started, review the following:

- Quantitative variable (Section 1.1, pp. 7–8)
- Continuous variable (Section 1.1, pp. 8–9)
- Discrete variable (Section 1.1, pp. 8–9)

Objectives	
1	Organize discrete data in tables
2	Construct histograms of discrete data
3	Organize continuous data in tables
4	Construct histograms of continuous data
5	Draw stem-and-leaf plots
6	Draw dot plots
7	Identify the shape of a distribution

In summarizing quantitative data, we first determine whether the data are discrete or continuous. If the data are discrete and there are relatively few different values of the variable, then the categories of data (called **classes**) will be the observations (as in qualitative data). If the data are discrete, but there are many different values of the variables or if the data are continuous, then the categories of data (the *classes*) must be created using intervals of numbers. We will first present the techniques required to organize discrete quantitative data when there are relatively few different values and then proceed to organizing continuous quantitative data.

1 Organize Discrete Data in Tables

We use the values of a discrete variable to create the classes when the number of distinct data values is small.

EXAMPLE 1 **Constructing Frequency and Relative Frequency Distributions from Discrete Data**

Problem: The manager of a Wendy's fast-food restaurant is interested in studying the typical number of customers who arrive during the lunch hour. The data in Table 8 represent the number of customers who arrive at Wendy's for 40 randomly selected 15-minute intervals of time during lunch. For example, during one 15-minute interval, seven customers arrived. Construct a frequency and relative frequency distribution.

Table 8							
Number of Arrivals at Wendy's							
7	6	6	6	4	6	2	6
5	6	6	11	4	5	7	6
2	7	1	2	4	8	2	6
6	5	5	3	7	5	4	6
2	2	9	7	5	9	8	5

Approach: The number of people arriving could be 0, 1, 2, 3, ... From Table 8, we see that there are 11 categories of data from this study: 1, 2, 3, . . . , 11. We tally the number of observations for each category, count each tally, and create the frequency and relative frequency distributions.

Solution: The frequency and relative frequency distributions are shown in Table 9.

Table 9			
Number of Customers	Tally	Frequency	Relative Frequency
1	|	1	$\frac{1}{40} = 0.025$
2	ⵌⵌ |	6	0.15
3	|	1	0.025
4	||||	4	0.1
5	ⵌⵌ ||	7	0.175
6	ⵌⵌ ⵌⵌ |	11	0.275
7	ⵌⵌ	5	0.125
8	||	2	0.05
9	||	2	0.05
10		0	0.0
11	|	1	0.025

On the basis of the relative frequencies, 27.5% of the 15-minute intervals had 6 customers arrive at Wendy's during the lunch hour.

Now Work Problems 31(a)–(e)

2 Construct Histograms of Discrete Data

As with qualitative data, quantitative data may be represented graphically. We begin our discussion with a graph called the *histogram*, which is similar to the bar graph drawn for qualitative data.

Definition

A **histogram** is constructed by drawing rectangles for each class of data. The height of each rectangle is the frequency or relative frequency of the class. The width of each rectangle is the same and the rectangles touch each other.

EXAMPLE 2   **Drawing a Histogram for Discrete Data**

Problem: Construct a frequency histogram and a relative frequency histogram using the data summarized in Table 9.

Approach: On the horizontal axis, we place the value of each category of data (number of customers). The vertical axis will be the frequency or relative frequency of each category. Rectangles of equal width are drawn, with the center of each rectangle located at the value of each category. For example, the first rectangle is centered at 1. For the frequency histogram, the height of the rectangle will be the frequency of the category. For the relative frequency histogram, the height of the rectangle will be the relative frequency of the category. Remember, the rectangles touch for histograms.

 The rectangles in histograms touch, while the rectangles in bar graphs do not touch.

Solution: Figure 7(a) on the next page shows the frequency histogram. Figure 7(b) shows the relative frequency histogram.

Figure 7

Arrivals at Wendy's

(a)

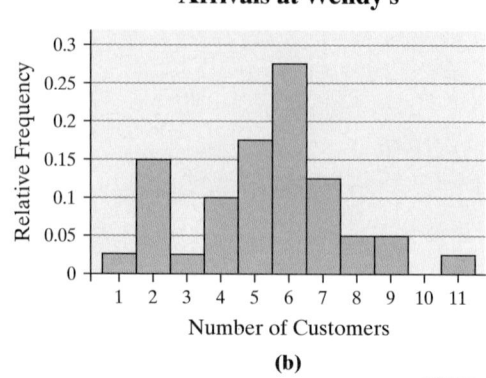

Arrivals at Wendy's

(b)

Now Work Problems 31(f)–(g)

③ Organize Continuous Data in Tables

Classes are the categories by which data are grouped. When a data set consists of a relatively small number of different discrete data values, the classes for the corresponding frequency distribution are predetermined to be those data values (as in Example 1). However, when a data set consists of a large number of different discrete data values or when a data set consists of continuous data, then no such predetermined classes exist. Therefore, the classes must be created by using intervals of numbers.

Table 10 is a typical frequency distribution created from continuous data. The data represent the number of U.S. residents between the ages of 25 and 74 who have earned a bachelor's degree or higher. The data are based on the Current Population Survey conducted in 2006.

In the table, we notice that the data are categorized, or grouped, by intervals of numbers. Each interval represents a class. For example, the first class is 25- to 34-year-old residents of the United States who have a bachelor's degree or higher. We read this interval as follows: "The number of residents of the United States in 2006 who were between 25 and 34 years of age and have a bachelor's degree or higher was 11,806,000." There are five classes in the table, each with a *lower class limit* and an *upper class limit*. The **lower class limit** of a class is the smallest value within the class, while the **upper class limit** of a class is the largest value within the class. The lower class limit for the first class in Table 10 is 25; the upper class limit is 34. The **class width** is the difference between consecutive lower class limits. The class width for the data in Table 10 is $35 - 25 = 10$.

Notice that the classes in Table 10 do not overlap. This is necessary to avoid confusion as to which class a data value belongs. Notice also that the class widths are equal for all classes. One exception to this requirement is in open-ended tables. A table is **open ended** if the first class has no lower class limit or the last class does not have an upper class limit. The data in Table 11 represent the number of persons under sentence of death as of December 31, 2006, in the United States. The last class in the table, "60 and older," is open ended.

Table 10	
Age	**Number (in thousands)**
25–34	11,806
35–44	13,387
45–54	12,571
55–64	9,035
65–74	3,953

Source: Current Population Survey, 2006

Table 11	
Age	**Number**
20–29	382
30–39	1,078
40–49	1,122
50–59	535
60 and older	137

Source: U.S. Justice Department

EXAMPLE 3 **Organizing Continuous Data into a Frequency and Relative Frequency Distribution**

In Other Words

For qualitative and many discrete data, the classes are formed by using the data. For continuous data, the classes are formed by using intervals of numbers, such as 30–39.

Problem: Suppose you are considering investing in a Roth IRA. You collect the data in Table 12, which represent the 3-year rate of return (in percent, adjusted for sales charges) for a simple random sample of 40 small-capitalization growth mutual funds. Construct a frequency and relative frequency distribution of the data.

Approach: To construct a frequency distribution, we first create classes of equal width. There are 40 observations in Table 12, and they range from 10.06 to 23.76, so

Table 12							
Three-Year Rate of Return of Mutual Funds (as of 10/31/07)							
13.50	13.16	10.53	14.74	13.20	12.24	12.61	19.11
14.47	12.29	13.92	16.16	12.07	10.99	15.07	10.06
14.14	12.77	19.74	12.76	13.34	11.32	15.41	17.37
13.51	15.44	15.10	17.13	12.37	16.34	11.34	10.57
15.70	13.28	23.76	22.68	14.81	23.54	19.65	14.07

Source: TD Ameritrade

CAUTION Watch out for tables with class widths that overlap, such as a first class of 20–30 and a second class of 30–40.

we decide to create the classes such that the lower class limit of the first class is 10 (a little smaller than the smallest data value) and the class width is 2. There is nothing magical about the choice of 2 as a class width. We could have selected a class width of 8 (or any other class width, as well). We choose a class width that we think will nicely summarize the data. If our choice doesn't accomplish this, we can always try another one. The lower class limit of the second class will be $10 + 2 = 12$. Because the classes must not overlap, the upper class limit of the first class is 11.99. Continuing in this fashion, we obtain the following classes:

$$10 - 11.99$$
$$12 - 13.99$$
$$\vdots$$
$$22 - 23.99$$

This gives us seven classes. We tally the number of observations in each class, count the tallies, and create the frequency distribution. The relative frequency distribution would be created by dividing each class's frequency by 40, the number of observations.

Solution: We tally the data as shown in the second column of Table 13. The third column in the table shows the frequency of each class. From the frequency distribution, we conclude that a 3-year rate of return between 12% and 13.99% occurs with the most frequency. The fourth column in the table shows the relative frequency of each class. So, 35% of the small-capitalization growth mutual funds had a 3-year rate of return between 12% and 13.99%.

Historical Note

Florence Nightingale was born in Italy on May 12, 1820. She was named after the city of her birth. Nightingale was educated by her father, who attended Cambridge University. Between 1849 and 1851, she studied nursing throughout Europe. In 1854, she was asked to oversee the introduction of female nurses into the military hospitals in Turkey. While there, she greatly improved the mortality rate of wounded soldiers. She collected data and invented graphs (the polar area diagram), tables, and charts to show that improving sanitary conditions would lead to decreased mortality rates. In 1869, Nightingale founded the Nightingale School Home for Nurses. After a long and eventful life as a reformer of health care and contributor to graphics in statistics, Florence Nightingale died on August 13, 1910.

Table 13			
Class (3-year rate of return)	**Tally**	**Frequency**	**Relative Frequency**
10–11.99	IIII I	6	6/40 = 0.15
12–13.99	IIII IIII IIII	14	14/40 = 0.35
14–15.99	IIII IIII	10	10/40 = 0.25
16–17.99	IIII	4	0.1
18–19.99	III	3	0.075
20–21.99		0	0
22–23.99	III	3	0.075

Three mutual funds had 3-year rates of return between 22% and 23.99%. We might consider these mutual funds worthy of our investment. This type of information would be more difficult to obtain from the raw data.

The choices of the lower class limit of the first class and the class width were rather arbitrary. Though formulas and procedures exist for creating frequency distributions from raw data, they do not necessarily provide better summaries. There is no one correct frequency distribution for a particular set of data. However, some frequency distributions will likely better illustrate patterns within the data than will others. So constructing frequency distributions is somewhat of an art form. The distribution that seems to provide the best overall summary of the data is the one that should be used.

Consider the frequency distributions in Tables 14 and 15, which also summarize the 3-year rate-of-return data discussed in Example 3. In both tables, the lower class limit of the first class is 10, but the class widths are 4 and 1, respectively. Do you think Table 13, 14, or 15 provides the best summary of the distribution of 3-year rates of return? In forming your opinion, consider the following: Too few classes will cause a bunching effect. Too many classes will spread the data out, thereby not revealing any pattern.

Table 14		
Class	**Tally**	**Frequency**
10–13.99	ЖЖ ЖЖ ЖЖ ЖЖ	20
14–17.99	ЖЖ ЖЖ IIII	14
18–21.99	III	3
22–25.99	III	3

Table 15		
Class	**Tally**	**Frequency**
10–10.99	IIII	4
11–11.99	II	2
12–12.99	ЖЖ II	7
13–13.99	ЖЖ II	7
14–14.99	ЖЖ	5
15–15.99	ЖЖ	5
16–16.99	II	2
17–17.99	II	2
18–18.99		0
19–19.99	III	3
20–20.99		0
21–21.99		0
22–22.99	I	1
23–23.99	II	2

Now Work Problems 33(a)–(b)

The goal in constructing a frequency distribution is to reveal interesting features of the data. With that said, when constructing frequency distributions, we typically want the number of classes to be between 5 and 20. When the data set is small, we usually want fewer classes. When the data set is large, we usually want more classes. Why do you think this is reasonable?

Remember, there is no "right" frequency distribution. However, there are bad frequency distributions. The following guidelines should be used to help determine an appropriate lower class limit of the first class and the class width.

In Other Words

Creating the classes for summarizing continuous data is an art form. There is no such thing as the correct frequency distribution. However, there can be less desirable frequency distributions. The larger the class width, the fewer classes a frequency distribution will have.

Note to Instructor

You could present Sturge's Formula for the number of classes, m.

$$m = 1 + 3.3 \log n$$

where n is the number of observations.

Guidelines for Determining the Lower Class Limit of the First Class and Class Width

Choosing the Lower Class Limit of the First Class

Choose the smallest observation in the data set or a convenient number slightly lower than the smallest observation in the data set. For example, in Table 12, the smallest observation is 10.06. A convenient lower class limit of the first class is 10.

Determining the Class Width

- Decide on the number of classes. Generally, there should be between 5 and 20 classes. The smaller the data set, the fewer classes you should have. For example, we might choose 8 classes for the data in Table 12.

In Other Words
Rounding up is different from rounding off. For example, 6.2 rounded up would be 7, while 6.2 rounded off would be 6.

- Determine the class width by computing

$$\text{Class width} \approx \frac{\text{largest data value} - \text{smallest data value}}{\text{number of classes}}$$

Round this value *up* to a convenient number. For example, using the data in Table 12, we obtain class width $\approx \dfrac{23.76 - 10.06}{8} = 1.7125$. We would round this up to 2 because this is an easy number to work with. Rounding up may result in fewer classes than were originally intended.

Now Work Problems 37(a)–(c)

Using these guidelines, we would end up with the frequency distribution shown in Table 13.

 Construct Histograms of Continuous Data

We are now ready to draw histograms of continuous data.

EXAMPLE 4 | **Drawing a Histogram of Continuous Data**

*Note to Instructor
Have students think about the factors to consider in determining an appropriate class width. Are there any ways that a histogram can be used to distort the data?*

Problem: Construct a frequency and relative frequency histogram of the 3-year rate-of-return data discussed in Example 3.

Approach: To draw the frequency histogram, we will use the frequency distribution in Table 13. We label the lower class limits of each class on the horizontal axis. Then, for each class, we draw a rectangle whose width is the class width and whose height is the frequency. To construct the relative frequency histogram, we let the height of the rectangle be the relative frequency, instead of the frequency.

Solution: Figure 8(a) represents the frequency histogram, and Figure 8(b) represents the relative frequency histogram.

Figure 8

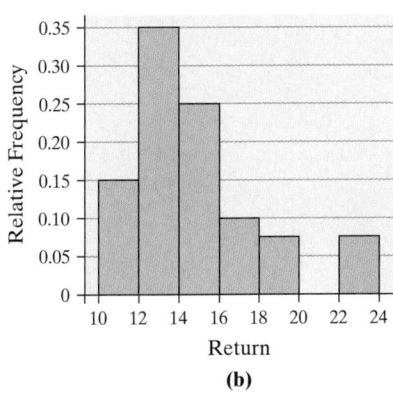

EXAMPLE 5 | **Drawing a Histogram for Continuous Data Using Technology**

Problem: Construct a frequency and relative frequency histogram of the 3-year rate-of-return data discussed in Example 3.

Approach: We will use MINITAB to construct the frequency and relative frequency histograms. The steps for constructing the graphs using the TI-83/84 Plus graphing calculators, MINITAB, and Excel are given in the Technology Step-by-Step on page 101.

Solution: Figure 9(a) shows the frequency histogram and Figure 9(b) shows the relative frequency histogram obtained from MINITAB. Note that MINITAB expresses relative frequencies using percent.

Figure 9

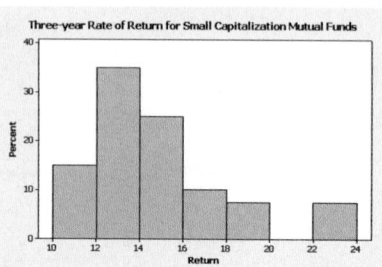

Now Work Problems 33(c)–(d)

Using technology to construct histograms is a convenient and efficient way to explore patterns in data using different class widths.

 Draw Stem-and-Leaf Plots

A **stem-and-leaf plot** is another way to represent quantitative data graphically. In a stem-and-leaf plot (sometimes called simply a *stem plot*), we use the digits to the left of the rightmost digit to form the **stem**. Each rightmost digit forms a **leaf**. For example, a data value of 147 would have 14 as the stem and 7 as the leaf.

EXAMPLE 6   **Constructing a Stem-and-Leaf Plot**

Problem: The data in Table 16 represent the two-year average percentage of persons living in poverty, by state for the years 2005–2006. Draw a stem-and-leaf plot of the data.

Approach

Step 1: We will treat the integer portion of the number as the stem and the decimal portion as the leaf. For example, the stem of Alabama will be 15 and the leaf will be 5. The stem of 15 will include all data from 15.0 to 15.9.

Step 2: Write the stems vertically in ascending order, and then draw a vertical line to the right of the stems.

Step 3: Write the leaves corresponding to the stem.

Step 4: Within each stem, rearrange the leaves in ascending order. Title the plot and provide a legend to indicate what the values represent.

Solution

Step 1: The stem from Alabama is 15 and the corresponding leaf is 5. The stem from Alaska is 9 and its leaf is 4, and so on.

Step 2: Since the lowest data value is 5.5 and the highest data value is 20.4, we need the stems to range from 5 to 20. We write the stems vertically in Figure 10(a), along with a vertical line to the right of the stem.

Step 3: We write the leaves corresponding to each stem. See Figure 10(b).

Step 4: We rearrange the leaves in ascending order, give the plot a title, and provide a legend. See Figure 10(c).

Table 16

Two-Year Average Percentage of Persons Living in Poverty (2005–2006)

State	Percent	State	Percent	State	Percent
Alabama	15.5	Kentucky	15.8	North Dakota	11.3
Alaska	9.4	Louisiana	17.6	Ohio	12.2
Arizona	14.8	Maine	11.4	Oklahoma	15.4
Arkansas	15.8	Maryland	9.1	Oregon	11.9
California	12.7	Massachusetts	11.1	Pennsylvania	11.3
Colorado	10.6	Michigan	12.6	Rhode Island	11.3
Connecticut	8.7	Minnesota	8.1	South Carolina	13.1
Delaware	9.3	Mississippi	20.4	South Dakota	11.3
D.C.	19.8	Missouri	11.5	Tennessee	14.9
Florida	11.3	Montana	13.7	Texas	16.3
Georgia	13.5	Nebraska	9.9	Utah	9.2
Hawaii	8.9	Nevada	10.1	Vermont	7.7
Idaho	9.7	New Hampshire	5.5	Virginia	8.9
Illinois	11.0	New Jersey	7.8	Washington	9.1
Indiana	11.6	New Mexico	17.4	West Virginia	15.3
Iowa	10.8	New York	14.3	Wisconsin	10.2
Kansas	12.7	North Carolina	13.5	Wyoming	10.3

Source: U.S. Census Bureau, *Current Population Survey*, 2006

Figure 10   **Percentage of Persons Living in Poverty**

```
   5 |           5 | 5           5 | 5
   6 |           6 |             6 |
   7 |           7 | 8 7         7 | 7 8
   8 |           8 | 7 9 1 9     8 | 1 7 9 9
   9 |           9 | 4 3 7 1 9 2 1   9 | 1 1 2 3 4 7 9
  10 |          10 | 6 8 1 2 3   10 | 1 2 3 6 8
  11 |          11 | 3 0 6 4 1 5 3 9 3 3 3   11 | 0 1 3 3 3 3 3 4 5 6 9
  12 |          12 | 7 7 6 2     12 | 2 6 7 7
  13 |          13 | 5 7 5 1     13 | 1 5 5 7
  14 |          14 | 8 3 9       14 | 3 8 9
  15 |          15 | 5 8 8 4 3   15 | 3 4 5 8 8
  16 |          16 | 3           16 | 3
  17 |          17 | 6 4         17 | 4 6
  18 |          18 |             18 |
  19 |          19 | 8           19 | 8
  20 |          20 | 4           20 | 4
                                Legend: 5/5 represennts 5.5%
  (a)             (b)              (c)
```

The following summarizes the method for constructing a stem-and-leaf plot.

Construction of a Stem-and-Leaf Plot

Step 1: The stem of a data value will consist of the digits to the left of the right-most digit. The leaf of a data value will be the rightmost digit.

Step 2: Write the stems in a vertical column in increasing order. Draw a vertical line to the right of the stems.

Step 3: Write each leaf corresponding to the stems to the right of the vertical line.

Step 4: Within each stem, rearrange the leaves in ascending order, title the plot, and provide a legend to indicate what the values represent.

EXAMPLE 7

Constructing a Stem-and-Leaf Plot Using Technology

Problem: Construct a stem-and-leaf plot of the poverty data discussed in Example 6.

Approach: We will use MINITAB to construct the stem-and-leaf plot. The steps for constructing the graphs using MINITAB are given in the Technology Step-by-Step on page 101. **Note:** The TI graphing calculators and Excel are not capable of drawing stem-and-leaf plots.

Solution: Figure 11 shows the stem-and-leaf plot obtained from MINITAB.

Using Technology
In MINITAB, there is a column of numbers left of the stem. The (11) indicates that there are 11 observations in the class containing the middle value (called the *median*). The values above the (11) represent the number of observations less than or equal to the upper class limit of the class. For example, 14 states have percentages in poverty less than or equal to 9.9. The values in the left column below the (11) indicate the number of observations greater than or equal to the lower class limit of the class. For example, 10 states have percentages in poverty greater than or equal to 15.0.

Now Work Problem 39(a)

Figure 11

```
   1    5    5
   1    6
   3    7    78
   7    8    1799
  14    9    1123479
  19   10    12368
 (11)  11    01333334569
  21   12    2677
  17   13    1557
  13   14    389
  10   15    34588
   5   16    3
   4   17    46
   2   18
   2   19    8
   1   20    4
```

If you look at the stem-and-leaf plot carefully, you'll notice that it looks much like a histogram turned on its side. The stem serves as the class. For example, the stem 10 contains all data from 10.0 to 10.9. The leaves represent the frequency (height of the rectangle). Therefore, it is important to space the leaves equally when drawing a stem-and-leaf plot.

One advantage of the stem-and-leaf plot over frequency distributions and histograms is that the raw data can be retrieved from the stem-and-leaf plot.

Once a frequency distribution or histogram of continuous data is created, the raw data are lost. However, the raw data can be retrieved from the stem-and-leaf plot.

On the other hand, stem-and-leaf plots lose their usefulness when data sets are large or when they consist of a large range of values. In addition, the steps listed for creating stem-and-leaf plots sometimes must be modified to meet the needs of the data. Consider the next example.

In Other Words
The choice of the stem in the construction of a stem-and-leaf diagram is also an art form. It acts just like the class width. For example, the stem of 7 in Figure 11 represents the class 7.0–7.9. The stem of 8 represents the class 8.0–8.9. Notice that the class width is 1.0. The number of leaves is the frequency of each category.

EXAMPLE 8

Constructing a Stem-and-Leaf Plot after Modifying the Data

Problem: Construct a stem-and-leaf plot of the 3-year, rate-of-return data listed in Table 12 on page 85.

Approach

Step 1: If we use the approach from Example 6 and use the integer portion as the stem and the decimals as the leaves, the stems will be 10, 11, 12, ..., 23. This is fine. However, the leaves will be two digits (such as 50, 16, and so on). This is not acceptable since each leaf must be a single digit. To address this problem, we will round the data to the nearest tenth. Then the stem can be the whole numbers 10, 11, 12, ..., 23, and the leaves will be the decimal portion.

Step 2: Create a vertical column of the whole-number stems in increasing order.

Step 3: Write the leaves corresponding to each stem.

Step 4: Rearrange the leaves in ascending order, title the plot, and provide a legend.

Solution

Step 1: We round the data to the nearest tenth as shown in Table 17.

Table 17							
13.5	13.2	10.5	14.7	13.2	12.2	12.6	19.1
14.5	12.3	13.9	16.2	12.1	11.0	15.1	10.1
14.1	12.8	19.7	12.8	13.3	11.3	15.4	17.4
13.5	15.4	15.1	17.1	12.4	16.3	11.3	10.6
15.7	13.3	23.8	22.7	14.8	23.5	19.7	14.1

Step 2: Write the stems vertically in ascending order as shown in Figure 12(a).

Step 3: Write the leaves corresponding to each stem as shown in Figure 12(b).

Step 4: Rearrange the leaves in ascending order, title the plot, and provide a legend as shown in Figure 12(c).

Note to Instructor
Discuss the similarities and differences of histograms and stem-and-leaf diagrams. Remind students that they can determine the shape of the distribution just as they did with histograms, by turning the stem-and-leaf plot on its side.

Figure 12   **Three-Year Rate of Return of Mutual Funds**

```
10 |                10 | 5 1 6          10 | 1 5 6
11 |                11 | 0 3 3          11 | 0 3 3
12 |                12 | 2 6 3 1 8 8 4  12 | 1 2 3 4 6 8 8
13 |                13 | 5 2 2 9 3 5 3  13 | 2 2 3 3 5 5 9
14 |                14 | 7 5 1 8 1      14 | 1 1 5 7 8
15 |                15 | 1 4 4 1 7      15 | 1 1 4 4 7
16 |                16 | 2 3            16 | 2 3
17 |                17 | 4 1            17 | 1 4
18 |                18 |                18 |
19 |                19 | 1 7 7          19 | 1 7 7
20 |                20 |                20 |
21 |                21 |                21 |
22 |                22 | 7             22 | 7
23 |                23 | 8 5           23 | 5 8
```

Legend: 10|1 represents 10.1%

(a)   (b)   (c)

In Other Words
Stem-and-leaf plots are best used when the data set is small and the range of values is not too wide.

Note that altering the data to construct the graph in Figure 12(c) means that we lose the benefit of being able to retrieve the original data (though we can retrieve the altered data). A second limitation appearing in Example 8 is that we were effectively forced to use a "class width" of 1.0 even though a larger "width" may be more desirable. This illustrates that we must weigh the advantages against the disadvantages when determining the type of graph to use in constructing our data summaries.

Split Stems

In Other Words
Using split stems is like adding more classes to a frequency distribution.

Consider the data shown in Table 18. The data range from 11 to 48. If we draw a stem-and-leaf plot using the tens digit as the stem and the ones digit as the leaf, we obtain the result shown in Figure 13. The data appear rather bunched. To resolve this problem, we can use **split stems**. For example, rather than using one stem for the class of data 10–19, we could use two stems, one for the 10–14 interval and the second for the 15–19 interval. We do this in Figure 14.

Table 18				
27	17	11	24	36
13	29	22	18	17
23	30	12	46	17
32	48	11	18	23
18	32	26	24	38
24	15	13	31	22
18	21	27	20	16
15	37	19	19	29

Figure 13

```
1 | 1 1 2 3 3 5 5 6 7 7 7 8 8 8 8 9 9
2 | 0 1 2 2 3 3 4 4 4 6 7 7 9 9
3 | 0 1 2 2 6 7 8
4 | 6 8
```

Legend: 1|1 represents 11

Figure 14

```
1 | 1 1 2 3 3
1 | 5 5 6 7 7 7 8 8 8 8 9 9
2 | 0 1 2 2 3 3 4 4 4
2 | 6 7 7 9 9
3 | 0 1 2 2
3 | 6 7 8
4 |
4 | 6 8
```

Legend: 1|1 represents 11

The stem-and-leaf plot shown in Figure 14 reveals the distribution of the data better. As with the determination of class intervals in the creation of frequency histograms, judgment plays a major role. There is no such thing as the correct stem-and-leaf plot. However, a quick comparison of Figures 13 and 14 shows that some plots are better than others.

Now Work Problem 45

6 Draw Dot Plots

One more graph! A **dot plot** is drawn by placing each observation horizontally in increasing order and placing a dot above the observation each time it is observed. Though limited in usefulness, dot plots can be used to quickly visualize the data.

EXAMPLE 9 **Drawing a Dot Plot**

Problem: Draw a dot plot for the number of arrivals at Wendy's data from Table 8 on page 82.

Approach: The smallest observation in the data set is 1 and the largest is 11. We write the numbers 1 through 11 horizontally. For each observation, we place a dot above the value of the observation.

Solution: Figure 15 shows the dot plot.

Figure 15

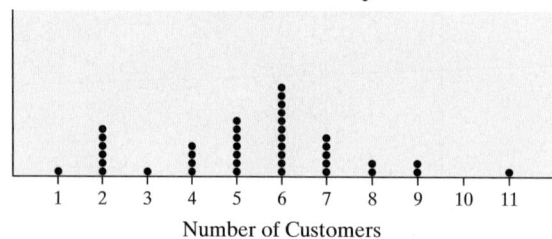

Arrivals at Wendy's

Number of Customers

Now Work Problem 49

7 Identify the Shape of a Distribution

One way that a variable is described is through the shape of its distribution. Distribution shapes are typically classified as symmetric, skewed left, or skewed right. Figure 16 displays various histograms and the shape of the distribution.

Figures 16(a) and (b) display symmetric distributions. These distributions are symmetric because, if we split the histogram down the middle, the right and left sides of the histograms are mirror images. Figure 16(a) is a **uniform distribution**, because the frequency of each value of the variable is evenly spread out across the values of the variable. Figure 16(b) displays a **bell-shaped distribution**, because the highest frequency occurs in the middle and frequencies tail off to the left and right of the middle. Figure 16(c) illustrates a distribution that is **skewed right**. Notice that

Note to Instructor
Give examples of data sets that may be uniform, bell shaped, and skewed right. For example, rolling a single die, IQ scores, and income, respectively.

⬥ **CAUTION** We do not describe qualitative data as skewed left, skewed right, or uniform.

⬥ **CAUTION** It is important to recognize that data will not always exhibit behavior that perfectly matches any of the shapes given in Figure 16. To identify the shape of a distribution, some flexibility is required. In addition, people may disagree on the shape, since identifying shape is subjective.

Figure 16

(a) Uniform (symmetric)

(b) Bell-shaped (symmetric)

(c) Skewed Right

(d) Skewed Left

the tail to the right of the peak is longer than the tail to the left of the peak. Finally, Figure 16(d) illustrates a distribution that is **skewed left**, because the tail to the left of the peak is longer than the tail to the right of the peak.

EXAMPLE 10   **Identifying the Shape of a Distribution**

Problem: Figure 17 displays the histogram obtained in Example 4 for the 3-year rate of return for small-capitalization mutual funds. Describe the shape of the distribution.

Approach: We compare the shape of the distribution displayed in Figure 17 with those in Figure 16.

Solution: Since the histogram looks most like Figure 16(c), the distribution is skewed right.

Figure 17

Three-Year Rate of Return for Small Capitalization Mutual Funds

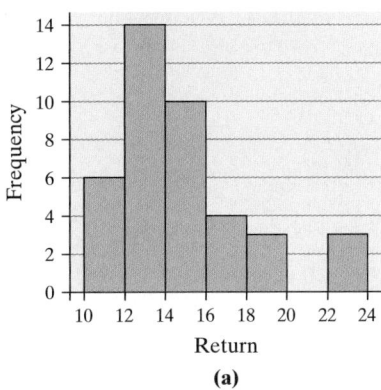

(a)

Now Work Problem 33(e)

IN CLASS ACTIVITY

Random-Number Generators, Pulse Rate, and Household Size

1. We saw in Chapter 1 how to use a graphing calculator or statistical software to generate random numbers. Using either of these, randomly generate 200 integers between 0 and 20, inclusive. That is, the integer can be any value greater than or equal to 0 or less than or equal to 20. Store these data in your calculator or spreadsheet.

2. Class members should determine their resting pulse rates. Collect these data for the class and store them in your calculator or spreadsheet.

3. Class members should share how many people live in their households. Collect the data for the class, and input them into your calculator or spreadsheet.

  (a) What shape do you expect the distribution of random integers to have? Why?

  (b) What shape do you expect the distribution of pulse rates to have? Why?

  (c) What shape do you expect the distribution of household size to have? Why?

  (d) Draw a histogram of each data set. For the random integer data, use a class width of 2.

  (e) What shape did each have? Are you surprised?

2.2 ASSESS YOUR UNDERSTANDING

Concepts and Vocabulary

1. Discuss circumstances under which it is preferable to use relative frequency distributions instead of frequency distributions.

2. Why shouldn't classes overlap when one summarizes continuous data?

3. Discuss the advantages and disadvantages of histograms versus stem-and-leaf plots.

4. Contrast the differences between histograms and bar graphs.

5. _____ are the categories by which data are grouped. *Classes*

6. The histogram represents the total rainfall for each time it rained in Chicago during the month of August since 1871. The histogram was taken from the *Chicago Tribune* on August 14, 2001. What is wrong with the histogram?

Total August Rain Events
Since 1871 in Chicago

7. *True or False*: There is not one particular frequency distribution that is correct, but there are frequency distributions that are less desirable than others. *True*

8. *True or False*: Stem-and-leaf plots are particularly useful for large sets of data. *False*

9. *True or False*: The shape of the distribution shown is best classified as skewed left. *False*

10. *True or False*: The shape of the distribution shown is best classified as uniform. *False*

Skill Building

11. **Rolling the Dice** An experiment was conducted in which two fair dice were thrown 100 times. The sum of the pips showing on the dice was then recorded. The following frequency histogram gives the results.

Sum of Two Dice

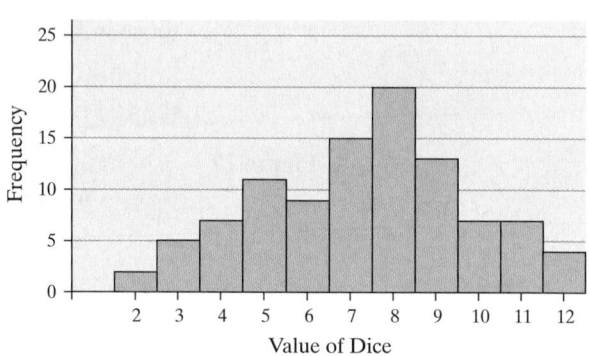

(a) What was the most frequent outcome of the experiment? *8*

(b) What was the least frequent? *2*

(c) How many times did we observe a 7? *15*

(d) How many more 5's were observed than 4's? *4*

(e) Determine the percentage of time a 7 was observed. *15%*

(f) Describe the shape of the distribution. *Bell shaped*

12. **Car Sales** A car salesman records the number of cars he sold each week for the past year. The following frequency histogram shows the results.

Cars Sold per Week

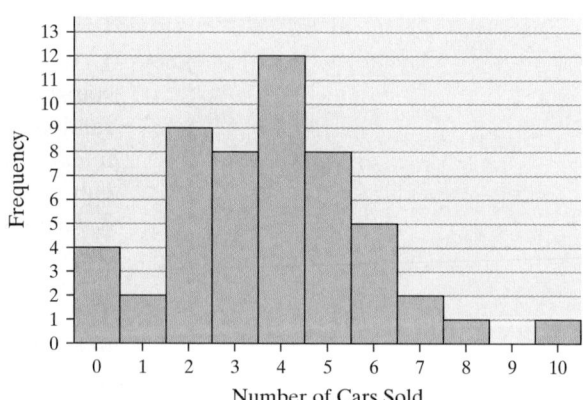

(a) What is the most frequent number of cars sold in a week? *4*

(b) For how many weeks were two cars sold? *9*

(c) Determine the percentage of time two cars were sold.

(d) Describe the shape of the distribution. *Skewed right*

12. (c) 17.3%

13. **IQ Scores** The following frequency histogram represents the IQ scores of a random sample of seventh-grade students. IQs are measured to the nearest whole number. The frequency of each class is labeled above each rectangle.

IQs of 7th Grade Students

(a) How many students were sampled?   200
(b) Determine the class width.   10
(c) Identify the classes and their frequencies.
(d) Which class has the highest frequency?   100–109
(e) Which class has the lowest frequency?   150–159

14. **Alcohol-Related Traffic Fatalities** The following frequency histogram represents the number of alcohol-related traffic fatalities by state (including Washington, D.C.) in 2006 according to the National Highway Traffic Safety Administration.

Alcohol-Related Traffic Fatalities

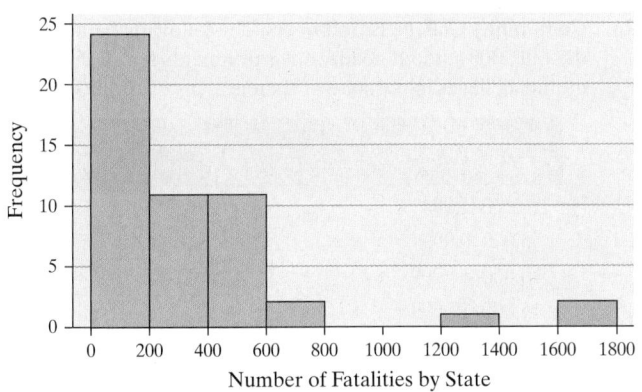

(a) Determine the class width.   200
(b) Identify the classes.
(c) Which class has the highest frequency?   0–199
(d) Describe the shape of the distribution.   Skewed right
(e) A reporter writes the following statement: "According to the data, Texas had 1677 alcohol-related deaths, while Vermont had only 29. So the roads in Vermont are much safer." Explain what is wrong with this statement and how a fair comparison can be made between alcohol-related traffic fatalities in Texas versus Vermont.

In Problems 15 and 16, for each variable presented, state whether you would expect a histogram of the data to be bell-shaped, uniform, skewed left, or skewed right. Justify your reasoning.

15. (a) Annual household incomes in the United States
    (b) Scores on a standardized exam such as the SAT
    (c) Number of people living in a household
    (d) Ages of patients diagnosed with Alzheimer's disease
    15. (a) skewed right   15. (b) bell shaped   15. (c) skewed right
    15. (d) skewed left

16. (a) Number of alcoholic drinks consumed per week
    (b) Ages of students in a public school district   uniform
    (c) Ages of hearing-aid patients   skewed left
    (d) Heights of full-grown men   bell shaped
    16. (a) skewed right

Applying the Concepts

17. **Predicting School Enrollment** To predict future enrollment, a local school district wants to know the number of children in the district under the age of 5. Fifty households within the district were sampled, and the head of household was asked to disclose the number of children under the age of 5 living in the household. The results of the survey are presented in the following table.

Number of Children under 5	Number of Households
0	16
1	18
2	12
3	3
4	1

(a) Construct a relative frequency distribution of the data.
(b) What percentage of households has two children under the age of 5?   24%
(c) What percentage of households has one or two children under the age of 5?   60%

18. **Free Throws** A basketball player habitually makes 70% of her free throws. In an experiment, a researcher asks this basketball player to record the number of free throws she shoots until she misses. The experiment is repeated 50 times. The following table lists the distribution of the number of free throws attempted until a miss is recorded.

Number of Free Throws until a Miss	Frequency
1	16
2	11
3	9
4	7
5	2
6	3
7	0
8	1
9	0
10	1

(a) Construct a relative frequency distribution of the data.
(b) What percentage of the time did she first miss on her fourth free throw?   14%
(c) What percentage of the time did she make nine in a row and then miss the tenth free throw?   2%
(d) What percentage of the time did she make at least five in a row?   10%

In Problems 19–22, determine the original set of data.

19.

```
1 | 0 1 4
2 | 1 4 4 7 9
3 | 3 5 5 5 7 7 8
4 | 0 0 1 2 6 6 8 9 9
5 | 3 3 5 8
6 | 1 2
```
Legend: 1|0 represents 10

20.

```
24 | 0 4 7
25 | 2 2 3 9 9
26 | 3 4 5 8 8 9
27 | 0 1 1 3 6 6
28 | 2 3 8
```
Legend: 24|0 represents 240

21.

```
1 | 2 4 6
2 | 1 4 7 7 9
3 | 3 3 3 5 7 7 8
4 | 0 1 1 3 6 6 8 8 9
5 | 3 4 5 8
6 | 2 4
```
Legend: 1|2 represents 1.2

22.

```
12 | 3 7 9 9
13 | 0 4 5 7 8 9 9
14 | 2 4 4 7 7 8 9
15 | 1 2 2 5 6
16 | 0 3
```
Legend: 12|3 represents 12.3

In Problems 23–26, find (a) the number of classes, (b) the class limits, and (c) the class width.

23. Undergraduate Tuition The following data represent the cost of undergraduate tuition and fees for all 4-year public and private nonprofit colleges in the United States in 2006–2007. (a) 19 (b) $2000

Tuition (dollars)	Number of 4-Year Colleges
0–1,999	19
2,000–3,999	132
4,000–5,999	308
6,000–7,999	180
8,000–9,999	106
10,000–11,999	99
12,000–13,999	89
14,000–15,999	98
16,000–17,999	125
18,000–19,999	116
20,000–21,999	117
22,000–23,999	100
24,000–25,999	83
26,000–27,999	53
28,000–29,999	45
30,000–31,999	36
32,000–33,999	46
34,000–35,999	32
36,000–37,999	6

Source: Chronicle of Higher Education, *Tuition and Fees*, 2006–2007

24. Earthquakes The following data represent the number of earthquakes in 2007 worldwide whose magnitude was less than 8.0 (as of November 26, 2007). (a) 18 (b) 1.0

Magnitude	Number
0–0.9	1,600
1.0–1.9	33
2.0–2.9	2,983
3.0–3.9	8,028
4.0–4.9	10,465
5.0–5.9	1,466
6.0–6.9	151
7.0–7.9	11

Source: U.S. Geological Survey, Earthquake Hazards Program

25. Live Births The following data represent the number of live births in the United States in 2005 for women 15 to 44 years old. (a) 6 (b) 5

Age	Live Births
15–19	414,406
20–24	1,040,399
25–29	1,132,293
30–34	952,013
35–39	483,401
40–44	104,644

Source: National Center for Health Statistics, Preliminary Data for 2005

26. Community College Enrollments The following data represent the fall 2006 student headcount enrollments for all public community colleges in the state of Illinois. (a) 6 (b) 5000

Number of Students Enrolled	Number of Community Colleges[a]
0–4,999	15
5,000–9,999	16
10,000–14,999	9
15,000–19,999	4
20,000–24,999	0
25,000–29,999	1

Source: Illinois Board of Higher Education, Report to the Governor and General Assembly, December 2007

[a] Treats the City Colleges of Chicago as seven distinct institutions, but all other multicampus districts as single institutions.

In Problems 27–30, construct (a) a relative frequency distribution, (b) a frequency histogram, and (c) a relative frequency histogram for the given data. Then answer the questions that follow.

27. Using the data in Problem 23, what percentage of 4-year colleges have tuition and fees below $4,000? What percentage of 4-year colleges have tuition and fees of $30,000 or more? 8.44%; 6.70%

28. Using the data in Problem 24, what percentage of earthquakes registered 4.0 to 4.9? What percentage of earthquakes registered 4.9 or less? 42.31%; 93.42%

29. Using the data in Problem 25, what percentage of live births was to women 40 to 44 years old? What percentage of live births was to women 24 years or younger? 2.54%; 35.25%

30. Using the data in Problem 26, what percentage of public community colleges in Illinois enrolled between 5,000 and 9,999 students? What percentage of public community colleges in Illinois enrolled 15,000 or more students? 35.56%; 11.11%

31. Televisions in the Household A researcher with A. C. Nielsen
NW wanted to determine the number of color televisions in households. He conducts a survey of 40 randomly selected households and obtains the following data.

1	1	4	2	3	3	5	1
1	2	2	4	1	1	0	3
1	2	2	1	3	1	1	3
2	3	2	2	1	2	3	2
1	2	2	2	2	1	3	1

Source: Based on data from the U.S. Department of Energy

(a) Are these data discrete or continuous? Explain. Discrete
(b) Construct a frequency distribution of the data.
(c) Construct a relative frequency distribution of the data.
(d) What percentage of households in the survey have 3 color televisions? 20%
(e) What percentage of households in the survey have 4 or more color televisions? 7.5%
(f) Construct a frequency histogram of the data.
(g) Construct a relative frequency histogram of the data.
(h) Describe the shape of the distribution. Skewed right

32. Waiting The following data represent the number of customers waiting for a table at 6:00 P.M. for 40 consecutive Saturdays at Bobak's Restaurant:

11	5	11	3	6	8	6	7
4	5	13	9	6	4	14	11
13	10	9	6	8	10	9	5
10	8	7	3	8	8	7	8
7	9	10	4	8	6	11	8

(a) Are these data discrete or continuous? Explain. Discrete
(b) Construct a frequency distribution of the data.
(c) Construct a relative frequency distribution of the data.
(d) What percentage of the Saturdays had 10 or more customers waiting for a table at 6:00 P.M.? 27.5%
(e) What percentage of the Saturdays had 5 or fewer customers waiting for a table at 6:00 P.M.? 20%
(f) Construct a frequency histogram of the data.
(g) Construct a relative frequency histogram of the data.
(h) Describe the shape of the distribution. bell shaped

33. Average Income The following data represent the per capita
NW (average) disposable income (income after taxes) for the 50 states and the District of Columbia in 2006.

With the first class having a lower class limit of 24,000 and a class width of 3000:

(a) Construct a frequency distribution.
(b) Construct a relative frequency distribution.
(c) Construct a frequency histogram of the data.
(d) Construct a relative frequency histogram of the data.
(e) Describe the shape of the distribution. skewed right

28,185	33,595	27,763	25,112	33,373	34,332
40,973	33,683	47,515	31,635	28,109	31,856
26,754	33,419	28,979	29,808	30,935	26,104
28,553	28,777	37,574	38,794	30,117	33,494
24,360	29,066	27,419	30,676	32,290	34,964
39,840	26,839	35,407	28,339	29,515	29,223
28,895	29,310	32,222	32,734	26,406	31,116
29,456	31,012	25,792	30,317	33,628	33,334
25,204	30,439	36,176			

Source: U.S. Bureau of Economic Analysis, March 2007

(f) Repeat parts (a)–(e) using a class width of 4,000.
(g) Does one frequency distribution provide a better summary of the data than the other? Explain.

34. Uninsured Rates The following data represent the percentage of people without health insurance for the 50 states and the District of Columbia in 2006.

15.2	16.5	20.9	18.9	18.8	17.2
9.4	12.1	11.6	21.2	17.7	8.9
15.4	14.0	11.8	10.5	12.3	15.6
21.9	9.3	13.8	10.4	10.5	9.2
20.8	13.3	17.1	12.3	19.6	11.5
15.5	22.9	14.0	17.9	12.2	10.1
18.9	17.9	10.0	8.6	15.9	11.8
13.7	24.5	17.4	10.2	13.3	11.8
13.5	8.8	14.6			

Source: Illinois Hospital Association, September 2007

With the first class having a lower class limit of 8 and a class width of 2:

(a) Construct a frequency distribution.
(b) Construct a relative frequency distribution.
(c) Construct a frequency histogram of the data.
(d) Construct a relative frequency histogram of the data.
(e) Describe the shape of the distribution. skewed right
(f) Repeat parts (a)–(e) using a class width of 1.
(g) Does one frequency distribution provide a better summary of the data than the other? Explain.

35. Serum HDL Dr. Paul Oswiecmiski randomly selects 40 of his 20- to 29-year-old patients and obtains the following data regarding their serum HDL cholesterol:

70	56	48	48	53	52	66	48
36	49	28	35	58	62	45	60
38	73	45	51	56	51	46	39
56	32	44	60	51	44	63	50
46	69	53	70	33	54	55	52

Source: Paul Oswiecmiski

With the first class having a lower class limit of 20 and a class width of 10:

(a) Construct a frequency distribution.
(b) Construct a relative frequency distribution.
(c) Construct a frequency histogram of the data.

(d) Construct a relative frequency histogram of the data.
(e) Describe the shape of the distribution.   *Bell shaped*
(f) Repeat parts (a)–(e) using a class width of 5.
(g) Which frequency distribution seems to provide a better summary of the data?

36. Dividend Yield A dividend is a payment from a publicly traded company to its shareholders. The dividend yield of a stock is determined by dividing the annual dividend of a stock by its price. The following data represent the dividend yields (in percent) of a random sample of 28 publicly traded stocks of companies with a value of at least $5 billion.

1.7	0	1.15	0.62	1.06	2.45	2.38
2.83	2.16	1.05	1.22	1.68	0.89	0
2.59	0	1.7	0.64	0.67	2.07	0.94
2.04	0	0	1.35	0	0	0.41

Source: Yahoo! Finance

With the first class having a lower class limit of 0 and a class width of 0.40:

(a) Construct a frequency distribution.
(b) Construct a relative frequency distribution.
(c) Construct a frequency histogram of the data.
(d) Construct a relative frequency histogram of the data.
(e) Describe the shape of the distribution.   *Skewed right*
(f) Repeat parts (a)–(e) using a class width of 0.8.
(g) Which frequency distribution seems to provide a better summary of the data?

37. Volume of Altria Group Stock The volume of a stock is the number of shares traded on a given day. The following data, in millions, so that 6.42 represents 6,420,000 shares traded, represent the volume of Altria Group stock traded for a random sample of 35 trading days in 2007.

6.42	23.59	18.91	7.85	7.76
8.51	9.05	14.83	14.43	8.55
6.37	10.30	10.16	10.90	11.20
13.57	9.13	7.83	15.32	14.05
7.84	7.88	17.10	16.58	7.68
7.69	10.22	10.49	8.41	7.85
10.94	20.15	8.97	15.39	8.32

Source: TD Ameritrade

(a) If six classes are to be formed, choose an appropriate lower class limit for the first class and a class width.
(b) Construct a frequency distribution.
(c) Construct a relative frequency distribution.
(d) Construct a frequency histogram of the data.
(e) Construct a relative frequency histogram of the data.
(f) Describe the shape of the distribution.   *skewed right*

38. Violent Crimes Violent crimes include murder, forcible rape, robbery, and aggravated assault. The following data represent the violent-crime rate (crimes per 100,000 population) by state plus the District of Columbia in 2005.

(a) If eight classes are to be formed, choose an appropriate lower class limit for the first class and a class width.
(b) Construct a frequency distribution.
(c) Construct a relative frequency distribution.
(d) Construct a frequency histogram of the data.

432	708	594	287	351	530
632	449	112	607	509	227
513	255	703	132	287	120
528	257	457	355	425	283
526	552	552	702	251	346
397	323	297	446	761	273
275	291	278	468	176	242
632	387	525	98	753	230
1459	267	282			

Source: Federal Bureau of Investigation

(e) Construct a relative frequency histogram of the data.
(f) Describe the shape of the distribution.   *skewed right*

In Problems 39–42, (a) construct a stem-and-leaf plot and (b) describe the shape of the distribution.

39. Age at Inauguration The following data represent the ages of the presidents of the United States (from George Wahington through George W. Bush) on their first days in office.

Note: President Cleveland's age is listed twice, 47 and 55, because he is historically counted as two different presidents, numbers 22 and 24, since his terms were not consecutive.   *(b) Bell shaped*

42	48	51	52	54	56	57	61	65
43	49	51	54	55	56	57	61	68
46	49	51	54	55	56	58	62	69
46	50	51	54	55	57	60	64	
47	50	52	54	55	57	61	64	

Source: factmonster.com

40. Divorce Rates The following data represent the divorce rate (per 1,000 population) for most states in the United States in the year 2004.

Note: The list includes the District of Columbia, but excludes California, Georgia, Hawaii, Indiana, Louisiana, and Oklahoma because of failure to report.   *(b) Bell shaped*

4.7	4.8	4.2	6.3	4.4	2.9	3.7
1.7	4.8	5.1	2.6	2.8	3.3	4.9
3.6	3.1	2.2	3.5	2.8	4.5	3.8
3.8	3.6	6.4	3.9	3.0	4.6	3.0
4.4	2.8	3.7	4.1	2.5	3.0	3.2
3.2	5.0	3.6	3.9	3.9	4.0	4.1
4.7	3.1	5.3				

Source: U.S. Census Bureau, *Statistical Abstract of the United States*, 2006

41. Grams of Fat in a McDonald's Breakfast The following data represent the number of grams of fat in breakfast meals offered at McDonald's.   *(b) Bell shaped*

12	22	27	3	25	30
32	37	27	31	11	16
21	32	22	46	51	55
59	16	36	30	9	24

Source: McDonald's Corporation, *McDonald's USA Nutrition Facts*, November 2007

42. Gasoline Mileages The following data represent the number of miles per gallon achieved on the highway for small cars for the model year 2008. (b) Slightly skewed right (or bell shaped)

33	36	27	37	29	33	26	33	32
32	29	34	28	31	31	35	33	35
29	33	45	33	28	32	32	35	30
32	31	31	32	32	36	31	23	29
29	31	25	29	34	29	34	28	33
27	35	29	32	27	24	33	30	28

Source: U.S. Department of Energy (fueleconomy.gov)

43. Electric Rates The following data represent the average retail prices for electricity (cents/kWh) in 2006 for the 50 states plus the District of Columbia.

7.07	12.84	8.24	6.99	12.82	7.61
14.83	10.13	11.08	10.45	7.63	20.72
4.92	7.07	6.46	7.01	6.89	5.43
8.30	11.80	9.95	15.45	8.14	6.98
8.33	6.30	6.91	6.07	9.63	13.84
11.88	7.37	15.27	7.53	6.21	7.71
7.30	6.53	8.68	13.98	6.98	6.70
6.97	10.34	5.99	11.37	6.86	6.14
5.04	8.13	5.27			

Source: Energy Information Administration, *State Electric Profiles: 2006 Edition*, November 2007

(a) Round each observation to the nearest tenth of a cent and draw a stem-and-leaf plot.

(b) Describe the shape of the distribution. Skewed right

(c) Hawaii has the highest retail price for electricity. What is Hawaii's average retail price for electricity? Why might Hawaii's rate be so much higher than the others? 20.72 cents/kWh

44. Housing Price Index The housing price index (HPI) serves as an indicator of housing price trends by measuring average price changes in repeat sales or refinancing on the same property. The following data represent the change in HPI from the third quarter of 2002 to the third quarter of 2007 for a random sample of 40 U.S. cities.

12.27	18.82	13.50	42.22	77.96
39.65	40.33	113.82	55.69	20.18
36.34	87.23	72.54	27.83	42.02
36.92	15.91	24.22	91.92	29.04
14.26	17.78	24.11	41.02	25.88
94.41	63.45	81.15	56.90	41.23
73.57	71.77	29.15	76.02	26.08
18.57	38.74	81.40	19.31	30.97

Source: Office of Federal Housing Enterprise Oversight

(a) Round each observation to the nearest whole percent and draw a stem-and-leaf plot.

(b) Describe the shape of the distribution. Skewed right

---

45. Dependability Survey J. D. Power and Associates regularly surveys car owners and asks them about the reliability of their cars. The following data represent the number of problems per 100 vehicles over a 3-year period for the 2004 model year for all makes.

Make	Problems per 100 Vehicles	Make	Problems per 100 Vehicles	Make	Problems per 100 Vehicles
Lexus	162	Saab	265	Jeep	314
Buick	187	Saturn	267	Oldsmobile	314
Infiniti	189	Ford	276	Mercedes-Benz	327
Lincoln	194	Nissan	280	Mitsubishi	327
Cadillac	196	Chrysler	285	Volvo	346
Honda	209	Mazda	285	Suzuki	365
Acura	212	Subaru	288	Hyundai	375
Toyota	216	Plymouth	289	Volkswagen	386
Mercury	224	Audi	295	Isuzu	393
Porsche	240	Pontiac	297	Daewoo	411
Chevrolet	262	Dodge	298	Kia	432
GMC	262	Jaguar	310	Land Rover	472
BMW	264				

Source: J. D. Power and Associates, *2004 Vehicle Dependability Study*

(a) Draw a stem-and-leaf plot, using the ones position as the leaf.

(b) Round the data to the nearest ten (for example, round 162 as 160).

(c) Draw a stem-and-leaf plot, treating the hundreds position as the stem and the tens position as the leaf (so that 1|6 represents 160).

(d) Redraw the stem-and-leaf plot using split stems.

(e) In your opinion, which of these plots best summarizes the data? Why?

46. **Violent Crimes** Use the violent crime rate data from Problem 38 to answer each of the following:
    (a) Round the data to the nearest ten (for example, round 432 as 430).
    (b) Draw a stem-and-leaf plot, treating the hundreds position as the stem and the tens position as the leaf (so that 4|3 represents 430).
    (c) Redraw the stem-and-leaf plot using split stems.
    (d) In your opinion, which of these plots best summarizes the data? Why?

In Problems 47 and 48, we compare data sets. A great way to compare two data sets is through back-to-back stem-and-leaf plots. The figure represents the number of grams of fat in 20 sandwiches served at McDonald's and 20 sandwiches served at Burger King.

Source: McDonald's Corporation, *McDonald's USA Nutrition Facts,* November 2007; Burger King Corporation, *Nutritional Information,* October 2007

Fat (g) in Fast Food Sandwiches
McDonald's   Burger King

```
        98 | 0 | 7
 98766420 | 1 | 223667
988664331 | 2 | 129
          | 3 | 0399
        2 | 4 | 47
          | 5 | 47
          | 6 | 58
```

Legend: 8 |0|7 represents 8 g of fat for McDonalds and 7 g of fat for Burger King

47. **Academy Award Winners** The following data represent the ages on the ceremony date of the Academy Award winners for Best Actor and Best Actress in a leading role for the 30 years from 1977 to 2006.

Best Actor Ages					
30	40	42	37	76	39
53	45	36	62	43	51
32	42	54	52	37	38
32	45	60	46	40	36
47	29	43	37	38	45

Best Actress Ages					
32	41	33	31	74	33
49	38	61	21	41	26
80	42	29	33	36	45
49	39	34	26	25	33
35	35	28	30	29	61

(a) Construct a back-to-back stem-and-leaf display.
(b) Compare the two populations. What can you conclude form the back-to-back stem-and-leaf display?

48. **Home Run Distances** In 1998, Mark McGwire of the St. Louis Cardinals set the record for the most home runs hit in a season by hitting 70 home runs. Three years later in 2001, Barry Bonds of the San Francisco Giants broke McGwire's record by hitting 73 home runs. The following data represent the distances, in feet, of each player's home runs in his record-setting season.

Mark McGwire						
360	370	370	430	420	340	460
410	440	410	380	360	350	527
380	550	478	420	390	420	425
370	480	390	430	388	423	410
360	410	450	350	450	430	461
430	470	440	400	390	510	430
450	452	420	380	470	398	409
385	369	460	390	510	500	450
470	430	458	380	430	341	385
410	420	380	400	440	377	370

Barry Bonds						
420	417	440	410	390	417	420
410	380	430	370	420	400	360
410	420	391	416	440	410	415
436	430	410	400	390	420	410
420	410	410	450	320	430	380
375	375	347	380	429	320	360
375	370	440	400	405	430	350
396	410	380	430	415	380	375
400	435	420	420	488	361	394
410	411	365	360	440	435	454
442	404	385				

(a) Construct a back-to-back stem-and-leaf display.
(b) Compare the two populations. What can you conclude from the back-to-back stem-and-leaf display?

49. **Televisions in the Household** Draw a dot plot of the televisions per household data from Problem 31.

50. **Waiting** Draw a dot plot of the waiting data from Problem 32.

51. **Putting It Together: Time Viewing a Web Page** Nielsen/NetRatings is an Internet media and market research firm. One variable they measure is the amount of time an individual spends viewing a specific Webpage. The following data represent the amount of time, in seconds, a random sample of 40 surfers spent viewing a Webpage. Decide on an appropriate graphical summary and create the graphical summary. Write a few sentences that describe the data. Be sure to include in your description any interesting features the data may exhibit.

19	86	27	42	11	12	13	5
27	20	83	4	69	10	12	65
15	26	75	27	19	31	23	14
111	185	51	51	156	48	16	81
9	73	45	27	104	257	40	114

Source: Based on information provided by Nielsen/NetRatings

TECHNOLOGY STEP-BY-STEP

Drawing Histograms and Stem-and-Leaf Plots

TI-83/84 Plus

Histograms

1. Enter the raw data in L1 by pressing STAT and selecting 1: Edit.

2. Press 2nd Y = to access the StatPlot menu. Select 1: Plot1.

3. Place the cursor on "ON" and press ENTER.

4. Place the cursor on the histogram icon (see the figure) and press ENTER. Press 2nd QUIT to exit Plot 1 menu.

5. Press WINDOW. Set Xmin to the lower class limit of the first class. Set Xmax to the lower class limit of the class following the class containing the largest value. For example, if the first class is 0–9, set Xmin to 0. If the class width is 10 and the last class is 90–99, set Xmax to 100. Set Xscl to the class width. Set Ymin to 0. Set Ymax to a value larger than the frequency of the class with the highest frequency.

6. Press GRAPH.

Helpful Hints: To determine each class frequency, press TRACE and use the arrow keys to scroll through each class. If you decrease the value of Ymin to a value such as −5, you can see the values displayed on the screen easier. The TI graphing calculators do not draw stem-and-leaf plots or dot plots.

MINITAB

Histograms

1. Enter the raw data in C1.

2. Select the **Graph** menu and highlight **Histogram** . . .

3. Highlight the "simple" icon and press OK.

4. Put the cursor in the "Graph variables" box. Highlight C1 and press Select. Click SCALE

and select the Y-Scale Type tab. For a frequency histogram, click the frequency radio button. For a relative frequency histogram, click the percent radio button. Click OK twice.

Note: To adjust the class width and to change the labels on the horizontal axis to the lower class limit, double-click inside one of the bars in the histogram. Select the "binning" tab in the window that opens. Click the cutpoint button and the midpoint/cutpoint positions radio button. In the midpoint/cutpoint box, enter the lower class limits of each class. Click OK.

Stem-and-Leaf Plots

1. With the raw data entered in C1, select the **Graph** menu and highlight **Stem-and-Leaf**.

2. Select the data in C1 and press OK.

Dot Plots

1. Enter the raw data in C1.

2. Select the **Graph** menu and highlight **Dotplot**.

3. Highlight the "simple" icon and press OK.

4. Put the cursor in the "Graph variables" box. Highlight C1 and press Select. Click OK.

Excel

Histograms

1. Enter the raw data in column A.

2. Select **Tools** and **Data Analysis** . . .

3. Select Histogram from the list.

4. With the cursor in the Input Range cell, use the mouse to highlight the raw data. Select the Chart Output box and press OK.

5. Double-click on one of the bars in the histogram. Select the Options tab from the menu that appears. Reduce the gap width to zero.

Excel does not draw stem-and-leaf plots. Dot plots can be drawn in Excel using the DDXL plug-in. See the Excel technology manual.

2.3 ADDITIONAL DISPLAYS OF QUANTITATIVE DATA

Objectives	
1	Construct frequency polygons
2	Create cumulative frequency and relative frequency tables
3	Construct frequency and relative frequency ogives
4	Draw time-series graphs

Note to Instructor
The material in this section may be omitted without loss of continuity, depending on the time constraints. One suggestion is to have students read the section on their own.

In this section, we continue to organize and summarize quantitative data by presenting additional displays that are commonly used in statistical analysis. Specifically, we examine *frequency polygons*, *cumulative distributions*, *ogives*, and *time-series graphs*.

1 Construct Frequency Polygons

Another way of graphically representing quantitative data sets is through *frequency polygons*. They provide the same information as histograms. Before we can provide a method for constructing frequency polygons, we must learn how to obtain the *class midpoint* of a class.

Definition   The **class midpoint** is found by adding consecutive lower class limits and dividing the result by 2.

The class midpoint is used to draw frequency polygons.

Definition   A **frequency polygon** is a graph that uses points, connected by line segments, to represent the frequencies for the classes. It is constructed by plotting a point above each class midpoint on a horizontal axis at a height equal to the frequency of the class. After the points for each class are plotted, line segments are drawn connecting consecutive points. Two additional line segments are drawn connecting each end of the graph with the horizontal axis.

Suppose we wish to construct a frequency polygon of the data summarized in Table 13 on page 85 from Section 2.2. First we need to determine the class midpoints of each class, as shown in Table 19.

Table 19			
Class (3-year rate of return)	**Class Midpoint**	**Frequency**	**Relative Frequency**
10–11.99	$\frac{10 + 12}{2} = 11$	6	0.15
12–13.99	$\frac{12 + 14}{2} = 13$	14	0.35
14–15.99	15	10	0.25
16–17.99	17	4	0.1
18–19.99	19	3	0.075
20–21.99	21	0	0
22–23.99	23	3	0.075

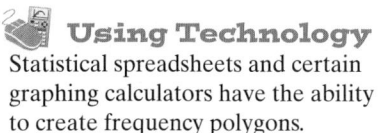

Using Technology
Statistical spreadsheets and certain graphing calculators have the ability to create frequency polygons.

We then plot points whose x-coordinates are the class midpoints and y-coordinates are the frequencies. We connect these points with line segments. Next, we determine the midpoint of the class that would precede the first class to be 9 and the midpoint of the class that would follow the last class to be 25. (Do you see why?) Finally, we connect each end of the graph with the horizontal axis at $(9, 0)$ and $(25, 0)$, respectively, and obtain Figure 18.

Figure 18

Three-Year Rate of Return

Now Work Problem 19(c)

2   Create Cumulative Frequency and Relative Frequency Tables

Since quantitative data can be ordered (that is, written in ascending or descending order), they can be summarized in a *cumulative frequency distribution* and a *cumulative relative frequency distribution*.

Definitions

A **cumulative frequency distribution** displays the aggregate frequency of the category. In other words, for discrete data, it displays the total number of observations less than or equal to the category. For continuous data, it displays the total number of observations less than or equal to the upper class limit of a class.

A **cumulative relative frequency distribution** displays the proportion (or percentage) of observations less than or equal to the category for discrete data and the proportion (or percentage) of observations less than or equal to the upper class limit for continuous data.

The cumulative frequency for a class is obtained by adding the frequencies of the classes less than or equal to the upper class limit of the class. For example, the cumulative frequency for the second class is the sum of the frequencies of classes 1 and 2, the cumulative frequency for the third class is the sum of the frequencies of classes 1, 2, and 3, and so on.

The cumulative relative frequency for continuous data is obtained using the same procedures used in creating the cumulative frequency distribution, except that we use the relative frequencies instead of the frequencies.

Table 20 displays the cumulative frequency and cumulative relative frequency of the data summarized in Table 13 in Section 2.2. From Table 20, we see that 34 of the 40 mutual funds had 3-year rates of return of 17.99% or less. The cumulative relative frequency distribution is shown in the fifth column of the table. We see that 85% of the mutual funds had a 3-year rate of return of 17.99% or less. We can also see that a mutual fund with a 3-year rate of return of 22% or higher is outperforming 92.5% of its peers.

Now Work Problems 19(a)–(b)

		Table 20		
Class (3-year rate of return)	Frequency	Relative Frequency	Cumulative Frequency	Cumulative Relative Frequency
10–11.99	6	0.15	6	0.15
12–13.99	14	0.35	6 + 14 = 20	0.15 + 0.35 = 0.5
14–15.99	10	0.25	20 + 10 = 30	0.50 + 0.25 = 0.75
16–17.99	4	0.1	34	0.85
18–19.99	3	0.075	37	0.925
20–21.99	0	0	37	0.925
22–23.99	3	0.075	40	1

 Construct Frequency and Relative Frequency Ogives

Recall that the cumulative frequency of a class is the aggregate frequency less than or equal to the upper class limit.

Definition　An **ogive** (read as "oh jīve") is a graph that represents the cumulative frequency or cumulative relative frequency for the class. It is constructed by plotting points whose *x*-coordinates are the upper class limits and whose *y*-coordinates are the cumulative frequencies or cumulative relative frequencies. After the points for each class are plotted, line segments are drawn connecting consecutive points. An additional line segment is drawn connecting the point for the first class to the horizontal axis at a location representing the upper limit of the class that would precede the first class (if it existed).

We can construct a relative frequency ogive using the data in Table 20 by plotting points whose *x*-coordinates are the upper class limits and whose *y*-coordinates are the cumulative relative frequencies of the classes. We then connect the points with line segments. See Figure 19.

Figure 19

Relative Frequency Ogive

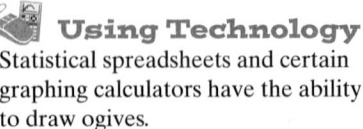 **Using Technology**
Statistical spreadsheets and certain graphing calculators have the ability to draw ogives.

Now Work Problems 19(d) and (e)

From Figure 19 we can see that 75% of the mutual funds had a 3-year rate of return less than or equal to 15.99%.

 Draw Time-Series Graphs

If the value of a variable is measured at different points in time, the data are referred to as **time-series data**. The closing price of Cisco Systems stock each month for the past 12 years is an example of time-series data.

Definition

A **time-series plot** is obtained by plotting the time in which a variable is measured on the horizontal axis and the corresponding value of the variable on the vertical axis. Line segments are then drawn connecting the points.

Time-series plots are very useful in identifying trends in the data over time.

EXAMPLE 1   **Drawing a Time-Series Plot**

Problem: The data in Table 21 represent the closing price of Cisco Systems stock at the end of each month from January 2006 through December 2007. Construct a time-series plot of the data.

Table 21			
Date	**Closing Price**	**Date**	**Closing Price**
1/06	18.57	1/07	26.62
2/06	20.24	2/07	25.94
3/06	21.67	3/07	25.53
4/06	20.95	4/07	26.74
5/06	19.68	5/07	26.92
6/06	19.53	6/07	27.85
7/06	17.88	7/07	28.91
8/06	21.99	8/07	31.92
9/06	22.98	9/07	33.13
10/06	24.13	10/07	33.06
11/06	26.91	11/07	28.02
12/06	27.33	12/07	27.07

Source: TD Ameritrade

Approach

Step 1: Plot points for each month, with the date on the horizontal axis and the closing price on the vertical axis.

Step 2: Connect the points with line segments.

Solution: Figure 20 shows the graph of the time-series plot. The overall 2-year trend bodes fairly well for investors of Cisco Systems stock. However, the development shown after October 2007 may be cause for concern.

Figure 20

Closing Price of Cisco Systems

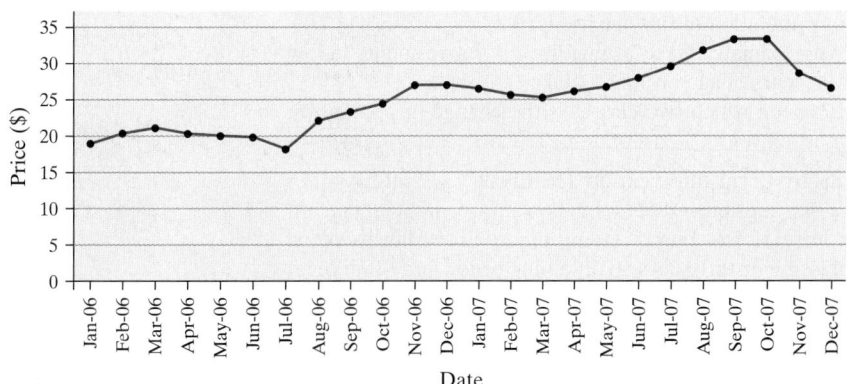

Using Technology

Statistical spreadsheets, such as Excel or MINITAB, and certain graphing calculators, such as the TI-83 or TI-84 Plus, have the ability to create time-series graphs.

Now Work Problem 21

7. (g) Most: between 50–59 and 60–69. Least: between 10–19 and 20–29

2.3 ASSESS YOUR UNDERSTANDING

Concepts and Vocabulary

1. Which do you prefer, histograms, stem-and-leaf plots, or frequency polygons? Be sure to support your opinion. Are there circumstances in which one might be preferred over another?

2. The cumulative relative frequency for the last class must always be 1. Why?

3. What is an ogive?

4. What are time-series data?

5. *True or False*: When plotting an ogive, the plotted points have *x*-coordinates that are equal to the upper limits of each class. True

6. *True or False*: When plotting a frequency polygon, we plot the percentages for each class above the midpoint and connect the points with line segments. False

Skill Building

7. **Age of Population** The following frequency polygon shows the number of U.S. residents below 100 years of age on July 1, 2006.

   Source: U.S. Census Bureau, *Annual Estimates of the Population*, May 2007.

Age of 2006 U.S. Population

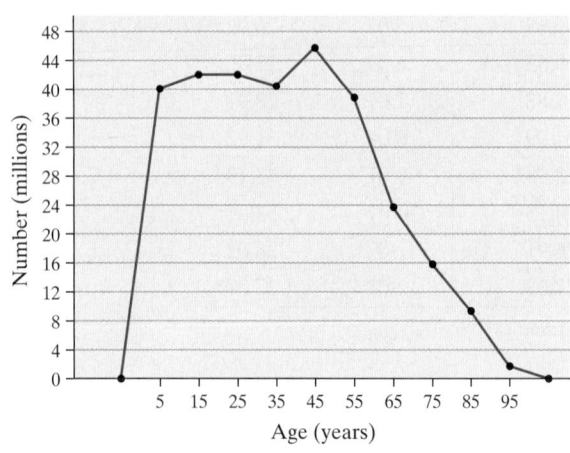

(a) What is the class width? How many classes are represented in the graph? 10; 10

(b) What is the midpoint of the first class? What are the lower and upper limits of the first class? 5; 0–9

(c) What is the midpoint of the last class? What are the lower and upper limits of the last class? 95; 90–99

(d) Which age group has the highest population? Estimate population of this age group. 40–49; ≈45 million

(e) Which age group has the lowest population? Estimate its population of this age group. 90–99; ≈1.2 million

(f) Approximate the total number of U.S. residents below 100 years of age on July 1, 2006. 300 million

(g) Between which two classes is the change in population most extreme? Least extreme?

8. **Deaths by Legal Intervention** Deaths by legal intervention refers to injuries inflicted by law-enforcement agents in the course of arresting or attempting to arrest lawbreakers, suppressing disturbances, maintaining order, and other legal action (including legal execution). In 2004, 372 such deaths occurred in the United States. The following frequency polygon represents these deaths by age.

   Source: National Center for Health Statistics, *National Vital Statistics Reports*, 55(19), 2007.

U.S. Deaths by Legal Intervention

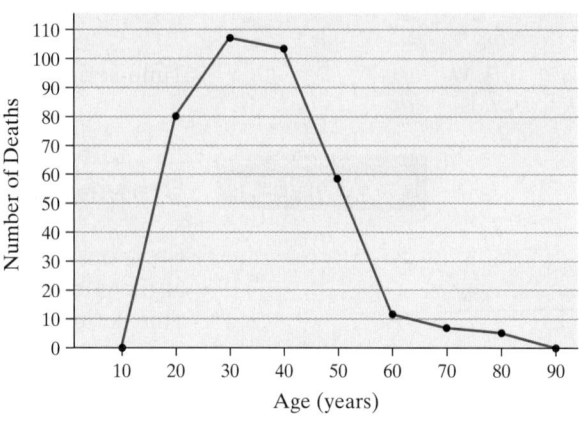

(a) What is the class width? How many classes are represented in the graph? 10; 7

(b) What is the midpoint of the first class? What are the lower and upper limits of the first class? 20; 15–24

(c) What is the midpoint of the last class? What are the lower and upper limits of the last class? 80; 75–84

(d) Which age group has the highest number of deaths due to legal intervention? Estimate the number of deaths for this age group. 25–34; 106

(e) Which age group has the lowest number of deaths due to legal intervention? Estimate the number of deaths for this age group. 75–84; 5

(f) Estimate the relative frequency for the first class. 0.215

9. **ACT Scores** The following relative frequency ogive represents the ACT composite score for the high school graduating class of 2007.

   Source: ACT, *ACT High School Profile Report: The Graduating Class of 2007, National*

   9. (c) 33–36

Class of 2007 ACT Composite Score

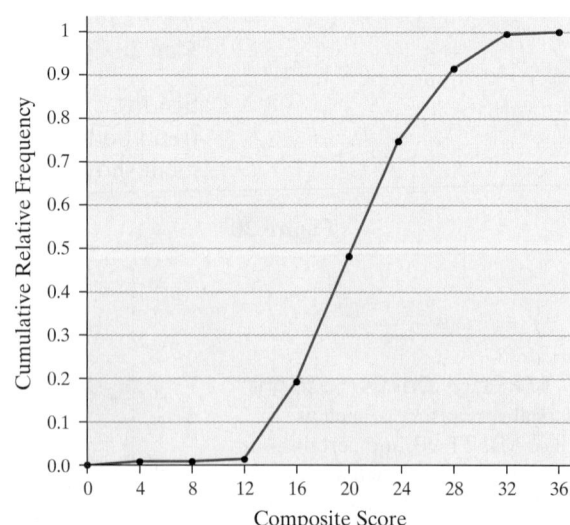

(a) What is the class width? How many classes are represented in the graph? 4; 9

(b) What are the lower and upper limits of the first class? 1–4

(c) What are the lower and upper limits of the last class?

10. (b) 201–250 10. (c) 751–800

(d) Estimate the percentage of students who had a composite score of 24 or below. 76%

(e) Estimate the percentage of students who had a composite score above 28. 8%

(f) If 1,300,599 students from the class of 2007 took the ACT exam, approximately how many students had a score of 24 or below? Above 28? 988,455; 104,048

10. **SAT Writing Scores** The following frequency ogive represents the SAT writing scores of 300 randomly selected college-bound students.

Source: Based on data from The College Board, *2007 College-Bound Seniors Total Group Profile Report*, 2007

SAT Writing Scores

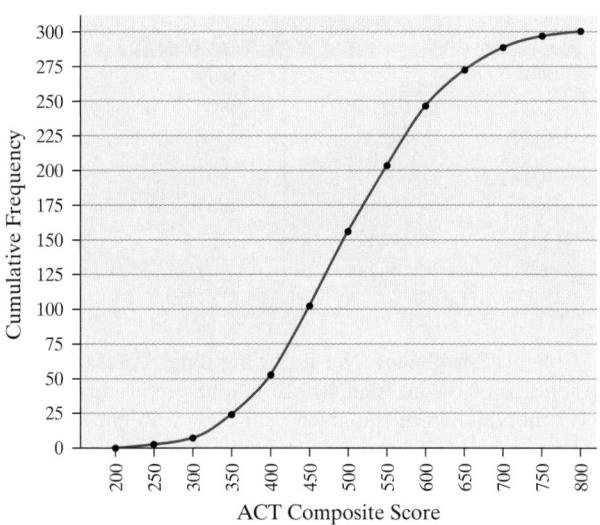

(a) What is the class width? How many classes are represented in the graph? 50; 12

(b) What are the lower and upper limits of the first class?

(c) What are the lower and upper limits of the last class?

(d) Estimate the number of students who had a writing score of 350 or below. 25

(e) Estimate the number of students who had a writing score above 650. 28

(f) In which class did the most students fall? Estimate the number of students in this class. 501–550; 54

11. **MasterCard, Inc.** The following time-series graph shows the closing price of MasterCard stock at the end of each month since it first went public in May 2006.

Source: TD Ameritrade

Closing Price of MasterCard, Inc.

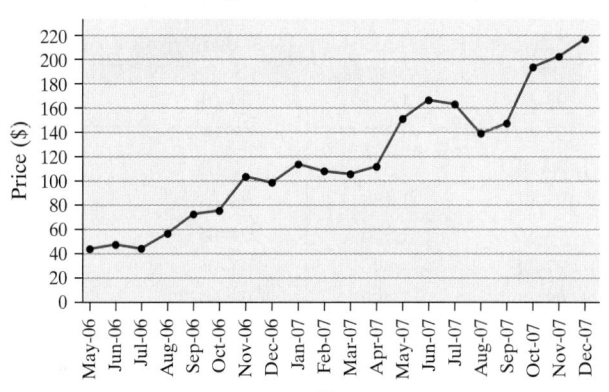

(a) Estimate the closing price of the stock at the end of May 2006. $45

(b) Estimate the closing price of the stock at the end of December 2007. $215

(c) Use your results from (a) and (b) to estimate the percent increase in the price from the end of May 2006 to the end of December 2007. 378%

(d) Estimate the percent decrease in the price from the end of June 2007 to the end of August 2007. 17%

12. **Motor Vehicle Production** The following time-series graph shows the annual U.S. motor vehicle production from 1991 through 2006.

Source: Bureau of Transportation Statistics

Annual U.S. Motor Vehicle Production

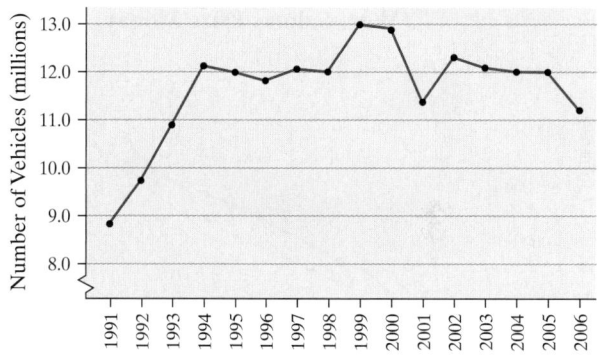

(a) Estimate the number of motor vehicles produced in the United States in 1991. 8.8 million

(b) Estimate the number of motor vehicles produced in the United States in 1999. 13.0 million

(c) Use your results from (a) and (b) to estimate the percent increase in the number of motor vehicles produced from 1991 to 1999. 47.7%

(d) Estimate the percent decrease in the number of vehicles produced from 1999 to 2006. 13.1%

13. **Unemployment and Inflation** The following time-series plot shows the annual unemployment and inflation rates for the years 1988 through 2006.

Source: www.miseryindex.us

Unemployment & Inflation Rates

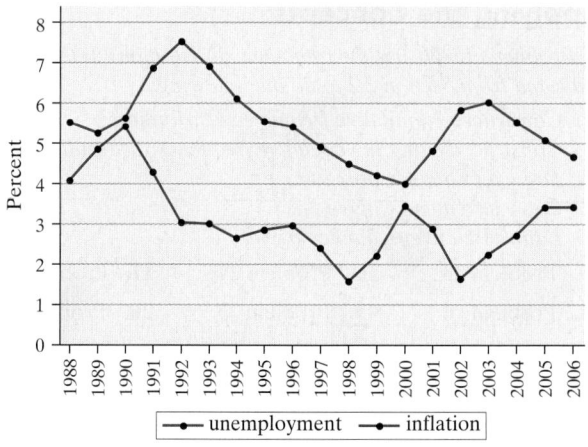

14. (d) Equal prize money was awarded; £700,000 each; 14. (e) 6.9%; 12.0%

(a) Estimate the unemployment and inflation rates for 1992. 7.5%; 3.0%
(b) Estimate the unemployment and inflation rates for 2006. 4.6%; 3.4%
(c) The misery index is defined as the sum of the unemployment rate and the inflation rate. Use your results from (a) and (b) to estimate the misery index for the years 1992 and 2006. 10.5%; 8.0%
(d) Describe any relationship that might exist between the unemployment rate and inflation rate over the time period shown.

14. **Prize Money at Wimbledon** The following time-series plot shows the prize money (in pounds) awarded at the Wimbledon Tennis Championship to the winners of the men's singles and ladies' singles competitions from 1990 through 2007.

Source: www.wimbledon.org

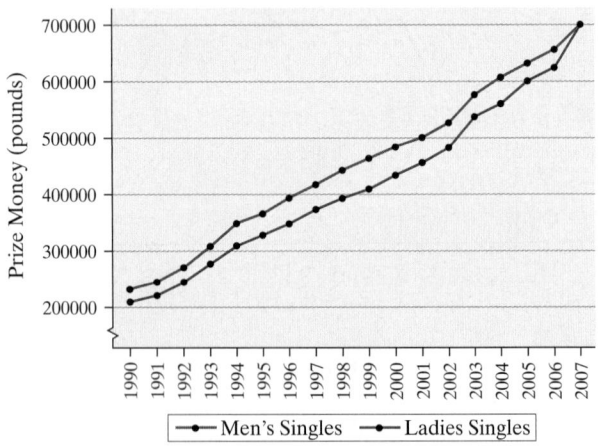

Wimbledon's Prize Money

(a) Estimate the prize money awarded to each for men's and ladies' singles in 1990. £230,000; £207,000
(b) Estimate the prize money awarded to each for men's and ladies' singles in 2006. £655,000; £625,000
(c) Describe any relationship that might exist between the prize money awarded for men's and ladies' singles over the time period shown.
(d) Use the graph to determine what happened for the first time in 2007. Estimate the prize money awarded for each championship in 2007.
(e) Estimate the percent increase in prize money awarded to each for men's and ladies' singles from 2006 to 2007.

Applying the Concepts

In Problems 15–20, use the frequency distributions in the problem indicated from Section 2.2 to do the following:

(a) *Construct a cumulative frequency distribution.*
(b) *Construct a cumulative relative frequency distribution.*
(c) *Draw a frequency polygon.*
(d) *Draw a frequency ogive.*
(e) *Draw a relative frequency ogive.*

15. Problem 23   16. Problem 24   17. Problem 25
18. Problem 26   19. Problem 33   20. Problem 34
     NW

21. **Walt Disney Company** The following data represent the
    NW stock price for the Walt Disney Company at the end of each month in 2007. Construct a time-series plot and comment on any trends.

Date	Closing Price	Date	Closing Price
1/07	34.50	7/07	33.00
2/07	33.60	8/07	33.60
3/07	33.78	9/07	34.39
4/07	34.32	10/07	34.63
5/07	34.77	11/07	33.15
6/07	34.14	12/07	32.28

Source: TD Ameritrade

22. **Google, Inc.** The following data represent the closing stock price for Google, Inc. at the end of each quarter since it first went public in 2004 until the end of 2007. Construct a time-series plot and comment on any trends.

Date	Closing Price	Date	Closing Price
9/04	129.60	6/06	419.33
12/04	192.79	9/06	401.90
3/05	180.51	12/06	460.48
6/05	294.15	3/07	458.18
9/05	316.46	6/07	522.70
12/05	414.86	9/07	567.27
3/06	390.00	12/07	691.31

Source: TD Ameritrade

23. **College Enrollment** The following data represent the percentage of recent high school graduates (graduated within 12 months before the given year-end) who enrolled in college in the fall. Construct a time-series plot and comment on any trends.

Year	Percent Enrolled	Year	Percent Enrolled
1988	58.9	1998	65.6
1989	59.6	1999	62.9
1990	60.1	2000	63.3
1991	62.5	2001	61.7
1992	61.9	2002	65.2
1993	62.6	2003	63.9
1994	61.9	2004	66.7
1995	61.9	2005	68.6
1996	65.0	2006	65.8
1997	67.0		

Source: U.S. Center for Education Statistics

24. **Shaq** Shaquille O'Neal began playing in the NBA in the 1992–1993 season. The following data represent the number of points per season scored by Shaq through the 2006–2007 season. Construct a time-series plot and comment on any trends.

Season	Points	Season	Points
92–93	1,893	00–01	2,125
93–94	2,377	01–02	1,822
94–95	2,315	02–03	1,841
95–96	1,434	03–04	1,439
96–97	1,336	04–05	1,669
97–98	1,699	05–06	1,181
98–99	1,289	06–07	690
99–00	2,344		

Source: www.nba.com

25. Rates of Return of Stocks Stocks may be categorized by industry. The following data represent the 5-year rates of return for a sample of financial stocks and retail stocks ending December 21, 2007.

Financial Stocks				
−19.75	55.74	55.39	58.44	59.94
0.45	102.29	52.27	195.61	−1.82
44.35	46.14	177.43	85.34	19.57
196.67	57.37	106.80	24.36	93.07
78.51	85.12	176.32	14.83	116.35
130.77	6.18	40.52	51.88	14.35
38.88	29.07	65.50	50.89	70.36

Retail Stocks				
31.74	26.45	199.19	24.87	47.03
75.17	9.04	−6.83	159.04	76.08
228.41	−15.81	98.69	51.24	0.96
103.92	32.85	42.49	109.18	31.70
34.65	137.32	187.26	34.35	−2.78
155.86	24.53	−3.64	88.13	29.79
226.34	90.66	22.13	77.58	58.53

Sources: CNNmoney.com; TD Ameritrade

(a) Construct a frequency distribution for each industry. To make an easy comparison, create each frequency distribution so that the lower class limit of the first class is −20 and the class width is 20.

(b) Construct a relative frequency distribution for each industry.

(c) On the same graph, construct a relative frequency polygon for the two industries.

(d) On the same graph, construct a relative frequency ogive for the two industries.

(e) Which industry appears to have the better performance for the 5-year period? Support your opinion.

26. American League versus National League The following data represent the earned-run average (ERA) of the top 40 pitchers in both the American League and National League in 2007.

Note: ERA is the average number of earned runs given up per 9 innings.

(a) Why would it be appropriate to use frequencies to compare the two leagues?

(b) Construct a frequency distribution for each league. To make an easy comparison, create each frequency distribution so that the lower class limit of the first class is 2.5 and the class width is 0.50.

(c) On the same graph, construct a frequency polygon for the American and National Leagues.

(d) On the same graph, construct a frequency ogive for the American and National Leagues.

(e) Which league appears to have better pitchers? Support your opinion.

Note: Be sure to take into account the fact that the National League does not have a designated hitter.

American League				
3.01	3.06	3.07	3.16	3.21
3.27	3.33	3.40	3.48	3.63
3.66	3.67	3.70	3.70	3.71
3.74	3.75	3.85	3.87	3.91
3.92	3.95	4.05	4.08	4.13
4.19	4.23	4.29	4.32	4.32
4.40	4.42	4.48	4.59	4.76
4.76	5.01	5.10	5.15	5.16

National League				
2.54	3.01	3.03	3.11	3.12
3.18	3.33	3.39	3.56	3.65
3.70	3.73	3.76	3.83	3.88
3.88	3.91	3.92	3.92	3.95
4.12	4.14	4.22	4.23	4.24
4.25	4.30	4.45	4.53	4.58
4.60	4.62	4.63	4.65	4.93
4.94	4.94	5.01	5.02	5.10

Source: www.baseball-reference.com

27. Putting It Together: Shark! The following two graphics represent the number of reported shark attacks worldwide since 1900 and the worldwide fatality rate of shark attacks since 1900. Write a report about the trends in the graphs. In your report discuss the apparent contradiction between the increase in shark attacks, but the decrease in fatality rate.

Source: Florida Museum of Natural History

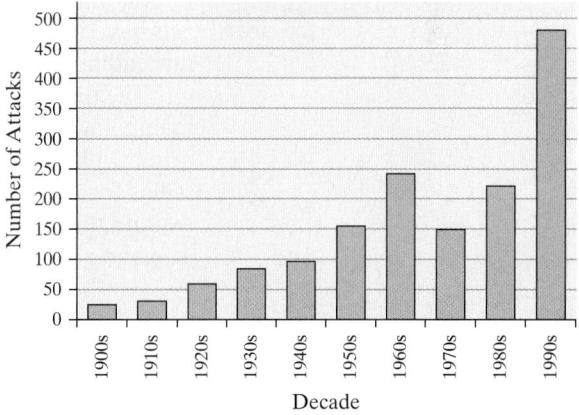

Unprovoked Shark Attacks Over the Last Century Worldwide

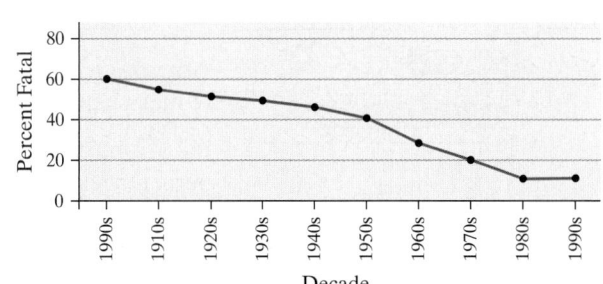

Worldwide Shark Attack Fatality Rate, 1900–1999

TECHNOLOGY **Drawing Frequency Polygons, Ogives, and Time-Series Plots**

TECHNOLOGY **Drawing Frequency Polygons, Ogives, and Time-Series Plots**

TI-83/84 Plus
The TI-83 and TI-84 Plus are capable of drawing all three of these graphs.

MINITAB
MINITAB is capable of drawing all three of these graphs.

Excel
Excel is capable of drawing all three of these graphs.

2.4 GRAPHICAL MISREPRESENTATIONS OF DATA

Objective		Describe what can make a graph misleading or deceptive

Describe What Can Make a Graph Misleading or Deceptive

Statistics: The only science that enables different experts using the same figures to draw different conclusions.—EVAN ESAR

Note to Instructor
The material in this section can be omitted without loss of continuity. For those instructors who are pressed for time, it can be assigned for reading.

Often, statistics gets a bad rap for having the ability to manipulate data to support any position desired. One method of distorting the truth is through graphics. We mentioned in Section 2.1 how visual displays send more powerful messages than raw data or even tables of data. Since graphics are so powerful, care must be taken both in constructing graphics and interpreting the messages they are trying to convey. Sometimes graphics *mislead*; other times they *deceive*. We will call graphs misleading if they unintentionally create an incorrect impression. We consider graphs deceptive if they purposely attempt to create an incorrect impression. Regardless of the intentions of the graph's creator, an incorrect impression on the reader's part can have serious consequences. Therefore, it is important to be able to recognize misleading and deceptive graphs.

The most common graphical misrepresentation of data is accomplished through manipulation of the scale of the graph, typically in the form of an inconsistent scale or a misplaced origin. Increments between tick marks should remain constant, and scales for comparative graphs should be the same. In addition, readers will usually assume that the baseline, or zero point, is at the bottom of the graph. Starting the graph at a higher or lower value can be misleading.

EXAMPLE 1 Misrepresentation of Data

Figure 21

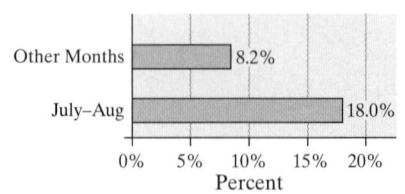

Problem: A home security company puts out a summer ad campaign with the slogan "When you leave for vacation, burglars leave for work." According to the FBI, roughly 18% of home burglaries in 2004 occurred during the peak vacation months of July and August. The advertisement contains the graph shown in Figure 21. Explain what is wrong with the graphic.

Approach: We need to look at the graph for any characteristics that may mislead a reader, such as inconsistent scales or poorly defined categories.

Solution: Let's consider how the categories of data are defined. The sum of the percentages (the relative frequencies) over all 12 months should be 1. Because $10(0.082) + 0.18 = 1$, it is clear that the bar for Other Months represents an average percent for *each* month, while the bar for July–August represents the average percent for the months July and August *combined*. By combining months, the unsuspecting reader is mislead into thinking that July and August each have a much higher burglary rate.

Figure 22 gives a better picture of the burglary distribution. While there is an increase during the months of July and August, the increase is not as dramatic as the bar graph in Figure 21 implies. In fact, Figure 21 would be considered deceitful because the security company is intentionally trying to convince consumers that July and August are much higher burglary months.

Figure 22

Burglaries in the U.S., 2004

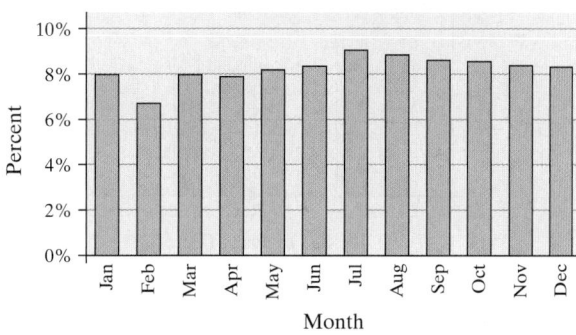

Source: FBI, Crime in the United States, 2004

Now Work Problem 5

EXAMPLE 2 | **Misrepresentation of Data by Manipulating the Vertical Scale**

Problem: In 2005, Terri Schiavo was the center of a right-to-die battle that drew international attention. At issue was whether her husband had the right to remove her feeding tube on which she had been dependent for the previous 15 years. A CNN/USA Today/Gallup poll conducted March 18–20, 2005, asked respondents, "*As you may know, on Friday the feeding tube keeping Terri Schiavo alive was removed. Based on what you have heard or read about the case, do you think that the feeding tube should or should not have been removed?*" The results were presented in a graph similar to Figure 23. Explain what is wrong with the graphic.

Figure 23

Opinion Regarding Schiavo Case

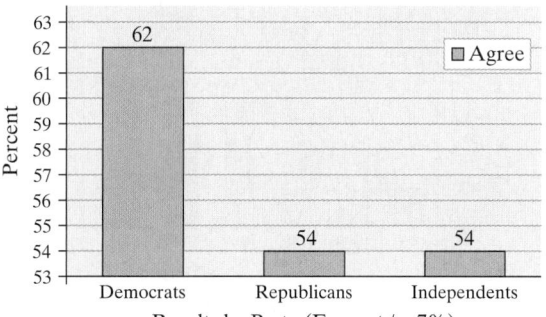

Results by Party (Error: +/− 7%)

Approach: We need to look at the graph for any characteristics that may mislead a reader, such as manipulation of the vertical scale.

Solution: The graphic seems to indicate that Democrats overwhelmingly supported the removal of the feeding tube, much more so than either Republicans or Independents. Because the vertical scale does not begin at 0, it may appear that Democrats are 9 times more likely to support the decision (because the bar is 9 times as high as the others) when there is really only an 8 percentage point difference. The dramatic difference in bar heights overshadows the data being presented. Note that the majority of each party sampled supported the decision to remove the feeding tube. In addition, given a ±7 percentage point margin of error for each sample, the actual difference of 8 percentage points would not be *statistically significant* (we will learn more about this later in the text). Ultimately, CNN posted a corrected graphic similar to the one in Figure 24. Note how starting the vertical scale at 0 allows for a more accurate comparison.

Figure 24

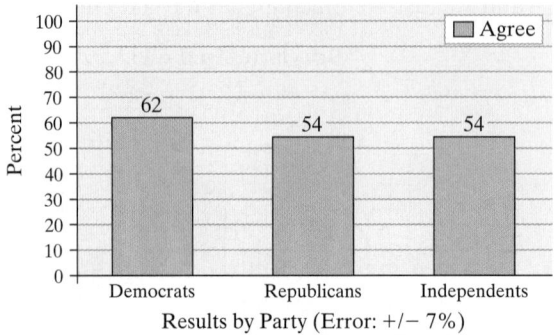

Recall from Section 1.5 that the order of words in a question can affect responses and lead to potential *response bias*. In the question presented in Example 2, the order of the choices ("should," and "should not") were not rotated. The first choice given was "should," and the majority of respondents stated that the feeding tube should be removed. It is possible that the position of the choice in the question could have affected the responses. A better way to present the question would be, "*As you may know, on Friday the feeding tube keeping Terri Schiavo alive was removed. Based on what you have heard or read about the case, do you [Rotated – agree (or) disagree] that the feeding tube should have been removed?*"

EXAMPLE 3 | **Misrepresentation of Data by Manipulating the Vertical Scale**

Problem: The time-series graph shown in Figure 25 depicts the average SAT math scores of college-bound seniors for the years 1991–2007. Determine why this graph might be considered misrepresentative. (*Source: College Board, College-Bound Seniors*, 2007)

Figure 25

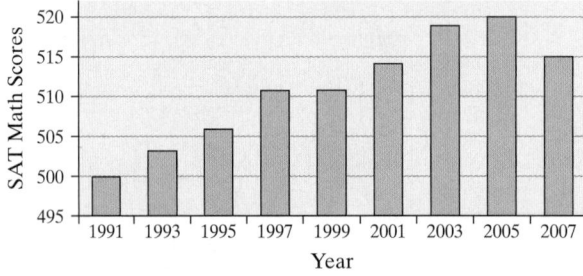

Approach: We need to look at the graph for any characteristics that may mislead a reader, such as manipulation of the vertical scale.

Solution: The graph in the figure may lead a reader to believe that SAT math scores have increased substantially since 1991. While SAT math scores have been increasing, they have not doubled or quadrupled (since the point for 2007 is 4 times as high as the point for 1991). We notice in the figure that the vertical axis begins at 495 instead of the baseline of 200 (the minimum score for the math portion of the SAT). This type of scaling is common when the smallest observed data value is a rather large number. It is not necessarily done purposely to confuse or mislead the reader. Often, the main purpose in graphs (particularly time-series graphs) is to discover a trend, rather than the actual differences in the data. The trend is clearer in Figure 25 than in Figure 26, where the vertical axis begins at the baseline. Remember that the goal of a good graph is to make the data stand out. When displaying time-series data, as in this example, it is better to use a time-series plot to discover any trends. In addition, instead of beginning the axis of a graph at 0 as in Figure 26, scales are frequently truncated so they begin at a value slightly less than the smallest value in the data set. There is nothing inherently wrong with doing this, but special care must be taken to make the reader aware of the scaling that is used. Figure 27 shows the proper construction of the graph of the SAT math scores, with the graph beginning at 495. The symbol ⭙ is used to indicate that the scale has been truncated and the graph has a gap in it. Notice that the lack of bars allows us to focus on the trend in the data, rather than the relative size (or area) of the bars.

Figure 26

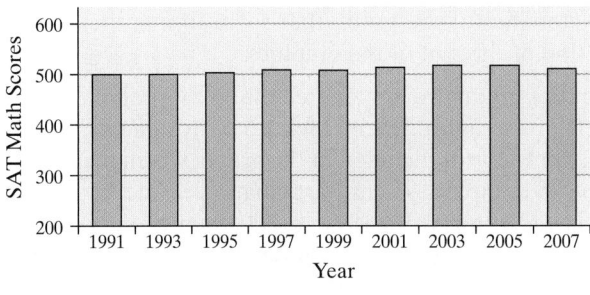

Average SAT Math Scores Over Time

Figure 27

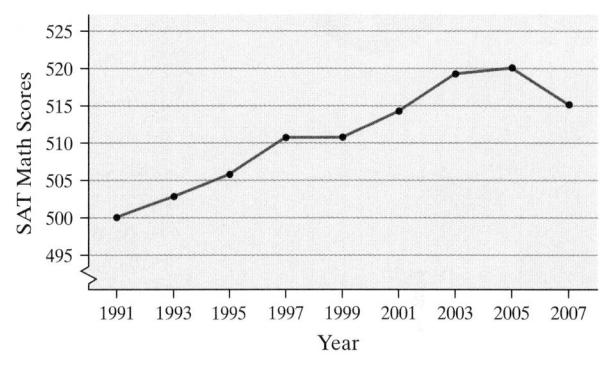

Average SAT Math Score Over Time

Now Work Problem 3

EXAMPLE 4 **Misrepresentation of Data**

Figure 28

Now Work Problem 11

Problem: The bar graph illustrated in Figure 28 is a *USA Today*-type graph. A survey was conducted by Impulse Research for Quilted Northern Confidential in which individuals were asked how they would flush a toilet when the facilities are not sanitary. What's wrong with the graphic?

Approach: We need to compare the vertical scales of each bar to see if they accurately depict the percentages given.

Solution: First, it is unclear whether the bars include the roll of toilet paper or not. In either case, the roll corresponding to "use shoe" should be 2.4 (= 41/17) times longer than the roll corresponding to "paper towel." If we include the roll of toilet paper, then the bar corresponding to "use shoe" is less than double the length of "paper towel." If we do not include the roll of toilet paper, then the bar corresponding to "use shoe" is almost exactly double the length of the bar corresponding to "paper towel." The vertical scaling is incorrect.

Newspapers, magazines, and Websites often go for a "wow" factor when displaying graphs. In many cases, the graph designer is more interested in catching the reader's eye than making the data stand out. The two most commonly used tactics are 3-D graphs and pictograms (graphs that use pictures to represent the data). The use of 3-D effects is strongly discouraged, because such graphs are often difficult to read, add little value to the graph, and distract the reader from the data.

When comparing bars that represent different quantities, our eyes are really comparing the *areas* of the bars. In our discussion of bar graphs and histograms, we emphasized that the bars or classes should be of the same width. The advantage of having uniform width is that the area of the bar is then proportional to its height, so we can simply compare the heights of the bars for the different quantities. However, when we use two-dimensional pictures in place of the bars, it is not possible to obtain a uniform width. To avoid distorting the picture when values increase or decrease, both the height and width of the picture must be adjusted. This often leads to misleading graphs.

| EXAMPLE 5 | Misleading Graphs |

Figure 29

Soccer Participation

1991   2006

Problem: Soccer continues to grow in popularity as a sport in the United States. High-profile players such as Mia Hamm and Landon Donovan have helped to generate renewed interest in the sport at various age levels. In 1991 there were approximately 10 million participants in the United States aged 7 years or older. By 2006 this number had climbed to 14 million. To illustrate this increase, we could create a graphic like the one shown in Figure 29. Describe how the graph may be misleading. (*Source*: U.S. Census Bureau; National Sporting Goods Association.)

Approach: We look for characteristics of the graph that seem to manipulate the facts, such as an incorrect depiction of the size of the graphics.

Solution: The graph on the right of the figure has an area that is more than 4 times the area of the graph on the left of the figure. While the number of participants is given in the problem statement, they are not included in the graph, which makes the reader rely on the graphic alone to compare soccer participation in the two years. There was a 40% increase in participation from 1991 to 2006, not the more than 300% indicated by the graphic. To be correct, the graph on the right of the figure should have an area that is only 40% more than the area of the graph on the left of the figure. Adding the data values to the graphic would help reduce the chance of misinterpretation due to the oversized graph.

Now Work Problem 17

Figure 30

Soccer Participation

1991 ⚽⚽⚽⚽⚽⚽⚽⚽⚽⚽

2006 ⚽⚽⚽⚽⚽⚽⚽⚽⚽⚽⚽⚽⚽⚽

⚽ = 1 million participants

A variation on pictograms is to use a smaller picture repeatedly, with each picture representing a certain quantity. For example, we could present the data from Figure 29 by using a smaller soccer ball to represent 1 million participants. The resulting graphic is displayed in Figure 30. Note how the uniform size of the graphic allows us to make a more accurate comparison of the two quantities.

| EXAMPLE 6 | Misleading Graphs |

Problem: Figure 31 represents the number of active-duty military personnel in the United States as of August 2007. Describe how this graph is misleading. (*Source*: infoplease.com.)

Figure 31

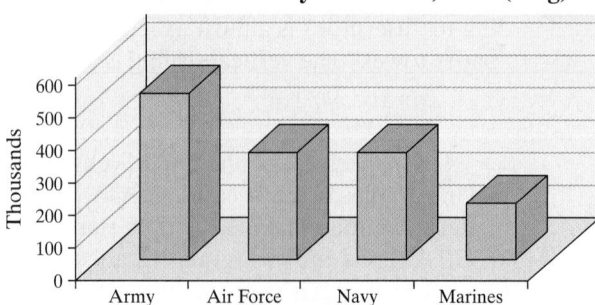

Active Duty Personnel, 2007 (Aug)

Approach: Again, we look for characteristics of the graph that seem to distort the facts or distract the reader.

Solution: The three-dimensional bar graph in the figure may draw the reader's attention, but the bars seem to stand out more than the data they represent. The perspective angle of the graph makes it difficult to estimate the data values being presented, actually resulting in estimates that are typically lower than the true values. This in turn makes comparison of the data difficult. The only dimension that matters is bar height, so this is what should be emphasized. Figure 32 displays the same data in a two-dimensional bar graph. Which graphic is easier to read?

Figure 32

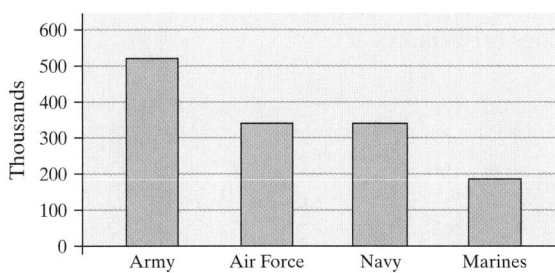

The material presented in this section is by no means all-inclusive. There are many ways to create graphs that mislead. Two popular texts written about ways that graphs mislead or deceive are *How to Lie with Statistics* (W. W. Norton & Company, Inc., 1982) by Darrell Huff and *The Visual Display of Quantitative Information* (Graphics Press, 2001) by Edward Tufte.

We conclude this section with some guidelines for constructing good graphics.

- Title and label the graphic axes clearly, providing explanations if needed. Include units of measurement and a data source when appropriate.
- Avoid distortion. Never lie about the data.
- Minimize the amount of white space in the graph. Use the available space to let the data stand out. If scales are truncated, be sure to clearly indicate this to the reader.
- Avoid clutter, such as excessive gridlines and unnecessary backgrounds or pictures. Don't distract the reader.
- Avoid three dimensions. Three-dimensional charts may look nice, but they distract the reader and often lead to misinterpretation of the graphic.
- Do not use more than one design in the same graphic. Sometimes graphs use a different design in one portion of the graph to draw attention to that area. Don't try to force the reader to any specific part of the graph. Let the data speak for themselves.
- Avoid relative graphs that are devoid of data or scales.

2.4 ASSESS YOUR UNDERSTANDING

Applying the Concepts

1. Inauguration Cost The following is a *USA Today*-type graph. Explain how it is misleading.

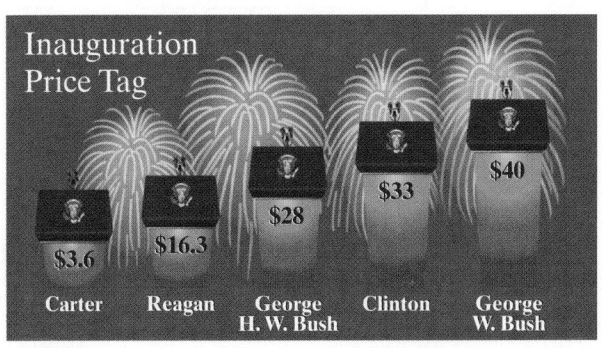

2. Burning Calories The following is a *USA Today*-type graph.

(a) Explain how it is misleading.
(b) What could be done to improve the graphic?

3. Median Earnings The following graph shows the median earnings for females from 2002 to 2006 in constant 2006 dollars.

Source: U.S. Census Bureau, Income, Poverty, and Health Insurance Coverage in the United States, 2006

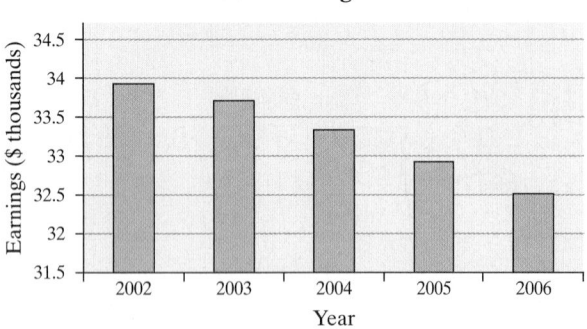

Median Earnings for Females

(a) How is the bar graph misleading? What does the graph seem to convey?
(b) Redraw the graph so that it is not misleading. What does the new graph seem to convey?

4. Union Membership The following relative frequency histogram represents the proportion of employed people aged 25 to 64 years old who were members of a union.

Source: U.S. Bureau of Labor Statistics

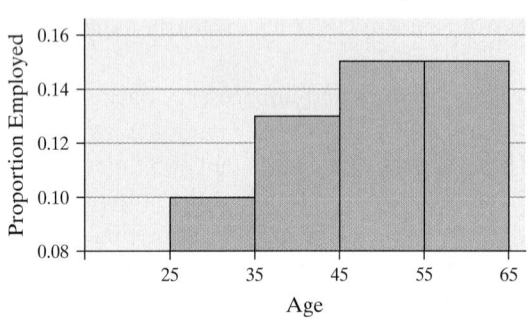

Union Membership

(a) Describe how this graph is misleading. What might a reader conclude from the graph?
(b) Redraw the histogram so that it is not misleading.

5. Robberies A newspaper article claimed that the afternoon hours were the worst in terms of robberies and provided the following graph in support of this claim. Explain how this graph is misleading.

Source: U.S. Statistical Abstract, 2008

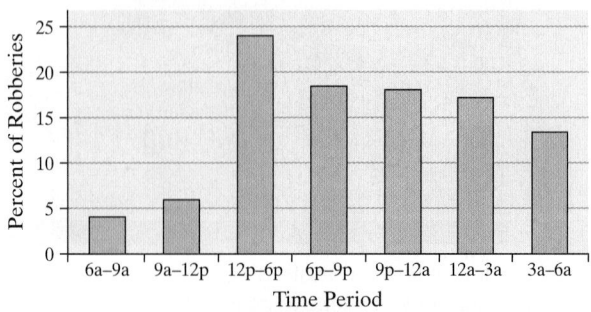

Hourly Crime Distribution (Robbery)

6. Car Accidents An article in a student newspaper claims that younger drivers are safer than older drivers and provides the following graph to support the claim. Explain how this graph is misleading.

Source: U.S. Statistical Abstract, 2008

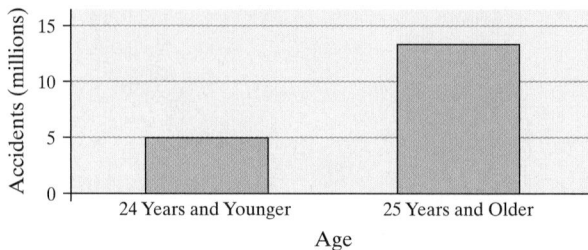

Number of Motor Vehicle Accidents, 2005

7. Health Insurance The following relative frequency histogram represents the proportion of people aged 25 to 64 years old not covered by any health insurance in 2006.

Source: U.S. Census Bureau

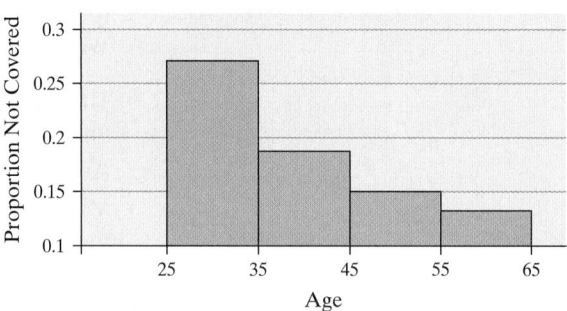

Proportion Not Covered by Health Insurance

(a) Describe how this graph is misleading. What might a reader conclude from the graph?
(b) Redraw the histogram so that it is not misleading.

8. New Homes The following time-series plot shows the number of new homes built in the Midwest from 2000 to 2006.

Source: U.S. Statistical Abstract, 2008

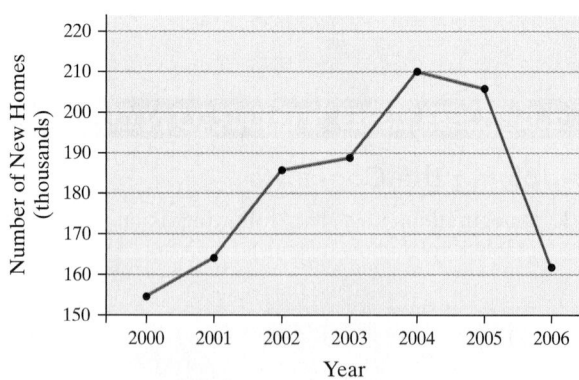

New Homes in Midwest

(a) Describe how this graph is misleading.
(b) What is the graph trying to convey?
(c) In January 2006, the National Association of Realtors reported, "*A lot of demand has been met over the last five years, and a modest rise in mortgage interest rates is causing some market cooling. Along with regulatory tightening on nontraditional mortgages, there will be fewer investors in the market this year.*" Does the graph support this view? Explain why or why not.

9. Median Income The following time-series plot shows the median household income for the years 2001 to 2006 in constant 2006 dollars.

Source: U.S. Census Bureau

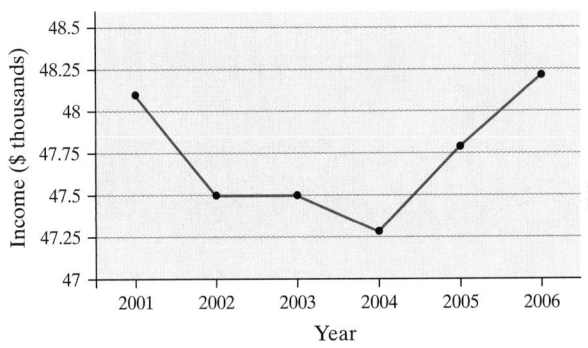

U.S. Median Household Income

(a) Describe how the graph is misleading.
(b) What is the graph trying to convey?
(c) Redraw the graph so that Median Household Income appears to be relatively stable for the years shown.

10. You Explain It! Oil Reserves The U.S. Strategic Oil Reserve is a government-owned stockpile of crude oil. It was established after the oil embargo in the mid-1970s and is meant to serve as a national defense fuel reserve, as well as to offset reductions in commercial oil supplies that would threaten the U.S. economy.

Source: U.S. Energy Information Administration

**U.S. Strategic Oil Reserves
(millions of barrels)**

696.3

7.5

1977   2007

(a) How many times larger should the graphic for 2007 be than the 1977 graphic (to the nearest whole number)?
(b) The United States imported approximately 10.1 million barrels of oil per day in 2007. At that rate, assuming no change in U.S. oil production, how long would the U.S. strategic oil reserve last if no oil were imported?

11. Cost of Kids The following is a *USA Today*-type graph
NW based on data from the Department of Agriculture. It represents the percentage of income a middle-income family will spend on their children.

Cost of Raising Kids

Housing   33%
Food   18%
Transportation 15%
Other   11%

(a) How is the graphic misleading?
(b) What could be done to improve the graphic?

12. Electricity The following table gives the average per kilowatt-hour prices of electricity in the United States for the years 2001 to 2007.

Source: U.S. Energy Information Administration

Year	2001	2002	2003	2004	2005	2006	2007
Price per kWh (cents)	8.58	8.44	8.72	8.95	9.45	10.40	10.65

(a) Construct a misleading graph indicating that the price per kilowatt-hour has more than tripled since 2001.
(b) Construct a graph that is not misleading.

13. ACT Composite The following table gives the average ACT composite scores for the years 2003–2007.

Year	2003	2004	2005	2006	2007
Average ACT composite	20.8	20.9	20.9	21.1	21.2

(a) Construct a misleading time-series plot that indicates the average ACT composite score has risen sharply over the given time period.
(b) Construct a time-series plot that is not misleading.
(c) Which of the two graphs would you prefer if you were merely looking for trends in the data? Explain.

14. Worker Injury The safety manager at Klutz Enterprises provides the following graph to the plant manager and claims that the rate of worker injuries has been reduced by 67% over a 12-year period. Does the graph support his claim? Explain.

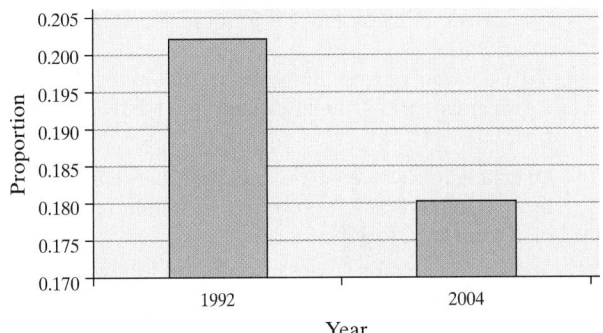

Proportion of Workers Injured

10. (a) 93 times   10. (b) About 69 days

15. Health Care Expenditures The following data represent health care expenditures as a percentage of the U.S. gross domestic product (GDP) from 2001 to 2007. Gross domestic product is the total value of all goods and services created during the course of the year.

Source: Center for Medicare and Medicad Services, Office of the Actuary

Year	Health Care as a Percent of GDP
2001	14.5
2002	15.3
2003	15.8
2004	15.9
2005	16.0
2006	16.0
2007	16.2

(a) Construct a time-series plot that a politician would create to support the position that health care expenditures, as a percentage of GDP, are increasing and must be slowed.
(b) Construct a time-series plot that the health care industry would create to refute the opinion of the politician.
(c) Construct a time-series plot that is not misleading.

16. Motor Vehicle Death Rates The following data represent the number of motor vehicle deaths (within 30 days of accident) and the traffic death rates (number of deaths per 100,000 licensed drivers) from 2001 to 2005.

Year	Motor Vehicle Deaths (in thousands)	Traffic Death Rate (per 100,000 licensed drivers)
2001	42.2	22.1
2002	43.0	22.0
2003	42.9	21.9
2004	42.8	21.5
2005	43.4	21.7

Source: U.S. Statistical Abstract, 2008

(a) Construct a time-series graph to support the belief that the roads are becoming less safe.
(b) Construct a time-series graph to support the belief that the roads are becoming safer.
(c) Which graph do you feel better represents the situation?

17. Gas Hike The average per gallon price for regular unleaded gasoline in the United States rose from $1.46 in 2001 to $4.01 in 2008.

Source: U.S. Energy Information Administration

(a) Construct a graphic that is not misleading to depict this situation.
(b) Construct a misleading graphic that makes it appear the average price roughly quadrupled between 2001 and 2007.

18. Overweight Between 1980 and 2006, the number of adults in the United States who were overweight more than doubled from 15% to 34%.

Source: Centers for Disease Control and Prevention

(a) Construct a graphic that is not misleading to depict this situation.

(b) Construct a misleading graphic that makes it appear that the percent of overweight adults has more than quadrupled between 1980 and 2006.

19. Corn Production The following *USA Today*-type graphic illustrates U.S. corn production in billions of bushels for the years 1998 to 2007.

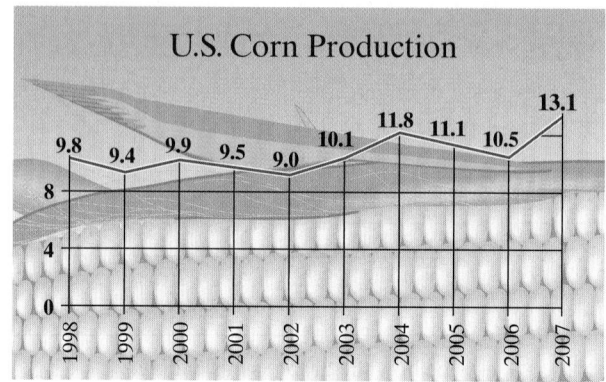

(a) What type of graph is being displayed? Time-series
(b) Describe some of the problems with this graphic.
(c) Construct a new graphic that is not misleading and makes the data stand out.

20. Putting It Together: College Costs The cover of the *Ithaca Times* from December 7, 2000 is shown.

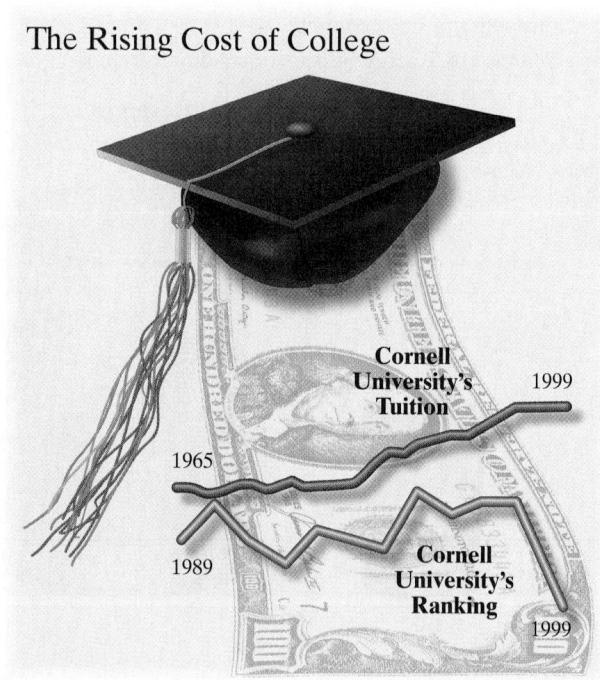

(a) Identify the two variables being graphed and describe them in terms of type and measurement level.
(b) What type of data collection method was likely used to create this graph?
(c) What type of graph is displayed? Time-series
(d) What message does the graph convey to you? How might this graph be misleading?
(e) Describe at least three things that are wrong with the graph.

CHAPTER 2 REVIEW

Summary

Raw data are first organized into tables. Data are organized by creating classes into which they fall. Qualitative data and discrete data have values that provide clear-cut categories of data. However, with continuous data the categories, called classes, must be created. Typically, the first table created is a frequency distribution, which lists the frequency with which each class of data occurs. Other types of distributions include the relative frequency distribution and the cumulative frequency distribution.

Once data are organized into a table, graphs are created. For data that are qualitative, we can create bar charts and pie charts. For data that are quantitative, we can create histograms, stem-and-leaf plots, frequency polygons, and ogives.

In creating graphs, care must be taken not to draw a graph that misleads or deceives the reader. If a graph's vertical axis does not begin at zero, the symbol ⌁ should be used to indicate the gap that exists in the graph.

Vocabulary

Raw data (p. 66)
Frequency distribution (p. 67)
Relative frequency (p. 68)
Relative frequency
  distribution (p. 68)
Bar graph (p. 69)
Pareto chart (p. 70)
Side-by-side bar graph (p. 70)
Pie chart (p. 72)
Class (p. 82)
Histogram (p. 83)

Lower and upper class limits (p. 84)
Class width (p. 84)
Open ended (p. 84)
Stem-and-leaf plot (p. 88)
Stem (p. 88)
Leaf (p. 88)
Split stems (p. 91)
Dot plot (p. 92)
Uniform distribution (p. 92)
Bell-shaped distribution (p. 92)
Skewed right (p. 92)

Skewed left (p. 92)
Class midpoint (p. 102)
Frequency polygon (p. 102)
Cumulative frequency
  distribution (p. 103)
Cumulative relative frequency
  distribution (p. 103)
Ogive (p. 104)
Time-series data (p. 104)
Time series plot (p. 105)

Objectives

Section	You should be able to . . .	Example	Review Exercises
2.1	**1** Organize qualitative data in tables (p. 67)	1, 2	2(a), 4(a) and (b)
	2 Construct bar graphs (p. 69)	3 through 5	2(c) and (d), 4(c)
	3 Construct pie charts (p. 72)	6	2(e), 4(d)
2.2	**1** Organize discrete data in tables (p. 82)	1	5(a) and (b)
	2 Construct histograms of discrete data (p. 83)	2	5(e) and (f)
	3 Organize continuous data in tables (p. 84)	3	3(a), 6(a) and (b), 7(a) and (b)
	4 Construct histograms of continuous data (p. 87)	4, 5	3(d) and (e), 6(e) and (f), 7(e) and (f)
	5 Draw stem-and-leaf plots (p. 88)	6 through 8	8
	6 Draw dot plots (p. 92)	9	5(i)
	7 Identify the shape of a distribution (p. 92)	10	3(d), 6(e), 7(e), 8
2.3	**1** Construct frequency polygons (p. 102)	pp. 102–103	3(f)
	2 Create cumulative frequency and relative frequency tables (p. 103)	pp. 103–104	3(b) and (c), 5(c) and (d), 6(c) and (d), 7(c) and (d)
	3 Construct frequency and relative frequency ogives (p. 104)	p. 104	3(h) and (i)
	4 Draw time-series graphs (p. 104)	1	9
2.4	**1** Describe what can make a graph misleading or deceptive (p. 110)	1 through 6	10, 11, 12(b)

Review Exercises

1. Energy Consumption The following bar chart represents the energy consumption of the United States (in quadrillion Btu) in 2006.
Source: Energy Information Administration

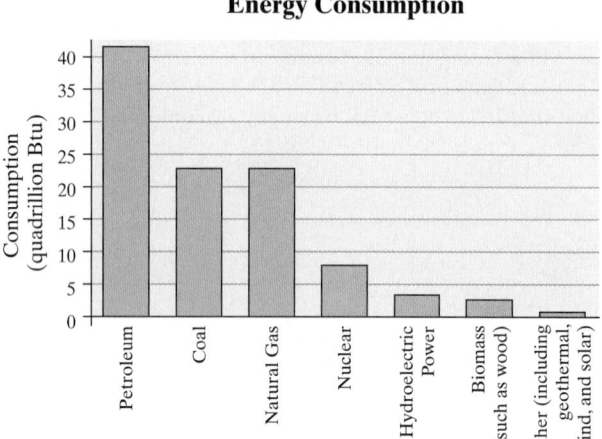

Energy Consumption

(a) Approximately how much energy did the United States consume from natural gas? 22.5 quadrillion Btu
(b) Approximately how much energy did the United States consume from biomass? 3 quadrillion Btu
(c) Approximate the total energy consumption of the United States in 2006. 100 quadrillion Btu
(d) Which category has the lowest frequency? Other
(e) Is it appropriate to describe the shape of the distribution as skewed right? Why or why not? No; qualitative data

2. Weapons Used in Homicide The following frequency distribution represents the cause of death in homicides for the year 2005.

Type of Weapon	Frequency
Firearms	10,075
Knives or cutting instruments	1,902
Blunt objects (clubs, hammers, etc.)	609
Personal weapons (hands, fists, etc.)	892
Strangulation	208
Fire	119
Other weapon or not stated	1,040

Source: *Crime in the United States, 2005*, FBI, Uniform Crime Reports

(a) Construct a relative frequency distribution.
(b) What percentage of homicides was committed using a blunt object? 4.1%
(c) Construct a frequency bar graph.
(d) Construct a relative frequency bar graph.
(e) Construct a pie chart.

3. Live Births The following frequency distribution represents the number of live births (in thousands) in the United States in 2006 by age of mother.

Age of Mother (years)	Births (thousands)
10–14	6
15–19	435
20–24	1081
25–29	1182
30–34	950
35–39	499
40–44	105

Source: National Center for Health Statistics

(a) Construct a relative frequency distribution.
(b) Construct a cumulative frequency distribution.
(c) Construct a cumulative relative frequency distribution.
(d) Construct a frequency histogram. Describe the shape of the distribution.
(e) Construct a relative frequency histogram.
(f) Construct a frequency polygon.
(g) Construct a relative frequency polygon.
(h) Construct a frequency ogive.
(i) Construct a relative frequency ogive.
(j) What percentage of live births were to mothers aged 20 to 24? 25.4%
(k) What percentage of live births were to mothers of age 30 or older? 36..5%

4. Political Affiliation A sample of 100 randomly selected registered voters in the city of Naperville was asked their political affiliation: Democrat (D), Republican (R), or Independent (I). The results of the survey are as follows:

D	R	D	R	D	R	D	D	R	D
R	D	D	D	R	R	D	D	D	D
R	R	I	I	D	R	D	R	R	R
I	D	D	R	I	I	R	D	R	R
D	I	R	D	D	D	D	I	I	R
R	I	R	R	I	D	D	D	D	R
D	I	I	D	D	R	R	R	R	D
D	R	R	R	D	D	I	I	D	D
D	D	I	D	R	I	D	D	D	D
R	R	R	R	R	D	R	D	R	D

(a) Construct a frequency distribution of the data.
(b) Construct a relative frequency distribution of the data.
(c) Construct a relative frequency bar graph of the data.
(d) Construct a pie chart of the data.
(e) What appears to be the most common political affiliation in Naperville? Democrat

5. Family Size A random sample of 60 couples married for 7 years were asked to give the number of children they have. The results of the survey are as follows:

0	0	3	1	2	3
3	4	3	3	0	3
1	2	1	3	0	3
4	2	3	2	2	4
2	1	3	4	1	3
0	3	3	3	2	1
2	0	3	1	2	3
4	3	3	5	2	0
4	2	2	2	3	3
2	4	2	2	2	2

(a) Construct a frequency distribution of the data.
(b) Construct a relative frequency distribution of the data.
(c) Construct a cumulative frequency distribution of the data.
(d) Construct a cumulative relative frequency distribution of the data.
(e) Construct a frequency histogram of the data. Describe the shape of the distribution.   bell shaped
(f) Construct a relative frequency histogram of the data.
(g) What percentage of couples married 7 years has two children?   30%
(h) What percentage of couples married 7 years has at least two children?   76.7%
(i) Draw a dot plot of the data.

6. Crime Rate by State The following data represent the crime rate (per 100,000 population) for each state and the District of Columbia in 2005.

State	Crime Rate	State	Crime Rate	State	Crime Rate
Alabama	4,324	Kentucky	2,798	North Dakota	2,076
Alaska	4,245	Louisiana	4,277	Ohio	4,014
Arizona	5,351	Maine	2,525	Oklahoma	4,551
Arkansas	4,586	Maryland	4,247	Oregon	4,687
California	3,849	Massachusetts	2,821	Pennsylvania	2,842
Colorado	4,437	Michigan	3,643	Rhode Island	2,970
Connecticut	2,833	Minnesota	3,381	South Carolina	5,100
Delaware	3,743	Mississippi	3,538	South Dakota	1,952
District of Columbia	6,206	Missouri	4,453	Tennessee	5,029
Florida	4,716	Montana	3,425	Texas	4,862
Georgia	4,621	Nebraska	3,710	Utah	4,096
Hawaii	5,048	Nevada	4,849	Vermont	2,401
Idaho	2,955	New Hampshire	1,928	Virginia	2,921
Illinois	3,632	New Jersey	2,688	Washington	5,239
Indiana	3,780	New Mexico	4,850	West Virginia	2,898
Iowa	3,125	New York	2,555	Wisconsin	2,902
Kansas	4,174	North Carolina	4,543	Wyoming	3,385

Source: *Crime in the United States, 2005.* FBI, Uniform Crime Reports.

In (a)–(f), start the first class at a lower class limit of 1,800 and maintain a class width of 400.

(a) Construct a frequency distribution.
(b) Construct a relative frequency distribution.
(c) Construct a cumulative frequency distribution.
(d) Construct a cumulative relative frequency distribution.
(e) Construct a frequency histogram. Describe the shape of the distribution.   Roughly symmetric
(f) Construct a relative frequency histogram.
(g) Repeat (a)–(f) using a class width of 1,000. In your opinion, which class width provides the better summary of the data? Why?

7. Diameter of a Cookie The following data represent the diameter (in inches) of a random sample of 34 Keebler Chips Deluxe™ Chocolate Chip Cookies.

2.3414	2.3010	2.2850	2.3015	2.2850	2.3019	2.2400
2.3005	2.2630	2.2853	2.3360	2.3696	2.3300	2.3290
2.2303	2.2600	2.2409	2.2020	2.3223	2.2851	2.2382
2.2438	2.3255	2.2597	2.3020	2.2658	2.2752	2.2256
2.2611	2.3006	2.2011	2.2790	2.2425	2.3003	

Source: Trina S. McNamara, student at Joliet Junior College

(a) Construct a frequency distribution.
(b) Construct a relative frequency distribution.
(c) Construct a cumulative frequency distribution.
(d) Construct a cumulative relative frequency distribution.
(e) Construct a frequency histogram. Describe the shape of the distribution.
(f) Construct a relative frequency histogram.

8. **Time Online** The following data represent the average number of hours per week that a random sample of 40 college students spend online.

18.9	14.0	24.4	17.4	13.7	16.5	14.8	20.8
22.9	22.2	13.4	18.8	15.1	21.9	21.1	14.7
18.6	18.0	21.1	15.6	16.6	20.6	17.3	17.9
15.2	16.4	14.5	17.1	25.7	17.4	18.8	17.1
13.6	20.1	15.3	19.2	23.4	14.5	18.6	23.8

The data are based on the ECAR Study of Undergraduate Students and Information Technology, 2007. Construct a stem-and-leaf diagram of the data, and comment on the shape of the distribution.   *Skewed right*

9. **Eliminating Syphilis** Syphilis is a highly infectious sexually transmitted disease. The disease is treatable, but if left untreated can lead to serious health problems and even death. The prevalence of syphilis can be tracked by means of incidence rates (the number of reported cases per 100,000 population). The following data are the incidence rates for primary and secondary syphilis (the most infectious) from 1990 to 1999.

Year	Rate	Year	Rate
1990	20.3	1995	6.2
1991	17.0	1996	4.2
1992	13.3	1997	3.1
1993	10.2	1998	2.5
1994	7.8	1999	2.4

(a) Construct a time plot for the data. Comment on the apparent trend.
(b) The low rate and localized occurrence led the Centers for Disease Control and Prevention (CDC) to develop the National Plan to Eliminate Syphilis in 1999. Construct a time-series plot for incidence rates from 2000 to 2006.

Year	Rate	Year	Rate
2000	2.1	2004	2.7
2001	2.1	2005	2.8
2002	2.4	2006	3.3
2003	2.5		

(c) The CDC's plan to eliminate syphilis was revised in 2006. Why do you think this was necessary?
(d) Would a histogram of incidence rates of syphilis allow a researcher to observe trends in the data? Explain.

10. **Misleading Graphs** The following graph was found in a magazine advertisement for skin cream. How is this graph misleading?

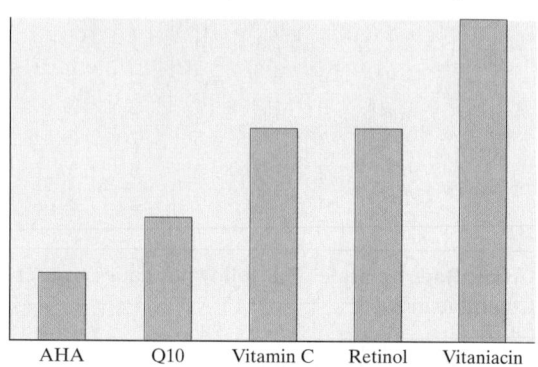

Skin Health (Moisture Retention)

11. **Misleading Graphs** In 2005 the average earnings of a high school graduate were $29,448. At $54,689, the average earnings of a recipient of a bachelor's degree were about 86% higher.

Source: U.S. Census Bureau, Current Population Survey, 2006
(a) Construct a misleading graph that a college recruiter might create to convince high school students that they should attend college.
(b) Construct a graph that does not mislead.

12. **High Heels** The following graphic is a *USA Today*-type graph displaying women's preference for shoes.

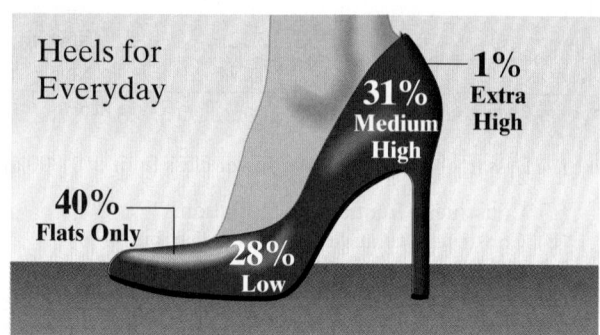

(a) Which type of shoe is preferred the most? The least?
(b) How is the graph misleading?

CHAPTER TEST

1. The following graph shows the country represented by the champion of the men's singles competition at the Wimbledon Tennis Championship from 1968 (when professional players were first allowed to participate in the tournament) through 2007.

   Source: www.wimbledon.org

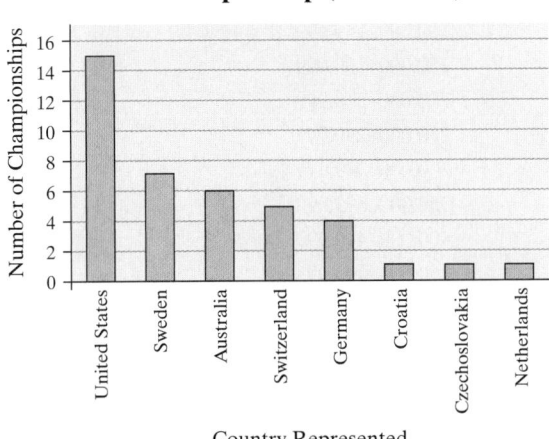

Wimbledon Men's Singles Championship (1968–2007)

   1. (a) *United States; 15*

   (a) Which country's representatives won the most championships from 1968 to 2007? How many did they win?
   (b) How many more championships were won by representatives of Australia than Germany?   2

   (c) What percentage of championships from 1968 to 2007 was won by representatives of Sweden?   17.5%
   (d) Is it appropriate to describe the shape of the distribution as skewed right? Why or why not? *No; qualitative data*

2. The following frequency distribution represents the total greenhouse emissions in millions of metric tons in 2006 in the United States.

Gas	Emissions
Carbon dioxide	5,934.4
Methane	605.1
Nitrous oxide	378.6
Hydrofluorocarbons, perfluorocarbons, and sulfur hexafluoride	157.6

Source: Energy Information Administration, *Emissions of Greenhouse Gases in the United States 2006*, November 2007

2. (b) *83.87%*

   (a) Construct a relative frequency distribution.
   (b) What percent of emissions was due to carbon dioxide?
   (c) Construct a frequency bar graph.
   (d) Construct a relative frequency bar graph.
   (e) Construct a pie chart.

3. The Metra Train Company was interested in knowing the educational background of its customers. The company contracted a marketing firm to conduct a survey with a random sample of 50 commuters at the train station. In the survey, commuters were asked to disclose their educational attainment. The following results were obtained:

No high school diploma	Some college	Advanced degree	High school graduate	Advanced degree
High school graduate	High school graduate	High school graduate	High school graduate	No high school diploma
Some college	High school graduate	Bachelor's degree	Associate's degree	High school graduate
No high school diploma	Bachelor's degree	Some college	High school graduate	No high school diploma
Associate's degree	High school graduate	High school graduate	No high school diploma	Some college
Bachelor's degree	Bachelor's degree	Some college	High school graduate	Some college
Bachelor's degree	Advanced degree	No high school diploma	Advanced degree	No high school diploma
High school graduate	Bachelor's degree	No high school diploma	High school graduate	No high school diploma
Associate's degree	Bachelor's degree	High school graduate	Bachelor's degree	Some college
Some college	Associate's degree	High school graduate	Some college	High school graduate

   (a) Construct a frequency distribution of the data.
   (b) Construct a relative frequency distribution of the data.
   (c) Construct a relative frequency bar graph of the data.
   (d) Construct a pie chart of the data.
   (e) What is the most common educational level of a commuter?   *High school graduate*

4. The following data represent the number of cars that arrived at a McDonald's drive-through between 11:50 A.M. and 12:00 noon each Wednesday for the past 50 weeks:
   (a) Construct a frequency distribution of the data.
   (b) Construct a relative frequency distribution of the data.
   (c) Construct a cumulative frequency distribution of the data.

1	7	3	8	2	3	8	2	6	3
6	5	6	4	3	4	3	8	1	2
5	3	6	3	3	4	3	2	1	2
4	4	9	3	5	2	3	5	5	5
2	5	6	1	7	1	5	3	8	4

(d) Construct a cumulative relative frequency distribution of the data.

(e) Construct a frequency histogram of the data. Describe the shape of the distribution. *Skewed right*

(f) Construct a relative frequency histogram of the data.

(g) What percentage of weeks did exactly three cars arrive between 11:50 A.M. and 12:00 noon? *24%*

(h) What percentage of weeks did three or more cars arrive between 11:50 A.M. and 12:00 noon? *76%*

(i) Draw a dot plot of the data.

5. The following data represent the serving sizes (in grams) of 40 sandwiches served at McDonald's and Burger King.

Sources: McDonald's Corporation, *McDonald's USA Nutrition Facts*, November 2007; Burger King Corporation, *Nutritional Information*, October 2007

100	114	165	169	198
279	214	206	220	143
147	209	226	229	260
263	246	249	118	125
269	294	352	376	434
459	147	149	121	133
164	189	190	250	311
273	244	284	190	122

5. (a) 100 grams; 50 grams

(a) If eight classes are to be formed, choose an appropriate lower class limit for the first class and a class width.

(b) Construct a frequency distribution.

(c) Construct a relative frequency distribution.

(d) Construct a frequency histogram. Describe the shape of the distribution. *Skewed right*

(e) Construct a relative frequency histogram.

6. The following frequency distribution represents the closing prices (in dollars) of homes sold in a Midwest city.

Closing Price ($)	Number of Houses
50,000–99,999	4
100,000–149,999	13
150,000–199,999	19
200,000–249,999	7
250,000–299,999	3
300,000–349,999	2
350,000–399,999	1
400,000–449,999	0
450,000–499,999	1

(a) Construct a cumulative frequency distribution.

(b) Construct a cumulative relative frequency distribution.

(c) What percent of homes sold for less than $200,000? *72%*

(d) Construct a frequency polygon. Describe the shape of the distribution. *Skewed right*

(e) Construct a frequency ogive.

(f) Construct a relative frequency ogive.

---

7. The following data represent the fertility rate (births per 1,000 women aged 15 to 44) for each state and the District of Columbia in 2006.

State	Fertility Rate	State	Fertility Rate	State	Fertility Rate
Alabama	67.0	Kentucky	67.2	North Dakota	68.7
Alaska	76.7	Louisiana	70.6	Ohio	64.7
Arizona	81.6	Maine	54.5	Oklahoma	74.7
Arkansas	72.3	Maryland	64.2	Oregon	65.5
California	71.8	Massachusetts	57.0	Pennsylvania	60.6
Colorado	70.2	Michigan	61.7	Rhode Island	56.6
Connecticut	58.8	Minnesota	68.7	South Carolina	69.7
Delaware	67.3	Mississippi	75.8	South Dakota	78.4
District of Columbia	58.5	Missouri	67.9	Tennessee	67.5
Florida	67.3	Montana	69.5	Texas	78.8
Georgia	72.4	Nebraska	75.1	Utah	94.1
Hawaii	73.9	Nevada	78.0	Vermont	52.2
Idaho	80.9	New Hampshire	53.4	Virginia	66.3
Illinois	66.8	New Jersey	64.4	Washington	65.2
Indiana	68.3	New Mexico	74.7	West Virginia	59.4
Iowa	69.1	New York	61.1	Wisconsin	64.0
Kansas	73.3	North Carolina	69.0	Wyoming	75.9

Source: National Center for Health Statistics, *National Vital Statistics Reports*, Vol. 56, No. 7, December 5, 2007

(a) Round each observation to the nearest whole number and draw a stem-and-leaf diagram using split stems.

(b) Describe the shape of the distribution. *Slightly skewed right*

8. The following data represent the average price (in dollars) of a gallon of reduced fat (2%) milk in the United States at the beginning of each month in the years 2006 and 2007. Construct a time-series plot and comment on any trends.

Month	Average Price	Month	Average Price
1/06	3.19	1/07	3.19
2/06	3.15	2/07	3.18
3/06	3.15	3/07	3.21
4/06	3.11	4/07	3.22
5/06	3.09	5/07	3.30
6/06	3.06	6/07	3.47
7/06	3.03	7/07	3.70
8/06	3.06	8/07	3.77
9/06	3.05	9/07	3.80
10/06	3.09	10/07	3.76
11/06	3.06	11/07	3.77
12/06	3.11	12/07	3.74

Source: Agricultural Marketing Service, U.S. Department of Agriculture

9. The following is a *USA Today*-type graph.

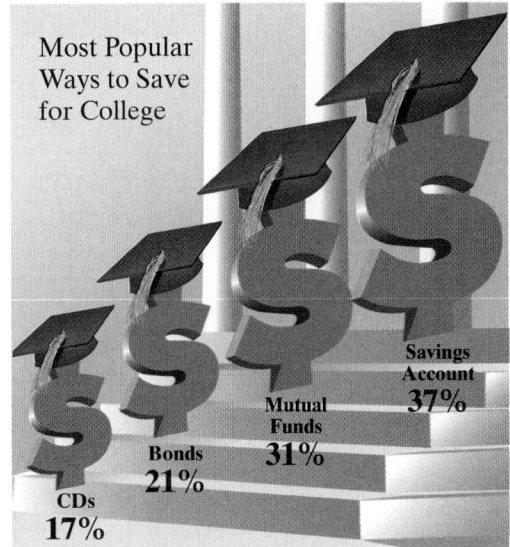

Most Popular Ways to Save for College

CDs 17%

Bonds 21%

Mutual Funds 31%

Savings Account 37%

Do you think the graph is misleading? Why? If you think it is misleading, what might be done to improve the graph?

MAKING AN INFORMED DECISION

Tables or Graphs?

You work for the school newspaper. Your editor approaches you with a special reporting assignment. Your task is to write an article that describes the "typical" student at your school, complete with supporting information. To write this article, you have to survey at least 40 students and ask them to respond to a questionnaire. The editor would like to have at least two qualitative and two quantitative variables that describe the typical student. The results of the survey will be presented in your article, but you are unsure whether you should present tabular or graphical summaries, so you decide to perform the following experiment.

1. Develop a questionnaire that results in obtaining the values of two qualitative and two quantitative variables. Administer the questionnaire to at least 40 students on your campus.
2. Summarize the data in both tabular and graphical form.
3. Select 20 individuals. (They don't have to be students at your school.) Give the tabular summaries to 10 individuals and the graphical summaries to the other 10. Ask each individual to study the table or graph for 5 seconds. After 1 minute, give a questionnaire that asks various questions regarding the information contained in the table or graph. For example, if you summarize age data, ask the individual which age group has the highest frequency. Record the number of correct answers for each individual. Which summary results in a higher percentage of correct answers, the tables or the graphs? Write a report that discusses your findings.
4. Now use the data collected from the questionnaire to create some misleading graphs. Again, select 20 individuals. Give 10 individuals the misleading graphs and 10 individuals the correct graphs. Ask each individual to study each graph for 5 seconds. After 1 minute has elapsed, give a questionnaire that asks various questions regarding the information contained in the graphs. Record the number of correct answers for each individual. Did the misleading graphs mislead? Write a report that discusses your findings.

Note: Be sure to check with your school's administration regarding privacy laws and policies regarding studies involving human subjects. ◀

The Day the Sky Roared

Shortly after daybreak on April 3, 1974, thunder began to rumble through the dark skies that covered much of the midwestern United States. Lightning struck areas from the Gulf Coast states to the Canadian border. By the predawn hours of the next day, the affected region of around 490,000 acres was devastated by more than 100 tornadoes. This "super outbreak" was responsible for the deaths of more than 300 people in 11 states. More than 6,100 people were injured by the storms, with approximately 27,500 families suffering some kind of loss. The total cost attributed to the disaster was more than $600 million. Amazingly, the storm resulted in six category 5 tornadoes with wind speeds exceeding 261 miles per hour. To put this figure in perspective, the region endured about one decade's worth of category 5 tornadoes in a single 24-hour period!

Fujita Wind Damage Scale		
F-scale	Wind Speed (mph)	Damage
F-0	Up to 72	Light
F-1	73 to 112	Moderate
F-2	113 to 157	Considerable
F-3	158 to 206	Severe
F-4	207 to 260	Devastating
F-5	Above 260	Incredible

Structural engineers and meteorologists are interested in understanding catastrophic events such as this tornado outbreak. Variables such as tornado intensity (as described by the F-scale), tornado duration (time spent by the tornado in contact with the ground), and death demographics can provide insights into these events and their impact on the human population. The following table lists the duration time and F-scale for each tornado in the April 1974 super outbreak.

Tornado Duration Times for Outbreak of April 3–4, 1974	
F-scale	Tornado Duration (minutes)
F-0	1, 1, 5, 1, 1, 6, 4, 10, 5, 4, 1, 1, 1, 1, 1, 1, 1, 1, 1, 30, 1, 9
F-1	16, 13, 9, 8, 13, 10, 15, 1, 17, 23, 10, 8, 12, 5, 20, 31, 12, 5, 30, 13, 7, 1, 5, 13, 1, 2, 5, 10, 1, 20, 5
F-2	7, 15, 2, 10, 23, 10, 7, 12, 8, 1, 8, 19, 5, 10, 15, 20, 10, 13, 20, 15, 13, 14, 1, 4, 2, 15, 30, 91, 11, 5
F-3	9, 20, 8, 16, 26, 36, 10, 20, 50, 17, 26, 31, 21, 30, 23, 28, 23, 18, 35, 35, 15, 25, 30, 15, 22, 18, 58, 19, 23, 31, 13, 26, 40, 14, 11
F-4	120, 23, 23, 42, 47, 25, 22, 22, 34, 50, 38, 28, 39, 29, 28, 25, 34, 16, 40, 55, 124, 30, 30, 31
F-5	37, 69, 23, 52, 61, 122

The following tables present the number of deaths as a function of F-scale and community size:

Deaths as a Function of F-scale for April 3–4, 1974, Tornadoes	
F-Scale	**Deaths**
F-0	0
F-1	0
F-2	14
F-3	32
F-4	129
F-5	130

Deaths as a Function of Community Size for Tornado Super Outbreak of April 3–4, 1974	
Community Size	**Deaths**
Rural areas	99
Small communities	77
Small cities	63
Medium cities	56
Large cities	10

Create a report that graphically displays and discusses the tornado-related data. Your report should include the following:

1. A bar graph or pie chart (or both) that depicts the number of tornadoes by F-scale. Generally, only a little more than 1% of all tornadoes exceed F-3 on the Fujita Wind Damage Scale. How does the frequency of the most severe tornadoes of the April 3–4, 1974, outbreak compare with normal tornado formation?

2. A single histogram that displays the distribution of tornado duration for all the tornadoes.

3. Six histograms displaying tornado duration for each of the F-scale categories. Does there appear to be a relationship between duration and intensity? If so, describe this relationship.

4. A bar chart that shows the relationship between the number of deaths and tornado intensity. Ordinarily, the most severe tornadoes (F-4 and F-5) account for more than 70% of deaths. Is the death distribution of this outbreak consistent with this observation?

5. A bar chart that shows the relationship between the number of deaths and community size. Are tornadoes more likely to strike rural areas? Include a discussion describing the number of deaths as a function of community size.

6. A general summary of your findings and conclusions.

Data Source: Abbey, Robert F., and T. Theodore Fujita. "Tornadoes: The Tornado Outbreak of 3–4 April 1974." In *The Thunderstorm in Human Affairs*, 2nd ed, edited by Edwin Kessler, 37–66. Norman, OK: University of Oklahoma Press, 1983. The death figures presented in this case study are based on approximations made from charts by Abbey and Fujita. Additional descriptions of events and normal tornado statistics are derived from Jack Williams's *The Weather Book* (New York: Vintage Books, 1992).

Numerically Summarizing Data

Outline

3.1 Measures of Central Tendency

3.2 Measures of Dispersion

3.3 Measures of Central Tendency and Dispersion from Grouped Data

3.4 Measures of Position and Outliers

3.5 The Five-Number Summary and Boxplots

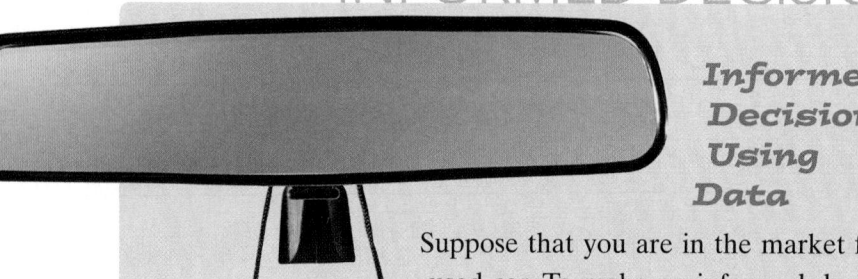

Informed Decisions Using Data

Suppose that you are in the market for a used car. To make an informed decision regarding your purchase, you decide to collect as much information as possible. What information is important in helping you make this decision? See the Decisions project on page 189.

PUTTING IT TOGETHER

When we look at a distribution of data, we should consider three characteristics of the distribution: shape, center, and spread. In the last chapter, we discussed methods for organizing raw data into tables and graphs. These graphs (such as the histogram) allow us to identify the shape of the distribution. Recall that we describe the shape of a distribution as symmetric (in particular, bell shaped or uniform), skewed right, or skewed left.

The center and spread are numerical summaries of the data. The center of a data set is commonly called the *average*. There are many ways to describe the *average* value of a distribution. In addition, there are many ways to measure the spread of a distribution. The most appropriate measure of center and spread depends on the shape of the distribution.

Once these three characteristics of the distribution are known, we can analyze the data for interesting features, including unusual data values, called *outliers*.

3.1 MEASURES OF CENTRAL TENDENCY

Preparing for This Section   Before getting started, review the following:

- Population versus sample (Section 1.1, p. 5)
- Parameter versus statistic (Section 1.1, p. 5)
- Quantitative data (Section 1.1, p. 9)
- Qualitative data (Section 1.1, p. 9)
- Simple random sampling (Section 1.3, pp. 22–27)

Objectives

1. Determine the arithmetic mean of a variable from raw data
2. Determine the median of a variable from raw data
3. Explain what it means for a statistic to be resistant
4. Determine the mode of a variable from raw data

Note to Instructor
If you like, you can print out and distribute the Preparing for this Section quiz located in the Instructor's Resource Center.

Note to Instructor
Discuss with students that we describe distributions using three characteristics: shape, center, and spread. Shape can be determined from pictures of data, like the histogram. Center is discussed in this section, and spread is discussed in Section 3.2.

CAUTION Whenever you hear the word *average*, be aware that the word may not always be referring to the mean. One average could be used to support one position, while another average could be used to support a different position.

A measure of central tendency numerically describes the average or typical data value. We hear the word *average* in the news all the time:

- The average miles per gallon of gasoline of the 2008 Chevrolet Corvette in city driving is 15 miles.
- According to the U.S. Census Bureau, the national average commute time to work in 2006 was 24.0 minutes.
- According to the U.S. Census Bureau, the average household income in 2006 was $48,201.
- The average American woman is 5′4″ tall and weighs 142 pounds.

In this chapter, we discuss three measures of central tendency: the *mean*, the *median*, and the *mode*. While other measures of central tendency exist, these three are the most widely used. When the word *average* is used in the media (newspapers, reporters, and so on) it usually refers to the mean. But beware! Some reporters use the term *average* to refer to the median or mode. As we shall see, these three measures of central tendency can give very different results!

1 Determine the Arithmetic Mean of a Variable from Raw Data

When used in everyday language, the word *average* often represents the arithmetic mean. To compute the arithmetic mean of a set of data, the data must be quantitative.

Definitions

The **arithmetic mean** of a variable is computed by determining the sum of all the values of the variable in the data set and dividing by the number of observations. The **population arithmetic mean**, μ (pronounced "mew"), is computed using all the individuals in a population. The population mean is a parameter.

The **sample arithmetic mean**, $\bar{x}$ (pronounced "x-bar"), is computed using sample data. The sample mean is a statistic.

In Other Words
To find the mean of a set of data, add up all the observations and divide by the number of observations.

While other types of means exist (see Problems 45 and 46), the arithmetic mean is generally referred to as the **mean**. We will follow this practice for the remainder of the text.

Typically, Greek letters are used to represent parameters, and Roman letters are used to represent statistics. Statisticians use mathematical expressions to describe the method for computing means.

If $x_1, x_2, \ldots, x_N$ are the N observations of a variable from a population, then the population mean, μ, is

$$\mu = \frac{x_1 + x_2 + \cdots + x_N}{N} = \frac{\sum x_i}{N} \qquad (1)$$

If $x_1, x_2, \ldots, x_n$ are n observations of a variable from a sample, then the sample mean, $\bar{x}$, is

$$\bar{x} = \frac{x_1 + x_2 + \cdots + x_n}{n} = \frac{\sum x_i}{n} \tag{2}$$

Note that N represents the size of the population, while n represents the size of the sample. The symbol Σ (the Greek letter capital sigma) tells us the terms are to be added. The subscript i is used to make the various values distinct and does not serve as a mathematical operation. For example, x_1 is the first data value, x_2 is the second, and so on.

Let's look at an example to help distinguish the population mean and sample mean.

EXAMPLE 1   Computing a Population Mean and a Sample Mean

Problem: The data in Table 1 represent the first exam score of 10 students enrolled in a section of Introductory Statistics.

(a) Compute the population mean.

(b) Find a simple random sample of size $n = 4$ students.

(c) Compute the sample mean of the sample obtained in part (b).

Approach

(a) To compute the population mean, we add up all the data values (test scores) and then divide by the number of individuals in the population.

(b) Recall from Section 1.3 that we can use either Table I in Appendix A, a calculator with a random-number generator, or computer software to obtain simple random samples. We will use a TI-84 Plus graphing calculator.

(c) The sample mean is found by adding the data values that correspond to the individuals selected in the sample and then dividing by $n = 4$, the sample size.

Table 1

Student	Score
1. Michelle	82
2. Ryanne	77
3. Bilal	90
4. Pam	71
5. Jennifer	62
6. Dave	68
7. Joel	74
8. Sam	84
9. Justine	94
10. Juan	88

Solution

(a) We compute the population mean by adding the scores of all 10 students:

$$\sum x_i = x_1 + x_2 + x_3 + \cdots + x_{10}$$
$$= 82 + 77 + 90 + 71 + 62 + 68 + 74 + 84 + 94 + 88$$
$$= 790$$

Divide this result by 10, the number of students in the class.

$$\mu = \frac{\sum x_i}{N} = \frac{790}{10} = 79$$

Although it was not necessary in this problem, we will agree to round the mean to one more decimal place than that in the raw data.

(b) To find a simple random sample of size $n = 4$ from a population whose size is $N = 10$, we will use the TI-84 Plus random-number generator with a seed of 54. (Recall that this gives the starting point that the calculator uses to generate the list of random numbers.) Figure 1 shows the students in the sample. Bilal (90), Ryanne (77), Pam (71), and Michelle (82) are in the sample.

(c) We compute the sample mean by first adding the scores of the individuals in the sample.

$$\sum x_i = x_1 + x_2 + x_3 + x_4$$
$$= 90 + 77 + 71 + 82$$
$$= 320$$

Figure 1

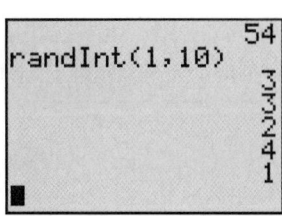

Divide this result by 4, the number of individuals in the sample.

$$\overline{x} = \frac{\sum x_i}{n} = \frac{320}{4} = 80$$

Now Work Problem 23

Note to Instructor
The purpose of this activity is to introduce the students to sampling variability. It should take about 15 to 20 minutes. It can be used to illustrate the ideas in Example 1. Keep the data collected so you can use it to illustrate other concepts later in the course. If you decided to postpone the discussion of Sections 1.2–1.6, do not attempt this activity.

Figure 2

Scores on First Exam

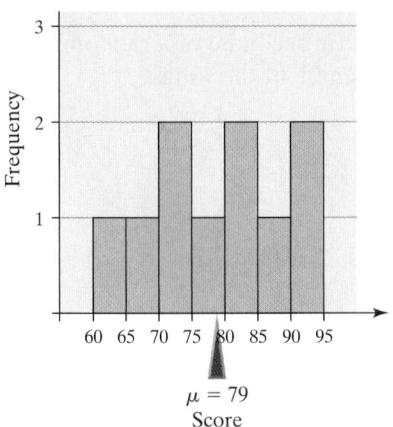

$\mu = 79$
Score

IN CLASS ACTIVITY

Population Mean versus Sample Mean

Treat the students in the class as a population. All the students in the class should determine their pulse rates.

(a) Compute the population mean pulse rate.

(b) Obtain a simple random sample of $n = 4$ students and compute the sample mean. Does the sample mean equal the population mean?

(c) Obtain a second simple random sample of $n = 4$ students and compute the sample mean. Does the sample mean equal the population mean?

(d) Are the sample means the same? Why?

It is helpful to think of the mean of a data set as the center of gravity. In other words, the mean is the value such that a histogram of the data is perfectly balanced, with equal weight on each side of the mean. Figure 2 shows a histogram of the data in Table 1 with the mean labeled. The histogram balances at $\mu = 79$.

IN CLASS ACTIVITY

The Mean as the Center of Gravity

Find a yardstick, a fulcrum, and three objects of equal weight (maybe 1-kilogram weights from the physics department). Place the fulcrum at 18 inches so that the yardstick balances like a teeter-totter. Now place one weight on the yardstick at 12 inches, another at 15 inches, and the third at 27 inches. See Figure 3.

Figure 3

Does the yardstick balance? Now compute the mean of the location of the three weights. Compare this result with the location of the fulcrum. Conclude that the mean is the center of gravity of the data set.

② ## Determine the Median of a Variable from Raw Data

A second measure of central tendency is the median. To compute the median of a set of data, the data must be quantitative.

Definition   The **median** of a variable is the value that lies in the middle of the data when arranged in ascending order. We use M to represent the median.

To determine the median of a set of data, we use the following steps:

Steps in Finding the Median of a Data Set

Step 1: Arrange the data in ascending order.

Step 2: Determine the number of observations, n.

Step 3: Determine the observation in the middle of the data set.

- If the number of observations is odd, then the median is the data value that is exactly in the middle of the data set. That is, the median is the observation that lies in the $\frac{n+1}{2}$ position.

- If the number of observations is even, then the median is the mean of the two middle observations in the data set. That is, the median is the mean of the observations that lie in the $\frac{n}{2}$ position and the $\frac{n}{2} + 1$ position.

EXAMPLE 2

Determining the Median of a Data Set with an Odd Number of Observations

Problem: The data in Table 2 represent the length (in seconds) of a random sample of songs released in the 1970s. Find the median length of the songs.

Approach: We will follow the steps listed above.

Solution

Step 1: Arrange the data in ascending order:

$$179, 201, 206, 208, 217, 222, 240, 257, 284$$

Step 2: There are $n = 9$ observations.

Step 3: Since there are an odd number of observations, the median will be the observation exactly in the middle of the data set. The median, M, is 217 seconds (the $\frac{n+1}{2} = \frac{9+1}{2} = $ 5th data value). We list the data in ascending order, with the median in blue.

$$179, 201, 206, 208, 217, 222, 240, 257, 284$$

Notice there are four observations to the left and four observations to the right of the median.

Table 2	
Song Name	**Length**
"Sister Golden Hair"	201
"Black Water"	257
"Free Bird"	284
"The Hustle"	208
"Southern Nights"	179
"Stayin' Alive"	222
"We Are Family"	217
"Heart of Glass"	206
"My Sharona"	240

EXAMPLE 3

Determining the Median of a Data Set with an Even Number of Observations

Problem: Find the median score of the data in Table 1 on page 130.

Approach: We will follow the steps listed above.

Solution

Step 1: Arrange the data in ascending order:

$$62, 68, 71, 74, 77, 82, 84, 88, 90, 94$$

Step 2: There are $n = 10$ observations.

Step 3: Because there are $n = 10$ observations, the median will be the mean of the two middle observations. The median is the mean of the fifth $\left(\frac{n}{2} = \frac{10}{2} = 5 \right)$ and sixth $\left(\dfrac{n}{2} + 1 = \dfrac{10}{2} + 1 = 6 \right)$ observations with the data written in ascending order. So the median is the mean of 77 and 82:

$$M = \frac{77 + 82}{2} = 79.5$$

Notice that there are five observations to the left and five observations to the right of the median, as follows:

$$62, 68, 71, 74, 77, 82, 84, 88, 90, 94$$

$$M = 79.5$$

We conclude that 50% (or half) of the students scored less than 79.5 and 50% (or half) of the students scored above 79.5.

Now compute the median of the data in Problem 15 by hand

EXAMPLE 4   **Finding the Mean and Median Using Technology**

Problem: Use statistical software or a calculator to determine the population mean and median of the student test score data in Table 1 on page 130.

Figure 4

	Student Scores
Mean	79
Standard Error	3.272783389
Median	79.5
Mode	#N/A

Approach: We will use Excel to obtain the mean and median. The steps for calculating measures of central tendency using the TI-83/84 Plus graphing calculator, MINITAB, or Excel are given in the Technology Step-by-Step on page 142.

Solution: Figure 4 shows the output obtained from Excel.

---

3   **Explain What It Means for a Statistic to be Resistant**

Thus far, we have discussed two measures of central tendency, the mean and the median. Perhaps you are asking yourself which measure is better. It depends.

EXAMPLE 5   **Comparing the Mean and the Median**

Note to Instructor
If you collected pulse data, change the largest observation to something extreme, like 120. Ask students to recompute the mean and median. Discuss the results.

Problem: Yolanda wants to know how much time she typically spends on her cell phone. She goes to her phone's website and records the phone call length for a random sample of 12 calls and obtains the data in Table 3. Find the mean and median length of a cell phone call. Which measure of central tendency better describes the length of a typical phone call?

Table 3			
1	7	4	1
2	4	3	48
3	5	3	6

Source: Yolanda Sullivan's cell phone records

Approach: We will find the mean and median using MINITAB. To help judge which is the better measure of central tendency, we will also draw a dot plot of the data using MINITAB.

Solution: Figure 5 indicates that the mean talk time is $\bar{x} = 7.3$ minutes and the median talk time is 3.5 minutes. Figure 6 shows a dot plot of the data using MINITAB.

Figure 5

Descriptive Statistics: TalkTime

```
Variable  N N* Mean SE Mean StDev Minimum   Q1 Median   Q3 Maximum
TalkTime 12  0 7.25    3.74 12.96    1.00 2.25   3.50 5.75   48.00
```

Figure 6

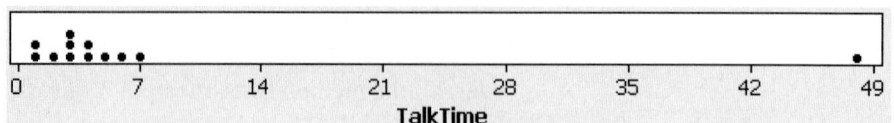

Which measure of central tendency do you think better describes the typical amount of time Yolanda spends on a phone call? Given the fact that only one phone call has a talk time greater than the mean, we conclude that the mean is not representative of the typical talk time. So the median is the better measure of central tendency.

Look back at the data in Table 3. Suppose Yolanda's 48-minute phone call was actually a 5-minute phone call. Then the mean talk time would be 3.7 minutes and the median talk time would still be 3.5 minutes. So the one extreme observation (48 minutes) can cause the mean to increase substantially, but have no effect on the median. In other words, the mean is sensitive to extreme values while the median is not. In fact, if Yolanda's 48-minute phone call had actually been a 148-minute phone call, the median would still be 3.5 minutes, but the mean would increase to 15.6 minutes. The median is unchanged because it is based on the value of the middle observation, so the value of the largest observation does not play a role in its computation. Because extreme values do not affect the value of the median, we say that the median is *resistant*.

Definition   A numerical summary of data is said to be **resistant** if extreme values (very large or small) relative to the data do not affect its value substantially.

So the median is resistant, while the mean is not resistant.

When data are either skewed left or skewed right, there are extreme values in the tail, which tend to pull the mean in the direction of the tail. For example, in skewed-right distributions, there are large observations in the right tail. These observations tend to increase the value of the mean, while having little effect on the median. Similarly, in distributions that are skewed left, the mean will tend to be smaller than the median. In distributions that are symmetric, the mean and the median are close in value. We summarize these ideas in Table 4 and Figure 7.

Table 4	
Relation Between the Mean, Median, and Distribution Shape	
Distribution Shape	**Mean versus Median**
Skewed left	Mean substantially smaller than median
Symmetric	Mean roughly equal to median
Skewed right	Mean substantially larger than median

Figure 7
Mean or median versus skewness

  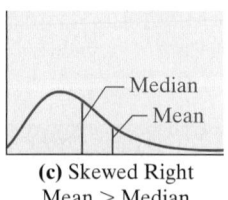

(a) Skewed Left   **(b)** Symmetric   **(c)** Skewed Right
Mean < Median   Mean = Median   Mean > Median

A word of caution is in order. The relation between the mean, median, and skewness are guidelines. The guidelines tend to hold up well for continuous data, but, when the data are discrete, the rules can be easily violated. See Problem 47.*

A question you may be asking yourself is, "Why would I ever compute the mean?" After all, the mean and median are close in value for symmetric data, and

*This idea is discussed in "Mean, Median, and Skew: Correcting a Textbook Rule" by Paul T. von Hippel. *Journal of Statistics Education*, Volume 13, Number 2 (2005).

the median is the better measure of central tendency for skewed data. The reason we compute the mean is that much of the statistical inference that we perform is based on the mean. We will have more to say about this in Chapter 8.

| EXAMPLE 6 | **Describing the Shape of a Distribution** |

Problem: The data in Table 5 represent the birth weights (in pounds) of 50 randomly sampled babies.

(a) Find the mean and the median.

(b) Describe the shape of the distribution.

(c) Which measure of central tendency better describes the average birth weight?

Approach

(a) This can be done either by hand or technology. We will use a TI-84 Plus to compute the mean and the median.

(b) We will draw a histogram to identify the shape of the distribution.

(c) If the data are roughly symmetric, the mean is a good measure of central tendency. If the data are skewed, the median is a good measure of central tendency.

Solution

(a) Using a TI-84 Plus, we find $\bar{x} = 7.49$ and $M = 7.35$. See Figure 8.

Table 5

5.8	7.4	9.2	7.0	8.5	7.6
7.9	7.8	7.9	7.7	9.0	7.1
8.7	7.2	6.1	7.2	7.1	7.2
7.9	5.9	7.0	7.8	7.2	7.5
7.3	6.4	7.4	8.2	9.1	7.3
9.4	6.8	7.0	8.1	8.0	7.5
7.3	6.9	6.9	6.4	7.8	8.7
7.1	7.0	7.0	7.4	8.2	7.2
7.6	6.7				

Figure 8

   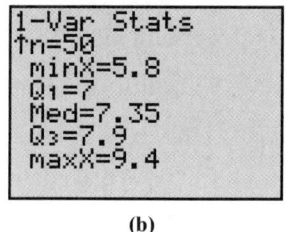

(a)   (b)

(b) See Figure 9 for the frequency histogram with the mean and median labeled. The distribution is bell shaped. We have further evidence of the shape because the mean and median are close to each other.

Figure 9
Birth weights of 50 randomly selected babies

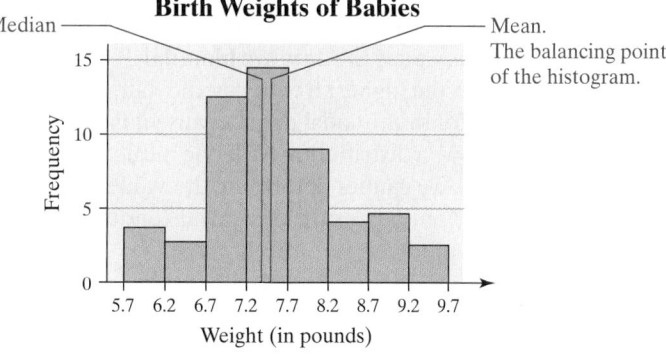

(c) Because the mean and median are close in value, we use the mean as the measure of central tendency.

Now Work Problem 27

4   Determine the Mode of a Variable from Raw Data

A third measure of central tendency is the mode. The mode can be computed for either quantitative or qualitative data.

Definition

The **mode** of a variable is the most frequent observation of the variable that occurs in the data set.

To compute the mode, tally the number of observations that occur for each data value. The data value that occurs most often is the mode. A set of data can have no mode, one mode, or more than one mode. If no observation occurs more than once, we say the data have **no mode**.

| EXAMPLE 7 | **Finding the Mode of Quantitative Data** |

Problem: The following data represent the number of O-ring failures on the shuttle *Columbia* for its 17 flights prior to its fatal flight:

$$0, 0, 0, 0, 0, 0, 0, 0, 0, 0, 0, 1, 1, 1, 1, 2, 3$$

Find the mode number of O-ring failures.

Approach: We tally the number of times we observe each data value. The data value with the highest frequency is the mode.

Solution: The mode is 0 because it occurs most frequently (11 times).

| EXAMPLE 8 | **Finding the Mode of Quantitative Data** |

Problem: Find the mode of the exam score data listed in Table 1 on page 130.

Approach: Tally the number of times we observe each data value. The data value with the highest frequency is the mode.

Solution: For convenience, the data are listed next:

$$82, 77, 90, 71, 62, 68, 74, 84, 94, 88$$

Since each data value occurs only once, there is no mode.

Figure 10

Mode
(a) One mode

Mode   Mode
(b) Bimodal

> Now compute the mode of the data in Problem 15

A data set can have more than one mode. For example, suppose the instructor recorded the scores of Pam and Sam incorrectly and they actually scored 77 and 88, respectively. The data set in Table 1 would now have two modes: 77 and 88. In this case, we say the data are **bimodal**. If a data set has three or more data values that occur with the highest frequency, the data set is **multimodal**. The mode is usually not reported for multimodal data because it is not representative of a typical value. Figure 10(a) shows a distribution with one mode. Figure 10(b) shows a distribution that is bimodal.

We cannot determine the value of the mean or median of data that are nominal. The only measure of central tendency that can be determined for nominal data is the mode.

| EXAMPLE 9 | **Determining the Mode of Qualitative Data** |

Problem: The data in Table 6 represent the location of injuries that required rehabilitation by a physical therapist. Determine the mode location of injury.

In Other Words
Remember, nominal data are qualitative data that cannot be written in any meaningful order.

Table 6					
Back	Back	Hand	Neck	Knee	Knee
Wrist	Back	Groin	Shoulder	Shoulder	Back
Elbow	Back	Back	Back	Back	Back
Back	Shoulder	Shoulder	Knee	Knee	Back
Hip	Knee	Hip	Hand	Back	Wrist

Source: Krystal Catton, student at Joliet Junior College

Approach: Determine the location of injury that occurs with the highest frequency.

Solution: The mode location of injury is the back, with 12 instances.

Now Work Problem 33

Summary

We conclude this section with the following chart, which addresses the circumstances under which each measure of central tendency should be used.

Measure of Central Tendency	Computation	Interpretation	When to Use
Mean	Population mean: $\mu = \dfrac{\Sigma x_i}{N}$ Sample mean: $\overline{x} = \dfrac{\Sigma x_i}{n}$	Center of gravity	When data are quantitative and the frequency distribution is roughly symmetric
Median	Arrange data in ascending order and divide the data set in half	Divides the bottom 50% of the data from the top 50%	When the data are quantitative and the frequency distribution is skewed left or skewed right
Mode	Tally data to determine most frequent observation	Most frequent observation	When the most frequent observation is the desired measure of central tendency or the data are qualitative

Note to Instructor   If you postponed discussion of Sections 1.2–1.6, do not assign Problems 23 or 24.

3.1 ASSESS YOUR UNDERSTANDING

Concepts and Vocabulary

1. What does it mean if a statistic is resistant? Why is the median resistant, but the mean is not?

2. In the 2000 census conducted by the U.S. Census Bureau, two average household incomes were reported: $41,349 and $55,263. One of these averages is the mean and the other is the median. Which is the mean? Support your answer.   Mean = $55,263

3. The U.S. Department of Housing and Urban Development (HUD) uses the median to report the average price of a home in the United States. Why do you think HUD uses the median?   Data skewed right

4. A histogram of a set of data indicates that the distribution of the data is skewed right. Which measure of central tendency will likely be larger, the mean or the median? Why?   Mean

5. If a data set contains 10,000 values arranged in increasing order, where is the median located?

6. *True or False*: A data set will always have exactly one mode.
   False

Skill Building

In Problems 7–10, find the population mean or sample mean as indicated.

7. Sample: 20, 13, 4, 8, 10 $\overline{x} = 11$

8. Sample: 83, 65, 91, 87, 84 $\overline{x} = 82$

9. Population: 3, 6, 10, 12, 14 $\mu = 9$

10. Population: 1, 19, 25, 15, 12, 16, 28, 13, 6 $\mu = 15$

11. For Super Bowl XL, CBS television sold 65 ad slots for a total revenue of roughly $162.5 million. What was the mean price per ad slot? $2.5 million

12. The median for the given set of six ordered data values is 26.5. What is the missing value? 7 12 21 ___32___ 41 50

13. **Crash Test Results** The Insurance Institute for Highway Safety crashed the 2007 Audi A4 four times at 5 miles per hour. The costs of repair for each of the four crashes were

$976, $2038, $918, $1899

Compute the mean, median, and mode cost of repair.

14. **Cell Phone Use** The following data represent the monthly cell phone bill for my wife's phone for six randomly selected months.

$35.34, $42.09, $39.43, $38.93, $43.39, $49.26

Compute the mean, median, and mode phone bill.

15. **Concrete Mix** A certain type of concrete mix is designed to NW withstand 3,000 pounds per square inch (psi) of pressure. The strength of concrete is measured by pouring the mix into casting cylinders 6 inches in diameter and 12 inches tall. The concrete is allowed to set for 28 days. The concrete's strength is then measured. The following data represent the strength of nine randomly selected casts (in psi).

3960, 4090, 3200, 3100, 2940, 3830, 4090, 4040, 3780

Compute the mean, median, and mode strength of the concrete (in psi). 3670; 3830; 4090

16. **Flight Time** The following data represent the flight time (in minutes) of a random sample of seven flights from Las Vegas, Nevada, to Newark, New Jersey, on Continental Airlines.

282, 270, 260, 266, 257, 260, 267

Compute the mean, median, and mode flight time.

5. The median is between the 5000th and 5001st ordered values

13. $1,457.75; $1,437.50; none   14. $41.41; $40.76; none
16. 266; 266; 260

17. For each of the three histograms shown, determine whether the mean is greater than, less than, or approximately equal to the median. Justify your answer. (a) $\bar{x} > M$ (b) $\bar{x} = M$ (c) $\bar{x} < M$

(a)

(b)

(c)

18. Match the histograms shown to the summary statistics:

	Mean	Median
I	42	42
II	31	36
III	31	26
IV	31	32

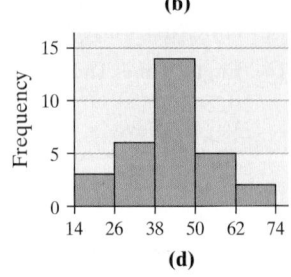

(a) IV (b) III (c) II (d) I

19. Mean versus Median Applet Load the mean versus median applet that is located on the CD that accompanies the text. Change the lower limit to 0 and the upper limit to 10 and click Update.

(a) Create a data set of at least eight observations such that the mean and median are roughly 2.

(b) Add a single observation near 9. How does this new value affect the mean? How does this new value affect the median?

(c) Change the upper limit to 25 and click Update. Remove the single value added from part (b). Add a single observation near 24. How does this new value affect the mean? the median?

(d) Refresh the page. Change the lower limit to 0 and the upper limit to 50 and click Update. Create a data set of at least eight observations such that the mean and median are roughly 40.

(e) Add a single observation near 35. How does this new value affect the mean? the median? Now "grab" this point with your mouse cursor and drag it toward 0. What happens to the value of the mean? What happens to the value of the median? Why?

20. Mean versus Median Applet Load the mean versus median applet that is located on the CD that accompanies the text. Change the lower limit to 0 and the upper limit to 10 and click Update.

(a) Create a data set of at least 10 observations such that the mean equals the median.

(b) Create a data set of at least 10 observations such that the mean is greater than the median.

(c) Create a data set of at least 10 observations such that the mean is less than the median.

(d) Comment on the shape of each distribution from parts (a)–(c).

(e) Can you create a distribution that is skewed left, but has a mean that is greater than the median?

Applying the Concepts

21. pH in Water The acidity or alkalinity of a solution is measured using pH. A pH less than 7 is acidic; a pH greater than 7 is alkaline. The following data represent the pH in samples of bottled water and tap water.

21. (a) Tap: $\bar{x} = 7.50$; $M = 7.485$; mode $= 7.47$
Bottled: $\bar{x} = 5.194$, $M = 5.22$, mode $= 5.26$

Tap	7.64	7.45	7.47	7.50	7.68	7.69
	7.45	7.10	7.56	7.47	7.52	7.47
Bottled	5.15	5.09	5.26	5.20	5.02	5.23
	5.28	5.26	5.13	5.26	5.21	5.24

Source: Emily McCarney, student at Joliet Junior College

(a) Compute the mean, median, and mode pH for each type of water. Comment on the differences between the two water types.

(b) Suppose the pH of 7.10 in tap water was incorrectly recorded as 1.70. How does this affect the mean? the median? What property of the median does this illustrate? $\bar{x} = 7.05$, $M = 7.485$; resistance

22. Reaction Time In an experiment conducted online at the University of Mississippi, study participants are asked to react to a stimulus. In one experiment, the participant must

22. (a) Blue: 0.551 sec; 0.5315 sec; none; Red: 0.458 sec; 0.432 sec; none

press a key upon seeing a blue screen. The time (in seconds) to press the key is measured. The same person is then asked to press a key upon seeing a red screen, again with the time to react measured. The table shows the results for six study participants.

(a) Compute the mean, median, and mode reaction time for both blue and red.

(b) Does there appear to be a difference in the reaction time? What might account for any difference? How might this information be used?

(c) Suppose the reaction time of 0.841 for blue was incorrectly recorded as 8.41. How does this affect the mean? the median? What property of the median does this illustrate? $\bar{x} = 1.8125$; $M = 0.5315$; resistance

Participant Number	Reaction Time to Blue	Reaction Time to Red
1	0.582	0.408
2	0.481	0.407
3	0.841	0.542
4	0.267	0.402
5	0.685	0.456
6	0.450	0.533

Source: PsychExperiments at the University of Mississippi (www.olemiss.edu/psychexps)

23. **Pulse Rates** The following data represent the pulse rates
NW (beats per minute) of nine students enrolled in a section of Sullivan's Introductory Statistics course. Treat the nine students as a population.

Student	Pulse
Perpectual Bempah	76
Megan Brooks	60
Jeff Honeycutt	60
Clarice Jefferson	81
Crystal Kurtenbach	72
Janette Lantka	80
Kevin McCarthy	80
Tammy Ohm	68
Kathy Wojdyla	73

(a) Compute the population mean pulse. 72.2

(b) Determine three simple random samples of size 3 and compute the sample mean pulse of each sample.

(c) Which samples result in a sample mean that overestimates the population mean? Which samples result in a sample mean that underestimates the population mean? Do any samples lead to a sample mean that equals the population mean?

24. **Travel Time** The following data (table on top of next column) represent the travel time (in minutes) to school for nine students enrolled in Sullivan's College Algebra course. Treat the nine students as a population.

(a) Compute the population mean for travel time. 26.4 min

(b) Determine three simple random samples of size 4 and compute the sample mean for travel time of each sample.

Student	Travel Time	Student	Travel Time
Amanda	39	Scot	45
Amber	21	Erica	11
Tim	9	Tiffany	12
Mike	32	Glenn	39
Nicole	30		

(c) Which samples result in a sample mean that overestimates the population mean? Which samples result in a sample mean that underestimates the population mean? Do any samples lead to a sample mean that equals the population mean?

25. **Carbon Dioxide Emissions** The given data represent the carbon dioxide (CO_2) emissions (in thousands of metric tons) of the top 10 emitters in 2004.

Country	Emissions	Per Capita Emissions
United States	6,049,435	5.61
China	5,010,170	1.05
Russia	1,524,993	2.89
India	1,342,962	0.34
Japan	1,257,963	2.69
Germany	808,767	2.67
Canada	639,403	5.46
United Kingdom	587,261	2.67
South Korea	465,643	2.64
Italy	449,948	2.12

Source: Carbon Dioxide Information Analysis Center

(a) Determine the mean CO_2 emissions of the top 10 countries. 1,813,654.5 thousand metric tons

(b) Explain why the total emissions of a country is likely not the best gauge of CO_2 emissions; instead, the emissions per capita (total emissions divided by population size) is the better gauge.

(c) Determine the mean and median per capita CO_2 emissions of the top 10 countries. Which measure would an environmentalist likely use to support the position that per capita CO_2 emissions are too high? Why? 2.814 thousand metric tons; 2.67 thousand metric tons; mean

26. **Tour de Lance** Lance Armstrong won the Tour de France seven consecutive years (1999–2005). The following table gives the winning times, distances, speeds, and margin of victory.

Year	Winning Time (h)	Distance (km)	Winning Speed (km/h)	Winning Margin (min)
1999	91.538	3687	40.28	7.617
2000	92.552	3662	39.56	6.033
2001	86.291	3453	40.02	6.733
2002	82.087	3278	39.93	7.283
2003	83.687	3427	40.94	1.017
2004	83.601	3391	40.56	6.317
2005	86.251	3593	41.65	4.667

Source: cyclingnews.com

26. (d) Method 1: mean = 40.420 km/h; method 2: mean = 40.414 km/h; method 3: mean = 40.414 km/h

(a) Compute the mean and median of his winning times for the seven races. Mean = 86.572 h; median = 86.251 h

(b) Compute the mean and median of the distances for the seven races. Mean = 3498.7 km; median = 3453 km

(c) Compute the mean and median of his winning time margins. Mean = 5.667 min; median = 6.317 min

(d) Compute the mean winning speed by finding the mean of the data values in the table. Next, compute the mean winning speed by finding the total of the seven distances and dividing by the total of the seven winning times. Finally, compute the mean winning speed by dividing the mean distance by the mean winning time. Do the three values agree or are there differences?

27. **Connection Time** A histogram of the connection time, in seconds, to an Internet service provider for 30 randomly selected connections is shown. The mean connection time is 39.007 seconds and the median connection time is 39.065 seconds. Identify the shape of the distribution. Which measure of central tendency better describes the "center" of the distribution? Symmetric; mean

Connection Time

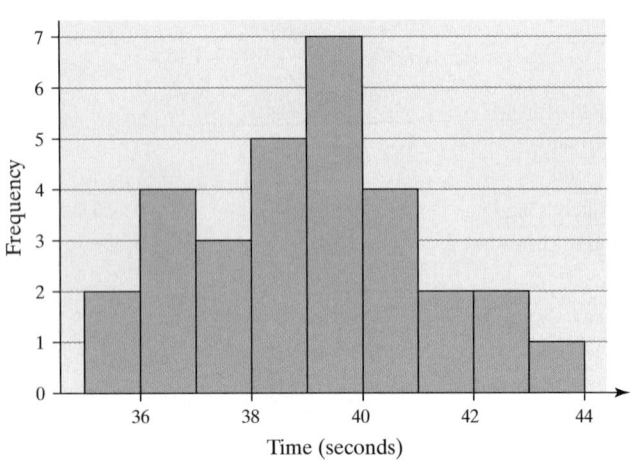

Source: Nicole Spreitzer, student at Joliet Junior College

28. **Journal Costs** A histogram of the annual subscription cost (in dollars) for 26 biology journals is shown. The mean subscription cost is $1846 and the median subscription cost is $1142. Identify the shape of the distribution. Which measure

Cost of Biology Journals

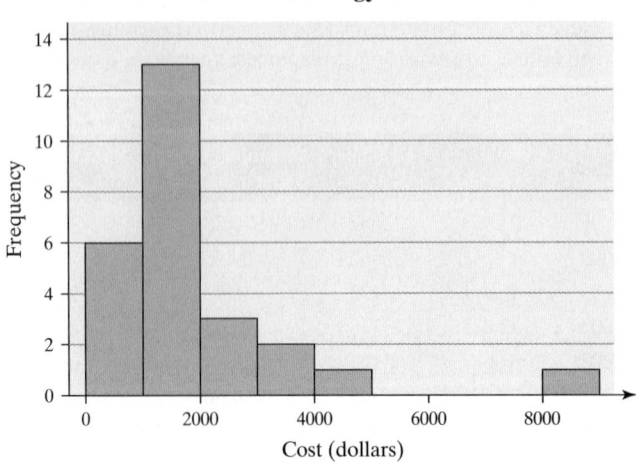

Source: Carol Wesolowski, student at Joliet Junior College

of central tendency better describes the "center" of the distribution? Skewed right; median

29. **M&Ms** The following data represent the weights (in grams) of a simple random sample of 50 M&M plain candies.

0.87	0.88	0.82	0.90	0.90	0.84	0.84
0.91	0.94	0.86	0.86	0.86	0.88	0.87
0.89	0.91	0.86	0.87	0.93	0.88	
0.83	0.95	0.87	0.93	0.91	0.85	
0.91	0.91	0.86	0.89	0.87	0.84	
0.88	0.88	0.89	0.79	0.82	0.83	
0.90	0.88	0.84	0.93	0.81	0.90	
0.88	0.92	0.85	0.84	0.84	0.86	

Source: Michael Sullivan

Symmetric; $\bar{x}$ = 0.875 g; M = 0.875 g; mean
Determine the shape of the distribution of weights of M&Ms by drawing a frequency histogram. Compute the mean and median. Which measure of central tendency better describes the weight of a plain M&M?

30. **Old Faithful** We have all heard of the Old Faithful geyser in Yellowstone National Park. However, there is another, less famous, Old Faithful geyser in Calistoga, California. The following data represent the length of eruption (in seconds) for a random sample of eruptions of the California Old Faithful.

108	108	99	105	103	103	94
102	99	106	90	104	110	110
103	109	109	111	101	101	
110	102	105	110	106	104	
104	100	103	102	120	90	
113	116	95	105	103	101	
100	101	107	110	92	108	

Source: Ladonna Hansen, Park Curator

Symmetric; $\bar{x}$ = 104.1 s, M = 104 s; mean
Determine the shape of the distribution of length of eruption by drawing a frequency histogram. Compute the mean and median. Which measure of central tendency better describes the length of eruption?

31. **Hours Working** A random sample of 25 college students was asked, "How many hours per week typically do you work outside the home?" Their responses were as follows:

0	0	15	20	30
40	30	20	35	35
28	15	20	25	25
30	5	0	30	24
28	30	35	15	15

Determine the shape of the distribution of hours worked by drawing a frequency histogram. Compute the mean and median. Which measure of central tendency better describes hours worked? Skewed left; $\bar{x}$ = 22 hrs; M = 25 hrs; median

32. **A Dealer's Profit** The following data represent the profit (in dollars) of a new-car dealer for a random sample of 40 sales.

781	1,038	453	1,446	3,082
501	451	1,826	1,348	3,001
1,342	1,889	580	0	2,909
2,883	480	1,664	1,064	2,978
149	1,291	507	261	540
543	87	798	673	2,862
1,692	1,783	2,186	398	526
730	2,324	2,823	1,676	4,148

Source: Ashley Hudson, student at Joliet Junior College

Determine the shape of the distribution of new-car profit by drawing a frequency histogram. Compute the mean and median. Which measure of central tendency better describes the profit? Skewed right; $\bar{x}$ = \$1,392.83; M = \$1,177.50; median

33. Political Views A sample of 30 registered voters was surveyed in which the respondents were asked, "Do you consider your political views to be conservative, moderate, or liberal?" The results of the survey are shown in the table.

Liberal	Conservative	Moderate
Moderate	Liberal	Moderate
Liberal	Moderate	Conservative
Moderate	Conservative	Moderate
Moderate	Moderate	Liberal
Liberal	Moderate	Liberal
Conservative	Moderate	Moderate
Liberal	Conservative	Liberal
Liberal	Conservative	Liberal
Conservative	Moderate	Conservative

Source: Based on data from the General Social Survey

(a) Determine the mode political view. Moderate

(b) Do you think it would be a good idea to rotate the choices conservative, moderate, or liberal in the question? Why? Yes, to avoid response bias

34. Hospital Admissions The following data represent the diagnosis of a random sample of 20 patients admitted to a hospital.

Cancer	Motor vehicle accident	Congestive heart failure
Gunshot wound	Fall	Gunshot wound
Gunshot wound	Motor vehicle accident	Gunshot wound
Assault	Motor vehicle accident	Gunshot wound
Motor vehicle accident	Motor vehicle accident	Gunshot wound
Motor vehicle accident	Gunshot wound	Motor vehicle accident
Fall	Gunshot wound	

Source: Tamela Ohm, student at Joliet Junior College

Determine the mode diagnosis. Gunshot wound

35. Resistance and Sample Size Each of the following three data sets represents the IQ scores of a random sample of adults. IQ scores are known to have a mean and median of 100. For each data set, compute the mean and median. For each data set recalculate the mean and median, assuming that the individual whose IQ is 106 is accidentally recorded as 160. For each sample size, state what happens to the mean and the median? Comment on the role the number of observations plays in resistance.

Sample of Size 5				
106	92	98	103	100

Sample of Size 12					
106	92	98	103	100	102
98	124	83	70	108	121

Sample of Size 30					
106	92	98	103	100	102
98	124	83	70	108	121
102	87	121	107	97	114
140	93	130	72	81	90
103	97	89	98	88	103

36. Mr. Zuro finds the mean height of all 14 students in his statistics class to be 68.0 inches. Just as Mr. Zuro finishes explaining how to get the mean, Danielle walks in late. Danielle is 65 inches tall. What is the mean height of the 15 students in the class? 67.8 inches

37. A researcher with the Department of Energy wants to determine the mean natural gas bill of households throughout the United States. He knows the mean natural gas bill of households for each state, so he adds together these 50 values and divides by 50 to arrive at his estimate. Is this a valid approach? Why or why not? No

38. Net Worth According to the *Statistical Abstract of the United States*, the mean net worth of all households in the United States in 2004 was \$448,200, while the median net worth was \$93,100.

(a) Which measure do you believe better describes the typical U.S. household's net worth? Support your opinion. Median

(b) What shape would you expect the distribution of net worth to have? Why? Skewed right

(c) What do you think causes the disparity in the two measures of central tendency?

39. You are negotiating a contract for the Players Association of the NBA. Which measure of central tendency will you use to support your claim that the average player's salary needs to be increased? Why? As the chief negotiator for the owners, which measure would you use to refute the claim made by the Players Association?

40. In January 2008, the mean amount of money lost per visitor to a local riverboat casino was \$135. Do you think the median was more than, less than, or equal to this amount? Why?

41. Missing Exam Grade A professor has recorded exam grades for 20 students in his class, but one of the grades is no longer readable. If the mean score on the exam was 82 and the mean of the 19 readable scores is 84, what is the value of the unreadable score? 44

42. For each of the following situations, determine which measure of central tendency is most appropriate and justify your reasoning.

42. (d) Median   43. (a) Mean = 50; median = 50; mode = 50

(a) Average price of a home sold in Pittsburgh, Pennsylvania in 2009 Median

(b) Most popular major for students enrolled in a statistics course Mode

(c) Average test score when the scores are distributed symmetrically Mean

(d) Average test score when the scores are skewed right

(e) Average income of a player in the National Football League Median

(f) Most requested song at a radio station Mode

43. **Linear Transformations** Benjamin owns a small Internet business. Besides himself, he employs nine other people. The salaries earned by the employees are given next in thousands of dollars (Benjamin's salary is the largest, of course):

30, 30, 45, 50, 50, 50, 55, 55, 60, 75

(a) Determine the mean, median, and mode for salary.

(b) Business has been good! As a result, Benjamin has a total of $25,000 in bonus pay to distribute to his employees. One option for distributing bonuses is to give each employee (including himself) $2,500. Add the bonuses under this plan to the original salaries to create a new data set. Recalculate the mean, median, and mode. How do they compare to the originals? mean = 52.5; median = 52.5; mode = 52.5

(c) As a second option, Benjamin can give each employee a bonus of 5% of his or her original salary. Add the bonuses under this second plan to the original salaries to create a new data set. Recalculate the mean, median, and mode. How do they compare to the originals?

(d) As a third option, Benjamin decides not to give his employees a bonus at all. Instead, he keeps the $25,000 for himself. Use this plan to create a new data set. Recalculate the mean, median, and mode. How do they compare to the originals? mean = 52.5; median = 50; mode = 50

44. **Linear Transformations** Use the five test scores of 65, 70, 71, 75, and 95 to answer the following questions:

(a) Find the sample mean. 75.2

(b) Find the median. 71

(c) Which measure of central tendency best describes the typical test score? Median

43. (c) mean = 52.5; median = 52.5; mode = 52.5

(d) Suppose the professor decides to curve the exam by adding 4 points to each test score. Compute the sample mean based on the adjusted scores. 79.2

(e) Compare the unadjusted test score mean with the curved test score mean. What effect did adding 4 to each score have on the mean?

45. **Trimmed Mean** Another measure of central tendency is the trimmed mean. It is computed by determining the mean of a data set after deleting the smallest and largest observed values. Compute the trimmed mean for the data in Problem 29. Is the trimmed mean resistant? Explain. 0.875

46. **Midrange** The midrange is also a measure of central tendency. It is computed by adding the smallest and largest observed values of a data set and dividing the result by 2; that is,

$$\text{Midrange} = \frac{\text{largest data value} + \text{smallest data value}}{2}$$

Compute the midrange for the data in Problem 29. Is the midrange resistant? Explain. 0.87; no

47. **Putting It Together: Shape, Mean and Median** As part of a semester project in a statistics course, Carlos surveyed a sample of 40 high school students and asked, "How many days in the past week have you consumed an alcoholic beverage?" The results of the survey are shown next.

0	0	1	4	1	1	1	5	1	3
0	1	0	1	0	4	0	1	0	1
0	0	0	0	2	0	0	0	0	0
1	0	2	0	0	0	1	2	1	1
2	0	1	0	1	3	1	1	0	3

(a) Is this data discrete or continuous? Discrete

(b) Draw a histogram of the data and describe its shape.

(c) Based on the shape of the histogram, do you expect the mean to be more than, equal to, or less than the median? $\bar{x} > M$

(d) Compute the mean and the median. What does this tell you? Mean: 0.94; Median: 1

(e) Determine the mode. 0

(f) Do you believe that Carlos' survey suffers from sampling bias? Why? Yes

47. (b) Skewed right

TECHNOLOGY STEP-BY-STEP Determining the Mean and Median

TI-83/84 Plus

1. Enter the raw data in L1 by pressing STAT and selecting 1:Edit.

2. Press STAT, highlight the CALC menu, and select 1:1-Var Stats.

3. With 1-Var Stats appearing on the HOME screen, press 2nd then 1 to insert L1 on the HOME screen. Press ENTER.

MINITAB

1. Enter the data in C1.

2. Select the **Stat** menu, highlight **Basic Statistics**, and then highlight **Display Descriptive Statistics**.

3. In the **Variables** window, enter C1. Click OK.

Excel

1. Enter the data in column A.

2. Select the **Tools** menu and highlight **Data Analysis . . .**

3. In the Data Analysis window, highlight **Descriptive Statistics** and click OK.

4. With the cursor in the **Input Range** window, use the mouse to highlight the data in column A.

5. Select the **Summary statistics** option and click OK.

3.2 MEASURES OF DISPERSION

Objectives

1 Compute the range of a variable from raw data

2 Compute the variance of a variable from raw data

3 Compute the standard deviation of a variable from raw data

4 Use the Empirical Rule to describe data that are bell shaped

5 Use Chebyshev's inequality to describe any set of data

In Section 3.1, we discussed measures of central tendency. The purpose of these measures is to describe the typical value of a variable. In addition to measuring the central tendency of a variable, we would also like to know the amount of *dispersion* in the variable. By **dispersion**, we mean the degree to which the data are spread out. An example should help to explain why measures of central tendency are not sufficient in describing a distribution.

EXAMPLE 1 **Comparing Two Sets of Data**

Problem: The data in Table 7 represent the IQ scores of a random sample of 100 students from two different universities. For each university, compute the mean IQ score and draw a histogram, using a lower class limit of 55 for the first class and a class width of 15. Comment on the results.

Table 7																			
University A										**University B**									
73	103	91	93	136	108	92	104	90	78	86	91	107	94	105	107	89	96	102	96
108	93	91	78	81	130	82	86	111	93	92	109	103	106	98	95	97	95	109	109
102	111	125	107	80	90	122	101	82	115	93	91	92	91	117	108	89	95	103	109
103	110	84	115	85	83	131	90	103	106	110	88	97	119	90	99	96	104	98	95
71	69	97	130	91	62	85	94	110	85	87	105	111	87	103	92	103	107	106	97
102	109	105	97	104	94	92	83	94	114	107	108	89	96	107	107	96	95	117	97
107	94	112	113	115	106	97	106	85	99	98	89	104	99	99	87	91	105	109	108
102	109	76	94	103	112	107	101	91	107	116	107	90	98	98	92	119	96	118	98
107	110	106	103	93	110	125	101	91	119	97	106	114	87	107	96	93	99	89	94
118	85	127	141	129	60	115	80	111	79	104	88	99	97	106	107	112	97	94	107

Approach: We will use MINITAB to compute the mean and draw a histogram for each university.

Solution: We enter the data into MINITAB and determine that the mean IQ score of both universities is 100.0. Figure 11 shows the histograms.

Figure 11

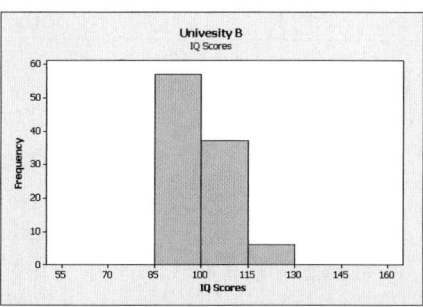

Note to Instructor
You may want to share with students that the smallest data value is also referred to as the minimum and the largest data value is referred to as the maximum, as a preview of the five-number summary.

Note to Instructor
Consider continuing with the data collected from the population mean versus sample mean activity to illustrate Examples 2 through 6.

Both universities have the same mean IQ, but the histograms indicate the IQs from University A are more spread out, that is, more dispersed. While an IQ of 100.0 is typical for both universities, it appears to be a more reliable description of the typical student from University B than from University A. That is, a higher proportion of students from University B have IQ scores within, say, 15 points of the mean of 100.0 than students from University A.

Our goal in this section is to discuss numerical measures of dispersion so that we can quantify the spread of data. In this section, we discuss three numerical measures for describing the dispersion, or spread, of data: the range, variance, and standard deviation. In Section 3.4, we will discuss another measure of dispersion, the *interquartile range* (IQR).

① Compute the Range of a Variable from Raw Data

The simplest measure of dispersion is the range. To compute the range, the data must be quantitative.

Definition

The **range, *R*,** of a variable is the difference between the largest data value and the smallest data value. That is,

$$\text{Range} = R = \text{largest data value} - \text{smallest data value}$$

EXAMPLE 2 **Computing the Range of a Set of Data**

Table 8	
Student	**Score**
1. Michelle	82
2. Ryanne	77
3. Bilal	90
4. Pam	71
5. Jennifer	62
6. Dave	68
7. Joel	74
8. Sam	84
9. Justine	94
10. Juan	88

Problem: The data in Table 8 represent the scores on the first exam of 10 students enrolled in a section of Introductory Statistics. Compute the range.

Approach: The range is found by computing the difference between the largest and smallest data values.

Solution: The highest test score is 94 and the lowest test score is 62. The range is

$$R = 94 - 62 = 32$$

All the students in the class scored between 62 and 94 on the exam. The difference between the best score and the worst score is 32 points.

Now compute the range of the data in Problem 19

Notice that the range is affected by extreme values in the data set, so the range is not resistant. If Jennifer did not study and scored 28, the range becomes $R = 94 - 28 = 66$. In addition, the range is computed using only two values in the data set (the largest and smallest). The *variance* and the *standard deviation*, on the other hand, use all the data values in the computations.

② Compute the Variance of a Variable from Raw Data

Note to Instructor
Stress to the students that the variance is difficult to interpret because it is measured in units squared (such as points squared). However, the variance plays an important role in statistical inference.

Just as there is a population mean and sample mean, we also have a population variance and a sample variance. Measures of dispersion are meant to describe how spread out data are. Another way to think about this is to describe how far, on average, each observation is from the mean. Variance is based on the **deviation**

about the mean. For a population, the deviation about the mean for the ith observation is $x_i - \mu$. For a sample, the deviation about the mean for the ith observation is $x_i - \overline{x}$. The further an observation is from the mean, the larger the absolute value of the deviation.

The sum of all deviations about the mean must equal zero. That is,

$$\sum (x_i - \mu) = 0 \quad \text{and} \quad \sum (x_i - \overline{x}) = 0$$

In other words, observations greater than the mean are offset by observations less than the mean. Because the sum of deviations about the mean is zero, we cannot use the average deviation about the mean as a measure of spread. However, squaring a nonzero number always results in a positive number, so we could find the average *squared* deviation.

Definition

The **population variance** of a variable is the sum of the squared deviations about the population mean divided by the number of observations in the population, N. That is, it is the mean of the squared deviations about the population mean. The population variance is symbolically represented by σ^2 (lowercase Greek sigma squared).

CAUTION

In using Formula (1), do not round until the last computation. Use as many decimal places as allowed by your calculator to avoid round-off errors.

$$\sigma^2 = \frac{(x_1 - \mu)^2 + (x_2 - \mu)^2 + \cdots + (x_N - \mu)^2}{N} = \frac{\sum (x_i - \mu)^2}{N} \quad \textbf{(1)}$$

where $x_1, x_2, \ldots, x_N$ are the N observations in the population and μ is the population mean.

A formula that is equivalent to Formula (1), called the **computational formula** for determining the population variance, is

Note to Instructor
Be sure to let students know which, if any, formula you prefer.

$$\sigma^2 = \frac{\sum x_i^2 - \dfrac{\left(\sum x_i\right)^2}{N}}{N} \quad \textbf{(2)}$$

where $\sum x_i^2$ means to square each observation and then sum these squared values, and $\left(\sum x_i\right)^2$ means to add up all the observations and then square the sum.

We illustrate how to use both formulas for computing the variance in the next example.

EXAMPLE 3   **Computing a Population Variance**

Problem: Compute the population variance of the test scores presented in Table 8.

Approach Using Formula (1)

Step 1: Create a table with four columns. Enter the population data in the first column. In the second column, enter the population mean.

Step 2: Compute the deviation about the mean for each data value. That is, compute $x_i - \mu$ for each data value. Enter these values in column 3.

Step 3: Square the values in column 3, and enter the results in column 4.

Step 4: Sum the squared deviations in column 4, and divide this result by the size of the population, N.

Approach Using Formula (2)

Step 1: Create a table with two columns. Enter the population data in the first column. Square each value in the first column and enter the result in the second column.

Step 2: Sum the entries in the first column. That is, find $\sum x_i$. Sum the entries in the second column. That is, find $\sum x_i^2$.

Step 3: Substitute the values found in Step 2 and the value for N into the computational formula and simplify.

Solution

Step 1: See Table 9. Column 1 lists the observations in the data set, and column 2 contains the population mean.

		Table 9	
Score, x_i	Population Mean, μ	Deviation about the Mean, $x_i - \mu$	Squared Deviations about the Mean, $(x_i - \mu)^2$
82	79	$82 - 79 = 3$	$3^2 = 9$
77	79	$77 - 79 = -2$	$(-2)^2 = 4$
90	79	11	121
71	79	−8	64
62	79	−17	289
68	79	−11	121
74	79	−5	25
84	79	5	25
94	79	15	225
88	79	9	81
		$\sum(x_i - \mu) = 0$	$\sum(x_i - \mu)^2 = 964$

Step 2: Compute the deviations about the mean for each observation, as shown in column 3. For example, the deviation about the mean for Michelle is $82 - 79 = 3$. It is a good idea to add up the entries in this column to make sure they sum to 0.

Step 3: Column 4 shows the squared deviations about the mean. Notice the further an observation is from the mean, the larger the squared deviation.

Step 4: We sum the entries in column 4 to obtain the numerator of Formula (1). We compute the population variance by dividing the sum of the entries in column 4 by the number of students, 10:

$$\sigma^2 = \frac{\sum(x_i - \mu)^2}{N} = \frac{964}{10} = 96.4 \text{ points}^2$$

Solution

Step 1: See Table 10. Column 1 lists the observations in the data set, and column 2 contains the values in column 1 squared.

Table 10	
Score, x_i	Score Squared, x_i^2
82	$82^2 = 6{,}724$
77	$77^2 = 5{,}929$
90	8,100
71	5,041
62	3,844
68	4,624
74	5,476
84	7,056
94	8,836
88	7,744
$\sum x_i = 790$	$\sum x_i^2 = 63{,}374$

Step 2: The last row of columns 1 and 2 show that $\sum x_i = 790$ and $\sum x_i^2 = 63{,}374$.

Step 3: We substitute 790 for $\sum x_i$, 63,374 for $\sum x_i^2$, and 10 for N into the computational Formula (2).

$$\sigma^2 = \frac{\sum x_i^2 - \dfrac{\left(\sum x_i\right)^2}{N}}{N} = \frac{63{,}374 - \dfrac{(790)^2}{10}}{10}$$

$$= \frac{964}{10}$$

$$= 96.4 \text{ points}^2$$

Note to Instructor

In-class concept check: Ask students to explain why $\sum(x_i - \bar{x}) = 0$? When calculating $\sum(x_i - \bar{x})$, why does it sometimes turn out to be a little more or less than 0?

The unit of measure of the variance in Example 3 is points squared. This unit of measure results from squaring the deviations about the mean. Because points squared does not have any obvious meaning, the interpretation of the variance is limited.

The sample variance is computed using sample data.

Definition   The **sample variance**, s^2, is computed by determining the sum of the squared deviations about the sample mean and dividing this result by $n - 1$. The formula for the sample variance from a sample of size n is

$$s^2 = \frac{\sum(x_i - \bar{x})^2}{n - 1} = \frac{(x_1 - \bar{x})^2 + (x_2 - \bar{x})^2 + \cdots + (x_n - \bar{x})^2}{n - 1} \quad \textbf{(3)}$$

where $x_1, x_2, \ldots, x_n$ are the n observations in the sample and $\bar{x}$ is the sample mean.

⬥ CAUTION When using Formula (3), be sure to use $\bar{x}$ with as many decimal places as possible to avoid round-off error.

A computational formula that is equivalent to Formula (3) for computing the sample variance is

$$s^2 = \frac{\sum x_i^2 - \dfrac{\left(\sum x_i\right)^2}{n}}{n - 1} \tag{4}$$

When computing the sample variance, be sure to divide by $n - 1$, not n.

Notice that the sample variance is obtained by dividing by $n - 1$. If we divided by n, as we might expect, the sample variance would consistently underestimate the population variance. Whenever a statistic consistently overestimates or underestimates a parameter, it is called **biased**. To obtain an unbiased estimate of the population variance, we divide the sum of the squared deviations about the sample mean by $n - 1$.

To help understand the idea of a biased estimator, consider the following situation: Suppose you work for a carnival in which you must guess a person's age. After 20 people come to your booth, you notice that you have a tendency to underestimate people's age. (You guess too low.) What would you do about this? In all likelihood, you would adjust your guesses higher so that you don't underestimate anymore. In other words, before the adjustment, your guesses were biased. To remove the bias, you increase your guess. This is what dividing by $n - 1$ in the sample variance formula accomplishes. Dividing by n results in an underestimate, so we divide by a smaller number to increase our "guess."

Although a proof that establishes why we divide by $n - 1$ is beyond the scope of the text, we can provide an explanation that has intuitive appeal. We already know that the sum of the deviations about the mean, $\Sigma(x_i - \overline{x})$, must equal zero. Therefore, if the sample mean is known and the first $n - 1$ observations are known, then the nth observation must be the value that causes the sum of the deviations to equal zero. For example, suppose $\overline{x} = 4$ based on a sample of size 3. In addition, if $x_1 = 2$ and $x_2 = 3$, then we can determine x_3.

$$\frac{x_1 + x_2 + x_3}{3} = \overline{x}$$

$$\frac{2 + 3 + x_3}{3} = 4 \qquad x_1 = 2, x_2 = 3, \overline{x} = 4$$

$$5 + x_3 = 12$$

$$x_3 = 7$$

Note to Instructor

To help students understand the concept of bias, draw a dart board on the board. Have all the darts congregate in the upper-left quadrant of the board.

Note to Instructor

A visual to help students understand degrees of freedom: Suppose there are six doughnuts in a box. The first five people to pick a doughnut have a choice (or freedom) about which doughnut to pick. The sixth person does not.

In Other Words

We have $n - 1$ degrees of freedom in the computation of s^2 because an unknown parameter, μ, is estimated with $\overline{x}$. For each parameter estimated, we lose 1 degree of freedom.

We call $n - 1$ the **degrees of freedom** because the first $n - 1$ observations have freedom to be whatever value they wish, but the nth value has no freedom. It must be whatever value forces the sum of the deviations about the mean to equal zero.

Again, you should notice that typically Greek letters are used for parameters, while Roman letters are used for statistics. Do not use rounded values of the sample mean in Formula (3).

EXAMPLE 4   **Computing a Sample Variance**

Problem: Compute the sample variance of the sample obtained in Example 1(b) on page 130 from Section 3.1.

Approach: We follow the same approach that we used to compute the population variance, but this time using the sample data. In looking back at Example 1(b) from Section 3.1, we see that Bilal (90), Ryanne (77), Pam (71), and Michelle (82) are in the sample.

Solution Using Formula (3)

Step 1: Create a table with four columns. Enter the sample data in the first column. In the second column, enter the sample mean. See Table 11.

Table 11			
Score, x_i	Sample Mean, $\bar{x}$	Deviation about the Mean, $x_i - \bar{x}$	Squared Deviations about the Mean, $(x_i - \bar{x})^2$
90	80	$90 - 80 = 10$	$10^2 = 100$
77	80	-3	9
71	80	-9	81
82	80	2	4
		$\sum (x_i - \bar{x}) = 0$	$\sum (x_i - \bar{x})^2 = 194$

Step 2: Compute the deviations about the mean for each observation, as shown in column 3. For example, the deviation about the mean for Bilal is $90 - 80 = 10$. It is a good idea to add up the entries in this column to make sure they sum to 0.

Step 3: Column 4 shows the squared deviations about the mean.

Step 4: We sum the entries in column 4 to obtain the numerator of Formula (3). We compute the population variance by dividing the sum of the entries in column 4 by one fewer than the number of students, $4 - 1$:

$$s^2 = \frac{\sum (x_i - \bar{x})^2}{n - 1} = \frac{194}{4 - 1} = 64.7$$

Solution Using Formula (4)

Step 1: See Table 12. Column 1 lists the observations in the data set, and column 2 contains the values in column 1 squared.

Table 12	
Score, x_i	Score squared, x_i^2
90	$90^2 = 8,100$
77	$77^2 = 5,929$
71	5,041
82	6,724
$\sum x_i = 320$	$\sum x_i^2 = 25,794$

Step 2: The last rows of columns 1 and 2 show that $\Sigma x_i = 320$ and $\Sigma x_i^2 = 25,794$.

Step 3: We substitute 320 for Σx_i, 25,794 for Σx_i^2, and 4 for n into the computational Formula (4).

$$s^2 = \frac{\sum x_i^2 - \frac{\left(\sum x_i\right)^2}{n}}{n - 1} = \frac{25,794 - \frac{(320)^2}{4}}{4 - 1}$$

$$= \frac{194}{3}$$

$$= 64.7$$

Notice that the sample variance obtained for this sample is an underestimate of the population variance we found in Example 3. This discrepancy does not violate our definition of an unbiased estimator, however. A biased estimator is one that *consistently* under- or overestimates.

③ Compute the Standard Deviation of a Variable from Raw Data

The standard deviation and the mean are the most popular methods for numerically describing the distribution of a variable. This is because these two measures are used for most types of statistical inference.

Definitions

The **population standard deviation**, σ, is obtained by taking the square root of the population variance. That is,

$$\sigma = \sqrt{\sigma^2}$$

The **sample standard deviation**, s, is obtained by taking the square root of the sample variance. That is,

$$s = \sqrt{s^2}$$

EXAMPLE 5 **Obtaining the Standard Deviation for a Population and a Sample**

Problem: Use the results obtained in Examples 3 and 4 to compute the population and sample standard deviation score on the statistics exam.

Approach: The population standard deviation is the square root of the population variance. The sample standard deviation is the square root of the sample variance.

Solution: The population standard deviation is

$$\sigma = \sqrt{\sigma^2} = \sqrt{\frac{\sum(x_i - \mu)^2}{N}} = \sqrt{\frac{964}{10}} = 9.8 \text{ points}$$

The sample standard deviation for the sample obtained in Example 1 from Section 3.1 is

⬥ **CAUTION** Never use the rounded variance to compute the standard deviation.

$$s = \sqrt{s^2} = \sqrt{\frac{\sum(x_i - \bar{x})^2}{n - 1}} = \sqrt{\frac{194}{4 - 1}} = 8.0 \text{ points}$$

To avoid round-off error, never use the rounded value of the variance to compute the standard deviation.

Now Work Problem 25

IN CLASS ACTIVITY

The Sample Standard Deviation

Using the pulse data from Section 3.1, page 131, do the following:

(a) Obtain a simple random sample of $n = 4$ students and compute the sample standard deviation.

(b) Obtain a second simple random sample of $n = 4$ students and compute the sample standard deviation.

(c) Are the sample standard deviations the same? Why?

EXAMPLE 6   **Determining the Variance and Standard Deviation Using Technology**

Problem: Use statistical software or a calculator to determine the population standard deviation of the data listed in Table 8. Also determine the sample standard deviation of the sample data from Example 4.

Approach: We will use a TI-84 Plus graphing calculator to obtain the population standard deviation and sample standard deviation score on the statistics exam. The steps for determining the standard deviation using the TI-83 or TI-84 Plus graphing calculator, MINITAB, or Excel are given in the Technology Step-by-Step on page 159.

Solution: Figure 12(a) shows the population standard deviation, and Figure 12(b) shows the sample standard deviation. Notice the TI graphing calculators provide both a population and sample standard deviation as output. This is because the calculator does not know whether the data entered are population data or sample data. It is up to the user of the calculator to choose the correct standard deviation. The results agree with those obtained in Example 5. To get the variance, we need to square the standard deviation. For example, the population variance is $9.818350167^2 = 96.4 \text{ points}^2$.

Figure 12

Population standard deviation

Sample standard deviation

(a)   (b)

Is the standard deviation resistant? To help determine the answer, suppose Jennifer's exam score (Table 8 on page 144) is 26, not 62. The population standard deviation increases from 9.8 to 18.3. Clearly, the standard deviation is *not* resistant.

Interpretations of the Standard Deviation

Note to Instructor
To help students understand the concept of standard deviation, ask them whether they would prefer to invest in a stock with a standard deviation rate of return of 8% or one of 20%. Why? Or would they rather stand in a line with a standard deviation wait time of 3 minutes or 6 minutes? Why? In both examples, assume the means are equal.

The standard deviation is used in conjunction with the mean to numerically describe distributions that are bell shaped and symmetric. The mean measures the center of the distribution, while the standard deviation measures the spread of the distribution. So how does the value of the standard deviation relate to the dispersion of the distribution?

Loosely, we can interpret the standard deviation as the typical deviation from the mean. So, in the data from Table 8, a typical deviation from the mean, $\mu = 79$ points, is 9.8 points.

If we are comparing two populations, then **the larger the standard deviation, the more dispersion the distribution has** provided that the variable of interest from the two populations has the same unit of measure. The units of measure must be the same so that we are comparing apples with apples. For example, $100 is not the same as 100 Japanese yen, because $1 is equivalent to about 109 yen. This means a standard deviation of $100 is substantially higher than a standard deviation of 100 yen.

EXAMPLE 7   **Comparing the Standard Deviation of Two Data Sets**

Problem: Refer to the data in Example 1. Use the standard deviation to determine whether University A or University B has more dispersion in the IQ scores of its students.

Approach: We will use MINITAB to compute the standard deviation of IQ for each university. The university with the higher standard deviation will be the university with more dispersion in IQ scores. Recall that, on the basis of the histograms, it was apparent that University A had more dispersion. Therefore, we would expect University A to have a higher sample standard deviation.

Solution: We enter the data into MINITAB and compute the descriptive statistics. See Figure 13.

Figure 13   **Descriptive statistics**

Variable	N	N*	Mean	SE Mean	StDev	Minimum
Univ A	100	0	100.00	1.61	16.08	60
Univ B	100	0	100.00	0.83	8.35	86

Variable	Q1	Median	Q3	Maximum
Univ A	90	102	110	141
Univ B	94	98	107	119

The sample standard deviation is larger for University A (16.1) than for University B (8.4). Therefore, University A has IQ scores that are more dispersed.

 Use the Empirical Rule to Describe Data That Are Bell Shaped

If data have a distribution that is bell shaped, the *Empirical Rule* can be used to determine the percentage of data that will lie within k standard deviations of the mean.

The Empirical Rule

If a distribution is roughly bell shaped, then

- Approximately 68% of the data will lie within 1 standard deviation of the mean. That is, approximately 68% of the data lie between $\mu - 1\sigma$ and $\mu + 1\sigma$.
- Approximately 95% of the data will lie within 2 standard deviations of the mean. That is, approximately 95% of the data lie between $\mu - 2\sigma$ and $\mu + 2\sigma$.
- Approximately 99.7% of the data will lie within 3 standard deviations of the mean. That is, approximately 99.7% of the data lie between $\mu - 3\sigma$ and $\mu + 3\sigma$.

Note: We can also use the empirical rule based on sample data with $\bar{x}$ used in place of μ and s used in place of σ.   ◄

Figure 14 illustrates the Empirical Rule.

Figure 14

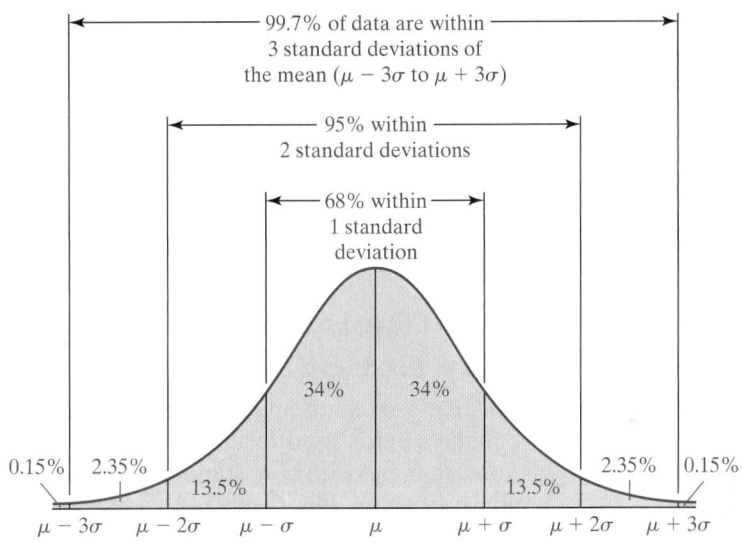

Let's revisit the data from University A in Table 7.

EXAMPLE 8   **Using the Empirical Rule**

Problem: Use the data from University A in Table 7.

(a) Determine the percentage of students who have IQ scores within 3 standard deviations of the mean according to the Empirical Rule.

(b) Determine the percentage of students who have IQ scores between 67.8 and 132.2 according to the Empirical Rule.

(c) Determine the actual percentage of students who have IQ scores between 67.8 and 132.2.

(d) According to the Empirical Rule, what percentage of students will have IQ scores above 132.2?

Approach: To use the Empirical Rule, a histogram of the data must be roughly bell shaped. Figure 15 shows the histogram of the data from University A.

Solution: The histogram of the data drawn in Figure 15 is roughly bell shaped. From Example 7 we know that the mean IQ score of the students enrolled in University A is 100 and the standard deviation is 16.1. To help organize our thoughts and make the analysis easier, we draw a bell-shaped curve like the one in Figure 14, with the $\bar{x} = 100$ and $s = 16.1$. See Figure 16.

Figure 15

University A IQ Scores

Figure 16

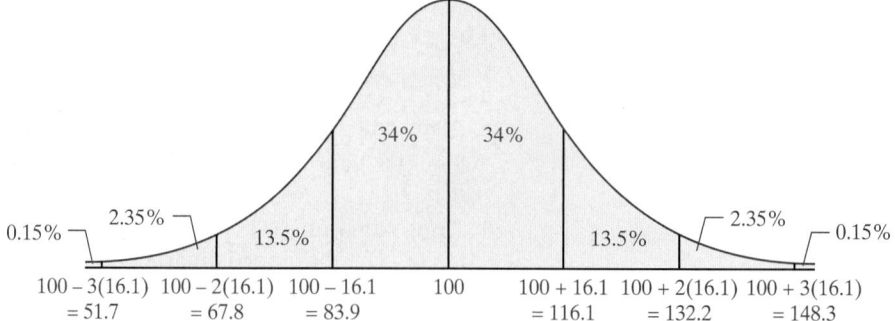

100 − 3(16.1)   100 − 2(16.1)   100 − 16.1   100   100 + 16.1   100 + 2(16.1)   100 + 3(16.1)
= 51.7   = 67.8   = 83.9   = 116.1   = 132.2   = 148.3

(a) According to the Empirical Rule, approximately 99.7% of the IQ scores will be within 3 standard deviations of the mean. That is, approximately 99.7% of the data will be greater than or equal to $100 - 3(16.1) = 51.7$ and less than or equal to $100 + 3(16.1) = 148.3$.

(b) Since 67.8 is exactly 2 standard deviations below the mean $[100 - 2(16.1) = 67.8]$ and 132.2 is exactly 2 standard deviations above the mean $[100 + 2(16.1) = 132.2]$, we use the Empirical Rule to determine that approximately 95% of all IQ scores lie between 67.8 and 132.2.

(c) Of the 100 IQ scores listed in Table 7, 96, or 96%, are between 67.8 and 132.2. This is very close to the approximation given by the Empirical Rule.

(d) Based on Figure 16, approximately $2.35\% + 0.15\% = 2.5\%$ of students at University A will have IQ scores above 132.2.

> Now Work Problem 35

⑤ Use Chebyshev's Inequality to Describe Any Set of Data

The Russian mathematician Pafnuty Chebyshev (1821–1894) developed an inequality that is used to determine a lower bound on the percentage of observations that lie within k standard deviations of the mean, where $k > 1$. What's amazing about this result is that the bound is obtained regardless of the basic shape of the distribution (skewed left, skewed right, or symmetric).

Note to Instructor

If you are pressed for time, Chebyshev's Inequality can be skipped without loss of continuity.

Chebyshev's Inequality

For any data set, regardless of the shape of the distribution, at least $\left(1 - \dfrac{1}{k^2}\right)100\%$ of the observations will lie within k standard deviations of the mean, where k is any number greater than 1. That is, at least $\left(1 - \dfrac{1}{k^2}\right)100\%$ of the data will lie between $\mu - k\sigma$ and $\mu + k\sigma$ for $k > 1$.

Note: We can also use Chebyshev's Inequality based on sample data. ◄

⬥ **CAUTION** The Empirical Rule holds only if the distribution is bell shaped. Chebyshev's Inequality holds regardless of the shape of the distribution.

For example, at least $\left(1 - \dfrac{1}{2^2}\right)100\% = 75\%$ of all observations will lie within $k = 2$ standard deviations of the mean and at least $\left(1 - \dfrac{1}{3^2}\right)100\% = 88.9\%$ of all observations will lie within $k = 3$ standard deviations of the mean.

Notice the result does not state that exactly 75% of all observations lie within 2 standard deviations of the mean, but instead states that 75% or more of the observations will lie within 2 standard deviations of the mean.

EXAMPLE 9	Using Chebyshev's Inequality

Problem: Using the data from University A in Table 7.

(a) Determine the minimum percentage of students who have IQ scores within 3 standard deviations of the mean according to Chebyshev's Inequality.

(b) Determine the minimum percentage of students who have IQ scores between 67.8 and 132.2, according to Chebyshev's Inequality.

(c) Determine the actual percentage of students who have IQ scores between 67.8 and 132.2.

Approach

(a) We use Chebyshev's Inequality with $k = 3$.

(b) We have to determine the number of standard deviations 67.8 and 132.2 are from the mean of 100.0. We then substitute this value of k into Chebyshev's Inequality.

(c) We refer to Table 7 and count the number of observations between 67.8 and 132.2. We divide this result by 100, the number of observations in the data set.

Solution

(a) We use Chebyshev's Inequality with $k = 3$ and determine that at least $\left(1 - \dfrac{1}{3^2}\right)100\% = 88.9\%$ of all students have IQ scores within 3 standard deviations of the mean. Since the mean of the data set is 100.0 and the standard deviation is 16.1, at least 88.9% of the students have IQ scores between $\bar{x} - ks = 100.0 - 3(16.1) = 51.7$ and $\bar{x} + ks = 100 + 3(16.1) = 148.3$.

(b) Since 67.8 is exactly 2 standard deviations below the mean $[100 - 2(16.1) = 67.8]$ and 132.2 is exactly 2 standard deviations above the mean $[100 + 2(16.1) = 132.2]$, we use Chebyshev's Inequality with $k = 2$ to determine that at least $\left(1 - \dfrac{1}{2^2}\right)100\% = 75\%$ of all IQ scores lie between 67.8 and 132.2.

(c) Of the 100 IQ scores listed, 96 or 96% is between 67.8 and 132.2. Notice that Chebyshev's inequality provides a rather conservative result.

Now Work Problem 39

Because the Empirical Rule requires that the distribution be bell shaped, while Chebyshev's Inequality applies to all distributions, the Empirical Rule provides results that are more precise.

3.2 ASSESS YOUR UNDERSTANDING

Concepts and Vocabulary

1. Would it be appropriate to say that a distribution with a standard deviation of 10 centimeters is more dispersed than a distribution with a standard deviation of 5 inches? Support your position.

2. What is meant by the phrase *degrees of freedom* as it pertains to the computation of the sample variance?

3. Are any of the measures of dispersion mentioned in this section resistant? Explain.

4. The sum of the deviations about the mean always equals ___zero___.

5. What does it mean when a statistic is biased?

6. What makes the range less desirable than the standard deviation as a measure of dispersion?

7. In one of Sullivan's statistics sections, the standard deviation of the heights of all students was 3.9 inches. The standard deviation of the heights of males was 3.4 inches and the standard deviation of females was 3.3 inches. Why is the standard deviation of the entire class more than the standard deviation of the males and females considered separately?

8. The standard deviation is used in conjunction with the ___mean___ to numerically describe distributions that are bell shaped. The ___mean___ measures the center of the distribution, while the standard deviation measures the _spread_ of the distribution.

9. *True or False:* When comparing two populations, the larger the standard deviation, the more dispersion the distribution has, provided that the variable of interest from the two populations has the same unit of measure. True

10. *True or False:* Chebyshev's Inequality applies to all distributions regardless of shape, but the Empirical Rule holds only for distributions that are bell shaped. True

Skill Building

19. 1150; 211,275; 459.6

In Problems 11–16, find the population variance and standard deviation or the sample variance and standard deviation as indicated.

11. Sample: 20, 13, 4, 8, 10 $s^2 = 36$; $s = 6$
12. Sample: 83, 65, 91, 87, 84 $s^2 = 100$; $s = 10$
13. Population: 3, 6, 10, 12, 14 $\sigma^2 = 16$; $\sigma = 4$
14. Population: 1, 19, 25, 15, 12, 16, 28, 13, 6 $\sigma^2 = 64$; $\sigma = 8$
15. Sample: 6, 52, 13, 49, 35, 25, 31, 29, 31, 29 $s^2 = 196$; $s = 14$
16. Population: 4, 10, 12, 12, 13, 21 $\sigma^2 = 25$; $\sigma = 5$

17. **Crash Test Results** The Insurance Institute for Highway Safety crashed the 2007 Audi A4 four times at 5 miles per hour. The costs of repair for each of the four crashes are as follows:

$976, $2038, $918, $1899

Compute the range, sample variance, and sample standard deviation cost of repair. $1120; 351,601.6; $593.0

18. **Cell Phone Use** The following data represent the monthly cell phone bill for my wife's phone for six randomly selected months:

$35.34, $42.09, $39.43, $38.93, $43.39, $49.26

Compute the range, sample variance, and sample standard deviation phone bill. $13.92; 22.584; $4.752

19. **Concrete Mix** A certain type of concrete mix is designed to NW withstand 3,000 pounds per square inch (psi) of pressure. The strength of concrete is measured by pouring the mix into casting cylinders 6 inches in diameter and 12 inches tall. The concrete is allowed to set up for 28 days. The concrete's strength is then measured (in psi). The following data represent the strength of nine randomly selected casts:

3960, 4090, 3200, 3100, 2940, 3830, 4090, 4040, 3780

Compute the range, sample variance, and sample standard deviation for the strength of the concrete (in psi).

20. **Flight Time** The following data represent the flight time (in minutes) of a random sample of seven flights from Las Vegas, Nevada, to Newark, New Jersey, on Continental Airlines.

282, 270, 260, 266, 257, 260, 267

Compute the range, sample variance, and sample standard deviation of flight time. 25; 71 min²; 8.4 min

21. Which histogram depicts a higher standard deviation? Justify your answer. (b)

(a)

(b)

22. Match the histograms to the summary statistics given.

	Mean	Median	Standard Deviation
I	53	53	1.8
II	60	60	11
III	53	53	10
IV	53	53	22

(a) III (b) I (c) IV (d) II

(a)

(b)

(c)

(d)

Applying the Concepts

23. (a) Tap water (0.59 vs. 0.26)

23. **pH in Water** The acidity or alkalinity of a solution is measured using pH. A pH less than 7 is acidic, while a pH greater than 7 is alkaline. The following data represent the pH in samples of bottled water and tap water.

(a) Which type of water has more dispersion in pH using the range as the measure of dispersion?

(b) Which type of water has more dispersion in pH using the standard deviation as the measure of dispersion?
Tap water (0.154 vs. 0.081)

Tap	7.64	7.45	7.47	7.50	7.68	7.69
	7.45	7.10	7.56	7.47	7.52	7.47
Bottled	5.15	5.09	5.26	5.20	5.02	5.23
	5.28	5.26	5.13	5.26	5.21	5.24

Source: Emily McCarney, student at Joliet Junior College

24. **Reaction Time** In an experiment conducted online at the University of Mississippi, study participants are asked to react to a stimulus. In one experiment, the participant must press a key upon seeing a blue screen. The time (in seconds) to press the key is measured. The same person is then asked to press a key upon seeing a red screen, again with the time to react measured. The results for six study participants are listed in the table.

(a) Which color has more dispersion using the range as the measure of dispersion? Blue

(b) Which color has more dispersion using the standard deviation as the measure of dispersion? Blue

Participant Number	Reaction Time to Blue	Reaction Time to Red
1	0.582	0.408
2	0.481	0.407
3	0.841	0.542
4	0.267	0.402
5	0.685	0.456
6	0.450	0.533

Source: PsychExperiments at the University of Mississippi (www.olemiss.edu/psychexps)

25. Pulse Rates The following data represent the pulse rates
NW (beats per minute) of nine students enrolled in a section of
Sullivan's course in Introductory Statistics. Treat the nine
students as a population.   25. (a) 7.7 beats per minute

Student	Pulse
Perpectual Bempah	76
Megan Brooks	60
Jeff Honeycutt	60
Clarice Jefferson	81
Crystal Kurtenbach	72
Janette Lantka	80
Kevin McCarthy	80
Tammy Ohm	68
Kathy Wojdyla	73

(a) Compute the population standard deviation.
(b) Determine three simple random samples of size 3, and
compute the sample standard deviation of each sample.
(c) Which samples underestimate the population standard
deviation? Which overestimate the population standard
deviation?

26. Travel Time The following data represent the travel time
(in minutes) to school for nine students enrolled in
Sullivan's College Algebra course. Treat the nine students
as a population.

Student	Travel Time	Student	Travel Time
Amanda	39	Scot	45
Amber	21	Erica	11
Tim	9	Tiffany	12
Mike	32	Glenn	39
Nicole	30		

(a) Compute the population standard deviation. 12.8 minutes
(b) Determine three simple random samples of size 4, and
compute the sample standard deviation of each sample.
(c) Which samples underestimate the population standard
deviation? Which overestimate the population standard
deviation?

27. A Fish Story Ethan and Drew went on a 10-day fishing trip.
The number of smallmouth bass caught and released by the
two boys each day was as follows:

Ethan	9	24	8	9	5	8	9	10	8	10
Drew	15	2	3	18	20	1	17	2	19	3

(a) Find the population mean and the range for the number
of smallmouth bass caught per day by each fisherman. Do
these values indicate any differences between the two
fishermen's catches per day? Explain. $\mu = 10$; range $= 19$
(b) Find the population standard deviation for the number of
smallmouth bass caught per day by each fisherman. Do
these values present a different story about the two fishermen's catches per day? Which fisherman has the more
consistent record? Explain. Ethan: $\sigma = 4.9$; Drew: $\sigma = 7.9$
(c) Discuss limitations of the range as a measure of
dispersion.

28. Soybean Yield The following data represent the number of
pods on a sample of soybean plants for two different plot
types. Which plot type do you think is superior? Why? Liberty

Plot Type	Pods								
Liberty	32	31	36	35	44	31	39	37	38
No Till	35	31	32	30	43	33	37	42	40

Source: Andrew Dieter and Brad Schmidgall, students at Joliet Junior
College

29. The Empirical Rule The following data represent the weights
(in grams) of a random sample of 50 M&M plain candies.

0.87	0.88	0.82	0.90	0.90	0.84	0.84
0.91	0.94	0.86	0.86	0.86	0.88	0.87
0.89	0.91	0.86	0.87	0.93	0.88	
0.83	0.95	0.87	0.93	0.91	0.85	
0.91	0.91	0.86	0.89	0.87	0.84	
0.88	0.88	0.89	0.79	0.82	0.83	
0.90	0.88	0.84	0.93	0.81	0.90	
0.88	0.92	0.85	0.84	0.84	0.86	

Source: Michael Sullivan

(a) Determine the sample standard deviation weight. Express
your answer rounded to three decimal places. 0.036 gram
(b) On the basis of the histogram drawn in Section 3.1,
Problem 29, comment on the appropriateness of using
the Empirical Rule to make any general statements
about the weights of M&Ms. Okay to use
(c) Use the Empirical Rule to determine the percentage of
M&Ms with weights between 0.803 and 0.947 gram.
Hint: $\bar{x} = 0.875$. 95%
(d) Determine the actual percentage of M&Ms that weigh
between 0.803 and 0.947 gram, inclusive. 96%
(e) Use the Empirical Rule to determine the percentage of
M&Ms with weights more than 0.911 gram. 16%
(f) Determine the actual percentage of M&Ms that weigh
more than 0.911 gram. 12%

30. The Empirical Rule The following data represent the length
of eruption for a random sample of eruptions at the Old
Faithful geyser in Calistoga, California.

108	108	99	105	103	103	94
102	99	106	90	104	110	110
103	109	109	111	101	101	
110	102	105	110	106	104	
104	100	103	102	120	90	
113	116	95	105	103	101	
100	101	107	110	92	108	

Source: Ladonna Hansen, Park Curator

(a) Determine the sample standard deviation length of
eruption. Express your answer rounded to the nearest
whole number. 6 seconds
(b) On the basis of the histogram drawn in Section 3.1,
Problem 30, comment on the appropriateness of using
the Empirical Rule to make any general statements
about the length of eruptions. Okay to use

(c) Use the Empirical Rule to determine the percentage of eruptions that last between 92 and 116 seconds. *Hint*: $\bar{x}$ = 104. 95%

(d) Determine the actual percentage of eruptions that last between 92 and 116 seconds, inclusive. 93%

(e) Use the Empirical Rule to determine the percentage of eruptions that last less than 98 seconds. 16%

(f) Determine the actual percentage of eruptions that last less than 98 seconds. 11%

31. Which Car Would You Buy? Suppose that you are in the market to purchase a car. With gas prices on the rise, you have narrowed it down to two choices and will let gas mileage be the deciding factor. You decide to conduct a little experiment in which you put 10 gallons of gas in the car and drive it on a closed track until it runs out gas. You conduct this experiment 15 times on each car and record the number of miles driven.

Car 1				
228	223	178	220	220
233	233	271	219	223
217	214	189	236	248

Car 2				
277	164	326	215	259
217	321	263	160	257
239	230	183	217	230

Describe each data set. That is, determine the shape, center, and spread. Which car would you buy and why?

32. Which Investment Is Better? You have received a year-end bonus of $5,000. You decide to invest the money in the stock market and have narrowed your investment options down to two mutual funds. The following data represent the historical quarterly rates of return of each mutual fund for the past 20 quarters (5 years).

Mutual Fund A				
1.3	−0.3	0.6	6.8	5.0
5.2	4.8	2.4	3.0	1.8
7.3	8.6	3.4	3.8	−1.3
6.4	1.9	−0.5	−2.3	3.1

Mutual Fund B				
−5.4	6.7	11.9	4.3	4.3
3.5	10.5	2.9	3.8	5.9
−6.7	1.4	8.9	0.3	−2.4
−4.7	−1.1	3.4	7.7	12.9

Describe each data set. That is, determine the shape, center, and spread. Which mutual fund would you invest in and why?

33. Rates of Return of Stocks Stocks may be categorized by industry. The following data represent the 5-year rates of return (in percent) for a sample of financial stocks and energy stocks ending December 3, 2007.

(a) Compute the mean and the median rate of return for each industry. Which sector has the higher mean rate of return? Which sector has the higher median rate of return?

(b) Compute the standard deviation for each industry. In finance, the standard deviation rate of return is called

Financial Stocks				
16.01	29.66	8.58	61.90	16.27
18.30	47.16	31.40	26.57	12.15
0.86	25.95	16.54	15.21	25.89
14.44	77.82	50.75	15.52	1.05
7.82	8.30	10.01	7.24	13.53

Energy Stocks				
44.39	7.22	18.82	106.05	41.29
42.79	23.10	44.87	34.18	40.67
29.32	39.08	20.35	52.94	42.56
39.89	13.07	71.03	28.68	33.76
24.75	17.39	41.29	26.61	22.26

Source: morningstar.com

risk. Typically, an investor "pays" for a higher return by accepting more risk. Is the investor paying for higher returns in this instance? Do you think the higher returns are worth the cost?

34. Temperatures It is well known that San Diego has milder weather than Chicago, but which city has more dispersion in temperatures over the course of a month? In particular, which city has more dispersion in high temperatures in the month of November? Use the following data, which represent the daily high temperatures for each day in November, 2007. In which city would you rather be a meteorologist? Why?

Daily High Temperature, Chicago (°F)					
54.0	43.0	52.0	39.9	51.8	39.2
57.2	42.8	66.0	44.6	41.0	39.0
55.4	52.0	60.8	42.8	30.9	48.2
53.6	48.0	55.4	61.0	37.9	48.0
53.6	51.1	46.4	61.0	37.9	35.6

Daily High Temperature, San Diego (°F)					
66.0	63.0	64.4	64.9	64.4	71.1
64.9	63.0	70.0	63.0	64.0	71.1
66.2	63.0	80.6	63.0	62.6	73.9
64.4	63.0	84.0	62.6	69.8	73.9
64.9	66.0	84.0	62.1	72.0	71.1

Source: National Climatic Data Center

35. The Empirical Rule One measure of intelligence is the Stanford–Binet Intelligence Quotient (IQ). IQ scores have a bell-shaped distribution with a mean of 100 and a standard deviation of 15.

(a) What percentage of people has an IQ score between 70 and 130? 95%

(b) What percentage of people has an IQ score less than 70 or greater than 130? 5%

(c) What percentage of people has an IQ score greater than 130? 2.5%

33. (a) Financial: $\bar{x}$ = 22.357%, M = 16.01%; Energy: $\bar{x}$ = 36.254%, M = 34.18%; Energy; energy   33. (b) Financial: s = 18.936%; Energy: s = 20.080%; yes   34. Chicago: R = 35.1°F; σ = 8.54°F San Diego: R = 21.9°F; σ = 6.14°F; Chicago has more dispersion

40. (c) 88.9%   42. (a) $R = \$45, \sigma^2 = 160, \sigma = \$12.6$ 42. (c) $R = 47.25, \sigma^2 = 176.4, \sigma = 13.3$

36. The Empirical Rule SAT Math scores have a bell-shaped distribution with a mean of 515 and a standard deviation of 114.

Source: College Board, 2007   36. (a) 68%

   (a) What percentage of SAT scores is between 401 and 629?

   (b) What percentage of SAT scores is less than 401 or greater than 629? 32%

   (c) What percentage of SAT scores is greater than 743? 2.5%

37. The Empirical Rule The weight, in grams, of the pair of kidneys in adult males between the ages of 40 and 49 have a bell-shaped distribution with a mean of 325 grams and a standard deviation of 30 grams.   37. (a) 265 and 385 grams

   (a) About 95% of kidney pairs will be between what weights?

   (b) What percentage of kidney pairs weighs between 235 grams and 415 grams? 99.7%

   (c) What percentage of kidney pairs weighs less than 235 grams or more than 415 grams? 0.3%

   (d) What percentage of kidney pairs weighs between 295 grams and 385 grams? 81.5%

38. The Empirical Rule The distribution of the length of bolts has a bell shape with a mean of 4 inches and a standard deviation of 0.007 inch.

   (a) About 68% of bolts manufactured will be between what lengths? 3.993 and 4.007 inches

   (b) What percentage of bolts will be between 3.986 inches and 4.014 inches? 95%

   (c) If the company discards any bolts less than 3.986 inches or greater than 4.014 inches, what percentage of bolts manufactured will be discarded? 5%

   (d) What percentage of bolts manufactured will be between 4.007 inches and 4.021 inches? 15.85%

39. Chebyshev's Inequality In December 2007, the average price of regular unleaded gasoline excluding taxes in the United States was $3.06 per gallon, according to the Energy Information Administration. Assume that the standard deviation price per gallon is $0.06 per gallon to answer the following.

   (a) What minimum percentage of gasoline stations had prices within 3 standard deviations of the mean? 88.9%

   (b) What minimum percentage of gasoline stations had prices within 2.5 standard deviations of the mean? What are the gasoline prices that are within 2.5 standard deviations of the mean? 84%; $2.91 to $3.21

   (c) What is the minimum percentage of gasoline stations that had prices between $2.94 and $3.18? 75%

40. Chebyshev's Inequality According to the U.S. Census Bureau, the mean of the commute time to work for a resident of Boston, Massachusetts, is 27.3 minutes. Assume that the standard deviation of the commute time is 8.1 minutes to answer the following: 40. (a) 75%

   (a) What minimum percentage of commuters in Boston has a commute time within 2 standard deviations of the mean?

   (b) What minimum percentage of commuters in Boston has a commute time within 1.5 standard deviations of the mean? What are the commute times within 1.5 standard deviations of the mean? 55.6%; 15.15 minutes to 39.45 minutes

   (c) What is the minimum percentage of commuters who have commute times between 3 minutes and 51.6 minutes?

41. Comparing Standard Deviations The standard deviation of batting averages of all teams in the American League is 0.008. The standard deviation of all players in the American League is 0.02154. Why is there less variability in team batting averages?

42. Linear Transformations Benjamin owns a small Internet business. Besides himself, he employs nine other people. The salaries earned by the employees are given next in thousands of dollars (Benjamin's salary is the largest, of course):

$$30, 30, 45, 50, 50, 50, 55, 55, 60, 75$$

   (a) Determine the range, population variance, and population standard deviation for the data.

   (b) Business has been good! As a result, Benjamin has a total of $25,000 in bonus pay to distribute to his employees. One option for distributing bonuses is to give each employee (including himself) $2,500. Add the bonuses under this plan to the original salaries to create a new data set. Recalculate the range, population variance, and population standard deviation. How do they compare to the originals? $R = \$45, \sigma^2 = 160, \sigma = \$12.6$

   (c) As a second option, Benjamin can give each employee a bonus of 5% of his or her original salary. Add the bonuses under this second plan to the original salaries to create a new data set. Recalculate the range, population variance, and population standard deviation. How do they compare to the originals?

   (d) As a third option, Benjamin decides not to give his employees a bonus at all. Instead, he keeps the $25,000 for himself. Use this plan to create a new data set. Recalculate the range, population variance, and population standard deviation. How do they compare to the originals? $R = \$70, \sigma^2 = 341.3, \sigma = \$18.5$

43. Resistance and Sample Size Each of the following three data sets represents the IQ scores of a random sample of adults. IQ scores are known to have a mean and median of 100. For each data set, determine the sample standard deviation. Then recompute the sample standard deviation assuming that the individual whose IQ is 106 is accidentally recorded as 160. For each sample size, state what happens to the standard deviation. Comment on the role that the number of observations plays in resistance.

Sample of Size 5				
106	92	98	103	100

Sample of Size 12					
106	92	98	103	100	102
98	124	83	70	108	121

Sample of Size 30					
106	92	98	103	100	102
98	124	83	70	108	121
102	87	121	107	97	114
140	93	130	72	81	90
103	97	89	98	88	103

44. Identical Values Compute the sample standard deviation of the following test scores: 78, 78, 78, 78. What can be said about a data set in which all the values are identical? $s = 0$

45. Blocking and Variability Recall that blocking refers to the idea that we can reduce the variability in a variable by segmenting the data by some other variable. The given data represent the recumbent length (in centimeters) of a sample of 10 males and 10 females who are 40 months of age.

Males		Females	
104.0	94.4	102.5	100.8
93.7	97.6	100.4	96.3
98.3	100.6	102.7	105.0
86.2	103.0	98.1	106.5
90.7	100.9	95.4	114.5

Source: National Center for Health Statistics

(a) Determine the standard deviation of recumbent length for all 20 observations. 6.11 cm
(b) Determine the standard deviation of recumbent length for the males. 5.67 cm
(c) Determine the standard deviation of recumbent length for the females. 5.59 cm
(d) What effect does blocking by gender have on the standard deviation of recumbent length for each gender?

46. Coefficient of Variation The coefficient of variation is a measure that allows for the comparison of two or more variables measured on a different scale. It measures the relative variability in terms of the mean and does not have a unit of measure. The lower the coefficient of variation is, the less the data vary. The coefficient of variation is defined as

$$CV = \frac{\text{standard deviation}}{\text{mean}} \cdot 100\%$$

For example, suppose the senior class of a school district has a mean ACT score of 23 with a standard deviation of 4 and a mean SAT score of 1,100 with a standard deviation of 150. Which test has more variability? The coefficient of variation for the ACT exam is $\frac{4}{23} \cdot 100\% = 17.4\%$; the coefficient of variation for the SAT exam is $\frac{150}{1100} \cdot 100\% = 13.6\%$. The ACT has more variability.

(a) Suppose the systolic blood pressure of a random sample of 100 students before exercising has a sample mean of 121, with a standard deviation of 14.1. The systolic blood pressure after exercising is 135.9, with a standard deviation of 18.1. Is there more variability in systolic blood pressure before exercise or after exercise? After
(b) An investigation of intracellular calcium and blood pressure was conducted by Erne, Bolli, Buergisser, and Buehler in 1984 and published in the *New England Journal of Medicine*, 310:1084–1088. The researchers measured the free calcium concentration in the blood platelets of 38 people with normal blood pressure and 45 people with high blood pressure. The mean and standard deviation of the normal blood pressure group were 107.9 and 16.1, respectively. The mean and standard deviation of the high blood pressure group were 168.2 and 31.7, respectively. Is there more variability in free calcium concentration in the normal blood pressure or the high blood pressure group? High blood pressure group

47. Mean Absolute Deviation Another measure of variation is the mean absolute deviation. It is computed using the formula

$$MAD = \frac{\sum |x_i - \bar{x}|}{n}$$

Compute the mean absolute deviation of the data in Problem 17 and compare the results with the sample standard deviation. MAD = $510.75; s = $592.96

48. Coefficient of Skewness Karl Pearson developed a measure that describes the skewness of a distribution, called the **coefficient of skewness**. The formula is

$$\text{Skewness} = \frac{3(\text{mean} - \text{median})}{\text{standard deviation}}$$

The value of this measure generally lies between −3 and +3. The closer the value lies to −3, the more the distribution is skewed left. The closer the value lies to +3, the more the distribution is skewed right. A value close to 0 indicates a symmetric distribution. Find the coefficient of skewness of the following distributions and comment on the skewness.

(a) Mean = 50, median = 40, standard deviation = 10 3
(b) Mean = 100, median = 100, standard deviation = 15 0
(c) Mean = 400, median = 500, standard deviation = 120 −2.50
(d) Compute the coefficient of skewness for the data in Problem 29. 0
(e) Compute the coefficient of skewness for the data in Problem 30. 0.05

49. Diversification A popular theory in investment states that you should invest a certain amount of money in foreign investments to reduce your risk. The risk of a portfolio is defined as the standard deviation of the rate of return. Refer to the following graph, which depicts the relation between risk (standard deviation of rate of return) and reward (mean rate of return).

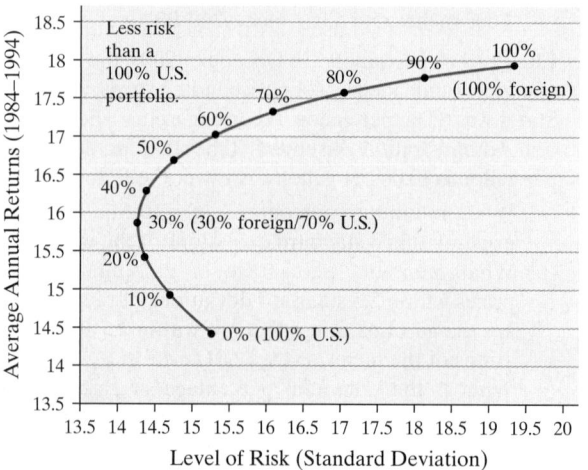

How Foreign Stocks Benefit a Domestic Portfolio

Source: T. Rowe Price

(a) Determine the average annual return and level of risk in a portfolio that is 10% foreign.
(b) Determine the percentage that should be invested in foreign stocks to best minimize risk. 30%
(c) Why do you think risk initially decreases as the percent of foreign investments increases?
(d) A portfolio that is 30% foreign and 70% American has a mean rate of return of about 15.8%, with a standard deviation of 14.3%. According to Chebyshev's inequality, at least 75% of returns will be between what values? According to Chebyshev's inequality, at least 88.9% of returns will be between what two values? Should an investor be surprised if she has a negative rate of return? Why? Between −12.8% and 44.4%; between −27.1% and 58.7%; no

Consumer Reports® Basement Waterproofing Coatings

A waterproofing coating can be an inexpensive and easy way to deal with leaking basements. But how effective are they? In a study, *Consumer Reports* tested nine waterproofers to rate their effectiveness in controlling water seepage though concrete foundations.

To compare the products' ability to control water seepage, we applied two coats of each product to slabs cut from concrete block. For statistical validity, this process was repeated at least six times. In each test run, four blocks (each coated with a different product) were simultaneously placed in a rectangular aluminum chamber. See the picture.

The chamber was sealed and filled with water and the blocks were subjected to progressively increasing hydrostatic pressures. Water that leaked out during each period was channeled to the bottom of the chamber opening, collected, and weighed.

The table contains a subset of the data collected for two of the products tested. Using these data:

(a) Calculate the mean, median, and mode weight of water collected for product A.

(b) Calculate the standard deviation of the weight of water collected for product A.

(c) Calculate the mean, median, and mode weight of water collected for product B.

(d) Calculate the standard deviation of the weight of water collected for product B.

(e) Construct back-to-back stem-and-leaf diagrams for these data.

Product	Replicate	Weight of Collected Water (grams)
A	1	91.2
A	2	91.2
A	3	90.9
A	4	91.3
A	5	90.8
A	6	90.8
B	1	87.1
B	2	87.2
B	3	86.8
B	4	87.0
B	5	87.2
B	6	87.0

Does there appear to be a difference in these two products' abilities to mitigate water seepage? Why?

Note to Readers: *In many cases, our test protocol and analytical methods are more complicated than described in these examples. The data and discussions have been modified to make the material more appropriate for the audience.*

Basement Waterproofer Test Chamber

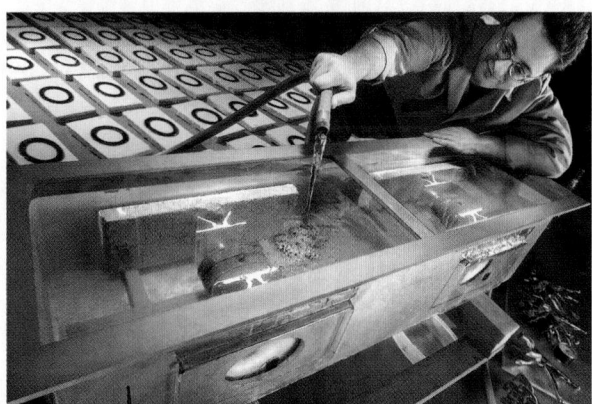

TECHNOLOGY STEP-BY-STEP   Determining the Range, Variance, and Standard Deviation

The same steps followed to obtain the measures of central tendency from raw data can be used to obtain the measures of dispersion.

3.3 MEASURES OF CENTRAL TENDENCY AND DISPERSION FROM GROUPED DATA

Preparing for This Section   Before getting started, review the following:

- Organizing discrete data in tables (Section 2.2, pp. 82–83)
- Organizing continuous data in tables (Section 2.2, pp. 84–87)
- Class midpoint (Section 2.3, p. 102)

Objectives

 Approximate the mean of a variable from grouped data

2 Compute the weighted mean

3 Approximate the variance and standard deviation of a variable from grouped data

---

Note to Instructor

This section can be skipped without loss of continuity. If covered, the formulas used in this section can be overwhelming. Therefore, it is recommended that "by hand" computations be de-emphasized.

We have discussed how to compute descriptive statistics from raw data, but many times the data that we have access to have already been summarized in frequency distributions (grouped data). While we cannot obtain exact values of the mean or standard deviation without raw data, these measures can be approximated using the techniques discussed in this section.

1 Approximate the Mean of a Variable from Grouped Data

Note to Instructor

If you like, you can print out and distribute the Preparing for this Section quiz located in the Instructor's Resource Center.

Since raw data cannot be retrieved from a frequency table, we assume that, within each class, the mean of the data values is equal to the class midpoint. We then multiply the class midpoint by the frequency. This product is expected to be close to the sum of the data that lie within the class. We repeat the process for each class and sum the results. This sum approximates the sum of all the data.

Definition

Approximate Mean of a Variable from a Frequency Distribution

Population Mean

$$\mu = \frac{\sum x_i f_i}{\sum f_i} = \frac{x_1 f_1 + x_2 f_2 + \cdots + x_N f_N}{f_1 + f_2 + \cdots + f_N} \tag{1a}$$

Sample Mean

$$\bar{x} = \frac{\sum x_i f_i}{\sum f_i} = \frac{x_1 f_1 + x_2 f_2 + \cdots + x_n f_n}{f_1 + f_2 + \cdots + f_n} \tag{1b}$$

where x_i is the midpoint or value of the ith class

f_i is the frequency of the ith class

n is the number of classes

In Formula (1), $x_1 f_1$ approximates the sum of all the data values in the first class, $x_2 f_2$ approximates the sum of all the data values in the second class, and so on. Notice that the formulas for the population mean and sample mean are essentially identical, just as they were for computing the mean from raw data.

EXAMPLE 1   **Approximating the Mean for Continuous Quantitative Data from a Frequency Distribution**

Problem: The frequency distribution in Table 13 represents the 3-year rate of return of a random sample of 40 small-capitalization growth mutual funds. Approximate the mean 3-year rate of return.

Table 13	
Class (3-year rate of return)	**Frequency**
10–11.99	6
12–13.99	14
14–15.99	10
16–17.99	4
18–19.99	3
20–21.99	0
22–23.99	3

Approach: We perform the following steps to approximate the mean.

Step 1: Determine the class midpoint of each class. The class midpoint is found by adding consecutive lower class limits and dividing the result by 2.

Step 2: Compute the sum of the frequencies, Σf_i.

Step 3: Multiply the class midpoint by the frequency to obtain $x_i f_i$ for each class.

Step 4: Compute $\Sigma x_i f_i$.

Step 5: Substitute into Formula (1b) to obtain the mean from grouped data.

Solution

Step 1: The lower class limit of the first class is 10. The lower class limit of the second class is 12. Therefore, the class midpoint of the first class is $\dfrac{10 + 12}{2} = 11$, so $x_1 = 11$. The remaining class midpoints are listed in column 2 of Table 14.

Step 2: We add the frequencies in column 3 to obtain $\Sigma f_i = 6 + 14 + \cdots + 3 = 40$.

Step 3: Compute the values of $x_i f_i$ by multiplying each class midpoint by the corresponding frequency and obtain the results shown in column 4 of Table 14.

Step 4: We add the values in column 4 of Table 14 to obtain $\Sigma x_i f_i = 592$.

Table 14			
Class (3-year rate of return)	**Class Midpoint, x_i**	**Frequency, f_i**	**$x_i f_i$**
10–11.99	$\dfrac{10 + 12}{2} = 11$	6	$(11)(6) = 66$
12–13.99	13	14	$(13)(14) = 182$
14–15.99	15	10	150
16–17.99	17	4	68
18–19.99	19	3	57
20–21.99	21	0	0
22–23.99	23	3	69
		$\Sigma f_i = 40$	$\Sigma x_i f_i = 592$

Step 5: Substituting into Formula (1b), we obtain

$$\bar{x} = \frac{\Sigma x_i f_i}{\Sigma f_i} = \frac{592}{40} = 14.8$$

The approximate mean 3-year rate of return is 14.8%.

CAUTION We computed the mean from grouped data in Example 1 even though the raw data is available. The reason for doing this was to illustrate how close the two values can be. In practice, use raw data whenever possible.

The mean 3-year rate of return from the raw data listed in Example 3 on page 84 from Section 2.2 is 14.8%. The approximate mean from grouped data is equal to the actual mean!

Now compute the mean of the frequency distribution in Problem 3

2 Compute the Weighted Mean

Sometimes, certain data values have a higher importance or weight associated with them. In this case, we compute the *weighted mean*. For example, your grade-point average is a weighted mean, with the weights equal to the number of credit hours in each course. The value of the variable is equal to the grade converted to a point value.

Note to Instructor
Idea for a classroom discussion: Suppose a company owns three cars that get 20 miles per gallon, two cars that get 22 miles per gallon, and one car that gets 24 miles per gallon. Would the mean miles per gallon be 22? Discuss.

Definition

The **weighted mean**, $\bar{x}_w$, of a variable is found by multiplying each value of the variable by its corresponding weight, summing these products, and dividing the result by the sum of the weights. It can be expressed using the formula

$$\bar{x}_w = \frac{\sum w_i x_i}{\sum w_i} = \frac{w_1 x_1 + w_2 x_2 + \cdots + w_n x_n}{w_1 + w_2 + \cdots + w_n} \tag{2}$$

where w_i is the weight of the ith observation

x_i is the value of the ith observation

EXAMPLE 2 **Computing the Weighted Mean**

Problem: Marissa just completed her first semester in college. She earned an A in her 4-hour statistics course, a B in her 3-hour sociology course, an A in her 3-hour psychology course, a C in her 5-hour computer programming course, and an A in her 1-hour drama course. Determine Marissa's grade-point average.

Approach: We must assign point values to each grade. Let an A equal 4 points, a B equal 3 points, and a C equal 2 points. The number of credit hours for each course determines its weight. So a 5-hour course gets a weight of 5, a 4-hour course gets a weight of 4, and so on. We multiply the weight of each course by the points earned in the course, sum these products, and divide the sum by the number of credit hours.

Solution

$$\text{GPA} = \bar{x}_w = \frac{\sum w_i x_i}{\sum w_i} = \frac{4(4) + 3(3) + 3(4) + 5(2) + 1(4)}{4 + 3 + 3 + 5 + 1} = \frac{51}{16} = 3.19$$

Marissa's grade-point average for her first semester is 3.19.

Now Work Problem 11

---

③ Approximate the Variance and Standard Deviation of a Variable from Grouped Data

The procedure for approximating the variance and standard deviation from grouped data is similar to that of finding the mean from grouped data. Again, because we do not have access to the original data, the variance is approximate.

Definition

Approximate Variance of a Variable from a Frequency Distribution

Population Variance	**Sample Variance**	
$\sigma^2 = \dfrac{\sum (x_i - \mu)^2 f_i}{\sum f_i}$	$s^2 = \dfrac{\sum (x_i - \bar{x})^2 f_i}{\left(\sum f_i\right) - 1}$	(3)

where x_i is the midpoint or value of the ith class

f_i is the frequency of the ith class

An algebraically equivalent formula for the population variance is

$$\frac{\sum x_i^2 f_i - \dfrac{\left(\sum x_i f_i\right)^2}{\sum f_i}}{\sum f_i}$$

We approximate the standard deviation by taking the square root of the variance.

EXAMPLE 3 **Approximating the Variance and Standard Deviation from a Frequency Distribution**

Problem: The data in Table 13 on page 161 represent the 3-year rate of return of a random sample of 40 small-capitalization growth mutual funds. Approximate the variance and standard deviation of the 3-year rate of return.

Approach: We will use the sample variance Formula (3).

Step 1: Create a table with the class in the first column, the class midpoint in the second column, the frequency in the third column, and the unrounded mean in the fourth column.

Step 2: Compute the deviation about the mean, $x_i - \overline{x}$, for each class, where x_i is the class midpoint of the ith class and $\overline{x}$ is the sample mean. Enter the results in column 5.

Step 3: Square the deviation about the mean and multiply this result by the frequency to obtain $(x_i - \overline{x})^2 f_i$. Enter the results in column 6.

Step 4: Add the entries in columns 3 and 6 to obtain Σf_i and $\Sigma(x_i - \overline{x})^2 f_i$.

Step 5: Substitute the values obtained in Step 4 into Formula (3) to obtain an approximate value for the sample variance.

Solution

Step 1: We create Table 15. Column 1 contains the classes. Column 2 contains the class midpoint of each class. Column 3 contains the frequency of each class. Column 4 contains the unrounded sample mean obtained in Example 1.

Step 2: Column 5 of Table 15 contains the deviation about the mean, $x_i - \overline{x}$, for each class.

Step 3: Column 6 contains the values of the squared deviation about the mean multiplied by the frequency, $(x_i - \overline{x})^2 f_i$.

Step 4: We add the entries in columns 3 and 6 and obtain $\Sigma f_i = 40$ and $\Sigma(x_i - \overline{x})^2 f_i = 406.4$.

Table 15					
Class (3-year rate of return)	Class Midpoint, x_i	Frequency, f_i	$\overline{x}$	$x_i - \overline{x}$	$(x_i - \overline{x})^2 f_i$
10–11.99	11	6	14.8	−3.8	86.64
12–13.99	13	14	14.8	−1.8	45.36
14–15.99	15	10	14.8	0.2	0.4
16–17.99	17	4	14.8	2.2	19.36
18–19.99	19	3	14.8	4.2	52.92
20–21.99	21	0	14.8	6.2	0
22–23.99	23	3	14.8	8.2	201.72
		$\sum f_i = 40$			$\sum(x_i - \overline{x})^2 f_i = 406.4$

Step 5: Substitute these values into Formula (3) to obtain an approximate value for the sample variance.

$$s^2 = \frac{\sum(x_i - \overline{x})^2 f_i}{\left(\sum f_i\right) - 1} = \frac{406.4}{39} \approx 10.42$$

Take the square root of the unrounded estimate of the sample variance to obtain an approximation of the sample standard deviation.

$$s = \sqrt{s^2} = \sqrt{\frac{406.4}{39}} \approx 3.23$$

We approximate the sample standard deviation 3-year rate of return to be 3.23%.

EXAMPLE 4 | **Approximating the Mean and Standard Deviation of Grouped Data Using Technology**

Problem: Approximate the mean and standard deviation of the 3-year rate of return data in Table 13 using a TI-83/84 Plus graphing calculator.

Approach: The steps for approximating the mean and standard deviation of grouped data using the TI-83/84 Plus graphing calculator are given in the Technology Step-by-Step on page 166.

Solution: Figure 17 shows the result from the TI-84 Plus.

Figure 17

Approximate mean

Approximate sample standard deviation

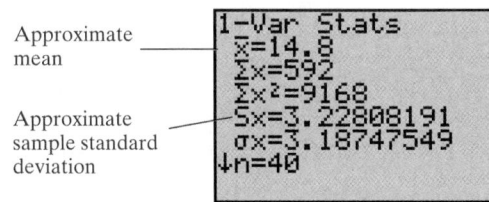

```
1-Var Stats
 x̄=14.8
 Σx=592
 Σx²=9168
 Sx=3.22808191
 σx=3.18747549
↓n=40
```

From the output, we can see that the approximate mean is 14.8% and the approximate standard deviation is 3.23%. The results agree with our by-hand solutions.

From the raw data listed in Example 3 in Section 2.2, we find that the sample standard deviation is 3.41%. The approximate sample standard deviation from grouped data is close to, but a little lower than, the sample standard deviation from the raw data!

> Now compute the standard deviation from the frequency distribution in Problem 3

3·3 ASSESS YOUR UNDERSTANDING

Concepts and Vocabulary

1. Explain the role of the class midpoint in the formulas to approximate the mean and the standard deviation.

2. In Section 3.1, the mean is given by $\bar{x} = \dfrac{\Sigma x_i}{n}$. Explain how this is a special case of the weighted mean, $\bar{x}_w$.

Applying the Concepts

3. **Birth Weight** The following frequency distribution repre-
NW sents the birth weight of all babies born in the United States in 2004. Approximate the mean and standard deviation birth weight. $\mu = 3289.5$ g; $\sigma = 657.2$ g

Weight (grams)	Number of Babies (thousands)
0–999	30
1,000–1,999	97
2,000–2,999	935
3,000–3,999	2,698
4,000–4,999	344
5,000–5,999	5

Source: National Vital Statistics Report, Volume 55, No. 1

4. **Square Footage of Housing** The following frequency distribution represents the square footage of a random sample of 500 houses that are owner occupied year round. Approximate the mean and standard deviation square footage. $\bar{x} = 2419$ sq ft; $s = 907.0$ sq ft

Square Footage	Frequency
0–499	5
500–999	17
1,000–1,499	36
1,500–1,999	121
2,000–2,499	119
2,500–2,999	81
3,000–3,499	47
3,500–3,999	45
4,000–4,499	22
4,500–4,999	7

Source: Based on data from the U.S. Census Bureau

5. **Household Winter Temperature** Often, frequency distributions are reported using unequal class widths because the frequencies of some groups would otherwise be small or very

large. Consider the following data, which represent the daytime household temperature the thermostat is set to when someone is home for a random sample of 750 households. Determine the class midpoint, if necessary, for each class and approximate the mean and standard deviation temperature. $\bar{x} = 70.6°F; s = 3.5°F$

Temperature (°F)	Frequency
61–64	31
65–67	67
68–69	198
70	195
71–72	120
73–76	89
77–80	50

Source: Based on data from the U.S. Department of Energy

6. **Living in Poverty** (See Problem 5) The following frequency distribution represents the age of people living in poverty in 2006 (in thousands). In this frequency distribution, the class widths are not the same for each class. Approximate the mean and standard deviation age of a person living in poverty. For the open-ended class 65 and older use 70 as the class midpoint. $\mu = 30.5$ years; $\sigma = 20.8$ years

Age	Frequency
0–17	12,827
18–24	5,047
25–34	4,920
35–44	4,049
45–54	3,399
55–59	1,468
60–64	1,357
65 and older	3,394

Source: U.S. Census Bureau

7. **Multiple Births** The following data represent the number of live multiple-delivery births (three or more babies) in 2004 for women 15 to 54 years old.

Age	Number of Multiple Births
15–19	84
20–24	431
25–29	1,753
30–34	2,752
35–39	1,785
40–44	378
45–49	80
50–54	9

Source: National Vital Statistics Reports, Vol. 55, No. 10, September 29, 2006

(a) $\mu = 32.5$ years; $\sigma \approx 5.4$ years
(a) Approximate the mean and standard deviation for age.
(b) Draw a frequency histogram of the data to verify that the distribution is bell shaped.
(c) According to the Empirical Rule, 95% of mothers of multiple births will be between what two ages?
21.7 years and 43.3 years

8. **SAT Scores** The following data represent SAT Mathematics scores for 2006.

SAT Math Score	Number
200–249	13,159
250–299	23,083
300–349	59,672
350–399	124,616
400–449	202,883
450–499	243,569
500–549	247,435
550–599	213,880
600–649	156,057
650–699	120,933
700–749	54,108
750–800	35,136

Source: The College Board

(a) Approximate the mean and standard deviation of the score. $\mu = 519.1; \sigma \approx 114.5$
(b) Draw a frequency histogram of the data to verify that the distribution is bell shaped.
(c) According to the Empirical Rule, 95% of these students will have SAT Mathematics scores between what two values? 290.1 and 748.1

9. **Serum HDL** Use the frequency distribution whose class width is 10 obtained in Problem 35 in Section 2.2 to approximate the mean and standard deviation for serum HDL. Compare these results to the actual mean and standard deviation. $\bar{x} = 51.8; s = 12.1$

10. **Dividend Yield** Use the frequency distribution whose class width is 0.4 obtained in Problem 36 in Section 2.2 to approximate the mean and standard deviation of the dividend yield. Compare these results to the actual mean and standard deviation. $\bar{x} \approx 1.214\%; s \approx 0.865\%$

11. **Grade-Point Average** Marissa has just completed her second semester in college. She earned a B in her 5-hour calculus course, an A in her 3-hour social work course, an A in her 4-hour biology course, and a C in her 3-hour American literature course. Assuming that an A equals 4 points, a B equals 3 points, and a C equals 2 points, determine Marissa's grade-point average for the semester. 3.27

12. **Computing Class Average** In Marissa's calculus course, attendance counts for 5% of the grade, quizzes count for 10% of the grade, exams count for 60% of the grade, and the final exam counts for 25% of the grade. Marissa had a 100% average for attendance, 93% for quizzes, 86% for exams, and 85% on the final. Determine Marissa's course average. 87.15%

13. **Mixed Chocolates** Michael and Kevin want to buy chocolates. They can't agree on whether they want chocolate-covered almonds, chocolate-covered peanuts, or chocolate-covered raisins. They agree to create a mix. They bought 4 pounds of chocolate-covered almonds at $3.50 per pound, 3 pounds of chocolate-covered peanuts for $2.75 per pound, and 2 pounds of chocolate-covered raisins for $2.25 per pound. Determine the cost per pound of the mix. $2.97

14. **Nut Mix** Michael and Kevin return to the candy store, but this time they want to purchase nuts. They can't decide among peanuts, cashews, or almonds. They again agree to create a mix. They bought 2.5 pounds of peanuts for $1.30 per pound,

16. (a) $\mu \approx 25.5$ years; $\sigma \approx 5.4$ years   16. (b) $\mu \approx 27.9$ years; $\sigma \approx 6.3$ years

4 pounds of cashews for $4.50 per pound, and 2 pounds of almonds for $3.75 per pound. Determine the price per pound of the mix. $3.38

15. **Population** The following data represent the male and female population, by age, of the United States in July 2006.

Age	Male Resident Pop (in thousands)	Female Resident Pop (in thousands)
0–9	20,518	19,607
10–19	22,496	20,453
20–29	21,494	20,326
30–39	20,629	20,261
40–49	22,461	22,815
50–59	18,872	19,831
60–69	11,216	12,519
70–79	6,950	8,970
80–89	3,327	5,678
90–99	524	1,356
100–109	14	59

Source: U.S. Census Bureau

(a) Approximate the population mean and standard deviation of age for males. $\mu \approx 35.9$ years; $\sigma \approx 21.8$ years
(b) Approximate the population mean and standard deviation of age for females. $\mu \approx 38.5$ years; $\sigma \approx 23.1$ years
(c) Which gender has the higher mean age? Female
(d) Which gender has more dispersion in age? Female

16. **Age of Mother** The following data represent the age of the mother at childbirth for 1980 and 2004.

Age	1980 Births (thousands)	2004 Births (thousands)
10–14	9.8	6.8
15–19	551.9	415.3
20–24	1226.4	1034.5
25–29	1108.2	1104.5
30–34	549.9	965.7
35–39	140.7	475.6
40–44	23.2	103.7
45–49	1.1	5.7

Source: National Vital Statistics Reports, Vol. 55, No. 10

(a) Approximate the population mean and standard deviation of age for mothers in 1980.
(b) Approximate the population mean and standard deviation of age for mothers in 2004.
(c) Which year has the higher mean age? 2004
(d) Which year has more dispersion in age? 2004

Problems 17–20 use the following steps to approximate the median from grouped data.

Approximating the Median from Grouped Data

Step 1: Construct a cumulative frequency distribution.
Step 2: Identify the class in which the median lies. Remember, the median can be obtained by determining the observation that lies in the middle.
Step 3: Interpolate the median using the formula

$$\text{Median} = M = L + \frac{\frac{n}{2} - CF}{f} \cdot (i)$$

where L is the lower class limit of the class containing the median

n is the number of data values in the frequency distribution

CF is the cumulative frequency of the class immediately preceding the class containing the median

f is the frequency of the median class

i is the class width of the class containing the median

17. Approximate the median of the frequency distribution in Problem 3. 3367.9 g
18. Approximate the median of the frequency distribution in Problem 4. 2298.3 ft^2
19. Approximate the median of the frequency distribution in Problem 7. 32.5 years
20. Approximate the median of the frequency distribution in Problem 8. 516.2

Problems 21 and 22, use the following definition of the modal class. The **modal class** of a variable can be obtained from data in a frequency distribution by determining the class that has the largest frequency.

21. Determine the modal class of the frequency distribution in Problem 3. 3000–3999 g
22. Determine the modal class of the frequency distribution in Problem 4. 1500–1999 ft^2

TECHNOLOGY STEP-BY-STEP **Determining the Mean and Standard Deviation from Grouped Data**

TI-83/84 Plus
1. Enter the class midpoint in L1 and the frequency or relative frequency in L2 by pressing STAT and selecting 1:Edit.
2. Press STAT, highlight the CALC menu, and select 1:1-Var Stats
3. With 1-Var Stats appearing on the HOME screen, press 2nd then 1 to insert L1 on the

HOME screen. Then press the comma and press 2nd 2 to insert L2 on the HOME screen. So the HOME screen should have the following:

1-Var Stats L1, L2

Press ENTER to obtain the mean and standard deviation.

3.4 MEASURES OF POSITION AND OUTLIERS

Objectives
1 Determine and interpret z-scores
2 Interpret percentiles
3 Determine and interpret quartiles
4 Determine and interpret the interquartile range
5 Check a set of data for outliers

In Section 3.1, we determined measures of central tendency. Measures of central tendency are meant to describe the "typical" data value. Section 3.2 discussed measures of dispersion, which describe the amount of spread in a set of data. In this section, we discuss measures of position; that is, we wish to describe the relative position of a certain data value within the entire set of data.

1 Determine and Interpret z-Scores

At the end of the 2007 season, the New York Yankees led the American League with 968 runs scored, while the Philadelphia Phillies led the National League with 892 runs scored. A quick comparison might lead one to believe that the Yankees are the better run-producing team. However, this comparison is unfair because the two teams play in different leagues. The Yankees play in the American League, where the designated hitter bats for the pitcher, whereas the Phillies play in the National League, where the pitcher must bat (pitchers are typically poor hitters). To compare the two teams' scoring of runs we need to determine their relative standings in their respective leagues. This can be accomplished using a *z-score*.

Definition

The **z-score** represents the distance that a data value is from the mean in terms of the number of standard deviations. It is obtained by subtracting the mean from the data value and dividing this result by the standard deviation. There is both a population z-score and a sample z-score; their formulas follow:

$$\text{Population } z\text{-Score} \qquad \text{Sample } z\text{-Score} \tag{1}$$
$$z = \frac{x - \mu}{\sigma} \qquad\qquad z = \frac{x - \bar{x}}{s}$$

The z-score is unitless. It has mean 0 and standard deviation 1.

In Other Words

z-Scores provide a way to compare apples to oranges by converting variables with different centers and/or spreads to variables with the same center (0) and spread (1).

If a data value is larger than the mean, the z-score will be positive. If a data value is smaller than the mean, the z-score will be negative. If the data value equals the mean, the z-score will be zero. z-Scores measure the number of standard deviations an observation is above or below the mean. For example, a z-score of 1.24 is interpreted as "the data value is 1.24 standard deviations above the mean." A z-score of -2.31 is interpreted as "the data value is 2.31 standard deviations below the mean."

We are now prepared to determine whether the Yankees or Phillies had a better year in run production.

EXAMPLE 1   **Comparing z-Scores**

Problem: Determine whether the New York Yankees or the Philadelphia Phillies had a relatively better run producing season. The Yankees scored 968 runs and play in the American League, where the mean number of runs scored was $\mu = 793.9$ and the standard deviation was $\sigma = 73.5$ runs. The Phillies scored 892 runs and play in the National League, where the mean number of runs scored was $\mu = 763.0$ and the standard deviation was $\sigma = 58.9$ runs.

Approach: To determine which team had the relatively better run-producing season with respect to each league, we compute each team's z-score. The team with the higher z-score had the better season. Because we know the values of the population parameters, we will compute the population z-score.

Solution: First, we compute the z-score for the Yankees. z-Scores are typically rounded to two decimal places.

$$z\text{-score} = \frac{x - \mu}{\sigma} = \frac{968 - 793.9}{73.5} = 2.37$$

Next we compute the z-score for the Phillies.

$$z\text{-score} = \frac{x - \mu}{\sigma} = \frac{892 - 763.0}{58.9} = 2.19$$

So the Yankees had run production 2.37 standard deviations above the mean, while the Phillies had run production 2.19 standard deviations above the mean. Therefore, the Yankees had a relatively better year at scoring runs, with respect to the American League, than did the Phillies, with respect to the National League.

Note to Instructor
It really does not make sense to talk about percentiles (other than quartiles) for small data sets. After all, how can one divide a data set with 40 observations into 100 parts? When data sets are large, it makes more sense to determine percentiles using a model, such as the normal model. For that reason, we will postpone determining percentiles until we can use the normal model to find their values.

Now Work Problem 9

2 Interpret Percentiles

Recall that the median divides the lower 50% of a set of data from the upper 50%. The median is a special case of a general concept called the *percentile*.

Definition The **kth percentile**, denoted P_k, of a set of data is a value such that k percent of the observations are less than or equal to the value.

So percentiles divide a set of data that is written in ascending order into 100 parts; thus 99 percentiles can be determined. For example, P_1 divides the bottom 1% of the observations from the top 99%, P_2 divides the bottom 2% of the observations from the top 98%, and so on. Figure 18 displays the 99 possible percentiles.

Figure 18

Percentiles are used to give the relative standing of an observation. Many standardized exams, such as the SAT college entrance exam, use percentiles to provide students with an understanding of how they scored on the exam in relation to all other students who took the exam.

EXAMPLE 2 **Interpret a Percentile**

Problem: Jennifer just received the results of her SAT exam. Her SAT Composite of 1,710 is at the 73rd percentile. What does this mean?

Approach: In general, the kth percentile of an observation means that k percent of the observations are less than or equal to the observation.

Interpretation: A percentile rank of 73% means that 73% of SAT Composite scores are less than or equal to 1,710 and 27% of the scores are greater than 1,710. So about 27% of the students who took the exam scored better than Jennifer.

Now Work Problem 17

3 **Determine and Interpret Quartiles**

In Other Words

The first quartile, Q_1, is equivalent to the 25th percentile, P_{25}. The 2nd quartile, Q_2, is equivalent to the 50th percentile, P_{50}, which is equivalent to the median, M. Finally, the third quartile, Q_3, is equivalent to the 75th percentile, P_{75}.

The most common percentiles are quartiles. **Quartiles** divide data sets into fourths, or four equal parts. The first quartile, denoted Q_1, divides the bottom 25% of the data from the top 75%. Therefore, the first quartile is equivalent to the 25th percentile. The second quartile divides the bottom 50% of the data from the top 50%, so the second quartile is equivalent to the 50th percentile, which is equivalent to the median. Finally, the third quartile divides the bottom 75% of the data from the top 25%, so that the third quartile is equivalent to the 75th percentile. Figure 19 illustrates the concept of quartiles.

Figure 19

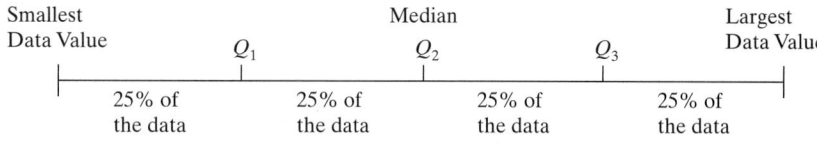

Smallest Data Value ——— Q_1 ——— Median Q_2 ——— Q_3 ——— Largest Data Value

25% of the data   25% of the data   25% of the data   25% of the data

 Using Technology

The technique presented here agrees with the method used by TI graphing calculators. It will agree with MINITAB output when the number of observations is odd. When the number of observations is even, MINITAB gives different results.

Finding Quartiles

Step 1: Arrange the data in ascending order.
Step 2: Determine the median, M, or second quartile, Q_2.
Step 3: Determine the first and third quartiles, Q_1 and Q_3, by dividing the data set into two halves; the bottom half will be the observations below (to the left of) the location of the median and the top half will be the observations above (to the right of) the location of the median. The first quartile is the median of the bottom half and the third quartile is the median of the top half.

| EXAMPLE 3 | **Finding and Interpreting Quartiles** |

In Other Words

To find Q_2, determine the median of the data set. To find Q_1, determine the median of the "lower half" of the data set. To find Q_3, determine the median of the "upper half" of the data set.

Note to Instructor

Ask your students whether quartiles are resistant.

Problem: The Highway Loss Data Institute routinely collects data on collision coverage claims. Collision coverage insures against physical damage to an insured individual's vehicle. The data in Table 16 represent a random sample of 18 collision coverage claims based on data obtained from the Highway Loss Data Institute for 2004 models. Find and interpret the first, second, and third quartiles for collision coverage claims.

Table 16					
$6,751	$9,908	$3,461	$2,336	$21,147	$2,332
$189	$1,185	$370	$1,414	$4,668	$1,953
$10,034	$735	$802	$618	$180	$1,657

Approach: We follow the steps given above.

Solution
Step 1: The data written in ascending order are given as follows:

$180 $189 $370 $618 $735 $802 $1,185 $1,414 $1,657
$1,953 $2,332 $2,336 $3,461 $4,668 $6,751 $9,908 $10,034 $21,147

Step 2: There are $n = 18$ observations, so the median, or second quartile, Q_2, is the mean of the 9th and 10th observations. Therefore, $M = Q_2 = \dfrac{\$1,657 + \$1,953}{2} = \$1,805$.

Step 3: The median of the bottom half of the data is the first quartile, Q_1. The bottom half of the data is the observations less than the median, or

$$\$180 \quad \$189 \quad \$370 \quad \$618 \quad \$735 \quad \$802 \quad \$1185 \quad \$1414 \quad \$1657$$
$$\uparrow$$
$$Q_1$$

The median of these data is the 5th observation. Therefore, $Q_1 = \$735$.

 The median of the top half of the data is the third quartile, Q_3. The top half of the data is the observations greater than the median, or

$$\$1,953 \quad \$2,332 \quad \$2,336 \quad \$3,461 \quad \$4,668 \quad \$6,751 \quad \$9,908 \quad \$10,034 \quad \$21,147$$
$$\uparrow$$
$$Q_3$$

The median of these data is the 5th observation. Therefore, $Q_3 = \$4,668$.

Interpretation: We interpret the quartiles as percentiles. For example, 25% of the collision claims are less than or equal to the first quartile, $735, and 75% of the collision claims are greater than $735. Also, 50% of the collision claims are less than or equal to $1,805, the second quartile, and 50% of the collision claims are greater than $1,805. Finally, 75% of the collision claims are less than or equal to $4,668, the third quartile, and 25% of the collision claims are greater than $4,668.

EXAMPLE 4   **Finding Quartiles Using Technology**

 Using Technology

Statistical packages may use different formulas for obtaining the quartiles, so results may differ slightly.

Problem: Find the quartiles of the collision coverage claims data in Table 16.

Approach: We will use both a TI-84 Plus graphing calculator and MINITAB to obtain the quartiles. The steps for obtaining quartiles using a TI-83/84 Plus graphing calculator, MINITAB, or Excel are given in the Technology Step-by-Step on page 175.

Solution: Figure 20(a) shows the results obtained from a TI-84 Plus graphing calculator. Figure 20(b) shows the results obtained from MINITAB. The results presented by the TI-84 agree with our "by hand" solution. Notice that the first quartile, 706, and the third quartile, 5,189, reported by MINITAB disagree with our "by hand" and TI-84 result. This difference is due to the fact that the TI-84 Plus and MINITAB use different algorithms for obtaining quartiles.

Figure 20

```
1-Var Stats
↑n=18
 minX=180
 Q₁=735
 Med=1805
 Q₃=4668
 maxX=21147
```

(a)

Note to Instructor
Ask students to conjecture the method that MINITAB uses in finding the quartiles.

Descriptive statistics: Claim

Variable	N	N*	Mean	SE Mean	StDev	Minimum	Q1	Median	Q3	Maximum
Claim	18	0	3874	1250	5302	180	706	1805	5189	2114

(b)

Now Work Problem 21(b)

 Determine and Interpret the Interquartile Range

In Section 3.2 we introduced two measures of dispersion, the range and the standard deviation, neither of which are resistant to extreme values. Quartiles, on the other hand, are resistant to extreme values. For this reason, it would be preferable to find a measure of dispersion that is based on quartiles.

Definition

The **interquartile range**, denoted **IQR**, is the range of the middle 50% of the observations in a data set. That is, the IQR is the difference between the first and third quartiles and is found using the formula

$$IQR = Q_3 - Q_1$$

The interpretation of the interquartile range is similar to that of the range and standard deviation. That is, the more spread a set of data has, the higher the interquartile range will be.

EXAMPLE 5 | **Determining and Interpreting the Interquartile Range**

Problem: Determine and interpret the interquartile range of the collision claim data from Example 3.

Approach: We will use the quartiles found by hand in Example 3. The interquartile range, IQR, is found by computing the difference between the first and third quartiles. It represents the range of the middle 50% of the observations.

Solution: The interquartile range is

$$
\begin{aligned}
IQR &= Q_3 - Q_1 \\
&= \$4,668 - \$735 \\
&= \$3,933
\end{aligned}
$$

Interpretation: The range of the middle 50% of the observations in the collision claim data is $3,933.

Now Work Problem 21(c)

Let's compare the measures of central tendency and dispersion discussed thus far for the collision claim data. The mean collision claim is $3874.4 and the median is $1,805. The median is more representative of the "center" because the data are skewed to the right (only 5 of the 18 observations are greater than the mean). The range is $21,147 − $180 = $20,967. The standard deviation is $5,301.6 and the interquartile range is $3,933. The values of the range and standard deviation are affected by the extreme claim of $21,147. In fact, if this claim had been $120,000 (let's say the claim was for a totaled Mercedes S-class AMG), then the range and standard deviation would increase to $119,820 and $27,782.5, respectively. The interquartile range is not affected. Therefore, when the distribution of data is highly skewed or contains extreme observations, it is best to use the interquartile range as the measure of dispersion because it is resistant.

Summary: Which Measures to Report		
Shape of Distribution	**Measure of Central Tendency**	**Measure of Dispersion**
Symmetric	Mean	Standard deviation
Skewed left or skewed right	Median	Interquartile range

For the remainder of this text, the direction **describe the distribution** will mean to describe its shape (skewed left, skewed right, symmetric), its center (mean or median), and its spread (standard deviation or interquartile range).

5 Check a Set of Data for Outliers

Whenever performing any type of data analysis, we should always check for extreme observations in the data set. Extreme observations are referred to as **outliers**. Whenever outliers are encountered, their origin must be investigated. They can occur by

⬦ **CAUTION** Outliers distort both the mean and the standard deviation, because neither is resistant. Because these measures often form the basis for most statistical inference, any conclusions drawn from a set of data that contains outliers can be flawed.

chance, because of error in the measurement of a variable, during data entry, or from errors in sampling. For example, in the 2000 presidential election, a precinct in New Mexico accidentally recorded 610 absentee ballots for Al Gore as 110. Workers in the Gore camp discovered the data-entry error through an analysis of vote totals.

Sometimes extreme observations are common within a population. For example, suppose we wanted to estimate the mean price of a European car. We might take a random sample of size 5 from the population of all European automobiles. If our sample included a Ferrari F430 Spider (approximately $175,000), it probably would be an outlier, because this car costs much more than the typical European automobile. The value of this car would be considered *unusual* because it is not a typical value from the data set.

We can use the following steps to check for outliers using quartiles.

Note to Instructor
A second method for identifying outliers uses z-scores. If the z-score is less than −2 or greater than 2, the data value can be considered to be an outlier. However, this method should be used only if the distribution is symmetric, because it is based on the Empirical Rule.

Checking for Outliers by Using Quartiles

Step 1: Determine the first and third quartiles of the data.

Step 2: Compute the interquartile range.

Step 3: Determine the fences. **Fences** serve as cutoff points for determining outliers.

$$\text{Lower fence} = Q_1 - 1.5(\text{IQR})$$

$$\text{Upper fence} = Q_3 + 1.5(\text{IQR})$$

Step 4: If a data value is less than the lower fence or greater than the upper fence, it is considered an outlier.

EXAMPLE 6	**Checking for Outliers**

Problem: Check the data that represent the collision coverage claims for outliers.

Approach: We follow the preceding steps. Any data value that is less than the lower fence or greater than the upper fence will be considered an outlier.

Solution

Step 1: We will use the quartiles found by hand in Example 3. So $Q_1 = \$735$ and $Q_3 = \$4,668$.

Step 2: The interquartile range, IQR, is

$$\begin{aligned} \text{IQR} &= Q_3 - Q_1 \\ &= \$4,668 - \$735 \\ &= \$3,933 \end{aligned}$$

Step 3: The lower fence, LF, is

$$\begin{aligned} \text{LF} &= Q_1 - 1.5(\text{IQR}) \\ &= \$735 - 1.5(\$3,933) \\ &= -\$5,164.5 \end{aligned}$$

The upper fence, UF, is

$$\begin{aligned} \text{UF} &= Q_3 + 1.5(\text{IQR}) \\ &= \$4,668 + 1.5(\$3,933) \\ &= \$10,567.5 \end{aligned}$$

Step 4: There are no outliers below the lower fence. However, there is an outlier above the upper fence, corresponding to the claim of $21,147.

Now Work Problem 21(d)

3.4 ASSESS YOUR UNDERSTANDING

Concepts and Vocabulary

1. Write a paragraph that explains the meaning of percentiles.

2. Suppose you received the highest score on an exam. Your friend scored the second-highest score, yet you both were in the 99th percentile. How can this be?

3. Morningstar is a mutual fund rating agency. It ranks a fund's performance by using one to five stars. A one-star mutual fund is in the bottom 20% of its investment class; a five-star mutual fund is in the top 20% of its investment class. Interpret the meaning of a four-star mutual fund.

4. When outliers are discovered, should they always be removed from the data set before further analysis?

5. Mensa is an organization designed for people of high intelligence. One qualifies for Mensa if one's intelligence is measured at or above the 98th percentile. Explain what this means.

6. Explain the advantage of using z-scores to compare observations from two different data sets.

7. Explain the circumstances for which the interquartile range is the preferred measure of dispersion. What is an advantage that the standard deviation has over the interquartile range?

8. Explain what each quartile represents.

Applying the Concepts

9. **Birth Weights** In 2005, babies born after a gestation period of 32 to 35 weeks had a mean weight of 2,600 grams and a standard deviation of 660 grams. In the same year, babies born after a gestation period of 40 weeks had a mean weight of 3,500 grams and a standard deviation of 470 grams. Suppose a 34-week gestation period baby weighs 2,400 grams and a 40-week gestation period baby weighs 3,300 grams. What is the z-score for the 34-week gestation period baby? What is the z-score for the 40-week gestation period baby? Which baby weighs less relative to the gestation period?

10. **Birth Weights** In 2005, babies born after a gestation period of 32 to 35 weeks had a mean weight of 2,600 grams and a standard deviation of 660 grams. In the same year, babies born after a gestation period of 40 weeks had a mean weight of 3,500 grams and a standard deviation of 470 grams. Suppose a 34-week gestation period baby weighs 3,000 grams and a 40-week gestation period baby weighs 3,900 grams. What is the z-score for the 34-week gestation period baby? What is the z-score for the 40-week gestation period baby? Which baby weighs less relative to the gestation period?

11. **Men versus Women** The average 20- to 29-year old man is 69.6 inches tall, with a standard deviation of 3.0 inches, while the average 20- to 29-year old woman is 64.1 inches tall, with a standard deviation of 3.8 inches. Who is relatively taller, a 75-inch man or a 70-inch woman? Man

Source: CDC Vital and Health Statistics, Advance Data, Number 361, July 5, 2005

12. **Men versus Women** The average 20- to 29-year-old man is 69.6 inches tall, with a standard deviation of 3.0 inches, while the average 20- to 29-year-old woman is 64.1 inches tall, with a standard deviation of 3.8 inches. Who is relatively taller, a 67-inch man or a 62-inch woman? Woman

Source: CDC Vital and Health Statistics, Advance Data, Number 361, July 5, 2005

13. **ERA Champions** In 2007, Jake Peavy of the San Diego Padres had the lowest earned-run average (ERA is the mean number of runs yielded per nine innings pitched) of any starting pitcher in the National League, with an ERA of 2.54. Also in 2007, John Lackey of the Los Angeles Angels had the lowest ERA of any starting pitcher in the American League with an ERA of 3.01. In the National League, the mean ERA in 2007 was 4.119 and the standard deviation was 0.697. In the American League, the mean ERA in 2007 was 4.017 and the standard deviation was 0.678. Which player had the better year relative to his peers, Peavy or Lackey? Why? Peavy

14. **Batting Champions** The highest batting average ever recorded in Major League Baseball was by Ted Williams in 1941 when he hit 0.406. That year, the mean and standard deviation for batting average were 0.2806 and 0.0328. In 2007, Magglio Ordonez was the American League batting champion, with a batting average of 0.363. In 2007, the mean and standard deviation for batting average were 0.2848 and 0.0273. Who had the better year relative to his peers, Williams or Ordonez? Why?

15. **School Admissions** A highly selective boarding school will only admit students who place at least 1.5 standard deviations above the mean on a standardized test that has a mean of 200 and a standard deviation of 26. What is the minimum score that an applicant must make on the test to be accepted? 239

16. **Quality Control** A manufacturer of bolts has a quality-control policy that requires it to destroy any bolts that are more than 2 standard deviations from the mean. The quality-control engineer knows that the bolts coming off the assembly line have a mean length of 8 cm with a standard deviation of 0.05 cm. For what lengths will a bolt be destroyed?

17. **You Explain It! Percentiles** Explain the meaning of the following percentiles.
Source: Advance Data from Vital and Health Statistics, Number 361, July 7, 2005.

   (a) The 15th percentile of the head circumference of males 3 to 5 months of age is 41.0 cm.

   (b) The 90th percentile of the waist circumference of females 2 years of age is 52.7 cm.

   (c) Anthropometry involves the measurement of the human body. One goal of these measurements is to assess how body measurements may be changing over time. The following table represents the standing height of males aged 20 years or older for various age groups. Based on the percentile measurements of the different age groups, what might you conclude?

Age	Percentile				
	10th	**25th**	**50th**	**75th**	**90th**
20–29	166.8	171.5	176.7	181.4	186.8
30–39	166.9	171.3	176.0	181.9	186.2
40–49	167.9	172.1	176.9	182.1	186.0
50–59	166.0	170.8	176.0	181.2	185.4
60–69	165.3	170.1	175.1	179.5	183.7
70–79	163.2	167.5	172.9	178.1	181.7
80 or older	161.7	166.1	170.5	175.3	179.4

9. −0.30; −0.43; 40-week gestation   10. 0.61; 0.85; 34-week gestation   14. Williams   16. <7.9 cm or >8.1 cm

22. (d) 6.23 g/dL; 14.03 g/dL; Yes, 5.7 g/dL   23. (a) −0.02; 0.035; 0.095   24. (a) 1.61; 2.165; 2.68

18. **You Explain It! Percentiles** Explain the meaning of the following percentiles.

    Source: National Center for Health Statistics.

    (a) The 5th percentile of the weight of males 36 months of age is 12.0 kg.

    (b) The 95th percentile of the length of newborn females is 53.8 cm.

19. **You Explain It! Quartiles** A violent crime includes rape, robbery, assault, and homicide. The following is a summary of the violent-crime rate (violent crimes per 100,000 population) for all 50 states in the United States plus Washington, D.C., in 2005.

    $$Q_1 = 272.8 \quad Q_2 = 387.4 \quad Q_3 = 529.7$$

    (a) Provide an interpretation of these results.

    (b) Determine and interpret the interquartile range. 256.9

    (c) The violent-crime rate in Washington, D.C., in 2005 was 1,459. Would this be an outlier? Yes

    (d) Do you believe that the distribution of violent-crime rates is skewed or symmetric? Why? Skewed right

20. **You Explain It! Quartiles** One variable that is measured by online homework systems is the amount of time a student spends on homework for each section of the text. The following is a summary of the number of minutes a student spends for each section of the text for the fall 2007 semester in a College Algebra class at Joliet Junior College.

    $$Q_1 = 42 \quad Q_2 = 51.5 \quad Q_3 = 72.5$$

    (a) Provide an interpretation of these results.

    (b) Determine and interpret the interquartile range. 30.5

    (c) Suppose a student spent 2 hours doing homework for a section. Would this be an outlier? Yes

    (d) Do you believe that the distribution of time spent doing homework is skewed or symmetric? Why? Skewed right

21. **April Showers** The following data represent the number of inches of rain in Chicago, Illinois, during the month of April for 20 randomly selected years.

0.97	2.47	3.94	4.11	5.79
1.14	2.78	3.97	4.77	6.14
1.85	3.41	4.00	5.22	6.28
2.34	3.48	4.02	5.50	7.69

    Source: NOAA, Climate Diagnostics Center

    (a) Compute the z-score corresponding to the 1971 rainfall of 0.97 inch. Interpret this result. −1.70

    (b) Determine the quartiles. 2.625 in.; 3.985 in.; 5.36 in.

    (c) Compute and interpret the interquartile range, IQR. 2.735

    (d) Determine the lower and upper fences. Are there any outliers, according to this criterion? −1.478 in.; 9.463 in.; No

22. **Hemoglobin in Cats** The following data represent the hemoglobin (in g/dL) for 20 randomly selected cats.

5.7	8.9	9.6	10.6	11.7
7.7	9.4	9.9	10.7	12.9
7.8	9.5	10.0	11.0	13.0
8.7	9.6	10.3	11.2	13.4

    Source: Joliet Junior College Veterinarian Technology Program

(a) Compute the z-score corresponding to the hemoglobin of Blackie, 7.8 g/dL. Interpret this result. −1.21

(b) Determine the quartiles. 9.15 g/dL; 9.95 g/dL; 11.1 g/dL

(c) Compute and interpret the interquartile range, IQR. 1.95

(d) Determine the lower and upper fences. Are there any outliers, according to this criterion?

23. **Rate of Return of Google** The following data represent the monthly rate of return of Google common stock from its inception in August 2004 through November 2007.

    (a) Determine and interpret the quartiles.

    (b) Check the data set for outliers. 0.47

0.26	0.26	0.04	0.06	0.06	−0.04	−0.04	0.22
0.47	0.06	−0.16	0.19	0.05	0.18	0.09	0.02
−0.05	−0.02	0.08	0.02	−0.02	0.13	−0.08	−0.02
0.06	−0.01	0.07	−0.05	0.01	−0.10	0.02	0.03
0.01	0.11	−0.11	0.09	0.10	0.25	−0.02	0.03

    Source: Yahoo!Finance

24. **CO_2 Emissions** The following data represent the carbon dioxide emissions per capita (total carbon dioxide emissions, in tons, divided by total population) for the countries of Western Europe in 2004.

    (a) Determine and interpret the quartiles.

    (b) Is the observation corresponding to Luxembourg, 6.81, an outlier? Yes

2.34	1.34	3.86	1.40	2.08	2.39	2.68
2.64	3.44	2.07	1.67	1.61	6.81	2.21
2.09	1.64	2.87	2.38	1.47	1.53	
1.44	3.65	2.12	5.22	2.67	1.01	

    Source: Carbon Dioxide Information Analysis Center

25. **Fraud Detection** As part of its "Customers First" program, a cellular phone company monitors monthly phone usage. The goal of the program is to identify unusual use and alert the customer that their phone may have been used by an unscrupulous individual. The following data represent the monthly phone use in minutes of a customer enrolled in this program for the past 20 months.

346	345	489	358	471
442	466	505	466	372
442	461	515	549	437
480	490	429	470	516

    The phone company decides to use the upper fence as the cutoff point for the number of minutes at which the customer should be contacted. What is the cutoff point? 574 minutes

26. **Stolen Credit Card** A credit card company decides to enact a fraud-detection service. The goal of the credit card company is to determine if there is any unusual activity on the credit card. The company maintains a database of daily charges on a customer's credit card. Days when the card was inactive are excluded from the database. If a day's worth of charges appears unusual, the customer is contacted to make sure that the credit card has not been compromised. Use the following daily charges (rounded to the nearest dollar) to determine the amount the daily charges must exceed before the customer is contacted. $219

143	166	113	188	133
90	89	98	95	112
111	79	46	20	112
70	174	68	101	212

27. Student Survey of Income A survey of 50 randomly selected full-time Joliet Junior College students was conducted during the Fall 2007 semester. In the survey, the students were asked to disclose their weekly income from employment. If the student did not work, $0 was entered.

0	262	0	635	0
244	521	476	100	650
12,777	567	310	527	0
83	159	0	547	188
719	0	367	316	0
479	0	82	579	289
375	347	331	281	628
0	203	149	0	403
0	454	67	389	0
671	95	736	300	181

(a) Check the data set for outliers. $12,777
(b) Draw a histogram of the data and label the outliers on the histogram.
(c) Provide an explanation for the outliers.

28. Student Survey of Entertainment Spending A survey of 40 randomly selected full-time Joliet Junior College students was conducted in the Fall 2007 semester. In the survey, the students were asked to disclose their weekly spending on entertainment. The results of the survey are as follows:

21	54	64	33	65	32	21	16
22	39	67	54	22	51	26	14
115	7	80	59	20	33	13	36
36	10	12	101	1,000	26	38	8
28	28	75	50	27	35	9	48

(a) Check the data set for outliers. $115 and $1,000
(b) Draw a histogram of the data and label the outliers on the histogram.
(c) Provide an explanation for the outliers.

29. Pulse Rate Use the results of Problem 23 in Section 3.1 and Problem 25 in Section 3.2 to compute the z-scores for all the students. Compute the mean and standard deviation of these z-scores.

30. Travel Time Use the results of Problem 24 in Section 3.1 and Problem 26 in Section 3.2 to compute the z-scores for all the students. Compute the mean and standard deviation of these z-scores.

31. Fraud Detection Revisited Use the fraud-detection data from Problem 25 to do the following.
(a) Determine the standard deviation and interquartile range of the data.   58.0 min; 56.5 min
(b) Suppose the month in which the customer used 346 minutes was not actually that customer's phone. That particular month, the customer did not use her phone at all, so 0 minutes were used. How does changing the observation from 346 to 0 affect the standard deviation and interquartile range? What property does this illustrate?
$S = 115.0$ min; $IQR = 56.5$ min

TECHNOLOGY STEP-BY-STEP   Determining Quartiles

TI-83/84 Plus
Follow the same steps given to compute the mean and median from raw data. (Section 3.1)

MINITAB
Follow the same steps given to compute the mean and median from raw data. (Section 3.1)

Excel
1. Enter the raw data into column A.
2. With the data analysis Tool Pak enabled, select the **Tools** menu and highlight **Data Analysis**....
3. Select **Rank and Percentile** from the Data Analysis window.
4. With the cursor in the **Input Range** cell, highlight the data. Press OK.

3.5 THE FIVE-NUMBER SUMMARY AND BOXPLOTS

Objectives	1	Compute the five-number summary
	2	Draw and interpret boxplots

Let's pause for a minute and consider where we have come up to this point. In Chapter 2, we discussed techniques for graphically representing data. These summaries included bar graphs, pie charts, histograms, stem-and-leaf plots, and timeseries graphs. In Sections 3.1–3.4, we presented techniques for measuring the center of a distribution, spread in a distribution, and relative position of observations in a distribution of data. Why do we want these summaries? What purpose do they serve?

Historical Note

John Tukey was born on July 16, 1915, in New Bedford, Massachusetts. His parents graduated numbers 1 and 2 from Bates College and were elected "the couple most likely to give birth to a genius." In 1936, Tukey graduated from Brown University with an undergraduate degree in chemistry. He went on to earn a master's degree in chemistry from Brown. In 1939, Tukey earned his doctorate in mathematics from Princeton University. He remained at Princeton and, in 1965, became the founding chair of the Department of Statistics. Among his many accomplishments, Tukey is credited with coining the terms *software* and *bit*. In the early 1970s, he discussed the negative effects of aerosol cans on the ozone layer. In December 1976 he published *Exploratory Data Analysis*, from which the following quote appears. "Exploratory data analysis can never be the whole story, but nothing else can serve as the foundation stone—as the first step." (p. 3). Tukey also recommended that the 1990 Census be adjusted by means of statistical formulas. John Tukey died in New Brunswick, New Jersey, on July 26, 2000.

Well, the reason we want these summaries is to gain a sense as to what the data are trying to tell us. We are *exploring* the data to see if they contain any interesting information that may be useful in our research. The summaries make this exploration much easier. In fact, because these summaries represent an exploration, a famous statistician, named John Tukey, called this material **exploratory data analysis**.

Tukey defined exploratory data analysis as "detective work—numerical detective work—or graphical detective work." He believed it is best to treat the exploration of data as a detective would search for evidence when investigating a crime. Our goal is only to collect and present evidence. Drawing conclusions (or inference) is like the deliberations of the jury. So, what we have done up to this point falls under the category of exploratory data analysis. We have not come to any conclusions; we have only collected information and presented summaries.

We have already looked at one of Tukey's graphical summaries, the stem-and-leaf plot. In this section, we look at two more summaries: the five-number summary and the boxplot.

① Compute the Five-Number Summary

Remember that the median is a measure of central tendency that divides the lower 50% of the data from the upper 50% of the data. It is resistant to extreme values and is the preferred measure of central tendency when data are skewed right or left.

The three measures of dispersion presented in Section 3.2 (range, variance, and standard deviation) are not resistant to extreme values. However, the interquartile range, $Q_3 - Q_1$, is resistant. It measures the spread of the data by determining the difference between the 25th and 75th percentiles. It is interpreted as the range of the middle 50% of the data. However, the median, Q_1 and Q_3 do not provide information about the extremes of the data. To get this information, we need to know the smallest and largest values in the data set.

The **five-number summary** of a set of data consists of the smallest data value, Q_1, the median, Q_3, and the largest data value. Symbolically, the five-number summary is presented as follows:

Five-Number Summary

   MINIMUM Q_1 M Q_3 MAXIMUM

EXAMPLE 1   **Obtaining the Five-Number Summary**

Problem: The data shown in Table 17 show the finishing times (in minutes) of the men in the 60- to 64-year-old age group in a 5-kilometer race. Determine the five-number summary of the data.

Table 17						
19.95	23.25	23.32	25.55	25.83	26.28	42.47
28.58	28.72	30.18	30.35	30.95	32.13	49.17
33.23	33.53	36.68	37.05	37.43	41.42	54.63

Source: Laura Gillogly, student at Joliet Junior College

Approach: The five-number summary requires that we determine the minimum data value, Q_1, M (the median), Q_3, and the maximum data value. We need to arrange the data in ascending order and then use the procedures introduced in Section 3.4 to obtain Q_1, M, and Q_3.

Solution: The data in ascending order are as follows:

19.95, 23.25, 23.32, 25.55, 25.83, 26.28, 28.58, 28.72, 30.18, 30.35, 30.95,
32.13, 33.23, 33.53, 36.68, 37.05, 37.43, 41.42, 42.47, 49.17, 54.63

The smallest number (the fastest time) in the data set is 19.95. The largest number in the data set is 54.63. The first quartile, Q_1, is 26.06. The median, M, is 30.95. The third quartile, Q_3, is 37.24. The five-number summary is

19.95 26.06 30.95 37.24 54.63

EXAMPLE 2   **Obtaining the Five-Number Summary Using Technology**

Problem: Using statistical software or a graphing calculator, determine the five-number summary of the data presented in Table 17.

Approach: We will use MINITAB to obtain the five-number summary.

Solution: Figure 21 shows the output supplied by MINITAB. The five-number summary is highlighted.

Figure 21

Descriptive statistics: Times

Variable	N	N*	Mean	SE Mean	StDev	Minimum	Q1	Median	Q3	Maximum
Times	21	0	33.37	2.20	10.10	19.95	26.06	30.95	37.24	54.63

---

2   ## Draw and Interpret Boxplots

The five-number summary can be used to create another graph, called the **boxplot**.

> **Drawing a Boxplot**
>
> **Step 1:** Determine the lower and upper fences:
>
> $$\text{Lower fence} = Q_1 - 1.5(\text{IQR})$$
> $$\text{Upper fence} = Q_3 + 1.5(\text{IQR})$$
>
> Remember, IQR $= Q_3 - Q_1$.
>
> **Step 2:** Draw vertical lines at Q_1, M, and Q_3. Enclose these vertical lines in a box.
>
> **Step 3:** Label the lower and upper fences.
>
> **Step 4:** Draw a line from Q_1 to the smallest data value that is larger than the lower fence. Draw a line from Q_3 to the largest data value that is smaller than the upper fence. These lines are called **whiskers**.
>
> **Step 5:** Any data values less than the lower fence or greater than the upper fence are outliers and are marked with an asterisk (*).

Note to Instructor
Some call the boxplot described here the modified boxplot.

EXAMPLE 3   **Constructing a Boxplot**

Problem: Use the results from Example 1 to a construct a boxplot of the finishing times of the men in the 60- to 64-year-old age group.

Approach: Follow the steps presented above.

Solution: From the results of Example 1, we know that $Q_1 = 26.06$, $M = 30.95$, and $Q_3 = 37.24$. Therefore, the interquartile range $= \text{IQR} = Q_3 - Q_1 = 37.24 - 26.06 = 11.18$. The difference between the 75th percentile and 25th percentile is a time of 11.18 minutes.

Step 1: We compute the lower and upper fences:

$$\text{Lower fence} = Q_1 - 1.5(\text{IQR}) = 26.06 - 1.5(11.18) = 9.29$$

$$\text{Upper fence} = Q_3 + 1.5(\text{IQR}) = 37.24 + 1.5(11.18) = 54.01$$

Step 2: Draw a horizontal number line with a scale that will accommodate our graph. Draw vertical lines at $Q_1 = 26.06$, $M = 30.95$, and $Q_3 = 37.24$. Enclose these lines in a box. See Figure 22(a).

Figure 22(a)

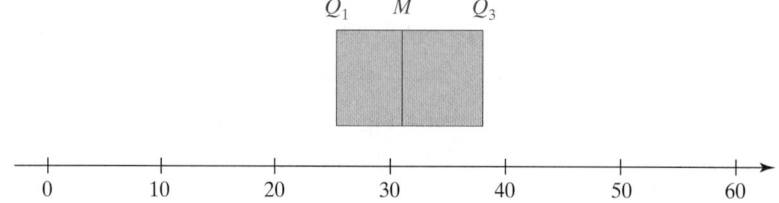

Step 3: Temporarily mark the location of the lower and upper fence with brackets ([and]). See Figure 22(b).

Figure 22(b)

Step 4: The smallest data value that is larger than 9.29 (the lower fence) is 19.95. The largest data value that is smaller than 54.01 (the upper fence) is 49.17. We draw horizontal lines from Q_1 to 19.95 and from Q_3 to 49.17. See Figure 22(c).

Figure 22(c)

Step 5: Plot any values less than 9.29 (the lower fence) or greater than 54.01 (the upper fence) using an asterisk (*). These values are outliers. So 54.63 is an outlier. Remove the brackets from the graph. See Figure 22(d).

Figure 22(d)

Using a Boxplot and Quartiles to Describe the Shape of a Distribution

Figure 23 shows three histograms and their corresponding boxplots with the five-number summary labeled. We should notice the following from the figure.

- In Figure 23(a), the histogram shows the distribution is skewed right. Notice that the median is left of center in the box, and the right whisker is longer than the left whisker. Further notice the distance from the median to the first quartile is less than the distance from the median to the third quartile. Also, the distance from the median to the minimum value in the data set is less than the distance from the median to the maximum value in the data set.

- In Figure 23(b), the histogram shows the distribution is symmetric. Notice that the median is in the center of the box, and the left and right whiskers are roughly the same length. Further notice the distance from the median to the first quartile is the same as the distance from the median to the third quartile. Also, the distance from the median to the minimum value in the data set is the same as the distance from the median to the maximum value in the data set.

- In Figure 23(c), the histogram shows the distribution is skewed left. Notice that the median is right of center in the box, and the left whisker is longer than the right whisker. Further notice the distance from the median to the first quartile is more than the distance from the median to the third quartile. Also, the distance from the median to the minimum value in the data set is more than the distance from the median to the maximum value in the data set.

CAUTION Identifying the shape of a distribution from a boxplot (or from a histogram, for that matter) is subjective. When identifying the shape of a distribution from a graph, be sure to support your opinion.

Figure 23

(a) Skewed right

(b) Symmetric

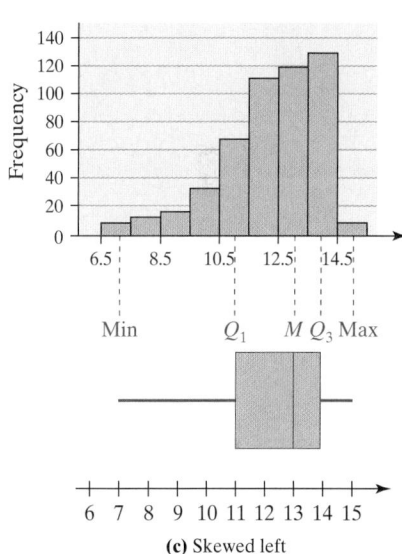

(c) Skewed left

The boxplot in Figure 22(d) suggests that the distribution is skewed right, since the right whisker is longer than the left whisker and the median is left of center in the box. We can also assess the shape using the quartiles. The distance from the median to the first quartile is 4.89 ($= 30.95 - 26.06$), while the distance from the median to the third quartile is 6.29 ($= 37.24 - 30.95$). Plus, the distance from the median to the minimum value is 11 ($= 30.95 - 19.95$), while the distance from the median to the maximum value is 23.68 ($= 54.63 - 30.95$).

Now Work Problem 11

| EXAMPLE 4 | **Comparing Two Distributions by Using Boxplots** |

Problem: In the Spacelab Life Sciences 2, 14 male rats were sent to space. Upon their return, the red blood cell mass (in milliliters) of the rats was determined. A control group of 14 male rats was held under the same conditions (except for space-flight) as the space rats, and their red blood cell mass was also determined when the space rats returned. The project was led by Paul X. Callahan. The data in Table 18 were obtained. Construct side-by-side boxplots for red blood cell mass for the flight group and control group. Does it appear that the flight to space affected the red blood cell mass of the rats?

Table 18							
Flight				**Control**			
7.43	7.21	8.59	8.64	8.65	6.99	8.40	9.66
9.79	6.85	6.87	7.89	7.62	7.44	8.55	8.70
9.30	8.03	7.00	8.80	7.33	8.58	9.88	9.94
6.39	7.54			7.14	9.14		

Source: NASA Life Sciences Data Archive

Approach: When comparing two data sets, we draw side-by-side boxplots on the same horizontal number line to make the comparison easy. Graphing calculators with advanced statistical features, as well as statistical spreadsheets such as MINITAB and Excel, have the ability to draw boxplots. We will use MINITAB to draw the boxplots. The steps for drawing boxplots using a TI-83/84 Plus graphing calculator, MINITAB, or Excel are given in the Technology Step-by-Step on page 183.

Solution: Figure 24 shows the side-by-side boxplots drawn in MINITAB. From the boxplots, it appears that the space flight has reduced the red blood cell mass of the rats since the median for the flight group (M ≈ 7.7) is less than the median for the control group (M ≈ 8.6). The spread, as measured by the interquartile range, appears to be similar for both groups.

Figure 24

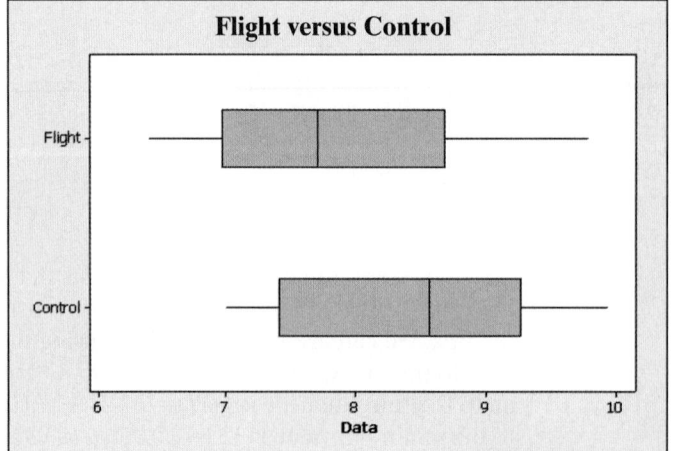

3·5 ASSESS YOUR UNDERSTANDING

Concepts and Vocabulary

1. Explain how to determine the shape of a distribution using the boxplot and quartiles.

2. In a boxplot, if the median is to the left of the center of the box and the right whisker is substantially longer than the left whisker, the distribution is skewed ___right___.

Skill Building

In Problems 3 and 4, (a) identify the shape of the distribution and (b) determine the five-number summary. Assume that each number in the five-number summary is an integer.

3.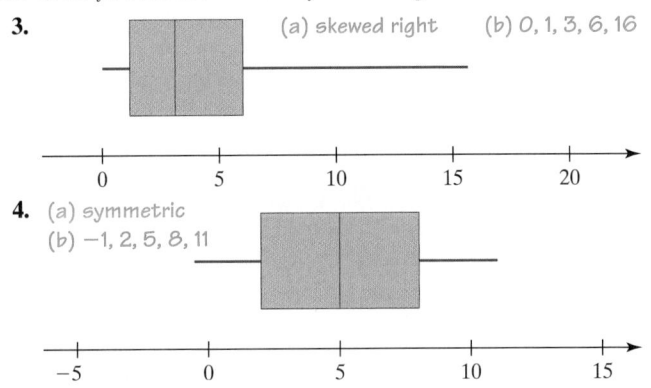
   (a) skewed right   (b) 0, 1, 3, 6, 16

4. (a) symmetric
   (b) −1, 2, 5, 8, 11
   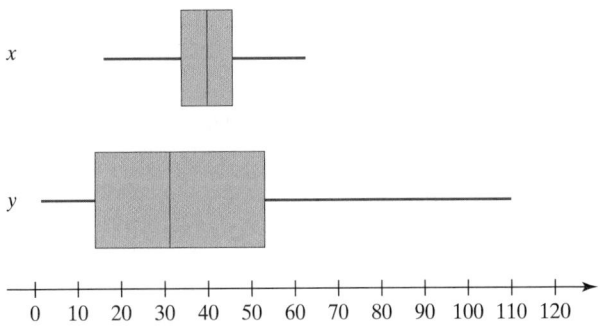

5. Use the side-by-side boxplots shown to answer the questions that follow.

   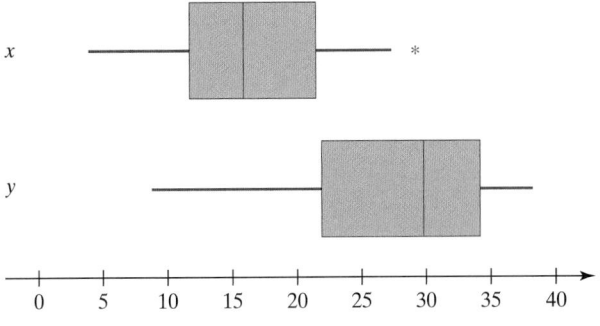

   (a) To the nearest integer, what is the median of variable *x*? 40
   (b) To the nearest integer, what is the third quartile of variable *y*? 52
   (c) Which variable has more dispersion? Why? y
   (d) Describe the shape of the variable *x*. Support your position. Symmetric
   (e) Describe the shape of the variable *y*. Support your position. Skewed right

6. Use the side-by-side boxplots shown to answer the questions that follow.

(a) To the nearest integer, what is the median of variable *x*? 16
(b) To the nearest integer, what is the first quartile of variable *y*? 22
(c) Which variable has more dispersion? Why? y
(d) Does the variable *x* have any outliers? If so, what is the value of the outlier? Yes; 30
(e) Describe the shape of the variable *y*. Support your position. Skewed left

7. **Exam Scores** After giving a statistics exam, Professor Dang determined the following five-number summary for her class results: 60 68 77 89 98. Use this information to draw a boxplot of the exam scores.

8. **Speed Reading** Jessica enrolled in a course that promised to increase her reading speed. To help judge the effectiveness of the course, Jessica measured the number of words per minute she could read prior to enrolling in the course. She obtained the following five-number summary: 110 140 157 173 205. Use this information to draw a boxplot of the reading speed.

Applying the Concepts

9. **Age at Inauguration** The following data represent the age of U.S. presidents on their respective inauguration days.

42	48	51	52	54	56	57	61	65
43	49	51	54	55	56	57	61	68
46	49	51	54	55	56	58	62	69
46	50	51	54	55	57	60	64	
47	50	52	54	55	57	61	64	

Source: factmonster.com

(a) Find the five-number summary. 42, 51, 55, 58, 69
(b) Construct a boxplot.
(c) Comment on the shape of the distribution.   symmetric

10. **Carpoolers** The following data represent the percentage of workers who carpool to work for the fifty states plus Washington D.C. Note: The minimum observation of 7.2% corresponds to Maine and the maximum observation of 16.4% corresponds to Hawaii.

7.2	8.5	9.0	9.4	10.0	10.3	11.2	11.5	13.8
7.8	8.6	9.1	9.6	10.0	10.3	11.2	11.5	14.4
7.8	8.6	9.2	9.7	10.0	10.3	11.2	11.7	16.4
7.9	8.6	9.2	9.7	10.1	10.7	11.3	12.4	
8.1	8.7	9.2	9.9	10.2	10.7	11.3	12.5	
8.3	8.8	9.4	9.9	10.3	10.9	11.3	13.6	

Source: 2004 American Community Survey by the U.S. Census Bureau

(a) Find the five-number summary. 7.2, 9.0, 10.0, 11.2, 16.4
(b) Construct a boxplot.
(c) Comment on the shape of the distribution.   Skewed right

11. Got a Headache? The following data represent the weight
NW (in grams) of a random sample of 25 Tylenol tablets.

0.608	0.601	0.606	0.602	0.611
0.608	0.610	0.610	0.607	0.600
0.608	0.608	0.605	0.609	0.605
0.610	0.607	0.611	0.608	0.610
0.612	0.598	0.600	0.605	0.603

Source: Kelly Roe, student at Joliet Junior College

(a) Construct a boxplot.
(b) Use the boxplot and quartiles to describe the shape of
the distribution.   Skewed left

12. CO₂ Emissions Revisited The following data represent the
carbon dioxide emissions per capita (total carbon dioxide
emissions, in tons, divided by total population) for the countries of Western Europe in 2004. In Problem 24 from Section 3.4, you found the quartiles.

(a) Construct a boxplot.
(b) Use the boxplot and quartiles to describe the shape of
the distribution.   Skewed right

2.34	1.34	3.86	1.40	2.08
2.64	3.44	2.07	1.67	1.61
2.09	1.64	2.87	2.38	1.47
1.44	3.65	2.12	5.22	2.67
2.68	2.39	6.81	1.53	1.01
2.21				

Source: Carbon Dioxide Information Analysis Center

13. M&Ms In Problem 29 from Section 3.1, we drew a histogram of the weights of M&Ms and found that the distribution is symmetric. Draw a boxplot of these data. Use the
boxplot and quartiles to confirm the distribution is symmetric. For convenience, the data are displayed again.

0.87	0.88	0.82	0.90	0.90	0.84	0.84
0.91	0.94	0.86	0.86	0.86	0.88	0.87
0.89	0.91	0.86	0.87	0.93	0.88	
0.83	0.95	0.87	0.93	0.91	0.85	
0.91	0.91	0.86	0.89	0.87	0.84	
0.88	0.88	0.89	0.79	0.82	0.83	
0.90	0.88	0.84	0.93	0.81	0.90	
0.88	0.92	0.85	0.84	0.84	0.86	

Source: Michael Sullivan

14. Old Faithful In Problem 30 from Section 3.1, we drew a histogram of the length of eruption of California's Old Faithful
geyser and found that the distribution is symmetric. Draw a
boxplot of these data. Use the boxplot and quartiles to confirm the distribution is symmetric. For convenience, the data
are displayed again.

108	108	99	105	103	103	94
102	99	106	90	104	110	110
103	109	109	111	101	101	
110	102	105	110	106	104	
104	100	103	102	120	90	
113	116	95	105	103	101	
100	101	107	110	92	108	

Source: Ladonna Hansen, Park Curator

15. Dissolving Rates of Vitamins A student wanted to know
NW whether Centrum vitamins dissolve faster than the corresponding generic brand. The student used vinegar as a proxy
for stomach acid and measured the time (in minutes) it took
for a vitamin to completely dissolve. The results are shown
next.

Centrum					Generic Brand				
2.73	3.07	3.30	3.35	3.12	6.57	6.23	6.17	7.17	5.77
2.95	2.15	2.67	2.80	2.25	6.73	5.78	5.38	5.25	5.55
2.60	2.57	4.02	3.02	2.15	5.50	6.50	7.42	6.47	6.30
3.03	3.53	2.63	2.30	2.73	6.33	7.42	5.57	6.35	5.92
3.92	2.38	3.25	4.00	3.63	5.35	7.25	7.58	6.50	4.97
3.02	4.17	4.33	3.85	2.23	7.13	5.98	6.60	5.03	7.18

Source: Amanda A. Sindewald, student at Joliet Junior College

(a) Draw side-by-side boxplots for each vitamin type.
(b) Which vitamin type has more dispersion?   Generic
(c) Which vitamin type appears to dissolve faster?   Centrum

16. Chips per Cookie Do store-brand chocolate chip cookies
have fewer chips per cookie than Keebler's Chips Deluxe
Chocolate Chip Cookies? To find out, a student randomly
selected 21 cookies of each brand and counted the number
of chips in the cookies. The results are shown next.

Keebler			Store Brand		
32	23	28	21	23	24
28	28	29	24	25	27
25	20	25	26	26	21
22	21	24	18	16	24
21	24	21	21	30	17
26	28	24	23	28	31
33	20	31	27	33	29

Source: Trina McNamara, student at Joliet Junior College

(a) Draw side-by-side boxplots for each brand of cookie.
(b) Does there appear to be a difference in the number of
chips per cookie?   Not really
(c) Does one brand have a more consistent number of chips
per cookie?   Keebler

17. Putting It Together: Paternal Smoking It is well-documented that active maternal smoking during pregnancy is associated with lower birth weight babies. Researchers Fernando D. Martinez and associates wanted to determine if there is a relationship between paternal smoking habits and birth weight. The researchers administered a questionnaire to each parent of newborn infants. One question asked whether the individual smoked regularly. Because the survey was administered within 15 days of birth, it was assumed that any regular smokers were also regular smokers during pregnancy. Birthweights for the babies (in grams) of nonsmoking mothers were obtained and divided into two groups, non-smoking fathers and smoking fathers. The given data are representative of the data collected by the researchers. The researchers concluded that the birth weight of babies whose father smoked was less than the birth weight of babies whose father did not smoke.

Source: "The Effect of Paternal Smoking on the Birthweight of Newborns Whose Mothers Did Not Smoke" Fernando D.

Martinez, Anne L. Wright, Lynn M. Taussig, *American Journal of Public Health* Vol. 84, No. 9

(a) Is this an observational study or a designed experiment? Why? *Observational study*
(b) What is the explanatory variable? What is the response variable? *Whether the father smoked or not; birth weight*
(c) Can you think of any lurking variables that may affect the results of the study?
(d) In the article, the researchers stated that, "birthweights were adjusted for possible confounders . . . .". What does this mean?
(e) Determine summary statistics (mean, median, standard deviation, quartiles) for each group.
(f) Interpret the first quartile for both the nonsmoker and smoker group.
(g) Draw a side-by-side boxplot of the data. Does the side-by-side boxplot confirm the conclusions of the study?

Nonsmokers						Smokers					
4194	3128	3522	3290	3454	3423	3998	3686	3455	2851	3066	3145
3062	3471	3771	4354	3783	3544	3150	3807	2986	3548	2918	4104
3544	3994	3746	2976	4019	4067	4216	3963	3502	3892	3457	2768
4054	3732	3518	3823	3884	3302	3493	3769	3255	3509	3234	3629
4248	3436	3719	3976	3668	3263	2860	4131	3282	3129	2746	4263

TECHNOLOGY STEP-BY-STEP   Drawing Boxplots Using Technology

TI-83/84 Plus
1. Enter the raw data into L1.
2. Press 2nd Y= and select 1:Plot 1.
3. Turn the plots ON. Use the cursor to highlight the modified boxplot icon. Your screen should look as follows:

4. Press ZOOM and select 9:ZoomStat.

MINITAB
1. Enter the raw data into column C1.
2. Select the **Graph** menu and highlight **Boxplot . . .**
3. For a single boxplot, select One Y, simple. For two or more boxplots, **select** Multiple Y's, simple.
4. Select the data to be graphed. If you want the boxplot to be horizontal rather than vertical, select the Scale button, then transpose value and category scales. Click OK.

Excel
1. Load the DDXL Add-in.
2. Enter the raw data into column A. If you are drawing side-by-side boxplots, enter all the data in column A and use index values to identify which group the data belongs to in column B. Consider Example 4, we might use 1 for the flight group and 2 for the control group. Highlight the data.
3. Select the **DDXL** menu and highlight **Charts and Plots**. If you are drawing a single boxplot, select "Boxplot" from the pull-down menu; if you drawing side-by-side boxplots, select "Boxplot by Groups" from the pull-down menu.
4. Put the cursor in the "Quantitative Variable" window. From the Names and Columns window, select the column of the data and click the ◄ arrow. If you are drawing side-by-side boxplots, place the cursor in the "Group Variable" window. From the Names and Columns window, select the column of the indices and click the ◄ arrow. If the first row contains the variable name, check the "First row is variable names" box. Click OK.

CHAPTER 3 REVIEW

Summary

This chapter concentrated on describing distributions numerically. Measures of central tendency are used to indicate the typical value in a distribution. Three measures of central tendency were discussed. The mean measures the center of gravity of the distribution. The median separates the bottom 50% of the data from the top 50%. The data must be quantitative to compute the mean. The data must be at least ordinal to compute the median. The mode measures the most frequent observation. The data can be either quantitative or qualitative to compute the mode. The median is resistant to extreme values, while the mean is not.

Measures of dispersion describe the spread in the data. The range is the difference between the highest and lowest data values. The variance measures the average squared deviation about the mean. The standard deviation is the square root of the variance. The range, variance, and standard deviation are not resistant. The mean and standard deviation are used in many types of statistical inference.

The mean, median, and mode can be approximated from grouped data. The variance and standard deviation can also be approximated from grouped data.

We can determine the relative position of an observation in a data set using z-scores and percentiles. A z-score denotes how many standard deviations an observation is from the mean. Percentiles determine the percent of observations that lie above and below an observation. The interquartile range is a resistant measure of dispersion. The upper and lower fences can be used to identify potential outliers. Any potential outlier must be investigated to determine whether it was the result of a data-entry error or some other error in the data-collection process, or of an unusual value in the data set.

The five-number summary provides an idea about the center and spread of a data set through the median and the interquartile range. The length of the tails in the distribution can be determined from the smallest and largest data values. The five-number summary is used to construct boxplots. Boxplots can be used to describe the shape of the distribution and to visualize outliers.

Vocabulary

Arithmetic mean (p. 129)
Population arithmetic mean (p. 129)
Sample arithmetic mean (p. 129)
Mean (p. 129)
Median (p. 131)
Resistant (p. 134)
Mode (p. 135)
No mode (p. 136)
Bimodal (p. 136)
Multimodal (p. 136)
Dispersion (p. 143)
Range (p. 144)

Deviation about the mean (pp. 144–145)
Population variance (p. 145)
Computational formula (p. 145)
Sample variance (p. 146)
Biased (p. 147)
Degrees of freedom (p. 147)
Population standard deviation (p. 148)
Sample standard deviation (p. 148)
The Empirical Rule (p. 150)
Chebyshev's Inequality (p. 152)
Weighted mean (p. 162)
z-score (p. 167)

kth percentile (p. 168)
Quartiles (p. 169)
Interquartile range (p. 171)
Describe the distribution (p. 171)
Outlier (p. 171)
Fences (p. 172)
Exploratory data analysis (p. 176)
Five-number summary (p. 176)
Boxplot (p. 177)
Whiskers (p. 177)

Formulas

Population Mean

$$\mu = \frac{\sum x_i}{N}$$

Sample Mean

$$\bar{x} = \frac{\sum x_i}{n}$$

Population Variance

$$\sigma^2 = \frac{\sum (x_i - \mu)^2}{N} = \frac{\sum x_i^2 - \frac{(\sum x_i)^2}{N}}{N}$$

Sample Variance

$$s^2 = \frac{\sum (x_i - \bar{x})^2}{n - 1} = \frac{\sum x_i^2 - \frac{(\sum x_i)^2}{n}}{n - 1}$$

Population Standard Deviation

$$\sigma = \sqrt{\sigma^2}$$

Sample Standard Deviation

$$s = \sqrt{s^2}$$

Range = Largest Data Value − Smallest Data Value

Weighted Mean

$$\bar{x}_w = \frac{\sum w_i x_i}{\sum w_i}$$

Population Mean from Grouped Data

$$\mu = \frac{\sum x_i f_i}{\sum f_i}$$

Sample Mean from Grouped Data

$$\bar{x} = \frac{\sum x_i f_i}{\sum f_i}$$

Population Variance from Grouped Data

$$\sigma^2 = \frac{\sum (x_i - \mu)^2 f_i}{\sum f_i}$$

Sample Variance from Grouped Data

$$s^2 = \frac{\sum (x_i - \bar{x})^2 f_i}{\left(\sum f_i\right) - 1}$$

Population z-Score

$$z = \frac{x - \mu}{\sigma}$$

Sample z-Score

$$z = \frac{x - \bar{x}}{s}$$

Interquartile Range

$$IQR = Q_3 - Q_1$$

Lower and Upper Fences

Lower Fence $= Q_1 - 1.5(IQR)$
Upper Fence $= Q_3 + 1.5(IQR)$

Objectives

Section	You should be able to . . .	Example	Review Exercises
3.1	1 Determine the arithmetic mean of a variable from raw data (p. 129)	1, 4, 6	1(a), 2(a), 3(a), 4(c), 10(a)
	2 Determine the median of a variable from raw data (p. 131)	2, 3, 4, 6	1(a), 2(a), 3(a), 4(c), 10(a)
	3 Explain what it means for a statistic to be resistant (p. 133)	5	2(c), 10(h), 10(i), 12
	4 Determine the mode of a variable from raw data (p. 135)	7, 8, 9	3(a), 4(d)
3.2	1 Compute the range of a variable from raw data (p. 144)	2	1(b), 2(b), 3(b)
	2 Compute the variance of a variable from raw data (p. 144)	3, 4, 6	1(b)
	3 Compute the standard deviation of a variable from raw data (p. 148)	5, 6, 7	1(b), 2(b), 3(b), 10(d)
	4 Use the Empirical Rule to describe data that are bell shaped (p. 150)	8	5(a)–(d)
	5 Use Chebyshev's inequality to describe any set of data (p. 152)	9	5(e)–(f)
3.3	1 Approximate the mean of a variable from grouped data (p. 160)	1, 4	6(a)
	2 Compute the weighted mean (p. 161)	2	7
	3 Approximate the variance and standard deviation of a variable from grouped data (p. 162)	3, 4	6(b)
3.4	1 Determine and interpret z-scores (p. 167)	1	8
	2 Interpret percentiles (p. 168)	2	11
	3 Determine and interpret quartiles (p. 169)	3, 4	10(b)
	4 Determine and interpret the interquartile range (p. 170)	5	2(b), 10(d)
	5 Check a set of data for outliers (p. 171)	6	10(e)
3.5	1 Compute the five-number summary (p. 176)	1, 2	10(c)
	2 Draw and interpret boxplots (p. 177)	3, 4	9, 10(f)–10(g)

Review Exercises

1. **Muzzle Velocity** The following data represent the muzzle velocity (in meters per second) of rounds fired from a 155-mm gun.

793.8	793.1	792.4	794.0	791.4
792.4	791.7	792.3	789.6	794.4

   Source: Christenson, Ronald, and Blackwood, Larry, "Tests for Precision and Accuracy of Multiple Measuring Devices," *Technometrics,* 35(4): 411–421, 1993.

   1. (a) $\bar{x} = 792.51$ m/s, M $= 792.40$ m/s
   (a) Compute the sample mean and median muzzle velocity.
   (b) Compute the range, sample variance, and sample standard deviation. Range $= 4.8$ m/s, $s^2 = 2.03$, $s = 1.42$ m/s

2. **Price of Chevy Cobalts** The following data represent the sales price in dollars for nine 2-year-old Chevrolet Cobalts in the Los Angeles area.

14,050	13,999	12,999	10,995	9,980
8,998	7,889	7,200	5,500	

   Source: cars.com

   2. (a) $\bar{x} = \$10,178.9$; M $= \$9,980$
   (a) Determine the sample mean and median price.
   (b) Determine the range, sample standard deviation, and interquartile range. Range $= \$8,550$, $s = \$3,074.9$, IQR $= \$5,954.5$
   (c) Redo (a) and (b) if the data value 14,050 was incorrectly entered as 41,050. How does this change affect the mean? the median? the range? the standard deviation? the interquartile range? Which of these values is resistant? Median and IQR are resistant.

3. **Chief Justices** The following data represent the ages of chief justices of the U.S. Supreme Court when they were appointed.

Justice	Age
John Jay	44
John Rutledge	56
Oliver Ellsworth	51
John Marshall	46
Roger B. Taney	59
Salmon P. Chase	56
Morrison R. Waite	58
Melville W. Fuller	55
Edward D. White	65
William H. Taft	64
Charles E. Hughes	68
Harlan F. Stone	69
Frederick M. Vinson	56
Earl Warren	62
Warren E. Burger	62
William H. Rehnquist	62
John G. Roberts	50

Source: Information Please Almanac

(a) Compute the population mean, median, and mode ages. $\mu = 57.8$, $M = 58.0$, bimodal: 56 and 62
(b) Compute the range and population standard deviation ages. Range = 25, $\sigma = 7.0$
(c) Obtain two simple random samples of size 4, and compute the sample mean and sample standard deviation ages.

4. Number of Tickets Issued As part of a statistics project, a student surveys 30 randomly selected students and asks them how many speeding tickets they have been issued in the past month. The results of the survey are as follows:

1	1	0	1	0	0
0	0	0	1	0	1
0	1	2	0	1	1
0	0	0	0	1	1
0	0	0	0	1	0

(a) Draw a frequency histogram of the data and describe its shape. Skewed right
(b) Based on the shape of the histogram, do you expect the mean to be more than, equal to, or less than the median? Mean > median
(c) Compute the mean and the median of the number of tickets issued. $\bar{x} = 0.4$; $M = 0$
(d) Determine the mode of the number of tickets issued. 0

5. Chebyshev's Inequality and the Empirical Rule Suppose that a random sample of 200 light bulbs has a mean life of 600 hours and a standard deviation of 53 hours.

(a) A histogram of the data indicates the sample data follow a bell-shaped distribution. According to the Empirical Rule, 99.7% of light bulbs have lifetimes between ___441___ and ___759___ hours.
(b) Assuming the data are bell shaped, determine the percentage of light bulbs that will have a life between 494 and 706 hours? 95%

(c) Assuming the data are bell shaped, what percentage of light bulbs will last between 547 and 706 hours? 81.5%
(d) If the company that manufactures the light bulb guarantees to replace any bulb that does not last at least 441 hours, what percentage of light bulbs can the firm expect to have to replace, according to the Empirical Rule? 0.15%
(e) Use Chebyshev's Inequality to determine the minimum percentage of light bulbs with a life within 2.5 standard deviations of the mean. 84%
(f) Use Chebyshev's Inequality to determine the minimum percentage of light bulbs with a life between 494 and 706 hours. 75%

6. Travel Time to Work The frequency distribution listed in the table represents the travel time to work (in minutes) for a random sample of 895 U.S. adults.

Travel Time (minutes)	Frequency
0–9	28
10–19	151
20–29	177
30–39	206
40–49	94
50–59	93
60–69	88
70–79	45
80–89	13

Source: Based on data from the 2006 American Community Survey

(a) Approximate the mean travel time to work for U.S. adults in 2006. 37.5 minutes
(b) Approximate the standard deviation travel time to work for U.S. adults in 2006. 19.2 minutes

7. Weighted Mean Michael has just completed his first semester in college. He earned an A in his 5-hour calculus course, a B in his 4-hour chemistry course, an A in his 3-hour speech course, and a C in his 3-hour psychology course. Assuming an A equals 4 points, a B equals 3 points, and a C equals 2 points, determine Michael's grade-point average if grades are weighted by class hours. 3.33

8. Weights of Males versus Females According to the National Center for Health Statistics, the mean weight of a 20- to 29-year-old female is 156.5 pounds, with a standard deviation of 51.2 pounds. The mean weight of a 20- to 29-year-old male is 183.4 pounds, with a standard deviation of 40.0 pounds. Who is relatively heavier: a 20- to 29-year-old female who weights 160 pounds or a 20- to 29-year-old male who weighs 185 pounds? Female

9. Population Density The side-by-side boxplot shows the density (population per square kilometer) of the 50 United States (USA) and the fifteen countries in the European Union (EU).

(a) Is the USA or the EU more densely populated? Why? EU
(b) Does the USA or the EU have more dispersion in density? Why?

(c) Are there any outliers in the density for the EU? If so, approximate their values. *490*

(d) What is the shape of each distribution? *Skewed right*

Population Density

10. **Presidential Inaugural Addresses** Ever wonder how many words are in a typical inaugural address? The following data represent the lengths of all the inaugural addresses (measured in word count) for all presidents up to George W. Bush's second address. (a) *μ = 2,363 words; M = 2,144 words*

1,425	1,125	1,128	5,433	2,242	2,283
135	1,172	1,337	1,802	2,446	1,507
2,308	3,838	2,480	1,526	2,449	2,170
1,729	8,445	2,978	3,318	1,355	1,571
2,158	4,776	1,681	4,059	1,437	
1,175	996	4,388	3,801	2,130	
1,209	3,319	2,015	1,883	1,668	
3,217	2,821	3,967	1,807	1,087	
4,467	3,634	2,217	1,340	2,463	
2,906	698	985	559	2,546	

Source: infoplease.com

(a) Determine the mean and median number of words in a presidential inaugural address.

(b) Determine and interpret the quartiles for the number of words in a presidential inaugural address.

(c) Determine the five-number summary for the number of words in a presidential inaugural address.

(d) Determine the standard deviation and interquartile range for the number of words in a presidential inaugural address. *σ = 1,418 words; IQR = 1,623 words*

(e) Are there any outliers in the data set? If so, what is (are) the value(s)? *Yes, 5433 and 8445*

(f) Draw a boxplot of the data.

(g) Describe the shape of the distribution. Support your position using the boxplot and quartiles. *Skewed right*

(h) Which measure of central tendency do you think better describes the typical number of words in an inaugural address? Why? *Median*

(i) Which measure of dispersion do you think better describes the spread of the typical number of words in an inaugural address? Why? *IQR*

11. **You Explain It! Percentiles** According to the National Center for Health Statistics, a 19-year-old female whose height is 67.1 inches has a height that is at the 85th percentile. Explain what this means.

12. **Skinfold Thickness Procedure** One method of estimating body fat is through skinfold thickness measurement. The measurement can use from three to nine different standard anatomical sites around the body. The right side is usually only measured (for consistency). The tester pinches the skin at the appropriate site to raise a double layer of skin and the underlying adipose tissue, but not the muscle. Calipers are then applied 1 centimeter below and at right angles to the pinch and a reading is taken 2 seconds later. The mean of two measurements should be taken. If the two measurements differ greatly, a third should be done and then the median value taken. Explain why a median is used as the measure of central tendency when three measures are taken, rather than the mean. *Resistance*

10. (b) 1,355; 2,144; 2,978 words
10. (c) 135, 1355, 2144, 2978, 8445

CHAPTER TEST

1. The following data represent the amount of snowfall (in inches) received at Mammoth Mountain in the Sierra Mountains from the 1996–1997 ski season to the 2005–2006 ski season. Treat these data as a sample of all ski seasons.

399	542	347	381	400
289	358	439	602	661

Source: Mammoth Mountain

(a) Determine the mean amount of snowfall. *441.8 inches*

(b) Determine the median amount of snowfall. *399.5 inches*

(c) Suppose the observation 661 inches was incorrectly recorded at 1661 inches. Recompute the mean and the median. What do you notice? What property of the median does this illustrate? *x̄ = 541.8 inches; M = 399.5 inches; resistance*

2. The Federal Bureau of Investigation classifies various larcenies. The following data represent the type of larcenies based on a random sample of 15 larcenies. What is the mode type of larceny? *From motor vehicles*

Pocket picking and purse snatching	Bicycles	From motor vehicles
From motor vehicles	From motor vehicles	From buildings
From buildings	Shoplifiting	Motor vehicle accessories
From motor vehicles	Shoplifiting	From motor vehicles
From motor vehicles	Pocket picking and purse snatching	From motor vehicles

3. Determine the range of the snowfall data from Problem 1.
372 inches

4. (a) Determine the standard deviation of the snowfall data from Problem 1. 120.4 inches

    (b) By hand, determine and interpret the interquartile range of the snowfall data from Problem 1. 184 inches

    (c) Which of these two measures of dispersion is resistant? Why? IQR

5. In a random sample of 250 toner cartridges, the mean number of pages a toner cartridge can print is 4,302 and the standard deviation is 340.

    (a) Suppose a histogram of the data indicates that the sample data follow a bell-shaped distribution. According to the Empirical Rule, 99.7% of toner cartridges will print between 3,282 and 5,322 pages.

    (b) Assuming that the distribution of the data are bell shaped, determine the percentage of toner cartridges whose print total is between 3,622 and 4,982 pages. 95%

    (c) If the company that manufactures the toner cartridges guarantees to replace any cartridge that does not print at least 3,622 pages, what percent of cartridges can the firm expect to be responsible for replacing, according to the Empirical Rule? 2.5%

    (d) Use Chebyshev's inequality to determine the minimum percentage of toner cartridges with a page count within 1.5 standard deviations of the mean. 55.6%

    (e) Use Chebyshev's inequality to determine the minimum percentage of toner cartridges that print between 3,282 and 5,322 pages. 88.9%

6. The following data represent the length of time (in minutes) between eruptions of Old Faithful in Yellowstone National Park.

Time (minutes)	Frequency
40–49	8
50–59	44
60–69	23
70–79	6
80–89	107
90–99	11
100–109	1

    (a) Approximate the mean length of time between eruptions. 74.9 minutes

    (b) Approximate the standard deviation length of time between eruptions. 14.7 minutes

7. Yolanda wishes to develop a new type of meatloaf to sell at her restaurant. She decides to combine 2 pounds of ground sirloin (cost $2.70 per pound), 1 pound of ground turkey (cost $1.30 per pound), and $\frac{1}{2}$ pound of ground pork (cost $1.80 per pound). What is the cost per pound of the meatloaf? $2.17

8. An engineer is studying bearing failures for two different materials in aircraft gas turbine engines. The following data are failure times (in millions of cycles) for samples of the two material types.

Material A		Material B	
3.17	5.88	5.78	9.65
4.31	6.91	6.71	13.44
4.52	8.01	6.84	14.71
4.66	8.97	7.23	16.39
5.69	11.92	8.20	24.37

    (a) Compute the sample mean failure time for each material.

    (b) By hand, compute the median failure time for each material.

    (c) Compute the sample standard deviation of the failure times for each material. Which material has its failure times more dispersed?

    (d) By hand, compute the five-number summary for each material.

    (e) On the same graph, draw boxplots for the two materials. Annotate the graph with some general remarks comparing the failure times.

    (f) Describe the shape of the distribution of each material using the boxplot and quartiles. Skewed right

9. The following data represent the weights (in grams) of 50 randomly selected quarters. Determine and interpret the quartiles. Does the data set contain any outliers?
5.58 g; 5.60 g; 5.67 g; yes, 5.84 g

5.49	5.58	5.60	5.62	5.68
5.52	5.58	5.60	5.63	5.70
5.53	5.58	5.60	5.63	5.71
5.53	5.58	5.60	5.63	5.71
5.53	5.58	5.60	5.65	5.72
5.56	5.58	5.60	5.66	5.73
5.57	5.59	5.60	5.66	5.73
5.57	5.59	5.61	5.66	5.73
5.57	5.59	5.62	5.67	5.74
5.57	5.59	5.62	5.67	5.84

10. Armando is filling out a college application. The application requires that Armando supply either his SAT math score, or his ACT math score. Armando scored 610 on the SAT math and 27 on the ACT math. Which score should Armando report, given that the mean SAT math score is 515 with a standard deviation of 114, and the mean ACT math scores is 21.0 with a standard deviation of 5.1? Why? ACT

11. According to the National Center for Health Statistics, a 10-year-old male whose height is 53.5 inches has a height that is at the 15th percentile. Explain what this means.

12. The distribution of income tends to be skewed to the right. Suppose you are running for a congressional seat and wish to portray that the average income in your district is low. Which measure of central tendency, the mean or the median, would you report? Why? Median

8. (a) $\bar{x}_A$ = 6.404 million cycles; $\bar{x}_B$ = 11.332 million cycles   8. (b) M_A = 5.785 million cycles; M_B = 8.925 million cycles

8. (c) s_A = 2.626 million cycles; s_B = 5.900 million cycles; Material B   8. (d) A (in million cycles); 3.17, 4.52, 5.785, 8.01, 11.92
                                       B (in million cycles); 5.78, 6.84, 8.925, 14.71, 24.37

13. Answer the following based on the histograms shown.

(a) Which measure of central tendency would you recommend reporting for the data whose histogram is shown in Figure I? Why? *Mean*

(b) Which one has more dispersion? Explain. I

◨ MAKING AN INFORMED DECISION

What Car Should I Buy?

Suppose you are in the market to purchase a used car. To make an informed decision regarding your purchase, you would like to collect as much information as possible. Among the information you might consider are the typical price of the car, the typical number of miles the car should have, and its crash test results, insurance costs, and expected repair costs.

1. Make a list of at least three cars that you would consider purchasing. To be fair, the cars should be in the same class (such as compact, mid-size, and so on). They should also be of the same age.

2. Collect information regarding the three cars in your list by finding at least eight cars of each type that are for sale. Obtain such information as the asking price and the number of miles the car has. Sources of data include your local newspaper, classified ads, and car websites (such as www.cars.com and www.vehix.com). Compute summary statistics for asking price, number of miles, and other variables of interest. Using the same scale, draw boxplots of each variable considered.

3. Go to the Insurance Institute for Highway Safety website (www.hwysafety.org). Select the Vehicle Ratings link. Choose the make and model for each car you are considering. Obtain information regarding crash testing for each car under consideration. Compare cars in the same class. How does each car compare? Is one car you are considering substantially safer than the others? What about repair costs? Compute summary statistics for crash tests and repair costs.

4. Obtain information about insurance costs. Contact various insurance companies to determine the cost of insuring the cars you are considering. Compute summary statistics for insurance costs and draw boxplots.

5. Write a report supporting your conclusion regarding which car you would purchase.

Which colonial patriot penned the VINDEX essay in the January 8, 1770, issue of *The Boston Gazette and Country Journal*? Who wrote the 12 contested *Federalist* papers? Such questions about authorship of unattributed documents are one of the many problems confronting historians. Statistical analyses, when combined with other historical facts, often help resolve these mysteries.

One such historical conundrum is the identity of the writer known simply as A MOURNER. A letter appeared in the February 26, 1770, issue of *The Boston Gazette and Country Journal*. The text of the letter is as follows:

> The general Sympathy and Concern for the Murder of the Lad by the base and infamous Richardson on the 22d Instant, will be sufficient Reason for your Notifying the Publick that he will be buried from his Father's House in Frogg Lane, opposite Liberty-Tree, on Monday next, when all the Friends of Liberty may have an Opportunity of paying their last Respects to the Remains of this little Hero and first Martyr to the noble Cause—Whose manly Spirit (after this Accident happened) appear'd in his discreet Answers to his Doctor, his Thanks to the Clergymen who prayed with him, and Parents, and while he underwent the greatest Distress of bodily Pain; and with which he met the King of Terrors. These Things, together with the several heroic Pieces found in his Pocket, particularly *Wolfe's Summit of human Glory*, gives Reason to think he had a *martial Genius*, and would have made a clever Man.
>
> A MOURNER.

The Lad the writer refers to is Christopher Sider, an 11-year-old son of a poor German immigrant. Young Sider was shot and killed on February 22, 1770, in a civil disturbance involving schoolboys, patriot supporters of the nonimportation agreement, and champions of the English crown. This event preceded the bloody Boston Massacre by just a couple of weeks. Of Sider's funeral, John Adams wrote, "My eyes never beheld such a funeral. The Procession extended further than can be well imagined." (Diary of John Adams entry for 1770. MONDAY FEB. 26 OR THEREABOUTS.)

From a historical perspective, the identity of A MOURNER remains a mystery. However, it seems clear from the letter's text that the author supported the patriot position. This assumption somewhat narrows the field of possible writers.

Ordinarily, a statistical analysis of the frequencies of various words contained in the contested document, when compared with frequency analyses for known authors, would permit an identity inference to be drawn. Unfortunately, in this case, the letter is too short for this strategy to be useful. Another possibility is based on the frequencies of word lengths. In this instance, a simple count of letters is generated for each word in the document. Proper names, numbers, abbreviations, and titles are removed from consideration, because these do not represent normal vocabulary use. Care must be taken in choosing comparison texts, since colonial publishers habitually incorporated their own spellings into the essays they printed. Therefore, it is desirable to get comparison texts from the same printer the contested material came from.

The following table contains the summary analysis for six passages printed in *The Boston Gazette, and Country Journal* in early 1770. The Tom Sturdy (probably a pseudonym) text was included because of the use of the phrase "Friends of Liberty," which appears in A MOURNER's letter, as opposed to the more familiar "Sons of Liberty." John Hancock, James Otis, and Samuel Adams are included because they are well-known patriots who frequently wrote articles that were carried by the Boston papers. In the case of Samuel Adams, the essay used in this analysis was signed VINDEX, one of his many pseudonyms. The table presents three summaries

CASE STUDY

	Tom Sturdy	John Hancock	James Otis	Samuel Adams-1	Samuel Adams-2	Samuel Adams-1 & 2
Summary Statistics of Word Length from Sample Passages by Various Potential Authors of the Letter Signed A MOURNER						
Mean	4.08	4.69	4.58	4.60	4.52	4.56
Median	4	4	4	3	4	4
Mode	2	3	2	2	2	2
Standard deviation	2.17	2.60	2.75	2.89	2.70	2.80
Sample variance	4.70	6.76	7.54	8.34	7.30	7.84
Range	13	9	14	12	16	16
Minimum	1	1	1	1	1	1
Maximum	14	10	15	13	17	17
Sum	795	568	842	810	682	1492
Count	195	121	184	176	151	27

of work penned by Adams. The first two originate from two separate sections of the VINDEX essay. The last summary is a compilation of the first two.

1. Acting as a historical detective, generate a data set consisting of the length of each word used in the letter signed by A MOURNER. Be sure to disregard any text that uses proper names, numbers, abbreviations, or titles.

2. Calculate the summary statistics for the letter's word lengths. Compare your findings with those of the known authors, and speculate about the identity of A MOURNER.

3. Compare the two Adams summaries. Discuss the viability of word-length analysis as a tool for resolving disputed documents.

4. What other information would be useful to identify A MOURNER?

Describing the Relation between Two Variables

Outline

4.1 Scatter Diagrams and Correlation

4.2 Least-Squares Regression

4.3 Diagnostics on the Least-Squares Regression Line

4.4 Contingency Tables and Association

4.5 Nonlinear Regression: Transformations (on CD)

Note to Instructor

Remind students that Problems 15 to 17 in Section 3.5 discussed how we can graphically represent relations between a quantitative and qualitative variable. We now look at a graph of two quantitative variables. Section 4.4 will look at relations between two qualitative variables.

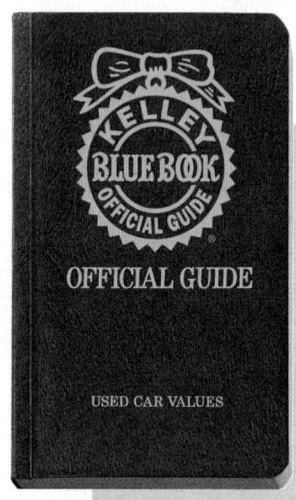

MAKING AN INFORMED DECISION

You are still in the market to buy a car. Because cars lose value over time at different rates, you want to look at the depreciation rates of the cars you are considering. After all, the higher the depreciation rate is, the more value the car loses each year. See the Decision Project on page 254.

PUTTING IT TOGETHER

In Chapters 2 and 3 we examined data in which a single variable was measured for each individual in the study (**univariate data**), such as the 3-year rate of return (the variable) for various mutual funds (the individuals). We obtained descriptive measures for the variable that were both graphical and numerical.

In this chapter, we discuss graphical and numerical methods for describing *bivariate data*. **Bivariate data** are data in which two variables are measured on an individual. For example, we might want to know whether the amount of cola consumed per week is related to one's bone density. The individuals would be the people in the study, and the two variables are amount of cola and bone density. In this scenario, both variables are quantitative. We present methods for describing the relation between two quantitative variables in Sections 4.1–4.3.

Suppose we want to know whether level of education is related to one's employment status (employed or unemployed). Here, both variables are qualitative. We will present methods for describing the relation between two qualitative variables in Section 4.4.

Situations may also occur in which one variable is quantitative while the other is qualitative. We have already presented a technique for describing this situation. Look back at Example 4 in Section 3.5 where we considered whether spaceflight affected red blood cell mass. There, spaceflight is qualitative (one group of rats was sent to space and the other was not, so this is a yes/no variable) and red blood cell mass is quantitative.

4.1 SCATTER DIAGRAMS AND CORRELATION

Preparing for This Section   Before getting started, review the following:

- Mean (Section 3.1, pp. 129–131)
- Standard deviation (Section 3.2, pp. 144–150)
- z-scores (Section 3.4, pp. 167–168)
- Lurking variable and confounding (Section 1.2, pp. 17–18)

Objectives		
	1	Draw and interpret scatter diagrams
	2	Describe the properties of the linear correlation coefficient
	3	Compute and interpret the linear correlation coefficient
	4	Determine whether a linear relation exists between two variables
	5	Explain the difference between correlation and causation

Note to Instructor

If you like, you can print out and distribute the Preparing for This Section quiz located in the Instructor's Resource Center. The purpose of the quiz is to verify that the students have the prerequisite knowledge for the section.

Before we can graphically represent bivariate data, a fundamental question must be asked. Am I interested in using the value of one variable to predict the value of the other variable? For example, it seems reasonable to think that as the speed at which a golf club is swung increases, the distance the golf ball travels also increases. Therefore, we might use club-head speed to predict distance. We call distance the *response* (or *dependent*) *variable* and club-head speed the *explanatory* (or *predictor* or *independent*) *variable*.

Definition   The **response variable** is the variable whose value can be explained by the value of the **explanatory** or **predictor variable**.

In Other Words

We use the term *explanatory variable* because it helps to explain variability in the response variable.

1 Draw and Interpret Scatter Diagrams

The first step in identifying the type of relation that might exist between two variables is to draw a picture. Bivariate data can be represented graphically through a *scatter diagram*.

Definition   A **scatter diagram** is a graph that shows the relationship between two quantitative variables measured on the same individual. Each individual in the data set is represented by a point in the scatter diagram. The explanatory variable is plotted on the horizontal axis, and the response variable is plotted on the vertical axis.

EXAMPLE 1   **Drawing a Scatter Diagram**

Table 1

Club-Head Speed (mph)	Distance (yards)
100	257
102	264
103	274
101	266
105	277
100	263
99	258
105	275

Source: Paul Stephenson, student at Joliet Junior College

Problem: A golf pro wanted to investigate the relation between the club-head speed of a golf club (measured in miles per hour) and the distance (in yards) that the ball will travel. He realized that there are other variables besides club-head speed that determine the distance a ball will travel (such as club type, ball type, golfer, and weather conditions). To eliminate the variability due to these variables, the pro used a single model of club and ball. One golfer was chosen to swing the club on a clear, 70-degree day with no wind. The pro recorded the club-head speed, measured the distance that the ball traveled, and collected the data in Table 1. Draw a scatter diagram of the data.

Approach: Because the pro wants to use club-head speed to predict the distance the ball travels, club-head speed is the explanatory variable (horizontal axis) and distance is the response variable (vertical axis). We plot the ordered pairs (100, 257), (102, 264), and so on, in a rectangular coordinate system.

Solution: The scatter diagram is shown in Figure 1.

Figure 1

Driving Distance vs. Club-head Speed

CAUTION Do not connect points when drawing a scatter diagram.

It appears from the graph that as club-head speed increases the distance that the ball travels increases as well.

It is not always clear which variable should be considered the response variable and which the explanatory variable. For example, does high school GPA predict a student's SAT score or can the SAT score be used to predict GPA? The researcher must determine which variable plays the role of explanatory variable based on the questions he or she wants answered. For example, if the researcher is interested in predicting SAT scores on the basis of high school GPA, then high school GPA will play the role of explanatory variable.

Now Work Problems 23(a) and 23(b)

Scatter diagrams show the type of relation that exists between two variables. Our goal in interpreting scatter diagrams will be to distinguish scatter diagrams that imply a linear relation from those that imply a nonlinear relation and those that imply no relation. Figure 2 displays various scatter diagrams and the type of relation implied.

Figure 2

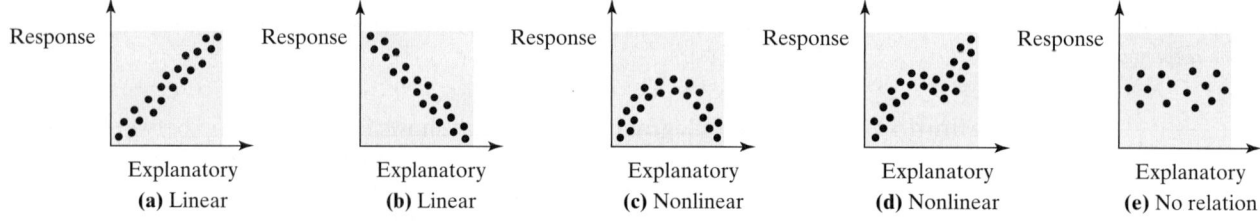

As we compare Figure 2(a) with Figure 2(b), we notice a distinct difference. In Figure 2(a), the data follow a linear pattern that slants upward to the right; the data in Figure 2(b) follow a linear pattern that slants downward to the right. Figures 2(c) and 2(d) show scatter diagrams of nonlinear relations. Figure 2(e) shows a scatter diagram in which there is no relation between the explanatory and response variables.

Definitions

In Other Words
If two variables are positively associated, then as one goes up the other also tends to go up. If two variables are negatively associated, then as one goes up the other tends to go down.

Two variables that are linearly related are said to be **positively associated** when above-average values of one variable are associated with above-average values of the other variable and below-average values of one variable are associated with below-average values of the other variable. That is, two variables are positively associated if, whenever the value of one variable increases, the value of the other variable also increases.

Two variables that are linearly related are said to be **negatively associated** when above-average values of one variable are associated with below-average values of the other variable. That is, two variables are negatively associated if, whenever the value of one variable increases, the value of the other variable decreases.

Now Work Problem 9

So the scatter diagram from Figure 1 implies that club-head speed is positively associated with the distance a golf ball travels.

② Describe the Properties of the Linear Correlation Coefficient

It is dangerous to use only a scatter diagram to determine if two variables follow a linear relation. Suppose that we redraw the scatter diagram in Figure 1 using a different vertical scale, as shown in Figure 3.

Figure 3

Note to Instructor
The correlation by eye applet can be used to illustrate many of the properties of the linear correlation coefficient. See Problems 44–46 at the end of this section.

⬦ CAUTION   The horizontal or vertical scale of a scatter diagram should be set so that the scatter diagram does not mislead a reader.

It is more difficult to conclude that club-head speed and distance are related in Figure 3 than in Figure 1. The moral of the story is this: Just as we can manipulate the scale of graphs of univariate data, we can also manipulate the scale of the graphs of bivariate data, possibly resulting in incorrect conclusions. Therefore, numerical summaries of bivariate data should be used in conjunction with graphs to determine the type of relation, if any, that exists between two variables.

Definition

The **linear correlation coefficient** or **Pearson product moment correlation coefficient** is a measure of the strength and direction of the linear relation between two quantitative variables. We use the Greek letter ρ (rho) to represent the population correlation coefficient and r to represent the sample correlation coefficient. We present only the formula for the sample correlation coefficient.

Sample Linear Correlation Coefficient*

$$r = \frac{\sum \left(\dfrac{x_i - \overline{x}}{s_x} \right)\left(\dfrac{y_i - \overline{y}}{s_y} \right)}{n - 1}$$ **(1)**

where $\overline{x}$ is the sample mean of the explanatory variable

s_x is the sample standard deviation of the explanatory variable

$\overline{y}$ is the sample mean of the response variable

s_y is the sample standard deviation of the response variable

n is the number of individuals in the sample

*An equivalent computational formula for the linear correlation coefficient is

$$r = \frac{\sum x_i y_i - \dfrac{\sum x_i \sum y_i}{n}}{\sqrt{\left(\sum x_i^2 - \dfrac{(\sum x_i)^2}{n} \right)}\sqrt{\left(\sum y_i^2 - \dfrac{(\sum y_i)^2}{n} \right)}}$$

Historical Note

Karl Pearson was born March 27, 1857. Pearson's proficiency as a statistician was recognized early in his life. It is said that his mother told him not to suck his thumb, because otherwise his thumb would wither away. Pearson analyzed the size of each thumb and said to himself, "They look alike to me. I can't see that the thumb I suck is any smaller than the other. I wonder if she could be lying to me."

Karl Pearson graduated from Cambridge University in 1879. From 1893 to 1911, he wrote 18 papers on genetics and heredity. Through this work, he developed ideas regarding correlation and the chi-square test. (See Chapter 12.) In addition, Pearson coined the term *standard deviation*.

Pearson and Ronald Fisher (see page 46) didn't get along. Their dispute was severe enough that Fisher turned down the post of chief statistician at the Galton Laboratory in 1919 because it would have meant working under Pearson.

Pearson died on April 27, 1936.

The Pearson linear correlation coefficient is named in honor of Karl Pearson (1857–1936).

Properties of the Linear Correlation Coefficient

1. The linear correlation coefficient is always between -1 and 1, inclusive. That is, $-1 \leq r \leq 1$.

2. If $r = +1$, then a perfect positive linear relation exists between the two variables. See Figure 4(a).

3. If $r = -1$, then a perfect negative linear relation exists between the two variables. See Figure 4(d).

4. The closer r is to $+1$, the stronger is the evidence of positive association between the two variables. See Figures 4(b) and 4(c).

5. The closer r is to -1, the stronger is the evidence of negative association between the two variables. See Figures 4(e) and 4(f).

6. If r is close to 0, then little or no evidence exists of a *linear* relation between the two variables. Because the linear correlation coefficient is a measure of the strength of the linear relation, **r close to 0 does not imply no relation, just no** *linear* relation. See Figures 4(g) and 4(h).

7. The linear correlation coefficient is a unitless measure of association. So the unit of measure for x and y plays no role in the interpretation of r.

8. The correlation coefficient is not resistant. Therefore, an observation that does not follow the overall pattern of the data could affect the value of the linear correlation coefficient.

Figure 4

(a) Perfect positive linear relation, $r = 1$

(b) Strong positive linear relation, $r \approx 0.9$

(c) Moderate positive linear relation, $r \approx 0.4$

(d) Perfect negative linear relation, $r = -1$

(e) Strong negative linear relation, $r \approx -0.9$

(f) Moderate negative linear relation, $r \approx -0.4$

(g) No linear relation, r close to 0.

(h) No linear relation, r close to 0.

CAUTION A linear correlation coefficient close to 0 does not imply that there is no relation, just no linear relation. For example, although the scatter diagram drawn in Figure 4(h) indicates that the two variables are related, the linear correlation coefficient of these data is close to 0.

In looking carefully at Formula (1), we should notice that the numerator in the formula is the sum of the products of z-scores for the explanatory (x) and response (y) variables. A positive linear correlation coefficient means that the sum of the products of the z-scores for x and y must be positive. Under what circumstances does this occur? Figure 5 shows a scatter diagram that implies a positive association between x and y. The vertical dashed line represents the value of $\bar{x}$, and the horizontal dashed line represents the value of $\bar{y}$. These two dashed lines divide our scatter diagram into four quadrants, labeled I, II, III, and IV.

Consider the data in quadrants I and III. If a certain x-value is above its mean, $\bar{x}$, then the corresponding y-value will be above its mean, $\bar{y}$. If a certain x-value is below its mean, $\bar{x}$, then the corresponding y-value will be below its mean, $\bar{y}$. Therefore, for

Figure 5

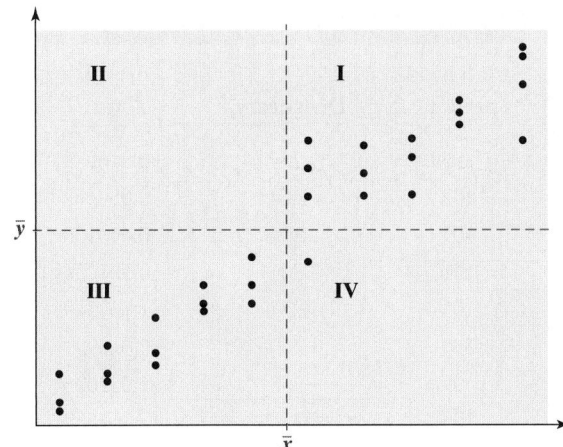

data in quadrant I, we have $\dfrac{x_i - \overline{x}}{s_x}$ positive and $\dfrac{y_i - \overline{y}}{s_y}$ positive, so their product is

positive. For data in quadrant III, we have $\dfrac{x_i - \overline{x}}{s_x}$ negative and $\dfrac{y_i - \overline{y}}{s_y}$ negative, so

their product is positive. The sum of these products is positive, and therefore we have a positive linear correlation coefficient. A similar argument can be made for negative correlation.

Now suppose that the data are equally dispersed in the four quadrants. Then the negative products (resulting from data in quadrants II and IV) will offset the positive products (resulting from data in quadrants I and III). The result is a linear correlation coefficient close to 0.

Now Work Problem 13

❸ Compute and Interpret the Linear Correlation Coefficient

Now that we have an understanding of the properties of the linear correlation coefficient, we are ready to compute and interpret its value.

EXAMPLE 2   Computing and Interpreting the Correlation Coefficient

Problem: In Table 2, columns 1 and 2 represent the club-head speed (in miles per hour) and the distance the ball travels (in yards). Compute and interpret the linear correlation coefficient.

Approach: We treat club-head speed as the explanatory variable, x, and distance as the response variable, y.

Step 1: Compute $\overline{x}$, s_x, $\overline{y}$, and s_y.

Step 2: Determine $\dfrac{x_i - \overline{x}}{s_x}$ and $\dfrac{y_i - \overline{y}}{s_y}$ for each observation.

Step 3: Compute $\left(\dfrac{x_i - \overline{x}}{s_x}\right)\left(\dfrac{y_i - \overline{y}}{s_y}\right)$ for each observation.

Step 4: Determine $\sum\left(\dfrac{x_i - \overline{x}}{s_x}\right)\left(\dfrac{y_i - \overline{y}}{s_y}\right)$ and substitute this value into Formula (1).

Solution

Step 1: We compute $\overline{x}$, s_x, $\overline{y}$, and s_y:

$$\overline{x} = 101.875 \quad s_x = 2.29518 \quad \overline{y} = 266.75 \quad s_y = 7.74135$$

To avoid round-off error when using Formula (1), do not round the statistics.

		Table 2		
Club-head Speed, x_i	Distance, y_i	$\dfrac{x_i - \bar{x}}{s_x}$	$\dfrac{y_i - \bar{y}}{s_y}$	$\left(\dfrac{x_i - \bar{x}}{s_x}\right)\left(\dfrac{y_i - \bar{y}}{s_y}\right)$
100	257	−0.816929	−1.259470	1.028898
102	264	0.054462	−0.355235	−0.019347
103	274	0.490158	0.936529	0.459047
101	266	−0.381234	−0.096882	0.036935
105	277	1.361549	1.324058	1.802770
100	263	−0.816929	−0.484412	0.395730
99	258	−1.252625	−1.130294	1.415835
105	275	1.361549	1.065706	1.451011

$$\sum \left(\frac{x_i - \bar{x}}{s_x}\right)\left(\frac{y_i - \bar{y}}{s_y}\right) = 6.570879$$

Step 2: We determine $\dfrac{x_i - \bar{x}}{s_x}$ and $\dfrac{y_i - \bar{y}}{s_y}$ in columns 3 and 4 in Table 2.

Step 3: We multiply the entries in columns 3 and 4 to obtain the entries in column 5.

Step 4: We add the entries in column 5 to obtain

$$\sum \left(\frac{x_i - \bar{x}}{s_x}\right)\left(\frac{y_i - \bar{y}}{s_y}\right) = 6.570879$$

Substitute this value into Formula (1) to obtain the correlation coefficient.

$$r = \frac{\sum \left(\dfrac{x_i - \bar{x}}{s_x}\right)\left(\dfrac{y_i - \bar{y}}{s_y}\right)}{n - 1} = \frac{6.570879}{8 - 1} = 0.938697$$

We will agree to round the correlation coefficient to three decimal places. The linear correlation between club-head speed and distance is 0.939, indicating a strong positive association between the two variables. The faster the club-head speed, the farther the golf ball tends to travel.

Notice in Example 2 that we carry many decimal places in the computation of the correlation coefficient to avoid rounding error. Also, compare the signs of the entries in columns 3 and 4. Notice that negative values in column 3 correspond to negative values in column 4 and that positive values in column 3 correspond to positive values in column 4 (except for the second trial of the experiment). This means that above-average values of x are associated with above-average values of y, and below-average values of x are associated with below-average values of y. This is why the linear correlation coefficient is positive.

EXAMPLE 3   **Drawing a Scatter Diagram and Determining the Linear Correlation Coefficient Using Technology**

Problem: Use a statistical spreadsheet or a graphing calculator with advanced statistical features to draw a scatter diagram of the data in Table 1. Then determine the linear correlation between club-head speed and distance.

Approach: We will use Excel to draw the scatter diagram and obtain the linear correlation coefficient. The steps for drawing scatter diagrams and obtaining the linear correlation coefficient using MINITAB, Excel, or the TI-83/84 Plus graphing calculators are given in the Technology Step-by-Step on pages 208–209.

Solution: Figure 6(a) shows the scatter diagram, and Figure 6(b) shows the linear correlation coefficient obtained from Excel. Notice that Excel provides a **correlation matrix**, which means that for every pair of columns in the spreadsheet it will compute and display the correlation in the bottom triangle of the matrix.

Figure 6

	Driving Distance	Club Head Speed
Driving Distance	1	
Club Head Speed	0.938695838	1

(a)   (b)

Now Work Problem 23(c)

We stated in Property 8 that the linear correlation coefficient is not resistant. For example, suppose the golfer described in Examples 1 through 3 decides to hit one more golf ball. As he is swinging, a car driving by blows its horn, which distracts the golfer. His swing speed is measured at 105 mph, but the mis-hit golf ball only travels 255 yards. The linear correlation coefficient with this additional observation decreases to 0.535.

IN CLASS ACTIVITY

Correlation

Randomly select six students from the class and have them determine their at-rest pulse rates and then discuss the following:

1. When determining each at-rest pulse rate, would it be better to count beats for 30 seconds and multiply by 2 or count beats for 1 full minute? Explain. What are some other ways to find the at-rest pulse rate? Do any of these methods have an advantage?

2. What effect will physical activity have on pulse rate?

3. Do you think the at-rest pulse rate will have any effect on the pulse rate after physical activity? If so, how? If not, why not?

Have the same six students jog in place for 3 minutes and then immediately determine their pulse rates using the same technique as for the at-rest pulse rates.

4. Draw a scatter diagram for the pulse data using the at-rest data as the explanatory variable.

5. Comment on the relationship, if any, between the two variables. Is this consistent with your expectations?

6. Based on the graph, estimate the linear correlation coefficient for the data. Then compute the correlation coefficient and compare it to your estimate.

Determine Whether a Linear Relation Exists between Two Variables

A question you may be asking yourself is "How do I know the correlation between two variables is strong enough for me to conclude that there is a linear relation between the variables?" While rigorous tests exist that can answer this question, for now we will be content with a simple comparison test that is based on the more rigorous approach.

In Other Words
We use two vertical bars to denote absolute value, as in |5| or |−4|. Recall, |5| = 5, |−4| = 4, and |0| = 0.

To test whether the correlation between the explanatory and response variables is strong enough, determine the absolute value of the correlation coefficient. If the absolute value of the correlation coefficient is greater than the critical value in Table II in Appendix A for the given sample size, then we say a linear relation exists between the two variables. Otherwise, no linear relation exists.

EXAMPLE 4 **Does a Linear Relation Exist?**

Problem: Using the data from Example 2, determine whether a linear relation exists between club-head speed and distance. Comment on the type of relation that appears to exist between club-head speed and distance.

Note to Instructor
We are conducting this test using a 0.05 level of significance.

Approach: We compare the absolute value of the linear correlation coefficient to the critical value in Table II with $n = 8$. If the absolute value of the linear correlation coefficient is greater than the critical value, we conclude that a linear relation exists between club-head speed and distance.

Solution: The linear correlation coefficient between club-head speed and distance was found to be 0.939 in Example 2. We find the critical value for correlation in Table II with $n = 8$ to be 0.707. Since $|0.939| = 0.939 > 0.707$ (0.939 is greater than 0.707), we conclude a positive linear relation exists between club-head speed and distance.

Now Work Problem 23(d)

Explain the Difference between Correlation and Causation

In Chapter 1 we stated that there are two types of studies: observational studies and designed experiments. The data examined in Examples 1 to 3 are the result of an experiment. Therefore, we can claim that a faster club-head speed causes the golf ball to travel a longer distance.

CAUTION A linear correlation coefficient that implies a strong positive or negative association does not imply causation if it was computed using observational data.

If data used in a study are observational, we cannot conclude the two correlated variables have a causal relationship. For example, the correlation between teenage birthrate and homicide rate since 1993 is 0.9987, but we cannot conclude that higher teenage birthrates cause a higher homicide rate because the data are observational. In fact, it is often the case that time-series data are correlated because both variables happen to be moving in the same direction over time. In this circumstance, both teenage birthrates and homicide rates have been declining since 1993. It is this relation that leads to the high correlation.

Is there any other way two variables can be correlated without there being a causal relation? Yes—through a *lurking variable*. A **lurking variable** is related to both the explanatory variable and response variable. For example, air-conditioning bills can be used to explain crime rates. As air-conditioning bills increase, so does the crime rate. Does this mean that folks should turn off their air conditioners so that crime rates decrease? Certainly not! In this case, the lurking variable is air temperature. As air temperatures rise, air-conditioning bills and crime rates both rise.

| EXAMPLE 5 | **Lurking Variables in a Bone Mineral Density Study** |

Table 3

Number of Colas per Week	Bone Mineral Density (g/cm²)
0	0.893
0	0.882
1	0.891
1	0.881
2	0.888
2	0.871
3	0.868
3	0.876
4	0.873
5	0.875
5	0.871
6	0.867
7	0.862
7	0.872
8	0.865

Source: Based on data obtained from Katherine L. Tucker et. al., "Colas, but not other carbonated beverages, are associated with low bone mineral density in older women: The Framingham Osteoporosis Study." *American Journal of Clinical Nutrition* 2006, 84:936–942.

Problem: Because colas tend to replace healthier beverages and colas contain caffeine and phosphoric acid, researchers Katherine L. Tucker and associates wanted to know whether consumption of cola is associated with lower bone mineral density in women. The data shown in Table 3 represent the typical number of cans of soda consumed in a week and the bone mineral density of the femoral neck for a sample of 15 women. The data were collected through a prospective cohort study.

Figure 7 shows the scatter diagram of the data. The correlation between number of colas per week and bone mineral density is -0.806. The critical value for correlation with $n = 15$ from Table II in Appendix A is 0.514. Because $|-0.806| > 0.514$, we conclude a negative linear relation exists between number of colas consumed and bone mineral density. Can the authors conclude that an increase in the number of colas consumed causes a decrease in bone mineral density? Identify some lurking variables in the study.

Figure 7

Bone Mineral Density vs Colas Consumed per Week

Approach: To claim causality, we must collect the data through a designed experiment. Remember, lurking variables are related to both the explanatory and response variables in the study.

Solution: Prospective cohort studies are studies in which the data are collected on a group of subjects through questionnaires and surveys over time. Therefore, the data are observational. So the researchers cannot claim that increased cola consumption causes a decrease in bone mineral density.

The authors of the study identified a number of lurking variables that could confound the results. The following quote is from the article:

In Other Words

Confounding means that any relation that may exist between two variables may be due to some other variable not accounted for in the study.

> Variables that could potentially confound the relation between cola consumption and bone mineral density . . . included the following: age, body mass index, height, smoking, average daily intakes of alcohol, calcium, caffeine, total energy intake, physical activity, season of measurement, estrogen use, and menopause status.

Although the authors employed advanced statistical techniques to account for these potential lurking variables, they were still careful to say that increased cola consumption is *associated* with lower bone mineral density. They never stated that increased cola consumption *causes* lower bone mineral density.

Now Work Problem 37

4.1 ASSESS YOUR UNDERSTANDING

Concepts and Vocabulary

1. Describe the difference between univariate and bivariate data.

2. What does it mean to say that two variables are positively associated?

3. What does it mean to say that the linear correlation coefficient between two variables equals 1? What would the scatter diagram look like?

4. What does it mean if $r = 0$?

5. Explain what is wrong with the following statement: "We have concluded that a high correlation exists between the gender of drivers and rates of automobile accidents."

6. Write a statement that explains the concept of correlation. Include a discussion of the role that $x_i - \bar{x}$ and $y_i - \bar{y}$ play in the computation.

7. Explain what is meant by a lurking variable. Provide an example.

8. Explain the difference between correlation and causation. When does a linear correlation coefficient that indicates a correlation exists also imply causation?

Skill Building

In Problems 9–12, determine whether the scatter diagram indicates that a linear relation may exist between the two variables. If the relation is linear, determine whether it indicates a positive or negative association between the variables.

9. Nonlinear
NW

10. Linear, negative

11. Linear, positive

12. Nonlinear

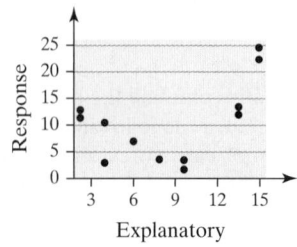

13. Match the linear correlation coefficient to the scatter diagram. The scales on the x- and y-axes are the same for each scatter diagram.
NW

(a) $r = 0.787$ III

(b) $r = 0.523$ IV

(c) $r = 0.053$ II

(d) $r = 0.946$ I

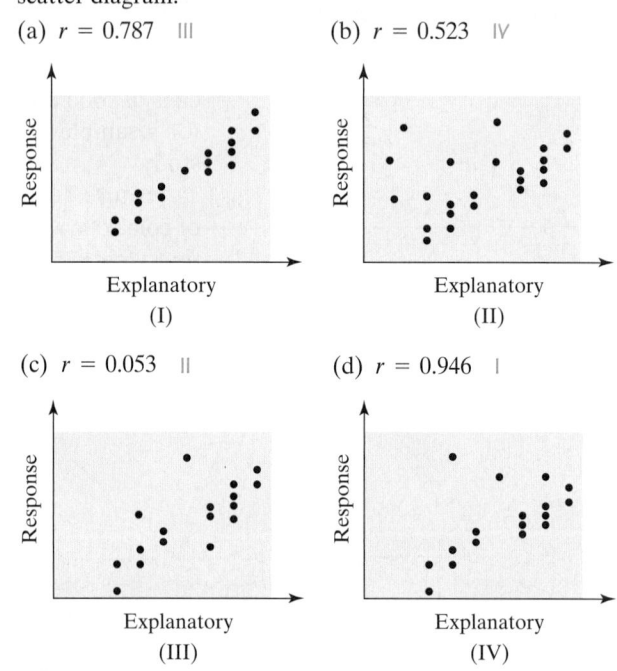

14. Match the linear correlation coefficient to the scatter diagram. The scales on the x- and y-axes are the same for each scatter diagram.

(a) $r = -0.969$ IV

(b) $r = -0.049$ III

(c) $r = -1$ I

(d) $r = -0.992$ II

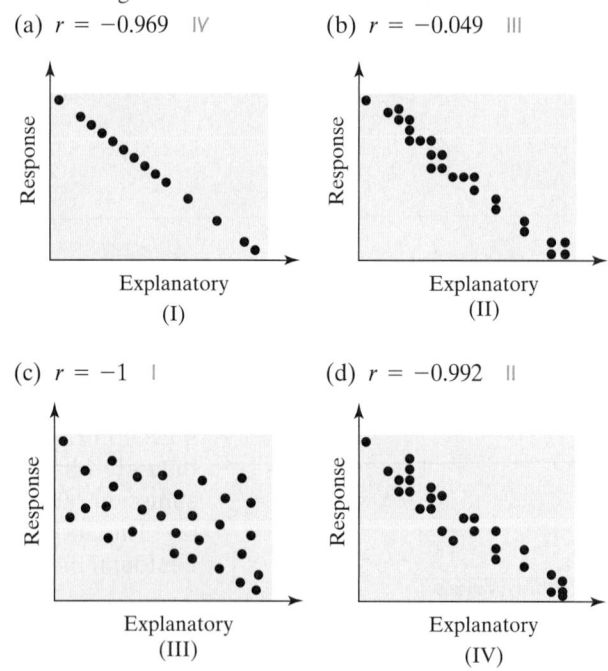

15. Does Education Pay? The scatter diagram drawn in MINITAB shows the relation between the percentage of the population of a state plus Washington D.C. that has at least a bachelor's degree and the median income (in dollars) of the state for 2006.

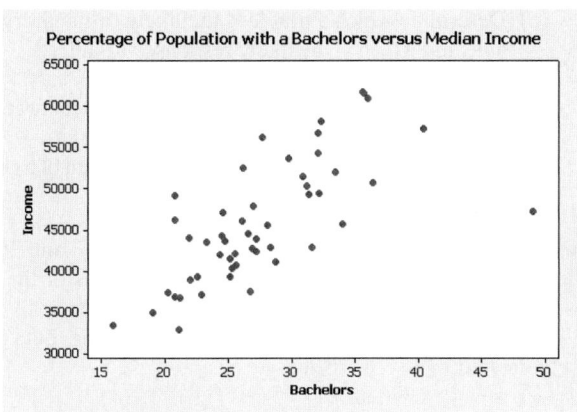

Percentage of Population with a Bachelors versus Median Income

Source: U.S. Census Bureau

15. (a) Linear; positive association

(a) Describe any relation that exists between level of education and median income.
(b) One observation appears to stick out from the rest. Which one? This particular observation is for Washington DC. Can you think of any reasons why Washington DC might have a high percentage of residents with a bachelor's degree, but a lower than expected median income?
(c) The correlation coefficient between the percentage of the population with a bachelor's degree and median income with Washington DC included in the data set is 0.693; the correlation coefficient without Washington, DC, included is 0.790. What property does this illustrate about the linear correlation coefficient? Not resistant

16. **Relation between Income and Birthrate?** The following scatter diagram drawn in Excel shows the relation between median income (in dollars) in a state and birthrate (births per 100,000 population).

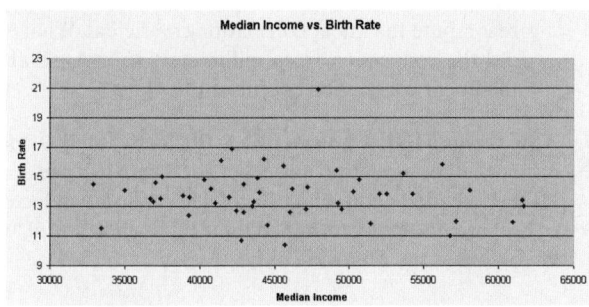

(a) Describe any relation that exists between median income and birthrate.
(b) One observation sticks out from the rest. Which one? This particular observation is for the state of Utah. Are there any explanations for this result?
(c) The correlation coefficient between median income and birthrate is −0.072. What does this imply about the relation between median income and birthrate? No linear relation

In Problems 17–20, (a) draw a scatter diagram of the data, (b) by hand, compute the correlation coefficient, and (c) determine whether there is a linear relation between x and y.

17.

x	2	4	6	6	7
y	4	8	10	13	20

(b) r = 0.896
(c) linear relation

18.

x	2	3	5	6	6
y	10	9	7	4	2

(b) r = −0.933
(c) linear relation

19.

x	2	6	6	7	9
y	8	7	6	9	5

(b) r = −0.496
(c) no linear relation

20.

x	0	5	7	8	9
y	3	8	6	9	4

(b) r = 0.440
(c) no linear relation

21. **Name the Relation, Part I** For each of the following statements, explain whether you think the variables will have positive correlation, negative correlation, or no correlation. Support your opinion.   21. (b) Negative

(a) Number of children in the household under the age of 3 and expenditures on diapers   Positive
(b) Interest rates on car loans and number of cars sold
(c) Number of hours per week on the treadmill and cholesterol level   Negative
(d) Price of a Big Mac and number of McDonald's French fries sold in a week   Negative
(e) Shoe size and IQ   No correlation

22. **Name the Relation, Part II** For each of the following statements, explain whether you think the variables will have positive correlation, negative correlation, or no correlation. Support your opinion.

(a) Number of cigarettes smoked by a pregnant woman each week and birth weight of her baby   Negative
(b) Years of education and annual salary   Positive
(c) Number of doctors on staff at a hospital and number of administrators on staff.   Positive
(d) Head circumference and IQ.   No correlation
(e) Number of movie goers and movie ticket price   Negative

Applying the Concepts

23. **Height versus Head Circumference** A pediatrician wants to
NW   determine the relation that may exist between a child's height and head circumference. She randomly selects eleven 3-year-old children from her practice, measures their heights and head circumferences and obtains the data shown in the table.

Height (inches)	Head Circumference (inches)	Height (inches)	Head Circumference (inches)
27.75	17.5	26.5	17.3
24.5	17.1	27	17.5
25.5	17.1	26.75	17.3
26	17.3	26.75	17.5
25	16.9	27.5	17.5
27.75	17.6		

Source: Denise Slucki, student at Joliet Junior College

(a) If the pediatrician wants to use height to predict head circumference, determine which variable is the explanatory variable and which is the response variable.
Explanatory: height; Response: head circumference

(b) Draw a scatter diagram.

(c) Compute the linear correlation coefficient between the height and head circumference of a child. *0.911*

(d) Does a linear relation exist between height and head circumference? *Yes; positive association*

24. **American Black Bears** The American black bear (*Ursus Americanus*) is one of eight bear species in the world. It is the smallest North American bear and the most common bear species on the planet. In 1969, Dr. Michael R. Pelton of the University of Tennessee initiated a long-term study of the population in the Great Smoky Mountains National Park. One aspect of the study was to develop a model that could be used to predict a bear's weight (since it is not practical to weigh bears in the field). One variable thought to be related to weight is the length of the bear. The following data represent the lengths and weights of 12 American black bears.

Total Length (cm)	Weight (kg)
139.0	110
138.0	60
139.0	90
120.5	60
149.0	85
141.0	100
141.0	95
150.0	85
166.0	155
151.5	140
129.5	105
150.0	110

Source: fieldtripearth.org

(a) Which variable is the explanatory variable based on the goals of the research? *Length*

(b) Draw a scatter diagram of the data.

(c) Determine the linear correlation coefficient between weight and height. *0.704*

(d) Does a linear relation exist between the weight of the bear and its height? *Yes; positive association*

25. **Weight of a Car versus Miles per Gallon** An engineer wanted to determine how the weight of a car affects gas mileage. The following data represent the weights of various domestic cars and their gas mileages in the city for the 2008 model year.

Car	Weight (lb)	Miles per Gallon
Buick Lucerne	3,765	19
Cadillac DeVille	3,984	18
Chevrolet Malibu	3,530	21
Chrysler Sebring Sedan	3,175	22
Dodge Neon	2,580	27
Dodge Charger	3,730	18
Ford Focus	2,605	26
Lincoln LS	3,772	17
Mercury Sable	3,310	20
Pontiac G5	2,991	25
Saturn Ion	2,752	26

Source: www.roadandtrack.com

(a) Determine which variable is the likely explanatory variable and which is the likely response variable.

(b) Draw a scatter diagram of the data. *Explanatory: weight*

(c) Compute the linear correlation coefficient between the weight of a car and its miles per gallon in the city. *−0.964*

(d) Does a linear relation exist between the weight of a car and its miles per gallon in the city? *Yes; negative association*

26. **Bone Length** Research performed at NASA and led by Emily R. Morey-Holton measured the lengths of the right humerus and right tibia in 11 rats that were sent to space on Spacelab Life Sciences 2. The following data were collected.

Right Humerus (mm)	Right Tibia (mm)	Right Humerus (mm)	Right Tibia (mm)
24.80	36.05	25.90	37.38
24.59	35.57	26.11	37.96
24.59	35.57	26.63	37.46
24.29	34.58	26.31	37.75
23.81	34.20	26.84	38.50
24.87	34.73		

Source: NASA Life Sciences Data Archive

26. (c) Yes; positive association

(a) Draw a scatter diagram treating the length of the right humerus as the explanatory variable and the length of the right tibia as the response variable.

(b) Compute the linear correlation coefficient between the length of the right humerus and the length of the right tibia. *0.951*

(c) Does a linear relation exist between the length of the right humerus and the length of the right tibia?

(d) Convert the data to inches (1 mm = 0.03937 inch), and recompute the linear correlation coefficient. What effect did the conversion from millimeters to inches have on the linear correlation coefficient? *None*

27. **Age versus HDL Cholesterol** A doctor wanted to determine whether a relation exists between a male's age and his HDL (so-called good) cholesterol. He randomly selected 17 of his patients and determined their HDL cholesterol levels. He obtained the following data.

Age	HDL Cholesterol	Age	HDL Cholesterol
38	57	38	44
42	54	66	62
46	34	30	53
32	56	51	36
55	35	27	45
52	40	52	38
61	42	49	55
61	38	39	28
26	47		

Source: Data based on information obtained from the National Center for Health Statistics

(a) Draw a scatter diagram of the data treating age as the explanatory variable. What type of relation, if any, appears to exist between age and HDL cholesterol?

(b) Compute the linear correlation coefficient between age and HDL cholesterol.   *−0.164*

(c) Does a linear relation exist between age and HDL cholesterol?   *No*

28. Intensity of a Light Bulb Cathy is conducting an experiment to measure the relation between a light bulb's intensity and the distance from the light source. She measures a 100-watt light bulb's intensity 1 meter from the bulb and at 0.1-meter intervals up to 2 meters from the bulb and obtains the following data.

Distance (m)	Intensity	Distance (m)	Intensity
1.0	0.29645	1.6	0.11450
1.1	0.25215	1.7	0.10243
1.2	0.20547	1.8	0.09231
1.3	0.17462	1.9	0.08321
1.4	0.15342	2.0	0.07342
1.5	0.13521		

(a) Draw a scatter diagram of the data treating distance as the explanatory variable.

(b) Do you think that it is appropriate to compute the linear correlation coefficient between distance and intensity? Why?   *No; nonlinear relation*

29. Does Size Matter? Researchers wondered whether the size of a person's brain was related to the individual's mental capacity. They selected a sample of right-handed introductory psychology students who had SAT scores higher than 1,350. The subjects took the Wechsler Adult Intelligence Scale-Revised to obtain their IQ scores. MRI scans were performed at the same facility for the subjects. The scans consisted of 18 horizontal MR images. The computer counted all pixels with a nonzero gray scale in each of the 18 images, and the total count served as an index for brain size.

Gender	MRI Count	IQ	Gender	MRI Count	IQ
Female	816,932	133	Male	949,395	140
Female	951,545	137	Male	1,001,121	140
Female	991,305	138	Male	1,038,437	139
Female	833,868	132	Male	965,353	133
Female	856,472	140	Male	955,466	133
Female	852,244	132	Male	1,079,549	141
Female	790,619	135	Male	924,059	135
Female	866,662	130	Male	955,003	139
Female	857,782	133	Male	935,494	141
Female	948,066	133	Male	949,589	144

Source: L. Willerman, R. Schultz, J. N. Rutledge, and E. Bigler (1991). "In Vivo Brain Size and Intelligence," *Intelligence*, 15, 223–228.

(a) Draw a scatter diagram treating MRI count as the explanatory variable and IQ as the response variable. Comment on what you see.

(b) Compute the linear correlation coefficient between MRI count and IQ. Are MRI count and IQ linearly related?   *0.548; yes*

(c) A lurking variable in the analysis is gender. Draw a scatter diagram treating MRI count as the explanatory variable and IQ as the response variable, but use a different plotting symbol for each gender. For example, use a circle for males and a triangle for females. What do you notice?   *Linear relation goes away*

(d) Compute the linear correlation coefficient between MRI count and IQ for females. Compute the linear correlation coefficient between MRI count and IQ for males. Are MRI count and IQ linearly related? What is the moral?   *F: 0.359; M: 0.236; no*

30. Male versus Female Drivers The following data represent the number of licensed drivers in various age groups and the number of fatal accidents within the age group by gender.

Age	Number of Male Licensed Drivers (000s)	Number of Fatal Crashes	Number of Female Licensed Drivers (000s)	Number of Fatal Crashes
<16	12	227	12	77
16–20	6,424	5,180	6,139	2,113
21–24	6,941	5,016	6,816	1,531
25–34	18,068	8,595	17,664	2,780
35–44	20,406	7,990	20,063	2,742
45–54	19,898	7,118	19,984	2,285
55–64	14,340	4,527	14,441	1,514
65–74	8,194	2,274	8,400	938
>74	4,803	2,022	5,375	980

Source: National Highway and Traffic Safety Institute

(a) On the same graph, draw a scatter diagram for both males and females. Be sure to use a different plotting symbol for each group. For example, use a square (□) for males and a plus sign (+) for females. Treat number of licensed drivers as the explanatory variable.

(b) Based on the scatter diagrams, do you think that insurance companies are justified in charging different insurance rates for males and females? Why?

(c) Compute the linear correlation coefficient between number of licensed drivers and number of fatal crashes for males.   *0.883*

(d) Compute the linear correlation coefficient between number of licensed drivers and number of fatal crashes for females.   *0.836*

(e) Which gender has the stronger linear relation between number of licensed drivers and number of fatal crashes. Why?   *Males*

31. Weight of a Car versus Miles per Gallon Suppose that we add the Ford Taurus to the data in Problem 25. A Ford Taurus weighs 3,305 pounds and gets 19 miles per gallon.

(a) Redraw the scatter diagram with the Taurus included.

(b) Recompute the linear correlation coefficient with the Taurus included.   *−0.943*

(c) Compare the results of parts (a) and (b) with the results of Problem 25. Why are the results here reasonable?

(d) Now suppose that we add the Toyota Prius to the data in Problem 25 (remove the Taurus). A Toyota Prius weighs 2,890 pounds and gets 60 miles per gallon. Redraw the scatter diagram with the Prius included. What do you notice?

(e) Recompute the linear correlation coefficient with the Prius included. How did this new value affect your result? *−0.507*

(f) Why does this observation not follow the pattern of the data?

32. **American Black Bears** The website that contained the American black bear data listed in Problem 24 actually had a bear whose height is 141.0 cm and weight is 100 kg incorrectly listed as 41.0 cm tall.

(a) Redraw the scatter diagram with the incorrect entry.

(b) Recompute the linear correlation coefficient using the data with the incorrect entry. *0.254*

(c) Explain how the scatter diagram can be used to identify incorrectly entered data values. Explain how the incorrectly entered data value affects the correlation coefficient.

33. **Draw Your Data!** Consider the four data sets shown to the right.

(a) Compute the linear correlation coefficient for each data set. *1: 0.816; 2: 0.817; 3: 0.816; 4: 0.817*

Data Set 1		Data Set 2		Data Set 3		Data Set 4	
x	y	x	y	x	y	x	y
10	8.04	10	9.14	10	7.46	8	6.58
8	6.95	8	8.14	8	6.77	8	5.76
13	7.58	13	8.74	13	12.74	8	7.71
9	8.81	9	8.77	9	7.11	8	8.84
11	8.33	11	9.26	11	7.81	8	8.47
14	9.96	14	8.10	14	8.84	8	7.04
6	7.24	6	6.13	6	6.08	8	5.25
4	4.26	4	3.10	4	5.39	8	5.56
12	10.84	12	9.13	12	8.15	8	7.91
7	4.82	7	7.26	7	6.42	8	6.89
5	5.68	5	4.47	5	5.73	19	12.50

Source: Frank Anscombe. "Graphs in Statistical Analysis," *American Statistician* 27: 17–21, 1993.

(b) Draw a scatter diagram for each data set. Conclude that linear correlation coefficients and scatter diagrams must be used together in any statistical analysis of bivariate data.

34. **The Best Predictor of the Winning Percentage** The ultimate goal in any sport (besides having fun) is to win. One measure of how well a team does is the winning percentage. In baseball, a lot of effort goes into figuring out the variable that best predicts a team's winning percentage. The following data represent the winning percentages of teams in the National League along with potential explanatory variables based on the 2007 season. Which variable do you think is the best predictor of winning percentage? Why?

Team	Winning Percentage	Runs Scored	Home Runs	Team Batting Average	On-Base Percentage	Batting Average against Team	Team Earned-Run Average
Arizona	0.556	712	171	0.250	0.321	0.262	4.13
Atlanta	0.519	810	176	0.275	0.339	0.259	4.11
Chicago Cubs	0.525	752	151	0.271	0.333	0.246	4.04
Cincinnati	0.444	783	204	0.267	0.335	0.282	4.94
Colorado	0.522	860	171	0.280	0.354	0.266	4.32
Florida	0.438	790	201	0.267	0.336	0.285	4.94
Houston	0.451	723	167	0.260	0.330	0.273	4.68
Los Angeles	0.506	735	129	0.275	0.337	0.261	4.20
Milwaukee	0.512	801	231	0.262	0.329	0.269	4.41
New York Mets	0.543	804	177	0.275	0.342	0.255	4.26
Philadelphia	0.549	892	213	0.274	0.354	0.276	4.73
Pittsburgh	0.420	724	148	0.263	0.325	0.288	4.93
San Diego	0.546	741	171	0.251	0.322	0.250	3.70
San Francisco	0.438	683	131	0.254	0.322	0.261	4.19
St. Louis	0.481	725	141	0.274	0.337	0.271	4.65
Washington	0.451	673	123	0.256	0.325	0.269	4.58

Source: espn.com

35. **Diversification** One basic theory of investing is diversification. The idea is that you want to have a basket of stocks that do not all "move in the same direction." In other words, if one investment goes down, you don't want a second investment in your portfolio that is also likely to go down. One hallmark of a good portfolio is a low correlation between investments. The following data represent the annual rates of return for various stocks. If you only wish to invest in two stocks, which two would you select if your goal is to have low correlation between the two investments? Which two would you select if your goal is to have one stock go up when the other goes down? *GE and TECO; Cisco and TECO*

| Year | Rate of Return | | | | |
	Cisco Systems	Walt Disney	General Electric	Exxon Mobil	TECO Energy
1996	0.704	0.204	0.565	0.405	−0.012
1997	0.314	0.448	0.587	0.342	0.223
1998	1.50	−0.080	0.451	0.254	0.050
1999	1.31	−0.015	0.574	0.151	−0.303
2000	−0.286	−0.004	−0.055	0.127	0.849
2001	−0.527	−0.277	−0.151	−0.066	−0.150
2002	−0.277	−0.203	−0.377	−0.089	−0.369
2003	0.850	0.444	0.308	0.206	0.004
2004	−0.203	0.202	0.207	0.281	0.128
2005	0.029	−0.129	−0.014	0.118	0.170
2006	0.434	0.443	0.093	0.391	0.051
2007	0.044	−0.043	0.126	0.243	0.058

Source: Yahoo!Finance

36. Lyme Disease versus Drownings Lyme disease is an inflammatory disease that results in a skin rash and flulike symptoms. It is transmitted through the bite of an infected deer tick. The following data represent the number of reported cases of Lyme disease and the number of drowning deaths for a rural county in the United States.

Month	J	F	M	A	M	J	J	A	S	O	N	D
Cases of Lyme Disease	3	2	2	4	5	15	22	13	6	5	4	1
Drowning Deaths	0	1	2	1	2	9	16	5	3	3	1	0

(a) Draw a scatter diagram of the data using cases of Lyme disease as the explanatory variable.
(b) Compute the correlation coefficient for the data. *0.961*
(c) Based on your results from parts (a) and (b), what type of relation exists between the number of reported cases of Lyme disease and drowning deaths? Do you believe that an increase in cases of Lyme disease causes an increase in drowning deaths? What is a likely lurking variable between cases of Lyme disease and drowning deaths?

37. Television Stations and Life Expectancy Based on data obtained from the *CIA World Factbook*, the linear correlation coefficient between the number of television stations in a country and the life expectancy of residents of the country is 0.599. What does this correlation imply? Do you believe that the more television stations a country has, the longer its population can expect to live? Why or why not? What is a likely lurking variable between number of televisions and life expectancy?

38. Obesity In a study published in the *Journal of the American Medical Association*, researchers found that the length of time a mother breast-feeds is negatively associated with the likelihood a child is obese. In an interview, the head investigator stated, "It's not clear whether breast milk has obesity-preventing properties or the women who are breast-feeding are less likely to have obese kids because they are less likely to be obese themselves." Using the researcher's statement, explain what might be wrong with concluding that breast-feeding prevents obesity. Identify some lurking variables in the study.

39. Crime Rate and Cell Phones The linear correlation between violent crime rate and percentage of the population that has a cell phone is −0.918 for years since 1995. Do you believe that increasing the percentage of the population that has a cell phone will decrease the violent crime rate? What might be a lurking variable between percentage of the population with a cell phone and violent crime rate?

40. Faulty Use of Correlation On the basis of the scatter diagram, explain what is wrong with the following statement: "Because the linear correlation coefficient between age and median income is 0.012, there is no relation between age and median income."

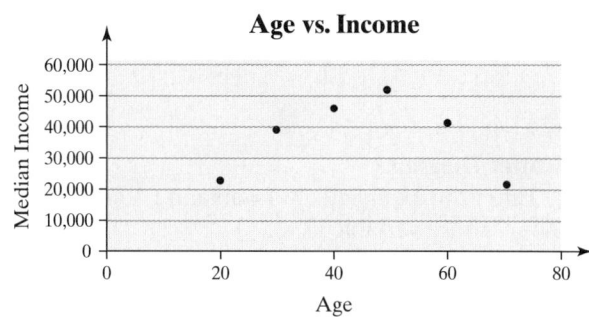

Age vs. Income

41. Influential Consider the following set of data:

x	2.2	3.7	3.9	4.1	2.6	4.1	2.9	4.7
y	3.9	4.0	1.4	2.8	1.5	3.3	3.6	4.9

(a) Draw a scatter diagram of the data and compute the linear correlation coefficient. *0.228*
(b) Draw a scatter diagram of the data and compute the linear correlation coefficient with the additional data point (10.4, 9.3). Comment on the effect the additional data point has on the linear correlation coefficient. Explain why correlations should always be reported with scatter diagrams. *0.860*

42. Transformations Consider the following data set:

x	5	6	7	7	8	8	8	8
y	4.2	5	5.2	5.9	6	6.2	6.1	6.9
x	9	9	10	10	11	11	12	12
y	7.2	8	8.3	7.4	8.4	7.8	8.5	9.5

(a) Draw a scatter diagram with the x-axis starting at 0 and ending at 30 and with the y-axis starting at 0 and ending at 20.
(b) Compute the linear correlation coefficient. *0.952*
(c) Now multiply both x and y by 2.
(d) Draw a scatter diagram of the new data with the x-axis starting at 0 and ending at 30 and with the y-axis starting at 0 and ending at 20. Compare the scatter diagrams.
(e) Compute the linear correlation coefficient. *0.952*
(f) Conclude that multiplying each value in the data set by a nonzero constant does not affect the correlation between the variables. Explain why this is the case.

43. RateMyProfessors.com Professors Theodore Coladarci and Irv Kornfield from the University of Maine found a correlation of 0.68 between responses to questions on the RateMyProfessors.com website and typical in-class evaluations. Use this correlation to make an argument in favor of the validity of RateMyProfessors.com as a legitimate evaluation tool. RateMyProfessors.com also has a chili pepper icon, which is meant to indicate a "hotness scale" for the professor. This hotness scale serves as a proxy for the sexiness of the professor. It was found that the correlation between quality and sexiness is 0.64. In addition, it was found that the correlation between easiness of the professor and quality is 0.85 for instructors with at least 70 posts. Use this information to make an argument against RateMyProfessors.com as a legitimate evaluation tool.

Source: Theodore Coladarci and Irv Kornfield. "RateMyProfessors.com versus Formal In-class Student Evaluations of Teaching," *Practical Assessment, Research, & Evaluation*, 12:6, May, 2007.

44. Correlation Applet Load the correlation by eye applet.
(a) In the lower-left corner of the applet, add 10 points that line up with a positive slope so that the linear correlation between the points is about 0.8. Click "show r" to show the correlation.
(b) Add another point in the upper-right corner of the applet that roughly lines up with the 10 points you have in the lower-left corner. Comment on how the linear correlation coefficient changes.
(c) Drag the point in the upper-right corner straight down. Take note of the change in the linear correlation coefficient. Notice how a single point can have a substantial impact on the linear correlation coefficient.

45. Correlation Applet Load the correlation by eye applet. Add about 10 points that form an upside-down U. Certainly, a relation between exists x and y, but what is the value of the linear correlation coefficient? Conclude that a low linear correlation coefficient does not imply that no relation exists between two variables; it means no *linear* relation exists between two variables.

46. Correlation Applet Load the correlation by eye applet.
(a) Plot about 10 points that follow a linear trend and have a linear correlation coefficient that is close to 0.8.
(b) Clear the applet. Plot about 6 points vertically on top of each other on the left side of the applet. Add a seventh point to the right of the applet. Move the point until the linear correlation coefficient is close to 0.8.
(c) Clear the applet. Plot about 7 points in a U-shaped curve. Add an eighth point and move it around the applet until the linear correlation coefficient is close to 0.8.
(d) Conclude that a linear correlation coefficient can result from data that have many patterns, and so you should always plot your data.

TECHNOLOGY STEP-BY-STEP   Drawing Scatter Diagrams and Determining the Correlation Coefficient

TI-83/84 Plus
Scatter Diagrams
1. Enter the explanatory variable in L1 and the response variable in L2.
2. Press 2nd Y = to bring up the StatPlot menu. Select 1: Plot1.
3. Turn Plot 1 on by highlighting the On button and pressing ENTER.
4. Highlight the scatter diagram icon (see the figure) and press ENTER. Be sure that Xlist is L1 and Ylist is L2.
5. Press ZOOM and select 9: ZoomStat.

Correlation Coefficient
1. Turn the diagnostics on by selecting the catalog (2nd Ø). Scroll down and select

DiagnosticOn. Hit ENTER twice to activate diagnostics.
2. With the explanatory variable in L1 and the response variable in L2, press STAT, highlight CALC and select 4: LinReg (ax + b). With LinReg on the HOME screen, press ENTER.

MINITAB
Scatter Diagrams
1. Enter the explanatory variable in C1 and the response variable in C2. You may want to name the variables.
2. Select the **Graph** menu and highlight **Scatterplot . . . .**
3. Highlight the Simple icon and click OK.
4. With the cursor in the Y column, select the response variable. With the cursor in the X column, select the explanatory variable. Click OK.

Correlation Coefficient
1. With the explanatory variable in C1 and the response variable in C2, select the **Stat** menu and highlight **Basic Statistics**. Highlight **Correlation**.
2. Select the variables whose correlation you wish to determine and click OK.

Excel
Scatter Diagrams
1. Enter the explanatory variable in column A and the response variable in column B.

2. Highlight both sets of data and select the Chart Wizard icon.
3. Select XY (Scatter).
4. Click Finish.

Correlation Coefficient
1. Be sure the Data Analysis Tool Pak is activated by selecting the **Tools** menu and highlighting **Add-Ins** . . . . Check the box for the Analysis ToolPak and select OK.
2. Select **Tools** and highlight **Data Analysis** . . . . Highlight **Correlation** and select OK.
3. With the cursor in the Input Range, highlight the data. Select OK.

4.2 LEAST-SQUARES REGRESSION

Preparing for This Section   Before getting started, review the following:

• Lines (Appendix B on CD, pp. B1–B5)

Objectives		
	1	Find the least-squares regression line and use the line to make predictions
	2	Interpret the slope and the *y*-intercept of the least-squares regression line
	3	Compute the sum of squared residuals

Note to Instructor
If you like, you can print out and distribute the Preparing for This Section quiz located in the Instructor's Resource Center. The purpose of the quiz is to verify that the students have the prerequisite knowledge for the section.

Once the scatter diagram and linear correlation coefficient indicate that a linear relation exists between two variables, we proceed to find a linear equation that describes the relation between the two variables. One way to obtain a line that describes the relation is to select two points from the data that appear to provide a good fit and to find the equation of the line through these points.

EXAMPLE 1   **Finding an Equation That Describes Linearly Related Data**

Note to Instructor
Encourage students to review lines in Appendix B on the CD.

Problem: The data in Table 4 represent the club-head speed and the distance a golf ball travels for eight swings of the club. We determined that these data are linearly related in the previous section.

CAUTION   Example 1 *does not* present the least-squares method. It is used to set up the concepts of determining the line that best fits the data.

Table 4		
Club-head Speed (mph) *x*	**Distance (yd) *y***	**(*x*, *y*)**
100	257	(100, 257)
102	264	(102, 264)
103	274	(103, 274)
101	266	(101, 266)
105	277	(105, 277)
100	263	(100, 263)
99	258	(99, 258)
105	275	(105, 275)

Source: Paul Stephenson, student at Joliet Junior College

(a) Find a linear equation that relates club-head speed, x (the explanatory variable), and distance, y (the response variable), by selecting two points and finding the equation of the line containing the points.

(b) Graph the line on the scatter diagram.

(c) Use the equation to predict the distance a golf ball will travel if the club-head speed is 104 miles per hour.

Approach

(a) To answer part (a), we perform the following steps:

Step 1: Select two points so that a line drawn through the points appears to give a good fit. Call the points (x_1, y_1) and (x_2, y_2). Refer to Figure 1 for the scatter diagram.

In Other Words

A good fit means that the line drawn appears to describe the relation between the two variables well.

Step 2: Find the slope of the line containing the two points using $m = \dfrac{y_2 - y_1}{x_2 - x_1}$.

Step 3: Use the point–slope formula, $y - y_1 = m(x - x_1)$, to find the equation of the line through the points selected in Step 1. Express the equation in the form $y = mx + b$, where m is the slope and b is the y-intercept.

(b) For part (b), draw a line through the points selected in Step 1 of part (a).

(c) Finally, for part (c), we let $x = 104$ in the equation found in part (a) to find the predicted distance.

Solution

(a) **Step 1:** We select $(x_1, y_1) = (99, 258)$ and $(x_2, y_2) = (105, 275)$, because a line drawn through these two points seems to give a good fit.

Step 2: $m = \dfrac{y_2 - y_1}{x_2 - x_1} = \dfrac{275 - 258}{105 - 99} = \dfrac{17}{6} = 2.8333$

Step 3: We use the point–slope formula to find the equation of the line.

⚠ **CAUTION** The line found in Step 3 of Example 1 is not the least-squares regression line.

$$y - y_1 = m(x - x_1)$$
$$y - 258 = 2.8333(x - 99) \qquad \textcolor{gray}{m = 2.8333, x_1 = 99, y_1 = 258}$$
$$y - 258 = 2.8333x - 280.4967$$
$$y = 2.8333x - 22.4967 \tag{1}$$

The slope of the line is 2.8333, and the y-intercept is -22.4967.

(b) Figure 8 shows the scatter diagram along with the line drawn through the points $(99, 258)$ and $(105, 275)$.

Figure 8

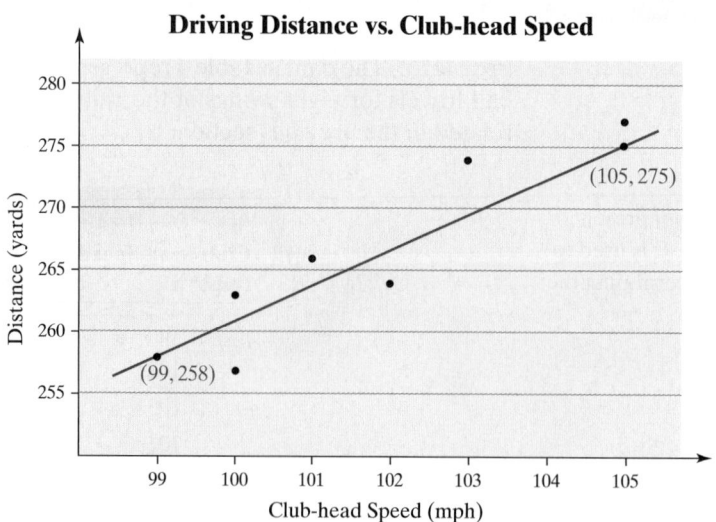

Driving Distance vs. Club-head Speed

⚠ **CAUTION** Unless otherwise noted, we will round to four decimal places. As always, do not round until the last computation.

(c) We let $x = 104$ in equation (1) to predict the distance a golf ball travels when hit with a club-head speed of 104 miles per hour.

$$y = 2.8333(104) - 22.4967$$
$$= 272.2 \text{ yards}$$

We predict that a golf ball will travel 272.2 yards when it is hit with a club-head speed of 104 miles per hour.

Now Work Problems 11(a)–(c)

 Find the Least-Squares Regression Line and Use the Line to Make Predictions

The line that we found in Example 1 appears to describe the relation between club-head speed and distance quite well. However, is there a line that fits the data better? Is there a line that fits the data *best*?

Whenever we are attempting to determine the best of something, we need a criterion for determining best. For example, suppose that we are trying to identify the best domestic car. What do we mean by best? Best gas mileage? Best horsepower? Best reliability? In attempting to find the best line for describing the relation between two variables, we need a criterion for determining the best line as well. To understand this criterion, consider Figure 9. Each y-coordinate on the line corresponds to a predicted distance for a given club-head speed. For example, if club-head speed is 103 miles per hour, the predicted distance the ball will travel is $2.8333(103) - 22.4967 = 269.3$ yards. The observed distance for this club-head speed is 274 yards. The difference between the observed value of y and the predicted value of y is the error, or **residual**. For a club-head speed of 103 miles per hour, the residual is

In Other Words
The residual represents how close our prediction comes to the actual observation. The smaller the residual, the better the prediction.

$$\text{Residual} = \text{observed } y - \text{predicted } y$$
$$= 274 - 269.3$$
$$= 4.7 \text{ yards}$$

The residual for a club-head speed of 103 miles per hour is labeled in Figure 9.

Figure 9

The criterion for determining the line that *best* describes the relation between two variables is based on the residuals. The most popular technique for making the residuals as small as possible is the *method of least squares*, developed by Adrien Marie Legendre.

Definition   **Least-Squares Regression Criterion**

The **least-squares regression line** is the line that minimizes the sum of the squared errors (or residuals). It is the line that minimizes the sum of the squared vertical distance between the observed values of y and those predicted by the line, $\hat{y}$ (read "y-hat"). We represent this as

$$\text{Minimize } \sum \text{residuals}^2$$

Adrien Marie Legendre was born on September 18, 1752, into a wealthy family and was educated in mathematics and physics at the College Mazarin in Paris. From 1775 to 1780, he taught at École Militaire. On March 30, 1783, Legendre was appointed an adjoint in the Académie des Sciences. On May 13, 1791, he became a member of the committee of the Académie des Sciences and was charged with the task of standardizing weights and measures. The committee worked to compute the length of the meter. During the French Revolution, Legendre lost his small fortune. In 1794, Legendre published *Eléments de géométrie*, which was the leading elementary text in geometry for around 100 years. In 1806, Legendre published a book on orbits, in which he developed the theory of least squares. He died on January 10, 1833.

The advantage of the least-squares criterion is that it allows for statistical inference on the predicted value and slope (Chapter 14). Another advantage of the least-squares criterion is explained by Legendre in his text *Nouvelles méthodes pour la determination des orbites des cométes*, published in 1806.

Of all the principles that can be proposed for this purpose, I think there is none more general, more exact, or easier to apply, than that which we have used in this work; it consists of making the sum of squares of the errors a *minimum*. By this method, a kind of equilibrium is established among the errors which, since it prevents the extremes from dominating, is appropriate for revealing the state of the system which most nearly approaches the truth.

Equation of the Least-Squares Regression Line

The equation of the least-squares regression line is given by

$$\hat{y} = b_1 x + b_0$$

where

$$b_1 = r \cdot \frac{s_y}{s_x} \text{ is the \textbf{slope} of the least-squares regression line*} \qquad (2)$$

and

$$b_0 = \bar{y} - b_1 \bar{x} \text{ is the \textbf{y-intercept} of the least-squares regression line} \qquad (3)$$

Note: $\bar{x}$ is the sample mean and s_x is the sample standard deviation of the explanatory variable x; $\bar{y}$ is the sample mean and s_y is the sample standard deviation of the response variable y. ◄

---

*An equivalent formula is

$$b_1 = \frac{S_{xy}}{S_{xx}} = \frac{\sum x_i y_i - \frac{\left(\sum x_i\right)\left(\sum y_i\right)}{n}}{\sum x_i^2 - \frac{\left(\sum x_i\right)^2}{n}}$$

The notation $\hat{y}$ is used in the least-squares regression line to serve as a reminder that it is a predicted value of y for a given value of x. An interesting property of the least-squares regression line, $\hat{y} = b_1 x + b_0$, is that the line always contains the point $(\bar{x}, \bar{y})$. This property can be useful when drawing the least-squares regression line by hand.

Since s_y and s_x must both be positive, the sign of the linear correlation coefficient and the sign of the slope of the least-squares regression line are the same. For example, if r is positive, then the slope of the least-squares regression line will also be positive.

EXAMPLE 2 | **Finding the Least-Squares Regression Line**

Problem: For the data in Table 4 on page 209.

(a) Find the least-squares regression line.

(b) Predict the distance a golf ball will travel when hit with a club-head speed of 103 miles per hour (mph).

(c) The observed distance the ball traveled when the swing speed was 103 mph was 274 yards. Is this distance above average or below average among all balls hit with a swing speed of 103 mph?

(d) Draw the least-squares regression line on the scatter diagram of the data.

Approach

(a) From Example 2 in Section 4.1, we have the following unrounded values:

$$r = 0.938697 \quad \bar{x} = 101.875 \quad s_x = 2.29518 \quad \bar{y} = 266.75 \quad s_y = 7.74135$$

We substitute these values into Formula (2) to find the slope of the least-squares regression line. We use Formula (3) to find the intercept of the least-squares regression line.

(b) Substitute $x = 103$ into the least-squares regression line found in part (a) to find $\hat{y}$.

(c) Any point on the least-squares regression line is an estimate of the mean value of the response variable for a given value of the explanatory variable. To determine if a certain value of the response variable is above or below average, we determine the predicted value of the response variable and compare it to the observed value of the response variable. If the residual is positive, then the observed value is greater than the predicted value, which means the observed value is above average. If the residual is negative, the observed value is below average.

(d) To draw the least-squares regression line, select two values of x and use the equation to find the predicted values of y. Plot these points on the scatter diagram and draw a line through the points.

Solution

(a) Substituting $r = 0.938698$, $s_x = 2.29518$, and $s_y = 7.74135$ into Formula (2), we obtain

$$b_1 = r \cdot \frac{s_y}{s_x} = 0.938697 \cdot \frac{7.74135}{2.29518} = 3.1661$$

We have that $\bar{x} = 101.875$ and $\bar{y} = 266.75$. Substituting these values into Formula (3), we obtain

$$b_0 = \bar{y} - b_1\bar{x} = 266.75 - 3.1661(101.875) = -55.7964$$

The least-squares regression line is

$$\hat{y} = 3.1661x - 55.7964$$

(b) We let $x = 103$ in the equation $y = 3.1661x - 55.7964$ to predict the distance a golf ball hit with a club-head speed of 103 mph will travel.

$$\hat{y} = 3.1661(103) - 55.7964$$
$$= 270.3 \text{ yards}$$

We predict that the distance the ball will travel is 270.3 yards.

(c) The observed distance the ball traveled when the swing speed is 103 mph was 274 yards. The residual is

$$\text{Residual} = \text{observed } y - \text{predicted } y$$
$$= y - \hat{y}$$
$$= 274 - 270.3$$
$$= 3.7 \text{ yards}$$

Since the residual is positive (or the observed value is greater than the predicted value), the distance of 274 yards is above average for a swing speed of 103 mph.

(d) Figure 10 shows the graph of the least-squares regression line drawn on the scatter diagram with the residual labeled.

CAUTION Throughout the text, we will round the slope and y-intercept values to four decimal places. Predictions will be rounded to one more decimal place than the response variable.

Figure 10

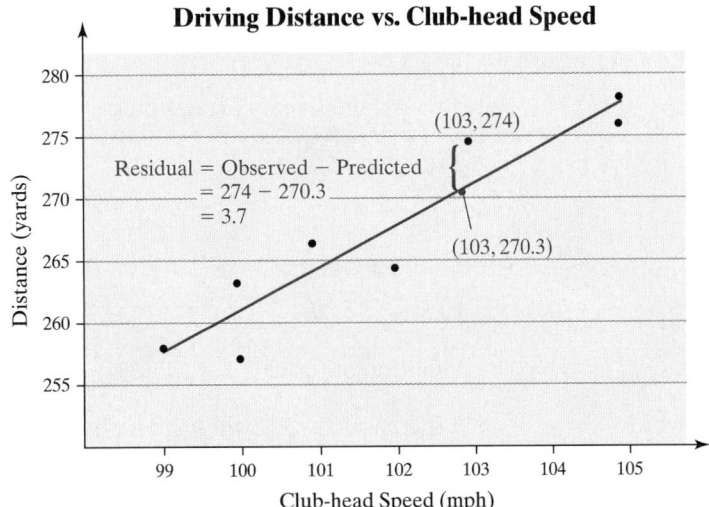

Driving Distance vs. Club-head Speed

We have presented the procedure for determining the least-squares regression equation by hand. In practice, however, statistical software or a calculator with advanced statistical features is used to determine the least-squares regression line.

EXAMPLE 3

Finding the Least-Squares Regression Line Using Technology

Problem: Use statistical software or a graphing calculator with advanced statistical features to find the least-squares regression line of the data in Table 4.

Approach: Because technology plays a major role in obtaining the least-squares regression line, we will use a TI-84 Plus graphing calculator, MINITAB, and Excel to obtain the least-squares regression line. The steps for obtaining these lines are given in the Technology Step-by-Step on page 223.

Solution: Figure 11(a) shows the output obtained from a TI-84 Plus graphing calculator, Figure 11(b) shows the output obtained from MINITAB with the slope and y-intercept highlighted, and Figure 11(c) shows partial output from Excel with the slope and y-intercept highlighted.

Figure 11

(a) TI-84 Plus output

```
The regression equation is
Distance (yards) = -55.8 + 3.17 Club Head Speed (mph)
Predictor                    Coef    SE Coef        T        P
Constant                   -55.80      48.37    -1.15    0.293
Club Head Speed (mph)      3.1661     0.4747     6.67    0.001

S = 2.88264     R - Sq = 88.1%    R - Sq(adj) = 86.1%
```

(b) MINITAB output

	Coefficients	Standard Error	t Stat	P-value
Intercept	-55.79661017	48.37134953	-1.153505344	0.29257431
Club Head Speed (mph)	3.166101695	0.47470539	6.669613957	0.00054983

(c) Excel output

CAUTION If the explanatory and response variables are negatively associated, then the linear correlation coefficient from MINITAB is $r = -\sqrt{R - \text{Sq}}$.

Now Work Problems 11(d) and 11(e)

Note: To get the linear correlation coefficient from MINITAB, use $r = \sqrt{R - \text{Sq}}$. So $r = \sqrt{0.881} = 0.939$.

---

2 ## Interpret the Slope and y-Intercept of the Least-Squares Regression Line

The definition of the slope of a line is $\dfrac{\text{Rise}}{\text{Run}}$ or $\dfrac{\text{Change in } y}{\text{Change in } x}$. For a line whose slope is $\dfrac{2}{3}$, if x increases by 3, y will *increase* by 2. Or, if the slope of a line is $-4 = \dfrac{-4}{1}$, if x increases by 1, y will *decrease* by 4.

The *y*-intercept of any line is the point where the graph intersects the vertical axis. It is found by letting $x = 0$ in an equation and solving for *y*.

We found the regression equation in Example 2 to be $\hat{y} = 3.1661x - 55.7964$.

Interpretation of Slope: The slope of the regression line is 3.1661. If the club-head speed increases by 1 mile per hour, the distance the ball travels increases by 3.1661 yards, on average.

Interpretation of the *y*-Intercept: The *y*-intercept of the regression line is -55.7964. To interpret the *y*-intercept, we must first ask two questions:

1. Is 0 a reasonable value for the explanatory variable?
2. Do any observations near $x = 0$ exist in the data set?

If the answer to either of these questions is no, we do not give an interpretation to the *y*-intercept. In the regression equation of Example 2, a swing speed of 0 miles per hour does not make sense, so an interpretation of the *y*-intercept is unreasonable.

In general, to interpret a *y*-intercept, we would say that it is the value of the response variable when the value of the explanatory variable is 0.

The second condition for interpreting the *y*-intercept is especially important, because we should not use the regression model to make predictions *outside the scope of the model*. **Outside the scope of the model** refers to using the regression model to make predictions for values of the explanatory variable that are much larger or much smaller than those observed. This is a dangerous practice because we cannot be certain of the behavior of data for which we have no observations.

For example, it is inappropriate to use the line we determined in Example 2 to predict distance when club-head speed is 140 miles per hour. The highest observed club-head speed in our data set is 105 miles per hour. We cannot be certain that the linear relation between distance and club-head speed will continue. See Figure 12.

> ⟨**CAUTION**⟩   Be careful when using the least-squares regression line to make predictions for values of the explanatory variable that are much larger or much smaller than those observed.

Figure 12

Driving Distance vs. Club-head Speed

Now Work Problem 17

Predictions When There Is No Linear Relation

When the correlation coefficient indicates that no linear relation exists between the explanatory and response variables and the scatter diagram indicates no relation at all between the variables, then we use the mean value of the response variable as the predicted value. That is, if the linear correlation coefficient indicates that there is no linear relation between the explanatory and response variables, then $\hat{y} = \overline{y}$.

Note to Instructor

The purpose of this activity is to illustrate how regression can be used to forecast or make predictions. The issue of extrapolation should be discussed, particularly when predicting the thickness of 0 pages. Students should consider two ways of estimating the thickness of one page of the text: using the slope or evaluating the model for x = 1. Another good discussion topic is variability in measurement. Students should see that there is variability from student to student, even for the same number of pages. In addition, assuming that each page is the same thickness, there is often variability within each student's measurements. (For example, the thickness for 200 pages is not twice the thickness for 100 pages). Time limit: 45 to 60 minutes, depending on discussions.

IN CLASS ACTIVITY

Paper Thin (Regression)

Each student, or small group of students, will need a ruler with both inches and centimeters.

1. Use the ruler to measure the thickness of a single page of the text. Which unit of measurement did you use and why?

2. Grouping pages (one page is one sheet), complete the following table:

No. of pages	25	50	75	150	200	225
Thickness						

3. Compute the least-squares regression line for your data.

4. Compare your data and your regression line to those around you. Did everyone get the same measurements and model? Explain why or why not.

5. Use your model to estimate the thickness of a single page of the text by letting $x = 1$. Is the value you obtained reasonable?

6. Use your model to estimate the thickness of a single page of the text by interpreting the slope. Is the value you obtained reasonable?

7. What, if anything, could you do to improve the model?

Note to Instructor

The purpose of this material is to allow students to see that the least-squares regression line has the smallest sum of squared residuals. It can be skipped without loss of continuity.

③ Compute the Sum of Squared Residuals

Recall that the least-squares regression line is the line that minimizes the sum of the squared residuals. This means that the sum of the squared residuals, Σ residuals^2, for the least-squares line will be smaller than for any other line that may describe the relation between the two variables. In particular, the sum of the squared residuals for the line obtained in Example 2 using the method of least squares will be smaller than the sum of the squared residuals for the line obtained in Example 1. It is worthwhile to verify this result.

EXAMPLE 4 | **Comparing the Sum of Squared Residuals**

Problem: Compare the sum of squared residuals for the lines obtained in Examples 1 and 2.

Approach: We compute Σ residuals^2 using the predicted values of y, $\hat{y}$, for the equations obtained in Examples 1 and 2. This is best done by creating a table of values.

Solution: We create Table 5, which contains the value of the explanatory variable in column 1. Column 2 contains the corresponding response variable. Column 3 contains the predicted values using the equation obtained in Example 1, $\hat{y} = 2.8333x - 22.4967$. In column 4, we compute the residuals for each observation: residual = observed y − predicted $y = y - \hat{y}$. For example, the first residual using the equation found in Example 1 is $y - \hat{y} = 257 - 260.8 = -3.8$. Column 5 contains the squares of the residuals obtained in column 4. Column 6 contains the predicted values using the least-squares regression equation obtained in Example 2: $\hat{y} = 3.1661x - 55.7964$. Column 7 represents the residuals for each observation, and column 8 represents the squared residuals.

Table 5							
Club-head Speed (mph)	**Distance (yd)**	**Example 1** $(\hat{y} = 2.8333x - 22.4967)$	**Residual** $y - \hat{y}$	**Residual^2** $(y - \hat{y})^2$	**Example 2** $(\hat{y} = 3.1661x - 55.7964)$	**Residual** $y - \hat{y}$	**Residual^2** $(y - \hat{y})^2$
100	257	260.8	−3.8	14.44	260.8	−3.8	14.44
102	264	266.5	−2.5	6.25	267.2	−3.2	10.24
103	274	269.3	4.7	22.09	270.3	3.7	13.69
101	266	263.7	2.3	5.29	264.0	2.0	4.00
105	277	275.0	2.0	4.00	276.6	0.4	0.16
100	263	260.8	2.2	4.84	260.8	2.2	4.84
99	258	258.0	0.0	0.00	257.6	0.4	0.16
105	275	275.0	0.0	0.00	276.6	−1.6	2.56
				$\sum \text{residual}^2$ = 56.91			$\sum \text{residual}^2$ = 50.09

The sum of the squared residuals for the line found in Example 1 is 56.91; the sum of the squared residuals for the least-squares regression line is 50.09. Again, any line that describes the relation between distance and club-head speed will have a sum of squared residuals that is greater than 50.09.

Now Work Problems 11(f)–(h)

We draw the graphs of the two lines obtained in Examples 1 and 2 on the same scatter diagram in Figure 13 to help the reader visualize the difference.

Figure 13

Driving Distance vs. Club-head Speed

4.2 ASSESS YOUR UNDERSTANDING

Concepts and Vocabulary

1. Explain the least-squares regression criterion.

2. What is a residual? What does it mean when a residual is positive?

3. Explain the phrase *outside the scope of the model*. Why is it dangerous to make predictions outside the scope of the model?

4. If the linear correlation between two variables is negative, what can be said about the slope of the regression line? Negative

5. In your own words, explain the meaning of Legendre's quote given on page 212.

6. *True or False*: The least-squares regression line always travels through the point $(\bar{x}, \bar{y})$. True

7. In your own words, explain what each point on the least-squares regression line represents.

8. If the linear correlation coefficient is 0, what is the equation of the least-squares regression line? $\hat{y} = \bar{y}$

Skill Building

9. For the data set

x	0	2	3	5	6	6
y	5.8	5.7	5.2	2.8	1.9	2.2

(a) Draw a scatter diagram. Comment on the type of relation that appears to exist between x and y.

(b) Given that $\bar{x} = 3.6667$, $s_x = 2.4221$, $\bar{y} = 3.9333$, $s_y = 1.8239$, and $r = -0.9477$, determine the least-squares regression line. $\hat{y} = -0.7136x + 6.5498$

(c) Graph the least-squares regression line on the scatter diagram drawn in part (a).

10. For the data set

x	2	4	8	8	9
y	1.4	1.8	2.1	2.3	2.6

(a) Draw a scatter diagram. Comment on the type of relation that appears to exist between x and y.

(b) Given that $\bar{x} = 6.2$, $s_x = 3.03315$, $\bar{y} = 2.04$, $s_y = 0.461519$, and $r = 0.957241$, determine the least-squares regression line. $\hat{y} = 0.1457x + 1.1370$

(c) Graph the least-squares regression line on the scatter diagram drawn in part (a).

In Problems 11–16,

(a) *Draw a scatter diagram treating x as the explanatory variable and y as the response variable.*

(b) *Select two points from the scatter diagram and find the equation of the line containing the points selected.*

(c) *Graph the line found in part (b) on the scatter diagram.*

(d) *Determine the least-squares regression line.*

(e) *Graph the least-squares regression line on the scatter diagram.*

(f) *Compute the sum of the squared residuals for the line found in part (b).*

(g) *Compute the sum of the squared residuals for the least-squares regression line found in part (d).*

(h) *Comment on the fit of the line found in part (b) versus the least-squares regression line found in part (d).*

11.
NW
x	3	4	5	7	8
y	4	6	7	12	14

12.
x	3	5	7	9	11
y	0	2	3	6	9

13.
x	-2	-1	0	1	2
y	-4	0	1	4	5

14.
x	-2	-1	0	1	2
y	7	6	3	2	0

15.
x	20	30	40	50	60
y	100	95	91	83	70

16.
x	5	10	15	20	25
y	2	4	7	11	18

17. **You Explain It! Video Games and GPAs** A student at Joliet
NW Junior College conducted a survey of 20 randomly selected full-time students to determine the relation between the number of hours of video game playing each week, x, and grade-point average, y. She found that a linear relation exists between the two variables. The least-squares regression line that describes this relation is $\hat{y} = -0.0526x + 2.9342$.

(a) Predict the grade-point average of a student who plays video games 8 hours per week. 2.51

(b) Interpret the slope.

(c) If appropriate, interpret the y-intercept.

(d) A student who plays video games 7 hours per week has a grade-point average of 2.68. Is this student's grade-point average above or below average among all students who play video games 7 hours per week? Above

18. **You Explain It! Study Time and Exam Scores** After the first exam in a statistics course, Professor Katula surveyed 14 randomly selected students to determine the relation between the amount of time they spent studying for the exam and exam score. She found that a linear relation exists between the two variables. The least-squares regression line that describes this relation is $\hat{y} = 6.3333x + 53.0298$.

(a) Predict the exam score of a student who studied 2 hours.

(b) Interpret the slope.

(c) What is the mean score of students who did not study?

(d) A student who studied 5 hours for the exam scored 81 on the exam. Is this student's exam score above or below average among all students who studied 5 hours? Below

19. **You Explain It! Winning Percentage and On-base Percentage** In his best-selling book *Moneyball*, author Michael Lewis discusses how statistics can be used to judge both a baseball player's potential and a team's ability to win games. One aspect of this analysis is that a team's on-base percentage is the best predictor of winning percentage. The on-base percentage is the proportion of time a player reaches a base. For example, an on-base percentage of 0.3 would mean the

18. (a) 65.7   18. (c) 53.0

player safely reaches bases 3 times out of 10, on average. For the 2007 baseball season, winning percentage, y, and on-base percentage, x, are linearly related by the least-squares regression equation $\hat{y} = 2.94x - 0.4871$.

Source: espn.com

(a) Interpret the slope.

(b) For 2007, the lowest on-base percentage was 0.318 and the highest on-base percentage was 0.366. Use this information to explain why it does not make sense to interpret the y-intercept.

(c) Would it be a good idea to use this model to predict the winning percentage of a team whose on-base percentage was 0.250? Why or why not? Bad idea

(d) The San Diego Padres had an on-base percentage of 0.322 and a winning percentage of 0.546. What is the residual for San Diego? How would you interpret this residual? 0.0864

20. **You Explain It! CO$_2$ and Energy Production** The least-squares regression equation $\hat{y} = 0.7668x - 9011$ relates the carbon dioxide emissions (in thousands of tons), y, and energy produced (thousands of megawatts), x, for all countries in the world in 2007.

Source: CARMA (www.carma.org)

(a) Interpret the slope.

(b) Is the y-intercept of the model reasonable? Why? What would you expect the y-intercept of the model to equal? Why? No; expect it to be 0.

(c) For 2007, the lowest energy-producing country was Liberia, which produced 0.957 thousand megawatts of energy. The highest energy-producing country was the United States, which produced 3,970,000 thousand megawatts of energy in 2007. Would it be reasonable to use this model to predict the CO$_2$ emissions of a country if it produced 6,394,000 thousand megawatts of energy in 2007? Why or why not? No

(d) In 2007, China produced 2,410,000 thousand megawatts of energy and emitted 2,680,000 thousand tons of carbon dioxide. What is the residual for China? How would you interpret this residual? 841,023 thousand tons

Applying the Concepts

Problems 21–24 use the results from Problems 23–26 in Section 4.1.

21. **Height versus Head Circumference** (Refer to Problem 23, Section 4.1) A pediatrician wants to determine the relation that exists between a child's height, x, and head circumference, y. She randomly selects 11 children from her practice, measures their heights and head circumferences and obtains the following data.

Height, x (inches)	Head Circumference, y (inches)	Height, x (inches)	Head Circumference, y (inches)
27.75	17.5	26.5	17.3
24.5	17.1	27	17.5
25.5	17.1	26.75	17.3
26	17.3	26.75	17.5
25	16.9	27.5	17.5
27.75	17.6		

Source: Denise Slucki, student at Joliet Junior College

(a) Find the least-squares regression line treating height as the explanatory variable and head circumference as the response variable. $\hat{y} = 0.1827x + 12.4932$

(b) Interpret the slope and y-intercept, if appropriate.

(c) Use the regression equation to predict the head circumference of a child who is 25 inches tall. 17.06 inches

(d) Compute the residual based on the observed head circumference of the 25-inch-tall child in the table. Is the head circumference of this child above average or below average? −0.16 inches; below

(e) Draw the least-squares regression line on the scatter diagram of the data and label the residual from part (d).

(f) Notice that two children are 26.75 inches tall. One has a head circumference of 17.3 inches; the other has a head circumference of 17.5 inches. How can this be?

(g) Would it be reasonable to use the least-squares regression line to predict the head circumference of a child who was 32 inches tall? Why? No

22. **American Black Bears** (Refer to Problem 24 in Section 4.1) The American black bear (*Ursus americanus*) is one of eight bear species in the world. It is the smallest North American bear and the most common bear species on the planet. In 1969, Dr. Michael R. Pelton of the University of Tennessee initiated a long-term study of the population in Great Smoky Mountains National Park. One aspect of the study was to develop a model that could be used to predict a bear's weight (since it is not practical to weigh bears in the field). One variable thought to be related to weight is the length of the bear. The following data represent the lengths of 12 American black bears.

Total Length (cm)	Weight (kg)
139.0	110
138.0	60
139.0	90
120.5	60
149.0	85
141.0	100
141.0	95
150.0	85
166.0	155
151.5	140
129.5	105
150.0	110

Source: fieldtripearth.org

(a) Find the least-squares regression line, treating total length as the explanatory variable and weight as the response variable. $\hat{y} = 1.6942x - 142.4709$

(b) Interpret the slope and y-intercept, if appropriate.

(c) Suppose a 149.0-cm bear is captured in the field. Use the least-squares regression line to predict the weight of the bear. 110.0 kg

(d) What is the residual of the bear from part (c)? Is this bear's weight above or below average for a bear of this length? −25.0 kg; below

23. **Weight of a Car versus Miles per Gallon** (Refer to Problem 25, Section 4.1) An engineer wants to determine how the weight of a car, x, affects gas mileage, y. The following

data represent the weights of various domestic cars and their miles per gallon in the city for the 2008 model year.

Car	Weight (pounds), x	Miles per Gallon, y
Buick Lucerne	3,765	19
Cadillac DeVille	3,984	18
Chevrolet Malibu	3,530	21
Chrysler Sebring Sedan	3,175	22
Dodge Neon	2,580	27
Dodge Charger	3,730	18
Ford Focus	2,605	26
Lincoln LS	3,772	17
Mercury Sable	3,310	20
Pontiac G5	2,991	25
Saturn Ion	2,752	26

Source: www.roadandtrack.com

(a) Find the least-squares regression line treating weight as the explanatory variable and miles per gallon as the response variable. $\hat{y} = -0.0070x + 44.8793$
(b) Interpret the slope and y-intercept, if appropriate.
(c) A Chevy Cobalt weighs 2,780 pounds and gets 22 miles per gallon. Is the miles per gallon of a Cobalt above average or below average for cars of this weight? *Below*
(d) Would it be reasonable to use the least-squares regression line to predict the miles per gallon of a Toyota Prius, a hybrid gas and electric car? Why or why not? *No*

24. **Bone Length** (Refer to Problem 26, Section 4.1) Research performed at NASA and led by Emily R. Morey-Holton measured the lengths of the right humerus and right tibia in 11 rats that were sent to space on Spacelab Life Sciences 2. The following data were collected.

Right Humerus (mm), x	Right Tibia (mm), y	Right Humerus (mm), x	Right Tibia (mm), y
24.80	36.05	25.90	37.38
24.59	35.57	26.11	37.96
24.59	35.57	26.63	37.46
24.29	34.58	26.31	37.75
23.81	34.20	26.84	38.50
24.87	34.73		

Source: NASA Life Sciences Data Archive

24. (a) $\hat{y} = 1.3902x + 1.1140$

(a) Find the least-squares regression line treating the length of the right humerus, x, as the explanatory variable and the length of the right tibia, y, as the response variable.
(b) Interpret the slope and y-intercept, if appropriate.
(c) Determine the residual if the length of the right humerus is 26.11 mm and the actual length of the right tibia is 37.96 mm. Is the length of this tibia above or below average? *0.548 mm; above*

(d) Draw the least-squares regression line on the scatter diagram and label the residual from part (c).
(e) Suppose one of the rats sent to space experienced a broken right tibia due to a severe landing. The length of the right humerus is determined to be 25.31 mm. Use the least-squares regression line to estimate the length of the right tibia. *36.300 mm*

25. **Cola Consumption vs. Bone Density** Example 5 in Section 4.1 on page 201 discussed the effect of cola consumption on bone mineral density in the femoral neck of women.
(a) Find the least-squares regression line treating cola consumption per week as the explanatory variable.
(b) Interpret the slope. 25. (a) $\hat{y} = -0.0029x + 0.8861$
(c) Interpret the intercept.
(d) Predict the bone mineral density of the femoral neck of a woman who consumes four colas per week. *0.8745 g/cm²*
(e) The researchers found a woman who consumed four colas per week to have a bone mineral density of 0.873 g/cm². Is this woman's bone mineral density above or below average among all women who consume four colas per week? *Below*
(f) Would you recommend using the model found in part (a) to predict the bone mineral density of a woman who consumes two cans of cola per day? Why?

No; outside the scope of the model

26. **Attending Class** The following data represent the number of days absent, x, and the final grade, y, for a sample of college students in a general education course at a large state university.

No. of absences, x	0	1	2	3	4	5	6	7	8	9
Final grade, y	89.2	86.4	83.5	81.1	78.2	73.9	64.3	71.8	65.5	66.2

Source: College Teaching, 53(1), 2005.

26. (c) 74.60; −0.70; below

(a) Find the least-squares regression line treating number of absences as the explanatory variable and final grade as the response variable. $\hat{y} = -2.8273x + 88.7327$
(b) Interpret the slope and y-intercept, if appropriate.
(c) Predict the final grade for a student who misses five class periods and compute the residual. Is the final grade above or below average for this number of absences?
(d) Draw the least-squares regression line on the scatter diagram of the data and label the residual.
(e) Would it be reasonable to use the least-squares regression line to predict the final grade for a student who has missed 15 class periods? Why or why not? *No*

27. **Does Size Matter?** (Refer to Problem 29, Section 4.1) Researchers wondered whether the size of a person's brain was related to the individual's mental capacity. They selected a sample of right-handed introductory psychology students who had SAT scores higher than 1,350. The subjects

were administered the Wechsler Adult Intelligence Scale-Revised to obtain their IQ scores. MRI scans, performed at the same facility, consisted of 18 horizontal MR images. The computer counted all pixels with nonzero gray scale in each of the 18 images, and the total count served as an index for brain size. The resulting data for the females in the study are presented in the table.

MRI Count, x	IQ, y
816,932	133
951,545	137
991,305	138
833,868	132
856,472	140
852,244	132
790,619	135
866,662	130
857,782	133
948,066	133

Source: L. Willerman, R. Schultz, J. N. Rutledge, and E. Bigler. "In Vivo Brain Size and Intelligence." *Intelligence*, 15: 223–228, 1991.

(a) Find the least-squares regression line for females treating MRI count as the explanatory variable and IQ as the response variable. $\hat{y} = 0.00002x + 119.1662$

(b) What do you notice about the value of the slope? Why does this result seem reasonable based on the scatter diagram and linear correlation coefficient obtained in Problem 29(d) of Section 4.1?

(c) When there is no relation between the explanatory and response variable, we use the mean value of the response variable, $\bar{y}$, to predict. Predict the IQ of a female whose MRI count is 1,000,000. Predict the IQ of a female whose MRI count is 830,000. $134.3; 134.3$

28. **Male versus Female Drivers** (Refer to Problem 30, Section 4.1) The following data represent the number of licensed drivers in various age groups and the number of fatal accidents within the age group by gender.
(a) Males: $\hat{y} = 0.3428x + 998.4488$; Females: $\hat{y} = 0.1045x + 514.1520$

Age	Number of Male Licensed Drivers (000s)	Number of Fatal Crashes	Number of Female Licensed Drivers (000s)	Number of Fatal Crashes
<16	12	227	12	77
16–20	6,424	5,180	6,139	2,113
21–24	6,941	5,016	6,816	1,531
25–34	18,068	8,595	17,664	2,780
35–44	20,406	7,990	20,063	2,742
45–54	19,898	7,118	19,984	2,285
55–64	14,340	4,527	14,441	1,514
65–74	8,194	2,274	8,400	938
>74	4,803	2,022	5,375	980

Source: National Highway and Traffic Safety Institute

(a) Find the least-squares regression line for males treating number of licensed drivers as the explanatory variable, x, and number of fatal crashes, y, as the response variable. Repeat this procedure for females.

(b) Interpret the slope of the least-squares regression line for each gender, if appropriate. How might an insurance company use this information?

(c) Was the number of fatal accidents for 16 to 20 year old males above or below average? Was the number of fatal accidents for 21 to 24 year old males above or below average? Was the number of fatal accidents for males greater than 74 years old above or below average? How might an insurance company use this information? Does the same relationship hold for females?

29. Mark Twain, in his book *Life on the Mississippi* (1884), makes the following observation:

Therefore, the Mississippi between Cairo and New Orleans was twelve hundred and fifteen miles long one hundred and seventy-six years ago. It was eleven hundred and eighty after the cut-off of 1722. It was one thousand and forty after the American Bend cut-off. It has lost sixty-seven miles since. Consequently its length is only nine hundred and seventy-three miles at present.

Now, if I wanted to be one of those ponderous scientific people, and "let on" to prove what had occurred in the remote past by what had occurred in a given time in the recent past, or what will occur in the far future by what has occurred in late years, what an opportunity is here! Geology never had such a chance, nor such exact data to argue from! Nor "development of species," either! Glacial epochs are great things, but they are vague—vague. Please observe:

In the space of one hundred and seventy-six years the Lower Mississippi has shortened itself two hundred and forty-two miles. That is an average of a trifle over one mile and a third per year. Therefore, any calm person, who is not blind or idiotic, can see that in the Old Oolitic Silurian Period, just a million years ago next November, the Lower Mississippi River was upwards of one million three hundred thousand miles long, and stuck out over the Gulf of Mexico like a fishing-rod. And by the same token any person can see that seven hundred and forty-two years from now the Lower Mississippi will be only a mile and three-quarters long, and Cairo and New Orleans will have joined their streets together, and be plodding comfortably along under a single mayor and a mutual board of aldermen. There is something fascinating about science. One gets such wholesale returns of conjecture out of such a trifling investment of fact.

Discuss how Twain's observation relate to the material presented in this section.

30. **Regression Applet** Load the regression by eye applet. Create a scatter diagram with 12 points and a positive linear association. Try to choose the points so that the correlation is about 0.7.
(a) Draw a line that you believe describes the relation between the two variables well.

(b) Now click the Show Least-squares Line on the applet. Compare the sum of squared residuals for the line that you draw to the sum of squared residuals for the least-squares regression line. Repeat parts (a) and (b) as often as you like. Does your eyeballed line ever coincide with the least-squares regression line?

31. Putting It Together: Housing Prices One of the biggest factors in determining the value of a home is the square footage. The following data represent the square footage and asking price (in thousands of dollars) for a random sample of homes for sale in Naples, Florida, in December 2007.

31. (a) Square footage

Square Footage, x	Asking Price ($000s), y
1,148	154
1,096	159.9
1,142	169
1,288	169.9
1,322	170
1,466	179.9
1,344	180
1,544	189
1,494	189.9

Source: realtor.com

(a) Which variable is the explanatory variable?
(b) Draw a scatter diagram of the data.
(c) Determine the linear correlation coefficient between square footage and asking price.   *0.916*
(d) Is there a linear relation between the square footage and asking price?   *Yes*
(e) Find the least-squares regression line treating square footage as the explanatory variable. $\hat{y} = 0.0686x + 83.2366$
(f) Interpret the slope.   *31. (h) Above*
(g) Is it reasonable to *y*-interpret the intercept? Why?   *No*
(h) One home that is 1,092 square feet is listed at $189,900. Is this home's price above or below average for a home of this size? What might be some reasons for this price?

32. Putting It Together: Smoking and Birth Weight It is well known that women should not smoke while pregnant, but what is the effect of smoking on a baby's birth weight? Researchers Ira M. Bernstein and associates "sought to estimate how the pattern of maternal smoking throughout pregnancy influences newborn size." To conduct this study, 160 pregnant, smoking women were enrolled in a prospective study. During the third trimester of pregnancy, the woman self-reported the number of cigarettes smoked. Urine samples were collected to measure cotinine levels (to assess nicotine levels). Birth weights (in grams) of the babies were obtained upon delivery.

Source: Ira M. Bernstein et. al. "Maternal Smoking and Its Association with Birthweight." *Obstetrics & Gynecology* 106 (Part 1) 5, 2005.

(a) The histogram, drawn in MINITAB, shows the birth weight of babies whose mothers did not smoke in the third trimester of pregnancy (but did smoke prior to the third trimester). Describe the shape of the distribution. What is the class width of the histogram?
Bell-shaped; 200

32. (b) Observational study

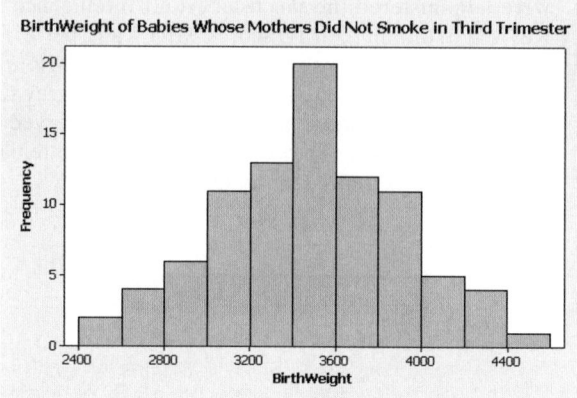

(b) Is this an observational study or a designed experiment?
(c) What does it mean for the study to be prospective?
(d) Why would the researchers conduct a urinalysis to measure cotinine levels?
(e) What is the explanatory variable in the study? What is the response variable?   *Cigarettes; birth weight*
(f) The scatter diagram of the data drawn using MINITAB is shown next. What type of relation appears to exist between cigarette consumption in the third trimester and birth weight?   *Negative association*

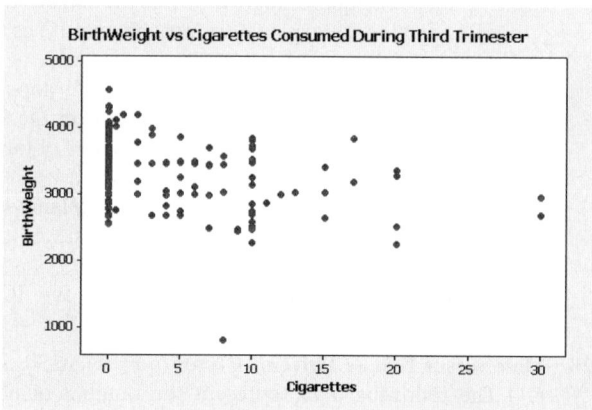

Regression Analysis: BirthWeight versus Cigarettes

```
The regression equation is
BirthWeight = 3456 − 31.0 Cigarettes

Predictor          Coef    SE Coef       T       P
Constant        3456.04      45.44   76.07   0.000
Cigarettes       −31.014      6.498   −4.77   0.000

S = 482.603     R − Sq = 12.6%     R − Sq(adj) = 12.0%
```

(g) Use the given regression output from MINITAB to find the linear correlation between cigarette consumption and birth weight.   *−0.355*
(h) Use the regression output from MINITAB to report the least-squares regression line between cigarette consumption and birth weight. $\hat{y} = -31.014x + 3456.04$

(i) Interpret the slope.

(j) Interpret the *y*-intercept.

(k) Would you recommend using this model to predict the birth weight of a baby whose mother smoked 10 cigarettes per day during the third trimester? Why?   No

(l) Does this study demonstrate that smoking during the third trimester causes lower-birth-weight babies?   No

(m) Cite some lurking variables that may confound the results of the study.

TECHNOLOGY STEP-BY-STEP   Determining the Least-Squares Regression Line

TI-83/84 Plus

Use the same steps that were followed to obtain the correlation coefficient. (See Section 4.1).

MINITAB

1. With the explanatory variable in C1 and the response variable in C2, select the **Stat** menu and highlight **Regression**. Highlight **Regression . . . .**

2. Select the explanatory (predictor) variable and response variable and click OK.

Excel

1. Be sure the Data Analysis Tool Pak is activated by selecting the **Tools** menu and highlighting **Add-Ins . . . .** Check the box for the Analysis ToolPak and select OK.

2. Enter the explanatory variable in column A and the response variable in column B.

3. Select the **Tools** menu and highlight **Data Analysis . . . .**

4. Select the **Regression** option.

5. With the cursor in the Y-range cell, highlight the column that contains the response variable. With the cursor in the X-range cell, highlight the column that contains the explanatory variable. Select the Output Range. Press OK.

4.3 DIAGNOSTICS ON THE LEAST-SQUARES REGRESSION LINE

Preparing for This Section   Before getting started, review the following:

- Outliers (Section 3.4, pp. 171–172)

Objectives	
1	Compute and interpret the coefficient of determination
2	Perform residual analysis on a regression model
3	Identify influential observations

In Section 4.2, we discussed the procedure for obtaining the least-squares regression line. In this section, we discuss additional characteristics of the least-squares regression line, along with graphical diagnostic tests that should be performed on every least-squares regression line.

1 Compute and Interpret the Coefficient of Determination

In Other Words

Just as a doctor performs tests to diagnose a patient, a researcher must use tests to diagnose the least-squares regression line.

Consider the club-head speed versus distance data introduced in Section 4.1. If we were asked to predict the distance of a randomly selected shot, what would be a good guess? Our best guess might be the average distance of all shots taken. Since we don't know this value, we use the average distance from the sample data given in Table 1, $\bar{y} = 266.75$ yards.

Now suppose we were told this particular shot resulted from a swing with a club-head speed of 103 mph. Knowing that a linear relation exists between club-head speed and distance allows us to improve our estimate of the distance of the shot. In fact, we could use the least-squares regression line to adjust our guess to $\hat{y} = 3.1661(103) - 55.7964 = 270.3$ yards. In statistical terms, we say that some of the variation in distance is explained by the linear relation between club-head speed and distance.

The proportion of variation in the response variable that is explained by the least-squares regression line is called the *coefficient of determination*.

<table><tr><td>Definition</td><td>The **coefficient of determination, R^2**, measures the proportion of total variation in the response variable that is explained by the least-squares regression line.</td></tr></table>

In Other Words

The coefficient of determination is a measure of how well the least-squares regression line describes the relation between the explanatory and response variable. The closer R^2 is to 1, the better the line describes how changes in the explanatory variable affect the value of the response variable.

The coefficient of determination is a number between 0 and 1, inclusive. That is, $0 \leq R^2 \leq 1$. If $R^2 = 0$, the least-squares regression line has no explanatory value. If $R^2 = 1$, the least-squares regression line explains 100% of the variation in the response variable.

Consider Figure 14, where a horizontal line is drawn at $\bar{y} = 266.75$. This value represents the predicted distance of a shot without any knowledge of club-head speed. Armed with the additional information that the club-head speed is 103 miles per hour, we increased our guess to 270.3 yards. The difference between the predicted distance of 266.75 yards and the predicted distance of 270.3 yards is due to the fact that the club head-speed is 103 miles per hour. In other words, the difference between the prediction of $\hat{y} = 270.3$ and $\bar{y} = 266.75$ is explained by the linear relation between club-head speed and distance. The observed distance when club-head speed is 103 miles per hour is 274 yards (see Table 4 on page 209). The difference between our predicted value, $\hat{y} = 270.3$, and the actual value, $y = 274$, is due to factors (variables) other than the club-head speed and also is due to random error. The differences just discussed are called **deviations**.

Figure 14

In Other Words

The word deviations comes from deviate. To deviate means "to stray".

The deviation between the observed value of the response variable, y, and the mean value of the response variable, $\bar{y}$, is called the **total deviation**, so total deviation = $y - \bar{y}$. The deviation between the predicted value of the response variable, $\hat{y}$, and the mean value of the response variable, $\bar{y}$, is called the **explained deviation**, so explained deviation = $\hat{y} - \bar{y}$. Finally, the deviation between the observed value of the response variable, y, and the predicted value of the response variable, $\hat{y}$, is called the **unexplained deviation**, so unexplained deviation = $y - \hat{y}$. See Figure 15.

Figure 15

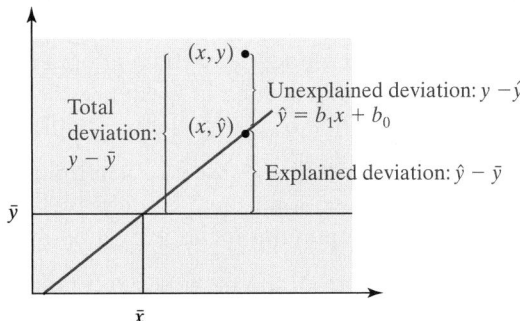

From the figure, it should be clear that

Total deviation = unexplained deviation + explained deviation

or

$$y - \bar{y} = (y - \hat{y}) + (\hat{y} - \bar{y})$$

Although beyond the scope of this text, it can be shown that

$$\sum (y - \bar{y})^2 = \sum (y - \hat{y})^2 + \sum (\hat{y} - \bar{y})^2$$

or

Total variation = unexplained variation + explained variation

Dividing both sides by total variation, we obtain

$$1 = \frac{\text{unexplained variation}}{\text{total variation}} + \frac{\text{explained variation}}{\text{total variation}}$$

Subtracting $\dfrac{\text{unexplained variation}}{\text{total variation}}$ from both sides, we obtain

$$R^2 = \frac{\text{explained variation}}{\text{total variation}} = 1 - \frac{\text{unexplained variation}}{\text{total variation}}$$

> **CAUTION** Squaring the linear correlation coefficient to obtain the coefficient of determination works only for the least-squares linear regression model
> $$\hat{y} = b_1 x + b_0$$
> The method does not work in general.

Unexplained variation is found by summing the squares of the residuals, $\sum \text{residuals}^2 = \sum (y - \hat{y})^2$. So the smaller the sum of squared residuals, the smaller the unexplained variation and, therefore, the larger R^2 will be. Therefore, the closer the observed y's are to the regression line (the predicted y's), the larger R^2 will be.

The coefficient of determination, R^2, is the square of the linear correlation coefficient for the least-squares regression model. Written in symbols, $R^2 = r^2$.

EXAMPLE 1   **Computing the Coefficient of Determination, R^2**

Problem: Compute and interpret the coefficient of determination, R^2, for the club-head speed versus distance data shown in Table 2 on page 198.

Approach: To compute R^2, we square the linear correlation coefficient, r, found in Example 2 from Section 4.1 on page 197.

Solution: $R^2 = r^2 = 0.939^2 = 0.882 = 88.2\%$

Interpretation: 88.2% of the variation in distance is explained by the least-squares regression line, and 11.8% of the variation in distance is explained by other factors.

| EXAMPLE 2 | **Determining the Coefficient of Determination Using Technology** |

Problem: Determine the coefficient of determination, R^2, for the club-head speed versus distance data found in Example 2 from Section 4.1 using statistical software or graphing calculator with advanced statistical features.

Figure 16

Summary Output

Approach: We will use Excel to determine R^2. The steps for obtaining the coefficient of determination using Excel, MINITAB, and the TI-83/84 Plus graphing calculators are given in the Technology Step-by-Step on page 238.

Solution: Figure 16 shows the results obtained from Excel. The coefficient of determination, R^2, is highlighted.

Regression Statistics	
Multiple R	0.938695838
R Square	0.881149876
Adjusted R Square	0.861341522
Standard Error	2.882638465
Observations	8

Now Work Problems 15 and 25(a)

To help reinforce the concept of the coefficient of determination, consider the three data sets in Table 6.

Table 6					
Data Set A		**Data Set B**		**Data Set C**	
x	*y*	*x*	*y*	*x*	*y*
3.6	8.9	3.1	8.9	2.8	8.9
8.3	15.0	9.4	15.0	8.1	15.0
0.5	4.8	1.2	4.8	3.0	4.8
1.4	6.0	1.0	6.0	8.3	6.0
8.2	14.9	9.0	14.9	8.2	14.9
5.9	11.9	5.0	11.9	1.4	11.9
4.3	9.8	3.4	9.8	1.0	9.8
8.3	15.0	7.4	15.0	7.9	15.0
0.3	4.7	0.1	4.7	5.9	4.7
6.8	13.0	7.5	13.0	5.0	13.0

Figure 17(a) represents the scatter diagram of data set A, Figure 17(b) represents the scatter diagram of data set B, and Figure 17(c) represents the scatter diagram of data set C.

Figure 17

(a)

(b)

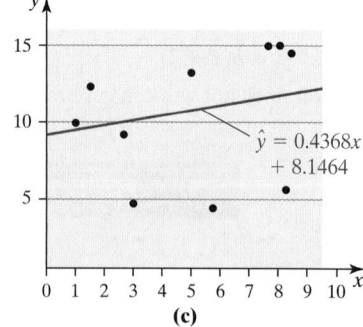
(c)

Notice that the y-values in each of the three data sets are the same. The variance of y is 17.49. If we look at the scatter diagram in Figure 17(a), we notice that almost 100% of the variability in y can be explained by the least-squares regression line, because the data almost lie perfectly on a straight line. In Figure 17(b), a high percentage of the variability in y can be explained by the least-squares regression line because the data have a strong linear relation. Higher x-values are associated with higher y-values. Finally, in Figure 17(c), a low percentage of the variability in y is explained by the least-squares regression line. If x increases, we cannot easily predict the change in y. If we compute the coefficient of determination, R^2, for the three data sets in Table 6, we obtain the following results:

Data Set	Coefficient of Determination, R^2	Interpretation
A	99.99%	99.99% of the variability in y is explained by the least-squares regression line.
B	94.7%	94.7% of the variability in y is explained by the least-squares regression line.
C	9.4%	9.4% of the variability in y is explained by the least-squares regression line.

Notice that, as the explanatory ability of the line decreases, the coefficient of determination, R^2, also decreases.

② Perform Residual Analysis on a Regression Model

Recall that a residual is the difference between the observed value of y and the predicted value, $\hat{y}$. Residuals play an important role in determining the adequacy of the linear model. We will analyze residuals for the following purposes:

- To determine whether a linear model is appropriate to describe the relation between the explanatory and response variables
- To determine whether the variance of the residuals is constant
- To check for outliers

Is a Linear Model Appropriate?

In Section 4.1 we learned how to use the correlation coefficient to determine whether a linear relation exists between the explanatory variable and response variable. However, does a correlation coefficient that indicates a linear relation exists between two variables mean that the relation is linear? No! To determine if a linear model is appropriate, we also need to draw a **residual plot**, which is a scatter diagram with the residuals on the vertical axis and the explanatory variable on the horizontal axis.

If a plot of the residuals against the explanatory variable shows a discernible pattern, such as a curve, then the explanatory and response variable may not be linearly related.

Figure 18 shows two residual plots. The residual plot in Figure 18(a) does not show any pattern, so a linear model is appropriate. However, the residual plot in Figure 18(b) shows a U-shaped pattern, which indicates that a linear model is inappropriate.

Figure 18

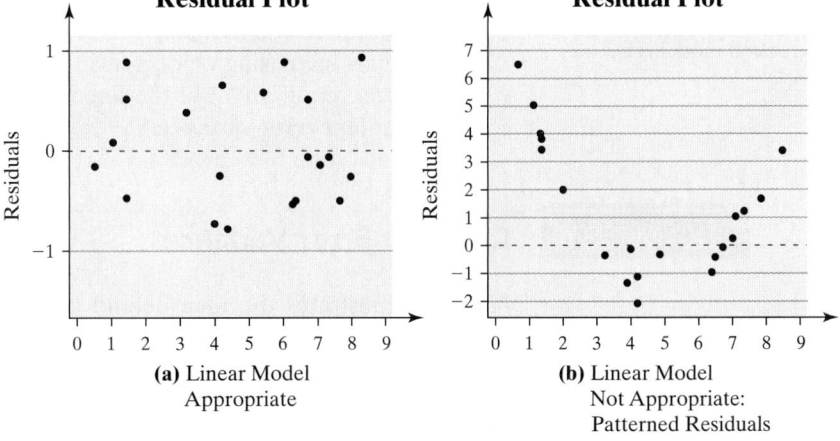

(a) Linear Model Appropriate

(b) Linear Model Not Appropriate: Patterned Residuals

EXAMPLE 3 Is a Linear Model Appropriate?

Table 7

Time (seconds)	Temperature (°F)
1	164.5
3	163.2
5	162.0
7	160.5
9	158.6
11	156.8
13	155.1

Source: Michael Sullivan

Problem: The data in Table 7 were collected by placing a the temperature probe in a portable heater, removing the probe, and then recording the temperature (in degrees Fahrenheit) over time (in seconds). Determine whether the relation between the temperature of the probe and time is linear.

Approach: We find the least-squares regression line and determine the residuals. Then, plot the residuals against the explanatory variable, time. If an obvious pattern results, we conclude that the linear model is not appropriate. If no pattern results, a linear model is appropriate.

Solution: Enter the data into statistical software or a graphing calculator with advanced statistical features. Figure 19(a) shows a scatter diagram of the data. It appears that perhaps temperature and time are linearly related with a negative slope. In fact, the linear correlation coefficient between these two variables is -0.998. We use statistical software to compute the least-squares regression line and store the residuals. Figure 19(b) shows a plot of the residuals versus the explanatory variable, time. The upside-down U-shaped pattern in the plot indicates that the linear model is not appropriate. The predicted values overestimate the temperature for early and late times, whereas they underestimate the temperature for the middle times.

Figure 19

(a)

(b)

Is the Variance of the Residuals Constant?

To determine whether the variance of the residuals is constant, we plot the residuals against the explanatory variable.

CAUTION If the model does not have constant error variance, statistical inference (the subject of Chapter 14) using the regression model is not reliable.

> If a plot of the residuals against the explanatory variable shows the spread of the residuals increasing or decreasing as the explanatory variable increases, then a strict requirement of the linear model is violated. This requirement is called **constant error variance**.*

EXAMPLE 4 Constant Error Variance

Figure 20 illustrates the idea behind constant error variance. Notice that in Figure 20(a) the data appear more spread out about the regression line when x is large. From the residual plot in Figure 20(b), we see that the absolute value of the residuals

*The statistical term for constant error variance is **homoscedasticity**.

is larger when x is larger and smaller when x is smaller. This means that the predictions made using the regression equation will be less reliable when x is large because there is more variability in y.

Figure 20

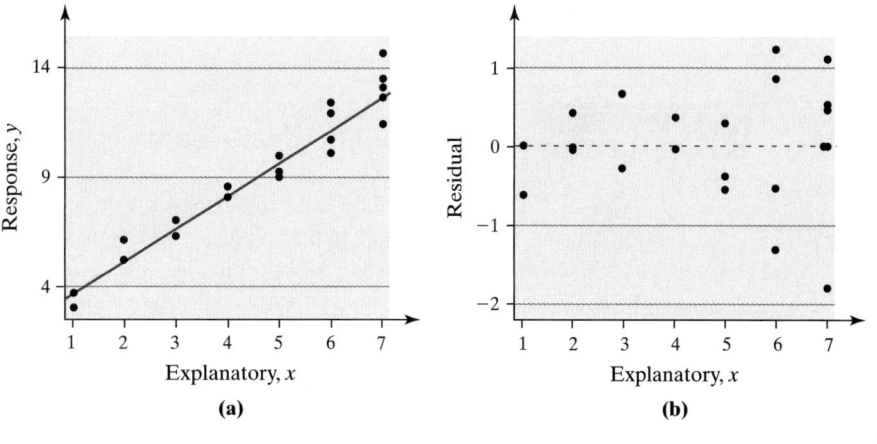

(a)   (b)

Note to Instructor
Many statistical software packages will identify potential outliers in the output of the least-squares regression analysis. Software typically uses the z-score to identify outliers. A data value is an outlier if its z-score is less than −2 or greater than +2. This method works only with normally distributed residuals, a topic that hasn't been discussed yet.

Are There Any Outliers?

In Section 3.4 we stated that outliers are extreme observations. An **outlier** can also be thought of as an observation that does not fit the overall pattern of the data. To determine outliers, we can either construct a plot of residuals against the explanatory variable or draw a boxplot of the residuals.

We can find outliers from the residual plot because the residual will lie far from the rest of the plot. Outliers can be found from a boxplot of residuals because they will appear as asterisks (*) in the plot.

EXAMPLE 5   **Identifying Outliers**

Problem: Figure 21(a) shows a scatter diagram of a set of data. After the least-squares regression line was obtained, the residual plot in Figure 21(b) and the boxplot of the residuals in Figure 21(c) were obtained. Do the data have any outliers?

Approach: We examine the residual plot and boxplot for outliers.

Solution: We can see that the data do contain an outlier. We label the outlier in the scatter diagram given in Figure 21(a).

Figure 21

(a)   (b)   (c)

We will follow the practice of removing outliers only if they are the result of an error in recording, a miscalculation, or some other obvious blunder in the data-collection process (such as the observation not being from the population under study). If none of these are reasons for the outlier, we recommend that a statistician be consulted.

EXAMPLE 6 **Graphical Residual Analysis**

Problem: The data in Table 4 on page 209 represent the club-head speed, the distance the golf ball traveled, and the residuals (column 7) for eight swings of a golf club. Construct a residual plot and boxplot of the residuals and comment on the appropriateness of the least-squares regression model.

Approach: We plot the residuals on the vertical axis and the corresponding values of the explanatory variable on the horizontal axis. We then look for any violations of the requirements of the regression model. We use a boxplot of the residuals to identify any outliers.

Solution: Figure 22 shows the residual plot. Figure 23 shows the boxplot.

Figure 22

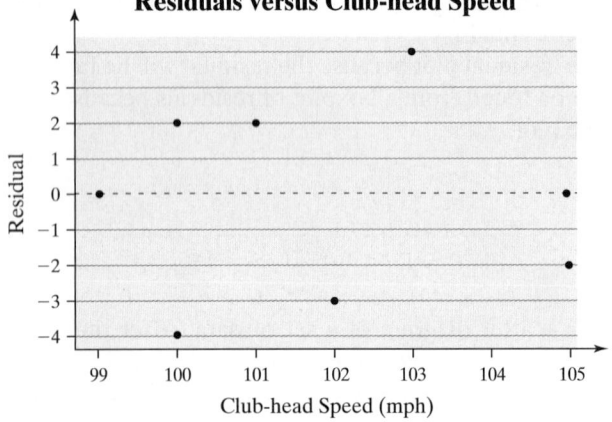

Residuals versus Club-head Speed

Figure 23

Because there is no discernible pattern in the residual plot, describing the relation between club-head speed and distance using a linear model is appropriate. The residuals display constant error variance, and no outliers appear in the boxplot of the residuals.

 Now Work Problems 21 and 25(b)–(c)

---

3 **Identify Influential Observations**

An **influential observation** is an observation that significantly affects the value of the slope and/or y-intercept of the least-squares regression line. An influential observation will also significantly affect the value of the correlation coefficient. How do we identify influential observations? We first remove the point that is believed to be influential from the data set, and then we recompute the correlation or regression line. If the correlation coefficient, slope, or y-intercept changes significantly, we say that the removed point is influential. Consider the scatter diagram in Figure 24.

Figure 24

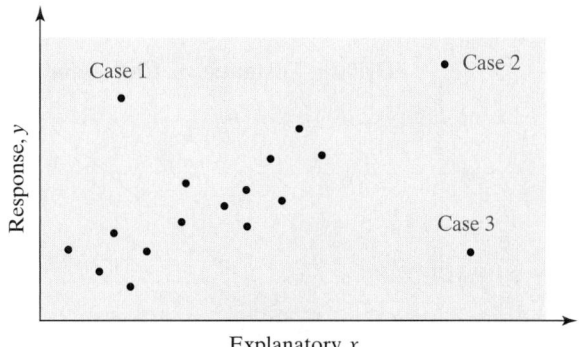

In Other Words

Draw a boxplot of the explanatory variable. If an outlier appears, the observation corresponding to the outlier may be influential.

Case 1 would be an outlier because its *y*-value is large relative to its *x*-value. Notice, however, that there are enough points to offset the effect case 1 would have on the correlation coefficient or least-squares regression, so it is not influential. Case 2 is large relative to both its *x*-value and *y*-value. It may or may not be influential because the point appears to lie along the linear pattern of the data. Case 3 is large relative to its *x*-value, and its *y*-value is not consistent with the pattern of the data. This point would influence the values of the slope and *y*-intercept in the regression equation and would also affect the value of the correlation coefficient. We conclude the following:

> Influential observations typically exist when the point is an outlier relative to the values of the explanatory variable.

EXAMPLE 7 **Identifying Influential Observations**

Problem: Suppose that our driving of the golf ball experiment called for nine trials, but the player that we were using hurt his wrist. Luckily, Tiger Woods is practicing on the same range and graciously agrees to participate in our experiment. His club-head speed is measured at 120 miles per hour and he hits the golf ball 305 yards. Is Tiger Woods' shot an influential observation? The least-squares regression line without Woods is $\hat{y} = 3.1661x - 55.7964$.

Approach: To determine whether Tiger Woods is influential, we recompute the least-squares regression line with Woods included. If the slope or *y*-intercept of the least-squares regression line changes substantially, we will conclude that Woods is influential.

Solution: Figure 25 shows a partial output obtained from MINITAB with Woods included in the data set.

Figure 25 **Regression Analysis: Distance (yards) versus Club Head Speed (mph)**

```
The regression equation is
Distance (yards) = 39.5 + 2.23 Club Head Speed (mph)

Predictor                 Coef    SE Coef      T       P
Constant                  39.46    20.15     1.96    0.091
Club Head Speed (mph)      2.2287   0.1937   11.51    0.000

S = 3.51224    R - Sq = 95.0%    R - Sq(adj) = 94.3%
```

The least-squares regression line with Woods included in the data set is

$$\hat{y} = 2.2287x + 39.46$$

We graph the regression lines with Woods included (red) and with Woods excluded (blue) on the same scatter diagram. See Figure 26.

Figure 26

The inclusion of Woods in the data set causes the slope of the regression line to decrease (from 3.1661 to 2.2287) and the y-intercept to increase substantially (from -55.80 to $+39.46$). In other words, the Woods data pulls the least-squares regression line toward his observation. His data point is influential.

Using Technology

MINITAB will alert you when a data value is influential.

As with outliers, influential observations should be removed only if there is justification to do so. When an influential observation occurs in a data set and its removal is not warranted, two popular courses of action are to (1) collect more data so that additional points near the influential observation are obtained or (2) use techniques that reduce the influence of the influential observation. (These techniques are beyond the scope of this text.) In the case of Example 7, we are justified in removing Tiger Woods from the data set because our experiment called for the same player to swing the club for each trial.

Now Work Problem 17

4.3 ASSESS YOUR UNDERSTANDING

Concepts and Vocabulary

1. It is determined that $R^2 = 0.75$ when a linear regression is performed. Interpret this result.

2. Explain what is meant by total deviation, explained deviation, and unexplained deviation.

3. What does it mean if a plot of the residuals against the explanatory variable shows a discernible pattern (such as U-shaped)?

4. What is constant error variance? Why is it important?

5. What is an influential observation? If an influential observation is identified, what should be done?

6. Explain the difference between an outlier and an influential observation.

7. Explain how an influential observation affects the least-squares regression line.

8. Explain how a violation of the constant error variance assumption might affect the confidence placed on a predicted value.

9. If R^2 is 0.81, can you determine the value of r? If so, what is its value? If not, what else do you need to know?

10. Explain why it is important to do residual analysis after obtaining a least-squares regression line.

Skill Building

In Problems 11–14, analyze the residual plots and identify which, if any, of the conditions for an adequate linear model is not met.

11. Constant error variance

12. None

13. Outlier

14. Patterned residuals

19. No

20. Yes

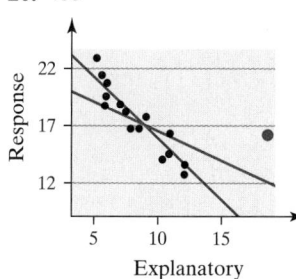

15. Match the coefficient of determination to the scatter diagram. The scales on the horizontal and vertical axis are the same for each scatter diagram.

(a) $R^2 = 0.58$ III
(b) $R^2 = 0.90$ II
(c) $R^2 = 1$ IV
(d) $R^2 = 0.12$ I

(I)

(II)

(III)

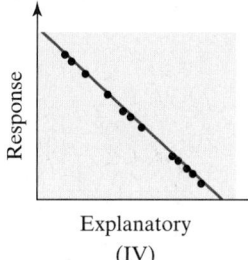

(IV)

16. Use the linear correlation coefficient given to determine the coefficient of determination, R^2. Interpret each R^2.

(a) $r = -0.32$ $R^2 = 10.24\%$
(b) $r = 0.13$ $R^2 = 1.69\%$
(c) $r = 0.40$ $R^2 = 16\%$
(d) $r = 0.93$ $R^2 = 86.49\%$

In Problems 17–20, a scatter diagram is given with one of the points drawn in blue. In addition, two least-squares regression lines are drawn: The line drawn in red is the least-squares regression line with the point in blue excluded. The line drawn in blue is the least-squares regression line with the point in blue included. On the basis of these graphs, do you think the point in blue is influential? Why?

17. Yes

18. No

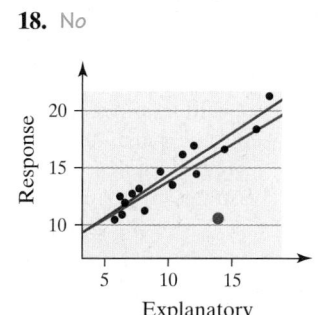

Applying the Concepts

21. The Other Old Faithful Perhaps you are familiar with the famous Old Faithful geyser in Yellowstone National Park. Another Old Faithful geyser is located in Calistoga in California's Napa Valley. The following data represent the time (in minutes) between eruptions and the length of eruption for 11 randomly selected eruptions.

Time between Eruptions, x	Length of Eruption, y	Time between Eruptions, x	Length of Eruption, y
12.17	1.88	11.70	1.82
11.63	1.77	12.27	1.93
12.03	1.83	11.60	1.77
12.15	1.83	11.72	1.83
11.30	1.70		

Source: Ladonna Hansen, Park Curator

(a) A scatter diagram of the data is shown next. What type of relation appears to exist between time between eruptions and length of eruption? Linear, positive association

Time between Eruptions vs Length of Eruption

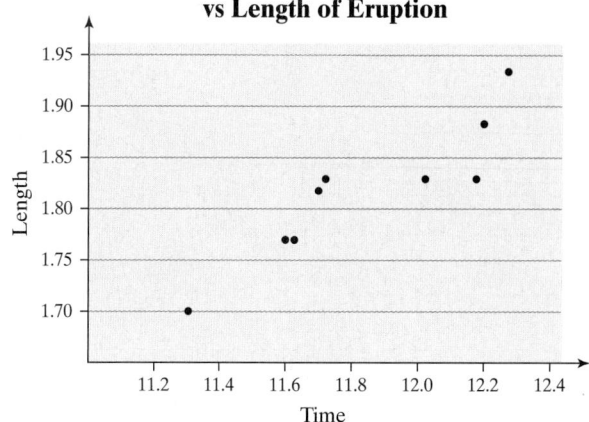

(b) The following residual plot was obtained after finding the least-squares regression line. Does the residual plot confirm that the relation between time between eruptions and length of eruption is linear? Yes

Residuals versus Time

Residuals versus 7 Day

(c) The coefficient of determination is 83.0%. Provide an interpretation of this value.

(c) The coefficient of determination is 57.5%. Provide an interpretation of this value.

22. Concrete As concrete cures, it gains strength. The following data represent the 7-day and 28-day strength (in pounds per square inch) of a certain type of concrete.

7-Day Strength, x	28-Day Strength, y	7-Day Strength, x	28-Day Strength, y
2,300	4,070	2,480	4,120
3,390	5,220	3,380	5,020
2,430	4,640	2,660	4,890
2,890	4,620	2,620	4,190
3,330	4,850	3,340	4,630

(a) A scatter diagram of the data is shown next. What type of relation appears to exist between 7-day strength and 28-day strength? *Positive association*

28 Day vs 7 Day Concrete Strength

(b) The following residual plot was obtained after finding the least-squares regression line. Does the residual plot confirm that the relation between 7-day and 28-day strength is linear? *Yes*

23. Calories versus Sugar The following data represent the number of calories per serving and the number of grams of sugar per serving for a random sample of high-fiber cereals.

Calories, x	Sugar, y	Calories, x	Sugar, y
200	18	210	23
210	23	210	16
170	17	210	17
190	20	190	12
200	18	190	11
180	19	200	11

Source: Consumer Reports

(a) Draw a scatter diagram of the data treating calories as the explanatory variable. What type of relation appears to exist between calories and sugar content?

(b) Determine the correlation between calories and sugar content. Is there a linear relation between calories and sugar content? *0.261; no*

(c) Suppose that we add Kellogg's All-Bran cereal, which has 80 calories and 6 grams of sugar per serving, to the data set. Redraw the scatter diagram and recompute the correlation between calories and sugar content. Is there a linear relation between calories and sugar content with All-Bran included in the data set? Is All-Bran an influential observation? *0.649; yes; yes*

(d) Explain why it is necessary to show a scatter diagram with the correlation coefficient when claiming that a linear relation exists between two variables.

24. Education and Teen Birthrates The scatter diagram represents the percentage of the population with a bachelor's degree, x, and teen birthrates, y, for the 50 states and Washington, DC, in 2006.

Source: U.S. Census Bureau

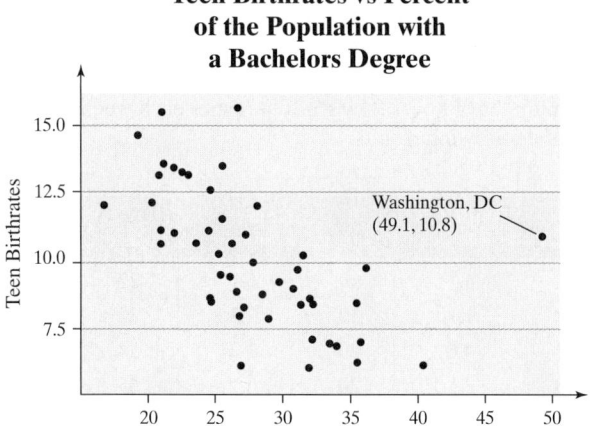

**Teen Birthrates vs Percent
of the Population with
a Bachelors Degree**

Washington, DC
(49.1, 10.8)

(a) The least-squares regression with Washington, DC, included is $\hat{y} = -0.2452x + 16.820$. The least-squares regression line with Washington, DC, excluded is $\hat{y} = -0.3436x + 19.373$. Do you think the point corresponding to Washington, DC, may be influential? Why?
(b) Washington, DC, often appears as an influential observation in regression analysis. What is it about Washington, DC, that makes it influential?
(c) Would you say that higher levels of education cause lower teen birthrates?

Problems 25–28 use the results from Problems 23–26, in Section 4.1 and Problems 21–24 in Section 4.2.

25. Height versus Head Circumference Use the results from Problem 23 in Section 4.1 and Problem 21 in Section 4.2 to:

(a) Compute the coefficient of determination, R^2. *83.0%*
(b) Construct a residual plot to verify the requirements of the least-squares regression model.
(c) Interpret the coefficient of determination and comment on the adequacy of the linear model.

26. American Black Bears Use the results from Problem 24 in Section 4.1 and Problem 22 in Section 4.2 to:

(a) Compute the coefficient of determination, R^2. *49.5%*
(b) Construct a residual plot to verify the requirements of the least-squares regression model.
(c) Interpret the coefficient of determination and comment on the adequacy of the linear model.

27. Weight of a Car versus Miles per Gallon Use the results from Problem 25 in Section 4.1 and Problem 23 in Section 4.2.

(a) What proportion of the variability in miles per gallon is explained by the relation between weight of the car and miles per gallon? *92.9%*
(b) Construct a residual plot to verify the requirements of the least-squares regression model.
(c) Interpret the coefficient of determination and comment on the adequacy of the linear model.

28. Bone Length Use the results from Problem 26 in Section 4.1 and Problem 24 in Section 4.2.

(a) What proportion of the variability in the length of the right tibia is explained by the relation between the length of the right humerus and the length of the right tibia? *90.5%*
(b) Construct a residual plot to verify the requirements of the least-squares regression model.

(c) Interpret the coefficient of determination and comment on the adequacy of the linear model.

29. Kepler's Law of Planetary Motion The time it takes for a planet to complete its orbit around the sun is called the planet's sidereal year. In 1618, Johann Kepler discovered that the sidereal year of a planet is related to the distance the planet is from the sun. The following data show the distances of the planets, and the dwarf planet Pluto, from the sun and their sidereal years. *29. (c) $\hat{y} = 0.0657x - 12.4967$*

Planet	Distance from Sun, x (millions of miles)	Sidereal Year, y
Mercury	36	0.24
Venus	67	0.62
Earth	93	1.00
Mars	142	1.88
Jupiter	483	11.9
Saturn	887	29.5
Uranus	1,785	84.0
Neptune	2,797	165.0
Pluto	3,675	248.0

(a) Draw a scatter diagram of the data treating distance from the sun as the explanatory variable.
(b) Determine the correlation between distance and sidereal year. Does this imply a linear relation between distance and sidereal year? *0.989; yes*
(c) Compute the least-squares regression line.
(d) Plot the residuals against the distance from the sun.
(e) Do you think the least-squares regression line is a good model? Why? *No*

30. Wind Chill Factor The wind chill factor depends on wind speed and air temperature. The following data represent the wind speed (in mph) and wind chill factor at an air temperature of 15° Fahrenheit.

Wind Speed, x (mph)	Wind Chill Factor, y	Wind Speed, x (mph)	Wind Chill Factor, y
5	12	25	−22
10	−3	30	−25
15	−11	35	−27
20	−17		

Source: Information Please Almanac

(a) Draw a scatter diagram of the data treating wind speed as the explanatory variable.
(b) Determine the correlation between wind speed and wind chill factor. Does this imply a linear relation between wind speed and wind chill factor? *−0.952; yes*
(c) Compute the least-squares regression line.
(d) Plot the residuals against the wind speed.
(e) Do you think the least-squares regression line is a good model? Why? *No*

31. Weight of a Car versus Miles per Gallon Suppose that we add the Dodge Viper to the data in Problem 23 in Section 4.2. A Dodge Viper weighs 3,425 pounds and gets 11 miles per gallon.
30. (c) $\hat{y} = -1.2286x + 11.2857$

(a) Compute the coefficient of determination of the expanded data set. What effect does the addition of the Viper to the data set have on R^2? *60.0%; decreases*

(b) Is the point corresponding to the Dodge Viper influential? Is it an outlier? *No; yes*

32. **American Black Bears** Suppose that we find a bear that is 205 cm tall and weighs 187 kg and add the bear to the data in Problem 22 from Section 4.2.

(a) Compute the coefficient of determination of the expanded data set. What effect does the additional bear have on R^2? *71.7%; increases*

(b) Is the new bear influential? Is it an outlier? *Yes; yes*

33. **CO_2 Emissions and Energy** The following data represent the carbon dioxide emissions (in thousands of tons), y, and energy generated (thousands of megawatts), x, for a random sample of 14 power plants in Wyoming. Is there anything unusual about the Laramie River Power Plant, which produces 24,800 thousand megawatts of energy and emits 10,100 thousand tons of CO_2? What about the Jim Bridger power plant, which produces 14,700 thousand megawatts of energy and emits 16,500 thousand tons of CO_2?

Energy	Carbon
14,700	16,500
24,800	10,100
5,773	6,959
5,215	5,778
2,712	3,475
2,493	1,147
1,211	1,070
219	379
412	258
127	86
448	30
541	6
55	5
4	4

Source: CARMA (www.carma.org)

34. **Height versus Weight** The following data represent the heights and weights of various professional baseball players. In what regard is Derek Jeter unusual?

Player	Height, x (in.)	Weight, y (lb)
Alex Rodriguez	75	225
Derek Jeter	75	195
Josh Beckett	77	222
Randy Johnson	82	230
Magglio Ordonez	72	215
Torii Hunter	74	225
Andruw Jones	73	210
Matt Holliday	76	235
Aramis Ramirez	73	215

Source: Yahoo! Sports

35. **Age versus Study Time** Professor Katula feels that there is a relation between the number of hours a statistics student studies each week and the student's age. She conducts a survey in which 26 statistics students are asked their age and the number of hours they study statistics each week. She obtains the following results:

Age, x	Hours Studying, y	Age, x	Hours Studying, y	Age, x	Hours Studying, y
18	4.2	19	5.1	22	2.1
18	1.1	19	2.3	22	3.6
18	4.6	20	1.7	24	5.4
18	3.1	20	6.1	25	4.8
18	5.3	20	3.2	25	3.9
18	3.2	20	5.3	26	5.2
19	2.8	21	2.5	26	4.2
19	2.3	21	6.4	35	8.1
19	3.2	21	4.2		

(a) Draw a scatter diagram of the data. Comment on any potential influential observations.

(b) Find the least-squares regression line using all the data points. $\hat{y} = 0.2320x - 0.9204$

(c) Find the least-squares regression line with the data point $(35, 8.1)$ removed. $\hat{y} = 0.1549x + 0.6346$

(d) Draw each least-squares regression line on the scatter diagram obtained in part (a).

(e) Comment on the influence that the point $(35, 8.1)$ has on the regression line.

36. **Regression Applet** Load the regression by eye applet. Create a scatter diagram with about 12 points clustered in the upper-left corner that have a strong, negative linear association.

(a) Click the "Show least-squares line" on the applet.

(b) Now add a thirteenth point in the bottom-right corner of the applet. The point should be near the least-squares regression line. How does the regression line change? Is this point influential?

(c) Drag the point in the bottom-right corner straight up. What makes this point influential?

(d) Clear the applet. Create a scatter diagram with 12 points that are spread out. The scatter diagram should have a strong, negative linear association. Click the "Show least-squares line."

(e) Now add a thirteenth point at the point near the mean of X and mean of Y. Does the least-squares regression line change?

(f) Drag the thirteenth point straight up. Does the least-squares regression line change much? Why or why not?

37. **Putting It Together: Building a Financial Model** In Section 3.2, we introduced one measure of risk used by financial analysts, the standard deviation of rate of return. In this problem we will learn about a second measure of risk of a stock, the *beta* of a stock. The following data represent the annual rate of return of General Electric (GE) stock and the annual rate of return of the Standard & Poor's 500 (S&P 500) Index for the past 12 years.

Year	Rate of Return of S&P 500	Rate of Return of GE
1996	0.203	0.402
1997	0.310	0.510
1998	0.267	0.410
1999	0.195	0.536
2000	−0.101	−0.060
2001	−0.130	−0.151
2002	−0.234	−0.377
2003	0.264	0.308
2004	0.090	0.207
2005	0.030	−0.014
2006	0.128	0.093
2007	−0.035	0.027

Source: finance.yahoo.com

(a) Draw a scatter diagram of the data treating the rate of return of the S&P 500 as the explanatory variable.

(b) Determine the correlation coefficient between rate of return of the S&P 500 and GE stock. *0.942*

(c) Based on the scatter diagram and correlation coefficient, is there a linear relation between rate of return of the S&P 500 and GE? *Yes*

(d) Find the least-squares regression line treating the rate of return of the S&P 500 as the explanatory variable.

(e) Predict the rate of return of GE stock if the rate of return of the S&P 500 is 0.10 (10%). *0.1846*

(f) If the actual rate of return for GE was 13.2% when the rate of return of the S&P 500 was 10%, was GE's performance above or below average among all years the S&P 500 returns were 10%? *Below*

(g) Interpret the slope.

(h) Interpret the intercept, if appropriate.

(i) What proportion of the variability in GE's rate of return is explained by the variability in the rate of return of the S&P 500? *88.8%*

(j) Plot residuals against the rate of return of the S&P 500. Does the residual plot confirm that the relation between the rate of return of the S&P 500 and GE stock is linear?

(k) Are there any years where GE's rate of return was unusual? *No*

37. (d) $\hat{y} = 1.5208x + 0.0325$

Consumer Reports® Fit to Drink

The taste, color, and clarity of the water coming out of home faucets have long concerned consumers. Recent reports of lead and parasite contamination have made unappetizing water a health, as well as an esthetic, concern. Water companies are struggling to contain cryptosporidium, a parasite that has caused outbreaks of illness that may be fatal to people with a weakened immune system. Even chlorination, which has rid drinking water of infectious organisms that once killed people by the thousands, is under suspicion as an indirect cause of miscarriages and cancer.

Concerns about water quality and taste have made home filtering increasingly popular. To find out how well they work, technicians at Consumer Reports tested 14 models to determine how well they filtered contaminants and whether they could improve the taste of our cabbage-soup testing mixture.

To test chloroform and lead removal, we added concentrated amounts of both to our water, along with calcium nitrate to increase water hardness. Every few days we analyzed the water to measure chloroform and lead content. The table contains the lead measurements for one of the models tested.

(a) Construct a scatter diagram of the data using % Lead Removed as the response variable.

(b) Does the relationship between No. Gallons Processed and % Lead Removed appear to be linear? If not, describe the relationship.

(c) Calculate the linear correlation coefficient between No. Gallons Processed and % Lead Removed. Based on the scatter diagram constructed in part (a) and your answer to part (b), is this measure useful? What is R^2? Interpret R^2.

(d) Fit a linear regression model to these data. Using this model, construct a residual plot. What does the residual plot suggest?

No. Gallons Processed	% Lead Removed
25	85
26	87
73	86
75	88
123	90
126	87
175	92
177	94

(e) Using statistical software or a graphing calculator with advanced statistical features, fit a quadratic model to these data. Construct a residual plot. What is R^2? Which model appears to fit the data better?

(f) Given the nature of the variables being measured, describe the type of curve you would expect to show the true relationship between these variables (linear, quadratic, exponential, S-shaped). Support your position.

Note to Readers: *In many cases, our test protocol and analytical methods are more complicated than described in these examples. The data and discussions have been modified to make the material more appropriate for the audience.*

TECHNOLOGY STEP-BY-STEP Determining R^2 and Residual Plots

TI-83/84 Plus

The Coefficient of Determination, R^2
Use the same steps that were followed to obtain the correlation coefficient to obtain R^2. Diagnostics must be on.

Residual Plots
1. Enter the raw data in L1 and L2. Obtain the least-squares regression line.
2. Access STAT PLOTS. Select Plot1. Choose the scatter diagram icon and let XList be L1. Let YList be RESID by moving the cursor to YList, pressing 2nd STAT, and choosing the list entitled RESID under the NAMES menu.
3. Press ZOOM and select 9: ZoomStat.

MINITAB
The Coefficient of Determination, R^2
This is provided in the standard regression output.

Residual Plots
Follow the same steps as those used to obtain the regression output (Section 4.2). Before selecting OK, click GRAPHS. In the cell that says "Residuals versus the variables," enter the name of the explanatory variable. Click OK.

Excel
The Coefficient of Determination, R^2
This is provided in the standard regression output.

Residual Plots
Follow the same steps as those used to obtain the regression output (Section 4.2). Before selecting OK, click **Residual Plots**. Click OK.

4.4 CONTINGENCY TABLES AND ASSOCIATION

Preparing for This Section   Before getting started, review the following:
- Side-by-side bar graphs (Section 2.1, pp. 70–72)

Objectives		
	1	Compute the marginal distribution of a variable
	2	Use the conditional distribution to identify association among categorical data
	3	Explain Simpson's Paradox

In Sections 4.1 to 4.3, we looked at techniques for summarizing relations between two quantitative variables. We now look at techniques for summarizing relations between two qualitative variables.

Consider the data (measured in thousands) in Table 8, which represent the employment status and level of education of all U.S. residents 25 years old or older in 2006. By definition, an individual is unemployed if he or she is actively seeking work but is unable to find work. An individual is considered not to be in the labor force if he or she is not employed and is not actively seeking employment.

	Table 8			
	Level of Education			
Employment Status	**Did Not Finish High School**	**High School Graduate**	**Some College**	**Bachelor's Degree or Higher**
Employed	11,892	36,702	34,143	41,649
Unemployed	866	1,798	1,267	863
Not in the labor force	14,783	22,391	13,601	12,059

Source: Bureau of Labor Statistics

Table 8 is referred to as a **contingency table**, or a **two-way table**, because it relates two categories of data. The **row variable** is employment status, because each row in the table describes the employment status of a group. The **column variable** is level of education. Each box inside the table is referred to as a **cell**. For example, the cell corresponding to employed individuals who are high school graduates is in the first row, second column. Each cell contains the frequency of the category: There were 11,892 thousand employed individuals who did not finish high school in 2006.

The data presented in Table 8 describe two characteristics regarding the population of U.S. residents who are 25 years or older: their employment status and their level of education. We want to investigate whether the two variables are associated. For example, are individuals who have a higher level of education more likely to be employed? Just as we did in Sections 4.1 to 4.3, we will discuss both numerical and graphical methods for summarizing the data.

 Compute the Marginal Distribution of a Variable

The first step in summarizing data in a contingency table is to look at the distribution of each variable separately. To determine the distribution of either the column variable or the row variable, we create a *marginal distribution*.

Definition

A **marginal distribution** of a variable is a frequency or relative frequency distribution of either the row or column variable in the contingency table.

In Other Words

The distributions are called marginal distributions because they appear in the right and the bottom margin of the contingency table.

A marginal distribution removes the effect of either the row variable or the column variable in the contingency table.

To create a marginal distribution for a variable, we calculate the row and column totals for each category of the variable. The row totals for each category are found by adding up the cell entries in each column of that row. The row totals represent the distribution of the row variable. The column totals for each category are found by adding up the cell entries in each row of that column. The column totals represent the distribution of the column variable.

EXAMPLE 1 **Determining Frequency Marginal Distributions**

Problem: Find the frequency marginal distributions for employment status and level of education from the data in Table 8.

Approach: The row total for the category "employed" is found by adding the number of employed individuals who did not finish high school, the number of employed individuals who finished high school, and so on. We repeat this process for each category of employment status.

The column total for the category "did not finish high school" is found by adding the number of employed individuals who did not finish high school, the number of unemployed individuals who did not finish high school, and the number of individuals not in the labor force who did not finish high school. We repeat this process for each level of education.

Solution: In Table 9, the blue entries represent the marginal distribution of the row variable "employment status." For example, there were 11,892 + 36,702 + 34,143 + 41,649 = 124,386 thousand employed individuals in 2006. The red entries represent the marginal distribution of the column variable "level of education."

The marginal distribution for employment status removes the effect of level of education; the marginal distribution for level of education removes the effect of employment status. From the marginal distribution of employment status, we can see that there were about twice as many employed Americans as there were Americans

	Table 9				
	Level of Education				
Employment Status	**Did Not Finish High School**	**High School Graduate**	**Some College**	**Bachelor's Degree or Higher**	Totals
Employed	11,892	36,702	34,143	41,649	124,386
Unemployed	866	1,798	1,267	863	4,794
Not in the labor force	14,783	22,391	13,601	12,059	62,834
Totals	**27,541**	**60,891**	**49,011**	**54,571**	**192,014**

not in the labor force (124,386 thousand versus 62,834 thousand) in 2006. From the marginal distribution of level of education, we can see that 60,891 thousand Americans were high school graduates. We can also learn from the table that there were 192,014 thousand U.S. residents 25 years old or older.

Now Work Problem 9(a)

We can use the row and column totals obtained in Example 1 to calculate the relative frequency marginal distribution for level of education and employment status.

EXAMPLE 2 **Determining Relative Frequency Marginal Distributions**

Problem: Determine the relative frequency marginal distribution for level of education and employment status from the data in Table 9.

Approach: The relative frequency marginal distribution for the row variable, employment status, is found by dividing the row total for each employment status by the table total, 192,014. The relative frequency marginal distribution for the column variable, level of education, is found by dividing the column total for each level of education by the table total.

CAUTION For relative frequency marginal distributions (such as in Table 10), row or column totals might not sum exactly to 1, due to rounding.

Solution: Table 10 represents the relative frequency marginal distribution for each variable.

	Table 10				
	Level of Education				
Employment Status	**Did Not Finish High School**	**High School Graduate**	**Some College**	**Bachelor's Degree or Higher**	Relative Frequency Marginal Distribution
Employed	11,892	36,702	34,143	41,649	$\frac{124,386}{192,014} = 0.648$
Unemployed	866	1,798	1,267	863	$\frac{4,794}{192,014} = 0.025$
Not in the labor force	14,783	22,391	13,601	12,059	$\frac{62,834}{192,014} = 0.327$
Relative Frequency Marginal Distribution	$\frac{27,541}{192,014} = 0.143$	$\frac{60,891}{192,014} = 0.317$	$\frac{49,011}{192,014} = 0.255$	$\frac{54,571}{192,014} = 0.284$	**1**

From Table 10, we learn that 14.3% of U.S. residents 25 years old or older did not graduate from high school. We also learn that 64.8% of U.S. residents 25 years old or older were employed in 2006.

Now Work Problems 9(b) and (c)

2 Use the Conditional Distribution to Identify Association among Categorical Data

As we look at the information contained in Tables 9 and 10, we might ask whether there is a relation between employment status and level of education. In other words, is a higher level of education associated with a higher likelihood of being employed? If level of education does not play any role, we would expect the relative frequencies for employment status at each level of education to be close to the relative frequency marginal distribution for employment status given in blue in Table 10. So we would expect 64.8% of individuals who did not finish high school to be employed, 64.8% of individuals who finished high school to be employed, 64.8% of individuals with some college to be employed, and 64.8% of individuals with at least a bachelor's degree to be employed. If the relative frequencies for the various levels of education are different, we might associate this difference with the level of education.

The marginal distributions in Tables 9 and 10 allow us to see the distribution of either the row variable, employment status, or the column variable, level of education, but we do not get a sense of association from these tables.

When describing any association between two categories of data, we must use relative frequencies instead of frequencies, because frequencies are difficult to compare when there are different numbers of observations for the categories of a variable.

⚠️ **CAUTION** To describe the association between two categorical variables, relative frequencies must be used, because there are different numbers of observations for the categories.

EXAMPLE 3 | **Comparing Two Categories of a Variable**

Problem

(a) What proportion of the individuals who did not finish high school is employed?

(b) What proportion of high school graduates is employed?

(c) What proportion of the individuals who finished some college is employed?

(d) What proportion of the individuals who have at least a bachelor's degree is employed?

Approach: For the first question, we are asking, "Of the individuals who did not finish high school, what proportion is employed?" To determine this proportion, we divide the number of employed individuals who did not finish high school by the number of people who did not finish high school. We repeat this process to answer the remaining three questions.

Solution

(a) In 2006, a total of 27,541 thousand individuals 25 years old or older did not finish high school. (See Table 9.) Of this number, 11,892 thousand were employed. Therefore, $\frac{11,892}{27,541} = 0.432$ represents the proportion of employed individuals who did not finish high school.

(b) In 2006, a total of 60,891 thousand individuals 25 years old or older were high school graduates. Of this number, 36,702 thousand were employed. Therefore, $\frac{36,702}{60,891} = 0.603$ represents the proportion of employed individuals who graduated from high school.

(c) In 2006, a total of 49,011 thousand individuals 25 years old or older had some college. Of this number, 34,143 thousand were employed. Therefore, $\frac{34,143}{49,011} = 0.697$ were employed.

In Other Words

Since we are finding the conditional distribution of employment status by level of education, the level of education is the explanatory variable and the employment status is the response variable.

(d) In 2006, a total of 54,571 thousand individuals 25 years old or older had at least a bachelor's degree. Of this number, 41,649 thousand were employed. Therefore, $\frac{41,649}{54,571} = 0.763$ were employed.

From these relative frequencies, we can see that as the level of education increases, the proportion of individuals employed increases.

The results in Example 3 are only partial. In general, we create a relative frequency distribution for each value of the explanatory variable. For our example, this means we would construct a relative frequency distribution for individuals who did not finish high school, a second relative frequency distribution for individuals who are high school graduates, and so on. These relative frequency distributions are called *conditional distributions*.

Definition   A **conditional distribution** lists the relative frequency of each category of a variable, given a specific value of the other variable in the contingency table.

An example should help to solidify our understanding of the definition.

EXAMPLE 4   **Constructing a Conditional Distribution**

Problem: Find the conditional distribution of the variable "employment status" by level of education for the data in Table 8. What is the association between level of education and employment status?

Approach: We first compute the relative frequency for each employment status, given that the individual did not finish high school. We next compute the relative frequency for each employment status, given that the individual is a high school graduate. Then we compute the relative frequency for each employment status, given that the individual had some college. Finally, we compute the relative frequency for each employment status, given that the individual had at least a bachelor's degree. This is the same approach taken in Example 3 for employed individuals.

Solution: We start with the individuals who did not finish high school. We use the number of individuals who did not finish high school (27,541 thousand) as the denominator in computing the relative frequencies.

We then compute the relative frequency for each employment status, given that the individual is a high school graduate. In this case, since we know the individual is a high school graduate, we use the number of individuals who graduated from high school as the denominator in computing relative frequencies.

Next, compute the relative frequency for each employment status, given that the individual had some college and then given that the individual had at least a bachelor's degree. We obtain Table 11. Notice that the Employed row in Table 11 shows the results from Example 3.

	Table 11			
	Level of Education			
Employment Status	**Did Not Finish High School**	**High School Graduate**	**Some College**	**Bachelor's Degree or Higher**
Employed	$\dfrac{11,892}{27,541} = 0.432$	$\dfrac{36,702}{60,891} = 0.603$	$\dfrac{34,143}{49,011} = 0.697$	$\dfrac{41,649}{54,571} = 0.763$
Unemployed	$\dfrac{866}{27,541} = 0.031$	$\dfrac{1,798}{60,891} = 0.030$	$\dfrac{1,267}{49,011} = 0.026$	$\dfrac{863}{54,571} = 0.016$
Not in the labor force	$\dfrac{14,783}{27,541} = 0.537$	$\dfrac{22,391}{60,891} = 0.368$	$\dfrac{13,601}{49,011} = 0.278$	$\dfrac{12,059}{54,571} = 0.221$
Totals	1	1	1	1

Looking at the conditional distributions of employment status by level of education, associations become apparent. Read the information in Table 11 from left to right. As the amount of schooling increases, the proportion employed within each category also increases. As the amount of schooling increases, the proportion unemployed and the proportion not in the labor force decrease.

Information about individuals' levels of education provides some insight into their employment status. For example, suppose that we are asked to predict the number of employed individuals out of 100. We might predict that about 65 of the 100 are employed, because the employment rate for the entire United States is 64.8%. (See Table 10.) However, if we are given the additional information that all the 100 individuals had at least a bachelor's degree, we would increase our guess to about 76. Do you see why? The association between level of education and employment status allows us to adjust our predictions.

Now Work Problem 9(d)

We could also construct a conditional distribution of level of education by employment status. The procedure is the same, except the distribution uses the rows instead of the columns. In this case, the explanatory variable is employment status and the response variable is level of education.

As is usually the case, a graph can provide a powerful depiction of the data.

EXAMPLE 5   **Drawing a Bar Graph of a Conditional Distribution**

Problem: Using the results of Example 4, draw a bar graph that represents the conditional distribution of employment status by level of education.

Approach: We will draw three bars, side by side, for each employment status. The horizontal axis will represent the level of education and the vertical axis will represent the relative frequency.

Solution: Figure 27 contains the bar graph: The blue bars represent the proportion employed for each level of education, the green bars represent the proportion unemployed for each level of education, and the purple bars represent the proportion not in the labor force for each level of education.

Figure 27   **Employment Status by Level of Education**

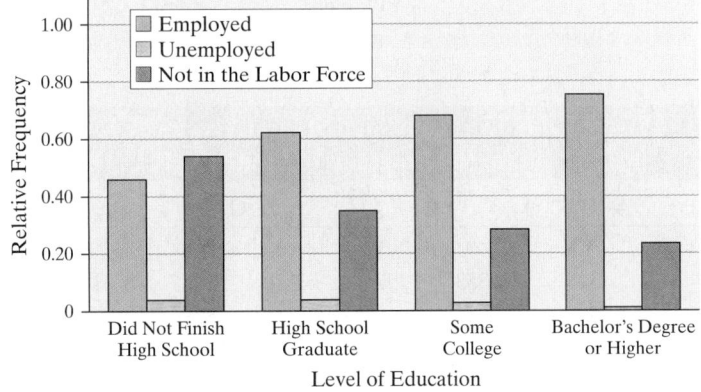

The graph contains the same information as that obtained from Table 11. The proportion employed increases as the level of education increases. We also see that the proportion of individuals unemployed or not in the labor force decreases as the level of education increases.

Now Work Problems 9(e) and (f)

The methods presented in this section for identifying the association between two categorical variables are different from the methods for measuring association between two quantitative variables. The measure of association in this section is based on whether there are differences in the relative frequencies of the response variable (employment status) for the different categories of the explanatory variable (level of education). If differences exist, we might attribute these differences to the explanatory variable.

In addition, because the data in Example 4 are observational, we do not make any statements regarding causation. Level of education is not said to be a cause of employment status, because a controlled experiment was not conducted. We do not make statements about causation when the data are observational.

3 Explain Simpson's Paradox

In Section 4.1 we discussed how a lurking variable can cause two quantitative variables to be correlated even though they are unrelated. This same phenomenon exists when exploring the relation between two qualitative variables.

EXAMPLE 6 **Gender Bias at the University of California, Berkeley**

Problem: The data in Table 12 show the admission status and gender of students who applied to the University of California, Berkeley. From the data in Table 12, the proportion of accepted applications is $\frac{1,748}{4,785} = 0.395$. The proportion of accepted men is $\frac{1,191}{2,950} = 0.460$ and the proportion of accepted women is $\frac{557}{1,835} = 0.304$. On the basis of these proportions, a gender bias suit was brought against the university. The university was shocked and claimed that program of study is a lurking variable that created the apparent association between admission status and gender. The university supplied Table 13 in its defense. Develop a conditional distribution by program of study to defend the university's admission policies.

Source: P. J. Bickel, E. A. Hammel, and J. W. O'Connell. "Sex Bias in Graduate Admissions: Data from Berkeley." *Science* 187(4175): 398–404, 1975.

Table 12			
	Accepted (A)	**Not Accepted (NA)**	**Total**
Men	1,191	1,399	**2,950**
Women	557	1,278	**1,835**
Total	**1,748**	**2,677**	**4,785**

Table 13   Admission Status (Accepted, A, or Not Accepted, NA), for Six Programs of Study (A, B, C, D, E, F) by Gender

	A		B		C		D		E		F	
	A	NA	A	NA	A	NA	A	NA	A	NA	A	NA
Men	511	314	353	207	120	205	138	279	53	138	16	256
	A	NA	A	NA	A	NA	A	NA	A	NA	A	NA
Women	89	19	17	8	202	391	131	244	94	299	24	317

Approach: We will determine the proportion of accepted men for each program of study and separately determine the proportion of accepted women for each program of study. If a significant difference between the proportions of men and women accepted within each program of study exists, we may have evidence of discrimination; otherwise, the university should be exonerated.

Solution: The proportion of men who applied to program A and were accepted is $\frac{511}{511 + 314} = 0.619$. The proportion of women who applied to program A and were accepted is $\frac{89}{89 + 19} = 0.824$. So, within program A, a higher proportion of women were accepted. Table 14 shows the conditional distribution for the remaining programs.

Table 14 Conditional Distribution of Applicants Admitted for Men and Women by Program of Admission						
	A	**B**	**C**	**D**	**E**	**F**
Men	$\dfrac{511}{825} = 0.619$	0.630	0.369	0.331	0.277	0.059
Women	0.824	0.680	0.341	0.349	0.239	0.070

Figure 28 shows the bar graph of the conditional distribution in Table 14. The blue bars represent the proportion of men admitted for each program; the green bars represent the proportion of women admitted for each program.

Figure 28

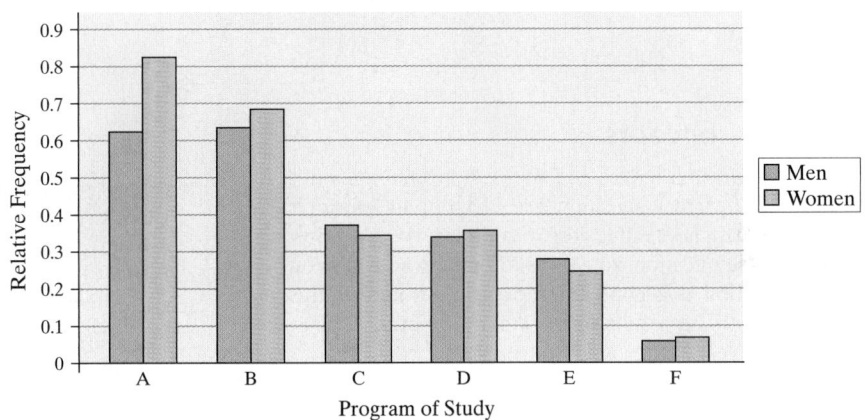

Notice that four out of the six programs actually had a higher proportion of women accepted! And the proportion of men accepted in programs C and E is not much higher than the proportion of women.

What causes the overall proportion of accepted men to be so much higher than the overall proportion of accepted women within the entire university, yet within each program the proportions differ very little and, in fact, may imply that women are accepted at a higher rate? The initial analysis did not account for the lurking variable, program of study. There were many more male applicants in programs A and B than female applicants, and these two programs happen to have higher acceptance rates. It is the higher acceptance rates in these programs that led to the false conclusion that the University of California, Berkeley, was biased against gender in its admissions.

In Example 6, the association between gender and admission reverses when the lurking variable program of study is accounted for in the analysis. This illustrates a phenomenon known as *Simpson's Paradox*. **Simpson's Paradox** represents a situation in which an association between two variables inverts or goes away when a third variable is introduced to the analysis. The results of Example 6 serve as a warning that any type of association between two variables may not be the result of an actual association, but rather the effect of some third variable that was not accounted for in the study.

Now Work Problem 13

4.4 ASSESS YOUR UNDERSTANDING

Concepts and Vocabulary

1. What is meant by a marginal distribution? What is meant by a conditional distribution?

2. Refer to Table 8. Is constructing a conditional distribution by level of education different from constructing a conditional distribution by employment status? If they are different, explain the difference.

3. Explain why we use the term *association* rather than *correlation* when describing the relation between two variables in this section.

4. Explain the idea behind Simpson's Paradox.

Skill Building

In Problems 5 and 6,

(a) *Construct a frequency marginal distribution.*
(b) *Construct a relative frequency marginal distribution.*
(c) *Construct a conditional distribution by x.*
(d) *Draw a bar graph of the conditional distribution found in part (c).*

5.

	x_1	x_2	x_3
y_1	20	25	30
y_2	30	25	50

6.

	x_1	x_2	x_3
y_1	35	25	20
y_2	65	75	80

Applying the Concepts

7. **Immigration** The immigration debate is raging among politicians. In an effort to gauge how the U.S. population feels about the issue, the Gallup organization surveyed adult Americans. One question asked was, "On the whole, do you think immigration is a good thing or a bad thing for this country today?" The results of the survey, by ethnicity, are given in the table.

	Non-Hispanic Whites	Blacks	Hispanics	Total
Good thing	180	154	144	478
Bad thing	107	101	33	241
Good and bad	9	14	12	35
No opinion	9	11	6	26
Total	305	280	195	780

Source: Based on the results of a Gallup poll conducted June 2007.

(a) How many adult Americans were surveyed? How many Hispanics were surveyed? 780; 195
(b) Construct a relative frequency marginal distribution.
(c) What proportion of adult Americans feel that immigration is a good thing for this country? 0.613
(d) Construct a conditional distribution of immigration opinion by ethnicity.
(e) Draw a bar graph of the conditional distribution found in part (d).
(f) Is ethnicity associated with opinion regarding immigration? If so, how? Yes

8. **Method of Delivery** Is there an association between method of delivery and ethnicity? The following data (in thousands) represent the method of delivery and ethnicity of mothers who had a baby in 2005.

	Non-Hispanic Whites	Blacks	Hispanics	Total
Vaginal	1,580	392	698	2,670
Cesarean	690	189	285	1,164
Total	2,270	581	983	3,834

Source: National Vital Statistics Report, 56(9), 2007.

(a) How many births were there in 2005? How many births had Hispanic mothers? 3,834 thousand; 983 thousand
(b) Construct a relative frequency marginal distribution.
(c) What proportion of births was vaginal in 2005? 0.696
(d) Construct a conditional distribution of method of delivery by ethnicity.
(e) Draw a bar graph of the conditional distribution found in part (d).
(f) Is ethnicity associated with method of delivery? If so, how No

9. **Party Affiliation** Is there an association between party affiliation and gender? The following data represent the gender and party affiliation of registered voters based on a random sample of 802 adults.

	Female	Male
Republican	105	115
Democrat	150	103
Independent	150	179

Source: Star Tribune Minnesota Poll

(a) Construct a frequency marginal distribution.
(b) Construct a relative frequency marginal distribution.
(c) What proportion of registered voters considers themselves to be Independent? 0.410
(d) Construct a conditional distribution of party affiliation by gender.
(e) Draw a bar graph of the conditional distribution found in part (d).
(f) Is gender associated with party affiliation? If so, how? Yes

10. **Feelings on Abortion** The Pew Research Center for the People and the Press conducted a poll in which it asked about the availability of abortion. The table is based on the results of the survey.

	High School or Less	Some College	College Graduate
Generally available	90	72	113
Allowed, but more limited	51	60	77
Illegal, with few exceptions	125	94	69
Never permitted	51	14	17

Source: Pew Research Center for the People and the Press

(a) Construct a frequency marginal distribution.
(b) Construct a relative frequency marginal distribution.
(c) What proportion of college graduates feel that abortion should never be permitted? 0.062
(d) Construct a conditional distribution of people's feelings about the availability of abortion by level of education.
(e) Draw a bar graph of the conditional distribution found in part (d).
(f) Is level of education associated with opinion on the availability of abortion? If so, how? Yes

11. **Health and Happiness** The General Social Survey asks questions about one's happiness and health. One would think that health plays a role in one's happiness. Use the data in the table to determine whether healthier people tend to also be happier.

	Poor	Fair	Good	Excellent	Total
Not too happy	696	1,386	1,629	732	4,443
Pretty happy	950	3,817	9,642	5,195	19,604
Very happy	350	1,382	4,520	5,095	11,347
Total	1,996	6,585	15,791	11,022	35,394

Source: General Social Survey

12. **Happy in Your Marriage?** The General Social Survey asks questions about one's happiness in marriage. Is there an association between gender and happiness in marriage? Use the data in the table to determine if gender is associated with happiness in marriage.

	Male	Female	Total
Very happy	7,609	7,942	15,551
Pretty happy	3,738	4,447	8,185
Not too happy	259	460	719
Total	11,606	12,849	24,455

Source: General Social Survey

13. **Smoking Is Healthy?** Could it be that smoking actually increases survival rates among women? The following data represent the NW 20-year survival status and smoking status of 1,314 English women who participated in a cohort study from 1972 to 1992.

	Smoking Status		Total
	Smoker (S)	Nonsmoker (NS)	
Dead	139	230	369
Alive	443	502	945
Total	582	732	1,314

Source: David R. Appleton et. al. "Ignoring a Covariate: An Example of Simpson's Paradox." *American Statistician* 50(4), 1996

(a) What proportion of the smokers was dead after 20 years? What proportion of the nonsmokers was dead after 20 years? What does this imply about the health consequences of smoking? *0.239; 0.314*

The data in the table do not take into account a variable that is strongly related to survival status, age. The data shown next give the survival status of women and their age at the beginning of the study. For example, 14 women who were 35 to 44 at the beginning of the study were smokers and dead after 20 years.

	Age Group													
	18–24		25–34		35–44		45–54		55–64		65–74		75 or older	
	S	NS	S	NS	S	NS	S	NS	S	NS	S	NS	S	NS
Dead	2	1	3	5	14	7	27	12	51	40	29	101	13	64
Alive	53	61	121	152	95	114	103	66	64	81	7	28	0	0

(b) Determine the proportion of 18- to 24-year-old smokers who were dead after 20 years. Determine the proportion of 18- to 24-year-old nonsmokers who were dead after 20 years. *0.036; 0.016*

(c) Repeat part (b) for the remaining age groups to create a conditional distribution of survival status by smoking status for each age group.

(d) Draw a bar graph of the conditional distribution from part (c).

(e) Write a short report detailing your findings.

14. **Treating Kidney Stones** Researchers conducted a study to determine which of two treatments, A or B, is more effective in the treatment of kidney stones. The results of their experiment are given in the table.

	Treatment A	Treatment B	Total
Effective	273	289	562
Not effective	77	61	138
Total	350	350	700

Source: C. R. Charig, D. R. Webb, S. R. Payne, and O. E. Wickham. "Comparison of Treatment Real Calculi by Operative Surgery, Precutaneous Nephrolithotomi, and Extracorporeal Shock Wave Lithoripsy." *British Medical Journal* 292(6524): 879–882.

(a) Which treatment appears to be more effective? Why?

The data in the table do not take into account the size of the kidney stone. The data shown next indicate the effectiveness of each treatment for both large and small kidney stones.

	Small Stones		Large Stones	
	A	B	A	B
Effective	81	234	273	55
Not effective	6	36	77	25

(b) Determine the proportion of small kidney stones that were effectively dealt with using treatment A. Determine the proportion of small kidney stones that were effectively dealt with using treatment B. *0.931; 0.867*

(c) Repeat part (b) for the large stones to create a conditional distribution of effectiveness by treatment for each stone size. *0.78; 0.688*

(d) Draw a bar graph of the conditional distribution from part (c).

(e) Write a short report detailing your findings.

CHAPTER 4 REVIEW

Summary

In this chapter we looked at describing the relation between two quantitative variables (Sections 4.1 to 4.3) and between two qualitative variables (Section 4.4).

The first step in describing the relation between two quantitative variables is to draw a scatter diagram. The explanatory variable is plotted on the horizontal axis and the corresponding response variable on the vertical axis. The scatter diagram can be used to discover whether the relation between the explanatory and the response variables is linear. In addition, for linear relations, we can judge whether the linear relation shows positive or negative association.

A numerical measure for the strength of linear relation between two quantitative variables is the linear correlation coefficient. It is a number between −1 and 1 inclusive. Values of the correlation coefficient near −1 are indicative of a negative linear relation between the two variables. Values of the correlation coefficient near +1 indicate a positive linear relation between the two variables. If the correlation coefficient is near 0, then little *linear* relation exists between the two variables.

Be careful! Just because the correlation coefficient between two quantitative variables indicates that the variables are linearly related, it does not mean that a change in one variable *causes* a change in a second variable. It could be that the correlation is the result of a lurking variable.

Once a linear relation between the two variables has been discovered, we describe the relation by finding the least-squares regression line. This line best describes the linear relation between the explanatory and response variables. We can use the least-squares regression line to predict a value of the response variable for a given value of the explanatory variable.

The coefficient of determination, R^2, measures the percent of variation in the response variable that is explained by the least-squares regression line. It is a measure between 0 and 1 inclusive. The closer R^2 is to 1, the more explanatory value the line has. Whenever a least-squares regression line is obtained, certain diagnostics must be performed. These include verifying that the linear model is appropriate, verifying the residuals have constant variance, and checking for outliers and influential observations.

Section 4.4 introduced methods that allow us to describe any association that might exist between two qualitative variables. This is done through contingency tables. Both marginal and conditional distributions allow us to describe the effect one variable might have on the other variable in the study. We also construct bar graphs to see the association between the two variables in the study. Again, just because two qualitative variables are associated does not mean that a change in one variable *causes* a change in a second variable. We also looked at Simpson's Paradox, which represents situations in which as association between two variables inverts or goes away when a third (lurking) variable is introduced into the analysis.

Vocabulary

Bivariate data (p. 192)
Response variable (p. 193)
Explanatory variable (p. 193)
Predictor variable (p. 193)
Scatter diagram (p. 193)
Positively associated (p. 194)
Negatively associated (p. 194)
Linear correlation coefficient (p. 195)
Correlation matrix (p. 199)
Lurking variable (p. 200)
Residuals (p. 211)

Least-squares regression line (p. 211)
Slope (p. 212)
y-intercept (p. 212)
Outside the scope of the model (p. 215)
Coefficient of determination (p. 224)
Deviation (p. 224)
Total deviation (p. 224)
Explained deviation (p. 224)
Unexplained deviation (p. 224)
Residual plot (p. 227)

Constant error variance (p. 228)
Outlier (p. 229)
Influential observation (p. 230)
Contingency (or two-way) table (p. 239)
Row variable (p. 239)
Column variable (p. 239)
Cell (p. 239)
Marginal distribution (p. 239)
Conditional distribution (p. 242)
Simpson's Paradox (p. 245)

Formulas

Correlation Coefficient

$$r = \frac{\sum \left(\dfrac{x_i - \bar{x}}{s_x} \right)\left(\dfrac{y_i - \bar{y}}{s_y} \right)}{n - 1}$$

Equation of the Least-Squares Regression Line

$$\hat{y} = b_1 x + b_0$$

where

$\hat{y}$ is the predicted value of the response variable

$b_1 = r \cdot \dfrac{s_y}{s_x}$ is the slope of the least-squares regression line

$b_0 = \bar{y} - b_1\bar{x}$ is the y-intercept of the least-squares regression line

Coefficient of Determination, R^2

$$R^2 = \frac{\text{explained variation}}{\text{total variation}}$$

$$= 1 - \frac{\text{unexplained variation}}{\text{total variation}}$$

$$= r^2 \text{ for the least-squares regression model } \hat{y} = b_1 x + b_0$$

Objectives

Section	You should be able to . . .	Example	Review Exercises
4.1	1 Draw and interpret scatter diagrams (p. 193)	1, 3	1(b), 2(a), 5(a), 12(a)
	2 Describe the properties of the linear correlation coefficient (p. 195)	page 196	17
	3 Compute and interpret the linear correlation coefficient (p. 197)	2, 3	1(c), 2(b), 12(b)
	4 Determine whether a linear relation exists between two variables (p. 200)	4	1(d), 2(c)
	5 Explain the difference between correlation and causation (p. 200)	5	13, 16
4.2	1 Find the least-squares regression line and use the line to make predictions (p. 211)	2, 3	3(a), 3(d), 4(a), 4(c), 5(d), 11(a), 12(c), 18(c)
	2 Interpret the slope and y-intercept of the least-squares regression line (p. 214)	page 215	3(c), 4(b), 18(b)
	3 Compute the sum of squared residuals (p. 216)	4	5(f), 5(g)
4.3	1 Compute and interpret the coefficient of determination (p. 223)	1, 2	9(a), 10(a)
	2 Perform residual analysis on a regression model (p. 227)	3–6	6–8, 9(b) and (c), 10(b) and (c), 12(d) and (e), 18(d)
	3 Identify influential observations (p. 230)	7	9(d), 9(e), 10(d), 11(b), 18(e)
4.4	1 Compute the marginal distribution of a variable (p. 239)	1 and 2	14(b)
	2 Use the conditional distribution to identify association among categorical data (p. 241)	3–5	14(d), 14(e), 14(f)
	3 Explain Simpson's Paradox (p. 244)	6	15

Review Exercises

1. **Fat and Calories in Cheeseburgers** A nutritionist was interested in developing a model that describes the relation between the amount of fat (in grams) in cheeseburgers at fast-food restaurants and the number of calories. She obtains the following data from the websites of the companies.

Sandwich (Restaurant)	Fat Content (g)	Calories
Quarter-pound Single with Cheese (Wendy's)	20	430
Whataburger (Whataburger)	39	750
Cheeseburger (In-n-Out)	27	480
Big Mac (McDonald's)	29	540
Quarter-pounder with cheese (McDonald's)	26	510
Whopper with cheese (Burger King)	47	760
Jumbo Jack (Jack in the Box)	35	690
Double Steakburger with cheese (Steak 'n Shake)	38	632

Source: Each company's Web site

(a) The researcher wants to use fat content to predict calories. Which is the explanatory variable?   Fat content
(b) Draw a scatter diagram of the data.
(c) Compute the linear correlation coefficient between fat content and calories.   0.944
(d) Does a linear relation exist between fat content and calories in fast-food restaurant sandwiches?   Yes

2. **Apartments** The following data represent the square footage and rent for apartments in the borough of Queens and Nassau County, New York.

2. (b) Queens: 0.909; Nassau: 0.867

Queens (New York City)		Nassau County (Long Island)	
Square Footage, x	Rent per Month, y	Square Footage, x	Rent per Month, y
500	650	1,100	1,875
588	1,215	588	1,075
1,000	2,000	1,250	1,775
688	1,655	556	1,050
825	1,250	825	1,300
460	1,805	743	1,475
1,259	2,700	660	1,315
650	1,200	975	1,400
560	1,250	1,429	1,900
1,073	2,350	800	1,650
1,452	3,300	1,906	4,625
1,305	3,100	1,077	1,395

Source: apartments.com

(a) On the same graph, draw a scatter diagram for both Queens and Nassau County apartments treating square footage as the explanatory variable. Be sure to use a different plotting symbol for each group.
(b) Compute the linear correlation coefficient between square footage and rent for each location.
(c) Does a linear relation exist between the two variables for each location?   Yes
(d) Does location appear to be a factor in rent?

3. Using the data and results from Problem 1, do the following:
(a) Find the least-squares regression line treating fat content as the explanatory variable. $\hat{y} = 13.7334x + 150.9469$
(b) Draw the least-squares regression line on the scatter diagram.

(c) Interpret the slope and y-intercept, if appropriate.

(d) Predict the number of calories in a sandwich that has 30 grams of fat. *562.9 calories*

(e) A cheeseburger from Sonic has 700 calories and 42 grams of fat. Is the number of calories for this sandwich above or below average among all sandwiches with 42 grams? *Below*

4. Using the Queens data and results from Problem 2, do the following:

(a) Find the least-squares regression line, treating square footage as the explanatory variable. $\hat{y} = 2.2091x - 34.3148$

(b) Interpret the slope and y-intercept, if appropriate.

(c) Is the rent on the 825-square-foot apartment in the data above or below average among 825-square-foot apartments? *Below*

5.

x	10	14	17	18	21
y	105	94	82	76	63

(a) Draw a scatter diagram treating x as the explanatory variable and y as the response variable.

(b) Select two points from the scatter diagram, and find the equation of the line containing the points selected.

(c) Graph the line found in part (b) on the scatter diagram.

(d) Determine the least-squares regression line.

(e) Graph the least-squares regression line on the scatter diagram.

(f) Compute the sum of the squared residuals for the line found in part (b). *5.(d) $\hat{y} = -3.8429x + 145.4857$*

(g) Compute the sum of the squared residuals for the least-squares regression line found in part (d). *16.271*

(h) Comment on the fit of the line found in part (b) versus the least-squares regression line found in part (d).

In Problems 6–8, a residual plot is given. From the residual plot, determine whether or not a linear model is appropriate. If not, state your reason.

6. Yes

7. No

8. No

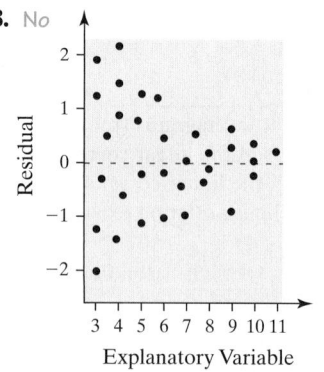

9. Use the results from Problems 1 and 3 for the following:

(a) Compute and interpret R^2. *89.1%*

(b) Plot the residuals against fat content.

(c) Based on the residual plot drawn in part (b), is a linear model appropriate for describing the relation between fat content and calories? *Yes*

(d) Are there any outliers or influential observations? *No*

(e) Suppose a White Castle cheeseburger (affectionately known as a slyder) is added to the data set. Slyders have 9 grams of fat and 80 calories. Is this observation an outlier or influential? *Outlier and influential*

10. Use Queens data and the results from Problems 2 and 4 for the following:

(a) Compute and interpret R^2. *82.7%*

(b) Plot the residuals against square footage.

(c) For the graph obtained in part (b), is a linear model appropriate? *Yes*

(d) Are there any outliers or influential observations? *Yes*

11. **Apartment Rents** Using the Nassau County apartment rent data and the results of Problem 2, do the following:

(a) Find the least-squares regression line treating square footage as the explanatory variable.

(b) Are there any outliers or influential observations? *Yes*

12. **Depreciation** The following data represent the price of a random sample of used Chevy Camaros, by age.

Age, x (years)	Price, y (dollars)	Age, x (years)	Price, y (dollars)
2	15,900	1	20,365
5	10,988	2	16,463
2	16,980	6	10,824
5	9,995	1	19,995
4	11,995	1	18,650
5	10,995	4	10,488

Source: www.onlineauto.com

(a) Draw a scatter diagram treating the age of the car as the explanatory variable and price as the response variable.

(b) Find the correlation coefficient between age and price. Based on the correlation coefficient, is there a linear relation between age and price? *−0.954*

(c) Find the least-squares regression line treating age as the explanatory variable. $\hat{y} = -2054.6460x + 20,976.2124$

(d) Plot the residuals against the age of the car.

(e) Do you think that a linear model is appropriate for describing the relation between the age of the car and price? Why? *No*

11. (a) $\hat{y} = 2.0995x - 347.3641$

13. **Shark Attacks** The correlation between the number of visitors in the state of Florida and the number of shark attacks since 1990 is 0.946. Should the number of visitors to Florida be reduced in an attempt to reduce shark attacks? Explain your reasoning.

    Source: Florida Museum of Natural History

14. **New versus Used Car Satisfaction** Are you more likely to be satisfied with your automobile purchase when it is new or used? The following data represent the level of satisfaction of the buyer for both new and used cars.

	New	Used	Total
Not too satisfied	11	25	36
Pretty satisfied	78	79	157
Extremely satisfied	118	85	203
Total	207	189	396

    Source: General Social Survey

    (a) How many were extremely satisfied with their automobile purchase? *203*
    (b) Construct a relative frequency marginal distribution.
    (c) What proportion of consumers was extremely satisfied with their automobile purchase? *0.513*
    (d) Construct a conditional distribution of satisfaction by purchase type (new or used).
    (e) Draw a bar graph of the conditional distribution found in part (d).
    (f) Do you think that the purchase type (new versus used) is associated with satisfaction? *Yes*

15. **An Unhealthy Hospital** The following contingency table relates the number of patients admitted for surgery to Palos Community Hospital (PCH) and General Hospital (GH) along with their survival status for the month of July.

	PCH	GH
Survived	150	230
Died	20	55

    15. (b) PCH: 0.118; GH: 0.193
    (a) Construct a conditional distribution of survival status by hospital.
    (b) What proportion of surgeries at PCH resulted in death? What proportion of surgeries at GH resulted in death?
    (c) What might you conclude about GH?

    A lurking variable is the type of hospital. General Hospital is a trauma center, so emergency or high-risk patients (such as gunshot wounds) are directed to GH. Palos Community Hospital typically does planned procedures. The following table shows survival by type of surgical procedure.

	Planned		Emergency	
	PCH	GH	PCH	GH
Survived	138	160	12	70
Died	12	13	8	42

    (d) What proportion of planned surgeries at PCH had patients that survived? What proportion of planned surgeries at GH had patients that survived? *0.92; 0.925*

    (e) What proportion of emergency surgeries at PCH had patients that survived? What proportion of emergency surgeries at GH had patients that survived? *0.6; 0.625*
    (f) Notice that for both the planned and emergency surgeries a higher proportion of survivors were at GH, yet for all surgeries PCH has a higher proportion of survivors! When the lurking variable "type of surgery" is considered, the apparent superiority of Palos Community Hospital goes away. Explain carefully how the bias disappears when the type of surgery is considered.

16. (a) The correlation between number of married residents and number of unemployed residents in 2006 for the 50 states is 0.865. A scatter diagram of the data drawn in MINITAB is shown. What type of relation appears to exist between number of marriages and number unemployed?

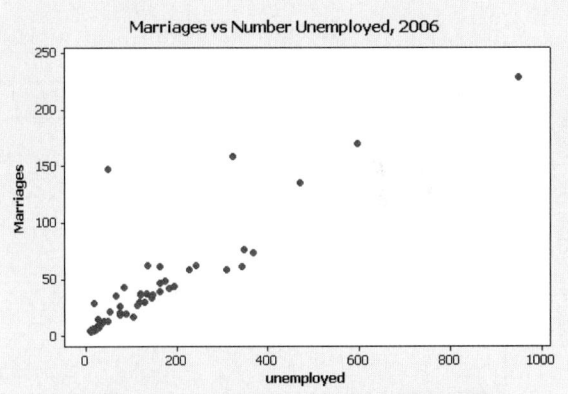

    (b) A lurking variable is in the relation presented in part (a). Use the following correlation matrix to explain how population is a lurking variable.

    Correlations: Unemployed, Population, Marriages

	Unemployed	Population
Population	0.985	
Marriages	0.865	0.899

    Cell Contents: Pearson correlation

    (c) The correlation between unemployment rate (number unemployed divided by population size) and marriage rate (number married divided by population size) in 2006 for the 50 states is −0.200. A scatter diagram between unemployment rate and marriage rate drawn in MINITAB is shown next. What type of relation appears to exist between unemployment rate and marriage rate?

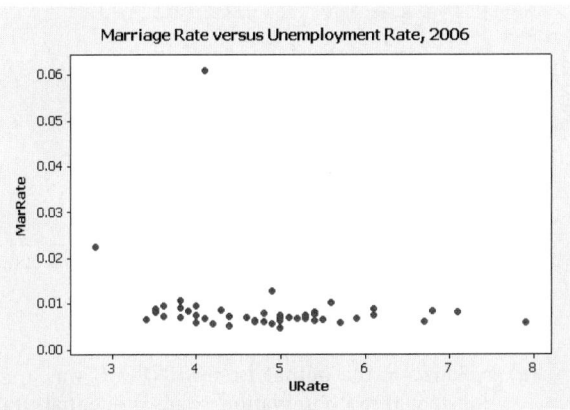

(d) Write a few sentences to explain the danger in using correlation to conclude that a relation exists between two variables without considering lurking variables.

17. List the eight properties of the linear correlation coefficient.

18. **Analyzing a Newspaper Article** In a newspaper article written in the *Chicago Tribune* on September 29, 2002, it was claimed that poorer school districts have shorter school days.

    (a) The following scatter diagram was drawn using the data supplied in the article. In this scatter diagram, the response variable is length of the school day (in hours) and the explanatory variable is percent of the population that is low income. The correlation between length and income is −0.461. Do you think that the scatter diagram and correlation coefficient support the position of the article?

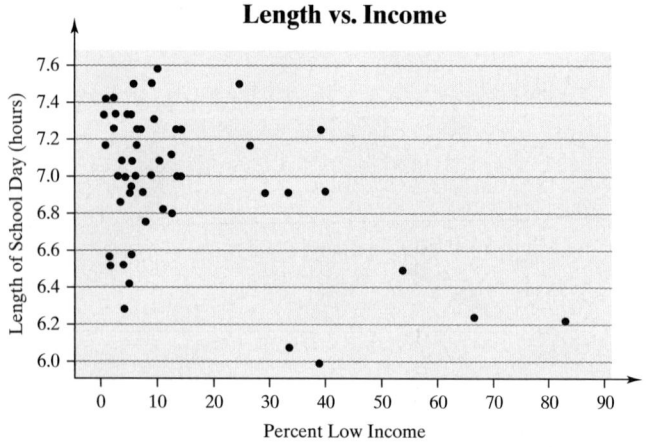

Length vs. Income

18. (c) 6.91 hours

    (b) The least-squares regression line between length, *y*, and income, *x*, is $\hat{y} = -0.0102x + 7.11$. Interpret the slope of this regression line. Does it make sense to interpret the *y*-intercept? If so, interpret the *y*-intercept.
    (c) Predict the length of the school day for a district in which 20% of the population is low income by letting $x = 20$.
    (d) Based on the following residual plot, do you think a linear model is appropriate for describing the relation between length of school day and income? Why?

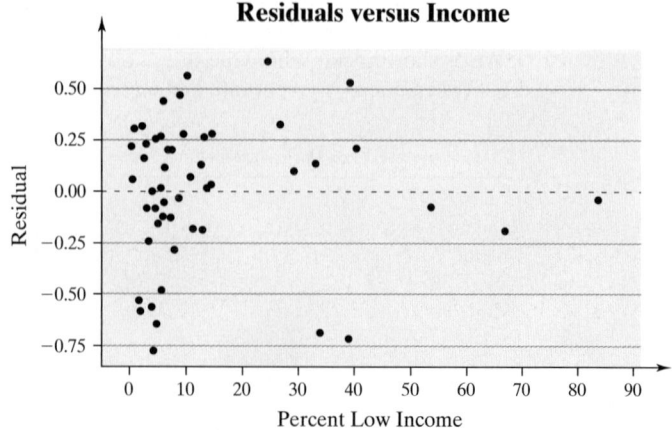

Residuals versus Income

    (e) Included in the output from MINITAB was a notification that three observations were influential. Based on

the scatter diagram in part (a), which three observations do you think might be influential?

    (f) We should not remove influential observations just because they are influential. What suggestions would you make to the author of the article to improve the study and therefore give more credibility to the conclusions?
    (g) This same article included average Prairie State Achievement Examination (PSAE) scores for each district. The article implied that shorter school days result in lower PSAE scores. The correlation between PSAE score and length of school day is 0.517. A scatter diagram treating PSAE as the response variable is shown next. Do you believe that a longer school day is positively associated with a higher PSAE score?

PSAE vs Length

    (h) The correlation between percentage of the population that is low income and PSAE score is −0.720. A scatter diagram treating PSAE score as the response variable is shown below. Do you believe that percentage of the population that is low income is negatively associated with PSAE score?

PSAE vs Income

    (i) Can you think of any lurking variables that are playing a role in this study?

CHAPTER TEST

1. Crickets make a chirping noise by sliding their wings rapidly over each other. Perhaps you have noticed that the number of chirps seems to increase with the temperature. The following data list the temperature (in degrees Fahrenheit) and the number of chirps per second for the striped ground cricket.

Temperature, x	Chirps per Second, y	Temperature, x	Chirps per Second, y
88.6	20.0	71.6	16.0
93.3	19.8	84.3	18.4
80.6	17.1	75.2	15.5
69.7	14.7	82.0	17.1
69.4	15.4	83.3	16.2
79.6	15.0	82.6	17.2
80.6	16.0	83.5	17.0
76.3	14.4		

Source: George W. Pierce. *The Songs of Insects*. Cambridge, MA: Harvard University Press, 1949, pp. 12–21.

(a) What is the likely explanatory variable in these data? Why? Temperature
(b) Draw a scatter diagram of the data.
(c) Compute the linear correlation coefficient between temperature and chirps per second.   0.835
(d) Does a linear relation exist between temperature and chirps per second? Yes
(e) Find the least-squares regression line treating temperature as the explanatory variable and chirps per second as the response variable. $\hat{y} = 0.2119x - 0.3091$
(f) Interpret the slope and y-intercept, if appropriate.
(g) Predict the chirps per second if it is 83.3°F.   17.3
(h) A cricket chirps 15 times per second when the temperature is 82°F. Is this rate of chirping above or below average at this temperature? Below
(i) It is 55°F outside. Would you recommend using the linear model found in part (e) to predict the number of chirps per second of a cricket? Why or why not? No
(j) Compute and interpret R^2. 69.7%
(k) A plot of residuals against temperature is shown next. Based on the residual plot, do you think a linear model is appropriate for describing the relation between temperature and chirps per second? Yes

Residuals versus Temperature

2. A cricket chirps 14.5 times per second when it is 92°F outside. Is this observation influential? Why? Yes

3. The following data represent the speed of a car (in miles per hour) and its braking distance (feet) on dry asphalt. Is the relation between speed and braking distance linear? Why? No

Speed (mph)	Braking Distance (ft)
30	48
40	79
50	123
60	184
70	243
80	315

4. A researcher collects data regarding the percent of all births to unmarried women and the number of violent crimes for the 50 states and Washington, DC. The scatter diagram along with the least-squares regression line obtained from MINITAB is shown. The correlation between percent of births to unmarried women and the number of violent crimes is 0.667. A politician looks over the data and claims that, for each 1% decrease in births to single mothers, violent crimes will decrease by 23. Therefore, percent of births to single mothers needs to be reduced in an effort to decrease violent crimes. Explain his faulty reasoning to the politician.

5. What is the relationship between education and belief in Heaven? The following data represent the highest level of education and belief in Heaven for a random sample of adult Americans.
(a) Construct a relative frequency marginal distribution.

	Yes, Definitely	Yes, Probably	No, Probably Not	No, Definitely Not	Total
Less than high school	316	66	21	9	**412**
High school	956	296	122	65	**1,439**
Bachelor's	267	131	62	64	**524**
Total	**1,539**	**493**	**205**	**138**	**2,375**

Source: General Social Survey

(b) What proportion of adult Americans in the survey definitely believe in Heaven? 0.648

(c) Construct a conditional distribution of belief in Heaven by level of education.

(d) Draw a bar graph of the conditional distribution found in part (c).

(e) Is there an association between level of education and belief in Heaven? Yes

6. Consider the following contingency table, which relates the number of applicants accepted to a college.

	Accepted	Denied
Male	98	522
Female	90	200

(a) Construct a conditional distribution of acceptance status by gender.

(b) What proportion of males was accepted? What proportion of females was accepted? 0.158; 0.310

(c) What might you conclude about the admittance policies of the school?

A lurking variable is the type of school applied to. This particular college has two programs of study: business and social work. The following table shows applications by type of school.

	Business School		Social Work School	
	Accepted	Denied	Accepted	Denied
Male	90	510	8	12
Female	10	60	80	140

(d) What proportion of males who applied to the business school was accepted? What proportion of females who applied to the business school was accepted? 0.15; 0.143

(e) What proportion of males who applied to the social work school was accepted? What proportion of females who applied to the social work school was accepted? 0.4; 0.364

(f) Explain carefully how the bias disappears when type of school is considered.

7. What would you say about a set of quantitative bivariate data whose linear correlation coefficient is −1? What would a scatter diagram of the data look like?

8. If the slope of a least-squares regression line is negative, what could be said about the correlation between the explanatory and response variable? Negative

9. What does it mean if a linear correlation coefficient is close to zero? No linear relation

MAKING AN INFORMED DECISION

What Car Should I Buy?

You are still in the market to buy a car. As we all know, cars lose value over time. Therefore, another item to consider when purchasing a car is its depreciation rate. The higher the depreciation rate is, the more value the car loses each year. Using the same three cars that you used in the Chapter 3 Decision, answer the following questions to determine depreciation rate.

1. Collect information regarding the three cars in your list by finding at least 12 cars of each car model that are for sale. Obtain the asking price and age of the car. Sources of data include your local newspaper classified ads or car websites, such as www.cars.com and www.vehix.com.

2. For each car type, draw a scatter diagram, treating age of the car as the explanatory variable and asking price as the response variable. Does the relation between the two variables appear linear?

3. The asking price of a car and the age of a car are related through the exponential equation $y = ab^x$, where y is the price of the car and x is the age of the car. The depreciation rate is $1 - b$. To estimate the values of a and b using least-squares regression, we need to transform the equation into a linear equation. This is accomplished by computing the logarithm of the asking price. For example, if the asking price of a car is $8,000, compute $\log(8,000) = 3.9031$. Compute the logarithm of each asking price for each car.

4. For each car model, draw a scatter diagram treating age of the car as the explanatory variable and the logarithm of asking price as the response variable. Does the relation between age and the logarithm of asking price appear to be linear?

5. For each car model, find the least-squares regression line treating age of the car as the explanatory variable and the logarithm of asking price as the response variable. The line will be

$$Y = \log a + (\log b) x = A + Bx$$

6. To determine a and b for the exponential equation $y = ab^x$, let $a = 10^A$ and $b = 10^B$. Graph the exponential equation on each scatter diagram from question 2.

7. For each exponential equation determined in question 6, the depreciation rate is $1 - b$. What are the depreciation rates for the three cars considered? Will this result affect your decision about which car to buy?

CASE STUDY

In 1798, Thomas Malthus published *An Essay on the Principle of Population* in which he stated

> Population, when unchecked, increases in a geometrical ratio. Subsistence increases only in an arithmetical ratio. A slight acquaintance with numbers will show the immensity of the first power in comparison of the second.

What did he mean by this? Essentially he is claiming that population grows exponentially and food production increases linearly. The assumption is that the population grows unchecked. That is, without interference from human-caused or natural disasters such as war, famine, disease, and so on. Malthus also stated,

> By that law of our nature which makes food necessary to the life of man, the effects of these two unequal powers must be kept equal. This implies a strong and constantly operating check on population from the difficulty of subsistence. This difficulty must fall somewhere and must necessarily be severely felt by a large portion of mankind.

(a) Read the article *Food, Land, Population, and the American Economy* from Carrying Capacity Network. (*Source*: www.carryingcapacity.org/resources.html)

(b) Use the historic census data from the U.S. Census Bureau at www.census.gov for the United States for the years 1790 to present to find an exponential model of the form $P = a \cdot b^t$, where t is the number of years after 1790. To do this, first take the logarithm of P. Now find the least-squares regression line between $\log P$ and t. The least-squares model is of the form $\log P = \log a + t \log b$. To find estimates of a and b, compute $10^{\log a}$, where $\log a$ is the intercept and $10^{\log b}$ is the slope of the least-squares regression line. The quantity $b - 1$ is the growth rate as a decimal. For example, if $b = 1.01$, then the annual growth rate is $1.01 - 1 = 0.01$ or 1%.

(c) Multiply your model obtained in part (b) by 1.2 to obtain a function for the number of arable acres of land A required to have a diverse diet in the United States (as a function of time). [*Hint*: The model is $A = 1.2P$].

(d) Go the *Statistical Abstract of the United States* and look up the number of acres of farmland A in the United States for the most recent 9 years for which data are available. Find the least-squares regression line treating year as the explanatory variable.

(e) Determine when the United States will no longer be capable of providing a diverse diet for its entire population by setting the model in part (c) equal to the model in part (d) and solving for the year t.

(f) Does this result seem reasonable? Discuss some reasons why this prediction might be affected or changed. For example, rather than looking at the number of arable acres of land required to have a diverse diet, consider total food production. Compare the results using this variable as a measure of subsistence.

PART 3

Probability and Probability Distributions

CHAPTER 5
Probability

CHAPTER 6
Discrete Probability Distributions

CHAPTER 7
The Normal Probability Distribution

We now take a break from the statistical process. Why? In Chapter 1, we mentioned that inferential statistics uses methods that generalize results obtained from a sample to the population and measures their reliability. But how can we measure their reliability? It turns out that the methods we use to generalize results from a sample to a population are based on probability and probability models. Probability is a measure of the likelihood that something occurs. This part of the course will focus on methods for determining probabilities.

5 Probability

Outline

5.1 Probability Rules

5.2 The Addition Rule and Complements

5.3 Independence and the Multiplication Rule

5.4 Conditional Probability and the General Multiplication Rule

5.5 Counting Techniques

5.6 Putting It Together: Which Method Do I Use?

5.7 Bayes's Rule (on CD)

MAKING AN INFORMED DECISION

Have you ever watched a sporting event on television in which the announcer cites an obscure statistic? Where do these numbers come from? Well, pretend that you are the statistician for your favorite sports team. Your job is to compile strange or obscure probabilities regarding your favorite team and a competing team. See the Decisions project on page 326.

PUTTING IT TOGETHER

In Chapter 1, we learned the methods of collecting data. In Chapters 2 through 4, we learned how to summarize raw data using tables, graphs, and numbers. As far as the statistical process goes, we have discussed the collecting, organizing, and summarizing parts of the process.

Before we can proceed with the analysis of data, we introduce probability, which forms the basis of inferential statistics. Why? Well, we can think of the probability of an outcome as the likelihood of observing that outcome. If something has a high likelihood of happening, it has a high probability (close to 1). If something has a small chance of happening, it has a low probability (close to 0). For example, in rolling a single die, it is unlikely that we would roll five straight sixes, so this result has a low probability. In fact, the probability of rolling five straight sixes is 0.0001286. So, if we were playing a game that entailed throwing a single die, and one of the players threw five sixes in a row, we would consider the player to be lucky (or a cheater) because it is such an unusual occurrence. Statisticians use probability in the same way. If something occurs that has a low probability, we investigate to find out "what's up."

5.1 PROBABILITY RULES

Preparing for This Section Before getting started, review the following:

- Relative frequency (Section 2.1, p. 68)

Objectives	
1	Apply the rules of probabilities
2	Compute and interpret probabilities using the empirical method
3	Compute and interpret probabilities using the classical method
4	Use simulation to obtain data based on probabilities
5	Recognize and interpret subjective probabilities

Note to Instructor

If you like, you can print out and distribute the Preparing for This Section quiz located in the Instructor's Resource Center. The purpose of the quiz is to verify that the students have the prerequisite knowledge for the section.

Note to Instructor

Probabilities can be expressed as fractions, decimals, or percents. You may want to give a brief review of how to convert from one form to the other.

Probability is a measure of the likelihood of a random phenomenon or chance behavior. Probability describes the long-term proportion with which a certain **outcome** will occur in situations with short-term uncertainty.

The long-term predictability of chance behavior is best understood through a simple experiment. Flip a coin 100 times and compute the proportion of heads observed after each toss of the coin. Suppose the first flip is tails, so the proportion of heads is $\frac{0}{1}$; the second flip is heads, so the proportion of heads is $\frac{1}{2}$; the third flip is heads, so the proportion of heads is $\frac{2}{3}$; and so on. Plot the proportion of heads versus the number of flips and obtain the graph in Figure 1(a). We repeat this experiment with the results shown in Figure 1(b).

Figure 1

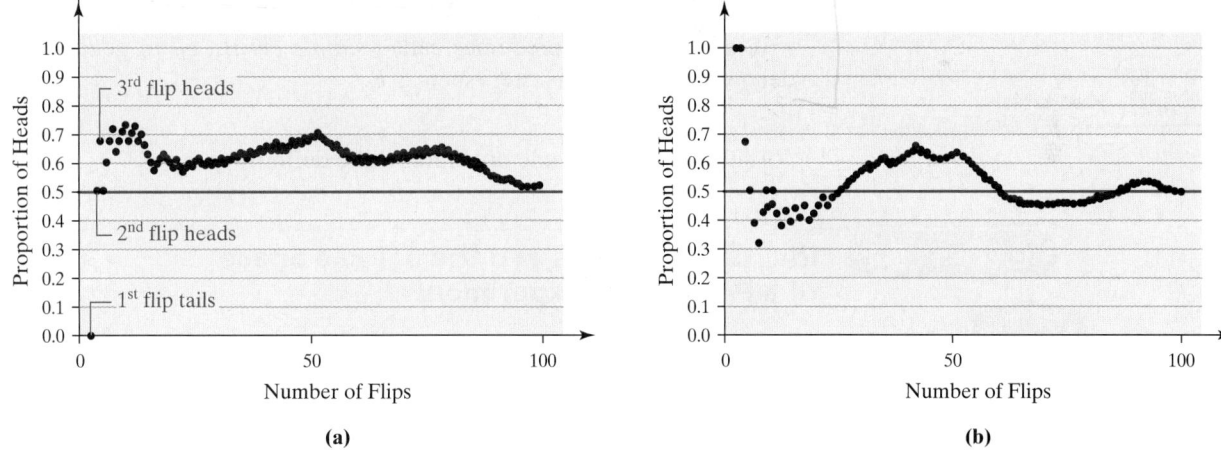

(a)   (b)

In Other Words

Probability describes how likely it is that some event will happen. If we look at the proportion of times an event has occurred over a long period of time (or over a large number of trials), we can be more certain of the likelihood of its occurrence.

Looking at the graphs in Figures 1(a) and (b), we notice that in the short term (fewer flips of the coin) the observed proportion of heads is different and unpredictable for each experiment. As the number of flips of the coin increases, however, both graphs tend toward a proportion of 0.5. This is the basic premise of probability. Probability deals with experiments that yield random short-term results or **outcomes** yet reveal long-term predictability. **The long-term proportion with which a certain outcome is observed is the probability of that outcome.** So we say that the probability of observing a head is $\frac{1}{2}$ or 50% or 0.5 because, as we flip the coin more times, the proportion of heads tends toward $\frac{1}{2}$. This phenomenon is referred to as the *Law of Large Numbers*.

> **The Law of Large Numbers**
>
> As the number of repetitions of a probability experiment increases, the proportion with which a certain outcome is observed gets closer to the probability of the outcome.

Note to Instructor
In-class activity: Have each student flip a
coin three times. Use the results to find
the probability of a head. Repeat this
experiment a few times. Use the cumulative results to illustrate the Law of Large
Numbers. You may also want to use the
probability applet to demonstrate the
Law of Large Numbers. See Problem 57.

The Law of Large Numbers is illustrated in Figure 1. For a few flips of the coin, the proportion of heads fluctuates wildly around 0.5, but as the number of flips increases, the proportion of heads settles down near 0.5. Jakob Bernoulli (a major contributor to the field of probability) believed that the Law of Large Numbers was common sense. This is evident in the following quote from his text *Ars Conjectandi*: "For even the most stupid of men, by some instinct of nature, by himself and without any instruction, is convinced that the more observations have been made, the less danger there is of wandering from one's goal."

In probability, an **experiment** is any process with uncertain results that can be repeated. The result of any single trial of the experiment is not known ahead of time. However, the results of the experiment over many trials produce regular patterns that enable us to predict with remarkable accuracy. For example, an insurance company cannot know ahead of time whether a particular 16-year-old driver will be involved in an accident over the course of a year. However, based on historical records, the company can be fairly certain that about three out of every ten 16-year-old male drivers will be involved in a traffic accident during the course of a year. Therefore, of the 816,000 male 16-year-old drivers (816,000 repetitions of the experiment), the insurance company is fairly confident that about 30%, or 244,800, of the drivers will be involved in an accident. This prediction forms the basis for establishing insurance rates for any particular 16-year-old male driver.

We now introduce some terminology that we will need to study probability.

Definitions

The **sample space, S,** of a probability experiment is the collection of all possible outcomes.

In Other Words
An outcome is the result of one trial of a probability experiment. The sample space is a list of all possible results of a probability experiment.

An **event** is any collection of outcomes from a probability experiment. An event may consist of one outcome or more than one outcome. We will denote events with one outcome, sometimes called *simple events*, e_i. In general, events are denoted using capital letters such as E.

The following example illustrates these definitions.

EXAMPLE 1

A *fair die* is one in which each possible outcome is equally likely. For example, rolling a 2 is just as likely as rolling a 5. We contrast this with a *loaded* die, in which a certain outcome is more likely. For example, if rolling a 1 is more likely than rolling a 2, 3, 4, 5, or 6, the die is loaded.

Identifying Events and the Sample Space of a Probability Experiment

Problem: A probability experiment consists of rolling a single *fair* die.
(a) Identify the outcomes of the probability experiment.
(b) Determine the sample space.
(c) Define the event E = "roll an even number."

Approach: The outcomes are the possible results of the experiment. The sample space is a list of all possible outcomes.

Solution
(a) The outcomes from rolling a single fair die are e_1 = "rolling a one" = $\{1\}$, e_2 = "rolling a two" = $\{2\}$, e_3 = "rolling a three" = $\{3\}$, e_4 = "rolling a four" = $\{4\}$, e_5 = "rolling a five" = $\{5\}$, and e_6 = "rolling a six" = $\{6\}$.

(b) The set of all possible outcomes forms the sample space, S = $\{1, 2, 3, 4, 5, 6\}$. There are 6 outcomes in the sample space.

(c) The event E = "roll an even number" = $\{2, 4, 6\}$.

Now Work Problem 23

1 Apply the Rules of Probabilities

Probabilities have some rules that must be satisfied. In these rules, the notation $P(E)$ means "the probability that event E occurs."

In Other Words
Rule 1 states that probabilities less than
0 or greater than 1 are not possible.
Therefore, probabilities such as 1.32 or
−0.3 are not possible. Rule 2 states
when the probabilities of all outcomes
are added, the sum must be 1.

Rules of Probabilities

1. The probability of any event E, $P(E)$, must be greater than or equal to 0 and less than or equal to 1. That is, $0 \leq P(E) \leq 1$.

2. The sum of the probabilities of all outcomes must equal 1. That is, if the sample space $S = \{e_1, e_2, \ldots, e_n\}$, then

$$P(e_1) + P(e_2) + \cdots + P(e_n) = 1$$

A **probability model** lists the possible outcomes of a probability experiment and each outcome's probability. A probability model must satisfy rules 1 and 2 of the rules of probabilities.

EXAMPLE 2   **A Probability Model**

Table 1

Color	Probability
Brown	0.13
Yellow	0.14
Red	0.13
Blue	0.24
Orange	0.20
Green	0.16

Source: M&Ms

In a bag of plain M&M milk chocolate candies, the colors of the candies can be brown, yellow, red, blue, orange, or green. Suppose that a candy is randomly selected from a bag. Table 1 shows each color and the probability of drawing that color.

To verify that this is a probability model, we must show that rules 1 and 2 of the rules of probabilities are satisfied.

Each probability is greater than or equal to 0 and less than or equal to 1, so rule 1 is satisfied.

Because

$$0.13 + 0.14 + 0.13 + 0.24 + 0.20 + 0.16 = 1$$

rule 2 is also satisfied. The table is an example of a probability model.

Now Work Problem 11

Note to Instructor
The interpretation of probability given here is important to emphasize. We will use this interpretation again when we discuss confidence intervals.

If an event is **impossible**, the probability of the event is 0. If an event is a **certainty**, the probability of the event is 1.

The closer a probability is to 1, the more likely the event will occur. The closer a probability is to 0, the less likely the event will occur. For example, an event with probability 0.8 is more likely to occur than an event with probability 0.75. An event with probability 0.8 will occur about 80 times out of 100 repetitions of the experiment, whereas an event with probability 0.75 will occur about 75 times out of 100.

Be careful of this interpretation. Just because an event has a probability of 0.75 does not mean that the event *must* occur 75 times out of 100. It means that we *expect* the number of occurrences to be close to 75 in 100 trials of the experiment. The more repetitions of the probability experiment, the closer the proportion with which the event occurs will be to 0.75 (the Law of Large Numbers).

One goal of this course is to learn how probabilities can be used to identify *unusual events*.

Definition   An **unusual event** is an event that has a low probability of occurring.

In Other Words
An unusual event is an event that is not likely to occur.

Typically, an event with a probability less than 0.05 (or 5%) is considered unusual, but this *cutoff point* is not set in stone. The researcher and the context of the problem determine the probability that separates unusual events from *not so unusual events*.

For example, suppose that the probability of being wrongly convicted of a capital crime punishable by death is 3%. Even though 3% is below our 5% cutoff point, this probability is too high in light of the consequences (death for the wrongly convicted), so the event is not unusual (unlikely) enough. We would want this probability to be much closer to zero.

Note to Instructor
Ask students to cite some real-life examples of unusual events.

Now suppose that you are planning a picnic on a day for which there is a 3% chance of rain. In this context, you would consider "rain" an unusual (unlikely) event and proceed with the picnic plans.

CAUTION A probability of 0.05 should not always be used to separate unusual events from not so unusual events.

The point is this: Selecting a probability that separates unusual events from not so unusual events is subjective and depends on the situation. Statisticians typically use cutoff points of 0.01, 0.05, and 0.10. For many circumstances, any event that occurs with a probability of 0.05 or less will be considered unusual.

Next, we introduce three methods for determining the probability of an event: (1) the empirical method, (2) the classical method, and (3) the subjective method.

2 Compute and Interpret Probabilities Using the Empirical Method

Because probabilities deal with the long-term proportion with which a particular outcome is observed, it makes sense that we begin our discussion of determining probabilities using the idea of relative frequency. Probabilities computed in this manner rely on empirical evidence, that is, evidence based on the outcomes of a probability experiment.

> **Approximating Probabilities Using the Empirical Approach**
>
> The probability of an event E is approximately the number of times event E is observed divided by the number of repetitions of the experiment.
>
> $$P(E) \approx \text{relative frequency of } E = \frac{\text{frequency of } E}{\text{number of trials of experiment}} \quad (1)$$

The probability obtained using the empirical approach is approximate because different *runs* of the probability experiment lead to different outcomes and, therefore, different estimates of $P(E)$. Consider flipping a coin 20 times and recording the number of heads. Use the results of the experiment to estimate the probability of obtaining a head. Now repeat the experiment. Because the results of the second run of the experiment do not necessarily yield the same results, we cannot say the probability *equals* the relative frequency; rather we say the probability is *approximately* the relative frequency. As we increase the number of trials of a probability experiment, our estimate becomes more accurate (again, the Law of Large Numbers).

EXAMPLE 3   Using Relative Frequencies to Approximate Probabilities

A pit boss wanted to approximate the probability of rolling a seven using a pair of dice that have been in use for a while. To do this he rolls the dice 100 times and records 15 sevens. The probability of rolling a seven is approximately $\frac{15}{100} = 0.15$.

When we survey a random sample of individuals, the probabilities computed from the survey are approximate. In fact, we can think of a survey as a probability experiment, since the results of a survey are likely to be different each time the survey is conducted because different people are included.

EXAMPLE 4   Building a Probability Model from Survey Data

Table 2

Means of Travel	Frequency
Drive alone	153
Carpool	22
Public transportation	10
Walk	5
Other means	3
Work at home	7

Problem: The data in Table 2 represent the results of a survey in which 200 people were asked their means of travel to work.

(a) Use the survey data to build a probability model for means of travel to work.

(b) Estimate the probability that a randomly selected individual carpools to work. Interpret this result.

(c) Would it be unusual to randomly select an individual who walks to work?

Approach: To build a probability model, we estimate the probability of each outcome by determining its relative frequency.

Table 3	
Means of Travel	**Probability**
Drive alone	0.765
Carpool	0.11
Public transportation	0.05
Walk	0.025
Other means	0.015
Work at home	0.035

Now Work Problem 39

Solution

(a) There are $153 + 22 + \cdots + 7 = 200$ individuals in the survey. The individuals can be thought of as trials of the probability experiment. The relative frequency for "drive alone" is $\dfrac{153}{200} = 0.765$. We compute the relative frequency of the other outcomes similarly and obtain the probability model in Table 3.

(b) From Table 3, we estimate the probability to be 0.11 that a randomly selected individual carpools to work.

(c) The probability that an individual walks to work is approximately 0.025. It is somewhat unusual to randomly choose a person who walks to work.

③ Compute and Interpret Probabilities Using the Classical Method

When using the empirical method, we obtain an approximate probability of an event by conducting a probability experiment.

The classical method of computing probabilities does not require that a probability experiment actually be performed. Rather, we use counting techniques to determine the probability of an event.

The classical method of computing probabilities requires *equally likely outcomes*. An experiment is said to have **equally likely outcomes** when each outcome has the same probability of occurring. For example, in throwing a fair die once, each of the six outcomes in the sample space, $\{1, 2, 3, 4, 5, 6\}$, has an equal chance of occurring. Contrast this situation with a loaded die in which a five or six is twice as likely to occur as a one, two, three, or four.

> **Computing Probability Using the Classical Method**
>
> If an experiment has n equally likely outcomes and if the number of ways that an event E can occur is m, then the probability of E, $P(E)$, is
>
> $$P(E) = \frac{\text{number of ways that } E \text{ can occur}}{\text{number of possible outcomes}} = \frac{m}{n} \qquad (2)$$
>
> So, if S is the sample space of this experiment,
>
> $$P(E) = \frac{N(E)}{N(S)} \qquad (3)$$
>
> where $N(E)$ is the number of outcomes in E, and $N(S)$ is the number of outcomes in the sample space.

EXAMPLE 5 Computing Probabilities Using the Classical Method

Problem: A pair of fair dice is rolled.

(a) Compute the probability of rolling a seven.

(b) Compute the probability of rolling "snake eyes"; that is, compute the probability of rolling a two.

(c) Comment on the likelihood of rolling a seven versus rolling a two.

Approach: To compute probabilities using the classical method, we count the number of outcomes in the sample space and count the number of ways the event can occur.

Solution

(a) In rolling a pair of fair dice, there are 36 equally likely outcomes in the sample space, as shown in Figure 2.

Figure 2

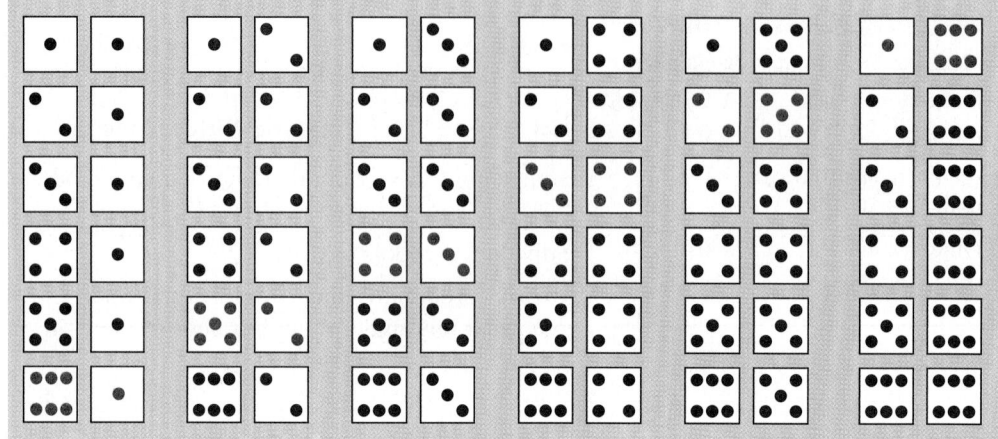

So, $N(S) = 36$. The event $E =$ "roll a seven" $= \{(1,6), (2,5), (3,4), (4,3), (5,2), (6,1)\}$ has six outcomes, so $N(E) = 6$. Using Formula (3), the probability of rolling a seven is

$$P(E) = P(\text{roll a seven}) = \frac{N(E)}{N(S)} = \frac{6}{36} = \frac{1}{6}$$

(b) The event $F =$ "roll a two" $= \{(1,1)\}$ has one outcome, so $N(F) = 1$. Using Formula (3), the probability of rolling a two is

$$P(F) = P(\text{roll a two}) = \frac{N(F)}{N(S)} = \frac{1}{36}$$

(c) Since $P(\text{roll a seven}) = \frac{6}{36}$ and $P(\text{roll a two}) = \frac{1}{36}$, rolling a seven is six times as likely as rolling a two. In other words, in 36 rolls of the dice, we *expect* to observe about 6 sevens and only 1 two.

If we compare the empirical probability of rolling a seven, 0.15, obtained in Example 3, to the classical probability of rolling a seven, $\frac{1}{6} \approx 0.167$, obtained in Example 5(a), we see that they are not too far apart. In fact, if the dice are fair, we expect the relative frequency of sevens to get closer to 0.167 as we increase the number of rolls of the dice. That is, if the dice are fair, the empirical probability will get closer to the classical probability as the number of trials of the experiment increases. If the two probabilities do not get closer together, we may suspect that the dice are not fair.

In simple random sampling, each individual has the same chance of being selected. Therefore, we can use the classical method to compute the probability of obtaining a specific sample.

EXAMPLE 6   **Computing Probabilities Using Equally Likely Outcomes**

Problem: Sophia has three tickets to a concert. Yolanda, Michael, Kevin, and Marissa have all stated they would like to go to the concert with Sophia. To be fair, Sophia decides to randomly select the two people who can go to the concert with her.

(a) Determine the sample space of the experiment. In other words, list all possible simple random samples of size $n = 2$.

(b) Compute the probability of the event "Michael and Kevin attend the concert."

Historical Note

Girolamo Cardano (in English Jerome Cardan) was born in Pavia, Italy, on September 24, 1501. He was an illegitimate child whose father was Fazio Cardano, a lawyer in Milan. Fazio was a part-time mathematician and taught Girolamo. In 1526, Cardano earned his medical degree. Shortly thereafter, his father died. Unable to maintain a medical practice, Cardano spent his inheritance and turned to gambling to help support himself. Cardano developed an understanding of probability that helped him to win. He wrote a booklet on probability, *Liber de Ludo Alaea*, which was not printed until 1663, 87 years after his death. The booklet is a practical guide to gambling, including cards, dice, and cheating. Eventually, Cardano became a lecturer of mathematics at the Piatti Foundation. This position allowed him to practice medicine and develop a favorable reputation as a doctor. In 1545, he published his greatest work, *Ars Magna*.

(c) Compute the probability of the event "Marissa attends the concert."

(d) Interpret the probability in part (c).

Approach: First, we determine the outcomes in the sample space by making a table. The probability of an event is the number of outcomes in the event divided by the number of outcomes in the sample space.

Solution

(a) The sample space is listed in Table 4.

Table 4		
Yolanda, Michael	Yolanda, Kevin	Yolanda, Marissa
Michael, Kevin	Michael, Marissa	Kevin, Marissa

(b) We have $N(S) = 6$, and there is one way the event "Michael and Kevin attend the concert" can occur. Therefore, the probability that Michael and Kevin attend the concert is $\frac{1}{6}$.

(c) We have $N(S) = 6$, and there are three ways the event "Marissa attends the concert" can occur. The probability that Marissa will attend is $\frac{3}{6} = 0.5 = 50\%$.

(d) If we conducted this experiment many times, about 50% of the experiments would result in Marissa attending the concert.

Now Work Problems 33 and 47

EXAMPLE 7 **Comparing the Classical Method and Empirical Method**

Problem: Suppose that a survey is conducted in which 500 families with three children are asked to disclose the gender of their children. Based on the results, it was found that 180 of the families had two boys and one girl.

(a) Estimate the probability of having two boys and one girl in a three-child family using the empirical method.

(b) Compute and interpret the probability of having two boys and one girl in a three-child family using the classical method, assuming boys and girls are equally likely.

Approach: To answer part (a), we determine the relative frequency of the event "two boys and one girl." To answer part (b), we must count the number of ways the event "two boys and one girl" can occur and divide this by the number of possible outcomes for this experiment.

Solution

(a) The empirical probability of the event $E =$ "two boys and one girl" is

$$P(E) \approx \text{relative frequency of } E = \frac{180}{500} = 0.36 = 36\%$$

There is about a 36% probability that a family of three children will have two boys and one girl.

(b) To determine the sample space, we construct a **tree diagram** to list the equally likely outcomes of the experiment. We draw two branches corresponding to the two possible outcomes (boy or girl) for the first repetition of the experiment (the first child). For the second child, we draw four branches: two branches originate from the first boy and two branches originate from the first girl. This is repeated for the third child. See Figure 3, where B stands for boy and G stands for girl.

Figure 3

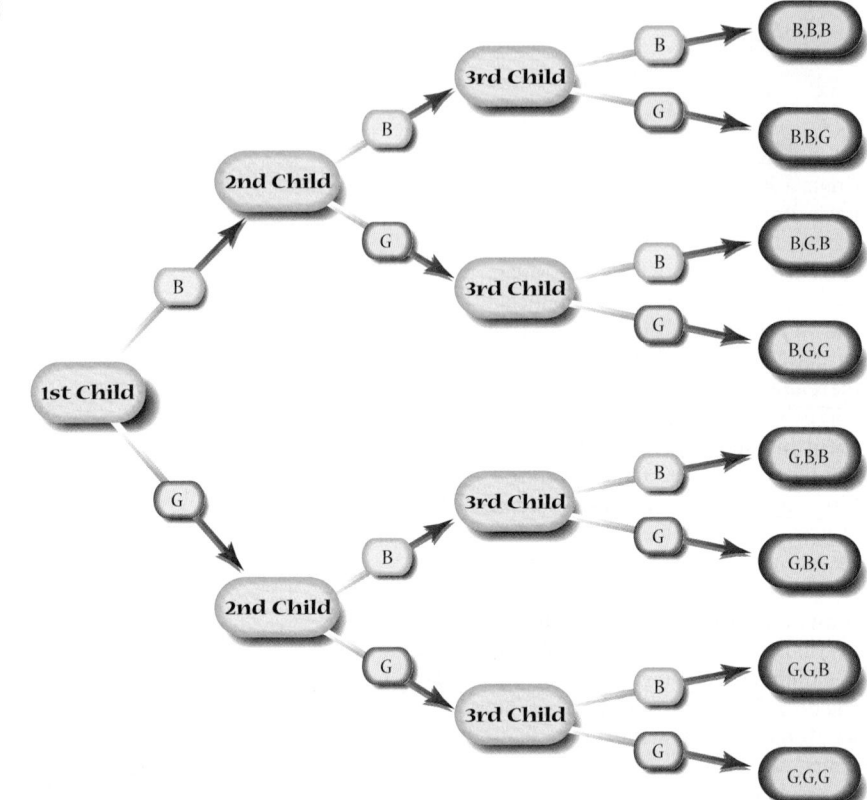

The sample space S of this experiment is found by following each branch to identify all the possible outcomes of the experiment:

$$S = \{BBB, BBG, BGB, BGG, GBB, GBG, GGB, GGG\}$$

So, $N(S) = 8$.

For the event $E =$ "two boys and a girl" $= \{BBG, BGB, GBB\}$, we have $N(E) = 3$. Since the outcomes are equally likely (for example, BBG is just as likely as BGB), the probability of E is

$$P(E) = \frac{N(E)}{N(S)} = \frac{3}{8} = 0.375 = 37.5\%$$

There is a 37.5% probability that a family of three children will have two boys and one girl. If we repeated this experiment 1000 times and the outcomes are equally likely (having a girl is just as likely as having a boy), we would expect about 375 of the trials to result in 2 boys and one girl.

In comparing the results of Examples 7(a) and 7(b), we notice that the two probabilities are slightly different. Empirical probabilities and classical probabilities often differ in value. As the number of repetitions of a probability experiment increases, the empirical probability should get closer to the classical probability. That is, the classical probability is the theoretical relative frequency of an event after a large number of trials of the probability experiment. However, it is also possible that the two probabilities differ because having a boy or having a girl are not equally likely events. (Maybe the probability of having a boy is 50.5% and the probability of having a girl is 49.5%.) If this is the case, the empirical probability will not get closer to the classical probability.

4 **Use Simulation to Obtain Data Based on Probabilities**

Suppose that we want to determine the probability of having a boy. Using classical methods, we would assume that having a boy is just as likely as having a girl, so the probability of having a boy is 0.5. We could also approximate this probability by looking in the *Statistical Abstract of the United States* under Vital Statistics and determining the number of boys and girls born for the most recent year for which data are available. In 2005, for example, 2,119,000 boys and 2,020,000 girls were born. Based on empirical evidence, the probability of a boy is approximately

$$\frac{2,119,000}{2,119,000 + 2,020,000} = 0.512 = 51.2\%.$$

Notice that the empirical evidence, which is based on a very large number of repetitions, differs from the value of 0.50 used for classical methods (which assumes boys and girls are equally likely). This empirical results serve as evidence against the belief that the probability of having a boy is 0.5.

Instead of obtaining data from existing sources, we could also simulate a probability experiment using a graphing calculator or statistical software to replicate the experiment as many times as we like. Simulation is particularly helpful for estimating the probability of more complicated events. In Example 7 we used a tree diagram and the classical approach to find the probability of an event (a three-child family will have two boys and one girl). In this next example, we use simulation to estimate the same probability.

EXAMPLE 8   Simulating Probabilities

Problem

(a) Simulate the experiment of sampling 100 three-child families to estimate the probability that a three-child family has two boys.

(b) Simulate the experiment of sampling 1,000 three-child families to estimate the probability that a three-child family has two boys.

Approach: To simulate probabilities, we use a random-number generator available in statistical software and most graphing calculators. We assume the outcomes "have a boy" and "have a girl" are equally likely.

Solution

(a) We use MINITAB to perform the simulation. Set the seed in MINITAB to any value you wish, say 1970. Use the Integer Distribution* to generate random data that simulate three-child families. If we agree to let 0 represent a girl and 1 represent a boy, we can approximate the probability of having 2 boys by summing each row (adding up the number of boys), counting the number of 2s, and dividing by 100, the number of repetitions of the experiment. See Figure 4.

Figure 4

---

*The Integer Distribution involves a mathematical formula that uses a seed number to generate a sequence of equally likely random integers. Consult the technology manuals for setting the seed and generating sequences of integers.

Historical Note

Blaise Pascal was born on June 19, 1623, in Clermont, France. Pascal's father felt that Blaise should not be taught mathematics before age 15. Pascal couldn't resist studying mathematics on his own, and at the age of 12 started to teach himself geometry. In December 1639, the Pascal family moved to Rouen, where Pascal's father had been appointed as a tax collector. Between 1642 and 1645, Pascal worked on developing a calculator to help his father collect taxes. In correspondence with Fermat, he helped develop the theory of probability. This correspondence consisted of five letters written in the summer of 1654. They considered the dice problem and the problem of points. The dice problem deals with determining the expected number of times a pair of dice must be thrown before a pair of sixes is observed. The problem of points asks how to divide the stakes if a game of dice is incomplete. They solved the problem of points for a two-player game, but did not solve it for three or more players.

Now Work Problem 51

Using MINITAB's Tally command, we can determine the number of 2s that MINITAB randomly generated. See Figure 5.

Figure 5

Tally for Discrete Variables: C4

C4	Count	Percent
0	14	14.00
1	40	40.00
2	32	32.00
3	14	14.00

N = 100

Based on this figure, we approximate that there is a 32% probability that a three-child family will have 2 boys.

(b) Again, set the seed to 1970. Figure 6 shows the result of simulating 1,000 three-child families.

Figure 6

Tally for Discrete Variables: C4

C4	Count	Percent
0	136	13.60
1	367	36.70
2	388	38.80
3	109	10.90

N = 1000

We approximate that there is a 38.8% probability of a three-child family having 2 boys. Notice that more repetitions of the experiment (100 repetitions versus 1,000 repetitions) results in a probability closer to 37.5% as found in Example 7 (b).

5 Recognize and Interpret Subjective Probabilities

Suppose that a sports reporter is asked what he thinks the chances are for the Boston Red Sox to return to the World Series. The sports reporter will likely process information about the Red Sox (their pitching staff, lead-off hitter, and so on) and then come up with an educated guess of the likelihood. The reporter may respond that there is a 20% chance the Red Sox will return to the World Series. This forecast is a probability although it is not based on relative frequencies. We cannot, after all, repeat the experiment of playing a season under the same circumstances (same players, schedule, and so on) over and over. Nonetheless, the forecast of 20% does satisfy the criterion that a probability be between 0 and 1, inclusive. This forecast is known as a *subjective probability*.

Definition   A **subjective probability** of an outcome is a probability obtained on the basis of personal judgment.

It is important to understand that subjective probabilities are perfectly legitimate and are often the only method of assigning likelihood to an outcome. As another example, a financial reporter may ask an economist about the likelihood the economy will fall into recession next year. Again, we cannot conduct an experiment *n* times to obtain a relative frequency. The economist must use his or her knowledge of the current conditions of the economy and make an educated guess as to the likelihood of recession.

5.1 ASSESS YOUR UNDERSTANDING

Concepts and Vocabulary

1. Describe the difference between classical and empirical probability.

2. What is the probability of an event that is impossible? Suppose that a probability is approximated to be zero based on empirical results. Does this mean the event is impossible? *0; no*

3. In computing classical probabilities, all outcomes must be equally likely. Explain what this means.

4. What does it mean for an event to be unusual? Why should the cutoff for identifying unusual events not always be 0.05?

5. *True or False*: In a probability model, the sum of the probabilities of all outcomes must equal 1. *True*

6. *True or False*: Probability is a measure of the likelihood of a random phenomenon or chance behavior. *True*

7. In probability, a(n) __experiment__ is any process that can be repeated in which the results are uncertain.

8. A(n) __event__ is any collection of outcomes from a probability experiment.

9. Explain why probability can be considered a long-term relative frequency.

10. Explain the purpose of a tree diagram.

Skill Building

11. Verify that the following is a probability model. What do we **NW** call the outcome "blue"? *Impossible event*

Color	Probability
Red	0.3
Green	0.15
Blue	0
Brown	0.15
Yellow	0.2
Orange	0.2

12. Verify that the following is a probability model. If the model represents the colors of M&M's in a bag of milk chocolate M&M's, explain what the model implies. *All of the M&M's are yellow*

Color	Probability
Red	0
Green	0
Blue	0
Brown	0
Yellow	1
Orange	0

13. Why is the following not a probability model? $P(green) < 0$

Color	Probability
Red	0.3
Green	−0.3
Blue	0.2
Brown	0.4
Yellow	0.2
Orange	0.2

14. Why is the following not a probability model? *Sum of probabilities not 1*

Color	Probability
Red	0.1
Green	0.1
Blue	0.1
Brown	0.4
Yellow	0.2
Orange	0.3

15. Which of the following numbers could be the probability of an event? *0, 0.01, 0.35, 1*

$$0, 0.01, 0.35, -0.4, 1, 1.4$$

16. Which of the following numbers could be the probability of an event?

$$1.5, \frac{1}{2}, \frac{3}{4}, \frac{2}{3}, 0, -\frac{1}{4} \quad \frac{1}{2}, \frac{3}{4}, \frac{2}{3}, 0$$

17. In five-card stud poker, a player is dealt five cards. The probability that the player is dealt two cards of the same value and three other cards of different value so that the player has a pair is 0.42. Explain what this probability means. If you play five-card stud 100 times, will you be dealt a pair exactly 42 times? Why or why not? *No*

18. In seven-card stud poker, a player is dealt seven cards. The probability that the player is dealt two cards of the same value and five other cards of different value so that the player has a pair is 0.44. Explain what this probability means. If you play seven-card stud 100 times, will you be dealt a pair exactly 44 times? Why or why not? *No*

19. Suppose that you toss a coin 100 times and get 95 heads and 5 tails. Based on these results, what is the estimated probability that the next flip results in a head? *0.95*

20. Suppose that you roll a die 100 times and get six 80 times. Based on these results, what is the estimated probability that the next roll results in six? *0.8*

21. Bob is asked to construct a probability model for rolling a pair of fair dice. He lists the outcomes as 2, 3, 4, 5, 6, 7, 8, 9, 10, 11, 12. Because there are 11 outcomes, he reasoned, the probability of rolling a two must be $\frac{1}{11}$. What is wrong with Bob's reasoning? *Not equally likely outcomes*

36. (a) $\dfrac{12}{365}$ 36. (b) $\dfrac{7}{365}$ 36. (c) $\dfrac{31}{365}$ 36. (d) $\dfrac{1}{365}$

22. Blood Types A person can have one of four blood types: A, B, AB, or O. If a person is randomly selected, is the probability they have blood type A equal to $\dfrac{1}{4}$? Why?   No

23. If a person rolls a six-sided die and then flips a coin, describe
NW the sample space of possible outcomes using 1, 2, 3, 4, 5, 6 for the die outcomes and H, T for the coin outcomes.

24. If a basketball player shoots three free throws, describe the sample space of possible outcomes using S for a made free throw and F for a missed free throw.

25. According to the U.S. Department of Education, 42.8% of 3-year-olds are enrolled in day care. What is the probability that a randomly selected 3-year-old is enrolled in day care?   0.428

26. According to the American Veterinary Medical Association, the proportion of households owning a dog is 0.372. What is the probability that a randomly selected household owns a dog?   0.372

For Problems 27–30, let the sample space be $S = \{1, 2, 3, 4, 5, 6, 7, 8, 9, 10\}$. Suppose the outcomes are equally likely.

27. Compute the probability of the event $E = \{1, 2, 3\}$.

28. Compute the probability of the event $F = \{3, 5, 9, 10\}$.

29. Compute the probability of the event $E =$ "an even number less than 9."

30. Compute the probability of the event $F =$ "an odd number."   27. $\dfrac{3}{10}$ 28. $\dfrac{2}{5}$ 29. $\dfrac{2}{5}$ 30. $\dfrac{1}{2}$

Applying the Concepts

31. Play Sports? A survey of 500 randomly selected high school students determined that 288 played organized sports.
   (a) What is the probability that a randomly selected high school student plays organized sports?   0.576
   (b) Interpret this probability.

32. Volunteer? In a survey of 1,100 female adults (18 years of age or older), it was determined that 341 volunteered at least once in the past year.
   (a) What is the probability that a randomly selected adult female volunteered at least once in the past year?   0.31
   (b) Interpret this probability.

33. Planting Tulips A bag of 100 tulip bulbs purchased from a
NW nursery contains 40 red tulip bulbs, 35 yellow tulip bulbs, and 25 purple tulip bulbs.
   (a) What is the probability that a randomly selected tulip bulb is red?   0.4
   (b) What is the probability that a randomly selected tulip bulb is purple?   0.25
   (c) Interpret these two probabilities.

34. Golf Balls The local golf store sells an "onion bag" that contains 80 "experienced" golf balls. Suppose the bag contains 35 Titleists, 25 Maxflis, and 20 Top-Flites.
   (a) What is the probability that a randomly selected golf ball is a Titleist?   0.4375
   (b) What is the probability that a randomly selected golf ball is a Top-Flite?   0.25
   (c) Interpret these two probabilities.

35. Roulette In the game of roulette, a wheel consists of 38 slots numbered 0, 00, 1, 2, ..., 36. (See the photo.) To play the game, a metal ball is spun around the wheel and is allowed to fall into one of the numbered slots.   35. (b) $\dfrac{1}{38}$ 35. (c) $\dfrac{9}{19}$

   (a) Determine the sample space. $\{0, 00, 1, 2, \ldots, 36\}$
   (b) Determine the probability that the metal ball falls into the slot marked 8. Interpret this probability.
   (c) Determine the probability that the metal ball lands in an odd slot. Interpret this probability.

36. Birthdays Exclude leap years from the following calculations and assume each birthday is equally likely:
   (a) Determine the probability that a randomly selected person has a birthday on the 1st day of a month. Interpret this probability.
   (b) Determine the probability that a randomly selected person has a birthday on the 31st day of a month. Interpret this probability.
   (c) Determine the probability that a randomly selected person was born in December. Interpret this probability.
   (d) Determine the probability that a randomly selected person has a birthday on November 8. Interpret this probability.
   (e) If you just met somebody and she asked you to guess her birthday, are you likely to be correct?   No
   (f) Do you think it is appropriate to use the methods of classical probability to compute the probability that a person is born in December?

37. Genetics A gene is composed of two alleles. An allele can be either dominant or recessive. Suppose that a husband and wife, who are both carriers of the sickle-cell anemia allele but do not have the disease, decide to have a child. Because both parents are carriers of the disease, each has one dominant normal-cell allele (S) and one recessive sickle-cell allele (s). Therefore, the genotype of each parent is Ss. Each parent contributes one allele to his or her offspring, with each allele being equally likely.   37. (a) $\{SS, Ss, sS, ss\}$
   (a) List the possible genotypes of their offspring.
   (b) What is the probability that the offspring will have sickle-cell anemia? In other words, what is the probability that the offspring will have genotype ss? Interpret this probability.
   (c) What is the probability that the offspring will not have sickle-cell anemia but will be a carrier? In other words, what is the probability that the offspring will have one dominant normal-cell allele and one recessive sickle-cell allele? Interpret this probability. $\dfrac{1}{2}$

   37. (b) $\dfrac{1}{4}$

38. (a) {SS, Ss, sS, ss} 38. (b) $\frac{1}{4}$ 38. (c) $\frac{3}{4}$

38. More Genetics In Problem 37, we learned that for some diseases, such as sickle-cell anemia, an individual will get the disease only if he or she receives both recessive alleles. This is not always the case. For example, Huntington's disease only requires one dominant gene for an individual to contract the disease. Suppose that a husband and wife, who both have a dominant Huntington's disease allele (S) and a normal recessive allele (s), decide to have a child.

(a) List the possible genotypes of their offspring.

(b) What is the probability that the offspring will not have Huntington's disease? In other words, what is the probability that the offspring will have genotype ss? Interpret this probability.

(c) What is the probability that the offspring will have Huntington's disease?

39. College Survey In a national survey conducted by the
NW Centers for Disease Control to determine college students' health-risk behaviors, college students were asked, "How often do you wear a seatbelt when riding in a car driven by someone else?" The frequencies appear in the following table:

Response	Frequency
Never	125
Rarely	324
Sometimes	552
Most of the time	1,257
Always	2,518

(a) Construct a probability model for seatbelt use by a passenger.

(b) Would you consider it unusual to find a college student who never wears a seatbelt when riding in a car driven by someone else? Why? Yes

40. College Survey In a national survey conducted by the Centers for Disease Control to determine college students' health-risk behaviors, college students were asked, "How often do you wear a seatbelt when driving a car?" The frequencies appear in the following table:

Response	Frequency
Never	118
Rarely	249
Sometimes	345
Most of the time	716
Always	3,093

(a) Construct a probability model for seatbelt use by a driver.

(b) Is it unusual for a college student to never wear a seatbelt when driving a car? Why? Yes

41. Larceny Theft A police officer randomly selected 642 police records of larceny thefts. The following data represent the number of offenses for various types of larceny thefts.

(a) Construct a probability model for type of larceny theft.

(b) Are purse snatching larcenies unusual? Yes

(c) Are bicycle larcenies unusual? No

Type of Larceny Theft	Number of Offenses
Pocket picking	4
Purse snatching	6
Shoplifting	133
From motor vehicles	219
Motor vehicle accessories	90
Bicycles	42
From buildings	143
From coin-operated machines	5

Source: U.S. Federal Bureau of Investigation

42. Multiple Births The following data represent the number of live multiple-delivery births (three or more babies) in 2005 for women 15 to 44 years old.

Age	Number of Multiple Births
15–19	83
20–24	465
25–29	1,635
30–34	2,443
35–39	1,604
40–44	344

Source: *National Vital Statistics Reports*, Vol. 56, No. 16, December 15, 2007

(a) Construct a probability model for number of multiple births.

(b) In the sample space of all multiple births, are multiple births for 15- to 19-year-old mothers unusual? Yes

(c) In the sample space of all multiple births, are multiple births for 40- to 44-year-old mothers unusual?

42. (c) Not too unusual

Problems 43–46 use the given table, which lists six possible assignments of probabilities for tossing a coin twice, to answer the following questions.

Assignments	Sample Space			
	HH	HT	TH	TT
A	$\frac{1}{4}$	$\frac{1}{4}$	$\frac{1}{4}$	$\frac{1}{4}$
B	0	0	0	1
C	$\frac{3}{16}$	$\frac{5}{16}$	$\frac{5}{16}$	$\frac{3}{16}$
D	$\frac{1}{2}$	$\frac{1}{2}$	$-\frac{1}{2}$	$\frac{1}{2}$
E	$\frac{1}{4}$	$\frac{1}{4}$	$\frac{1}{4}$	$\frac{1}{8}$
F	$\frac{1}{9}$	$\frac{2}{9}$	$\frac{2}{9}$	$\frac{4}{9}$

43. Which of the assignments of probabilities are consistent with the definition of a probability model? A, B, C, F

44. Which of the assignments of probabilities should be used if the coin is known to be fair? A

45. Which of the assignments of probabilities should be used if the coin is known to always come up tails?   B

46. Which of the assignments of probabilities should be used if tails is twice as likely to occur as heads?   F

47. Going to Disney World John, Roberto, Clarice, Dominique, NW and Marco work for a publishing company. The company wants to send two employees to a statistics conference in Orlando. To be fair, the company decides that the two individuals who get to attend will have their names randomly drawn from a hat.

(a) Determine the sample space of the experiment. That is, list all possible simple random samples of size $n = 2$.

(b) What is the probability that Clarice and Dominique attend the conference?   0.1

(c) What is the probability that Clarice attends the conference?   0.4

(d) What is the probability that John stays home?   0.6

48. Six Flags In 2008, Six Flags St. Louis had eight roller coasters: The Screamin' Eagle, The Boss, River King Mine Train, Batman the Ride, Mr. Freeze, Ninja, Tony Hawk's Big Spin, and Evel Knievel. Of these, The Boss, The Screamin' Eagle, and Evel Knievel are wooden coasters. Ethan wants to ride two more roller coasters before leaving the park (not the same one twice) and decides to select them by drawing names from a hat.

(a) Determine the sample space of the experiment. That is, list all possible simple random samples of size $n = 2$.

(b) What is the probability that Ethan will ride Mr. Freeze and Evel Knievel?   0.036

(c) What is the probability that Ethan will ride the Screamin' Eagle?   0.25

(d) What is the probability that Ethan will ride two wooden roller coasters?   0.107

(e) What is the probability that Ethan will not ride any wooden roller coasters?   0.357

49. Barry Bonds On October 5, 2001, Barry Bonds broke Mark McGwire's home-run record for a single season by hitting his 71st and 72nd home runs. Bonds went on to hit one more home run before the season ended, for a total of 73. Of the 73 home runs, 24 went to right field, 26 went to right center field, 11 went to center field, 10 went to left center field, and 2 went to left field.

Source: Baseball-almanac.com

(a) What is the probability that a randomly selected home run was hit to right field?

(b) What is the probability that a randomly selected home run was hit to left field?

(c) Was it unusual for Barry Bonds to hit a home run to left field? Explain.   Yes

50. Rolling a Die

(a) Roll a single die 50 times, recording the result of each roll of the die. Use the results to approximate the probability of rolling a three.

(b) Roll a single die 100 times, recording the result of each roll of the die. Use the results to approximate the probability of rolling a three.

(c) Compare the results of (a) and (b) to the classical probability of rolling a three.

51. Simulation Use a graphing calculator or statistical software NW to simulate rolling a six-sided die 100 times, using an integer distribution with numbers one through six.

(a) Use the results of the simulation to compute the probability of rolling a one.

(b) Repeat the simulation. Compute the probability of rolling a one.

(c) Simulate rolling a six-sided die 500 times. Compute the probability of rolling a one.

(d) Which simulation resulted in the closest estimate to the probability that would be obtained using the classical method?

52. Classifying Probability Determine whether the following probabilities are computed using classical methods, empirical methods, or subjective methods.

(a) The probability of having eight girls in an eight-child family is 0.390625%.   Classical

(b) On the basis of a survey of 1,000 families with eight children, the probability of a family having eight girls is 0.54%.

(c) According to a sports analyst, the probability that the Chicago Bears will win their next game is about 30%.

(d) On the basis of clinical trials, the probability of efficacy of a new drug is 75%.   Empirical

53. Checking for Loaded Dice You suspect a pair of dice to be loaded and conduct a probability experiment by rolling each die 400 times. The outcome of the experiment is listed in the following table:

Value of Die	Frequency
1	105
2	47
3	44
4	49
5	51
6	104

Do you think the dice are loaded? Why?   Yes

54. Conduct a survey in your school by randomly asking 50 students whether they drive to school. Based on the results of the survey, approximate the probability that a randomly selected student drives to school.

55. In 2006, the median income of families in the United States was $58,500. What is the probability that a randomly selected family has an income greater than $58,500?   0.5

56. The middle 50% of enrolled freshmen at Washington University in St. Louis had SAT math scores in the range 700–780. What is the probability that a randomly selected freshman at Washington University has a SAT math score of 700 or higher?   0.75

57. The Probability Applet Load the long-run probability applet on your computer.

(a) Choose the "simulating the probability of a head with a fair coin" applet and simulate flipping a fair coin 10 times. What is the estimated probability of a head based on these 10 trials?

(b) Reset the applet. Simulate flipping a fair coin 10 times a second time. What is the estimated probability of a

49. (a) $\dfrac{24}{73}$ 49. (b) $\dfrac{2}{73}$

head based on these 10 trials? Compare the results to part (a).

(c) Reset the applet. Simulate flipping a fair coin 1,000 times. What is the estimated probability of a head based on these 1,000 trials? Compare the results to part (a).

(d) Reset the applet. Simulate flipping a fair coin 1,000 times. What is the estimated probability of a head based on these 1,000 trials? Compare the results to part (c).

(e) Choose the "simulating the probability of head with an unfair coin [P(H) = 0.2]" applet and simulate flipping a coin 1,000 times. What is the estimated probability of a head based on these 1,000 trials? If you did not know that the probability of heads was set to 0.2, what would you conclude about the coin? Why?

58. Putting It Together: Drug Side Effects In placebo-controlled clinical trials for the drug Viagra, 734 subjects received Viagra and 725 subjects received a placebo (subjects did not know which treatment they received). The following table summarizes reports of various side effects that were reported.

(a) Is the variable "adverse effect" qualitative or quantitative? Qualitative

(b) Which type of graph would be appropriate to display the information in the table? Construct the graph. Side-by-side relative frequency bar graph

Adverse Effect	Viagra ($n = 734$)	Placebo ($n = 725$)
Headache	117	29
Flushing	73	7
Dyspepsia	51	15
Nasal congestion	29	15
Urinary tract infection	22	15
Abnormal vision	22	0
Diarrhea	22	7
Dizziness	15	7
Rash	15	7

(c) What is the estimated probability that a randomly selected subject from the Viagra group reported experiencing flushing? Would this be unusual? 0.099; no

(d) What is the estimated probability that a subject receiving a placebo would report experiencing flushing? Would this be unusual? 0.010; yes

(e) If a subject reports flushing after receiving a treatment, what might you conclude? They received the Viagra treatment

(f) What type of experimental design is this? Completely randomized design

TECHNOLOGY STEP-BY-STEP Simulation

TI-83/84 Plus

1. Set the seed by entering any number on the HOME screen. Press the STO ▶ button, press the MATH button, highlight the PRB menu, and highlight 1 : rand and hit ENTER. With the cursor on the HOME screen, hit ENTER.

2. Press the MATH button and highlight the PRB menu. Highlight 5:randInt (and hit ENTER.

3. After the randInt (on the HOME screen, type 1, n, number of repetitions of experiment), where n is the number of equally likely outcomes. For example, to simulate rolling a single die 50 times, we type

randInt(1, 6, 50)

4. Press the STO ▶ button and then 2nd 1, and hit ENTER to store the data in L1.

5. Draw a histogram of the data using the outcomes as classes. TRACE to obtain outcomes.

MINITAB

1. Set the seed by selecting the **Calc** menu and highlighting **Set Base**. . . . Insert any seed you wish into the cell and click OK.

2. Select the **Calc** menu, highlight **Random Data**, and then highlight **Integer**. To simulate rolling a single die 100 times, fill in the window as shown in Figure 4 on page 267.

3. Select the **Stat** menu, highlight **Tables**, and then highlight **Tally**. . . . Enter C1 into the variables cell. Make sure that the Counts box is checked and click OK.

Excel

1. With cell A1 selected, press the *fx* button.

2. Highlight Math & Trig in the Function category window. Then highlight RANDBETWEEN in the Function Name: window. Click OK.

3. To simulate rolling a die 50 times, enter 1 for the lower limit and 6 for the upper limit. Click OK.

4. Copy the contents of cell A1 into cells A2 through A50.

5.2 THE ADDITION RULE AND COMPLEMENTS

Preparing for this Section Before getting started, review the following:

- Contingency Tables (Section 4.4, p. 239)

> **Objectives**
> 1 Use the Addition Rule for disjoint events
> 2 Use the General Addition Rule
> 3 Compute the probability of an event using the Complement Rule

Note to Instructor

If you like, you can print out and distribute the Preparing for This Section quiz located in the Instructor's Resource Center. The purpose of the quiz is to verify that the students have the prerequisite knowledge for the section.

1 **Use the Addition Rule for Disjoint Events**

Now we introduce more rules for computing probabilities. However, before we present these rules, we must discuss *disjoint events*.

Definition Two events are **disjoint** if they have no outcomes in common. Another name for disjoint events is **mutually exclusive** events.

In Other Words

Two events are disjoint if they cannot occur at the same time.

It is often helpful to draw pictures of events. Such pictures, called **Venn diagrams**, represent events as circles enclosed in a rectangle. The rectangle represents the sample space, and each circle represents an event. For example, suppose we randomly select chips from a bag. Each chip is labeled $0, 1, 2, 3, 4, 5, 6, 7, 8, 9$. Let E represent the event "choose a number less than or equal to 2," and let F represent the event "choose a number greater than or equal to 8." Because E and F do not have any outcomes in common, they are disjoint. Figure 7 shows a Venn diagram of these disjoint events.

Figure 7

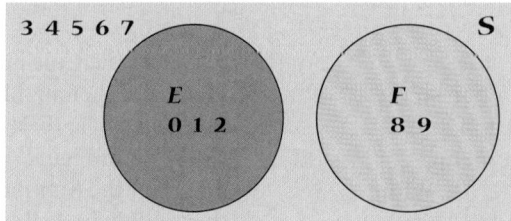

Notice that the outcomes in event E are inside circle E, and the outcomes in event F are inside the circle F. All outcomes in the sample space that are not in E or F are outside the circles, but inside the rectangle. From this diagram, we know that $P(E) = \dfrac{N(E)}{N(S)} = \dfrac{3}{10} = 0.3$ and $P(F) = \dfrac{N(F)}{N(S)} = \dfrac{2}{10} = 0.2$. In addition, $P(E \text{ or } F) = \dfrac{N(E \text{ or } F)}{N(S)} = \dfrac{5}{10} = 0.5$ and $P(E \text{ or } F) = P(E) + P(F) = 0.3 + 0.2 = 0.5$. This result occurs because of the Addition Rule for Disjoint Events.

In Other Words

The Addition Rule for Disjoint Events states that, if you have two events that have no outcomes in common, the probability that one or the other occurs is the sum of their probabilities.

Addition Rule for Disjoint Events

If E and F are disjoint (or mutually exclusive) events, then

$$P(E \text{ or } F) = P(E) + P(F)$$

The Addition Rule for Disjoint Events can be extended to more than two disjoint events. In general, if $E, F, G, \ldots$ each have no outcomes in common (they are pairwise disjoint), then

$$P(E \text{ or } F \text{ or } G \text{ or} \ldots) = P(E) + P(F) + P(G) + \cdots$$

Let event G represent "the number is a 5 or 6." The Venn diagram in Figure 8 illustrates the Addition Rule for more than two disjoint events using the chip example. Notice that no pair of events has any outcomes in common. So, from the Venn diagram, we can see that $P(E) = \dfrac{N(E)}{N(S)} = \dfrac{3}{10} = 0.3$, $P(F) = \dfrac{N(F)}{N(S)} = \dfrac{2}{10} = 0.2$, and $P(G) = \dfrac{N(G)}{N(S)} = \dfrac{2}{10} = 0.2$. In addition, $P(E \text{ or } F \text{ or } G) = P(E) + P(F) + P(G) = 0.3 + 0.2 + 0.2 = 0.7$.

Figure 8

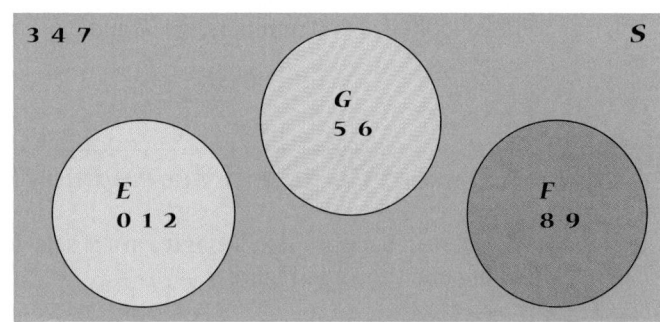

| EXAMPLE 1 | **Benford's Law and the Addition Rule for Disjoint Events** |

Problem: Our number system consists of the digits 0, 1, 2, 3, 4, 5, 6, 7, 8, and 9. Because we do not write numbers such as 12 as 012, the first significant digit in any number must be 1, 2, 3, 4, 5, 6, 7, 8, or 9. Although we may think that each digit appears with equal frequency so that each digit has a $\dfrac{1}{9}$ probability of being the first significant digit, this is, in fact, not true. In 1881, Simon Necomb discovered that digits do not occur with equal frequency. This same result was discovered again in 1938 by physicist Frank Benford. After studying lots and lots of data, he was able to assign probabilities of occurrence for each of the first digits, as shown in Table 5.

Table 5								
Digit	1	2	3	4	5	6	7	8	9
Probability	0.301	0.176	0.125	0.097	0.079	0.067	0.058	0.051	0.046

Source: The First Digit Phenomenon, T. P. Hill, *American Scientist*, July–August, 1998.

The probability model is now known as *Benford's Law* and plays a major role in identifying fraudulent data on tax returns and accounting books.

(a) Verify that Benford's Law is a probability model.

(b) Use Benford's Law to determine the probability that a randomly selected first digit is 1 or 2.

(c) Use Benford's Law to determine the probability that a randomly selected first digit is at least 6.

Approach: For part (a), we need to verify that each probability is between 0 and 1 and that the sum of all probabilities equals 1. For parts (b) and (c), we use the Addition Rule for Disjoint Events.

Solution

(a) In looking at Table 5, we see that each probability is between 0 and 1. In addition, the sum of all the probabilities is 1.

$$0.301 + 0.176 + 0.125 + \cdots + 0.046 = 1$$

Because rules 1 and 2 are satisfied, Table 5 represents a probability model.

(b)
$$P(1 \text{ or } 2) = P(1) + P(2)$$
$$= 0.301 + 0.176$$
$$= 0.477$$

If we looked at 100 numbers, we would expect about 48 to begin with 1 or 2.

(c)
$$P(\text{at least } 6) = P(6 \text{ or } 7 \text{ or } 8 \text{ or } 9)$$
$$= P(6) + P(7) + P(8) + P(9)$$
$$= 0.067 + 0.058 + 0.051 + 0.046$$
$$= 0.222$$

If we looked at 100 numbers, we would expect about 22 to begin with 6, 7, 8, or 9.

EXAMPLE 2 **A Deck of Cards and the Addition Rule for Disjoint Events**

Problem: Suppose that a single card is selected from a standard 52-card deck, such as the one shown in Figure 9.

Figure 9

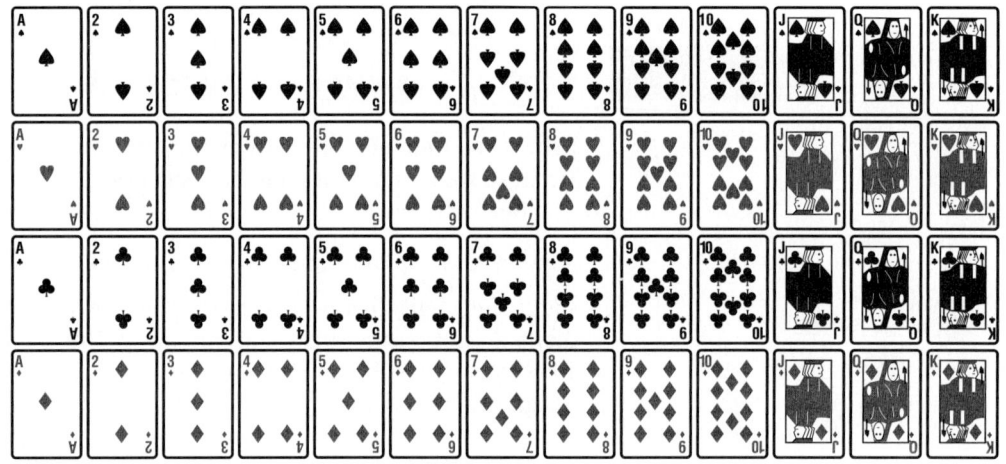

(a) Compute the probability of the event E = "drawing a king."

(b) Compute the probability of the event E = "drawing a king" or F = "drawing a queen."

(c) Compute the probability of the event E = "drawing a king" or F = "drawing a queen" or G = "drawing a jack."

Approach: We will use the classical method for computing the probabilities because the outcomes are equally likely and easy to count. We use the Addition Rule for Disjoint Events to compute the probabilities in parts (b) and (c) because the events are mutually exclusive. For example, you cannot simultaneously draw a king and a queen.

Solution: The sample space consists of the 52 cards in the deck, so $N(S) = 52$.

(a) A standard deck of cards has four kings, so $N(E) = 4$. Therefore,

$$P(\text{king}) = P(E) = \frac{N(E)}{N(S)} = \frac{4}{52} = \frac{1}{13}$$

(b) A standard deck of cards also has four queens. Because events E and F are mutually exclusive, we use the Addition Rule for Disjoint Events. So

$$P(\text{king or queen}) = P(E \text{ or } F)$$
$$= P(E) + P(F)$$
$$= \frac{4}{52} + \frac{4}{52} = \frac{8}{52} = \frac{2}{13}$$

(c) Because events E, F, and G are mutually exclusive, we use the Addition Rule for Disjoint Events extended to two or more disjoint events. So

$$P(\text{king or queen or jack}) = P(E \text{ or } F \text{ or } G)$$
$$= P(E) + P(F) + P(G)$$
$$= \frac{4}{52} + \frac{4}{52} + \frac{4}{52} = \frac{12}{52} = \frac{3}{13}$$

Now Work Problems 25(a)–(c)

2 Use the General Addition Rule

A question that you may be asking yourself is, "What if I need to compute the probability of two events that are not disjoint?"

Consider the chip example. Suppose that we are randomly selecting chips from a bag. Each chip is labeled 0, 1, 2, 3, 4, 5, 6, 7, 8, or 9. Let E represent the event "choose an odd number," and let F represent the event "choose a number less than or equal to 4." Because $E = \{1, 3, 5, 7, 9\}$ and $F = \{0, 1, 2, 3, 4\}$ have the outcomes 1 and 3 in common, the events are not disjoint. Figure 10 shows a Venn diagram of these events.

Figure 10

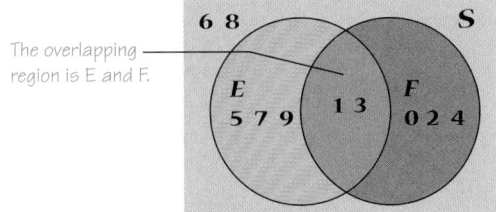

The overlapping region is E and F.

We can compute $P(E \text{ or } F)$ directly by counting because each outcome is equally likely. There are 8 outcomes in E or F and 10 outcomes in the sample space, so

$$P(E \text{ or } F) = \frac{N(E \text{ or } F)}{N(S)}$$
$$= \frac{8}{10} = \frac{4}{5}$$

If we attempt to compute $P(E \text{ or } F)$ using the Addition Rule for Disjoint Events, we obtain the following:

$$P(E \text{ or } F) = P(E) + P(F)$$
$$= \frac{5}{10} + \frac{5}{10}$$
$$= \frac{10}{10} = 1$$

This implies that the chips labeled 6 and 8 will never be selected, which contradicts our assumption that all the outcomes are equally likely. Our result is incorrect because we counted the outcomes 1 and 3 twice: once for event E and once for event F. To avoid this double counting, we have to subtract the probability corresponding to the overlapping region, E and F. That is, we have to subtract $P(E \text{ and } F) = \frac{2}{10}$ from the result and obtain

$$P(E \text{ or } F) = P(E) + P(F) - P(E \text{ and } F)$$
$$= \frac{5}{10} + \frac{5}{10} - \frac{2}{10}$$
$$= \frac{8}{10} = \frac{4}{5}$$

which agrees with the result we obtained by counting. These results can be generalized in the following rule:

The General Addition Rule

For any two events E and F,

$$P(E \text{ or } F) = P(E) + P(F) - P(E \text{ and } F)$$

EXAMPLE 3	**Computing Probabilities for Events That Are Not Disjoint**

Problem: Suppose that a single card is selected from a standard 52-card deck. Compute the probability of the event E = "drawing a king" or H = "drawing a diamond."

Approach: The events are not disjoint because the outcome "king of diamonds" is in both events, so we use the General Addition Rule.

Solution

$$P(\text{king or diamond}) = P(\text{king}) + P(\text{diamond}) - P(\text{king of diamonds})$$

$$= \frac{4}{52} + \frac{13}{52} - \frac{1}{52}$$

$$= \frac{16}{52} = \frac{4}{13}$$

Now Work Problem 31

Consider the data shown in Table 6, which represent the marital status of males and females 18 years old or older in the United States in 2006.

Table 6	Males (in millions)	Females (in millions)
Never married	30.3	25.0
Married	63.6	64.1
Widowed	2.6	11.3
Divorced	9.7	13.1

Source: U.S. Census Bureau, *Current Population Reports*

Table 6 is called a **contingency table** or **two-way table**, because it relates two categories of data. The **row variable** is marital status, because each row in the table describes the marital status of each individual. The **column variable** is gender. Each box inside the table is called a **cell**. For example, the cell corresponding to married individuals who are male is in the second row, first column. Each cell contains the frequency of the category: There were 63.6 million married males in the United States in 2006. Put another way, in the United States in 2006, there were 63.6 million individuals who were male *and* married.

EXAMPLE 4	**Using the Addition Rule with Contingency Tables**

Problem: Using the data in Table 6,

(a) Determine the probability that a randomly selected U.S. resident 18 years old or older is male.

(b) Determine the probability that a randomly selected U.S. resident 18 years old or older is widowed.

(c) Determine the probability that a randomly selected U.S. resident 18 years old or older is widowed or divorced.

(d) Determine the probability that a randomly selected U.S. resident 18 years old or older is male or widowed.

Approach: We first add up the entries in each row and column so that we get the total number of people in each category. We can then determine the probabilities using either the Addition Rule for Disjoint Events or the General Addition Rule.

Solution: Add the entries in each column. For example, in the "male" column we find that there are $30.3 + 63.6 + 2.6 + 9.7 = 106.2$ million males 18 years old or older in the United States. Add the entries in each row. For example, in the "never married" row we find there are $30.3 + 25.0 = 55.3$ million U.S. residents 18 years old or older who have never married. Adding the row totals or column totals, we find there are $106.2 + 113.5 = 55.3 + 127.7 + 13.9 + 22.8 = 219.7$ million U.S. residents 18 years old or older.

(a) There are 106.2 million males 18 years old or older and 219.7 million U.S. residents 18 years old or older. The probability that a randomly selected U.S. resident 18 years old or older is male is $\dfrac{106.2}{219.7} = 0.483$.

(b) There are 13.9 million U.S. residents 18 years old or older who are widowed. The probability that a randomly selected U.S. resident 18 years old or older is widowed is $\dfrac{13.9}{219.7} = 0.063$.

(c) The events widowed and divorced are disjoint. Do you see why? We use the Addition Rule for Disjoint Events.

$$P(\text{widowed or divorced}) = P(\text{widowed}) + P(\text{divorced})$$
$$= \frac{13.9}{219.7} + \frac{22.8}{219.7} = \frac{36.7}{219.7}$$
$$= 0.167$$

(d) The events male and widowed are not mutually exclusive. In fact, there are 2.6 million males who are widowed in the United States. Therefore, we use the General Addition Rule to compute $P(\text{male or widowed})$:

$$P(\text{male or widowed}) = P(\text{male}) + P(\text{widowed}) - P(\text{male and widowed})$$
$$= \frac{106.2}{219.7} + \frac{13.9}{219.7} - \frac{2.6}{219.7}$$
$$= \frac{117.5}{219.7} = 0.535$$

Now Work Problem 41

---

3 Compute the Probability of an Event Using the Complement Rule

Note to Instructor

There are a number of ways to denote the complement of an event, such as $\overline{E}, E'$, and $\sim E$ We choose E^c to avoid confusion with the notation for the sample mean.

Suppose that the probability of an event E is known and we would like to determine the probability that E does not occur. This can easily be accomplished using the idea of *complements*.

Definition

Complement of an Event
Let S denote the sample space of a probability experiment and let E denote an event. The **complement of E**, denoted E^c, is all outcomes in the sample space S that are not outcomes in the event E.

In Other Words

For any event, the event either happens or it doesn't. The Complement Rule is used when you know the probability that some event will occur and you want to know the opposite: the chance it will not occur.

Because E and E^c are mutually exclusive,

$$P(E \text{ or } E^c) = P(E) + P(E^c) = P(S) = 1$$

Subtracting $P(E)$ from both sides, we obtain

$$P(E^c) = 1 - P(E)$$

We have the following result.

Complement Rule

If E represents any event and E^c represents the complement of E, then

$$P(E^c) = 1 - P(E)$$

Figure 11 illustrates the Complement Rule using a Venn diagram.

Figure 11

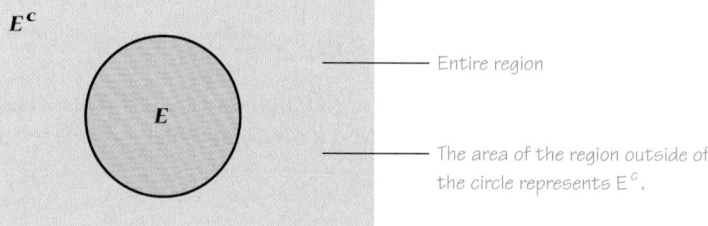

EXAMPLE 5   **Computing Probabilities Using Complements**

Problem: According to the National Gambling Impact Study Commission, 52% of Americans have played state lotteries. What is the probability that a randomly selected American has not played a state lottery?

Approach: Not playing a state lottery is the complement of playing a state lottery. We compute the probability using the Complement Rule.

Solution

$$P(\text{not played state lottery}) = 1 - P(\text{played state lottery}) = 1 - 0.52 = 0.48$$

There is a 48% probability of randomly selecting an American who has not played a state lottery.

EXAMPLE 6   **Computing Probabilities Using Complements**

Problem: The data in Table 7 represent the income distribution of households in the United States in 2006.

Table 7			
Annual Income	**Number (in thousands)**	**Annual Income**	**Number (in thousands)**
Less than $10,000	8,899	$50,000 to $74,999	21,222
$10,000 to $14,999	6,640	$75,000 to $99,999	13,215
$15,000 to $24,999	12,722	$100,000 to $149,999	12,164
$25,000 to $34,999	12,447	$150,000 to $199,999	3,981
$35,000 to $49,999	16,511	$200,000 or more	3,817

Source: U.S. Census Bureau

(a) Compute the probability that a randomly selected household earned $200,000 or more in 2006.

(b) Compute the probability that a randomly selected household earned less than $200,000 in 2006.

(c) Compute the probability that a randomly selected household earned at least $10,000 in 2006.

Approach: The probabilities will be determined by finding the relative frequency of each event. We have to find the total number of households in the United States in 2006.

Solution

(a) There were a total of $8,899 + 6,640 + \cdots + 3,817 = 111,528$ thousand households in the United States in 2006 and 3,817 thousand of them earned $200,000 or more. The probability that a randomly selected household in the United States earned $200,000 or more in 2006 is $\dfrac{3,817}{111,528} = 0.034$.

(b) We could compute the probability of randomly selecting a household that earned less than $200,000 in 2006 by adding the relative frequencies of each category less than $200,000, but it is easier to use complements. The complement of earning less than $200,000 is earning $200,000 or more. Therefore,

$$P(\text{less than } \$200,000) = 1 - P(\$200,000 \text{ or more})$$
$$= 1 - 0.034 = 0.966$$

There is a 96.6% probability of randomly selecting a household that earned less than $200,000 in 2006.

(c) The phrase *at least* means greater than or equal to. The complement of at least $10,000 is less than $10,000. In 2006, 8,899 thousand households earned less than $10,000. The probability of randomly selecting a household that earned at least $10,000 is

$$P(\text{at least } \$10,000) = 1 - P(\text{less than } \$10,000)$$
$$= 1 - \dfrac{8,899}{111,528} = 0.920$$

There is a 92.0% probability of randomly selecting a household that earned at least $10,000 in 2006.

Now Work Problems 25(d) and 29

5.2 ASSESS YOUR UNDERSTANDING

Concepts and Vocabulary

1. What does it mean when two events are disjoint?

2. If E and F are disjoint events, then $P(E \text{ or } F) = \underline{\hspace{1cm}}$.

3. If E and F are not disjoint events, then $P(E \text{ or } F) = \underline{\hspace{1cm}}$.

4. What does it mean when two events are complements?

Skill Building

In Problems 5–12, a probability experiment is conducted in which the sample space of the experiment is
$S = \{1, 2, 3, 4, 5, 6, 7, 8, 9, 10, 11, 12\}$. *Let event*
$E = \{2, 3, 4, 5, 6, 7\}$, *event* $F = \{5, 6, 7, 8, 9\}$, *event*
$G = \{9, 10, 11, 12\}$, *and event* $H = \{2, 3, 4\}$. *Assume that each outcome is equally likely.*

5. List the outcomes in E and F. Are E and F mutually exclusive?   {5, 6, 7}; no

2. $P(E) + P(F)$ 3. $P(E) + P(F) - P(E \text{ and } F)$

6. List the outcomes in F and G. Are F and G mutually exclusive?   {9}; no

7. List the outcomes in F or G. Now find $P(F \text{ or } G)$ by counting the number of outcomes in F or G. Determine $P(F \text{ or } G)$ using the General Addition Rule.   {5, 6, 7, 8, 9, 10, 11, 12}; $\frac{2}{3}$

8. List the outcomes in E or H. Now find $P(E \text{ or } H)$ by counting the number of outcomes in E or H. Determine $P(E \text{ or } H)$ using the General Addition Rule.   {2, 3, 4, 5, 6, 7}; $\frac{1}{2}$

9. List the outcomes in E and G. Are E and G mutually exclusive?   { }; yes

10. List the outcomes in F and H. Are F and H mutually exclusive?   { }; yes

11. List the outcomes in E^c. Find $P(E^c)$.   {1, 8, 9, 10, 11, 12}; $\frac{1}{2}$

12. List the outcomes in F^c. Find $P(F^c)$.   {1, 2, 3, 4, 10, 11, 12}; $\frac{7}{12}$

In Problems 13–18, find the probability of the indicated event if $P(E) = 0.25$ *and* $P(F) = 0.45$.

13. Find $P(E$ or $F)$ if $P(E$ and $F) = 0.15$. *0.55*

14. Find $P(E$ and $F)$ if $P(E$ or $F) = 0.6$. *0.1*

15. Find $P(E$ or $F)$ if E and F are mutually exclusive. *0.7*

16. Find $P(E$ and $F)$ if E and F are mutually exclusive. *0*

17. Find $P(E^c)$. *0.75*

18. Find $P(F^c)$. *0.55*

19. If $P(E) = 0.60$, $P(E$ or $F) = 0.85$, and $P(E$ and $F) = 0.05$, find $P(F)$. *0.30*

20. If $P(F) = 0.30$, $P(E$ or $F) = 0.65$, and $P(E$ and $F) = 0.15$, find $P(E)$. *0.50*

In Problems 21–24, a golf ball is selected at random from a golf bag. If the golf bag contains 9 Titleists, 8 Maxflis, and 3 Top-Flites, find the probability of each event.

21. The golf ball is a Titleist or Maxfli. $\dfrac{17}{20}$

22. The golf ball is a Maxfli or Top-Flite. $\dfrac{11}{20}$

23. The golf ball is not a Titleist. $\dfrac{11}{20}$

24. The golf ball is not a Top-Flite. $\dfrac{17}{20}$

Applying the Concepts

25. Weapon of Choice The following probability model shows
NW the distribution of murders by type of weapon for murder cases from 2002 to 2006.

Weapon	Probability
Gun	0.671
Knife	0.126
Blunt object	0.044
Personal weapon	0.063
Strangulation	0.010
Fire	0.009
Other	0.077

Source: U.S. Federal Bureau of Investigation

(a) Verify that this is a probability model.
(b) What is the probability that a randomly selected murder resulted from a gun or knife? Interpret this probability. *0.797*
(c) What is the probability that a randomly selected murder resulted from a knife, blunt object, or strangulation? Interpret this probability. *0.180*
(d) What is the probability that a randomly selected murder resulted from a weapon other than a gun? Interpret this probability. *0.329*
(e) Are murders by strangulation unusual? *Yes*

26. Doctorates Conferred The following probability model shows the distribution of doctoral degrees from U.S. universities in 2005 by area of study.

Area of Study	Probability
Engineering	0.148
Physical sciences	0.100
Life sciences	0.171
Mathematics	0.028
Computer sciences	0.026
Social sciences	0.172
Humanities	0.114
Education	0.144
Professional and other fields	0.097

Source: U.S. National Science Foundation

(a) Verify that this is a probability model.
(b) What is the probability that a randomly selected doctoral candidate who earned a degree in 2005 studied physical science or life science? Interpret this probability. *0.271*
(c) What is the probability that a randomly selected doctoral candidate who earned a degree in 2005 studied physical science, life science, mathematics, or computer science? Interpret this probability. *0.325*
(d) What is the probability that a randomly selected doctoral candidate who earned a degree in 2005 did not study mathematics? Interpret this probability. *0.972*
(e) Are doctoral degrees in mathematics unusual? Does this result surprise you? *Yes*

27. If events E and F are disjoint and the events F and G are disjoint, must the events E and G necessarily be disjoint? Give an example to illustrate your opinion. *No*

28. Draw a Venn diagram like that in Figure 10 that expands the general addition rule to three events. Use the diagram to write the General Addition Rule for three events.

29. Multiple Births The following data represent the number of
NW live multiple-delivery births (three or more babies) in 2005 for women 15 to 54 years old:

Age	Number of Multiple Births
15–19	83
20–24	465
25–29	1,635
30–34	2,443
35–39	1,604
40–44	344
45–54	120
Total	**6,694**

Source: National Vital Statistics Report, Vol. 56, No. 16, December 5, 2007

(a) Determine the probability that a randomly selected multiple birth in 2005 for women 15 to 54 years old involved a mother 30 to 39 years old. Interpret this probability. *0.605*
(b) Determine the probability that a randomly selected multiple birth in 2005 for women 15 to 54 years old involved a mother who was not 30 to 39 years old. Interpret this probability. *0.395*
(c) Determine the probability that a randomly selected multiple birth in 2005 for women 15 to 54 years old

involved a mother who was less than 45 years old. Interpret this probability. *0.982*

(d) Determine the probability that a randomly selected multiple birth in 2005 for women 15 to 54 years old involved a mother who was at least 20 years old. Interpret this probability. *0.988*

30. Housing The following probability model shows the distribution for the number of rooms in U.S. housing units.

Rooms	Probability
One	0.005
Two	0.011
Three	0.088
Four	0.183
Five	0.230
Six	0.204
Seven	0.123
Eight or more	0.156

Source: U.S. Census Bureau

30. (b) 0.896

(a) Verify that this is a probability model.
(b) What is the probability that a randomly selected housing unit has four or more rooms? Interpret this probability.
(c) What is the probability that a randomly selected housing unit has fewer than eight rooms? Interpret this probability. *0.844*
(d) What is the probability that a randomly selected housing unit has from four to six (inclusive) rooms? Interpret this probability. *0.617*
(e) What is the probability that a randomly selected housing unit has at least two rooms? Interpret this probability. *0.995*

31. A Deck of Cards A standard deck of cards contains 52 cards, as shown in Figure 9. One card is randomly selected from the deck.

(a) Compute the probability of randomly selecting a heart or club from a deck of cards. *1/2*
(b) Compute the probability of randomly selecting a heart or club or diamond from a deck of cards. *3/4*
(c) Compute the probability of randomly selecting an ace or heart from a deck of cards. *4/13*

32. A Deck of Cards A standard deck of cards contains 52 cards, as shown in Figure 9. One card is randomly selected from the deck.

(a) Compute the probability of randomly selecting a two or three from a deck of cards. *2/13*
(b) Compute the probability of randomly selecting a two or three or four from a deck of cards. *3/13*
(c) Compute the probability of randomly selecting a two or club from a deck of cards. *4/13*

33. Birthdays Exclude leap years from the following calculations:

(a) Compute the probability that a randomly selected person does not have a birthday on November 8. *364/365*
(b) Compute the probability that a randomly selected person does not have a birthday on the 1st day of a month.
(c) Compute the probability that a randomly selected person does not have a birthday on the 31st day of a month.
(d) Compute the probability that a randomly selected person was not born in December. *334/365*

33. (b) 353/365   33. (c) 358/365

34. Roulette In the game of roulette, a wheel consists of 38 slots numbered 0, 00, 1, 2, … 36. The odd-numbered slots are red, and the even-numbered slots are black. The numbers 0 and 00 are green. To play the game, a metal ball is spun around the wheel and is allowed to fall into one of the numbered slots.

(a) What is the probability that the metal ball lands on green or red? *10/19*
(b) What is the probability that the metal ball does not land on green? *18/19*

35. Health Problems According to the Centers for Disease Control, the probability that a randomly selected citizen of the United States has hearing problems is 0.151. The probability that a randomly selected citizen of the United States has vision problems is 0.093. Can we compute the probability of randomly selecting a citizen of the United States who has hearing problems or vision problems by adding these probabilities? Why or why not? *No*

36. Visits to the Doctor A National Ambulatory Medical Care Survey administered by the Centers for Disease Control found that the probability a randomly selected patient visited the doctor for a blood pressure check is 0.593. The probability a randomly selected patient visited the doctor for urinalysis is 0.064. Can we compute the probability of randomly selecting a patient who visited the doctor for a blood pressure check or urinalysis by adding these probabilities? Why or why not? *No*

37. Foster Care A social worker for a child advocacy center has a caseload of 24 children under the age of 18. Her caseload by age is as follows:

Age (yr)	Under 1	1–5	6–10	11–14	15–17
Cases	1	6	5	7	5

What is the probability that one of her clients, selected at random, is:

(a) Between 6 and 10 years old? Is this unusual? *0.208; no*
(b) More than 5 years old? *0.708*
(c) Less than 1 year old? Is this unusual? *0.042; yes*

38. Language Spoken at Home According to the U.S. Census Bureau, the probability that a randomly selected household speaks only English at home is 0.81. The probability that a randomly selected household speaks only Spanish at home is 0.12.

(a) What is the probability that a randomly selected household speaks only English or only Spanish at home? *0.93*
(b) What is the probability that a randomly selected household speaks a language other than only English or only Spanish at home? *0.07*
(c) What is the probability that a randomly selected household speaks a language other than only English at home? *0.19*
(d) Can the probability that a randomly selected household speaks only Polish at home equal 0.08? Why or why not? *No*

39. Getting to Work According to the U.S. Census Bureau, the probability that a randomly selected worker primarily drives a car to work is 0.867. The probability that a randomly selected worker primarily takes public transportation to work is 0.048.

(a) What is the probability that a randomly selected worker primarily drives a car or takes public transportation to work?   0.915

(b) What is the probability that a randomly selected worker neither drives a car nor takes public transportation to work?   0.085

(c) What is the probability that a randomly selected worker does not drive a car to work?   0.133

(d) Can the probability that a randomly selected worker walks to work equal 0.15? Why or why not?   No

40. Working Couples A guidance counselor at a middle school collected the following information regarding the employment status of married couples within his school's boundaries.

Worked	Number of Children under 18 Years Old			
	0	1	2 or More	Total
Husband only	172	79	174	**425**
Wife only	94	17	15	**126**
Both spouses	522	257	370	**1,149**
Total	**788**	**353**	**559**	**1,700**

(a) What is the probability that, for married couple selected at random, both spouses work?   0.676

(b) What is the probability that, for married couple selected at random, the couple has one child under the age of 18?   0.208

(c) What is the probability that, for married couple selected at random, the couple has two or more children under the age of 18 and both spouses work?   0.218

(d) What is the probability that, for married couple selected at random, the couple has no children or only the husband works?   0.612

(e) Would it be unusual to select a married couple at random for which only the wife works?   No

41. Cigar Smoking The data in the following table show the results of a national study of 137,243 U.S. men that investigated the association between cigar smoking and death from cancer. **Note:** Current cigar smoker means cigar smoker at time of death.

	Died from Cancer	Did Not Die from Cancer
Never smoked cigars	782	120,747
Former cigar smoker	91	7,757
Current cigar smoker	141	7,725

Source: Shapiro, Jacobs, and Thun. "Cigar Smoking in Men and Risk of Death from Tobacco-Related Cancers," *Journal of the National Cancer Institute,* February 16, 2000.

(a) If an individual is randomly selected from this study, what is the probability that he died from cancer?   0.007

(b) If an individual is randomly selected from this study, what is the probability that he was a current cigar smoker?   0.057

(c) If an individual is randomly selected from this study, what is the probability that he died from cancer and was a current cigar smoker?   0.001

(d) If an individual is randomly selected from this study, what is the probability that he died from cancer or was a current cigar smoker?   0.064

42. Civilian Labor Force The following table represents the employment status and gender of the civilian labor force ages 16 to 24 (in millions).

	Male	Female
Employed	9.9	9.5
Unemployed	1.4	1.0

Source: U.S. Bureau of Labor Statistics, December 2007

(a) What is the probability that a randomly selected 16- to 24-year-old individual from the civilian labor force is employed?   0.890

(b) What is the probability that a randomly selected 16- to 24-year-old individual from the civilian labor force is male?   0.518

(c) What is the probability that a randomly selected 16- to 24-year-old individual from the civilian labor force is employed and male?   0.454

(d) What is the probability that a randomly selected 16- to 24-year-old individual from the civilian labor force is employed or male?   0.954

43. Student Government Satisfaction Survey The Committee on Student Life at a university conducted a survey of 375 undergraduate students regarding satisfaction with student government. Results of the survey are shown in the table by class rank.

	Freshman	Sophomore	Junior	Senior	Total
Satisfied	57	49	64	61	**231**
Neutral	23	15	16	11	**65**
Not satisfied	21	18	14	26	**79**
Total	**101**	**82**	**94**	**98**	**375**

(a) If a survey participant is selected at random, what is the probability that he or she is satisfied with student government?   0.616

(b) If a survey participant is selected at random, what is the probability that he or she is a junior?   0.251

(c) If a survey participant is selected at random, what is the probability that he or she is satisfied and is a junior?   0.171

(d) If a survey participant is selected at random, what is the probability that he or she is satisfied or is a junior?   0.696

44. The Placebo Effect A company is testing a new medicine for migraine headaches. In the study, 150 women were given the new medicine and an additional 100 women were given a placebo. Each participant was directed to take the medicine when the first symptoms of a migraine occurred and then to record whether the headache went away within 45 minutes or lingered. The results are recorded in the following table:

	Headache Went Away	Headache Lingered
Given medicine	132	18
Given placebo	56	44

(a) If a study participant is selected at random, what is the probability she was given the placebo?   0.40

(b) If a study participant is selected at random, what is the probability her headache went away within 45 minutes?   0.752

(c) If a study participant is selected at random, what is the probability she was given the placebo and her headache went away within 45 minutes? *0.224*

(d) If a study participant is selected at random, what is the probability she was given the placebo or her headache went away within 45 minutes? *0.928*

45. Active Duty The following table represents the number of active-duty military personnel by rank in the four major branches of the military as of December 31, 2007.

	Officer	Enlisted	Total
Army	84,781	428,929	**513,710**
Navy	51,167	278,193	**329,360**
Air Force	64,927	260,798	**325,725**
Marines	19,631	166,711	**186,342**
Total	**220,506**	**1,134,631**	**1,355,137**

Source: U.S. Department of Defense

45. (b) 0.243

(a) If an active-duty military person is selected at random, what is the probability the individual is an officer? *0.163*

(b) If an active-duty military person is selected at random, what is the probability the individual is in the Navy?

(c) If an active-duty military person is selected at random, what is the probability the individual is a naval officer? *0.038*

(d) If an active-duty military person is selected at random, what is the probability the individual is an officer or is in the Navy? *0.368*

46. Driver Fatalities The following data represent the number of drivers in fatal crashes in the United States in 2005 by age group for male and female drivers:

Age	Males	Females	Total
Under 16	227	77	**304**
16–20	5,180	2,113	**7,293**
21–34	13,611	4,311	**17,922**
35–54	15,108	5,027	**20,135**
55–74	6,801	2,452	**9,253**
Over 74	2,022	980	**3,002**
Total	**42,949**	**14,960**	**57,909**

Source: *Traffic Safety Facts, 2005*, Federal Highway Administration, 2005

(a) Determine the probability that a randomly selected driver involved in a fatal crash was male. *0.742*

(b) Determine the probability that a randomly selected driver involved in a fatal crash was 16 to 20 years old. *0.126*

(c) Determine the probability that a randomly selected driver involved in a fatal crash was a 16- to 20-year-old male. *0.089*

(d) Determine the probability that a randomly selected driver involved in a fatal crash was male or 16 to 20 years old. *0.778*

(e) Would it be unusual for a randomly selected driver involved in a fatal crash to be a 16- to 20-year-old female? *Yes*

47. Putting It Together: Red Light Cameras In a study of the feasibility of a red-light camera program in the city of Milwaukee, the following data were provided summarizing the projected number of crashes at 13 selected intersections over a 5-year period.

Crash Type	Current System	With Red-Light Cameras
Reported injury	289	221
Reported property damage only	392	333
Unreported injury	78	60
Unreported property damage only	362	308
Total	**1,121**	**922**

Source: Krig, Moran, Regan. "An Analysis of a Red-Light Camera Program in the City of Milwaukee," Spring 2006, prepared for the city of Milwaukee Budget and Management Division

47. (e) Current: 86.2; Camera: 70.9

(a) Identify the variables presented in the table.

(b) State whether each variable is qualitative or quantitative. If quantitative, state whether it is discrete or continuous.

(c) Construct a relative frequency distribution for each system.

(d) Construct a side-by-side relative frequency bar graph for the data.

(e) Compute the mean number of crashes per intersection in the study, if possible. If not possible, explain why.

(f) Compute the standard deviation number of crashes, if possible. If not possible, explain why.

(g) Based on the data shown, does it appear that the red-light camera program will be beneficial in reducing crashes at the intersections? Explain.

(h) For the current system, what is the probability that a crash selected at random will have reported injuries? *0.258*

(i) For the camera system, what is the probability that a crash selected at random will have only property damage? *0.695*

The study classified crashes further by indicating whether they were red-light running crashes or rear-end crashes. The results are as follows:

Crash Type	Rear End Current	Rear End Cameras	Red-Light Running Current	Red-Light Running Cameras
Reported injury	67	77	222	144
Reported property damage only	157	180	235	153
Unreported injury	18	21	60	39
Unreported property damage only	145	167	217	141
Total	**387**	**445**	**734**	**477**

(j) Using Simpson's Paradox, explain how the additional classification affects your response to part (g).

(k) What recommendation would you make to the city council regarding the implementation of the red-light camera program? Would you need any additional information before making your recommendation? Explain.

5.3 INDEPENDENCE AND THE MULTIPLICATION RULE

Objectives	
1	Identify independent events
2	Use the Multiplication Rule for independent events
3	Compute at-least probabilities

1 Identify Independent Events

The Addition Rule for Disjoint Events deals with probabilities involving the word *or*. That is, it is used for computing the probability of observing an outcome in event *E* or event *F*. We now describe a probability rule for computing the probability that *E* and *F* both occur.

Before we can present this rule, we must discuss the idea of *independent events*.

Definition   Two events *E* and *F* are **independent** if the occurrence of event *E* in a probability experiment does not affect the probability of event *F*. Two events are **dependent** if the occurrence of event *E* in a probability experiment affects the probability of event *F*.

To help you understand the idea of independence, we again look at a simple situation—flipping a coin. Suppose that you flip a fair coin twice. Does the fact that you obtained a head on the first toss have any effect on the likelihood of obtaining a head on the second toss? Not unless you are a master coin flipper who can manipulate the outcome of a coin flip! For this reason, the outcome from the first flip is independent of the outcome from the second flip. Let's look at other examples.

EXAMPLE 1 | **Independent or Not?**

(a) Suppose that you flip a coin and roll a die. The events "obtain a head" and "roll a 5" are independent because the results of the coin flip do not affect the results of the die toss.

(b) Are the events "earned a bachelor's degree" and "earn more than $100,000 per year" independent? No, because knowing that an individual has a bachelor's degree affects the likelihood that the individual is earning more than $100,000 per year.

(c) Two 24-year-old male drivers who live in the United States are randomly selected. The events "male 1 gets in a car accident during the year" and "male 2 gets in a car accident during the year" are independent because the males were randomly selected. This means what happens with one of the drivers has nothing to do with what happens to the other driver.

In Other Words

In determining whether two events are independent, ask yourself whether the probability of one event is affected by the other event. For example, what is the probability that a 29-year-old male has high cholesterol? What is the probability that a 29-year-old male has high cholesterol, given that he eats fast food four times a week? Does the fact that the individual eats fast food four times a week change the likelihood that he has high cholesterol? If yes, the events are not independent.

In Example 1(c), we are able to conclude that the events "male 1 gets in an accident" and "male 2 gets in an accident" are independent because the individuals are randomly selected. By randomly selecting the individuals, it is reasonable to conclude that the individuals are not related in any way (related in the sense that they do not live in the same town, attend the same school, and so on). If the two individuals did have a common link between them (such as they both lived on the same city block), then knowing that one male had a car accident may affect the likelihood that the other male had a car accident. After all, they could hit each other!

Now Work Problem 7

Disjoint Events versus Independent Events

It is important that we understand that disjoint events and independent events are different concepts. Recall that two events are disjoint if they have no outcomes in common. In other words, two events are disjoint if, knowing that one of the events occurs, we know the other event did not occur. Independence means that one event occurring does not affect the probability of the other event occurring. Therefore, knowing two events are disjoint means that the events are not independent.

Consider the experiment of rolling a single die. Let E represent the event "roll an even number," and let F represent the event "roll an odd number." We can see that E and F are mutually exclusive because they have no outcomes in common. In addition, $P(E) = \dfrac{1}{2}$ and $P(F) = \dfrac{1}{2}$. However, if we are told that the roll of the die is going to be an even number, then what is the probability of event F? Because the outcome will be even, the probability of event F is now 0 (and the probability of event E is now 1).

② Use the Multiplication Rule for Independent Events

Suppose that you flip a fair coin twice. What is the probability that you obtain a head on both flips? Put another way, what is the probability that you obtain a head on the first flip *and* you obtain a head on the second flip? We can easily create a sample space that lists the outcomes of this experiment. In flipping a coin twice, where H represents the outcome "heads" and T represents the outcome "tails," we can obtain

$$S = \{HH, HT, TH, TT\}$$

There is one outcome with both heads. Because each outcome is equally likely, we have

$$P(\text{heads on the 1st flip and heads on the 2nd flip}) = \frac{N(\text{heads on the 1st and heads on the 2nd})}{N(S)}$$

$$= \frac{1}{4}$$

We may have intuitively been able to figure this out by recognizing $P(\text{head}) = \dfrac{1}{2}$ for each flip. So it seems reasonable that

$$P(\text{heads on the 1st flip and heads on the 2nd flip}) = P(\text{heads on 1st flip}) \cdot P(\text{heads on 2nd flip})$$

$$= \frac{1}{2} \cdot \frac{1}{2}$$

$$= \frac{1}{4}$$

Because both approaches result in the same answer, $\dfrac{1}{4}$, we conjecture that $P(E \text{ and } F) = P(E) \cdot P(F)$. Our conjecture is correct.

> **Multiplication Rule for Independent Events**
>
> If E and F are independent events, then
>
> $$P(E \text{ and } F) = P(E) \cdot P(F)$$

EXAMPLE 2 Computing Probabilities of Independent Events

Problem: In the game of roulette, the wheel has slots numbered 0, 00, and 1 through 36. A metal ball is allowed to roll around a wheel until it falls into one of the numbered slots. You decide to play the game and place a bet on the number 17. What is the probability that the ball will land in the slot numbered 17 two times in a row?

Approach: There are 38 outcomes in the sample space of the experiment. We use the classical method of computing probabilities because the outcomes are equally likely. In addition, we use the Multiplication Rule for Independent Events. The events "17 on first spin" and "17 on second spin" are independent because the ball does not remember it landed on 17 on the first spin, so this cannot affect the probability of landing on 17 on the second spin.

Solution: Because there are 38 possible outcomes to the experiment, the probability of the ball landing on 17 is $\frac{1}{38}$. Because the events "17 on first spin" and "17 on second spin" are independent, we have

$P(\text{ball lands in slot 17 on the first spin and ball lands in slot 17 on the second spin})$

$= P(\text{ball lands in slot 17 on the first spin}) \cdot P(\text{ball lands in slot 17 on the second spin})$

$= \frac{1}{38} \cdot \frac{1}{38} = \frac{1}{1,444} \approx 0.0006925$

It is very unlikely that the ball will land on 17 twice in a row. We expect the ball to land on 17 twice in a row about 7 times in 10,000 trials.

We can extend the Multiplication Rule for three or more independent events.

> **Multiplication Rule for n Independent Events**
> If events $E, F, G, \ldots$ are independent, then
> $$P(E \text{ and } F \text{ and } G \text{ and } \ldots) = P(E) \cdot P(F) \cdot P(G) \ldots$$

EXAMPLE 3   Life Expectancy

Problem: The probability that a randomly selected 24 year old male will survive the year is 0.9986 according to the National Vital Statistics Report, Vol. 56, No. 9. What is the probability that 3 randomly selected 24-year-old males will survive the year? What is the probability that 20 randomly selected 24-year-old males will survive the year?

Approach: We can safely assume that the outcomes of the probability experiment are independent, because there is no indication that the survival of one male affects the survival of the others. For example, if two of the males lived in the same house, a house fire could kill both males and we lose independence. (Knowledge that one male died in a house fire certainly affects the probability that the other died.) By randomly selecting the males, we minimize the chances that they are related in any way.

Solution

$$
\begin{aligned}
P(\text{all three males survive}) &= P(\text{1st survives and 2nd survives and 3rd survives}) \\
&= P(\text{1st survives}) \cdot P(\text{2nd survives}) \cdot P(\text{3rd survives}) \\
&= (0.9986)(0.9986)(0.9986) \\
&= 0.9958
\end{aligned}
$$

There is a 99.58% probability that all three males survive the year.

$$
\begin{aligned}
P(\text{all 20 males survive}) &= P(\text{1st survives and 2nd survives and} \ldots \text{and 20th survives}) \\
&= P(\text{1st survives}) \cdot P(\text{2nd survives}) \cdot \cdots \cdot P(\text{20th survives}) \\
&\qquad \uparrow \text{Independent events} \qquad \overbrace{\text{Multiply 0.9986 by itself 20 times.}} \\
&= (0.9986) \cdot (0.9986) \cdot \cdots \cdot (0.9986) \\
&= (0.9986)^{20} \\
&= 0.9724
\end{aligned}
$$

There is a 97.24% probability that all 20 males survive the year.

Now Work Problem 17(a) and (b)

3   Compute At-Least Probabilities

We now present an example in which we compute at-least probabilities. These probabilities use the Complement Rule. The phrase *at least* means "greater than or equal to". For example, a person must be at least 17 years old to see an R-rated movie.

EXAMPLE 4	**Computing At-Least Probabilities**

Note to Instructor

Remind students that at-least means greater than or equal to. At-least probabilities are usually determined using the Complement Rule. For Example 4, ask students to distinguish between $1 - 0.9986^{1,000}$ and $(1 - 0.9986)^{1,000}$.

Problem: Compute the probability that at least 1 male out of 1,000 aged 24 years will die during the course of the year if the probability that a randomly selected 24-year-old male survives the year is 0.9986.

Approach: The phrase *at least* means "greater than or equal to", so we wish to know the probability that 1 or 2 or 3 or ... or 1,000 males will die during the year. These events are mutually exclusive, so

$$P(1 \text{ or } 2 \text{ or } 3 \text{ or} \ldots \text{or } 1,000 \text{ die}) = P(1 \text{ dies}) + P(2 \text{ die}) + P(3 \text{ die}) + \cdots + P(1,000 \text{ die})$$

Computing these probabilities is very time consuming. However, we notice that the complement of "at least one dying" is "none die." We use the Complement Rule to compute the probability.

Solution

$$P(\text{at least one dies}) = 1 - P(\text{none die})$$
$$= 1 - P(\text{1st survives and 2nd survives and} \ldots \text{and 1,000th survives})$$
$$= 1 - P(\text{1st survives}) \cdot P(\text{2nd survives}) \cdot \cdots \cdot P(\text{1,000th survives}) \qquad \textit{Independent events}$$
$$= 1 - (0.9986)^{1,000}$$
$$= 1 - 0.2464$$
$$= 0.7536$$
$$= 75.36\%$$

There is a 75.36% probability that at least one 24-year-old male out of 1,000 will die during the course of the year.

Now Work Problem 17(c)

Summary: Rules of Probability

1. The probability of any event must be between 0 and 1, inclusive. If we let E denote any event, then $0 \le P(E) \le 1$.

2. The sum of the probabilities of all outcomes must equal 1. That is, if the sample space $S = \{e_1, e_2, \ldots, e_n\}$, then $P(e_1) + P(e_2) + \cdots + P(e_n) = 1$.

3. If E and F are disjoint events, then $P(E \text{ or } F) = P(E) + P(F)$. If E and F are not disjoint events, then $P(E \text{ or } F) = P(E) + P(F) - P(E \text{ and } F)$.

4. If E represents any event and E^c represents the complement of E, then $P(E^c) = 1 - P(E)$.

5. If E and F are independent events, then $P(E \text{ and } F) = P(E) \cdot P(F)$.

Notice that *or* probabilities use the Addition Rule, whereas *and* probabilities use the Multiplication Rule. Accordingly, *or* probabilities imply addition, while *and* probabilities imply multiplication.

5.3 ASSESS YOUR UNDERSTANDING

Concepts and Vocabulary

1. Two events E and F are _independent_ if the occurrence of event E in a probability experiment does not affect the probability of event F.

2. The word *and* in probability implies that we use the _Multiplication_ Rule.

3. The word *or* in probability implies that we use the _Addition_ Rule.

4. *True or False*: When two events are disjoint, they are also independent. _False_

5. If two events E and F are independent, $P(E \text{ and } F) =$ _$P(E) \cdot P(F)$_ .

6. Suppose events E and F are disjoint. What is $P(E \text{ and } F)$? _0_

Skill Building

7. Determine whether the events E and F are independent or **NW** dependent. Justify your answer.
   (a) E: Speeding on the interstate.
       F: Being pulled over by a police officer. _Dependent_
   (b) E: You gain weight.
       F: You eat fast food for dinner every night. _Dependent_
   (c) E: You get a high score on a statistics exam.
       F: The Boston Red Sox win a baseball game. _Independent_

8. Determine whether the events E and F are independent or dependent. Justify you answer.
   (a) E: The battery in your cell phone is dead.
       F: The batteries in your calculator are dead. _Independent_
   (b) E: Your favorite color is blue.
       F: Your friend's favorite hobby is fishing. _Independent_
   (c) E: You are late for school.
       F: Your car runs out of gas. _Dependent_

9. Suppose that events E and F are independent, $P(E) = 0.3$, and $P(F) = 0.6$. What is the $P(E \text{ and } F)$? _0.18_

10. Suppose that events E and F are independent, $P(E) = 0.7$, and $P(F) = 0.9$. What is the $P(E \text{ and } F)$? _0.63_

Applying the Concepts

11. **Flipping a Coin** What is the probability of obtaining five heads in a row when flipping a coin? Interpret this probability. _0.03125_

12. **Rolling a Die** What is the probability of obtaining 4 ones in a row when rolling a fair, six-sided die? Interpret this probability. _0.0008_

13. **Southpaws** About 13% of the population is left-handed. If two people are randomly selected, what is the probability that both are left-handed? What is the probability that at least one is right-handed? _0.0169; 0.9831_

14. **Double Jackpot** Shawn lives near the border of Illinois and Missouri. One weekend he decides to play $1 in both state lotteries in hopes of hitting two jackpots. The probability of winning the Missouri Lotto is about 0.00000028357 and the probability of winning the Illinois Lotto is about 0.000000098239.
    (a) Explain why the two lotteries are independent.
    (b) Find the probability that Shawn will win both jackpots. _0.0000000000000279_

15. **False Positives** The ELISA is a test to determine whether the HIV antibody is present. The test is 99.5% effective. This means that the test will accurately come back negative if the HIV antibody is not present. The probability of a test coming back positive when the antibody is not present (a false positive) is 0.005. Suppose that the ELISA is given to five randomly selected people who do not have the HIV antibody.
    (a) What is the probability that the ELISA comes back negative for all five people? _0.9752_
    (b) What is the probability that the ELISA comes back positive for at least one of the five people? _0.0248_

16. **Christmas Lights** Christmas lights are often designed with a series circuit. This means that when one light burns out the entire string of lights goes black. Suppose that the lights are designed so that the probability a bulb will last 2 years is 0.995. The success or failure of a bulb is independent of the success or failure of other bulbs.
    (a) What is the probability that in a string of 100 lights all 100 will last 2 years? _0.6058_
    (b) What is the probability that at least one bulb will burn out in 2 years? _0.3942_

17. **Life Expectancy** The probability that a randomly selected **NW** 40-year-old male will live to be 41 years old is 0.99757, according to the *National Vital Statistics Report*, Vol. 56, No. 9.
    (a) What is the probability that two randomly selected 40-year-old males will live to be 41 years old? _0.99515_
    (b) What is the probability that five randomly selected 40-year-old males will live to be 41 years old? _0.98791_
    (c) What is the probability that at least one of five randomly selected 40-year-old males will not live to be 41 years old? Would it be unusual if at least one of five randomly selected 40-year-old males did not live to be 41 years old? _0.01209; yes_

18. **Life Expectancy** The probability that a randomly selected 40-year-old female will live to be 41 years old is 0.99855 according to the *National Vital Statistics Report*, Vol. 56, No. 9.
    (a) What is the probability that two randomly selected 40-year-old females will live to be 41 years old? _0.99710_
    (b) What is the probability that five randomly selected 40-year-old females will live to be 41 years old? _0.99277_
    (c) What is the probability that at least one of five randomly selected 40-year-old females will not live to be 41 years old? Would it be unusual if at least one of five randomly selected 40-year-old females did not live to be 41 years old? _0.00723; yes_

19. **Blood Types** Blood types can be classified as either Rh^+ or Rh^-. According to the *Information Please Almanac*, 99% of the Chinese population has Rh^+ blood.
    (a) What is the probability that two randomly selected Chinese people have Rh^+ blood? _0.9801_
    (b) What is the probability that six randomly selected Chinese people have Rh^+ blood? _0.9415_
    (c) What is the probability that at least one of six randomly selected Chinese people has Rh^- blood? Would it be unusual that at least one of six randomly selected Chinese people has Rh^- blood? _0.0585; no_

20. **Quality Control** Suppose that a company selects two people who work independently inspecting two-by-four timbers.

Their job is to identify low-quality timbers. Suppose that the probability that an inspector does not identify a low-quality timber is 0.20.

(a) What is the probability that both inspectors do not identify a low-quality timber? *0.04*

(b) How many inspectors should be hired to keep the probability of not identifying a low-quality timber below 1%? *3*

(c) Interpret the probability from part (a).

21. Reliability For a parallel structure of identical components, the system can succeed if at least one of the components succeeds. Assume that components fail independently of each other and that each component has a 0.15 probability of failure.

(a) Would it be unusual to observe one component fail? Two components? *No; yes*

(b) What is the probability that a parallel structure with 2 identical components will succeed? *0.9775*

(c) How many components would be needed in the structure so that the probability the system will succeed is greater than 0.9999? *5*

22. E.P.T. Pregnancy Tests The packaging of an E.P.T. Pregnancy Test states that the test is "99% accurate at detecting typical pregnancy hormone levels." Assume that the probability that a test will correctly identify a pregnancy is 0.99 and that 12 randomly selected pregnant women with typical hormone levels are each given the test. *(a) 0.8864*

(a) What is the probability that all 12 tests will be positive?

(b) What is the probability that at least one test will not be positive? *0.1136*

23. Cold Streaks Players in sports are said to have "hot streaks" and "cold streaks." For example, a batter in baseball might be considered to be in a slump, or cold streak, if he has made 10 outs in 10 consecutive at-bats. Suppose that a hitter successfully reaches base 30% of the time he comes to the plate.

(a) Find the probability that the hitter makes 10 outs in 10 consecutive at-bats, assuming that at-bats are independent events. *Hint*: The hitter makes an out 70% of the time. *0.02825*

(b) Are cold streaks unusual? *Yes*

(c) Interpret the probability from part (a).

24. Hot Streaks In a recent basketball game, a player who makes 65% of his free throws made eight consecutive free throws. Assuming that free-throw shots are independent, determine whether this feat was unusual. *Unusual*

25. Bowling Suppose that Ralph gets a strike when bowling 30% of the time.

(a) What is the probability that Ralph gets two strikes in a row? *0.09*

(b) What is the probability that Ralph gets a turkey (three strikes in a row)? *0.027*

(c) When events are independent, their complements are independent as well. Use this result to determine the probability that Ralph gets a strike and then does not get a strike. *0.21*

26. NASCAR Fans Among Americans who consider themselves auto racing fans, 59% identify NASCAR stock cars as their favorite type of racing. Suppose that four auto racing fans are randomly selected.
Source: ESPN/TNS Sports, reported in *USA Today*

(a) What is the probability that all four will identify NASCAR stock cars as their favorite type of racing? *0.1212*

29. (b) 0.000313

(b) What is the probability that at least one will not identify NASCAR stock cars as his or her favorite type of racing? *0.8788*

(c) What is the probability that none will identify NASCAR stock cars as his or her favorite type of racing? *0.0283*

(d) What is the probability that at least one will identify NASCAR stock cars as his or her favorite type of racing? *0.9717*

27. Driving under the Influence Among 21- to 25-year-olds, 29% say they have driven while under the influence of alcohol. Suppose that three 21- to 25-year-olds are selected at random.
Source: U.S. Department of Health and Human Services, reported in *USA Today*

(a) What is the probability that all three have driven while under the influence of alcohol? *0.0244*

(b) What is the probability that at least one has not driven while under the influence of alcohol? *0.9756*

(c) What is the probability that none of the three has driven while under the influence of alcohol? *0.3579*

(d) What is the probability that at least one has driven while under the influence of alcohol? *0.6421*

28. Defense System Suppose that a satellite defense system is established in which four satellites acting independently have a 0.9 probability of detecting an incoming ballistic missile. What is the probability that at least one of the four satellites detects an incoming ballistic missile? Would you feel safe with such a system? *0.9999*

29. Audits For the fiscal year 2007, the IRS audited 1.77% of individual tax returns with income of $100,000 or more. Suppose this percentage stays the same for the current tax year.

(a) Would it be unusual for a return with income of $100,000 or more to be audited? *Yes*

(b) What is the probability that two randomly selected returns with income of $100,000 or more will be audited?

(c) What is the probability that two randomly selected returns with income of $100,000 or more will *not* be audited? *0.9649*

(d) What is the probability that at least one of two randomly selected returns with income of $100,000 or more will be audited? *0.0351*

30. Casino Visits According to a December 2007 Gallup poll, 24% of American adults have visited a casino in the past 12 months.

(a) What is the probability that 4 randomly selected adult Americans have visited a casino in the past 12 months? Is this result unusual? *0.0033; yes*

(b) What is the probability that 4 randomly selected adult Americans have *not* visited a casino in the past 12 months? Is this result unusual? *0.3336; no*

31. Betting on Sports According to a Gallup Poll, about 17% of adult Americans bet on professional sports. Census data indicate that 48.4% of the adult population in the United States is male.

(a) Are the events "male" and "bet on professional sports" mutually exclusive? Explain. *no*

(b) Assuming that betting is independent of gender, compute the probability that an American adult selected at random is a male and bets on professional sports. *0.0823*

(c) Using the result in part (b), compute the probability that an American adult selected at random is male or bets on professional sports. *0.5717*

(d) The Gallup poll data indicated that 10.6% of adults in the United States are males and bet on professional sports. What does this indicate about the assumption in part (b)?   *Not independent*

(e) How will the information in part (d) affect the probability you computed in part (c)?   *0.548*

32. Fingerprints Fingerprints are now widely accepted as a form of identification. In fact, many computers today use fingerprint identification to link the owner to the computer. In 1892, Sir Francis Galton explored the use of fingerprints to uniquely identify an individual. A fingerprint consists of ridgelines. Based on empirical evidence, Galton estimated the probability that a square consisting of six ridgelines that covered a fingerprint could be filled in accurately by an experienced fingerprint analyst as $\frac{1}{2}$.

(a) Assuming that a full fingerprint consists of 24 of these squares, what is the probability that all 24 squares could

$32.\ (a)\ \left(\frac{1}{2}\right)^{24} \approx 5.96 \times 10^{-8}$ $32.\ (b)\ \left(\frac{1}{2}\right)^{36} \approx 1.46 \times 10^{-11}$

be filled in correctly; assuming that success or failure in filling in one square is independent of success or failure in filling in any other square within the region? (This value represents the probability that two individuals would share the same ridgeline features within the 24-square region.)

(b) Galton further estimated that the likelihood of determining the fingerprint type (e.g. arch, left loop, whorl, etc.) as $\left(\frac{1}{2}\right)^4$ and the likelihood of the occurrence of the correct number of ridges entering and exiting each of the 24 regions as $\left(\frac{1}{2}\right)^8$. Assuming that all three probabilities are independent, compute Galton's estimate of the probability that a particular fingerprint configuration would occur in nature (that is, the probability that a fingerprint match occurs by chance).

5.4 CONDITIONAL PROBABILITY AND THE GENERAL MULTIPLICATION RULE

Objectives		Compute conditional probabilities
		Compute probabilities using the General Multiplication Rule

 Compute Conditional Probabilities

Note to Instructor

For instructors looking to offer a course that minimizes the coverage of probability, this section can be skipped without loss of continuity.

In the last section, we learned that when two events are independent the occurrence of one event has no effect on the probability of the second event. However, we cannot generally assume that two events will be independent. Will the probability of being in a car accident change depending on driving conditions? We would expect so. For example, we would expect the probability of an accident to be higher for nighttime driving on icy roads than of daytime driving on dry roads. What about the likelihood of contracting a sexually transmitted disease (STD)? Do you think the number of sexual partners will affect the likelihood of contracting an STD?

According to data from the Centers for Disease Control, 33.3% of adult men in the United States are obese. So the probability is 0.333 that a randomly selected adult male in the United States is obese. However, 28% of adult men aged 20 to 39 are obese compared to 40% of adult men aged 40 to 59. The probability is 0.28 that an adult male is obese, *given* that they are aged 20 to 39. The probability is 0.40 that an adult male is obese, *given* that they are aged 40 to 59. The probability that an adult male is obese changes depending on the age group in which the individual falls. This is called *conditional probability*.

Definition   **Conditional Probability**

The notation $P(F|E)$ is read "the probability of event F given event E." It is the probability that the event F occurs, given that the event E has occurred.

Let's look at an example.

EXAMPLE 1   **An Introduction to Conditional Probability**

Problem: Suppose that a single die is rolled. What is the probability that the die comes up 3? Now suppose that the die is rolled a second time, but we are told the outcome will be an odd number. What is the probability that the die comes up 3?

Approach: We assume that the die is fair and compute the probabilities using equally likely outcomes.

Solution: In the first instance, there are six possibilities in the sample space, $S = \{1, 2, 3, 4, 5, 6\}$, so $P(3) = \frac{1}{6}$. In the second instance, there are three possibilities in the sample space, because the only possible outcomes are odd, so $S = \{1, 3, 5\}$. We express this probability symbolically as $P(3|\text{outcome is odd}) = \frac{1}{3}$, which is read "the probability of rolling a 3, given that the outcome is odd, is one-third."

So conditional probabilities reduce the size of the sample space under consideration. Let's look at another example. The data in Table 8 represent the marital status of males and females 18 years old or older in the United States in 2006.

	Males (in millions)	Females (in millions)	Totals (in millions)
Never married	30.3	25.0	**55.3**
Married	63.6	64.1	**127.7**
Widowed	2.6	11.3	**13.9**
Divorced	9.7	13.1	**22.8**
Totals (in millions)	**106.2**	**113.5**	**219.7**

Table 8

Source: U.S. Census Bureau, Current Population Reports

We want to know the probability that a randomly selected individual 18 years old or older is widowed. This probability is found by dividing the number of widowed individuals by the total number of individuals who are 18 years old or older.

$$P(\text{widowed}) = \frac{13.9}{219.7}$$
$$= 0.063$$

Now suppose that we know the individual is female. Does this change the probability that she is widowed? Because the sample space now consists only of females, we can determine the probability that the individual is widowed, given that the individual is female, as follows:

$$P(\text{widowed}|\text{female}) = \frac{N(\text{widowed females})}{N(\text{females})}$$

$$= \frac{11.3}{113.5} = 0.100$$

So, knowing that the individual is female increases the likelihood that the individual is widowed. This leads to the following.

Conditional Probability Rule

If E and F are any two events, then

$$P(F|E) = \frac{P(E \text{ and } F)}{P(E)} = \frac{N(E \text{ and } F)}{N(E)} \qquad \textbf{(1)}$$

The probability of event F occurring, given the occurrence of event E, is found by dividing the probability of E and F by the probability of E. Or the probability of event F occurring, given the occurrence of event E, is found by dividing the number of outcomes in E and F by the number of outcomes in E.

We used the second method for computing conditional probabilities in the widow example.

EXAMPLE 2   **Conditional Probabilities on Marital Status and Gender**

Problem: The data in Table 8 represent the marital status and gender of the residents of the United States aged 18 years old or older in 2006.

(a) Compute the probability that a randomly selected male has never married.
(b) Compute the probability that a randomly selected individual who has never married is male.

Approach

(a) We are given that the randomly selected person is male, so we concentrate on the male column. There are 106.2 million males and 30.3 million males who never married, so $N(\text{male}) = 106.2$ million and $N(\text{male and never married}) = 30.3$ million. Compute the probability using the Conditional Probability Rule.

(b) We are given that the randomly selected person has never married, so we concentrate on the never married row. There are 55.3 million people who have never married and 30.3 million males who have never married, so $N(\text{never married}) = 55.3$ million and $N(\text{male and never married}) = 30.3$ million. Compute the probability using the Conditional Probability Rule.

Solution

(a) Substituting into Formula (1), we obtain

$$P(\text{never married}|\text{male}) = \frac{N(\text{never married and male})}{N(\text{male})} = \frac{30.3}{106.2} = 0.285$$

There is a 28.5% probability that the randomly selected individual has never married, given that he is male.

(b) Substituting into Formula (1), we obtain

$$P(\text{male}|\text{never married}) = \frac{N(\text{male and never married})}{N(\text{never married})} = \frac{30.3}{55.3} = 0.548$$

There is a 54.8% probability that the randomly selected individual is male, given that he or she has never married.

What is the difference between the results of Example 2(a) and (b)? In Example 2(a), we found that 28.5% of males have never married, whereas in Example 2(b) we found that 54.8% of individuals who have never married are male. Do you see the difference?

Now Work Problem 17

EXAMPLE 3   **Birth Weights of Preterm Babies**

Problem: In 2005, 12.64% of all births were preterm. (The gestation period of the pregnancy was less than 37 weeks.) Also in 2005, 0.22% of all births resulted in a preterm baby that weighed 8 pounds, 13 ounces or more. What is the probability that a randomly selected baby weighs 8 pounds, 13 ounces or more, given that the baby was preterm? Is this unusual?

Approach: We want to know the probability that the baby weighs 8 pounds, 13 ounces or more, given that the baby was preterm. We know that 0.22% of all babies weighed 8 pounds, 13 ounces or more and were preterm, so P(weighs 8 pounds, 13 ounces or more and preterm) = 0.22%. We also know that 12.64% of all births were preterm, so P(preterm) = 12.64%. We compute the probability by dividing the probability that a baby will weigh 8 pounds, 13 ounces or more *and* be preterm by the probability that a baby will be preterm.

Solution: P(weighs 8 pounds, 13 ounces or more|preterm)

$$= \frac{P(\text{weighs 8 pounds, 13 ounces or more and preterm})}{P(\text{preterm})}$$

$$= \frac{0.22\%}{12.64\%} = \frac{0.0022}{0.1264} \approx 0.0174 = 1.74\%$$

There is a 1.74% probability that a randomly selected baby will weigh 8 pounds, 13 ounces or more, given that the baby is preterm. It is unusual for preterm babies to weigh 8 pounds, 13 ounces or more.

Now Work Problem 13

---

2   **Compute Probabilities Using the General Multiplication Rule**

If we solve the Conditional Probability Rule for $P(E$ and $F)$, we obtain the General Multiplication Rule.

> **General Multiplication Rule**
>
> The probability that two events E and F both occur is
>
> $$P(E \text{ and } F) = P(E) \cdot P(F|E)$$
>
> In words, the probability of E and F is the probability of event E occurring times the probability of event F occurring, given the occurrence of event E.

EXAMPLE 4   **Using the General Multiplication Rule**

Problem: The probability that a driver who is speeding gets pulled over is 0.8. The probability that a driver gets a ticket, given that he or she is pulled over, is 0.9. What is the probability that a randomly selected driver who is speeding gets pulled over and gets a ticket?

Approach: Let E represent the event "driver who is speeding gets pulled over," and let F represent the event "driver gets a ticket." We use the General Multiplication Rule to compute $P(E$ and $F)$.

Solution: P(driver who is speeding gets pulled over and gets a ticket) = $P(E \text{ and } F) = P(E) \cdot P(F|E) = 0.8(0.9) = 0.72$. There is a 72% probability that a driver who is speeding gets pulled over and gets a ticket.

Now Work Problem 31

EXAMPLE 5   Acceptance Sampling

Problem: Suppose that a box of 100 circuits is sent to a manufacturing plant. Of the 100 circuits shipped, 5 are defective. The plant manager receiving the circuits randomly selects 2 and tests them. If both circuits work, she will accept the shipment. Otherwise, the shipment is rejected. What is the probability that the plant manager discovers at least 1 defective circuit and rejects the shipment?

Approach: We wish to determine the probability that at least one of the tested circuits is defective. There are four possibilities in this probability experiment: Neither of the circuits is defective, the first is defective while the second is not, the first is not defective while the second is defective, or both circuits are defective. We cannot compute this probability using the fact that there are four outcomes and three that result in at least 1 defective, because the outcomes are not equally likely. We need a different approach. One approach is to use a tree diagram to list all possible outcomes and the General Multiplication Rule to compute the probability for each outcome. We could then determine the probability of at least 1 defective by adding the probability that the first is defective while the second is not, the first is not defective while the second is defective, or both are defective, using the Addition Rule (because they are disjoint).

A second approach is to compute the probability that both circuits are not defective and use the Complement Rule to determine the probability of at least 1 defective.

We will illustrate both approaches.

Solution: We have 100 circuits and 5 of them are defective, so 95 circuits are not defective. To use our first approach, we construct a tree diagram to determine the possible outcomes for the experiment. We draw two branches corresponding to the two possible outcomes (defective or not defective) for the first repetition of the experiment (the first circuit). For the second circuit, we draw four branches: two branches originate from the first defective circuit and two branches originate from the first nondefective circuit. See Figure 12, where D stands for defective and G stands for good (not defective). Since the outcomes are not equally likely, we include the probabilities in our diagram to show how the probability of each outcome is obtained. The probability for each outcome is obtained by multiplying the individual probabilities along the corresponding path is the diagram.

Figure 12   **Probability**

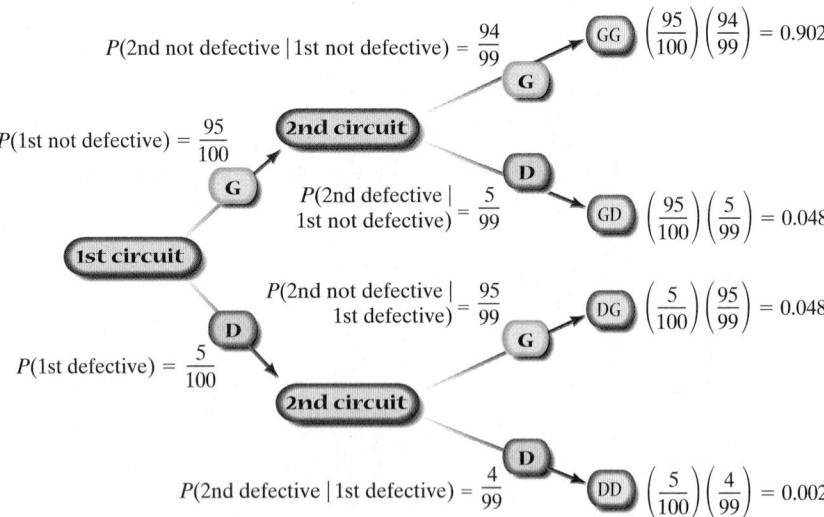

From our tree diagram, and using the Addition Rule, we can write

$$P(\text{at least 1 defective}) = P(\text{GD}) + P(\text{DG}) + P(\text{DD})$$
$$= 0.048 + 0.048 + 0.002$$
$$= 0.098$$

There is a 9.8% probability that the shipment will not be accepted.

For our second approach, we compute the probability that both circuits are not defective and use the Complement Rule to determine the probability of at least 1 defective.

$$P(\text{at least 1 defective}) = 1 - P(\text{none defective})$$
$$= 1 - P(\text{1st not defective}) \cdot P(\text{2nd not defective} \mid \text{1st not defective})$$
$$= 1 - \left(\frac{95}{100}\right) \cdot \left(\frac{94}{99}\right)$$
$$= 1 - 0.902$$
$$= 0.098$$

There is a 9.8% probability that the shipment will not accepted. This result is the same as that obtained using our tree diagram.

Now Work Problem 21

Whenever a small random sample is taken from a large population, it is reasonable to compute probabilities of events assuming independence. Consider the following example.

EXAMPLE 6   **Sickle-Cell Anemia**

Problem: A survey of 10,000 African Americans found that 27 had sickle-cell anemia.

(a) Suppose we randomly select 1 of the 10,000 African Americans surveyed. What is the probability that he or she will have sickle-cell anemia?

(b) If two individuals from this group are randomly selected, what is the probability that both have sickle-cell anemia?

(c) Compute the probability of randomly selecting two individuals from this group who have sickle-cell anemia, assuming independence.

Approach: We let the event E = "sickle-cell anemia," so $P(E)$ = number of African Americans who have sickle-cell anemia divided by the number in the survey. To answer part (b), we let E_1 = "first person has sickle-cell anemia" and E_2 = "second person has sickle-cell anemia," and then we compute $P(E_1 \text{ and } E_2) = P(E_1) \cdot P(E_2 \mid E_1)$. To answer part (c), we use the Multiplication Rule for Independent Events.

Solution

(a) If one individual is selected, $P(E) = \dfrac{27}{10,000} = 0.0027$.

(b) Using the Multiplication Rule, we have

$$P(E_1 \text{ and } E_2) = P(E_1) \cdot P(E_2 \mid E_1) = \frac{27}{10,000} \cdot \frac{26}{9,999} \approx 0.00000702$$

Notice that $P(E_2 \mid E_1) = \dfrac{26}{9,999}$ because we are sampling without replacement, so after event E_1 occurs there is one less person with sickle-cell anemia and one less person in the sample space.

(c) The assumption of independence means that the outcome of the first trial of the experiment does not affect the probability of the second trial. (It is like sampling with replacement.) Therefore, we assume that

$$P(E_1) = P(E_2) = \frac{27}{10,000}$$

Then

$$P(E_1 \text{ and } E_2) = P(E_1) \cdot P(E_2) = \frac{27}{10,000} \cdot \frac{27}{10,000} \approx 0.00000729$$

Historical Note

Andrei Nikolaevich Kolmogorov was born on April 25, 1903, in Tambov, Russia. His parents were not married. His mother's sister, Vera Yakovlena, raised Kolmogorov. In 1920, Kolmogorov enrolled in Moscow State University. He graduated from the university in 1925. That year he published eight papers, including his first on probability. In 1929, Kolmogorov received his doctorate. By this time he already had 18 publications. He became a professor at Moscow State University in 1931. Kolmogrov is quoted as saying, "The theory of probability as a mathematical discipline can and should be developed from axioms in exactly the same way as Geometry and Algebra." In addition to conducting research, Kolmogorov was interested in helping to educate gifted children. It did not bother him if the students did not become mathematicians; he simply wanted them to be happy. Andrei Kolmogorov died on October 20, 1987.

The probabilities in Examples 6(b) and 6(c) are extremely close in value. Based on these results, we infer the following principle:

> If small random samples are taken from large populations without replacement, it is reasonable to assume independence of the events. As a rule of thumb, if the sample size is less than 5% of the population size, we treat the events as independent.

For example, in Example 6, we can compute the probability of randomly selecting two African Americans who have sickle-cell anemia assuming independence because the sample size, 2, is less than 5% of the population size, 10,000:

$$2 < 0.05\,(10{,}000)$$
$$2 < 500$$

Now Work Problem 39

Conditional Probability and Independence

Two events are independent if the occurrence of event E in a probability experiment does not affect the probability of event F. We can now express independence using conditional probabilities.

Definition Two events E and F are independent if $P(E|F) = P(E)$ or, equivalently, if $P(F|E) = P(F)$.

If either condition in our definition is true, the other is as well. In addition, for independent events,

$$P(E \text{ and } F) = P(E) \cdot P(F).$$

So the Multiplication Rule for Independent Events is a special case of the General Multiplication Rule.

Look back at Table 8 on page 293. Because $P(\text{widowed}) = 0.063$ does not equal $P(\text{widowed}|\text{female}) = 0.100$, the events "widowed" and "female" are not independent. In fact, knowing an individual is female increases the likelihood that the individual is also widowed.

Now Work Problem 41

5.4 ASSESS YOUR UNDERSTANDING

Concepts and Vocabulary

1. The notation $P(F|E)$ means the probability of event __F__ given event __E__.

2. If $P(E) = 0.6$ and $P(E|F) = 0.34$, are events E and F independent? No

Skill Building

3. Suppose that E and F are two events and that $P(E \text{ and } F) = 0.6$ and $P(E) = 0.8$. What is $P(F|E)$? 0.75

4. Suppose that E and F are two events and that $P(E \text{ and } F) = 0.21$ and $P(E) = 0.4$. What is $P(F|E)$? 0.525

5. Suppose that E and F are two events and that $N(E \text{ and } F) = 420$ and $N(E) = 740$. What is $P(F|E)$? 0.568

6. Suppose that E and F are two events and that $N(E \text{ and } F) = 380$ and $N(E) = 925$. What is $P(F|E)$? 0.411

7. Suppose that E and F are two events and that $P(E) = 0.8$ and $P(F|E) = 0.4$. What is $P(E \text{ and } F)$? 0.32

8. Suppose that E and F are two events and that $P(E) = 0.4$ and $P(F|E) = 0.6$. What is $P(E \text{ and } F)$? 0.24

9. According to the U.S. Census Bureau, the probability that a randomly selected individual in the United States earns more than $75,000 per year is 9.5%. The probability that a randomly selected individual in the United States earns more than $75,000 per year, given that the individual has earned a bachelor's degree, is 21.5%. Are the events "earn more than $75,000 per year" and "earned a bachelor's degree" independent? No

10. The probability that a randomly selected individual in the United States 25 years and older has at least a bachelor's degree is 0.287. The probability that an individual in the United States 25 years and older has at least a bachelor's degree, given that the individual is Hispanic, is 0.127. Are the events "bachelor's degree" and "Hispanic" independent? No

    Source: Current Population Survey, 2007 Annual Social and Economic Supplement, U.S. Census Bureau.

Applying the Concepts

11. **Drawing a Card** Suppose that a single card is selected from a standard 52-card deck. What is the probability that the card drawn is a club? Now suppose that a single card is drawn from a standard 52-card deck, but we are told that the card is black. What is the probability that the card drawn is a club?

11. $\dfrac{1}{4}; \dfrac{1}{2}$

17. (b) 0.184

12. Drawing a Card Suppose that a single card is selected from a standard 52-card deck. What is the probability that the card drawn is a king? Now suppose that a single card is drawn from a standard 52-card deck, but we are told that the card is a heart. What is the probability that the card drawn is a king? Did the knowledge that the card is a heart change the probability that the card was a king? What term is used to describe this result? 1/13; 1/13; no; independence

13. Rainy Days For the month of June in the city of Chicago, NW 37% of the days are cloudy. Also in the month of June in the city of Chicago, 21% of the days are cloudy and rainy. What is the probability that a randomly selected day in June will be rainy if it is cloudy? 0.568

14. Cause of Death According to the U.S. National Center for Health Statistics, in 2005, 0.15% of deaths in the United States were 25- to 34-year-olds whose cause of death was cancer. In addition, 1.71% of all those who died were 25 to 34 years old. What is the probability that a randomly selected death is the result of cancer if the individual is known to have been 25 to 34 years old? 0.088

15. High School Dropouts According to the U.S. Census Bureau, 8.4% of high school dropouts are 16- to 17-year-olds. In addition, 6.2% of high school dropouts are white 16- to 17-year-olds. What is the probability that a randomly selected dropout is white, given that he or she is 16 to 17 years old? 0.738

16. Income by Region According to the U.S Census Bureau, 19.1% of U.S. households are in the Northeast. In addition, 4.4% of U.S. households earn $75,000 per year or more and are located in the Northeast. Determine the probability that a randomly selected U.S. household earns more than $75,000 per year, given that the household is located in the Northeast.

17. Health Insurance Coverage The following data represent, NW in thousands, the type of health insurance coverage of people by age in the year 2006.   16. 0.230

	Age				
	<18	**18–44**	**45–64**	**>64**	**Total**
Private health insurance	47,906	74,375	57,505	21,904	**201,690**
Government health insurance	22,109	12,375	11,304	33,982	**80,270**
No health insurance	8,661	27,054	10,737	541	**46,993**
Total	**78,676**	**114,304**	**79,546**	**56,427**	**328,953**

Source: U.S. Census Bureau

(a) What is the probability that a randomly selected individual who is less than 18 years old has no health insurance? 0.110

(b) What is the probability that a randomly selected individual who has no health insurance is less than 18 years old?

18. Cigar Smoking The data in the following table show the results of a national study of 137,243 U.S. men that investigated the association between cigar smoking and death from cancer.

Note: "Current cigar smoker" means cigar smoker at time of death.

	Died from Cancer	**Did Not Die from Cancer**
Never smoked cigars	782	120,747
Former cigar smoker	91	7,757
Current cigar smoker	141	7,725

Source: Shapiro, Jacobs, and Thun. "Cigar Smoking in Men and Risk of Death from Tobacco-Related Cancers," *Journal of the National Cancer Institute*, February 16, 2000

(a) What is the probability that a randomly selected individual from the study who died from cancer was a former cigar smoker? 0.090

(b) What is the probability that a randomly selected individual from the study who was a former cigar smoker died from cancer? 0.012

19. Traffic Fatalities The following data represent the number of traffic fatalities in the United States in 2005 by person type for male and female drivers.

Person Type	**Male**	**Female**	**Total**
Driver	20,795	6,598	**27,393**
Passenger	5,190	4,896	**10,086**
Total	**25,985**	**11,494**	**37,479**

Source: U.S. Department of Transportation, *Traffic Safety Facts, 2005*.

(a) What is the probability that a randomly selected traffic fatality who was female was a passenger? 0.426

(b) What is the probability that a randomly selected passenger fatality was female? 0.485

(c) Suppose you are a police officer called to the scene of a traffic accident with a fatality. The dispatcher states that the victim was driving, but the gender is not known. Is the victim more likely to be male or female? Why? Male

20. Marital Status The following data, in thousands, represent the marital status of Americans 25 years old or older and their levels of education in 2006.

	Did Not Graduate from High School	**High School Graduate**	**Some College**	**College Graduate**	**Total**
Never married	4,803	9,575	5,593	11,632	**31,603**
Married, spouse present	13,880	35,627	19,201	46,965	**115,673**
Married, spouse absent	1,049	1,049	503	944	**3,545**
Separated	1,162	1,636	790	1,060	**4,648**
Widowed	4,070	5,278	1,819	2,725	**13,892**
Divorced	2,927	7,725	4,639	7,232	**22,523**
Total	**27,891**	**60,890**	**32,545**	**70,558**	**191,884**

Source: *Current Population Survey*. U.S. Census Bureau, March 2006

(a) What is the probability that a randomly selected individual who has never married is a high school graduate? 0.303

(b) What is the probability that a randomly selected individual who is a high school graduate has never married? 0.157

21. **Acceptance Sampling** Suppose that you just received a
    [NW] shipment of six televisions. Two of the televisions are defec-
    tive. If two televisions are randomly selected, compute the
    probability that both televisions work. What is the probability
    that at least one does not work? *0.4; 0.6*

22. **Committee** A committee consists of four women and three
    men. The committee will randomly select two people to at-
    tend a conference in Hawaii. Find the probability that both
    are women. $\frac{2}{7}$

23. Suppose that two cards are randomly selected from a stan-
    dard 52-card deck.
    (a) What is the probability that the first card is a king and
        the second card is a king if the sampling is done without
        replacement?
    (b) What is the probability that the first card is a king and
        the second card is a king if the sampling is done with
        replacement? $\frac{1}{169}$ 23. (a) $\frac{1}{221}$

24. Suppose that two cards are randomly selected from a stan-
    dard 52-card deck.
    (a) What is the probability that the first card is a club and
        the second card is a club if the sampling is done without
        replacement?
    (b) What is the probability that the first card is a club and
        the second card is a club if the sampling is done with
        replacement? $\frac{1}{16}$ 24. (a) $\frac{1}{17}$

25. **Board Work** This past semester, I had a small business cal-
    culus section. The students in the class were Mike, Neta, Jinita,
    Kristin, and Dave. Suppose that I randomly select two peo-
    ple to go to the board to work problems. What is the proba-
    bility that Dave is the first person chosen to go to the board
    and Neta is the second? $\frac{1}{20}$

26. **Party** My wife has organized a monthly neighborhood party.
    Five people are involved in the group: Yolanda (my wife),
    Lorrie, Laura, Kim, and Anne Marie. They decide to ran-
    domly select the first and second home that will host the
    party. What is the probability that my wife hosts the first
    party and Lorrie hosts the second?

    Note: Once a home has hosted, it cannot host again until all
    other homes have hosted. $\frac{1}{20}$

27. **Playing a CD on the Random Setting** Suppose that a com-
    pact disk (CD) you just purchased has 13 tracks. After listen-
    ing to the CD, you decide that you like 5 of the songs. With
    the random feature on your CD player, each of the 13 songs
    is played once in random order. Find the probability that
    among the first two songs played
    (a) You like both of them. Would this be unusual? $\frac{5}{39}$; no
    (b) You like neither of them.
    (c) You like exactly one of them.
    (d) Redo (a)–(c) if a song can be replayed before all 13 songs
        are played (if, for example, track 2 can play twice in
        a row). $\frac{25}{169}, \frac{64}{169}, \frac{80}{169}$

28. **Packaging Error** Due to a manufacturing error, three cans
    of regular soda were accidentally filled with diet soda and
    placed into a 12-pack. Suppose that two cans are randomly
    selected from the 12-pack.
    (a) Determine the probability that both contain diet
        soda.
    27. (b) $\frac{14}{39}$ 27. (c) $\frac{20}{39}$ 28. (a) $\frac{1}{22}$

28. (b) $\frac{6}{11}$; no
    (b) Determine the probability that both contain regular
        soda. Would this be unusual?
    (c) Determine the probability that exactly one is diet and
        one is regular. $\frac{9}{22}$

29. **Planting Tulips** A bag of 30 tulip bulbs purchased from a
    nursery contains 12 red tulip bulbs, 10 yellow tulip bulbs, and
    8 purple tulip bulbs. Use a tree diagram like the one in
    Example 5 to answer the following:
    (a) What is the probability that two randomly selected tulip
        bulbs are both red? *0.152*
    (b) What is the probability that the first bulb selected is red
        and the second yellow? *0.138*
    (c) What is the probability that the first bulb selected is yel-
        low and the second is red? *0.138*
    (d) What is the probability that one bulb is red and the
        other yellow? *0.276*

30. **Golf Balls** The local golf store sells an "onion bag" that con-
    tains 35 "experienced" golf balls. Suppose that the bag con-
    tains 20 Titleists, 8 Maxflis, and 7 Top-Flites. Use a tree
    diagram like the one in Example 5 to answer the following:
    (a) What is the probability that two randomly selected golf
        balls are both Titleists? *0.319*
    (b) What is the probability that the first ball selected is a
        Titleist and the second is a Maxfli? *0.134*
    (c) What is the probability that the first ball selected is a
        Maxfli and the second is a Titleist? *0.134*
    (d) What is the probability that one golf ball is a Titleist and
        the other is a Maxfli? *0.269*

31. **Smokers** According to the National Center for Health
    [NW] Statistics, there is a 20.9% probability that a randomly se-
    lected resident of the United States aged 18 years or older
    is a smoker. In addition, there is a 33.4% probability that
    a randomly selected resident of the United States aged
    18 years or older is female, given that he or she smokes.
    What is the probability that a randomly selected resident of
    the United States aged 18 years or older is female and
    smokes? Would it be unusual to randomly select a resident
    of the United States aged 18 years or older who is female
    and smokes? *0.070; no*

32. **Multiple Jobs** According to the U.S. Bureau of Labor Sta-
    tistics, there is a 5.2% probability that a randomly selected
    employed individual has more than one job (a multiple-
    job holder). Also, there is a 50.4% probability that a ran-
    domly selected employed individual is male, given that he
    has more than one job. What is the probability that a ran-
    domly selected employed individual is a multiple-job holder
    and male? Would it be unusual to randomly select an
    employed individual who is a multiple-job holder and
    male? *0.026; yes*

33. **The Birthday Problem** Determine the probability that at
    least 2 people in a room of 10 people share the same birthday,
    ignoring leap years and assuming each birthday is equally
    likely by answering the following questions:
    (a) Compute the probability that 10 people have 10 different
        birthdays.

        Hint: The first person's birthday can occur 365 ways, the
        second person's birthday can occur 364 ways, because he
        or she cannot have the same birthday as the first person,
        the third person's birthday can occur 363 ways, because

he or she cannot have the same birthday as the first or second person, and so on. *0.883*

(b) The complement of "10 people have different birthdays" is "at least 2 share a birthday." Use this information to compute the probability that at least 2 people out of 10 share the same birthday. *0.117*

34. The Birthday Problem Using the procedure given in Problem 33, compute the probability that at least 2 people in a room of 23 people share the same birthday. *0.507*

35. Teen Communication The following data represent the number of different communication activities (e.g., cell phone, text messaging, and e-mail) used by a random sample of teenagers in a given week.

Activities	0	1–2	3–4	5–7	Total
Male	21	81	60	48	200
Female	21	52	56	71	200
Total	42	133	116	109	400

(a) Are the events "male" and "0 activities" independent? Justify your answer. *Yes*

(b) Are the events "female" and "5–7 activities" independent? Justify your answer. *No*

(c) Are the events "1–2 activities" and "3–4 activities" mutually exclusive? Justify your answer. *Yes*

(d) Are the events "male" and "1–2 activities" mutually exclusive? Justify your answer. *No*

36. 2008 Democratic Primary The following data represent political party by age from an entrance poll during the Iowa caucus.

	17–29	30–44	45–64	65+	Total
Republican	224	340	1075	561	2,200
Democrat	184	384	773	459	1,800
Total	408	724	1,848	1,020	4,000

(a) Are the events "Republican" and "30–44" independent? Justify your answer. *No*

(b) Are the events "Democrat" and "65+" independent? Justify your answer. *Yes*

(c) Are the events "17–29" and "45–64" mutually exclusive? Justify your answer. *Yes*

(d) Are the events "Republican" and "45–64" mutually exclusive? Justify your answer. *No*

37. A Flush A flush in the card game of poker occurs if a player gets five cards that are all the same suit (clubs, diamonds, hearts, or spades). Answer the following questions to obtain the probability of being dealt a flush in five cards.

(a) We initially concentrate on one suit, say clubs. There are 13 clubs in a deck. Compute $P(\text{five clubs}) = P(\text{first card is clubs and second card is clubs and third card is clubs and fourth card is clubs and fifth card is clubs})$. *0.000495*

(b) A flush can occur if we get five clubs or five diamonds or five hearts or five spades. Compute $P(\text{five clubs or five diamonds or five hearts or five spades})$. Note that the events are mutually exclusive. *0.002*

38. A Royal Flush A royal flush in the game of poker occurs if the player gets the cards Ten, Jack, Queen, King, and Ace all in the same suit. Use the procedure given in Problem 37 to compute the probability of being dealt a royal flush. *0.00000154*

39. Independence in Small Samples from Large Populations Suppose that a computer chip company has just shipped 10,000 computer chips to a computer company. Unfortunately, 50 of the chips are defective. *39. (a) 0.0000245*

(a) Compute the probability that two randomly selected chips are defective using conditional probability.

(b) There are 50 defective chips out of 10,000 shipped. The probability that the first chip randomly selected is defective is $\frac{50}{10,000} = 0.005 = 0.5\%$. Compute the probability that two randomly selected chips are defective under the assumption of independent events. Compare your results to part (a). Conclude that, when small samples are taken from large populations without replacement, the assumption of independence does not significantly affect the probability. *0.000025*

40. Independence in Small Samples from Large Populations Suppose that a poll is being conducted in the village of Lemont. The pollster identifies her target population as all residents of Lemont 18 years old or older. This population has 6,494 people.

(a) Compute the probability that the first resident selected to participate in the poll is Roger Cummings and the second is Rick Whittingham. *0.0000000237*

(b) The probability that any particular resident of Lemont is the first person picked is $\frac{1}{6,494}$. Compute the probability that Roger is selected first and Rick is selected second, assuming independence. Compare your results to part (a). Conclude that, when small samples are taken from large populations without replacement, the assumption of independence does not significantly affect the probability.

41. Independent? Refer to the contingency table in Problem 17 that relates age and health insurance coverage. Determine $P(<18 \text{ years old})$ and $P(<18 \text{ years old} \mid \text{no health insurance})$. Are the events "<18 years old" and "no health insurance" independent? *0.239; 0.184; no*

42. Independent? Refer to the contingency table in Problem 18 that relates cigar smoking and deaths from cancer. Determine $P(\text{died from cancer})$ and $P(\text{died from cancer} \mid \text{current cigar smoker})$. Are the events "died from cancer" and "current cigar smoker" independent? *0.007; 0.018; no*

43. Independent? Refer to the contingency table in Problem 19 that relates person type in a traffic fatality to gender. Determine $P(\text{female})$ and $P(\text{female} \mid \text{driver})$. Are the events "female" and "driver" independent? *0.307; 0.241; no*

44. Independent? Refer to the contingency table in Problem 20 that relates marital status and level of education. Determine $P(\text{divorced})$ and $P(\text{divorced} \mid \text{college graduate})$. Are the events "divorced" and "college graduate" independent?

45. Let's Make a Deal In 1991, columnist Marilyn Vos Savant posted her reply to a reader's question. The question posed was in reference to one of the games played on the gameshow *Let's Make a Deal* hosted by Monty Hall.

Suppose you're on a game show, and you're given the choice of three doors: Behind one door is a car; behind the others, goats. You pick a door, say No. 1, and the host, who knows what's behind the doors, opens another door, say No. 3, which has a goat. He then says to you. "Do you want to pick door No. 2?" Is it to your advantage to take the switch?

40. (b) 0.0000000237   *44. 0.117; 0.102; no*

Her reply generated a tremendous amount of backlash, with many highly educated individuals angrily responding that she was clearly mistaken in her reasoning.

(a) Using subjective probability, estimate the probability of winning if you switch.

(b) Load the *Let's Make a Deal* applet. Simulate the probability that you will win if you switch by going through the simulation at least 100 times. How does your simulated result compare to your answer to part (a)?

(c) Research the Monty Hall Problem as well as the reply by Marilyn Vos Savant. How does the probability she gives compare to the two estimates you obtained?

(d) Write a report detailing why Marilyn was correct. One approach is to use a random variable on a wheel similar to the one shown. On the wheel, the innermost ring indicates the door where the car is located, the middle ring indicates the door you selected, and the outer ring indicates the door(s) that Monty could show you. In the outer ring, green indicates you lose if you switch while purple indicates you win if you switch.

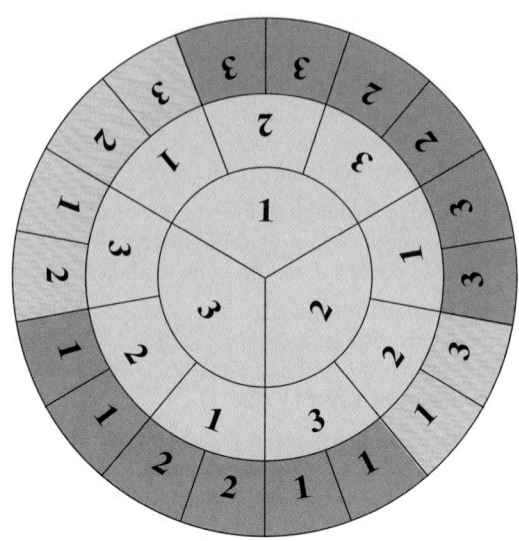

Consumer Reports®   His 'N' Hers Razor?

With so many men's and women's versions of different products, you might wonder how different they really are. To help answer this question, technicians at Consumers Union compared a new triple-edge razor for women with a leading double-edge razor for women and a leading triple-edge razor for men. The technicians asked 30 women panelists to shave with the razors over a 4-week period, following a random statistical design.

After each shave, the panelists were asked to answer a series of questions related to the performance of the razor. One question involved rating the razor. The following table contains a summary of the results for this question.

Using the information in the table, answer the following questions:

(a) Calculate the probability that a randomly selected razor scored Excellent.

(b) Calculate the probability that a randomly selected razor scored Poor.

(c) Calculate the probability of randomly selecting Razor B, given the score was Fair.

(d) Calculate the probability of receiving an Excellent rating, given that Razor C was selected.

(e) Are razor type and rating independent?

(f) Which razor would you choose based on the information given? Support your decision.

Note to Readers: *In many cases, our test protocol and analytical methods are more complicated than described in these examples. The data and discussions have been modified to make the material more appropriate for the audience.*

Source: © 2000 by Consumers Union of U.S., Inc., Yonkers, NY 10703-1057, a nonprofit organization. Reprinted with permission from the June 2000 issue of CONSUMER REPORTS® for educational purposes only. No commercial use or photocopying permitted. To learn more about Consumers Union, log onto www.ConsumersReports.org

Survey Results for Razor Study			
	Rating		
Razor	**Poor**	**Fair**	**Excellent**
A	1	8	21
B	0	11	19
C	6	11	13

5.5 COUNTING TECHNIQUES

Objectives
1. Solve counting problems using the Multiplication Rule
2. Solve counting problems using permutations
3. Solve counting problems using combinations
4. Solve counting problems involving permutations with nondistinct items
5. Compute probabilities involving permutations and combinations

1 Solve Counting Problems Using the Multiplication Rule

Note to Instructor
Most of the material in this section is optional. However, the material on combinations should be covered if you intend to present binomial probabilities (Section 6.2).

Counting plays a major role in many diverse areas, including probability. In this section, we look at special types of counting problems and develop general techniques for solving them.

We begin with an example that demonstrates a general counting principle.

EXAMPLE 1   **Counting the Number of Possible Meals**

Problem: The fixed-price dinner at Mabenka Restaurant provides the following choices:

Appetizer: soup or salad
Entrée: baked chicken, broiled beef patty, baby beef liver, or roast beef au jus
Dessert: ice cream or cheese cake

How many different meals can be ordered?

Approach: Ordering such a meal requires three separate decisions:

Choose an Appetizer	Choose an Entrée	Choose a Dessert
2 choices	4 choices	2 choices

Figure 13 is a tree diagram that lists the possible meals that can be ordered.

Figure 13

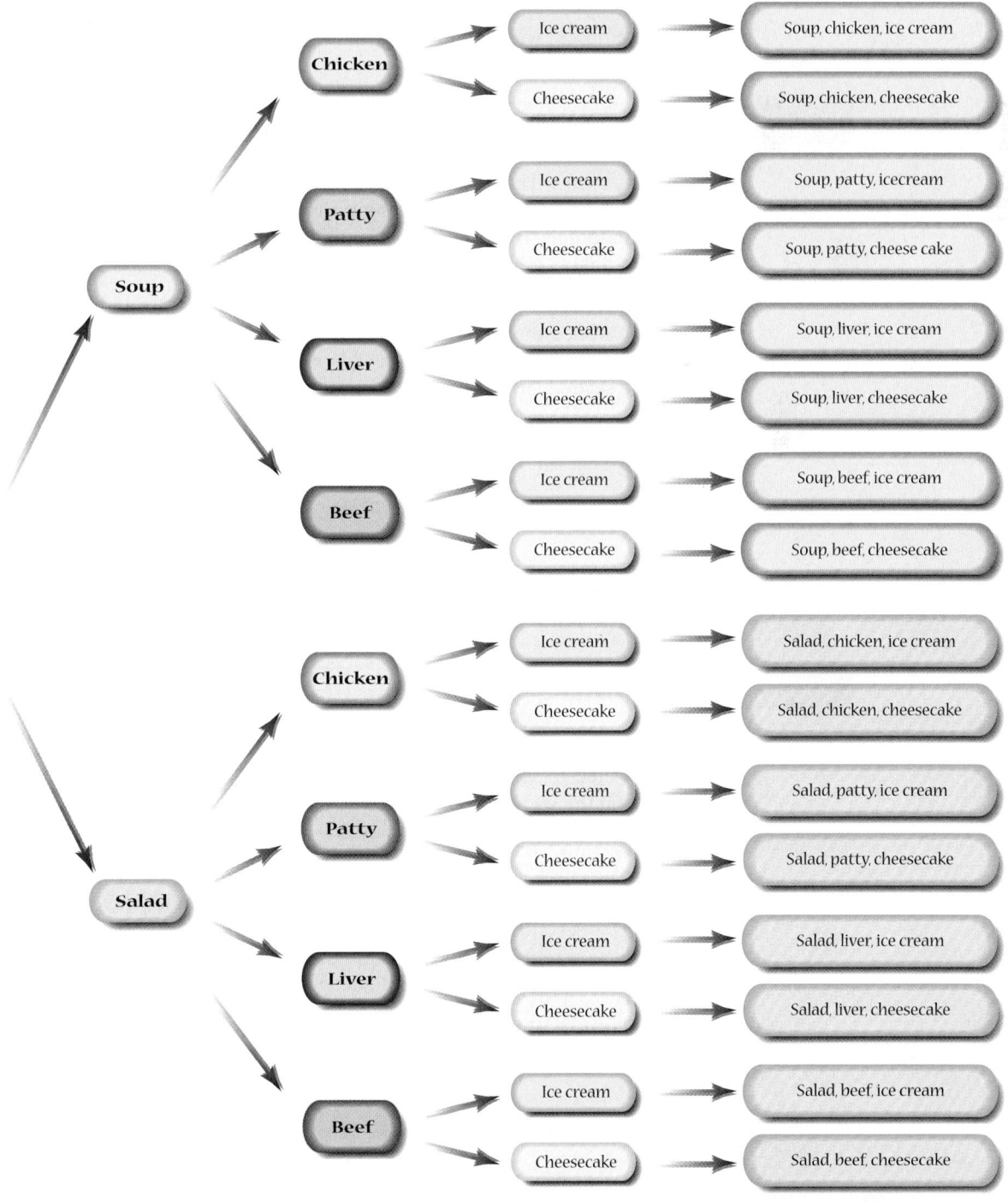

Solution: Look at the tree diagram in Figure 13. For each choice of appetizer, we have 4 choices of entrée, and that, for each of these $2 \cdot 4 = 8$ choices, there are 2 choices for dessert. A total of

$$2 \cdot 4 \cdot 2 = 16$$

different meals can be ordered.

Example 1 illustrates a general counting principle.

> **Multiplication Rule of Counting**
>
> If a task consists of a sequence of choices in which there are p selections for the first choice, q selections for the second choice, r selections for the third choice, and so on, then the task of making these selections can be done in
>
> $$p \cdot q \cdot r \cdot \cdots$$
>
> different ways.

EXAMPLE 2 **Counting Airport Codes (Repetition Allowed)**

Problem: The International Airline Transportation Association (IATA) assigns three-letter codes to represent airport locations. For example, the code for Fort Lauderdale International Airport is FLL. How many different airport codes are possible?

Approach: We are choosing 3 letters from 26 letters and arranging them in order. We notice that repetition of letters is allowed. We use the Multiplication Rule of Counting, recognizing we have 26 ways to choose the first letter, 26 ways to choose the second letter, and 26 ways to choose the third letter.

Solution: By the Multiplication Rule,

$$26 \cdot 26 \cdot 26 = 26^3 = 17,576$$

different airport codes are possible.

In Example 2, we were allowed to repeat letters. In the following example, repetition is not allowed.

EXAMPLE 3 **Counting without Repetition**

Problem: Three members from a 14-member committee are to be randomly selected to serve as chair, vice-chair, and secretary. The first person selected is the chair; the second is the vice-chair; and the third is the secretary. How many different committee structures are possible?

Approach: The task consists of making three selections. The first selection requires choosing from 14 members. Because a member cannot serve in more than one capacity, the second selection requires choosing from the 13 remaining members. The third selection requires choosing from the 12 remaining members. (Do you see why?) We use the Multiplication Rule to determine the number of possible committees.

Solution: By the Multiplication Rule,

$$14 \cdot 13 \cdot 12 = 2,184$$

different committee structures are possible.

Now Work Problem 31

The Factorial Symbol

We now introduce a special symbol that can assist us in representing certain types of counting problems.

Definition   If $n \geq 0$ is an integer, the **factorial symbol, $n!$**, is defined as follows:

$$n! = n(n - 1) \cdots \cdot 3 \cdot 2 \cdot 1$$
$$0! = 1 \qquad 1! = 1$$

 Using Technology
Your calculator has a factorial key. Use it to see how fast factorials increase in value. Find the value of 69!. What happens when you try to find 70!? In fact, 70! is larger than 10^{100} (a *googol*), the largest number most calculators can display.

For example, $2! = 2 \cdot 1 = 2, 3! = 3 \cdot 2 \cdot 1 = 6, 4! = 4 \cdot 3 \cdot 2 \cdot 1 = 24$, and so on. Table 9 lists the values of $n!$ for $0 \leq n \leq 6$.

Table 9						
n	0	1	2	3	4	5	6
$n!$	1	1	2	6	24	120	720

EXAMPLE 4   **The Traveling Salesperson**

Problem: You have just been hired as a book representative for Pearson Education. On your first day, you must travel to seven schools to introduce yourself. How many different routes are possible?

Approach: The seven schools are different. Let's call the schools A, B, C, D, E, F, and G. School A can be visited first, second, third, fourth, fifth, sixth, or seventh. So, we have seven choices for school A. We would then have six choices for school B, five choices for school C, and so on. We can use the Multiplication Rule and the factorial to find our solution.

Solution: $7 \cdot 6 \cdot 5 \cdot 4 \cdot 3 \cdot 2 \cdot 1 = 7! = 5{,}040$ different routes are possible.

Now Work Problems 5 and 33

2 Solve Counting Problems Using Permutations

Examples 3 and 4 illustrate a type of counting problem referred to as a *permutation*.

Definition   A **permutation** is an ordered arrangement in which r objects are chosen from n distinct (different) objects and repetition is not allowed. The symbol ${}_nP_r$ represents the number of permutations of r objects selected from n objects.

So we could represent the solution to the question posed in Example 3 as

$${}_nP_r = {}_{14}P_3 = 14 \cdot 13 \cdot 12 = 2{,}184$$

and the solution to Example 4 could be represented as

$${}_7P_7 = 7 \cdot 6 \cdot 5 \cdot 4 \cdot 3 \cdot 2 \cdot 1 = 5{,}040$$

To arrive at a formula for ${}_nP_r$, we note that there are n choices for the first selection, $n - 1$ choices for the second selection, $n - 2$ choices for the third selection, ..., and $n - (r - 1)$ choices for the rth selection. By the Multiplication Rule, we have

$$
\begin{array}{ccccccc}
 & & \text{1st} & \text{2nd} & \text{3rd} & & r\text{th} \\
{}_nP_r & = & n & \cdot & (n - 1) & \cdot & (n - 2) & \cdots \cdot & [n - (r - 1)] \\
 & = & n & \cdot & (n - 1) & \cdot & (n - 2) & \cdots \cdot & (n - r + 1)
\end{array}
$$

This formula for $_nP_r$ can be written in **factorial notation**:

$$_nP_r = n \cdot (n-1) \cdot (n-2) \cdots (n-r+1)$$

$$= n \cdot (n-1) \cdot (n-2) \cdots (n-r+1) \cdot \frac{(n-r) \cdots 3 \cdot 2 \cdot 1}{(n-r) \cdots 3 \cdot 2 \cdot 1}$$

$$= \frac{n!}{(n-r)!}$$

We have the following result.

> ### Number of Permutations of n Distinct Objects Taken r at a Time
>
> The number of arrangements of r objects chosen from n objects, in which
>
> **1.** the n objects are distinct,
> **2.** repetition of objects is not allowed, and
> **3.** order is important,
>
> is given by the formula
>
> $$_nP_r = \frac{n!}{(n-r)!} \tag{1}$$

EXAMPLE 5 | **Computing Permutations**

Problem: Evaluate:

(a) $_7P_5$ **(b)** $_8P_2$ **(c)** $_5P_5$

Approach: To answer (a), we use Formula (1) with $n = 7$ and $r = 5$. To answer (b), we use Formula (1) with $n = 8$ and $r = 2$. To answer (c), we use Formula (1) with $n = 5$ and $r = 5$.

Solution

(a) $_7P_5 = \dfrac{7!}{(7-5)!} = \dfrac{7!}{2!} = \dfrac{7 \cdot 6 \cdot 5 \cdot 4 \cdot 3 \cdot 2!}{2!} = \underbrace{7 \cdot 6 \cdot 5 \cdot 4 \cdot 3}_{5 \text{ factors}} = 2520$

(b) $_8P_2 = \dfrac{8!}{(8-2)!} = \dfrac{8!}{6!} = \dfrac{8 \cdot 7 \cdot 6!}{6!} = \underbrace{8 \cdot 7}_{2 \text{ factors}} = 56$

(c) $_5P_5 = \dfrac{5!}{(5-5)!} = \dfrac{5!}{0!} = 5! = 5 \cdot 4 \cdot 3 \cdot 2 \cdot 1 = 120$

Example 5(c) illustrates a general result:

$$_rP_r = r!$$

EXAMPLE 6 | **Computing Permutations Using Technology**

Problem: Evaluate $_7P_5$ using statistical software or a graphing calculator with advanced statistical features.

Approach: We will use both Excel and a TI-84 Plus graphing calculator to evaluate $_7P_5$. The steps for computing permutations using Excel and the TI-83/84 Plus graphing calculator can be found in the Technology Step-by-Step on page 315.

Solution: Figure 14(a) shows the result in Excel, and Figure 14(b) shows the result on a TI-84 Plus graphing calculator.

Figure 14

(a)   (b)

Now Work Problem 11

EXAMPLE 7   **Betting on the Trifecta**

Problem: In how many ways can horses in a 10-horse race finish first, second, and third?

Approach: The 10 horses are distinct. Once a horse crosses the finish line, that horse will not cross the finish line again, and, in a race, order is important. We have a permutation of 10 objects taken 3 at a time.

Solution: The top three horses can finish a 10-horse race in

$$_{10}P_3 = \frac{10!}{(10-3)!} = \frac{10!}{7!} = \frac{10 \cdot 9 \cdot 8 \cdot 7!}{7!} = \underbrace{10 \cdot 9 \cdot 8}_{3\ factors} = 720\ \text{ways}$$

Now Work Problem 45

3 Solve Counting Problems Using Combinations

In a permutation, order is important. For example, the arrangements *ABC*, *ACB*, *BAC*, *BCA*, *CAB*, and *CBA* are considered different arrangements of the letters *A*, *B*, and *C*. If order is unimportant, the six arrangements of the letters *A*, *B*, and *C* given above are not different. That is, we do not distinguish *ABC* from *BAC*. In the card game of poker, the order in which the cards are received does not matter. The *combination* of the cards is what matters.

Definition   A **combination** is a collection, without regard to order, of *n* distinct objects without repetition. The symbol $_nC_r$ represents the number of combinations of *n* distinct objects taken *r* at a time.

EXAMPLE 8 **Listing Combinations**

Problem: Roger, Rick, Randy, and Jay are going to play golf. They will randomly select teams of two players each. List all possible team combinations. That is, list all the combinations of the four people Roger, Rick, Randy, and Jay taken two at a time. What is $_4C_2$?

Approach: We list the possible teams. We note that order is unimportant, so {Roger, Rick} is the same as {Rick, Roger}.

Solution: The list of all such teams (combinations) is

Roger, Rick;   Roger, Randy;   Roger, Jay;   Rick, Randy;   Rick, Jay;   Randy, Jay

So,

$$_4C_2 = 6$$

There are six ways of forming teams of two from a group of four players.

We can find a formula for $_nC_r$ by noting that the only difference between a permutation and a combination is that we disregard order in combinations. To determine $_nC_r$, we eliminate from the formula for $_nP_r$ the number of permutations that were rearrangements of a given set of r objects. In Example 8, for example, selecting {Roger, Rick} was the same as selecting {Rick, Roger}, so there were $2! = 2$ rearrangements of the two objects. This can be determined from the formula for $_nP_r$ by calculating $_rP_r = r!$. So, if we divide $_nP_r$ by $r!$, we will have the desired formula for $_nC_r$:

$$_nC_r = \frac{_nP_r}{r!} = \frac{n!}{r!(n-r)!}$$

We have the following result.

> **Number of Combinations of n Distinct Objects Taken r at a Time**
>
> The number of different arrangements of n objects using $r \leq n$ of them, in which
>
> **1.** the n objects are distinct,
> **2.** repetition of objects is not allowed, and
> **3.** order is not important
>
> is given by the formula
>
> $$_nC_r = \frac{n!}{r!(n-r)!} \qquad (2)$$

Using Formula (2) to solve the problem presented in Example 8, we obtain

$$_4C_2 = \frac{4!}{2!(4-2)!} = \frac{4!}{2!2!} = \frac{4 \cdot 3 \cdot 2!}{2 \cdot 1 \cdot 2!} = \frac{12}{2} = 6$$

EXAMPLE 9 **Using Formula (2)**

Problem: Use Formula (2) to find the value of each expression.
(a) $_4C_1$ **(b)** $_6C_4$ **(c)** $_6C_2$

Approach: We use Formula (2): $_nC_r = \dfrac{n!}{r!(n-r)!}$

Solution

(a) $_4C_1 = \dfrac{4!}{1!(4-1)!} = \dfrac{4!}{1! \cdot 3!} = \dfrac{4 \cdot 3!}{1 \cdot 3!} = 4$ $n = 4, r = 1$

(b) $_6C_4 = \dfrac{6!}{4!(6-4)!} = \dfrac{6!}{4! \cdot 2!} = \dfrac{6 \cdot 5 \cdot 4!}{4! \cdot 2 \cdot 1} = \dfrac{30}{2} = 15$ $n = 6, r = 4$

(c) $_6C_2 = \dfrac{6!}{2!(6-2)!} = \dfrac{6!}{2!4!} = \dfrac{6 \cdot 5 \cdot 4!}{2 \cdot 1 \cdot 4!} = \dfrac{30}{2} = 15$ $n = 6, r = 2$

Notice in Example 9 that $_6C_4 = {_6C_2}$. This result can be generalized:

$$_nC_r = {_nC_{n-r}}$$

EXAMPLE 10   Computing Combinations Using Technology

Problem: Evaluate $_6C_4$ using statistical software or a graphing calculator with advanced statistical features.

Approach: We will use both Excel and a TI-84 Plus graphing calculator to evaluate $_6C_4$. The steps for computing combinations using Excel and the TI-83/84 Plus graphing calculator can be found in the Technology Step-by-Step on page 315.

Solution: Figure 15(a) shows the result in Excel, and Figure 15(b) shows the result on a TI-84 Plus graphing calculator.

Figure 15

Here is the result. If you click OK, the result goes into the cell.

(a)   (b)

Now Work Problem 19

EXAMPLE 11   Simple Random Samples

Problem: How many different simple random samples of size 4 can be obtained from a population whose size is 20?

Approach: The 20 individuals in the population are distinct. In addition, the order in which individuals are selected is unimportant. Thus, the number of simple random samples of size 4 from a population of size 20 is a combination of 20 objects taken 4 at a time.

Solution: Use Formula (2) with $n = 20$ and $r = 4$:

$$_{20}C_4 = \dfrac{20!}{4!(20-4)!} = \dfrac{20!}{4!16!} = \dfrac{20 \cdot 19 \cdot 18 \cdot 17 \cdot 16!}{4 \cdot 3 \cdot 2 \cdot 1 \cdot 16!} = \dfrac{116{,}280}{24} = 4{,}845$$

There are 4,845 different simple random samples of size 4 from a population whose size is 20.

Now Work Problem 51

4 Solve Counting Problems Involving Permutations with Nondistinct Items

Sometimes we wish to arrange objects in order, but some of the objects are not distinguishable.

EXAMPLE 12 | **DNA Structure**

Problem: The DNA structure is a double helix, similar to a ladder that is twisted in a spiral shape. Each rung of the ladder consists of a pair of DNA bases. A DNA sequence consists of a series of letters representing a DNA strand that spells out the genetic code. A DNA nucleotide contains a molecule of sugar, a molecule of phosphoric acid, and a base molecule. There are four possible letters (A, C, G, and T), each representing a specific nucleotide base in the DNA strand (adenine, cytosine, guanine, and thymine, respectively). How many distinguishable sequences can be formed using two As, two Cs, three Gs, and one T? **Note:** Scientists estimate that the complete human genome contains roughly 3 billion nucleotide base pairs.

Approach: Each sequence formed will have eight letters. To construct each sequence, we need to fill in eight positions with the eight letters:

$$\overline{1} \quad \overline{2} \quad \overline{3} \quad \overline{4} \quad \overline{5} \quad \overline{6} \quad \overline{7} \quad \overline{8}$$

The process of forming a sequence consists of four tasks:

Task 1: Choose the positions for the two As.
Task 2: Choose the positions for the two Cs.
Task 3: Choose the positions for the three Gs.
Task 4: Choose the position for the one T.

Task 1 can be done in $_8C_2$ ways. This leaves 6 positions to be filled, so task 2 can be done in $_6C_2$ ways. This leaves 4 positions to be filled, so task 3 can be done in $_4C_3$ ways. The last position can be filled in $_1C_1$ way.

Solution: By the Multiplication Rule, the number of possible sequences that can be formed is

$$_8C_2 \cdot {}_6C_2 \cdot {}_4C_3 \cdot {}_1C_1 = \frac{8!}{6! \cdot 2!} \cdot \frac{6!}{4! \cdot 2!} \cdot \frac{4!}{3! \cdot 1!} \cdot \frac{1!}{1! \cdot 0!}$$

$$= \frac{8!}{2! \cdot 2! \cdot 3! \cdot 1! \cdot 0!}$$

$$= 1,680$$

There are 1,680 possible distinguishable sequences that can be formed.

The solution to Example 12 is suggestive of a general result. Had the letters in the sequence each been different, $_8P_8 = 8!$ possible sequences would have been formed. This is the numerator of the answer. The presence of two As, two Cs, and three Gs reduces the number of different sequences, as the entries in the denominator illustrate. We are led to the following result:

> **Permutations with Nondistinct Items**
>
> The number of permutations of n objects of which n_1 are of one kind, n_2 are of a second kind, ..., and n_k are of a kth kind is given by
>
> $$\frac{n!}{n_1! \cdot n_2! \cdots \cdot n_k!} \tag{3}$$
>
> where $n = n_1 + n_2 + \cdots + n_k$.

EXAMPLE 13   **Arranging Flags**

Problem: How many different vertical arrangements are there of 10 flags if 5 are white, 3 are blue, and 2 are red?

Approach: We seek the number of permutations of 10 objects, of which 5 are of one kind (white), 3 are of a second kind (blue), and 2 are of a third kind (red).

Solution: Using Formula (3), we find that there are

$$\frac{10!}{5! \cdot 3! \cdot 2!} = \frac{10 \cdot 9 \cdot 8 \cdot 7 \cdot 6 \cdot 5!}{5! \cdot 3! \cdot 2!}$$

$$= 2,520 \text{ different vertical arrangements}$$

Now Work Problem 55

Summary

To summarize the differences between combinations and the various types of permutations, we present Table 10.

	Table 10	
	Description	**Formula**
Combination	The selection of r objects from a set of n different objects when the order in which the objects is selected does not matter (so AB is the same as BA) and an object cannot be selected more than once (repetition is not allowed)	$_nC_r = \dfrac{n!}{r!(n-r)!}$
Permutation of Distinct Items with Replacement	The selection of r objects from a set of n different objects when the order in which the objects are selected matters (so AB is different from BA) and an object may be selected more than once (repetition is allowed)	n^r
Permutation of Distinct Items without Replacement	The selection of r objects from a set of n different objects when the order in which the objects are selected matters (so AB is different from BA) and an object cannot be selected more than once (repetition is not allowed)	$_nP_r = \dfrac{n!}{(n-r)!}$
Permutation of Nondistinct Items without Replacement	The number of ways n objects can be arranged (order matters) in which there are n_1 of one kind, n_2 of a second kind, ..., and n_k of a kth kind, where $n = n_1 + n_2 + \cdots + n_k$	$\dfrac{n!}{n_1! n_2! \cdots n_k!}$

  Compute Probabilities Involving Permutations and Combinations

The counting techniques presented in this section can be used to determine probabilities of certain events by using the classical method of computing probabilities. Recall that this method stated the probability of an event E is the number of ways event E can occur divided by the number of different possible outcomes of the experiment provided each outcome is equally likely.

EXAMPLE 14   **Winning the Lottery**

Problem: In the Illinois Lottery, an urn contains balls numbered 1 to 52. From this urn, six balls are randomly chosen without replacement. For a $1 bet, a player chooses two sets of six numbers. To win, all six numbers must match those chosen from the urn. The order in which the balls are selected does not matter. What is the probability of winning the lottery?

Approach: The probability of winning is given by the number of ways a ticket could win divided by the size of the sample space. Each ticket has two sets of six numbers, so there are two chances (for the two sets of numbers) of winning for each ticket. The size of the sample space S is the number of ways that 6 objects can be selected from 52 objects without replacement and without regard to order, so $N(S) = {}_{52}C_6$.

Solution: The size of the sample space is

$$N(S) = {}_{52}C_6 = \frac{52!}{6! \cdot (52 - 6)!} = \frac{52 \cdot 51 \cdot 50 \cdot 49 \cdot 48 \cdot 47 \cdot 46!}{6! \cdot 46!} = 20{,}358{,}520$$

Each ticket has two sets of 6 numbers, so a player has two chances of winning for each \$1. If E is the event "winning ticket," then $N(E) = 2$. The probability of E is

$$P(E) = \frac{2}{20{,}358{,}520} = 0.000000098$$

There is about a 1 in 10,000,000 chance of winning the Illinois Lottery!

EXAMPLE 15   **Probabilities Involving Combinations**

Problem: A shipment of 120 fasteners that contains 4 defective fasteners was sent to a manufacturing plant. The quality-control manager at the manufacturing plant randomly selects 5 fasteners and inspects them. What is the probability that exactly 1 fastener is defective?

Approach: The probability that exactly 1 fastener is defective is found by calculating the number of ways of selecting exactly 1 defective fastener in 5 fasteners and dividing this result by the number of ways of selecting 5 fasteners from 120 fasteners. To choose exactly 1 defective in the 5 requires choosing 1 defective from the 4 defectives and 4 nondefectives from the 116 nondefectives. The order in which the fasteners are selected does not matter, so we use combinations.

Solution: The number of ways of choosing 1 defective fastener from 4 defective fasteners is ${}_4C_1$. The number of ways of choosing 4 nondefective fasteners from 116 nondefectives is ${}_{116}C_4$. Using the Multiplication Rule, we find that the number of ways of choosing 1 defective and 4 nondefective fasteners is

$$({}_4C_1) \cdot ({}_{116}C_4) = 4 \cdot 7{,}160{,}245 = 28{,}640{,}980$$

The number of ways of selecting 5 fasteners from 120 fasteners is ${}_{120}C_5 = 190{,}578{,}024$. The probability of selecting exactly 1 defective fastener is

$$P(1 \text{ defective fastener}) = \frac{({}_4C_1)({}_{116}C_4)}{{}_{120}C_5} = \frac{28{,}640{,}980}{190{,}578{,}024} = 0.1503$$

There is a 15.03% probability of randomly selecting exactly 1 defective fastener.

Now Work Problem 61

5.5 ASSESS YOUR UNDERSTANDING

Concepts and Vocabulary

1. A <u>permutation</u> is an ordered arrangement of r objects chosen from n distinct objects without repetition.

2. A <u>combination</u> is an arrangement of r objects chosen from n distinct objects without repetition and without regard to order.

3. *True or False*: In a combination problem, order is not important. True

4. Explain the difference between a combination and a permutation.

Skill Building

In Problems 5–10, find the value of each factorial.

5. 5! 120
NW

6. 7! 5,040

7. 10! 3,628,800

8. 12! 479,001,600

9. 0! 1

10. 1! 1

In Problems 11–18, find the value of each permutation.

11. ${}_6P_2$ 30
NW

12. ${}_7P_2$ 42

13. ${}_4P_4$ 24

14. ${}_7P_7$ 5,040

15. $_5P_0$ 1

16. $_4P_0$ 1

17. $_8P_3$ 336

18. $_9P_4$ 3,024

In Problems 19–26, find the value of each combination.

19. $_8C_3$ 56
NW

20. $_9C_2$ 36

21. $_{10}C_2$ 45

22. $_{12}C_3$ 220

23. $_{52}C_1$ 52

24. $_{40}C_{40}$ 1

25. $_{48}C_3$ 17,296

26. $_{30}C_4$ 27,405

27. List all the permutations of five objects a, b, c, d, and e taken two at a time without repetition. What is $_5P_2$? 20

28. List all the permutations of four objects a, b, c, and d taken two at a time without repetition. What is $_4P_2$? 12

29. List all the combinations of five objects a, b, c, d, and e taken two at a time. What is $_5C_2$? 10

30. List all the combinations of four objects a, b, c, and d taken two at a time. What is $_4C_2$? 6

Applying the Concepts

31. Clothing Options A man has six shirts and four ties. Assuming that they all match, how many different shirt-and-tie combinations can he wear? 24
NW

32. Clothing Options A woman has five blouses and three skirts. Assuming that they all match, how many different outfits can she wear? 15

33. Arranging Songs on a CD Suppose Dan is going to burn a compact disk (CD) that will contain 12 songs. In how many ways can Dan arrange the 12 songs on the CD? 12!
NW

34. Arranging Students In how many ways can 15 students be lined up? 15!

35. Traveling Salesperson A salesperson must travel to eight cities to promote a new marketing campaign. How many different trips are possible if any route between cities is possible? 8!

36. Randomly Playing Songs A certain compact disk player randomly plays each of 10 songs on a CD. Once a song is played, it is not repeated until all the songs on the CD have been played. In how many different ways can the CD player play the 10 songs? 10!

37. Stocks on the NYSE Companies whose stocks are listed on the New York Stock Exchange (NYSE) have their company name represented by either one, two, or three letters (repetition of letters is allowed). What is the maximum number of companies that can be listed on the New York Stock Exchange? 18,278

38. Stocks on the NASDAQ Companies whose stocks are listed on the NASDAQ stock exchange have their company name represented by either four or five letters (repetition of letters is allowed). What is the maximum number of companies that can be listed on the NASDAQ? 12,338,352

39. Garage Door Code Outside a home there is a keypad that will open the garage if the correct four-digit code is entered.

44. 2,600,000

(a) How many codes are possible? 10,000

(b) What is the probability of entering the correct code on the first try, assuming that the owner doesn't remember the code? 0.0001

40. Social Security Numbers A Social Security number is used to identify each resident of the United States uniquely. The number is of the form xxx–xx–xxxx, where each x is a digit from 0 to 9. 40. (b) 1/10^9

(a) How many Social Security numbers can be formed? 10^9

(b) What is the probability of correctly guessing the Social Security number of the president of the United States?

41. User Names Suppose that a local area network requires eight letters for user names. Lower- and uppercase letters are considered the same. How many user names are possible for the local area network? 26^8

42. User Names How many additional user names are possible in Problem 41 if the last character could also be a digit?
$10 \cdot 26^7 \approx 8.03 \times 10^{10}$

43. Combination Locks A combination lock has 50 numbers on it. To open it, you turn counterclockwise to a number, then rotate clockwise to a second number, and then counterclockwise to the third number. Repetitions are allowed.

(a) How many different lock combinations are there? 50^3

(b) What is the probability of guessing a lock combination on the first try? 1/50^3

44. Forming License Plate Numbers How many different license plate numbers can be made by using one letter followed by five digits selected from the digits 0 through 9?

45. INDY 500 Suppose 40 cars start at the Indianapolis 500. In how many ways can the top 3 cars finish the race? 59,280
NW

46. Betting on the Perfecta In how many ways can the top 2 horses finish in a 10-horse race? 90

47. Forming a Committee Four members from a 20-person committee are to be selected randomly to serve as chairperson, vice-chairperson, secretary, and treasurer. The first person selected is the chairperson; the second, the vice-chairperson; the third, the secretary; and the fourth, the treasurer. How many different leadership structures are possible? 116,280

48. Forming a Committee Four members from a 50-person committee are to be selected randomly to serve as chairperson, vice-chairperson, secretary, and treasurer. The first person selected is the chairperson; the second, the vice-chairperson; the third, the secretary; and the fourth, the treasurer. How many different leadership structures are possible? $_{50}P_4$

49. Lottery A lottery exists where balls numbered 1 to 25 are placed in an urn. To win, you must match the four balls chosen in the correct order. How many possible outcomes are there for this game? 303,600

50. Forming a Committee In the U.S. Senate, there are 21 members on the Committee on Banking, Housing, and Urban Affairs. Nine of these 21 members are selected to be on the Subcommittee on Economic Policy. How many different committee structures are possible for this subcommittee? 293,930

51. Simple Random Sample How many different simple random samples of size 5 can be obtained from a population whose size is 50? 2,118,760
NW

52. **Simple Random Sample** How many different simple random samples of size 7 can be obtained from a population whose size is 100? $_{100}C_7$

53. **Children** A family has six children. If this family has exactly two boys, how many different birth and gender orders are possible? 15

54. **Children** A family has eight children. If this family has exactly three boys, how many different birth and gender orders are possible? 56

55. **DNA Sequences** (See Example 12) How many distinguishable DNA sequences can be formed using three As, two Cs, two Gs, and three Ts? 25,200
    NW

56. **DNA Sequences** (See Example 12) How many distinguishable DNA sequences can be formed using one A, four Cs, three Gs, and four Ts? 138,600

57. **Landscape Design** A golf-course architect has four linden trees, five white birch trees, and two bald cypress trees to plant in a row along a fairway. In how many ways can the landscaper plant the trees in a row, assuming that the trees are evenly spaced? 6,930

58. **Starting Lineup** A baseball team consists of three outfielders, four infielders, a pitcher, and a catcher. Assuming that the outfielders and infielders are indistinguishable, how many batting orders are possible? 2,520

59. **Little Lotto** In the Illinois Lottery game Little Lotto, an urn contains balls numbered 1 to 39. From this urn, 5 balls are chosen randomly, without replacement. For a $1 bet, a player chooses one set of five numbers. To win, all five numbers must match those chosen from the urn. The order in which the balls are selected does not matter. What is the probability of winning Little Lotto with one ticket? 1/575,757

60. **Mega Millions** In Mega Millions, an urn contains balls numbered 1 to 56, and a second urn contains balls numbered 1 to 46. From the first urn, 5 balls are chosen randomly, without replacement and without regard to order. From the second urn, 1 ball is chosen randomly. For a $1 bet, a player chooses one set of five numbers to match the balls selected from the first urn and one number to match the ball selected from the second urn. To win, all six numbers must match; that is, the player must match the first 5 balls selected from the first urn *and* the single ball selected from the second urn. What is the probability of winning Mega Millions with a single ticket? $1/(_{56}C_5 \cdot 46)$

61. **Selecting a Jury** The grade appeal process at a university requires that a jury be structured by selecting five individuals randomly from a pool of eight students and ten faculty.
    NW
    (a) What is the probability of selecting a jury of all students? 56/8,568 = 1/153
    (b) What is the probability of selecting a jury of all faculty? 252/8,568 = 1/34
    (c) What is the probability of selecting a jury of two students and three faculty? 3,360/8,568 — 20/51

62. **Selecting a Committee** Suppose that there are 55 Democrats and 45 Republicans in the U.S. Senate. A committee of seven senators is to be formed by selecting members of the Senate randomly.

    (a) What is the probability that the committee is composed of all Democrats? 0.0127
    (b) What is the probability that the committee is composed of all Republicans? 0.0028
    (c) What is the probability that the committee is composed of three Democrats and four Republicans? 0.2442

63. **Acceptance Sampling** Suppose that a shipment of 120 electronic components contains 4 defective components. To determine whether the shipment should be accepted, a quality-control engineer randomly selects 4 of the components and tests them. If 1 or more of the components is defective, the shipment is rejected. What is the probability that the shipment is rejected? 0.1283

64. **In the Dark** A box containing twelve 40-watt light bulbs and eighteen 60-watt light bulbs is stored in your basement. Unfortunately, the box is stored in the dark and you need two 60-watt bulbs. What is the probability of randomly selecting two 60-watt bulbs from the box? 0.3517

65. **Randomly Playing Songs** Suppose a compact disk (CD) you just purchased has 13 tracks. After listening to the CD, you decide that you like 5 of the songs. The random feature on your CD player will play each of the 13 songs once in a random order. Find the probability that among the first 4 songs played
    (a) you like 2 of them; 0.3916
    (b) you like 3 of them; 0.1119
    (c) you like all 4 of them. 0.0070

66. **Packaging Error** Through a manufacturing error, three cans marked "regular soda" were accidentally filled with diet soda and placed into a 12-pack. Suppose that three cans are randomly selected from the 12-pack.
    (a) Determine the probability that exactly two contain diet soda. 0.1227
    (b) Determine the probability that exactly one contains diet soda. 0.4909
    (c) Determine the probability that all three contain diet soda. 0.0045

67. **Three of a Kind** You are dealt 5 cards from a standard 52-card deck. Determine the probability of being dealt three of a kind (such as three aces or three kings) by answering the following questions:
    (a) How many ways can 5 cards be selected from a 52-card deck? 2,598,960
    (b) Each deck contains 4 twos, 4 threes, and so on. How many ways can three of the same card be selected from the deck? 52
    (c) The remaining 2 cards must be different from the 3 chosen and different from each other. For example, if we drew three kings, the 4th card cannot be a king. After selecting the three of a kind, there are 12 different ranks of card remaining in the deck that can be chosen. If we have three kings, then we can choose twos, threes, and so on. Of the 12 ranks remaining, we choose 2 of them and then select one of the 4 cards in each of the two chosen ranks. How many ways can we select the remaining 2 cards? $66 \cdot 4 \cdot 4 = 1,056$
    (d) Use the General Multiplication Rule to compute the probability of obtaining three of a kind. That is, what is the probability of selecting three of a kind and two cards that are not like? 0.0211

68. Two of a Kind Follow the outline presented in Problem 67 to determine the probability of being dealt exactly one pair. *0.4226*

69. Acceptance Sampling Suppose that you have just received a shipment of 20 modems. Although you don't know this, 3 of the modems are defective. To determine whether you will accept the shipment, you randomly select 4 modems and test them. If all 4 modems work, you accept the shipment. Otherwise, the shipment is rejected. What is the probability of accepting the shipment? *0.4912*

70. Acceptance Sampling Suppose that you have just received a shipment of 100 televisions. Although you don't know this, 6 are defective. To determine whether you will accept the shipment, you randomly select 5 televisions and test them. If all 5 televisions work, you accept the shipment; otherwise, the shipment is rejected. What is the probability of accepting the shipment? *0.7291*

71. Password Policy According to the Sefton Council Password Policy (August 2007), the UK government recommends the use of "*Environ passwords with the following format: consonant, vowel, consonant, consonant, vowel, consonant, number, number (for example, pinray45).*"

(a) Assuming passwords are not case sensitive, how many such passwords are possible (assume that there are 5 vowels and 21 consonants)? *486,202,500*

(b) How many passwords are possible if they are case sensitive? *$420^4 \approx 3.11 \times 10^{10}$*

TECHNOLOGY STEP-BY-STEP   Factorials, Permutations, and Combinations

TI-83/84 Plus

Factorials
1. To compute 7!, type 7 on the HOME screen.
2. Press MATH, then highlight PRB, and then select 4 : ! With 7! on the HOME screen, press ENTER again.

Permutations and Combinations
1. To compute $_7P_3$, type 7 on the HOME screen.
2. Press MATH, then highlight PRB, and then select 2 : $_nP_r$
3. Type 3 on the HOME screen, and press ENTER.
Note: To compute $_7C_3$, select 3 : $_nC_r$ instead of 2 : $_nP_r$.

Excel

Factorials or Combinations
1. Select Insert and then Function ....
2. Highlight Math & Trig in the Function category. For combinations, select COMBIN in the function name and fill in the appropriate cells. For a factorial, select FACT in the function name and fill in the appropriate cells.

Permutations
1. Select Insert and then Function ....
2. Highlight Statistical in the Function category. For permutations, select PERMUT in the function name and fill in the appropriate cells.

5.6 PUTTING IT TOGETHER: WHICH METHOD DO I USE?

Objectives		
	1	Determine the appropriate probability rule to use
	2	Determine the appropriate counting technique to use

1 Determine the Appropriate Probability Rule to Use

Working with probabilities can be challenging. The number of different probability rules can sometimes seem daunting. The material presented in this chapter is meant to provide the basic building blocks of probability theory. Knowing when to use a particular rule takes practice. To aid you in this learning process, consider the flowchart provided in Figure 16 on the following page. While not all situations can be handled directly with the formulas provided, they can be combined and expanded to many more situations. A firm understanding of the basic probability rules will help in understanding much of the later material in the text.

Figure 16

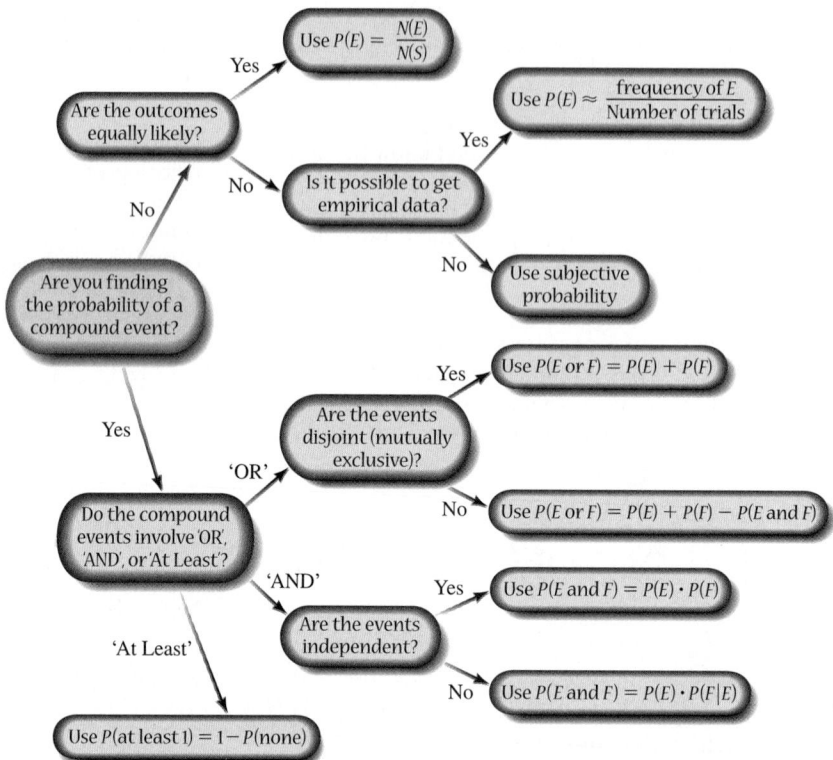

From this flowchart, the first step is to determine whether or not we are finding the probability of a compound event. If we are not dealing with a compound event, we must decide whether to use the classical method (equally likely outcomes), the empirical method (relative frequencies), or subjective assignment. For compound events, we must first decide which type of compound statement we will have. For compound events involving 'AND', we must know if the events are independent. For compound events involving 'OR', we need to know if the events are disjoint (mutually exclusive).

EXAMPLE 1 **Probability: Which Rule Do I Use?**

Problem: In the gameshow *Deal or No Deal?*, a contestant is presented with 26 suitcases that contain amounts ranging from $0.01 to $1,000,000. The contestant must pick an initial case that is set aside as the game progresses. The amounts are randomly distributed among the suitcases prior to the game. Consider the following breakdown:

Prize	Number of Suitcases
$0.01–$100	8
$200–$1000	6
$5,000–$50,000	5
$100,000–$1,000,000	7

What is the probability that the contestant picks a case worth at least $100,000?

Approach: We will follow the flowchart in Figure 16.

Solution: We are asked to find the probability of an event that is not compound. Therefore, we must decide among the empirical, classical, or subjective approaches for determining probability. The probability experiment in this situation is selecting a suitcase. Each prize amount is randomly assigned to one of the 26 suitcases, so the outcomes are equally likely. From the table we see that 7 of the cases contain at least $100,000. Letting $E =$ "worth at least $100,000," we compute $P(E)$ using the classical approach.

$$P(E) = \frac{N(E)}{N(S)} = \frac{7}{26} = 0.269$$

The chance the contestant selects a suitcase worth at least $100,000 is 26.9%. In 100 different games, we would expect about 27 games to result in a contestant choosing a suitcase worth at least $100,000.

| EXAMPLE 2 | **Probability: Which Rule Do I Use?** |

Problem: According to a Harris poll in January 2008, 14% of adult Americans have one or more tattoos, 50% have pierced ears, and 65% of those with one or more tattoos also have pierced ears. What is the probability that a randomly selected adult American has one or more tattoos and pierced ears?

Approach: We will follow the flowchart in Figure 16.

Solution: We are asked to find the probability of a compound event involving 'AND'. Letting E = "one or more tattoos" and F = "ears pierced," we are asked to find $P(E \text{ and } F)$. We need to determine if the two simple events, E and F, are independent. The problem statement tells us that $P(F) = 0.50$ and $P(F|E) = 0.65$. Because $P(F) \neq P(F|E)$, the two events are not independent. We can find $P(E \text{ and } F)$ using the General Multiplication Rule.

$$P(E \text{ and } F) = P(E) \cdot P(F|E)$$
$$= (0.14)(0.65)$$
$$= 0.091$$

So, the chance of selecting an adult American at random who has one or more tattoos and pierced ears is 9.1%.

---

② Determine the Appropriate Counting Technique to Use

To determine the appropriate counting technique to use we need the ability to distinguish between a sequence of choices and arrangement of items. We also need to determine whether order matters in the arrangements. To help in deciding which counting rule to use, we provide the flowchart in Figure 17. Keep in mind that it may be necessary to use several counting rules in one problem.

Figure 17

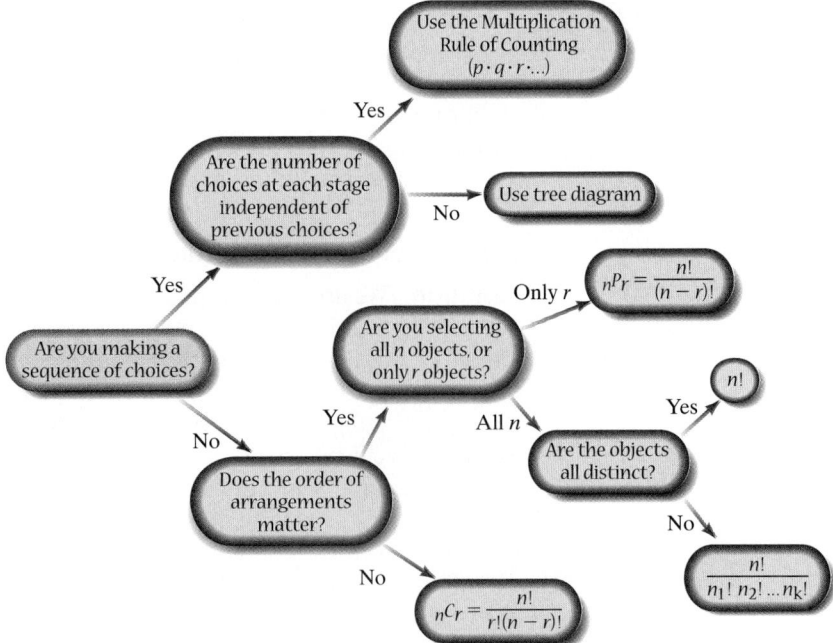

From the flowchart, we first must decide whether we are dealing with a sequence of choices or determining the number of arrangements of items. For a sequence of choices, we use the Multiplication Rule of Counting if the number of choices at each stage is independent of previous choices. This may involve the rules for arrangements, since each choice in the sequence could involve arranging items. If the number of choices at each stage is not independent of previous choices, we use a tree diagram. When determining the number of arrangements of items, we want to know whether the order of selection matters. If order matters, we also want to know whether we are arranging all the items available or a subset of the items.

EXAMPLE 3 | **Counting: Which Technique Do I Use?**

Problem: The Hazelwood city council consists of 5 men and 4 women. How many different subcommittees can be formed that consist of 3 men and 2 women?

Approach: We will follow the flowchart in Figure 17.

Solution: We are asked to find the number of subcommittees that can be formed using 3 men and 2 women. We have a sequence of events to consider: select the men, then select the women. Since the number of choices at each stage is independent of previous choices (the men chosen will not impact which women are chosen), we use the Multiplication Rule of Counting to obtain

$$N(\text{subcommittees}) = N(\text{ways to pick 3 men}) \cdot N(\text{ways to pick 2 women})$$

To select the men, we must consider the number of arrangements of 5 men taken 3 at a time. Since the order of selection does not matter, we use the combination formula.

$$N(\text{ways to pick 3 men}) = {}_5C_3 = \frac{5!}{3! \cdot 2!} = 10$$

To select the women, we must consider the number of arrangements of 3 women taken 2 at a time. Since the order of selection does not matter, we use the combination formula again.

$$N(\text{ways to pick 2 women}) = {}_3C_2 = \frac{3!}{2! \cdot 1!} = 3$$

Combining our results, we obtain $N(\text{subcommittees}) = 10 \cdot 3 = 30$. There are 30 possible subcommittees that contain 3 men and 2 women.

EXAMPLE 4 | **Counting: Which Technique Do I Use?**

Problem: On February 17, 2008, the Daytona International Speedway hosted the 50th running of the Daytona 500. Touted by many to be the most anticipated event in racing history, the race carried a record purse of almost $18.7 million. With 43 drivers in the race, in how many different ways could the top four finishers (1st, 2nd, 3rd, and 4th place) occur?

Approach: We will follow the flowchart in Figure 17.

Solution: We are asked to find the number of ways the top four finishers can be selected. We can view this as a sequence of choices, where the first choice is the first-place driver, the second choice is the second-place driver, and so on. There are 43 ways to pick the first driver, 42 ways to pick the second, 41 ways to pick the third, and 40 ways to pick the fourth. The number of choices at each stage is independent of previous choices, so we can use the Multiplication Rule of Counting. The number of ways the top four finishers can occur is

$$N(\text{top four}) = 43 \cdot 42 \cdot 41 \cdot 40 = 2,961,840$$

We could also approach this problem as an arrangement of units. Since each race position is distinguishable, order matters in the arrangements. We are arranging the

43 drivers taken 4 at a time, so we are only considering a subset of $r = 4$ distinct drivers in each arrangement. Using our permutation formula, we get

$$N(\text{top four}) = {}_{43}P_4 = \frac{43!}{(43-4)!} = \frac{43!}{39!} = 43 \cdot 42 \cdot 41 \cdot 40 = 2{,}961{,}840$$

Again there are 2,961,840 different ways that the top four finishers could occur.

5.6 ASSESS YOUR UNDERSTANDING

Concepts and Vocabulary

1. What is the difference between a permutation and a combination?

2. What method of assigning probabilities to a simple event uses relative frequencies?   *Empirical*

3. Which type of compound event is generally associated with multiplication? Which is generally associated with addition?   *'AND'; 'OR'*

Skill Building

4. Suppose that you roll a pair of dice 1,000 times and get seven 350 times. Based on these results, what is the probability that the next roll results in seven?   *0.35*

For Problems 5 and 6, let the sample space be $S = \{1, 2, 3, 4, 5, 6, 7, 8, 9, 10\}$. Suppose that the outcomes are equally likely.

5. Compute the probability of the event $E = \{1, 3, 5, 10\}$.   *0.4*

6. Compute the probability of the event F = "a number divisible by three."   *0.3*

7. List all permutations of five objects a, b, c, d, and e taken three at a time without replacement.

In Problems 8 and 9, find the probability of the indicated event if $P(E) = 0.7$ and $P(F) = 0.2$.

8. Find $P(E \text{ or } F)$ if E and F are mutually exclusive.   *0.9*

9. Find $P(E \text{ or } F)$ if $P(E \text{ and } F) = 0.15$.   *0.75*

In Problems 10–12, evaluate each expression.

10. $\dfrac{6!2!}{4!}$ *60*   11. ${}_7P_3$ *210*   12. ${}_9C_4$ *126*

13. Suppose that events E and F are independent, $P(E) = 0.8$ and $P(F) = 0.5$. What is $P(E \text{ and } F)$?   *0.4*

14. Suppose that E and F are two events and $P(E \text{ and } F) = 0.4$ and $P(E) = 0.9$. Find $P(F|E)$.

15. Suppose that E and F are two events and $P(E) = 0.9$ and $P(F|E) = 0.3$. Find $P(E \text{ and } F)$.   *0.27*

16. List all combinations of five objects a, b, c, d, and e taken three at a time without replacement.

Applying the Concepts   14. $\dfrac{4}{9} = 0.444$

17. **Soccer?** In a survey of 500 randomly selected Americans, it was determined that 22 play soccer. What is the probability that a randomly selected American plays soccer?   *0.044*

18. **Apartment Vacancy** A real estate agent conducted a survey of 200 landlords and asked how long their apartments remained vacant before a tenant was found. The results of the survey are shown in the table. The data are based on information obtained from the U.S. Census Bureau.

Duration of Vacancy	Frequency
Less than 1 month	42
1 to 2 months	38
2 to 4 months	45
4 to 6 months	30
6 to 12 months	24
1 to 2 years	13
2 years or more	8

(a) Construct a probability model for duration of vacancy.

(b) Is it unusual for an apartment to remain vacant for 2 years or more?   *Yes*

(c) Determine the probability that a randomly selected apartment is vacant for 1 to 4 months.   *0.415*

(d) Determine the probability that a randomly selected apartment is vacant for less than 2 years.   *0.96*

19. **Seating Arrangements** In how many ways can three men and three women be seated around a circular table (that seats six) assuming that women and men must alternate seats?   *36*

20. **Starting Lineups** Payton's futsal team consists of 10 girls, but only 5 can be on the field at any given time (four fielders and a goalie).

(a) How many starting lineups are possible if all players are selected without regard to position played?   *252*

(b) How many starting lineups are possible if either Payton or Jordyn must play goalie?   *252*

21. **Titanic Survivors** The following data represent the survival data for the ill-fated *Titanic* voyage by gender. The males are adult males and the females are adult females.

	Male	Female	Child	Total
Survived	338	316	57	**711**
Died	1,352	109	52	**1,513**
Total	**1,690**	**425**	**109**	**2,224**

(a) If a passenger is selected at random, what is the probability that the passenger survived?   *0.320*

(b) If a passenger is selected at random, what is the probability that the passenger was female?   *0.191*

(c) If a passenger is selected at random, what is the probability that the passenger was female or a child?   *0.240*

(d) If a passenger is selected at random, what is the probability that the passenger was female and survived?   *0.142*

(e) If a passenger is selected at random, what is the probability that the passenger was female or survived?   *0.369*

(f) If a female passenger is selected at random, what is the probability that she survived?   *0.744*

(g) If a child passenger is selected at random, what is the probability that the child survived? *0.523*

(h) If a male passenger is selected at random, what is the probability that he survived? *0.2*

(i) Do you think the adage "women and children first" was adhered to on the *Titanic*? *Yes*

(j) Suppose two females are randomly selected. What is the probability both survived? *0.552*

22. Marijuana Use According to the *Statistical Abstract of the United States*, about 17% of all 18- to 25-year-olds are current marijuana users.

(a) What is the probability that four randomly selected 18- to 25-year-olds are all marijuana users? *0.00084*

(b) What is the probability that among four randomly selected 18- to 25-year-olds at least one is a marijuana user? *0.525*

23. SAT Reports Shawn is planning for college and takes the SAT test. While registering for the test, he is allowed to select three schools to which his scores will be sent at no cost. If there are 12 colleges he is considering, how many different ways could he fill out the score report form? *220*

24. National Honor Society The distribution of National Honor Society members among the students at a local high school is shown in the table. A student's name is drawn at random.

Class	Total	National Honor Society
Senior	92	37
Junior	112	30
Sophomore	125	20
Freshman	120	0

(a) What is the probability that the student is a junior? *0.249*

(b) What is the probability that the student is a senior, given that the student is in the National Honor Society? *0.425*

25. Instant Winner In 2002, Valerie Wilson won $1 million in a scratch-off game (Cool Million) from the New York lottery. Four years later, she won $1 million in another scratch-off game ($3,000,000 Jubilee), becoming the first person in New York state lottery history to win $1 million or more in a scratch-off game twice. In the first game, she beat odds of 1 in 5.2 million to win. In the second, she beat odds of 1 in 705,600.

(a) What is the probability that an individual would win $1 million in both games if they bought one scratch-off ticket from each game? *≈ 0.00000000000027*

(b) What is the probability that an individual would win $1 million twice in the $3,000,000 Jubilee scratch-off game? *≈ 0.000000000002*

26. Text Twist In the game Text Twist, 6 letters are given and the player must form words of varying lengths using the letters provided. Suppose that the letters in a particular game are ENHSIC.

(a) How many different arrangements are possible using all 6 letters? *720*

(b) How many different arrangements are possible using only 4 letters? *360*

(c) The solution to this game has three 6-letter words. To advance to the next round, the player needs at least one of the 6-letter words. If the player simply guesses, what is the probability that he/she will get one of the 6-letter words on their first guess of six letters? $\frac{1}{240} = 0.0042$

27. Digital Music Players According to an October 2004 survey, 51% of teens own an iPod or other MP3 player. If the probability that both a teen and his or her parent own an iPod or other MP3 player is 0.220, what is the probability that a parent owns such a device given that his or her teenager owns one? *0.431*

28. Weather Forecast The weather forecast says there is a 10% chance of rain on Thursday. Jim wakes up on Thursday and sees overcast skies. Since it has rained for the past three days, he believes that the chance of rain is more likely 60% or higher. What method of probability assignment did Jim use? *Subjective*

29. Essay Test An essay test in European History has 12 questions. Students are required to answer 8 of the 12 questions. How many different sets of questions could be answered? *495*

30. Exercise Routines Todd is putting together an exercise routine and feels that the sequence of exercises can affect his overall performance. He has 12 exercises to select from, but only has enough time to do 9. How many different exercise routines could he put together? *79,833,600*

31. New Cars If the 2008 Hyundai Elantra has 2 transmission types, 3 vehicle styles, 2 option packages, 8 exterior color choices, and 2 interior color choices, how many different Elantras are possible? *192*

32. Lingo In the gameshow *Lingo*, the team that correctly guesses a mystery word gets a chance to pull two Lingo balls from a bin. Balls in the bin are labeled with numbers corresponding to the numbers remaining on their Lingo board. There are also three prize balls and three red "stopper" balls in the bin. If a stopper ball is drawn first, the team loses their second draw. To form a Lingo, the team needs five numbers in a vertical, horizontal, or diagonal row. Consider the sample Lingo board below for a team that has just guessed a mystery word.

L	I	N	G	O
10			48	66
		34		74
		22	58	68
4	16		40	70
	26	52		64

(a) What is the probability that the first ball selected is on the Lingo board? *0.714*

(b) What is the probability that the team draws a stopper ball on its first draw? *0.143*

(c) What is the probability that the team makes a Lingo on their first draw? *0*

(d) What is the probability that the team makes a Lingo on their second draw? *0.0143*

CHAPTER 5 REVIEW

Summary

In this chapter, we introduced the concept of probability. Probability is a measure of the likelihood of a random phenomenon or chance behavior. Because we are measuring a random phenomenon, there is short-term uncertainty. However, this short-term uncertainty gives rise to long-term predictability.

Probabilities are numbers between zero and one, inclusive. The closer a probability is to one, the more likely the event is to occur. If an event has probability zero, it is said to be impossible. Events with probability one are said to be certain.

We introduced three methods for computing probabilities: (1) the empirical method, (2) the classical method, and (3) subjective probabilities. Empirical probabilities rely on the relative frequency with which an event happens. Classical probabilities require the events in the experiment to be equally likely. We count the number of ways an event can happen and divide this by the number of possible outcomes of the experiment. Empirical probabilities require that an experiment be performed, whereas classical probability does not. Subjective probabilities are probabilities based on the opinion of the individual providing the probability. They are educated guesses about the likelihood of an event occurring, but still represent a legitimate way of assigning probabilities.

We are also interested in probabilities of multiple outcomes. For example, we might be interested in the probability that either event E or event F happens. The Addition Rule is used to compute the probability of E *or* F; the Multiplication Rule is used to compute the probability that both E *and* F occur. Two events are mutually exclusive (or disjoint) if they do not have any outcomes in common. That is, mutually exclusive events cannot happen at the same time. Two events E and F are independent if knowing that one of the events occurs does not affect the probability of the other. The complement of an event E, denoted E^c, is all the outcomes in the sample space that are not in E.

Finally, we introduced counting methods. The Multiplication Rule of Counting is used to count the number of ways a sequence of events can occur. Permutations are used to count the number of ways r items can be arranged from a set of n distinct items. Combinations are used to count the number of ways r items can be selected from a set of n distinct items without replacement and without regard to order. These counting techniques can be used to calculate probabilities using the classical method.

Vocabulary

Probability (p. 259)
Outcome (p. 259)
The Law of Large Numbers (p. 259)
Experiment (p. 260)
Sample space (p. 260)
Event (p. 260)
Probability model (p. 261)
Impossible event (p. 261)
Certainty (p. 261)
Unusual event (p. 261)

Equally likely outcomes (p. 263)
Tree diagram (p. 265)
Subjective probability (p. 268)
Disjoint (p. 274)
Mutually exclusive (p. 274)
Venn diagram (p. 274)
Contingency table (p. 278)
Two-way table (p. 278)
Row variable (p. 278)
Column variable (p. 278)

Cell (p. 278)
Complement (p. 279)
Independent (p. 286)
Dependent (p. 286)
Conditional probability (p. 292)
Factorial symbol (p. 305)
Permutation (p. 305)
Factorial notation (p. 306)
Combination (p. 307)

Formulas

Empirical Probability

$$P(E) \approx \frac{\text{frequency of } E}{\text{number of trials of experiment}}$$

Classical Probability

$$P(E) = \frac{\text{number of ways that } E \text{ can occur}}{\text{number of possible outcomes}} = \frac{N(E)}{N(S)}$$

Addition Rule for Disjoint Events
$$P(E \text{ or } F) = P(E) + P(F)$$

General Addition Rule
$$P(E \text{ or } F) = P(E) + P(F) - P(E \text{ and } F)$$

Probabilities of Complements
$$P(E^c) = 1 - P(E)$$

Multiplication Rule for Independent Events
$$P(E \text{ and } F) = P(E) \cdot P(F)$$

Multiplication Rule for n Independent Events
$$P(E \text{ and } F \text{ and } G \dots) = P(E) \cdot P(F) \cdot P(G) \cdot \dots$$

Conditional Probability Rule

$$P(F|E) = \frac{P(E \text{ and } F)}{P(E)} = \frac{N(E \text{ and } F)}{N(E)}$$

General Multiplication Rule
$$P(E \text{ and } F) = P(E) \cdot P(F|E)$$

Factorial Notation
$$n! = n \cdot (n-1) \cdot (n-2) \cdot \dots \cdot 3 \cdot 2 \cdot 1$$

Combination

$$_nC_r = \frac{n!}{r!(n-r)!}$$

Permutation

$$_nP_r = \frac{n!}{(n-r)!}$$

Permutations with Nondistinct Items

$$\frac{n!}{n_1! \cdot n_2! \cdot \dots \cdot n_k!}$$

Objectives

Section	You should be able to . . .	Examples	Review Exercises
5.1	1 Apply the rules of probabilities (p. 260)	2	1, 13(d), 15
	2 Compute and interpret probabilities using the empirical method (p. 262)	3, 4, 7(a)	14(a), 15, 16(a) and (b), 17(a), 30
	3 Compute and interpret probabilities using the classical method (p. 263)	5, 6, 7(b)	2–4, 13(a) and (d), 32(a) and (b)
	4 Use simulation to obtain data based on probabilities (p. 266)	8	27
	5 Recognize and interpret subjective probabilities (p. 268)		28
5.2	1 Use the Addition Rule for disjoint events (p. 274)	1 and 2	3, 4, 7, 13(b) and (c), 32(g)
	2 Use the General Addition Rule (p. 277)	3 and 4	6, 16(d)
	3 Compute the probability of an event using the Complement Rule (p. 279)	5 and 6	5, 14(b), 17(b)
5.3	1 Identify independent events (p. 286)	1	9, 16(g), 32(f)
	2 Use the Multiplication Rule for independent events (p. 287)	2 and 3	14(c) and (d), 17(c) and (e), 18, 19
	3 Compute at-least probabilities (p. 289)	4	14(e), 17(d) and (f)
5.4	1 Compute conditional probabilities (p. 292)	1 through 3	11, 16(f), 32(c) and (d)
	2 Compute probabilities using the General Multiplication Rule (p. 295)	4 through 6	10, 20, 29
5.5	1 Solve counting problems using the Multiplication Rule (p. 302)	1 through 4	21
	2 Solve counting problems using permutations (p. 305)	5 through 7	10(e) and (f), 22
	3 Solve counting problems using combinations (p. 307)	8 through 11	10(c) and (d), 24
	4 Solve counting problems involving permutations with nondistinct items (p. 310)	12 and 13	23
	5 Compute probabilities involving permutations and combinations (p. 311)	14 and 15	25, 26
5.6	1 Determine the appropriate probability rule to use (p. 315)	1, 2	13–20, 25, 26, 29(c) and (d), 30
	2 Determine the appropriate counting technique to use (p. 317)	3, 4	21–25

Review Exercises

1. (a) Which among the following numbers could be the probability of an event?

$$0, -0.01, 0.75, 0.41, 1.34 \quad 0, 0.75, 0.41$$

(b) Which among the following numbers could be the probability of an event?

$$\frac{2}{5}, \frac{1}{3}, -\frac{4}{7}, \frac{4}{3}, \frac{6}{7} \quad \frac{2}{5}, \frac{1}{3}, \frac{6}{7}$$

For Problems 2–5, let the sample space be S = {red, green, blue, orange, yellow}. Suppose that the outcomes are equally likely.

2. Compute the probability of the event E = {yellow}. $\frac{1}{5}$

3. Compute the probability of the event F = {green or orange}. $\frac{2}{5}$

4. Compute the probability of the event E = {red or blue or yellow}. $\frac{3}{5}$

5. Suppose that E = {yellow}. Compute the probability of E^c. $\frac{4}{5}$

6. Suppose that $P(E) = 0.76$, $P(F) = 0.45$, and $P(E \text{ and } F) = 0.32$. What is $P(E \text{ or } F)$? 0.89

7. Suppose that $P(E) = 0.36$, $P(F) = 0.12$, and E and F are mutually exclusive. What is $P(E \text{ or } F)$? 0.48

8. Suppose that events E and F are independent. In addition, $P(E) = 0.45$ and $P(F) = 0.2$. What is $P(E \text{ and } F)$? 0.09

9. Suppose that $P(E) = 0.8$, $P(F) = 0.5$, and $P(E \text{ and } F) = 0.24$. Are events E and F independent? Why? No

10. Suppose that $P(E) = 0.59$ and $P(F|E) = 0.45$. What is $P(E$ and $F)$? 0.2655

11. Suppose that $P(E \text{ and } F) = 0.35$ and $P(F) = 0.7$. What is $P(E|F)$? 0.5

12. Determine the value of each of the following:
    (a) 7! 5040
    (b) 0! 1
    (c) $_9C_4$ 126
    (d) $_{10}C_3$ 120
    (e) $_9P_2$ 72
    (f) $_{12}P_4$ $11,880$

13. **Roulette** In the game of roulette, a wheel consists of 38 slots, numbered 0, 00, 1, 2, . . . , 36. (See the photo in Problem 35 from Section 5.1.) To play the game, a metal ball is spun around the wheel and allowed to fall into one of the numbered slots. The slots numbered 0 and 00 are green, the odd numbers are red, and the even numbers are black.

    (a) Determine the probability that the metal ball falls into a green slot. Interpret this probability.
    (b) Determine the probability that the metal ball falls into a green or a red slot. Interpret this probability.
    (c) Determine the probability that the metal ball falls into 00 or a red slot. Interpret this probability.
    (d) Determine the probability that the metal ball falls into the number 31 and a black slot simultaneously. What term is used to describe this event? 0; impossible

13. (a) $\frac{1}{19}$ 13. (b) $\frac{10}{19}$ 13. (c) $\frac{19}{38} = \frac{1}{2}$

14. New Year's Holiday Between 6:00 P.M. December 30, 2005, and 5:59 A.M. January 3, 2006, there were 454 traffic fatalities in the United States. Of these, 193 were alcohol related.

 (a) What is the probability that a randomly selected traffic fatality that happened between 6:00 P.M. December 30, 2005, and 5:59 A.M. January 3, 2006, was alcohol related? *0.425*

 (b) What is the probability that a randomly selected traffic fatality that happened between 6:00 P.M. December 30, 2005, and 5:59 A.M. January 3, 2006, was not alcohol related? *0.575*

 (c) What is the probability that two randomly selected traffic fatalities that happened between 6:00 P.M. December 30, 2005, and 5:59 A.M. January 3, 2006, were both alcohol related? *0.181*

 (d) What is the probability that neither of two randomly selected traffic fatalities that happened between 6:00 P.M. December 30, 2005, and 5:59 A.M. January 3, 2006, were alcohol related? *0.330*

 (e) What is the probability that of two randomly selected traffic fatalities that happened between 6:00 P.M. December 30, 2005, and 5:59 A.M. January 3, 2006, at least one was alcohol related? *0.670*

15. Memphis Workers The following data represent the distribution of class of workers in Memphis, Tennessee, in 2006.

Class of Worker	Number of Workers
Private wage and salary worker	219,852
Government worker	39,351
Self-employed worker	17,060
Unpaid family worker	498

Source: U.S. Census Bureau, *American Community Survey*, 2006.

 (a) Construct a probability model for Memphis workers.
 (b) Is it unusual for a Memphis worker to be an unpaid family worker? *Yes*
 (c) Is it unusual for a Memphis worker to be self-employed? *No*

16. Gestation Period versus Weight The following data represent the birth weights (in grams) of babies born in 2005, along with the period of gestation.

Birth Weight (grams)	Preterm	Term	Postterm	Total
Less than 1000	29,764	223	15	**30,002**
1000–1999	84,791	11,010	974	**96,775**
2000–2999	252,116	661,510	37,657	**951,283**
3000–3999	145,506	2,375,346	172,957	**2,693,809**
4000–4999	8,747	292,466	27,620	**328,833**
Over 5000	192	3,994	483	**4,669**
Total	**521,116**	**3,344,549**	**239,706**	**4,105,371**

Source: National Vital Statistics Report, Vol. 56, No. 6, December 5, 2007

 (a) What is the probability that a randomly selected baby born in 2005 was postterm? *0.058*
 (b) What is the probability that a randomly selected baby born in 2005 weighed 3,000 to 3,999 grams? *0.656*
 (c) What is the probability that a randomly selected baby born in 2005 weighed 3,000 to 3,999 grams and was postterm? *0.042*

 (d) What is the probability that a randomly selected baby born in 2005 weighed 3,000 to 3,999 grams or was postterm? *0.672*
 (e) What is the probability that a randomly selected baby born in 2005 weighed less than 1,000 grams and was postterm? Is this event impossible? *0.000004; no*
 (f) What is the probability that a randomly selected baby born in 2005 weighed 3,000 to 3,999 grams, given the baby was postterm? *0.722*
 (g) Are the events "postterm baby" and "weighs 3,000 to 3,999 grams" independent? Why? *No*

17. Better Business Bureau The Better Business Bureau reported that approximately 72.2% of consumer complaints in 2006 were settled.

 (a) If a consumer complaint from 2006 is randomly selected, what is the probability that it was settled? *0.722*
 (b) What is the probability that is was not settled? *0.278*
 (c) If a random sample of five consumer complaints is selected, what is the probability that all five were settled?
 (d) If a random sample of five consumer complaints is selected, what is the probability that at least one was not settled? *0.804*
 (e) If a random sample of five consumer complaints is selected, what is the probability that none was settled?
 (f) If a random sample of five consumer complaints is selected, what is the probability that at least one was settled?

18. Pick 3 For the Illinois Lottery's PICK 3 game, a player must match a sequence of three repeatable numbers, ranging from 0 to 9, in exact order (for example, 3–7–2). With a single ticket, what is the probability of matching the three winning numbers? *0.001*

19. Pick 4 The Illinois Lottery's PICK 4 game is similar to PICK 3, except a player must match a sequence of four repeatable numbers, ranging from 0 to 9, in exact order (for example, 5–8–5–1). With a single ticket, what is the probability of matching the four winning numbers? *0.0001*

20. Drawing Cards Suppose that you draw 3 cards without replacement from a standard 52-card deck. What is the probability that all 3 cards are aces? *0.00018*

21. Forming License Plates A license plate is designed so that the first two characters are letters and the last four characters are digits (0 through 9). How many different license plates can be formed assuming that letters and numbers can be used more than once? *6,760,000*

22. Choosing a Seat If four students enter a classroom that has 10 vacant seats, in how many ways can they be seated? *5040*

23. Arranging Flags How many different vertical arrangements are there of 10 flags if 4 are white, 3 are blue, 2 are green, and 1 is red? *12,600*

24. Simple Random Sampling How many different simple random samples of size 8 can be obtained from a population whose size is 55? *$_{55}C_8$*

25. Arizona's Pick 5 In one of Arizona's lotteries, balls are numbered 1 to 35. Five balls are selected randomly, without replacement. The order in which the balls are selected does not matter. To win, your numbers must match the five selected. Determine your probability of winning Arizona's Pick 5 with one ticket. *1/324,632*

17. (c) 0.196   17. (e) 0.002   17. (f) 0.998

26. **Packaging Error** Because of a mistake in packaging, a case of 12 bottles of red wine contained 5 Merlot and 7 Cabernet, each without labels. All the bottles look alike and have an equal probability of being chosen. Three bottles are randomly selected. *26. (b) 0.3182*
    (a) What is the probability that all three are Merlot? *0.0455*
    (b) What is the probability that exactly two are Merlot?
    (c) What is the probability that none is a Merlot? *0.1591*

27. **Simulation** Use a graphing calculator or statistical software to simulate the playing of the game of roulette, using an integer distribution with numbers 1 through 38. Repeat the simulation 100 times. Let the number 37 represent 0 and the number 38 represent 00. Use the results of the simulation to answer the following questions.
    (a) What is the probability that the ball lands in the slot marked 7?
    (b) What is the probability that the ball lands either in the slot marked 0 or in the one marked 00?

28. Explain what is meant by a subjective probability. List some examples of subjective probabilities.

29. **Playing Five-Card Stud** In the game of five-card stud, one card is dealt face down to each player and the remaining four cards are dealt face up. After two cards are dealt (one down and one up), the players bet. Players continue to bet after each additional card is dealt. Suppose three cards have been dealt to each of five players at the table. You currently have three clubs in your hand, so you will attempt to get a flush (all cards in the same suit). Of the cards dealt, there are two clubs showing in other player's hands.
    (a) How many clubs are in a standard 52-card deck? *13*
    (b) How many cards remain in the deck or are not known by you? Of this amount, how many are clubs? *41; 8*
    (c) What is the probability that you get dealt a club on the next card? *8/41*
    (d) What is the probability that you get dealt two clubs in a row? *0.034*
    (e) Should you stay in the game?

30. **Mark McGwire** During the 1998 major league baseball season, Mark McGwire of the St. Louis Cardinals hit 70 home runs. Of the 70 home runs, 34 went to left field, 20 went to left center field, 13 went to center field, 3 went to right center field, and 0 went to right field. *Source*: Miklasz, B., et al. *Celebrating 70: Mark McGwire's Historic Season*, Sporting News Publishing Co., 1998, p. 179.
    (a) What is the probability that a randomly selected home run was hit to left field? Interpret this probability. *0.486*
    (b) What is the probability that a randomly selected home run was hit to right field? *0*
    (c) Was it impossible for Mark McGwire to hit a homer to right field? *No*

31. **Lottery Luck** In 1996, a New York couple won $2.5 million in the state lottery. Eleven years later, the couple won $5 million in the state lottery using the same set of numbers. The odds of winning the New York lottery twice are roughly 1 in 16 trillion, described by a lottery spokesperson as "galactically astronomical." Although it is highly unlikely that an individual will win the lottery twice, it is not unlikely that *someone* will win a lottery twice. Explain why this is the case.

32. **Coffee Sales** The following data represent the number of cases of coffee or filters sold by four sales reps in a recent sales competition.

Salesperson	Gourmet	Single Cup	Filters	Total
Connor	142	325	30	**497**
Paige	42	125	40	**207**
Bryce	9	100	10	**119**
Mallory	71	75	40	**186**
Total	**264**	**625**	**120**	**1,009**

   (a) What is the probability that a randomly selected case was sold by Bryce? Is this unusual? *0.118; no*
   (b) What is the probability that a randomly selected case was Gourmet? *0.262*
   (c) What is the probability that a randomly selected Single-Cup case was sold by Mallory? *0.120*
   (d) What is the probability that a randomly selected Gourmet case was sold by Bryce? Is this unusual? *0.034; yes*
   (e) What can be concluded from the results of parts (a) and (d)?
   (f) Are the events "Mallory" and "Filters" independent? Explain. *No*
   (g) Are the events "Paige" and "Gourmet" mutually exclusive? Explain. *No*

CHAPTER TEST

1. Which among the following numbers could be the probability of an event? $0.23, 0, \frac{3}{2}, \frac{3}{4}, -1.32$ *0.23, 0, 3/4*

For Problems 2–4, let the sample space by $S = \{$Chris, Adam, Elaine, Brian, Jason$\}$. Suppose that the outcomes are equally likely.

2. Compute the probability of the event $E = \{$Jason$\}$. *1/5*

3. Compute the probability of the event $E = \{$Chris or Elaine$\}$.

4. Suppose that $E = \{$Adam$\}$. Compute the probability of E^c.

5. Suppose that $P(E) = 0.37$ and $P(F) = 0.22$.
    (a) Find $P(E$ or $F)$ if E and F are mutually exclusive. *0.59*
    (b) Find $P(E$ and $F)$ if E and F are independent. *0.0814*

6. Suppose that $P(E) = 0.15$, $P(F) = 0.45$, and $P(F|E) = 0.70$.
    (a) What is $P(E$ and $F)$? *0.105*
    (b) What is $P(E$ or $F)$? *0.495*
    (c) What is $P(E|F)$? *0.233*
    (d) Are E and F independent? *No*

7. Determine the value of each of the following:
    (a) $8!$ *40,320*
    (b) $_{12}C_6$ *924*
    (c) $_{14}P_8$ *121,080,960*

8. Craps is a dice game in which two fair dice are cast. If the roller shoots a 7 or 11 on the first roll, he or she wins. If the roller shoots a 2, 3, or 12 on the first roll, he or she loses.
    (a) Compute the probability that the shooter wins on the first roll. Interpret this probability. $\frac{2}{9}$

3. 2/5   4. 4/5

(b) Compute the probability that the shooter loses on the first roll. Interpret this probability. $\frac{1}{9}$

9. The National Fire Protection Association reports that 32% of fires in 2006 were in structures. What is the probability that a randomly selected fire from 2006 was in a structure? What is the probability that a randomly selected fire from 2006 occurred somewhere other than in a structure? *0.32; 0.68*

10. The following probability model shows the distribution of the most-popular-selling Girl Scout Cookies®.

Cookie Type	Probability
Thin Mints	0.25
Samoas®/Caramel deLites™	0.19
Peanut Butter Patties®/Tagalongs™	0.13
Peanut Butter Sandwich/Do-si-dos™	0.11
Shortbread/Trefoils	0.09
Other varieties	0.23

Source: www.girlscouts.org

(a) Verify that this is a probability model.
(b) If a girl scout is selling cookies to people who randomly enter a shopping mall, what is the probability that the next box sold will be Peanut Butter Patties®/Tagalongs™ or Peanut Butter Sandwich/Do-si-dos™? *0.24*
(c) If a girl scout is selling cookies to people who randomly enter a shopping mall, what is the probability that the next box sold will be Thin Mints, Samoas®/Caramel deLites™, or Shortbread/Trefoils? *0.53*
(d) What is the probability that the next box sold will not be Thin Mints? *0.75*

11. The following data represent the medal tallies of the top eight countries at the 2006 Winter Olympics in Turin, Italy.

Country	Gold	Silver	Bronze	Total
Germany	11	12	6	29
USA	9	9	7	25
Austria	9	7	7	23
Russia	8	6	8	22
Canada	7	10	7	24
Sweden	7	2	5	14
Korea	6	3	2	11
Switzerland	5	4	5	14
Total	**62**	**53**	**47**	**162**

(a) If a medal is randomly selected from the top eight countries, what is the probability that it is gold? *0.383*
(b) If a medal is randomly selected from the top eight countries, what is the probability that it was won by Russia? *0.136*
(c) If a medal is randomly selected from the top eight countries, what is the probability that it is gold and was won by Russia? *0.049*
(d) If a medal is randomly selected from the top eight countries, what is the probability that it is gold or was won by Russia? *0.469*

(e) If a bronze medal is randomly selected from the top eight countries, what is the probability that it was won by Sweden? *0.106*
(f) If a medal that was won by Sweden is randomly selected, what is the probability that it is bronze? *0.357*

12. During the 2007 season, the Boston Red Sox won 59.3% of their games. Assuming that the outcomes of the baseball games are independent and that the percentage of wins this season will be the same as in 2007, answer the following questions:
(a) What is the probability that the Red Sox will win two games in a row? *0.352*
(b) What is the probability that the Red Sox will win seven games in a row? *0.026*
(c) What is the probability that the Red Sox will lose at least one of their next seven games? *0.974*

13. You just received a shipment of 10 DVD players. One DVD player is defective. You will accept the shipment if two randomly selected DVD players work. What is the probability that you will accept the shipment? *0.8*

14. In the game of Jumble, the letters of a word are scrambled. The player must form the correct word. In a recent game in a local newspaper, the Jumble "word" was LINCEY. How many different arrangements are there of the letters in this "word"? *6!*

15. The U.S. Senate Appropriations Committee has 29 members and a subcommittee is to be formed by randomly selecting 5 of its members. How many different committees could be formed? $_{29}C_5$

16. In Pennsylvania's Cash 5 lottery, balls are numbered 1 to 43. Five balls are selected randomly, without replacement. The order in which the balls are selected does not matter. To win, your numbers must match the five selected. Determine your probability of winning Pennsylvania's Cash 5 with one ticket. *1/962,598*

17. A local area network requires eight characters for a password. The first character must be a letter, but the remaining seven characters can be either a letter or a digit (0 through 9). Lower- and uppercase letters are considered the same. How many passwords are possible for the local area network? $26\cdot36^7$

18. In 1 second, a 3-GHz computer processor can generate about 3 million passwords. How long would it take such a processor to generate all the passwords for the scheme in Problem 17?

19. A survey distributed at the 28th Lunar and Planetary Science Conference in March 1997 asked respondents to estimate the chance that there was life on Mars. The median response was a 57% chance of life on Mars. Which method of finding probabilities was used to obtain this result? Explain why. *Subjective*

20. How many distinguishable DNA sequences can be formed using two As, four Cs, four Gs and five Ts? *9,459,450*

21. A student is taking a 40-question multiple-choice test. Each question has five possible answers. Since the student did not study for the test, he guesses on all the questions. Letting 0 or 1 indicate a correct answer, use the following line from a table of random digits to simulate the probability that the student will guess a question correctly. *0.225*

73634 79304 78871 25956 59109 30573 18513 61760

18. *679,156 seconds (7.9 days)*

MAKING AN
INFORMED DECISION

Sports Probabilities

Have you ever watched a sporting event on television in which the announcer cites an obscure statistic? Where do these numbers come from? Well, pretend that you are the statistician for your favorite sports team. Your job is to compile strange probabilities regarding your favorite team and a competing team. For example, during the 2007 baseball season, the Boston Red Sox won 68% of their day games. As statisticians, we represent this as a conditional probability as follows: $P(\text{win}|\text{day}) = 0.68$. Suppose that Boston was playing the Seattle Mariners during the day and that Seattle won 52% of the games that it played during the day. From these statistics, we predict that Boston will win the game. Other ideas for conditional probabilities include home versus road games, right- vs left-handed pitcher, weather, and so on. For basketball, consider conditional probabilities such as the probability of winning if the team's leading scorer scores fewer than 12 points.

Use the statistics and probabilities that you compile to make a prediction about which team will win. Write an article that presents your predictions along with the supporting numerical facts. Maybe the article could include such "keys to the game" as "Our crack statistician has found that our football team wins 80% of its games when it holds opposing teams to less than 10 points." Repeat this exercise for at least five games. Following each game, determine whether the team you chose has won or lost. Compute your winning percentage for the games you predicted. Did you predict the winner in more than 50% of the games?

A great source for these obscure facts can be found at www.espn.com. For baseball, a great site is www.mlb.com. For basketball, go to www.nba.com. For football, go to www.nfl.com. For hockey, go to www.nhl.com.

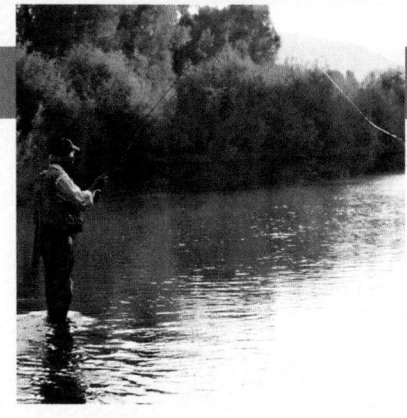

CASE STUDY

The late spring morning broke along the banks of a river. Robert Donkin, an elderly retiree with fishing pole in hand, slipped through the underbrush that lined the river's banks. As he neared the shore, he saw a rather large canvas bag floating in the water, held by foliage that leaned over the river. The bag appeared to be stuffed, well-worn, and heavily stained. Upon closer inspection, Mr. Donkin observed what he believed to be hair floating through the bag's opening. Marking the spot of his discovery, the fisherman fetched the authorities.

Preliminary investigation at the scene revealed a body in the bag. Unfortunately, it was impossible to identify the corpse's sex or race immediately. Estimating age was also out of the question. Forensics was assigned the task of identifying the victim and estimating the cause and time of death. While waiting for the forensics analysis, you, as the detective in charge, have gathered the information shown pages 327–328 concerning victim–offender relationships from recent reports from the FBI.

Using the information contained in the tables, you are to develop a preliminary profile of the victim and offender by determining the likelihood that:

1. The offender is at least 18.
2. The offender is white.
3. The offender is male.
4. The victim is a white female.
5. The victim is either white or female.
6. The victim and the offender are from the same age category.
7. The victim and the offender are from different age categories.
8. The victim and the offender are of the same race.
9. The victim and the offender are of different races.
10. The victim and the offender are of the same sex.
11. The victim and the offender are of different sexes.

12. Without knowing the contents of the forensic team's report, what is your best prediction of the age, race, and sex of the victim? Explain your reasoning.

13. What is your best prediction as to the age, race, and sex of the offender? Explain your reasoning.

Soon after you finished this analysis, the preliminary forensics report was delivered to your desk. Although no identification had been made, the autopsy suggested that the cause of death was blunt-force trauma and that the body had been in the water at least 2 weeks. By using a variety of techniques, it was also determined that the victim was a white female with blonde hair. She was estimated as being in her mid-thirties, showed no signs of having had children, and was wearing no jewelry.

Based on this new information, you develop a new offender profile by determining the likelihood that:

14. The offender is at least 18.
15. The offender is white.
16. The offender is male.

Victim–Offender Relationship by Age			
	Age of Offender		
Age of Victim	**Less Than 18**	**At Least 18**	**Unknown**
Less than 18	124	619	39
At least 18	290	5,628	480
Unknown	4	80	21

Victim–Offender Relationship by Sex

Sex of Victim	Sex of Offender		
	Male	Female	Unknown
Male	4,710	490	89
Female	1,735	150	24
Unknown	50	11	26

Victim–Offender Relationship by Race

Race of Victim	Race of Offender			
	White	Black	Other	Unknown
White	3,026	573	53	57
Black	208	3,034	12	49
Other	54	28	97	7
Unknown	30	27	4	26

Sex of Victim by Race of Offender

Sex of Victim	Race of Offender			
	White	Black	Other	Unknown
Male	2,162	2,935	103	89
Female	1,126	700	59	24
Unknown	30	27	4	26

Race of Victim by Sex of Offender

Race of Victim	Sex of Offender		
	Male	Female	Unknown
White	3,322	330	57
Black	2,964	290	49
Other	159	20	7
Unknown	50	11	26

Source: Uniform Crime Reports: Crime in the United States–2006.

Murder Victims by Race and Sex

Race	Sex		
	Male	Female	Unknown
White	5,067	1,883	6
Black	6,294	1,126	1
Other	301	105	0
Unknown	131	42	34

17. The victim and the offender are from the same age category.

18. The victim and the offender are from different age categories.

19. The victim and the offender are of the same race.

20. The victim and the offender are of different races.

21. The victim and the offender are of the same sex.

22. The victim and the offender are of different sexes.

23. What is your best prediction of the age, race, and sex of the offender? Explain your reasoning.

24. Did your answers to the offender questions change once you knew the age, race, and sex of the victim? Explain.

Suppose that 45% of murder victims were known to be related to or acquainted with the offender, that 15% were murdered by an unrelated stranger, and that for 40% of victims relationship to their killer is unknown. Based on all the information available, complete your offender profile for this case.

6 Discrete Probability Distributions

Outline

6.1 Discrete Random Variables

6.2 The Binomial Probability Distribution

6.3 The Poisson Probability Distribution

6.4 The Hypergeometric Probability Distribution (On CD)

MAKING AN INFORMED DECISION

A woman who was shopping in Los Angeles had her purse stolen by a young, blonde female who was wearing a ponytail. Because there were no eyewitnesses and no real evidence, the prosecution used probability to make its case against the defendant. Your job is to play the role of both the prosecution and defense attorney to make probabilistic arguments both for and against the defendant. See the Decisions project on page 369.

PUTTING IT TOGETHER

In Chapter 5, we discussed the idea of probability. The probability of an event is the long-term proportion with which the event is observed. That is, if we conduct an experiment 1,000 times and observe an outcome 300 times, we estimate that the probability of the outcome is 0.3. The more times we conduct the experiment, the more accurate this empirical probability will be. This is the Law of Large Numbers. We learned that we can use counting techniques to obtain theoretical probabilities provided that the outcomes in the experiment are equally likely. This is called *classical probability*.

We also learned that a probability model lists the possible outcomes to a probability experiment and each outcome's probability. A probability model must satisfy the rules of probability. In particular, all probabilities must be between 0 and 1, inclusive, and the sum of the probabilities must equal 1.

In this chapter, we introduce probability models for *random variables*. A random variable is a numerical measure of the outcome to a probability experiment. So, rather than listing specific outcomes for a probability experiment such as heads or tails, we might list the number of heads obtained in, say, three flips of a coin. In Section 6.1, we discuss random variables and describe the distribution of discrete random variables (shape, center, and spread). We then discuss two specific discrete probability distributions: *the binomial probability distribution* (Section 6.2) and *the Poisson probability distribution* (Section 6.3).

6.1 DISCRETE RANDOM VARIABLES

Preparing for This Section   Before getting started, review the following:

- Discrete versus continuous variables (Section 1.1, pp. 8–9)
- Relative frequency histograms for discrete data (Section 2.2, pp. 83–84)
- Mean (Section 3.1, pp. 129–131)

- Standard deviation (Section 3.2, pp. 148–150)
- Mean from grouped data (Section 3.3, pp. 160–161)
- Standard deviation from grouped data (Section 3.3, pp. 162–164)

Objectives

1. Distinguish between discrete and continuous random variables
2. Identify discrete probability distributions
3. Construct probability histograms
4. Compute and interpret the mean of a discrete random variable
5. Interpret the mean of a discrete random variable as an expected value
6. Compute the variance and standard deviation of a discrete random variable

---

1 **Distinguish between Discrete and Continuous Random Variables**

Note to Instructor

If you like, you can print out and distribute the Preparing for This Section quiz located in the Instructor's Resource Center. The purpose of the quiz is to verify that the students have the prerequisite knowledge for this section.

In Chapter 5, we presented the concept of a probability experiment and its outcomes. Suppose that we flip a coin two times. The possible outcomes of the experiment are {HH, HT, TH, TT}. Rather than being interested in a particular outcome, we might be interested in the number of heads. When experiments are conducted in a way such that the outcome is a numerical result, we say the outcome is a *random variable*.

Definition

A **random variable** is a numerical measure of the outcome of a probability experiment, so its value is determined by chance. Random variables are typically denoted using capital letters such as X.

So, in our coin-flipping example, if the random variable X represents the number of heads in two flips of a coin, the possible values of X are 0, 1, or 2.

We will follow the practice of using a capital letter to identify the random variable and a lowercase letter to list the possible values of the random variable, that is, the sample space of the experiment. For example, if an experiment is conducted in which a single die is cast, then X represents the number of pips showing on the die, and the possible values of X are $x = 1, 2, 3, 4, 5,$ or 6. As another example, suppose an experiment is conducted in which the time between arrivals of cars at a drive-through is measured. The random variable T might describe the time between arrivals, so the sample space of the experiment is $t > 0$.

There are two types of random variables, *discrete* and *continuous*.

Note to Instructor

To help students understand the difference between a discrete and continuous random variable, tell them that a discrete random variable would have values given by points on a number line, while continuous random variables would have possible values given by an interval on a number line.

Definitions

In Other Words

Discrete random variables typically result from counting, such as 0, 1, 2, 3, and so on. Continuous random variables are variables that result from measurement.

A **discrete random variable** has either a finite or countable number of values. The values of a discrete random variable can be plotted on a number line with space between each point. See Figure 1(a).

A **continuous random variable** has infinitely many values. The values of a continuous random variable can be plotted on a line in an uninterrupted fashion. See Figure 1(b).

Figure 1

0 1 2 3 4

(a) Discrete Random Variable

0 1 2 3 4

(b) Continuous Random Variable

EXAMPLE 1 Distinguishing between Discrete and Continuous Random Variables

(a) The number of A's earned in a section of statistics with 15 students enrolled is a discrete random variable because the value of the random variable results from counting. If we let the random variable X represent the number of A's, then the possible values of X are $x = 0, 1, 2, \ldots, 15$.

(b) The number of cars that travel through a McDonald's drive-through in the next hour is a discrete random variable because the value of the random variable results from counting. If we let the random variable X represent the number of cars that travel through the drive-through in the next hour, the possible values of X are $x = 0, 1, 2, \ldots$.

(c) The speed of the next car that passes a state trooper is a continuous random variable because speed is measured. If we let the random variable S represent the speed of the next car, the possible values of S are all positive real numbers; that is, $s > 0$.

CAUTION Even though a radar gun may report the speed of a car as 37 miles per hour, it is actually any number greater than or equal to 36.5 mph and less than 37.5 mph. That is, $36.5 \leq s < 37.5$.

Now Work Problem 7

In this chapter, we will concentrate on probabilities of discrete random variables. Probabilities for certain continuous random variables will be discussed in Chapter 7.

2 Identify Discrete Probability Distributions

Because the value of a random variable is determined by chance, probabilities correspond to the possible values of the random variable.

Definition The **probability distribution** of a discrete random variable X provides the possible values of the random variable and their corresponding probabilities. A probability distribution can be in the form of a table, graph, or mathematical formula.

EXAMPLE 2 A Discrete Probability Distribution

Table 1

x	$P(x)$
0	0.01
1	0.10
2	0.38
3	0.51

Suppose that we ask a basketball player to shoot three free throws. Let the random variable X represent the number of shots made, so $x = 0, 1, 2,$ or 3. Table 1 shows a probability distribution for the random variable X, assuming that the player historically makes 80% of her free-throw attempts.

From the probability distribution in Table 1, we can see that the probability that the player makes all three free-throw attempts is 0.51.

We will denote probabilities using the notation $P(x)$, where x is a specific value of the random variable. We read $P(x)$ as "the probability that the random variable X equals x." For example, $P(3) = 0.51$ is read "the probability that the random variable X equals 3 is 0.51."

Recall from Section 5.1 that probabilities must obey certain rules. We repeat the rules for a discrete probability distribution using the notation just introduced.

In Other Words

The first rule states that the sum of the probabilities must equal 1. The second rule states that each probability must be greater than or equal to 0 and less than or equal to 1.

Rules for a Discrete Probability Distribution

Let $P(x)$ denote the probability that the random variable X equals x; then

1. $\sum P(x) = 1$
2. $0 \leq P(x) \leq 1$

Table 1 from Example 2 is a probability distribution because the sum of the probabilities equals 1 and each probability is between 0 and 1, inclusive. You are encouraged to verify this.

EXAMPLE 3   **Identifying Discrete Probability Distributions**

Problem: Which of the following is a discrete probability distribution?

(a)

x	$P(x)$
1	0.20
2	0.35
3	0.12
4	0.40
5	−0.07

(b)

x	$P(x)$
1	0.20
2	0.25
3	0.10
4	0.14
5	0.49

(c)

x	$P(x)$
1	0.20
2	0.25
3	0.10
4	0.14
5	0.31

Approach: In a discrete probability distribution, the sum of the probabilities must equal 1, and all probabilities must be greater than or equal to 0 and less than or equal to 1.

Solution

(a) This is not a discrete probability distribution because $P(5) = -0.07$, which is less than 0.

(b) This is not a discrete probability distribution because

$$\sum P(x) = 0.20 + 0.25 + 0.10 + 0.14 + 0.49 = 1.18 \neq 1$$

(c) This is a discrete probability distribution because the sum of the probabilities equals 1, and each probability is greater than or equal to 0 and less than or equal to 1.

Now Work Problem 11

Table 1 is an example of a discrete probability distribution in table form. Probability distributions can also be represented through graphs or mathematical formulas. We discuss discrete probability distributions using graphs next and discuss probability distributions as mathematical formulas in the Sections 6.2 and 6.3.

③ Construct Probability Histograms

A graphical depiction of a discrete probability distribution is typically done with a *probability histogram*.

Definition   A **probability histogram** is a histogram in which the horizontal axis corresponds to the value of the random variable and the vertical axis represents the probability of each value of the random variable.

EXAMPLE 4   **Constructing a Probability Histogram**

Problem: Construct a probability histogram of the discrete probability distribution given in Table 1 from Example 2.

Approach: Probability histograms are constructed like relative frequency histograms, except that the vertical axis represents the probability of the random variable, rather than its relative frequency. Each rectangle is centered at the value of the discrete random variable.

Solution: Figure 2 presents the probability histogram of the probability distribution in Table 1.

Figure 2

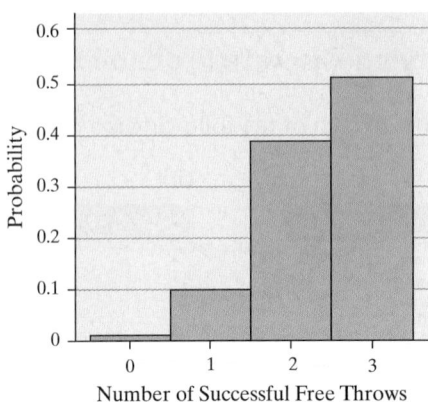

Shooting Three Free Throws

Notice that the area of each rectangle in the probability histogram equals the probability that the random variable assumes the particular value. For example, the area of the rectangle corresponding to the value $x = 2$ is $1 \cdot (0.38) = 0.38$, where 1 represents the width and 0.38 represents the height of the rectangle.

Probability histograms help us to determine the shape of the distribution. Recall that we describe distributions as skewed left, skewed right, or symmetric. For example, the probability histogram presented in Figure 2 is skewed left.

Now Work Problems 19(a) and (b)

 Compute and Interpret the Mean of a Discrete Random Variable

Remember, when we describe the distribution of a variable, we describe its center, spread, and shape. We will use the mean to describe the center of a random variable. We will use the variance and standard deviation to describe the spread.

To help see where the formula for computing the mean of a discrete random variable comes from, consider the following. One semester I had a small statistics class of 10 students. I asked them to disclose the number of people living in their households and obtained the following data:

$$2, 4, 6, 6, 4, 4, 2, 3, 5, 5$$

What is the mean number of people in the 10 households? Of course, we could find the mean by adding the observations and dividing by 10. But we will take a different approach. Letting the random variable X represent the number of people in the household, we obtain the probability distribution in Table 2.

Now we compute the mean as follows:

	Table 2	
x	**P(x)**	
2	$\dfrac{2}{10} = 0.2$	
3	$\dfrac{1}{10} = 0.1$	
4	$\dfrac{3}{10} = 0.3$	
5	$\dfrac{2}{10} = 0.2$	
6	$\dfrac{2}{10} = 0.2$	

$$\mu = \frac{\sum x_i}{N} = \frac{2 + 4 + 6 + 6 + 4 + 4 + 2 + 3 + 5 + 5}{10}$$

$$= \frac{\overbrace{2 + 2}^{2} + \overbrace{3}^{1} + \overbrace{4 + 4 + 4}^{3} + \overbrace{5 + 5}^{2} + \overbrace{6 + 6}^{2}}{10}$$

$$= \frac{2 \cdot 2 + 3 \cdot 1 + 4 \cdot 3 + 5 \cdot 2 + 6 \cdot 2}{10}$$

$$= 2 \cdot \frac{2}{10} + 3 \cdot \frac{1}{10} + 4 \cdot \frac{3}{10} + 5 \cdot \frac{2}{10} + 6 \cdot \frac{2}{10}$$

$$= 2 \cdot P(2) + 3 \cdot P(3) + 4 \cdot P(4) + 5 \cdot P(5) + 6 \cdot P(6)$$

$$= 2(0.2) + 3(0.1) + 4(0.3) + 5(0.2) + 6(0.2)$$

$$= 4.1$$

Based on the preceding computations, we conclude that the mean of a discrete random variable is found by multiplying each possible value of the random variable by its corresponding probability and then adding these products.

The Mean of a Discrete Random Variable

The mean of a discrete random variable is given by the formula

$$\mu_X = \sum [x \cdot P(x)] \tag{1}$$

where x is the value of the random variable and $P(x)$ is the probability of observing the value x.

In Other Words
To find the mean of a discrete random variable, multiply the value of each random variable by its probability. Then add these products.

EXAMPLE 5   **Computing the Mean of a Discrete Random Variable**

Problem: Compute the mean of the discrete random variable given in Table 1 from Example 2.

Approach: The mean of a discrete random variable is found by multiplying each value of the random variable by its probability and adding these products.

Solution: Refer to Table 3. The first two columns represent the discrete probability distribution. The third column represents $x \cdot P(x)$.

We substitute into Formula (1) to find the mean number of free throws made.

$$\mu_X = \sum [x \cdot P(x)] = 0(0.01) + 1(0.10) + 2(0.38) + 3(0.51) = 2.39 \approx 2.4$$

We will follow the practice of rounding the mean, variance, and standard deviation to one more decimal place than the values of the random variable.

Table 3		
x	$P(x)$	$x \cdot P(x)$
0	0.01	$0 \cdot 0.01 = 0$
1	0.10	$1 \cdot 0.1 = 0.1$
2	0.38	$2 \cdot 0.38 = 0.76$
3	0.51	$3 \cdot 0.51 = 1.53$

How to Interpret the Mean of a Discrete Random Variable

The mean of a discrete random variable can be thought of as the mean outcome of the probability experiment if we repeated the experiment many times. Consider the result of Example 5. If we repeated the experiment of shooting three free throws many times and recorded the number of free throws made, we would expect the average number of free throws made to be around 2.4.

In Other Words
We can think of the mean of a discrete random variable as the average outcome if the experiment is repeated many, many times.

Interpretation of the Mean of a Discrete Random Variable

Suppose that an experiment is repeated n independent times and the value of the random variable X is recorded. As the number of repetitions of the experiment increases, the mean value of the n trials will approach μ_X, the mean of the random variable X. In other words, let x_1 be the value of the random variable X after the first experiment, x_2 be the value of the random variable X after the second experiment, and so on. Then

$$\overline{x} = \frac{x_1 + x_2 + \cdots + x_n}{n}$$

The difference between $\overline{x}$ and μ_X gets closer to 0 as n increases.

EXAMPLE 6   **Illustrating the Interpretation of the Mean of a Discrete Random Variable**

Problem: The basketball player from Example 2 is asked to shoot three free throws 100 times. Compute the mean number of free throws made.

Approach: The player shoots three free throws and the number made is recorded. We repeat this experiment 99 more times and then compute the mean number of free throws made.

Solution: The results are presented in Table 4.

Table 4									
3	2	3	3	3	3	1	2	3	2
2	3	3	1	2	2	2	2	2	3
3	3	2	2	3	2	3	2	2	2
3	3	2	3	2	3	3	2	3	1
3	2	2	2	2	0	2	3	1	2
3	3	2	3	2	3	2	1	3	2
2	3	3	3	1	3	3	1	3	3
3	2	2	1	3	2	2	2	3	2
3	2	2	2	3	3	2	2	3	3
2	3	2	1	2	3	3	2	3	3

The first time the experiment was conducted, the player made all three free throws. The second time the experiment was conducted, the player made two out of three free throws. The hundredth time the experiment was conducted, the player made three out of three free throws. The mean number of free throws made was

$$\bar{x} = \frac{3 + 2 + 3 + \cdots + 3}{100} = 2.35$$

This is close to the theoretical mean of 2.4 (from Example 5). As the number of repetitions of the experiment increases, we expect $\bar{x}$ to get even closer to 2.4.

Figure 3(a) and Figure 3(b) further demonstrate the interpretation of the mean of a discrete random variable. Figure 3(a) shows the mean number of free throws made versus the number of repetitions of the experiment for the data in Table 4. Figure 3(b) shows the mean number of free throws made versus the number of repetitions of the experiment when the same experiment of shooting three free throws is conducted a second time for 100 repetitions. In both plots the player starts off "hot," since the mean number of free throws made is above the theoretical level of 2.4. However, both graphs approach the theoretical mean of 2.4 as the number of repetitions of the experiment increases.

Figure 3

(a) Number of Repetitions

(b) Number of Repetitions

Now Work Problem 19(c)

5 Interpret the Mean of a Discrete Random Variable as an Expected Value

In Other Words

The expected value of a discrete random variable is the mean of the discrete random variable.

Because the mean of a random variable represents what we would expect to happen in the long run, it is also called the **expected value**, $E(X)$. The interpretation of expected value is the same as the interpretation of the mean of a discrete random variable.

EXAMPLE 7   **Finding the Expected Value**

Problem: A term life insurance policy will pay a beneficiary a certain sum of money upon the death of the policyholder. These policies have premiums that must be paid annually. Suppose a life insurance company sells a $250,000 1-year term life insurance policy to an 18-year-old male for $350. According to the *National Vital Statistics Report*, Vol. 56, No. 9, the probability that the male will survive the year is 0.998936. Compute the expected value of this policy to the insurance company.

Approach: The experiment has two possible outcomes: survival or death. Let the random variable X represent the *payout* (money lost or gained), depending on survival or death of the insured. We assign probabilities to each payout and substitute these values into Formula (1).

Solution

Step 1: We have $P(\text{survives}) = 0.998936$, so $P(\text{dies}) = 0.001064$. From the point of view of the insurance company, if the client survives the year, the insurance company makes $350. Therefore, $x = \$350$ if the client survives the year. If the client dies during the year, the insurance company must pay $250,000 to the client's beneficiary. However, the company still keeps the $350 premium, so $x = \$350 - \$250,000 = -\$249,650$. The value is negative because it is money paid out by the insurance company. The probability distribution is listed in Table 5.

Step 2: Substituting into Formula (1), we obtain the expected value (from the point of view of the insurance company) of the policy.

Table 5	
x	*P(x)*
$350 (survives)	0.998936
−$249,650 (dies)	0.001064

$$E(X) = \mu_X = \sum xP(x) = \$350(0.998936) + (-\$249,650)(0.001064) = \$84.00$$

Interpretation: The company expects to make $84.00 for each 18-year-old male client it insures. The $84.00 profit of the insurance company is a long-term result. It does not make $84.00 on each 18-year-old male it insures, but rather the average profit per 18-year-old male insured is $84.00. Because this is a long-term result, the insurance "idea" will not work with only a few insured.

Now Work Problem 29

Historical Note

IN CLASS ACTIVITY

Expected Value

Consider the following game of chance. A player pays $1 and rolls a pair of fair dice. If the player rolls a 2, 3, 4, 10, 11, or 12, the player loses the $1 bet. If the player rolls 5, 6, 8, or 9, there is a "push" and the player gets his or her dollar back. If the player rolls a 7, the player wins $1.

(a) Construct a probability distribution that describes the game.

(b) Compute the expected value of the game from the player's point of view.

(c) Actually play the game in a small group. Keep track of the results on paper (no money should actually change hands). Compute the mean earnings to the player from the game. Are the results close to what you expected? If not, why?

Christiaan Huygens was born on April 14, 1629, into an influential Dutch family. He studied Law and Mathematics at the University of Leiden from 1645 to 1647. From 1647 to 1649, he continued to study Law and Mathematics at the College of Orange at Breda. Among his many great accomplishments, Huygens discovered the first moon of Saturn in 1655 and the shape of the rings of Saturn in 1656. While in Paris sharing his discoveries, he learned about probability through the correspondence of Fermat and Pascal. In 1657, Huygens published the first book on probability theory. In that text, Huygens introduced the idea of expected value.

Compute the Variance and Standard Deviation of a Discrete Random Variable

We now introduce a method for computing the variance and standard deviation of a discrete random variable.

Variance and Standard Deviation of a Discrete Random Variable

The variance of a discrete random variable is given by

$$\sigma_X^2 = \sum[(x - \mu_X)^2 \cdot P(x)] \qquad \text{(2a)}$$

$$= \sum[x^2 \cdot P(x)] - \mu_X^2 \qquad \text{(2b)}$$

In Other Words

The variance of a discrete random variable is a weighted average of the squared deviations for which the weights are the probabilities.

where x is the value of the random variable, μ_X is the mean of the random variable, and $P(x)$ is the probability of observing the random variable x.

To find the standard deviation of the discrete random variable, take the square root of the variance. That is, $\sigma_X = \sqrt{\sigma_X^2}$.

EXAMPLE 8 **Computing the Variance and Standard Deviation of a Discrete Random Variable**

Problem: Find the variance and standard deviation of the discrete random variable given in Table 1 from Example 2.

Approach: We will use Formula (2a) with the unrounded mean $\mu_X = 2.39$.

Approach: We will use Formula (2b) with the unrounded mean $\mu_X = 2.39$.

Solution: Refer to Table 6. The first two columns represent the discrete probability distribution. The third column represents $(x - \mu_X)^2 \cdot P(x)$. We sum the entries in the third column to get the variance.

Solution: Refer to Table 7. The first two columns represent the discrete probability distribution. The third column represents $x^2 \cdot P(x)$.

		Table 6	
x	$P(x)$	$(x - \mu_X)^2 \cdot P(x)$	
0	0.01	$(0 - 2.39)^2 \cdot 0.01 = 0.057121$	
1	0.10	$(1 - 2.39)^2 \cdot 0.10 = 0.19321$	
2	0.38	$(2 - 2.39)^2 \cdot 0.38 = 0.057798$	
3	0.51	$(3 - 2.39)^2 \cdot 0.51 = 0.189771$	
		$\sum(x - \mu_X)^2 \cdot P(x) = 0.4979$	

		Table 7	
x	$P(x)$	$x^2 \cdot P(x)$	
0	0.01	$0^2 \cdot 0.01 = 0$	
1	0.10	$1^2 \cdot 0.10 = 0.10$	
2	0.38	$2^2 \cdot 0.38 = 1.52$	
3	0.51	$3^2 \cdot 0.51 = 4.59$	
		$\sum x^2 \cdot P(x) = 6.21$	

The variance of the discrete random variable X is

$$\sigma_X^2 = \sum(x - \mu_X)^2 \cdot P(x) = 0.4979 \approx 0.5$$

The variance of the discrete random variable X is

$$\sigma_X^2 = \sum[x^2 \cdot P(x)] - \mu_X^2 = 6.21 - 2.39^2 = 0.4979 \approx 0.5$$

The standard deviation of the discrete random variable is found by taking the square root of the variance.

$$\sigma_X = \sqrt{\sigma_X^2} = \sqrt{0.4979} \approx 0.7$$

Now Work Problems 19(d) and (e)

EXAMPLE 9 **Obtaining the Mean and Standard Deviation of a Discrete Random Variable Using Technology**

Problem: Use statistical software or a graphing calculator to determine the mean and the standard deviation of the random variable whose distribution is given in Table 1.

Approach: We will use a TI-84 Plus graphing calculator to obtain the mean and standard deviation. The steps for determining the mean and standard deviation using a TI-83/84 Plus graphing calculator are given in the Technology Step-by-Step on page 342.

Solution: Figure 4 shows the results from a TI-84 Plus graphing calculator.

Note: The TI-84 does not find s_X when the sum of L_2 is 1.

Figure 4

μ_X —
σ_X —

```
1-Var Stats
 x̄=2.39
 Σx=2.39
 Σx²=6.21
 Sx=
 σx=.7056202945
↓n=1
```

6.1 ASSESS YOUR UNDERSTANDING

Concepts and Vocabulary

1. What is a random variable?

2. What is the difference between a discrete random variable and a continuous random variable? Provide your own examples of each.

3. What are the two requirements for a discrete probability distribution?

4. In your own words, provide an interpretation of the mean of a discrete random variable.

5. A baseball player historically hits 0.300. (This means that the player averages three hits in every 10 at-bats.) The player has zero hits in four at-bats in a game and enters the batter's box for the fifth time, whereupon the announcer declares that the player is "due for a hit." What is the flaw in the announcer's reasoning? If the player had four hits in the last four at-bats, is the player "due to make an out"?

6. A game is called a zero-sum game if the expected value of the game is zero. Explain what a game whose expected value is zero means.

Skill Building

In Problems 7–10, determine whether the random variable is discrete or continuous. In each case, state the possible values of the random variable.

7. (a) The number of light bulbs that burn out in the next week in a room with 20 bulbs. Discrete; x = 0, 1, . . . , 20

(b) The time it takes to fly from New York City to Los Angeles. Continuous; t > 0

(c) The number of hits to a website in a day.

(d) The amount of snow in Toronto during the winter.

8. (a) The time it takes for a light bulb to burn out.

(b) The weight of a T-bone steak. Continuous, w > 0

(c) The number of free-throw attempts before the first shot is made. Discrete, x = 1, 2, . . .

(d) In a random sample of 20 people, the number with type A blood. Discrete, x = 0, 1, . . . , 20

9. (a) The amount of rain in Seattle during April.

(b) The number of fish caught during a fishing tournament.

(c) The number of customers arriving at a bank between noon and 1:00 P.M. Discrete, x = 0, 1, 2, . . .

(d) The time required to download a file from the Internet.

10. (a) The number of defects in a roll of carpet.

(b) The distance a baseball travels in the air after being hit.

(c) The number of points scored during a basketball game.

(d) The square footage of a house. Continuous, a > 0

In Problems 11–16, determine whether the distribution is a discrete probability distribution. If not, state why.

11.

x	P(x)
0	0.2
1	0.2
2	0.2
3	0.2
4	0.2

Yes

12.

x	P(x)
0	0.1
1	0.5
2	0.05
3	0.25
4	0.1

Yes

13.

x	P(x)
10	0.1
20	0.23
30	0.22
40	0.6
50	−0.15

No; P(50) < 0

14.

x	P(x)
1	0
2	0
3	0
4	0
5	1

Yes

15.

x	P(x)
100	0.1
200	0.25
300	0.2
400	0.3
500	0.1

No; $\sum P(x) \neq 1$

16.

x	P(x)
100	0.25
200	0.25
300	0.25
400	0.25
500	0.25

No; $\sum P(x) \neq 1$

7. (c) Discrete, x = 0, 1, 2, . . .   7. (d) Continuous, s ≥ 0   8. (a) Continuous, t > 0   9. (a) Continuous, r ≥ 0

9. (b) Discrete, x = 0, 1, 2, . . .   9. (d) Continuous, t > 0   10. (a) Discrete, x = 0, 1, 2, . . .   10. (b) Continuous, d > 0

10. (c) Discrete, x = 0, 1, 2, . . .

In Problems 17 and 18, determine the required value of the missing probability to make the distribution a discrete probability distribution.

17.

x	$P(x)$
3	0.4
4	?
5	0.1
6	0.2

$P(4) = 0.3$

18.

x	$P(x)$
0	0.30
1	0.15
2	?
3	0.20
4	0.15
5	0.05

$P(2) = 0.15$

Applying the Concepts

19. Parental Involvement In the following probability distribution, the random variable X represents the number of activities a parent of a K–5th grade student is involved in.

x	$P(x)$
0	0.035
1	0.074
2	0.197
3	0.320
4	0.374

Source: U.S. National Center for Education Statistics

(a) Verify that this is a discrete probability distribution.
(b) Draw a probability histogram.
(c) Compute and interpret the mean of the random variable X. $\mu_X = 2.9$
(d) Compute the variance of the random variable X. $\sigma_X^2 = 1.2$
(e) Compute the standard deviation of the random variable X. $\sigma_X = 1.1$
(f) What is the probability that a randomly selected student has a parent involved in three activities?   0.320
(g) What is the probability that a randomly selected student has a parent involved in three or four activities? 0.694

20. Parental Involvement In the following probability distribution, the random variable X represents the number of activities a parent of a 6th–8th grade student is involved in.

x	$P(x)$
0	0.073
1	0.117
2	0.258
3	0.322
4	0.230

Source: U.S. National Center for Education Statistics

(a) Verify that this is a discrete probability distribution.
(b) Draw a probability histogram.
(c) Compute and interpret the mean of the random variable X. $\mu_X = 2.5$
(d) Compute the variance of the random variable X. $\sigma_X^2 = 1.4$
(e) Compute the standard deviation of the random variable X. $\sigma_X = 1.2$
(f) What is the probability that a randomly selected student has a parent involved in three activities?   0.322

(g) What is the probability that a randomly selected student has a parent involved in three or four activities?   0.552

21. Ichiro's Hit Parade In the 2004 baseball season, Ichiro Suzuki of the Seattle Mariners set the record for the most hits in a season with a total of 262 hits. In the following probability distribution, the random variable X represents the number of hits Ichiro obtained in a game.

x	$P(x)$
0	0.1677
1	0.3354
2	0.2857
3	0.1491
4	0.0373
5	0.0248

Source: Chicago Tribune

(a) Verify that this is a discrete probability distribution.
(b) Draw a probability histogram.
(c) Compute and interpret the mean of the random variable X. $\mu_X = 1.6$
(d) Compute the standard deviation of the random variable X. $\sigma_X = 1.2$
(e) What is the probability that in a randomly selected game Ichiro got 2 hits?   0.2857
(f) What is the probability that in a randomly selected game Ichiro got more than 1 hit?   0.4969

22. Waiting in Line A Wendy's manager performed a study to determine a probability distribution for the number of people, X, waiting in line during lunch. The results were as follows:

x	$P(x)$
0	0.011
1	0.035
2	0.089
3	0.150
4	0.186
5	0.172
6	0.132
7	0.098
8	0.063
9	0.035
10	0.019
11	0.002
12	0.006
13	0.001
14	0.001

(a) Verify that this is a discrete probability distribution.
(b) Draw a probability histogram.
(c) Compute and interpret the mean of the random variable X. $\mu_X = 4.9$
(d) Compute the variance of the random variable X. $\sigma_X^2 = 5.0$
(e) Compute the standard deviation of the random variable X. $\sigma_X = 2.2$
(f) What is the probability that eight people are waiting in line for lunch?   0.063
(g) What is the probability that 10 or more people are waiting in line for lunch? Would this be unusual?   0.029; yes

In Problems 23–26, (a) construct a discrete probability distribution for the random variable X [Hint: $P(x_i) = \dfrac{f_i}{N}$], (b) draw the probability histogram, (c) compute and interpret the mean of the random variable X, and (d) compute the standard deviation of the random variable X.

23. The World Series The following data represent the number of games played in each World Series from 1923 to 2007.

x (games played)	Frequency
4	17
5	16
6	18
7	33

Source: Major League Baseball

(c) $\mu_X = 5.8$ (d) $\sigma_X = 1.2$

24. Boy Scout Troop The following data represent the ages of boys belonging to a particular boy scout troop.

x (age)	Frequency
11	5
12	6
13	7
14	4
15	5
16	3
17	4

(c) $\mu_X = 13.7$ (d) $\sigma_X = 1.9$

25. Ideal Number of Children What is the ideal number of children to have in a family? The following data represent the ideal number of children for a random sample of 900 adult Americans.   (c) $\mu_X = 2.4$ (d) $\sigma_X = 0.8$

x (number of children)	Frequency
0	10
1	30
2	520
3	250
4	70
5	17
6	3

Source: Based on data from a Gallup poll conducted June 11–14, 2007

handwritten: .011   .033   .578   .278   .078   .019   .003

26. High School Enrollment The following data represent (in thousands) the total private and public enrollment levels in grades 9 to 12 in the United States in October 2005.

x (grade level)	Frequency
9	4,306
10	4,421
11	4,490
12	4,137

Source: Current Population Survey Reports, October 2005

(c) $\mu_X = 10.5$ (d) $\sigma_X = 1.1$

27. Number of Births The probability histogram that follows represents the number of live births by a mother 50 to 54 years old who had a live birth in 2005.
Source: National Vital Statistics Report, 56(6): December 5, 2007.

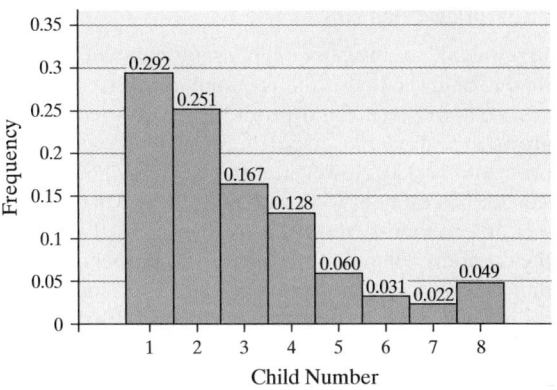

Number of Live Births, 50 to 54-Year-Old Mother

(a) What is the probability that a randomly selected 50- to 54-year-old mother who had a live birth in 2005 has had her fourth live birth?   0.128
(b) What is the probability that a randomly selected 50- to 54-year-old mother who had a live birth in 2005 has had her fourth or fifth live birth?   0.188
(c) What is the probability that a randomly selected 50- to 54-year-old mother who had a live birth in 2005 has had her sixth or more live birth?   0.102
(d) If a 50- to 54-year-old mother who had a live birth in 2005 is randomly selected, how many live births would you expect the mother to have had?   2.8

28. Rental Units The probability histogram that follows represents the number of rooms in rented housing units in 2005.
Source: 2005 American Housing Survey.

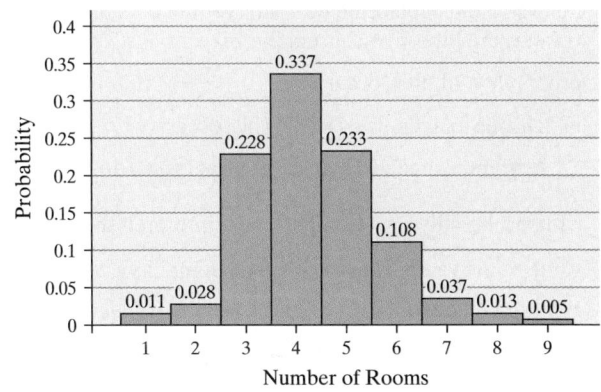

Number of Rooms in Rental Unit

(a) What is the probability that a randomly selected rental unit has five rooms?   0.233
(b) What is the probability that a randomly selected rental unit has five or six rooms?   0.341
(c) What is the probability that a randomly selected rental unit has seven or more rooms?   0.055
(d) If a rental unit is randomly selected, how many rooms would you expect the unit to have?   4.3

29. Life Insurance A life insurance company sells a $250,000 NW 1-year term life insurance policy to a 20-year-old female for $200. According to the *National Vital Statistics Report,* 56(9), the probability that the female survives the year is 0.999544.

Compute and interpret the expected value of this policy to the insurance company. *$86.00*

30. **Life Insurance** A life insurance company sells a $250,000 1-year term life insurance policy to a 20-year-old male for $350. According to the *National Vital Statistics Report*, 56(9), the probability that the male survives the year is 0.998734. Compute and interpret the expected value of this policy to the insurance company. *$33.50*

31. **Investment** An investment counselor calls with a hot stock tip. He believes that if the economy remains strong, the investment will result in a profit of $50,000. If the economy grows at a moderate pace, the investment will result in a profit of $10,000. However, if the economy goes into recession, the investment will result in a loss of $50,000. You contact an economist who believes there is a 20% probability the economy will remain strong, a 70% probability the economy will grow at a moderate pace, and a 10% probability the economy will slip into recession. What is the expected profit from this investment? *$12,000*

32. **Real Estate Investment** Shawn and Maddie purchase a foreclosed property for $50,000 and spend an additional $27,000 fixing up the property. They feel that they can resell the property for $120,000 with probability 0.15, $100,000 with probability 0.45, $80,000 with probability 0.25, and $60,000 with probability 0.15. Compute and interpret the expected profit for reselling the property. *$15,000*

33. **Roulette** In the game of roulette, a player can place a $5 bet on the number 17 and have a $\frac{1}{38}$ probability of winning. If the metal ball lands on 17, the player wins $175. Otherwise, the casino takes the player's $5. What is the expected value of the game to the player? If you played the game 1,000 times, how much would you expect to lose? *−$0.26; about $260*

34. **Connecticut Lottery** In the Cash Five Lottery in Connecticut, a player pays $1 for a single ticket with five numbers. Five balls numbered 1 through 35 are randomly chosen from a bin without replacement. If all five numbers on a player's ticket match the five chosen, the player wins $100,000. The probability of this occurring is $\frac{1}{324,632}$. If four numbers match, the player wins $300. This occurs with probability $\frac{1}{2,164}$. If three numbers match, the player wins $10. This occurs with probability $\frac{1}{75}$. Compute and interpret the expected value of the game from the player's point of view.

35. **Powerball** Powerball is a multi-state lottery. The following probability distribution represents the cash prizes of Powerball with their corresponding probabilities.

34. −$0.42   35. (b) $118,000,000

x (cash prize, $)	P(x)
Grand prize	0.00000000684
200,000	0.00000028
10,000	0.000001711
100	0.000153996
7	0.004778961
4	0.007881463
3	0.01450116
0	0.9726824222

Source: www.powerball.com

(a) If the grand prize is $15,000,000, find and interpret the expected cash prize. If a ticket costs $1, what is your expected profit from one ticket? *$0.30; −$0.70*

(b) To the nearest million, how much should the grand prize be so that you can expect a profit? Assume nobody else wins so that you do not have to share the grand prize.

(c) Does the size of the grand prize affect your chance of winning? Explain. *No*

36. **SAT Test Penalty** Some standardized tests, such as the SAT test, incorporate a penalty for wrong answers. For example, a multiple-choice question with five possible answers will have 1 point awarded for a correct answer and $\frac{1}{4}$ point deducted for an incorrect answer. Questions left blank are worth 0 points.

(a) Find the expected number of points received for a multiple-choice question with five possible answers when a student just guesses. *0*

(b) Explain why there is a deduction for wrong answers.

37. **Simulation** Use the probability distribution from Problem 21 and a DISCRETE command for some statistical software to simulate 100 repetitions of the experiment (100 games). The number of hits is recorded. Approximate the mean and standard deviation of the random variable X based on the simulation. Repeat the simulation by performing 500 repetitions of the experiment. Approximate the mean and standard deviation of the random variable. Compare your results to the theoretical mean and standard deviation. What property is being illustrated?

38. **Simulation** Use the probability distribution from Problem 22 and a DISCRETE command for some statistical software to simulate 100 repetitions of the experiment. Approximate the mean and standard deviation of the random variable X based on the simulation. Repeat the simulation by performing 500 repetitions of the experiment. Approximate the mean and standard deviation of the random variable. Compare your results to the theoretical mean and standard deviation. What property is being illustrated?

TECHNOLOGY STEP-BY-STEP

Finding the Mean and Standard Deviation of a Discrete Random Variable Using Technology

TI-83/84 Plus

1. Enter the values of the random variable in L1 and their corresponding probabilities in L2.
2. Press STAT, highlight CALC, and select 1: 1-Var Stats.

3. With 1-Var Stats on the HOME screen, type L1 followed by a comma, followed by L2 as follows:

```
1-Var Stats L1, L2
```

Hit ENTER.

6.2 THE BINOMIAL PROBABILITY DISTRIBUTION

Preparing for This Section   Before getting started, review the following:

- Empirical Rule (Section 3.2, pp. 150–152)
- Addition Rule for Disjoint Events (Section 5.2, pp. 274–277)
- Complement Rule (Section 5.2, pp. 279–281)

- Independence (Section 5.3, pp. 286–287)
- Multiplication Rule for Independent Events (Section 5.3, pp. 287–288)
- Combinations (Section 5.5, pp. 307–309)

Objectives

1. Determine whether a probability experiment is a binomial experiment
2. Compute probabilities of binomial experiments
3. Compute the mean and standard deviation of a binomial random variable
4. Construct binomial probability histograms

 Determine Whether a Probability Experiment Is a Binomial Experiment

Note to Instructor

If you like, you can print out and distribute the Preparing for This Section quiz located in the Instructor's Resource Center. The purpose of the quiz is to verify that the students have the prerequisite knowledge for this section.

In Other Words

The prefix *bi* means "two". This should help remind you that binomial experiments deal with situations in which there are only two outcomes: success and failure.

In Section 6.1, we stated that probability distributions could be presented using tables, graphs, or mathematical formulas. In this section, we introduce a specific type of discrete probability distribution that can be presented using a formula, the *binomial probability distribution*.

The binomial probability distribution is a discrete probability distribution that describes probabilities for experiments in which there are two mutually exclusive (disjoint) outcomes. These two outcomes are generally referred to as *success* and *failure*. For example, a basketball player can either make a free throw (success) or miss (failure). A new surgical procedure can result in either life (success) or death (failure).

Experiments in which only two outcomes are possible are referred to as *binomial experiments*, provided that certain criteria are met.

Criteria for a Binomial Probability Experiment

An experiment is said to be a **binomial experiment** if

1. The experiment is performed a fixed number of times. Each repetition of the experiment is called a **trial**.

2. The trials are independent. This means that the outcome of one trial will not affect the outcome of the other trials.

3. For each trial, there are two mutually exclusive (disjoint) outcomes: success or failure.

4. The probability of success is the same for each trial of the experiment.

Let the random variable X be the number of successes in n trials of a binomial experiment. Then X is called a **binomial random variable**. Before introducing the method for computing binomial probabilities, it is worthwhile to introduce some notation.

Notation Used in the Binomial Probability Distribution

- There are n independent trials of the experiment.
- Let p denote the probability of success for each trial so that $1 - p$ is the probability of failure for each trial.
- Let X denote the number of successes in n independent trials of the experiment. So, $0 \leq x \leq n$.

| EXAMPLE 1 | **Identifying Binomial Experiments** |

Historical Note

Jacob Bernoulli was born on December 27, 1654, in Basel, Switzerland. He studied philosophy and theology at the urging of his parents. (He resented this.) In 1671, he graduated from the University of Basel with a master's degree in philosophy. In 1676, he received a licentiate in theology. After earning his philosophy degree, Bernoulli traveled to Geneva to tutor. From there, he went to France to study with the great mathematicians of the time. One of Bernoulli's greatest works is *Ars Conjectandi*, published 8 years after his death. In this publication, Bernoulli proved the binomial probability formula. To this day, each trial in a binomial probability experiment is called a *Bernoulli trial*.

Problem: Determine which of the following probability experiments qualify as a binomial experiment. For those that are binomial experiments, identify the number of trials, probability of success, probability of failure, and possible values of the random variable X.

(a) An experiment in which a basketball player who historically makes 80% of his free throws is asked to shoot three free throws, and the number of made free throws is recorded.

(b) The number of people with blood type O-negative based on a simple random sample of size 10 is recorded. According to the American Red Cross, 7% of people in the United States have blood type O-negative.

(c) A probability experiment in which three cards are drawn from a deck without replacement and the number of aces is recorded.

Approach: We determine whether the four conditions for a binomial experiment are satisfied.

1. The experiment is performed a fixed number of times.
2. The trials are independent.
3. There are only two possible outcomes of the experiment.
4. The probability of success for each trial is constant.

Solution

(a) This is a binomial experiment because
   1. There are $n = 3$ trials.
   2. The trials are independent.
   3. There are two possible outcomes: make or miss.
   4. The probability of success (make) is 0.8 and the probability of failure (miss) is 0.2. The probabilities are the same for each trial.
   The random variable X is the number of free throws made with $x = 0, 1, 2,$ or 3.

(b) This is a binomial experiment because
   1. There are 10 trials (the 10 randomly selected people).
   2. The trials are independent.*
   3. There are two possible outcomes: finding a person with blood type O-negative or not.
   4. The probability of success is 0.07 and the probability of failure is 0.93.

   The random variable X is the number of people with blood type O-negative with $x = 0, 1, 2, 3, \ldots, 10$.

(c) This is not a binomial experiment because the trials are not independent. The probability of an ace on the first trial is $\frac{4}{52}$. Because we are sampling without replacement, if an ace is selected on the first trial, the probability of an ace on the second trial is $\frac{3}{51}$. If an ace is not selected on the first trial, the probability of an ace on the second trial is $\frac{4}{51}$.

Now Work Problem 9

It is worth mentioning that the word *success* does not necessarily imply that something positive has occurred. Success means that an outcome has occurred that

---

*In sampling from large populations without replacement, the trials are assumed to be independent, provided that the sample size is small in relation to the size of the population. As a rule of thumb, if the sample size is less than 5% of the population size, the trials are assumed to be independent, although they are technically dependent. See Example 6 in Section 5.4.

⬦ **CAUTION**
The probability of success, p, is always associated with the random variable X, the number of successes. So if X represents the number of 18-year-olds involved in an accident, then p represents the probability of an 18-year-old being involved in an accident.

corresponds with p, the probability of success. For example, a probability experiment might be to randomly select ten 18-year-old male drivers. We might let X denote the number who have been involved in an accident within the last year. In this case, a success would mean obtaining an 18-year-old male who was involved in an accident. This outcome is certainly not positive, but still represents a success as far as the experiment goes.

2 ## Compute Probabilities of Binomial Experiments

We are now prepared to compute probabilities for a binomial random variable X. We present three methods for obtaining binomial probabilities: (1) the binomial probability distribution formula, (2) a table of binomial probabilities, and (3) technology. We develop the binomial probability formula in Example 2.

EXAMPLE 2   ### Constructing a Binomial Probability Distribution

Problem: According to the American Red Cross, 7% of people in the United States have blood type O-negative. A simple random sample of size 4 is obtained, and the number of people X with blood type O-negative is recorded. Construct a probability distribution for the random variable X.

Approach: This is a binomial experiment with $n = 4$ trials. We define a success as selecting an individual with blood type O-negative. The probability of success, p, is 0.07, and X is the random variable representing the number of successes with $x = 0, 1, 2, 3,$ or 4.

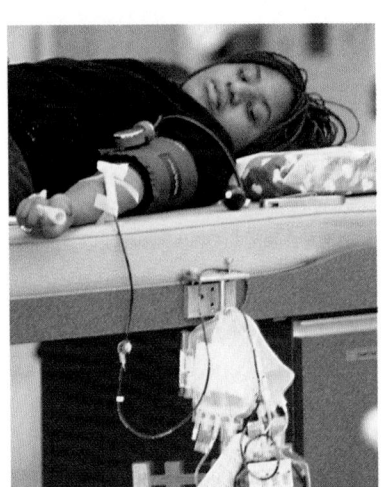

Step 1: Construct a tree diagram listing the various outcomes of the experiment by listing each outcome as S (success) or F (failure).
Step 2: Compute the probabilities for each value of the random variable X.
Step 3: Construct the probability distribution.

Solution

Step 1: Figure 5 on the following page contains a tree diagram listing the 16 possible outcomes of the experiment.
Step 2: We now compute the probability for each possible value of the random variable X. We start with $P(0)$:

$$P(0) = P(FFFF) = P(F) \cdot P(F) \cdot P(F) \cdot P(F) \quad \text{Multiplication Rule for Independent Events}$$
$$= (0.93)(0.93)(0.93)(0.93)$$
$$= (0.93)^4$$
$$= 0.74805$$

$$P(1) = P(SFFF \text{ or } FSFF \text{ or } FFSF \text{ or } FFFS)$$
$$= P(SFFF) + P(FSFF) + P(FFSF) + P(FFFS) \quad \text{Addition Rule for Disjoint Events}$$
$$= (0.07)^1(0.93)^3 + (0.07)^1(0.93)^3 + (0.07)^1(0.93)^3 + (0.07)^1(0.93)^3 \quad \text{Multiplication Rule for Independent Events}$$
$$= 4(0.07)^1(0.93)^3$$
$$= 0.22522$$

$$P(2) = P(SSFF \text{ or } SFSF \text{ or } SFFS \text{ or } FSSF \text{ or } FSFS \text{ or } FFSS)$$
$$= P(SSFF) + P(SFSF) + P(SFFS) + P(FSSF) + P(FSFS) + P(FFSS)$$
$$= (0.07)^2(0.93)^2 + (0.07)^2(0.93)^2 + (0.07)^2(0.93)^2 + (0.07)^2(0.93)^2 + (0.07)^2(0.93)^2 + (0.07)^2(0.93)^2$$
$$= 6(0.07)^2(0.93)^2$$
$$= 0.02543$$

Figure 5

1st Trial	2nd Trial	3rd Trial	4th Trial	Outcome	Number of Successes, x
			S	S,S,S,S	4
		S	F	S,S,S,F	3
	S	F	S	S,S,F,S	3
			F	S,S,F,F	2
S			S	S,F,S,S	3
	F	S	F	S,F,S,F	2
		F	S	S,F,F,S	2
			F	S,F,F,F	1
			S	F,S,S,S	3
		S	F	F,S,S,F	2
	S	F	S	F,S,F,S	2
			F	F,S,F,F	1
F			S	F,F,S,S	2
	F	S	F	F,F,S,F	1
		F	S	F,F,F,S	1
			F	F,F,F,F	0

Table 8

x	$P(x)$
0	0.74805
1	0.22522
2	0.02543
3	0.00128
4	0.00002

We compute $P(3)$ and $P(4)$ similarly and obtain $P(3) = 0.00128$ and $P(4) = 0.00002$. You are encouraged to verify these probabilities.

Step 3: We use these results and obtain the probability distribution in Table 8.

As we look back at the solution in Example 2, we note some interesting results. Consider the probability of obtaining $x = 1$ success:

$$P(1) = 4(0.07)^1 (0.93)^3$$

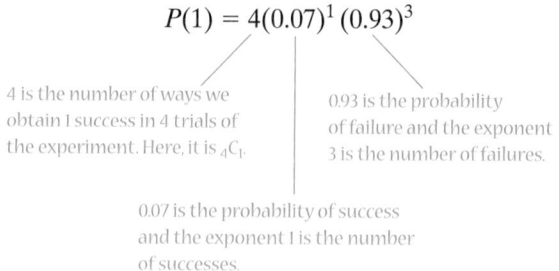

4 is the number of ways we obtain 1 success in 4 trials of the experiment. Here, it is $_4C_1$.

0.07 is the probability of success and the exponent 1 is the number of successes.

0.93 is the probability of failure and the exponent 3 is the number of failures.

The coefficient 4 is the number of ways of obtaining one success in four trials. In general, the coefficient will be $_nC_x$, the number of ways of obtaining x successes in n trials. The second factor in the formula, $(0.07)^1$, is the probability of success, p, raised to the number of successes, x. The third factor in the formula, $(0.93)^3$, is the probability of failure, $1 - p$, raised to the number of failures, $n - x$. This formula holds for all binomial experiments, and we have the *binomial probability distribution function (pdf)*.

CAUTION

Before using the binomial probability distribution function, be sure the requirements for a binomial experiment are satisfied.

Binomial Probability Distribution Function

The probability of obtaining x successes in n independent trials of a binomial experiment is given by

$$P(x) = {}_nC_x \, p^x(1 - p)^{n-x} \qquad x = 0, 1, 2, \ldots, n \qquad \textbf{(1)}$$

where p is the probability of success.

While reading probability problems, pay special attention to key phrases that translate into mathematical symbols. Table 9 lists various phrases and their corresponding mathematical equivalent.

Table 9	
Phrase	**Math Symbol**
"at least" or "no less than" or "greater than or equal to"	$\geq$
"more than" or "greater than"	$>$
"fewer than" or "less than"	$<$
"no more than" or "at most" or "less than or equal to"	$\leq$
"exactly" or "equals" or "is"	$=$

EXAMPLE 3   **Using the Binomial Probability Distribution Function**

Problem: According to Mediamark Research, Inc., 86% of all U.S. households own a cellular phone (one or more).
(a) In a random sample of 20 households, what is the probability that exactly 15 own a cellular phone?
(b) In a random sample of 20 households, what is the probability that at least 18 own a cellular phone?
(c) In a random sample of 20 households, what is the probability that fewer than 18 own a cellular phone?
(d) In a random sample of 20 households, what is the probability that the number of households owning a cellular phone is between 15 and 17, inclusive?

Approach: This is a binomial experiment with $n = 20$ independent trials. We define a success as selecting a household that owns a cellular phone. The probability of success, p, is equal to 0.86. The possible values of the random variable X are $x = 0, 1, 2, \ldots, 20$. We use Formula (1) to compute the probabilities.

Solution

(a) $P(15) = {}_{20}C_{15}\,(0.86)^{15}\,(1 - 0.86)^{20-15}$ $n = 20, x = 15, p = 0.86$

$\qquad = \dfrac{20!}{15!(20 - 15)!}(0.86)^{15}(0.14)^5$ ${}_nC_x = \dfrac{n!}{x!(n - x)!}$

$\qquad = 15{,}504(0.86)^{15}(0.14)^5$

$\qquad = 0.0868$

Note to Instructor
It is important to reinforce the relative frequency approach to interpreting probabilities. This will help students when we get to confidence intervals and P-values.

Interpretation: The probability of getting exactly 15 households out of 20 that own a cellular phone is 0.0868. In 100 trials of this experiment, (that is, if we surveyed 20 households 100 different times) we would expect about 9 trials to result in 15 households that own a cellular phone.

(b) The phrase *at least* means "greater than or equal to." The values of the random variable X greater than or equal to 18 are $x = 18, 19,$ or 20.

$P(X \geq 18) = P(18 \text{ or } 19 \text{ or } 20)$

$\qquad = P(18) + P(19) + P(20)$ Addition Ru nt Events

$\qquad = {}_{20}C_{18}(0.86)^{18}(1 - 0.86)^{20-18} + {}_{20}C_{19}(0.86)^{19}(1 - 0.86)^{20-19} + {}_{20}C_{20}(0.86)^{20}(1 - 0.86)^{20-20}$

$\qquad = 0.2466 + 0.1595 + 0.0490$

$\qquad = 0.4551$

Interpretation: There is a 0.4551 probability that, in a random sample of 20 households, at least 18 will own a cellular phone. In 100 trials of this experiment, we would expect about 46 trials to result in at least 18 households that own a cellular phone.

(c) The values of the random variable X less than 18 are $x = 0, 1, 2, \ldots, 17$. Rather than compute $P(X \leq 17)$ directly by computing $P(1) + P(2) + \cdots + P(17)$, we can use the Complement Rule.

$$P(X < 18) = P(X \leq 17) = 1 - P(X \geq 18) = 1 - 0.4551 = 0.5449$$

Interpretation: There is a 0.5449 probability that, in a random sample of 20 households, fewer than 18 will own a cellular phone. In 100 trials of this experiment, we would expect about 54 trials to result in fewer than 18 households that own a cellular phone.

(d) The word *inclusive* means "including," so we want to determine the probability that 15, 16, or 17 households have a cellular phone.

$$
\begin{aligned}
P(15 \leq X \leq 17) &= P(15 \text{ or } 16 \text{ or } 17) \\
&= P(15) + P(16) + P(17) \quad \text{\small Addition Rule for Disjoint Events} \\
&= {}_{20}C_{15}(0.86)^{15}(1 - 0.86)^{20-15} + {}_{20}C_{16}(0.86)^{16}(1 - 0.86)^{20-16} + {}_{20}C_{17}(0.86)^{17}(1 - 0.86)^{20-17} \\
&= 0.0868 + 0.1666 + 0.2409 \\
&= 0.4943
\end{aligned}
$$

Interpretation: The probability that the number of households owning a cellular phone is between 15 and 17, inclusive, is 0.4943. In 100 trials of this experiment, we would expect about 49 trials to result in 15 to 17 households that own a cellular phone.

Obtaining Binomial Probabilities from Tables

Another method for obtaining probabilities is the binomial probability table. Table III in Appendix A gives probabilities for a binomial random variable X taking on a specific value such as $P(10)$ for select values of n and p. Table IV in Appendix A gives cumulative probabilities of a binomial random variable X. This means that Table IV gives "less than or equal to" binomial probabilities such as $P(X \leq 6)$. We illustrate how to use Tables III and IV in Example 4.

EXAMPLE 4　**Computing Binomial Probabilities Using the Binomial Table**

Problem: According to the Cable and Telecommunications Association for Marketing, 30% of cable television subscribers owned a high-definition television (HDTV) in 2007.

(a) In a random sample of 15 cable television subscribers in 2007, what is the probability that exactly 5 owned an HDTV?

(b) In a random sample of 15 cable television subscribers in 2007, what is the probability that fewer than 9 owned an HDTV?

(c) In a random sample of 15 cable television subscribers in 2007, what is the probability that 9 or more owned an HDTV?

(d) In a random sample of 15 cable television subscribers in 2007, what is the probability that between 3 and 9, inclusive, owned an HDTV?

Approach: We use Tables III and IV in Appendix A to obtain the probabilities.

Solution
(a) We have $n = 15$, $p = 0.30$, and $x = 5$. In Table III, Appendix A, we go to the section that contains $n = 15$ and the column that contains $p = 0.30$. The value at which the $x = 5$ row intersects the $p = 0.30$ column is the probability we seek. See Figure 6. So $P(5) = 0.2061$.

Figure 6

n	x	0.01	0.05	0.10	0.15	0.20	0.25	0.30	0.35	0.40	0.45	0.50
15	0	0.8601	0.4633	0.2059	0.0874	0.0352	0.0134	0.0047	0.0016	0.0005	0.0001	0.0000+
	1	0.1303	0.3658	0.3432	0.2312	0.1319	0.0668	0.0305	0.0126	0.0047	0.0016	0.0005
	2	0.0092	0.1348	0.2669	0.2856	0.2309	0.1559	0.0916	0.0476	0.0219	0.0090	0.0032
	3	0.0004	0.0307	0.1285	0.2184	0.2501	0.2252	0.1700	0.1110	0.0634	0.0318	0.0139
	4	0.0000+	0.0049	0.0428	0.1156	0.1876	0.2252	0.2186	0.1792	0.1268	0.0780	0.0417
	5	0.0000+	0.0006	0.0105	0.0449	0.1032	0.1651	0.2061	0.2123	0.1859	0.1404	0.0916
	6	0.0000+	0.0000+	0.0019	0.0132	0.0430	0.0917	0.1472	0.1906	0.2066	0.1914	0.1527
	7	0.0000+	0.0000+	0.0003	0.0030	0.0138	0.0393	0.0811	0.1319	0.1771	0.2013	0.1964

Interpretation: There is a 0.2061 probability that, in a random sample of 15 cable television subscribers in 2007, exactly 5 owned an HDTV. In 100 trials of this experiment, we expect about 21 trials to result in exactly 5 cable subscribers who owned an HDTV.

(b) The values of the random variable X that are fewer than 9 are 0, 1, 2, 3, 4, 5, 6, 7, or 8. So $P(X < 9) = P(X \leq 8)$. To compute $P(X \leq 8)$, we use the cumulative binomial table, Table IV in Appendix A, which lists binomial probabilities less than or equal to a specified value. We have $n = 15$, $p = 0.30$. In Table IV, we go to the section that contains $n = 15$ and the column that contains $p = 0.30$. The value at which the $x = 8$ row intersects the $p = 0.30$ column represents $P(X \leq 8)$. See Figure 7. So $P(X < 9) = P(X \leq 8) = 0.9848$.

Figure 7

Note to Instructor

Be sure to inform students that discrepancies in answers can occur due to rounding in the binomial distribution table. For example, had we used Table III in Appendix A to solve part (b) of Example 4, we would obtain 0.0047 + 0.0305 + 0.0916 + 0.1700 + 0.2186 + 0.2061 + 0.1472 + 0.0811 + 0.0348 = 0.9846. Because of the rounding within Table III, this result differs from and is less accurate than the answer 0.9848 that we found by using the cumulative table, Table IV. Point out to students that it is generally better to use the cumulative binomial table when the binomial probabilities must be summed.

n	x	0.01	0.05	0.10	0.15	0.20	0.25	0.30	0.35	0.40	0.45	0.50
15	0	0.8601	0.4633	0.2059	0.0874	0.0352	0.0134	0.0047	0.0016	0.0005	0.0001	0.0000+
	1	0.9904	0.8290	0.5490	0.3186	0.1671	0.0802	0.0353	0.0142	0.0052	0.0017	0.0005
	2	0.9996	0.9638	0.8159	0.6042	0.3980	0.2361	0.1268	0.0617	0.0271	0.0107	0.0037
	3	1.0000-	0.9945	0.9444	0.8227	0.6482	0.4613	0.2969	0.1727	0.0905	0.0424	0.0176
	4	1.0000-	0.9994	0.9873	0.9383	0.8358	0.6865	0.5155	0.3519	0.2173	0.1204	0.0592
	5	1.0000-	0.9999	0.9978	0.9832	0.9389	0.8516	0.7216	0.5643	0.4032	0.2608	0.1509
	6	1.0000-	1.0000-	0.9997	0.9964	0.9819	0.9434	0.8689	0.7548	0.6098	0.4622	0.3036
	7	1.0000-	1.0000-	1.0000-	0.9994	0.9958	0.9827	0.9500	0.8868	0.7869	0.6535	0.5000
	8	1.0000-	1.0000-	1.0000-	0.9999	0.9992	0.9958	0.9848	0.9578	0.9050	0.8182	0.6964
	9	1.0000-	1.0000-	1.0000-	1.0000-	0.9999	0.9992	0.9963	0.9876	0.9662	0.9231	0.8491
	10	1.0000-	1.0000-	1.0000-	1.0000-	1.0000-	0.9999	0.9993	0.9972	0.9907	0.9745	0.9408

Interpretation: There is a 0.9848 probability that, in a random sample of 15 cable television subscribers in 2007, fewer than 9 owned an HDTV. In 100 trials of this experiment, we would expect about 98 trials to result in fewer than 9 cable subscribers who owned an HDTV.

(c) To obtain $P(X \geq 9)$, we use the Complement Rule and the results of part (b) as follows:

$$P(X \geq 9) = 1 - P(X < 9)$$
$$= 1 - P(X \leq 8)$$
$$= 1 - 0.9848$$
$$= 0.0152$$

Interpretation: There is a 0.0152 probability that, in a random sample of 15 cable television subscribers in 2007, at least 9 owned an HDTV. In 100 trials of this experiment, we expect about 2 trials to result in 9 or more cable subscribers who owned an HDTV. Because this event only happens about 2 out of 100 times, we consider it to be unusual.

(d) We obtain $P(3 \leq X \leq 9)$ by subtracting $P(X < 3)$ from $P(X \leq 9)$. To determine the values of $P(X < 3) = P(X \leq 2)$ and $P(X \leq 9)$, we use the cumulative binomial table. Within the $n = 15$ section of Table IV, the value at which the $x = 2$ row intersects the $p = 0.30$ column is 0.1268. See Figure 8. The value at which $x = 9$ row intersects the $p = 0.30$ column is 0.9963. So we have the following:

$$P(3 \leq X \leq 9) = P(X \leq 9) - P(X < 3)$$
$$= P(X \leq 9) - P(X \leq 2)$$
$$= 0.9963 - 0.1268$$
$$= 0.8695$$

Figure 8

n	x	0.01	0.05	0.10	0.15	0.20	0.25	0.30	0.35	0.40	0.45	0.50
15	0	0.8601	0.4633	0.2059	0.0874	0.0352	0.0134	0.0047	0.0016	0.0005	0.0001	0.0000+
	1	0.9904	0.8290	0.5490	0.3186	0.1671	0.0802	0.0353	0.0142	0.0052	0.0017	0.0005
	2	0.9996	0.9638	0.8159	0.6042	0.3980	0.2361	0.1268	0.0617	0.0271	0.0107	0.0037
	3	1.0000−	0.9945	0.9444	0.8227	0.6482	0.4613	0.2969	0.1727	0.0905	0.0424	0.0176
	4	1.0000−	0.9994	0.9873	0.9383	0.8358	0.6865	0.5155	0.3519	0.2173	0.1204	0.0592
	5	1.0000−	0.9999	0.9978	0.9832	0.9389	0.8516	0.7216	0.5643	0.4032	0.2608	0.1509
	6	1.0000−	1.0000−	0.9997	0.9964	0.9819	0.9434	0.8689	0.7548	0.6098	0.4622	0.3036
	7	1.0000−	1.0000−	1.0000−	0.9994	0.9958	0.9827	0.9500	0.8868	0.7869	0.6535	0.5000
	8	1.0000−	1.0000−	1.0000−	0.9999	0.9992	0.9958	0.9848	0.9578	0.9050	0.8182	0.6964
	9	1.0000−	1.0000−	1.0000−	1.0000−	0.9999	0.9992	0.9963	0.9876	0.9662	0.9231	0.8491
	10	1.0000−	1.0000−	1.0000−	1.0000−	1.0000−	0.9999	0.9993	0.9972	0.9907	0.9745	0.9408

Interpretation: In a random sample of 15 cable television subscribers in 2007, there is a 0.8695 probability that between 3 and 9 subscribers, inclusive, owned an HDTV. In 100 trials of this experiment, we would expect about 87 trials to result in 3 to 9 subscribers, inclusive, who owned an HDTV.

Obtaining Binomial Probabilities Using Technology

Statistical software and graphing calculators have the ability to compute binomial probabilities as well. We illustrate this approach to computing probabilities in the next example.

EXAMPLE 5   **Obtaining Binomial Probabilities Using Technology**

Problem: According to the Cable and Telecommunications Association for Marketing, 30% of cable television subscribers owned a high definition television (HDTV) in 2007.

(a) In a random sample of 15 cable television subscribers in 2007, what is the probability that exactly 5 owned an HDTV?

(b) In a random sample of 15 cable television subscribers in 2007, what is the probability that fewer than 9 owned an HDTV?

Approach: Statistical software or graphing calculators with advanced statistical features have the ability to determine binomial probabilities. The steps for determining binomial probabilities using MINITAB, Excel, and the TI-83/84 Plus graphing calculators can be found in the Technology Step-by-Step on page 358.

Solution: We will use Excel to determine the probability for part (a) and a TI-84 Plus to determine the probability for part (b).

(a) Using Excel's formula wizard, we obtain the results in Figure 9(a). So $P(5) = 0.2061$. This agrees with the results of Example 4(a).

(b) To compute probabilities such as $P(X < 9) = P(X \leq 8)$, it is best to use the **cumulative distribution function** (or **cdf**), which computes probabilities less than or equal to a specified value. Using a TI-84 Plus graphing calculator to compute $P(X \leq 8)$ with $n = 15$ and $p = 0.3$, we find $P(X \leq 8) = 0.9848$. See Figure 9(b).

Figure 9

Here is the probability

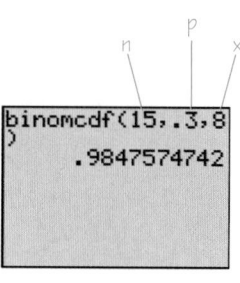

(a)   (b)

Now Work Problem 35

Compute the Mean and Standard Deviation of a Binomial Random Variable

We discussed finding the mean (or expected value) and standard deviation of a discrete random variable in Section 6.1. These formulas can be used to find the mean and standard deviation of a binomial random variable as well. However, a simpler method exists.

In Other Words
The mean of a binomial random variable equals the product of the number of trials of the experiment and the probability of success. It can be interpreted as the expected number of successes in n trials of the experiment.

Mean (or Expected Value) and Standard Deviation of a Binomial Random Variable

A binomial experiment with n independent trials and probability of success p has a mean and standard deviation given by the formulas

$$\mu_X = np \quad \text{and} \quad \sigma_X = \sqrt{np(1-p)} \qquad \textbf{(2)}$$

EXAMPLE 6   **Finding the Mean and Standard Deviation of a Binomial Random Variable**

Note to Instructor
You may want to construct a binomial probability distribution with $n = 3$ and $p = 0.4$. Then use the formulas from Section 6.1 to compute μ_X and σ_X. Now use Formula (2) to compute μ_X and σ_X.

Problem: According to Mediamark Research, Inc., 86% of all U.S. households in 2007 owned at least one cellular phone. In a simple random sample of 300 households, determine the mean and standard deviation number of households that own at least one cellular phone.

Approach: This is a binomial experiment with $n = 300$ and $p = 0.86$. We can use Formula (2) to find the mean and standard deviation, respectively.

Solution

$$\mu_X = np = 300(0.86) = 258$$

and

$$\sigma_X = \sqrt{np(1-p)} = \sqrt{300(0.86)(1-0.86)} = \sqrt{36.12} = 6.0$$

Interpretation: We expect that, in a random sample of 300 households, 258 will own at least one cellular phone.

Now Work Problems 29(a)–(c)

 Construct Binomial Probability Histograms

Constructing binomial probability histograms is no different from constructing other probability histograms.

EXAMPLE 7   **Constructing Binomial Probability Histograms**

Problem

(a) Construct a binomial probability histogram with $n = 10$ and $p = 0.2$. Comment on the shape of the distribution.

(b) Construct a binomial probability histogram with $n = 10$ and $p = 0.5$. Comment on the shape of the distribution.

(c) Construct a binomial probability histogram with $n = 10$ and $p = 0.8$. Comment on the shape of the distribution.

Approach: To construct a binomial probability histogram, we will first obtain the probability distribution. We then construct the probability histogram of the probability distribution.

Table 10	
x	*P(x)*
0	0.1074
1	0.2684
2	0.3020
3	0.2013
4	0.0881
5	0.0264
6	0.0055
7	0.0008
8	0.0001
9	0.0000
10	0.0000

Solution

(a) We obtain the probability distribution with $n = 10$ and $p = 0.2$. See Table 10 and note that $P(9) = 0.0000$. The probability is actually 0.000004096, but is written as 0.0000 to four significant digits. The same idea applies to $P(10)$. Figure 10 shows the corresponding probability histogram with the mean $\mu_X = 10(0.2) = 2$ labeled. The distribution is skewed right.

Figure 10

(b) We obtain the probability distribution with $n = 10$ and $p = 0.5$. See Table 11. Figure 11 shows the corresponding probability histogram with the mean $\mu_X = 10(0.5) = 5$ labeled. The distribution is symmetric and approximately bell shaped.

Table 11	
x	*P(x)*
0	0.0010
1	0.0098
2	0.0439
3	0.1172
4	0.2051
5	0.2461
6	0.2051
7	0.1172
8	0.0439
9	0.0098
10	0.0010

Figure 11

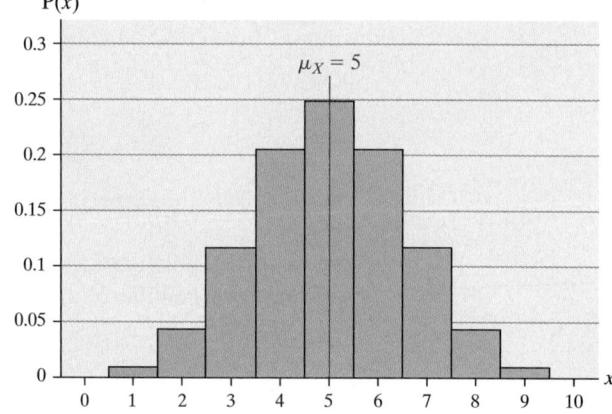

(c) We obtain the probability distribution with $n = 10$ and $p = 0.8$. See Table 12. Figure 12 shows the corresponding probability histogram with the mean $\mu_X = 10(0.8) = 8$ labeled. The distribution is skewed left.

Table 12	
x	*P(x)*
0	0.0000
1	0.0000
2	0.0001
3	0.0008
4	0.0055
5	0.0264
6	0.0881
7	0.2013
8	0.3020
9	0.2684
10	0.1074

Figure 12

Now Work Problem 29(d)

Based on the results of Example 7, we conclude that the binomial probability distribution is skewed right if $p < 0.5$, symmetric and approximately bell shaped if $p = 0.5$, and skewed left if $p > 0.5$. Notice that Figure 10 ($p = 0.2$) and Figure 12 ($p = 0.8$) are mirror images.

We have seen the role that p plays in the shape of a binomial distribution, but what role does n play in the shape of the distribution? To answer this question, we compare the binomial probability histogram with $n = 10$ and $p = 0.2$ [see Figure 13(a)] to the binomial probability histogram with $n = 30$ and $p = 0.2$ [Figure 13(b)] and the binomial probability histogram with $n = 70$ and $p = 0.2$ [Figure 13(c)].

Figure 13(a) is skewed right, Figure 13(b) is slightly skewed right, and Figure 13(c) appears bell shaped.

Figure 13

(a)   (b)   (c)

We conclude the following:

> For a fixed p, as the number of trials n in a binomial experiment increases, the probability distribution of the random variable X becomes bell shaped. As a rule of thumb, if $np(1 - p) \geq 10$,* the probability distribution will be approximately bell shaped.

In Other Words

Provided that $np(1 - p) \geq 10$, the interval $\mu - 2\sigma$ to $\mu + 2\sigma$ gives us an interval of "usual" observations. Any observation outside this interval may be considered unusual.

This result allows us to use the Empirical Rule to identify unusual observations in a binomial experiment. Recall that the Empirical Rule states that in a bell-shaped distribution about 95% of all observations lie within two standard deviations of the mean. That is, about 95% of the observations lie between $\mu - 2\sigma$ and $\mu + 2\sigma$. Any observation that lies outside this interval may be considered unusual because the observation occurs less than 5% of the time.

EXAMPLE 8 | **Using the Mean, Standard Deviation, and Empirical Rule to Check for Unusual Results in a Binomial Experiment**

Problem: According to Mediamark Research, Inc., 86% of all U.S. households in 2007 owned at least one cellular phone. In a simple random sample of 300 households, 275 owned at least one cellular phone. Is this result unusual?

---

*P. P. Ramsey and P. H. Ramsey, "Evaluating the Normal Approximation to the Binomial Test," *Journal of Educational Statistics* 13 (1998): 173–182.

Approach: Because $np(1 - p) = 300(0.86)(0.14) = 36.12 \geq 10$, the binomial probability distribution is approximately bell shaped. Therefore, we can use the Empirical Rule to check for unusual observations. If the observation is less than $\mu - 2\sigma$ or greater than $\mu + 2\sigma$, we say it is unusual.

Solution: From Example 6, we have $\mu = 258$ and $\sigma = 6.0$.

$$\mu - 2\sigma = 258 - 2(6.0) = 258 - 12.0 = 246$$

and

$$\mu + 2\sigma = 258 + 2(6.0) = 258 + 12.0 = 270$$

Interpretation: Since any value less than 246 or greater than 270 is unusual, 275 is an unusual result. We should attempt to identify the reason for its value. Perhaps the percentage of households that owns at least one cellular phone has increased since 2007.

Now Work Problem 45

6.2 ASSESS YOUR UNDERSTANDING

Concepts and Vocabulary

1. State the criteria for a binomial probability experiment.

2. What role does $_nC_x$ play in the binomial probability distribution function?

3. How can the Empirical Rule be used to identify unusual results in a binomial experiment? When can the Empirical Rule be used?

4. Describe how the value of n affects the shape of the binomial probability histogram.

5. Describe how the value of p affects the shape of the binomial probability histogram.

6. Explain what "success" means in a binomial experiment.

Skill Building

In Problems 7–16, determine which of the following probability experiments represents a binomial experiment. If the probability experiment is not a binomial experiment, state why.

7. A random sample of 15 college seniors is obtained, and the individuals selected are asked to state their ages. Not binomial

8. A random sample of 30 cars in a used car lot is obtained, and their mileages recorded. Not binomial

9. An experimental drug is administered to 100 randomly selected individuals, with the number of individuals responding favorably recorded. Binomial
NW

10. A poll of 1,200 registered voters is conducted in which the respondents are asked whether they believe Congress should reform Social Security. Binomial

11. Three cards are selected from a standard 52-card deck without replacement. The number of aces selected is recorded. Not binomial

12. Three cards are selected from a standard 52-card deck with replacement. The number of kings selected is recorded. Binomial

13. A basketball player who makes 80% of her free throws is asked to shoot free throws until she misses. The number of free-throw attempts is recorded. Not binomial

14. A baseball player who reaches base safely 30% of the time is allowed to bat until he reaches base safely for the third time. The number of at-bats required is recorded. Not binomial

15. One hundred randomly selected U.S. parents with at least one child under the age of 18 are surveyed and asked if they have ever spanked their child. The number of parents who have spanked their child is recorded. Binomial

16. In a poll conducted December 6–9, 2007, by Gallup, 82% of Americans identified themselves with a Christian religion. In a small town with 400 citizens, 100 randomly selected citizens are asked to identify their religion. The number who identify with a Christian religion is recorded. Not binomial

In Problems 17–28, a binomial probability experiment is conducted with the given parameters. Compute the probability of x successes in the n independent trials of the experiment.

17. $n = 10, p = 0.4, x = 3$ 0.2150

18. $n = 15, p = 0.85, x = 12$ 0.2184

19. $n = 40, p = 0.99, x = 38$ 0.0532

20. $n = 50, p = 0.02, x = 3$ 0.0607

21. $n = 8, p = 0.35, x = 3$ 0.2786

22. $n = 20, p = 0.6, x = 17$ 0.0123

23. $n = 9, p = 0.2, x \leq 3$ 0.9144

24. $n = 10, p = 0.65, x < 5$ 0.0949

25. $n = 7, p = 0.5, x > 3$ 0.5

26. $n = 20, p = 0.7, x \geq 12$ 0.8867

27. $n = 12, p = 0.35, x \leq 4$ 0.5833

28. $n = 11, p = 0.75, x \geq 8$ 0.7133

In Problems 29–34, (a) construct a binomial probability distribution with the given parameters; (b) compute the mean and standard deviation of the random variable using the methods of Section 6.1; (c) compute the mean and standard deviation, using the methods of this section; and (d) draw the probability histogram, comment on its shape, and label the mean on the histogram.

29. $n = 6, p = 0.3$ $\mu_X = 1.8, \sigma_X = 1.1$
NW

30. $n = 8, p = 0.5$ $\mu_X = 4, \sigma_X = 1.4$

31. $n = 9, p = 0.75$ $\mu_X = 6.75, \sigma_X = 1.3$

32. $n = 10, p = 0.2$ $\mu_X = 2, \sigma_X = 1.3$

33. $n = 10$, $p = 0.5$ $\mu_X = 5$, $\sigma_X = 1.6$
34. $n = 9$, $p = 0.8$ $\mu_X = 7.2$, $\sigma_X = 1.2$

35. (b) 0.2123
35. (c) 0.5643

Applying the Concepts

35. On-Time Flights According to flightstats.com, American Airlines flight 1247 from Orlando to Los Angeles is on time 65% of the time. Suppose fifteen flights are randomly selected, and the number of on-time flights is recorded.
(a) Explain why this is a binomial experiment.
(b) Find the probability that exactly 10 flights are on time.
(c) Find the probability that at least 10 flights are on time.
(d) Find the probability that fewer than 10 flights are on time. 0.4357
(e) Find the probability that between 7 and 10 flights, inclusive, are on time. 0.6059

36. Smokers According to the American Lung Association, 90% of adult smokers started smoking before turning 21 years old. Ten smokers 21 years old or older are randomly selected, and the number of smokers who started smoking before 21 is recorded.
(a) Explain why this is a binomial experiment.
(b) Find the probability that exactly 8 of them started smoking before 21 years of age. 0.1937
(c) Find the probability that at least 8 of them started smoking before 21 years of age. 0.9298
(d) Find the probability that fewer than 8 of them started smoking before 21 years of age. 0.0702
(e) Find the probability that between 7 and 9 of them, inclusive, started smoking before 21 years of age. 0.6385

37. Allergy Sufferers Clarinex-D is a medication whose purpose is to reduce the symptoms associated with a variety of allergies. In clinical trials of Clarinex-D, 5% of the patients in the study experienced insomnia as a side effect. A random sample of 20 Clarinex-D users is obtained, and the number of patients who experienced insomnia is recorded.
(a) Find the probability that exactly 3 experienced insomnia as a side effect. 0.0596
(b) Find the probability that 3 or fewer experienced insomnia as a side effect. 0.9841
(c) Find the probability that between 1 and 4 patients, inclusive, experienced insomnia as a side effect. 0.6389
(d) Would it be unusual to find 4 or more patients who experienced insomnia as a side effect? Why? Yes

38. Migraine Sufferers Depakote is a medication whose purpose is to reduce the pain associated with migraine headaches. In clinical trials of Depakote, 2% of the patients in the study experienced weight gain as a side effect. A random sample of 30 Depakote users is obtained, and the number of patients who experienced weight gain is recorded.
Source: Abbott Laboratories
(a) Find the probability that exactly 3 experienced weight gain as a side effect. 0.0188
(b) Find the probability that 3 or fewer experienced weight gain as a side effect. 0.9971
(c) Find the probability that 4 or more patients experienced weight gain as a side effect. 0.0029
(d) Find the probability that between 1 and 4 patients, inclusive, experienced weight gain as a side effect. 0.4542

39. Murder Clearances According to the *Uniform Crime Report, 2006*, nationwide, 61% of murders committed in 2006 were cleared by arrest or exceptional means. Twenty-five murders committed in 2006 are randomly selected, and the number cleared by arrest or exceptional means is recorded.
(a) Find the probability that exactly 20 of the murders were cleared. 0.0244
(b) Find the probability that between 16 and 18 of the murders, inclusive, were cleared. 0.3767
(c) Would it be unusual if fewer than 10 of the murders were cleared? Why or why not? Yes

40. College Enrollment According to the *2005 American Community Survey*, 43% of women aged 18 to 24 were enrolled in college in 2005. Twenty-five women aged 18 to 24 are randomly selected, and the number enrolled in college is recorded.
(a) Find the probability that exactly 15 of the women are enrolled in college. 0.0376
(b) Find the probability that between 11 and 13 of the women, inclusive, are enrolled in college. 0.4027
(c) Would it be unusual if more than 15 of the women are enrolled in college? Why or why not? Yes

41. Airline Satisfaction A CNN/USA Today/Gallup poll in April 2005 reported that 75% of adult Americans were satisfied with the job the nation's major airlines were doing. Ten adult Americans are selected at random, and the number who are satisfied is recorded.
(a) Find the probability that exactly 6 are satisfied with the airlines. 0.1460
(b) Find the probability that fewer than 7 are satisfied with the airlines. 0.2241
(c) Find the probability that 5 or more are satisfied with the airlines. 0.9803
(d) Find the probability that between 5 and 8, inclusive, are satisfied with the airlines. 0.7363
(e) Ten adult Americans are randomly selected, and 3 reported being satisfied with the job the nation's major airlines are doing. Would it be unusual to find 3 or fewer satisfied? What might you conclude? Yes

42. Broadband Video Consumers According to the report *Broadband Content and Services 2007*™ by Horowitz Associates, Inc., 6 out of 10 adult high-speed Internet users watch online video content at least once per week. Twenty adult high-speed Internet users are randomly selected, and the number who watch online video content at least once per week is recorded.
(a) Find the probability that exactly 5 users watch online video content at least once per week. 0.0013
(b) Find the probability that fewer than 8 users watch online video content at least once per week. Would this be unusual? 0.0210; yes
(c) Find the probability that at least 15 users watch online video content at least once per week. Would this be unusual? 0.1256; no
(d) Find the probability that between 8 and 12 users, inclusive, watch online video content at least once per week. 0.5631
(e) Suppose 20 adult high-speed Internet users are randomly selected and 17 report watching online video content at least once per week. Would it be unusual for 17 or more adult Internet users to watch online video content at least once per week? What might you conclude? Yes

43. Adult Children Living at Home According to the March 2005 *Current Population Survey*, 53% of males between the ages of 18 and 24 lived at home in 2005 (unmarried college students living in dorms are counted as living at home). A survey is administered at a community college to 20 randomly selected male students between the ages of 18 and 24 years, and 17 of them respond that they live at home.

(a) Based on the sample of 20 students, what proportion of community college males live at home? 0.85

(b) Find the probability that 17 or more out of 20 community college male students live at home, assuming that the proportion who live at home is 53%. 0.0029

(c) What might you conclude from this result?

44. Jury Selection Twelve jurors are randomly selected from a population of 3 million residents. Of these 3 million residents, it is known that 45% are Hispanic. Of the 12 jurors selected, 2 are Hispanic.

(a) What proportion of the jury described is Hispanic? 0.1667

(b) If 12 jurors are randomly selected from a population that is 45% Hispanic, what is the probability that 2 or fewer jurors will be Hispanic? 0.0421

(c) If you were the lawyer of the defendant, what might you argue?

45. On-Time Flights According to flightstats.com, American
NW Airlines flight 1247 from Orlando to Los Angeles is on time 65% of the time. Suppose 100 flights are randomly selected.

(a) Compute the mean and standard deviation of the random variable X, the number of on-time flights in 100 trials of the probability experiment. $\mu_X = 65, \sigma_X = 4.8$

(b) Interpret the mean.

(c) Would it be unusual to observe 75 on-time flights in a random sample of 100 flights from Orlando to Los Angeles? Why? Yes

46. Smokers According to the *American Lung Association*, 90% of adult smokers started smoking before turning 21 years old. 46. (a) $\mu_X = 180, \sigma_X = 4.2$

(a) Compute the mean and standard deviation of the random variable X, the number of smokers who started before turning 21 years old in 200 trials of the probability experiment.

(b) Interpret the mean.

(c) Would it be unusual to observe 185 smokers who started smoking before turning 21 years old in a random sample of 200 adult smokers? Why? No

47. Allergy Sufferers Clarinex-D is a medication whose purpose is to reduce the symptoms associated with a variety of allergies. In clinical trials of Clarinex-D, 5% of the patients in the study experienced insomnia as a side effect.

(a) If 240 users of Clarinex-D are randomly selected, how many would we expect to experience insomnia as a side effect? 12

(b) Would it be unusual to observe 20 patients experiencing insomnia as a side effect in 240 trials of the probability experiment? Why? Yes

48. Migraine Sufferers Depakote is a medication whose purpose is to reduce the pain associated with migraine headaches. In clinical trials and extended studies of Depakote, 2% of the patients in the study experienced weight gain as a side effect. Would it be unusual to observe 16 patients who experience weight gain in a random sample of 600 patients who take the medication? Why? No

49. Murder Clearances According to the *Uniform Crime Report*, *2006*, nationwide, 61% of murders committed in 2006 were cleared by arrest or exceptional means.

(a) For 250 randomly selected murders committed in 2006, compute the mean and standard deviation of the random variable X, the number of murders cleared by arrest or exceptional means. $\mu_X = 152.5, \sigma_X = 7.7$

(b) Interpret the mean.

(c) Of the 250 randomly selected murders, find the interval that would be considered "usual" for the number of murders that was cleared. 137–168

(d) Would it be unusual if more than 170 of the 250 murders were cleared? Why Yes

50. College Enrollment According to the *2005 American Community Survey*, 43% of women aged 18 to 24 were enrolled in college in 2005.

(a) For 500 randomly selected women ages 18 to 24 in 2005, compute the mean and standard deviation of the random variable X, the number of women who were enrolled in college. $\mu_X = 215; \sigma_X = 11.1$

(b) Interpret the mean.

(c) Of the 500 randomly selected women, find the interval that would be considered "usual" for the number of women who were enrolled in college. 193–237

(d) Would it be unusual if 200 of the 500 women were enrolled in college? Why? No

51. Internet Searches In August 2007, Google™ accounted for 53.6% of all U.S. Internet searches. Assuming this percentage is still accurate today, would it be unusual to observe 600 searches using Google™ in a random sample of 1,000 U.S. Internet searches? Why? Yes

Source: Nielsen NetRatings

52. Asthma Control Singulair is a medication whose purpose is to control asthma attacks. In clinical trials of Singulair, 18.4% of the patients in the study experienced headaches as a side effect. Would it be unusual to observe 86 patients who experience headaches in a random sample of 400 patients who use this medication? Why? No

53. Racial Profiling in New York City The following excerpt is from the *Racial Profiling Data Collection Resource Center* (www.racialprofilinganalysis.neu.edu/).

In 2006, the New York City Police Department stopped a half-million pedestrians for suspected criminal involvement. Raw statistics for these encounters suggest large racial disparities— 89 percent of the stops involved nonwhites. Do these statistics point to racial bias in police officers' decisions to stop particular pedestrians? Do they indicate that officers are particularly intrusive when stopping nonwhites?

Write a report that answers the questions posed using the fact that 44% of New York City residents were classified as white in 2006. In your report, cite some shortcomings in using the proportion of white residents in the city to formulate likelihoods.

54. Probability Applet Load the binomial applet on your computer.

(a) Set the probability of success, p, to 0.8 and the number of trials of the binomial experiment, n, to 10. Simulate shooting 10 free throws for $N = 1$. How many were made?

(b) Set the probability of success to 0.8 and the number of trials of the binomial experiment to 10. Simulate shooting 10 free throws $N = 1,000$ times. Use the results of the simulation to estimate the probability of making 10 out of 10 free throws.

(c) Use the binomial probability formula to compute the probability of making 10 out of 10 free throws if the probability of success is 0.8. *0.1074*

(d) Use the results of the simulation to estimate the probability of making at least 8 out of 10 free throws.

(e) Use the binomial probability formula to compute the probability of making at least 8 out of 10 free throws. *0.6778*

(f) Determine the mean number of free throws made for the 1,000 repetitions of the experiment. Is it close to the expected value?

55. Simulation According to the U.S. National Center for Health Statistics, there is a 98% probability that a 20-year-old male will survive to age 30.

(a) Using statistical software, simulate taking 100 random samples of size 30 from this population.

(b) Using the results of the simulation, compute the probability that exactly 29 of the 30 males survive to age 30.

(c) Compute the probability that exactly 29 of the 30 males survive to age 30, using the binomial probability distribution. Compare the results with part (b). *0.3340*

(d) Using the results of the simulation, compute the probability that at most 27 of the 30 males survive to age 30.

(e) Compute the probability that at most 27 of the 30 males survive to age 30, using the binomial probability distribution. Compare the results with part (d). *0.0217*

(f) Compute the mean number of male survivors in the 100 simulations of the probability experiment. Is it close to the expected value?

(g) Compute the standard deviation of the number of male survivors in the 100 simulations of the probability experiment. Compare the result to the theoretical standard deviation of the probability distribution.

(h) Did the simulation yield any unusual results?

56. Athletics Participation According to the 2006–07 High School Athletics Participation Survey, approximately 55% of students enrolled in high schools participate in athletic programs. You are performing a study of high school students and would like at least 11 students in the study to be participating in athletics.

Source: National Federation of State High School Associations

(a) How many high school students do you expect to have to randomly select? *20*

(b) How many high school students do you have to select to have a 99% probability that the sample contains at least 12 who participate in athletics? *33*

57. Educational Attainment According to the *2006 American Community Survey*, 27% of residents of the United States 25 years old or older had earned at least a bachelor's degree. You are performing a study and would like at least 10 people in the study to have earned at least a bachelor's degree.

(a) How many residents of the United States 25 years old or older do you expect to randomly select? *38*

(b) How many residents of the United States 25 years old or older do you have to randomly select to have a probability 0.99 that the sample contains at least 10 who have earned at least a bachelor's degree? *65*

58. Geometric Probability Distribution A probability distribution for the random variable X, the number of trials until a success is observed, is called the **geometric probability distribution**. It has the same criteria as the binomial distribution (see page 343), except that the number of trials is not fixed. Its probability distribution function (pdf) is

$$P(x) = p(1 - p)^{x-1}, \quad x = 1, 2, 3, \dots$$

where p is the probability of success.

(a) What is the probability that Shaquille O'Neal misses his first two free throws and makes the third? Over his career, he makes 52.4% of his free throws. That is, find $P(3)$. *0.1187*

(b) Construct a probability distribution for the random variable X, the number of free-throw attempts of Shaquille O'Neal until he makes a free throw. Construct the distribution for $x = 1, 2, 3, \dots, 10$. The probabilities are small for $x > 10$.

(c) Compute the mean of the distribution, using the formula presented in Section 6.1. *$\mu_X = 1.9$*

(d) Compare the mean obtained in part (c) with the value $\dfrac{1}{p}$. Conclude that the mean of a geometric probability distribution is $\mu_X = \dfrac{1}{p}$. How many free throws do we expect Shaq to take before we observe a made free throw? *$\mu_X = 1.9$*

59. Negative Binomial Probability Distribution The **negative binomial probability distribution** can be used to compute the probability of the random variable X, the number of trials necessary to observe r successes of a binomial experiment. The probability distribution function is given by

$$P(x) = (_{x-1}C_{r-1})p^r(1 - p)^{x-r}$$
$$x = r, r + 1, r + 2, \dots$$

Consider a roulette wheel. Remember, a roulette wheel has 2 green slots, 18 red slots, and 18 black slots.

(a) What is the probability that it will take $x = 1$ trial before observing $r = 1$ green? *0.0526*

(b) What is the probability that it will take $x = 20$ trials before observing $r = 2$ greens? *0.0199*

(c) What is the probability that it will take $x = 30$ trials before observing $r = 3$ greens? *0.0137*

(d) The expected number of trials before observing r successes is $\dfrac{r}{p}$. What is the expected number of trials before observing 3 greens? *57*

TECHNOLOGY STEP-BY-STEP Computing Binomial Probabilities via Technology

TI-83/84 Plus

Computing P(x)

1. Press 2nd VARS to access the probability distribution menu.
2. Highlight 0: binompdf(and hit ENTER.
3. With binompdf(on the HOME screen, type the number of trials n, the probability of success, p, and the number of successes, x. For example, with $n = 15$, $p = 0.3$, and $x = 8$, type

$$binompdf(15, 0.3, 8)$$

Then hit ENTER.

Computing P(X ≤ x)

1. Press 2nd VARS to access the probability distribution menu.
2. Highlight A: binomcdf(and hit ENTER.
3. With binomcdf(on the HOME screen, type the number of trials n, the probability of success, p, and the number of successes, x. For example, with $n = 15$, $p = 0.3$, and $x ≤ 8$, type

$$binomcdf(15, 0.3, 8)$$

Then hit ENTER. The result was shown in Figure 9(b).

MINITAB

Computing P(x)

1. Enter the possible values of the random variable X in C1. For example, with $n = 15$, $p = 0.3$, enter 0, 1, 2, ..., 15 into C1.
2. Select the **CALC** menu, highlight **Probability Distributions**, then highlight **Binomial** ....
3. Fill in the window as shown. Click OK.

Computing P(X ≤ x)

Follow the same steps as those for computing $P(x)$. In the window that comes up after selecting Binomial Distribution, select **Cumulative probability** instead of **Probability**.

Excel

Computing P(x)

1. Click on the fx icon. Highlight Statistical in the Function category window. Highlight BINOMDIST in the Function name window.
2. Fill in the window with the appropriate values. For example, if $x = 5$, $n = 10$, and $p = 0.2$, fill in the window as shown in Figure 9(a). Click OK.

Computing P(X ≤ x)

Follow the same steps as those presented for computing $P(x)$. In the BINOMDIST window, type TRUE in the cumulative cell.

6.3 THE POISSON PROBABILITY DISTRIBUTION

Objectives

1. Determine if a probability experiment follows a Poisson process
2. Compute probabilities of a Poisson random variable
3. Find the mean and standard deviation of a Poisson random variable

1 Determine If a Probability Experiment Follows a Poisson Process

Note to Instructor
This section is optional and may be omitted without loss of continuity.

We now introduce another discrete probability model, the *Poisson probability distribution*, named after Siméon Denis Poisson. This probability distribution can be used to compute probabilities of experiments in which the random variable X counts the number of occurrences (successes) of a particular event within a specified interval (usually time or space). Consider the following example.

| EXAMPLE 1 | **Illustrating a Poisson Process** |

A McDonald's manager knows from prior experience that cars arrive at the drive-through at an average rate of two cars per minute between the hours of 12:00 noon and 1:00 P.M. The random variable X, the number of cars that arrive between 12:20 and 12:40, follows a Poisson process.

We now present the criteria for a random variable to follow a *Poisson process*.

Definition   A random variable X, the number of successes in a fixed interval, follows a **Poisson process** provided the following conditions are met.

1. The probability of two or more successes in any sufficiently small subinterval* is 0.

2. The probability of success is the same for any two intervals of equal length.

3. The number of successes in any interval is independent of the number of successes in any other interval provided the intervals are not overlapping.

In the McDonald's example, if we divide the time interval into a sufficiently small length (say, 1 second), it is impossible for more than one car to arrive. This would satisfy part 1 of the definition. Part 2 of the definition is satisfied because the cars arrive at an average rate of 2 cars per minute over the 1-hour interval. Part 3 is satisfied because the number of cars that arrive in any 1-minute interval (say between 12:23 P.M. and 12:24 P.M.) is independent of the number of cars that arrive in any other 1-minute interval (say between 12:35 P.M. and 12:36 P.M.).

 Compute Probabilities of a Poisson Random Variable

If the random variable X follows a Poisson process, then we can use the following probability rule to compute Poisson probabilities.

In Other Words
Poisson probabilities are used to determine the probability of the number of successes in a fixed interval of time or space.

> **Poisson Probability Distribution Function**
>
> If X is the number of successes in an interval of fixed length t, then the probability of obtaining x successes in the interval is
>
> $$P(x) = \frac{(\lambda t)^x}{x!}e^{-\lambda t}, \quad x = 0, 1, 2, 3, \ldots \tag{1}$$
>
> where λ (the Greek letter lambda) represents the average number of occurrences of the event in some interval of length 1 and $e \approx 2.71828$.

| Now Work Problem 3 |

To clarify the roles of λ and t, let's revisit Example 1. In the McDonald's situation, $\lambda = 2$ cars per minute, while $t = 20$ minutes (the amount of time between 12:20 P.M. and 12:40 P.M.).

---

*For example, the fixed interval might be any time between 0 and 5 minutes. A subinterval could be any time between 1 and 2 seconds.

EXAMPLE 2

Historical Note

Siméon Denis Poisson was born on June 21, 1781, in Pithiviers, France. He was educated by his father, who wanted him to become a doctor. However, one of his first patients died within a few hours of Poisson's treatment, so Poisson decided never to practice medicine again. After this mishap, Poisson enrolled in the Polytechnic school. While there, he drew the attention of Lagrange, Legendre, and Laplace. In 1837, Poisson published *Récherches sur la probabilité des jugements*, in which he first presented the probability distribution named after him.

Computing Probabilities of a Poisson Process

Problem: A McDonald's manager knows that cars arrive at the drive-through at the rate of 2 cars per minute between the hours of 12 noon and 1:00 P.M. She needs to determine and interpret the probability of the following events:

(a) Exactly 6 cars arrive between 12 noon and 12:05 P.M.

(b) Fewer than 6 cars arrive between 12 noon and 12:05 P.M.

(c) At least 6 cars arrive between 12 noon and 12:05 P.M.

Approach: The manager first needs a method that can be used to determine the probabilities. The cars arrive at a constant rate of 2 per minute over the time interval between 12:00 noon and 1:00 P.M. We know from Example 1 that the random variable X follows a Poisson process, where $x = 0, 1, 2, \ldots$. The Poisson probability distribution function requires a value for λ and t. We are given that cars arrive at a rate of 2 per minute, so $\lambda = 2$. The interval of time we are interested in is 5 minutes, so $t = 5$.

Solution: We use the Poisson probability distribution function (1) to compute the probabilities.

(a) The probability that exactly six cars arrive between 12 noon and 12:05 P.M. is

$$P(6) = \frac{[2(5)]^6}{6!}e^{-2(5)} = \frac{1,000,000}{720}e^{-10} = 0.0631$$

Interpretation: On about 6 out of every 100 days, exactly 6 cars will arrive between 12:00 noon and 12:05 P.M.

(b) The probability that fewer than 6 cars arrive between 12:00 noon and 12:05 P.M. is

$$P(X < 6) = P(X \le 5)$$

$$= P(0) + P(1) + P(2) + P(3) + P(4) + P(5)$$

$$= \frac{[2(5)]^0}{0!}e^{-2(5)} + \frac{[2(5)]^1}{1!}e^{-2(5)} + \frac{[2(5)]^2}{2!}e^{-2(5)}$$

$$+ \frac{[2(5)]^3}{3!}e^{-2(5)} + \frac{[2(5)]^4}{4!}e^{-2(5)} + \frac{[2(5)]^5}{5!}e^{-2(5)}$$

$$= \frac{1}{1}e^{-10} + \frac{10}{1}e^{-10} + \frac{100}{2}e^{-10} + \frac{1,000}{6}e^{-10} + \frac{10,000}{24}e^{-10} + \frac{100,000}{120}e^{-10}$$

$$= 0.0671$$

Interpretation: On about 7 out of every 100 days, fewer than 6 cars will arrive between 12:00 noon and 12:05 P.M.

(c) The probability that at least 6 cars arrive between 12 noon and 12:05 P.M. is the complement of the probability that fewer than 6 cars arrive between 12 noon and 12:05 P.M. That is,

$$P(X \ge 6) = 1 - P(X < 6) = 1 - P(X \le 5) = 1 - 0.0671 = 0.9329$$

Interpretation: On about 93 out of every 100 days, at least six cars will arrive between 12:00 noon and 12:05 P.M.

Now Work Problem 11

⬧ CAUTION For a Poisson process, at-least and more-than probabilities must be computed by using the Complement Rule.

It is important to recognize that *at-least* and *more-than* probabilities for a Poisson process must be found using the complement. This is because the random variable X in a Poisson process can be any integer greater than or equal to 0.

③ Find the Mean and Standard Deviation of a Poisson Random Variable

If cars arrive at McDonald's at the rate of 2 per minute between 12:00 noon and 1:00 P.M., how many cars would you expect to arrive between 12:00 noon and 12:05 P.M.? Considering that 2 cars arrive every minute (on average) and we are observing the arrival of cars for 5 minutes, it seems reasonable to expect $2(5) = 10$ cars to arrive. Since the expected value of a random variable is the mean of the random variable, it is reasonable that $\mu_X = \lambda t$ for interval t.

Mean and Standard Deviation of a Poisson Random Variable

A random variable X that follows a Poisson process with parameter λ has mean (or expected value) and standard deviation given by the formulas

$$\mu_X = \lambda t \quad \text{and} \quad \sigma_X = \sqrt{\lambda t} = \sqrt{\mu_X}$$

where t is the length of the interval.

Because $\mu_X = \lambda t$, we restate the Poisson probability distribution function in terms of its mean.

Poisson Probability Distribution Function

If X is the number of successes in an interval of fixed length and X follows a Poisson process with mean μ, the probability distribution function for X is

$$P(x) = \frac{\mu^x}{x!}e^{-\mu} \qquad x = 0, 1, 2, 3 \dots.$$

EXAMPLE 3 | **Beetles and the Poisson Distribution**

Problem: A biologist performs an experiment in which 2,000 Asian beetles are allowed to roam in an enclosed area of 1,000 square feet. The area is divided into 200 subsections of 5 square feet each.

(a) Assuming that the beetles spread evenly throughout the enclosed area, how many beetles are expected to be within each subsection?

(b) What is the standard deviation of X, the number of beetles in a particular subsection?

(c) What is the probability of finding exactly 8 beetles in a particular subsection?

(d) Would it be unusual to find more than 16 beetles in a particular subsection?

Approach: If the beetles spread evenly throughout the enclosed region, we can model the distribution of the beetles using Poisson probabilities.

Solution

(a) Assuming the beetles spread evenly throughout the enclosed area, we expect

$$\mu_X = \frac{2,000 \text{ beetles}}{200 \text{ subsections}} = 10 \text{ beetles per subsection}$$

(b) $\sigma_X = \sqrt{\mu_X} = \sqrt{10} \approx 3.2$.

(c) We use the expected value $\mu_X = 10$ in the Poisson probability distribution function to compute the probability of finding exactly 8 beetles in a subsection.

$$P(8) = \frac{10^8}{8!}e^{-10} \qquad P(x) = \frac{\mu^x}{x!}e^{-\mu}, \mu = 10, x = 8$$

$$= 0.1126$$

Note to Instructor

If you wish, you can illustrate these results by computing the mean and standard deviation of a Poisson random variable with $\lambda = 2$ and $t = 5$. Construct the probability distribution and then use the formulas from Section 6.1 to obtain μ_x and σ_x. Compare the results to $\mu_x = \lambda t$ and $\sigma_x = \sqrt{\lambda t}$.

Figure 14

Interpretation: In 100 trials of this experiment, we expect to find 8 beetles in a particular subsection about 11 times.

(d) We compute $P(X > 16)$ using the Poisson probability distribution function, the Complement Rule, and a TI-84 Plus graphing calculator.

$$P(X > 16) = 1 - P(X \leq 16)$$
$$= 1 - 0.9730 \quad \text{\footnotesize See Figure 14.}$$
$$= 0.0270$$

Interpretation: According to the Poisson probability model, there will be more than 16 beetles in a subsection about 3 times in 100. To observe more than 16 beetles in a subsection is rather unusual.

6.3 ASSESS YOUR UNDERSTANDING

Concepts and Vocabulary

1. State the conditions required for a random variable X to follow a Poisson process.

2. Explain the role of λ and t in the Poisson probability formula.

Skill Building   3. $\lambda = 10, t = 5$

In Problems 3–6, state the values of λ and t for each Poisson process.

3. The hits to a website occur at the rate of 10 per minute between 7:00 P.M. and 9:00 P.M. The random variable X is the number of hits to the website between 7:30 P.M. and 7:35 P.M.

4. The phone calls to a computer software help desk occur at the rate of 5 per minute between 3:00 P.M. and 4:00 P.M. The random variable X is the number of phone calls to the help desk between 3:10 P.M. and 3:20 P.M. $\lambda = 5, t = 10$

5. The flaws in a piece of timber occur at the rate of 0.07 per linear foot. The random variable X is the number of flaws in the next 20 linear feet of timber. $\lambda = 0.07, t = 20$

6. The potholes on a major highway in the city of Madison occur at the rate of 3.4 per mile. The random variable X is the number of potholes in 10 miles of randomly selected highway. $\lambda = 3.4, t = 10$

In Problems 7 and 8, the random variable X follows a Poisson process with the given mean.

7. Assuming $\mu = 5$, compute
   (a) $P(6)$ 0.1462
   (b) $P(X < 6)$ 0.6160
   (c) $P(X \geq 6)$ 0.3840
   (d) $P(2 \leq X \leq 4)$ 0.4001

8. Assuming $\mu = 7$, compute
   (a) $P(10)$ 0.0710
   (b) $P(X < 10)$ 0.8305
   (c) $P(X \geq 10)$ 0.1695
   (d) $P(7 \leq X \leq 9)$ 0.3808

In Problems 9 and 10, the random variable X follows a Poisson process with the given value of λ and t.

9. Assuming $\lambda = 0.07$ and $t = 10$, compute
   (a) $P(4)$ 0.0050
   (b) $P(X < 4)$ 0.9942
   (c) $P(X \geq 4)$ 0.0058
   (d) $P(4 \leq X \leq 6)$ 0.0057
   (e) μ_X and σ_X 0.7, 0.8

10. Assuming $\lambda = 0.02$ and $t = 50$, compute
    (a) $P(2)$ 0.1839
    (b) $P(X < 2)$ 0.7358
    (c) $P(X \geq 2)$ 0.2642
    (d) $P(1 \leq X \leq 3)$ 0.6131
    (e) μ_X and σ_X 1, 1

Applying the Concepts

11. **Hits to a Website** The number of hits to a website follows a Poisson process; hits occur at the rate of 1.4 per minute between 7:00 P.M. and 9:00 P.M. Compute the probability that the number of hits to the website between 7:30 P.M. and 7:35 P.M. is
    (a) exactly seven. Interpret the result.   0.1490
    (b) fewer than seven. Interpret the result.   0.4497
    (c) at least seven. Interpret the result.   0.5503

12. **Calls to the Help Desk** The phone calls to a computer software help desk occur at the rate of 2.1 per minute between 3:00 P.M. and 4:00 P.M. Compute the probability that the number of calls to the help desk between 3:10 P.M. and 3:15 P.M. is
    (a) exactly eight. Interpret the result.   0.1009
    (b) fewer than eight. Interpret the result.   0.1785
    (c) at least eight. Interpret the result.   0.8215

13. **Insect Fragments** The Food and Drug Administration sets a Food Defect Action Level (FDAL) for the various foreign substances that inevitably end up in the food we eat and liquids we drink. For example, the FDAL level for insect filth in peanut butter is 0.3 insect fragment (larvae, eggs, body parts, and so on) per gram. Suppose that a supply of peanut butter contains 0.3 insect fragment per gram. Compute the probability that the number of insect fragments in a 5-gram sample of the peanut butter is
    (a) exactly two. Interpret the result.   0.2510
    (b) fewer than two. Interpret the result.   0.5578
    (c) at least two. Interpret the result.   0.4422
    (d) at least one. Interpret the result.   0.7769
    (e) Would it be unusual for a 5-gram sample of this supply of peanut butter to contain four or more insect fragments?   No

14. **Potholes** The potholes on a major highway in the city of Chicago occur at the rate of 3.4 per mile. Compute the probability that the number of potholes over 3 miles of randomly selected highway is   14. (d) No
    (a) exactly seven. Interpret the result.   0.0847
    (b) fewer than seven. Interpret the result.   0.1180
    (c) at least seven. Interpret the result.   0.8820
    (d) Would it be unusual for a randomly selected 3-mile stretch of highway in Chicago to contain more than 15 potholes?

15. **Airline Fatalities** According to the *Statistical Abstract of the United States*, airline fatalities occur at the rate of 0.03 death per 100 million miles (2005 data). Find the probability that, during the next 100 million miles of flight, there will be

(a) exactly zero deaths. Interpret the result.   *0.9704*
(b) at least one death. Interpret the result.   *0.0296*
(c) more than one death. Interpret the result.   *0.0004*

16. **Traffic Fatalities** According to the *Statistical Abstract of the United States*, traffic fatalities occur at the rate of 1.5 deaths per 100 million miles (2005 data). Find the probability that, during the next 100 million vehicle miles, there will be

(a) exactly zero deaths. Interpret the result.   *0.2231*
(b) at least one death. Interpret the result.   *0.7769*
(c) more than one death. Interpret the result.   *0.4422*
(d) Compare these results with the results in Problem 15. Given the choice, would you rather fly or drive?

17. **Florida Hurricanes** From 1900 to 2007 (108 years), Florida suffered 29 direct hits from major (category 3 to 5) hurricanes. Assume that this was typical and the number of hits per year follows a Poisson distribution.

Source: National Hurricane Center   17. (b) 0.2355; no

(a) What is the probability that Florida will not be hit by any major hurricanes in a single year?   *0.7645*
(b) What is the probability that Florida will be hit by at least one major hurricane in a single year? Is this unusual?
(c) What is the probability that Florida will be hit by at least three major hurricanes in a single year, as happened in 2004? Does this indicate that the 2004 hurricane season in Florida was unusual?   *0.0026; yes*
(d) What is the probability that Florida will be hit by at least two major hurricanes in a single year, as happened in 2005? Does this indicate that the 2005 hurricane season in Florida was unusual?   *0.0302; yes*

18. **Police Dispatch** Officer Thompson of the Bay Ridge Police Department works the graveyard shift. He averages 4.5 calls per shift from his dispatcher. Assume the number of calls follows a Poisson distribution. Would it be unusual for Officer Thompson to get fewer than 2 calls in a shift?   *0.0611; no*

19. **Wendy's Drive-Through** Cars arrive at Wendy's drive-through at a rate of 0.2 car per minute between the hours of 11:00 P.M. and 1:00 A.M. on Saturday evening. Wendy's begins an advertising blitz that touts its late-night service. After one week of advertising, Wendy's officials count the number of cars, X, arriving at Wendy's drive-through between the hours of 12:00 midnight and 12:30 A.M. at 200 of its restaurants. The results are shown in the following table:

x (number of cars arriving)	Frequency
1	4
2	5
3	13
4	23
5	25
6	28
7	25
8	27
9	21
10	15
11	5
12	3
13	2
14	2
15	0
16	2

(a) Construct a probability distribution for the random variable X, assuming it follows a Poisson process with $\lambda = 0.2$ and $t = 30$. This is the probability distribution of X before the advertising.
(b) Compute the expected number of restaurants that will have 0 arrivals, 1 arrival, and so on.
(c) Compare these results with the number of arrivals after the advertising. Does it appear the advertising was effective? Why?

20. **Quality Control** A builder ordered two hundred 8-foot grade A 2-by-4s for a construction job. To qualify as a grade A board, each 2-by-4 will have no knots and will average no more than 0.05 imperfection per linear foot. The following table lists the number of imperfections per 2-by-4 in the 200 ordered:

x (number of imperfections)	Frequency
0	124
1	51
2	20
3	5

(a) Construct a probability distribution for the random variable X, the number of imperfections per 8 feet of board, assuming that it follows a Poisson process with $\lambda = 0.05$ and $t = 8$.
(b) Compute the expected number of 2-by-4s that will have 0 imperfections, 1 imperfection, and so on.
(c) Compare these results with the number of actual imperfections. Does it appear the 2-by-4s are of grade A quality? Why?

21. **Prussian Army** In 1898, Ladislaus von Bortkiewicz published *The Law of Small Numbers*, in which he demonstrated the power of the Poisson probability law. Before his publication, the law was used exclusively to approximate binomial probabilities. He demonstrated the law's power, using the number of Prussian cavalry soldiers who were kicked to death by their horses. The Prussian army monitored 10 cavalry corps for 20 years and recorded the number X of annual fatalities due to horse kicks for the 200 observations. The following table shows the data:

Number of Deaths, x	Number of Times x Deaths Were Observed
0	109
1	65
2	22
3	3
4	1

Source: Adapted from *An Introduction to Mathematical Statistics* by Larsen et al., Prentice Hall, Upper Saddle River, NJ, 2001

(a) Compute the proportion of years in which there were 0 deaths, 1 death, 2 deaths, 3 deaths, and 4 deaths.
(b) From the data in the table, what was the mean number of deaths per year?   *0.61*
(c) Use the mean number of deaths per year found in part (b) and the Poisson probability law to determine the theoretical proportion of years that 0 deaths should occur. Repeat this for 1, 2, 3, and 4 deaths.
(d) Compare the observed proportions to the theoretical proportions. Do you think the data can be modeled by the Poisson probability law?

22. **Simulation** Data from the National Center for Health Statistics show that, in 1995, spina bifida occurred at the rate of 28 per 100,000 live births. Let the random variable X represent the number of occurrences of spina bifida in a random sample of 100,000 live births.

   (a) What is the expected number of children with spina bifida per 100,000 live births in any given year? 28

   (b) Using statistical software such as MINITAB, simulate taking 200 random samples of 100,000 live births, assuming $\mu = 28$.

   (c) Approximate the probability that fewer than 18 births per 100,000 result in spina bifida.

   (d) In 2005, 17.96 births per 100,000 resulted in babies born with spina bifida. In light of the results of parts (b) and (c), is this an unusual occurrence? What might you conclude?

23. **Simulation** According to the National Center for Health Statistics, the common cold occurs at the rate of 23.6 colds per 100 people during the course of a year in the 18- to 24-year-old age group. Let the random variable X represent the number of 18- to 24-year-olds out of a sample of 500 who have had a common cold in the past year.

   (a) What is the expected number of colds for every five hundred 18- to 24-year-olds? 118

   (b) Using statistical software, such as MINITAB, simulate taking 100 random samples of size 500 from this population.

   (c) Approximate the probability that at least 150 18- to 24-year-olds in a group of 500 will have experienced a common cold in the past year.

   (d) Approximate the probability that fewer than 100 18- to 24-year-olds in a group of 500 will have experienced the common cold in the past year.

   (e) Given the simulation, compute the mean number of 18- to 24-year-olds out of 500 who have experienced the common cold in the past year.

   (f) Given the simulation, compute the standard deviation of the number of 18- to 24-year-olds out of 500 who have experienced the common cold in the past year.

   (g) Compute the 5-number summary of the data. Did the simulation result in any unusual results?

24. **How Long Do I Have to Wait?** The number of hits to a website follows a Poisson process and occurs at the rate of 10 hits per minute between 7:00 P.M. and 9:00 P.M. How long should you expect to wait before the probability of at least 1 hit to the site is 95%?

   Hint: $P(X \geq 1) = 1 - P(0)$ 0.3 minute

Consumer Reports Quality Assurance in Customer Relations

The Customer Relations Department at Consumers Union (CU) receives thousands of letters and e-mails from customers each month. Some people write asking how well a product performed during CU's testing, some people write sharing their own experiences with their household products, and the remaining people write for an array of other reasons.

To respond to each letter and e-mail that is received, Customer Relations recently upgraded its customer contact database. Although much of the process has been automated, it still requires employees to manually draft the responses. Given the current size of the department, each Customer Relations representative is required to draft approximately 300 responses each month.

As part of a quality assurance program, the Customer Relations manager would like to develop a plan that allows him to evaluate the performance of his employees. From past experience, he knows the probability that a new employee will write an initial draft of a response that contains errors is approximately 10%. The manager would like to know how many of the 300 responses he should sample to have a cost-effective quality assurance program.

(a) Let X be a discrete random variable that represents the number of the $n = 300$ draft responses that contain errors. Describe the probability distribution for X. Be sure to include the name of the probability distribution, possible values for the random variable X, and values of the parameters.

(b) To be effective, the manager would like to have a 95% probability of finding at least one draft document that contains an error. If the probability that a draft document will have errors is known to be 10%, determine the appropriate sample size to satisfy the manager's requirements.

Hint: We are required to find the number of draft documents that must be sampled so that the probability of finding at least one document containing an error is 95%. In other words, we have to determine n by solving: $P(X \geq 1) = 0.95$.

(c) Suppose that the error rate is really 20%. What sample size will the manager have to review to have a 95% probability of finding one or more documents containing an error?

(d) Now let Y be a discrete random variable that represents the number of errors discovered in a single draft document. (It is possible for a single draft to contain more than one error.) The manager determined that errors occurred at the rate of 0.3 error per document. Describe the probability distribution for Y. Be sure to include the name of the probability distribution, possible values for the random variable Y, and values of the parameters.

(e) What is the probability that a document contains no errors? One error? At least two errors?

Note to Readers: *In many cases, our test protocol and analytical methods are more complicated than described in these examples. The data and discussions have been modified to make the material more appropriate for the audience.*

TECHNOLOGY STEP-BY-STEP Computing Poisson Probabilities via Technology

TI-83/84 Plus
Computing P(x)
1. Press 2nd VARS to access the probability distribution menu.
2. Highlight `poissonpdf (` and hit ENTER.
3. With `poissonpdf(` on the HOME screen, type the value of μ, followed by the number of successes, x. For example, with $\mu = 10$ and $x = 4$, type

$$poissonpdf\ (10,4)$$

Then hit ENTER.

Computing P(X ≤ x)
Instead of selecting `poissonpdf(`, select `poissoncdf(`. Everything else is the same.

MINITAB
Computing P(x)
1. Enter the desired values of the random variable X in C1.
2. Select the **CALC** menu, highlight **Probability Distributions**, then highlight **Poisson** ....
3. Select Probability, enter the mean, enter the input column as C1, and select C2 as the output column. Click OK.

Computing P(X ≤ x)
Follow the same steps as those followed for computing $P(x)$. In the window that comes up after selecting Poisson Distribution, select Cumulative probability instead of Probability.

Excel
Computing P(x)
1. Enter the desired values of the random variable X in column A.
2. With the cursor in cell B1, select the *fx* icon. Highlight Statistical in the Function category window. Highlight POISSON in the Function name window.
3. In the cell labeled X, enter A1. In the cell labeled mean, enter the mean. In the cell labeled cumulative, type FALSE. Click OK.

Computing P(X ≤ x)
Follow the same steps as those presented for computing $P(x)$. In the POISSON window, type TRUE in the cumulative cell.

CHAPTER 6 REVIEW

Summary

In this chapter, we discussed discrete probability distributions. A random variable represents the numerical measurement of the outcome from a probability experiment. Discrete random variables have either a finite or a countable number of outcomes. The term *countable* means that the values result from counting. Probability distributions must satisfy the following two criteria: (1) All probabilities must be between 0 and 1, inclusive, and (2) the sum of all probabilities must equal 1. Discrete probability distributions can be presented by a table, graph, or mathematical formula.

The mean and standard deviation of a random variable describe the center and spread of the distribution. The mean of a random variable is also called its expected value.

We discussed two discrete probability distributions in particular, the binomial and Poisson. A probability experiment is considered a binomial experiment if there is a fixed number, n, of independent trials of the experiment with only two outcomes. The probability of success, p, is the same for each trial of the experiment. Special formulas exist for computing the mean and standard deviation of a binomial random variable.

We also discussed the Poisson probability distribution. A Poisson process is one in which the following conditions are met: (1) The probability of two or more successes in any sufficiently small subinterval is 0. (2) The probability of success is the same for any two sufficiently short intervals of equal length. (3) The number of successes in any interval is independent of the number of successes in any other disjoint interval. Special formulas exist for computing the mean and standard deviation of a random variable that follows a Poisson process. For the Poisson distribution, the mean and variance are equal.

Vocabulary

Random variable (p. 331)
Discrete random variable (p. 331)
Continuous random variable (p. 331)
Probability distribution (p. 332)
Probability histogram (p. 333)
Expected value (p. 336)
Binomial experiment (p. 343)
Trial (p. 343)
Binomial random variable (p. 343)
Cumulative distribution function (p. 350)
Poisson process (p. 359)

Formulas

Mean (or Expected Value) of a Discrete Random Variable

$$\mu_X = E(X) = \sum xP(x)$$

Variance of a Discrete Random Variable

$$\sigma_X^2 = \sum (x - \mu_X)^2 \cdot P(x) = \sum [x^2 P(x)] - \mu_X^2$$

Binomial Probability Distribution Function

$$P(x) = {}_nC_x p^x (1 - p)^{n-x}, \quad x = 0, 1, 2, \ldots, n$$

Mean of a Binomial Random Variable

$$\mu_X = np$$

Standard Deviation of a Binomial Random Variable

$$\sigma_X = \sqrt{np(1 - p)}$$

Poisson Probability Distribution Function

$$P(x) = \frac{(\lambda t)^x}{x!} e^{-\lambda t} = \frac{\mu^x}{x!} e^{-\mu}, \quad x = 0, 1, 2, \ldots$$

Mean and Standard Deviation of a Poisson Random Variable

$$\mu_X = \lambda t \qquad \sigma_X = \sqrt{\lambda t} = \sqrt{\mu_X}$$

Objectives

Section	You should be able to . . .	Examples	Review Exercises
6.1	1 Distinguish between discrete and continuous random variables (p. 331)	1	1
	2 Identify discrete probability distributions (p. 332)	2 and 3	2, 3(a)
	3 Construct probability histograms (p. 333)	4	3(b)
	4 Compute and interpret the mean of a discrete random variable (p. 334)	5, 6, and 9	3(c)
	5 Interpret the mean of a discrete random variable as an expected value (p. 336)	7	4
	6 Compute the variance and standard deviation of a discrete random variable (p. 338)	8 and 9	3(d)
6.2	1 Determine whether a probability experiment is a binomial experiment (p. 343)	1	5
	2 Compute probabilities of binomial experiments (p. 345)	2–5	6(a)–(d), 7(a)–(d), 8(a),15
	3 Compute the mean and standard deviation of a binomial random variable (p. 351)	6	6(e), 7(e), 8(b)
	4 Construct binomial probability histograms (p. 351)	7	8(c)
6.3	1 Determine if a probability experiment follows a Poisson process (p. 358)	1	11
	2 Compute probabilities of a Poisson random variable (p. 359)	2 and 3	12(a)–(d), 13, 14
	3 Find the mean and standard deviation of a Poisson random variable (p. 361)	3	12(e)

Review Exercises

1. Determine whether the random variable is discrete or continuous. In each case, state the possible values of the random variable.
   (a) The number of students in a randomly selected elementary school classroom.   Discrete; $s = 0, 1, 2, \ldots$
   (b) The amount of snow that falls in Minneapolis during the winter season.   Continuous; $s \geq 0$
   (c) The flight time accumulated by a randomly selected Air Force fighter pilot.   Continuous; $h \geq 0$
   (d) The number of points scored by the Miami Heat in a randomly selected basketball game.   Discrete; $x = 0, 1, 2, \ldots$

2. Determine whether the distribution is a discrete probability distribution. If not, state why.

(a)

x	P(x)
0	0.34
1	0.21
2	0.13
3	0.04
4	0.01

No; $\sum P(x) = 0.73 \neq 1$

(b)

x	P(x)
0	0.40
1	0.31
2	0.23
3	0.04
4	0.02

Yes

3. **Stanley Cup** The Stanley Cup is a best-of-seven series to determine the champion of the National Hockey League. The following data represent the number of games played, X, in the Stanley Cup before a champion was determined from 1939 to 2007.

   Note: There was no champion in 2005. The season was cancelled due to a labor dispute.

x	Frequency
4	20
5	17
6	17
7	14

Source: Information Please Almanac

   (a) Construct a probability model for the random variable X, the number of games in the Stanley Cup.
   (b) Draw a probability histogram.
   (c) Compute and interpret the mean of the random variable X. $\mu_X = 5.4$
   (d) Compute the standard deviation of the random variable X. $\sigma_X = 1.1$

4. The Carnival A carnival game is played as follows: You draw a card from an ordinary deck. If you draw an ace, you win $5. You win $3 for a face card and $10 for the seven of spades. If you pick anything else, you lose $2. On average, how much money can the operator expect to make per customer? $0.08

5. Determine whether the probability experiment represents a binomial experiment. If not, explain why.

(a) According to the *Chronicle of Higher Education*, there is a 54% probability that a randomly selected incoming freshman will graduate from college within 6 years. Suppose that 10 incoming freshmen are randomly selected. After 6 years, each student is asked whether he or she graduated.   Binomial

(b) An experiment is conducted in which a single die is cast until a 3 comes up. The number of throws required is recorded.   Not binomial

6. High Cholesterol According to the National Center for Health Statistics, 8% of 20- to 34-year-old females have high serum cholesterol. In a random sample of 10 females 20 to 34 years old:

(a) Find the probability that exactly 0 have high serum cholesterol. Interpret this result.   0.4344

(b) Find the probability that exactly 2 have high serum cholesterol. Interpret this result.   0.1478

(c) Find the probability that at least 2 have high serum cholesterol. Interpret this result.   0.1879

(d) Find the probability that exactly 9 *will not* have high serum cholesterol. Interpret this result.   0.3777

(e) In a random sample of 250 females 20 to 34 years old, what is the expected number with high serum cholesterol? What is the standard deviation?   20; 4.3

(f) If a random sample of 250 females 20 to 34 years old resulted in 12 of them having high serum cholesterol, would this be unusual? Why?   No

7. Driving Age According to a Gallup poll conducted December 17–19, 2004, 60% of U.S. women 18 years old or older stated that the minimum driving age should be 18. In a random sample of 15 U.S. women 18 years old or older:

(a) Find the probability that exactly 10 believe that the minimum driving age should be 18.   0.1859

(b) Find the probability that fewer than 5 believe that the minimum driving age should be 18.   0.0093

(c) Find the probability that at least 5 believe that the minimum driving age should be 18.   0.9907

(d) Find the probability that between 7 and 12, inclusive, believe that the minimum driving age should be 18.   0.8779

(e) In a random sample of 200 U.S. women 18 years old or older, what is the expected number who believe that the minimum driving age should be 18? What is the standard deviation? $\mu_X = 120; \sigma_X = 6.9$

(f) If a random sample of 200 U.S. women 18 years old or older resulted in 110 who believe that the minimum driving age should be 18, would this be unusual? Why?   No

8. Consider a binomial probability distribution with parameters $n = 8$ and $p = 0.75$.

(a) Construct a binomial probability distribution with these parameters.

(b) Compute the mean and standard deviation of the distribution. $\mu_X = 6; \sigma_X = 1.2$

(c) Draw the probability histogram, comment on its shape, and label the mean on the histogram.

9. State the condition required to use the Empirical Rule to check for unusual observations in a binomial experiment.

10. In sampling without replacement, the assumption of independence required for a binomial experiment is violated. Under what circumstances can we sample without replacement and still use the binomial probability formula to approximate probabilities?

11. State the conditions required for a Poisson process.

12. The random variable X follows a Poisson process with $\lambda = 0.05$ and $t = 30$. Find each of the following:

(a) $P(2)$ 0.2510

(b) $P(X < 2)$ 0.5578

(c) $P(X \geq 2)$ 0.4422

(d) $P(1 \leq X \leq 3)$ 0.7112

(e) What are μ_X and σ_X?   1.5, 1.2

13. Carpet Flaws The mills at the Acme Carpet Company produce, on average, one flaw in every 500 yards of material they produce; the carpeting is sold in 100-yard rolls. If the number of flaws in a roll follows a Poisson distribution and the quality-control department rejects any roll with two or more flaws, what percent of the rolls is rejected?   1.75%

14. Copier Maintenance The student copy machine in the library requires a maintenance call an average of two times per month. Assuming that the number of required maintenance calls follows a Poisson distribution, would it be unusual for the copy machine to require more than four maintenance calls in any given month? Why or why not?   No

15. Self Injury According to the article "Self-injurious Behaviors in a College Population," 17% of undergraduate or graduate students have had at least one incidence of self-injurious behavior. The researchers conducted a survey of 40 college students who reported a history of emotional abuse and found that 12 of them have had at least one incidence of self-injurious behavior. What do the results of this survey tell you about college students who report a history of emotional abuse?

Source: Janis Whitlock, John Eckenrode, and Daniel Silverman. "Self-injurious Behaviors in a College Population," *Pediatrics* 117: 1939–1948

CHAPTER TEST

1. Determine whether the random variable is discrete or continuous. In each case, state the possible values of the random variable.
   (a) The number of days with measurable rainfall in Honolulu, Hawaii, during a year.   *Discrete:* $r = 0, 1, 2, \ldots, 365$
   (b) The miles per gallon of gasoline obtained by a randomly selected Toyota Prius.   *Continuous;* $m > 0$
   (c) The number of golf balls hit into the ocean on the famous 18th hole at Pebble Beach on a randomly selected Sunday.   *Discrete;* $x = 0, 1, 2, \ldots$
   (d) The weight (in grams) of a randomly selected robin egg.   *Continuous;* $w > 0$

2. Determine whether the distribution is a discrete probability distribution. If not, state why.

   (a)

x	$P(x)$
0	0.324
1	0.121
2	0.247
3	0.206
4	0.102

   Yes

   (b)

x	$P(x)$
0	0.34
1	0.28
2	0.26
3	0.23
4	−0.11

   No; P(4) is negative

3. At the Wimbledon Tennis Championship, to win a match in men's singles a player must win the best of five sets. The following data represent the number of sets played, X, in the men's singles final match for the years 1968 to 2007.

x	Frequency
3	18
4	10
5	12

   Source: www.wimbledon.org

   3. (c) $\mu_X = 3.9$ 3. (d) $\sigma_X = 0.9$

   (a) Construct a probability model for the random variable, X, the number of sets played in the Wimbledon men's singles final match.
   (b) Draw a probability histogram.
   (c) Compute and interpret the mean of the random variable X.
   (d) Compute the standard deviation of the random variable X.

4. A life insurance company sells a $100,000 one-year term life insurance policy to a 35-year-old male for $200. According to the *National Vital Statistics Report*, 56(9), the probability the male survives the year is 0.998725. Compute and interpret the expected value of this policy to the life insurance company.   *$72.50*

5. State the criteria that must be met for an experiment to be a binomial experiment.

6. Determine whether the probability experiment represents a binomial experiment. If not, explain why.
   (a) An urn contains 20 colored golf balls: 8 white, 6 red, 4 blue, and 2 yellow. A child is allowed to draw balls until he gets a yellow one. The number of draws required is recorded.   *Not binomial*
   (b) According to the *Uniform Crime Report, 2006*, 16% of property crimes committed in the United States were cleared by arrest or exceptional means. Twenty-five property crimes from 2006 are randomly selected and the number that was cleared is recorded.   *Binomial*

7. Nielsen Media Research determines ratings for television programs by placing meters on 5,000 televisions throughout the United States. The January 16, 2007, broadcast of *American Idol* resulted in a rating of 20, which means that 20% of households were tuned into the show. In a random sample of 20 households:
   (a) Find the probability that exactly 7 were tuned into the show.   *0.0545*
   (b) Find the probability that fewer than 5 were tuned into the show.   *0.6296*
   (c) Find the probability that at least 3 were tuned into the show.   *0.7939*
   (d) Find the probability that between 5 and 10, inclusive, were tuned into the show.   *0.3698*
   (e) In a random sample of 500 households, what is the expected number that was tuned into the show? What is the standard deviation?   *100; 8.9*
   (f) If a random sample of 500 households resulted in 125 that were tuned into the show, would this be unusual? Why?   *Yes*

8. The drug Zyban is meant to suppress the urge to smoke. In clinical trials, 35% of the study's participants experienced insomnia when taking 300 mg of Zyban per day. In a random sample of 25 users of Zyban:
   Source: GlaxoSmithKline
   (a) Find the probability that exactly 8 will experience insomnia.   *0.1607*
   (b) Find the probability that fewer than 4 will experience insomnia.   *0.0097*
   (c) Find the probability that at least 5 will experience insomnia.   *0.9680*
   (d) Find the probability that exactly 20 *will not* experience insomnia.   *0.0506*
   (e) In a random sample of 1,000 users of Zyban, what is the expected number who experience insomnia? What is the standard deviation?   *350; 15.1*
   (f) If a random sample of 1,000 users of Zyban results in 330 who experience insomnia, would this be unusual? Why?   *No*

9. Consider a binomial probability distribution with parameters $n = 5$ and $p = 0.2$.
   (a) Construct a binomial probability distribution with these parameters.
   (b) Compute the mean and standard deviation of the distribution. $\mu_X = 1$; $\sigma_X = 0.9$
   (c) Draw the probability histogram, comment on its shape, and label the mean on the histogram.

10. The random variable X follows a Poisson process with $\lambda = 0.05$ and $t = 8$. Find each of the following:
    (a) $P(3)$ *0.0072*
    (b) $P(X < 3)$ *0.9921*

(c) $P(X \geq 3)$ *0.0079*
(d) $P(3 \leq X \leq 5)$ *0.0079*
(e) What are μ_X and σ_X?   *0.4; 0.6*

11. The number of cars that arrive at a bank's drive-through window between 3:00 P.M. and 6:00 P.M. on Friday follows a Poisson process at the rate of 0.41 car every minute. Compute the probability that the number of cars that arrive at the bank between 4:00 P.M. and 4:10 P.M. is

(a) exactly four cars. Interpret this result.   *0.1951*
(b) fewer than four cars. Interpret this result.   *0.4142*
(c) at least four cars. Interpret this result.   *0.5858*
(d) What is the number of cars expected to arrive during this time?   *4.1*
(e) What is the standard deviation of the random variable X, the number of cars arriving between 4:00 P.M. and 4:10 P.M.?   *2.0*

◤ MAKING AN INFORMED DECISION

Should We Convict?

A woman who was shopping in Los Angeles had her purse stolen by a young, blonde female who was wearing a ponytail. The blonde female got into a yellow car that was driven by a black male who had a mustache and a beard. The police located a blonde female named Janet Collins who wore her hair in a ponytail and had a friend who was a black male who had a mustache and beard and also drove a yellow car. The police arrested the two subjects.

Because there were no eyewitnesses and no real evidence, the prosecution used probability to make its case against the defendants. The following probabilities were presented by the prosecution for the known characteristics of the thieves.

Characteristic	Probability
Yellow car	$\frac{1}{10}$
Man with a mustache	$\frac{1}{4}$
Woman with a ponytail	$\frac{1}{10}$
Woman with blonde hair	$\frac{1}{3}$
Black man with beard	$\frac{1}{10}$
Interracial couple in car	$\frac{1}{1,000}$

(a) Assuming that the characteristics listed are independent of each other, what is the probability that a randomly selected couple has all these characteristics? That is, what is P ("yellow car" and "man

with a mustache" and … and "interracial couple in a car")?
(b) Would you convict the defendants based on this probability? Why?
(c) Now let n represent the number of couples in the Los Angeles area who could have committed the crime. Let p represent the probability that a randomly selected couple has all six characteristics listed. Let the random variable X represent the number of couples who have all the characteristics listed in the table. Assuming that the random variable X follows the binomial probability function, we have

$$P(x) = {}_nC_x \cdot p^x (1-p)^{n-x}, \quad x = 0, 1, 2, \dots, n$$

Assuming that there are $n = 1{,}000{,}000$ couples in the Los Angeles area, what is the probability that more than one of them has the characteristics listed in the table? Does this result cause you to change your mind regarding the defendants' guilt?
(d) Now let's look at this case from a different point of view. We will compute the probability that more than one couple has the characteristics described, given that at least one couple has the characteristics.

$$\begin{aligned} P(X > 1 \mid X \geq 1) &= \frac{P(X > 1 \text{ and } X \geq 1)}{P(X \geq 1)} \\ &= \frac{P(X > 1)}{P(X \geq 1)} \quad \text{Conditional Probability Rule} \end{aligned}$$

Compute this probability, assuming that $n = 1{,}000{,}000$. Compute this probability again, but this time assume that $n = 2{,}000{,}000$. Do you think that the couple should be convicted "beyond all reasonable doubt"? Why?

Throughout the picturesque valleys of mid-18th-century Germany echoed the song of the *Neuländer* (newlander). Their song enticed journeymen who struggled to feed their families with the dream and promise of colonial America. Traveling throughout the German countryside, the typical *Neuländer* sought to sign up several families from a village for immigration to a particular colony. By registering a group of neighbors, rather than isolated families, the agent increased the likelihood that his signees would not stray to the equally enticing proposals of a competitor. Additionally, by signing large groups, the *Neuländer* fattened his purse, to the tune of one to two florins a head.

Generally, the Germans who chose to undertake the hardship of a trans-Atlantic voyage were poor, yet the cost of such a voyage was high. Records from a 1753 voyage indicate that the cost of an adult fare (one freight) from Rotterdam to Boston was 7.5 pistole. Children between the ages of 4 and 13 were assessed at half the adult rate (one-half freight). Children under 4 were not charged. To get a sense of the expense involved, it has been estimated that the adult fare, 7.5 pistoles, is equivalent to approximately $2,000! For a large family, the cost could easily be well beyond their means. Even though many immigrants did not have the necessary funds to purchase passage, they were determined to make the crossing. Years of indentured servitude for themselves and other family members were often the currency of last resort.

As a historian studying the influence of these German immigrants on colonial America, Hans Langenscheidt is interested in describing various demographic characteristics of these people. Unfortunately, accurate records are rare. In his research, he has discovered a partially reconstructed 1752 passenger list for a ship, the *St. Andrew*. This list contains the names of the heads of families, a list of family members traveling with them, their parish of origin, and the number of freights each family purchased. Unfortunately, some data are missing for some families. Langenscheidt believes that the demographic parameters of this passenger list are likely to be similar to those of the other numerous voyages taken from Germany to America during the mid-eighteenth century. Assuming that he is correct, he believes that it is appropriate to create a discrete probability distribution for a number of demographic variables for this population of German immigrants. His distributions are presented next.

Probability Distribution of the Number of Families per Parish of German Immigrants on Board the 1752 Voyage of the *St. Andrew*	
Number of Families per Parish	**Probability**
1	0.706
2	0.176
3	0.000
4	0.059
5	0.000
6	0.059

Probability Distribution of the Known Number of Freights Purchased by the German Families on Board the 1752 Voyage of the *St. Andrew*	
Number of Freights	Probability
1.0	0.075
1.5	0.025
2.0	0.425
2.5	0.150
3.0	0.125
3.5	0.100
4.0	0.050
5.0	0.025
6.0	0.025

Probability Distribution of the Known Number of People in a Family for the Germans on Board the 1752 Voyage of the *St. Andrew*	
Number in Family	Probability
1	0.322
2	0.186
3	0.136
4	0.102
5	0.051
6	0.136
7	0.034
8	0.017
9	0.016

Source: Wilford W. Whitaker and Gary T. Horlacher, *Broad Bay Pioneers* (Rockport, Maine: Picton Press, 1998), 63–68. Distributions created from the partially reconstructed 1752 passenger list of the *St. Andrew* presented by Whitaker and Horlacher.

1. Using the information provided, describe, through histograms and numerical summaries such as the mean and standard deviation, each probability distribution.

2. Does it appear that, on average, the Neuländers were successful in signing more than one family from a parish? Does it seem likely that most of the families knew one another prior to undertaking the voyage? Explain your answers for both questions.

3. Using the mean number of freights purchased per family, estimate the average cost of the crossing for a family in pistoles and in U.S. dollars.

4. Is it appropriate to estimate the average cost of the voyage from the mean family size? Why or why not?

5. Langenscheidt came across a fragment of another ship's passenger list. This fragment listed information for six families. Of these six, five families purchased more than four freights. Using the information contained in the appropriate probability distribution for the *St. Andrew*, calculate the probability that at least five of six German immigrant families purchased more than four freights. Does it seem likely that these families came from a population similar to that of the Germans on board the *St. Andrew*? Explain.

6. Summarize your findings in a report. Discuss any assumptions made throughout this analysis. What are the consequences to your calculations and conclusions if your assumptions are subsequently determined to be invalid?

7 The Normal Probability Distribution

Outline

7.1 Properties of the Normal Distribution

7.2 The Standard Normal Distribution

7.3 Applications of the Normal Distribution

7.4 Assessing Normality

7.5 The Normal Approximation to the Binomial Probability Distribution

MAKING AN INFORMED DECISION

You are interested in starting your own MENSA-type club. To qualify for the club, the potential member must have intelligence that is in the top 20% of all people. You must decide the baseline score that allows an individual to qualify. See the Decisions project on page 421.

PUTTING IT TOGETHER

In Chapter 6, we introduced discrete probability distributions and, in particular, the binomial probability distribution. We computed probabilities for this discrete distribution using its probability distribution function.

However, we could also determine the probability of any discrete random variable from its probability histogram. For example, the figure shows the probability histogram for the binomial random variable X with $n = 5$ and $p = 0.35$.

From the probability histogram, we can see $P(1) \approx 0.31$. Notice that the width of each rectangle in the probability histogram is 1. Since the area of a rectangle equals height times width, we can think of $P(1)$ as the area of the rectangle corresponding to $x = 1$. Thinking of probability in this fashion makes the transition from computing discrete probabilities to continuous probabilities much easier.

In this chapter, we discuss two continuous distributions, the *uniform distribution* and the *normal distribution*. The greater part of the discussion will focus on the normal distribution, which has many uses and applications.

Binomial Probability Histogram; $n = 5, p = 0.35$

7.1 PROPERTIES OF THE NORMAL DISTRIBUTION

Preparing for This Section   Before getting started, review the following:

- Continuous variable (Section 1.1, p. 8)
- The Empirical Rule (Section 3.2, pp. 150–152)
- *z*-score (Section 3.4, pp. 167–168)
- Rules for a discrete probability distribution (Section 6.1, p. 332)

Objectives

1 Utilize the uniform probability distribution

2 Graph a normal curve

3 State the properties of the normal curve

4 Explain the role of area in the normal density function

5 Describe the relation between a normal random variable and a standard normal random variable

---

1 **Utilize the Uniform Probability Distribution**

We illustrate a uniform distribution using an example. Using the uniform distribution makes it easy to see the relation between area and probability.

EXAMPLE 1   **The Uniform Distribution**

Note to Instructor

If you like, you can print out and distribute the Preparing for This Section quiz located in the Instructor's Resource Center. The purpose of the quiz is to verify that the students have the prerequisite knowledge for the section

Note to Instructor

To help students understand the relation between area and probability, we begin with a discussion of the uniform distribution. The graph of the uniform distribution is a rectangle. Tell students that we will be using the concept of area in this section and that the area of a rectangle is length times width.

Imagine that a friend of yours is always late. Let the random variable X represent the time from when you are supposed to meet your friend until he shows up. Further suppose that your friend could be on time ($x = 0$) or up to 30 minutes late ($x = 30$), with all intervals of equal time between $x = 0$ and $x = 30$ being equally likely. For example, your friend is just as likely to be from 3 to 4 minutes late as he is to be 25 to 26 minutes late. The random variable X can be any value in the interval from 0 to 30, that is, $0 \leq x \leq 30$. Because any two intervals of equal length between 0 and 30, inclusive, are equally likely, the random variable X is said to follow a **uniform probability distribution**.

When we compute probabilities for discrete random variables, we usually substitute the value of the random variable into a formula.

Things are not as easy for continuous random variables. Since an infinite number of outcomes are possible for continuous random variables, the probability of observing a particular value of a continuous random variable is zero. For example, the probability that your friend is exactly 12.9438823 minutes late is zero. This result is based on the fact that classical probability is found by dividing the number of ways an event can occur by the total number of possibilities. There is one way to observe 12.9438823, and there are an infinite number of possible values between 0 and 30, so we get a probability that is zero. To resolve this problem, we compute probabilities of continuous random variables over an interval of values. For example, we might compute the probability that your friend is between 10 and 15 minutes late. To find probabilities for continuous random variables, we use *probability density functions*.

Definition   A **probability density function (pdf)** is an equation used to compute probabilities of continuous random variables. It must satisfy the following two properties:

1. The total area under the graph of the equation over all possible values of the random variable must equal 1.

2. The height of the graph of the equation must be greater than or equal to 0 for all possible values of the random variable. That is, the graph of the equation must lie on or above the horizontal axis for all possible values of the random variable.

Property 1 is similar to the rule for discrete probability distributions that stated the sum of the probabilities must add up to 1. Property 2 is similar to the rule that stated all probabilities must be greater than or equal to 0.

Figure 1 illustrates the properties for the example about your friend who is always late. Since all possible values of the random variable between 0 and 30 are equally likely, the graph of the probability density function for uniform random variables is a rectangle. Because the random variable is any number between 0 and 30 inclusive, the width of the rectangle is 30. Since the area under the graph of the probability density function must equal 1, and the area of a rectangle equals height times width, the height of the rectangle must be $\frac{1}{30}$.

Figure 1

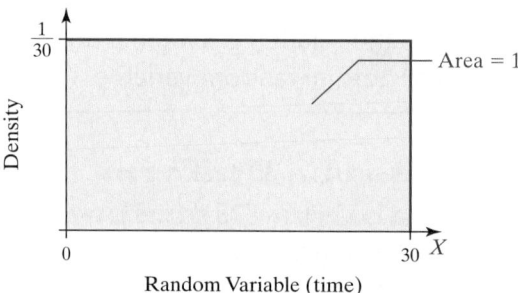

A pressing question remains: How do we use density functions to find probabilities of continuous random variables?

> The area under the graph of a density function over an interval represents the probability of observing a value of the random variable in that interval.

The following example illustrates this statement.

EXAMPLE 2 **Area as a Probability**

Problem: Refer to the situation presented in Example 1. What is the probability that your friend will be between 10 and 20 minutes late the next time you meet him?

Approach: Figure 1 presented the graph of the density function. We need to find the area under the graph between 10 and 20 minutes.

Solution: Figure 2 presents the graph of the density function with the area we wish to find shaded in green.

Figure 2

The width of the shaded rectangle is 10 and its height is $\frac{1}{30}$. Therefore, the area between 10 and 20 is $10\left(\frac{1}{30}\right) = \frac{1}{3}$. The probability that your friend is between 10 and 20 minutes late is $\frac{1}{3}$.

Now Work Problem 13

We introduced the uniform density function so that we could associate probability with area. We are now better prepared to discuss the most frequently used continuous distribution, the normal distribution.

Figure 3

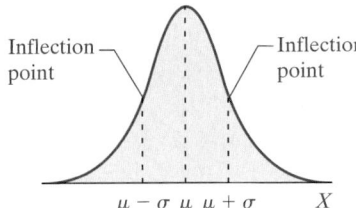

2 Graph a Normal Curve

Many continuous random variables, such as IQ scores, birth weights of babies, or weights of M&Ms, have relative frequency histograms that have a shape similar to Figure 3. Relative frequency histograms that have a shape similar to Figure 3 are said to have the shape of a **normal curve**.

Definition

A continuous random variable is **normally distributed,** or has a **normal probability distribution,** if the relative frequency histogram of the random variable has the shape of a normal curve.

Figure 4

Inflection point — — Inflection point

$\mu - \sigma \;\; \mu \;\; \mu + \sigma \qquad X$

Figure 4 shows a normal curve, demonstrating the roles that μ and σ play in drawing the curve. For any distribution, the mode represents the "high point" of the graph of the distribution. The median represents the point where 50% of the area under the distribution is to the left and 50% of the area under the distribution is to the right. The mean represents the balancing point of the graph of the distribution (see Figure 2 on page 131 in Section 3.1). For symmetric distributions with a single peak, such as the normal distribution, the mean = median = mode. Because of this, the mean, μ, is the high point of the graph of the distribution.

The points at $x = \mu - \sigma$ and $x = \mu + \sigma$ are the *inflection points* on the normal curve. The **inflection points** are the points on the curve where the curvature of the graph changes. To the left of $x = \mu - \sigma$ and to the right of $x = \mu + \sigma$, the curve is drawn upward $\left(\diagup \text{ or } \diagdown \right)$. In between $x = \mu - \sigma$ and $x = \mu + \sigma$, the curve is drawn downward $\left(\frown \right)$.*

Figure 5 shows how changes in μ and σ change the position or shape of a normal curve. In Figure 5(a), two normal density curves are drawn with the location of the inflection points labeled. One density curve has $\mu = 0, \sigma = 1$, and the other has $\mu = 3, \sigma = 1$. We can see that increasing the mean from 0 to 3 caused the graph to shift three units to the right but maintained its shape. In Figure 5(b), two normal density curves are drawn, again with the inflection points labeled. One density curve has $\mu = 0, \sigma = 1$, and the other has $\mu = 0, \sigma = 2$. We can see that increasing the standard deviation from 1 to 2 causes the graph to become flatter and more spread out but maintained its location of center.

Historical Note

Karl Pearson coined the phrase *normal curve*. He did not do this to imply that a distribution that is not normal is *abnormal*. Rather, Pearson wanted to avoid giving the name of the distribution a proper name, such as Gaussian (as in Carl Friedrich Gauss).

Figure 5

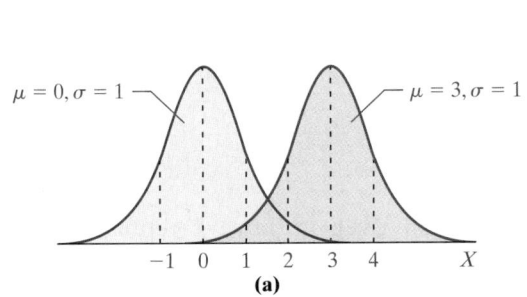

$\mu = 0, \sigma = 1$ — — $\mu = 3, \sigma = 1$

$$-1 \quad 0 \quad 1 \quad 2 \quad 3 \quad 4 \qquad X$$
(a)

$\mu = 0, \sigma = 1$

$\mu = 0, \sigma = 2$

$$-6 \quad -4 \quad -2 \quad 0 \quad 2 \quad 4 \quad 6 \qquad X$$
(b)

Now Work Problem 25

*The vertical scale on the graph, which indicates density, is purposely omitted. The vertical scale, while important, will not play a role in any of the computations using this curve.

3 **State the Properties of the Normal Curve**

The normal probability density function satisfies all the requirements that are necessary to have a probability distribution. We list the properties of the normal density curve next.

Properties of the Normal Density Curve

1. It is symmetric about its mean, μ.

2. Because mean = median = mode, there is a single peak and the highest point occurs at $x = \mu$.

3. It has inflection points at $\mu - \sigma$ and $\mu + \sigma$.

4. The area under the curve is 1.

5. The area under the curve to the right of μ equals the area under the curve to the left of μ, which equals $\frac{1}{2}$.

6. As x increases without bound (gets larger and larger), the graph approaches, but never reaches, the horizontal axis. As x decreases without bound (gets larger and larger in the negative direction), the graph approaches, but never reaches, the horizontal axis.

7. The Empirical Rule: Approximately 68% of the area under the normal curve is between $x = \mu - \sigma$ and $x = \mu + \sigma$. Approximately 95% of the area under the normal curve is between $x = \mu - 2\sigma$ and $x = \mu + 2\sigma$. Approximately 99.7% of the area under the normal curve is between $x = \mu - 3\sigma$ and $x = \mu + 3\sigma$. See Figure 6.

Figure 6

Normal Distribution

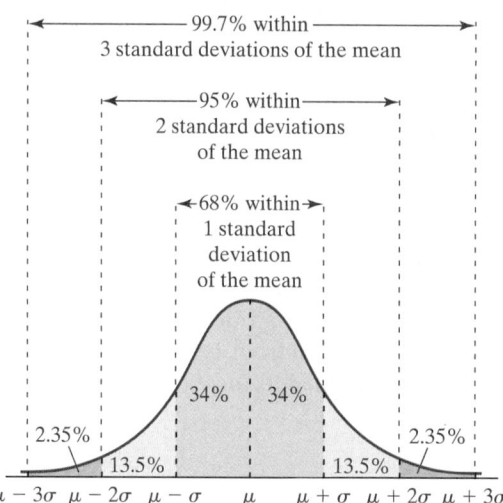

4 **Explain the Role of Area in the Normal Density Function**

Let's look at an example of a normally distributed random variable.

EXAMPLE 3   **A Normal Random Variable**

Problem: The relative frequency distribution given in Table 1 represents the heights of a pediatrician's 200 three-year-old female patients. The raw data indicate that the mean height of the patients is $\mu = 38.72$ inches with standard deviation $\sigma = 3.17$ inches.

(a) Draw a relative frequency histogram of the data. Comment on the shape of the distribution.

Table 1

Height (Inches)	Relative Frequency
29.0–29.9	0.005
30.0–30.9	0.005
31.0–31.9	0.005
32.0–32.9	0.025
33.0–33.9	0.02
34.0–34.9	0.055
35.0–35.9	0.075
36.0–36.9	0.09
37.0–37.9	0.115
38.0–38.9	0.15
39.0–39.9	0.12
40.0–40.9	0.11
41.0–41.9	0.07
42.0–42.9	0.06
43.0–43.9	0.035
44.0–44.9	0.025
45.0–45.9	0.025
46.0–46.9	0.005
47.0–47.9	0.005

(b) Draw a normal curve with $\mu = 38.72$ inches and $\sigma = 3.17$ inches on the relative frequency histogram. Compare the area of the rectangle for heights between 40 and 40.9 inches to the area under the normal curve for heights between 40 and 40.9 inches.

Approach

(a) Draw the relative frequency histogram. If the histogram is shaped like Figure 3, we say that height is approximately normal. We say "approximately normal," rather than "normal," because the normal curve is an "idealized" description of the data, and data rarely follow the curve exactly.

(b) Draw the normal curve on the histogram with the high point at μ and the inflection points at $\mu - \sigma$ and $\mu + \sigma$. Shade the rectangle corresponding to heights between 40 and 40.9 inches, and compare the area of the shaded region to the area under the normal curve between 40 and 40.9.

Solution

(a) Figure 7 shows the relative frequency distribution. The relative frequency histogram is symmetric and bell-shaped.

Figure 7

(b) In Figure 8, the normal curve with $\mu = 38.72$ and $\sigma = 3.17$ is superimposed on the relative frequency histogram. The figure demonstrates that the normal curve describes the heights of 3-year-old females fairly well. We conclude that the heights of 3-year-old females are approximately normal with $\mu = 38.72$ and $\sigma = 3.17$.

Figure 8 also shows the rectangle corresponding to heights between 40 and 40.9 inches. The area of this rectangle represents the proportion of 3-year-old females between 40 and 40.9 inches. Notice that the area of this shaded region is very close to the area under the normal curve for the same region, so we can use the area under the normal curve to approximate the proportion of 3-year-old females with heights between 40 and 40.9 inches!

Figure 8

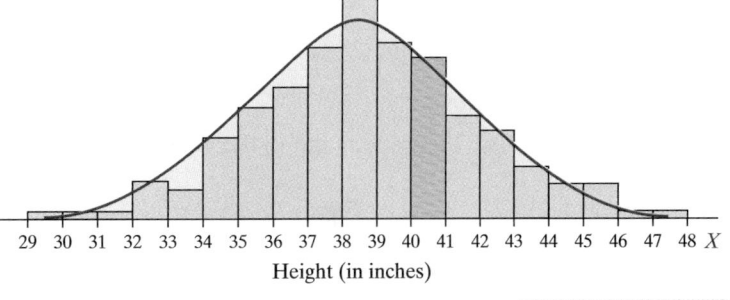

In Other Words
Models are not always mathematical. For example, a map can be thought of as a model of a highway system. The model does not show every detail of the highway system (such as traffic lights), but it does serve the purpose of describing how to get from point A to point B. Mathematical models do the same thing: They make assumptions to simplify the mathematics, while still trying to accomplish the goal of accurately describing reality.

The normal curve drawn in Figure 8 is a *model*. In mathematics, a **model** is an equation, table, or graph that is used to describe reality. The normal distribution, or normal curve, is a model that is used to describe variables that are approximately normally distributed. For example, the normal curve drawn in Figure 8 does a good job of describing the observed distribution of heights of 3-year-old females.

The equation (model) that is used to determine the probability of a continuous random variable is called a **probability density function** (or **pdf**). The **normal probability density function** is given by

$$y = \frac{1}{\sigma\sqrt{2\pi}} e^{\frac{-(x-\mu)^2}{2\sigma^2}} = \frac{1}{\sigma\sqrt{2\pi}} e^{-\frac{1}{2}\left(\frac{x-\mu}{\sigma}\right)^2}$$

where μ is the mean and σ is the standard deviation of the normal random variable. This equation represents the normal distribution. Don't feel threatened by this equation, because we will not be using it in this text. Instead, we will use the normal distribution in graphical form by drawing the normal curve, as we did in Figure 5.

We now summarize the role area plays in the normal curve.

Area under a Normal Curve

Suppose that a random variable X is normally distributed with mean μ and standard deviation σ. The area under the normal curve for any interval of values of the random variable X represents either

- the proportion of the population with the characteristic described by the interval of values or
- the probability that a randomly selected individual from the population will have the characteristic described by the interval of values.

EXAMPLE 4 **Interpreting the Area under a Normal Curve**

Problem: The serum total cholesterol for males 20 to 29 years old is approximately normally distributed with mean $\mu = 180$ and $\sigma = 36.2$, based on data obtained from the National Health and Nutrition Examination Survey.

(a) Draw a normal curve with the parameters labeled.

(b) An individual with total cholesterol greater than 200 is considered to have high cholesterol. Shade the region under the normal curve to the right of $x = 200$.

(c) Suppose that the area under the normal curve to the right of $x = 200$ is 0.2903. (You will learn how to find this area in Section 7.3.) Provide two interpretations of this result.

Approach

(a) Draw the normal curve with the mean $\mu = 180$ labeled at the high point and the inflection points at $\mu - \sigma = 180 - 36.2 = 143.8$ and $\mu + \sigma = 180 + 36.2 = 216.2$.

(b) Shade the region under the normal curve to the right of $x = 200$.

(c) The two interpretations of this shaded region are (1) the proportion of 20- to 29-year-old males who have high cholesterol and (2) the probability that a randomly selected 20- to 29-year-old male has high cholesterol.

Solution

(a) Figure 9(a) shows the graph of the normal curve.

Figure 9

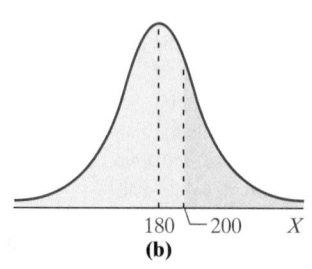

143.8 180 216.2 X
(a)

180 200 X
(b)

Historical Note

The normal probability distribution is often referred to as the Gaussian distribution in honor of Carl Gauss, the individual thought to have discovered the idea. However, it was actually Abraham de Moivre who first wrote down the equation of the normal distribution. Gauss was born in Brunswick, Germany, on April 30, 1777. Mathematical prowess was evident early in Gauss's life. At age 8 he was able to instantly add the first 100 integers. In 1799, Gauss earned his doctorate. The subject of his dissertation was the Fundamental Theorem of Algebra. In 1809, Gauss published a book on the mathematics of planetary orbits. In this book, he further developed the theory of least-squares regression by analyzing the errors. The analysis of these errors led to the discovery that errors follow a normal distribution. Gauss was considered to be "glacially cold" as a person and had troubled relationships with his family. Gauss died on February 23, 1855.

(b) Figure 9(b) shows the region under the normal curve to the right of $x = 200$ shaded.

(c) The two interpretations for the area of this shaded region are (1) the proportion of 20- to 29-year-old males that have high cholesterol is 0.2903 and (2) the probability that a randomly selected 20- to 29-year-old male has high cholesterol is 0.2903.

Now Work Problems 29 and 33

 Describe the Relation between a Normal Random Variable and a Standard Normal Random Variable

At this point, we know that a random variable X is approximately normally distributed if its relative frequency histogram has the shape of a normal curve. We use a normal random variable with mean μ and standard deviation σ to model the distribution of X. The area below the normal curve (model of X) represents the proportion of the population with a given characteristic or the probability that a randomly selected individual from the population will have a given characteristic.

Note to Instructor

The material in Objective 5 can be skipped if you only plan on using technology to find areas under normal curves.

The question now becomes, "How do I find the area under the normal curve?" Finding the area under a curve requires techniques introduced in calculus, which are beyond the scope of this text. An alternative would be to use a series of tables to find areas. However, this would result in an infinite number of tables being created for each possible mean and standard deviation!

A solution to the problem lies in the z-score. Recall that the z-score allows us to transform a random variable X with mean μ and standard deviation σ into a random variable Z with mean 0 and standard deviation 1.

Standardizing a Normal Random Variable

Suppose that the random variable X is normally distributed with mean μ and standard deviation σ. Then the random variable

$$Z = \frac{X - \mu}{\sigma}$$

is normally distributed with mean $\mu = 0$ and standard deviation $\sigma = 1$. The random variable Z is said to have the **standard normal distribution**.

This result is powerful! We need only one table of areas corresponding to the standard normal distribution. If a normal random variable has mean different from 0 or standard deviation different from 1, we transform the normal random variable into a standard normal random variable Z, and then we use a table to find the area and, therefore, the probability.

In Other Words

To find the area under any normal curve, we first find the z-score of the normal random variable. Then we use a table to find the area.

We demonstrate the idea behind standardizing a normal random variable in the next example.

EXAMPLE 5   **Relation between a Normal Random Variable and a Standard Normal Random Variable**

Problem: The heights of a pediatrician's 200 three-year-old female patients are approximately normal with mean $\mu = 38.72$ inches and $\sigma = 3.17$ inches. We wish to demonstrate that the area under the normal curve between 35 and 38 inches is equal to the area under the standard normal curve between the z-scores corresponding to heights of 35 and 38 inches.

Approach

Step 1: Draw a normal curve and shade the area representing the proportion of 3-year-old females between 35 and 38 inches tall.

Step 2: Standardize the values $x = 35$ and $x = 38$ using

$$z = \frac{x - \mu}{\sigma}$$

Step 3: Draw the standard normal curve with the standardized values of $x = 35$ and $x = 38$ labeled. Shade the area that represents the proportion of 3-year-old females between 35 and 38 inches tall. Comment on the relation between the two shaded regions.

Solution

Step 1: Figure 10(a) shows the normal curve with mean $\mu = 38.72$ and $\sigma = 3.17$. The region between $x = 35$ and $x = 38$ is shaded.

Step 2: With $\mu = 38.72$ and $\sigma = 3.17$, the standardized version of $x = 35$ is

$$z = \frac{x - \mu}{\sigma} = \frac{35 - 38.72}{3.17} = -1.17$$

The standardized version of $x = 38$ is

> **CAUTION**
> Recall that we round z-scores to two decimal places.

$$z = \frac{x - \mu}{\sigma} = \frac{38 - 38.72}{3.17} = -0.23$$

Step 3: Figure 10(b) shows the standard normal curve with the region between $z = -1.17$ and $z = -0.23$ shaded.

Figure 10

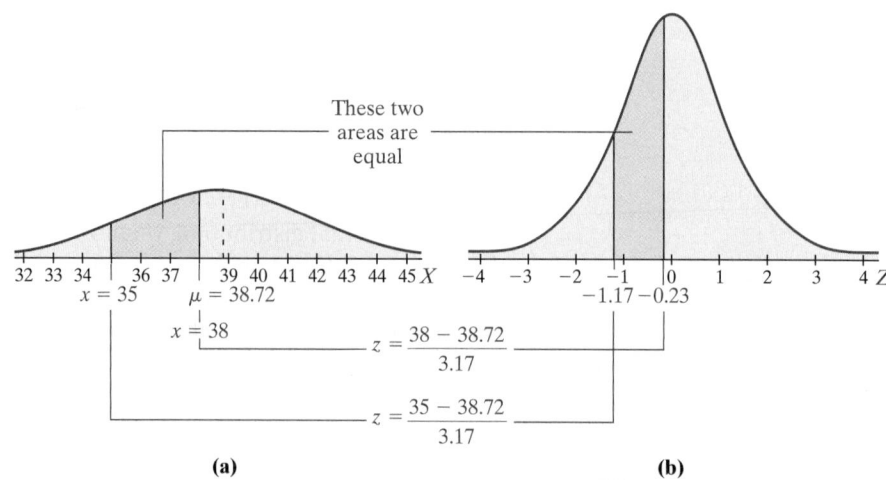

(a)   (b)

The area under the normal curve with $\mu = 38.72$ inches and $\sigma = 3.17$ inches bounded to the left by $x = 35$ and bounded to the right by $x = 38$ is equal to the area under the standard normal curve bounded to the left by $z = -1.17$ and bounded to the right by $z = -0.23$.

Now Work Problem 35

7.1 ASSESS YOUR UNDERSTANDING

Concepts and Vocabulary

1. State the two characteristics of the graph of a probability density function.

2. To find the probabilities for continuous random variables, we do not use probability _distribution_ functions, but instead we use probability _density_ functions.

3. Provide two interpretations of the area under the graph of a probability density function.

4. Why do we standardize normal random variables to find the area under any normal curve?

5. The points at $x = \underline{\mu - \sigma}$ and $x = \underline{\mu + \sigma}$ are the inflection points on the normal curve.

6. As σ increases, the normal density curve becomes more spread out. Knowing that the area under the density curve must be 1, what effect does increasing σ have on the height of the curve?

For Problems 7–12, determine whether the graph can represent a normal density function. If it cannot, explain why.

7. No

8. Yes

9. No

10. No

11. Yes

12. No

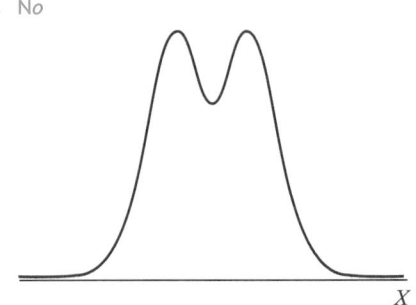

Skill Building

Problems 13–16 use the information presented in Examples 1 and 2.

13. **NW** Find the probability that your friend is between 5 and 10 minutes late. 1/6

14. Find the probability that your friend is between 15 and 25 minutes late. 1/3

15. Find the probability that your friend is at least 20 minutes late. 1/3

16. Find the probability that your friend is no more than 5 minutes late. 1/6

17. **Uniform Distribution** The random-number generator on calculators randomly generates a number between 0 and 1. The random variable X, the number generated, follows a uniform probability distribution.

    (a) Draw the graph of the uniform density function.
    (b) What is the probability of generating a number between 0 and 0.2? 0.2
    (c) What is the probability of generating a number between 0.25 and 0.6? 0.35
    (d) What is the probability of generating a number greater than 0.95? 0.05
    (e) Use your calculator or statistical software to randomly generate 200 numbers between 0 and 1. What proportion of the numbers are between 0 and 0.2? Compare the result with part (b).

18. Uniform Distribution The reaction time X (in minutes) of a certain chemical process follows a uniform probability distribution with $5 \leq X \leq 10$.

(a) Draw the graph of the density curve.

(b) What is the probability that the reaction time is between 6 and 8 minutes?   2/5

(c) What is the probability that the reaction time is between 5 and 8 minutes?   3/5

(d) What is the probability that the reaction time is less than 6 minutes?   1/5

In Problems 19–22, determine whether or not the histogram indicates that a normal distribution could be used as a model for the variable.

19. Birth Weights The following relative frequency histogram represents the birth weights (in grams) of babies whose term was 36 weeks.   Normal

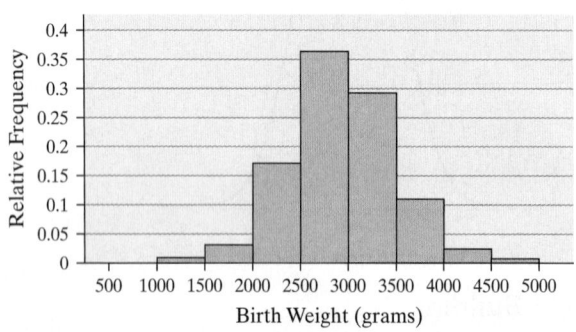

Birth Weights of Babies Whose Term Was 36 Weeks

20. Waiting in Line The following relative frequency histogram represents the waiting times in line (in minutes) for the Demon Roller Coaster for 2000 randomly selected people on a Saturday afternoon in the summer.   Not normal

Waiting Time for the Demon Roller Coaster

21. Length of Phone Calls The following relative frequency histogram represents the length of phone calls on my wife's cell phone during the month of September.   Not normal

Length of Phone Calls

22. Incubation Times The following relative frequency histogram represents the incubation times of a random sample of Rhode Island Red hens' eggs.   Normal

Rhode Island Red Hen Incubation Times

23. One graph in the following figure represents a normal distribution with mean $\mu = 10$ and standard deviation $\sigma = 3$. The other graph represents a normal distribution with mean $\mu = 10$ and standard deviation $\sigma = 2$. Determine which graph is which and explain how you know.
A: $\mu = 10, \sigma = 2$; B: $\mu = 10, \sigma = 3$

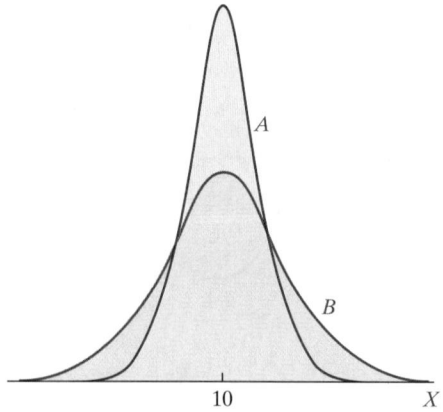

24. One graph in the following figure represents a normal distribution with mean $\mu = 8$ and standard deviation $\sigma = 2$. The other graph represents a normal distribution with mean $\mu = 14$ and standard deviation $\sigma = 2$. Determine which graph is which and explain how you know.
A: $\mu = 8, \sigma = 2$; B: $\mu = 14, \sigma = 2$

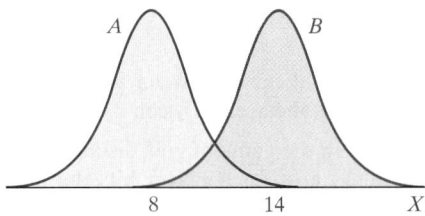

In Problems 25–28, the graph of a normal curve is given. Use the graph to identify the value of μ and σ.

25. μ = 2, σ = 3
NW

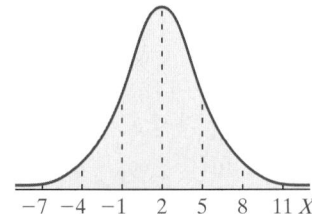

26. μ = 5, σ = 2

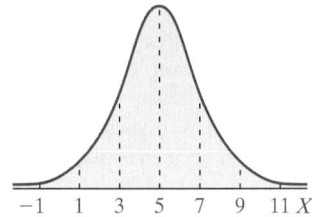

27. μ = 100, σ = 15

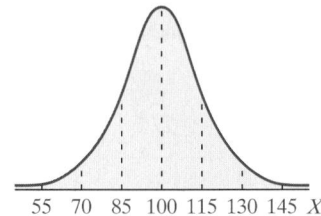

28. μ = 530, σ = 100

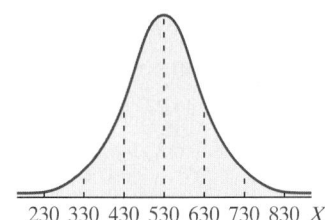

Applying the Concepts

29. You Explain It! Cell Phone Rates Monthly charges for cell
NW phone plans in the United States are normally distributed
with mean μ = $62 and standard deviation σ = $18.

Source: Based on information from *Consumer Reports*

(a) Draw a normal curve with the parameters labeled.

(b) Shade the region that represents the proportion of plans that charge less than $44.

(c) Suppose that the area under the normal curve to the left of x = $44 is 0.1587. Provide two interpretations of this result.

30. You Explain It! Refrigerators The lives of refrigerators are normally distributed with mean μ = 14 years and standard deviation σ = 2.5 years.

Source: Based on information from *Consumer Reports*

(a) Draw a normal curve with the parameters labeled.

(b) Shade the region that represents the proportion of refrigerators that last for more than 17 years.

(c) Suppose that the area under the normal curve to the right of x = 17 is 0.1151. Provide two interpretations of this result.

31. You Explain It! Birth Weights The birth weights of full-term babies are normally distributed with mean μ = 3,400 grams and σ = 505 grams.

Source: Based on data obtained from the *National Vital Statistics Report*, Vol. 48, No. 3

(a) Draw a normal curve with the parameters labeled.

(b) Shade the region that represents the proportion of full-term babies who weigh more than 4,410 grams.

(c) Suppose that the area under the normal curve to the right of x = 4,410 is 0.0228. Provide two interpretations of this result.

32. You Explain It! Height of 10-Year-Old Males The heights of 10-year-old males are normally distributed with mean μ = 55.9 inches and σ = 5.7 inches.

(a) Draw a normal curve with the parameters labeled.

(b) Shade the region that represents the proportion of 10-year-old males who are less than 46.5 inches tall.

(c) Suppose that the area under the normal curve to the left of x = 46.5 is 0.0496. Provide two interpretations of this result.

33. You Explain It! Gestation Period The lengths of human
NW pregnancies are normally distributed with μ = 266 days and σ = 16 days.

(a) The following figure represents the normal curve with μ = 266 days and σ = 16 days. The area to the right of x = 280 is 0.1908. Provide two interpretations of this area.

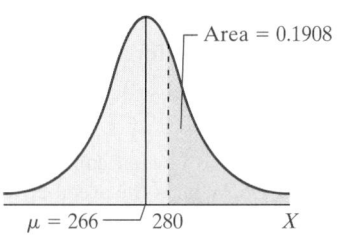

(b) The following figure represents the normal curve with μ = 266 days and σ = 16 days. The area between

$x = 230$ and $x = 260$ is 0.3416. Provide two interpretations of this area.

Area = 0.3416

230   260 $\mu = 266$ X

34. You Explain It! Miles per Gallon Elena conducts an experiment in which she fills up the gas tank on her Toyota Camry 40 times and records the miles per gallon for each fill-up. A histogram of the miles per gallon indicates that a normal distribution with mean of 24.6 miles per gallon and a standard deviation of 3.2 miles per gallon could be used to model the gas mileage for her car.

(a) The following figure represents the normal curve with $\mu = 24.6$ miles per gallon and $\sigma = 3.2$ miles per gallon. The area under the curve to the right of $x = 26$ is 0.3309. Provide two interpretations of this area.

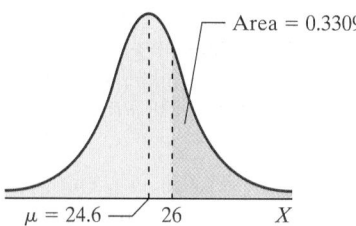

Area = 0.3309

$\mu = 24.6$ 26 X

(b) The following figure represents the normal curve with $\mu = 24.6$ miles per gallon and $\sigma = 3.2$ miles per gallon. The area under the curve between $x = 18$ and $x = 21$ is 0.1107. Provide two interpretations of this area.

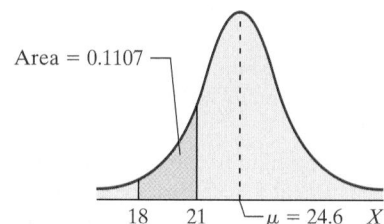

Area = 0.1107

18   21 $\mu = 24.6$ X

35. A random variable X is normally distributed with $\mu = 10$
NW and $\sigma = 3$.

(a) Compute $z_1 = \dfrac{x_1 - \mu}{\sigma}$ for $x_1 = 8$. -0.67

(b) Compute $z_2 = \dfrac{x_2 - \mu}{\sigma}$ for $x_2 = 12$. 0.67

(c) The area under the normal curve between $x_1 = 8$ and $x_2 = 12$ is 0.495. What is the area between z_1 and z_2?

36. A random variable X is normally distributed with $\mu = 25$ and $\sigma = 6$.

(a) Compute $z_1 = \dfrac{x_1 - \mu}{\sigma}$ for $x_1 = 18$. -1.17

35. (c) 0.495   36. (c) 0.6760

(b) Compute $z_2 = \dfrac{x_2 - \mu}{\sigma}$ for $x_2 = 30$. 0.83

(c) The area under the normal curve between $x_1 = 18$ and $x_2 = 30$ is 0.6760. What is the area between z_1 and z_2?

37. Hitting a Pitching Wedge In the game of golf, distance control is just as important as how far a player hits the ball. Michael went to the driving range with his range finder and hit 75 golf balls with his pitching wedge and measured the distance each ball traveled (in yards). He obtained the following data:

100	97	101	101	103	100	99	100	100
104	100	101	98	100	99	99	97	101
104	99	101	101	101	100	96	99	99
98	94	98	107	98	100	98	103	100
98	94	104	104	98	101	99	97	103
102	101	101	100	95	104	99	102	95
99	102	103	97	101	102	96	102	99
96	108	103	100	95	101	103	105	100
94	99	95						

(a) Use MINITAB or some other statistical software to construct a relative frequency histogram. Comment on the shape of the distribution.

(b) Use MINITAB or some other statistical software to draw a normal density function on the relative frequency histogram.

(c) Do you think the normal density function accurately describes the distance Michael hits with a pitching wedge? Why?

38. Heights of 5-Year-Old Females The following frequency distribution represents the heights (in inches) of eighty randomly selected 5-year-old females.

44.5	42.4	42.2	46.2	45.7	44.8	43.3	39.5
45.4	43.0	43.4	44.7	38.6	41.6	50.2	46.9
39.6	44.7	36.5	42.7	40.6	47.5	48.4	37.5
45.5	43.3	41.2	40.5	44.4	42.6	42.0	40.3
42.0	42.2	38.5	43.6	40.6	45.0	40.7	36.3
44.5	37.6	42.2	40.3	48.5	41.6	41.7	38.9
39.5	43.6	41.3	38.8	41.9	40.3	42.1	41.9
42.3	44.6	40.5	37.4	44.5	40.7	38.2	42.6
44.0	35.9	43.7	48.1	38.7	46.0	43.4	44.6
37.7	34.6	42.4	42.7	47.0	42.8	39.9	42.3

(a) Use MINITAB or some other statistical software to construct a relative frequency histogram. Comment on the shape of the distribution.

(b) Use MINITAB or some other statistical software to draw a normal density curve on the relative frequency histogram.

(c) Do you think the normal density function accurately describes the heights of 5-year-old females? Why?

7.2 THE STANDARD NORMAL DISTRIBUTION

Preparing for This Section   Before getting started, review the following:

• The Complement Rule (Section 5.2, pp. 279–281)

Objectives		
	1	Find the area under the standard normal curve
	2	Find z-scores for a given area
	3	Interpret the area under the standard normal curve as a probability

Note to Instructor

If you like, you can print out and distribute the Preparing for This Section quiz located in the Instructor's Resource Center. The purpose of the quiz is to verify that the students have the prerequisite knowledge for the section.

In Section 7.1, we introduced the normal distribution. We learned that, if X is a normally distributed random variable, we can use the area under the normal density function to obtain the proportion of a population with a certain characteristic, or the probability that a randomly selected individual from the population has the characteristic. To find the area under the normal curve by hand, we first convert the random variable X to a standard normal random variable Z and find the area under the standard normal curve. In this section we discuss methods for finding area under the standard normal curve.

Properties of the Standard Normal Distribution

Figure 11

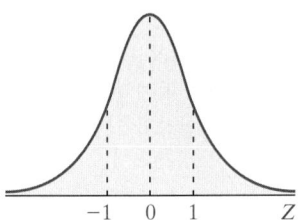

The standard normal distribution has a mean of 0 and a standard deviation of 1. The standard normal curve, therefore, has its high point located at 0 and inflection points located at −1 and +1. We use Z to represent a standard normal random variable. The graph of the standard normal curve is presented in Figure 11.

Although we stated the properties of normal curves in Section 7.1, it is worthwhile to restate them here in terms of the standard normal curve.

Figure 12

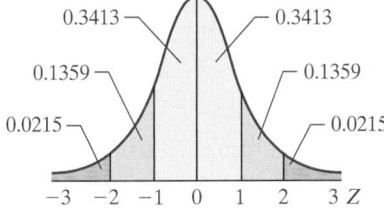

> **Properties of the Standard Normal Curve**
>
> **1.** It is symmetric about its mean, $\mu = 0$, and has standard deviation $\sigma = 1$.
> **2.** The mean = median = mode = 0. Its highest point occurs at $z = 0$.
> **3.** It has inflection points at $\mu - \sigma = 0 - 1 = -1$ and $\mu + \sigma = 0 + 1 = 1$.
> **4.** The area under the curve is 1.
> **5.** The area under the curve to the right of $\mu = 0$ equals the area under the curve to the left of $\mu = 0$, which equals $\frac{1}{2}$.
> **6.** As the value of Z increases, the graph approaches, but never equals, zero. As the value of Z decreases, the graph approaches, but never equals, zero.
> **7.** The Empirical Rule: Approximately 68% of the area under the standard normal curve is between $z = -1$ and $z = 1$. Approximately 95% of the area under the standard normal curve is between $z = -2$ and $z = 2$. Approximately 99.7% of the area under the standard normal curve is between $z = -3$ and $z = 3$. See Figure 12.

We now discuss the procedure for finding area under the standard normal curve.

Figure 13

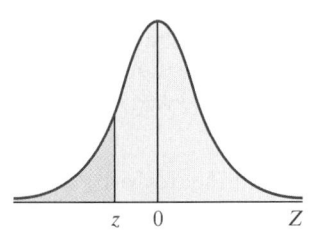

1   **Find the Area under the Standard Normal Curve**

We discuss two methods for finding area under the standard normal curve. The first method uses a table of areas that has been constructed for various values of Z. The second method involves the use of statistical software or a graphing calculator with advanced statistical features.

Table V, which can be found on the inside back cover of the text and in Appendix A, gives areas under the standard normal curve for values to the left of a specified z-score, z, as shown in Figure 13.

The shaded region represents the area under the standard normal curve to the left of z. When finding area under a normal curve, you should always sketch the normal curve and shade the area in question. This practice will help to minimize errors.

EXAMPLE 1 **Finding Area under the Standard Normal Curve to the Left of a z-Score**

Problem: Find the area under the standard normal curve that lies to the left of $z = 1.68$.

Approach
Step 1: Draw a standard normal curve with $z = 1.68$ labeled, and shade the area under the curve to the left of $z = 1.68$.

Step 2: The rows in Table V represent the ones and tenths digits of z, while the columns represent the hundredths digit. To find the area under the curve to the left of $z = 1.68$, we split 1.68 into 1.6 and 0.08. Find the row that represents 1.6 and the column that represents 0.08 in Table V. Identify where the row and column intersect. This value is the area.

Solution
Step 1: Figure 14 shows the graph of the standard normal curve with $z = 1.68$ labeled. The area to the left of $z = 1.68$ is shaded.

Step 2: A portion of Table V is presented in Figure 15. We have enclosed the row that represents 1.6 and the column that represents 0.08. The value located where the row and column intersect is the area we are seeking. The area to the left of $z = 1.68$ is 0.9535.

Figure 14

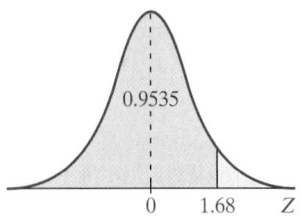

Figure 15

z	.00	.01	.02	.03	.04	.05	.06	.07	.08	.09
0.0	0.5000	0.5040	0.5080	0.5120	0.5160	0.5199	0.5239	0.5279	0.5319	0.5359
0.1	0.5398	0.5438	0.5478	0.5517	0.5557	0.5596	0.5636	0.5675	0.5714	0.5753
0.2	0.5793	0.5832	0.5871	0.5910	0.5948	0.5987	0.6026	0.6064	0.6103	0.6141
0.3	0.6179	0.6217	0.6255	0.6293	0.6331	0.6368	0.6406	0.6443	0.6480	0.6517
1.3	0.9032	0.9049	0.9066	0.9082	0.9099	0.9115	0.9131	0.9147	0.9162	0.9177
1.4	0.9192	0.9207	0.9222	0.9236	0.9251	0.9265	0.9279	0.9292	0.9306	0.9319
1.5	0.9332	0.9345	0.9357	0.9370	0.9382	0.9394	0.9406	0.9418	0.9429	0.9441
1.6	0.9452	0.9463	0.9474	0.9484	0.9495	0.9505	0.9515	0.9525	0.9535	0.9545
1.7	0.9554	0.9564	0.9573	0.9582	0.9591	0.9599	0.9608	0.9616	0.9625	0.9633
1.8	0.9641	0.9649	0.9656	0.9664	0.9671	0.9678	0.9686	0.9693	0.9699	0.9706

The area under a standard normal curve may also be determined using statistical software or a graphing calculator with advanced statistical features.

EXAMPLE 2 **Finding the Area under a Standard Normal Curve Using Technology**

Problem: Find the area under the standard normal curve to the left of $z = 1.68$ using statistical software or a graphing calculator with advanced statistical features.

Approach: We will use MINITAB and a TI-84 Plus graphing calculator to find the area. The steps for determining the area under the standard normal curve using MINITAB, Excel, and the TI-83/84 Plus graphing calculators are given in the Technology Step-by-Step on page 396.

Solution: Figure 16(a) shows the results from MINITAB, and Figure 16(b) shows the results from a TI-84 Plus graphing calculator.

Figure 16 **Cumulative Distribution Function**

Normal with mean = 0 and standard deviation = 1

x	P(X <= x)
1.68	0.953521

```
normalcdf(-1E99,
1.68,0,1)
           .9535213678
```

(a)

(b)

Notice that the output for MINITAB is titled Cumulative Distribution Function. Remember, the word *cumulative* means "less than or equal to," so MINITAB is giving the area under the standard normal curve for values of Z less than or equal to 1.68. The command required by the TI-84 Plus is `normalcdf(`. The cdf stands for *cumulative distribution function*. The TI-graphing calculators require a left and right bound. We use $-1\text{E}99$ for the left bound when obtaining areas "less than or equal to" some value.

Now Work Problem 5

Often, rather than being interested in the area under the standard normal curve to the left of z, we are interested in obtaining the area to the right of z. The solution to this type of problem uses the Complement Rule and the fact that the area under the entire standard normal curve is 1. Therefore,

In Other Words

Area right = 1 − area left

$$\left(\begin{matrix}\text{Area under the normal curve}\\\text{to the right of } z\end{matrix}\right) = 1 - \left(\begin{matrix}\text{area to the left}\\\text{of } z\end{matrix}\right)$$

$$P(Z > z) \qquad\quad = 1 - \quad P(Z \le z)$$

EXAMPLE 3 **Finding Area under the Standard Normal Curve to the Right of a z-Score**

Problem: Find the area under the standard normal curve to the right of $z = -0.46$.

Approach

Step 1: Draw a standard normal curve with $z = -0.46$ labeled, and shade the area under the curve to the right of $z = -0.46$.

Figure 17

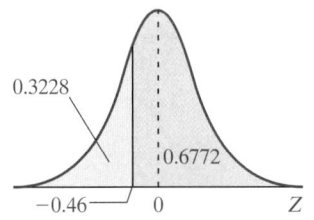

0.3228

0.6772

−0.46   0   Z

Step 2: Find the row that represents −0.4 and the column that represents 0.06 in Table V. Identify where the row and column intersect. This value is the area to the *left* of $z = -0.46$.

Step 3: The area under the standard normal curve to the right of $z = -0.46$ is 1 minus the area to the left of $z = -0.46$.

Solution

Step 1: Figure 17 shows the graph of the standard normal curve with $z = -0.46$ labeled. The area to the right of $z = -0.46$ is shaded.

Step 2: A portion of Table V is presented in Figure 18. We have enclosed the row that represents −0.4 and the column that represents 0.06. The value where the row and column intersect is the area to the left of $z = -0.46$. The area to the left of $z = -0.46$ is 0.3228.

Figure 18

z	.00	.01	.02	.03	.04	.05	.06	.07	.08	.09
−3.4	0.0003	0.0003	0.0003	0.0003	0.0003	0.0003	0.0003	0.0003	0.0003	0.0002
−3.3	0.0005	0.0005	0.0005	0.0004	0.0004	0.0004	0.0004	0.0004	0.0004	0.0003
−3.2	0.0007	0.0007	0.0006	0.0006	0.0006	0.0006	0.0006	0.0005	0.0005	0.0005
−3.1	0.0010	0.0009	0.0009	0.0009	0.0008	0.0008	0.0008	0.0008	0.0007	0.0007
−3.0	0.0013	0.0013	0.0013	0.0012	0.0012	0.0011	0.0011	0.0011	0.0010	0.0010
−0.5	0.3085	0.3050	0.3015	0.2981	0.2946	0.2912	0.2877	0.2843	0.2810	0.2776
−0.4	0.3446	0.3409	0.3372	0.3336	0.3300	0.3264	0.3228	0.3192	0.3156	0.3121
−0.3	0.3821	0.3783	0.3745	0.3707	0.3669	0.3632	0.3594	0.3557	0.3520	0.3483
−0.2	0.4207	0.4168	0.4129	0.4090	0.4052	0.4013	0.3974	0.3936	0.3897	0.3859
−0.1	0.4602	0.4562	0.4522	0.4483	0.4443	0.4404	0.4364	0.4325	0.4286	0.4247
−0.0	0.5000	0.4960	0.4920	0.4880	0.4840	0.4801	0.4761	0.4721	0.4681	0.4641

Using Technology

Statistical software and graphing calculators can also find areas under the standard normal curve to the right of a z-score. A TI-84 Plus can directly find the area to the right. MINITAB and Excel require the user to find the area to the left and use this result to find the area to the right (as we did in Example 3).

Now Work Problem 7

Step 3: The area under the standard normal curve to the right of $z = -0.46$ is 1 minus the area to the left of $z = -0.46$.

$$\text{Area right of } -0.46 = 1 - (\text{area left of } -0.46)$$
$$= 1 - 0.3228$$
$$= 0.6772$$

The area to the right of $z = -0.46$ is 0.6772.

The next example presents a situation in which we are interested in the area between two z-scores.

EXAMPLE 4

Find the Area under the Standard Normal Curve between Two z-Scores

Problem: Find the area under the standard normal curve between $z = -1.35$ and $z = 2.01$.

Approach

Step 1: Draw a standard normal curve with $z = -1.35$ and $z = 2.01$ labeled. Shade the area under the curve between $z = -1.35$ and $z = 2.01$.

Step 2: Find the area to the left of $z = -1.35$. Find the area to the left of $z = 2.01$.

Step 3: The area under the standard normal curve between $z = -1.35$ and $z = 2.01$ is the area to the left of $z = 2.01$ minus the area to the left of $z = -1.35$.

Figure 19

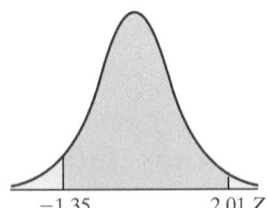

Solution

Step 1: Figure 19 shows the standard normal curve with the area between $z = -1.35$ and $z = 2.01$ shaded.

Step 2: Based upon Table V, the area to the left of $z = -1.35$ is 0.0885. The area to the left of $z = 2.01$ is 0.9778.

Step 3: The area between $z = -1.35$ and $z = 2.01$ is

$$(\text{Area between } z = -1.35 \text{ and } z = 2.01) = (\text{area left of } z = 2.01) - (\text{area left of } z = -1.35)$$

Using Technology

A TI-84 Plus can directly find the area between two z-values. For example, the command `normalcdf(-1.35, 2.01, 0, 1)` will give the results of Example 4. MINITAB and Excel require the user to first find the area to the left of 2.01 and then subtract the area to the left of −1.35, as we did in Example 4.

Now Work Problem 9

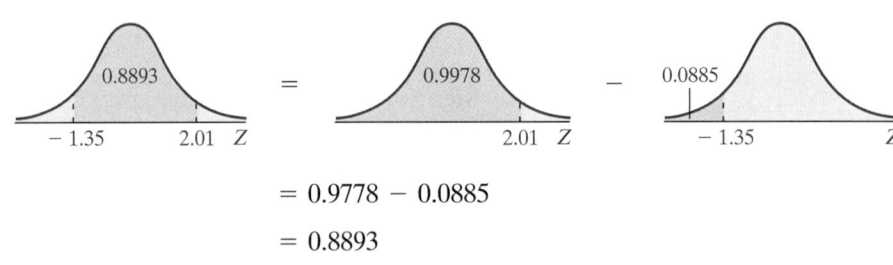

$$= 0.9778 - 0.0885$$
$$= 0.8893$$

The area between $z = -1.35$ and $z = 2.01$ is 0.8893.

CAUTION State the area under the standard normal curve to the left of $z = -3.90$ as <0.0001 (not 0). State the area under the standard normal curve to the left of $z = 3.90$ as >0.9999 (not 1).

We summarize the methods for obtaining area under the standard normal curve in Table 2.

Because the normal curve extends indefinitely in both directions on the Z-axis, there is no z-value for which the area under the curve to the left of the z-value is 1. For example, the area to the left of $z = 10$ is less than 1, even though graphing calculators and statistical software state that the area is 1, because they can only compute a limited number of decimal places. We will follow the practice of stating the area to the left of $z = -3.90$ or to the right of $z = 3.90$ as <0.0001. The area under the standard normal curve to the left of $z = 3.90$ or to the right of $z = -3.90$ will be stated as >0.9999.

Table 2 Finding Areas under the Standard Normal Curve		
Problem	**Approach**	**Solution**
Find the area to the left of z.	Shade the area to the left of z.	Use Table V to find the row and column that correspond to z. The area is the value where the row and column intersect. Or, use technology to find the area.
Find the area to the right of z.	Shade the area to the right of z.	Use Table V to find the area left of z. The area to the right of z is 1 minus the area to the left of z. Or, use technology to find the area.
Find the area between z_1 and z_2.	Shade the area between z_1 and z_2.	Use Table V to find the area to the left of z_1 and to the left of z_2. The area between z_1 and z_2 is (area to the left of z_2) − (area to the left of z_1). Or, use technology to find the area.

② Find z-Scores for a Given Area

Up to this point, we have found areas given the value of a z-score. Often, we are interested in finding a z-score that corresponds to a given area. The procedure to follow is the reverse of the procedure for finding areas given z-scores.

EXAMPLE 5   Finding a z-Score from a Specified Area to Its Left

Problem: Find the z-score so that the area to the left of the z-score is 0.32.

Approach

Step 1: Draw a standard normal curve with the area and corresponding unknown z-score labeled.

Step 2: Look for the area in the table closest to 0.32.

Step 3: Find the z-score that corresponds to the area closest to 0.32.

Figure 20

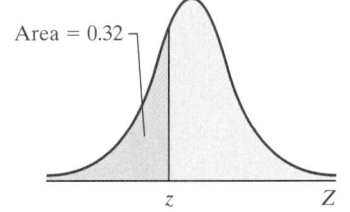

Area = 0.32

Solution

Step 1: Figure 20 shows the graph of the standard normal curve with the area of 0.32 labeled. We know that z must be less than 0. Do you know why?

Step 2: We refer to Table V and look in the body of the table for an area closest to 0.32. The area closest to 0.32 is 0.3192. Figure 21 on the following page shows a portion of Table V with 0.3192 labeled.

Figure 21

z	.00	.01	.02	.03	.04	.05	.06	.07	.08	.09
−3.4	0.0003	0.0003	0.0003	0.0003	0.0003	0.0003	0.0003	0.0003	0.0003	0.0002
−3.3	0.0005	0.0005	0.0005	0.0004	0.0004	0.0004	0.0004	0.0004	0.0004	0.0003
−3.2	0.0007	0.0007	0.0006	0.0006	0.0006	0.0006	0.0006	0.0005	0.0005	0.0005
−3.1	0.0010	0.0009	0.0009	0.0009	0.0008	0.0008	0.0008	0.0008	0.0007	0.0007
−3.0	0.0013	0.0013	0.0013	0.0012	0.0012	0.0011	0.0011	0.0011	0.0010	0.0010
−0.7	0.2420	0.2389	0.2358	0.2327	0.2296	0.2266	0.2236	0.2206	0.2177	0.2148
−0.6	0.2743	0.2709	0.2676	0.2643	0.2611	0.2578	0.2546	0.2514	0.2483	0.2451
−0.5	0.3085	0.3050	0.3015	0.2981	0.2946	0.2912	0.2877	0.2843	0.2810	0.2776
−0.4	0.3446	0.3409	0.3372	0.3336	0.3300	0.3264	0.3228	0.3192	0.3156	0.3121
−0.3	0.3821	0.3783	0.3745	0.3707	0.3669	0.3632	0.3594	0.3557	0.3520	0.3483
−0.2	0.4027	0.4168	0.4129	0.4090	0.4052	0.4013	0.3974	0.3936	0.3897	0.3859

Figure 22

Area ≈ 0.32

−0.47   Z

Step 3: From reading the table in Figure 21, we see that the approximate z-score that corresponds to an area of 0.32 to its left is −0.47. So, $z = -0.47$. See Figure 22.

Statistical software or graphing calculators with advanced statistical features can also be used to determine a z-score corresponding to a specified area.

EXAMPLE 6 | **Finding a z-Score from a Specified Area to Its Left Using Technology**

Problem: Find the z-score such that the area to the left of the z-score is 0.32 using statistical software or a graphing calculator with advanced statistical features.

Approach: We will use Excel and a TI-84 Plus graphing calculator to find the z-score. The steps for determining the z-score for MINITAB, Excel, and the TI-83/84 Plus graphing calculators are given in the Technology Step-by-Step on page 396.

Solution: Figure 23(a) shows the results from Excel, and Figure 23(b) shows the results from a TI-84 Plus graphing calculator.

Figure 23

Here is the z-score

(a)

invNorm(.32,0,1)
            -.4676988012

(b)

The z-score that corresponds to an area of 0.32 to its left is −0.47, so $z = -0.47$.

Now Work Problem 15

It is useful to remember that if the area to the left of the z-score is less than 0.5 the z-score must be less than 0. If the area to the left of the z-score is greater than 0.5, the z-score must be greater than 0.

The next example deals with situations in which the area to the right of some unknown z-score is given. The solution uses the fact that the total area under the normal curve is 1.

| EXAMPLE 7 | **Finding a z-Score from a Specified Area to Its Right** |

Problem: Find the z-score so that the area to the right of the z-score is 0.4332.

Approach

CAUTION   To find a z-score, given the area to the right, you must first determine the area to the left if you are using Table V.

Step 1: Draw a standard normal curve with the area and corresponding unknown z-score labeled.

Step 2: Determine the area to the left of the unknown z-score.

Step 3: Look for the area in the table closest to the area determined in Step 2 and record the z-score that corresponds to the closest area.

Solution

Step 1: Figure 24 shows the standard normal curve with the area and unknown z-score labeled.

Figure 24

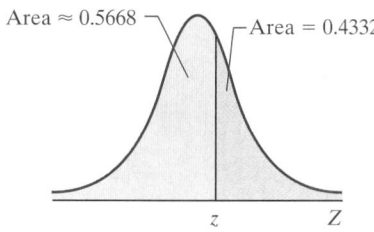
Area ≈ 0.5668   Area = 0.4332

Step 2: Since the area under the entire normal curve is 1, the area to the left of the unknown z-score is 1 minus the area right of the unknown z-score. Therefore,

$$\text{Area to the left} = 1 - \text{area to the right}$$
$$= 1 - 0.4332$$
$$= 0.5668$$

Step 3: We look in the body of Table V for an area closest to 0.5668. See Figure 25. The area closest to 0.5668 is 0.5675.

Figure 25

z	.00	.01	.02	.03	.04	.05	.06	.07	.08	.09
0.0	0.5000	0.5040	0.5080	0.5120	0.5160	0.5199	0.5239	0.5279	0.5319	0.5359
0.1	0.5398	0.5438	0.5478	0.5517	0.5557	0.5596	0.5636	0.5675	0.5714	0.5753
0.2	0.5793	0.5832	0.5871	0.5910	0.5948	0.5987	0.6026	0.6064	0.6103	0.6141
0.3	0.6179	0.6217	0.6255	0.6293	0.6331	0.6368	0.6406	0.6443	0.6480	0.6517

The approximate z-score that corresponds to a right-tail area of 0.4332 is 0.17. Therefore, $z = 0.17$. See Figure 26.

Figure 26

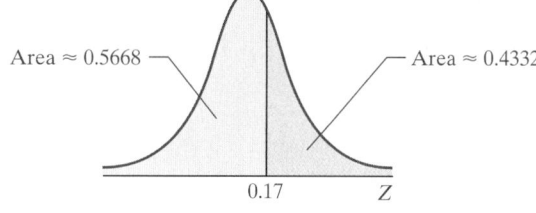
Area ≈ 0.5668   Area ≈ 0.4332

0.17   Z

Now Work Problem 19

In upcoming chapters, we will be interested in finding z-scores that separate the middle area of the standard normal curve from the area in its tails.

| EXAMPLE 8 | **Finding z-Scores from an Area in the Middle** |

Problem: Find the z-scores that separates the middle 90% of the area under the standard normal curve from the area in the tails.

Approach

Step 1: Draw a standard normal curve with the middle 90% = 0.9 of the area separated from the area of 5% = 0.05 in each of the two tails. Label the unknown z-scores z_1 and z_2.

Figure 27

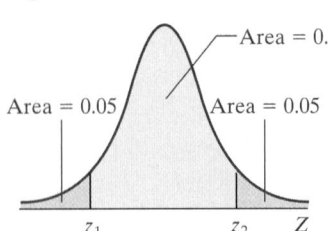

Step 2: Look in the body of Table V to find the area closest to 0.05.

Step 3: Determine the z-score for the left tail.

Step 4: The area to the right of z_2 is 0.05. Therefore, the area to the left of z_2 is 0.95. Look in Table V for an area of 0.95 and find the corresponding z-score.

Solution

Step 1: Figure 27 shows the standard normal curve with the middle 90% of the area separated from the area in the two tails.

Step 2: We look in the body of Table V for an area closest to 0.05. See Figure 28. Notice that 0.0495 and 0.0505 are equally close to 0.05.

Figure 28

z	.00	.01	.02	.03	.04	.05	.06	.07	.08	.09
−3.4	0.0003	0.0003	0.0003	0.0003	0.0003	0.0003	0.0003	0.0003	0.0003	0.0002
−3.3	0.0005	0.0005	0.0005	0.0004	0.0004	0.0004	0.0004	0.0004	0.0004	0.0003
−3.2	0.0007	0.0007	0.0006	0.0006	0.0006	0.0006	0.0006	0.0005	0.0005	0.0005
−1.8	0.0359	0.0351	0.0344	0.0336	0.0329	0.0322	0.0314	0.0307	0.0301	0.0294
−1.7	0.0446	0.0436	0.0427	0.0418	0.0409	0.0401	0.0392	0.0384	0.0375	0.0367
−1.6	0.0548	0.0537	0.0526	0.0516	0.0505	0.0495	0.0485	0.0475	0.0465	0.0455
−1.5	0.0668	0.0655	0.0643	0.0630	0.0618	0.0606	0.0594	0.0582	0.0571	0.0559

Step 3: We agree to take the mean of the two z-scores corresponding to the areas. The z-score corresponding to an area of 0.0495 is −1.65. The z-score corresponding to an area of 0.0505 is −1.64. Therefore, the approximate z-score corresponding to an area of 0.05 to its left is

$$z = \frac{-1.65 + (-1.64)}{2} = -1.645$$

Figure 29

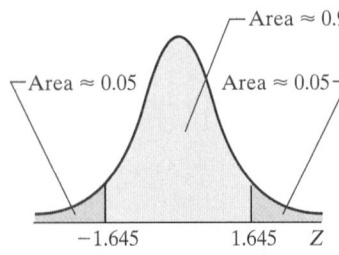

Step 4: The area to the right of z_2 is 0.05. Therefore, the area to the left of $z_2 = 1 - 0.05 = 0.95$. In Table V, we find an area of 0.9495 corresponding to $z = 1.64$ and an area of 0.9505 corresponding to $z = 1.65$. Consequently, the approximate z-score corresponding to an area of 0.05 to the right is

$$z_2 = \frac{1.65 + 1.64}{2} = 1.645$$

See Figure 29.

Now Work Problem 23

Note to Instructor
Remind students that the standard normal curve is symmetric about its mean, 0. Therefore, once the left z-score is known, the right is found by symmetry.

Figure 30

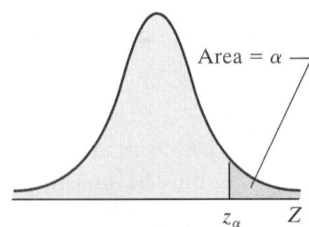

We could also obtain the solution to Example 8 using symmetry. Because the standard normal curve is symmetric about its mean, 0, the z-score that corresponds to an area of 0.05 to the left will be the additive inverse (i.e., opposite) of the z-score that corresponds to an area of 0.05 to the right. Since the area to the left of $z = -1.645$ is 0.05, the area to the right of $z = 1.645$ is also 0.05.

We are often interested in finding the z-score that has a specified area to the right. For this reason, we have special notation to represent this situation.

> The notation z_α (pronounced "z sub alpha") is the z-score such that the area under the standard normal curve to the right of z_α is α. Figure 30 illustrates the notation.

EXAMPLE 9 **Finding the Value of z_α**

Problem: Find the value of $z_{0.10}$.

Approach: We wish to find the z-value such that the area under the standard normal curve to the right of the z-value is 0.10.

By Hand Solution: The area to the right of the unknown z-value is 0.10, so the area to the left of the z-value is $1 - 0.10 = 0.90$. We look in Table V for the area closest to 0.90. The closest area is 0.8997, which corresponds to a z-value of 1.28. Therefore, $z_{0.10} = 1.28$.

Technology Solution: The area to the right of the unknown z-value is 0.10, so the area to the left is $1 - 0.10 = 0.90$. A TI-84 Plus is used to find that the z-value such that the area to the left is 0.90 is 1.28. See Figure 31. Therefore, $z_{0.10} = 1.28$.

Figure 31

Figure 32 shows the z-value on the normal curve.

Figure 32

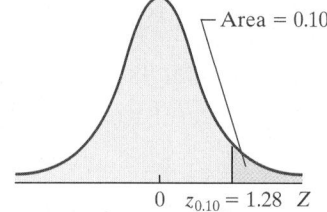

Now Work Problem 27

3 Interpret the Area under the Standard Normal Curve as a Probability

Recall that the area under a normal curve can be interpreted either as a probability or as the proportion of the population with a given characteristic (as represented by an interval of numbers). When interpreting the area under the standard normal curve as a probability, we use the notation introduced in Chapter 6. For example, in Example 8, we found that the area under the standard normal curve to the left of $z = -1.645$ is 0.05; therefore, the probability of randomly selecting a standard normal random variable, Z, that is less than -1.645 is 0.05. We write this statement with the notation $P(Z < -1.645) = 0.05$.

We will use the following notation to denote probabilities of a standard normal random variable, Z.

Notation for the Probability of a Standard Normal Random Variable	
$P(a \le Z \le b)$	represents the probability that a standard normal random variable is between a and b.
$P(Z > a)$	represents the probability that a standard normal random variable is greater than a.
$P(Z < a)$	represents the probability that a standard normal random variable is less than a.

EXAMPLE 10 **Finding Probabilities of Standard Normal Random Variables**

Problem: Evaluate: $P(Z < 1.26)$

Approach

Step 1: Draw a standard normal curve with the area that we desire shaded.

Figure 33

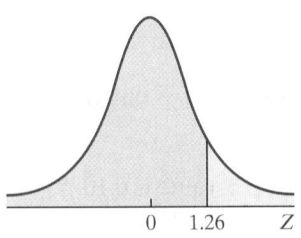

Now Work Problem 33

Step 2: Use Table V to find the area of the shaded region. This area represents the probability.

Solution

Step 1: Figure 33 shows the standard normal curve with the area to the left of $z = 1.26$ shaded.

Step 2: Using Table V, we find that the area under the standard normal curve to the left of $z = 1.26$ is 0.8962. Therefore, $P(Z < 1.26) = 0.8962$.

Note to Instructor
Be sure to emphasize this concept with students.

For any continuous random variable, the probability of observing a specific value of the random variable is 0. For example, for a standard normal random variable, $P(a) = 0$ for any value of a. This is because there is no area under the standard normal curve associated with a single value, so the probability must be 0. Therefore, the following probabilities are equivalent:

$$P(a < Z < b) = P(a \le Z < b) = P(a < Z \le b) = P(a \le Z \le b)$$

For example, $P(Z < 1.26) = P(Z \le 1.26) = 0.8962$.

7.2 ASSESS YOUR UNDERSTANDING

Concepts and Vocabulary

1. State the properties of the standard normal curve.

2. If the area under the standard normal curve to the left of $z = 1.20$ is 0.8849, what is the area under the standard normal curve to the right of $z = 1.20$?   *0.1151*

3. *True or False*: The area under the standard normal curve to the left of $z = 5.30$ is 1. Support your answer.   *False*

4. Explain why $P(Z < -1.30) = P(Z \le -1.30)$.

Skill Building

In Problems 5–12, find the indicated areas. For each problem, be sure to draw a standard normal curve and shade the area that is to be found.

5. Determine the area under the standard normal curve that NW lies to the left of
(a) $z = -2.45$ *0.0071*
(b) $z = -0.43$ *0.3336*
(c) $z = 1.35$ *0.9115*
(d) $z = 3.49$ *0.9998*

6. Determine the area under the standard normal curve that lies to the left of
(a) $z = -3.49$ *0.0002*
(b) $z = -1.99$ *0.0233*
(c) $z = 0.92$ *0.8212*
(d) $z = 2.90$ *0.9981*

7. Determine the area under the standard normal curve that NW lies to the right of
(a) $z = -3.01$ *0.9987*
(b) $z = -1.59$ *0.9441*

(c) $z = 1.78$ *0.0375*
(d) $z = 3.11$ *0.0009*

8. Determine the area under the standard normal curve that lies to the right of
(a) $z = -3.49$ *0.9998*
(b) $z = -0.55$ *0.7088*
(c) $z = 2.23$ *0.0129*
(d) $z = 3.45$ *0.0003*

9. Determine the area under the standard normal curve that NW lies between
(a) $z = -2.04$ and $z = 2.04$ *0.9586*
(b) $z = -0.55$ and $z = 0$ *0.2088*
(c) $z = -1.04$ and $z = 2.76$ *0.8479*

10. Determine the area under the standard normal curve that lies between
(a) $z = -2.55$ and $z = 2.55$ *0.9892*
(b) $z = -1.67$ and $z = 0$ *0.4525*
(c) $z = -3.03$ and $z = 1.98$ *0.9749*

11. Determine the total area under the standard normal curve
(a) to the left of $z = -2$ or to the right of $z = 2$ *0.0456*
(b) to the left of $z = -1.56$ or to the right of $z = 2.56$
(c) to the left of $z = -0.24$ or to the right of $z = 1.20$

12. Determine the total area under the standard normal curve
(a) to the left of $z = -2.94$ or to the right of $z = 2.94$
(b) to the left of $z = -1.68$ or to the right of $z = 3.05$
(c) to the left of $z = -0.88$ or to the right of $z = 1.23$

11. (b) 0.0646   11. (c) 0.5203   12. (a) 0.0032
12. (b) 0.0476   12. (c) 0.2987

In Problems 13 and 14, find the area of the shaded region for each standard normal curve.

13. (a)   *0.8877*

(b)   *0.0500*

(c)   *0.9802*

14. (a)   *0.0198*

(b)   *0.3686*

(c)   *0.9500*

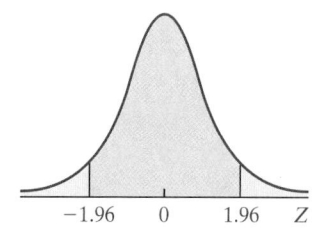

In Problems 15–26, find the indicated z-score. Be sure to draw a standard normal curve that depicts the solution.

15. Find the *z*-score such that the area under the standard normal curve to its left is 0.1.   *−1.28*

16. Find the *z*-score such that the area under the standard normal curve to its left is 0.2.   *−0.84*

17. Find the *z*-score such that the area under the standard normal curve to its left is 0.98.   *2.05*

18. Find the *z*-score such that the area under the standard normal curve to its left is 0.85.   *1.04*

19. Find the *z*-score such that the area under the standard normal curve to its right is 0.25.   *0.67*

20. Find the *z*-score such that the area under the standard normal curve to its right is 0.35.   *0.39*

21. Find the *z*-score such that the area under the standard normal curve to its right is 0.89.   *−1.23*

22. Find the *z*-score such that the area under the standard normal curve to its right is 0.75.   *−0.67*

23. Find the *z*-scores that separate the middle 80% of the distribution from the area in the tails of the standard normal distribution.   *−1.28; 1.28*

24. Find the *z*-scores that separate the middle 70% of the distribution from the area in the tails of the standard normal distribution.   *−1.04; 1.04*

25. Find the *z*-scores that separate the middle 99% of the distribution from the area in the tails of the standard normal distribution.   *−2.575; 2.575*

26. Find the *z*-scores that separate the middle 94% of the distribution from the area in the tails of the standard normal distribution.   *−1.88; 1.88*

In Problems 27–32, find the value of z_α.

27. $z_{0.05}$ *1.645*   **28.** $z_{0.35}$ *0.39*

29. $z_{0.01}$ *2.33*   **30.** $z_{0.02}$ *2.05*

31. $z_{0.20}$ *0.84*   **32.** $z_{0.15}$ *1.04*

In Problems 33–44, find the indicated probability of the standard normal random variable Z.

33. $P(Z < 1.93)$ *0.9732*

34. $P(Z < -0.61)$ *0.2709*

35. $P(Z > -2.98)$ *0.9986*

36. $P(Z > 0.92)$ *0.1788*

37. $P(-1.20 \le Z < 2.34)$ *0.8753*

38. $P(1.23 < Z \le 1.56)$ *0.0499*

39. $P(Z \ge 1.84)$ *0.0329*

40. $P(Z \ge -0.92)$ *0.8212*

41. $P(Z \le 0.72)$ *0.7642*

42. $P(Z \le -2.69)$ *0.0036*

43. $P(Z < -2.56 \text{ or } Z > 1.39)$ *0.0875*

44. $P(Z < -0.38 \text{ or } Z > 1.93)$ *0.3788*

Applying the Concepts

45. The Empirical Rule The Empirical Rule states that about 68% of the data in a bell-shaped distribution lies within 1 standard deviation of the mean. For the standard normal distribution, this means about 68% of the data lies between $z = -1$ and $z = 1$. Verify this result. Verify that about 95% of the data lies within 2 standard deviations of the mean. Finally, verify that about 99.7% of the data lies within 3 standard deviations of the mean.

46. According to Table V, the area under the standard normal curve to the left of $z = -1.34$ is 0.0901. Without consulting Table V, determine the area under the standard normal curve to the right of $z = 1.34$.   *0.0901*

47. According to Table V, the area under the standard normal curve to the left of $z = -2.55$ is 0.0054. Without consulting Table V, determine the area under the standard normal curve to the right of $z = 2.55$.   *0.0054*

48. According to Table V, the area under the standard normal curve between $z = -1.50$ and $z = 0$ is 0.4332. Without consulting Table V, determine the area under the standard normal curve between $z = 0$ and $z = 1.50$.   *0.4332*

49. According to Table V, the area under the standard normal curve between $z = -1.24$ and $z = -0.53$ is 0.1906. Without consulting Table V, determine the area under the standard normal curve between $z = 0.53$ and $z = 1.24$.   *0.1906*

50. (a) If $P(Z < a) = 0.9938$, find a.   *2.50*
(b) If $P(Z \geq a) = 0.4404$, find a.   *0.15*
(c) If $P(-b < Z < b) = 0.8740$, find b.   *1.53*
(d) If $P(0 \leq Z \leq a) = 0.4838$, find a.   *2.14*

TECHNOLOGY STEP-BY-STEP   The Standard Normal Distribution

TI-83/84 Plus

Finding Areas under the Standard Normal Curve
1. From the HOME screen, press 2nd VARS to access the DISTRibution menu.
2. Select `2:normalcdf(`
3. With `normalcdf(` on the HOME screen, type *lowerbound, upperbound, 0, 1)*. For example, to find the area left of $z = 1.26$ under the standard normal curve, type

    `normalcdf(-1E99, 1.26, 0, 1)`

and hit ENTER.

Note: When there is no lowerbound, enter $-1E99$. When there is no upperbound, enter $1E99$. The E shown is scientific notation; it is selected by pressing 2nd then ,.

Finding Z-Scores Corresponding to an Area
1. From the HOME screen, press 2nd VARS to access the DISTRibution menu.
2. Select `3:invNorm(`.
3. With `invNorm(` on the HOME screen, type *"area left", 0, 1)*. For example, to find the z-score such that the area under the normal curve to the left of the z-score is 0.79, type

    `invNorm(0.79, 0 , 1)`

and hit ENTER.

MINITAB

Finding Areas under the Standard Normal Curve
1. MINITAB will find an area to the left of a specified z-score. Select the **Calc** menu, highlight **Probability Distributions**, and highlight **Normal.** . . .

2. Select **Cumulative Probability**. Set the mean to 0 and the standard deviation to 1. Select **Input Constant**, and enter the specified z-score. Click OK.

Finding z-Scores Corresponding to an Area
1. MINITAB will find the z-score for an area to the left of an unknown z-score. Select the **Calc** menu, highlight **Probability Distributions**, and highlight **Normal.** . . .
2. Select **Inverse Cumulative Probability**. Set the mean to 0 and the standard deviation to 1. Select **Input Constant**, and enter the specified area. Click OK.

Excel

Finding Areas under the Standard Normal Curve
1. Excel will find the area to the left of a specified z-score. Select the fx button from the tool bar. In **Function Category:**, select "Statistical". In **Function Name:**, select "NORMSDIST". Click OK.
2. Enter the specified z-score. Click OK.

Finding z-Scores Corresponding to an Area
1. Excel will find the z-score for an area to the left of an unknown z-score. Select the fx button from the tool bar. In **Function Category:**, select "Statistical". In **Function Name:**, select "NORMSINV". Click OK.
2. Enter the specified area. Click OK.

7.3 APPLICATIONS OF THE NORMAL DISTRIBUTION

Preparing for This Section   Before getting started, review the following:

• Percentiles (Section 3.4, p. 168)

Objectives		
	1	Find and interpret the area under a normal curve
	2	Find the value of a normal random variable

---

1   **Find and Interpret the Area under a Normal Curve**

Note to Instructor
If you like, you can print out and distribute the Preparing for This Section quiz located in the Instructor's Resource Center. The purpose of the quiz is to verify that the students have the prerequisite knowledge for the section.

From the discussions in Section 7.1, we know that finding the area under a normal curve by hand requires that we transform values of a normal random variable X with mean μ and standard deviation σ into values of the standard normal random variable Z with mean 0 and standard deviation 1. This is accomplished by letting $Z = \dfrac{X - \mu}{\sigma}$ and using Table V to find the area under the standard normal curve. This idea is illustrated in Figure 34.

Figure 34

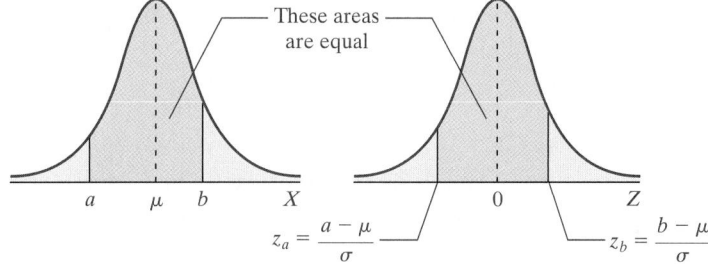

Now that we have the ability to find the area under a standard normal curve, we can find the area under any normal curve. We summarize the procedure next.

Finding the Area under Any Normal Curve

Step 1: Draw a normal curve and shade the desired area.

Step 2: Convert the values of X to z-scores using $z = \dfrac{x - \mu}{\sigma}$.

Step 3: Draw a standard normal curve and shade the desired area.

Step 4: Find the area under the standard normal curve. This area is equal to the area under the normal curve drawn in Step 1.

EXAMPLE 1   **Finding Area under a Normal Curve**

Note to Instructor
Be sure to emphasize to students that they should draw the nonstandard normal curve and the corresponding standard normal curve to reinforce their conceptual understanding for finding area under any normal curve.

Problem: A pediatrician obtains the heights of her 200 three-year-old female patients. The heights are approximately normally distributed, with mean 38.72 inches and standard deviation 3.17 inches. Use the normal model to determine the proportion of the 3-year-old females that have a height less than 35 inches.

Approach: Follow Steps 1 through 4.

Solution

Step 1: Figure 35 shows the normal curve with the area to the left of 35 shaded.

Step 2: We convert $x = 35$ to a z-score.

$$z = \frac{x - \mu}{\sigma} = \frac{35 - 38.72}{3.17} = -1.17$$

Step 3: Figure 36 shows the standard normal curve with the area to the left of $z = -1.17$ shaded. The area to the left of $z = -1.17$ is equal to the area to the left of $x = 35$.

Figure 35

Figure 36

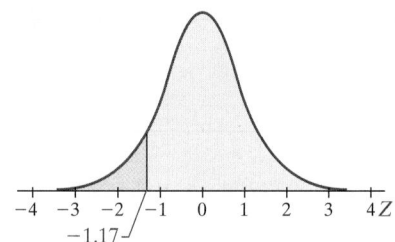

Step 4: Using Table V, we find that the area to the left of $z = -1.17$ is 0.1210. The normal model indicates that the proportion of the pediatrician's 3-year-old females that is less than 35 inches tall is 0.1210.

Table 3	
Height (inches)	**Relative Frequency**
29.0–29.9	0.005
30.0–30.9	0.005
31.0–31.9	0.005
32.0–32.9	0.025
33.0–33.9	0.02
34.0–34.9	0.055
35.0–35.9	0.075
36.0–36.9	0.09
37.0–37.9	0.115
38.0–38.9	0.15
39.0–39.9	0.12
40.0–40.9	0.11
41.0–41.9	0.07
42.0–42.9	0.06
43.0–43.9	0.035
44.0–44.9	0.025
45.0–45.9	0.025
46.0–46.9	0.005
47.0–47.9	0.005

According to the results of Example 1, the proportion of 3-year-old females who are shorter than 35 inches is 0.1210. If the normal curve is a good model for determining proportions (or probabilities), then about 12.1% of the 200 three-year-olds in Table 1 should be shorter than 35 inches. For convenience, the information provided in Table 1 is repeated in Table 3.

From the relative frequency distribution in Table 3, we determine that $0.005 + 0.005 + 0.005 + 0.025 + 0.02 + 0.055 = 0.115 = 11.5\%$ of the 3-year-old females are less than 35 inches tall. The results based on the normal curve are in close agreement with the actual results. The normal curve accurately models the heights of 3-year-old females.

Because the area under the normal curve represents a proportion, we can also use the area to find percentile ranks of scores. Recall that the kth percentile divides the lower $k\%$ of a data set from the upper $(100 - k)\%$. In Example 1, 12% of the females have a height less than 35 inches, and 88% of the females have a height greater than 35 inches. Therefore, a child whose height is 35 inches is at the 12th percentile.

Statistical software and graphing calculators with advanced statistical features can also be used to find areas under any normal curve.

EXAMPLE 2 **Finding Area under a Normal Curve Using Technology**

Problem: Find the percentile rank of a 3-year-old female whose height is 43 inches using statistical software or a graphing calculator with advanced statistical features. From Example 1, we know that the heights are approximately normally distributed, with a mean of 38.72 inches and standard deviation of 3.17 inches.

Approach: We will use a TI-84 Plus graphing calculator to find the area. The steps for determining the area under any normal curve for MINITAB, Excel, and the

Figure 37

```
normalcdf(-1E99,
43,38.72,3.17)
        .9115172428
```

TI-83/84 Plus graphing calculators are given in the Technology Step-by-Step on pages 404–405.

Solution: Figure 37 shows the results from a TI-84 Plus graphing calculator. The area under the normal curve to the left of 43 is approximately 0.91. Therefore, 91% of the heights are less than 43 inches, and 9% of the heights are more than 43 inches. A 3-year-old female whose height is 43 inches is at the 91st percentile.

EXAMPLE 3   **Finding the Probability of a Normal Random Variable**

Problem: For the pediatrician presented in Example 1, use the normal distribution to compute the probability that a randomly selected 3-year-old female is between 35 and 40 inches tall, inclusive. That is, find $P(35 \le X \le 40)$.

Approach: We follow the Steps 1 through 4 on page 397.

Solution

Step 1: Figure 38 shows the normal curve with the area between $x_1 = 35$ and $x_2 = 40$ shaded.

Step 2: Convert the values $x_1 = 35$ and $x_2 = 40$ to z-scores.

$$z_1 = \frac{x_1 - \mu}{\sigma} = \frac{35 - 38.72}{3.17} = -1.17$$

$$z_2 = \frac{x_2 - \mu}{\sigma} = \frac{40 - 38.72}{3.17} = 0.40$$

Step 3: Figure 39 shows the graph of the standard normal curve with the area between $z_1 = -1.17$ and $z_2 = 0.40$ shaded.

Figure 38   **Figure 39**

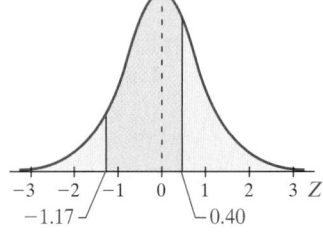

Using Technology
Due to rounding in the by-hand approach, technology answers will often differ. For example, finding the probability in Example 3 using technology, we obtain

$$P(35 \le X \le 40) = 0.5365$$

When answers between "by-hand" computation and technology differ, we will report both results.

Step 4: Using Table V, we find that the area to the left of $z_2 = 0.40$ is 0.6554 and the area to the left of $z_1 = -1.17$ is 0.1210. Therefore, the area between $z_1 = -1.17$ and $z_2 = 0.40$ is $0.6554 - 0.1210 = 0.5344$. We conclude that the probability that a randomly selected 3-year-old female is between 35 and 40 inches tall is 0.5344. That is, $P(35 \le X \le 40) = P(-1.17 \le Z \le 0.40) = 0.5344$. If we randomly selected one 3-year-old female 100 times, we would expect to select a child who is between 35 and 40 inches tall about 53 times.

Now Work Problem 19

In Other Words
The normal probability density function is used to model random variables that appear to be normal (such as girls' heights). A good model is one that yields results that are close to reality.

According to the relative frequency distribution in Table 3, the proportion of the 200 three-year-old females with heights between 35 and 40 inches is $0.075 + 0.09 + 0.115 + 0.15 + 0.12 = 0.55 = 55\%$. This is very close to the probability obtained in Example 3!

② Find the Value of a Normal Random Variable

Often, rather than being interested in the proportion, probability or percentile for a value of a normal random variable, we are interested in calculating the value of a normal random variable required for the value to correspond to a certain proportion, probability, or percentile. For example, we might want to know the height of a 3-year-old girl at the 20th percentile. This means that we want to know the height of a 3-year-old girl who is taller than 20% of all 3-year-old girls.

> **Procedure for Finding the Value of a Normal Random Variable Corresponding to a Specified Proportion, Probability, or Percentile**
>
> **Step 1:** Draw a normal curve and shade the area corresponding to the proportion, probability, or percentile.
>
> **Step 2:** Use Table V to find the z-score that corresponds to the shaded area.
>
> **Step 3:** Obtain the normal value from the formula $x = \mu + z\sigma$.*

EXAMPLE 4 **Finding the Value of a Normal Random Variable**

Problem: The heights of a pediatrician's 200 three-year-old females are approximately normally distributed, with mean 38.72 inches and standard deviation 3.17 inches. Find the height of a 3-year-old female at the 20th percentile. That is, find the height of a 3-year-old female that separates the bottom 20% from the top 80%.

Approach: We follow Steps 1 through 3.

Solution

Step 1: Figure 40 shows the normal curve with the unknown value of X separating the bottom 20% of the distribution from the top 80% of the distribution.

Step 2: From Table V, the area closest to 0.20 is 0.2005. The corresponding z-score is -0.84.

Figure 40

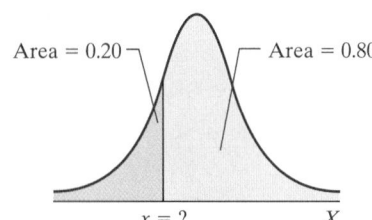

Step 3: The height of a 3-year-old female that separates the bottom 20% of the data from the top 80% is computed as follows:

$$x = \mu + z\sigma$$
$$= 38.72 + (-0.84)(3.17)$$
$$= 36.1 \text{ inches}$$

The height of a 3-year-old female at the 20th percentile is 36.1 inches.

EXAMPLE 5 **Finding the Value of a Normal Random Variable Using Technology**

Problem: Use statistical software or a graphing calculator with advanced statistical features to verify the results of Example 4. That is, find the height for a 3-year-old female that is at the 20th percentile, assuming their heights are approximately normally distributed, with a mean of 38.72 inches and a standard deviation of 3.17 inches.

---

*The formula provided in Step 3 is simply the formula for computing a z-score, solved for x.

$z = \dfrac{x - \mu}{\sigma}$ Formula for standardizing a value, x, for a random variable X

$z\sigma = x - \mu$ Multiply both sides by σ.

$x = \mu + z\sigma$ Add μ to both sides.

Approach: We will use MINITAB to find the height at the 20th percentile. The steps for determining the value of a normal random variable given an area for MINITAB, Excel, and the TI-83/84 Plus graphing calculators are given in the Technology Step-by-Step on pages 404–405.

Solution: Figure 41 shows the results obtained from MINITAB. The height of a 3-year-old female at the 20th percentile is 36.1 inches.

Figure 41   **Inverse Cumulative Distribution Function**

Normal with mean = 38.7200 and standard deviation = 3.17000

```
P ( x <= x)        x
   0.2000      36.0521
```

Now Work Problem 25(a)

EXAMPLE 6   **Finding the Value of a Normal Random Variable**

Problem: The heights of a pediatrician's 200 three-year-old females are approximately normally distributed, with mean 38.72 inches and standard deviation 3.17 inches. The pediatrician wishes to determine the heights that separate the middle 98% of the distribution from the bottom 1% and top 1%. In other words, find the 1st and 99th percentiles.

Figure 42

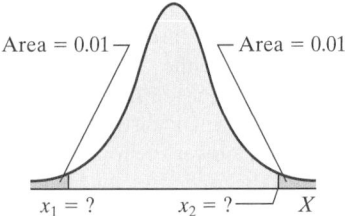

Approach: We follow Steps 1 through 3 given on page 400.

Solution

Step 1: Figure 42 shows the normal curve with the unknown values of x separating the bottom and top 1% of the distribution from the middle 98% of the distribution.

Step 2: First, we will find the z-score that corresponds to an area of 0.01 to the left. From Table V, the area closest to 0.01 is 0.0099. The corresponding z-score is -2.33. The z-score that corresponds to an area of 0.01 to the right is the z-score that has area 0.99 to the left. The area closest to 0.99 is 0.9901. The corresponding z-score is 2.33.

Step 3: The height of a 3-year-old female that separates the bottom 1% of the distribution from the top 99% is

$$x_1 = \mu + z\sigma$$
$$= 38.72 + (-2.33)(3.17)$$
$$= 31.3 \text{ inches}$$

The height of a 3-year-old female that separates the top 1% of the distribution from the bottom 99% is

$$x_2 = \mu + z\sigma$$
$$= 38.72 + (2.33)(3.17)$$
$$= 46.1 \text{ inches}$$

A 3-year-old female whose height is less than 31.3 inches is in the bottom 1% of all 3-year-old females, and a 3-year-old female whose height is more than 46.1 inches is in the top 1% of all 3-year-old females. The pediatrician might use this information to identify those patients who have unusual heights.

CAUTION If you are given a value of the random variable and asked to find the probability, proportion, or percentile corresponding to the value, convert the value to a z-score using $z = \dfrac{x - \mu}{\sigma}$ and find the area from the table. If you are using a TI-83/84 Plus graphing calculator, use `normalcdf(`.

If you are asked to find the value of a random variable corresponding to a probability, proportion, or percentile, find the area that represents the given probability, proportion, or percentile and use $x = \mu + z\sigma$ to find the value of the random variable. If you are using a TI-83/84 Plus graphing calculator, use `invNorm(`.

Now Work Problem 25(b)

7.3 ASSESS YOUR UNDERSTANDING

Concepts and Vocabulary

1. Describe the procedure for finding the area under any normal curve.

2. Describe the procedure for finding the value of a normal random variable corresponding to a probability, proportion, or percentile.

Skill Building

In Problems 3–12, assume that the random variable X is normally distributed, with mean $\mu = 50$ and standard deviation $\sigma = 7$. Compute the following probabilities. Be sure to draw a normal curve with the area corresponding to the probability shaded.

3. $P(X > 35)$ 0.9838
4. $P(X > 65)$ 0.0162
5. $P(X \leq 45)$ 0.2389
6. $P(X \leq 58)$ 0.8729
7. $P(40 < X < 65)$ 0.9074
8. $P(56 < X < 68)$ 0.1898
9. $P(55 \leq X \leq 70)$ 0.2368
10. $P(40 \leq X \leq 49)$ 0.3679
11. $P(38 < X \leq 55)$ 0.7175
12. $P(56 \leq X < 66)$ 0.1839

In Problems 13–16, assume that the random variable X is normally distributed, with mean $\mu = 50$ and standard deviation $\sigma = 7$. Find each indicated percentile for X.

13. The 9th percentile   40.62
14. The 90th percentile   58.96
15. The 81st percentile   56.16
16. The 38th percentile   47.83

Applying the Concepts

17. **Egg Incubation Times** The mean incubation time of fertilized chicken eggs kept at 100.5°F in a still-air incubator is 21 days. Suppose that the incubation times are approximately normally distributed with a standard deviation of 1 day.

    Source: University of Illinois Extension

    (a) What is the probability that a randomly selected fertilized chicken egg hatches in less than 20 days?   0.1587
    (b) What is the probability that a randomly selected fertilized chicken egg takes over 22 days to hatch?   0.1587
    (c) What is the probability that a randomly selected fertilized chicken egg hatches between 19 and 21 days?   0.4772
    (d) Would it be unusual for an egg to hatch in less than 18 days? Why?   Yes

18. **Reading Rates** The reading speed of sixth-grade students is approximately normal, with a mean speed of 125 words per minute and a standard deviation of 24 words per minute.

    (a) What is the probability that a randomly selected sixth-grade student reads less than 100 words per minute?
    (b) What is the probability that a randomly selected sixth-grade student reads more than 140 words per minute?
    (c) What is the probability that a randomly selected sixth-grade student reads between 110 and 130 words per minute?   0.3189
    (d) Would it be unusual for a sixth-grader to read more than 200 words per minute? Why?   Yes

19. **Chips Ahoy! Cookies** The number of chocolate chips in an 18-ounce bag of Chips Ahoy! chocolate chip cookies is approximately normally distributed with a mean of 1,262 chips and standard deviation 118 chips according to a study by cadets of the U.S. Air Force Academy.

    Source: Brad Warner and Jim Rutledge, *Chance* 12(1): 10–14, 1999

    (a) What is the probability that a randomly selected 18-ounce bag of Chips Ahoy! contains between 1,000 and 1,400 chocolate chips, inclusive?   0.8658
    (b) What is the probability that a randomly selected 18-ounce bag of Chips Ahoy! contains fewer than 1,000 chocolate chips?   0.0132
    (c) What proportion of 18-ounce bags of Chips Ahoy! contains more than 1,200 chocolate chips?   0.7019
    (d) What proportion of 18-ounce bags of Chips Ahoy! contains fewer than 1,125 chocolate chips?   0.1230
    (e) What is the percentile rank of an 18-ounce bag of Chips Ahoy! that contains 1,475 chocolate chips?
    (f) What is the percentile rank of an 18-ounce bag of Chips Ahoy! that contains 1,050 chocolate chips?

20. **Wendy's Drive-Through** Fast-food restaurants spend quite a bit of time studying the amount of time cars spend in their drive-throughs. Certainly, the faster the cars get through the drive-through, the more the opportunity for making money. In 2007, *QSR Magazine* studied drive-through times for fast-food restaurants and Wendy's had the best time, with a mean time spent in the drive-through of 138.5 seconds. Assuming drive-through times are normally distributed with a standard deviation of 29 seconds, answer the following.

    (a) What is the probability that a randomly selected car will get through Wendy's drive-through in less than 100 seconds?   0.0918
    (b) What is the probability that a randomly selected car will spend more than 160 seconds in Wendy's drive-through?
    (c) What proportion of cars spend between 2 and 3 minutes in Wendy's drive-through?   0.6625
    (d) Would it be unusual for a car to spend more than 3 minutes in Wendy's drive-through? Why?   No

21. **Gestation Period** The lengths of human pregnancies are approximately normally distributed, with mean $\mu = 266$ days and standard deviation $\sigma = 16$ days.

    (a) What proportion of pregnancies lasts more than 270 days?   0.4013
    (b) What proportion of pregnancies lasts less than 250 days?
    (c) What proportion of pregnancies lasts between 240 and 280 days?   0.7590
    (d) What is the probability that a randomly selected pregnancy lasts more than 280 days?   0.1894
    (e) What is the probability that a randomly selected pregnancy lasts no more than 245 days?   0.0951
    (f) A "very preterm" baby is one whose gestation period is less than 224 days. Are very preterm babies unusual?   Yes; 0.0043

22. **Light Bulbs** General Electric manufactures a decorative Crystal Clear 60-watt light bulb that it advertises will last 1,500 hours. Suppose that the lifetimes of the light bulbs are approximately normally distributed, with a mean of 1,550 hours and a standard deviation of 57 hours.

18. (a) 0.1492   18. (b) 0.2643   19. (e) 96th percentile   19. (f) 4th percentile   20. (b) 0.2296   21. (b) 0.1587

(a) What proportion of the light bulbs will last less than the advertised time? *0.1894*

(b) What proportion of the light bulbs will last more than 1,650 hours? *0.0401*

(c) What is the probability that a randomly selected GE Crystal Clear 60-watt light bulb will last between 1,625 and 1,725 hours? *0.0923*

(d) What is the probability that a randomly selected GE Crystal Clear 60-watt light bulb will last longer than 1400 hours? *0.9957*

23. **Manufacturing** Steel rods are manufactured with a mean length of 25 centimeter (cm). Because of variability in the manufacturing process, the lengths of the rods are approximately normally distributed, with a standard deviation of 0.07 cm.

(a) What proportion of rods has a length less than 24.9 cm?

(b) Any rods that are shorter than 24.85 cm or longer than 25.15 cm are discarded. What proportion of rods will be discarded? *0.0324*

(c) Using the results of part (b), if 5,000 rods are manufactured in a day, how many should the plant manager expect to discard? *162*

(d) If an order comes in for 10,000 steel rods, how many rods should the plant manager manufacture if the order states that all rods must be between 24.9 cm and 25.1 cm? *11,804*

24. **Manufacturing** Ball bearings are manufactured with a mean diameter of 5 millimeters (mm). Because of variability in the manufacturing process, the diameters of the ball bearings are approximately normally distributed, with a standard deviation of 0.02 mm.

(a) What proportion of ball bearings has a diameter more than 5.03 mm? *0.0668*

(b) Any ball bearings that have a diameter less than 4.95 mm or greater than 5.05 mm are discarded. What proportion of ball bearings will be discarded? *0.0124*

(c) Using the results of part (b), if 30,000 ball bearings are manufactured in a day, how many should the plant manager expect to discard? *372*

(d) If an order comes in for 50,000 ball bearings, how many bearings should the plant manager manufacture if the order states that all ball bearings must be between 4.97 mm and 5.03 mm? *57,711*

25. **Egg Incubation Times** The mean incubation time of fertilized chicken eggs kept at 100.5°F in a still-air incubator is 21 days. Suppose that the incubation times are approximately normally distributed with a standard deviation of 1 day.

Source: University of Illinois Extension

(a) Determine the 17th percentile for incubation times of fertilized chicken eggs. *20 days*

(b) Determine the incubation times that make up the middle 95% of fertilized chicken eggs? *19–23 days*

26. **Reading Rates** The reading speed of sixth-grade students is approximately normal, with a mean speed of 125 words per minute and a standard deviation of 24 words per minute.

(a) What is the reading speed of a sixth-grader whose reading speed is at the 90th percentile. *156 words per minute*

(b) A school psychologist wants to determine reading rates for unusual students (both slow and fast). Determine the reading rates of the middle 95% of all sixth-grade students. What are the cutoff points for unusual readers?

27. **Chips Ahoy! Cookies** The number of chocolate chips in an 18-ounce bag of Chips Ahoy! chocolate chip cookies is approximately normally distributed, with a mean of 1,262 chips and a standard deviation of 118 chips, according to a study by cadets of the U.S. Air Force Academy.

Source: Brad Warner and Jim Rutledge, *Chance* 12(1): 10–14, 1999   27. (b) *958 to 1,566 chips*

(a) Determine the 30th percentile for the number of chocolate chips in an 18-ounce bag of Chips Ahoy! cookies.

(b) Determine the number of chocolate chips in a bag of Chips Ahoy! that make up the middle 99% of bags.

28. **Wendy's Drive-Through** Fast-food restaurants spend quite a bit of time studying the amount of time cars spend in their drive-through. Certainly, the faster the cars get through the drive-through, the more the opportunity for making money. In 2007, *QSR Magazine* studied drive-through times for fast-food restaurants, and Wendy's had the best time, with a mean time a car spent in the drive-through equal to 138.5 seconds. Assume that drive-through times are normally distributed, with a standard deviation of 29 seconds. Suppose that Wendy's wants to institute a policy at its restaurants that it will not charge any patron that must wait more than a certain amount of time for an order. Management does not want to give away free meals to more than 1% of the patrons. What time would you recommend Wendy's advertise as the maximum wait time before a free meal is awarded? *206 seconds*

29. **Speedy Lube** The time required for Speedy Lube to complete an oil change service on an automobile approximately follows a normal distribution, with a mean of 17 minutes and a standard deviation of 2.5 minutes.

(a) Speedy Lube guarantees customers that the service will take no longer than 20 minutes. If it does take longer, the customer will receive the service for half-price. What percent of customers receive the service for half price?

(b) If Speedy Lube does not want to give the discount to more than 3% of its customers, how long should it make the guaranteed time limit? *22 minutes*

30. **Putting It Together: Birth Weights** The following data represent the distribution of birth weights (in grams) for babies in which the pregnancy went full term (37 to 41 weeks).

Birth Weight (g)	Number of Live Births
0–499	22
500–999	201
1,000–1,499	1,645
1,500–1,999	9,365
2,000–2,499	92,191
2,500–2,999	569,319
3,000–3,499	1,387,335
3,500–3,999	988,011
4,000–4,499	255,700
4,500–4,999	36,766
5,000–5,499	3,994

Source: National Vital Statistics Report 56(6): Dec 5, 2007.

23. (a) *0.0764*   26. (b) *78 and 172 words per minute*   27. (a) *1,201 chips*   29. (a) *11.51%*

(a) Construct a relative frequency distribution for birth weight.

(b) Draw a relative frequency histogram for birth weight. Describe the shape of the distribution.

(c) Determine the mean and standard deviation birth weight. $\mu = 3,375$ g; $\sigma = 493$ g

(d) Use the normal model to determine the proportion of babies in each class.

(e) Compare the proportions predicted by the normal model to the relative frequencies found in part (a). Do you believe that the normal model is effective in describing the birth weights of babies? Yes

Consumer Reports® *Sunscreens*

More than 1 million skin cancers are expected to be diagnosed in the United States this year, accounting for almost half of all cancers diagnosed. The prevalence of skin cancer is attributable in part to a history of unprotected or underprotected sun exposure. Sunscreens have been shown to prevent certain types of lesions associated with skin cancer. They also protect skin against exposure to light that contributes to premature aging. As a result, sunscreen is now in moisturizers, lip balms, shampoos, hair-styling products, insect repellents, and makeup.

Consumer Reports tested 23 sunscreens and two moisturizers, all with a claimed sun-protection factor (SPF) of 15 or higher. SPF is defined as the degree to which a sunscreen protects the skin from UVB, the ultraviolet rays responsible for sunburn. (Some studies have shown that UVB, along with UVA, can increase the risk of skin cancers.) A person with untreated skin who can stay in the sun for 5 minutes before becoming sunburned should be able to stay in the sun for $15 \times 5 = 75$ minutes using a sunscreen rated at SPF 15.

To test whether products met their SPF claims for UVB, we used a solar simulator (basically a sun lamp) to expose people to measured amounts of sunlight. First we determined the exposure time (in minutes) that caused each person's untreated skin to turn pink within 24 hours. Then we applied sunscreen to new areas of skin and made the same determination. To avoid potential sources of bias, samples of the sunscreens were applied to randomly assigned sites on the subjects' skin.

To determine the SPF rating of a sunscreen for a particular individual, the exposure time with sunscreen was divided by the exposure time without sunscreen. The following table contains the mean and standard deviation of the SPF measurements for two particular sunscreens.

Product	Mean	Std Dev
A	15.5	1.5
B	14.7	1.2

(a) In designing this experiment, why is it important to obtain the exposure time without sunscreen first and then determine the exposure time with sunscreen for each person?

(b) Why is the random assignment of people and application sites to each treatment (the sunscreen) important?

(c) Assuming that the SPF ratings are approximately normal, calculate the proportion of SPF measurements that you expect to be less than 15, the advertised level of protection for each of the products.

(d) Calculate the proportion of SPF measurements that you expect to be greater than 17.5 for product A. Repeat this for product B.

(e) Calculate the proportion of SPF measurements that you expect to fall between 14.5 and 15.5 for product A. Repeat this for product B.

(f) Which product appears to be superior, A or B? Support your conclusion.

Note to Readers: *In many cases, our test protocol and analytical methods are more complicated than described in these examples. The data and discussions have been modified to make the material more appropriate for the audience.*

Source: © 2001 by Consumers Union of U.S., Inc., Yonkers, NY 10703-1057, a nonprofit organization. Reprinted with permission from the June 2001 issue of CONSUMER REPORTS® for educational purposes only. No commercial use or photocopying permitted. To learn more about Consumers Union, log onto www.ConsumersReports.org.

TECHNOLOGY STEP-BY-STEP The Normal Distribution

TI-83/84 Plus

Finding Areas under the Normal Curve

1. From the HOME screen, press 2nd VARS to access the DISTRibution menu.

2. Select 2:normalcdf(.

3. With normalcdf(on the HOME screen, type *lowerbound, upperbound,* μ, σ). For example, to find the area to the left of $x = 35$ under the normal curve with $\mu = 40$ and $\sigma = 10$, type

```
normalcdf(-1E99, 35, 40, 10)
```

and hit ENTER.

Note: When there is no lowerbound, enter $-1E99$. When there is no upperbound, enter

1E99. The E shown is scientific notation; it is selected by pressing 2nd then , .

Finding Normal Values Corresponding to an Area

1. From the HOME screen, press 2nd VARS to access the DISTRibution menu.

2. Select 3:invNorm(.

3. With invNorm(on the HOME screen, type "*area left*", μ, σ). For example, to find the normal value such that the area under the normal curve to the left of the value is 0.68, with $\mu = 40$ and $\sigma = 10$, type

```
invNorm(0.68, 40, 10)
```

and hit ENTER.

MINITAB

Finding Areas under the Normal Curve
1. Select the <u>C</u>alc menu, highlight **Probability**
Distributions, and highlight **Normal . . .** .
2. Select **Cumulative Probability**. Enter the mean,
μ, and the standard deviation, σ. Select **Input**
Constant, and enter the observation. Click OK.

Finding Normal Values Corresponding to an Area
1. Select the <u>C</u>alc menu, highlight **Probability**
Distributions, and highlight **Normal . . .** .
2. Select **Inverse Cumulative Probability**. Enter
the mean, μ, and the standard deviation, σ.
Select **Input Constant**, and enter the area to the
left of the unknown normal value. Click OK.

Excel

Finding Areas under the Normal Curve
1. Select the *fx* button from the tool bar.
In **Function Category:**, select "Statistical."
In **Function Name:**, select "NORMDIST".
Click OK.
2. Enter the specified observation, μ, and σ,
and set **Cumulative** to True. Click OK.

Finding Normal Values Corresponding to an Area
1. Select the *fx* button from the tool bar. In
Function Category:, select "Statistical." In
Function Name:, select "NORMINV". Click OK.
2. Enter the area left of the unknown normal
value, μ, and σ. Click OK.

7.4 ASSESSING NORMALITY

Preparing for This Section   Before getting started, review the following:

• Shape of a distribution (Section 2.2, pp. 92–93)

Objective		Use normal probability plots to assess normality

Suppose that we obtain a simple random sample from a population whose distribution is unknown. Many of the statistical tests that we perform on small data sets (sample size less than 30) require that the population from which the sample is drawn be normally distributed.

Up to this point, we have said that a random variable X is normally distributed, or at least approximately normal, provided the histogram of the data is symmetric and bell-shaped. This method works well for large data sets, but the shape of a histogram drawn from a small sample of observations does not always accurately represent the shape of the population. For this reason, we need additional methods for assessing the normality of a random variable X when we are looking at a small set of sample data.

 ## Use Normal Probability Plots to Assess Normality

In Other Words
Normal probability plots are used to
assess normality in small data sets.

A **normal probability plot** is a graph that plots observed data versus *normal scores*. A **normal score** is the expected z-score of the data value, assuming that the distribution of the random variable is normal. The expected z-score of an observed value depends on the number of observations in the data set.

Drawing a normal probability plot requires the following steps:

> **Drawing a Normal Probability Plot**
>
> **Step 1:** Arrange the data in ascending order.
>
> **Step 2:** Compute $f_i = \dfrac{i - 0.375}{n + 0.25}$, * where i is the index (the position of the data value in the ordered list) and n is the number of observations. The expected proportion of observations less than or equal to the ith data value is f_i.
>
> **Step 3:** Find the z-score corresponding to f_i from Table V.
>
> **Step 4:** Plot the observed values on the horizontal axis and the corresponding expected z-scores on the vertical axis.

*The derivation of this formula is beyond the scope of this text.

Figure 43

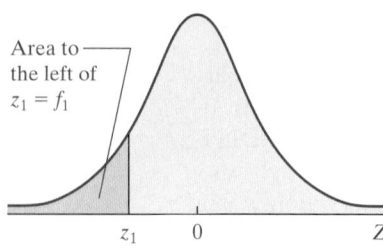

The idea behind finding the expected z-score is that, if the data come from a population that is normally distributed, we should be able to predict the area to the left of each data value. The value of f_i represents the expected area to the left of the ith observation when the data come from a population that is normally distributed. For example, f_1 is the expected area to the left of the smallest data value, f_2 is the expected area to the left of the second-smallest data value, and so on. Figure 43 illustrates the idea.

Once we determine each f_i, we find the z-scores corresponding to f_1, f_2, and so on. The smallest observation in the data set will be the smallest expected z-score, and the largest observation in the data set will be the largest expected z-score. Also, because of the symmetry of the normal curve, the expected z-scores are always paired as positive and negative values.

Values of normal random variables and their z-scores are linearly related ($x = \mu + z\sigma$), so a plot of observations of normal variables against their expected z-scores will be linear. We conclude the following:

> If sample data are taken from a population that is normally distributed, a normal probability plot of the observed values versus the expected z-scores will be approximately linear.

Normal probability plots are typically drawn using graphing calculators or statistical software. However, it is worthwhile to go through an example that demonstrates the procedure so that we can better understand the results supplied by technology.

EXAMPLE 1   **Constructing a Normal Probability Plot**

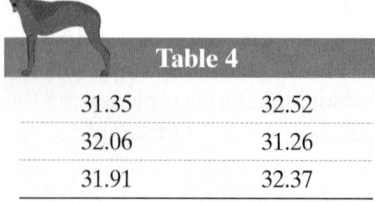

Table 4

31.35	32.52
32.06	31.26
31.91	32.37

Source: Greyhound Park, Dubuque, IA

Problem: The data in Table 4 represent the finishing time (in seconds) for six randomly selected races of a greyhound named Barbies Bomber in the $\frac{5}{16}$-mile race at Greyhound Park in Dubuque, Iowa. Is there evidence to support the belief that the variable "finishing time" is normally distributed?

Approach: We follow Steps 1 through 4.

Solution

Step 1: The first column in Table 5 represents the index i. The second column represents the observed values in the data set, written in ascending order.

Step 2: The third column in Table 5 represents $f_i = \dfrac{i - 0.375}{n + 0.25}$ for each observation. This value is the expected area under the normal curve to the left of the ith observation, assuming normality. For example, $i = 1$ corresponds to the finishing time of 31.26, and

$$f_1 = \frac{1 - 0.375}{6 + 0.25} = 0.1$$

So, the area under the normal curve to the left of 31.26 is 0.1, if the sample data come from a population that is normally distributed.

Step 3: We use Table V to find the z-scores that correspond to each f_i. The expected z-scores are listed in the fourth column of Table 5. Look in Table V for the area closest to $f_1 = 0.1$. The expected z-score is -1.28. Notice that for each negative expected z-score there is a corresponding positive expected z-score, as a result of the symmetry of the normal curve.

Sample Size, n	Critical Value
5	0.880
6	0.888
7	0.898
8	0.906
9	0.912
10	0.918
11	0.923
12	0.928
13	0.932
14	0.935
15	0.939
16	0.941
17	0.944
18	0.946
19	0.949
20	0.951
21	0.952
22	0.954
23	0.956
24	0.957
25	0.959
30	0.960

Source: S. W. Looney and T. R. Gulledge, Jr. "Use of the Correlation Coefficient with Normal Probability Plots," *American Statistician* 39(Feb. 1985): 75–79.

Table 5			
Index, i	**Observed Value**	f_i	**Expected z-score**
1	31.26	$\dfrac{1 - 0.375}{6 + 0.25} = 0.1$	−1.28
2	31.35	$\dfrac{2 - 0.375}{6 + 0.25} = 0.26$	−0.64
3	31.91	0.42	−0.20
4	32.06	0.58	0.20
5	32.37	0.74	0.64
6	32.52	0.9	1.28

Step 4: We plot the actual observations on the horizontal axis and the expected z-scores on the vertical axis. See Figure 44.

Figure 44

Although the normal probability plot in Figure 44 does show some curvature, it is roughly linear.* We conclude that the finishing times of Barbies Bomber in the $\frac{5}{16}$-mile race are approximately normally distributed.

Typically, normal probability plots are drawn using either a graphing calculator with advanced statistical features or statistical software. Certain software, such as MINITAB, will provide bounds that the data must lie within to support the belief that the sample data come from a population that is normally distributed.

EXAMPLE 2   **Assessing Normality Using Technology**

Problem: Using MINITAB or some other statistical software, draw a normal probability plot of the data in Table 4 and determine whether the sample data come from a population that is normally distributed.

Approach: We will construct a normal probability plot using MINITAB, which provides curved *bounds* that can be used to assess normality. If the normal probability plot is roughly linear and all the data lie within the bounds provided by the software, we have reason to believe the data come from a population that is approximately normal. The steps for constructing normal probability plots using MINITAB, Excel, or the TI-83/84 Plus graphing calculators can be found on page 411.

*In fact, the correlation between the observed value and expected z-score is 0.970.

Solution: Figure 45 shows the normal probability plot. Notice that MINITAB gives the area to the left of the expected z-score, rather than the z-score. For example, the area to the left of the expected z-score of -1.28 is 0.10. MINITAB writes 0.10 as 10 percent.

Figure 45

Note to Instructor
As an alternative to using MINITAB to assess the linearity of the normal probability plot, we can use the linear correlation coefficient, using the following steps. **Step 1:** Compute the linear correlation between the data and the expected z-scores. **Step 2:** Compare the linear correlation coefficient to the critical values supplied on page 407 ($\alpha = 0.05$). If the linear correlation coefficient is greater than or equal to the critical value, there is evidence to support the belief that the data come from a normally distributed population.

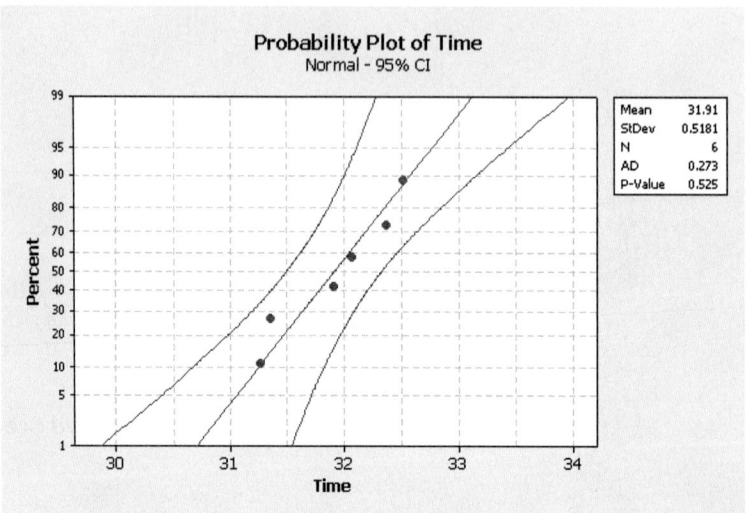

The normal probability plot is roughly linear, and all the data lie within the bounds provided by MINITAB. We conclude that the sample data could come from a population that is normally distributed.

Throughout the text, we will provide normal probability plots drawn with MINITAB so that assessing normality is straightforward.

EXAMPLE 3   Assessing Normality

Problem: The data in Table 6 represent the time spent waiting in line (in minutes) for the Demon Roller Coaster for 100 randomly selected riders. Is the random variable "wait time" normally distributed?

Table 6																	
7	3	5	107	8	37	16	41	7	25	22	19	1	40	1	29	93	
33	76	14	8	9	45	15	81	94	10	115	18	0	18	11	60	34	
30	6	21	0	86	6	11	1	1	3	9	79	41	2	9	6	19	
4	3	2	7	18	0	93	68	6	94	16	13	24	6	12	121	30	
35	39	9	15	53	9	47	5	55	64	51	80	26	24	12	0		
94	18	4	61	38	38	21	61	9	80	18	21	8	14	47	56		

Approach: We will use MINITAB to draw a normal probability plot. If the normal probability plot is roughly linear and the data lie within the bounds provided by MINITAB, we will conclude that it is reasonable to believe that the sample data come from a population that follows a normal distribution.

Solution: Figure 46 shows a normal probability plot of the data drawn using MINITAB. Since the normal probability plot is not linear, the random variable "wait time" is not normally distributed. Figure 47 shows a histogram of the data in Table 6. The histogram indicates that the data are skewed right.

Figure 46

Figure 47

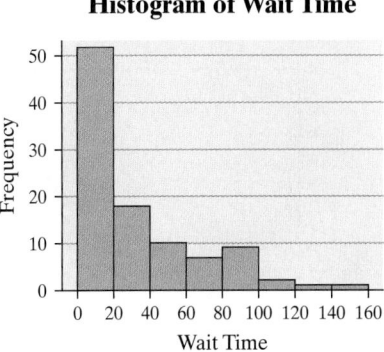

Now Work Problems 3 and 7

7.4 ASSESS YOUR UNDERSTANDING

Concepts and Vocabulary

1. Explain why normal probability plots should be linear if the data are normally distributed.

2. What does f_i represent?

Skill Building

In Problems 3–8, determine whether the normal probability plot indicates that the sample data could have come from a population that is normally distributed.

3. Not normal
NW

4. Normal

5. Not normal

6. Not normal

7. Normal

NW

8. Normal

Applying the Concepts

9. Chips per Bag In a 1998 advertising campaign, Nabisco claimed that every 18-ounce bag of Chips Ahoy! cookies contained at least 1,000 chocolate chips. Brad Warner and Jim Rutledge tried to verify the claim. The following data represent the number of chips in an 18-ounce bag of Chips Ahoy! based on their study.

1,087	1,098	1,103	1,121	1,132
1,185	1,191	1,199	1,200	1,213
1,239	1,244	1,247	1,258	1,269
1,307	1,325	1,345	1,356	1,363
1,135	1,137	1,143	1,154	1,166
1,214	1,215	1,219	1,219	1,228
1,270	1,279	1,293	1,294	1,295
1,377	1,402	1,419	1,440	1,514

Source: Chance 12 (1): 10–14, 1999

(a) Use the following normal probability plot to determine if the data could have come from a normal distribution. Normal

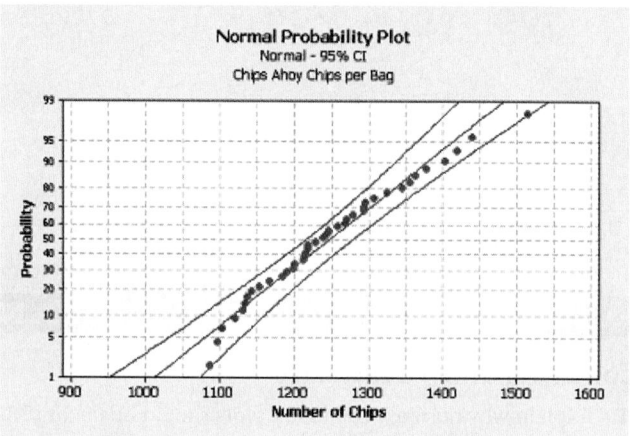

(b) Determine the mean and standard deviation of the sample data. $\bar{x} = 1247.4$, $s = 101.0$

(c) Using the sample mean and sample standard deviation obtained in part (b) as estimates for the population mean and population standard deviation, respectively, draw a graph of a normal model for the distribution of chips in a bag a Chips Ahoy!.

(d) Using the normal model from part (c), find the probability that an 18-ounce bag of Chips Ahoy! selected at random contains at least 1,000 chips. 0.9929

(e) Using the normal model from part (c), determine the proportion of 18-ounce bags of Chips Ahoy! that contains between 1,200 and 1,400 chips, inclusive. 0.6153

10. Hours of TV A random sample of college students aged 18 to 24 years was obtained, and the number of hours of television watched last week was recorded.

36.1	30.5	2.9	17.5	21.0
23.5	25.6	16.0	28.9	29.6
7.8	20.4	33.8	36.8	0.0
9.9	25.8	19.5	19.1	18.5
22.9	9.7	39.2	19.0	8.6

(a) Use the following normal probability plot to determine if the data could have come from a normal distribution. Normal

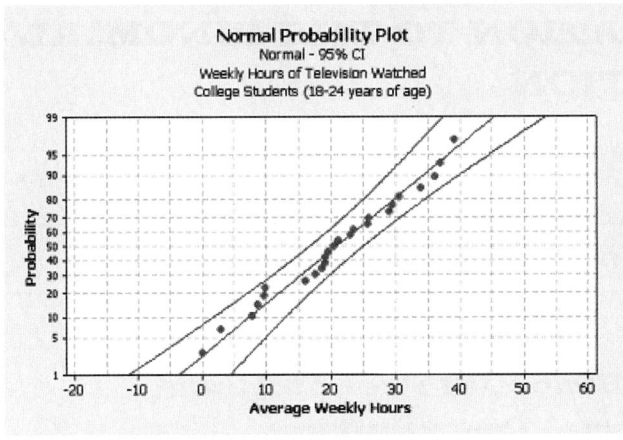

0.276	0.274	0.275	0.274	0.277
0.273	0.276	0.276	0.279	0.274
0.273	0.277	0.275	0.277	0.277
0.276	0.277	0.278	0.275	0.276

12. Customer Service A random sample of weekly work logs at an automobile repair station was obtained, and the average number of customers per day was recorded. *Normal*

26	24	22	25	23
24	25	23	25	22
21	26	24	23	24
25	24	25	24	25
26	21	22	24	24

(b) Determine the mean and standard deviation of the sample data. $\bar{x} = 20.90$, $s = 10.52$

(c) Using the sample mean and sample standard deviation obtained in part (b) as estimates for the population mean and population standard deviation, respectively, draw a graph of a normal model for the distribution of weekly hours of television watched.

(d) Using the normal model from part (c), find the probability that a college student aged 18 to 24 years, selected at random, watches between 20 and 35 hours of television each week. *0.4457*

(e) Using the normal model from part (c), determine the proportion of college students aged 18 to 24 years who watch more than 40 hours of television per week. *0.0344*

13. School Loans A random sample of 20 undergraduate students receiving student loans was obtained, and the amount of their loans for the 2007–2008 school year was recorded. *Not normal*

2,500	1,000	2,000	14,000	1,800
3,800	10,100	2,200	900	1,600
500	2,200	6,200	9,100	2,800
2,500	1,400	13,200	750	12,000

14. Memphis Snowfall A random sample of 25 years between 1890 and 2007 was obtained, and the amount of snowfall, in inches, for Memphis was recorded. *Not normal*

24.0	7.9	1.5	0.0	0.3
0.4	8.1	4.3	0.0	0.5
3.6	2.9	0.4	2.6	0.1
16.6	1.4	23.8	25.1	1.6
12.2	14.8	0.4	3.7	4.2

Source: National Oceanic and Atmospheric Administration

In Problems 11–14, use a normal probability plot to assess whether the sample data could have come from a population that is normally distributed.

11. O-Ring Thickness A random sample of O-rings was obtained, and the wall thickness (in inches) of each was recorded. *Normal*

TECHNOLOGY STEP-BY-STEP **Normal Probability Plots**

TI-83/84 Plus
1. Enter the raw data into L1.
2. Press 2nd Y= access STAT PLOTS.
3. Select 1:Plot1.
4. Turn Plot1 on by highlighting On and pressing ENTER. Press the down-arrow key. Highlight the *normal probability plot* icon. It is the icon in the lower-right corner under Type:. Press ENTER to select this plot type. The Data List should be set at L1. The Data axis should be the *x*-axis.
5. Press ZOOM, and select 9:ZoomStat.

MINITAB
1. Enter the raw data into C1.
2. Select the **Graph** menu. Highlight **Probability Plot....** Select "Single." Click OK.

3. In the Graph variables cell, enter the column that contains the raw data. Make sure Distribution is set to Normal. Click OK.

Excel
1. Install Data Desk XL.
2. Enter the raw data into column A.
3. Select the **DDXL** menu. Highlight **Charts and Plots**.
4. In the pulldown menu, select Normal Probability Plot. Drag the column containing the data to the Quantitative Variable cell and click OK. If the first row contains the variable name, check the "First row is variable name" box.

7.5 THE NORMAL APPROXIMATION TO THE BINOMIAL PROBABILITY DISTRIBUTION

Preparing for This Section Before getting started, review the following:

• Binomial probability distribution (Section 6.2, pp. 343–354)

| **Objective** | **1** | Approximate binomial probabilities using the normal distribution |

Note to Instructor

If you like, you can print out and distribute the Preparing for This Section quiz located in the Instructor's Resource Center. The purpose of the quiz is to verify that the students have the prerequisite knowledge for the section.

Note to Instructor

The material in this section is optional and can be omitted without loss of continuity.

Note to Instructor

The concepts in this section can be illustrated using the Normal Approximation to the Binomial applet.

1   **Approximate Binomial Probabilities Using the Normal Distribution**

In Section 6.2, we discussed the binomial probability distribution. Below, we remind you of the criteria for a probability experiment to be a binomial experiment.

Criteria for a Binomial Probability Experiment

A probability experiment is said to be a binomial experiment if all the following are true:

1. The experiment is performed n independent times. Each repetition of the experiment is called a **trial**. Independence means that the outcome of one trial will not affect the outcome of the other trials.

2. For each trial, there are two mutually exclusive outcomes—success or failure.

3. The probability of success, p, is the same for each trial of the experiment.

The binomial probability formula can be used to compute probabilities of events in a binomial experiment. When there is a large number of trials of a binomial experiment, the binomial probability formula can be difficult to use. For example, for 500 trials of a binomial experiment, we wish to compute the probability of 400 or more successes. Using the binomial probability formula requires that we compute the following probabilities:

$$P(X \geq 400) = P(400) + P(401) + \cdots + P(500)$$

This would be time consuming to compute by hand! Fortunately, we have an alternate means for approximating binomial probabilities, provided that certain conditions are met.

Recall, for a fixed p, as the number of trials n in a binomial experiment increases, the probability histogram becomes more nearly symmetric and bell-shaped (see page 353). We restate the conclusion here.

Historical Note

The normal approximation to the binomial was discovered by Abraham de Moivre in 1733. With the advance of computing technology, its importance has been diminished.

For a fixed p, as the number of trials n in a binomial experiment increases, the probability distribution of the random variable X becomes more nearly symmetric and bell-shaped. As a rule of thumb, if $np(1 - p) \geq 10$, the probability distribution will be approximately symmetric and bell-shaped.

Because of this result, we might be inclined to think that binomial probabilities can be approximated by the area under a normal curve, provided that $np(1 - p) \geq 10$. This intuition is correct.

The Normal Approximation to the Binomial Probability Distribution

If $np(1 - p) \geq 10$, the binomial random variable X is approximately normally distributed, with mean $\mu_X = np$ and standard deviation $\sigma_X = \sqrt{np(1 - p)}$.

Figure 48 shows a probability histogram for the binomial random variable X, with $n = 40$ and $p = 0.5$, and a normal curve, with $\mu_X = np = 40(0.5) = 20$ and standard deviation $\sigma_X = \sqrt{np(1 - p)} = \sqrt{40(0.5)(0.5)} = \sqrt{10}$. Notice that $np(1 - p) = 40(0.5)(1 - 0.5) = 10$.

Figure 48

Binomial Histogram, $n = 40, p = 0.5$

We know from Section 6.2 that the area of the rectangle corresponding to $x = 18$ represents $P(18)$. The width of each rectangle is 1, so the rectangle extends from $x = 17.5$ to $x = 18.5$. The area under the normal curve from $x = 17.5$ to $x = 18.5$ is approximately equal to the area of the rectangle corresponding to $x = 18$. Therefore, the area under the normal curve between $x = 17.5$ and $x = 18.5$ is approximately equal to $P(18)$, where X is a binomial random variable with $n = 40$ and $p = 0.5$. We add and subtract 0.5 from $x = 18$ as a **correction for continuity**, because we are using a continuous density function to approximate a discrete probability.

Suppose that we want to approximate $P(X \leq 18)$. Figure 49 illustrates the situation.

⬥ CAUTION Don't forget about the correction for continuity. It is needed because we are using a continuous density function to approximate the probability of a discrete random variable.

Figure 49

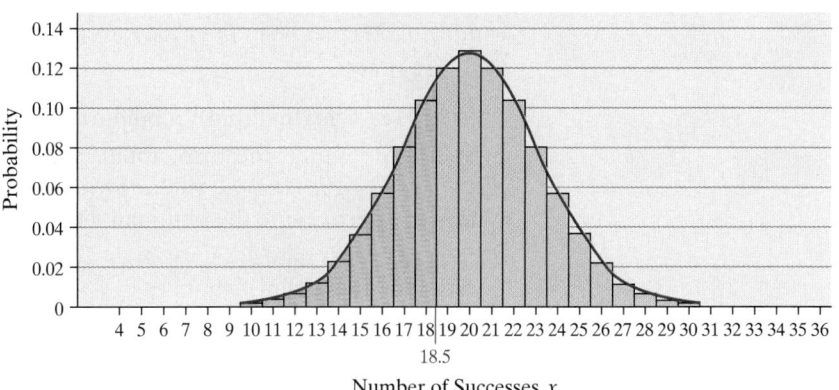

Binomial Histogram, $n = 40, p = 0.5$

To approximate $P(X \leq 18)$, we compute the area under the normal curve for $x < 18.5$. Do you see why?

If we want to approximate $P(X \geq 18)$, we compute $P(X \geq 17.5)$. Do you see why? Table 7 summarizes how to use the correction for continuity.

Table 7		
Exact Probability Using Binomial	**Approximate Probability Using Normal**	**Graphical Depiction**
$P(a)$	$P(a - 0.5 \leq X \leq a + 0.5)$	
$P(X \leq a)$	$P(X \leq a + 0.5)$	
$P(X \geq a)$	$P(X \geq a - 0.5)$	
$P(a \leq X \leq b)$	$P(a - 0.5 \leq X \leq b + 0.5)$	

A question remains, however. What do we do if the probability is of the form $P(X > a)$, $P(X < a)$, or $P(a < X < b)$? The solution is to rewrite the inequality in a form with $\leq$ or $\geq$. For example, $P(X > 4) = P(X \geq 5)$ and $P(X < 4) = P(X \leq 3)$ for binomial random variables, because the values of the random variables must be whole numbers.

EXAMPLE 1 **The Normal Approximation to a Binomial Random Variable**

Problem: According to the *American Red Cross*, 7% of people in the United States have blood type O-negative. What is the probability that, in a simple random sample of 500 people in the U.S., fewer than 30 have blood type O-negative?

Approach
Step 1: We verify that this is a binomial experiment.
Step 2: Computing the probability by hand would be very tedious. Verify $np(1 - p) \geq 10$. Then we will know that the condition for using the normal distribution to approximate the binomial distribution is met.
Step 3: Approximate $P(X < 30) = P(X \leq 29)$ by using the normal approximation to the binomial distribution.

Solution
Step 1: There are 500 independent trials with each trial having a probability of success equal to 0.07. This is a binomial experiment.
Step 2: We verify $np(1 - p) \geq 10$.

$$np(1 - p) = 500(0.07)(0.93) = 32.55 \geq 10$$

We can use the normal distribution to approximate the binomial distribution.

Figure 50

Figure 51

binomcdf(500,.07
,29)
        .1677676733

Now Work Problem 21

Step 3: We wish to know the probability that fewer than 30 people in the sample have blood type O-negative; that is, we wish to know $P(X < 30) = P(X \leq 29)$. This is approximately equal to the area under the normal curve to the left of $x = 29.5$, with $\mu_X = np = 500(0.07) = 35$ and $\sigma_X = \sqrt{np(1 - p)} = \sqrt{500(0.07)(1 - 0.07)} = \sqrt{32.55} \approx 5.71$. See Figure 50. We convert $x = 29.5$ to a z-score.

$$z = \frac{29.5 - 35}{\sqrt{32.55}} = -0.96$$

From Table V, we find that the area to the left of $z = -0.96$ is 0.1685. Therefore, the approximate probability that fewer than 30 people will have blood type O-negative is $0.1685 = 16.85\%$.

Using the *binomcdf(* command on a TI-84 Plus graphing calculator, we find that the exact probability is 0.1678. See Figure 51. The approximate result is close indeed!

EXAMPLE 2   **A Normal Approximation to the Binomial**

Problem: According to the Federal Communications Commission, 70% of all U.S. households have cable television. Erica selects a random sample of 1,000 households in DuPage County and finds that 734 of them have cable.

(a) Assuming that 70% of households have cable, what is the probability of obtaining a random sample of at least 734 households with cable from a sample of size 1,000?

(b) Does the result from part (a) contradict the FCC information? Explain.

Approach: This is a binomial experiment with $n = 1,000$ and $p = 0.70$. Erica needs to determine the probability of obtaining a random sample of at least 734 households with cable from a sample of size 1,000, assuming 70% of households have cable. Computing this using the binomial probability formula would be difficult, so Erica will compute the probability using the normal approximation to the binomial, since $np(1 - p) = 1,000(0.70)(0.30) = 210 \geq 10$. We approximate $P(X \geq 734)$ by computing the area under the standard normal curve to the right of $x = 733.5$, with $\mu_X = np = 1,000(0.70) = 700$ and $\sigma_X = \sqrt{np(1 - p)} = \sqrt{1,000(0.70)(1 - 0.70)} = \sqrt{210} \approx 14.491$.

Solution

(a) Figure 52 shows the area we wish to compute. We convert $x = 733.5$ to a z-score.

$$z = \frac{733.5 - 700}{\sqrt{210}} = 2.31$$

The area under the standard normal curve to the right of $z = 2.31$ is $1 - 0.9896 = 0.0104$. There is a 1.04% probability of obtaining 734 or more households with cable from a sample of 1,000 households, assuming that the percentage of households with cable is 70%.

(b) The result from part (a) means that about 1 sample in every 100 samples will have 734 or more households with cable if the true proportion is 0.7. Erica is not inclined to believe that her sample is one of the 1 in 100. She would conclude that the proportion of households in DuPage County with cable is higher than 0.70.

Figure 52

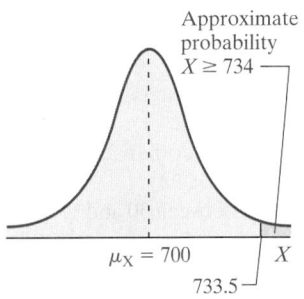

Now Work Problem 27

7.5 ASSESS YOUR UNDERSTANDING

Concepts and Vocabulary

1. List the conditions required for a binomial experiment.

2. Under what circumstances can the normal distribution be used to approximate binomial probabilities?

3. Why must we use a correction for continuity when using the normal distribution to approximate binomial probabilities?

4. *True or False:* Suppose that X is a binomial random variable. To approximate $P(3 \leq X < 7)$ using the normal probability distribution, we compute $P(3.5 \leq X < 7.5)$.   False

Skill Building

In Problems 5–14, a discrete random variable is given. Assume the probability of the random variable will be approximated using the normal distribution. Describe the area under the normal curve that will be computed. For example, if we wish to compute the probability of finding at least five defective items in a shipment, we would approximate the probability by computing the area under the normal curve to the right of $x = 4.5$.

5. The probability that at least 40 households have a gas stove   Right of x = 39.5

6. The probability of no more than 20 people who want to see *Roe v. Wade* overturned   Left of x = 20.5

7. The probability that exactly eight defective parts are in the shipment   Between x = 7.5 and x = 8.5

8. The probability that exactly 12 students pass the course

9. The probability that the number of people with blood type O-negative is between 18 and 24, inclusive

10. The probability that the number of tornadoes that occur in the month of May is between 30 and 40, inclusive

11. The probability that more than 20 people want to see the marriage tax penalty abolished   Right of x = 20.5

12. The probability that fewer than 40 households have a pet

13. The probability that more than 500 adult Americans support a bill proposing to extend daylight savings time

14. The probability that fewer than 35 people support the privatization of Social Security   Left of x = 34.5

In Problems 15–20, compute $P(x)$ using the binomial probability formula. Then determine whether the normal distribution can be used as an approximation for the binomial distribution. If so, approximate $P(x)$ and compare the result to the exact probability.

15. $n = 60$, $p = 0.4$, $x = 20$ 0.0616; 0.0618

16. $n = 80$, $p = 0.15$, $x = 18$ 0.0221; 0.0216

17. $n = 40$, $p = 0.25$, $x = 30$ <0.0001; cannot be used

18. $n = 100$, $p = 0.05$, $x = 50$ <0.0001; cannot be used

19. $n = 75$, $p = 0.75$, $x = 60$ 0.0677; 0.0630

20. $n = 85$, $p = 0.8$, $x = 70$ 0.0970; 0.0926

8. Between x = 11.5 and x = 12.5   9. Between x = 17.5 and x = 24.5   10. Between x = 29.5 and x = 40.5
12. Left of x = 39.5   13. Right of x = 500.5

Applying the Concepts

21. **On-Time Flights** According to American Airlines, Flight
    NW 215 from Orlando to Los Angeles is on time 90% of the time. Randomly select 150 flights and use the normal approximation to the binomial to
    (a) approximate the probability that exactly 130 flights are on time.   0.0444
    (b) approximate the probability that at least 130 flights are on time.   0.9332
    (c) approximate the probability that fewer than 125 flights are on time.   0.0021
    (d) approximate the probability that between 125 and 135 flights, inclusive, are on time.   0.5536

22. **Smokers** According to *Information Please Almanac*, 80% of adult smokers started smoking before they were 18 years old. Suppose 100 smokers 18 years old or older, are randomly selected. Use the normal approximation to the binomial to
    (a) approximate the probability that exactly 80 of them started smoking before they were 18 years old.   0.1034
    (b) approximate the probability that at least 80 of them started smoking before they were 18 years old.   0.5517
    (c) approximate the probability that fewer than 70 of them started smoking before they were 18 years old.   0.0043
    (d) approximate the probability that between 70 and 90 of them, inclusive, started smoking before they were 18 years old.   0.9914

23. **Migraine Sufferers** In clinical trials of a medication whose purpose is to reduce the pain associated with migraine headaches, 2% of the patients in the study experienced weight gain as a side effect. A random sample of 600 users of this medication is obtained. Use the normal approximation to the binomial to
    (a) approximate the probability that exactly 20 will experience weight gain as a side effect.   0.0077
    (b) approximate the probability that 20 or fewer will experience weight gain as a side effect.   0.9934
    (c) approximate the probability that 22 or more patients will experience weight gain as a side effect.   0.0028
    (d) approximate the probability that between 20 and 30 patients, inclusive, will experience weight gain as a side effect.   0.0143

24. **Murder by Firearms** According to the *Uniform Crime Report, 2005*, 67.8% of murders are committed with a firearm. Suppose that 50 murders are randomly selected. Use the normal approximation to the binomial to
    (a) approximate the probability that exactly 40 murders are committed using a firearm.   0.0227
    (b) approximate the probability that at least 35 murders are committed using a firearm.   0.4286
    (c) approximate the probability that fewer than 25 murders are committed using a firearm.   0.0022
    (d) approximate the probability that between 30 and 35 murders, inclusive, are committed using a firearm.   0.5926

25. **Males Living at Home** According to the *Current Population Survey* (Internet release date: September 15, 2004), 55% of males between the ages of 18 and 24 years lived at home in

2003. (Unmarried college students living in a dorm are counted as living at home.) A survey is administered at a community college to 200 randomly selected male students between the ages of 18 and 24 years, and 130 of them respond that they live at home.

(a) Approximate the probability that such a survey will result in at least 130 of the respondents living at home under the assumption that the true percentage is 55%.   *0.0028*

(b) Does the result from part (a) contradict the results of the *Current Population Survey*? Explain.   Yes

26. **Females Living at Home** According to the *Current Population Survey* (Internet release date: September 15, 2004), 46% of females between the ages of 18 and 24 years lived at home in 2003. (Unmarried college students living in a dorm are counted as living at home.) A survey is administered at a community college to 200 randomly selected female students between the ages of 18 and 24 years, and 110 of them respond that they live at home.

(a) Approximate the probability that such a survey will result in at least 110 of the respondents living at home under the assumption that the true percentage is 46%.   *0.0066*

(b) Does the result from part (a) contradict the results of the *Current Population Survey*? Explain.   Yes

27. **Boys Are Preferred** In a Gallup poll conducted June 11–14, 2007, 37% of survey respondents said that, if they only had one child, they would prefer the child to be a boy. You conduct a survey of 150 randomly selected students on your campus and find that 80 of them would prefer a boy.

(a) Approximate the probability that, in a random sample of 150 students, at least 75 would prefer a boy, assuming the true percentage is 37%.   *0.0007*

(b) Does this result contradict the Gallup poll? Explain.   Yes

28. **Liars** According to a *USA Today* "Snapshot," 3% of Americans surveyed lie frequently. You conduct a survey of 500 college students and find that 20 of them lie frequently.

(a) Compute the probability that, in a random sample of 500 college students, at least 20 lie frequently, assuming the true percentage is 3%.   *0.1190*

(b) Does this result contradict the *USA Today* "Snapshot"? Explain.   No

CHAPTER 7 REVIEW

Summary

In this chapter, we introduced continuous random variables and the normal probability density function. A continuous random variable is said to be approximately normally distributed if a histogram of its values is symmetric and bell-shaped. In addition, we can draw normal probability plots that are based on expected z-scores. If these normal probability plots are approximately linear, we say the distribution of the random variable is approximately normal. The area under the normal density function can be used to find proportions, probabilities, or percentiles for normal random variables. Also, we can find the value of a normal random variable that corresponds to a specific proportion, probability, or percentile.

If X is a binomial random variable with $np(1 - p) \geq 10$, we can use the area under the normal curve to approximate the probability of a binomial random variable. The parameters of the normal curve are $\mu_X = np$ and $\sigma_X = \sqrt{np(1 - p)}$, where n is the number of trials of the binomial experiment and p is the probability of success.

Vocabulary

Uniform probability distribution (p. 373)
Probability density function (p. 373)
Normal curve (p. 375)
Normally distributed (p. 375)
Normal probability distribution (p. 375)

Inflection points (p. 375)
Normal density curve (p. 376)
Model (p. 377)
Normal probability density function (p. 378)
Standard normal distribution (p. 379)
Standard normal curve (p. 385)

Normal probability plot (p. 405)
Normal score (p. 405)
Trial (p. 412)
Normal approximation to the binomial distribution (p. 413)
Correction for continuity (p. 413)

Formulas

Standardizing a Normal Random Variable

$$z = \frac{x - \mu}{\sigma}$$

Finding the Score

$$x = \mu + z\sigma$$

Objectives

Section	You should be able to . . .	Examples	Review Exercises
7.1	1 Utilize the uniform probability distribution (p. 373)	1 and 2	22
	2 Graph a normal curve (p. 375)	page 375	11–13
	3 State the properties of the normal curve (p. 376)	page 376	23
	4 Explain the role of area in the normal density function (p. 376)	3 and 4	1
	5 Describe the relation between a normal random variable and a standard normal random variable (p. 379)	5	2
7.2	1 Find the area under the standard normal curve (p. 385)	1–4	3, 4
	2 Find z-scores for a given area (p. 389)	5–9	8–10
	3 Interpret the area under the standard normal curve as a probability (p. 393)	10	5–7
7.3	1 Find and interpret the area under a normal curve (p. 397)	1–3	11–13, 14(a)–(c), 15(a)–(d), 16
	2 Find the value of a normal random variable (p. 400)	4–6	14(d), 15(e)–(f)
7.4	1 Draw normal probability plots to assess normality (p. 405)	1–3	18–20, 24
7.5	1 Approximate binomial probabilities using the normal distribution (p. 412)	1 and 2	17, 21

Review Exercises

1. Use the figure to answer the questions that follow:

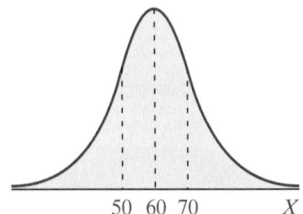

50 60 70 X

(a) What is μ? 60
(b) What is σ? 10
(c) Suppose that the area under the normal curve to the right of $x = 75$ is 0.0668. Provide two interpretations for this area.
(d) Suppose that the area under the normal curve between $x = 50$ and $x = 75$ is 0.7745. Provide two interpretations for this area.

2. A random variable X is approximately normally distributed, with $\mu = 20$ and $\sigma = 4$.

(a) Compute $z_1 = \dfrac{x_1 - \mu}{\sigma}$ for $x_1 = 18$. -0.5

(b) Compute $z_2 = \dfrac{x_2 - \mu}{\sigma}$ for $x_2 = 21$. 0.25

(c) The area under the normal curve between $x_1 = 18$ and $x_2 = 21$ is 0.2912. What is the area between z_1 and z_2? 0.2912

In Problems 3 and 4, draw a standard normal curve and shade the area indicated. Then find the area of the shaded region.

3. The area to the left of $z = -1.04$. 0.1492

4. The area between $z = -0.34$ and $z = 1.03$. 0.4816

In Problems 5–7, find the indicated probability of the standard normal random variable Z.

5. $P(Z < 1.19)$ 0.8830   **6.** $P(Z \ge 1.61)$ 0.0537

7. $P(-1.21 < Z \le 2.28)$ 0.8756

8. Find the z-score such that the area to the right of the z-score is 0.483. 0.04

9. Find the z-scores that separate the middle 92% of the data from the area in the tails of the standard normal distribution. $-1.75, 1.75$

10. Find the value of $z_{0.20}$. 0.84

In Problems 11–13, draw the normal curve with the parameters indicated. Then find the probability of the random variable X. Shade the area that represents the probability.

11. $\mu = 50, \sigma = 6, P(X > 55)$ 0.2033

12. $\mu = 30, \sigma = 5, P(X \le 23)$ 0.0808

13. $\mu = 70, \sigma = 10, P(65 < X < 85)$ 0.6247

14. Tire Wear Suppose that Dunlop Tire manufactures tires having the property that the mileage the tire lasts approximately follows a normal distribution with mean 70,000 miles and standard deviation 4,400 miles.

(a) What proportion of the tires will last at least 75,000 miles? 0.1271
(b) Suppose that Dunlop warrants the tires for 60,000 miles. What proportion of the tires will last 60,000 miles or less? 0.0116
(c) What is the probability that a randomly selected Dunlop tire lasts between 65,000 and 80,000 miles? 0.8613
(d) Suppose that Dunlop wants to warrant no more than 2% of its tires. What mileage should the company advertise as its warranty mileage? 60,980 miles

15. Wechsler Intelligence Scale The Wechsler Intelligence Scale for Children is approximately normally distributed, with mean 100 and standard deviation 15.

(a) What is the probability that a randomly selected test taker will score above 125? 0.0475
(b) What is the probability that a randomly selected test taker will score below 90? 0.2514
(c) What proportion of test takers will score between 110 and 140? 0.2476
(d) If a child is randomly selected, what is the probability that she scores above 150? 0.0004
(e) What intelligence score will place a child in the 98th percentile? 131

(f) If normal intelligence is defined as scoring in the middle 95% of all test takers, figure out the scores that differentiate normal intelligence from abnormal intelligence.   71–129

16. Major League Baseballs According to major league baseball rules, the ball must weigh between 5 and 5.25 ounces. A factory produces baseballs whose weights are approximately normally distributed, with mean 5.11 ounces and standard deviation 0.062 ounces.

Source: www.baseball-almanac.com

(a) What proportion of the baseballs produced by this factory are too heavy for use by major league baseball?   0.0119

(b) What proportion of the baseballs produced by this factory are too light for use by major league baseball?   0.0384

(c) What proportion of the baseballs produced by this factory can be used by major league baseball?   0.9497

(d) If 8,000 baseballs are ordered, how many baseballs should be manufactured, knowing that some will need to be discarded?   8,424

17. America Reads According to a Gallup poll conducted May 20–22, 2005, 46% of Americans 18 years old or older stated that they had read at least six books (fiction and nonfiction) within the past year. You conduct a random sample of 250 Americans 18 years old or older.

(a) Verify that the conditions for using the normal distribution to approximate the binomial distribution are met.

(b) Approximate the probability that exactly 125 read at least six books within the past year. Interpret this result.   0.0214

(c) Approximate the probability that fewer than 120 read at least six books within the past year. Interpret this result.   0.7157

(d) Approximate the probability that at least 140 read at least six books within the past year. Interpret this result.   0.0009

(e) Approximate the probability that between 100 and 120, inclusive, read at least six books within the past year. Interpret this result.   0.7336

In Problems 18 and 19, a normal probability plot of a simple random sample of data from a population whose distribution is unknown was obtained. Given the normal probability plot, is there reason to believe the population is normally distributed?

18.   Normal

19.   Not normal

20. Density of Earth In 1798, Henry Cavendish obtained 27 measurements of the density of Earth, using a torsion balance. The following data represent his estimates, given as a multiple of the density of water. Is it reasonable to conclude that the sample data come from a population that is normally distributed?   No

5.50	5.57	5.42	5.61	5.53
5.47	4.88	5.62	5.63	4.07
5.29	5.34	5.26	5.44	5.55
5.34	5.30	5.36	5.79	5.29
5.10	5.86	5.58	5.27	5.85
5.65	5.39			

Source: S. M. Stigler. "Do Robust Estimators Work with Real Data?" *Annals of Statistics* 5(1977), 1055–1078.

21. Creative Thinking According to a *USA Today* "Snapshot," 20% of adults surveyed do their most creative thinking while driving. You conduct a survey of 250 adults and find that 30 do their most creative thinking while driving.

(a) Compute the probability that, in a random sample of 250 adults, 30 or fewer do their most creative thinking while driving.   0.0010

(b) Does this result contradict the *USA Today* "Snapshot"? Explain.   Yes

22. A continuous random variable X is uniformly distributed with $0 \le X \le 20$.

(a) Draw a graph of the uniform density function.

(b) What is $P(0 \le X \le 5)$?   0.25

(c) What is $P(10 \le X \le 18)$?   0.4

23. List the properties of the standard normal curve.

24. Explain how to use a normal probability plot to assess normality.

CHAPTER TEST

1. Use the figure to answer the questions that follow:

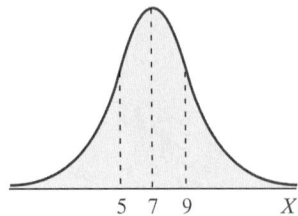

(a) What is μ? _7_
(b) What is σ? _2_
(c) Suppose that the area under the normal curve to the left of $x = 10$ is 0.9332. Provide two interpretations for this area.
(d) Suppose that the area under the normal curve between $x = 5$ and $x = 8$ is 0.5328. Provide two interpretations for this area.

2. A random variable X is approximately normally distributed with $\mu = 50$ and $\sigma = 8$.

(a) Compute $z_1 = \dfrac{x_1 - \mu}{\sigma}$ for $x_1 = 48$. _−0.25_

(b) Compute $z_2 = \dfrac{x_2 - \mu}{\sigma}$ for $x_2 = 60$. _1.25_

(c) The area under the normal curve between $x_1 = 48$ and $x_2 = 60$ is 0.4931. What is the area between z_1 and z_2? _0.4931_

3. Draw a standard normal curve and shade the area to the right of $z = 2.04$. Then find the area of the shaded region. _0.0207_

4. Find $P(0.21 < Z < 1.69)$. _0.3713_

5. Find the z-scores that separate the middle 88% of the data from the area in the tails of the standard normal distribution. _−1.555, 1.555_

6. Find the value of $z_{0.04}$. _1.75_

7. (a) Draw a normal curve with $\mu = 20$ and $\sigma = 3$.
(b) Shade the region that represents $P(22 \leq X \leq 27)$ and find the probability. _0.2415_

8. Suppose that the talk time on the Apple iPhone is approximately normally distributed with mean 7 hours and standard deviation 0.8 hour.
(a) What proportion of the time will a fully charged iPhone last at least 6 hours? _0.8944_
(b) What is the probability a fully charged iPhone will last less than 5 hours? _0.0062_
(c) What talk time would represent the cutoff for the top 5% of all talk times? _8.3 hours_
(d) Would it be unusual for the phone to last more than 9 hours? Why? _Yes_

9. The waist circumference of males 20 to 29 years old is approximately normally distributed, with mean 92.5 cm and standard deviation 13.7 cm.

Source: M. A. McDowell, C. D. Fryar, R. Hirsch, and C. L. Ogden. *Anthropometric Reference Data for Children and Adults: U.S. Population, 1999–2002*. Advance data from vital and health statistics; No. 361. Hyattsville, MD: National Center for Health Statistics, 2005.

(a) Use the normal model to determine the proportion of 20- to 29-year-old males whose waist circumference is less than 100 cm. _0.7088_
(b) What is the probability that a randomly selected 20- to 29-year-old male has a waist circumference between 80 and 100 cm? _0.5274_
(c) Determine the waist circumferences that represent the middle 90% of all waist circumferences. _70 to 115 cm_
(d) Determine the waist circumference that is at the 10th percentile _75 cm_

10. In a poll conducted by the Gallup organization August 13–16, 2007, 16% of adult, employed Americans were dissatisfied with the amount of their vacation time. You conduct a survey of 500 adult, employed Americans.
(a) Approximate the probability that exactly 100 are dissatisfied with their amount of vacation time. _0.0025_
(b) Approximate the probability that less than 60 are dissatisfied with their amount of vacation time. _0.0062_

11. Jane obtained a random sample of 15 college students and asked how many hours they studied last week. Is it reasonable to believe that hours studied is normally distributed based on the following normal probability plot? _No; not normal_

12. A continuous random variable X is uniformly distributed with $10 \leq X \leq 50$.
(a) Draw a graph of the uniform density function.
(b) What is $P(20 \leq X \leq 30)$? _0.25_
(c) What is $P(X < 15)$? _0.125_

MAKING AN INFORMED DECISION

Join the Club

You are interested in starting your own MENSA-type club. To qualify for the club, the potential member must have intelligence that is in the top 20% of all people. The problem that you face is that you do not have a baseline for measuring what qualifies as a top 20% score. To gather data, you must obtain a random sample of at least 25 volunteers to take an online intelligence test. Many online intelligence tests are available, but you need to make sure that the test will supply scored exams. One suggested site is www.queendom.com/tests/iq/classical_iq_r2_access.html.

Once you have obtained your sample of at least 25 test scores, answer the following questions.

(a) What is the mean test score? What is the standard deviation of the test scores?

(b) Do the sample data come from a population that is normally distributed? How do you know this?

(c) Assuming that the sample data come from a population that is normally distributed, determine the test score that would be required to join your club. That is, determine the test score that serves as a cutoff point for the top 20%. You can use this score to determine which potential members may join!

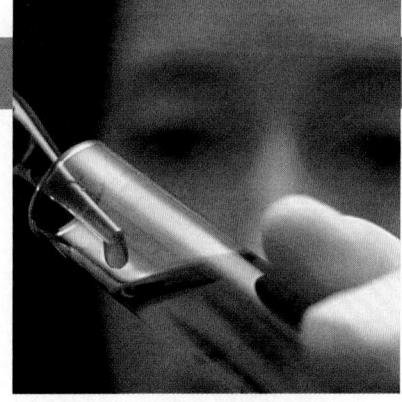

CASE STUDY

A Tale of Blood Chemistry and Health

Abby Tudor recently turned 40 years old. Her knees ache, and she often feels short of breath during exercise. She is experiencing fatigue and often feels that she is going in slow motion. Periodic dizziness plagues her during most days. According to the drugstore machine, her blood pressure is elevated. Her family has a history of cardiac disease, with both of her parents having experienced heart attacks. Additionally, an aunt on her mother's side has diabetes. Hypothyroidism also runs throughout her immediate family. Abby is approximately 20 pounds overweight. She has tried various diet and exercise programs in an attempt to lose weight. Her results have been disappointing.

With the advice of her physician, she scheduled an appointment for a full physical exam, including a complete blood workup. Her doctor is particularly interested in the level of various blood components that might shed some light on Abby's reported symptoms. Specifically, he wants to examine her white blood cell count, red blood cell count, hemoglobin, and hematocrit figures for indications of infection or anemia. Her serum glucose level will provide information concerning the possibility of the onset of diabetes. Cholesterol and triglyceride levels will provide insight into potential cardiac problems. Additionally, the possibility of hypothyroidism will be investigated by examining Abby's serum TSH level.

As instructed, two weeks before her doctor's appointment, she reported to her doctor's lab for a blood test. She confirmed for the lab technician that she had fasted for the 12 hours immediately preceding the exam.

During her physical, Abby's doctor went over the blood test report with her. He expressed concern over some of the results, but Abby was not convinced that she had a problem. Additional blood tests were not a viable option because it takes a good deal of time to get a sample of readings and they are expensive. At the time of her doctor's appointment, she was unwilling to accept the offered prescriptions. She chose to do a little research before committing herself to any drug regimen.

Her research revealed that many medical measurements, such as cholesterol, are normally distributed in healthy populations. Unfortunately, the lab report did not provide the means and standard deviations necessary for Abby to calculate the various probabilities of interest. However, the report did provide the appropriate reference intervals. Assuming that the reference intervals represent the range of values for each blood component for a healthy adult population, it is possible to estimate the various means and standard deviations for this population. Abby estimated each mean by taking the midpoint of its reference interval. Using the Range Rule of Thumb ($\sigma \approx$ range/4), standard deviations were estimated by dividing the reference interval range by 4. The following table lists Abby's blood test results, as well as the mean and standard deviation for a number of blood test components for the population of normal healthy adults.

For any blood component measurement that was below its population mean, Abby decided to calculate the probability that she would get a test value less than or equal to the value obtained, given that she was a member of the healthy population. For example, her HDL cholesterol reading (42 mg/dL) was below the mean of the healthy population (92.5 mg/dL), so she calculated the following probability:

$$P(X \leq 42 \text{ mg/dL})$$

Blood Test Components for Healthy Adults and the Blood Test Results for Abby Tudor*				
Abby's Blood Test Component	Unit	Standard Mean	Abby's Absolute Deviation	Result
White blood cell count	10^3/mL	7.25	1.625	5.3
Red blood cell count	10^6/mL	4.85	0.375	4.62
Hemoglobin	g/dL	14.75	1.125	14.6
Hematocrit	%	43.0	3.5	41.7
Glucose, serum	mg/dL	87.0	11.0	95.0
Creatine, serum	mg/dL	1.00	0.25	0.8
Sodium, serum	mEq/L	141.5	3.25	143.0
Potassium, serum	mEq/L	4.5	0.5	5.1
Chloride, serum	mEq/L	102.5	3.25	100.0
Carbon dioxide, total	mEq/L	26.0	3.0	25.0
Calcium, serum	mg/dL	9.55	0.525	10.1
Total cholesterol	mg/dL	149.5	24.75	253.0
Triglycerides	mg/dL	99.5	49.75	150.0
HDL cholesterol	mg/dL	92.5	28.75	42.0
LDL cholesterol	mg/dL	64.5	32.25	181.0
LDL/HDL ratio	Ratio	1.8	0.72	4.3
TSH, high sensitivity, serum	mcIU/mL	2.925	1.2875	3.15

*Population means and standard deviations were estimated from the reference intervals derived from an actual blood test report provided by TA LabCorp, Tampa, Florida. Means were estimated by taking the midpoints of the reference intervals. Standard deviations were estimated by dividing the reference interval ranges by 4. Test results attributed to Abby Tudor are actual results obtained from an anonymous patient.

Similarly, for any blood component measurement reading exceeding its population mean, Abby decided to calculate the probability that she would get a test value greater than or equal to the value obtained, given that she was a member of the healthy population. For example, her LDL cholesterol value (181 mg/dL) exceeds the mean of the healthy population (64.5 mg/dL), so she calculated the following probability:

$$P(X \geq 181 \text{ mg/dL})$$

To help her interpret the calculated probabilities, Abby decided to be concerned about only those blood components that had a probability of less than 0.025. By choosing this figure, she is acknowledging that it is unlikely that she could have such an extreme blood component reading and still be part of the healthy population.

1. The reference interval for HDL cholesterol is 35 to 150 mg/dL. Use this information to confirm the mean and standard deviation provided for this blood component.

2. Using Abby's criteria and the means and standard deviations provided in her blood test report, determine which blood components should be a cause of concern for Abby. Write up a summary report of your findings. Be sure to include a discussion concening your assumptions and any limitations to your conclusions.

PART 4

Inference: From Samples to Population

CHAPTER 8
Sampling Distributions

CHAPTER 9
Estimating the Value of a Parameter Using Confidence Intervals

CHAPTER 10
Hypothesis Tests Regarding a Parameter

CHAPTER 11
Inferences on Two Samples

CHAPTER 12
Inference on Categorical Data

CHAPTER 13
Comparing Three or More Means

CHAPTER 14
Inference on the Least-Squares Regression Model and Multiple Regression

CHAPTER 15
Nonparametric Statistics

In Chapter 1, we presented the following process of statistics:

Step 1: Identify the research objective.

Step 2: Collect the data needed to answer the question(s) posed in Step 1.

Step 3: Describe the data.

Step 4: Perform inference.

The methods for conducting Steps 1 and 2 were discussed in Chapter 1. The methods for conducting Step 3 were discussed in Chapters 2 through 4. We took a break from the statistical process in Chapters 5 through 7 so that we could develop skills that allow us to tackle Step 4.

If the information (data) collected is from the entire population, we can use the summaries obtained in Step 3 to draw conclusions about the population being studied and the statistical process is over.

However, it is often difficult or impossible to gain access to populations, so the information obtained in Step 2 is often sample data. The sample data are used to make inferences about the population. For example, we might compute a sample mean from the data collected in Step 2 and use this information to draw conclusions regarding the population mean. The last part of this text discusses how sample data are used to draw conclusions about populations.

8 Sampling Distributions

Outline

8.1 Distribution of the Sample Mean

8.2 Distribution of the Sample Proportion

◢ MAKING AN INFORMED DECISION

The American Time Use Survey is a survey of adult Americans conducted by the Bureau of Labor Statistics. The purpose of the survey is to learn how Americans allocate their time during a day. As a reporter for the school newspaper, you wish to file a report that compares the typical student at your school to other Americans. See the Decisions project on page 453.

PUTTING IT TOGETHER

In Chapters 6 and 7, we learned about random variables and their probability distributions. A random variable is a numerical measure of the outcome to a probability experiment. A probability distribution provides a way to assign probabilities to the possible values of the random variable. For discrete random variables, we discussed the binomial probability distribution and the Poisson probability distribution. We assigned probabilities using a formula. For continuous random variables, we discussed the normal probability distribution. To compute probabilities for a normal random variable, we found the area under a normal density curve.

In this chapter, we continue our discussion of probability distributions where statistics, such as $\bar{x}$, will be the random variable. Statistics are random variables because the value of a statistic varies from sample to sample. For this reason, statistics have probability distributions associated with them. For example, there is a probability distribution for the sample mean, sample variance, and so on. We use probability distributions to make probability statements regarding the statistic. So, this chapter discusses the shape, center, and spread of statistics such as $\bar{x}$.

8.1 DISTRIBUTION OF THE SAMPLE MEAN

Preparing for This Section   Before getting started, review the following:

- Simple random sampling (Section 1.2, pp. 22–27)
- The mean (Section 3.1, pp. 129–131)
- The standard deviation (Section 3.2, pp. 148–150)
- Applications of the normal distribution (Section 7.3, pp. 397–401)

Objectives Describe the distribution of the sample mean—samples from normal populations

 Describe the distribution of the sample mean—samples from a population that is not normal

---

Note to Instructor

If you like, you can print out and distribute the Preparing for This Section quiz located in the Instructor's Resource Center. The purpose of the quiz is to verify that the students have the prerequisite knowledge for the section.

Suppose that the government wanted to determine the mean income of all U.S. households. One approach the government could take is to literally survey each household in the United States to determine the population mean, μ. This would be a very expensive and time-consuming survey!

A second approach that the government could (and does) take is to survey a random sample of U.S. households and use the results of the survey to estimate the mean household income. This is done through the American Community Survey. The survey is administered to approximately 250,000 randomly selected households each month. Among the many questions on the survey, respondents are asked to report the income of each individual in the household. From this information, the federal government obtains a sample mean household income for U.S. households. For example, in 2006 the mean annual household income in the United States was estimated to be $\overline{x} = \$65{,}527$. The government might infer from this result that the mean annual household income of *all* U.S. households in 2006 was $\mu = \$65{,}527$.

The households that were administered the American Community Survey were determined by chance (random sampling). A second random sample of households would likely lead to a different sample mean, such as $\overline{x} = \$65{,}731$, and a third random sample of households would likely lead to a third sample mean, such as $\overline{x} = \$64{,}978$. Because the households selected to be in the sample will vary from sample to sample, the sample mean of household income will also vary from sample to sample. For this reason, the sample mean $\overline{x}$ is a random variable, so it has a probability distribution associated with it. Our goal in this section is to describe the distribution of the sample mean. Remember, when we describe a distribution, we do so in terms of its shape, center, and spread.

Definitions   The **sampling distribution** of a statistic is a probability distribution for all possible values of the statistic computed from a sample of size n.

The **sampling distribution of the sample mean** $\overline{x}$ is the probability distribution of all possible values of the random variable $\overline{x}$ computed from a sample of size n from a population with mean μ and standard deviation σ.

The idea behind obtaining the sampling distribution of the mean is as follows:

In Other Words

If the number of individuals in a population is a positive integer, we say the population is finite. Otherwise, the population is infinite.

Step 1: Obtain a simple random sample of size n.

Step 2: Compute the sample mean.

Step 3: Assuming that we are sampling from a finite population, repeat Steps 1 and 2 until all distinct simple random samples of size n have been obtained.

Note: Once a particular sample is obtained, it cannot be obtained a second time.

IN CLASS ACTIVITY

Sampling Distributions

Randomly select six students from the class to treat as a population. Choose a quantitative variable (such as pulse rate, age, or number of siblings) to use for this activity, and gather the data appropriately. Compute μ for the population. Divide the class into four groups and have one group list all samples of size $n = 2$, another group list all samples of size $n = 3$, and other groups list all samples of size $n = 4$ and $n = 5$. Each group should do the following:

(a) Compute the sample mean of each sample.

(b) Form the probability distribution for the sample mean.

(c) Draw a probability histogram of the probability distribution.

(d) Verify that $\mu_{\bar{x}} = \mu$.

Compare the spread in each probability distribution using the probability histogram. What does this result imply about the standard deviation of the sample mean?

1 Describe the Distribution of the Sample Mean—Samples from Normal Populations

The probability distribution of the sample mean is determined from statistical theory. We will use simulation to help justify the result that statistical theory provides. We consider two possibilities. In the first case (Examples 1, 2, and 3), we sample from a population that is known to be normally distributed. In the second case (Examples 4 and 5), we sample from a distribution that is not normally distributed.

EXAMPLE 1 **Sampling Distribution of the Sample Mean—Normal Population**

Using Technology
We are using MINITAB's <u>R</u>andom Data command under the <u>C</u>alc menu to generate these data. Select Normal . . . from the <u>R</u>andom Data menu.

Problem: An intelligence quotient, or IQ, is a measurement of intelligence derived from a standardized test. One such test is the Stanford–Binet IQ test, which is normally distributed with a mean score of 100 and a standard deviation of 15. What is the sampling distribution of the sample mean for a sample of size $n = 9$?

Approach: To determine the sampling distribution of the sample mean of size $n = 9$, we need to determine the shape, center, and spread of the distribution of the sample mean. Remember, the sampling distribution of the sample mean would be the distribution of *all* possible sample means of size $n = 9$. To get a sense of this distribution, we use MINITAB to simulate obtaining 1,000 samples of size $n = 9$ by randomly generating 1,000 rows of IQs over 9 columns. Each row represents a random sample of size 9. For each of the 1,000 samples (the 1,000 rows), we determine the mean IQ score. We draw a histogram to gauge the shape of the distribution of the sample mean, we determine the mean of the 1,000 sample means to approximate the mean of the sampling distribution, and we determine the standard deviation of the 1,000 sample means to approximate the standard deviation of the sampling distribution.

Solution: Figure 1 shows partial output from MINITAB. Row 1 contains the first sample, where the IQ scores of the nine individuals are 90, 74, 95, 88, 91, 91, 102, 91, and 96. The mean of these nine IQ scores is 90.9. Row 2 represents a second sample with nine different IQ scores; row 3 represents a third sample, and so on. The values in column C10 (xbar) represent the sample means obtained for each of the different samples.

Figure 1

↓	C1	C2	C3	C4	C5	C6	C7	C8	C9	C10 xbar	
1	90	74	95	88	91	91	102	91	96	90.9	$\bar{x} = 90.9$
2	114	86	96	82	80	68	93	136	111	96.2	$\bar{x} = 96.2$
3	89	89	86	98	96	96	89	99	107	94.3	
4	87	94	89	116	92	124	115	83	111	101.3	
5	107	103	86	86	109	104	94	82	110	97.8	
6	113	84	101	89	92	71	89	86	108	92.7	
7	75	116	107	118	112	86	104	97	106	102.4	
8	118	117	81	96	86	94	109	96	104	100.1	
9	91	91	79	80	109	89	97	81	99	90.6	
10	112	98	115	73	95	104	76	95	87	95.0	
11	103	92	100	75	95	108	105	125	62	96.1	
12	75	124	101	113	91	85	121	115	85	101.2	
13	104	103	81	134	111	108	101	88	115	105.1	
14	121	85	118	88	96	84	103	77	102	97.1	
15	119	84	119	80	99	98	88	88	89	95.9	
16	71	86	94	101	95	84	124	105	83	93.7	

Sample 1 corresponds to row 1; *Sample 2* corresponds to row 2.

Figure 2(a) shows the distribution of the population, and Figure 2(b) shows the distribution of the sample means from column C10 (using MINITAB). The shape of the distribution of the population is normal. The histogram in Figure 2(b) indicates that the shape of the distribution of the sample means is also normal. In addition, we notice that the center of the distribution of the sample means is the same as the center of the distribution of the population, but the spread of the distribution of the sample means is smaller than the spread of the distribution of the population. In fact, the mean of the 1,000 sample means in column C10 (xbar) is 99.92, and the standard deviation of the sample means is 4.88. Notice that the mean of the sample means is close to the population mean, 100, and the standard deviation of the sample means is less than the population standard deviation, 15.

Figure 2

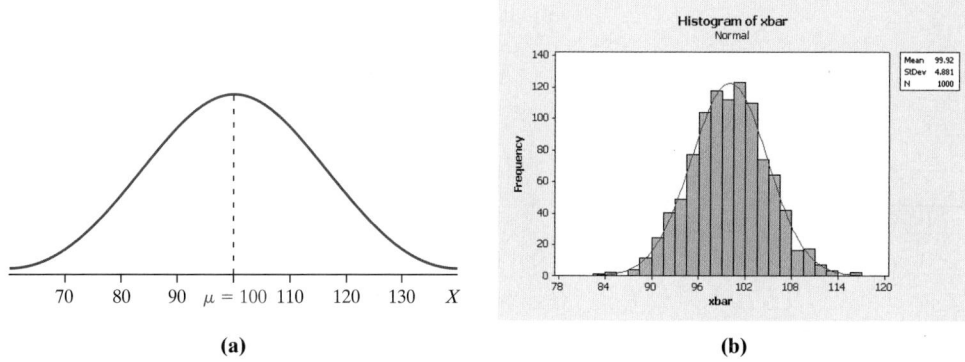

(a)   (b)

We conclude the following:

- **Shape:** The shape of the distribution of the sample mean is normal.
- **Center:** The mean of the distribution of the sample mean equals the mean of the population, 100.
- **Spread:** The standard deviation of the sample mean is less than the standard deviation of the population.

Why is the standard deviation of the sample mean less than the standard deviation of the population? Let's think of it this way. If we randomly select any one individual, there is about a 68% likelihood that the individual's IQ score is between 85 and 115 (in other words, there is a 68% likelihood that the individual's IQ score is within 1 standard deviation of the mean). Now, what if we had a sample of 9 individuals? Do you think there is a 68% likelihood that the mean IQ of these 9 individuals is between 85 and 115? We do not expect there to be as much spread in the sample as there is for a single individual, since individuals in the sample with lower IQs will offset individuals in the sample with higher IQs, resulting in a sample mean closer to the expected value of 100. Look back at Figure 1. In the first sample (row 1), the low-IQ individual (IQ = 74) is offset by the higher-IQ individual (IQ = 102), which is why the sample mean is closer to 100. In the second sample (row 2), the low-IQ individual (IQ = 68) is offset by the higher-IQ individual (IQ = 136), so the sample mean of the second sample is closer to 100. Therefore, the spread in the distribution of sample means should be less than the spread in the population from which the sample is drawn.

Based on this, what role do you think n, the sample size, plays in the sampling distribution of the sample mean $\bar{x}$? In particular, what role do you think n plays in the standard deviation of the distribution of the sample mean?

EXAMPLE 2 | **The Impact of Sample Size on Sampling Variability**

Problem: Repeat the problem in Example 1 with a sample of size $n = 25$.

Approach: The approach will be identical to that presented in Example 1, except we let $n = 25$ instead of $n = 9$.

Solution: Figure 3 shows the histogram of the sample means. Notice that the distribution of the sample means appear to be normally distributed with the center of the distribution at 100. The histogram in Figure 3 shows less dispersion than the histogram in Figure 2(b). This implies that there is less variability in the distribution of $\bar{x}$ with $n = 25$ than there is in the distribution of $\bar{x}$ with $n = 9$. In fact, the mean of the 1,000 sample means is 99.99, and the standard deviation of the 1,000 sample means is 3.00.

Figure 3

From the results of Examples 1 and 2, we conclude that, as the sample size n increases, the standard deviation of the distribution of $\bar{x}$ decreases. Although the proof is beyond the scope of this text, we should be convinced that the following result is reasonable.

In Other Words

Regardless of the distribution of the population, the sampling distribution of $\bar{x}$ will have a mean equal to the mean of the population and a standard deviation equal to the standard deviation of the population divided by the square root of the sample size!

> ### The Mean and Standard Deviation of the Sampling Distribution of $\bar{x}$
>
> Suppose that a simple random sample of size n is drawn from a large population with mean μ and standard deviation σ. The sampling distribution of $\bar{x}$ will have mean $\mu_{\bar{x}} = \mu$ and standard deviation $\sigma_{\bar{x}} = \dfrac{\sigma}{\sqrt{n}}$. The standard deviation of the sampling distribution of $\bar{x}$, $\sigma_{\bar{x}}$, is called the **standard error of the mean**.*

For the population presented in Example 1, if we draw a simple random sample of size $n = 9$, the sampling distribution $\bar{x}$ will have mean $\mu_{\bar{x}} = 100$ and standard deviation

$$\sigma_{\bar{x}} = \frac{\sigma}{\sqrt{n}} = \frac{15}{\sqrt{9}} \approx 5$$

Notice that this standard error of the mean is close to the approximate standard error of 4.88 found in our simulation in Example 1.

For the population presented in Example 2, if we draw a simple random sample of size $n = 25$, the sampling distribution of $\bar{x}$ will have mean $\mu_{\bar{x}} = 100$ and standard deviation

$$\sigma_{\bar{x}} = \frac{\sigma}{\sqrt{n}} = \frac{15}{\sqrt{25}} = 3$$

Notice that this standard error of the mean equals the approximate standard error found in our simulation in Example 2.

Now Work Problem 11

IN CLASS ACTIVITY

Variability in Individuals versus Variability in Means

The purpose of this activity is to explore the amount of dispersion that exists in values of a variable for individuals versus the variability in means.

1. Each student should determine his or her at-rest pulse rate.

2. We will treat the students in class as a sample of all students at the school. Determine the sample standard deviation at-rest pulse rate.

3. Obtain a simple random sample of $n = 5$ students from the class. Compute the mean pulse rate of the students. Repeat this at least 5 more times.

4. Compute the sample standard deviation of the mean pulse rates found in part 3. Which has more dispersion, the standard deviation of the individual pulse rates, or the standard deviation of the mean pulse rates? Why?

5. If a simple random sample of $n = 10$ students from class was used instead, do you think the standard deviation of the mean pulse rates would be higher or lower than the standard deviation of the mean pulse rates with $n = 5$ students? Why?

*Technically, we assume that we are drawing a simple random sample from an infinite population. For populations of finite size N, $\sigma_{\bar{x}} = \sqrt{\dfrac{N - n}{N - 1}} \cdot \dfrac{\sigma}{\sqrt{n}}$. However, if the sample size is less than 5% of the population size ($n < 0.05N$), the effect of $\sqrt{\dfrac{N - n}{N - 1}}$ (the finite population correction factor) can be ignored without significantly affecting the results.

Now that we know how to determine the mean and standard deviation for any sampling distribution of $\bar{x}$, we can concentrate on the shape of the distribution. Refer back to Figures 2(b) and 3 from Examples 1 and 2. Recall that the population from which the sample was drawn was normal. The shapes of these histograms imply that the sampling distribution of $\bar{x}$ is also normal. This leads us to believe that, if the population is normal, then the distribution of the sample mean is also normal.

Figure 4

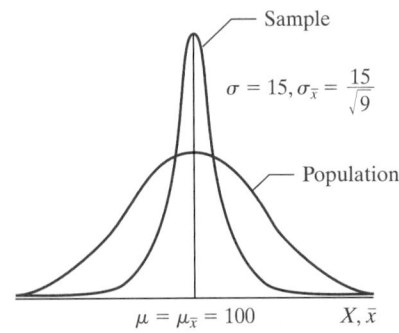

The Shape of the Sampling Distribution of $\bar{x}$ If X Is Normal

If a random variable X is normally distributed, the distribution of the sample mean, $\bar{x}$, is normally distributed.

For example, the IQ scores of individuals are modeled by a normal random variable with mean $\mu = 100$ and standard deviation $\sigma = 15$. The distribution of the sample mean, $\bar{x}$, the mean IQ of a simple random sample of $n = 9$ individuals, is normal, with mean $\mu_{\bar{x}} = 100$ and standard deviation $\sigma_{\bar{x}} = \dfrac{15}{\sqrt{9}}$. See Figure 4.

EXAMPLE 3 Describing the Distribution of the Sample Mean

Problem: The IQ, X, of humans is approximately normally distributed with mean $\mu = 100$ and standard deviation $\sigma = 15$. Compute the probability that a simple random sample of size $n = 10$ results in a sample mean greater than 110. That is, compute $P(\bar{x} > 110)$.

Approach: The random variable X is normally distributed, so the sampling distribution of $\bar{x}$ will also be normally distributed. The mean of the sampling distribution is $\mu_{\bar{x}} = \mu$, and its standard deviation is $\sigma_{\bar{x}} = \dfrac{\sigma}{\sqrt{n}}$. We convert the sample mean $\bar{x} = 110$ to a z-score and then find the area under the standard normal curve to the right of this z-score.

Solution: The sample mean is normally distributed, with mean $\mu_{\bar{x}} = 100$ and standard deviation $\sigma_{\bar{x}} = \dfrac{\sigma}{\sqrt{n}} = \dfrac{15}{\sqrt{10}} = 4.743$.

Figure 5

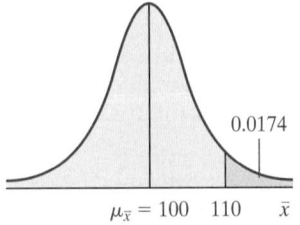

Figure 5 displays the normal curve with the area we wish to compute shaded. We convert $\bar{x} = 110$ to a z-score and obtain

$$z = \frac{\bar{x} - \mu_{\bar{x}}}{\sigma_{\bar{x}}} = \frac{\bar{x} - \mu_{\bar{x}}}{\dfrac{\sigma}{\sqrt{n}}} = \frac{110 - 100}{\dfrac{15}{\sqrt{10}}} = 2.11$$

The area to the right of $z = 2.11$ is $1 - 0.9826 = 0.0174$.

Interpretation: The probability of obtaining a sample mean IQ greater than 110 from a population whose mean is 100 is 0.0174. That is, $P(\bar{x} \geq 110) = 0.0174$. If we take 100 simple random samples of $n = 10$ individuals from this population and if the population mean is 100, about 2 of the samples will result in a mean IQ that is greater than 110.

Now Work Problem 21

② Describe the Distribution of the Sample Mean—Samples from a Population That Is Not Normal

What if the population from which the sample is drawn is not normal?

| EXAMPLE 4 | **Sampling from a Population That Is Not Normal** |

Problem: The data in Table 1 represent the probability distribution of the number of people living in households in the United States. Figure 6 shows a histogram of the data. From the data in Table 1, we determine the mean and standard deviation number of people living in households in the United States to be $\mu = 2.9$ and $\sigma = 1.48$.

Clearly, the distribution is not normal. Approximate the sampling distribution of the sample mean $\overline{x}$ by obtaining, through simulation, 1,000 samples of size (a) $n = 4$, (b) $n = 10$, and (c) $n = 30$ from the population distribution.

Table 1	
Number in Household	**Proportion**
1	0.147
2	0.361
3	0.187
4	0.168
5	0.083
6	0.034
7	0.012
8	0.004
9	0.002
10	0.002

Source: General Social Survey

Figure 6

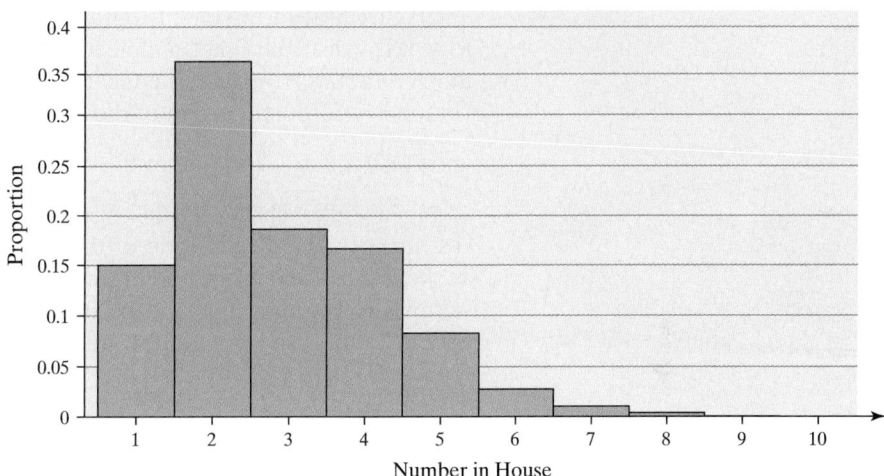

Approach: We use MINITAB to obtain 1,000 random samples of size $n = 4$ from the population. This simulates going to 4 households 1,000 times and determining the number of people living in the household. We then compute the mean of each of the 1,000 random samples. Finally, we draw a histogram of the 1,000 sample means, determine the mean of the 1,000 sample means, and determine the standard deviation of the 1,000 sample means. We will repeat this for samples of size $n = 10$ and $n = 30$.

Solution: Figure 7 shows partial output from MINITAB for random samples of size $n = 4$. The first two columns represent the probability distribution. Each row in columns 3 through 6 represents the number of individuals in the household for each sample. Column 7 (xbar) represents the sample mean for each sample (each row). For example, in the first sample (row 1), there are 4 individuals in the first house surveyed, and 2 individuals in the second, third, and fourth houses surveyed. The mean number of individuals in the household for the first sample is 2.5.

Figure 7

↓	C1 Number	C2 Proportion	C3	C4	C5	C6	C7 xbar
1	1	0.147	4	2	2	2	2.50
2	2	0.361	1	3	4	2	2.50
3	3	0.187	4	4	2	4	3.50
4	4	0.168	5	4	2	6	4.25
5	5	0.083	7	2	4	4	4.25
6	6	0.034	2	2	6	2	3.00
7	7	0.012	4	8	3	1	4.00
8	8	0.004	3	2	2	2	2.25
9	9	0.002	2	2	4	2	2.50
10	10	0.002	2	2	4	1	2.25
11			2	1	7	2	3.00
12			3	7	2	1	3.25
13			5	3	2	3	3.25
14			1	5	2	2	2.50
15			1	1	4	7	3.25

Figure 8(a) shows the histogram of the 1,000 sample means for a sample of size $n = 4$. The distribution of sample means is skewed right (just like the parent population, but not as strongly). The mean of the 1,000 samples is 2.9, and the standard deviation is 0.73. So, the mean of the 1,000 samples, $\mu_{\bar{x}}$, equals the population mean μ, and the standard deviation of the 1,000 samples, $\sigma_{\bar{x}}$, is close to $\dfrac{\sigma}{\sqrt{n}} = \dfrac{1.48}{\sqrt{4}} = 0.74$.

Figure 8(b) shows the histogram of the 1,000 sample means for a sample of size $n = 10$. The distribution of these sample means is also skewed right, but not as skewed as the distribution of sample means in Figure 8(a). The mean of the 1,000 samples is 2.9, and the standard deviation is 0.47. So, the mean of the 1,000 samples, $\mu_{\bar{x}}$ equals the population mean, μ, and the standard deviation of the 1,000 samples, $\sigma_{\bar{x}}$, equals $\dfrac{\sigma}{\sqrt{n}} = \dfrac{1.48}{\sqrt{10}} = 0.47$.

Figure 8(c) shows the histogram of the 1,000 sample means for a sample of size $n = 30$. The distribution of sample means is approximately normal! The mean of the 1,000 samples is 2.9, and the standard deviation is 0.27. So, the mean of the 1,000 samples, $\mu_{\bar{x}}$, equals the population mean, μ, and the standard deviation of the 1,000 samples, $\sigma_{\bar{x}}$, equals $\dfrac{\sigma}{\sqrt{n}} = \dfrac{1.48}{\sqrt{30}} = 0.27$.

Figure 8

(a)

(b)

(c)

There are two key concepts to understand in Example 4.

1. The mean of the sampling distribution is equal to the mean of the underlying population, and the standard deviation of the sampling distribution of the sample mean is $\dfrac{\sigma}{\sqrt{n}}$, regardless of the sample size.

In Other Words

For any population, regardless of its shape, as the sample size increases, the shape of the distribution of the sample mean becomes more "normal."

2. The shape of the distribution of the sample mean becomes approximately normal as the sample size n increases, regardless of the shape of the underlying population. We formally state point 2 as the *Central Limit Theorem*.

> **The Central Limit Theorem**
>
> Regardless of the shape of the underlying population, the sampling distribution of $\bar{x}$ becomes approximately normal as the sample size, n, increases.

So, if the random variable X is normally distributed, the sampling distribution of $\bar{x}$ will also be exactly normal. If the sample size is large enough, the sampling distribution of $\bar{x}$ will be approximately normal, *regardless of the shape of the distribution of X*. But how large does the sample size need to be before we can say that the sampling distribution of $\bar{x}$ is approximately normal? The answer depends on the shape of the distribution of the underlying population. Distributions that are highly skewed will require a larger sample size for the distribution of $\bar{x}$ to become approximately normal.

⚠ CAUTION   The Central Limit Theorem only has to do with the shape of the distribution of $\bar{x}$, not the center or spread. Regardless of the sample size $\mu_{\bar{x}} = \mu$ and $\sigma_{\bar{x}} = \dfrac{\sigma}{\sqrt{n}}$.

For example, from Example 4 we see that this right-skewed distribution required a sample size of about 30 before the distribution of the sample mean became approximately normal. However, Figure 9(a) shows a uniform distribution for $0 \leq X \leq 10$. Figure 9(b) shows the distribution of the sample mean for $n = 3$. Figure 9(c) shows the distribution of the sample mean for $n = 12$, and Figure 9(d) shows the distribution of the sample mean for $n = 30$. Notice that even for $n = 3$ the distribution of the sample mean is approximately normal.

Figure 9

Uniform Distribution

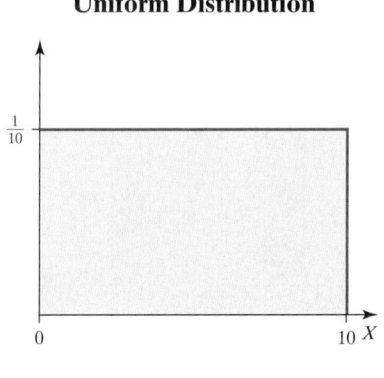

(a)

Distribution of $\bar{x}$ with $n = 3$

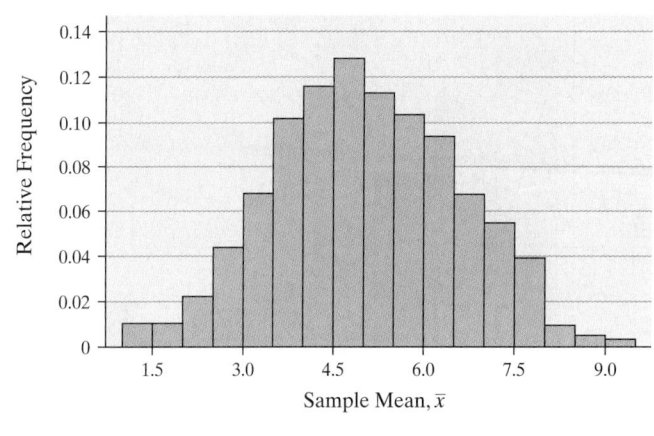

(b)

Distribution of $\bar{x}$ with $n = 12$

(c)

Distribution of $\bar{x}$ with $n = 30$

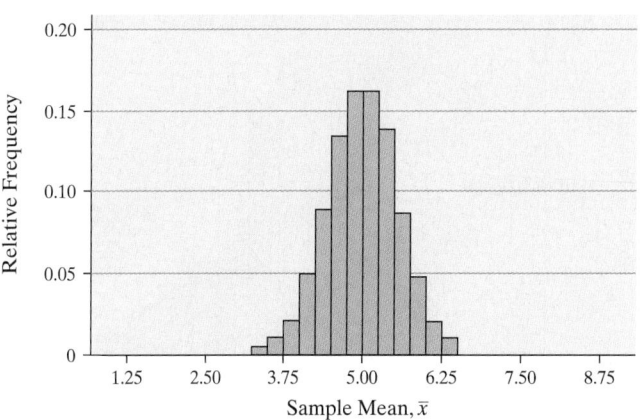

(d)

Table 2 shows the distribution of the cumulative number of children for 50- to 54-year-old mothers who had a live birth in 2005.

Table 2	
x (number of children)	P(x)
1	0.292
2	0.251
3	0.167
4	0.128
5	0.060
6	0.031
7	0.023
8	0.048

Source: U.S. Census Bureau

Figure 10(a) shows the probability histogram for this distribution. Figure 10(b) shows the distribution of the sample mean number of children for a random sample of $n = 3$ mothers. Figure 10(c) shows the distribution of the sample mean number of children for a random sample of $n = 12$ mothers, and Figure 10(d) shows the distribution of the sample mean for a random sample of $n = 30$ mothers. In this instance, the distribution of the sample mean is close to normal for $n = 12$.

Figure 10

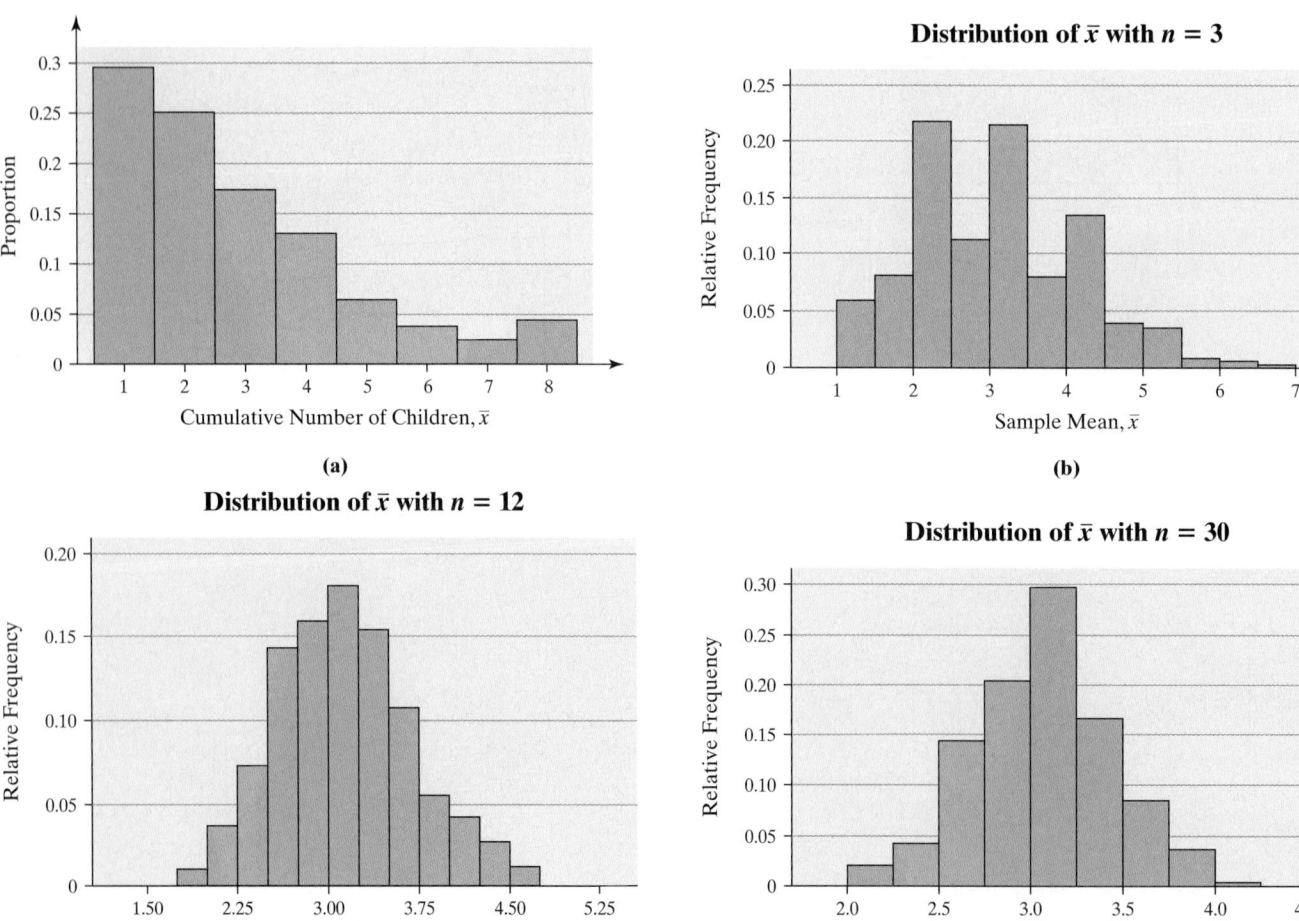

Cumulative Number of Children for 50–54 Year Old Mothers Who Had a Live Birth in 2005

(a)

Distribution of $\bar{x}$ with $n = 3$

(b)

Distribution of $\bar{x}$ with $n = 12$

(c)

Distribution of $\bar{x}$ with $n = 30$

(d)

Note to Instructor
While admittedly conservative, requiring $n \geq 30$ for nonnormal distributions provides a clear-cut decision rule for students to use.

The results of Example 4 and Figures 9 and 10 confirm that the shape of the distribution of the population dictates the size of the sample required before the distribution of the sample mean can be called normal. The more skewed the distribution of the population is, the larger the sample size needed to invoke the Central Limit Theorem. We will err on the side of caution and say that, if the distribution of the population is unknown or not normal, then the distribution of the sample mean is approximately normal provided that the sample size is greater than or equal to 30.

EXAMPLE 5   Weight Gain During Pregnancy

Historical Note

Pierre Simon Laplace was born on March 23, 1749, in Normandy, France. At age 16, Laplace attended Caen University, where he studied theology. While there, his mathematical talents were discovered, which led him to Paris, where he obtained a job as professor of mathematics at the École Militaire. In 1773, Laplace was elected to the Académie des Sciences. Laplace was not humble. It is reported that, in 1780, he stated that he was the best mathematician in Paris. In 1799, Laplace published the first two volumes of *Méchanique céleste*, in which he discussed methods for calculating the motion of the planets. On April 9, 1810, Laplace presented the Central Limit Theorem to the Academy.

Problem: The mean weight gain during pregnancy is 30 pounds, with a standard deviation of 12.9 pounds. Weight gain during pregnancy is skewed right. An obstetrician in a low-income neighborhood obtains a random sample of 35 of her patients and determines their mean weight gain during pregnancy was 36.2 pounds. Should the obstetrician be concerned?

Approach: Essentially, we want to know whether the sample mean obtained is unusual. So, we need to determine the likelihood of obtaining a sample mean of 36.2 pounds or higher (if a 36.2-pound weight gain is unusual, certainly any weight gain above 36.2 pounds is also unusual). We assume that the patients come from the population whose mean weight gain is 30 pounds. We can use the normal model to obtain the probability since our sample size is sufficiently large to use the Central Limit Theorem. So, we will determine the area under the normal curve to the right of 36.2 pounds with $\mu_{\bar{x}} = \mu = 30$ and $\sigma_{\bar{x}} = \dfrac{\sigma}{\sqrt{n}} = \dfrac{12.9}{\sqrt{35}}$.

Solution: The probability is represented by the area under the normal curve to the right of 36.2. See Figure 11.

Figure 11

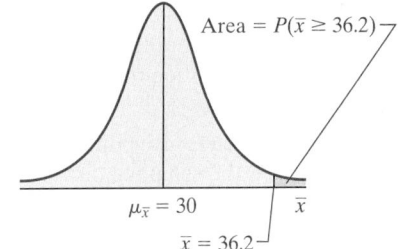

We compute $P(\bar{x} \geq 36.2)$ by converting the sample mean $\bar{x} = 36.2$ to a z-score.

$$z = \frac{\bar{x} - \mu_{\bar{x}}}{\sigma_{\bar{x}}} = \frac{36.2 - 30}{\dfrac{12.9}{\sqrt{35}}} = 2.84$$

Using Technology
If we use technology to find the area right of $\bar{x} = 36.2$, we obtain 0.0022.

So,

$$P(\bar{x} \geq 36.2) = P(Z \geq 2.84) = 1 - P(Z < 2.84) = 1 - 0.9977 = 0.0023$$

Interpretation: If the population from which this sample is drawn has a mean weight gain of 30 pounds, the probability that a random sample of 35 women will result in a sample mean weight gain of 36.2 pounds (or more) is 0.0023. This means that about 2 samples in 1,000 will result in a sample mean of 36.2 pounds or higher if the population mean is 30 pounds. We can conclude one of two things based on this result:

1. The mean weight gain for this obstetrician's patients is 30 pounds, and we happened to select women who, on average, gained more weight.

2. The mean weight gain for this obstetrician's patients is more than 30 pounds.

We are inclined to accept the second explanation over the first since our sample was obtained randomly. Therefore, the obstetrician should be concerned. Perhaps she should look at her patients' diets and/or lifestyles.

Now Work Problem 27

Summary: Shape, Center, and Spread of the Distribution of $\bar{x}$

Shape, Center, and Spread of the Population	Distribution of the Sample Mean		
	Shape	**Center**	**Spread**
Population is normal with mean μ and standard deviation σ	Regardless of the sample size n, the shape of the distribution of the sample mean is normal	$\mu_{\bar{x}} = \mu$	$\sigma_{\bar{x}} = \dfrac{\sigma}{\sqrt{n}}$
μ and standard deviation σ	As the sample size n increases, the distribution of the sample mean becomes approximately normal	$\mu_{\bar{x}} = \mu$	$\sigma_{\bar{x}} = \dfrac{\sigma}{\sqrt{n}}$

5. $\mu_{\bar{x}} = \mu; \sigma_{\bar{x}} = \dfrac{\sigma}{\sqrt{n}}$ 9. Normal, $\mu_{\bar{x}} = 30, \sigma_{\bar{x}} = \dfrac{8}{\sqrt{10}}$

8.1 ASSESS YOUR UNDERSTANDING

Concepts and Vocabulary

1. Explain what a sampling distribution is.

2. State the Central Limit Theorem.

3. The standard deviation of the sampling distribution of $\bar{x}$, denoted $\sigma_{\bar{x}}$, is called the <u>standard</u> <u>error</u> of the <u>mean</u>.

4. As the sample size increases, the difference between the sample mean, $\bar{x}$, and the population mean, μ, approaches <u>zero</u>.

5. What are the mean and standard deviation of the sampling distribution of $\bar{x}$, regardless of the distribution of the population from which the sample was drawn?

6. If a random sample of size $n = 6$ is taken from a population, what is required in order to say that the sampling distribution of $\bar{x}$ is approximately normal? Population is normal.

7. To cut the standard error of the mean in half, the sample size must be increased by a factor of <u>four</u>.

8. *True or False*: The distribution of the sample mean, $\bar{x}$, will be normally distributed if the sample is obtained from a population that is normally distributed, regardless of the sample size. True

9. A simple random sample of size $n = 10$ is obtained from a population that is normally distributed with $\mu = 30$ and $\sigma = 8$. What is the sampling distribution of $\bar{x}$?

10. A simple random sample of size $n = 40$ is obtained from a population with $\mu = 50$ and $\sigma = 4$. Does the population need to be normally distributed for the sampling distribution of $\bar{x}$ to be approximately normally distributed? Why? What is the sampling distribution of $\bar{x}$?

10. No; $n \geq 30$; Approx. normal, $\mu_{\bar{x}} = 50, \sigma_{\bar{x}} = \dfrac{4}{\sqrt{40}}$

Skill Building

In Problems 11–14, determine $\mu_{\bar{x}}$ and $\sigma_{\bar{x}}$ from the given parameters of the population and the sample size.

11. $\mu = 80, \sigma = 14, n = 49$ $\mu_{\bar{x}} = 80, \sigma_{\bar{x}} = 2$

12. $\mu = 64, \sigma = 18, n = 36$ $\mu_{\bar{x}} = 64, \sigma_{\bar{x}} = 3$

13. $\mu = 52, \sigma = 10, n = 21$ $\mu_{\bar{x}} = 52, \sigma_{\bar{x}} = \dfrac{10}{\sqrt{21}} \approx 2.182$

14. $\mu = 27, \sigma = 6, n = 15$ $\mu_{\bar{x}} = 27, \sigma_{\bar{x}} = \dfrac{6}{\sqrt{15}} \approx 1.549$

15. Answer the following questions for the sampling distribution of the sample mean shown.

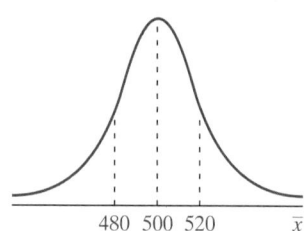

480 500 520 $\bar{x}$

(a) What is the value of $\mu_{\bar{x}}$? 500
(b) What is the value of $\sigma_{\bar{x}}$? 20
(c) If the sample size is $n = 16$, what must be true about the shape of the population? Normal   15. (d) 80
(d) If the sample size is $n = 16$, what is the standard deviation of the population from which the sample was drawn?

16. Answer the following questions for the sampling distribution of the sample mean shown.

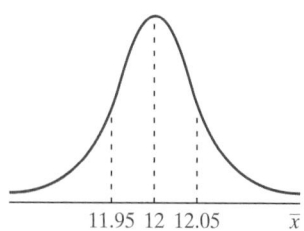

11.95 12 12.05 $\bar{x}$

(a) What is the value of $\mu_{\bar{x}}$? 12
(b) What is the value of $\sigma_{\bar{x}}$? 0.05
(c) If the sample size is $n = 9$, what must be true about the shape of the population? Normal   16. (d) 0.15
(d) If the sample size is $n = 9$, what is the standard deviation of the population from which the sample was drawn?

17. (a) Approximately normal with $\mu_{\bar{x}} = 80$ and $\sigma_{\bar{x}} = 2$
18. (a) Approximately normal with $\mu_{\bar{x}} = 64$ and $\sigma_{\bar{x}} = 3$

17. A simple random sample of size $n = 49$ is obtained from a population with $\mu = 80$ and $\sigma = 14$.

(a) Describe the sampling distribution of $\bar{x}$.

(b) What is $P(\bar{x} > 83)$?   0.0668

(c) What is $P(\bar{x} \le 75.8)$?   0.0179

(d) What is $P(78.3 < \bar{x} < 85.1)$?   0.7969

18. A simple random sample of size $n = 36$ is obtained from a population with $\mu = 64$ and $\sigma = 18$.

(a) Describe the sampling distribution of $\bar{x}$.

(b) What is $P(\bar{x} < 62.6)$?   0.3192

(c) What is $P(\bar{x} \ge 68.7)$?   0.0582

(d) What is $P(59.8 < \bar{x} < 65.9)$?   0.6549

19. A simple random sample of size $n = 12$ is obtained from a population with $\mu = 64$ and $\sigma = 17$.

(a) What must be true regarding the distribution of the population in order to use the normal model to compute probabilities involving the sample mean? Assuming that this condition is true, describe the sampling distribution of $\bar{x}$.

(b) Assuming that the requirements described in part (a) are satisfied, determine $P(\bar{x} < 67.3)$.   0.7486

(c) Assuming that the requirements described in part (a) are satisfied, determine $P(\bar{x} \ge 65.2)$.   0.4052

20. A simple random sample of size $n = 20$ is obtained from a population with $\mu = 64$ and $\sigma = 17$.

(a) What must be true regarding the distribution of the population in order to use the normal model to compute probabilities involving the sample mean? Assuming that this condition is true, describe the sampling distribution of $\bar{x}$.

(b) Assuming that the requirements described in part (a) are satisfied, determine $P(\bar{x} < 67.3)$.   0.8078

(c) Assuming that the requirements described in part (a) are satisfied, determine $P(\bar{x} \ge 65.2)$.   0.3745

(d) Compare the results obtained in parts (b) and (c) with the results obtained in parts (b) and (c) in Problem 19. What effect does increasing the sample size have on the probabilities? Why do you think this is the case?

Applying the Concepts

21. Gestation Period The length of human pregnancies is approximately normally distributed with mean $\mu = 266$ days and standard deviation $\sigma = 16$ days.

(a) What is the probability a randomly selected pregnancy lasts less than 260 days?   0.3520

(b) Suppose a random sample of 20 pregnancies is obtained. Describe the sampling distribution of the sample mean length of human pregnancies.

(c) What is the probability that a random sample of 20 pregnancies has a mean gestation period of 260 days or less?   0.0465

(d) What is the probability that a random sample of 50 pregnancies has a mean gestation period of 260 days or less?

(e) What might you conclude if a random sample of 50 pregnancies resulted in a mean gestation period of 260 days or less?

(f) What is the probability a random sample of size 15 will have a mean gestation period within 10 days of the mean?

22. Upper Leg Length The upper leg length of 20- to 29-year-old males is normally distributed with a mean length of 43.7 cm and a standard deviation of 4.2 cm.

Source: "Anthropometric Reference Data for Children and Adults: U.S. Population, 1999–2002; Volume 361, July 7, 2005.

(a) What is the probability that a randomly selected 20- to 29-year-old male has an upper leg length that is less than 40 cm?   0.1894

(b) A random sample of 9 males who are 20 to 29 years old is obtained. What is the probability that the mean upper leg length is less than 40 cm?   0.0041

(c) What is the probability that a random sample of 12 males who are 20 to 29 years old results in a mean upper leg length that is less than 40 cm?   0.0011

(d) What effect does increasing the sample size have on the probability? Provide an explanation for this result.

(e) A random sample of 15 males who are 20 to 29 years old results in a mean upper leg length of 46 cm. Do you find this result unusual? Why?   Yes; $P(\bar{x} \ge 46) = 0.0170$

23. Reading Rates The reading speed of second grade students is approximately normal, with a mean of 90 words per minute (wpm) and a standard deviation of 10 wpm.

(a) What is the probability a randomly selected student will read more than 95 words per minute?   0.3085

(b) What is the probability that a random sample of 12 second grade students results in a mean reading rate of more than 95 words per minute?   0.0418

(c) What is the probability that a random sample of 24 second grade students results in a mean reading rate of more than 95 words per minute?   0.0071

(d) What effect does increasing the sample size have on the probability? Provide an explanation for this result.

(e) A teacher instituted a new reading program at school. After 10 weeks in the program, it was found that the mean reading speed of a random sample of 20 second grade students was 92.8 wpm. What might you conclude based on this result? $P(\bar{x} \ge 92.8) = 0.1056$; program not effective

24. Old Faithful The most famous geyser in the world, Old Faithful in Yellowstone National Park, has a mean time between eruptions of 85 minutes. If the interval of time between eruptions is normally distributed with standard deviation 21.25 minutes, answer the following questions:

Source: www.unmuseum.org

(a) What is the probability that a randomly selected time interval between eruptions is longer than 95 minutes?

(b) What is the probability that a random sample of 20 time intervals between eruptions has a mean longer than 95 minutes?   0.0179

(c) What is the probability that a random sample of 30 time intervals between eruptions has a mean longer than 95 minutes?   0.0049

(d) What effect does increasing the sample size have on the probability? Provide an explanation for this result.

(e) What might you conclude if a random sample of 30 time intervals between eruptions has a mean longer than 95 minutes?

19. (a) Normal; normal with $\mu_{\bar{x}} = 64$ and $\sigma_{\bar{x}} = \dfrac{17}{\sqrt{12}}$ 20. (a) Normal; normal with $\mu_{\bar{x}} = 64$ and $\sigma_{\bar{x}} = \dfrac{17}{\sqrt{20}}$ 21. (b) Normal $\mu_{\bar{x}} = 266$;

$\sigma_{\bar{x}} = \dfrac{16}{\sqrt{20}}$ 21. (d) 0.0040   21. (f) 0.9844   22. (d) Decreases   23. (d) Decreases   24. (a) 0.3192   24. (d) Decreases

29. (b) $\mu_{\bar{x}} = 3$, $\sigma_{\bar{x}} = \dfrac{\sqrt{3}}{\sqrt{50}}$ 30. (b) $\mu_{\bar{x}} = 20$, $\sigma_{\bar{x}} = \dfrac{\sqrt{20}}{\sqrt{40}} = \sqrt{\dfrac{1}{2}}$

25. **Rates of Return in Stocks** The S&P 500 is a collection of 500 stocks of publicly traded companies. Using data obtained from Yahoo!Finance, the monthly rates of return of the S&P 500 since 1950 are normally distributed. The mean rate of return is 0.007233 (0.7233%), and the standard deviation for rate of return is 0.04135 (4.135%).   *25. (a) 0.5675*

    (a) What is the probability that a randomly selected month has a positive rate of return? That is, what is $P(x > 0)$?

    (b) Treating the next 12 months as a simple random sample, what is the probability that the mean monthly rate of return will be positive? That is, with $n = 12$, what is $P(\bar{x} > 0)$?   *0.7291*

    (c) Treating the next 24 months as a simple random sample, what is the probability that the mean monthly rate of return will be positive?   *0.8051*

    (d) Treating the next 36 months as a simple random sample, what is the probability that the mean monthly rate of return will be positive?   *0.8531*

    (e) Use the results of parts (b)–(d) to describe the likelihood of earning a positive rate of return on stocks as the investment time horizon increases.

26. **Gas Mileage** Based on tests of the Chevrolet Cobalt, engineers have found that the miles per gallon in highway driving are normally distributed, with a mean of 32 miles per gallon and a standard deviation 3.5 miles per gallon.

    (a) What is the probability that a randomly selected Cobalt gets more than 34 miles per gallon?   *0.2843*

    (b) Ten Cobalts are randomly selected and the miles per gallon for each car are recorded. What is the probability that the mean miles per gallon exceeds 34 miles per gallon?   *0.0351*

    (c) Twenty Cobalts are randomly selected and the miles per gallon for each car are recorded. What is the probability that the mean miles per gallon exceeds 34 miles per gallon? Would this result be unusual?   *0.0052; yes*

27. **Oil Change** The shape of the distribution of the time required to get an oil change at a 10-minute oil-change facility is unknown. However, records indicate that the mean time for an oil change is 11.4 minutes, and the standard deviation for oil-change time is 3.2 minutes.

    (a) To compute probabilities regarding the sample mean using the normal model, what size sample would be required?   *At least 30*

    (b) What is the probability that a random sample of $n = 40$ oil changes results in a sample mean time of less than 10 minutes?   *0.0028*

28. **Time Spent in the Drive-Through** The quality-control manager of a Long John Silver's restaurant wishes to analyze the length of time that a car spends at the drive-through window waiting for an order. According to records obtained from the restaurant, it is determined that the mean time spent at the window is 59.3 seconds with a standard deviation of 13.1 seconds. The distribution of time at the window is skewed right (data based on information provided by Danica Williams, student at Joliet Junior College).

    (a) To obtain probabilities regarding a sample mean using the normal model, what size sample is required?   *At least 30*

    (b) The quality-control manager wishes to use a new delivery system designed to get cars through the drive-through system faster. A random sample of 40 cars results in a sample mean time spent at the window of 56.8 seconds. What is the probability of obtaining a sample mean of 56.8 seconds or less, assuming that the population mean is 59.3 seconds? Do you think that the new system is effective?   *0.1131; no*

29. **Insect Fragments** The Food and Drug Administration sets Food Defect Action Levels (FDALs) for some of the various foreign substances that inevitably end up in the food we eat and liquids we drink. For example, the FDAL for insect filth in peanut butter is 3 insect fragments (larvae, eggs, body parts, and so on) per 10 grams. A random sample of 50 ten-gram portions of peanut butter is obtained and results in a sample mean of $\bar{x} = 3.6$ insect fragments per ten-gram portion.

    (a) Why is the sampling distribution of $\bar{x}$ approximately normal?   *Large sample size*

    (b) What is the mean and standard deviation of the sampling distribution of $\bar{x}$ assuming that $\mu = 3$ and $\sigma = \sqrt{3}$.

    (c) What is the probability that a simple random sample of 50 ten-gram portions results in a mean of at least 3.6 insect fragments? Is this result unusual? What might we conclude?   *0.0071; yes*

30. **Burger King's Drive-Through** Suppose that cars arrive at Burger King's drive-through at the rate of 20 cars every hour between 12:00 noon and 1:00 P.M. A random sample of 40 one-hour time periods between 12:00 noon and 1:00 P.M. is selected and has 22.1 as the mean number of cars arriving.

    (a) Why is the sampling distribution of $\bar{x}$ approximately normal?   *Large sample size*

    (b) What is the mean and standard deviation of the sampling distribution of $\bar{x}$ assuming that $\mu = 20$ and $\sigma = \sqrt{20}$.   *30. (c) 0.0015; yes*

    (c) What is the probability that a simple random sample of 40 one-hour time periods results in a mean of at least 22.1 cars? Is this result unusual? What might we conclude?

31. **Watching Television** The amount of time Americans spend watching television is closely monitored by firms such as A. C. Nielsen because this helps to determine advertising pricing for commercials.   *31. (a) No; skewed right*

    (a) Do you think the variable "weekly time spent watching television" would be normally distributed? If not, what shape would you expect the variable to have?

    (b) According to the American Time Use Survey, adult Americans spend 2.35 hours per day watching television on a weekday. Assume that the standard deviation for "time spent watching television on a weekday" is 1.93 hours. If a random sample of 40 adult Americans is obtained, describe the sampling distribution of $\bar{x}$, the mean amount of time spent watching television on a weekday.

    (c) Determine the probability that a random sample of 40 adult Americans results in a mean time watching television on a weekday of between 2 and 3 hours.   *0.8583*

    (d) One consequence of the popularity of the Internet is that it is thought to reduce television watching. Suppose that a random sample of 35 individuals who consider themselves to be avid Internet users results in a mean time of 1.89 hours watching television on a weekday. Determine the likelihood of obtaining a sample mean of 1.89 hours or less from a population whose mean is presumed to be 2.35 hours. Based on the result obtained, do you think avid Internet users watch less television?   *0.0793; no*

    31. (b) Approx. normal; $\mu_{\bar{x}} = 2.35$, $\sigma_{\bar{x}} = \dfrac{1.93}{\sqrt{40}}$

32. (b) Approx. normal; $\mu_{\bar{x}} = 60$; $\sigma_{\bar{x}} = \dfrac{35}{\sqrt{50}}$

32. ATM Withdrawals According to ATMDepot.com, the mean ATM withdrawal is \$60. Assume that the standard deviation for withdrawals is \$35.

  (a) Do you think the variable "ATM withdrawal" is normally distributed? If not, what shape would you expect the variable to have? *No; skewed right*

  (b) If a random sample of 50 ATM withdrawals is obtained, describe the sampling distribution of $\bar{x}$, the mean withdrawal amount.

  (c) Determine the probability of obtaining a sample mean withdrawal amount between \$70 and \$75. *0.0205*

33. Sampling Distributions The following data represent the ages of the winners of the Academy Award for Best Actor for the years 1999–2004.

2004: Jamie Foxx	37
2003: Sean Penn	43
2002: Adrien Brody	29
2001: Denzel Washington	47
2000: Russell Crowe	36
1999: Kevin Spacey	40

  (a) Compute the population mean, μ. $\mu \approx 38.7$ years
  (b) List all possible samples with size $n = 2$. There should be ${}_6C_2 = 15$ samples.
  (c) Construct a sampling distribution for the mean by listing the sample means and their corresponding probabilities. 33. (d) $\mu_{\bar{x}} \approx 38.7$ years
  (d) Compute the mean of the sampling distribution.
  (e) Compute the probability that the sample mean is within 3 years of the population mean age. *0.6*
  (f) Repeat parts (b)–(e) using samples of size $n = 3$. Comment on the effect of increasing the sample size.

34. Sampling Distributions The following data represent the running lengths (in minutes) of the winners of the Academy Award for Best Picture for the years 1999–2004.

2004: *Million Dollar Baby*	132
2003: *The Lord of the Rings: The Return of the King*	201
2002: *Chicago*	112
2001: *A Beautiful Mind*	134
2000: *Gladiator*	155
1999: *American Beauty*	120

  (a) Compute the population mean, μ. $\mu \approx 142.3$ minutes
  (b) List all possible samples with size $n = 2$. There should be ${}_6C_2 = 15$ samples.
  (c) Construct a sampling distribution for the mean by listing the sample means and their corresponding probabilities.
  (d) Compute the mean of the sampling distribution.
  (e) Compute the probability that the sample mean is within 15 minutes of the population mean running time. *0.4*
  (f) Repeat parts (b)–(e) using samples of size $n = 3$. Comment on the effect of increasing the sample size.

35. Simulation Scores on the Stanford–Binet IQ test are normally distributed with $\mu = 100$ and $\sigma = 15$.

  (a) Use MINITAB, Excel, or some other statistical software to obtain 400 random samples of size $n = 20$.

34. (d) $\mu_{\bar{x}} \approx 142.3$ minutes

  (b) Compute the sample mean for each of the 400 samples.
  (c) Draw a histogram of the 400 sample means. Comment on its shape.
  (d) What do you expect the mean and standard deviation of the sampling distribution of the mean to be?
  (e) Compute the mean and standard deviation of the 400 sample means. Are they close to the expected values?
  (f) Compute the probability that a random sample of 20 people results in a sample mean greater than 108. *0.0084*
  (g) What proportion of the 400 random samples had a sample mean IQ greater than 108? Is this result close to the theoretical value obtained in part (f)?

36. Sampling Distribution Applet Load the sampling distribution applet on your computer. Set the applet so that the population is bell shaped. Take note of the mean and standard deviation.

  (a) Obtain 1,000 random samples of size $n = 5$. Describe the distribution of the sample mean based on the results of the applet. According to statistical theory, what is the distribution of the sample mean?
  (b) Obtain 1,000 random samples of size $n = 10$. Describe the distribution of the sample mean based on the results of the applet. According to statistical theory, what is the distribution of the sample mean?
  (c) Obtain 1,000 random samples of size $n = 30$. Describe the distribution of the sample mean based on the results of the applet. According to statistical theory, what is the distribution of the sample mean?
  (d) Compare the results of parts (a)–(c). How are they the same? How are they different?

37. Sampling Distribution Applet Load the sampling distribution applet on your computer. Set the applet so that the population is skewed or draw your own skewed distribution. Take note of the mean and standard deviation.

  (a) Obtain 1,000 random samples of size $n = 5$. Describe the distribution of the sample mean based on the results of the applet.
  (b) Obtain 1,000 random samples of size $n = 10$. Describe the distribution of the sample mean based on the results of the applet.
  (c) Obtain 1,000 random samples of size $n = 50$. Describe the distribution of the sample mean based on the results of the applet. According to statistical theory, what is the distribution of the sample mean?
  (d) Compare the results of parts (a)–(c). How are they the same? How are they different? What effect does the sample size have on the shape of the distribution of the sample mean?

38. Sampling Distribution Applet Load the sampling distribution applet on your computer. Set the applet so that the population is uniform.

  (a) Obtain 1,000 random samples of size $n = 2$. Describe the distribution of the sample mean based on the results of the applet.
  (b) Obtain 1,000 random samples of size $n = 5$. Describe the distribution of the sample mean based on the results of the applet.
  (c) Obtain 1,000 random samples of size $n = 10$. Describe the distribution of the sample mean based on the results of the applet.
  (d) For what sample size does the distribution of the sample mean appear to be approximately normal? 35. (d) $\mu_{\bar{x}} = 100$, $\sigma_{\bar{x}} = \dfrac{15}{\sqrt{20}}$

39. Putting It Together: Playing Roulette In the game of roulette, a wheel consists of 38 slots numbered 0, 00, 1, 2, . . . , 36. (See the photo.) To play the game, a metal ball is spun around the wheel and is allowed to fall into one of the numbered slots. If the number of the slot the ball falls into matches the number you selected, you win $35; otherwise you lose $1.

(a) Construct a probability distribution for the random variable X, the winnings of each spin.

(b) Determine the mean and standard deviation of the random variable X. Round your results to the nearest penny. $\mu_x = -0.05$, $\sigma_x = 5.76$

(c) Suppose that you play the game 100 times so that $n = 100$. Describe the sampling distribution of $\bar{x}$, the mean amount won per game.

(d) What is the probability of being ahead after playing the game 100 times? That is, what is the probability that the sample mean is greater than 0 for $n = 100$? 0.4641

(e) What is the probability of being ahead after playing the game 200 times? 0.4522

(f) What is the probability of being ahead after playing the game 1,000 times? 0.3936

(g) Compare the results of parts (d) and (e). What lesson does this teach you?

$$39. \ (c) \ \mu_x = -0.05; \ \sigma_{\bar{x}} = \frac{5.76}{\sqrt{100}} = 0.576$$

8.2 DISTRIBUTION OF THE SAMPLE PROPORTION

Preparing for This Section   Before getting started, review the following:

- Applications of the Normal Distribution (Section 7.3, pp. 397–401)

Objectives		
	1	Describe the sampling distribution of a sample proportion
	2	Compute probabilities of a sample proportion

1 **Describe the Sampling Distribution of a Sample Proportion**

Suppose that we want to determine the proportion of households in a 100-house homeowners association that favor an increase in the annual assessments to pay for neighborhood improvements. One approach that we might take is to survey all households and determine which are in favor of higher assessments. If 65 of the 100 households favor the higher assessment, the population proportion, p, of households in favor of a higher assessment is

$$p = \frac{65}{100} = 0.65$$

Of course, it is rare to gain access to all the individuals in a population. For this reason, we usually obtain estimates of population parameters such as p.

Definition   Suppose that a random sample of size n is obtained from a population in which each individual either does or does not have a certain characteristic. The **sample proportion**, denoted $\hat{p}$ (read "p-hat"), is given by

$$\hat{p} = \frac{x}{n}$$

where x is the number of individuals in the sample with the specified characteristic.*
The sample proportion, $\hat{p}$, is a statistic that estimates the population proportion, p.

---

*For those who studied Section 6.2 on binomial probabilities, x can be thought of as the number of successes in n trials of a binomial experiment.

EXAMPLE 1 **Computing a Sample Proportion**

Problem: Opinion Dynamics Corporation conducted a survey of 1,000 adult Americans 18 years of age or older and asked, "Are you currently on some form of a low-carbohydrate diet?" Of the 1,000 individuals surveyed, 150 indicated that they were on a low-carb diet. Find the sample proportion of individuals surveyed who were on a low-carb diet.

Approach: The sample proportion of individuals on a low-carb diet is found using the formula $\hat{p} = \dfrac{x}{n}$, where $x = 150$, the number of individuals in the survey with the characteristic "on a low-carb diet," and $n = 1,000$.

Solution: Substituting $x = 150$ and $n = 1,000$ into the formula $\hat{p} = \dfrac{x}{n}$, we have that $\hat{p} = \dfrac{150}{1,000} = 0.15$. Opinion Dynamics Corporation estimates that 0.15 or 15% of adult Americans 18 years of age or older are on some form of low-carbohydrate diet.

If a second survey of 1,000 American adults is conducted, it is likely the estimate of the proportion of Americans on a low-carbohydrate diet will be different because there will be different individuals in the sample. Because the value of $\hat{p}$ varies from sample to sample, it is a random variable and has a probability distribution.

To get a sense of the shape, center, and spread of the sampling distribution of $\hat{p}$, we could repeat the exercise of obtaining simple random samples of 1,000 adult Americans over and over. This would lead to a list of sample proportions. Each sample proportion would correspond to a simple random sample of 1,000. A histogram of the sample proportions will give us a feel for the shape of the distribution of the sample proportion. The mean of the sample proportions will give us an idea of the center of the distribution and the standard deviation of the sample proportions will give us an idea of the spread of the distribution.

Rather than literally surveying 1,000 adult Americans over and over again, we will use simulation to get an idea of the shape, center, and spread of the sampling distribution of the proportion.

EXAMPLE 2 **Using Simulation to Describe the Distribution of the Sample Proportion**

Problem: Based on a study conducted by the Gallup organization, 82% of Americans believe that the state of moral values in the United States is getting worse. Describe the sampling distribution of the sample proportion for samples of size (a) $n = 10$, (b) $n = 40$, (c) $n = 80$.

Approach: Remember, to describe a distribution means to find its shape, center, and spread. The actual sampling distribution of the sample proportion would be the distribution of *all* possible sample proportions of size $n = 10$. It is virtually impossible to find all possible samples of size $n = 10$ from the population of Americans. To get a sense as to the shape, center, and spread of the sampling distribution of the sample proportion, we will use MINITAB's Bernoulli Random Data command with event probability 0.82 to simulate obtaining 1,000 samples of size $n = 10$ by randomly generating 1,000 rows of responses over 10 columns. Each row will consist of a 0 or 1, with 0 representing a failure (individual does not believe the state of moral values in the United States is getting worse) and 1 representing a success (individual believes the state of moral values in the United States is getting worse). For each of the 1,000 samples (the 1,000 rows), we determine the mean number of successes (the sample proportion). We draw a histogram of the 1,000 sample proportions to gauge the shape of the distribution of the sample proportions. We determine the mean of the 1,000 sample proportions to approximate the mean of the sampling distribution. We determine the standard deviation of the 1,000 sample proportions to approximate the standard deviation of the sampling distribution. We repeat this process for samples of size $n = 40$ and $n = 80$.

Solution: Figure 12 shows a partial output from MINITAB. Row 1 contains the first sample, where the results of the survey are 1 (success), 0 (failure), 0 (failure), . . . , 1 (success). The mean number of successes, and therefore the sample proportion, from the first sample of $n = 10$ adult Americans is 0.5.

Figure 12

	C1	C2	C3	C4	C5	C6	C7	C8	C9	C10	C11 phat	
Sample 1 — 1	1	0	0	1	0	1	1	0	0	1	0.5	— $\hat{p} = 0.5$
Sample 2 — 2	1	1	1	1	1	1	1	1	0	1	0.9	— $\hat{p} = 0.9$
3	1	1	1	1	1	1	1	1	1	1	1.0	
4	1	0	1	1	1	1	1	1	1	1	0.9	
5	0	1	0	0	1	1	0	1	1	1	0.6	
6	1	1	0	0	0	1	1	1	1	1	0.7	
7	1	1	1	0	1	1	0	1	1	1	0.8	
8	1	1	1	0	0	1	0	1	1	1	0.7	
9	1	1	1	1	1	1	1	1	1	0	0.9	
10	1	1	1	1	1	1	1	1	1	1	1.0	
11	0	1	1	1	1	1	0	1	1	1	0.8	
12	1	1	1	0	1	1	1	1	1	1	0.9	
13	1	1	1	1	1	1	1	0	1	1	0.9	
14	0	1	1	1	1	1	1	1	1	1	0.9	
15	1	1	1	1	1	1	1	1	1	1	1.0	
16	1	1	1	1	1	1	1	1	1	1	1.0	

Figure 13 shows the histogram of the 1,000 sample proportions from column C11. Notice that the shape of the distribution is skewed left.

Figure 13
Distribution of $\hat{p}$ with $n = 10$

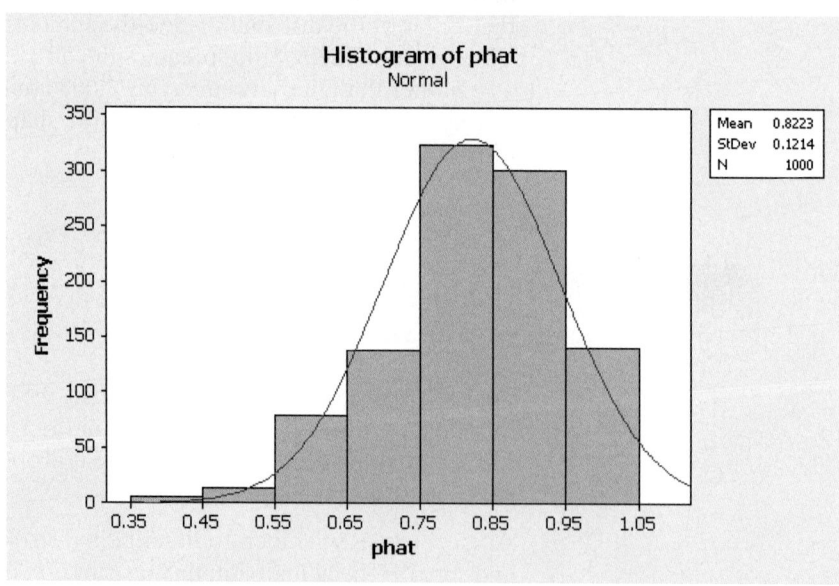

The mean of the 1,000 sample proportions is 0.82 and the standard deviation is 0.121. Notice that the mean of the sample proportions equals the population proportion.

We repeat the process described for samples of size $n = 40$. Figure 14 shows the histogram for 1,000 sample proportions from samples of size $n = 40$. Notice that the histogram is skewed left (although not as skewed as the histogram with $n = 10$). The mean of the 1,000 sample proportions for a sample of size $n = 40$ is 0.82 and the standard deviation is 0.060.

Figure 14
Distribution of $\hat{p}$ with $n = 40$

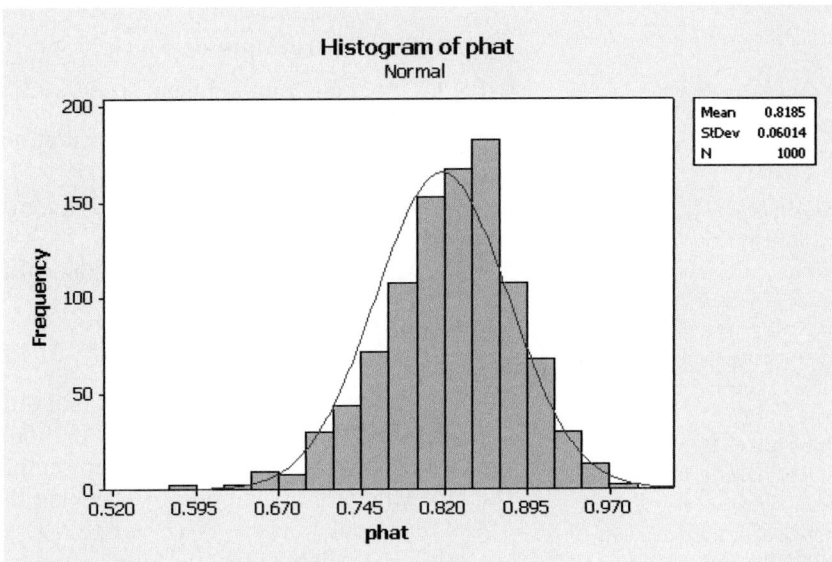

Figure 15 shows the histogram for 1,000 sample proportions from samples of size $n = 80$. Notice that the histogram is bell shaped. The mean of the 1,000 sample proportions is 0.82 and the standard deviation is 0.042.

Figure 15
Distribution of $\hat{p}$ with $n = 80$

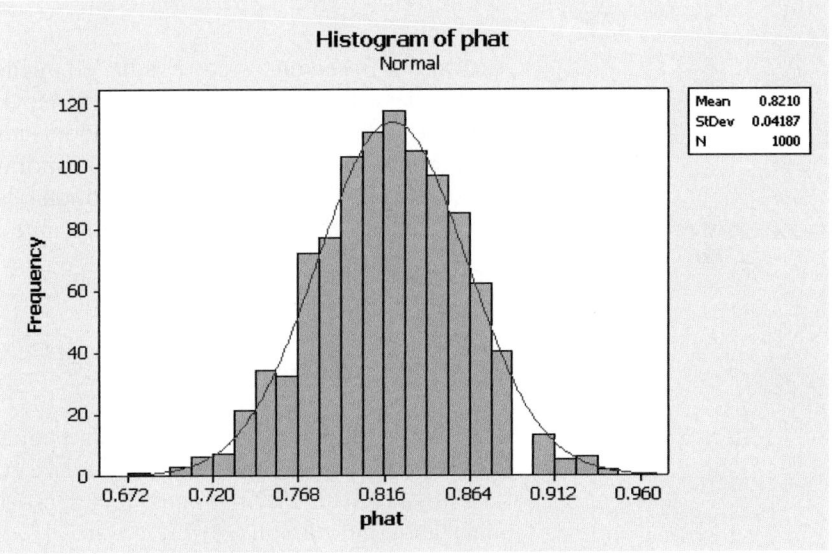

We notice the following regarding the sampling distribution of the sample proportion:

- **Shape:** As the size of the sample increases, the shape of the sampling distribution of the sample proportion becomes approximately normal.
- **Center:** The mean of the sample distribution of the sampling proportion equals the population proportion, p.
- **Spread:** The standard deviation of the sampling distribution of the sample proportion decreases as the sample size increases.

Although the proof is beyond the scope of this text, we should be convinced that the following results are reasonable.

Sampling Distribution of $\hat{p}$

For a simple random sample of size n with a population proportion p,

- The shape of the sampling distribution of $\hat{p}$ is approximately normal provided $np(1 - p) \geq 10$.
- The mean of the sampling distribution of $\hat{p}$ is $\mu_{\hat{p}} = p$.
- The standard deviation of the sampling distribution of $\hat{p}$ is $\sigma_{\hat{p}} = \sqrt{\dfrac{p(1 - p)}{n}}$.

In Other Words

The reason that the sample size cannot be more than 5% of the population size is because the success or failure of identifying an individual in the population that has the specified characteristic should not be affected by earlier observations. For example, in a population of size 100 where 14 of the individuals have brown hair, the probability that a randomly selected individual has brown hair is 14/100 = 0.14. The probability that a second randomly selected student has brown hair is 13/99 = 0.13. The probability changes because the sampling is done without replacement.

One requirement of this model is that the sampled values must be independent of each other. Remember, this means that one outcome does not affect the success or failure of any other outcome. When sampling from finite populations, we verify the independence assumption by checking that the sample size n is no more than 5% of the population size, N ($n \leq 0.05N$).

Also, regardless of whether $np(1 - p) \geq 10$ or not, the mean of the sampling distribution of $\hat{p}$ is p, and the standard deviation of the sampling distribution of $\hat{p}$ is $\sqrt{\dfrac{p(1 - p)}{n}}$.

EXAMPLE 3 **Describing the Sampling Distribution of the Sample Proportion**

Problem: Based on a study conducted by the Gallup organization, 82% of Americans believe that the state of moral values in the United States is getting worse. Suppose that we obtain a simple random sample of $n = 80$ Americans and determine which believe that the state of the moral values in the United States is getting worse. Describe the sampling distribution of the sample proportion for Americans who believe that the state of the moral values in the United States is getting worse.

Approach: If the sample size is less than 5% of the population size and $np(1 - p)$ is at least 10, the sampling distribution of $\hat{p}$ is approximately normal, with mean $\mu_{\hat{p}} = p$ and standard deviation $\sigma_{\hat{p}} = \sqrt{\dfrac{p(1 - p)}{n}}$.

Solution: There are over 300 million people in the United States. The sample of $n = 80$ is less than 5% of the population size. Also, $np(1 - p) = 80(0.82)(1 - 0.82) = 11.808 \geq 10$. The distribution of $\hat{p}$ is approximately normal, with mean $\mu_{\hat{p}} = 0.82$ and standard deviation

$$\sigma_{\hat{p}} = \sqrt{\frac{p(1 - p)}{n}} = \sqrt{\frac{0.82(1 - 0.82)}{80}} = 0.043$$

Notice that the standard deviation found in Example 3 (0.043) is very close to the standard deviation of the sample proportion found using simulation with $n = 80$ in Example 2 (0.042).

Now Work Problem 7

2 Compute Probabilities of a Sample Proportion

Now that we can describe the sampling distribution of the sample proportion, we can compute probabilities involving sample proportions.

| EXAMPLE 4 | **Compute Probabilities of a Sample Proportion** |

Problem: According to the National Center for Health Statistics, 15% of all Americans have hearing trouble.

(a) In a random sample of 120 Americans, what is the probability at most 12% have hearing trouble?

(b) Suppose that a random sample of 120 Americans who regularly listen to music using headphones results in 26 having hearing trouble. What might you conclude?

Approach: First, we determine whether the sampling distribution is approximately normal by verifying that the sample size is less than 5% of the population size and that $np(1 - p) \geq 10$. Then we can use the normal distribution to determine the probabilities.

Solution: There are over 300 million people in the United States. The sample size of $n = 120$ is definitely less than 5% of the population size. We are told that $p = 0.15$. Because $np(1 - p) = 120(0.15)(1 - 0.15) = 15.3 \geq 10$, the shape of the distribution of the sample proportion is approximately normal. The mean of the sample proportion $\hat{p}$ is $\mu_{\hat{p}} = 0.15$, and the standard deviation is $\sigma_{\hat{p}} = \sqrt{\dfrac{0.15(1 - 0.15)}{120}}$.

(a) We want to know the probability that a random sample of 120 Americans will result in a sample proportion of at most 12%, or 0.12. That is, we want to know $P(\hat{p} \leq 0.12)$. Figure 16(a) shows the normal curve with the area to the left of 0.12 shaded. To find this area, we convert $\hat{p} = 0.12$ to a z-score by subtracting the mean and dividing by the standard deviation. Don't forget that we round z to two decimal places.

$$z = \frac{\hat{p} - \mu_{\hat{p}}}{\sigma_{\hat{p}}} = \frac{0.12 - 0.15}{\sqrt{\dfrac{0.15(1 - 0.15)}{120}}} = -0.92$$

Figure 16(b) shows a standard normal curve with the area left of -0.92 shaded. Remember, the area to the left of $\hat{p} = 0.12$ is the same as the area to the left of $z = -0.92$.

Figure 16

The area to the left of $z = -0.92$ is 0.1788. Therefore,

$$P(\hat{p} \leq 0.12) = P(Z \leq -0.92) = 0.1788$$

Using Technology
If we use technology to find the area left of $\hat{p} = 0.12$, we obtain 0.1787.

Interpretation: The probability that a random sample of $n = 120$ Americans results in at most 12% having hearing trouble is 0.1788. This means that about 18 out of 100 random samples of size 120 will result in at most 12% having hearing trouble, if the population proportion of Americans with hearing trouble is 0.15.

(b) A random sample of 120 Americans results in 26 having hearing trouble. The sample proportion of Americans with hearing trouble is $\hat{p} = \dfrac{26}{120} = 0.217$. We want to know if obtaining a sample proportion of 0.217 from a population whose proportion is assumed to be 0.15 is unusual. To determine whether a sample proportion of 0.217 is unusual, we compute $P(\hat{p} \geq 0.217)$, because if a sample proportion of 0.217

is unusual, then any sample proportion more than 0.217 is also unusual. Figure 17(a) shows the normal curve with the area to the right of 0.217 shaded. To find this area, we convert $\hat{p} = 0.217$ to a z-score.

$$z = \frac{\hat{p} - \mu_{\hat{p}}}{\sigma_{\hat{p}}} = \frac{0.217 - 0.15}{\sqrt{\dfrac{0.15(1 - 0.15)}{120}}} = 2.06$$

Figure 17(b) shows a standard normal curve with the area right of 2.06 shaded. The area to the right of $\hat{p} = 0.217$ is the same as the area to the right of $z = 2.06$.

Figure 17

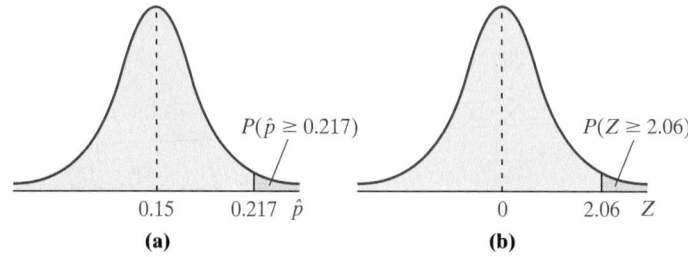

$P(\hat{p} \geq 0.217)$ $P(Z \geq 2.06)$

0.15   0.217 $\hat{p}$ 0   2.06   Z

(a)   (b)

Using Technology

If we use technology to find the area right of $\hat{p} = 0.217$, we obtain 0.0199.

The area to the right of $z = 2.06$ is 0.0197. Therefore,

$$P(\hat{p} \geq 0.217) = P(Z \geq 2.06) = 0.0197$$

Interpretation: About 2 samples in 100 will result in a sample proportion of 0.217 or more from a population whose proportion is 0.15. We obtained a result that should only happen about 2 times in 100, so the results obtained are indeed unusual. We could conclude one or two things:

- The population proportion of Americans with hearing trouble who regularly listen to music using headphones is 0.15, and we just happen to randomly select a higher proportion that have hearing trouble.

- The population proportion of Americans with hearing trouble who regularly listen to music using headphones is more than 0.15.

We are more likely to follow the second conclusion. It is likely that the proportion of Americans who regularly listen using headphones who have hearing trouble is higher than the general population.

Now Work Problem 17

11. (a) Approximately normal; $\mu_{\hat{p}} = 0.8$, $\sigma_{\hat{p}} \approx 0.046$

8.2 ASSESS YOUR UNDERSTANDING

Concepts and Vocabulary

1. In a town of 500 households, 220 have a dog. The population proportion of dog owners in this town (expressed as a decimal) is $p =$ ___0.44___ .

2. The _sample proportion_, denoted $\hat{p}$, is given by the formula $\hat{p} =$ ___$\frac{x}{n}$___ , where x is the number of individuals with a specified characteristic in a sample of n individuals.

3. *True or False*: The population proportion and sample proportion always have the same value.   False

4. *True or False*: The mean of the sampling distribution of $\hat{p}$ is p.   True   5. $n \leq 0.05N$, $np(1 - p) \geq 10$

5. Describe the circumstances under which the shape of the sampling distribution of $\hat{p}$ is approximately normal.

6. What happens to the standard deviation of $\hat{p}$ as the sample size increases? If the sample size is increased by a factor of 4, what happens to the standard deviation of $\hat{p}$?   Decreases; halved

8. Approximately normal; $\mu_{\hat{p}} = 0.7$, $\sigma_{\hat{p}} \approx 0.026$

Skill Building   7. Approximately normal; $\mu_{\hat{p}} = 0.4$, $\sigma_{\hat{p}} \approx 0.022$

In Problems 7–10, describe the sampling distribution of $\hat{p}$. Assume that the size of the population is 25,000 for each problem.

7. $n = 500$, $p = 0.4$ 8. $n = 300$, $p = 0.7$

9. $n = 1000$, $p = 0.103$ 10. $n = 1010$, $p = 0.84$

11. A simple random sample of size $n = 75$ is obtained from a population whose size is $N = 10,000$ and whose population proportion with a specified characteristic is $p = 0.8$.

(a) Describe the sampling distribution of $\hat{p}$.

(b) What is the probability of obtaining $x = 63$ or more individuals with the characteristic? That is, what is $P(\hat{p} \geq 0.84)$?   0.1922

(c) What is the probability of obtaining $x = 51$ or fewer individuals with the characteristic? That is, what is $P(\hat{p} \leq 0.68)$?   0.0047

9. Approximately normal; $\mu_{\hat{p}} = 0.103$, $\sigma_{\hat{p}} \approx 0.010$

10. Approximately normal; $\mu_{\hat{p}} = 0.84$, $\sigma_{\hat{p}} \approx 0.012$

12. (a) Approximately normal; $\mu_{\hat{p}} = 0.65$, $\sigma_{\hat{p}} \approx 0.034$
13. (a) Approximately normal; $\mu_{\hat{p}} = 0.35$, $\sigma_{\hat{p}} \approx 0.015$

12. A simple random sample of size $n = 200$ is obtained from a population whose size is $N = 25,000$ and whose population proportion with a specified characteristic is $p = 0.65$.

(a) Describe the sampling distribution of $\hat{p}$.

(b) What is the probability of obtaining $x = 136$ or more individuals with the characteristic? That is, what is $P(\hat{p} \geq 0.68)$? 0.1867

(c) What is the probability of obtaining $x = 118$ or fewer individuals with the characteristic? That is, what is $P(\hat{p} \leq 0.59)$? 0.0375

13. A simple random sample of size $n = 1,000$ is obtained from a population whose size is $N = 1,000,000$ and whose population proportion with a specified characteristic is $p = 0.35$.

(a) Describe the sampling distribution of $\hat{p}$.

(b) What is the probability of obtaining $x = 390$ or more individuals with the characteristic? 0.0040

(c) What is the probability of obtaining $x = 320$ or fewer individuals with the characteristic? 0.0233

14. A simple random sample of size $n = 1,460$ is obtained from a population whose size is $N = 1,500,000$ and whose population proportion with a specified characteristic is $p = 0.42$.

(a) Describe the sampling distribution of $\hat{p}$.

(b) What is the probability of obtaining $x = 657$ or more individuals with the characteristic? 0.0102

(c) What is the probability of obtaining $x = 584$ or fewer individuals with the characteristic? 0.0606

14. (a) Approximately normal; $\mu_{\hat{p}} = 0.42$, $\sigma_{\hat{p}} \approx 0.013$

Applying the Concepts

15. Are You Satisfied? According to a study conducted by the Gallup organization, the proportion of Americans who are satisfied with the way things are going in their lives is 0.82. Suppose that a random sample of 100 Americans is obtained.

(a) Describe the sampling distribution of $\hat{p}$.

(b) What is the probability that at least 85 Americans in the sample are satisfied with their lives? 0.2177

(c) What is the probability that 75 or fewer Americans in the sample are satisfied with their lives? Is this result unusual? 0.0344; yes

16. Text Messaging A nationwide study indicated that 80% of college students with cell phones send and receive text messages with their phones. A simple random sample of $n = 200$ college students with cell phones is obtained.

Source: medialifemagazine.com

(a) Describe the sampling distribution of $\hat{p}$, the sample proportion of college students with cell phones who send or receive text messages with their phones.

(b) What is the probability that 154 or fewer college students in the sample send and receive text messages with their cell phones? Is this result unusual? 0.1446; no

(c) What is the probability that 172 or more college students in the sample send and receive text messages with their cell phones? Is this result unusual? 0.0170; yes

17. Credit Cards According to a *USA Today* "Snapshot," 26% **NW** of adults do not have any credit cards. A simple random sample of 500 adults is obtained.

(a) Describe the sampling distribution of $\hat{p}$, the sample proportion of adults who do not have a credit card.

15. (a) Approximately normal; $\mu_{\hat{p}} = 0.82$, $\sigma_{\hat{p}} \approx 0.038$

16. (a) Approximately normal; $\mu_{\hat{p}} = 0.8$, $\sigma_{\hat{p}} \approx 0.028$

(b) In a random sample of 500 adults, what is the probability that less than 24% have no credit cards? 0.1539

(c) Would it be unusual if a random sample of 500 adults results in 150 having no credit cards?

18. Cell Phone Only According to a CNN report, 7% of the population do not have traditional phones and instead rely on only cell phones. A random sample of 750 telephone users is obtained.

(a) Describe the sampling distribution of $\hat{p}$, the sample proportion that are "cell-phone only." 18. (b) 0.1423

(b) In a random sample of 750 telephone users, what is the probability that more than 8% are "cell-phone only"?

(c) Would it be unusual if a random sample of 750 adults results in 40 or fewer being "cell-phone only"?

19. Afraid to Fly According to a study conducted by the Gallup organization, the proportion of Americans who were afraid to fly in 2006 was 0.10. A random sample of 1,100 Americans results in 121 indicating that they are afraid to fly. Explain why this is not necessarily evidence that the proportion of Americans who are afraid to fly has increased.

20. Phishing A report released in May 2005 by First Data Corp. indicated that 43% of adults had received a "phishing" contact (a bogus e-mail that replicates an authentic site for the purpose of stealing passwords). A random sample of 800 adults results in 328 indicating that they had received a phishing contact. Explain why this is not necessarily evidence that the proportion of adults who have received a phishing contact has decreased.

21. Social Security Reform A researcher studying public opinion of proposed Social Security changes obtains a simple random sample of 50 adult Americans and asks them whether or not they support the proposed changes. To say that the distribution of $\hat{p}$, the sample proportion of adults who respond yes, is approximately normal, how many more adult Americans does the researcher need to sample if

(a) 10% of all adult Americans support the changes? 62 more

(b) 20% of all adult Americans support the changes? 13 more

22. ADHD A researcher studying ADHD among teenagers obtains a simple random sample of 100 teenagers aged 13 to 17 and asks them whether or not they have ever been prescribed medication for ADHD. To say that the distribution of $\hat{p}$, the sample proportion of teenagers who respond no, is approximately normal, how many more teenagers aged 13 to 17 does the researcher need to sample if

(a) 90% of all teenagers aged 13 to 17 have never been prescribed medication for ADHD? 12 more

(b) 95% of all teenagers aged 13 to 17 have never been prescribed medication for ADHD? 111 more

23. Assessments Consider the homeowners association presented at the beginning of this section. A random sample of 20 households resulted in 15 indicating that they would favor an increase in assessments. Explain why the normal model could not be used to determine if a sample proportion of $\frac{15}{20} = 0.75$ or higher from a population whose proportion is 0.65 is unusual. Events are not independent

17. (a) Approximately normal; $\mu_{\hat{p}} = 0.26$, $\sigma_{\hat{p}} \approx 0.020$

17. (c) Yes; $P(x \geq 150) = P(\hat{p} \geq 0.3) = 0.0207$

18. (a) Approximately normal; $\mu_{\hat{p}} = 0.07$, $\sigma_{\hat{p}} \approx 0.009$

18. (c) Yes; $P(x \leq 40) = P(\hat{p} \leq 0.053) = 0.0344$

24. Simulation The following exercise is meant to illustrate the normality of the distribution of the sample proportion, $\hat{p}$.

(a) Using MINITAB, Excel, or some other statistical software, randomly generate 350 samples of size 25 from a population with $p = 0.3$. Store the number of successes in a column called x.

(b) Determine $\hat{p}$ for each of the 350 samples by computing $\frac{x}{25}$. Store each $\hat{p}$ in a column called *phat*.

(c) Draw a histogram of the 350 estimates of p. Comment on the shape of the distribution.

(d) Compute the mean and standard deviation of the sampling distribution of $\hat{p}$ in the simulation.

(e) Compute the theoretical mean and standard deviation of the sampling distribution of $\hat{p}$. Compare the theoretical results to the results of the simulation. Are they close?

25. The Sampling Distribution Applet Load the sampling distribution applet on your computer. Set the applet so that the population is binary with probability of success equal to 0.2.

(a) Obtain 1,000 random samples of size $n = 5$. Describe the distribution of the sample proportion based on the results of the applet.

(b) Obtain 1,000 random samples of size $n = 30$. Describe the distribution of the sample proportion based on the results of the applet.

(c) Obtain 1,000 random samples of size $n = 100$. Describe the distribution of the sample proportion based on the results of the applet.

(d) Compare the results of parts (a)–(c). How are they the same? How are they different?

26. Finite Population Correction Factor In this section, we assumed that the sample size was less than 5% of the size of the population. When sampling without replacement from a finite population in which $n > 0.05N$, the standard deviation of the distribution of $\hat{p}$ is given by

$$\sigma_{\hat{p}} = \sqrt{\frac{\hat{p}(1 - \hat{p})}{n - 1} \cdot \left(\frac{N - n}{N}\right)}$$

where N is the size of the population. A survey is conducted at a college having an enrollment of 6,502 students. The student council wants to estimate the percentage of students in favor of establishing a student union. In a random sample of 500 students, it was determined that 410 were in favor of establishing a student union.

(a) Obtain the sample proportion, $\hat{p}$, of students surveyed who favor establishing a student union. *0.82*

(b) Calculate the standard deviation of the sampling distribution of $\hat{p}$. *0.017*

Consumer Reports® Tanning Salons

Medical groups have long warned about the dangers of indoor tanning. The American Medical Association and the American Academy of Dermatology unsuccessfully petitioned the Food and Drug Administration in 1994 to ban cosmetic-tanning equipment. Three years later, the Federal Trade Commission warned the public to beware of advertised claims that "unlike the sun, indoor tanning will not cause skin cancer or skin aging" or that you can "tan indoors with absolutely no harmful side effects."

In February 1999, still under pressure from the medical community, the FDA announced that current recommendations "may allow higher exposures" to UV radiation "than are necessary." The agency proposed reducing recommended exposures and requiring simpler wording on consumer warnings. But it has not yet implemented either of these changes. An FDA spokeswoman told us that "the agency decided to postpone amendment of its standard pending the results of ongoing research and discussions with other organizations."

To make matters worse, only about half the states have any rules for tanning parlors. In some of these states, the regulation is minimal and may not require licensing, inspections, training, record keeping, or parental consent for minors. Despite this, millions of Americans, including a growing number of teenage girls, will visit tanning salons this year.

In a recent survey of 296 indoor-tanning facilities around the country, to our knowledge the first nationwide survey of its kind, we found evidence of widespread failures to inform customers about the possible risks, including premature wrinkling and skin cancer, and to follow recommended safety procedures, such as wearing eye goggles. Many facilities made questionable claims about indoor tanning: that it's safer than sunlight, for example, and is well controlled.

(a) In designing this survey, why is it important to sample a large number of facilities? And why is it important to sample these facilities in multiple cities?

(b) Given the fact that there are over 150,000 tanning facilities in the United States, is the condition for independence of survey results satisfied? Why?

(c) Sixty-seven of the 296 tanning facilities surveyed stated that "tanning in a salon is the same as tanning in the sun with respect to causing skin cancer." Assuming that the true proportion of facilities that believe this is 25%, describe the sampling distribution of $\hat{p}$, the sample proportion of tanning facilities that state "tanning in a salon is the same as tanning in the sun with respect to causing skin cancer." Calculate the probability that less than 22.6% of randomly selected tanning salon facilities would state that tanning in a salon is the same as tanning in the sun with respect to causing skin cancer.

(d) Forty-two of the 296 tanning facilities surveyed stated "tanning in a salon does not cause wrinkled skin." Assuming that the true proportion of facilities that believe this is 18%, describe the sampling distribution of $\hat{p}$, the sample proportion of tanning facilities that state "tanning in a salon does not cause wrinkled skin." Calculate the probability that at least 14.2% will state that tanning in a salon does not cause wrinkled skin. Would it be unusual for 50 or fewer facilities to state that tanning in a salon does not cause wrinkled skin?

Note to Readers: *In many cases, our test protocol and analytical methods are more complicated than described in this example. The data and discussion have been modified to make the material more appropriate for the audience.*

CHAPTER 8 REVIEW

Summary

This chapter forms the bridge between probability and statistical inference. In Section 8.1, we discussed the distribution of the sample mean. We learned that the mean of the distribution of the sample mean equals the mean of the population ($\mu_{\bar{x}} = \mu$) and that the standard deviation of the distribution of the sample mean is the standard deviation of the population divided by the square root of the sample size $\left(\sigma_{\bar{x}} = \dfrac{\sigma}{\sqrt{n}} \right)$. If the sample is obtained from a population that is known to be normally distributed, the shape of the distribution of the sample mean is also normal. If the sample is obtained from a population that is not normal, the shape of the distribution of the sample mean becomes approximately normal as the sample size increases. This result is known as the Central Limit Theorem.

In Section 8.2, we discussed the distribution of the sample proportion. We learned that the mean of the distribution of the sample proportion is the population proportion ($\mu_{\hat{p}} = p$) and that the standard deviation of the distribution of the sample proportion is $\sigma_{\hat{p}} = \sqrt{\dfrac{p(1 - p)}{n}}$. If $n \leq 0.05N$ and $np(1 - p) \geq 10$, then the shape of the distribution of $\hat{p}$ is approximately normal.

Vocabulary

Sampling distribution (p. 427)
Sampling distribution of the sample mean (p. 427)

Standard error of the mean (p. 431)
Central Limit Theorem (p. 435)

Sample proportion (p. 442)
Sampling distribution of $\hat{p}$ (p. 446)

Formulas

Mean and Standard Deviation of the Sampling Distribution of $\bar{x}$

$$\mu_{\bar{x}} = \mu \quad \text{and} \quad \sigma_{\bar{x}} = \frac{\sigma}{\sqrt{n}}$$

Sample Proportion

$$\hat{p} = \frac{x}{n}$$

Mean and Standard Deviation of the Sampling Distribution of $\hat{p}$

$$\mu_{\hat{p}} = p \quad \text{and} \quad \sigma_{\hat{p}} = \sqrt{\frac{p(1 - p)}{n}}$$

Standardizing a Normal Random Variable

$$z = \frac{\bar{x} - \mu}{\dfrac{\sigma}{\sqrt{n}}} \quad \text{or} \quad z = \frac{\hat{p} - p}{\sqrt{\dfrac{p(1 - p)}{n}}}$$

Objectives

Section	You should be able to . . .	Example	Review Exercises
8.1	1 Describe the distribution of the sample mean—samples from normal populations (p. 428)	1–3	2, 4, 5
	2 Describe the distribution of the sample mean—samples from a population that is not normal (p. 433)	4 and 5	2, 6, 7
8.2	1 Describe the sampling distribution of a sample proportion (p. 442)	2 and 3	3, 4, 8(a), 10(c)
	2 Compute probabilities of a sample proportion (p. 446)	4	8(b), (c), 9, 10(d), (e)

Review Exercises

4. $\mu_{\bar{x}} = \mu, \sigma_{\bar{x}} = \dfrac{\sigma}{\sqrt{n}}; \mu_{\hat{p}} = p, \sigma_{\hat{p}} = \sqrt{\dfrac{p(1 - p)}{n}}$ 5. (b) Normal; $\mu_{\bar{x}} = 2{,}600, \sigma_{\bar{x}} = \dfrac{50}{\sqrt{20}}$

1. In your own words, explain what a sampling distribution is.

2. Under what conditions is the sampling distribution of $\bar{x}$ normal? *Population normal; large sample size*

3. Under what conditions is the sampling distribution of $\hat{p}$ approximately normal? *when $np(1 - p) \geq 10$*

4. What are the mean and standard deviation of the sampling distribution of $\bar{x}$? What are the mean and standard deviation of the sampling distribution of $\hat{p}$?

5. **Energy Need during Pregnancy** The total energy need during pregnancy is normally distributed, with mean $\mu = 2{,}600$ kcal/day and standard deviation $\sigma = 50$ kcal/day.

   Source: American Dietetic Association

   (a) What is the probability that a randomly selected pregnant woman has an energy need of more than 2,625 kcal/day? Is this result unusual? *0.3085; no*

   (b) Describe the sampling distribution of $\bar{x}$, the sample mean daily energy requirement for a random sample of 20 pregnant women.

(c) What is the probability that a random sample of 20 pregnant women has a mean energy need of more than 2,625 kcal/day? Is this result unusual? *0.0125; yes*

6. **Copper Tubing** A machine at K&A Tube & Manufacturing Company produces a certain copper tubing component in a refrigeration unit. The tubing components produced by the manufacturer have a mean diameter of 0.75 inch with a standard deviation of 0.004 inch. The quality-control inspector takes a random sample of 30 components once each week and calculates the mean diameter of these components. If the mean is either less than 0.748 inch or greater than 0.752 inch, the inspector concludes that the machine needs an adjustment.

(a) Describe the sampling distribution of $\bar{x}$, the sample mean diameter, for a random sample of 30 such components.

(b) What is the probability that, based on a random sample of 30 such components, the inspector will conclude that the machine needs an adjustment when, in fact, the machine is correctly calibrated? *0.0062*

7. **Number of Televisions** Based on data obtained from A. C. Nielsen, the mean number of televisions in a household in the United States is 2.24. Assume that the population standard deviation number of television sets in the United States is 1.38.

(a) Do you believe the shape of the distribution of number of television sets follows a normal distribution? Why or why not? *No; skewed right*

(b) A random sample of 40 households results in a total of 102 television sets. What is the mean number of televisions in these 40 households? *2.55*

(c) What is the probability of obtaining the sample mean obtained in part (b) if the population mean is 2.24? Does the statistic from part (b) contradict the results reported by A. C. Nielsen? *0.0778; no*

8. **Entrepreneurship** A Gallup survey in March 2005 indicated that 72% of 18- to 29-year-olds, if given a choice, would prefer

to start their own business rather than work for someone else. A random sample of 600 18- to 29-year-olds is obtained today.

(a) Describe the sampling distribution of $\hat{p}$, the sample proportion of 18- to 29-year-olds who would prefer to start their own business.

(b) In a random sample of 600 18- to 29-year-olds, what is the probability that no more than 70% would prefer to start their own business? *0.1379*

(c) Would it be unusual if a random sample of 600 18- to 29-year-olds resulted in 450 or more who would prefer to start their own business? *a little unusual*

9. **Advanced Degrees** According to the U.S. Census Bureau, 10% of adults 25 years and older in the United States had advanced degrees in 2006. A researcher with the U.S. Department of Education surveys 500 randomly selected adults 25 years of age or older and finds that 60 of them have an advanced degree. Explain why this is not necessarily evidence that the proportion of adults 25 years of age or older with advanced degrees has increased.

10. **A Breakout Season?** In 2007, Orlando Cabrera had the highest batting average of his career. Suppose that Cabrera is intrinsically a 0.273 hitter (his career batting average), meaning he averages 273 hits for every 1,000 at-bats (think of this as 273 successes in 1,000 trials of an experiment). Therefore, the population proportion of hits for Cabrera is 0.273. Assume that each at-bat is independent of the other.

(a) In 2007, Cabrera had 192 hits in 638 at-bats. Determine the sample proportion of hits in 2007 for Cabrera. That is, determine his batting average. $\hat{p} = 0.301$

(b) Verify that the distribution of the sample proportion is approximately normal.

(c) Describe the distribution of the sample proportion.

(d) Was Cabrera's year all that unusual? *No*

(e) Would it be unusual for Cabrera to have 160 hits in 638 at-bats for a 0.251 batting average in 2008? *No; 0.1056 probability of hitting 0.251 or less*

6. (a) Approximately normal; $\mu_{\bar{x}} = 0.75$; $\sigma_{\bar{x}} = \dfrac{0.004}{\sqrt{30}}$

8. (a) Approximately normal; $\mu_{\hat{p}} = 0.72$, $\sigma_{\hat{p}} \approx 0.018$

10. (c) Approximately normal; $\mu_{\hat{p}} = 0.273$, $\sigma_{\hat{p}} \approx 0.018$

CHAPTER TEST

1. State the Central Limit Theorem.

2. If a random sample of 36 is obtained from a population with mean 50 and standard deviation 24, what is the mean and standard deviation of the sampling distribution of the sample mean?

3. The charge life of a certain lithium ion battery for camcorders is normally distributed, with mean 90 minutes and standard deviation 35 minutes.

(a) What is the probability that a randomly selected battery of this type lasts more than 100 minutes on a single charge? Is this result unusual? *0.3859; no*

(b) Describe the sampling distribution of $\bar{x}$, the sample mean charge life for a random sample of 10 such batteries.

(c) What is the probability that a random sample of 10 such batteries has a mean charge life of more than 100 minutes? Is this result unusual? *0.1841; no*

(d) What is the probability that a random sample of 25 such batteries has a mean charge of more than 100 minutes?

(e) Explain what causes the probabilities in parts (c) and (d) to be different.

4. A machine used for filling plastic bottles with a soft drink has a known standard deviation of $\sigma = 0.05$ liter. The target mean fill volume is $\mu = 2.0$ liters.

(a) Describe the sampling distribution of $\bar{x}$, the sample mean fill volume, for a random sample of 45 such bottles.

(b) A quality-control manager obtains a random sample of 45 bottles. He will shut down the machine if the sample mean of these 45 bottles is less than 1.98 liters or greater than 2.02 liters. What is the probability that the quality-control manager will shut down the machine even though the machine is correctly calibrated? *0.0074*

2. $\mu_{\bar{x}} = 50$, $\sigma_{\bar{x}} = \dfrac{24}{\sqrt{36}} = 4$ 3. (b) Normal; $\mu_{\bar{x}} = 90$, $\sigma_{\bar{x}} = \dfrac{35}{\sqrt{10}}$ 3. (d) 0.0764   4. (a) Approximately Normal; $\mu_{\bar{x}} = 2.0$, $\sigma_{\bar{x}} = \dfrac{0.05}{\sqrt{45}}$

5. According to the National Center for Health Statistics (2004), 22.4% of adults are smokers. A random sample of 300 adults is obtained.

(a) Describe the sampling distribution of $\hat{p}$, the sample proportion of adults who smoke.

(b) In a random sample of 300 adults, what is the probability that at least 50 are smokers? *0.9913*

(c) Would it be unusual if a random sample of 300 adults results in 18% or less being smokers? *Yes*

6. Peanut and tree nut allergies are considered to be the most serious food allergies. According to the National Institute of Allergy and Infectious Diseases, roughly 1% of Americans are allergic to peanuts or tree nuts. A random sample of 1,500 Americans is obtained.

(a) Explain why a large sample is needed for the distribution of the sample proportion to be approximately normal.

(b) Would it be unusual if a random sample of 1,500 Americans results in fewer than 10 with peanut or tree nut allergies? *No*

7. According to Wikipedia.com, net worth is defined as total assets (value of house, cars, money, etc.) minus total liabilities (mortgage balance, credit card debt, etc.). According to TNS Financial Services, 7% of American households had a net worth in excess of $1 million (excluding their primary residence) in 2006. A random sample of 1,000 American households results in 82 having a net worth in excess of $1 million. Explain why the results of this survey do not necessarily imply that the proportion of households with a net worth in excess of $1 million has increased.

5. (a) Normal; $\mu_{\hat{p}} = 0.224$, $\sigma_{\hat{p}} \approx 0.024$

◢MAKING AN
INFORMED DECISION

How Much Time Do You Spend in a Day . . . ?

The American Time Use Survey is a survey of adult Americans conducted by the Bureau of Labor Statistics. The purpose of the survey is to learn how Americans allocate their time in a day. As a reporter for the school newspaper, you wish to file a report that compares the typical student at your school to other Americans.

For those Americans who are currently attending school, the mean amount of time spent in class in a day is 5.11 hours, and the mean amount of time spent studying and doing homework is 2.50 hours. The mean amount of time Americans spend watching television each day is 2.57 hours.

Conduct a survey of 35 randomly selected full-time students at your school in which you ask the following questions:

(a) On average, how much time do you spend attending class each day?

(b) On average, how much time do you spend studying and doing homework each day?

(c) On average, how much time do you spend watching television each day? If you do not watch television, write 0 hours.

1. For each question, describe the sampling distribution of the sample mean. Use the national norms as estimates for the population means for each variable. Use the sample standard deviation as an estimate of the population standard deviation.

2. Compute probabilities regarding the values of the statistics obtained from the survey. Are any of the results unusual?

Write an article for your newspaper reporting your findings.

The exponential distribution is an example of a skewed distribution. It is defined by the density function

$$f(x) \geq \begin{cases} \lambda e^{\lambda x} = x \geq 0 \\ 0 \quad\;\; = x < 0 \end{cases}$$

with parameter λ. The mean of an exponential distribution is $\mu = \dfrac{1}{\lambda}$ and the median is $M = \dfrac{\ln 2}{\lambda}$.

The exponential distribution is used to model the failure rate of electrical components. For many electrical components, a plot of the failure rate over time appears to be shaped like a bathtub. The exponential distribution is used widely in reliability engineering for the constant hazard rate portion of the bathtub curve, where components spend most of their useful life. The portion of the curve prior to the constant rate is referred to as the burn-in period, and the portion after the constant rate is referred to as the wear-out period.

Another interesting property of the exponential distribution is the *memoryless property*. This says that the time to failure of a component does not depend on how long the component has been in use. For example, the probability that a component will fail in the next hour is the same whether the component has been in use for 10, 50, or 100 hours, and so on.

In our discussion of summary statistics, we have seen that the mean is used as a measure of the center for data sets whose distribution is (roughly) symmetric with no outliers. In the presence of outliers or skewness, we used the median as the measure of the center because it is resistant to extreme values. However, for skewed distributions, it is often difficult to determine which measure of center is most useful. In some cases, the mean, though not resistant, is easier to find than the median or is more intuitive to the reader within the context of the problem. Here we look at the sampling distributions of the mean and median for two different populations, one normal (symmetric) and one exponential (skewed).

1. Using statistical software, generate 250 samples (rows) of size $n = 80$ (columns) from a normal distribution with mean 50 and standard deviation 10.

2. Compute the mean for the first 10 values in each row and store the values in C81. You might label this column "n10mn" for normal distribution, sample size 10, mean.

3. Compute the median for the first 10 values in each row and store the values in C82. You might label this column "n10med" for normal distribution, sample size 10, median.

4. Repeat parts 2 and 3 for samples of size 20 (C1–C20), 40 (C1–C40), and 80 (C1–C80), storing the results in consecutive columns C83, C84, C85, and so on.

5. Compute the summary statistics for your data in columns C81 to C88.

6. How do the averages of your sample means compare to the actual population mean for the different sample sizes? How do the averages of your sample medians compare to the actual population median for the different sample sizes?

7. How does the standard deviation of sample means compare to the standard deviation of sample medians for different sample sizes?

8. Based on your results in parts 6 and 7, which measure of center seems more appropriate? Explain.

9. Construct histograms for each column of summary statistics. Describe the effect, if any, of increasing the sample size on the shape of the distribution of sample means and sample medians.

CASE STUDY

10. Using statistical software, generate 250 samples of size $n = 80$ from an exponential distribution with scale parameter 50. This could represent the distribution of failure times for a component with a failure rate of $\lambda = 0.02$.

Note: The threshold should be set to 0. Store the results in columns C101–C180.

11. Compute the mean for the first 10 values in each row and store the values in C181. You might label this column "e10mn" for exponential distribution, sample size 10, mean.

12. Compute the median for the first 10 values in each row and store the values in C182. You might label this column "e10med" for exponential distribution, sample size 10, median.

13. Repeat parts 11 and 12 for samples of size 20 (C101–C120), 40 (C101–C140), and 80 (C101–C180), storing the results in consecutive columns C183, C184, C185, and so on.

14. Compute the summary statistics for your data in columns C181 to C188.

15. How do the averages of your sample means compare to the actual population mean for the different sample sizes? How do the averages of your sample medians compare to the actual population median for the different sample sizes?

16. How does the standard deviation of sample means compare to the standard deviation of sample medians for different sample sizes?

17. Based on your results in parts 15 and 16, which measure of center seems more appropriate? Explain?

18. Construct histograms for each column of summary statistics. Describe the effect, if any, of increasing the sample size on the shape of the distribution of sample means and sample medians.

19. Can the Central Limit Theorem be used to explain any of the results in part 18? Why or why not?

9 Estimating the Value of a Parameter Using Confidence Intervals

Outline

9.1 The Logic in Constructing Confidence Intervals for a Population Mean When the Population Standard Deviation Is Known

9.2 Confidence Intervals for a Population Mean When the Population Standard Deviation Is Unknown

9.3 Confidence Intervals for a Population Proportion

9.4 Confidence Intervals for a Population Standard Deviation

9.5 Putting It Together: Which Procedure Do I Use?

MAKING AN INFORMED DECISION

One of the most difficult decisions that a person has to make while attending college is choosing a major field of study. This decision plays a large role in the career path of an individual. What major should you choose? The Decisions project on page 511 may help you decide.

PUTTING IT TOGETHER

Chapters 1 through 7 laid the groundwork for the remainder of the course. These chapters dealt with data collection (Chapter 1), descriptive statistics (Chapters 2 through 4), and probability (Chapters 5 through 7). Chapter 8 formed a bridge between probability and statistical inference by giving us a model we can use to make probability statements about the sample mean and sample proportion.

We know from Section 8.1 that the sample mean is a random variable and has a distribution associated with it. This distribution is called the sampling distribution of the sample mean. The mean of this distribution is equal to the mean of the population, μ and the standard deviation is $\frac{\sigma}{\sqrt{n}}$. The shape of the distribution of the sample mean is normal if the population is normal or approximately normal if the sample size is large. We learned in Section 8.2 that $\hat{p}$ is also a random variable whose mean is p and standard deviation is $\sqrt{\frac{p(1-p)}{n}}$. If $np(1-p) \geq 10$, the distribution of the random variable $\hat{p}$ is approximately normal.

We now discuss inferential statistics—the process of generalizing information obtained from a sample to a population. We will study two areas of inferential statistics: (1) estimation—sample data are used to estimate the value of unknown parameters such as μ or p, and (2) hypothesis testing—statements regarding a characteristic of one or more populations are tested using sample data. In this chapter, we discuss estimation of an unknown parameter, and in the next chapter, we discuss hypothesis testing.

Because the information collected from a sample does not contain all the information in the population, we will assign probabilities to our estimates. These probabilities serve as a way of measuring what will happen if we estimate the value of the parameter many times and provide a measure of confidence in our results.

9.1 THE LOGIC IN CONSTRUCTING CONFIDENCE INTERVALS FOR A POPULATION MEAN WHEN THE POPULATION STANDARD DEVIATION IS KNOWN

Preparing for This Section   Before getting started, review the following:

- Parameter versus statistic (Section 1.1, p. 5)
- Simple random sampling (Section 1.3, pp. 22–27)
- Sampling error (Section 1.5, p. 42)
- z_α notation (Section 7.2, pp. 392–393)

- Finding the value of a normal random variable (Section 7.3, pp. 400–401)
- Normal probability plots (Section 7.4, pp. 405–409)
- Distribution of the sample mean (Section 8.1, pp. 427–438)

Objectives

1. Compute a point estimate of the population mean
2. Construct and interpret a confidence interval for a population mean, assuming that the population standard deviation is known
3. Explain the role of margin of error in constructing a confidence interval
4. Determine the sample size necessary for estimating the population mean within a specified margin of error

---

Our goal in this section is to estimate the value of an unknown population mean. We begin introducing the approach to estimation by making the simplifying assumption that the population standard deviation, σ, is known. Granted, it is unlikely that we will know the population standard deviation while not knowing the population mean. However, the assumption is made because it allows us to use the normal distribution to develop the technique of estimation. Put simply, this assumption liberates us from details and allows us to focus on the concept of estimation. We will drop this assumption in the next section.

1 Compute a Point Estimate of the Population Mean

The goal of statistical inference is to use information obtained from a sample and generalize the results to the population that is being studied. The first step in estimating the value of an unknown parameter such as μ is to obtain a random sample and use the data from the sample to obtain a *point estimate* of the parameter.

Definition   A **point estimate** is the value of a statistic that estimates the value of a parameter.

For example, the sample mean, $\overline{x}$, is a point estimate of the population mean, μ.

EXAMPLE 1   **Computing a Point Estimate**

Problem: A two-lane highway with a posted speed limit of 45 miles per hour is located just outside a small 40-home subdivision. The residents of the neighborhood are concerned that the speed of cars on the highway is excessive and want an estimate of the population mean speed of the cars on the highway.

Table 1

57.4	56.1	70.3	65.6
44.2	58.6	66.1	57.3
62.2	60.4	64.5	52.7

Approach: The Department of Transportation estimates that 2,400 cars travel on the highway between the hours of 9 A.M. and 3 P.M. (nonpeak time). The residents decide to measure the speed of 12 cars on the highway during nonpeak times (congestion slows everyone down). The 12 cars will be selected using a simple random sample by determining 12 numbers between 1 and 2,400 and measuring the speed of the cars using a radar gun. The sample mean speed of the 12 cars will be the point estimate of the population mean.

Solution: Table 1 shows the speeds (in miles per hour) of the 12 randomly selected cars. The sample mean is

$$\bar{x} = \frac{57.4 + 44.2 + \cdots + 52.7}{12} = \frac{715.4}{12} = 59.62 \text{ miles per hour}$$

The point estimate of μ is 59.62 miles per hour.

Now Work Problem 35(a)

---

② Construct and Interpret a Confidence Interval for a Population Mean

What do we do with the point estimate obtained in Example 1? Would you go to the police department and ask for the speed on this highway to be monitored based on these 12 observations? Or would you like to have more evidence? After all, we know that statistics such as $\bar{x}$ vary from sample to sample. So a different random sample of 12 cars might result in a different point estimate of the population mean, such as $\bar{x} = 54.39$ miles per hour. Assuming the method used in selecting the cars was done appropriately, both point estimates would be reasonably good guesses of the population mean. Because of this variability in the sample mean, we are better off reporting a range (or interval) of values, with some measure of the likelihood that the interval includes the unknown population mean.

To help understand the idea of this interval, consider the following situation. Suppose you were asked to guess the mean age of the students in your statistics class. If the sample mean age based on a survey of five of the students is $\bar{x} = 24$, you might guess the mean age of *all* the students is 24 years. This would be a point estimate of μ, the mean age of all students in the class. As you look around the room, you realize that you did not survey everyone, so your guess is probably off. To account for this error, you might express your guess by producing a range of ages, such as 24 years old give or take 2 years (the *margin of error*). Mathematically, we write this as 24 ± 2. If asked how confident you are that the mean age is between 22 and 26, you might respond, "I am 80% confident that the mean age of all students in my statistics class is between 22 and 26 years." If asked to give a range for which your confidence increases to say, 90%, what do you think will happen to the interval? To have 90% confidence, you may need to increase your interval to between 20 and 28 years.

In statistics, we construct intervals for a population mean centered around a guess as well. The *guess* is the sample mean, the point estimate of the population mean.

In Other Words
The symbol $\pm$ is read "plus or minus." It means "to add and subtract the quantity following the $\pm$ symbol."

Definition

In Other Words
A confidence interval is a range of numbers, such as 22–30. The level of confidence is the proportion of intervals that will contain the unknown parameter if repeated samples are obtained.

- A **confidence interval** for an unknown parameter consists of an interval of numbers.
- The **level of confidence** represents the expected proportion of intervals that will contain the parameter if a large number of different samples is obtained. The level of confidence is denoted $(1 - \alpha) \cdot 100\%$.

For example, a 95% level of confidence ($\alpha = 0.05$) implies that if 100 different confidence intervals are constructed, each based on a different sample from the same population, then we will expect 95 of the intervals to include the parameter and 5 to not include the parameter.

Confidence interval estimates for the population mean are of the form

$$\text{Point estimate} \pm \text{margin of error}$$

The **margin of error** of a confidence interval estimate of a parameter is a measure of how accurate the point estimate is and depends on three factors:

1. *Level of confidence*: As the level of confidence increases, the margin of error also increases. This should seem logical based on the discussion presented earlier regarding estimating the mean age of students in your statistics class.

2. *Sample size*: As the size of the random sample increases, the margin of error decreases. This is a consequence of the Law of Large Numbers, which states that as the sample size increases the difference between the statistic and parameter decreases.

3. *Standard deviation of the population*: The more spread there is in the population, the wider our interval will be for a given sample size and level of confidence.

Now the question is "How do we construct a confidence interval for a population mean?" From Chapter 8, we know the following information about the distribution of the sample mean:

- The shape of the distribution of all possible sample means will be normal if the population is normal, or approximately normal if the population is not normal, but sample size is large ($n \geq 30$).
- The mean of the distribution of sample means equals the mean of the population. That is, $\mu_{\bar{x}} = \mu$.
- The standard deviation of the sample mean (the standard error) equals the standard deviation of the population divided by the square root of the sample size. That is, $\sigma_{\bar{x}} = \dfrac{\sigma}{\sqrt{n}}$.

The sample mean is a point estimate of the population mean, so we expect the value of $\bar{x}$ to be close to μ, but we do not know how close. Because the sample mean is normally distributed, we know 95% of all sample means lie within 1.96 standard deviations of the population mean, μ, and 2.5% of the sample means lie in each tail. See Figure 1. That is, 95% of all sample means are in the interval

$$\mu \quad - 1.96 \quad \cdot \quad \sigma_{\bar{x}} \quad < \quad \bar{x} \quad < \quad \mu \quad + 1.96 \quad \cdot \quad \sigma_{\bar{x}}$$
parameter − 1.96 (standard error) < point estimate < parameter + 1.96 (standard error)

With a little algebraic manipulation, we can rewrite this inequality with μ in the middle and obtain

$$\bar{x} \quad - 1.96 \quad \cdot \quad \sigma_{\bar{x}} \quad < \quad \mu \quad < \quad \bar{x} \quad + 1.96 \quad \cdot \quad \sigma_{\bar{x}} \quad \textbf{(1)}$$
point estimate − 1.96 (standard error) < parameter < point estimate + 1.96 (standard error)

This inequality states that 95% of *all* sample means will result in confidence interval estimates that contain the population mean. It is common to write the 95% confidence interval as

$$\bar{x} \quad \pm 1.96 \cdot \quad \sigma_{\bar{x}}$$
Point estimate ± 1.96 (standard error)

so that it is of the form

$$\text{Point estimate} \pm \text{margin of error}$$

To visually illustrate this idea, draw a normal curve of the sampling distribution of $\bar{x}$. Now create a "slider" that shows $\bar{x} - 1.96\,\sigma_{\bar{x}}$ and $\bar{x} + 1.96\,\sigma_{\bar{x}}$. As $\bar{x}$ goes into nonshaded region, the interval does not capture μ. See Figure 2.

Perhaps you are wondering where the 1.96 comes from in a 95% confidence interval. For a 95% confidence interval, we are capturing the middle 95% of all sample means, so 2.5% of the sample means are in each tail. Remember that the notation z_{α} is used to represent the z-value such that the area in the right tail is α.

Figure 1
Sampling distribution of $\bar{x}$

Figure 2

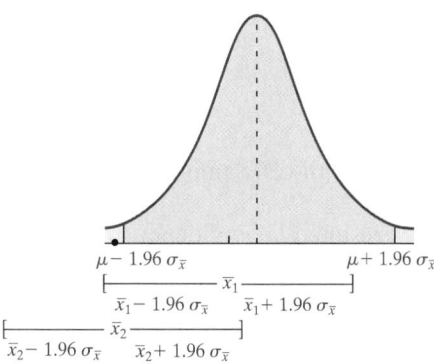

So $z_{0.025} = 1.96$ is the z-value such that 2.5% of the area under the standard normal curve is to the right.

Let's look at an example that illustrates the concept of a 95% confidence interval.

| EXAMPLE 2 | **Constructing 95% Confidence Intervals from 20 Samples** |

Problem: Scores on the Stanford–Binet IQ test are normally distributed with $\mu = 100$ and $\sigma = 15$. Use MINITAB, Excel, or some other statistical software to simulate obtaining 20 simple random samples of size $n = 9$. Use these 20 different samples to construct 95% confidence intervals for the population mean, μ.

Approach

Step 1: We use MINITAB to obtain 20 simple random samples of size $n = 9$ from a population that is normally distributed with mean $\mu = 100$ and standard deviation $\sigma = 15$. We then compute the mean of each of the 20 samples.

Step 2: Construct 95% confidence intervals by computing

$$\bar{x} - 1.96 \cdot \frac{\sigma}{\sqrt{n}} = \bar{x} - 1.96 \cdot \frac{15}{\sqrt{9}} \quad \text{and} \quad \bar{x} + 1.96 \cdot \frac{\sigma}{\sqrt{n}} = \bar{x} + 1.96 \cdot \frac{15}{\sqrt{9}}$$

Solution

Step 1: Table 2 shows the twenty samples and the twenty sample means from MINITAB. Each row represents a sample. The first 9 columns (C1–C9) represent the 9 individuals in the sample and column C10 (xbar) represents the sample mean for each sample.

Table 2

Worksheet 1 ***

↓	C1	C2	C3	C4	C5	C6	C7	C8	C9	C10 xbar
1	84	96	67	109	120	83	111	118	123	101.3
2	93	106	104	101	81	97	104	75	106	96.3
3	137	103	94	97	99	77	112	86	80	98.4
4	116	110	106	127	88	92	96	87	101	102.7
5	116	117	102	123	114	112	91	104	85	107.1
6	80	114	113	94	101	72	105	77	129	98.3
7	103	96	104	99	97	123	133	85	115	106.0
8	90	123	127	104	103	100	85	83	102	102.1
9	106	102	94	112	62	84	124	90	90	95.9
10	109	86	97	115	102	124	73	93	98	99.7
11	95	85	80	89	126	108	109	101	91	98.2
12	98	73	126	101	117	115	91	86	99	100.6
13	106	97	98	117	96	110	112	81	128	105.1
14	121	83	90	99	115	98	118	102	69	99.4
15	111	87	95	105	103	100	102	84	89	97.3
16	110	115	94	87	102	121	100	106	68	100.6
17	91	106	78	129	117	117	107	106	115	107.5
18	92	104	86	126	103	97	81	141	112	104.9
19	113	105	108	137	84	122	126	94	122	112.5
20	103	87	81	101	128	97	110	119	132	106.3

Step 2: We construct a confidence interval for each of the 20 sample means and present the results in Table 3.

We can see that 19 of the 20 (or 95%) samples resulted in confidence intervals that contain the value of the population mean, 100. Sample 19 resulted in a confidence interval that does not contain the population mean 100.

Figure 3 presents the sampling distribution of the sample mean along with the 20 confidence intervals. Any sample mean between 90.2 and 109.8 results in a confidence interval that includes the population mean, 100. Any sample mean less than

Figure 3

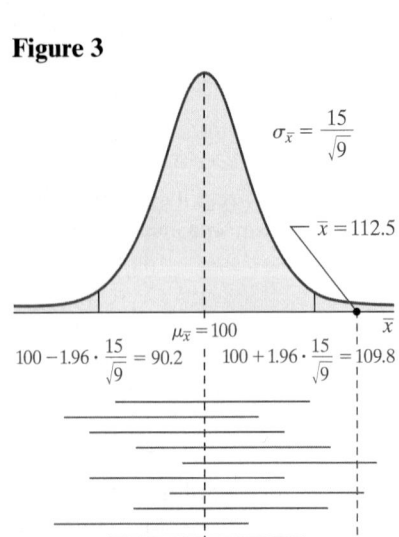

$\sigma_{\bar{x}} = \dfrac{15}{\sqrt{9}}$

$\bar{x} = 112.5$

$\mu_{\bar{x}} = 100$

$100 - 1.96 \cdot \dfrac{15}{\sqrt{9}} = 90.2$ $100 + 1.96 \cdot \dfrac{15}{\sqrt{9}} = 109.8$

		Table 3		
		Margin of Error	**Lower Bound**	**Upper Bound**
Sample	**Sample Mean, $\bar{x}$**	$1.96 \cdot \dfrac{\sigma}{\sqrt{n}} = 1.96 \cdot \dfrac{15}{\sqrt{9}} = 9.8$	$\bar{x} - 1.96 \cdot \dfrac{\sigma}{\sqrt{n}}$	$\bar{x} + 1.96 \cdot \dfrac{\sigma}{\sqrt{n}}$
1	101.3	9.8	$101.3 - 9.8 = 91.5$	$101.3 + 9.8 = 111.1$
2	96.3	9.8	$96.3 - 9.8 = 86.5$	$96.3 + 9.8 = 106.1$
3	98.4	9.8	88.6	108.2
4	102.7	9.8	92.9	112.5
5	107.1	9.8	97.3	116.9
6	98.3	9.8	88.5	108.1
7	106.0	9.8	96.2	115.8
8	102.1	9.8	92.3	111.9
9	95.9	9.8	86.1	105.7
10	99.7	9.8	89.9	109.5
11	98.2	9.8	88.4	108.0
12	100.6	9.8	90.8	110.4
13	105.1	9.8	95.3	114.9
14	99.4	9.8	89.6	109.2
15	97.3	9.8	87.5	107.1
16	100.6	9.8	90.8	110.4
17	107.5	9.8	97.7	117.3
18	104.9	9.8	95.1	114.7
19	112.5	9.8	102.7	122.3
20	106.3	9.8	96.5	116.1

90.2 or greater than 109.8 results in a confidence interval that does not include the population mean, 100. The proportion of sample means between 90.2 and 109.8 is 0.95; therefore, the proportion of sample means that result in intervals that include the population mean is 0.95.

We can generalize the results of Example 2. For a 95% confidence interval, any sample mean that lies within 1.96 standard errors of the population mean will result in a confidence interval that contains μ, and any sample mean that is more than 1.96 standard errors from the population mean will result in a confidence interval that does not contain μ. This is an extremely important point. **Whether a confidence interval contains μ depends solely on the sample mean, $\bar{x}$.** The population mean is a fixed value that either is or is not in the interval, and we will not know which of these possibilities is true for any computed confidence interval. However, if repeated values are taken, we do know 95% of the confidence intervals will contain the population mean.

Note: In the simulation of Example 2, exactly 95% of the samples resulted in intervals that contained μ. It is not always the case that exactly 95% of the sample means results in intervals that contain μ when performing this simulation. It could easily have been the case that all the intervals contained μ or that 17 out of the 20 contained μ. The interpretation of the confidence interval remains: In a 95% confidence interval, as the number of random samples of size n increases, the proportion of intervals that capture the population mean will approach 0.95. When we obtain only 20 samples, the exact proportion may be slightly different from 0.95. ◀

We are not interested in only constructing 95% confidence intervals, so we need a method for constructing any $(1 - \alpha) \cdot 100\%$ confidence interval. [When $\alpha = 0.05$ we are constructing a $(1 - 0.05) \cdot 100\% = 95\%$ confidence interval.]

We generalize Formula (1) given on page 459 by noting that $(1 - \alpha) \cdot 100\%$ of all sample means are in the interval

$$\mu - z_{\frac{\alpha}{2}} \cdot \frac{\sigma}{\sqrt{n}} < \bar{x} < \mu + z_{\frac{\alpha}{2}} \cdot \frac{\sigma}{\sqrt{n}}$$

as shown in Figure 4.

CAUTION   A 95% confidence interval does *not* mean that there is a 95% probability that the interval contains μ. Remember, probability describes the likelihood of undetermined events. Therefore, it does not make sense to talk about the probability that the interval contains μ, since the population mean is a fixed value. Think of it this way: I flip a coin and obtain a head. If I ask you to determine the probability that the flip resulted in a head, it would not be 0.5, because the outcome has already been determined. Instead, the probability is 0 or 1. Confidence intervals work the same way. Because μ is already determined, we do not say that there is a 95% probability that the interval contains μ.

Figure 4

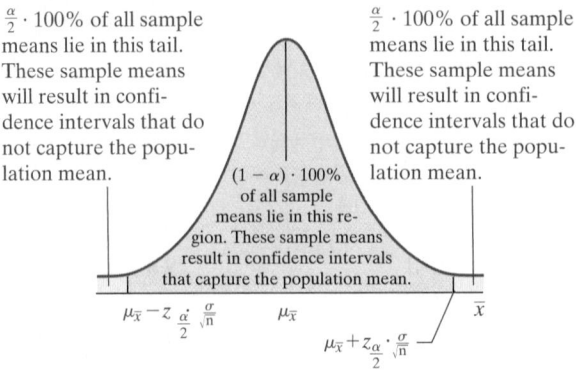

We rewrite this inequality with μ in the middle and obtain

$$\bar{x} - z_{\frac{\alpha}{2}} \cdot \frac{\sigma}{\sqrt{n}} < \mu < \bar{x} + z_{\frac{\alpha}{2}} \cdot \frac{\sigma}{\sqrt{n}}$$

So, $(1 - \alpha) \cdot 100\%$ of the sample means will result in confidence intervals that contain the population mean. The sample means that are in the tails of the distribution in Figure 4 will not have confidence intervals that include the population mean.

The value $z_{\frac{\alpha}{2}}$ is called the **critical value** of the distribution. Table 4 shows some of the common critical values used in the construction of confidence intervals.

Table 4		
Level of Confidence, $(1 - \alpha) \cdot 100\%$	**Area in Each Tail, $\dfrac{\alpha}{2}$**	**Critical Value, $z_{\frac{\alpha}{2}}$**
90%	0.05	1.645
95%	0.025	1.96
99%	0.005	2.575

We now present an interpretation of any confidence interval.

Interpretation of a Confidence Interval

A $(1 - \alpha) \cdot 100\%$ confidence interval indicates that $(1 - \alpha) \cdot 100\%$ of all simple random samples of size n from the population whose parameter is unknown will contain the parameter.

For example, a 90% confidence interval for a parameter means that 90% of all possible samples will result in an interval that includes the unknown parameter and 10% of the samples result in an interval that does not capture the parameter.

If we construct a 90% confidence interval with a lower bound of 12 and an upper bound of 18, we interpret the interval as follows: "We are 90% confident that the population mean, μ, is between 12 and 18." Be sure that you understand that the level of confidence refers to the confidence in the method, not the specific interval. So, a 90% confidence interval tells us that the method will result in an interval that contains the population mean, μ, 90% of the time. It *does not* tell us that there is a 90% probability that μ lies between 12 and 18.

We are now prepared to present a method for constructing a $(1 - \alpha) \cdot 100\%$ confidence interval about μ.

> ### Constructing a $(1 - \alpha) \cdot 100\%$ Confidence Interval for μ, σ Known
>
> Suppose that a simple random sample of size n is taken from a population with unknown mean, μ, and known standard deviation, σ. A $(1 - \alpha) \cdot 100\%$ confidence interval for μ is given by
>
> $$\text{Lower bound: } \overline{x} - z_{\frac{\alpha}{2}} \cdot \frac{\sigma}{\sqrt{n}} \qquad \text{Upper bound: } \overline{x} + z_{\frac{\alpha}{2}} \cdot \frac{\sigma}{\sqrt{n}} \qquad (2)$$
>
> where $z_{\frac{\alpha}{2}}$ is the critical z-value.
>
> **Note:** The sample size must be large ($n \geq 30$) or the population must be normally distributed. ◄

When constructing a confidence interval about the population mean, we must verify that the sample is big enough ($n \geq 30$) or comes from a population that is normally distributed so that we can use the normal model to construct the interval. Fortunately, the procedures for constructing confidence intervals presented in this section are **robust**, which means that minor departures from normality will not seriously affect the results. Nevertheless, it is important that the requirements for constructing confidence intervals be verified. We shall follow the practice of verifying the normality assumption for small sample sizes by drawing a normal probability plot and checking for outliers by drawing a boxplot.

Because the construction of the confidence interval with σ known uses z-scores, it is sometimes referred to as constructing a **Z-interval**.

EXAMPLE 3 | ### Constructing a Confidence Interval

Problem: In Example 1, we obtained a point estimate of 59.62 miles per hour for the population mean speed of cars on the highway outside a subdivision. We now wish to construct a 90% confidence interval about the population mean, μ. Assume that the population standard deviation speed of vehicles on the highway is known to be 8 miles per hour, based on past studies.

Approach

Step 1: We are treating the cars as a simple random sample of size $n = 12$. We have to verify that the data come from a population that is normally distributed with no outliers. We verify normality by constructing a normal probability plot. We check for outliers by drawing a boxplot.

Step 2: Since we are constructing a 90% confidence interval, $\alpha = 1 - 0.90 = 0.10$. Therefore, we have to identify the value of $z_{\frac{\alpha}{2}} = z_{\frac{0.1}{2}} = z_{0.05}$. This is the z-score such that the area under the standard normal curve to the right of $z_{0.05}$ is 0.05.

Step 3: We compute the lower and upper bounds on the interval with $\overline{x} = 59.62$, $\sigma = 8$, and $n = 12$.

Step 4: We interpret the result by stating, "We are 90% confident that the mean speed of all cars traveling on the highway outside the subdivision is somewhere between *lower bound* and *upper bound*."

Solution

Step 1: A normal probability plot of the data in Table 1 is provided in Figure 5(a). A boxplot is presented in Figure 5(b).

Figure 5

(a)   (b)

All the data values lie within the bounds on the normal probability plot, indicating that the data could come from a population that is normal. The boxplot does not show any outliers. The requirements for constructing a confidence interval are satisfied.

Step 2: We need to determine the value of $z_{0.05}$. We look in Table V in Appendix A for an area equal to 0.95 (remember, the table gives areas left of the z-scores). We have $z_{0.05} = 1.645$.

Step 3: Substitute into Formula (2).

Note to Instructor

In this text, we report a confidence interval as lower bound: upper bound: as in Lower bound: 55.82, Upper bound: 63.42. Some texts and technology will report the confidence interval as (lower bound, upper bound) as in (55.82, 63.42).

Lower bound: $\bar{x} - z_{\frac{\alpha}{2}} \cdot \dfrac{\sigma}{\sqrt{n}} = 59.62 - 1.645 \cdot \dfrac{8}{\sqrt{12}} = 59.62 - 3.80 = 55.82$

Upper bound: $\bar{x} + z_{\frac{\alpha}{2}} \cdot \dfrac{\sigma}{\sqrt{n}} = 59.62 + 1.645 \cdot \dfrac{8}{\sqrt{12}} = 59.62 + 3.80 = 63.42$

Step 4: We are 90% confident that the mean speed of all cars traveling on the highway outside the subdivision is between 55.82 and 63.42 miles per hour. Since the speed limit on the highway is 45 miles per hour, the residents now have some powerful evidence to bring to the police department.

EXAMPLE 4 **Constructing a Confidence Interval Using Technology**

Problem: Construct a 90% confidence interval for the mean speed of all cars on the highway outside the subdivision using the sample data from Table 1.

Approach: We use MINITAB to construct the confidence interval. The steps for constructing confidence intervals using TI-83/84 graphing calculators, MINITAB, and Excel are given in the Technology Step-by-Step on page 475.

Using Technology
Confidence intervals constructed by hand may differ from those using technology because of rounding.

Solution: Figure 6 shows the confidence interval obtained from MINITAB. The interval is reported in the form (*lower bound, upper bound*).

Figure 6 **One-Sample Z: Speed**
```
The assumed standard deviation = 8

Variable    N    Mean    StDev   SE Mean              90% CI
Speed      12   59.617  6.9563   2.3094   (55.8180, 63.4153)
```

Interpretation: We are 90% confident that the mean speed of all cars traveling on the highway outside the subdivision is between 55.82 and 63.42 miles per hour.

Now Work Problems 35(b)–(e)

❸ Explain the Role of the Margin of Error in Constructing a Confidence Interval

The width of the interval is determined by the *margin of error*.

Definition

The **margin of error**, E, in a $(1 - \alpha) \cdot 100\%$ confidence interval in which σ is known is given by

$$E = z_{\frac{\alpha}{2}} \cdot \frac{\sigma}{\sqrt{n}} \tag{3}$$

where n is the sample size.

In Other Words

The margin of error can be thought of as the "give or take" portion of the statement "The mean age of the class is 24, give or take 2 years."

Note: We require that the population from which the sample was drawn be normally distributed or the sample size n be greater than or equal to 30. ◀

As we look at the formula for obtaining the margin of error, we see that its value depends on three quantities:

1. Level of confidence, $1 - \alpha$
2. Standard deviation of the population, σ
3. Sample size, n

We cannot control the standard deviation of the population, but we certainly can control the level of confidence and/or the sample size. Let's see how changing these values affects the margin of error.

EXAMPLE 5   **Role of the Level of Confidence in the Margin of Error**

Problem: For the problem of estimating the population mean speed of all cars on the highway outside the subdivision presented in Example 3, determine the effect on margin of error of increasing the level of confidence from 90% to 99%.

Approach: With a 99% level of confidence, we have $\alpha = 1 - 0.99 = 0.01$. So, to compute the margin of error, E, we determine the value of $z_{\frac{\alpha}{2}} = z_{\frac{0.01}{2}} = z_{0.005}$. We then substitute this value into Formula (3) with $\sigma = 8$ and $n = 12$.

Solution: After consulting Table V, we determine that $z_{0.005} = 2.575$. Substituting into Formula (3), we obtain

$$E = z_{\frac{\alpha}{2}} \cdot \frac{\sigma}{\sqrt{n}} = 2.575 \cdot \frac{8}{\sqrt{12}} = 5.95$$

In Other Words

As the level of confidence increases, the margin of error also increases.

Notice that the margin of error has increased from 3.80 to 5.95 when the level of confidence increases from 90% to 99%. If we want to be more confident that the sample results in an interval containing the population mean, we need to increase the width of the interval.

| EXAMPLE 6 | **Role of Sample Size in the Margin of Error** |

Problem: For the problem of estimating the population mean speed of all cars on the highway outside the subdivision presented in Example 3, determine the effect of increasing the sample size from $n = 12$ to $n = 48$ on the margin of error. Leave the level of confidence at 90%.

Approach: We compute the margin of error with $n = 48$ instead of $n = 12$.

Solution: Substituting $z_{0.05} = 1.645$, $\sigma = 8$, and $n = 48$ into Formula (3), we obtain

$$E = z_{\frac{\alpha}{2}} \cdot \frac{\sigma}{\sqrt{n}} = 1.645 \cdot \frac{8}{\sqrt{48}} = 1.90$$

In Other Words
As the sample size increases, the margin of error decreases.

By increasing the sample size from $n = 12$ to $n = 48$, the margin of error, E, decreases from 3.80 to 1.90. Notice that by quadrupling the sample size the margin of error is cut in half.

This result should not be very surprising. Remember that the Law of Large Numbers states that as the sample size n increases the sample mean approaches the value of the population mean. The smaller margin of error supports this idea.

Now Work Problem 21

 Determine the Sample Size Necessary for Estimating the Population Mean within a Specified Margin of Error

Suppose that we want to know the number of cars that we should sample to estimate the mean speed of all cars traveling outside the subdivision within 2 miles per hour with 95% confidence. If we solve Formula (3) for n, we obtain a formula for determining sample size:

$$E = z_{\frac{\alpha}{2}} \cdot \frac{\sigma}{\sqrt{n}}$$

$$E\sqrt{n} = z_{\frac{\alpha}{2}} \cdot \sigma \qquad \text{Multiply both sides by } \sqrt{n}.$$

$$\sqrt{n} = \frac{z_{\frac{\alpha}{2}} \cdot \sigma}{E} \qquad \text{Divide both sides by } E.$$

$$n = \left(\frac{z_{\frac{\alpha}{2}} \cdot \sigma}{E}\right)^2 \qquad \text{Square both sides.}$$

> **Determining the Sample Size n**
>
> The sample size required to estimate the population mean, μ, with a level of confidence $(1 - \alpha) \cdot 100\%$ with a specified margin of error, E, is given by
>
> $$n = \left(\frac{z_{\frac{\alpha}{2}} \cdot \sigma}{E}\right)^2 \qquad \qquad (4)$$
>
> where n is rounded up to the nearest whole number.

⬦ CAUTION Rounding *up* is different from rounding *off*. We round 5.32 *up* to 6 and *off* to 5.

When σ is unknown, it is common practice to either conduct a preliminary study to determine s and use it as an estimate of σ or use results from previous studies to obtain an estimate of σ. When using this approach, the size of the sample should be at least 30.

Note to Instructor
Ask students to identify the reason we round up rather than round off.

EXAMPLE 7   **Determining Sample Size**

Problem: We once again consider the problem of estimating the population mean speed of all cars traveling on the highway outside the subdivision. How large a sample is required to estimate the mean speed within 2 miles per hour with 90% confidence?

Approach: The sample size required can be obtained using Formula (4) with $z_{\frac{\alpha}{2}} = z_{0.05} = 1.645$, $\sigma = 8$, and $E = 2$.

Solution: We substitute the values of z, σ, and E into Formula (4) and obtain

$$n = \left(\frac{z_{\frac{\alpha}{2}} \cdot \sigma}{E} \right)^2 = \left(\frac{1.645 \cdot 8}{2} \right)^2 = 43.2964$$

We round 43.2964 up to 44. A sample size of $n = 44$ results in an interval estimate of the population mean with a margin of error equal to 2 miles per hour with 90% confidence. If we obtain 100 samples of size $n = 44$, we expect about 90 intervals to capture the population mean, while 10 would not.

CAUTION Don't forget to round up when determining sample size.

Now Work Problem 43

Some Final Thoughts
Many requirements must be satisfied while performing any type of statistical inference. It is worthwhile to list the requirements for constructing a confidence interval about μ with σ known in a single location for quick reference.

> **Requirements for Constructing a Confidence Interval about μ if σ Is Known**
>
> **1.** *The data obtained come from a simple random sample.* In Chapter 1, we introduced other sampling techniques, such as stratified, cluster, and systematic samples. The techniques introduced in this section apply only to samples obtained through simple random sampling. Although methods exist for constructing confidence intervals when using the other sampling methods, they are beyond the scope of this text. If the data are obtained from a suspect sampling method, such as voluntary response or convenience sampling, no methods exist for constructing confidence intervals. If data are collected in a flawed manner, any statistical inference performed on the data is useless!
>
> **2.** *The data are obtained from a population that is normally distributed, or the sample size, n, is greater than or equal to 30.* When the sample size is small, we can use normal probability plots to help us judge whether the requirement of normality is satisfied. Remember, the techniques introduced in this section are robust. This means that minor departures from requirements will not have a severe effect on the results. However, we have to be aware that the sample mean is not resistant. Any outlier(s) in the data will affect the value of the sample mean and therefore affect the confidence interval. If the data contain outliers, we should proceed with caution when using the methods introduced in this section.
>
> **3.** *The population standard deviation, σ, is assumed to be known.* It is unlikely that the population standard deviation is known when the population mean is not. We will drop this assumption in the next section.

9.1 ASSESS YOUR UNDERSTANDING

Concepts and Vocabulary

1. The margin of error of a confidence interval for μ depends on three factors. What are they?

2. Why does the margin of error increase as the level of confidence increases?

3. Why does the margin of error decrease as the sample size n increases?

4. What does the level of confidence refer to in the construction of a confidence interval?

5. A student constructs a 95% confidence interval for the mean age of students at his college. The lower bound is 21.4 years and the upper bound is 28.8 years. He interprets the interval as "There is a 95% probability that the mean age of a student is between 21.4 years and 28.8 years." What is wrong with this interpretation? What could be done to increase the precision of the interval?

6. A professor in a class of 20 students wants to estimate the mean pulse rate of students prior to the final exam. Would it make sense for the professor to construct a 90% confidence interval for the population mean? Explain.

Skill Building

In Problems 7–12, a simple random sample of size n < 30 has been obtained. From the normal probability plot and boxplot, judge whether a Z-interval should be constructed.

7. No

8. No

9. No

10. No

11. Yes

12. Yes

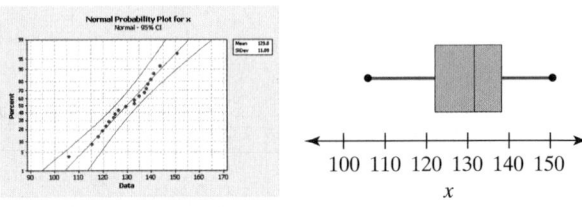

In Problems 13–16, determine the critical value $z_{\frac{\alpha}{2}}$ that corresponds to the given level of confidence.

13. 98%   2.33
14. 94%   1.88
15. 85%   1.44
16. 80%   1.28

In Problems 17–20, determine the point estimate of the population mean and margin of error for each confidence interval.

17. Lower bound: 18, upper bound: 24 $\bar{x} = 21, E = 3$

18. Lower bound: 20, upper bound: 30 $\bar{x} = 25, E = 5$

19. Lower bound: 5, upper bound: 23 $\bar{x} = 14, E = 9$

20. Lower bound: 15, upper bound: 35 $\bar{x} = 25, E = 10$

21. A simple random sample of size n is drawn from a population whose population standard deviation, σ, is known to be 5.3. The sample mean, $\bar{x}$, is determined to be 34.2.

   (a) Compute the 95% confidence interval for μ if the sample size, n, is 35.   (32.44, 35.96)

   (b) Compute the 95% confidence interval for μ if the sample size, n, is 50. How does increasing the sample size affect the margin of error, E?   (32.73, 35.67); decreases

   (c) Compute the 99% confidence interval for μ if the sample size, n, is 35. Compare the results to those obtained in part (a). How does increasing the level of confidence affect the size of the margin of error, E?   (31.89, 36.51); increases

   (d) Can we compute a confidence interval about μ based on the information given if the sample size is $n = 15$? Why? If the sample size is $n = 15$, what must be true regarding the population from which the sample was drawn?   Only if the population is normal

22. A simple random sample of size n is drawn from a population whose population standard deviation, σ, is known to be 3.8. The sample mean, $\bar{x}$, is determined to be 59.2.

   (a) Compute the 90% confidence interval for μ if the sample size, n, is 45.   (58.27, 60.13)

   (b) Compute the 90% confidence interval for μ if the sample size, n, is 55. How does increasing the sample size affect the margin of error, E?   (58.36, 60.04); decreases

   (c) Compute the 98% confidence interval for μ if the sample size, n, is 45. Compare the results to those obtained in part (a). How does increasing the level of confidence affect the size of the margin of error, E?

(d) Can we compute a confidence interval for μ based on the information given if the sample size is $n = 15$? Why? If the sample size is $n = 15$, what must be true regarding the population from which the sample was drawn?   Only if the population is normal

23. A simple random sample of size n is drawn from a population that is normally distributed with population standard deviation, σ, known to be 13. The sample mean, $\bar{x}$, is found to be 108.

(a) Compute the 96% confidence interval for μ if the sample size, n, is 25.   (102.7, 113.3)

(b) Compute the 96% confidence interval for μ if the sample size, n, is 10. How does decreasing the sample size affect the margin of error, E?   (99.6, 116.4); increases

(c) Compute the 88% confidence interval for μ if the sample size, n, is 25. Compare the results to those obtained in part (a). How does decreasing the level of confidence affect the size of the margin of error, E?   (104.0, 112.0); decreases

(d) Could we have computed the confidence intervals in parts (a)–(c) if the population had not been normally distributed? Why?   No

(e) If an analysis of the sample data revealed three outliers greater than the mean, how would this affect the confidence interval?

24. A simple random sample of size n is drawn from a population that is normally distributed with population standard deviation, σ, known to be 17. The sample mean, $\bar{x}$, is found to be 123.

(a) Compute the 94% confidence interval for μ if the sample size, n, is 20.   (115.9, 130.1)

(b) Compute the 94% confidence interval for μ if the sample size, n, is 12. How does decreasing the sample size affect the margin of error, E?   (113.8, 132.2); increases

(c) Compute the 85% confidence interval for μ if the sample size, n, is 20. Compare the results to those obtained in part (a). How does decreasing the level of confidence affect the size of the margin of error, E?   (117.5, 128.5); decreases

(d) Could we have computed the confidence intervals in parts (a)–(c) if the population had not been normally distributed? Why?   No

(e) If an analysis of the sample data revealed one outlier greater than the mean, how would this affect the confidence interval?

Applying the Concepts

25. **You Explain It! Hours Worked** In a survey conducted in August 2007, the Gallup organization asked 1,100 adult Americans how many hours they worked in the previous week. Based on the results, a 95% confidence interval for mean number of hours worked was lower bound: 42.7 and upper bound: 44.5. Which of the following represents a reasonable interpretation of the result? For those that are not reasonable, explain the flaw.   (b) is correct

(a) There is a 95% probability the mean number of hours worked by adult Americans in the previous week was between 42.7 hours and 44.5 hours.

(b) We are 95% confident that the mean number of hours worked by adult Americans in the previous week was between 42.7 hours and 44.5 hours.

(c) 95% of adult Americans worked between 42.7 hours and 44.5 hours last week.

(d) We are 95% confident that the mean number of hours worked by adults in Idaho in the previous week was between 42.7 hours and 44.5 hours.

26. **You Explain It! Sleeping** A 90% confidence interval for the number of hours that full-time college students sleep during a weekday is lower bound: 7.8 hours and upper bound: 8.8 hours. Which of the following represents a reasonable interpretation of the result? For those that are not reasonable, explain the flaw.   (d) is correct

(a) 90% of full-time college students sleep between 7.8 hours and 8.8 hours.

(b) We are 90% confident that the mean number of hours of sleep that full-time college students get any day of the week is between 7.8 hours and 8.8 hours.

(c) There is a 90% probability that the mean hours of sleep that full-time college students get during a weekday is between 7.8 hours and 8.8 hours.

(d) We are 90% confident that the mean hours of sleep that full-time college students get during a weekday is between 7.8 hours and 8.8 hours.

27. **You Explain It! Drive-Through Service Time** The trade magazine QSR routinely checks the drive-through service times of fast-food restaurants. A 90% confidence interval that results from examining 607 customers in Taco Bell's drive-through has a lower bound of 161.5 seconds and an upper bound of 164.7 seconds. What does this mean?

28. **You Explain It! MySpace.com** According to Nielsen/NetRatings, the mean amount of time spent on MySpace.com per user per month in July 2007 was 171.0 minutes. A 95% confidence interval for the mean amount of time spent on MySpace.com monthly has a lower bound of 151.4 minutes and an upper bound of 190.6 minutes. What does this mean?

29. **Hours Worked Revisited** For the "Hours Worked" survey conducted by Gallup in Problem 25, provide two recommendations for increasing the precision of the interval.

30. **Sleeping Revisited** Refer the "Sleeping" results from Problem 26. What could be done to increase the precision of the confidence interval?

31. **Blood Alcohol Concentration** A researcher for the National Highway Traffic Safety Administration (NHTSA) wishes to estimate the average blood alcohol concentration (BAC) for drivers involved in fatal accidents who are found to have positive BAC values. He randomly selects records from 1,200 such drivers and determines the sample mean BAC to be 0.16 g/dL.

Source: Based on data from NHTSA, August 2007.

(a) Assuming that the population standard deviation for the BAC of such drivers is 0.08 g/dL, construct and interpret a 90% confidence interval for the mean BAC.   (0.156, 0.164)

(b) All 50 states and the District of Columbia use a BAC of 0.08 g/dL as the legal intoxication level. Is it possible that the mean BAC of all drivers involved in fatal accidents who are found to have positive BAC values is less than the legal intoxication level? Explain.   Yes

32. **Hungry or Thirsty?** How much time do Americans spend eating or drinking? Based on a random sample of 1,120 Americans

15 years of age or older, the mean amount of time spent eating or drinking each day is 1.23 hours.

Source: American Time Use Survey conducted by the Bureau of Labor Statistics.

(a) Assuming that the population standard deviation for amount of time spent eating or drinking is 0.65 hour, construct and interpret a 90% confidence interval for the mean amount of time spent eating or drinking each day by Americans 15 years of age or older. (1.198, 1.262)

(b) Is it possible that adult Americans spend more than an hour and a half eating and drinking each day, on average? Explain. Yes

33. National Average Gasoline Price Every Monday, the Energy Information Administration (EIA) determines the national average gasoline price by collecting retail prices for gasoline from a sample of 900 retail gasoline outlets from across the nation. On July 14, 2008, the EIA reported the national average retail price for regular-grade gasoline to be $4.113 per gallon.

(a) Assuming that the population standard deviation is $\sigma = \$0.110$ per gallon, construct and interpret a 95% confidence interval for the national mean price per gallon for regular-grade gasoline on July 14, 2008. ($4.1058, $4.1202)

(b) An administrator of a rural town finds that the mean price of gasoline for all five gasoline stations in her town is $4.263 per gallon. Should she conclude that the interval obtained from the EIA is inaccurate? Why? No

34. Travel Time to Work An urban economist wishes to estimate the mean amount of time people spend traveling to work. He obtains a random sample of 50 individuals who are in the labor force and finds that the mean travel time is 24.2 minutes.

Source: Based on data from the American Community Survey

(a) Assuming that the population standard deviation of travel time is 18.5 minutes, construct and interpret a 95% confidence interval for the mean travel time to work.

Note: The standard deviation is large because many people work at home (travel time = 0 minutes) and many have commutes in excess of 1 hour. (19.07, 29.33)

(b) Could the interval in part (a) be used to estimate the mean travel time to work in a rural town? Why? No

35. Crash Test Results The Insurance Institute for Highway Safety (IIHS) routinely conducts crash tests on vehicles to determine the cost of repairs. The following data represent the vehicle repair costs for 2008-model minivans resulting from six front-corner and six rear-corner crash tests at 3 miles per hour.

Bumper Performance in Low-Speed Crash Tests **VEHICLE REPAIR COSTS ($)**		
Vehicle	**Front corner**	**Rear corner**
Honda Odyssey	$1,446	$743
Dodge Grand Caravan	$1,581	$483
Toyota Sienna	$767	$1,229
Chevrolet Uplander	$1,227	$1,045
Kia Sedona	$1,854	$1,126
Nissan Quest	$1,955	$995

Source: IIHS News Release, December 20, 2007

Treat these data as a simple random sample of 12 low-impact crashes, and answer the following questions assuming that $\sigma = \$450$.

(a) Use the data to compute a point estimate for the population mean cost of repairs. $1204.3

(b) Because the samples size is small, we must verify that the cost is approximately normally distributed and that the sample does not contain any outliers. The normal probability and boxplot are shown next. Are the conditions for constructing a Z-interval satisfied? Yes

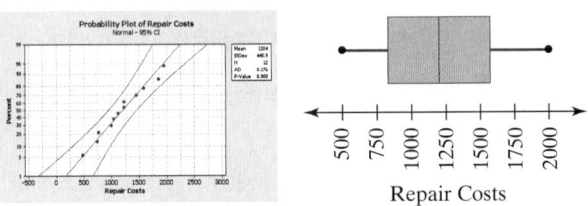

(c) Construct a 95% confidence interval for the repair costs. Interpret this interval. ($949.7, $1458.9)

(d) Construct a 90% confidence interval for the repair costs. Interpret this interval. ($990.6, $1418.0)

(e) What happened to the width of the interval when the level of confidence is decreased? Explain why this result is reasonable. Decreased

36. Retail Milk Prices To estimate the national average retail price for a gallon of reduced-fat (2%) milk, an economist surveys stores in 20 cities from across the United States and obtains the following data.

4.16	4.02	3.77	3.05	3.66
3.79	4.16	3.88	3.29	4.02
4.29	3.74	4.35	4.05	3.72
3.66	2.69	3.22	2.96	4.06

Source: Agricultural Marketing Service, February 2008

Treat these data as a simple random sample of 20 retail prices and answer the following questions, assuming that $\sigma = \$0.46$.

(a) Use the data to compute a point estimate for the population mean retail price. $3.727

(b) Because the sample size is small, we must verify that the price is approximately normally distributed and that the sample does not contain any outliers. The normal probability and boxplot are shown next. Are the conditions for constructing a Z-interval satisfied? Yes

(c) Construct a 95% confidence interval for the mean price of reduced fat milk. Interpret this interval. ($3.525, $3.929)

(d) Construct a 90% confidence interval for the mean price of reduced fat milk. Interpret this interval. ($3.558, $3.896)

(e) What happened to the width of the interval when the level of confidence is decreased? Explain why this result is reasonable. *Decreased*

37. Investment Home Buyers A study by the National Association of Realtors reports that second-home sales accounted for about one of every three residential real estate transactions in 2006. According to the report, the average age of a person buying a second home as an investment rental property was 39 years. A real estate agent wants to estimate the average age of investment-home buyers in his area. He randomly selects 20 such buyers and obtains the ages shown. Assume that $\sigma = 8.7$ years.

42	56	19	60	41
44	32	30	44	32
33	39	45	46	41
32	48	61	45	39

(a) Use the data to compute a point estimate for the population mean age of investment-home buyers in the agent's area. *41.5 years*

(b) Because the sample size is small, we must verify that buyer ages are approximately normally distributed and that the sample does not contain any outliers. The normal probability plot and boxplot are shown next. Are the conditions for constructing a Z-interval satisfied? *Yes*

(c) Construct a 95% confidence interval for the mean age of investment-home buyers in the agent's area. Interpret this interval. *(37.7, 45.3)*

(d) Do the investment-home buyers in the agent's area appear to differ in age from those in the general population? Why? *No*

38. Vacation-Home Buyers A study by the National Association of Realtors reports that second-home sales accounted for about one of every three residential real estate transactions in 2006. According to the report, the average age of a person buying a second home as a vacation home was 44 years. A real estate agent wants to estimate the average age of vacation-home buyers in her area. She randomly selects 20 such buyers and obtains the ages shown. Assume that $\sigma = 9.4$ years.

57	49	55	68	46
48	49	56	48	47
44	45	47	36	41
42	58	38	53	57

(a) Use the data to compute a point estimate for the population mean age of vacation-home buyers in the agent's area. *49.2 years*

(b) Because the sample size is small, we must verify that buyer ages are approximately normally distributed and that the sample does not contain any outliers. The normal probability plot and boxplot are shown next. Are the conditions for constructing a Z-interval satisfied? *Yes*

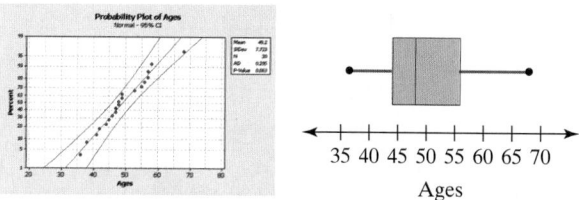

(c) Construct a 95% confidence interval for the mean age of vacation-home buyers in the agent's area. Interpret this interval. *(45.1, 53.3)*

(d) Do the vacation-home buyers in the agent's area appear to differ in age from those in the general population? Why? *Yes*

39. Dramas After watching a drama that seemed to last a long time, a student wondered how long a typical drama lasted. She obtained a random sample of 30 dramas and found the mean length of these movies to be 138.3 minutes. Assume that the population standard deviation length of a drama is 27.3 minutes.

(a) An analysis of the data indicated that the distribution of lengths of dramas is skewed right. Why does the student have to have a large sample size? *Population not normal*

(b) Construct and interpret a 99% confidence interval for the mean length of a drama. *(125.47, 151.13)*

40. What Is Wrong? The mean age of the 42 presidents of the United States on the day of inauguration is 54.8 years, with a standard deviation of 6.2 years. A researcher constructed a 95% confidence interval for the mean age of presidents on inauguration day. He wrote that he was 95% confident that the mean age of the president on inauguration day is between 53.0 and 56.7 years of age. What is wrong with the researcher's analysis? *Census data*

41. Miles on a Hummer A used-car dealer wants to estimate the mean number of miles on 4-year-old Hummer H2s. She finds a random sample of 34 such Hummer H2s in the Midwest and obtains the following mileages:

54,080	44,415	17,500	69,746	33,726
34,294	63,789	97,174	46,219	36,736
29,806	29,456	63,207	76,254	26,697
44,736	58,147	41,346	41,183	49,804
22,526	37,019	50,704	48,887	50,417
21,522	92,390	51,713	40,320	36,477
29,781	39,000	32,210	78,002	

Source: www.cars.com (collected February 24, 2008)

(a) Obtain a point estimate of the population mean number of miles on a 4-year-old Hummer H2. *46,743.6*

(b) A frequency histogram of the data is shown. Describe the shape of the distribution. *Skewed right*

Miles on a Hummer

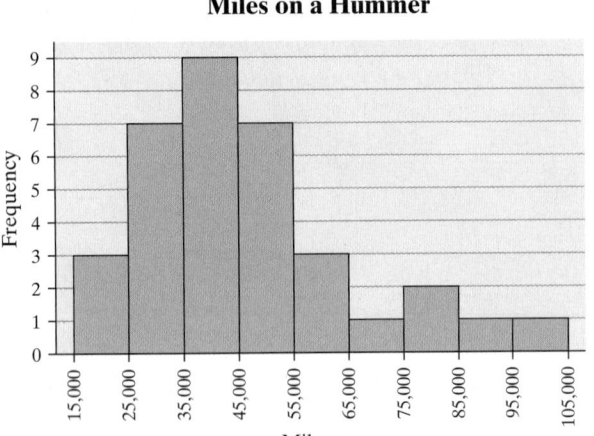

41. (c) *Central limit theorem is needed.*

(c) Explain why a large sample is necessary to construct a confidence interval for the population mean number of miles on a 4-year-old Hummer H2.

(d) Construct and interpret a 99% confidence interval for the population mean number of miles on a 4-year-old Hummer H2. Assume that $\sigma = 19{,}000$ miles.

(e) Construct and interpret a 95% confidence interval for the population mean number of miles on a 4-year-old Hummer H2. Assume that $\sigma = 19{,}000$ miles.

(f) What effect does decreasing the level of confidence have on the interval? *Decreases*

(g) Do the confidence intervals computed in parts (d) and (e) represent an estimate for the population mean number of miles on Hummer H2s in the United States? Why? *No*

42. **Wimbledon Match Lengths** A tennis enthusiast wants to estimate the mean length of men's singles matches held during the Wimbledon tennis tournament. From the Wimbledon history archives, he randomly selects 40 matches played during the tournament since the year 1968 (when professional players were first allowed to participate). The lengths of the 40 selected matches, in minutes, follow:

110	76	84	231	122	115	87	137
101	119	138	132	136	111	194	92
198	153	256	146	149	103	116	163
182	132	123	178	140	151	115	107
202	128	60	89	94	95	89	182

Source: www.wimbledon.org

42. (b) *Skewed right*   42. (c) *Central limit theorem is needed.*

(a) Obtain a point estimate of the population mean length of men's singles matches during Wimbledon. *133.4*

(b) A frequency histogram of the data is shown at top of the next column. Describe the shape of the distribution.

(c) Explain why a large sample is necessary to construct a confidence interval for the population mean length of men's singles matches during Wimbledon.

(d) Construct and interpret a 99% confidence interval for the population mean length of men's singles matches during Wimbledon. Assume that $\sigma = 45$ minutes. *(115.1, 151.7)*

41. (d) *(38,353.0, 55,134.2)*   41. (e) *(40,357.0, 53,130.2)*

Wimbledon Match Lengths

(e) Construct and interpret a 95% confidence interval for the population mean length of men's singles matches during Wimbledon. Assume that $\sigma = 45$ minutes. *(119.5, 147.3)*

(f) What effect does decreasing the level of confidence have on the interval? *Decreases*

(g) Do the confidence intervals computed in parts (d) and (e) represent an estimate for the population mean length of men's singles matches during all professional tennis tournaments? Why? *No*

43. **Sample Size** Dr. Paul Oswiecmiski wants to estimate the mean serum HDL cholesterol of all 20- to 29-year-old females. How many subjects are needed to estimate the mean serum HDL cholesterol of all 20- to 29-year-old females within 2 points with 99% confidence assuming that $\sigma = 13.4$? Suppose that Dr. Oswiecmiski would be content with 95% confidence. How does the decrease in confidence affect the sample size required? *298; 173; decreases*

44. **Sample Size** Dr. Paul Oswiecmiski wants to estimate the mean serum HDL cholesterol of all 20- to 29-year-old males. How many subjects are needed to estimate the mean serum HDL cholesterol of all 20- to 29-year-old males within 1.5 points with 90% confidence, assuming that $\sigma = 12.5$? Suppose that Dr. Oswiecmiski would prefer 98% confidence. How does the increase in confidence affect the sample size required? *188; 378; increases*

45. **How Much Do You Read?** A Gallup poll conducted May 20–22, 2005, asked Americans how many books, either hardback or paperback, they read during the previous year. How many subjects are needed to estimate the number of books Americans read the previous year within one book with 95% confidence? Initial survey results indicate that $\sigma = 16.6$ books. *1,059*

46. **Christmas Spending** A poll conducted on November 16–19, 2007, by American Research Group, Inc., asked Americans adults how much they planned to spend on gifts for Christmas. How many subjects are needed to estimate the amount of planned Christmas spending within $5 with 95% confidence? Initial survey results indicate that $\sigma = \$82.25$. *1,040*

47. **Miles on a Hummer** A used-car dealer wishes to estimate the mean number of miles on 4-year-old Hummer H2s.

(a) How many vehicles should be in a sample to estimate the mean number of miles within 2,000 miles with 90% confidence, assuming that $\sigma = 19{,}000$ miles. *245*

(b) How many vehicles should be in a sample to estimate the mean number of miles within 1,000 miles with 90% confidence, assuming that $\sigma = 19{,}000$ miles. *977*

47. (c) Quadruples

(c) What effect does doubling the required accuracy have on the sample size? Why is this the expected result?

48. **Wimbledon Match Lengths** A tennis enthusiast wants to estimate the mean length of men's singles matches held during the Wimbledon tennis tournament.

(a) How many matches should be in a sample to estimate the mean length within 10 minutes with 98% confidence, assuming that $\sigma = 45$ minutes.   110

(b) How many matches should be in a sample to estimate the mean length within 5 minutes with 98% confidence, assuming that $\sigma = 45$ minutes.   440

(c) What effect does doubling the required accuracy have on the sample size? Why is this the expected result?
   Quadruples

49. **Simulation** IQ scores as measured by the Stanford–Binet IQ test are normally distributed with $\mu = 100$ and $\sigma = 15$.

(a) Simulate obtaining 20 samples of size $n = 15$ from this population.

(b) Construct 95% confidence intervals for each of the 20 samples.

(c) How many of the intervals do you expect to include the population mean? How many actually contain the population mean?

50. **Simulation** Suppose that the arrival of cars at Burger King's drive-through follows a Poisson process with $\mu = 4$ cars every 10 minutes.

(a) Simulate obtaining 30 samples of size $n = 40$ from this population.

(b) Construct 90% confidence intervals for each of the 30 samples.

   Note: $\sigma = \sqrt{\mu}$ in a Poisson process.

(c) How many of the intervals do you expect to include the population mean? How many actually contain the population mean?

51. **Effect of Nonnormal Data** The *exponential probability distribution* is a probability distribution that can be used to model waiting time in line or the lifetime of electronic components. Its density function with $\mu = 5$ is shown in the accompanying figure. We can see that the distribution is skewed right.

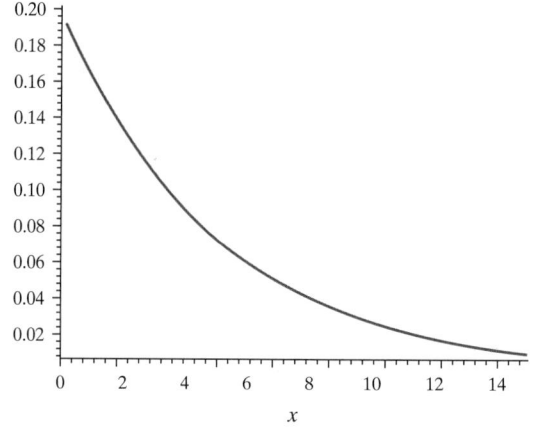

(a) Use MINITAB or some other statistical software to generate 100 random samples of size $n = 6$ from a population that follows the exponential probability distribution with $\mu = 5$. (It turns out that σ also equals 5.)

(b) Determine 95% confidence intervals for each of the 100 samples found in part (a) with $\sigma = 5$.

(c) How many of the intervals do we expect to contain $\mu = 5$? How many of the 100 intervals contain $\mu = 5$?

(d) What are the consequences of not having data from a normal population when the sample size is small?

52. **Effect of Outliers** The following small data set represents a simple random sample from a population whose mean is 50 and standard deviation is 10.

43	63	53	50	58	44
53	53	52	41	50	43

(a) A normal probability plot indicates that the data could come from a population that is normally distributed with no outliers. Compute a 95% confidence interval for this data set, assuming that $\sigma = 10$.   (44.6, 56.0)

(b) Suppose that the observation, 41, is inadvertently entered into the computer as 14. Verify that this observation is an outlier.

(c) Construct a 95% confidence interval on the data set with the outlier. What effect does the outlier have on the confidence interval?   (42.3, 53.7)

(d) Consider the following data set, which represents a simple random sample of size 36 from a population whose mean is 50 and standard deviation is 10.

43	63	53	50	58	44
53	53	52	41	50	43
47	65	56	58	41	52
49	56	57	50	38	42
59	54	57	41	63	37
46	54	42	48	53	41

52. (e) (47.0, 53.6); decreases width of interval

Verify that the sample mean for the large data set is the same as the sample mean for the small data set.

(e) Compute a 95% confidence interval for the large data set, assuming that $\sigma = 10$. Compare the results to part (a). What effect does increasing the sample size have on the confidence interval?

(f) Suppose that the last observation, 41, is inadvertently entered as 14. Verify that this observation is an outlier.

(g) Compute a 95% confidence interval for the large data set with the outlier, assuming that $\sigma = 10$. Compare the results to part (e). What effect does an outlier have on a confidence interval when the data set is large?   (46.2, 52.8)

53. By how many times does the sample size have to be increased to decrease the margin of error by a factor of $\frac{1}{2}$?   4 times

54. Population A has standard deviation $\sigma_A = 5$, and population B has standard deviation $\sigma_B = 10$. How many times larger than population A's sample size does population B's need to be to estimate μ with the same margin of error? [*Hint:* Compute n_B/n_A.]   4 times

55. **Resistance and Robustness** The data on the following page sets represent simple random samples from a population whose mean is 100 and standard deviation is 15.

(a) Compute the sample mean of each data set.

Data Set I				
106	122	91	127	88
74	77	108		

Data Set II				
106	122	91	127	88
74	77	108	87	88
111	86	113	115	97
122	99	86	83	102

Data Set III				
106	122	91	127	88
74	77	108	87	88
111	86	113	115	97
122	99	86	83	102
88	111	118	91	102
80	86	106	91	116

(b) For each data set, construct a 95% confidence interval about the population mean with $\sigma = 15$.

(c) What impact does the sample size n have on the width of the interval?

For parts (d)–(e), suppose that the data value 106 was accidentally recorded as 016.

(d) For each data set, construct a 95% confidence interval about the population mean with $\sigma = 15$ using the mis-entered data.

(e) Which intervals, if any, still capture the population mean, 100? What concept does this illustrate?

56. Confidence Interval Applet: The Role of Level of Confidence Load the confidence interval for a mean (the impact of a confidence level) applet.

(a) Set the shape to normal with mean = 50 and standard deviation = 10. Construct at least 1,000 confidence intervals with $n = 10$. For 95% confidence, what proportion of the intervals contains the population mean? What proportion did you expect to contain the population mean?

(b) Repeat part (a). Did the same proportion of intervals contain the population mean?

(c) For 99% confidence, what proportion of the intervals contain the population mean? What proportion did you expect to contain the population mean?

57. Confidence Interval Applet: The Role of Sample Size Load the confidence interval for a mean (the impact of a confidence level) applet.

(a) Set the shape to normal with mean = 50 and standard deviation = 10. Construct at least 1,000 confidence intervals with $n = 10$. What proportion of the 95% confidence intervals contains the population mean? What proportion did you expect to contain the population mean?

(b) Repeat part (a). Did the same proportion of intervals contain the population mean?

(c) Set the shape to normal with mean = 50 and standard deviation = 10. Construct at least 1,000 confidence intervals with $n = 50$. What proportion of the

59. (a) Completely randomized design. 59.(b) Cessation program; 2

95% confidence intervals contains the population mean? What proportion did you expect to contain the population mean? Does sample size have any effect on the proportion of intervals that captures the population mean?

(d) Compare the width of the intervals for the samples of size $n = 50$ obtained in part (c) to the width of the intervals for the samples of size $n = 10$ obtained in part (a). Which are wider? Why?

58. Confidence Interval Applet: The Role of Shape Load the confidence interval applet.

(a) Set the shape to normal with mean = 50 and standard deviation = 10. Construct at least 1,000 95% confidence intervals with $n = 40$. How many of the intervals contain the population mean? How many did you expect to contain the population mean?

(b) Set the shape to right skewed with mean = 50 and standard deviation = 10. Construct at least 1,000 95% confidence intervals with $n = 5$. How many of the intervals contain the population mean? How many did you expect to contain the population mean?

(c) What is the effect of nonnormal data on the confidence interval when the sample size is small?

59. Putting It Together: Smoking Cessation Study Researchers Havar Brendryen and Pal Kraft conducted a study in which 396 subjects were randomly assigned to either an experimental smoking cessation program or control group. The experimental program consisted of the Internet and phone-based Happy Ending Intervention, which lasted 54 weeks and consisted of more than 400 contacts by e-mail, web pages, interactive voice response, and short message service (SMS) technology. The control group received a self-help booklet. Both groups were offered free nicotine replacement therapy. Abstinence was defined as "not even a puff off smoke, for the last 7 days," and assessed by means of Internet surveys or telephone interviews. The response variable was abstinence after 12 months. Of the participants in the experimental program, 22.3% reported abstinence; of the participants in the control group, 13.1% reported abstinence. *Source:* "Happy Ending: A Randomized Controlled Trial of a Digital Multi-Media Smoking Cessation Intervention." Havar Brendryen and Pal Kraft. *Addiction* 103(3):478–484, 2008.

(a) What type of experimental design is this?

(b) What is the treatment? How many levels does it have?

(c) What is the response variable?

(d) What are the statistics reported by the authors?

(e) According to Wikipedia.com, an **odds ratio** is the ratio of the odds of an event occurring in one group to the odds of it occurring in another group. These groups might be men and women, an experimental group and a control group, or any other dichotomous classification. If the probabilities of the event in each of the groups are p (first group) and q (second group), then the odds ratio is

$$\frac{\dfrac{p}{(1-p)}}{\dfrac{q}{(1-q)}} = \frac{p(1-q)}{q(1-p)}$$

An odds ratio of 1 indicates that the condition or event under study is equally likely in both groups. An odds ratio greater than 1 indicates that the condition or event is more likely in the first group. And an odds ratio less than 1 indicates that the condition or event is less likely in the first group. The odds ratio must be greater than or equal to zero. As the odds of the first group approach zero, the odds ratio approaches zero. As the odds of the second group approach zero, the odds ratio approaches positive infinity. Verify that the odds ratio for this study is 1.90. What does this mean?

(f) The authors of the study reported a 95% confidence interval for the odds ratio to be *lower bound:* 1.12: and *upper bound:* 3.26. Interpret this result.

(g) Write a conclusion that generalizes the results of this study to the population of all smokers.

TECHNOLOGY STEP-BY-STEP Confidence Intervals about μ, σ Known

TI-83/84 Plus
1. If necessary, enter raw data in L1.
2. Press STAT, highlight TESTS, and select 7: ZInterval.
3. If the data are raw, highlight DATA. Make sure List1 is set to L1 and Freq to 1. If summary statistics are known, highlight STATS and enter the summary statistics. Following σ:, enter the population standard deviation.
4. Enter the confidence level following C-Level:.
5. Highlight Calculate; press ENTER.

MINITAB
1. If you have raw data, enter them in column C1.
2. Select the **Stat** menu, highlight **Basic Statistics**, then click **1-Sample Z . . . .**
3. If you have raw data, enter C1 in the cell marked "Samples in columns:". If you have

summarized data, select the summarized data radio button and enter the summarized values. Select **Options** and enter a confidence level. Click OK. In the cell marked Standard deviation, enter the value of σ. Click OK.

Excel
1. Enter raw data in column A. Highlight the data.
2. Load the Data Desk XL Add-in.
3. Select the **DDXL** menu, highlight **Confidence Intervals**, then highlight **1 Var z Interval** from the drop-down menu.
4. Select the column of data from the "Names and Columns" window. Check the "First row is variables names", if appropriate. Use the ◄ arrow to select the data. Click OK.
5. Select the level of confidence and enter the value of the population Standard deviation. Click Compute Interval.

9.2 CONFIDENCE INTERVALS FOR A POPULATION MEAN WHEN THE POPULATION STANDARD DEVIATION IS UNKNOWN

Preparing for This Section Before getting started, review the following:

- Parameter versus statistic (Section 1.1, p. 15)
- Simple random sampling (Section 1.3, pp. 22–27)
- Degrees of freedom (Section 3.2, p. 147)
- Normal probability plots (Section 7.4, pp. 405–409)
- Distribution of the sample mean (Section 8.1, pp. 427–438)

Objectives
1. State the properties of Student's *t*-distribution
2. Determine *t*-values
3. Construct and interpret a confidence interval for a population mean

In this section, we drop the assumption that σ is known and learn how to construct confidence intervals about a population mean in practice. That is, we learn how to construct confidence intervals about a population mean under the more realistic scenario that the population standard deviation is unknown.

Historical Note

William Sealey Gosset was born on June 13, 1876, in Canterbury, England. Gosset earned a degree in chemistry from New College in Oxford in 1899. He then got a job as a chemist for the Guinness Brewing Company in Dublin. Gosset, along with other chemists, was asked to find a way to make the best beer at the cheapest cost. This allowed him to concentrate on statistics. In 1904, Gosset wrote a paper on the brewing of beer that included a discussion of standard errors. In July 1905, Gosset met with Karl Pearson to learn about the theory of standard errors. Over the next few years, he developed his *t*-distribution. The Guinness Brewery did not allow its employees to publish, so Gosset published his research using the pen name Student. Gosset died on October 16, 1937.

1 State the Properties of Student's *t*-Distribution

In Section 9.1, we computed confidence intervals about a population mean, μ, under the assumption that the following conditions were met.

1. σ was known.

2. The population from which the sample was drawn followed a normal distribution or the sample size, n, was large ($n \geq 30$).

3. The sample was a simple random sample.

A $(1 - \alpha) \cdot 100\%$ confidence interval was then computed as

$$\bar{x} - z_{\frac{\alpha}{2}} \cdot \frac{\sigma}{\sqrt{n}} \quad \text{and} \quad \bar{x} + z_{\frac{\alpha}{2}} \cdot \frac{\sigma}{\sqrt{n}}$$

If σ is unknown, it seems reasonable to replace σ with s and proceed with the analysis. However, while it is true that $\dfrac{\bar{x} - \mu}{\frac{\sigma}{\sqrt{n}}}$ is normally distributed with mean 0 and standard deviation 1, we cannot replace σ with s and say that $\dfrac{\bar{x} - \mu}{\frac{s}{\sqrt{n}}}$ is normally distributed with mean 0 and standard deviation 1, because s itself is a random variable.

Instead, $\dfrac{\bar{x} - \mu}{\frac{s}{\sqrt{n}}}$ follows **Student's *t*-distribution**, developed by William Gosset.

Gosset was in charge of conducting experiments at the Guinness brewery to identify the best barley variety. At the time, the only available distribution was the standard normal distribution, but Gosset always performed experiments with small data sets and he did not know σ. This led Gosset to determine the sampling distribution of $\dfrac{\bar{x} - \mu}{\frac{s}{\sqrt{n}}}$. He published his findings under the pen name *Student*.

Student's *t*-Distribution

Suppose that a simple random sample of size n is taken from a population. If the population from which the sample is drawn follows a normal distribution, the distribution of

$$t = \frac{\bar{x} - \mu}{\frac{s}{\sqrt{n}}}$$

follows Student's *t*-distribution with $n - 1$ degrees of freedom,[*] where $\bar{x}$ is the sample mean and s is the sample standard deviation.

Note to Instructor

Consider the following to help students understand degrees of freedom: You have five pens of different colors and five students want to borrow a pen. The first four students have some freedom as to which pen to select; however, the last person has no freedom, but must choose the last available pen.

The interpretation of the *t*-statistic is the same as that of the *z*-score. The *t*-statistic represents the number of sample standard errors $\bar{x}$ is from the population mean, μ. It turns out that the shape of the *t*-distribution depends on the sample size, n.

To help see how the *t*-distribution differs from the standard normal (or *z*-) distribution and the role that the sample size n plays, we will go through the following simulation.

[*]The reader may wish to review the discussion of degrees of freedom in Section 3.2 on p. 147.

EXAMPLE 1   **Comparing the Standard Normal Distribution to the *t*-Distribution Using Simulation**

(a) Using statistical software such as MINITAB, obtain 1,000 simple random samples of size $n = 5$ from a normal population with $\mu = 50$ and $\sigma = 10$.

(b) Calculate the sample mean and sample standard deviation for each sample.

(c) Compute $z = \dfrac{\overline{x} - \mu}{\dfrac{\sigma}{\sqrt{n}}}$ and $t = \dfrac{\overline{x} - \mu}{\dfrac{s}{\sqrt{n}}}$ for each sample.

(d) Draw histograms for both z and t.

Solutions: We use MINITAB to obtain the 1,000 simple random samples and compute the 1,000 sample means and sample standard deviations. We then compute

$$z = \frac{\overline{x} - \mu}{\dfrac{\sigma}{\sqrt{n}}} = \frac{\overline{x} - 50}{\dfrac{10}{\sqrt{5}}} \quad \text{and} \quad t = \frac{\overline{x} - \mu}{\dfrac{s}{\sqrt{n}}} = \frac{\overline{x} - 50}{\dfrac{s}{\sqrt{5}}} \quad \text{for each of the 1,000 samples.}$$

Figure 7(a) shows the histogram for z, and Figure 7(b) shows the histogram for t.

Figure 7

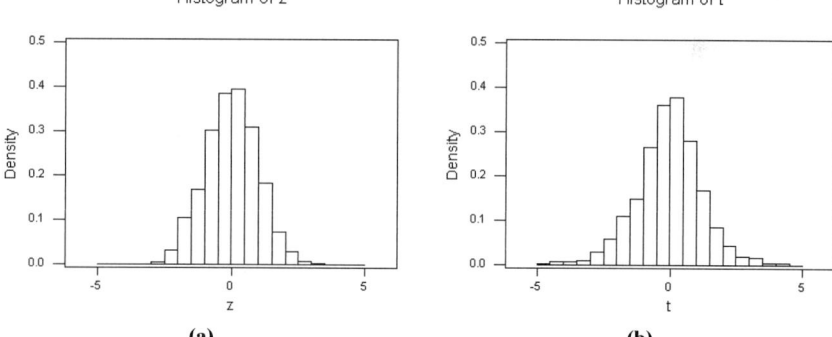

(a)   (b)

We notice that the histogram in Figure 7(a) is symmetric and bell shaped, with the center of the distribution at 0 and virtually all the rectangles between -3 and 3. In other words, z follows a standard normal distribution. The distribution of t is also symmetric and bell shaped and has its center at 0, but the distribution of t has longer tails (that is, t is more dispersed), so it is unlikely that t follows a standard normal distribution. The additional spread in the distribution of t can be attributed to the fact that we divide by $\dfrac{s}{\sqrt{n}}$ to find t instead of by $\dfrac{\sigma}{\sqrt{n}}$. Because the sample standard deviation is itself a random variable (rather than a constant such as σ), we have more dispersion in the distribution of t.

We now introduce the properties of the *t*-distribution.

Properties of the *t*-Distribution

1. The *t*-distribution is different for different degrees of freedom.

2. The *t*-distribution is centered at 0 and is symmetric about 0.

3. The area under the curve is 1. The area under the curve to the right of 0 equals the area under the curve to the left of 0, which equals $\dfrac{1}{2}$.

4. As t increases without bound, the graph approaches, but never equals, zero. As t decreases without bound, the graph approaches, but never equals, zero.

5. The area in the tails of the *t*-distribution is a little greater than the area in the tails of the standard normal distribution, because we are using s as an estimate of σ, thereby introducing further variability into the *t*-statistic.

Figure 8

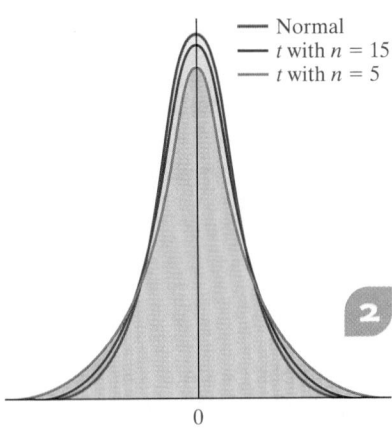

— Normal
— *t* with *n* = 15
— *t* with *n* = 5

0

6. As the sample size *n* increases, the density curve of *t* gets closer to the standard normal density curve. This result occurs because, as the sample size increases, the values of *s* get closer to the value of σ, by the Law of Large Numbers.

In Figure 8, we show the *t*-distribution for the sample sizes *n* = 5 and *n* = 15. As a point of reference, we have also drawn the standard normal density curve.

2 Determine *t*-Values

Recall that the notation z_α is used to represent the *z*-score whose area under the normal curve to the right of z_α is α. Similarly, we let t_α represent the *t*-value such that the area under the *t*-distribution to the right of t_α is α. See Figure 9.

The shape of the *t*-distribution depends on the sample size, *n*. Therefore, the value of t_α depends not only on α, but also on the degrees of freedom, *n* − 1. In Table VI in Appendix A, the far left column gives the degrees of freedom. The top row represents the area under the *t*-distribution to the right of some *t*-value.

Figure 9

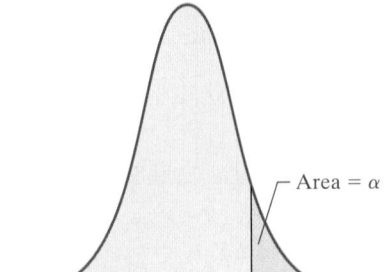

Area = α

t_α *t*

EXAMPLE 2 Finding *t*-Values

Problem: Find the *t*-value such that the area under the *t*-distribution to the right of the *t*-value is 0.10, assuming 15 degrees of freedom. That is, find $t_{0.10}$ with 15 degrees of freedom.

Approach: We will perform the following steps.

Step 1: Draw a *t*-distribution with the unknown *t*-value labeled. Shade the area under the curve to the right of the *t*-value, as in Figure 9.

Step 2: Find the row in Table VI that corresponds to 15 degrees of freedom and the column that corresponds to an area in the right tail of 0.10. Identify where the row and column intersect. This is the unknown *t*-value.

Figure 10

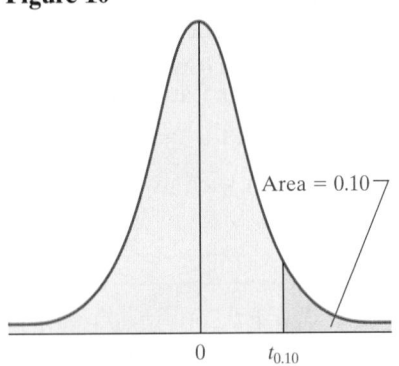

Area = 0.10

0   $t_{0.10}$

Solution

Step 1: Figure 10 shows the graph of the *t*-distribution with 15 degrees of freedom. The unknown value of *t* is labeled, and the area under the curve to the right of *t* is shaded.

Step 2: A portion of Table VI is reproduced in Figure 11. We have enclosed the row that represents 15 degrees of freedom and the column that represents the area 0.10 in the right tail. The value where the row and column intersect is the *t*-value we are seeking. The value of $t_{0.10}$ with 15 degrees of freedom is 1.341; that is, the area under the *t*-distribution to the right of *t* = 1.341 with 15 degrees of freedom is 0.10.

Figure 11

						Area in Right Tail						
df	**0.25**	**0.20**	**0.15**	**0.10**	**0.05**	**0.025**	**0.02**	**0.01**	**0.005**	**0.0025**	**0.001**	**0.0005**
1	1.000	1.376	1.963	3.078	6.314	12.710	15.890	31.820	63.660	127.300	318.300	636.600
2	0.816	1.061	1.386	1.886	2.920	4.303	4.849	6.965	9.925	14.090	22.330	31.600
3	0.765	0.978	1.250	1.638	2.353	3.182	3.482	4.541	5.841	7.453	10.210	12.920
13	0.694	0.870	1.079	1.350	1.771	2.160	2.282	2.650	3.012	3.372	3.852	4.221
14	0.692	0.868	1.076	1.345	1.761	2.145	2.264	2.624	2.977	3.326	3.787	4.140
15	0.691	0.866	1.074	1.341	1.753	2.131	2.249	2.602	2.947	3.286	3.733	4.073
16	0.690	0.865	1.071	1.337	1.746	2.120	2.235	2.583	2.921	3.252	3.686	4.015

The critical value of z with an area of to the right of 0.10 is approximately 1.28. Notice that the critical value for t is bigger than the corresponding critical value of z with an area to the right of 0.10. This is because the t-distribution has more spread than the z-distribution.

Now Work Problem 7

Using Technology
The TI-84 Plus graphing calculator has an invT feature, which finds the value of t given an area left of the unknown t-value and the degrees of freedom.

If the degrees of freedom we desire are not available in Table VI, we follow the practice of choosing the closest number of degrees of freedom available in the table. For example, if we have 43 degrees of freedom, we use 40 degrees of freedom from Table VI. In addition, the last row of Table VI provides the z-values from the standard normal distribution. We use these values for situations where the degrees of freedom are more than 1,000. This is acceptable because the t-distribution starts to behave like the standard normal distribution as n increases.

3 ## Construct and Interpret a Confidence Interval for a Population Mean

The construction of confidence intervals about μ with σ unknown follows the same logic as the construction of confidence intervals with σ known. The only difference is that we use s in place of σ and t in place of z.

Constructing a $(1 - \alpha) \cdot 100\%$ Confidence Interval for μ, σ Unknown

Suppose that a simple random sample of size n is taken from a population with unknown mean μ and unknown standard deviation σ. A $(1 - \alpha) \cdot 100\%$ confidence interval for μ is given by

$$\text{Lower bound: } \bar{x} - t_{\frac{\alpha}{2}} \cdot \frac{s}{\sqrt{n}} \qquad \text{Upper bound: } \bar{x} + t_{\frac{\alpha}{2}} \cdot \frac{s}{\sqrt{n}} \qquad (1)$$

where $t_{\frac{\alpha}{2}}$ is computed with $n - 1$ degrees of freedom.

Note: The interval is exact when the population is normally distributed. It is approximately correct for nonnormal populations, provided that n is large enough. ◀

Note to Instructor
Emphasize to students that we construct Z-intervals when σ is known and t-intervals when σ is unknown.

Because this confidence interval uses the t-distribution, it is often referred to as the **t-interval**.

Notice that a confidence interval about μ with σ unknown can be computed for nonnormal populations even though Student's t-distribution required the population from which the sample was obtained to be normal. This is because the procedure for constructing the confidence interval is robust; that is, the procedure is accurate despite moderate departures from the normality requirement. Notice that we said the procedure is accurate for *moderate* departures from normality. If a small data set has outliers, the results are compromised, because neither the sample mean, $\bar{x}$, nor the sample standard deviation, s, is resistant to outliers. Sample data should always be inspected for serious departures from normality and for outliers. This is easily done with normal probability plots and boxplots.

EXAMPLE 3 ## Constructing a Confidence Interval about a Population Mean

Problem: An arborist is interesting in determining the mean diameter of mature white oak trees. The data in Table 5 represent the diameter (in centimeters) 1 meter above the base for a random sample of seven mature white oak trees in a forest preserve. Treat the sample as a simple random sample of all white oak trees in the forest preserve. Construct a 95% confidence interval for the mean diameter of a mature white oak tree 1 meter from the base. Interpret this interval.

Table 5

64.0	33.4	45.8	56.0
51.5	29.2	63.7	

Source: Matt Gibson, instructor at Joliet West High School

Approach

Step 1: We draw a normal probability plot to verify the data come from a population that is normal and a boxplot to verify that there are no outliers.

Step 2: Compute $\bar{x}$ and s.

Step 3: Find the critical value $t_{\alpha/2}$ with $n - 1$ degrees of freedom.

Step 4: Compute the bounds on a $(1 - \alpha) \cdot 100\%$ confidence interval for μ, using the following:

$$\text{Lower bound: } \bar{x} - t_{\frac{\alpha}{2}} \cdot \frac{s}{\sqrt{n}} \qquad \text{Upper bound: } \bar{x} + t_{\frac{\alpha}{2}} \cdot \frac{s}{\sqrt{n}}$$

Step 5: Interpret the result.

Solution

Step 1: Because the sample size is small, we verify that the sample data come from a population that is normally distributed with no outliers. A normal probability plot of the data in Table 5 is shown in Figure 12(a). A boxplot is shown in Figure 12(b).

Figure 12

(a)   (b)

All the data lie within the bounds on the normal probability plot, indicating that the data could come from a population that is approximately normal. The boxplot does not display any outliers. The requirements for constructing the confidence interval are satisfied.

Step 2: We compute the sample mean and sample standard deviation using a calculator and find that $\bar{x} = 49.09$ centimeters and $s = 13.80$ centimeters.

Step 3: Because we wish to construct a 95% confidence interval, we have $\alpha = 0.05$. The sample size is $n = 7$. So we find $t_{\frac{0.05}{2}} = t_{0.025}$ with $7 - 1 = 6$ degrees of freedom. Referring to Table VI, we find that $t_{0.025} = 2.447$.

Step 4: Using Formula (1), we find the lower and upper bounds:

$$\text{Lower bound: } \bar{x} - t_{\frac{\alpha}{2}} \cdot \frac{s}{\sqrt{n}} = 49.09 - 2.447 \cdot \frac{13.80}{\sqrt{7}} = 49.09 - 12.76 = 36.33$$

$$\text{Upper bound: } \bar{x} + t_{\frac{\alpha}{2}} \cdot \frac{s}{\sqrt{n}} = 49.09 + 2.447 \cdot \frac{13.80}{\sqrt{7}} = 49.09 + 12.76 = 61.85$$

Step 5: We are 95% confident that the mean diameter, 1 meter above the base, of mature white oak trees in the forest preserve is between 36.33 and 61.85 centimeters.

Remember, 95% confidence refers to the method. If we obtained 100 samples of size $n = 7$ from the population of white oak trees, we would expect about 95 of the samples to result in confidence intervals that capture μ and 5 of the samples to result in intervals that do not capture μ. We do not know whether the interval in Example 3 is one of the intervals that captures μ or one of the intervals that does not capture μ.

EXAMPLE 4

Constructing a Confidence Interval about a Population Mean Using Technology

Problem: Construct a 95% confidence interval for the mean diameter of a mature white oak tree 1 meter above the base using the sample data in Table 5. Interpret this interval.

Approach: We will use a TI-84 Plus graphing calculator to construct the confidence interval. The steps for constructing confidence intervals using the TI-83/84 Plus graphing calculators, MINITAB, and Excel are given in the Technology Step-by-Step on page 487.

Solution: Figure 13 shows the results on a TI-84 Plus graphing calculator.

Figure 13

Using Technology
The results obtained from technology may differ from by-hand intervals due to rounding error.

Now Work Problem 23

Interpretation: We are 95% confident that the mean diameter, 1 meter above the base, of mature white oak trees in the forest preserve is between 36.33 and 61.85 centimeters.

EXAMPLE 5

The Effect of Outliers

Table 6				
30	29	34	41	37
16	18	30	24	25
29	16	80	19	30

Problem: The management of Disney World wanted to estimate the mean waiting time at the Dumbo ride. They randomly selected 15 riders and measured the amount of time (in minutes) that the riders spent waiting in line. The results are given in Table 6. Figure 14 shows a normal probability plot and boxplot for the data in the table. Figure 14(a) demonstrates that the sample data could have come from a population that is normally distributed except for the single outlier. Figure 14(b) shows the outlier as well. Determine a 95% confidence interval for the mean waiting time at the Dumbo ride both with, and without, the outlier in the data set. Comment on the effect the outlier has on the confidence interval.

Figure 14

Note to Instructor
Remind students that the mean and standard deviation are not resistant. This is why confidence intervals should not be constructed from sample data that have one or more outliers.

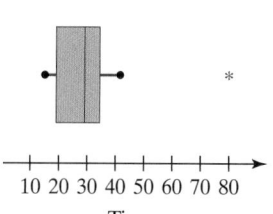

(a)

(b)

Approach: We use MINITAB to construct the confidence intervals.

Solution: Figure 15(a) shows the confidence interval with the outlier included. Figure 15(b) shows the confidence interval with the outlier removed.

Figure 15   **One-Sample T: Time(with outlier)**

Variable	N	Mean	StDev	SE Mean	95.0% CI
Time	15	30.53	15.59	4.02	(21.90, 39.17)

(a)

One-Sample T: Time(without outlier)

Variable	N	Mean	StDev	SE Mean	95.0% CI
Time	14	27.00	7.75	2.07	(22.53, 31.47)

(b)

The 95% confidence interval with the outlier has a lower bound of 21.90 minutes and an upper bound of 39.17 minutes. The 95% confidence interval with the outlier removed has a lower bound of 22.53 minutes and an upper bound of 31.47. We notice a few things.

- With the outlier included, the sample mean is larger (i.e., drawn toward the outlier), because the sample mean is not resistant.

- With the outlier included, the sample standard deviation is larger, because the sample standard deviation is not resistant.

- With the outlier removed, the width of the interval decreased from $39.17 - 21.90 = 17.27$ minutes to $31.47 - 22.53 = 8.94$ minutes. The confidence interval is nearly twice as wide when the outlier is included.

What should we do if the requirements to compute a t-interval are not met? One option is to increase the sample size beyond 30 observations. The other option is to try to use *nonparametric procedures*. **Nonparametric procedures** typically do not require normality, and the methods are resistant to outliers.

Now Work Problem 29

Note to Instructor

This activity allows students to generate their own data that can be used to construct a confidence interval to draw conclusions and reinforce the concept of a confidence interval. Time Limit: 20 to 30 minutes depending on discussions.

IN CLASS ACTIVITY

Confidence Intervals

What is the mean number of rolls of a die before a 1 is observed? Either as an individual or in a small group, roll a die until a 1 is observed. Repeat this process 30 times.

(a) Obtain a point estimate of the mean number of rolls of a die before a 1 is observed.

(b) The population standard deviation for the number of rolls before a 1 is observed is $\sqrt{30}$. Use this result to construct a 90% Z-interval for the mean number of rolls required before a 1 is observed.

(c) The population mean number of rolls before a 1 is observed is 6. Does your interval include 6? What proportion of the Z-intervals in the class includes 6? How many did you expect to include 6?

(d) Construct a 90% t-interval for the mean number of rolls required before a 1 is observed.

(e) The population mean number of rolls before a 1 is observed is 6. Does your interval include 6? What proportion of the t-intervals in the class includes 6? How many did you expect to include 6?

(f) Compare the Z-interval with the t-interval. Which has the smaller margin of error? Why?

9.2 ASSESS YOUR UNDERSTANDING

Concepts and Vocabulary

1. Explain the circumstances under which a Z-interval should be constructed. Under what circumstances should a t-interval be constructed? When can neither a Z- nor a t-interval be constructed?

2. Explain why the t-distribution has less spread as the number of degrees of freedom increases.

3. The procedures for constructing a t-interval are *robust*. Explain what this means.

4. Consider Figures 7(a) and (b). Why are the t-values more dispersed than the z-values?

5. Discuss the similarities and differences between the standard normal distribution and the t-distribution.

6. Explain what is meant by *degrees of freedom*.

Skill Building

7. (a) Find the t-value such that the area in the right tail is 0.10 with 25 degrees of freedom. 1.316
   (b) Find the t-value such that the area in the right tail is 0.05 with 30 degrees of freedom. 1.697
   (c) Find the t-value such that the area left of the t-value is 0.01 with 18 degrees of freedom. [*Hint*: Use symmetry.] -2.552
   (d) Find the critical t-value that corresponds to 90% confidence. Assume 20 degrees of freedom. 1.725

8. (a) Find the t-value such that the area in the right tail is 0.02 with 19 degrees of freedom. 2.205
   (b) Find the t-value such that the area in the right tail is 0.10 with 32 degrees of freedom. 1.309
   (c) Find the t-value such that the area left of the t-value is 0.05 with 6 degrees of freedom. [*Hint*: Use symmetry.] -1.943
   (d) Find the critical t-value that corresponds to 95% confidence. Assume 16 degrees of freedom. 2.120

9. A simple random sample of size n is drawn from a population that is normally distributed. The sample mean, $\bar{x}$, is found to be 108, and the sample standard deviation, s, is found to be 10.
   (a) Construct a 96% confidence interval for μ if the sample size, n, is 25. (103.7, 112.3)
   (b) Construct a 96% confidence interval for μ if the sample size, n, is 10. How does decreasing the sample size affect the margin of error, E? (100.4, 115.6); increases
   (c) Construct a 90% confidence interval for μ if the sample size, n, is 25. Compare the results to those obtained in part (a). How does decreasing the level of confidence affect the size of the margin of error, E? (104.6, 111.4); decreases
   (d) Could we have computed the confidence intervals in parts (a)–(c) if the population had not been normally distributed? Why? No

10. A simple random sample of size n is drawn from a population that is normally distributed. The sample mean, $\bar{x}$, is found to be 50, and the sample standard deviation, s, is found to be 8.
    (a) Construct a 98% confidence interval for μ if the sample size, n, is 20. (45.5, 54.5)
    (b) Construct a 98% confidence interval for μ if the sample size, n, is 15. How does decreasing the sample size affect the margin of error, E? (44.6, 55.4); increases

(c) Construct a 95% confidence interval for μ if the sample size, n, is 20. Compare the results to those obtained in part (a). How does decreasing the level of confidence affect the margin of error, E? (46.3, 53.7); decreases
(d) Could we have computed the confidence intervals in parts (a)–(c) if the population had not been normally distributed? Why? No

11. A simple random sample of size n is drawn. The sample mean, $\bar{x}$, is found to be 18.4, and the sample standard deviation, s, is found to be 4.5.
    (a) Construct a 95% confidence interval for μ if the sample size, n, is 35. (16.85, 19.95)
    (b) Construct a 95% confidence interval for μ if the sample size, n, is 50. How does increasing the sample size affect the margin of error, E? (17.12, 19.68); decreases
    (c) Construct a 99% confidence interval for μ if the sample size, n, is 35. Compare the results to those obtained in part (a). How does increasing the level of confidence affect the margin of error, E? (16.32, 20.48); increases
    (d) If the sample size is $n = 15$, what conditions must be satisfied to compute the confidence interval? Population must be normal.

12. A simple random sample of size n is drawn. The sample mean, $\bar{x}$, is found to be 35.1, and the sample standard deviation, s, is found to be 8.7.
    (a) Construct a 90% confidence interval for μ if the sample size, n, is 40. (32.78, 37.42)
    (b) Construct a 90% confidence interval for μ if the sample size, n, is 100. How does increasing the sample size affect the margin of error, E? (33.66, 36.54); decreases
    (c) Construct a 98% confidence interval for μ if the sample size, n, is 40. Compare the results to those obtained in part (a). How does increasing the level of confidence affect the margin of error, E? (31.76, 38.44); increases
    (d) If the sample size is $n = 18$, what conditions must be satisfied to compute the confidence interval? Population must be normal.

Applying the Concepts

13. **How Much Do You Read?** A Gallup poll conducted May 20–22, 2005, asked 1,006 Americans, "During the past year, about how many books, either hardcover or paperback, did you read either all or part of the way through?" Results of the survey indicated that $\bar{x} = 13.4$ books and $s = 16.6$ books. Construct a 99% confidence interval for the mean number of books that Americans read either all or part of during the preceding year. Interpret the interval. (12.05, 14.75)

14. **How Much Do You Read?** A Gallup poll conducted July 21–August 14, 1978, asked 1,006 Americans, "During the past year, about how many books, either hardcover or paperback, did you read either all or part of the way through?" Results of the survey indicated that $\bar{x} = 18.8$ books and $s = 19.8$ books.
    (a) Construct a 99% confidence interval for the mean number of books Americans read either all or part of during the preceding year. Interpret the interval. (17.19, 20.41)
    (b) Compare these results to those of Problem 13. Were Americans reading more in 1978 than in 2005? Yes

15. **The SARS Epidemic** Severe acute respiratory syndrome (SARS) is a viral respiratory illness. It has the distinction of

being the first new communicable disease of the 21st century. Based on interviews with 81 SARS patients, researchers found that the mean incubation period was 4.6 days, with a standard deviation of 15.9 days. Based on this information, construct a 95% confidence interval for the mean incubation period of the SARS virus. Interpret the interval. (1.08, 8.12)

Source: Gabriel M. Leung et al., "The Epidemiology of Severe Acute Respiratory Syndrome in the 2003 Hong Kong Epidemic: An Analysis of All 1755 Patients," *Annals of Internal Medicine* 141:662–673, 2004

16. **Tensile Strength** Tensile strength is the amount of stress a material can withstand before it breaks. Researchers wanted to determine the tensile strength of a resin cement used in bonding crowns to teeth. The researchers bonded crowns to 72 extracted teeth. Using a tensile resistance test, they found the mean tensile strength of the resin cement to be 242.2 newtons (N), with a standard deviation of 70.6 N. Based on this information, construct a 90% confidence interval for the mean tensile strength of the resin cement. (228.33, 256.07)

Source: Simonides Consani et al., "Effect of Cement Types on the Tensile Strength of Metallic Crowns Submitted to Thermocycling," *Brazilian Dental Journal* 14(3), 2003

17. **Commute to Work** A Gallup poll of 547 adult Americans employed full or part time conducted August 13–16, 2007, asked, "How much total time in minutes do you spend commuting to and from work in a typical day?" Survey results indicate that $\bar{x} = 45.6$ minutes and $s = 31.4$ minutes.

(a) Construct and interpret a 90% confidence interval for the mean commute time of adult Americans employed full or part time. (43.39, 47.81)

(b) Is it possible that the mean commute time is less than 40 minutes? Is it likely? Yes, no

18. **Ford Mustang Gas Mileage** For a simple random sample of forty 2007 Ford Mustangs (6-cylinder, 4-liter, 5-speed manual), the mean gas mileage was 20 miles per gallon with a standard deviation of 1.5 miles per gallon.

Source: Based on information from www.fueleconomy.com

(a) Construct and interpret a 95% confidence interval for the mean gas mileage of similar 2007 Ford Mustangs. (19.52, 20.48)

(b) Is it possible that the mean gas mileage is greater than 23 miles per gallon? Is it likely? Yes, no

19. **Exercise Habits** A researcher asked a random sample of 32 adults, "How many days per week do you participate in exercise activities?" The results are shown. Construct and interpret a 95% confidence interval for the mean number of days per week in which adults engage in exercise activities. (2.19, 3.81)

2	7	2	4	1	5	4	3
5	1	0	1	6	4	2	1
3	0	2	7	2	4	2	0
1	5	3	1	7	0	4	7

Source: Based on a Gallup poll conducted November 9–12, 2006

20. **Tips** A server at a restaurant wanted to estimate the mean tip percentage that she earns during dinner. She randomly selects 14 receipts from dinner, records the tip, and computes the tip rate. She obtains the following tip rates. The data are in percent,

so 16.5 represents 16.5%. Construct and interpret a 95% confidence interval for the tip percent. An analysis of the data indicates that it is reasonable to conclude that tip percent follows a normal distribution. The data have no outliers. (17.12, 20.30)

16.5	20.5	21.4	22.9	21.1
22.6	18.8	18.9	17.7	19.0
17.5	14.2	14.9	15.9	

Source: Pam Pimental, student at Joliet Junior College

21. **Harley-Davidson Stock Volume** The trade volume of a stock is the number of shares traded on a given day. The following data, in millions (so that 2.45 represents 2,450,000 shares traded), represent the volume of Harley-Davidson stock traded for a random sample of 40 trading days in 2007. 21. (a) 2.337 million

2.45	2.10	7.11	2.91	1.92	1.45	2.31	1.41
1.62	4.48	2.30	1.42	3.26	2.82	1.66	2.30
1.58	1.91	1.67	2.66	1.47	1.14	3.06	3.09
2.83	1.77	1.50	6.19	2.84	1.94	2.02	1.71
1.87	1.83	2.03	2.62	1.81	1.89	1.64	0.89

Source: TD Ameritrade

(a) Use the data to compute a point estimate for the population mean number of shares traded per day in 2007.

(b) Construct a 90% confidence interval for the population mean number of shares traded per day in 2007. Interpret the confidence interval. (2.013, 2.661)

(c) A second random sample of 40 days in 2007 resulted in the following data:

2.07	2.39	1.24	2.02	2.23	1.67	2.06	2.74
5.19	2.38	3.32	2.44	2.34	2.74	1.37	1.60
1.71	1.64	2.20	1.43	1.48	2.05	3.75	3.30
2.70	2.44	1.67	1.38	3.12	1.69	1.79	2.05
3.59	1.79	2.20	1.54	0.84	2.19	1.69	1.77

Construct another 90% confidence interval for the population mean number of shares traded per day in 2007. Interpret the confidence interval. (1.978, 2.412)

(d) Explain why the confidence intervals obtained in parts (b) and (c) are different.

22. **PepsiCo Stock Volume** The trade volume of a stock is the number of shares traded on a given day. The following data, in millions (so that 6.16 represents 6,160,000 shares traded), represent the volume of PepsiCo stock traded for a random sample of 40 trading days in 2007.

6.16	6.39	5.05	4.41	4.16	4.00	2.37	7.71
4.98	4.02	4.95	4.97	7.54	6.22	4.84	7.29
5.55	4.35	4.42	5.07	8.88	4.64	4.13	3.94
4.28	6.69	3.25	4.80	7.56	6.96	6.67	5.04
7.28	5.32	4.92	6.92	6.10	6.71	6.23	2.42

Source: TD Ameritrade

(a) Use the data to compute a point estimate for the population mean number of shares traded per day in 2007. 5.430 million

(b) Construct a 95% confidence interval for the population mean number of shares traded per day in 2007. Interpret the confidence interval.   (4.957, 5.903)

(c) A second random sample of 40 days in 2007 resulted in the following data:

6.12	5.73	6.85	5.00	4.89	3.79	5.75	6.04
4.49	6.34	5.90	5.44	10.96	4.54	5.46	6.58
8.57	3.65	4.52	7.76	5.27	4.85	4.81	6.74
3.65	4.80	3.39	5.99	7.65	8.13	6.69	4.37
6.89	5.08	8.37	5.68	4.96	5.14	7.84	3.71

Construct another 95% confidence interval for the population mean number of shares traded per day in 2007. Interpret the confidence interval.   (5.298, 6.322)

(d) Explain why the confidence intervals obtained in parts (b) and (c) are different.

23. **Crawling Babies** The following data represent the age NW (in weeks) at which babies first crawl based on a survey of 12 mothers conducted by Essential Baby.

| 52 | 30 | 44 | 35 | 39 | 26 |
| 47 | 37 | 56 | 26 | 39 | 28 |

Source: www.essentialbaby.com

(a) Because the sample size is small, we must verify that the data come from a population that is normally distributed and that the sample does not contain any outliers. The normal probability plot and boxplot are shown next. Are the conditions for constructing a confidence interval about the mean satisfied?   Yes

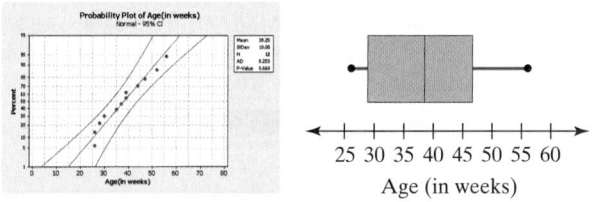

Age (in weeks)

(b) Construct a 95% confidence interval for the mean age at which a baby first crawls.   (31.9, 44.7)

(c) What could be done to increase the accuracy of the interval without changing the level of confidence?   Increase the sample size

24. **Battery Life** The following data represent the battery life, in hours, for a random sample of 10 full charges on a fifth-generation iPod™ music player.

| 7.3 | 10.2 | 12.9 | 10.8 | 12.1 |
| 6.6 | 10.2 | 9.0 | 8.5 | 7.1 |

(a) Because the sample size is small, we must verify that the data come from a population that is normally distributed and that the sample does not contain any outliers. The normal probability plot and boxplot are shown next. Are the conditions for constructing a confidence interval about the mean satisfied?   Yes

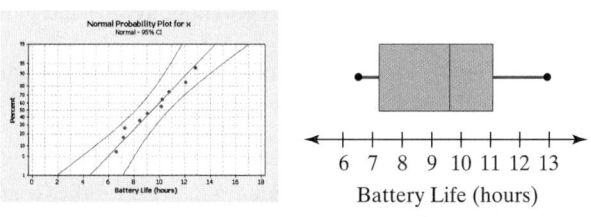

Battery Life (hours)

24. (b) (8.23, 10.71)

(b) Construct a 90% confidence interval for the mean number of hours that the battery will last on this player.

(c) Suppose that you wanted more accuracy. What can be done to increase the accuracy of the interval without changing the level of confidence?   Increase the sample size

25. **The Growing Season** An agricultural researcher is interested in estimating the mean length of the growing season in the Chicago area. Treating the last 10 years as a simple random sample, he obtains the following data, which represent the number of days of the growing season.

| 155 | 162 | 146 | 144 | 168 |
| 188 | 215 | 180 | 166 | 151 |

Source: Midwest Climate Center

(a) Because the sample size is small, we must verify that the data come from a population that is normally distributed and that the sample does not contain any outliers. The normal probability plot and boxplot are shown next. Are the conditions for constructing a confidence interval about the mean satisfied?   Yes

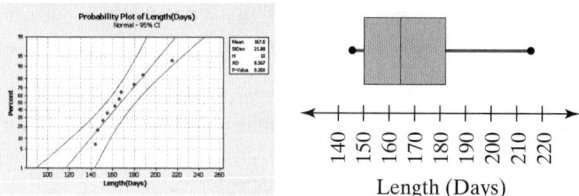

Length (Days)

(b) Construct a 95% confidence interval for the mean length of the growing season in the Chicago area.   (151.8, 183.2)

(c) What can be done to increase the accuracy of the interval without changing the level of confidence?   Increase the sample size

26. **Disc Weight** When playing disc golf, the weight of the disc has a huge effect on disc performance. Lighter discs tend to fly farther, but are less stable. Heavier discs tend to give better control and are better suited for strong winds. The following data represent the weights, in grams, of a random sample of 12 discs produced by a certain manufacturer.

| 172 | 168 | 170 | 173 | 172 | 173 |
| 171 | 175 | 173 | 171 | 169 | 173 |

(a) Because the sample size is small, we must verify that the data come from a population that is normally distributed and that the sample does not contain any outliers. The normal probability plot and boxplot are shown next. Are the conditions for constructing a confidence interval about the mean satisfied?   Yes

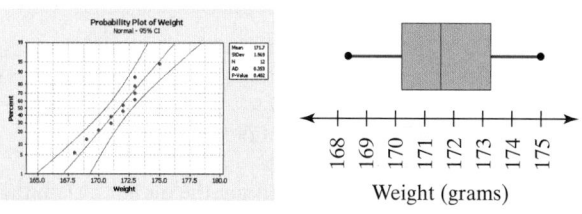

Weight (grams)

(b) Construct a 95% confidence interval for disc weight. Interpret the interval.   (170.4, 173.0)

27. **Age Married** The 2006 General Social Survey asked respondents, "If ever married, how old were you when you first married?" The results are summarized in the MINITAB excerpt that follows:

One-Sample T: AGEWED

```
Variable      N    Mean  StDev  SE Mean      95.0% CI
AGEWED    26540  22.150  4.885    0.030  (22.091, 22.209)
```

(a) Use the summary to determine the point estimate of the population mean and margin of error for the confidence interval. $\bar{x} = 22.150$, $E = 0.059$
(b) Interpret the confidence interval.
(c) Verify the results by computing a 95% confidence interval with the information provided.

28. **Sexual Relations** A question on the 2006 General Social Surveys was this: "About how many times did you engage in intercourse during the month?" The question was only asked of participants who had previously indicated that they had engaged in sexual intercourse during the past month. The results are summarized in the MINITAB excerpt that follows:

One-Sample T: SEXFREQ2

```
Variable     N  Mean  StDev  SE Mean      95.0% CI
SEXFREQ2   357  7.678  6.843    0.362  (6.966, 8.390)
```

(a) Use the summary to determine the point estimate of the population mean and margin of error for the confidence interval. $\bar{x} = 7.678$, $E = 0.712$
(b) Interpret the confidence interval.
(c) Verify the results by computing a 95% confidence interval with the information provided.

29. **Effect of Outliers** The following data represent the asking price for a simple random sample of homes for sale in Lexington, Kentucky, in December 2007.

NW

$245,900 $154,000 $496,600 $323,900 $299,900 $225,000

$159,900 $259,900 $237,500 $173,500 $202,500 $286,000

(a) Construct a boxplot to identify the outlier.
(b) Construct a 99% confidence interval with the outlier included. ($171,599.1, $339,167.6)
(c) Construct a 99% confidence interval with the outlier removed. ($178,920.8, $287,988.2)
(d) Comment on the effect that the outlier has on the confidence interval.

30. **Effect of Outliers** The following data represent a simple random sample of ages of West Nile virus victims in the United States during 2007.

60	48	73	65	63	81
56	86	80	77	72	25

(a) Construct a boxplot to identify the outlier.
(b) Construct a 99% confidence interval with the outlier included. (50.3, 80.7)
(c) Construct a 99% confidence interval with the outlier removed. (57.9, 80.5)
(d) Comment on the effect that the outlier has on the confidence interval.

31. **Simulation** IQ scores based on the Wechsler Intelligence Scale for Children (WISC) are known to be normally distributed with $\mu = 100$ and $\sigma = 15$.

34. (e) Yes: P(eight or more) = 0.0082

(a) Simulate obtaining 20 samples of size $n = 15$ from this population.
(b) Obtain the sample mean and sample standard deviation for each of the 20 samples.
(c) Construct 95% t-intervals for each of the 20 samples.
(d) How many of the intervals do you expect to include the population mean? How many actually contain the population mean?

32. **Simulation** The arrival of cars at a Burger King drive-through follows a Poisson process with $\mu = 4$ cars every 10 minutes.
(a) Simulate obtaining 30 samples of size $n = 35$ from this population.
(b) Obtain the sample mean and sample standard deviation for each of the 30 samples.
(c) Construct 90% t-intervals for each of the 30 samples.
(d) How many of the intervals do you expect to include the population mean? How many actually contain the population mean?

33. **Confidence Interval Applet: The Role of Right Skewed Data** Load the confidence intervals for a mean (the effect of not knowing the standard deviation) applet.
(a) Set the shape to normal with mean = 100 and standard deviation = 15. Construct at least 1,000 confidence intervals with $n = 10$. Compare the proportion of the 95% Z-intervals and t-intervals that contains the population mean. Is this what you would expect?
(b) Set the shape to skewed right with mean = 100 and standard deviation = 15. Construct at least 1,000 confidence intervals with $n = 10$. Compare the proportion of the 95% Z-intervals and t-intervals that contains the population mean. Is this what you would expect?

34. **Putting It Together: How Many Drinks?** A question on the 2006 General Social Survey was "When you drink, how many drinks do you have?" The results are shown next.

Number of Drinks	Frequency
1	119
2	66
3	27
4	12
5	8
6	5
7	4
8	1
9	0
10	0
11	0
12	1

(a) Draw a histogram of the data and comment on the shape of the distribution. Skewed right
(b) Determine the mean and standard deviation for number of drinks. $\bar{x} = 2.0$; $s = 1.6$
(c) What is the mode number of drinks? One drink
(d) What is the probability a randomly selected individual consumes two drinks? 0.2716
(e) Would it be unusual to observe an individual who consumes at least eight drinks? Why?
(f) What shape will the distribution of the sample mean have? Why? Approximately normal; Central Limit Theorem
(g) Construct a 95% confidence interval for the mean number of drinks. Interpret this interval. (1.8, 2.2)

Consumer Reports   *Consumer Reports Tests Tires*

Consumer Reports' specialized auto-test facility is the largest, most sophisticated consumer-based auto-testing facility in the world. Located on 327 acres in East Haddam, Connecticut, the facility is staffed by a team of experienced engineers and test personnel who buy and test more than 40 new cars, SUVs, minivans, and light trucks each year. For each vehicle, Consumer Reports conducts more than 46 individual tests, ranging from emergency handling, acceleration, and braking to fuel-economy measurements, noise-level evaluations, and bumper-impact tests.

As part of testing vehicles, Consumer Reports tests tires. Our tire evaluations include dry and wet braking from 60 mph, braking on ice, snow traction on a flat surface, snow traction on a snow hill, emergency handling, routine cornering, ride comfort, rolling resistance, and noise. All the test data are recorded using an optical instrument that provides precise speed and distance measurements.

The following table contains the dry brake stopping distance (in feet) data for one brand of tires recently tested.

Measurement	Distance
1	131.8
2	123.2
3	132.9
4	139.8
5	140.3
6	128.3
7	129.3
8	129.5
9	134.0

(a) A normal probability plot of the dry brake distance data is shown. What does this plot suggest about the distribution of the brake data?

(b) Does the data set contain any outliers?

(c) Use these data to construct a 95% confidence interval for the mean dry braking distance for this brand of tires. Write a statement that explains the meaning of this confidence interval to the readers of *Consumer Reports* magazine.

Note to Readers: *In many cases, our test protocol and analytical methods are more complicated than described in these examples. The data and discussions have been modified to make the material more appropriate for the audience.*

TECHNOLOGY STEP-BY-STEP

TI-83/84 Plus
1. If necessary, enter raw data in L1.
2. Press STAT, highlight TESTS, and select
8: TInterval.
3. If the data are raw, highlight DATA. Make sure List1 is set to L1 and Freq to 1. If summary statistics are known, highlight STATS and enter the summary statistics.
4. Enter the confidence level following C-Level:.
5. Highlight Calculate; press ENTER.

MINITAB
1. If you have raw data, enter them in column C1.
2. Select the **Stat** menu, highlight **Basic Statistics**, then highlight **1-Sample t . . . .**
3. If you have raw data, enter C1 in the cell marked "Samples in columns". If you have summarized data,

Confidence Intervals for μ, σ Unknown

select the "Summarized data" radio button and enter the summarized data. Select **Options . . .** and enter a confidence level. Click OK twice.

Excel
1. Enter raw data in column A. Highlight the data.
2. Load the Data Desk XL Add-in.
3. Select the **DDXL** menu, highlight **Confidence Intervals**, then highlight **1 Var t-Interval** from the drop-down menu.
4. Select the column of data from the "Names and Columns" window. Check the box for "First row is variable names", if necessary. Use the ◄ arrow to select the data. Click OK.
5. Select the level of confidence and click Compute Interval.

9.3 CONFIDENCE INTERVALS FOR A POPULATION PROPORTION

Preparing for This Section Before getting started, review the following:

• Distribution of the sample proportion (Section 8.2, pp. 442–448)

Objectives

1. Obtain a point estimate for the population proportion
2. Construct and interpret a confidence interval for the population proportion
3. Determine the sample size necessary for estimating a population proportion within a specified margin of error

---

Note to Instructor

Don't forget about the Preparing for This Section quiz on the Instructor's Resource Center.

In Other Words

The symbol ± is read "plus or minus." It means "to add and subtract the quantity following the ± symbol."

Probably the most frequently reported confidence interval is one involving the proportion of a population. Researchers are often interested in estimating the proportion of the population that has a certain characteristic. For example, in a poll conducted by the Gallup organization in early December, 2006, a random sample of 1,004 Americans resulted in 84% of the respondents stating that they are satisfied with the way things are going in their personal lives. The poll had a margin of error of 3% with 95% confidence. Based on discussions in Sections 9.1 and 9.2, we know that this means the pollsters are 95% confident that the true proportion of Americans who are satisfied with the way things are going in their personal lives is between 81% and 87% (84% ± 3%). Remember, this level of confidence refers to the method; it is not a probability. So the method works (i.e., captures the true population proportion) in 95% of all possible simple random samples of size 1,004. We don't know if the interval computed is one of the 95% that captures the population proportion, p, or one of the 5% that does not.

In this section, we will discuss the techniques for estimating the population proportion population, p. In addition, we present methods for determining the sample size required to estimate the population proportion.

1 Obtain a Point Estimate for the Population Proportion

A point estimate is an unbiased estimator of the parameter. The point estimate for the population proportion is $\hat{p} = \dfrac{x}{n}$, where x is the number of individuals in the sample with the specified characteristic and n is the sample size.

EXAMPLE 1 | **Obtaining a Point Estimate of a Population Proportion**

Problem: The Pew Internet and American Life Project conducted a poll between October 23 and November 19, 2006, in which a simple random sample of 935 teenagers between the ages of 12 and 17 was asked whether they participate in any form of content creation for the Internet. Content creation included the development of web pages, posts to blogs, and social networks. Of the 935 teenagers surveyed, 598 reported that they participate in content creation. Obtain a point estimate for the proportion of teenagers between the ages of 12 and 17 that participate is some form of content creation for the Internet.

Approach: The point estimate of the population proportion is $\hat{p} = \dfrac{x}{n}$, where $x = 598$ and $n = 935$.

Solution: Substituting into the formula, we obtain $\hat{p} = \dfrac{x}{n} = \dfrac{598}{935} = 0.640 = 64.0\%$.
We estimate that 64% of teenagers between the ages of 12 and 17 participate in some form of content creation for the Internet.

> Now Work Problem 19(a)

② Construct and Interpret a Confidence Interval for the Population Proportion

The point estimate obtained in Example 1 is a single estimate of the unknown parameter, p. We recognize it is unlikely that the sample proportion will equal the population proportion. Therefore, rather than reporting the value of the sample proportion alone, it is preferred to report an interval about the sample proportion along with a level of confidence in our results.

In Section 8.2, we discussed the sampling distribution of the sample proportion, $\hat{p}$. For convenience, we repeat the sampling distribution of $\hat{p}$ here.

Sampling Distribution of $\hat{p}$

For a simple random sample of size n, the sampling distribution of $\hat{p}$ is approximately normal, with mean $\mu_{\hat{p}} = p$ and standard deviation $\sigma_{\hat{p}} = \sqrt{\dfrac{p(1 - p)}{n}}$, provided that $np(1 - p) \geq 10$.

Note: We also require that each trial be independent. When sampling from finite populations, this means that the sample size can be no more than 5% of the population size $(n \leq 0.05N)$.   ◄

We use the sampling distribution of $\hat{p}$ to construct a confidence interval for the population proportion, p.

Constructing a $(1 - \alpha) \cdot 100\%$ Confidence Interval for a Population Proportion

Suppose that a simple random sample of size n is taken from a population. A $(1 - \alpha) \cdot 100\%$ confidence interval for p is given by the following quantities:

$$\text{Lower bound:}\quad \hat{p} - z_{\frac{\alpha}{2}} \cdot \sqrt{\dfrac{\hat{p}(1 - \hat{p})}{n}}$$

$$\text{Upper bound:}\quad \hat{p} + z_{\frac{\alpha}{2}} \cdot \sqrt{\dfrac{\hat{p}(1 - \hat{p})}{n}}$$

(1)

Note: It must be the case that $n\hat{p}(1 - \hat{p}) \geq 10$ and $n \leq 0.05N$ to construct this interval.   ◄

Notice that we use $\hat{p}$ in place of p in the standard deviation. This is because p is unknown, and $\hat{p}$ is the best point estimate of p.

EXAMPLE 2 | **Constructing a Confidence Interval for a Population Proportion**

Problem: The Pew Internet and American Life Project conducted a poll between October 23 and November 19, 2006, in which a simple random sample of 935 teenagers between the ages of 12 and 17 was asked whether they participate in any form of content creation for the Internet. Content creation included the development of web pages, posts to blogs, and social networks. Of the 935 teenagers surveyed, 598 reported that they participate in content creation. Obtain a 95% confidence interval for the proportion of teenagers who participate in some form of content creation for the Internet.

Approach
Step 1: Compute the value of $\hat{p}$.
Step 2: We can compute a 95% confidence interval for p provided that $n\hat{p}(1 - \hat{p}) \geq 10$ and $n \leq 0.05N$.
Step 3: Determine the critical value, $z_{\frac{\alpha}{2}}$.
Step 4: Determine the lower and upper bounds of the confidence interval.
Step 5: Interpret the result.

Solution

Step 1: From Example 1 we have that $\hat{p} = 0.640$.

Step 2: $n\hat{p}(1 - \hat{p}) = 935(0.640)(1 - 0.640) = 215.424 \geq 10$. There are about 20 million teenagers between 12 and 17 years of age in the United States, so our sample size is definitely less than 5% of the population size. The independence requirement is satisfied. We can proceed to construct the confidence interval.

Step 3: Because we want a 95% confidence interval, we have $\alpha = 1 - 0.95 = 0.05$, so $z_{\frac{\alpha}{2}} = z_{\frac{0.05}{2}} = z_{0.025} = 1.96$.

Step 4: Substituting into Formula (1) with $n = 935$, we obtain the lower and upper bounds of the confidence interval:

$$\text{Lower bound:} \quad \hat{p} - z_{\frac{\alpha}{2}} \cdot \sqrt{\frac{\hat{p}(1 - \hat{p})}{n}} = 0.640 - 1.96 \cdot \sqrt{\frac{0.640(1 - 0.640)}{935}}$$
$$= 0.640 - 0.031 = 0.609$$

$$\text{Upper bound:} \quad \hat{p} + z_{\frac{\alpha}{2}} \cdot \sqrt{\frac{\hat{p}(1 - \hat{p})}{n}} = 0.640 + 1.96 \cdot \sqrt{\frac{0.640(1 - 0.640)}{935}}$$
$$= 0.640 + 0.031 = 0.671$$

Step 5: We are 95% confident that the proportion of teenagers between the ages of 12 and 17 who contribute content to the Internet is between 0.609 and 0.671.

EXAMPLE 3 | **Constructing a Confidence Interval about a Population Proportion Using Technology**

Problem: The Pew Internet and American Life Project conducted a poll between October 23 and November 19, 2006, in which a simple random sample of 935 teenagers between the ages of 12 and 17 was asked whether they participate in any form of content creation for the Internet. Content creation included the development of web pages, posts to blogs, and social networks. Of the 935 teenagers surveyed, 598 reported that they participate in content creation. Obtain a 95% confidence interval for the proportion of teenagers who participate in some form of content creation for the Internet.

Approach: We will use MINITAB to construct the confidence interval. The steps for constructing confidence intervals using MINITAB, Excel, and the TI-83/84 graphing calculators are given in the Technology Step-by-Step on page 496.

Solution: Figure 16 shows the results obtained from MINITAB.

Figure 16

Test and CI for One Proportion

```
Sample    X    N    Sample p        95% CI
1        598  935   0.639572   (0.607861, 0.670401)
```

Using Technology

The results obtained using technology may differ from those obtained by hand due to rounding.

The lower bound is 0.608 and the upper bound is 0.670.

Interpretation: We are 95% confident that the proportion of teenagers between the ages of 12 and 17 who contribute content to the Internet is between 0.608 and 0.670.

CAUTION Beware of surveys that do not report a margin of error. Survey results should also report sample size, sampling technique, and the population that was being studied.

It is important to remember the correct interpretation of a confidence interval. The statement "95% confident" means that, if 100 samples of size 935 were taken, about 95 of the intervals will contain the parameter p and about 5 will not. Unfortunately, we cannot know whether the interval we computed in Examples 2 and 3 is one of the 95 intervals that contains p or one of the 5 that does not contain p.

Often polls will report their results by giving the value of $\hat{p}$ obtained from the sample data along with the margin of error, rather than reporting a confidence interval. In Examples 2 and 3, the Pew Internet and American Life Project might say, "In a survey conducted between October 23 and November 19, 2006, we found that 64% of teenage Americans between 12 and 17 years of age participate in some form of content creation for the Internet. The survey results have a margin of error of 3.1%."

Now Work Problems 19(b), (c), and (d)

Note to Instructor

The purpose of this activity is to illustrate the meaning of a confidence interval estimate. Remind students not to eat any of the candies until they are counted. It is helpful to determine up front how to deal with partial candies. Time Limit: 30 to 40 minutes depending on discussions.

IN CLASS ACTIVITY

Confidence Intervals (M&Ms)

Mars, Inc., reports that the proportion of Plain M&M's it produces that are blue is 0.24. However, you suspect that this is not the case.

(a) Each student should obtain a 1-pound bag of plain M&M candies and bring it to class unopened. We will treat each bag as a simple random sample of M&M's.

(b) In class, count the number of candies in your bag for each of the six colors (red, brown, blue, yellow, green, and orange).

(c) Obtain a point estimate for the population proportion of blue candies.

(d) Verify that the requirements for constructing a confidence interval about $\hat{p}$ are satisfied. If the conditions are not met, what could you do to rectify the situation?

(e) Construct a 95% confidence interval for the proportion of blue candies. Interpret the interval. Does your interval contain 0.24?

(f) Compare your interval with those of the rest of the class. What proportion of intervals found in the class does not contain 0.24? Is this result what you would expect?

3 Determine the Sample Size Necessary for Estimating a Population Proportion within a Specified Margin of Error

In Section 9.1, we introduced a method for determining the sample size, n, required to estimate the population mean within a certain margin of error for a specified level of confidence. The formula was obtained by solving the margin of error, $E = z_{\frac{\alpha}{2}} \cdot \dfrac{\sigma}{\sqrt{n}}$, for n. We can follow the same approach to determine sample size when estimating a population proportion. In Formula (1) on page 489, we notice that the margin of error is given by $E = z_{\frac{\alpha}{2}} \cdot \sqrt{\dfrac{\hat{p}(1 - \hat{p})}{n}}$. We solve for n and obtain

$$n = \hat{p}(1 - \hat{p})\left(\frac{z_{\frac{\alpha}{2}}}{E}\right)^2.$$

The problem with this formula is that it depends on $\hat{p}$, and $\hat{p} = \dfrac{x}{n}$ depends on the sample size, n, which is what we are trying to determine in the first place! How do we resolve this issue? There are two possibilities: (1) We could determine a preliminary value for $\hat{p}$ based on a pilot study or an earlier study, or (2) we could let $\hat{p} = 0.5$. When $\hat{p} = 0.5$, the maximum value of $\hat{p}(1 - \hat{p}) = 0.25$ is obtained, as illustrated in Figure 17. Using the maximum value gives the largest possible value of n for a given level of confidence and a given margin of error.

Figure 17

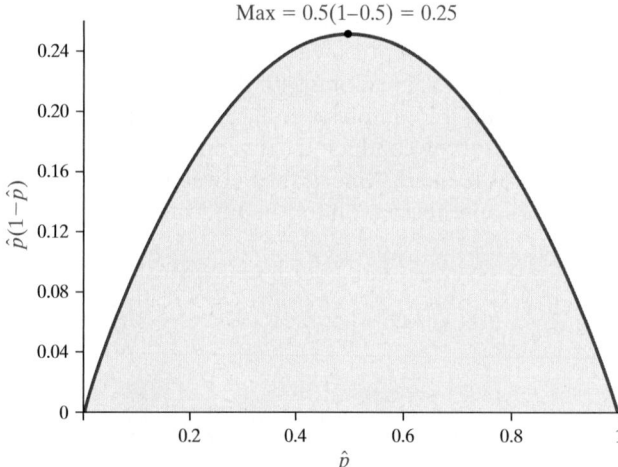

The disadvantage of the second option is that it could lead to a larger sample size than is necessary. Because of the time and expense of sampling, it is desirable to avoid too large a sample.

Sample Size Needed for Estimating the Population Proportion p

The sample size required to obtain a $(1 - \alpha) \cdot 100\%$ confidence interval for p with a margin of error E is given by

$$n = \hat{p}(1 - \hat{p})\left(\frac{z_{\frac{\alpha}{2}}}{E}\right)^2 \qquad (2)$$

In Other Words
There are two formulas for determining sample size when estimating the population proportion. Formula (2) requires a prior estimate of p; Formula (3) does not.

(rounded up to the next integer), where $\hat{p}$ is a prior estimate of p. If a prior estimate of p is unavailable, the sample size required is

$$n = 0.25\left(\frac{z_{\frac{\alpha}{2}}}{E}\right)^2 \qquad (3)$$

rounded up to the next integer. The margin of error should always be expressed as a decimal when using Formulas (2) and (3).

| EXAMPLE 4 | **Determining Sample Size** |

Problem: With gas prices on the rise, an economist wants to know if the proportion of the U.S. population who commutes to work via car-pooling is on the rise. What size sample should be obtained if the economist wants an estimate within 2 percentage points of the true proportion with 90% confidence if

(a) the economist uses the 2006 estimate of 10.7% obtained from the American Community Survey?

(b) the economist does not use any prior estimates?

Approach: In both cases, we have $E = 0.02$ ($2\% = 0.02$) and $z_{\alpha/2} = z_{0.1/2} = z_{0.05} = 1.645$. To answer part (a), we let $p = 0.107$ in Formula (2). To answer part (b), we use Formula (3).

Solution

(a) Substituting $E = 0.02$, $z_{0.05} = 1.645$, and $\hat{p} = 0.107$ into Formula (2), we obtain

$$n = \hat{p}(1 - \hat{p})\left(\frac{z_{\frac{\alpha}{2}}}{E}\right)^2 = 0.107(1 - 0.107)\left(\frac{1.645}{0.02}\right)^2 = 646.4$$

We always round up when determining sample size.

We round this value up to 647, so the economist must survey 647 randomly selected residents of the United States.

(b) Substituting $E = 0.02$ and $z_{0.05} = 1.645$ into Formula (3), we obtain

$$n = 0.25\left(\frac{z_{\frac{\alpha}{2}}}{E}\right)^2 = 0.25\left(\frac{1.645}{0.02}\right)^2 = 1{,}691.3$$

We round this value up to 1,692, so the economist must survey 1,692 randomly selected residents of the United States.

We can see the effect of not having a prior estimate of p: In this case, the required sample size more than doubled!

Now Work Problem 25

9.3 ASSESS YOUR UNDERSTANDING

Concepts and Vocabulary

1. What is the best point estimate of a population proportion?

2. What are the requirements that must be satisfied to construct a confidence interval about a population proportion?

3. When determining the sample size required to obtain an estimate for a population proportion, is the researcher better off using a prior estimate of p or no prior estimate of p? Why? List some pros and cons for each scenario.

4. Explain why you should be wary of surveys that do not report a margin of error.

Skill Building

In Problems 5–10, construct a confidence interval of the population proportion at the given level of confidence.

5. $x = 30$, $n = 150$, 90% confidence   (0.146, 0.254)

6. $x = 80$, $n = 200$, 98% confidence   (0.319, 0.481)

7. $x = 120$, $n = 500$, 99% confidence   (0.191, 0.289)

8. $x = 400$, $n = 1{,}200$, 95% confidence   (0.306, 0.360)

9. $x = 860$, $n = 1{,}100$, 94% confidence   (0.759, 0.805)

10. $x = 540$, $n = 900$, 96% confidence   (0.567, 0.633)

In Problems 11–14, determine the point estimate of the population proportion, the margin of error for each confidence interval, and the number of individuals in the sample with the specified characteristic, x, for the sample size provided.

11. Lower bound: 0.201, upper bound: 0.249, $n = 1{,}200$
    $\hat{p} = 0.225$, $E = 0.024$, $x = 270$

12. Lower bound: 0.051, upper bound: 0.074, $n = 1{,}120$
    $\hat{p} = 0.0625$, $E = 0.0115$, $x = 70$

13. Lower bound: 0.462, upper bound: 0.509, $n = 1{,}680$
    $\hat{p} = 0.4855$, $E = 0.0235$, $x = 816$

14. Lower bound: 0.853, upper bound: 0.871, $n = 10{,}732$
    $\hat{p} = 0.862$, $E = 0.009$, $x = 9{,}251$

Applying the Concepts

15. **You Explain It! Roman Catholics** A Gallup poll of 1,027 adult Americans conducted December 6–9, 2007 found that 23% identified themselves as Roman Catholic. The margin of error was 3 percentage points with 95% confidence. Which of the following represents a reasonable interpretation of the survey results? For those that are not reasonable, explain the flaw.   (c) is correct

    (a) We are 95% confident that 23% of adult Americans identify themselves as Roman Catholic.

    (b) We are between 92% and 98% confident that 23% of adult Americans identify themselves as Roman Catholic.

(c) We are 95% confident that the proportion of adult Americans who identify themselves as Roman Catholic is between 20% and 26%.

(d) In 95% of samples of adult Americans, the proportion who identify themselves as Roman Catholics is between 20% and 26%.

16. **You Explain It! Superstition** A *USA Today*/Gallup poll conducted February 9–11, 2007 asked 1,006 adult Americans how much it would bother them to stay in a room on the 13th floor of a hotel. Interestingly, 13% said it would bother them. The margin of error was 3 percentage points with 95% confidence. Which of the following represents a reasonable interpretation of the survey results? For those not reasonable, explain the flaw. (a) is correct

(a) We are 95% confident that the proportion of adult Americans who would be bothered to stay in a room on the 13th floor is between 10% and 16%.

(b) We are between 92% and 98% confident that 13% of adult Americans would be bothered to stay in a room on the 13th floor.

(c) In 95% of samples of adult Americans, the proportion who would be bothered to stay in a room on the 13th floor is between 10% and 16%.

(d) We are 95% confident that 13% of adult Americans would be bothered to stay in a room on the 13th floor.

17. **You Explain It! Valentine's Day** A Rasmussen Reports national survey of 1,000 adult Americans released on February 14, 2008 found that 18% dreaded Valentine's Day. The margin of error for the survey was 4.5 percentage points with 95% confidence. Explain what this means.

18. **You Explain It! A Stressful Commute?** A Gallup poll of 547 adult Americans employed full or part time conducted August 13–16, 2007 asked, "Generally speaking, would you say your commute to work is—very stressful, somewhat stressful, not that stressful, or not stressful at all?" Gallup reported that 24% of American workers said that their commute was "very" or "somewhat" stressful. The margin of error was 4 percentage points with 95% confidence. Explain what this means.

19. **Lipitor** The drug Lipitor™ is meant to lower cholesterol levels. In a clinical trial of 863 patients who received 10-mg doses of Lipitor daily, 47 reported a headache as a side effect.

(a) Obtain a point estimate for the population proportion of Lipitor users who will experience a headache as a side effect. *0.054*

(b) Verify that the requirements for constructing a confidence interval about *p* are satisfied.

(c) Construct a 90% confidence interval for the population proportion of Lipitor users who will report a headache as a side effect. *(0.042, 0.067)*

(d) Interpret the confidence interval.

20. **Pepcid** A study of 74 patients with ulcers was conducted in which they were prescribed 40 mg of Pepcid™. After 8 weeks, 58 reported ulcer healing.

(a) Obtain a point estimate for the proportion of patients with ulcers receiving Pepcid who will report ulcer healing. *0.784*

(b) Verify that the requirements for constructing a confidence interval about *p* are satisfied.

(c) Construct a 99% confidence interval for the proportion of patients with ulcers receiving Pepcid who will report ulcer healing. *(0.661, 0.907)*

(d) Interpret the confidence interval.

21. **Out of Touch?** A Zogby Interactive survey conducted February 20–21, 2008 found that 1,322 of 1,979 randomly selected adult Americans believe that traditional journalism is out of touch with what Americans want from their news.

(a) Obtain a point estimate for the proportion of adult Americans who believe that traditional journalism is out of touch. $\hat{p} = 0.668$

(b) Verify that the requirements for constructing a confidence interval for *p* are satisfied.

(c) Construct a 96% confidence interval for the proportion of adult Americans who believe that traditional journalism is out of touch with what Americans want from their news. *(0.646, 0.690)*

(d) Is it possible that the proportion of adult Americans who believe that traditional journalism is out of touch is below 60%? Is this likely? Yes, no

22. **Family Values** In a *USA Today*/Gallup poll conducted November 2–4, 2007, 768 of 1,024 randomly selected adult Americans aged 18 or older stated that a candidates' positions on the issue of family values are extremely or very important in determining their votes for president.

(a) Obtain a point estimate for the proportion of adult Americans aged 18 or older for which the issue of family values is extremely or very important in determining their votes for president. $\hat{p} = 0.75$

(b) Verify that the requirements for constructing a confidence interval for *p* are satisfied.

(c) Construct a 98% confidence interval for the proportion of adult Americans aged 18 or older for which the issue of family values is extremely or very important in determining their votes for president. *(0.718, 0.782)*

(d) Is it possible that the proportion of adult Americans aged 18 or older for which the issue of family values is extremely or very important in determining their votes for president is below 65%? Is this likely? Yes, no

23. **Body Art** A Harris Interactive poll conducted in the United States between January 15 and 22, 2008, found that 322 of 2,302 adults aged 18 or older have at least one tattoo.

(a) Obtain a point estimate for the proportion of adults who have at least one tattoo. $\hat{p} = 0.140$

(b) Verify that the requirements for constructing a confidence interval for *p* are satisfied.

(c) Construct a 90% confidence interval for the proportion of adults with at least one tattoo. *(0.128, 0.152)*

(d) Construct a 98% confidence interval for the proportion of adults with at least one tattoo. *(0.123, 0.157)*

(e) What is the effect of increasing the level of confidence on the width of the interval? The interval gets wider.

24. **Pet Ownership** A Gallup poll conducted December 11–14, 2006 found that 604 of 1,010 Americans own at least one pet.

(a) Obtain a point estimate for the proportion of adults who own at least one pet. $\hat{p} = 0.598$

(b) Verify that the requirements for constructing a confidence interval for *p* are satisfied.

(c) Construct a 95% confidence interval for the proportion of adults with at least one tattoo. *(0.568, 0.628)*

(d) Construct a 99% confidence interval for the proportion of adults with at least one tattoo. *(0.558, 0.638)*

(e) What is the effect of increasing the level of confidence on the width of the interval? *The interval gets wider.*

25. **High-Speed Internet Access** A researcher wishes to estimate the proportion of adults who have high-speed Internet access. What size sample should be obtained if she wishes the estimate to be within 0.03 with 99% confidence if

(a) she uses a 2007 estimate of 0.69 obtained from Nielsen NetRatings? *1,576*

(b) she does not use any prior estimates? *1,842*

26. **Home Ownership** An urban economist wishes to estimate the proportion of Americans who own their homes. What size sample should be obtained if he wishes the estimate to be within 0.02 with 90% confidence if

(a) he uses a 2007 estimate of 0.681 obtained from the U.S. Census Bureau? *1,470*

(b) he does not use any prior estimates? *1,692*

27. **A Penny for Your Thoughts** A researcher for the U.S. Department of the Treasury wishes to estimate the percentage of Americans who support abolishing the penny. What size sample should be obtained if he wishes the estimate to be within 2 percentage points with 98% confidence if

(a) he uses an August 2006 estimate of 15% obtained from a Coinstar National Currency Poll? *1,731*

(b) he does not use any prior estimate? *3,394*

28. **Credit-Card Debt** A school administrator is concerned about the amount of credit-card debt that college students have. She wishes to conduct a poll to estimate the percentage of full-time college students who have credit-card debt of $2,000 or more. What size sample should be obtained if she wishes the estimate to be within 2.5 percentage points with 94% confidence if

(a) a pilot study indicates that the percentage is 34%? *1,269*

(b) no prior estimates are used? *1,414*

29. **Football Fans** A television sports commentator wants to estimate the proportion of Americans who "follow professional football." What sample size should be obtained if he wants to be within 3 percentage points with 95% confidence if

(a) he uses a 2006 estimate of 48% obtained from a Harris poll? *1,066*

(b) he does not use any prior estimates? *1,068*

(c) Why are the results from parts (a) and (b) so close?

30. **Affirmative Action** A sociologist wishes to conduct a poll to estimate the percentage of Americans who favor affirmative action programs for women and minorities for admission to colleges and universities. What sample size should be obtained if she wishes to be within 4 percentage points with 90% confidence if

(a) she uses a 2003 estimate of 55% obtained from a Gallup Youth Survey? *419*

(b) she does not use any prior estimates? *423*

(c) Why are the results from parts (a) and (b) so close?

31. **Death Penalty** In a Gallup poll conducted in October 2007, 69% of the people polled answered yes to the following question: "Are you in favor of the death penalty for a person convicted of murder?" The margin of error in the poll was 3%, and the estimate was made with 95% confidence. At least how many people were surveyed? *914*

32. **Gun Control** In an ABC News Poll conducted April 22, 2007, 61% of the people polled answered "favor" to the following question: "Do you favor or oppose stricter gun-control laws in this country?" The margin of error in the poll was 3.5%, and the estimate was made with 95% confidence. At least how many people were surveyed? *747*

33. **2004 Presidential Election** The Gallup organization conducted a poll of 2,014 likely voters just prior to the 2004 presidential election. The results of the survey indicated that George W. Bush would receive 49% of the popular vote and John Kerry would receive 47% of the popular vote. The margin of error was reported to be 3%. The Gallup organization reported that the race was too close to call. Use the concept of a confidence interval to explain what this means.

34. **Confidence Interval Applet: The Role of Level of Confidence** Load the confidence interval for proportions applet.

(a) Construct at least 1,000 confidence intervals for the population proportion with $n = 100$, $p = 0.3$. What proportion of the 95% confidence intervals contain the population proportion? What proportion did you expect to contain the population proportion?

(b) Repeat part (a). Did the same proportion of intervals contain the population proportion?

(c) Construct at least 1,000 confidence intervals for the population proportion with $n = 100$, $p = 0.3$. What proportion of the 99% confidence intervals contain the population proportion 0.3? What proportion did you expect to contain the population proportion?

35. **Confidence Interval Applet: The Role of Sample Size** Load the confidence interval for proportions applet.

(a) Construct at least 1,000 confidence intervals for the population proportion with $n = 10$, $p = 0.3$. What proportion of the 95% confidence intervals contains the population proportion 0.3?

(b) Construct at least 1,000 confidence intervals for the population proportion with $n = 40$, $p = 0.3$. What proportion of the 95% confidence intervals contains the population proportion 0.3?

(c) Construct at least 1,000 confidence intervals for the population proportion with $n = 100$, $p = 0.3$. What proportion of the 95% confidence intervals contains the population proportion, 0.3?

(d) What happens to the proportion of intervals that capture the population proportion as the sample size, n, increases?

36. **Putting It Together: Hand Washing** The American Society for Microbiology (ASM) and the Soap and Detergent Association (SDA) jointly commissioned two separate studies during 2007, both of which were conducted by Harris Interactive. In one of the studies, 1,001 adults were interviewed by telephone and asked about their hand-washing habits. In the other study, the hand-washing behavior of 6,067 adults was inconspicuously observed within public rest rooms in four U.S. cities.

(a) In the telephone interviews, 921 of the adults said they always wash their hands in public rest rooms. Use this result to obtain a point estimate for the proportion of adults who say they always wash their hands in public rest rooms. $\hat{p} = 0.920$

(b) Verify that the requirements for constructing a confidence interval for p from part (a) are satisfied.

29. (c) 0.48(0.52) = 0.2496 is close to 0.25.   30. (c) 0.55(0.45) = 0.2475 is close to 0.25.

(c) Using the results from the telephone interviews, construct a 95% confidence interval for the proportion of adults who say they always wash their hands in public rest rooms.   *(0.903, 0.937)*

(d) Is it possible that the proportion of adults who say they always wash their hands in public rest rooms is less than 0.85? Is this likely?   *Yes, no*

(e) In the observational study, 4,679 of the 6,076 adults were observed washing their hands. Use this result to obtain a point estimate for the proportion of adults who wash their hands in public rest rooms. $\hat{p} = 0.770$

(f) Verify that the requirements for constructing a confidence interval for p from part (e) are satisfied.

(g) Using the results from the observational study, construct a 95% confidence interval for the proportion of adults who wash their hands in public rest rooms.   *(0.759, 0.781)*

(h) Is it possible that the proportion of adults who wash their hands in public rest rooms is greater than 0.85? Is this likely?   *Yes, no*

(i) Based on your findings in parts (a) through (h), what might you conclude about the proportion of adults who *say* they always wash their hands versus the proportion of adults who actually wash their hands in public rest rooms? Why do you think this is?   *The proportion who say they wash their hands is larger than the proportion who actually do.*

TECHNOLOGY STEP-BY-STEP   Confidence Intervals about p

TI-83/84 Plus
1. Press STAT, highlight TESTS, and select A: 1-PropZInt ...
2. Enter the values of x and n.
3. Enter the confidence level following C-Level:
4. Highlight Calculate; press ENTER.

MINITAB
1. If you have raw data, enter the data in column C1.
2. Select the **Stat** menu, highlight **Basic Statistics**, then highlight **1 Proportion . . . .**
3. Enter C1 in the cell marked "Samples in Columns" if you have raw data. If you have summary statistics, click "Summarized data" and enter the number of trials, n, and the number of events (successes) x.
4. Click the **Options . . .** button. Enter a confidence level. Click "Use test based on a normal distribution"

(provided that the assumptions stated are satisfied). Click OK twice.

Excel
1. Load the **Data Desk XL** Add-in.
2. If necessary, enter raw data in column A. Highlight the data. Select the **DDXL** menu, highlight **Confidence Intervals**, then highlight **1 Var Prop Interval** if you have raw data or **Summ 1 Var Prop Interval** if you have summarized data.
3. For raw data, select the column of data from the "Names and Columns" window. Use the ◀ arrow to select the data. Click OK. For summarized data, click the pencil icon and enter the number of trials and the number of successes. Click OK.
4. Select the level of confidence. Click Compute Interval.

9.4 CONFIDENCE INTERVALS FOR A POPULATION STANDARD DEVIATION

Objectives		
		Find critical values for the chi-square distribution
		Construct and interpret confidence intervals for the population variance and standard deviation

Note to Instructor
This section can be omitted without loss of continuity, except that you might need to refer to Objective 1 from this section when covering Section 12.1.

In this section, we discuss methods for estimating a population variance or standard deviation. Just as we discovered the sampling distribution of $\bar{x}$ and $\hat{p}$, we must find s^2, the point estimate of σ^2, and the sampling distribution of s^2. We then construct intervals about the point estimate of σ^2, using this sampling distribution.

Why might we be interested in obtaining estimates of σ^2? Many production processes not only require accuracy on average (the mean); they also require consistency. Consider a filling machine (such as a coffee machine) that consistently over- and underfills cups, but, on average, fills correctly. Certainly, customers will not be happy if the machine underfills their cups, and they might be dissatisfied even if it overfills, because of spilling. A machine that consistently delivers the correct amount of liquid is desired.

As another example, consider a mutual fund that claims an average rate of return of 12% per year over the past 20 years. An investor might prefer consistent year-to-year returns near 12% over returns that fluctuated wildly yet resulted in a mean return of 12%. Both of these situations illustrate the importance of measuring variability, the topic of this section.

① Find Critical Values for the Chi-Square Distribution

We begin by exploring the sampling distribution of s^2 through a simulation. Suppose that we obtain 2,000 samples of size $n = 10$ from a population that is known to be normally distributed with mean 100 and standard deviation 15. We then perform the following steps:

Step 1: Compute the sample variance of each of the 2,000 samples.

Step 2: Compute $\dfrac{(n-1)s^2}{\sigma^2} = \dfrac{9s^2}{15^2}$ for each sample.

Step 3: Draw a histogram of these values as shown in Figure 18.

Figure 18

Note to Instructor
You may want to demonstrate this concept using the sampling distribution applet.

Chi-Square Distribution

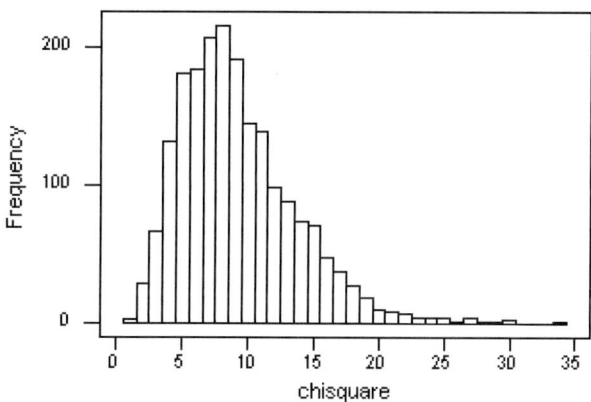

The histogram represents the sampling distribution of $\dfrac{(n-1)s^2}{\sigma^2}$. We can see that the histogram does not imply that the sampling distribution of $\dfrac{(n-1)s^2}{\sigma^2}$ is normal. Rather, the histogram appears to be skewed right, as indicated by the extended right tail of the histogram. In fact, the distribution follows a *chi-square distribution*.

Chi-Square Distribution

If a simple random sample of size n is obtained from a normally distributed population with mean μ and standard deviation σ, then

$$\chi^2 = \frac{(n-1)s^2}{\sigma^2}$$

has a **chi-square distribution** with $n - 1$ degrees of freedom.

The symbol χ^2, chi-square, is pronounced "kigh-square" (to rhyme with "sky-square"). We can find critical values of the chi-square distribution in Table VII in Appendix A of the text. Before discussing how to read Table VII, we introduce characteristics of the chi-square distribution.

Figure 19

Characteristics of the Chi-Square Distribution

1. It is not symmetric.

2. The shape of the chi-square distribution depends on the degrees of freedom, just like the Student's t-distribution.

3. As the number of degrees of freedom increases, the chi-square distribution becomes more nearly symmetric. See Figure 19.

4. The values of χ^2 are nonnegative; that is, values of χ^2 are always greater than or equal to 0.

Because the χ^2 distribution is not symmetric, we cannot construct a confidence interval for σ^2 by computing "point estimate ± margin of error." Instead, we must determine the left and right bounds by using different critical values.

Table VII is structured similarly to Table VI for the t-distribution. The left column represents the degrees of freedom, and the top row represents the area under the chi-square distribution to the right of the critical value. We use the notation χ^2_α to denote the critical χ^2-value such that the area under the chi-square distribution to the right of χ^2_α is α.

EXAMPLE 1 **Finding Critical Values for the Chi-Square Distribution**

Problem: Find the critical values that separate the middle 90% of the chi-square distribution from the 5% area in each tail, assuming 15 degrees of freedom.

Approach: We perform the following steps to obtain the critical values.
Step 1: Draw a chi-square distribution with the critical values and areas labeled.
Step 2: Use Table VII to find the critical values.

Solution

Step 1: Figure 20 shows the chi-square distribution with 15 degrees of freedom and the unknown critical values labeled. The area to the right of the right critical value is 0.05. We denote this critical value $\chi^2_{0.05}$. The area to the right of the left critical value is $1 - 0.05 = 0.95$. We denote this critical value $\chi^2_{0.95}$.

Figure 20

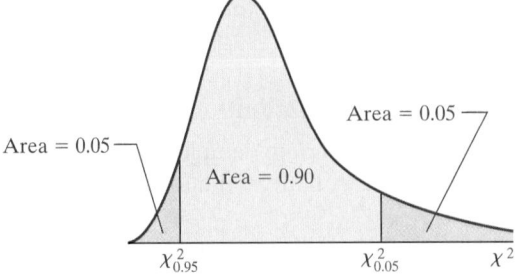

Step 2: Figure 21 shows a partial representation of Table VII. The row containing 15 degrees of freedom is boxed. The columns corresponding to an area to the right of 0.95 and 0.05 are also boxed. The critical values are $\chi^2_{0.95} = 7.261$ and $\chi^2_{0.05} = 24.996$.

Figure 21

Degrees of Freedom	Area to the Right of the Critical Value									
	0.995	0.99	0.975	0.95	0.90	0.10	0.05	0.025	0.01	0.005
1	—	—	0.001	0.004	0.016	2.706	3.841	5.024	6.635	7.879
2	0.010	0.020	0.051	0.103	0.211	4.605	5.991	7.378	9.210	10.597
3	0.072	0.115	0.216	0.352	0.584	6.251	7.815	9.348	11.345	12.838
12	3.074	3.571	4.404	5.226	6.304	18.549	21.026	23.337	26.217	28.299
13	3.565	4.107	5.009	5.892	7.042	19.812	22.362	24.736	27.688	29.819
14	4.075	4.660	5.629	6.571	7.790	21.064	23.685	26.119	29.141	31.319
15	4.601	5.229	6.262	7.261	8.547	22.307	24.996	27.488	30.578	32.801
16	5.142	5.812	6.908	7.962	9.312	23.542	26.296	28.845	32.000	34.267
17	5.697	6.408	7.564	8.672	10.085	24.769	27.587	30.191	33.409	35.718
18	6.365	7.215	8.231	9.288	10.265	25.200	28.601	31.595	24.265	36.456

In studying Table VII, we notice that the degrees of freedom are numbered 1 to 30 inclusive, then 40, 50, 60, ..., 100. If the number of degrees of freedom is not found in the table, we follow the practice of choosing the degrees of freedom closest to that desired. If the degrees of freedom are exactly between two values, find the mean of the values. For example, to find the critical value corresponding to 75 degrees of freedom, compute the mean of the critical values corresponding to 70 and 80 degrees of freedom.

Now Work Problem 5

Figure 22

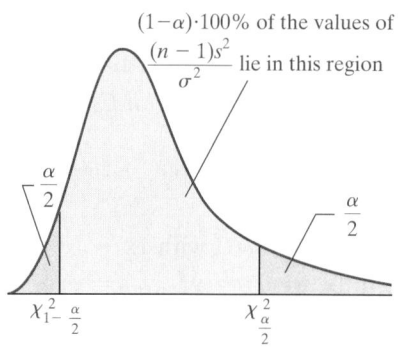

$(1-\alpha)\cdot100\%$ of the values of $\dfrac{(n-1)s^2}{\sigma^2}$ lie in this region

2 Construct and Interpret Confidence Intervals for the Population Variance and Standard Deviation

The sample variance, s^2, is the best point estimate of the population variance, σ^2. We use the sample standard deviation, s, as the point estimate of the population standard deviation, σ.*

We now must develop a method for constructing a confidence interval for the population variance. Suppose that we take a simple random sample of size n from a population that is normally distributed with mean μ and standard deviation σ; then $\chi^2 = \dfrac{(n-1)s^2}{\sigma^2}$ follows a chi-square distribution with $n-1$ degrees of freedom. Therefore, $(1-\alpha)\cdot100\%$ of the values of χ^2 will lie between $\chi^2_{1-\alpha/2}$ and $\chi^2_{\alpha/2}$. Figure 22 illustrates the situation.

So $(1-\alpha)\cdot100\%$ of the values of $\dfrac{(n-1)s^2}{\sigma^2}$ lie within the interval defined by the inequality

$$\chi^2_{1-\alpha/2} < \frac{(n-1)s^2}{\sigma^2} < \chi^2_{\alpha/2}$$

If we rewrite this inequality with σ^2 in the center, we have the formula for a $(1-\alpha)\cdot100\%$ confidence interval for σ^2:

$$\frac{(n-1)s^2}{\chi^2_{\alpha/2}} < \sigma^2 < \frac{(n-1)s^2}{\chi^2_{1-\alpha/2}}$$

*Although the sample standard deviation is a biased estimator of σ, it is common practice to use s as the estimator of σ.

A confidence interval about the population variance or standard deviation is not of the form "point estimate ± margin of error" because the sampling distribution of the sample variance is not symmetric.

A $(1 - \alpha) \cdot 100\%$ Confidence Interval about σ^2

If a simple random sample of size n is taken from a normal population with mean μ and standard deviation σ, then a $(1 - \alpha) \cdot 100\%$ confidence interval about σ^2 is given by

$$\text{Lower bound:} \quad \frac{(n-1)s^2}{\chi^2_{\alpha/2}} \qquad \text{Upper bound:} \quad \frac{(n-1)s^2}{\chi^2_{1-\alpha/2}} \qquad \textbf{(1)}$$

To find a $(1 - \alpha) \cdot 100\%$ confidence interval about σ, take the square root of the lower bound and upper bound.

EXAMPLE 2 ### Constructing a Confidence Interval for a Population Variance and Standard Deviation

Problem: Table 7 shows the sale price of 12 randomly selected 3-year-old Chevy Corvettes. Construct a 90% confidence interval for the population variance and standard deviation of the price of a 3-year-old Chevy Corvette.

Approach: We perform the following steps to construct the confidence interval:

Step 1: Check to see whether it is reasonable to conclude that the data come from a normally distributed population.

Step 2: Compute the sample variance.

Step 3: Determine the critical values.

Step 4: Use Formula (1) to construct the confidence interval for the population variance.

Step 5: Compute the square root of the lower bound and upper bound to obtain the confidence interval for the population standard deviation.

Table 7

$41,844	$41,500	$39,995
$36,995	$40,990	$37,995
$41,995	$38,900	$42,995
$36,995	$43,995	$35,950

Source: cars.com

Solution

Step 1: A normal probability plot and boxplot indicate that the price of Corvettes could be normally distributed and no outliers are present.

Step 2: The sample standard deviation is $2,615.19. The sample variance is $(\$2,615.19)^2$.

Step 3: For 90% confidence, we have $\alpha = 0.10$. Using Table VII with $12 - 1 = 11$ degrees of freedom, we find the left critical value to be $\chi^2_{1-\alpha/2} = \chi^2_{1-0.10/2} = \chi^2_{0.95} = 4.575$. We find the right critical value to be $\chi^2_{\alpha/2} = \chi^2_{0.10/2} = \chi^2_{0.05} = 19.675$. See Figure 23.

Step 4: Substitute these values into Formula (1), yielding

$$\text{Lower bound:} \quad \frac{(n-1)s^2}{\chi^2_{\alpha/2}} = \frac{11(2,615.19)^2}{19.675} = 3,823,705.52$$

$$\text{Upper bound:} \quad \frac{(n-1)s^2}{\chi^2_{1-\alpha/2}} = \frac{11(2,615.19)^2}{4.575} = 16,444,023.19$$

Step 5: Taking the square root of each part,* we obtain

Lower bound: $1,955   Upper bound: $4,055

We are 90% confident that the population standard deviation of the price of a 3-year-old Chevy Corvette is between $1,955 and $4,055.

Figure 23

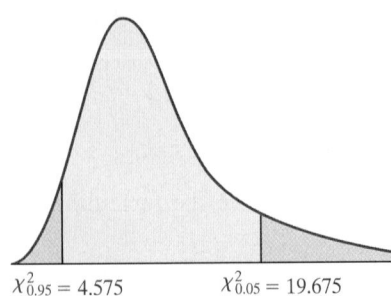

$\chi^2_{0.95} = 4.575$ $\chi^2_{0.05} = 19.675$

---

*Be sure to take the square root of the *unrounded* values.

The formula presented for constructing the confidence interval for a population variance requires that the data come from a normal distribution. Confidence intervals for the population mean and population proportion are robust (not sensitive to moderate departures from normality), but the intervals computed for the population variance (or standard deviation) are not robust. Therefore, it is vital that the requirement of normality be verified before proceeding.

Now Work Problem 11

9.4 ASSESS YOUR UNDERSTANDING

Concepts and Vocabulary

1. State the characteristics of the chi-square distribution.

2. How must the population be distributed to construct a confidence interval about a population standard deviation?

3. Explain how to obtain a confidence interval for the population standard deviation.

4. A 95% confidence interval for the population standard deviation of calories in a 1-ounce serving of American cheese is found to be lower bound: 15.1 calories and upper bound: 26.5 calories. Can we say that the point estimate is $s = 20.8$ calories with margin of error $E = 5.7$ calories? Why? No; confidence interval is not symmetric

Skill Building

In Problems 5–8, find the critical values $\chi^2_{1-\alpha/2}$ and $\chi^2_{\alpha/2}$ for the given level of confidence and sample size.

5. 90% confidence; $n = 20$ 10.117; 30.144

6. 95% confidence, $n = 25$ 12.401; 39.364

7. 98% confidence, $n = 23$ 9.542; 40.289

8. 99% confidence, $n = 14$ 3.565; 29.819

9. A simple random sample of size n is drawn from a population that is known to be normally distributed. The sample variance, s^2, is determined to be 12.6.
   (a) Construct a 90% confidence interval for σ^2 if the sample size, n, is 20.   (7.94, 23.66)
   (b) Construct a 90% confidence interval for σ^2 if the sample size, n, is 30. How does increasing the sample size affect the width of the interval?   (8.59, 20.63); decreases
   (c) Construct a 98% confidence interval for σ^2 if the sample size, n, is 20. Compare the results with those obtained in part (a). How does increasing the level of confidence affect the confidence interval?   (6.61, 31.36); increases

10. A simple random sample of size n is drawn from a population that is known to be normally distributed. The sample variance, s^2, is determined to be 19.8.
    (a) Construct a 95% confidence interval for σ^2 if the sample size, n, is 10.   (9.37, 66.00)
    (b) Construct a 95% confidence interval for σ^2 if the sample size, n, is 25. How does increasing the sample size affect the width of the interval?   (12.07, 38.32); decreases
    (c) Construct a 99% confidence interval for σ^2 if the sample size, n, is 10. Compare the results with those obtained in part (a). How does increasing the level of confidence affect the confidence interval?   (7.55, 102.71); increases

Applying the Concepts

11. **Crawling Babies** The following data represent the age (in weeks) at which babies first crawl based on a survey of 12 mothers conducted by Essential Baby.

52	30	44	35	39	26
47	37	56	26	39	28

Source: www.essentialbaby.com

In Problem 23 from Section 9.2, it was verified that the data are normally distributed and that $s = 10.00$ weeks. Construct a 95% confidence interval for the population standard deviation of the age (in weeks) at which babies first crawl. Interpret the interval.   (7.08, 16.98)

12. **Battery Life** The following data represent the battery life, in hours, for a random sample of 10 full charges on a fifth-generation iPod music player.

7.3	10.2	12.9	10.8	12.1
6.6	10.2	9.0	8.5	7.1

In Problem 24 from Section 9.2, it was verified that the data are normally distributed and that $s = 2.14$ hours. Construct a 95% confidence interval for the population standard deviation of the battery life (in hours). Interpret the interval.   (1.47, 3.91)

13. **The Growing Season** An agricultural researcher is interested in estimating the variation in the length of the growing season in the Chicago area. Treating the last 10 years as a simple random sample, he obtains the following data, which represent the number of days of the growing season.

155	162	146	144	168
188	215	180	166	151

Source: Midwest Climate Center

In Problem 25 from Section 9.2, it was verified that the data are normally distributed and that $s = 21.88$ days. Construct a 99% confidence interval for the population standard deviation of the number of days in the growing season. Interpret the interval.   (13.51, 49.83)

14. **Disc Weight** When playing disc golf, the weight of the disc has a huge effect on disc performance. Lighter discs tend to fly farther, but are less stable. Heavier discs tend to give better control and are better suited for strong winds. The following

data represent the weights, in grams, of a random sample of 12 discs produced by a certain manufacturer.

172	168	170	173	172	173
171	175	173	171	169	173

In Problem 26 from Section 9.2, it was verified that the data are normally distributed and that $s = 1.97$ grams. Construct a 99% confidence interval for the population standard deviation of the disc weight (in grams). Interpret the interval.   (1.26, 4.05)

15. **Peanuts** A jar of peanuts is supposed to have 16 ounces of peanuts. The filling machine inevitably experiences fluctuations in filling, so a quality-control manager randomly samples 12 jars of peanuts from the storage facility and measures their contents. She obtains the following data:

15.94	15.74	16.21	15.36	15.84	15.84
15.52	16.16	15.78	15.51	16.28	16.53

(a) Verify that the data are normally distributed by constructing a normal probability plot.
(b) Determine the sample standard deviation.   0.349 oz
(c) Construct a 90% confidence interval for the population standard deviation of the number of ounces of peanuts.   (0.261, 0.541)
(d) The quality control manager wants the machine to have a population standard deviation below 0.20 ounce. Does the confidence interval validate this desire?   No

16. **Investment Risk** Investors not only desire a high return on their money, but they would also like the rate of return to be stable from month to month. An investment manager invests with the goal of reducing volatility (month-to-month fluctuations in the rate of return). The following data represent the rate of return (in percent) for his mutual fund for the past 12 months.

13.8	15.9	10.0	12.4	11.3	6.6
9.6	12.4	10.3	8.7	14.9	6.7

(a) Verify that the data are normally distributed by constructing a normal probability plot.
(b) Determine the sample standard deviation.   2.98 percent
(c) Construct a 95% confidence interval for the population standard deviation of the rate of return.   (2.11, 5.06)
(d) The investment manager wants to have a population standard deviation for the rate of return below 6%. Does the confidence interval validate this desire?   Yes

17. **Critical Values** Sir R. A. Fisher, a famous statistician, showed that the critical values of a chi-square distribution can be approximated by the standard normal distribution

$$\chi_k^2 = \frac{(z_k + \sqrt{2v - 1})^2}{2}$$

where v is the degrees of freedom and z_k is the z-score such that the area under the standard normal curve to the right of z_k is k. Use Fisher's approximation to find $\chi_{0.975}^2$ and $\chi_{0.025}^2$ with 100 degrees of freedom. Compare the results with those found in Table VII.   73.772; 129.070

TECHNOLOGY STEP-BY-STEP   Confidence Intervals for σ

TI-83/84 Plus
The TI-83/84 Plus do not construct confidence intervals about σ.

MINITAB
1. Enter raw data in column C1.
2. Select the **Stat** menu, highlight **Basic Statistics**, then highlight **Graphical Summary** . . . .
3. Enter C1 in the cell marked "Variables."
4. Enter the confidence level desired. Click OK. The confidence interval for sigma is reported in the output.

Excel
1. Enter the raw data in column A. Highlight the data.

2. Load the Data Desk XL Add-in.
3. Select the **DDXL** menu, highlight **Confidence Intervals**, then highlight **Chi-square Conf Ints for SD** in the drop-down menu.
4. Select the column of raw data from the "Names and Columns" window. Check the box for "First row is variable names", if necessary. Use the ◄ arrow to select the data. Click OK.
5. Select the level of confidence and click Compute Interval.

9.5 PUTTING IT TOGETHER: WHICH PROCEDURE DO I USE?

Objective	**1** Determine the appropriate confidence interval to construct

1 Determine the Appropriate Confidence Interval to Construct

Perhaps the most difficult aspect of constructing a confidence interval is determining which type of confidence interval to construct. To assist in your decision making, we present Figure 24.

Figure 24

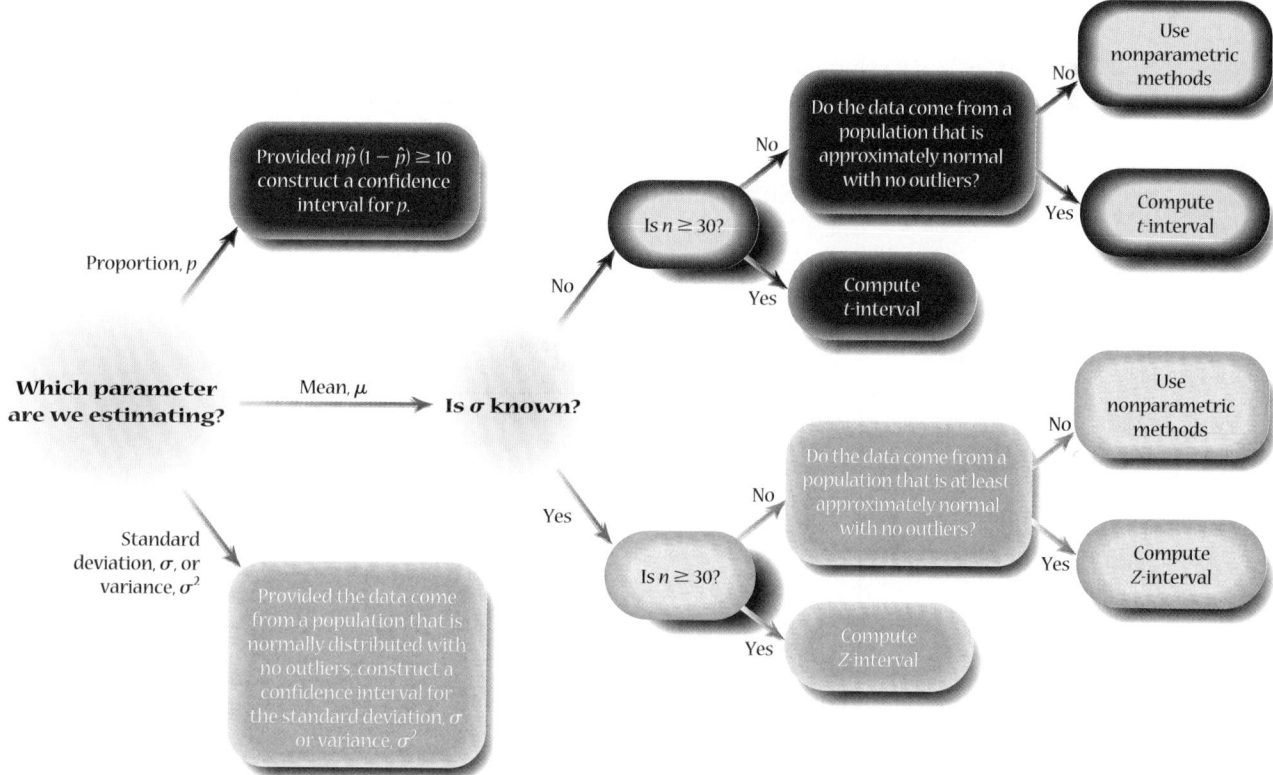

From the flow chart, the first step is to determine which parameter we wish to estimate. If we are estimating a proportion, standard deviation, or variance, we verify the requirements to construct the interval and proceed. However, if we are estimating a mean, then we have another decision to make. We must determine whether the population standard deviation is known or not. If the population standard deviation is not known, we construct a *t*-interval (provided the sample size is large or the sample data come from a population that is normally distributed with no outliers). If the population standard deviation is known, we construct a *Z*-interval (again provided the sample size is large or the sample data come from a population that is normally distributed with no outliers).

| EXAMPLE 1 | **Constructing a Confidence Interval: Which Method Do I Use?** |

Problem: Robert wishes to estimate the mean number of miles that his Buick Rendezvous can be driven on a full tank of gas. He fills up his car with regular unleaded gasoline from the same gas station 10 times and records the number of miles that he drives until his low-tank indicator light comes on. He obtains the data shown in Table 8. Construct a 95% confidence interval for the mean number of miles driven on a full tank of gas.

Table 8				
323.9	326.8	370.6	398.8	417.5
450.7	368.8	423.8	382.7	343.1

Approach: We will follow the flow chart given in Figure 24.

Solution: The problem is asking us to construct a confidence interval for the *mean* number of miles driven. So, we wish to estimate the population mean, μ. No information is given about the value of the population standard deviation, so σ is unknown. Because the sample size is small, we need to verify that the data come from a population that is normally distributed with no outliers. Figure 25 shows a normal probability plot and boxplot.

Figure 25

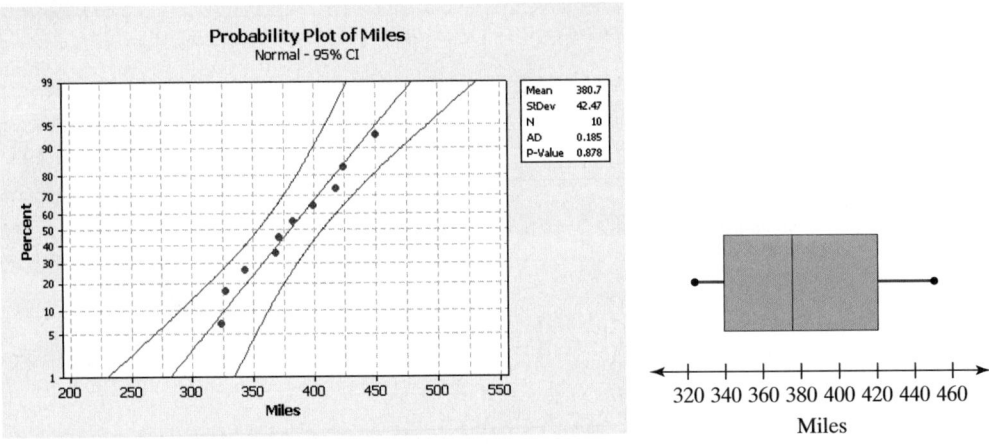

The normal probability plot indicates that the sample data could come from a population that is normally distributed, and the boxplot indicates that there are no outliers, so we construct a t-interval. Based on the sample data from Table 8, we have that $n = 10, \bar{x} = 380.67$, and $s = 42.47$. For a 95% confidence interval with $n - 1 = 10 - 1 = 9$ degrees of freedom, we have that $t_{\frac{\alpha}{2}} = t_{\frac{0.05}{2}} = t_{0.025} = 2.262$.

$$\text{Lower bound: } \quad \bar{x} - t_{\frac{\alpha}{2}} \cdot \frac{s}{\sqrt{n}} = 380.67 - 2.262 \cdot \frac{42.47}{\sqrt{10}} = 350.29$$

$$\text{Upper bound: } \quad \bar{x} - t_{\frac{\alpha}{2}} \cdot \frac{s}{\sqrt{n}} = 380.67 + 2.262 \cdot \frac{42.47}{\sqrt{10}} = 411.05$$

Robert is 95% confident that the mean number of miles he can drive on a full tank of gas is between 350.29 and 411.05 miles.

9.5 ASSESS YOUR UNDERSTANDING

Concepts and Vocabulary

1. State the circumstances under which we construct a *t*-interval. What are the circumstances under which we construct a *Z*-interval?

2. What are the requirements that must be satisfied before we can construct a confidence interval about a population proportion?

Skill Building

In Problems 3–12, construct the appropriate confidence interval.

3. A simple random sample of size $n = 14$ is drawn from a population that is normally distributed with $\sigma = 20$. The sample mean is found to be $\bar{x} = 60$. Construct a 95% confidence interval for the population mean. *(49.5, 70.5)*

4. A simple random sample of size $n = 22$ is drawn from a population that is normally distributed with $\sigma = 37$. The sample mean is found to be $\bar{x} = 122.5$. Construct a 90% confidence interval for the population mean. *(109.52, 135.48)*

5. A simple random sample of size $n = 300$ individuals who are currently employed is asked if they work at home at least once per week. Of the 300 employed individuals surveyed, 35 responded that they did work at home at least once per week. Construct a 99% confidence interval for the population proportion of employed individuals who work at home at least once per week. *(0.069, 0.165)*

6. A simple random sample of size $n = 785$ adults was asked if they follow college football. Of the 785 surveyed, 275 responded that they did follow college football. Construct a 95% confidence interval for the population proportion of adults who follow college football. *(0.317, 0.383)*

7. A simple random sample of size $n = 12$ is drawn from a population that is normally distributed. The sample mean is found to be $\bar{x} = 45$, and the sample standard deviation is found to be $s = 14$. Construct a 90% confidence interval for the population mean. *(37.74, 52.26)*

8. A simple random sample of size $n = 17$ is drawn from a population that is normally distributed. The sample mean is found to be $\bar{x} = 3.25$, and the sample standard deviation is found to be $s = 1.17$. Construct a 95% confidence interval for the population mean. *(2.65, 3.85)*

9. A simple random sample of size $n = 40$ is drawn from a population. The sample mean is found to be $\bar{x} = 120.5$, and the sample standard deviation is found to be $s = 12.9$. Construct a 99% confidence interval for the population mean. *(114.98, 126.02)*

10. A simple random sample of size $n = 210$ is drawn from a population. The sample mean is found to be $\bar{x} = 20.1$, and the sample standard deviation is found to be $s = 3.2$. Construct a 90% confidence interval for the population mean. *(19.73, 20.47)*

11. A simple random sample of size $n = 12$ is drawn from a population that is normally distributed. The sample variance is found to be $s^2 = 23.7$. Construct a 90% confidence interval for the population variance. *(13.25, 56.98)*

12. A simple random sample of size $n = 25$ is drawn from a population that is normally distributed. The sample variance is found to be $s^2 = 3.97$. Construct a 95% confidence interval for the population standard deviation. *(1.56, 2.77)*

Applying the Concepts

13. **Aggravated Assault** In a random sample of 40 felons convicted of aggravated assault, it was determined that the mean length of sentencing was 54 months, with a standard deviation of 8 months. Construct and interpret a 95% confidence interval for the mean length of sentence for an aggravated assault conviction.

    Source: Based on data from the U.S. Department of Justice. *(51.4, 56.6)*

14. **Click It** In a February 2007 Harris Poll, 881 of 1,013 randomly selected adults said that they always wear seat belts. Construct and interpret a 98% confidence interval for the proportion of adults who always wear seat belts. *(0.845, 0.895)*

15. **Estate Tax Returns** In a random sample of 100 estate tax returns that was audited by the Internal Revenue Service, it was determined that the mean amount of additional tax owed was $3,421. Assuming that the population standard deviation of the additional amount owed is $2,583, construct and interpret a 90% confidence interval for the mean additional amount of tax owed for estate tax returns. *($2996.1, $3845.9)*

16. **Muzzle Velocity** Fifty rounds of a new type of ammunition were fired from a test weapon, and the muzzle velocity of the projectile was measured. The sample had a mean muzzle velocity of 863 meters per second and a standard deviation of 2.7 meters per second. Construct and interpret a 99% confidence interval for the mean muzzle velocity. *(861.98, 864.02)*

17. **Worried about Retirement?** In a survey of 1,008 adult Americans conducted April 2–5, 2007, the Gallup organization asked, "Are you worried or not worried about having enough money for retirement?" Of the 1,008 surveyed, 567 stated that they were worried about having enough money for retirement. Construct a 90% confidence interval for the proportion of adult Americans who are worried about having enough money for retirement. *(0.537, 0.589)*

18. **Theme Park Spending** In a random sample of 40 visitors to a certain theme park, it was determined that the mean amount of money spent per person at the park (including ticket price) was $93.43 per day. Assuming that the population standard deviation of the amount spent per person is $15, construct and interpret a 95% confidence interval for the mean amount spent daily per person at the theme park. *($88.78, $98.08)*

In Problems 19–24, construct a 95% Z-interval or a 95% t-interval about the population mean. If neither can be constructed, state the reason why. For convenience, a normal probability plot and box-plot are given.

19. **Height of Males** The heights of 20- to 29-year-old males are known to have a population standard deviation of 2.9 inches.

A simple random sample of $n = 15$ males 20 to 29 years old results in the following data: *Z-Interval; (68.38, 71.32)*

65.5	72.3	68.2	65.6	68.8
66.7	69.6	72.6	72.9	67.5
71.8	73.8	70.7	67.9	73.9

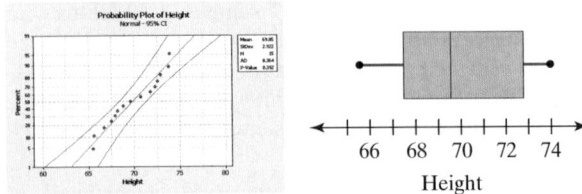

Height

20. Gestation Period The gestation period of humans has a population standard deviation of 16 days. A simple random sample of $n = 12$ live births results in the following data: *Z-Interval; (258.7, 276.8)*

266	270	277	278	258	275
261	260	270	269	252	277

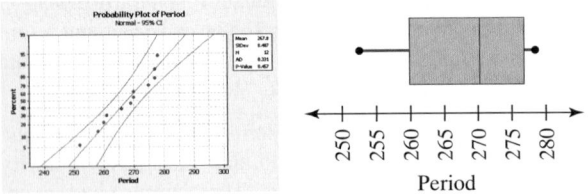

Period

21. Officer Friendly A police officer hides behind a billboard to catch speeders. The following data represent the number of minutes he waits before first observing a car that is exceeding the speed limit by more than 10 miles per hour on 10 randomly selected days: *Neither, outlier*

1.0	5.4	0.8	10.7	0.5
0.9	3.9	0.4	2.5	3.9

Time

22. M&Ms A quality-control engineer wanted to estimate the mean weight (in grams) of a random sample of 12 plain M&M candies. *t-Interval; (0.851, 0.894)*

0.87	0.88	0.82	0.90	0.86	0.86
0.84	0.84	0.91	0.94	0.88	0.87

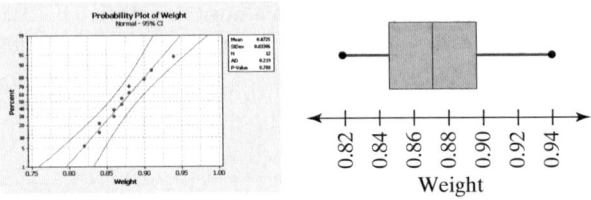

Weight

23. Pulse Fifteen randomly selected women were asked to work on a StairMaster for 3 minutes. After the 3 minutes, their pulses (in beats per minute) were measured and the following data were obtained: *t-Interval; (101.3, 117.3)*

117	102	98	100	116
113	91	92	96	136
134	126	104	113	102

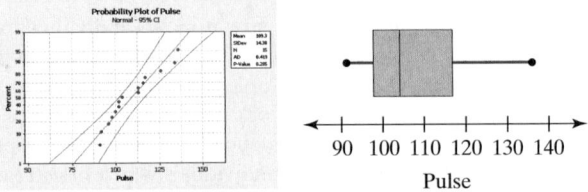

Pulse

24. Law Graduate Salaries A random sample of recent graduates of law school was obtained in which the graduates were asked to report their starting salary. The data, based on results reported by the National Association for Law Placement, are as follows: *Neither; nonnormal data*

54,400	115,000	132,000	45,000	137,500
60,500	56,250	63,500	125,000	47,250
47,000	160,000	112,500	78,000	58,000
142,000	46,500	57,000	55,000	115,000

Source: NALP *Bulletin*. "Salaries for New Lawyers: How Did We Get Here?" January, 2008.

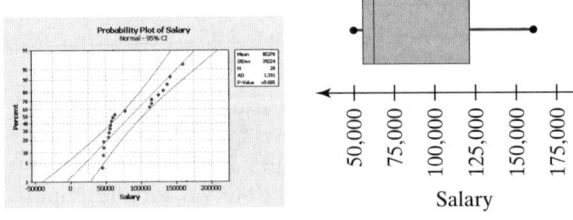

Salary

CHAPTER 9 REVIEW

Summary

In this chapter, we discussed estimation methods. We estimated the values of the parameters μ, p, and σ. We started by estimating the population mean under the assumption that the population standard deviation was known. This assumption allowed us to construct a confidence interval about μ by utilizing the standard normal distribution. To construct the interval, we required either that the population from which the sample was drawn be normal or that the sample size, n, be greater than or equal to 30. Also, the sampling method had to be simple random sampling. With these requirements satisfied, the $(1 - \alpha) \cdot 100\%$ confidence interval for μ is $\bar{x} \pm z_{\frac{\alpha}{2}} \cdot \dfrac{\sigma}{\sqrt{n}}$. We have $(1 - \alpha) \cdot 100\%$ confidence that the unknown value of μ lies within the interval.

In Section 9.2, we dropped the assumption that the population standard deviation be known. With σ unknown, the sampling distribution of $t = \dfrac{\bar{x} - \mu}{s/\sqrt{n}}$ follows Student's t-distribution with $n - 1$ degrees of freedom. We use the t-distribution to construct the confidence interval for μ. To construct this interval, either the population from which the sample was drawn must be normal or the sample size must be large. Also, the sampling method must be simple random sampling. With these requirements satisfied, the $(1 - \alpha) \cdot 100\%$ confidence interval for μ is $\bar{x} \pm t_{\alpha/2} \cdot \dfrac{s}{\sqrt{n}}$, where $t_{\alpha/2}$ has $n - 1$ degrees of freedom. This means that the procedure results in an interval that contains μ, the population mean, $(1 - \alpha) \cdot 100\%$ of the time.

In Section 9.3, a confidence interval for the population proportion, p, was constructed. This confidence interval is constructed for the binomial parameter p. Provided that the sample is obtained by simple random sampling, $n\hat{p}(1 - \hat{p}) \geq 10$, and the sample is less than 5% of the population size, the $(1 - \alpha) \cdot 100\%$ confidence interval about p is $\hat{p} \pm z_{\alpha/2} \cdot \sqrt{\dfrac{\hat{p}(1 - \hat{p})}{n}}$. We have $(1 - \alpha) \cdot 100\%$ confidence that the unknown value of p lies within the interval.

Finally, we introduced a method for estimating the population standard deviation. To perform this estimation, the population from which the sample is drawn must be normal, and the sampling method must be simple random sampling. If these requirements are satisfied, then $\chi^2 = \dfrac{(n - 1)s^2}{\sigma^2}$ follows cthe hi-square distribution with $n - 1$ degrees of freedom. The $(1 - \alpha) \cdot 100\%$ confidence interval about σ^2 is $\dfrac{(n - 1)s^2}{\chi^2_{\alpha/2}} < \sigma^2 < \dfrac{(n - 1)s^2}{\chi^2_{1-\alpha/2}}$. To construct the $(1 - \alpha) \cdot 100\%$ confidence interval for σ, we take the square root of each part of the inequality and obtain $\sqrt{\dfrac{(n - 1)s^2}{\chi^2_{\alpha/2}}} < \sigma < \sqrt{\dfrac{(n - 1)s^2}{\chi^2_{1-\alpha/2}}}$. We have $(1 - \alpha) \cdot 100\%$ confidence that the unknown value of σ lies within the interval.

Vocabulary

Point estimate (p. 457)
Confidence interval (p. 458)
Level of confidence (p. 458)
Margin of error (pp. 459, 465)

Critical value (p. 462)
Robust (p. 463)
Z-interval (p. 463)
Student's t-distribution (p. 476)

t-Interval (p. 479)
Nonparametric procedures (p. 482)
Chi-square distribution (p. 497)
Bootstrapping (p. 511)

Formulas

Confidence Intervals

- A $(1 - \alpha) \cdot 100\%$ confidence interval for μ with σ known is $\bar{x} \pm z_{\frac{\alpha}{2}} \cdot \dfrac{\sigma}{\sqrt{n}}$, provided that the population from which the sample was drawn is normal or that the sample size is large $(n \geq 30)$.

- A $(1 - \alpha) \cdot 100\%$ confidence interval for μ with σ unknown is $\bar{x} \pm t_{\frac{\alpha}{2}} \cdot \dfrac{s}{\sqrt{n}}$, where $t_{\alpha/2}$ has $n - 1$ degrees of freedom, provided that the population from which the sample was drawn is normal or that the sample size is large $(n \geq 30)$.

- A $(1 - \alpha) \cdot 100\%$ confidence interval for p is $\hat{p} \pm z_{\frac{\alpha}{2}} \cdot \sqrt{\dfrac{\hat{p}(1 - \hat{p})}{n}}$, provided that $n\hat{p}(1 - \hat{p}) \geq 10$ and $n \leq 0.05 N$.

- A $(1 - \alpha) \cdot 100\%$ confidence interval for σ^2 is $\dfrac{(n - 1)s^2}{\chi^2_{\alpha/2}} < \sigma^2 < \dfrac{(n - 1)s^2}{\chi^2_{1-\alpha/2}}$, where χ^2 has $n - 1$ degrees of freedom, provided that the population from which the sample was drawn is normal.

Sample Size

- To estimate the population mean within a margin of error E at a $(1 - \alpha) \cdot 100\%$ level of confidence requires a sample of size $n = \left(\dfrac{z_{\frac{\alpha}{2}} \cdot \sigma}{E} \right)^2$ (rounded up to the next integer).

- To estimate the population proportion within a margin of error E at a $(1 - \alpha) \cdot 100\%$ level of confidence requires a sample of size $n = \hat{p}(1 - \hat{p}) \left(\dfrac{z_{\frac{\alpha}{2}}}{E} \right)^2$ (rounded up to the next integer), where $\hat{p}$ is a prior estimate of the population proportion.

- To estimate the population proportion within a margin of error E at a $(1 - \alpha) \cdot 100\%$ level of confidence requires a sample of size $n = 0.25 \left(\dfrac{z_{\frac{\alpha}{2}}}{E} \right)^2$ (rounded up to the next integer) when no prior estimate is available.

Objectives

Section	You should be able to . . .	Examples	Review Exercises
9.1	**1** Compute a point estimate of the population mean (p. 457)	1	15(a)
	2 Construct and interpret a confidence interval for a population mean, assuming that the population standard deviation is known (p. 458)	2–4	9, 11(b), 11(c)
	3 Explain the role of margin of error in constructing a confidence interval (p. 465)	5 and 6	9(b), 9(c)
	4 Determine the sample size necessary for estimating the population mean within a specified margin of error (p. 466)	7	11(d)
9.2	**1** State the properties of Student's t-distribution (p. 476)	1	6–8
	2 Determine t-values (p. 478)	2	1
	3 Construct and interpret a confidence interval for a population mean (p. 479)	3–5	10(b), 10(c), 12(b), 13(b), 13(d), 14(b), 14(c), 15(c)
9.3	**1** Obtain a point estimate for the population proportion (p. 488)	1	16(a)
	2 Construct and interpret a confidence interval for the population proportion (p. 489)	2 and 3	16(b)
	3 Determine the sample size necessary for estimating a population proportion within a specified margin of error (p. 492)	4	16(c), 16(d)
9.4	**1** Find critical values for the chi-square distribution (p. 497)	1	2
	2 Construct and interpret confidence intervals for the population variance and standard deviation (p. 499)	2	10(d), 15(d)
9.5	**1** Determine the appropriate confidence interval to construct (p. 503)	1	9–16

4. 90% of samples result in intervals that include the unknown parameter.

10. (b) (98.86, 109.74); decreases

Review Exercises

1. Find the critical t-value for constructing a confidence interval for a population mean at the given level of confidence for the given sample size, n.
   (a) 99% confidence; $n = 18$ 2.898
   (b) 90% confidence; $n = 27$ 1.706

2. Find the critical values $\chi^2_{1-\alpha/2}$ and $\chi^2_{\alpha/2}$ required to construct a confidence interval for σ for the given level of confidence and sample size.
   (a) 95% confidence; $n = 22$ 10.283, 35.479
   (b) 99% confidence; $n = 12$ 2.603, 26.757

3. **IQ Scores** Many of the examples and exercises in the text have dealt with IQ scores. We now know that IQ scores based on the Stanford–Binet IQ test are normally distributed with a mean of 100 and standard deviation 15. If you were to obtain 100 different simple random samples of size 20 from the population of all adult humans and determine 95% confidence intervals for each of them, how many of the intervals would you expect to include 100? What causes a particular interval to not include 100?   95; chance in sampling

4. What does the 90% represent in a 90% confidence interval?

5. For what proportion of samples will a 90% confidence interval for a population mean not capture the true population mean?   10%

6. The area under the t-distribution with 18 degrees of freedom to the right of $t = 1.56$ is 0.0681. What is the area under the t-distribution with 18 degrees of freedom to the left of $t = -1.56$? Why?   0.0681

7. Which is larger, the area under the t-distribution with 10 degrees of freedom to the right of $t = 2.32$ or the area under the standard normal distribution to the right of $z = 2.32$? Why?
   t-distribution

8. State the properties of Student's t-distribution.

9. A simple random sample of size n is drawn from a population that is known to be normally distributed. The sample mean, $\bar{x}$, is determined to be 54.8.   9. (a) (50.94, 58.66)
   (a) Construct the 90% confidence interval for the population mean if the population standard deviation, σ, is known to be 10.5 and the sample size, n, is 20.
   (b) Construct the 90% confidence interval for the population mean if the population standard deviation, σ, is known to be 10.5 and the sample size, n, is 30. How does increasing the sample size affect the width of the interval?   (51.65, 57.95); decreases
   (c) Construct the 99% confidence interval for the population mean if the population standard deviation, σ, is known to be 10.5 and the sample size, n, is 20. Compare the results to those obtained in part (a). How does increasing the level of confidence affect the confidence interval?
   (48.75, 60.85); increases width

10. A simple random sample of size n is drawn from a population that is known to be normally distributed. The sample mean, $\bar{x}$, is determined to be 104.3 and the sample standard deviation, s, is determined to be 15.9.
    (a) Construct the 90% confidence interval for the population mean if the sample size, n, is 15.   (97.07, 111.53)
    (b) Construct the 90% confidence interval for the population mean if the sample size, n, is 25. How does increasing the sample size affect the width of the interval?
    (c) Construct the 95% confidence interval for the population mean if the sample size, n, is 15. Compare the results to those obtained in part (a). How does increasing the level of confidence affect the confidence interval?
    (d) Construct the 90% confidence interval for the population standard deviation if the sample size, n, is 15.
    (12.22, 23.21)   10. (c) (95.49; 113.11); increases width

11. **Tire Wear** Michelin wishes to estimate the mean mileage for its HydroEdge tire. In a random sample of 40 tires, the sample mean mileage was $\bar{x} = 100,294$.

(a) Why can we say that the sampling distribution of $\bar{x}$ is approximately normal? *Large sample*

(b) Construct a 90% confidence interval for the mean mileage for all HydroEdge tires, assuming that $\sigma = 4{,}600$ miles. Interpret this interval. *(99,098, 101,490)*

(c) Construct a 95% confidence interval for the mean mileage for all HydroEdge tires, assuming that $\sigma = 4{,}600$ miles. Interpret this interval. *(98,868, 101,720)*

(d) How many tires would Michelin require to estimate the mean mileage for all HydroEdge tires within 1,500 miles with 99% confidence? *63*

12. **E-mail** One question asked in the General Social Survey was this: "How many e-mails do you send in a day?" The results of 928 respondents indicate that the mean number of e-mails sent in a day is 10.4, with a standard deviation of 28.5.

(a) Given the fact that 1 standard deviation to the left of the mean results in a negative number of e-mails being sent, what shape would you expect the distribution of e-mails sent to have? *Skewed right*

(b) Construct and interpret a 90% confidence interval for the mean number of e-mails sent per day. *(8.86, 11.94)*

13. **Caffeinated Sports Drinks** Researchers conducted an experiment to determine the effectiveness of a commercial caffeinated carbohydrate–electrolyte sports drink compared with a placebo. Sixteen highly trained cyclists each completed trials of prolonged cycling in a warm environment, one while receiving the sports drink and another while receiving a placebo. For a given trial, one beverage treatment was administered throughout a 2-hour variable-intensity cycling bout followed by a 15-minute performance ride. Total work (in kilojoules) performed during the final 15 minutes was used to measure performance. The beverage order for individual subjects was randomly assigned with a period of at least five days separating the trials. Assume that the researchers verified the normality of the population of total work performed for each treatment.

Source: Kirk J. Cureton, Gordon L. Warren, et al., "Caffeinated Sports Drink: Ergogenic Effects and Possible Mechanisms." *International Journal of Sport Nutrition and Exercise Metabolism* 17(1):35–55, 2007

(a) Why do you think the sample size was small ($n = 16$) for this experiment?

(b) For the sports-drink treatment, the mean total work performed during the performance ride for the $n = 16$ riders was 218 kilojoules, with standard deviation 31 kilojoules. Construct and interpret a 95% confidence interval for the population mean total work performed. *(201.5, 234.5)*

(c) Is it possible for the population mean total work performed for the sports-drink treatment to be less than 198 kilojoules? Do you think this is likely? *Yes, no*

(d) For the placebo treatment, the mean total work performed during the performance ride for the $n = 16$ riders was 178 kilojoules, with standard deviation 31 kilojoules. Construct and interpret a 95% confidence interval for the population mean total work performed. *(161.5, 194.5)*

(e) Is it possible for the population mean total work performed for the placebo treatment to be more than 198 kilojoules? Do you think this is likely? *Yes, no*

(f) The researchers concluded that the caffeinated carbohydrate–electrolyte sports drink substantially enhanced physical performance during prolonged exercise compared with the placebo. Do your findings in parts (b) and (d) support the researchers' conclusion? Explain. *Yes*

14. **Family Size** A random sample of 60 married couples who have been married 7 years was asked the number of children they have. The results of the survey are as follows:

0	0	0	3	3	3	1	3	2	2	3	1
3	2	4	0	3	3	3	1	0	2	3	3
1	4	2	3	1	3	3	5	0	2	3	0
4	4	2	2	3	2	2	2	2	3	4	3
2	2	1	4	3	2	4	2	1	2	3	2

Note: $\bar{x} = 2.27$, $s = 1.22$.

(a) What is the shape of the distribution of the sample mean? Why? *Normal*

(b) Compute a 95% confidence interval for the mean number of children of all couples who have been married 7 years. Interpret this interval. *(1.95, 2.59)*

(c) Compute a 99% confidence interval for the mean number of children of all couples who have been married 7 years. Interpret this interval. *(1.85, 2.69)*

15. **Diameter of Douglas Fir Trees** The diameter of the Douglas fir tree is measured at a height of 1.37 meters. The following data represent the diameter in centimeters of a random sample of 12 Douglas firs in the western Washington Cascades.

156	190	147	173	159	181
162	130	101	147	113	109

Source: L. Winter. "Live Tree and Tree-Ring Records to Reconstruct the Structural Development of an Old-Growth Douglas Fir/Western Hemlock Stand in the Western Washington Cascades." Corvallis, OR: Forest Science Data Bank, 2005.

(a) Obtain a point estimate for the mean and standard deviation diameter of a Douglas fir tree in the western Washington Cascades. $\bar{x} = 147.3$, $s = 28.8$

(b) Because the sample size is small, we must verify that the data come from a population that is normally distributed and that the data do not contain any outliers. The figures show the normal probability plot and boxplot. Are the conditions for constructing a confidence interval for the population mean diameter satisfied? *Yes*

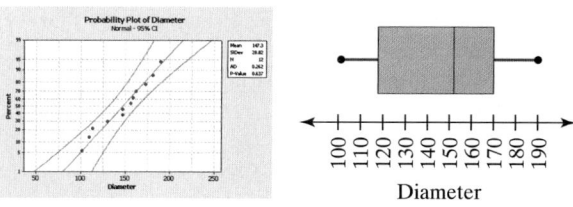

Diameter

(c) Construct a 95% confidence interval for the mean diameter of a Douglas fir tree in the western Washington Cascades. *(129.0, 165.6)*

(d) Construct a 95% confidence interval for the standard deviation diameter of a Douglas fir tree in the western Washington Cascades. *(20.4, 48.9)*

16. **Hypertension** In a random sample of 678 adult males 20 to 34 years of age, it was determined that 58 of them have hypertension (high blood pressure).

Source: The Centers for Disease Control.

(a) Obtain a point estimate for the proportion of adult males 20 to 34 years of age who have hypertension. *0.086*

(b) Construct a 95% confidence interval for the proportion of adult males 20 to 34 years of age who have hypertension. Interpret the confidence interval. *(0.065, 0.107)*

(c) You wish to conduct your own study to determine the proportion of adult males 20 to 34 years old who have hypertension. What sample size would be needed for the estimate to be within 3 percentage points with 95% confidence if you use the point estimate obtained in part (a)? _336_

(d) You wish to conduct your own study to determine the proportion of adult males 20 to 34 years old who have hypertension. What sample size would be needed for the estimate to be within 3 percentage points with 95% confidence if you don't have a prior estimate? _1068_

CHAPTER TEST

1. State the properties of the Student's t-distibution.

2. Find the critical t-value for constructing a confidence interval about a population mean at the given level of confidence for the given sample size, n.
   (a) 96% confidence; $n = 26$ _2.167_
   (b) 98% confidence; $n = 18$ _2.567_

3. Find the critical values $\chi^2_{1-\alpha/2}$ and $\chi^2_{\alpha/2}$ required to construct a confidence interval about σ for the given level of confidence and sample size.
   (a) 98% confidence; $n = 16$ _5.229, 30.578_
   (b) 90% confidence; $n = 30$ _17.708, 42.557_

4. Determine the point estimate of the population mean and margin of error if the confidence interval has lower bound: 125.8 and upper bound: 152.6 _$\bar{x} = 139.2, E = 13.4$_

5. Suppose that Motorola wishes to estimate the mean talk time for its V505 camera phone before the battery must be recharged. In a random sample of 35 phones, the sample mean talk time was 325 minutes.
   (a) Why can we say that the sampling distribution of the sample mean is approximately normal? _Large sample_
   (b) Construct a 94% confidence interval for the mean talk time for all Motorola V505 camera phones, assuming that $\sigma = 31$ minutes. Interpret this interval. _(315.1, 334.9)_
   (c) Construct a 98% confidence interval for the mean talk time for all Motorola V505 camera phones, assuming that $\sigma = 31$ minutes. Interpret this interval. _(312.8, 337.2)_
   (d) How many phones would Motorola need to test to estimate the mean talk time for all V505 camera phones within 5 minutes with 95% confidence? _148_

6. A question on the 2006 General Social Survey was this: "How many family members do you know that are in prison?" The results of 499 respondents indicate that the mean number of family members in jail is 1.22, with a standard deviation of 0.59.
   (a) What shape would you expect the distribution of this variable to have? Why? _Skewed right_
   (b) Construct and interpret a 99% confidence interval for the mean number of family members in jail. _(1.151, 1.289)_

7. A random sample of 50 recent college graduates results in a mean time to graduate of 4.58 years, with a standard deviation of 1.10 years.
   Source: Based on data from *The Toolbox Revisited* by Clifford Adelman, U.S. Department of Education
   (a) Compute and interpret a 90% confidence interval for time to graduate with a bachelor's degree. _(4.319, 4.841)_
   (b) Does this evidence contradict the widely held belief that it takes 4 years to complete a bachelor's degree? Why? _Yes_

8. The campus at Joliet Junior College has a lake. A student used a Secchi disk to measure the clarity of the lake's water by lowering the disk into the water and measuring the distance below the water surface at which the disk is no longer visible. The following measurements (in inches) were taken on the lake at various points in time over the course of a year.

82	64	62	66	68	43
38	26	68	56	54	66

Source: Virginia Piekarski, Joliet Junior College

8. (a) $\bar{x} = 57.8, s = 15.4$

(a) Use the data to compute a point estimate for the population mean and population standard deviation.
(b) Because the sample size is small, we must verify that the data are normally distributed and do not contain any outliers. The figures show the normal probability plot and boxplot. Are the conditions for constructing a confidence interval about μ satisfied? _Yes_

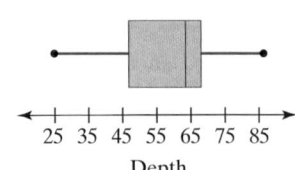

Depth

(c) Construct a 95% confidence interval for the mean Secchi disk measurement. Interpret this interval. _(48.0, 67.6)_
(d) Construct a 99% confidence interval for the mean Secchi disk measurement. Interpret this interval. _(44.0, 71.6)_
(e) Construct a 95% confidence interval for the population standard deviation Secchi disk measurement. Interpret this interval. _(10.9, 26.2)_

9. From a random sample of 1,201 Americans, it was discovered that 1,139 of them lived in neighborhoods with acceptable levels of carbon monoxide.
   Source: Environmental Protection Agency.
   (a) Obtain a point estimate for the proportion of Americans who live in neighborhoods with acceptable levels of carbon monoxide. _0.948_
   (b) Construct a 99% confidence interval for the proportion of Americans who live in neighborhoods with acceptable levels of carbon monoxide. _(0.932, 0.964)_
   (c) You wish to conduct your own study to determine the proportion of Americans who live in neighborhoods with acceptable levels of carbon monoxide. What sample size would be needed for the estimate to be within 1.5 percentage points with 90% confidence if you use the estimate obtained in part (a)? _593_
   (d) You wish to conduct your own study to determine the proportion of Americans who live in neighborhoods with acceptable levels of carbon monoxide. What sample size would be needed for the estimate to be within 1.5 percentage points with 90% confidence if you do not have a prior estimate? _3007_

▗▌MAKING AN
INFORMED DECISION

What's Your Major?

One of the most difficult decisions a person has to make while attending college is choosing a major field of study. This decision plays a huge role in the career path of the individual. The purpose of this project is to help you make a more informed decision regarding your major.

Randomly select people who have recently graduated in the major that you have chosen or randomly select individuals who have recently secured a job in a career that you are considering. If you have not yet chosen a major, select one that interests you. Create a survey that will allow you to make a more informed decision regarding your major field of study. Some suggested sample questions follow:

(a) What was your major in college?

(b) Does your job relate to your major?

(c) On average, how many hours do you work each week?

(d) Approximately how long (in weeks) did it take you to find your job?

(e) What was your starting annual salary?

(f) Are you satisfied or dissatisfied with your career?

(g) Do you believe you have job security?

(h) If you were to search for a job again, would you choose the same job?

Administer the survey. Be sure to explain the purpose of the survey and make it look professional. Because it is important that we obtain accurate results, make sure that the surveys are completed anonymously. We will treat the randomly selected individuals as a simple random sample.

Estimate the unknown parameter for each question asked. For example, in question (c), estimate the population "mean number of hours worked each week." In question (f), estimate the proportion of individuals satisfied with their career. Then construct 95% confidence intervals for each parameter. Write a report detailing your findings.

CASE STUDY

When Model Requirements Fail

In this chapter, we learned how to construct confidence intervals for population means, proportions, and standard deviations. For all three of these intervals, we needed to verify that certain requirements were satisfied prior to utilizing the techniques. For example, to estimate a population mean, we required that the sample size be large or the data come from a population that is normal with no outliers. To estimate a population proportion, we required that $n\hat{p}(1 - \hat{p}) \geq 10$ so that we could use the normal model. But what if these requirements are not satisfied? Is there anything we can do to estimate the parameter? Fortunately, the answer is yes. In this Case Study we will look at methods that can be used to estimate the population mean and proportion when the model requirements are not satisfied. We start with methods for estimating the population mean.

Bootstrapping to Estimate the Population Mean

Suppose that we wish to estimate a population mean, but the sample data come from a population that is not normal, and increasing the sample size so that we can utilize the Central Limit Theorem is not possible. **Bootstrapping** is sampling with replacement from a sample that is representative of the population whose parameters we wish to estimate. The name *bootstrapping* comes from the phrase "to pull up by your own bootstraps." It is said that this phrase comes from the Baron Münchhausen, who claimed to escape from a muddy swamp by pulling his boots up by their straps. Essentially, the phrase has come to mean that one should use whatever resources one has to solve a problem. The bootstrap method was invented by Brad Efron of Stanford University in 1979. Follow parts (a) through (i) to work through the bootstrap method. You will need to use Excel to do this problem.

The idea behind the bootstrap method is to obtain many random samples with replacement from the sample data. We then compute the mean of each random sample. For a 95% confidence interval, we find the cutoff points for the middle 95% of the sample means. That is, we find the 2.5th and 97.5th percentiles. These cutoff points represent the lower and upper bounds of the confidence interval.

The survival time, in years, of patients with a rare disease are listed in the table.

1.0	0.7	0.6	0.5
0.3	1.4	3.1	0.2

(a) To use the t-distribution to obtain a confidence interval for the mean, we require that the data come from a population that is normal (because we have a small sample size) and that the data have no outliers. Verify that 3.1 is an outlier.

(b) Open an Excel spreadsheet and enter the sample above in rows 1 and 2 and columns A through D.

(c) Now we need to sample with replacement from our sample data. To do so, enter the following in cell A4:

=index(a1:d2,rows(a1:d2)*rand()+1,columns(a1:d2)*rand()+1)

Copy the contents in cell A4 to cells B4 through H4 (because the size of the original sample is $n = 8$, each of our resamples will also have $n = 8$ observations). This creates the first random sample with replacement of size $n = 8$. Copy the contents in cell A4 through H4 to cells A5:H5 through A203:H203. You now have 200 random samples with replacement of size $n = 8$.

(d) Determine the mean of each of the 200 random samples by entering

=average(A4:H4)

into cell J4. Copy cell J4 into cells J5 through J203. You now have 200 sample means.

(e) We want to find the middle $(1 - \alpha)100\%$ of the data. Enter the level of confidence (as a decimal) into cell L1. In cell L2, enter=1 – L1 to get the value of α. Then enter the following into cell L3 to determine the number of sample means:

=count(J4:J203)

(f) Find the lower bound. For example, if the level of confidence is 95%, the lower bound will be the cutoff point that separates the bottom 2.5% of the data from the top 97.5 of the data. To do so, enter the following into cell L4:

=small(J4:J203,L2/2*L3)

(g) Find the upper bound. For example, if the level of confidence is 95%, the upper bound will be the cutoff point that separates the bottom 97.5% of the data from the top 2.5% of the data. To do so, enter the following into cell L5:

=small(J4:J203,(1-L2/2)*L3)

Interpret your confidence interval.

Note: If you move the cursor to an empty cell and press the "delete" key, a new set of random numbers is generated. Generate a new sample and new bounds. How do the lower and upper bound change? ◀

(h) What could be done to increase the precision of the confidence intervals?

(i) The following data represent the age (in months) at which a random sample of 8 babies first talk (words such as "mama" or "dada")

6	5.5	7	8
6.5	5	4.5	7

Construct a 95% confidence interval using the *t*-distribution. Now construct a confidence interval using the bootstrap method. Compare the two.

Note: We obtained 200 resamples, but you can adjust the Excel spreadsheet to obtain as many resamples as you like (within spreadsheet limits). ◄

Estimating the Population Proportion When the Normality Requirement Is Not Satisfied

(j) To construct a confidence interval about a population proportion using the normal model, we require that $np(1 - p) \geq 10$. What are the consequences if this requirement is not satisfied?

(k) Using MINITAB or some other statistical software, generate 100 Bernoulli samples of size $n = 20$ with $p = 0.15$. Construct a 95% confidence interval for each of the 100 Bernoulli samples using the normal model. What proportion of the intervals do you expect to include the population proportion, 0.15? What proportion of the intervals actually captures the population proportion? Why do we obtain unexpected results?

(l) To deal with issues such as the one encountered in part (h), A. Agresti and B. Coull ("Approximate Is Better Than 'Exact' for Interval Estimation of Binomial Proportion." *American Statistician*, 52:119–126, 1998) proposed a modified approach. A $(1 - \alpha)100\%$ confidence interval is given by

$$\text{Lower bound:} \tilde{p} - z_{\frac{\alpha}{2}}\sqrt{\frac{\tilde{p}(1 - \tilde{p})}{n + 4}} \qquad \text{Upper Bound:} \tilde{p} + z_{\frac{\alpha}{2}}\sqrt{\frac{\tilde{p}(1 - \tilde{p})}{n + 4}}$$

where $\quad \tilde{p} = \dfrac{x + 2}{n + 4}$

In other words, add two to the number of successes and 4 to the number of trials (which amounts to also adding 2 to the number of failures).

1. Jane wants to estimate the proportion of students on her campus who eat cauliflower. After surveying 10 students, she finds 1 who eats cauliflower. Obtain and interpret a 95% confidence interval for the proportion of students who eat cauliflower on Jane's campus using Agresti and Coull's method.

2. Alan wants to estimate the proportion of adults who walk to work. In a survey of 12 adults, he finds 0 walk to work. Explain why a standard 95% confidence interval yields silly results. Compute and interpret a 95% confidence interval for the proportion of adults who walk to work using Agresti and Coull's method.

10 Hypothesis Tests Regarding a Parameter

Outline

10.1 The Language of Hypothesis Testing

10.2 Hypothesis Tests for a Population Mean—Population Standard Deviation Known

10.3 Hypothesis Tests for a Population Mean—Population Standard Deviation Unknown

10.4 Hypothesis Tests for a Population Proportion

10.5 Hypothesis Tests for a Population Standard Deviation

10.6 Putting It Together: Which Method Do I Use?

10.7 The Probability of a Type II Error and the Power of the Test

MAKING AN INFORMED DECISION

Many of the products we buy have labels that indicate the net weight of the contents. For example, a candy bar wrapper might state that the net weight of the candy bar is 4 ounces. Should we believe the manufacturer? See the Making an Informed Decision project on page 579.

PUTTING IT TOGETHER

In Chapter 9, we mentioned that there are two types of inferential statistics: (1) estimation and (2) hypothesis testing. We have already discussed procedures for estimating the population mean, the population proportion, and the population standard deviation.

We now focus our attention on hypothesis testing. Hypothesis testing is used to test statements regarding a characteristic of one or more populations. In this chapter, we will test hypotheses regarding a single population parameter. The hypotheses that we test concern the population mean, the population proportion, and the population standard deviation.

10.1 THE LANGUAGE OF HYPOTHESIS TESTING

Preparing for This Section Before getting started, review the following:

- Parameter versus statistic (Section 1.1, p. 5)
- Simple random sampling (Section 1.3, pp. 23–27)
- Table 9 (Section 6.2, p. 347)
- Sampling distribution of $\bar{x}$ (Section 8.1, pp. 427–438)

Objectives
1. Determine the null and alternative hypotheses
2. Explain Type I and Type II errors
3. State conclusions to hypothesis tests

We begin with an example.

EXAMPLE 1   **Is Your Friend Cheating You?**

Problem: A friend of yours wants to play a simple game in which a coin is flipped. If the coin comes up heads, you win; if it comes up tails, your friend wins. Suppose that the outcome of five plays of the game is T, T, T, T, T. Is your friend cheating you?

Approach: To determine whether your friend is cheating, we need to determine the likelihood of obtaining five tails in a row. To determine this likelihood, we assume that the coin is fair so that $P(\text{tail}) = P(\text{head}) = {}^1/_2$ and the flips of the coin are independent. Then we ask, "Is it unusual to obtain five tails in a row with a fair coin?"

Solution: We will determine the probability of obtaining five tails in a row, assuming that the coin is fair. The flips of the coin are independent, so

$$
\begin{aligned}
P(\text{five tails in a row}) &= P(\text{T and T and T and T and T}) \\
&= P(\text{T}) \cdot P(\text{T}) \cdot P(\text{T}) \cdot P(\text{T}) \cdot P(\text{T}) \\
&= \frac{1}{2} \cdot \frac{1}{2} \cdot \frac{1}{2} \cdot \frac{1}{2} \cdot \frac{1}{2} \\
&= \left(\frac{1}{2}\right)^5 \\
&= 0.03125
\end{aligned}
$$

Note to Instructor

If you like, you can print out and distribute the Preparing for This Section quiz located in the Instructor's Resource Center. The purpose of the quiz is to verify that the students have the prerequisite knowledge for the section.

Note to Instructor

Before starting this section, divide your students into groups. Each group should define the following (along with the symbolic representation): population mean, sample mean, population standard deviation, sample standard deviation, and standard error of the mean.

Note to Instructor

We intentionally do not answer the question as to whether the friend actually is cheating. This can form a basis for classroom discussion. Survey the class to determine who is willing to accuse his or her friend of cheating. Plus, address the fact that, in reality, we will not know for sure the friend is (or is not) cheating.

If we flipped a *fair* coin 5 times 100 different times, we would expect about 3 of the 100 experiments to result in all tails. So, what we observed is possible, but it is not likely. You can come to one of two conclusions:

1. Your friend is not cheating you and happens to be lucky.

2. Your friend is not using a fair coin (i.e., the probability of obtaining a tail is greater than ${}^1/_2$) and is cheating you.

Are you willing to accuse your friend of cheating, or did you just happen to experience an unusual result from a fair coin?

This is at the heart of *hypothesis testing*. We make an assumption about reality (in this case, the probability of obtaining a tail is ${}^1/_2$). We then look at (or gather) sample evidence to determine whether it contradicts our assumption.

❶ Determine the Null and Alternative Hypotheses

What is a *hypothesis*? According to *dictionary.com*, a **hypothesis** is a proposition assumed as a premise in an argument. The word hypothesis comes from the Greek word *hypotithenai*, which means "to suppose." We present the definition of *hypothesis* in a statistical setting next.

Definition

A **hypothesis** is a statement regarding a characteristic of one or more populations.

In this chapter, we look at hypotheses regarding a single population parameter. Consider the following:

(A) According to a Gallup poll conducted in 1995, 74% of Americans felt that men were more aggressive than women. A researcher wonders if the percentage of Americans that feel men are more aggressive than women is different today (a statement regarding a population proportion).

(B) The packaging on a light bulb states that the bulb will last 500 hours under normal use. A consumer advocate would like to know if the mean lifetime of a bulb is less than 500 hours (a statement regarding the population mean).

(C) The standard deviation of the rate of return for a certain class of mutual funds is 0.08. A mutual fund manager believes the standard deviation of the rate of return for his fund is less than 0.08 (a statement regarding the population standard deviation).

We test these types of statements using sample data, because it is usually impossible or impractical to gain access to the entire population. The procedure (or process) that we use to test such statements is called *hypothesis testing*.

> ◆**CAUTION** If population data are available, there is no need for inferential statistics.

Definition

Hypothesis testing is a procedure, based on sample evidence and probability, used to test statements regarding a characteristic of one or more populations.

The basic steps in conducting a hypothesis test are these:

> **Steps in Hypothesis Testing**
> 1. A statement is made regarding the nature of the population.
> 2. Evidence (sample data) is collected to test the statement.
> 3. The data are analyzed to assess the plausibility of the statement.

Note to Instructor
Emphasize that sample data cannot prove that a hypothesis is true.

Because we use sample data to test hypotheses, we cannot state with 100% certainty that the statement is true; we can only determine whether the sample data support the statement or not. In fact, because the statement can be either true or false, hypothesis testing is based on two types of hypotheses.

Definitions

The **null hypothesis**, denoted H_0 (read "H-naught"), is a statement to be tested. The null hypothesis is a statement of no change, no effect, or no difference. The null hypothesis is assumed true until evidence indicates otherwise. In this chapter, it will be a statement regarding the value of a population parameter.

The **alternative hypothesis**, denoted H_1 (read "H-one"), is a statement that we are trying to find evidence to support. In this chapter, it will be a statement regarding the value of a population parameter.

In Other Words
The null hypothesis is a statement of status quo or no difference and always contains a statement of equality. The null hypothesis is assumed to be true until we have evidence to the contrary. We seek evidence that supports the statement in the alternative hypothesis.

In this chapter, there are three ways to set up the null and alternative hypotheses.

1. Equal hypothesis versus not equal hypothesis **(two-tailed test)**
   H_0: parameter = some value
   H_1: parameter ≠ some value

2. Equal versus less than (**left-tailed test**)

H_0: parameter = some value

H_1: parameter < some value

3. Equal versus greater than (**right-tailed test**)

H_0: parameter = some value

H_1: parameter > some value

Left- and right-tailed tests are referred to as **one-tailed tests**. Notice that in the left-tailed test the direction of the inequality sign in the alternative hypothesis points to the left ($<$), while in the right-tailed test the direction of the inequality sign in the alternative hypothesis points to the right ($>$). In all three tests, the null hypothesis contains a statement of equality.

Refer to the three hypotheses made on page 516. In Situation A, the null hypothesis would be expressed using the notation H_0: $p = 0.74$. This is a statement of *status quo* or no difference. The Latin phrase *status quo* means "the existing state or condition." So, the statement in the null hypothesis means that American opinions have not changed from 1995. We are trying to show that the proportion is different today, so the alternative hypothesis is H_1: $p \neq 0.74$. In Situation B, the null hypothesis is H_0: $\mu = 500$. This is a statement of no difference between the population mean and the lifetime stated on the label. We are trying to show that the mean lifetime is less than 500 hours, so the alternative hypothesis is H_1: $\mu < 500$. In Situation C, the null hypothesis is H_0: $\sigma = 0.08$. This is a statement of no difference between the population standard deviation rate of return of the manager's mutual fund and all mutual funds. The alternative hypothesis is H_1: $\sigma < 0.08$. Do you see why?

The statement we are trying to gather evidence for, which is dictated by the researcher before any data are collected, determines the structure of the alternative hypothesis (two-tailed, left-tailed, or right-tailed). For example, the label on a can of soda states that the can contains 12 ounces of liquid. A consumer advocate would be concerned only if the mean contents are less than 12 ounces, so the alternative hypothesis is H_1: $\mu < 12$. However, a quality-control engineer for the soda manufacturer would be concerned if there is too little or too much soda in the can, so the alternative hypothesis would be H_1: $\mu \neq 12$. In both cases, however, the null hypothesis is a statement of no difference between the manufacturer's assertion on the label and the actual mean contents of the can, so the null hypothesis is H_0: $\mu = 12$.

| EXAMPLE 2 | **Forming Hypotheses** |

In-Class Discussion

Ask students to explain why the alternative in Example 2(a) is $p > 0.02$, rather than $p \neq 0.02$. Ask similar questions for (b) and (c). When would a researcher use a $\neq$ alternative instead of $>$ or $<$? Answer: when he or she is not sure of the direction of the alternative.

In Other Words

Structuring the null and alternative hypotheses:

1. Identify the parameter to be tested.

2. Determine the status quo value of the parameter.

3. Determine the statement that reflects what we are trying to gather evidence for.

Problem: Determine the null and alternative hypotheses. State whether the test is two-tailed, left-tailed, or right-tailed.

(a) The Medco pharmaceutical company has just developed a new antibiotic for children. Among the competing antibiotics, 2% of children who take the drug experience headaches as a side effect. A researcher for the Food and Drug Administration wishes to know if the percentage of children taking the new antibiotic who experience headaches as a side effect is more than 2%.

(b) The *Blue Book* value of a used 3-year-old Chevy Corvette is $37,500. Grant wonders if the mean price of a used 3-year-old Chevy Corvette in the Miami metropolitan area is different from $37,500.

(c) The standard deviation of the contents in a 64-ounce bottle of detergent using an old filling machine was known to be 0.23 ounce. The company purchased a new filling machine and wants to know if there is less variability with the new filling machine.

Approach: In each case, we must determine the parameter to be tested. We then determine the statement of no change or no difference (status quo), and finally we identify the statement we are attempting to gather evidence for.

Solution

(a) The hypothesis deals with a population proportion, p. If the new drug is no different from current drugs on the market, the proportion of individuals taking the new drug who experience a headache will be 0.02, so the null hypothesis is $H_0: p = 0.02$. We are trying to determine if the proportion of individuals who experience a headache is "more than" 0.02. Therefore, the alternative hypothesis is $H_1: p > 0.02$. This is a right-tailed test because the alternative hypothesis contains a $>$ symbol.

(b) The hypothesis deals with a population mean, μ. If the mean price of a 3-year-old Corvette in Miami is no different from the *Blue Book* price, then the population mean in Miami will be $37,500, so the null hypothesis is $H_0: \mu = 37,500$. Grant wishes to determine if the mean price is different from $37,500, so the alternative hypothesis is $H_1: \mu \neq 37,500$. This is a two-tailed test because the alternative hypothesis contains a $\neq$ symbol.

(c) The hypothesis deals with a population standard deviation, σ. If the new machine is no different from the old machine, the standard deviation of the amount in the bottles filled by the new machine will be 0.23 ounce, so the null hypothesis is $H_0: \sigma = 0.23$. The company wants to know if the new machine has *less* variability than the old machine, so the alternative hypothesis is $H_1: \sigma < 0.23$. This is a left-tailed test because the alternative hypothesis contains a $<$ symbol.

Now Work Problem 17(a)

In Other Words

Look for key phrases when forming the alternative hypothesis. For example, *more than means* $>$; *different from means* $\neq$; *less than means* $<$; and so on. See Table 9 on page 347 for a list of key phrases and the symbols they translate into.

In Other Words

When you are testing a hypothesis, there is always the possibility that your conclusion will be wrong. To make matters worse, you won't know whether you are wrong or not! Don't fret, however; we have tools to help manage these incorrect conclusions.

2 Explain Type I and Type II Errors

As stated earlier, we use sample data to determine whether to reject or not reject the statement in the null hypothesis. Because the decision to reject or not reject the null hypothesis is based on incomplete (sample) information, there is always the possibility of making an incorrect decision. In fact, there are four possible outcomes from hypothesis testing.

Four Outcomes from Hypothesis Testing

1. We reject the null hypothesis when the alternative hypothesis is true. This decision would be correct.

2. We do not reject the null hypothesis when the null hypothesis is true. This decision would be correct.

3. We reject the null hypothesis when the null hypothesis is true. This decision would be incorrect. This type of error is called a **Type I error**.

4. We do not reject the null hypothesis when the alternative hypothesis is true. This decision would be incorrect. This type of error is called a **Type II error**.

Note to Instructor

Discuss the idea of a false positive or false negative as it relates to Type I and Type II errors.

Figure 1 illustrates the two types of errors that can be made in hypothesis testing.

Figure 1

Conclusion		Reality	
		H_0 Is True	H_1 Is True
	Do Not Reject H_0	Correct Conclusion	Type II Error
	Reject H_0	Type I Error	Correct Conclusion

Note to Instructor

Discuss the difference between 'beyond all reasonable doubt' and 'beyond all doubt', and how this relates to hypothesis testing.

We illustrate the idea of Type I and Type II errors by looking at hypothesis testing from the point of view of a criminal trial. In any trial, the defendant is assumed to be innocent. (We give the defendant the benefit of the doubt.) The district attorney must collect and present evidence proving that the defendant is guilty beyond all reasonable doubt.

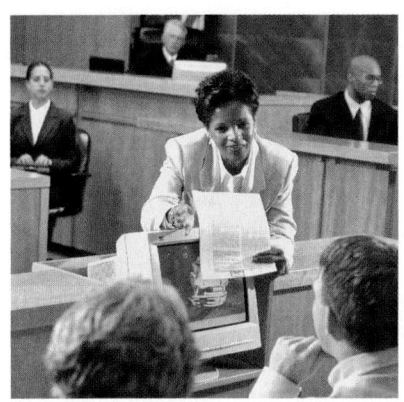

Because we are seeking evidence for guilt, it becomes the alternative hypothesis. Innocence is assumed, so it is the null hypothesis. The hypotheses for a trial are written

$$H_0: \text{the defendant is innocent}$$
$$H_1: \text{the defendant is guilty}$$

The trial is the process whereby the jury obtains information (sample data). The jury then deliberates about the evidence (the data analysis). Finally, the jury either convicts the defendant (rejects the null hypothesis) or declares the defendant not guilty (fails to reject the null hypothesis).

Note that the defendant is never declared innocent. That is, we never conclude that the null hypothesis is true. Using this analogy, the two correct decisions are to conclude that an innocent person is not guilty or conclude that a guilty person is guilty. The two incorrect decisions are to convict an innocent person (a Type I error) or to let a guilty person go free (a Type II error). It is helpful to think in this way when trying to remember the difference between a Type I and a Type II error.

In Other Words

A Type I error is like putting an innocent person in jail. A Type II error is like letting a guilty person go free.

EXAMPLE 3 | **Type I and Type II Errors**

Problem: The Medco pharmaceutical company has just developed a new antibiotic. Among the competing antibiotics, 2% of children who take the drug experience headaches as a side effect. A researcher for the Food and Drug Administration wishes to know if the percentage of children taking the new antibiotic who experience a headache as a side effect is more than 2%. The researcher conducts a hypothesis test with $H_0: p = 0.02$ and $H_1: p > 0.02$. Provide statements explaining what it would mean to make (a) a Type I error and (b) a Type II error.

Approach: A Type I error occurs if the null hypothesis is rejected when, in fact, the null hypothesis is true. A Type II error occurs if the null hypothesis is not rejected when, in fact, the alternative hypothesis is true.

Solution

(a) A Type I error is made if the sample evidence leads the researcher to believe that $p > 0.02$ (that is, we reject the null hypothesis) when, in fact, the proportion of children who experience a headache is not greater than 0.02.

(b) A Type II error is made if the researcher does not reject the null hypothesis that the proportion of children experiencing a headache is equal to 0.02 when, in fact, the proportion of children who experience a headache is more than 0.02. In other words, the sample evidence led the researcher to believe $p = 0.02$ when in fact the true proportion is some value larger than 0.2.

Now Work Problems 17(b) and (c)

The Probability of Making a Type I or Type II Error

Recall from Chapter 9 that we never know whether or not a confidence interval contains the unknown parameter. We only know the likelihood that a confidence interval captures the parameter. Similarly, we never know whether or not the conclusion of a hypothesis test is correct. However, just as we place a level of confidence in the construction of a confidence interval, we can determine the probability of making errors when testing hypotheses. The following notation is commonplace:

$$\alpha = P(\text{Type I error}) = P(\text{rejecting } H_0 \text{ when } H_0 \text{ is true})$$
$$\beta = P(\text{Type II error}) = P(\text{not rejecting } H_0 \text{ when } H_1 \text{ is true})$$

The symbol β is the Greek letter beta (pronounced "BAY tah"). The probability of making a Type I error, α, is chosen by the researcher *before* the sample data are collected. This probability is referred to as the *level of significance*.

Definition   The **level of significance**, α, is the probability of making a Type I error.

The choice of the level of significance depends on the consequences of making a Type I error. If the consequences are severe, the level of significance should be small (say, $\alpha = 0.01$). However, if the consequences of making a Type I error are not severe, a higher level of significance can be chosen (say $\alpha = 0.05$ or $\alpha = 0.10$).

Why is the level of significance not always set at $\alpha = 0.01$? By reducing the probability of making a Type I error, you increase the probability of making a Type II error, β. Using our court analogy, a jury is instructed that the prosecution must provide proof of guilt "beyond all reasonable doubt." This implies that we are choosing to make α small so that the probability of sending an innocent person to jail is very small. The consequence of the small α, however, is a large β, which means many guilty defendants will go free. For now, we are content to recognize the inverse relation between α and β (as one goes up the other goes down).

In Other Words
As the probability of a Type I error increases, the probability of a Type II error decreases, and vice versa.

 We never *accept* the null hypothesis, because, without having access to the entire population, we don't know the exact value of the parameter stated in the null hypothesis. Rather, we say that we do not reject the null hypothesis. This is just like the court system. We never declare a defendant innocent, but rather say the defendant is not guilty.

③ State Conclusions to Hypothesis Tests

Once the decision to reject or not reject the null hypothesis is made, the researcher must state his or her conclusion. It is important to recognize that we never *accept* the null hypothesis. Again, the court system analogy helps to illustrate the idea. The null hypothesis is H_0: innocent. When the evidence presented to the jury is not enough to convict beyond all reasonable doubt, the jury comes back with a verdict of "not guilty."

Notice that the verdict does not state that the null hypothesis of innocence is true; it states that there is not enough evidence to conclude guilt. This is a huge difference. Being told that you are not guilty is very different from being told that you are innocent!

So, sample evidence can never prove the null hypothesis to be true. When we do not reject the null hypothesis, we are saying that the evidence indicates that the null hypothesis *could* be true. That is, there is not enough evidence to reject our assumption that the null hypothesis is true.

EXAMPLE 4   **Stating the Conclusion**

Problem: The Medco pharmaceutical company has just developed a new antibiotic. Among the competing antibiotics, 2% of children who take the drug experience a headache as a side effect. A researcher for the Food and Drug Administration believes that the proportion of children taking the new antibiotic who experience a headache as a side effect is more than 0.02. From Example 2(a), we know the null hypothesis is H_0: $p = 0.02$ and the alternative hypothesis is H_1: $p > 0.02$.

(a) Suppose that the sample evidence indicates that the null hypothesis is rejected. State the conclusion.

(b) Suppose that the sample evidence indicates that the null hypothesis is not rejected. State the conclusion.

Approach: When the null hypothesis is rejected, we say that there is sufficient evidence to support the statement in the alternative hypothesis. When the null hypothesis is not rejected, we say that there is not sufficient evidence to support the statement in the alternative hypothesis. We never say that the null hypothesis is true!

Solution

(a) The statement in the alternative hypothesis is that the proportion of children taking the new antibiotic who experience a headache as a side effect is more than 0.02. Because the null hypothesis ($p = 0.02$) is rejected, we conclude that there is sufficient evidence to conclude that the proportion of children who experience a headache as a side effect is more than 0.02.

(b) Because the null hypothesis is not rejected, we conclude that there is not sufficient evidence to say that the proportion of children who experience a headache as a side effect is more than 0.02. Put another way, the sample evidence is consistent with a population proportion of children who experience a headache as a side effect equaling 0.02.

Now Work Problem 25

10.1 ASSESS YOUR UNDERSTANDING

Concepts and Vocabulary

1. Explain what it means to make a Type I error. Explain what it means to make a Type II error.

2. If the consequences of making a Type I error are severe, would you choose the level of significance, α, to equal 0.01, 0.05, or 0.10? Why?

3. What happens to the probability of making a Type II error, β, as the level of significance, α, decreases? Why is this result intuitive?

4. If a hypothesis is tested at the $\alpha = 0.05$ level of significance, what is the probability of making a Type I error?

5. The following is a quotation from Sir Ronald A. Fisher, a famous statistician.

    For the logical fallacy of believing that a hypothesis has been proved true, merely because it is not contradicted by the available facts, has no more right to insinuate itself in statistics than in other kinds of scientific reasoning.... It would, therefore, add greatly to the clarity with which the tests of significance are regarded if it were generally understood that tests of significance, when used accurately, are capable of rejecting or invalidating hypotheses, in so far as they are contradicted by the data: but that they are never capable of establishing them as certainly true....

    In your own words, explain what this quotation means.

6. In your own words, explain the difference between "beyond all reasonable doubt" and "beyond all doubt."

7. *True or False*: Sample evidence can prove that a null hypothesis is true. False

8. *True or False*: Type I and Type II errors are independent events. False

Skill Building

In Problems 9–14, the null and alternative hypotheses are given. Determine whether the hypothesis test is left-tailed, right-tailed, or two-tailed. What parameter is being tested?

9. $H_0: \mu = 5$ Right-tailed, μ
   $H_1: \mu > 5$

10. $H_0: p = 0.2$ Left-tailed, p
    $H_1: p < 0.2$

11. $H_0: \sigma = 4.2$ Two-tailed, σ
    $H_1: \sigma \neq 4.2$

12. $H_0: p = 0.76$ Right-tailed, p
    $H_1: p > 0.76$

13. $H_0: \mu = 120$ Left-tailed, μ
    $H_1: \mu < 120$

14. $H_0: \sigma = 7.8$ Two-tailed, σ
    $H_1: \sigma \neq 7.8$

In Problems 15–22, (a) determine the null and alternative hypotheses, (b) explain what it would mean to make a Type I error, and (c) explain what it would mean to make a Type II error.

15. **Teenage Mothers** According to the U.S. Census Bureau, 10.2% of registered births in the United States in 2005 were to teenage mothers. A sociologist believes that this percentage has increased since then. $H_0: p = 0.102$; $H_1: p > 0.102$

16. **Charitable Contributions** According to *Giving and Volunteering in the United States, 2001 Edition*, the mean charitable contribution per household in the United States in 2000 was $1,623. A researcher believes that the level of giving has changed since then. $H_0: \mu = \$1,623$; $H_1: \mu \neq \$1,623$

17. **Single-Family Home Price** According to the Federal Housing Finance Board, the mean price of a single-family home in 2005 was $299,800. A real estate broker believes that because of the recent credit crunch, the mean price has decreased since then. $H_0: \mu = \$299,800$; $H_1: \mu < \$299,800$

18. **Fair Packaging and Labeling** Federal law requires that a jar of peanut butter that is labeled as containing 32 ounces must contain at least 32 ounces. A consumer advocate feels that a certain peanut butter manufacturer is shorting customers by underfilling the jars. $H_0: \mu = 32$ ounces; $H_1: \mu < 32$ ounces

19. **Valve Pressure** The standard deviation in the pressure required to open a certain valve is known to be $\sigma = 0.7$ psi. Due to changes in the manufacturing process, the quality-control manager feels that the pressure variability has been reduced. $H_0: \sigma = 0.7$ psi; $H_1: \sigma < 0.7$ psi

20. **Overweight** According to the Centers for Disease Control and Prevention, 16% of children aged 6 to 11 years are overweight. A school nurse thinks that the percentage of 6- to 11-year-olds who are overweight is higher in her school district. $H_0: p = 0.16$; $H_1: p > 0.16$

21. **Cell Phone Service** According to the *CTIA–The Wireless Association*, the mean monthly cell phone bill was $49.94 in 2007. A researcher suspects that the mean monthly cell phone bill is different today. $H_0: \mu = \$49.94$; $H_1: \mu \neq \$49.94$

22. **SAT Math Scores** In 2007, the standard deviation SAT score on the Reasoning Test for all students taking the exam was 113. A teacher believes that, due to changes to high school curricula, the standard deviation of SAT math scores has decreased. $H_0: \sigma = 113$; $H_1: \sigma < 113$

In Problems 23–34, state the conclusion based on the results of the test.

23. For the hypotheses in Problem 15, the null hypothesis is rejected.

24. For the hypotheses in Problem 16, the null hypothesis is not rejected.

25. For the hypotheses in Problem 17, the null hypothesis is not rejected.

26. For the hypotheses in Problem 18, the null hypothesis is rejected.

27. For the hypotheses in Problem 19, the null hypothesis is not rejected.

28. For the hypotheses in Problem 20, the null hypothesis is not rejected.

29. For the hypotheses in Problem 21, the null hypothesis is rejected.

30. For the hypotheses in Problem 22, the null hypothesis is not rejected.

31. For the hypotheses in Problem 15, the null hypothesis is not rejected.

32. For the hypotheses in Problem 16, the null hypothesis is rejected.

33. For the hypotheses in Problem 17, the null hypothesis is rejected.

34. For the hypotheses in Problem 18, the null hypothesis is not rejected.

Applying the Concepts

35. Popcorn Consumption According to popcorn.org, the mean consumption of popcorn annually by Americans is 54 quarts. The marketing division of popcorn.org unleashes an aggressive campaign designed to get Americans to consume even more popcorn.

(a) Determine the null and alternative hypothesis that would be used to test the effectiveness of the marketing campaign. $H_0: \mu = 54$ quarts; $H_1: \mu > 54$ quarts

(b) A sample of 800 Americans provides enough evidence to conclude that the marketing campaign was effective. Provide a statement that should be put out by the marketing department.

(c) Suppose, in fact, that the mean annual consumption of popcorn after the marketing campaign is 53.4 quarts. Has a Type I or Type II error been made by the marketing department? If they tested the hypothesis at the $\alpha = 0.05$ level of significance, what is the probability of making a Type I error? Type I error; 0.05

36. Test Preparation The mean score on the SAT Math Reasoning exam is 518. A test preparation company states that the mean score of students who take its course is higher than 518.

(a) Determine the null and alternative hypotheses.

(b) If sample data indicate that the null hypothesis should not be rejected, state the conclusion of the company.

(c) Suppose, in fact, that the mean score of students taking the preparatory course is 522. Has a Type I or Type II error been made? If we tested this hypothesis at the $\alpha = 0.01$ level, what is the probability of committing a Type I error? Type II; 0.01

(d) If we wanted to decrease the probability of making a Type II error, would we need to increase or decrease the level of significance? Increase

37. Marijuana Use According to the Centers for Disease Control and Prevention, in 2005, 15.2% of tenth-grade students had tried marijuana. The Drug Abuse and Resistance Education (DARE) program underwent several major changes to keep up with technology and issues facing students in the 21st century. After the changes, a school resource officer (SRO) thinks that the proportion of tenth-grade students who have tried marijuana has decreased from the 2005 level.

(a) Determine the null and alternative hypotheses.

(b) If sample data indicate that the null hypothesis should not be rejected, state the conclusion of the SRO.

(c) Suppose, in fact, that the proportion of tenth-grade students who have tried marijuana is 14.7%. Was a Type I or Type II error committed? Type II

38. Migraines According to the Centers for Disease Control, 15.2% of American adults experience migraine headaches. Stress is a major contributor to the frequency and intensity of headaches. A massage therapist feels that she has a technique that can reduce the frequency and intensity of migraine headaches.

(a) Determine the null and alternative hypothesis that would be used to test the effectiveness of the massage therapist's techniques. $H_0: p = 0.152$; $H_1: p < 0.152$

(b) A sample of 500 American adults who participated in the massage therapist's program results in data that indicate that the null hypothesis should be rejected. Provide a statement that supports the massage therapist's program.

(c) Suppose, in fact, that the percentage of patients in the program who experience migraine headaches is 15.3%. Was a Type I or Type II error committed? Type I error

39. Consumer Reports The following is an excerpt from a *Consumer Reports* article.

The platinum Gasaver makes some impressive claims. The device, $188 for two, is guaranteed to increase gas mileage by 22% says the manufacturer, National Fuelsaver. Also, the company quotes "the government" as concluding, "Independent testing shows greater fuel savings with Gasaver *than the 22 percent claimed by the developer." Readers have told us they want to know more about it.*

The Environmental Protection Agency (EPA), after its lab tests of the Platinum Gasaver, concluded, "Users of the device would not be expected to realize either an emission or fuel economy benefit." The Federal Trade Commission says, "No government agency endorses gas-saving products for cars."

Determine the null and alternative hypotheses that the EPA used to draw the conclusion stated in the second paragraph.

40. Prolong Engine Treatment The manufacturer of Prolong Engine Treatment claims that if you add one 12-ounce bottle of its $20 product your engine will be protected from excessive wear. An infomercial claims that a woman drove 4 hours without oil, thanks to Prolong. *Consumer Reports* magazine tested engines in which they added Prolong to the motor oil, ran the engines, drained the oil, and then determined the time until the engines seized.

(a) Determine the null and alternative hypotheses that *Consumer Reports* will test.

(b) Both engines took exactly 13 minutes to seize. What conclusion might *Consumer Reports* draw based on this evidence? Prolong's claim not true

41. Refer to the claim made in Problem 18. Researchers must choose the level of significance based on the consequences of making a Type I error. In your opinion, is a Type I error or Type II error more serious? Why? On the basis of your answer, decide on a level of significance, α. Be sure to support your opinion.

36. (a) $H_0: \mu = 518$; $H_1: \mu > 518$ 37. (a) $H_0: p = 0.152$; $H_1: p < 0.152$ 39. $H_0: \mu = 0$; $H_1: \mu > 0$, where μ is the mean increase
40. (a) $H_0: \mu = 4$ hours; $H_1: \mu < 4$ hours

10.2 HYPOTHESIS TESTS FOR A POPULATION MEAN— POPULATION STANDARD DEVIATION KNOWN

Preparing for This Section Before getting started, review the following:

- Using probabilities to identify unusual events (Section 5.1, pp. 261–262)
- z_α notation (Section 7.2, pp. 392–393)

- Sampling distribution of $\bar{x}$ (Section 8.1, pp. 427–438)
- Computing normal probabilities (Section 7.3, pp. 397–399)

Objectives

① Explain the logic of hypothesis testing

② Test hypotheses about a population mean with σ known using the classical approach

③ Test hypotheses about a population mean with σ known using P-values

④ Test hypotheses about a population mean with σ known using confidence intervals

⑤ Distinguish between statistical significance and practical significance

---

Historical Note

Jerzy Neyman was born on April 16, 1894, in Bendery, Russia. In 1921, he moved to Poland. He received his Ph.D. from the University of Warsaw in 1924. He read some of Karl Pearson's works and became interested in statistics; however, Neyman was not impressed with Pearson's mathematical abilities. In 1927, he met Pearson's son, Egon Pearson, who was working on a formal approach to hypothesis testing. It was Neyman who provided the mathematical rigor to their work. Together, they developed the phrases *null hypothesis* and *alternative hypothesis*. In 1938, Neyman joined the faculty at the University of California at Berkeley. He died on August 5, 1981.

① **Explain the Logic of Hypothesis Testing**

In this section, we present three approaches to testing hypotheses about a population mean, μ. As we did for confidence intervals, we begin by assuming that we know the value of the population standard deviation, σ. The assumption is made because it allows us to use the normal model to test hypotheses regarding the population mean. Because the normal model is fairly easy to use, we can concentrate on the techniques of hypothesis testing without getting bogged down with other details. The assumption that σ is known will be dropped in the next section.

To test hypotheses regarding the population mean assuming the population standard deviation is known, two requirements must be satisfied:

1. A simple random sample is obtained.

2. The population from which the sample is drawn is normally distributed or the sample size is large ($n \geq 30$).

If these requirements are met, then the distribution of $\bar{x}$ is normal, with mean μ and standard deviation $\dfrac{\sigma}{\sqrt{n}}$.

The first method that we use in testing hypotheses regarding a population mean is referred to as the classical (traditional) approach, the second method is the P-value approach, and the third method uses confidence intervals. Your instructor may choose to cover one, two, or all three approaches to hypothesis testing. Do not be alarmed if one or two of the approaches are not covered by your instructor.

Let's first lay out a scenario that will be used to help understand both the classical approach to hypothesis testing and the P-value approach. Suppose that a consumer advocate is concerned that a manufacturer of potato chips is underfilling its bags. The bag states that the contents weigh 12.5 ounces. In hypothesis testing we assume that the manufacturer is "not guilty," which means we assume that the population mean contents of the bags of chips is $\mu = 12.5$ ounces. We look for evidence that shows the manufacturer is underfilling the bags. We have the following hypotheses:

$$H_0: \mu = 12.5 \quad \text{versus} \quad H_1: \mu < 12.5$$

The consumer advocate gathers evidence by obtaining a simple random sample of $n = 36$ bags of chips, weighing the contents, and calculating the sample mean of

12.45 ounces. Do the results of this sample suggest that the manufacturer is under-filling its bags? Put another way, would it be unusual to obtain a sample mean of 12.45 ounces or less from a population whose mean is 12.5 ounces? What is convincing or *statistically significant* evidence?

Definition When observed results are unlikely under the assumption that the null hypothesis is true, we say the result is **statistically significant**. When results are found to be statistically significant, we reject the null hypothesis.

Before we can test the hypothesis, we need to know the distribution of the sample mean, since a different sample of 36 bags of chips will likely result in a different sample mean. Since the sample size is large, the Central Limit Theorem says that the shape of the distribution of the sample mean is approximately normal. The mean of the distribution of the sample mean is $\mu_{\bar{x}} = \mu = 12.5$ ounces, because we assume the statement in the null hypothesis to be true until we have evidence to the contrary. Suppose that the population standard deviation is known to be 0.12 ounce; then the standard deviation of the distribution of the sample mean is

Figure 2

$$\sigma_{\bar{x}} = \frac{\sigma}{\sqrt{n}} = \frac{0.12}{\sqrt{36}} = 0.02 \text{ ounce. Figure 2 shows the sampling distribution of the}$$

sample mean for our potato chip example.

Now that we have a model that describes the distribution of the sample mean, we use it to look at the logic of the classical and *P*-value approach to test if the potato chip company is underfilling the bags.

The Logic of the Classical Approach

One criterion we may use for sufficient evidence is to reject the null hypothesis if the sample mean is too many standard deviations below the assumed (or status quo) population mean of 12.5 ounces. For example, our criterion might be to reject the null hypothesis if the sample mean is more than 2 standard deviations below the assumed mean of 12.5 ounces.

Recall that $z = \dfrac{\bar{x} - \mu}{\dfrac{\sigma}{\sqrt{n}}}$ represents the number of standard deviations that $\bar{x}$

is from the population mean, μ. Our simple random sample of 36 bags results in a sample mean weight of $\bar{x} = 12.45$ ounces, so under the assumption that the null hypothesis is true we have

$$z = \frac{\bar{x} - \mu}{\dfrac{\sigma}{\sqrt{n}}} = \frac{12.45 - 12.5}{\dfrac{0.12}{\sqrt{36}}} = -2.5$$

The sample mean is 2.5 standard deviations below the hypothesized mean. Because the sample mean is more than 2 standard deviations (that is, "too far") below the hypothesized population mean, we will reject the null hypothesis and conclude that there is sufficient evidence to conclude that the average bag has less than 12.5 ounces of potato chips. This conclusion will lead the consumer advocate to wage a "truth in advertising campaign" against the potato chip manufacturer.

Why does it make sense to reject the null hypothesis if the sample mean is more than 2 standard deviations away from the hypothesized mean? The area under the standard normal curve to the left of $z = -2$ is 0.0228, as shown in Figure 3.

Figure 4 shows that, if the null hypothesis is true (that is, if the population mean is 12.5 ounces), then 97.72% of all sample means will be 12.46 ounces or more and only 2.28% of the sample means will be less than 12.46 ounces. Remember, the 12.46 comes from the fact that 12.46 is 2 standard deviations below the hypothesized mean of 12.5 ounces. If a sample mean lies in the blue region, we are inclined to believe that it came from a population whose mean is less than 12.5, rather than believe that the population mean equals 12.5 and our sample just happened to result in an unusual outcome (a bunch of underfilled bags).

Note to Instructor

If you only wish to cover the *P*-value approach, skip to page 525.

CAUTION We always test hypotheses assuming that the null hypothesis is true.

Figure 3

Figure 4

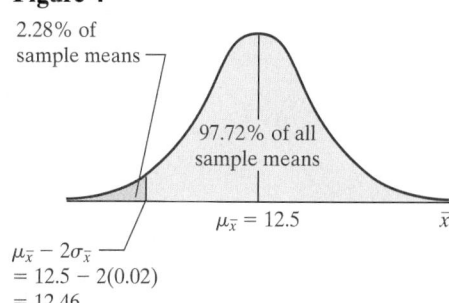

Notice that our criterion for rejecting the null hypothesis will lead to making a Type I error (rejecting a true null hypothesis) 2.28% of the time. That is, the probability of making a Type I error is 2.28% (0.0228). This is because 2.28% of all sample means are less than 12.46 ounces, even though the population mean is 12.5 ounces.

The previous discussion leads to the following premise of hypothesis testing using the classical approach:

> If the sample mean is too many standard deviations from the mean stated in the null hypothesis, we reject the null hypothesis.

The Logic of the *P*-Value Approach

A second criterion we may use for sufficient evidence to support the belief that the manufacturer is underfilling the bags is to compute how likely it is to obtain a sample mean of 12.45 ounces or less from a population whose mean is assumed to be 12.5 ounces. If a sample mean of 12.45 or less is unlikely (or unusual), we have evidence against the null hypothesis. If the sample mean of 12.45 is not unlikely (not unusual), we do not have sufficient evidence against the null hypothesis.

We can compute the probability of obtaining a sample mean of 12.45 or less from a population whose mean is 12.5 using the normal model. Figure 5 shows the area that represents $P(\overline{x} < 12.45)$.

Figure 5

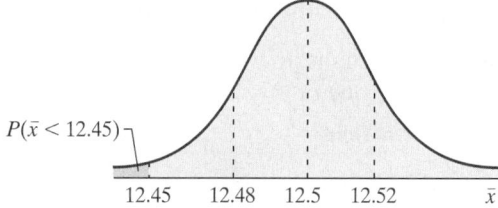

Because

$$z = \frac{\overline{x} - \mu}{\sigma_{\overline{x}}} = \frac{12.45 - 12.5}{0.02} = -2.5$$

we compute

$$P(\overline{x} \leq 12.45) = P(Z \leq -2.5) = 0.0062$$

The probability of obtaining a sample mean of 12.45 ounces or less from a population whose mean is 12.5 ounces is 0.0062. This means that fewer than 1 sample in 100 will give a mean as low or lower than the one we obtained *if* the population mean really is 12.5 ounces. Because these results are so unusual, we take this as evidence against the statement in the null hypothesis.

This discussion leads to the following premise of testing a hypothesis using the *P*-value approach:

> Assuming that H_0 is true, if the probability of getting a sample mean as extreme or more extreme than the one obtained is small, we reject the null hypothesis.

Figure 6 further illustrates the situation for both the classical and P-value approaches. The distribution in red shows the distribution of the sample mean assuming that the statement in the null hypothesis is true. The sample mean of 12.45 is too far from the assumed population mean of 12.5. Therefore, we reject the null hypothesis that $\mu = 12.5$ and conclude that the sample came from a population with some population mean less than 12.5 ounces, as indicated by the distribution in blue. We don't know what the population mean weight of the bags is, but we have evidence that it is less than 12.5 ounces.

Figure 6

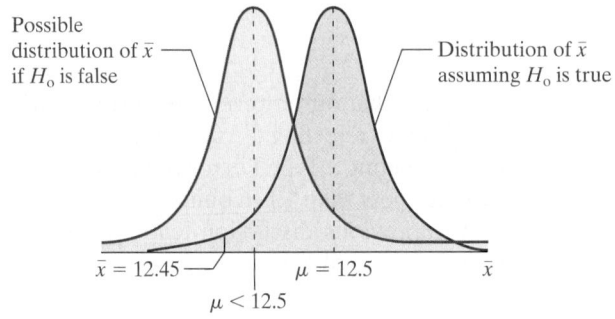

Possible distribution of $\bar{x}$ if H_o is false

Distribution of $\bar{x}$ assuming H_o is true

$\bar{x} = 12.45$ $\mu = 12.5$ $\bar{x}$

$\mu < 12.5$

Test Hypotheses about a Population Mean with σ Known Using the Classical Approach

Note to Instructor
If you only wish to teach the P-value approach to hypothesis testing, this objective can be skipped without loss of continuity.

We now formalize the procedure for testing hypotheses regarding the population mean when the population standard deviation, σ, is known using the classical approach.

Testing Hypotheses Regarding the Population Mean with σ Known Using the Classical Approach

To test hypotheses regarding the population mean with σ known, we can use the steps that follow, provided that two requirements are satisfied:

1. The sample is obtained using simple random sampling.
2. The sample has no outliers, and the population from which the sample is drawn is normally distributed or the sample size, n, is large ($n \geq 30$).

Step 1: Determine the null and alternative hypotheses. The hypotheses can be structured in one of three ways:

Two-Tailed	Left-Tailed	Right-Tailed
$H_0: \mu = \mu_0$	$H_0: \mu = \mu_0$	$H_0: \mu = \mu_0$
$H_1: \mu \neq \mu_0$	$H_1: \mu < \mu_0$	$H_1: \mu > \mu_0$

Note: μ_0 is the assumed or status quo value of the population mean.

Step 2: Select a level of significance, α, based on the seriousness of making a Type I error.

Step 3: Provided that the population from which the sample is drawn is normal, or the sample size is large ($n \geq 30$), and the population standard deviation, σ, is known, the distribution of the sample mean, $\bar{x}$, is normal with mean μ_0 and standard deviation $\dfrac{\sigma}{\sqrt{n}}$. Therefore,

$$z_0 = \frac{\bar{x} - \mu_0}{\dfrac{\sigma}{\sqrt{n}}}$$

represents the number of standard deviations that the sample mean is from the assumed mean, μ_0. This value is called the **test statistic**.

Step 4: The level of significance is used to determine the *critical value*. The **critical value** represents the maximum number of standard deviations that the sample mean can be from μ_0 before the null hypothesis is rejected. For example, the critical value in the left-tailed test is $-z_\alpha$. The shaded region(s) represents the *critical (or rejection) region(s)*. The **critical region** or **rejection region** is the set of all values such that the null hypothesis is rejected.

	Two-Tailed	Left-Tailed	Right-Tailed

Step 5: Compare the critical value with the test statistic:

Two-Tailed	Left-Tailed	Right-Tailed
If $z_0 < -z_{\frac{\alpha}{2}}$ or $z_0 > z_{\frac{\alpha}{2}}$, reject the null hypothesis.	If $z_0 < -z_\alpha$, reject the null hypothesis.	If $z_0 > z_\alpha$, reject the null hypothesis.

The comparison of the test statistic and critical value is called the **decision rule**.

Step 6: State the conclusion.

The procedure is **robust**, which means that minor departures from normality will not adversely affect the results of the test. However, for small samples, if the data have outliers, the procedure should not be used.

For small samples, we will verify that the data come from a population that is normal by constructing normal probability plots (to assess normality) and boxplots (to determine whether there are outliers). If the normal probability plot indicates that the data do not come from a population that is normally distributed or the boxplot reveals outliers, nonparametric tests (Chapter 15) should be performed.

EXAMPLE 1

The Classical Approach to Hypothesis Testing: Right-Tailed, Large Sample

Problem: The mean SAT math reasoning score in 2007 was 515, with a standard deviation of 114. An educational psychologist believes that students who take at least 4 years of English courses in high school score better on the SAT math reasoning exam. [**Note:** It is perfectly reasonable for a student to have more than 4 years of credits in a particular discipline. The student simply takes more than one course in the discipline in any given year.] The psychologist obtains a random sample of 40 high school students who completed at least 4 years of English courses in high school and finds that their mean SAT math reasoning exam score is 540. Conduct an appropriate test at the $\alpha = 0.05$ level of significance to determine if the psychologist's beliefs are supported by the data. *Source*: Based on results supplied by the College Board.

Approach: We assume there is no difference between the population of all students and those who take at least 4 years of English courses. We want to know if the mean score of students who complete at least 4 years of English is higher than 515. We will perform a hypothesis test about the mean using the classical approach. If the sample mean is "too far" from the assumed population mean of 515, we have evidence against the assumption that the population mean of students who take at least 4 years of English is also 515. Because the sample size is large, we can proceed to Steps 1 through 6.

Solution

Step 1: The psychologist wants to know if the students who take at least 4 years of English score better than 515 on the SAT math reasoning exam. We can write this as

Note to Instructor

Emphasize to students that they should always draw graphs like Figure 7 (on page 528) so that they can "see" the criteria for rejecting H_0.

Figure 7

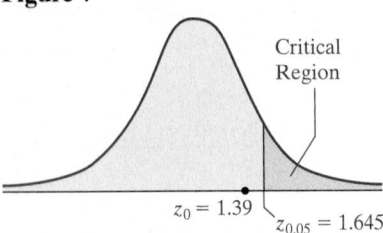

Critical Region

$z_0 = 1.39$

$z_{0.05} = 1.645$

CAUTION In Example 1, we do not have enough evidence to reject the statement in the null hypothesis. In other words, it is not unusual to obtain a sample mean of 540 from a population whose mean is 515. However, this does not imply that we are accepting the statement in the null hypothesis (that is, we are not saying that the mean equals 515). We are only saying we do not have enough evidence to conclude that the mean score is greater than 515. Be sure that you understand the difference between "accepting" and "not rejecting." It is similar to the difference between being declared "innocent" versus "not guilty."

$\mu > 515$. The statement of "no difference" is $\mu = 515$ (that is, no difference between the general population of SAT test takers and those who take at least 4 years of English). This is a right-tailed test and we have

$$H_0: \mu = 515 \qquad \text{versus} \qquad H_1: \mu > 515$$

Step 2: The level of significance is $\alpha = 0.05$.

Step 3: The sample mean of the 40 students who took at least 4 years of English is 540. The test statistic is

$$z_0 = \frac{\overline{x} - \mu_0}{\dfrac{\sigma}{\sqrt{n}}} = \frac{540 - 515}{\dfrac{114}{\sqrt{40}}} = 1.39$$

Step 4: Because this is a right-tailed test, we determine the critical value at the $\alpha = 0.05$ level of significance to be $z_{0.05} = 1.645$. The critical region is displayed in Figure 7.

Step 5: Because the test statistic $z_0 = 1.39$ is less than the critical value $z_{0.05} = 1.645$, we do not reject (fail to reject) the null hypothesis. That is, the value of the test statistic does not lie in the critical region, so we do not reject the null hypothesis. See Figure 7.

Step 6: There is not sufficient evidence at the $\alpha = 0.05$ level of significance to support the belief that students who take at least 4 years of English score better on the SAT math reasoning exam.

Now Work Problem 21 Using the Classical Approach

Now let's look at a two-tailed hypothesis test.

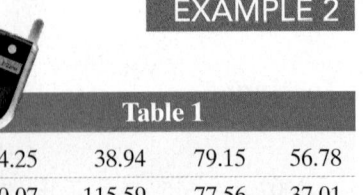

| EXAMPLE 2 | **The Classical Approach to Hypothesis Testing: Two-Tailed, Small Sample** |

Table 1

94.25	38.94	79.15	56.78
70.07	115.59	77.56	37.01
55.00	76.05	27.29	52.48

Problem: According to CTIA–The Wireless Association, the mean monthly cell phone bill in 2004 was $50.64. A market researcher believes that the mean monthly cell phone bill is different today, but is not sure whether bills have declined because of technological advances or increased due to additional use. The researcher phones a simple random sample of 12 cell phone subscribers and obtains the monthly bills shown in Table 1.

Assuming that $\sigma = \$18.49$, use these data to determine whether the mean monthly cell phone bill is different from $50.64 at the $\alpha = 0.05$ level of significance.

Approach: We assume that there is no difference between cell phone bills in 2004 and today. We then determine whether the sample data are consistent with this assumption. Because the sample size, n, is less than 30, we must verify that the data come from a population that is approximately normal with no outliers. We construct a normal probability plot and boxplot to verify these requirements. We then proceed to follow Steps 1 through 6.

Solution: Figure 8 displays the normal probability plot and boxplot. The normal probability plot indicates that the data could come from a population that is normal. The boxplot does not show any outliers.

Step 1: The market researcher wants to know if the mean cell phone bill is different from $50.64, which can be written $\mu \neq 50.64$. This is a two-tailed test and we have

$$H_0: \mu = 50.64 \qquad \text{versus} \qquad H_1: \mu \neq 50.64$$

Step 2: The level of significance is $\alpha = 0.05$.

Figure 8

Step 3: From the data in Table 1, the sample mean is computed to be \$65.014. The test statistic is

$$z_0 = \frac{\overline{x} - \mu_0}{\frac{\sigma}{\sqrt{n}}} = \frac{65.014 - 50.64}{\frac{18.49}{\sqrt{12}}} = 2.69$$

The sample mean of \$65.014 is 2.69 standard deviations above the assumed population mean of \$50.64.

Step 4: Because this is a two-tailed test, we determine the critical values at the $\alpha = 0.05$ level of significance to be $-z_{0.05/2} = -1.96$ and $z_{0.05/2} = 1.96$. The critical regions are displayed in Figure 9.

Figure 9

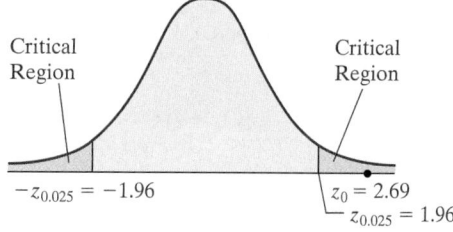

$-z_{0.025} = -1.96$

$z_0 = 2.69$

$z_{0.025} = 1.96$

Note to Instructor
Ask students how this problem will change if the researcher thinks that cell phone bills have risen since 2004.

Step 5: Because the test statistic, $z_0 = 2.69$, is greater than the critical value $z_{0.025} = 1.96$, we reject the null hypothesis. That is, the value of the test statistic falls within the critical region, so we reject H_0. We label this point in Figure 9.

Step 6: There is sufficient evidence at the $\alpha = 0.05$ level of significance to conclude that the mean monthly cell phone bill is different from the mean amount in 2004, \$50.64.

Now Work Problem 25 Using the Classical Approach

3   **Test Hypotheses about a Population Mean with σ Known Using P-Values**

Note to Instructor
Stress to students that the interpretation of P-values is the same for all hypothesis tests. Therefore, P-values are more versatile.

Now let's look at testing hypotheses with *P*-values.

Definition

A **P-value** is the probability of observing a sample statistic as extreme or more extreme than the one observed under the assumption that the null hypothesis is true. Put another way, the *P*-value is the likelihood or probability that a sample will result in a sample mean such as the one obtained if the null hypothesis is true.

A small *P*-value implies that the sample mean is unlikely if the null hypothesis is true and is considered evidence against the null hypothesis.

The following procedures can be used to compute *P*-values when testing a hypothesis about a population mean with σ known.

Testing Hypotheses Regarding the Population Mean Using *P*-Values

To test hypotheses regarding the population mean with σ known, we can use the steps that follow to compute the *P*-value, provided that the following two requirements are satisfied.

1. The sample is obtained using simple random sampling.

2. The sample has no outliers, and the population from which the sample is drawn is normally distributed or the sample size, n, is large ($n \geq 30$).

Step 1: Determine the null and alternative hypotheses. The hypotheses can be structured in one of three ways:

Two-Tailed	Left-Tailed	Right-Tailed
$H_0: \mu = \mu_0$	$H_0: \mu = \mu_0$	$H_0: \mu = \mu_0$
$H_1: \mu \neq \mu_0$	$H_1: \mu < \mu_0$	$H_1: \mu > \mu_0$

Note: μ_0 is the assumed value of the population mean.

Step 2: Decide on a level of significance, α, depending on the seriousness of making a Type I error.

Step 3: Compute the test statistic, $z_0 = \dfrac{\overline{x} - \mu_0}{\dfrac{\sigma}{\sqrt{n}}}$.

Step 4: Determine the *P*-value.

Two-Tailed	Left-Tailed	Right-Tailed
P-value $= P(Z < -\lvert z_0 \rvert \text{ or } Z > \lvert z_0 \rvert)$ $= 2P(Z > \lvert z_0 \rvert)$	*P*-value $= P(Z < z_0)$	*P*-value $= P(Z > z_0)$

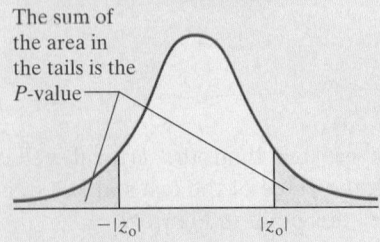

The sum of the area in the tails is the *P*-value

The area left of z_0 is the *P*-value

The area right of z_0 is the *P*-value

Interpretation: The *P*-value is the probability of obtaining a sample mean that is more than $\lvert z_0 \rvert$ standard deviations away from the mean stated in the null hypothesis, μ_0.

Interpretation: The *P*-value is the probability of obtaining a sample mean of $\overline{x}$ or smaller under the assumption that H_0 is true. In other words, it is the probability of obtaining a sample mean that is more than $\lvert z_0 \rvert$ standard deviations to the left of μ_0.

Interpretation: The *P*-value is the probability of obtaining a sample mean of $\overline{x}$ or larger under the assumption that H_0 is true. In other words, it is the probability of obtaining a sample mean that is more than z_0 standard deviations to the right of μ_0.

Step 5: Reject the null hypothesis if the *P*-value is less than the level of significance, α. The comparison of the *P*-value and the level of significance is called the **decision rule**.

Step 6: State the conclusion.

EXAMPLE 3	The *P*-Value Approach to Hypothesis Testing: Right-Tailed, Large Sample

Problem: The mean SAT math reasoning score in 2007 was 515 with a standard deviation of 114. An educational psychologist believes that students who take at least 4 years of English courses in high school score better on the SAT math reasoning exam. [**Note:** It is perfectly reasonable for a student to have more than 4 years of credits in a particular discipline. The student simply takes more than one course in the discipline in any given year.] The psychologist obtains a random sample of 40 high school students who completed at least 4 years of English courses in high school and finds that their mean SAT math reasoning exam score is 540. Conduct an appropriate test at the $\alpha = 0.05$ level of significance to determine if the psychologist's beliefs are supported by the data using the *P*-value approach. *Source*: Based on results supplied by the College Board.

Approach: We assume there is no difference between the population of all students and those who take at least 4 years of English. We want to know if the mean score of students who complete at least 4 years of English is higher than 515. We perform a hypothesis test about the mean using the *P*-value approach. The *P*-value will tell us the likelihood of obtaining a sample mean of 540 or higher from a population whose mean is 515. If the *P*-value is low, we have evidence against the assumption that the population mean of students who take at least 4 years of English is also 515. Because the sample size is large, we can proceed to Steps 1 through 6.

Solution

Step 1: The psychologist wants to know if the students who take at least 4 years of English score better than 515 on the SAT math reasoning exam. We can write this as $\mu > 515$. The statement of "no difference" would be $\mu = 515$ (that is, no difference between the general population of SAT test takers and those who took at least 4 years of English). This is a right-tailed test and we have

$$H_0\text{: } \mu = 515 \qquad \text{versus} \qquad H_1\text{: } \mu > 515$$

So, we want to know the likelihood of obtaining a sample mean of 540 from a population where mean is assumed to be 515.

Step 2: The level of significance is $\alpha = 0.05$.

Step 3: The sample mean of the 40 students who took at least 4 years of English is 540. The test statistic is

$$z_0 = \frac{\bar{x} - \mu_0}{\frac{\sigma}{\sqrt{n}}} = \frac{540 - 515}{\frac{114}{\sqrt{40}}} = 1.39$$

Note to Instructor

Emphasize to students that they should always draw graphs like Figure 10 so that they can see the area that represents the P-value.

Step 4: Because this is a right-tailed test, we determine

$$P(Z > z_0) = P(Z > 1.39)$$

We need to determine the area under the standard normal curve to the right of 1.39. This is equivalent to finding the area under the normal curve to the right of 540. See Figure 10.

Using Table V, we have

$$P(Z > 1.39) = 1 - P(Z \le 1.39) = 1 - 0.9177 = 0.0823$$

The probability of obtaining a sample mean of 540 or higher from a population whose mean is 515 is 0.0823. The *P*-value of 0.0823 means that we would expect about 8 out of 100 random samples of size 40 to result in a sample mean of 540 or higher *if* the population mean is 515 (that is, assuming that the statement in the null hypothesis is true). The results we obtained are not unusual assuming the null hypothesis is true.

Step 5: If the *P*-value is less than the level of significance, we reject the null hypothesis. Because $0.0823 > 0.05$, we do not reject the null hypothesis. The sample data obtained are not inconsistent with a population mean of 515. Put another way, we could have obtained the sample mean of 540 (or higher) from a population whose mean is 515 by random chance.

Step 6: There is not sufficient evidence at the $\alpha = 0.05$ level of significance to support the belief that students who take at least four years of English score better on the SAT math reasoning exam.

Figure 10

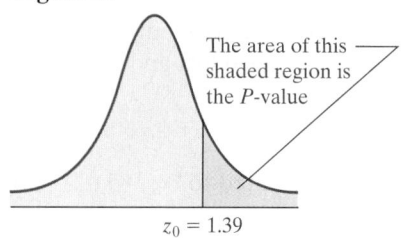

The area of this shaded region is the *P*-value

$z_0 = 1.39$

In Other Words

If *P*-value $< \alpha$, then reject the null hypothesis. Put another way—If the *P*-value is low, the null must go!

⬦CAUTION⬦ In Example 3, we do not have enough evidence to reject the statement in the null hypothesis. In other words, it is not unusual to obtain a sample mean of 540 from a population whose mean is 515. However, this does not imply that we are accepting the statement in the null hypothesis (that is, we are not saying that the mean equals 515). We are only saying we do not have enough evidence to conclude that the mean score is greater than 515. Be sure that you understand the difference between "accepting" and "not rejecting." It is similar to the difference between being declared "innocent" versus "not guilty."

Also, be sure you understand that the P-value is the probability of obtaining a sample mean as extreme or more extreme than the one observed *if* the statement in the null hypothesis is true. The P-value does not represent the probability that the null hypothesis is true. The statement in the null hypothesis is either true or false, we just don't which.

In practice, the level of significance is not reported using the P-value approach. Instead, only the P-value is given, and the reader of the study must interpret its value and judge its significance.

Now Work Problem 21 Using the P-Value Approach

EXAMPLE 4 | **The P-Value Approach of Hypothesis Testing: Two-Tailed, Small Sample**

Table 2

94.25	38.94	79.15	56.78
70.07	115.59	77.56	37.01
55.00	76.05	27.29	52.48

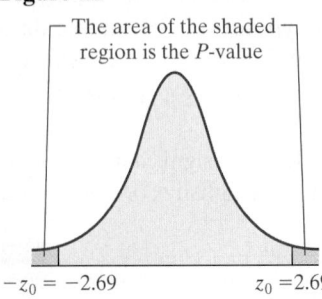

Problem: According to CTIA–The Wireless Association, the mean monthly cell phone bill in 2004 was $50.64. A market researcher believes that the mean monthly cell phone bill is different today, but is not sure whether bills have declined because of technological advances or increased due to additional use. The researcher phones a simple random sample of 12 cell phone subscribers and obtains the monthly bills shown in Table 2.

Assuming that $\sigma = \$18.49$, use these data to determine whether the mean monthly cell phone bill is different from $50.64 at the $\alpha = 0.05$ level of significance. Use the P-value approach.

Approach: We want to know if the mean cell phone bill is *different from* $50.64. Because the sample size, n, is less than 30, we must verify that the data come from a population that is approximately normal with no outliers. We construct a normal probability plot and boxplot to verify these requirements. We then proceed to follow Steps 1 through 6.

Solution: Figure 8 on page 529 displays the normal probability plot and boxplot. The normal probability plot indicates that the data could come from a population that is normal. The boxplot does not show any outliers.

Step 1: The market researcher wants to know if the mean cell phone bill is different from $50.64, which can be written $\mu \neq 50.64$. This is a two-tailed test and we have

$$H_0: \mu = 50.64 \quad \text{versus} \quad H_1: \mu \neq 50.64$$

Step 2: The level of significance is $\alpha = 0.05$.

Step 3: From the data in Table 2, the sample mean is computed to be $65.014 and $n = 12$. We assume that $\sigma = \$18.49$. The test statistic is

$$z_0 = \frac{\overline{x} - \mu_0}{\frac{\sigma}{\sqrt{n}}} = \frac{65.014 - 50.64}{\frac{18.49}{\sqrt{12}}} = 2.69$$

Figure 11

The area of the shaded region is the P-value

$-z_0 = -2.69 \qquad z_0 = 2.69$

The sample mean of $65.014 is 2.69 standard deviations above the assumed population mean of $50.64.

Step 4: Because we are performing a two-tailed test,

$$P\text{-value} = P(Z < -2.69 \text{ or } Z > 2.69)$$

We need to determine the area under the standard normal curve to the right of $z_0 = 2.69$ and to the left of $z_0 = -2.69$, as shown in Figure 11.

In Other Words

To find the P-value for a two-tailed test, first determine whether the test statistic, z_0, is positive or negative. If z_0 is negative, determine the area under the standard normal curve to the left of z_0 and then multiply this area by 2. If z_0 is positive, find the area under the standard normal curve to the right of z_0 and double this value.

Using Table V, we have

$$P\text{-value} = P(Z < -2.69 \text{ or } Z > 2.69) = P(Z < -2.69) + P(Z > 2.69)$$
$$= 2P(Z > 2.69)$$
$$= 2[1 - P(Z \le 2.69)]$$
$$= 2(1 - 0.9964)$$
$$= 2(0.0036)$$
$$= 0.0072$$

The probability of obtaining a sample mean that is more than 2.69 standard deviations away from the status quo population mean of $50.64 is 0.0072. This means that less than 1 sample in 100 will result in a sample mean such as the one we obtained *if* the statement in the null hypothesis is true. The results we obtained are not consistent with the assumption that $\mu = \$50.64$.

Step 5: Because the *P*-value is less than the level of significance (0.0072 < 0.05), we reject the null hypothesis.

Step 6: There is sufficient evidence at the $\alpha = 0.05$ level of significance to conclude that the mean monthly cell phone bill is different from $50.64, the mean amount in 2004. It would appear to be the case that monthly cell phone bills have changed since 2004.

Now Work Problem 25 Using the *P*-Value Approach

EXAMPLE 5 **Testing Hypotheses about a Population Mean Using Technology**

Problem: According to CTIA–The Wireless Association, the mean monthly cell phone bill in 2004 was $50.64. A market researcher believes that the mean monthly cell phone bill is different today, but is not sure whether bills have declined because of technological advances or increased due to additional use. The researcher phones a simple random sample of 12 cell phone subscribers and obtains the data in Table 2.
   Assuming that $\sigma = \$18.49$, use these data to determine whether the mean monthly cell phone bill is different from $50.64 at the $\alpha = 0.05$ level of significance.

Approach: We will use MINITAB to test $H_0: \mu = 50.64$ versus $H_1: \mu \ne 50.64$. The steps for testing hypotheses about a population mean with σ known using the TI-83/84 Plus graphing calculators, MINITAB, and Excel are given in the Technology Step-by-Step on page 540.

Solution: Figure 12 shows the results obtained from MINITAB.

Figure 12   **One-Sample Z: Cell Phone Bill**

```
Test of mu = 50.64 vs not = 50.64
The assumed standard deviation = 18.49

Variable       N    Mean    StDev  SE Mean         95% CI         Z      P
Cell Phone
Bill          12  65.0142  25.4587  5.3376  (54.5527, 75.4757)  2.69  0.007
```

The *P*-value is highlighted. From MINITAB, we have *P*-value = 0.007.

Interpretation: A *P*-value of 0.007 means that less than 1 sample in 100 will result in a sample mean as extreme or more extreme than the one we obtained *if* the null hypothesis is true. Because the *P*-value is less than the level of significance (0.007 < 0.05), we reject the null hypothesis. There is sufficient evidence at the $\alpha = 0.05$ level of significance to conclude that the mean monthly cell phone bill is different from $50.64, the mean amount in 2004.

Using Technology

The *P*-value obtained from technology may be slightly different from the *P*-value obtained by hand because of rounding.

Note to Instructor
Throughout the text, we will give the level
of significance, α, to use in the decision
rule. You may want to point out to stu-
dents that journal articles rarely (if ever)
provide levels of significance; they leave it
to the reader to judge significance.

One advantage of using *P*-values over the classical approach in hypothesis testing is that *P*-values provide information regarding the strength of the evidence. In Example 2, we rejected the null hypothesis, but did not learn much about the strength of the evidence against the null hypothesis. Example 4 tested the same hypothesis using *P*-values. The *P*-value was 0.0072. This result not only led us to reject the null hypothesis, but also indicates the strength of the evidence against the null hypothesis: Less than 1 sample in 100 would give us the sample mean that we got if the null hypothesis, H_0: μ = 50.64, were true.

Another advantage of *P*-values is that they are interpreted the same way regardless of the type of hypothesis test being performed. The lower the *P*-value, the stronger the evidence against the statement in the null hypothesis.

4 Test Hypotheses about a Population Mean with σ Known Using Confidence Intervals

Recall that the level of confidence in a confidence interval represents the percentage of intervals that will contain μ if repeated samples are obtained. The level of confidence is denoted $(1 - \alpha) \cdot 100\%$. We can use confidence intervals to test H_0: $\mu = \mu_0$ versus H_1: $\mu \neq \mu_0$ using the following criterion.

> When testing H_0: $\mu = \mu_0$ versus H_1: $\mu \neq \mu_0$, if a $(1 - \alpha) \cdot 100\%$ confidence interval contains μ_0, we do not reject the null hypothesis. However, if the confidence interval does not contain μ_0, we have sufficient evidence that supports the statement in the alternative hypothesis and conclude that $\mu \neq \mu_0$ at the level of significance, α.

EXAMPLE 6 | **Testing Hypotheses about a Population Mean Using a Confidence Interval**

Problem: Test the hypotheses presented in Examples 2 and 4 at the $\alpha = 0.05$ level of significance by constructing a 95% confidence interval about μ, the population mean monthly cell phone bill.

Approach: We construct the 95% confidence interval using the data in Table 1 or Table 2. If the interval contains the status quo mean of $50.64, we do not reject the null hypothesis.

Solution: We use the formula on page 463 to find the lower and upper bounds with $\bar{x} = \$65.014$, $\sigma = \$18.49$, and $n = 12$.

Lower bound: $\bar{x} - z_{\alpha/2} \cdot \dfrac{\sigma}{\sqrt{n}} = \$65.014 - 1.96 \cdot \dfrac{18.49}{\sqrt{12}} = \$65.014 - \$10.462 = \$54.552$

Upper bound: $\bar{x} + z_{\alpha/2} \cdot \dfrac{\sigma}{\sqrt{n}} = \$65.014 + 1.96 \cdot \dfrac{18.49}{\sqrt{12}} = \$65.014 + \$10.462 = \$75.476$

We are 95% confident that the mean monthly cell phone bill is between $54.552 and $75.476. Because the mean stated in the null hypothesis, H_0: $\mu = 50.64$, is not included in this interval, we reject the null hypothesis. There is sufficient evidence at the $\alpha = 0.05$ level of significance to conclude that the mean monthly cell phone bill is different from $50.64.

Now Work Problem 33

In Other Words
Results are statistically significant
if the difference between the observed
result and the statement made in the
null hypothesis is unlikely to occur due
to chance alone.

5 Distinguish between Statistical Significance and Practical Significance

When a large sample size is used in a hypothesis test, the results could be statistically significant even though the difference between the sample statistic and mean stated in the null hypothesis may have no *practical significance*.

Definition   **Practical significance** refers to the idea that, while small differences between the statistic and parameter stated in the null hypothesis are statistically significant, the difference may not be large enough to cause concern or be considered important.

EXAMPLE 7   **Statistical versus Practical Significance**

Problem: According to the American Community Survey, the mean travel time to work in Dallas, Texas, in 2006 was 25.3 minutes. The Department of Transportation in Dallas just reprogrammed all the traffic lights in an attempt to reduce travel time. To determine if there is evidence that indicates that travel times in Dallas have decreased as a result of the reprogramming, the Department of Transportation obtains a sample of 2,500 commuters, records their travel time to work, and obtains a sample mean of 24.9 minutes. Assuming that the population standard deviation travel time to work is known to be 8.4 minutes, determine whether travel times in Dallas have decreased as a result of the reprogramming at the $\alpha = 0.05$ level of significance.

Approach: We will use both the classical approach and P-value approach to test the hypotheses.

Solution

Step 1: The Department of Transportation wants to know if the mean travel time to work has decreased from 25.3 minutes, which can be written $\mu < 25.3$. This is a left-tailed test and we have

$$H_0: \mu = 25.3 \quad \text{versus} \quad H_1: \mu < 25.3$$

Step 2: The level of significance is $\alpha = 0.05$.

Step 3: The test statistic is

$$z_0 = \frac{\bar{x} - \mu_0}{\frac{\sigma}{\sqrt{n}}} = \frac{24.9 - 25.3}{\frac{8.4}{\sqrt{2500}}} = -2.38$$

Classical Approach

Step 4: This is a left-tailed test. With $\alpha = 0.05$, the critical value is $-z_{0.05} = -1.645$.

Step 5: Because the test statistic is less than the critical value (the critical value falls in the critical region), we reject the null hypothesis.

P-Value Approachh

Step 4: Because this is a left-tailed test, the P-value is $P\text{-value} = P(Z < z_0) = P(Z < -2.38) = 0.0087$.

Step 5: Because the P-value is less than the level of significance $(0.0087 < 0.05)$, we reject the null hypothesis.

Step 6: There is sufficient evidence at the $\alpha = 0.05$ level of significance to conclude that the mean travel time to work has decreased.

While the difference between 24.9 and 25.3 is statistically significant, it really has no practical meaning. After all, is 0.4 minute (24 seconds) really going to make anyone feel better about his or her commute to work?

The reason that the results from Example 7 were statistically significant had to do with the large sample size. The moral of the story is this:

CAUTION Beware of studies with large sample sizes that claim statistical significance because the differences may not have any practical meaning.

Large sample sizes can lead to results that are statistically significant, while the difference between the statistic and parameter in the null hypothesis is not enough to be considered practically significant.

10.2 ASSESS YOUR UNDERSTANDING

Concepts and Vocabulary

1. State the requirements that must be satisfied to test a hypothesis regarding a population mean with σ known.

2. Determine the critical value for a right-tailed test regarding a population mean with σ known at the $\alpha = 0.01$ level of significance. 2.33

3. Determine the critical value for a two-tailed test regarding a population mean with σ known at the $\alpha = 0.05$ level of significance. ± 1.96

4. The procedures for testing a hypothesis regarding a population mean with σ known are robust. What does this mean?

5. Explain what a *P*-value is. What is the criterion for rejecting the null hypothesis using the *P*-value approach?

6. Suppose that we are testing the hypotheses $H_0: \mu = 100$ versus $H_1: \mu < 100$ and we find the *P*-value to be 0.23. Explain what this means. Would you reject H_0? Why?

7. Suppose that we are testing the hypotheses $H_0: \mu = 50$ versus $H_1: \mu \neq 50$ and we find the *P*-value to be 0.02. Explain what this means. Would you reject H_0? Why?

8. Discuss the advantages and disadvantages of using the classical approach to hypothesis testing. Discuss the advantages and disadvantages of using the *P*-value approach to hypothesis testing.

9. In your own words, explain the difference between *statistical significance* and *practical significance*.

10. *True or False*: To test $H_0: \mu = \mu_0$ versus $H_1: \mu \neq \mu_0$ using a 5% level of significance, we could construct a 95% confidence interval. True

Skill Building

11. To test $H_0: \mu = 50$ versus $H_1: \mu < 50$, a random sample of size $n = 24$ is obtained from a population that is known to be normally distributed with $\sigma = 12$.
    (a) If the sample mean is determined to be $\bar{x} = 47.1$, compute the test statistic. $z_0 = -1.18$
    (b) If the researcher decides to test this hypothesis at the $\alpha = 0.05$ level of significance, determine the critical value. $-z_{0.05} = -1.645$
    (c) Draw a normal curve that depicts the critical region.
    (d) Will the researcher reject the null hypothesis? Why? No

12. To test $H_0: \mu = 40$ versus $H_1: \mu > 40$, a random sample of size $n = 25$ is obtained from a population that is known to be normally distributed with $\sigma = 6$.
    (a) If the sample mean is determined to be $\bar{x} = 42.3$, compute the test statistic. $z_0 = 1.92$
    (b) If the researcher decides to test this hypothesis at the $\alpha = 0.1$ level of significance, determine the critical value. $z_{0.1} = 1.28$
    (c) Draw a normal curve that depicts the critical region.
    (d) Will the researcher reject the null hypothesis? Why? Yes

13. To test $H_0: \mu = 100$ versus $H_1: \mu \neq 100$, a random sample of size $n = 23$ is obtained from a population that is known to be normally distributed with $\sigma = 7$.

(a) If the sample mean is determined to be $\bar{x} = 104.8$, compute the test statistic. $z_0 = 3.29$
(b) If the researcher decides to test this hypothesis at the $\alpha = 0.01$ level of significance, determine the critical values. $-z_{0.005} = -2.575$; $z_{0.005} = 2.575$
(c) Draw a normal curve that depicts the critical regions.
(d) Will the researcher reject the null hypothesis? Why? Yes

14. To test $H_0: \mu = 80$ versus $H_1: \mu < 80$, a random sample of size $n = 22$ is obtained from a population that is known to be normally distributed with $\sigma = 11$.
    (a) If the sample mean is determined to be $\bar{x} = 76.9$, compute the test statistic. $z_0 = -1.32$
    (b) If the researcher decides to test this hypothesis at the $\alpha = 0.02$ level of significance, determine the critical value. $-z_{0.02} = -2.05$
    (c) Draw a normal curve that depicts the critical region.
    (d) Will the researcher reject the null hypothesis? Why? No

15. To test $H_0: \mu = 20$ versus $H_1: \mu < 20$, a random sample of size $n = 18$ is obtained from a population that is known to be normally distributed with $\sigma = 3$.
    (a) If the sample mean is determined to be $\bar{x} = 18.3$, compute and interpret the *P*-value. 0.0082
    (b) If the researcher decides to test this hypothesis at the $\alpha = 0.05$ level of significance, will the researcher reject the null hypothesis? Why? Yes

16. To test $H_0: \mu = 4.5$ versus $H_1: \mu > 4.5$, a random sample of size $n = 13$ is obtained from a population that is known to be normally distributed with $\sigma = 1.2$.
    (a) If the sample mean is determined to be $\bar{x} = 4.9$, compute and interpret the *P*-value. 0.1151
    (b) If the researcher decides to test this hypothesis at the $\alpha = 0.1$ level of significance, will the researcher reject the null hypothesis? Why? No

17. To test $H_0: \mu = 105$ versus $H_1: \mu \neq 105$, a random sample of size $n = 35$ is obtained from a population whose standard deviation is known to be $\sigma = 12$.
    (a) Does the population need to be normally distributed to compute the *P*-value? No
    (b) If the sample mean is determined to be $\bar{x} = 101.2$, compute and interpret the *P*-value. 0.0614
    (c) If the researcher decides to test this hypothesis at the $\alpha = 0.05$ level of significance, will the researcher reject the null hypothesis? Why? No
    (d) Construct a 95% confidence interval to test the hypothesis. (97.22, 105.18); do not reject H_0

18. To test $H_0: \mu = 45$ versus $H_1: \mu \neq 45$, a random sample of size $n = 40$ is obtained from a population whose standard deviation is known to be $\sigma = 8$.
    (a) Does the population need to be normally distributed to compute the *P*-value? No
    (b) If the sample mean is determined to be $\bar{x} = 48.3$, compute and interpret the *P*-value. 0.0090
    (c) If the researcher decides to test this hypothesis at the $\alpha = 0.05$ level of significance, will the researcher reject the null hypothesis? Why? Yes
    (d) Construct a 95% confidence interval to test the hypothesis. (45.82, 50.78); reject H_0

Applying the Concepts

19. You Explain It! ATM Withdrawals According to the Crown ATM Network, the mean ATM withdrawal is $67. PayEase, Inc., manufacturers an ATM that allows one to pay bills (electric, water, parking tickets, and so on), as well as withdraw money. A review of 40 withdrawals shows the mean withdrawal is $73 from a PayEase ATM machine. Do people withdraw more money from a PayEase ATM machine?

(a) Determine the appropriate null and alternative hypotheses to answer the question. $H_0: \mu = 67$; $H_1: \mu > 67$

(b) Suppose the *P*-value for this test is 0.02. Explain what this value represents.

(c) Write a conclusion for this hypothesis test assuming an $\alpha = 0.05$ level of significance.

20. You Explain It! Are Women Getting Taller? In 1990, the mean height of women 20 years of age or older was 63.7 inches based on data obtained from the Centers for Disease Control and Prevention's *Advance Data Report*, No. 347. Suppose that a random sample of 45 women who are 20 years of age or older today results in a mean height of 63.9 inches.

(a) State the appropriate null and alternative hypotheses to assess whether women are taller today.

(b) Suppose the *P*-value for this test is 0.35. Explain what this value represents.

(c) Write a conclusion for this hypothesis test assuming an $\alpha = 0.10$ level of significance.

21. Ready for College? The ACT is a college entrance exam. In addition to administering this exam, researchers at ACT gauge high school students' readiness for college-level subjects. For example, the mean ACT score of all students who took the exam in 2007 was 21.2, with a standard deviation of 4.9. ACT recommends that students who plan to attend college take a minimum set of core mathematics courses. This core is 1 year of credit each in Algebra I, Algebra II, and Geometry. A random sample of 200 students who completed at least this core set of mathematics courses resulted in a mean score of 21.9 on the 2007 ACT.

(a) State the appropriate null and alternative hypotheses to assess whether students score better on the ACT when they take the core mathematics curriculum.

(b) Use the classical or *P*-value approach at the $\alpha = 0.05$ level of significance to test the hypothesis in part (a).

(c) Write a conclusion based on your results to part (b).

22. SAT Exam Scores A school administrator wonders if students whose first language is not English score differently on the math portion of the SAT exam than students whose first language is English. The mean SAT math score of students whose first language is English is 516, on the basis of data obtained from the College Board. A simple random sample of 20 students whose first language is not English results in a sample mean SAT math score of 522. SAT math scores are normally distributed, with a population standard deviation of 114.

(a) Why is it necessary for SAT math scores to be normally distributed to test the hypotheses using the methods of this section? Small sample

(b) Determine the appropriate null and alternative hypotheses to assess whether students whose first language is

not English score differently on the math portion of the SAT exam. $H_0: \mu = 516$; $H_1: \mu \neq 516$

(c) Use the classical or *P*-value approach at the $\alpha = 0.1$ level of significance to test the hypothesis in part (b).

(d) Write a conclusion based on your results to part (c).

23. Calcium in Rainwater Calcium is essential to tree growth because it promotes the formation of wood and maintains cell walls. In 1990, the concentration of calcium in precipitation in Chautauqua, New York, was 0.11 milligrams per liter (mg/L). A random sample of 10 precipitation dates in 2007 results in the following data:

0.065	0.087	0.070	0.262	0.126
0.183	0.120	0.234	0.313	0.108

Source: National Atmospheric Deposition Program

(a) Because the sample size is small, we must verify that calcium concentrations are normally distributed and the sample does not have any outliers. The normal probability plot and boxplot are shown. Are the conditions for conducting the hypothesis test satisfied? Yes

(b) Does the sample evidence suggest that calcium concentrations have changed since 1990? Assume that $\sigma = 0.08$ and use the $\alpha = 0.05$ level of significance. Yes; reject H_0

24. Acid Rain In 2002, the mean pH level of the rain in the Columbia River Gorge, Washington, was 5.27. A biologist wonders if the acidity of rain has changed. From a random sample of 16 rain dates in 2007, she obtains the following data:

5.11	5.70	5.27	5.59
4.98	5.13	5.49	4.81
5.23	5.16	5.58	5.86
5.20	5.54	5.34	5.39

Source: National Atmospheric Deposition Program

(a) Because the sample size is small, she must verify that the pH level is normally distributed and the sample does not contain any outliers. The normal probability plot and boxplot are shown. Are the conditions for testing the hypothesis satisfied? Yes

(b) Does the sample evidence suggest that the acidity of rain has changed? Assume that $\sigma = 0.27$. Use the $\alpha = 0.01$ level of significance.

25. **Filling Bottles** A certain brand of apple juice is supposed to have 64 ounces of juice. Because the punishment for under-filling bottles is severe, the target mean amount of juice is 64.05 ounces. However, the filling machine is not precise, and the exact amount of juice varies from bottle to bottle. The quality-control manager wishes to verify that the mean amount of juice in each bottle is 64.05 ounces so that she can be sure that the machine is not over- or underfilling. She randomly samples 22 bottles of juice, measures the content, and obtains the following data:

64.05	64.05	64.03	63.97	63.95	64.02
64.01	63.99	64.00	64.01	64.06	63.94
63.98	64.05	63.95	64.01	64.08	64.01
63.95	63.97	64.10	63.98		

(a) Because the sample size is small, she must verify that the amount of juice is normally distributed and the sample does not contain any outliers. The normal probability plot and boxplot are shown. Are the conditions for testing the hypothesis satisfied? Yes

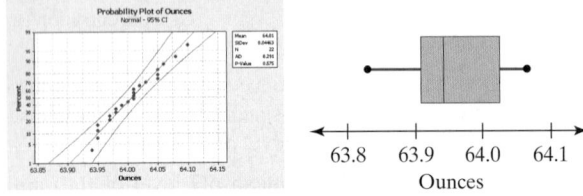

(b) Should the assembly line be shut down so that the machine can be recalibrated? Assume that $\sigma = 0.06$ ounces and use a 0.01 level of significance. Yes

(c) Explain why a level of significance of $\alpha = 0.01$ might be more reasonable than $\alpha = 0.1$. [*Hint:* Consider the consequences of incorrectly rejecting the null hypothesis.]

26. **Fuel Catalyst** To improve fuel efficiency and reduce pollution, the owner of a trucking fleet decides to install a new fuel catalyst in all his semitrucks. He feels that the catalyst will help to increase the number of miles per gallon. Before the installation, his trucks had a mean gas mileage of 5.6 miles per gallon. A random sample of 12 trucks after the installation gave the following gas mileages:

5.9	6.7	6.9	6.4	6.6	6.3
6.2	5.9	6.2	6.4	6.6	5.6

(a) Because the sample size is small, he must verify that mileage is normally distributed and the sample does not contain any outliers. The normal probability plot and boxplot are shown. Are the conditions for testing the hypothesis satisfied? Yes

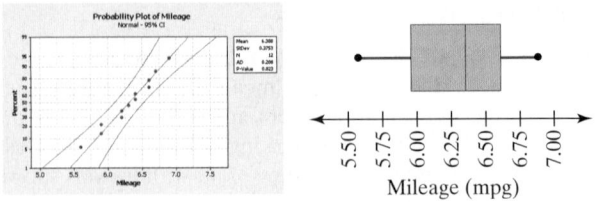

(b) Is the fuel catalyst effective? Assume that $\sigma = 0.5$ mile per gallon. Use the 0.05 level of significance. Reject H_0

27. **Real Estate Taxes** Real estate taxes are used to fund local education institutions, police protection, libraries, and other local public services. A household's real estate tax bill is based on the value of the house. In 2005, the mean real estate tax bill per \$1,000 assessed value for all households in the United States was \$11.38 with a standard deviation of \$8.02. A random sample of 50 rural households results in a sample mean real estate bill per \$1,000 assessed value of \$11.09

(a) What shape would you expect the distribution of the assessed value of a home have? Why? Based on this, why do we need a large sample size to conduct any hypothesis tests on assessed valuation? Skewed right

(b) Do you believe that rural homes pay less real estate taxes per \$1,000 of assessed value? Why or why not? No

28. **Birth Weight of Babies** The mean birth weight of all babies born in 2005 (the latest year that data were available) was 3,270 grams with a standard deviation of 610 grams. A random sample of 15 births to mothers who were less than 15 years of age results in a sample mean birth weight of 3,080 grams.

(a) To conduct a hypothesis test, what must be true about the population of birth weights? Normal

(b) Assuming that the requirement from part (a) is satisfied, does the evidence suggest that mothers less than 15 years of age have lower-birth-weight babies? Assume that $\sigma = 610$ grams. Use a 0.10 level of significance.

29. **Volume of Dell Computer Stock** The mean daily volume of Dell Computer stock in 2002 was $\mu = 24.1$ million shares with a standard deviation of $\sigma = 7.6$ million shares, according to Yahoo!Finance. A random sample of 40 trading days in 2007 resulted in a sample mean of 21.97 million shares traded.

(a) Based on the histogram and boxplot shown, why is a large sample necessary to conduct a hypothesis about the mean? Not normal with outliers

(b) Does the sample evidence suggest that the volume of Dell Computer stock is different today than it was in 2002? Use $\alpha = 0.05$ as the level of significance. No

30. **Volume of Google Stock** Google became a publicly traded company in August 2004. In 2005, its first full year as a publicly traded stock, the mean daily volume of the stock was

$\mu = 10.7$ million shares, with a standard deviation of $\sigma = 5.7$ million shares, according to Yahoo!Finance. A random sample of 35 trading days in 2007 resulted in a sample mean of 5.97 million shares traded.

(a) Based on the histogram and boxplot shown, why is a large sample necessary to conduct a hypothesis about the mean? *Skewed right with outliers*

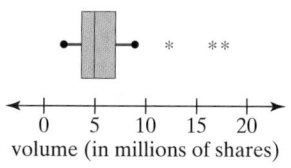

volume (in millions of shares)

(b) Does the sample evidence suggest that the volume of Google stock is different today than it was in 2005? Use $\alpha = 0.05$ as the level of significance. What does this say about the allure of the stock? *Yes*

31. Using Confidence Intervals to Test Hypotheses Test the hypotheses in Problem 23 by constructing a 99% confidence interval. *(0.0917, 0.2219); do not reject H_0*

32. Using Confidence Intervals to Test Hypotheses Test the hypotheses in Problem 24 by constructing a 95% confidence interval. *(5.204, 5.468); reject H_0*

33. Using Confidence Intervals to Test Hypotheses Test the hypotheses in Problem 29 by constructing a 95% confidence interval. *(19.615, 24.325); do not reject H_0*

NW

34. Using Confidence Intervals to Test Hypotheses Test the hypotheses in Problem 30 by constructing a 95% confidence interval. *(4.082, 7.858); reject H_0*

35. Statistical Significance versus Practical Significance A math teacher claims that she has developed a review course that increases the scores of students on the math portion of the SAT exam. Based on data from the College Board, SAT scores are normally distributed with $\mu = 515$ and $\sigma = 114$. The teacher obtains a random sample of 1,800 students, puts them through the review class, and finds that the mean SAT math score of the 1,800 students is 519.

(a) State the null and alternative hypotheses.
(b) Test the hypothesis at the $\alpha = 0.10$ level of significance. Is a mean SAT math score of 519 significantly higher than 515? *Reject H_0*
(c) Do you think that a mean SAT math score of 519 versus 515 will affect the decision of a school admissions administrator? In other words, does the increase in the score have any practical significance?
(d) Test the hypothesis at the $\alpha = 0.10$ level of significance with $n = 400$ students. Assume that the sample mean is still 519. Is a sample mean of 519 significantly more than 515? Conclude that large sample sizes cause P-values to shrink substantially, all other things being the same.

36. Statistical Significance versus Practical Significance The manufacturer of a daily dietary supplement claims that its product will help people lose weight. The company obtains a random sample of 950 adult males aged 20 to 74 who take the supplement and finds their mean weight loss after 8 weeks to be 0.9 pound. Assume that the population standard deviation weight loss is $\sigma = 7.2$ pounds.

35. (d) Do not reject H_0

(a) State the null and alternative hypotheses.
(b) Test the hypothesis at the $\alpha = 0.1$ level of significance. Is a mean weight loss of 0.9 pound significant?
(c) Do you think that a mean weight loss of 0.9 pound is worth the expense and commitment of a daily dietary supplement? In other words, does the weight loss have any practical significance?
(d) Test the hypothesis at the $\alpha = 0.1$ level of significance with $n = 40$ subjects. Assume that the sample mean weight loss is still 0.9 pound. Is a sample mean weight loss of 0.9 pound significantly more than 0 pounds? Conclude that large sample sizes cause P-values to shrink substantially, all other things being the same.

36. (a) H_0: $\mu = 0$ pound; H_1: $\mu > 0$ pound

37. Simulation Simulate drawing 50 simple random samples of size $n = 20$ from a population that is normally distributed with mean 80 and standard deviation 7.

(a) Test the null hypothesis H_0: $\mu = 80$ versus the alternative hypothesis H_1: $\mu \neq 80$.
(b) If we test this hypothesis at the $\alpha = 0.1$ level of significance, how many of the 50 samples would you expect to result in a Type I error? *5*
(c) Count the number of samples that lead to a rejection of the null hypothesis. Is it close to the expected value determined in part (b)?
(d) Describe how we know that a rejection of the null hypothesis results in making a Type I error in this situation.

36. (b) $z_0 = 3.85$; P-value < 0.0001; reject H_0

38. Simulation Simulate drawing 40 simple random samples of size $n = 35$ from a population that is exponentially distributed, with mean 8 and standard deviation $\sqrt{8}$.

(a) Test the null hypothesis H_0: $\mu = 8$ versus the alternative hypothesis H_1: $\mu \neq 8$.
(b) If we test this hypothesis at the $\alpha = 0.05$ level of significance, how many of the 40 samples would you expect to result in a Type I error? *2*
(c) Count the number of samples that lead to a rejection of the null hypothesis. Is it close to the expected value determined in part (b)?
(d) Describe how we know that a rejection of the null hypothesis results in making a Type I error in this situation.

39. What's the Problem? The head of institutional research at a university believed that the mean age of full-time students was declining. In 1995, the mean age of a full-time student was known to be 27.4 years. After looking at the enrollment records of all 4,934 full-time students in the current semester, he found that the mean age was 27.1 years, with a standard deviation of 7.3 years. He conducted a hypothesis of H_0: $\mu = 27.4$ years versus H_1: $\mu < 27.4$ years and obtained a P-value of 0.0019. He concluded that the mean age of full-time students did decline. Is there anything wrong with his research?

40. Putting It Together: Analyzing a Study An abstract in a journal article is a short synopsis of the study. The following abstract is from an article in the *British Medical Journal* (BMJ). The article uses *relative risk* in the analysis, which is common in health-related studies. **Relative risk** represents how many times more likely an individual is to have some condition when compared to an individual who does not have the condition.

36. (d) $z_0 = 0.79$; P-value $= 0.2148$; do not reject H_0

Childhood Cancer in Relation to Distance from High Voltage Power Lines in England and Wales: A Case-Control Study

Objective To determine whether there is an association between distance of home address at birth from high voltage power lines and the incidence of leukemia and other cancers in children in England and Wales.

Design Case-control study.

Setting Cancer registry and National Grid records.

Subjects Records of 29,081 children with cancer, including 9,700 with leukemia. Children were aged 0–14 years and born in England and Wales, 1962–95. Controls were individually matched for sex, approximate date of birth, and birth registration district. No active participation was required.

Main outcome measures Distance from home address at birth to the nearest high voltage overhead power line in existence at the time.

Results Compared with those who lived >600 m from a line at birth, children who lived within 200 m had a relative risk of leukemia of 1.69 (95% confidence interval 1.13 to 2.53); those born between 200 and 600 m had a relative risk of 1.23 (1.02 to 1.49). There was a significant (P-value < 0.01) trend in risk in relation to the reciprocal of distance from the line. No excess risk in relation to proximity to lines was found for other childhood cancers.

Conclusions There is an association between childhood leukemia and proximity of home address at birth to high voltage power lines, and the apparent risk extends to a greater distance than would have been expected from previous studies. About 4% of children in England and Wales live within 600 m of high voltage lines at birth. If the association is causal, about 1% of childhood leukemia in England and Wales would be attributable to these lines, though this estimate has considerable statistical uncertainty. There is no accepted biological mechanism to explain the epidemiological results; indeed, the relation may be due to chance or confounding.

Source: BMJ 2005;330:1290 (4 June), doi:10.1136/bmj.330.7503.1290

(a) Describe the statistical process. Include an interpretation of the confidence interval and P-value.
(b) Why is this study an observational study? What is a case-control study? Explain why a research objective such as this does not lend itself to a designed experiment.

TECHNOLOGY STEP-BY-STEP Hypothesis Tests Regarding μ, σ Known

TI-83/84 Plus
1. If necessary, enter raw data in L1.
2. Press STAT, highlight TESTS, and select 1:Z-Test.
3. If the data are raw, highlight DATA; make sure that List1 is set to L1 and Freq is set to 1. If summary statistics are known, highlight STATS and enter the summary statistics. Following σ, enter the population standard deviation. For the value of μ_0, enter the value of the mean stated in the null hypothesis.
4. Select the direction of the alternative hypothesis.
5. Highlight Calculate or Draw and press ENTER.

MINITAB
1. Enter raw data in column C1, if necessary.
2. Select the **Stat** menu, highlight **Basic Statistics**, and then highlight **1-Sample Z** . . . .
3. Click Options. In the cell marked "Alternative," select the appropriate direction for the alternative hypothesis. Click OK.
4. If you have raw data, enter C1 in the cell marked "Samples in columns:". If you have summary statistics, select the "Summarized data" radio button.

Enter the value of the sample size and sample mean. Enter the population standard deviation. Check the box for "Perform hypothesis test" and enter and the hypothesized mean (this is the value of the mean stated in the null hypothesis). Click OK.

Excel
1. Enter the raw data into column A. Highlight the data.
2. Load the DDXL Add-in, if necessary.
3. Select the **DDXL** menu and highlight **Hypothesis Tests**. From the drop-down menu under Function Type:, select 1 Var z Test.
4. Select the column that contains the raw data from the "Names and Columns" window. Use the ◀ arrow to select the data. Click OK.
5. Fill in the DataDesk window. In Step 1, click "Enter $\mu\varnothing$ and sd." Enter the value of the hypothesized mean (this is the value of the mean stated in the null hypothesis) and population standard deviation. In Step 2, select the level of significance. In Step 3, select the direction in the alternative hypothesis. Click Compute.

10.3 HYPOTHESIS TESTS FOR A POPULATION MEAN—POPULATION STANDARD DEVIATION UNKNOWN

Preparing for This Section   Before getting started, review the following:

- Sampling distribution of $\bar{x}$ (Section 8.1, pp. 427–438)
- The *t*-distribution (Section 9.2, pp. 476–479)

- Using probabilities to identify unusual events (Section 5.1, pp. 261–262)

Objective		Test hypotheses about a population mean with σ unknown

Note to Instructor

If you like, you can print out and distribute the Preparing for This Section quiz located in the Instructor's Resource Center. The purpose of the quiz is to verify that the students have the prerequisite knowledge for the section.

In Other Words

When σ is known, use Z; when σ is unknown, use t.

In Section 10.2, we assumed that the population standard deviation, σ, was known when testing hypotheses regarding the population mean. We now introduce procedures for testing hypotheses regarding a population mean when σ is not known. The only difference from the situation where σ is known is that we must use the *t*-distribution rather than the Z-distribution.

We do not replace σ with s and say that $\dfrac{\bar{x} - \mu}{\dfrac{s}{\sqrt{n}}}$ is normally distributed, with

mean 0 and standard deviation 1. Instead, $\dfrac{\bar{x} - \mu}{\dfrac{s}{\sqrt{n}}}$ follows **Student's *t*-distribution**

with $n - 1$ degrees of freedom. Let's review the properties of the *t*-distribution.

Properties of the *t*-Distribution

1. The *t*-distribution is different for different degrees of freedom.

2. The *t*-distribution is centered at 0 and is symmetric about 0.

3. The area under the curve is 1. Because of the symmetry, the area under the curve to the right of 0 equals the area under the curve to the left of 0, which equals $\frac{1}{2}$.

4. As t increases without bound, the graph approaches, but never equals, zero. As t decreases without bound, the graph approaches, but never equals, zero.

5. The area in the tails of the *t*-distribution is a little greater than the area in the tails of the standard normal distribution, because using s as an estimate of σ introduces more variability to the *t*-statistic.

6. As the sample size n increases, the density curve of t gets closer to the standard normal density curve. This result occurs because, as the sample size n increases, the values of s get closer to the values of σ, by the Law of Large Numbers.

 ### Test Hypotheses about a Population Mean with σ Unknown

From Section 10.2, we know that there are two approaches (besides using confidence intervals) that we can use to test hypotheses regarding a population mean, the classical approach and the *P*-value approach. We will present both methods here. Your instructor may choose one or both approaches.

Both the classical and the *P*-value approaches to testing a hypotheses about μ with σ unknown follow the exact same logic as testing a hypotheses about μ with σ

known. The only difference is that we use Student's t-distribution, rather than the normal distribution.

Testing Hypotheses Regarding a Population Mean with σ Unknown

To test hypotheses regarding the population mean with σ unknown, we use the following steps, provided that

1. The sample is obtained using simple random sampling.
2. The sample has no outliers, and the population from which the sample is drawn is normally distributed or the sample size, n, is large ($n \geq 30$).

Step 1: Determine the null and alternative hypotheses. The hypotheses can be structured in one of three ways:

Two-Tailed	Left-Tailed	Right-Tailed
$H_0: \mu = \mu_0$	$H_0: \mu = \mu_0$	$H_0: \mu = \mu_0$
$H_1: \mu \neq \mu_0$	$H_1: \mu < \mu_0$	$H_1: \mu > \mu_0$

Note: μ_0 is the assumed value of the population mean.

Step 2: Select a level of significance α, depending on the seriousness of making a Type I error.

Step 3: Compute the **test statistic**

$$t_0 = \frac{\bar{x} - \mu_0}{\dfrac{s}{\sqrt{n}}}$$

which follows Student's t-distribution with $n - 1$ degrees of freedom.

Classical Approach

Step 4: Use Table VI to determine the critical value using $n - 1$ degrees of freedom.

	Two-Tailed	Left-Tailed	Right-Tailed
Critical value(s)	$-t_{\frac{\alpha}{2}}$ and $t_{\frac{\alpha}{2}}$	$-t_\alpha$	t_α
Critical region			

Step 5: Compare the critical value with the test statistic.

Two-Tailed	Left-Tailed	Right-Tailed
If $t_0 < -t_{\frac{\alpha}{2}}$ or $t_0 > t_{\frac{\alpha}{2}}$, reject the null hypothesis.	If $t_0 < -t_\alpha$, reject the null hypothesis.	If $t_0 > t_\alpha$, reject the null hypothesis.

P-Value Approach

Step 4: Use Table VI to estimate the P-value using $n - 1$ degrees of freedom.

Two-Tailed	Left-Tailed	Right-Tailed

Step 5: If the P-value $< \alpha$, reject the null hypothesis.

Step 6: State the conclusion.

Notice that the procedure just presented requires either that the population from which the sample was drawn be normal or that the sample size be large ($n \geq 30$). The procedure is robust, so minor departures from normality will not adversely affect the results of the test. However, if the data include outliers, the procedure should not be used.

Just as we did for hypothesis tests with σ known, we will verify these assumptions by constructing normal probability plots (to assess normality) and boxplots (to discover whether there are outliers). If the normal probability plot indicates that the data do not come from a normal population or if the boxplot reveals outliers, nonparametric tests should be performed (Chapter 15).

Before we look at a couple of examples, it is important to understand that we cannot find exact *P*-values using the *t*-distribution table (Table VI) because the table provides *t*-values only for certain areas. However, we can use the table to calculate lower and upper bounds on the *P*-value. To find exact *P*-values, we use statistical software or a graphing calculator with advanced statistical features.

In Other Words

When σ is unknown, exact *P*-values can be found using technology.

EXAMPLE 1   ### Testing a Hypothesis about a Population Mean, Large Sample

Problem: According to the Centers for Disease Control, the mean number of cigarettes smoked per day by individuals who are daily smokers is 18.1. Do retired adults who are daily smokers smoke less than the general population of daily smokers? To answer this question, we obtain a random sample of 40 retired adults who are current daily smokers and record the number of cigarettes smoked on a randomly selected day. The data result in a sample mean of 16.8 cigarettes and a standard deviation of 4.7 cigarettes. Is there sufficient evidence at the $\alpha = 0.1$ level of significance to conclude that retired adults who are daily smokers smoke less than the general population of daily smokers?

Approach: We assume that there is no difference between the general population and retired adults regarding their smoking habits. We then determine the likelihood of obtaining a sample mean of 16.8 from a population whose mean is 18.1. If this result is unlikely, we will reject the assumption that the population mean number of cigarettes smoked by retired adults is the same as it is for the general population in favor of the more likely notion that the mean number of cigarettes smoked by retired adults daily is some value less than 18.1. However, if a sample mean of 16.8 from a population whose mean is 18.1 is not unusual and could occur due to sampling error, we will not reject the assumption that the population mean number of cigarettes smoked by retired adults is 18.1. Because the sample size is large, we follow the steps for testing hypotheses about a population mean on page 542.

Solution

Step 1: The researcher wants to know if retired adults who are daily smokers smoke less than the general population of daily smokers. The mean number of cigarettes smoked per day by individuals who are daily smokers is 18.1, so we have

$$H_0: \mu = 18.1 \quad \text{versus} \quad H_1: \mu < 18.1$$

This is a left-tailed test.

Step 2: The level of significance is $\alpha = 0.1$.

Step 3: The sample mean is $\bar{x} = 16.8$ cigarettes, and the sample standard deviation is $s = 4.7$ cigarettes. How likely is it to obtain a sample mean of 16.8 from a population whose mean is assumed to be 18.1? The test statistic is

$$t_0 = \frac{\bar{x} - \mu_0}{\frac{s}{\sqrt{n}}} = \frac{16.8 - 18.1}{\frac{4.7}{\sqrt{40}}} = -1.749$$

Classical Approach

Step 4: Because this is a left-tailed test, we determine the critical t-value at the $\alpha = 0.1$ level of significance with $n - 1 = 40 - 1 = 39$ degrees of freedom to be $-t_{0.1} = -1.304$. The critical region is displayed in Figure 13.

Figure 13

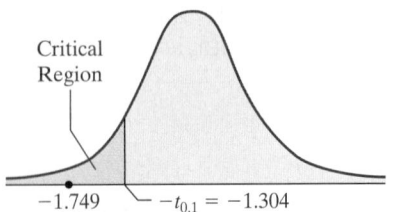

Critical Region

-1.749 $-t_{0.1} = -1.304$

Step 5: Because the test statistic $t_0 = -1.749$ is less than the critical value $-t_{0.1} = -1.304$, the researcher rejects the null hypothesis. We label this point in Figure 13.

P-Value Approach

Step 4: Because this is a left-tailed test, the P-value is the area under the t-distribution with $n - 1 = 40 - 1 = 39$ degrees of freedom to the left of the test statistic, $t_0 = -1.749$, as shown in Figure 14(a). That is, P-value $= P(t < t_0) = P(t < -1.749)$, with 39 degrees of freedom.

Because of the symmetry of the t-distribution, the area under the distribution to the left of -1.749 equals the area under the distribution to the right of 1.749. So, P-value $= P(t < -1.749) = P(t > 1.749)$. See Figure 14(b).

Figure 14

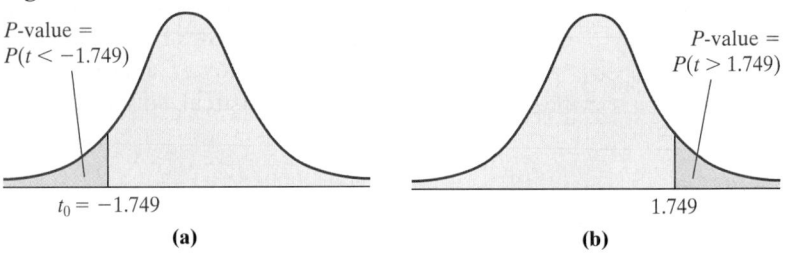

P-value = $P(t < -1.749)$

$t_0 = -1.749$

(a)

P-value = $P(t > 1.749)$

1.749

(b)

Using Table VI, we find the row that corresponds to 39 degrees of freedom. The value 1.749 lies between 1.685 and 2.023. The value of 1.685 has an area of 0.05 to the right under the t-distribution with 39 degrees of freedom. The area under the t-distribution with 39 degrees of freedom to the right of 2.023 is 0.025. See Figure 15.

Because 1.749 is between 1.685 and 2.023, the P-value is between 0.025 and 0.05. So

$$0.025 < P\text{-value} < 0.05$$

So fewer than 5 samples in 100 will result in a sample mean of 16.8 or less *if* the population mean is 18.1. The results we obtained do not seem to be consistent with the assumption that $\mu = 18.1$.

Step 5: Because the P-value is less than the level of significance $\alpha = 0.1$, we reject the null hypothesis. Put another way, the P-value is telling us that we obtained unusual results based on the assumption $\mu = 18.1$. Therefore, our assumption may be incorrect.

Step 6: There is sufficient evidence to conclude that retired adults who smoke daily smoke less than the general population of daily smokers at the $\alpha = 0.1$ level of significance.

Figure 15

					Area in Right Tail							
df	0.25	0.20	0.15	0.10	0.05	0.025	0.02	0.01	0.005	0.0025	0.001	0.0005
1	1.000	1.376	1.963	3.078	6.314	12.706	15.894	31.821	63.657	127.321	318.289	636.558
2	0.816	1.061	1.386	1.886	2.920	4.303	4.849	6.965	9.925	14.089	22.328	31.600
3	0.765	0.978	1.250	1.638	2.353	3.182	3.482	4.541	5.841	7.453	10.214	12.924
37	0.681	0.851	1.051	1.305	1.687	2.026	2.129	2.431	2.715	2.985	3.326	3.574
38	0.681	0.851	1.051	1.304	1.686	2.024	2.127	2.429	2.712	2.980	3.339	3.566
39	0.681	0.851	1.050	1.304	1.685	2.023	2.125	2.426	2.708	2.976	3.313	3.558
40	0.681	0.851	1.050	1.303	1.684	2.021	2.123	2.423	2.704	2.971	3.307	3.551
50	0.679	0.849	1.047	1.299	1.676	2.009	2.109	2.403	2.678	2.937	3.261	3.496
60	0.679	0.848	1.045	1.296	1.671	2.000	2.099	2.390	2.660	2.915	3.232	3.460

Obtaining the approximate *P*-value in Example 1 was somewhat challenging. With the aid of technology, we can find the exact *P*-value quite painlessly.

EXAMPLE 2   **Testing a Hypothesis for a Population Mean Using Technology**

Problem: Obtain an exact *P*-value for the problem in Example 1 using statistical software or a graphing calculator with advanced statistical features.

Approach: We will use a TI-84 Plus graphing calculator to obtain the *P*-value. The steps for testing hypotheses about a population mean with σ unknown using the TI-83/84 Plus graphing calculators, MINITAB, and Excel are given in the Technology Step-by-Step on page 552.

Solution: Figure 16(a) shows the results from the TI-84 Plus using the Calculate option. Figure 16(b) shows the results using the Draw option. The *P*-value is 0.044. Notice that the *P*-value is between 0.025 and 0.05. This agrees with the results in Example 1.

Figure 16

(a) Calculate Option   (b) Draw Option

Now Work Problem 13

EXAMPLE 3   **Testing a Hypothesis about a Population Mean, Small Sample**

Table 3		
19.68	20.66	19.56
19.98	20.65	19.61
20.55	20.36	21.02
21.50	19.74	

Source: Michael Carlisle, student at Joliet Junior College

Problem: The "fun size" of a Snickers bar is supposed to weigh 20 grams. Because the punishment for selling candy bars that weigh less than 20 grams is so severe, the manufacturer calibrates the machine so that the mean weight is 20.1 grams. The quality-control engineer at M&M–Mars, the company that manufactures Snickers bars, is concerned that the machine that manufactures the candy is miscalibrated. She obtains a random sample of 11 candy bars, weighs them, and obtains the data in Table 3. Should the machine be shut down and calibrated? Because shutting down the plant is very expensive, she decides to conduct the test at the $\alpha = 0.01$ level of significance.

Approach: We assume that the machine is calibrated correctly. That is, we assume there is "no difference" between the actual mean weight of the candy and the expected mean weight. We want to know whether the machine is incorrectly calibrated, which would result in a mean weight that is too high or too low. Therefore, this is a two-tailed test.

Before we can perform the hypothesis test, we must verify that the data come from a population that is normally distributed with no outliers. We construct a normal probability plot and boxplot to verify these requirements. We then proceed to follow Steps 1 through 6.

Solution: Figure 17 on the next page displays the normal probability plot and boxplot. The normal probability plot indicates that the data could come from a population that is approximately normal. The boxplot does not show any outliers. We can proceed with the hypothesis test.

Figure 17

Step 1: The quality-control engineer wishes to determine whether the Snickers have a mean weight of 20.1 grams or not. The hypotheses can be written

$$H_0: \mu = 20.1 \quad \text{versus} \quad H_1: \mu \neq 20.1$$

This is a two-tailed test.

Step 2: The level of significance is $\alpha = 0.01$.

Step 3: From the data in Table 3, the sample mean is $\bar{x} = 20.3$, and the sample standard deviation is $s = 0.64$. How likely is it to obtain a sample mean of 20.3 ounces from a population whose mean is 20.1 ounces? The test statistic is

$$t_0 = \frac{\bar{x} - \mu_0}{\dfrac{s}{\sqrt{n}}} = \frac{20.3 - 20.1}{\dfrac{0.64}{\sqrt{11}}} = 1.036$$

Classical Approach

Step 4: Because this is a two-tailed test, we determine the critical t-values at the $\alpha = 0.01$ level of significance with $n - 1 = 11 - 1 = 10$ degrees of freedom to be $-t_{0.01/2} = -t_{0.005} = -3.169$ and $t_{0.01/2} = t_{0.005} = 3.169$. The critical regions are displayed in Figure 18.

Figure 18

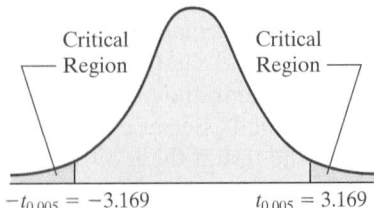

Step 5: The test statistic is $t_0 = -1.036$. Because the test statistic is between the critical values $-t_{0.005} = -3.169$ and $t_{0.005} = 3.169$, the quality-control engineer does not reject the null hypothesis.

P-Value Approach

Step 4: Because this is a two-tailed test, the P-value is the area under the t-distribution with $n - 1 = 11 - 1 = 10$ degrees of freedom to the left of $-t_0 = -1.036$ and to the right of $t_0 = 1.036$, as shown in Figure 19. That is, P-value $= P(t < -1.036) + P(t > 1.036) = 2P(t > 1.036)$, with 10 degrees of freedom.

Using Table VI, we find the row that corresponds to 10 degrees of freedom. The value 1.036 lies between 0.879 and 1.093. The value of 0.879 has an area of 0.20 to the right under the t-distribution. The area under the t-distribution with 10 degrees of freedom to the right of 1.093 is 0.15.

Because 1.036 is between 0.879 and 1.093, the P-value is between 2(0.15) and 2(0.20). So

$$0.30 < P\text{-value} < 0.40$$

Using MINITAB, we find that the exact P-value is 0.323. About 32 out of 100 samples would result in a sample mean as extreme or more extreme than the one we obtained *if* the true mean is 20.1 ounces. The result we obtained is not unusual.

Figure 19

The sum of these two areas is the P-value

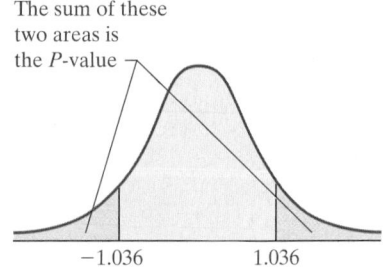

Step 5: Because the P-value is greater than the level of significance (0.323 > 0.01), the quality-control engineer does not reject the null hypothesis.

Step 6: There is not sufficient evidence to conclude that the Snickers do not have a mean weight of 20.1 grams at the $\alpha = 0.01$ level of significance. The machine should not be shut down.

Now Work Problem 21

Sections 10.2 and 10.3 discussed performing hypothesis tests about a population mean. The main criterion for choosing which test to use is whether the population standard deviation, σ, is known. Provided that the population from which the sample is drawn is normal or that the sample size is large,

- if σ is known, use the Z-test procedures from Section 10.2;
- if σ is unknown, use the t-test procedures from Section 10.3.

In Section 10.4, we will discuss testing hypotheses about a population proportion.

Note to Instructor

The purpose of this activity is to give students a hands-on experience with hypothesis testing involving means. Be sure to tell students the length of the rope only after all estimates have been reported. The activity could be elaborated to include discussion of bias and reliability in measurements or other related topics. Time limit: 30 to 45 minutes depending on discussion.

IN CLASS ACTIVITY

Stringing Them Along (Part I)

How skilled are people at estimating the length of a piece of rope? Do you think that they will tend to overestimate its length? Underestimate? Or are you not sure?

(a) Look at the piece of rope that your instructor is holding and estimate the length of the rope in inches.

(b) Using the null hypothesis $H_0: \mu = \mu_0$, where μ_0 represents the actual length of the rope, select an appropriate alternative hypothesis and a level of significance based on your responses to the questions posed at the beginning of the activity.

(c) Obtain the actual length of the rope from your instructor. Combine the data for the entire class and test the hypothesis formed in part (b). What did you conclude?

[**Note:** Save the class data for use in another activity.]

10.3 ASSESS YOUR UNDERSTANDING

Concepts and Vocabulary

1. State the requirements that must be satisfied to test hypotheses about a population mean with σ unknown.

2. Determine the critical value for a right-tailed test of a population mean with σ unknown at the $\alpha = 0.01$ level of significance with 15 degrees of freedom.   2.602

3. Determine the critical value for a two-tailed test of a population mean with σ unknown at the $\alpha = 0.05$ level of significance with 12 degrees of freedom. $-2.179; 2.179$

4. Determine the critical value for a left-tailed test of a population mean with σ unknown at the $\alpha = 0.05$ level of significance with 19 degrees of freedom. -1.729

Skill Building

5. To test $H_0: \mu = 50$ versus $H_1: \mu < 50$, a simple random sample of size $n = 24$ is obtained from a population that is known to be normally distributed.

   (a) If $\bar{x} = 47.1$ and $s = 10.3$, compute the test statistic.
   $t_0 = -1.379$
   (b) If the researcher decides to test this hypothesis at the $\alpha = 0.05$ level of significance, determine the critical value. $-t_{0.05} = -1.714$
   (c) Draw a t-distribution that depicts the critical region.
   (d) Will the researcher reject the null hypothesis? Why? No

6. To test $H_0: \mu = 40$ versus $H_1: \mu > 40$, a simple random sample of size $n = 25$ is obtained from a population that is known to be normally distributed.   6. (a) $t_0 = 2.674$

   (a) If $\bar{x} = 42.3$ and $s = 4.3$, compute the test statistic.
   (b) If the researcher decides to test this hypothesis at the $\alpha = 0.1$ level of significance, determine the critical value. $t_{0.1} = 1.318$
   (c) Draw a t-distribution that depicts the critical region.
   (d) Will the researcher reject the null hypothesis? Why? Yes

7. To test $H_0: \mu = 100$ versus $H_1: \mu \neq 100$, a simple random sample of size $n = 23$ is obtained from a population that is known to be normally distributed.   7. (a) $t_0 = 2.502$

   (a) If $\bar{x} = 104.8$ and $s = 9.2$, compute the test statistic.
   (b) If the researcher decides to test this hypothesis at the $\alpha = 0.01$ level of significance, determine the critical values. $-t_{0.005} = -2.819; t_{0.005} = 2.819$
   (c) Draw a t-distribution that depicts the critical region.
   (d) Will the researcher reject the null hypothesis? Why? No
   (e) Construct a 99% confidence interval to test the hypothesis.

8. To test $H_0: \mu = 80$ versus $H_1: \mu < 80$, a simple random sample of size $n = 22$ is obtained from a population that is known to be normally distributed.   8. (a) $t_0 = -1.711$

   (a) If $\bar{x} = 76.9$ and $s = 8.5$, compute the test statistic.
   (b) If the researcher decides to test this hypothesis at the $\alpha = 0.02$ level of significance, determine the critical value. $-t_{0.02} = -2.189$

   7. (e) $(99.39, 110.21)$; do not reject H_0

(c) Draw a t-distribution that depicts the critical region.

(d) Will the researcher reject the null hypothesis? Why? No

9. To test $H_0: \mu = 20$ versus $H_1: \mu < 20$, a simple random sample of size $n = 18$ is obtained from a population that is known to be normally distributed.   9. (a) $t_0 = -1.677$

(a) If $\bar{x} = 18.3$ and $s = 4.3$, compute the test statistic.

(b) Draw a t-distribution with the area that represents the P-value shaded.

(c) Approximate and interpret the P-value. 0.0559

(d) If the researcher decides to test this hypothesis at the $\alpha = 0.05$ level of significance, will the researcher reject the null hypothesis? Why? No

10. To test $H_0: \mu = 4.5$ versus $H_1: \mu > 4.5$, a simple random sample of size $n = 13$ is obtained from a population that is known to be normally distributed.   10. (a) $t_0 = 1.109$

(a) If $\bar{x} = 4.9$ and $s = 1.3$, compute the test statistic.

(b) Draw a t-distribution with the area that represents the P-value shaded.

(c) Approximate and interpret the P-value. 0.1445

(d) If the researcher decides to test this hypothesis at the $\alpha = 0.1$ level of significance, will the researcher reject the null hypothesis? Why? No

11. To test $H_0: \mu = 105$ versus $H_1: \mu \neq 105$, a simple random sample of size $n = 35$ is obtained.   11. (b) $t_0 = -3.108$

(a) Does the population have to be normally distributed to test this hypothesis by using the methods presented in this section? Why? No

(b) If $\bar{x} = 101.9$ and $s = 5.9$, compute the test statistic.

(c) Draw a t-distribution with the area that represents the P-value shaded.

(d) Approximate and interpret the P-value. 0.0038

(e) If the researcher decides to test this hypothesis at the $\alpha = 0.01$ level of significance, will the researcher reject the null hypothesis? Why? Yes

12. To test $H_0: \mu = 45$ versus $H_1: \mu \neq 45$, a simple random sample of size $n = 40$ is obtained.   12. (b) $t_0 = 2.455$

(a) Does the population have to be normally distributed to test this hypothesis by using the methods presented in this section? Why? No

(b) If $\bar{x} = 48.3$ and $s = 8.5$, compute the test statistic.

(c) Draw a t-distribution with the area that represents the P-value shaded.

(d) Determine and interpret the P-value. 0.0186

(e) If the researcher decides to test this hypothesis at the $\alpha = 0.01$ level of significance, will the researcher reject the null hypothesis? Why? No

(f) Construct a 99% confidence interval to test the hypothesis. (44.66, 51.94); do not reject H_0

Applying the Concepts

13. **Effects of Alcohol on the Brain** In a study published in the *American Journal of Psychiatry* (157:737–744, May 2000), researchers wanted to measure the effect of alcohol on the development of the hippocampal region in adolescents. The hippocampus is the portion of the brain responsible for long-term memory storage. The researchers randomly selected 12 adolescents with alcohol use disorders. They wanted to determine whether the hippocampal volumes in the alcoholic adolescents were less than the normal volume of 9.02 cubic centimeters (cm³). An analysis of the sample data revealed that the hippocampal volume is approximately

normal with $\bar{x} = 8.10$ and $s = 0.7$. Conduct the appropriate test at the $\alpha = 0.01$ level of significance. Reject H_0

14. **Effects of Plastic Resin** Para-nonylphenol is found in polyvinyl chloride (PVC) used in the food processing and packaging industries. Researchers wanted to determine the effect this substance had on the organ weight of first-generation mice when both parents were exposed to 50 micrograms per liter (μg/L) of para-nonylphenol in drinking water for 4 weeks. After 4 weeks, the mice were bred. After 100 days, the off-spring of the exposed parents were sacrificed and the kidney weights were determined. The mean weight of the 12 offspring was found to be 396.9 milligrams (mg), with a standard deviation of 45.4 mg. Is there significant evidence to conclude that the kidney weight of the offspring whose parents were exposed to 50 μg/L of para-nonylphenol in drinking water for 4 weeks is greater than 355.7 mg, the mean weight of kidneys in normal 100-day old mice at the $\alpha = 0.05$ level of significance? Reject H_0

Source: Vendula Kyselova et al., "Effects of p-nonylphenol and resveratrol on body and organ weight and in vivo fertility of outbred CD-1 mice," *Reproductive Biology and Endocrinology*, 2003

15. **Credit Scores** A Fair Isaac Corporation (FICO) score is used by credit agencies (such as mortgage companies and banks) to assess the creditworthiness of individuals. Its value ranges from 300 to 850. An individual with a FICO score over 700 is considered to be a quality credit risk. According to Fair Isaac Corporation, the mean FICO score is 703.5. A credit analyst wondered whether high-income individuals (incomes in excess of \$100,000 per year) had higher credit scores. He obtained a random sample of 40 high-income individuals and found the sample mean credit score to be 714.2 with a standard deviation of 83.2. Conduct the appropriate test to determine if high-income individuals have higher FICO scores at the $\alpha = 0.05$ level of significance. Do not reject H_0

16. **TVaholics** According to the American Time Use Survey, the typical American spends 154.8 minutes (2.58 hours) per day watching television. Do Internet users spend less time each day watching television? A survey of 50 Internet users results in a mean time watching television per day of 128.7 minutes, with a standard deviation of 46.5 minutes. Conduct the appropriate test to determine if Internet users spend less time watching television at the $\alpha = 0.05$ level of significance.

Source: Norman H. Nie and D. Sunshine Hillygus. "Where Does Internet Time Come From? A Reconnaissance." *IT & Society*, 1(2) Reject H_0

17. **Normal Temperature** Carl Reinhold August Wunderlich said that the mean temperature of humans is 98.6°F. Researchers Philip Mackowiak, Steven Wasserman, and Myron Levine [*JAMA*, Sept. 23–30 1992; 268(12):1578–80] thought that the mean temperature of humans is less than 98.6°F. They measured the temperature of 148 healthy adults 1 to 4 times daily for 3 days, obtaining 700 measurements. The sample data resulted in a sample mean of 98.2°F and a sample standard deviation of 0.7°F.

(a) Test whether the mean temperature of humans is less than 98.6°F at the $\alpha = 0.01$ level of significance using the classical approach. $t_0 = -15.119$; reject H_0

(b) Determine and interpret the P-value.

18. **Normal Temperature** Carl Reinhold August Wunderlich said that the mean temperature of humans is 98.6°F. Researchers

Philip Mackowiak, Steven Wasserman, and Myron Levine [*JAMA*, Sept. 23–30 1992; 268(12):1578–80] measured the temperatures of 26 females 1 to 4 times daily for 3 days to get a total of 123 measurements. The sample data yielded a sample mean of 98.4°F and a sample standard deviation of 0.7°F.

(a) Using the classical approach, judge whether the normal temperature of women is less than 98.6°F at the $\alpha = 0.01$ level of significance. $t_0 = -3.164$; reject H_0

(b) Determine and interpret the *P*-value.   *P*-value = 0.001

19. **Age of Death-Row Inmates** In 2002, the mean age of an inmate on death row was 40.7 years, according to data obtained from the U.S. Department of Justice. A sociologist wondered whether the mean age of a death-row inmate has changed since then. She randomly selects 32 death-row inmates and finds that their mean age is 38.9, with a standard deviation of 9.6. Construct a 95% confidence interval about the mean age. What does the interval imply?   (35.44, 42.36)

20. **Energy Consumption** In 2001, the mean household expenditure for energy was $1,493, according to data obtained from the U.S. Energy Information Administration. An economist wanted to know whether this amount has changed significantly from its 2001 level. In a random sample of 35 households, he found the mean expenditure (in 2001 dollars) for energy during the most recent year to be $1,618, with standard deviation $321. Construct a 95% confidence interval about the mean energy expenditure. What does the interval imply?

21. **Conforming Golf Balls** The U.S. Golf Association requires that golf balls have a diameter that is 1.68 inches. To determine if Maxfli XS golf balls conform to USGA standards, a random sample of Maxfli XS golf balls was selected. Their diameters are shown in the table.

1.683	1.677	1.681
1.685	1.678	1.686
1.684	1.684	1.673
1.685	1.682	1.674

Source: Michael McCraith, Joliet Junior College

(a) Because the sample size is small, the engineer must verify that the diameter is normally distributed and the sample does not contain any outliers. The normal probability plot and boxplot are shown. Are the conditions for testing the hypothesis satisfied?   Yes

(b) Do the golf balls conform to USGA standards? Use the $\alpha = 0.05$ level of significance.

22. **Reading Rates** Michael Sullivan, son of the author, decided to enroll in a reading course that allegedly increases reading speed and comprehension. Prior to enrolling in the class, Michael read 198 words per minute (wpm). The following data represent the words per minute read for 10 different passages read after the course.

206	217	197	199	210
210	197	212	227	209

(a) Because the sample size is small, we must verify that reading speed is normally distributed and the sample does not contain any outliers. The normal probability plot and boxplot are shown. Are the conditions for testing the hypothesis satisfied?   Yes

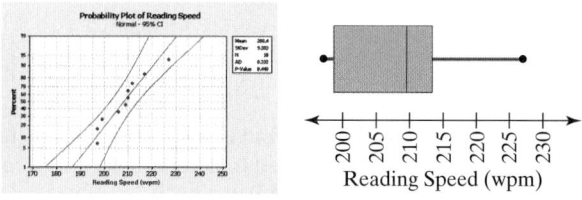

(b) Was the class effective? Use the $\alpha = 0.10$ level of significance.   Yes; $t_0 = 3.499$; reject H_0

23. **Waiting in Line** The mean waiting time at the drive-through of a fast-food restaurant from the time an order is placed to the time the order is received is 84.3 seconds. A manager devises a new drive-through system that he believes will decrease wait time. He initiates the new system at his restaurant and measures the wait time for 10 randomly selected orders. The wait times are provided in the table.

108.5	67.4	58.0	75.9	65.1
80.4	95.5	86.3	70.9	72.0

(a) Because the sample size is small, the manager must verify that wait time is normally distributed and the sample does not contain any outliers. The normal probability plot and boxplot are shown. Are the conditions for testing the hypothesis satisfied?   Yes

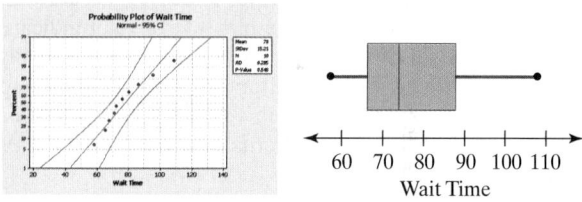

(b) Is the new system effective? Use the $\alpha = 0.1$ level of significance.   No; $t_0 = -1.310$; do not reject H_0

24. **Calibrating a pH Meter** An engineer wants to measure the bias in a pH meter. She uses the meter to measure the pH in 14 neutral substances (pH = 7.0) and obtains the data shown in the table.

7.01	7.04	6.97	7.00	6.99	6.97	7.04
7.04	7.01	7.00	6.99	7.04	7.07	6.97

(a) Because the sample size is small, the engineer must verify that pH is normally distributed and the sample does not contain any outliers. The normal probability plot and boxplot are shown. Are the conditions for testing the hypothesis satisfied?   Yes

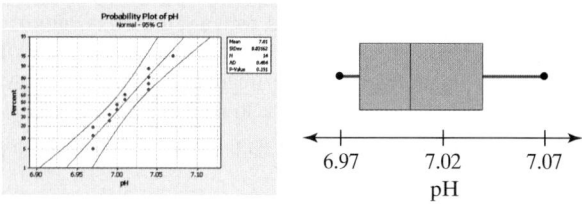

(b) Is there evidence to support that the pH meter is correctly calibrated? Use the $\alpha = 0.05$ level of significance.   No; $t_0 = 1.183$; do not reject H_0

25. Earnings Predictions One of the most important factors in judging the value of a publicly traded company is its earnings. Therefore, stock analysts will attempt to predict the earnings of a company. The following data represent the deviation from the actual earnings of General Electric for 2007. Negative values mean the actual earnings were less than predicted, while positive values mean that the actual earnings were more than predicted.

Note: General Electric earned $2.17 per share in 2007.

0.02	−0.03	0.00	0.02	−0.05	−0.02
−0.01	−0.04	0.01	−0.03	−0.03	−0.02

A normal probability plot and boxplot indicate that the data could come from a population that is normally distributed with no outliers. A researcher wanted to determine if, on average, stock analyst's earnings estimates were on target. The following display shows output from MINITAB.

One-Sample T: Deviation

```
Test of mu = 0 vs not = 0

Variable    N     Mean    StDev  SE Mean         95% CI           T       P
Deviation  12  -0.01500  0.02316  0.00669  (-0.02971, -0.00029)  -2.24   0.046
```

(a) Explain why the researcher tested $H_0: \mu = 0$ versus $H_1: \mu \neq 0$.

(b) Based on the output, what should the researcher conclude if she uses an $\alpha = 0.05$ level of significance.

(c) The researcher's boss does not think it would be good for the industry to state that analyst's earnings estimates are incorrect, on average. So he tells the researcher to change her level of significance to $\alpha = 0.01$. Explain why this is an example of bad statistics.

---

26. How Accurate Is the Weather Forecast? The following data represent the deviation of the actual high temperature for randomly selected days from the predicted temperature. Negative values mean that the actual high temperature is less than predicted, while positive values mean that the actual high temperature is more than predicted. Does the sample evidence imply that the weather forecast is accurate, on average? A normal probability plot and boxplot indicate that the data could come from a population that is normally distributed with no outliers. Output from a TI-84 Plus graphing calculator is supplied to help you answer the question. Be sure to state the null and alternative hypothesis, the P-value, and a conclusion.

−1	1	2	0	0
2	4	−3	1	−1

```
T-Test
μ≠0
t=.8075728531
p=.4401575297
x̄=.5
Sx=1.957890021
n=10
```

27. Soybean Yield The mean yield per acre of soybeans on farms in the United States in 2008 was 43 bushels, according to data obtained from the U.S. Department of Agriculture. A farmer in Iowa believed the yield was higher than the reported mean. He randomly sampled 35 acres on his farm and determined the mean yield to be 45.1 bushels, with a standard deviation of 2.5 bushels. He computed the P-value to be less than 0.0001 and concluded that the U.S. Department of Agriculture was wrong. Why should his conclusions be looked on with skepticism?

28. Significance Test Applet Load the hypothesis tests for a mean applet.

(a) Set the shape to normal, the mean to 100, and the standard deviation to 15. These parameters describe the distribution of IQ scores. Obtain 1,000 simple random samples of size $n = 10$ from this population, and test whether the mean is different from 100. How many samples led to a rejection of the null hypothesis if $\alpha = 0.05$? How many would we expect to lead to a rejection of the null hypothesis? For this level of significance, what is the probability of a Type I error?

(b) Set the shape to normal, the mean to 100, and the standard deviation to 15. These parameters describe the distribution of IQ scores. Obtain 1,000 simple random samples of size $n = 30$ from this population, and test whether the mean is different from 100. How many samples led to a rejection of the null hypothesis if $\alpha = 0.05$? How many would we expect to lead to a rejection of the null hypothesis? For this level of significance, what is the probability of a Type I error?

(c) Compare the results of parts (a) and (b). Did the sample size have any effect on the number of samples that incorrectly rejected the null hypothesis?

29. Significance Test Applet: Violating Assumptions Load the hypothesis tests for a mean applet.

(a) Set the shape to right skewed, the mean to 50, and the standard deviation to 10. Obtain 1,000 simple random samples of size $n = 8$ from this population, and test whether the mean is different from 50. How many of the samples led to a rejection of the null hypothesis if $\alpha = 0.05$? How many would we expect to lead to a rejection of the null hypothesis if $\alpha = 0.05$? What might account for any discrepancies?

(b) Set the shape to right skewed, the mean to 50, and the standard deviation to 10. Obtain 1,000 simple random samples of size $n = 40$ from this population, and test whether the mean is different from 50. How many of the samples led to a rejection of the null hypothesis if $\alpha = 0.05$? How many would we expect to lead to a rejection of the null hypothesis if $\alpha = 0.05$?

30. Simulation Simulate drawing 40 simple random samples of size $n = 20$ from a population that is normally distribution with mean 50 and standard deviation 10.

(a) Test the null hypothesis H_0: $\mu = 50$ versus the alternative hypothesis H_1: $\mu \neq 50$ for each of the 40 samples using a t-test.

(b) If we were testing this hypothesis at the $\alpha = 0.05$ level of significance, how many of the 40 samples would you expect to result in a Type I error?

(c) Count the number of samples that lead to a rejection of the null hypothesis. Is it close to the expected value determined in part (b)?

(d) Describe why we know a rejection of the null hypothesis results in making a Type I error in this situation.

Consumer Reports® Eyeglass Lenses

Eyeglasses are part medical device and part fashion statement, a marriage that has always made them a tough buy. Aside from the thousands of different frames the consumer has to choose from, various lens materials and coatings can add to the durability, and the cost, of a pair of eyeglasses. One manufacturer even goes so far as to claim that its lenses are "the most scratch-resistant plastic lenses ever made." With a claim like that, we had to test the lenses.

One test involved tumbling the lenses in a drum containing scrub pads of grit of varying size and hardness. Afterward, readings of the lenses' haze were taken on a spectrometer to determine how scratched they had become. To evaluate their scratch resistance, we measured the difference between the haze reading before and after tumbling.

The photo illustrates the difference between an uncoated lens (on the left) and the manufacturer's "scratch-resistant" lens (on the right).

The following table contains the haze measurements both before and after the scratch resistance test for this manufacturer. Haze difference is measured by subtracting the before score from the after score. In other words, haze difference is computed as After – Before.

Before	After	Difference
0.18	0.72	0.54
0.16	0.85	0.69
0.20	0.71	0.51
0.17	0.42	0.25
0.21	0.76	0.55
0.21	0.51	0.30

(a) Suppose it is known that the closest competitor to the manufacturer's lens has a mean haze difference of 0.6. Does the evidence indicate that this manufacturer's lenses are more scratch resistant?

(b) Write a paragraph for the readers of *Consumer Reports* magazine that explains your findings.

Note to Readers: *In many cases, our test protocol and analytical methods are more complicated than described in these examples. The data and discussions have been modified to make the material more appropriate for the audience.*

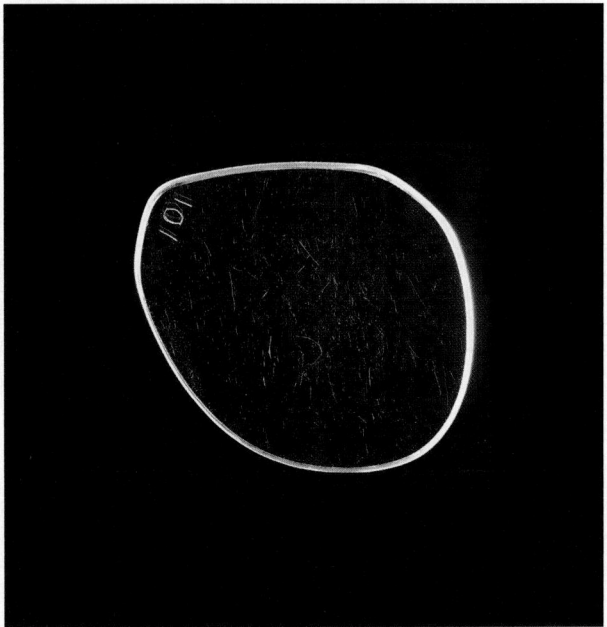

TECHNOLOGY STEP-BY-STEP   Hypothesis Tests Regarding μ, σ Unknown

TI-83/84 Plus

1. If necessary, enter raw data in L1.

2. Press STAT, highlight TESTS, and select 2:T-Test.

3. If the data are raw, highlight DATA; make sure that List1 is set to L1 and Freq is set to 1. If summary statistics are known, highlight STATS and enter the summary statistics. For the value of μ_0, enter the value of the mean stated in the null hypothesis.

4. Select the direction of the alternative hypothesis.

5. Highlight **Calculate** or **Draw** and press ENTER. The TI-83/84 gives the *P*-value.

MINITAB

1. Enter raw data in column C1.

2. Select the **Stat** menu, highlight **Basic Statistics**, then highlight **1-Sample t . . . .**

3. If you have raw data, enter C1 in the cell marked "Samples in columns.": If you have summary statistics, select the "Summarized data" radio button. Enter the value of the sample size, sample mean, and

sample standard deviation. Check the box for "Perform hypothesis test" and enter the hypothesized mean (this is the value of the mean stated in the null hypothesis). Click OK.

Excel

1. Enter the raw data into column A. Highlight the data.

2. Load the DDXL Add-in, if necessary.

3. Select the **DDXL** menu and highlight **Hypothesis Tests**. From the drop-down menu under Function Type:, select 1 Var t Test.

4. Select the column that contains the raw data from the "Names and Columns" window. Use the ◀ arrow to select the data. Click OK.

5. Fill in the DataDesk window. In Step 1, click "Set $\mu\varnothing$" and enter the value of the hypothesized mean (this is the value of the mean stated in the null hypothesis). In Step 2, select the level of significance. In Step 3, select the direction in the alternative hypothesis. Click Compute.

10.4 HYPOTHESIS TESTS FOR A POPULATION PROPORTION

Preparing for This Section   Before getting started, review the following:

- Binomial probability distribution (Section 6.2, pp. 343–354)

- Distribution of the sample proportion (Section 8.2, pp. 442–448)

Objectives	
1	Test hypotheses about a population proportion
2	Test hypotheses about a population proportion using the binomial probability distribution

1 Test Hypotheses about a Population Proportion

Recall that the best point estimate of *p*, the proportion of the population with a certain characteristic, is given by

$$\hat{p} = \frac{x}{n}$$

where *x* is the number of individuals in the sample with the specified characteristic and *n* is the sample size. Recall from Section 8.2 that the sampling distribution of $\hat{p}$ is approximately normal, with mean $\mu_{\hat{p}} = p$ and standard deviation

$\sigma_{\hat{p}} = \sqrt{\dfrac{p(1 - p)}{n}}$, provided that the following requirements are satisfied.

1. The sample is a simple random sample.

2. $np(1 - p) \geq 10$.

3. The sampled values are independent of each other.

CAUTION When determining the standard error for the sampling distribution of $\hat{p}$ for hypothesis testing, use the assumed value of the population proportion, p_0.

Testing hypotheses for the population proportion, p, follows the same logic as the testing of hypotheses about a population mean with σ known. The only difference is that the **test statistic** is

$$z_0 = \frac{\hat{p} - p_0}{\sqrt{\dfrac{p_0(1 - p_0)}{n}}}$$

where p_0 is the value of the population proportion stated in the null hypothesis.

Notice that we are using p_0 in computing the standard error rather than $\hat{p}$ (as we did in computing confidence intervals about p). This is because, when we test a hypothesis, the null hypothesis is always assumed true. Therefore, we are assuming that the population proportion is p_0.

Testing Hypotheses Regarding a Population Proportion, p

To test hypotheses regarding the population proportion, we can use the following steps, provided that

1. The sample is obtained by simple random sampling.
2. $np_0(1 - p_0) \geq 10$.
3. The sampled values are independent of each other.

Step 1: Determine the null and alternative hypotheses. The hypotheses can be structured in one of three ways:

Two-Tailed	Left-Tailed	Right-Tailed
$H_0: p = p_0$	$H_0: p = p_0$	$H_0: p = p_0$
$H_1: p \neq p_0$	$H_1: p < p_0$	$H_1: p > p_0$

Note: p_0 is the assumed value of the population proportion.

Step 2: Select a level of significance α, depending on the seriousness of making a Type I error.

Step 3: Compute the **test statistic**

$$z_0 = \frac{\hat{p} - p_0}{\sqrt{\dfrac{p_0(1 - p_0)}{n}}}$$

Classical Approach

Step 4: Use Table V to determine the critical value.

	Two-Tailed	Left-Tailed	Right-Tailed
Critical value	$-z_{\frac{\alpha}{2}}$ and $z_{\frac{\alpha}{2}}$	$-z_\alpha$	z_α

Critical region

Step 5: Compare the critical value with the test statistic.

Two-Tailed	Left-Tailed	Right-Tailed
If $z_0 < -z_{\frac{\alpha}{2}}$ or $z_0 > z_{\frac{\alpha}{2}}$, reject the null hypothesis.	If $z_0 < -z_\alpha$, reject the null hypothesis.	If $z_0 > z_\alpha$, reject the null hypothesis.

P-Value Approach

Step 4: Use Table V to determine the P-value.

Two-Tailed	Left-Tailed	Right-Tailed
The sum of the area in the tails is the P-value	The area left of z_0 is the P-value	The area right of z_0 is the P-value

Step 5: If P-value $< \alpha$, reject the null hypothesis.

Step 6: State the conclusion.

| EXAMPLE 1 | **Testing Hypotheses about a Population Proportion: Right-Tailed Test** |

Problem: There are two major college entrance exams that a majority of colleges accept for admission, the SAT and ACT. ACT looked at historical records and established 22 as the minimum score on the ACT math portion of the exam for a student to be considered prepared for college mathematics. [**Note:** "Being prepared" means there is a 75% probability of successfully completing College Algebra in college.] An official with the Illinois State Department of Education wonders whether less than half of the students in her state are prepared for College Algebra. She obtains a simple random sample of 500 records of students who have taken the ACT and finds that 219 are prepared for college mathematics (that is, 219 scored at least 22 on the math portion of the ACT). Does this represent significant evidence that less than half of the students in the state of Illinois are prepared for college mathematics upon graduation from a high school? Use the $\alpha = 0.05$ level of significance. *Source:* ACT High School Profile Report.

Approach: This problem deals with a hypothesis test of the proportion of high school students who are prepared for college mathematics. We want to gather evidence that shows that less than half of the students are prepared for college mathematics. Symbolically, we represent this as $p < \frac{1}{2}$ or $p < 0.5$.

We must verify the requirements to perform the hypothesis test; that is, the sample must be a simple random sample, $np_0(1 - p_0) \geq 10$, and the sample size cannot be more than 5% of the population size (for independence). Then we follow Steps 1 through 6.

Solution: We want to know if $p < 0.5$. The sample is a simple random sample. Also, $np_0(1 - p_0) = 500(0.5)(1 - 0.5) = 125 > 10$. Provided that there are over 10,000 students in the state, the sample size is less than 5% of the population size. Assuming that this is the case, the requirements are satisfied. We now proceed to Steps 1 through 6.

Step 1: The burden of proof lies in showing $p < 0.5$. We assume there is no effect, which means we assume the proportion of students ready for college math is the same as the proportion of students not ready for college math. Therefore, the statement in the null hypothesis is that $p = 0.5$. So we have

$$H_0: p = 0.5 \qquad \text{versus} \qquad H_1: p < 0.5$$

Step 2: The level of significance is $\alpha = 0.05$.

Step 3: The assumed value of the population proportion is $p_0 = 0.5$. The sample proportion is $\hat{p} = \frac{x}{n} = \frac{219}{500} = 0.438$. Here is the question: Is it likely to obtain a sample proportion of 0.438 from a population whose proportion is 0.5? Or is this result so unusual that we are forced to believe that the population proportion is some value less than 0.5?

The test statistic is

$$z_0 = \frac{\hat{p} - p_0}{\sqrt{\dfrac{p_0(1 - p_0)}{n}}} = \frac{0.438 - 0.5}{\sqrt{\dfrac{0.5(1 - 0.5)}{500}}} = -2.77$$

Classical Approach

Step 4: Because this is a left-tailed test, we determine the critical value at the $\alpha = 0.05$ level of significance to be $z_{0.05} = -1.645$. The critical region is displayed in Figure 20.

P-Value Approach

Step 4: Because this is a left-tailed test, the P-value is the area under the standard normal distribution to the left of the test statistic, $z_0 = -2.77$, as shown in Figure 21. That is, P-value $= P(Z < z_0) = P(Z < -2.77) = 0.0028$.

Figure 20

This means that *if* the null hypothesis were true we would expect to get the results we obtained in less than 1 sample in 100! Our results are unusual, indeed.

Figure 21

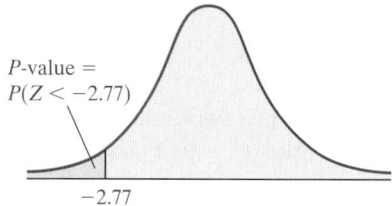

Step 5: The test statistic is $z_0 = -2.77$. We label this point in Figure 20. Because the test statistic is less than the critical value ($-2.77 < -1.645$), we reject the null hypothesis.

Step 5: Because the *P*-value is less than the level of significance $\alpha = 0.05$ ($0.0028 < 0.05$), we reject the null hypothesis.

Step 6: There is sufficient evidence at the $\alpha = 0.05$ level of significance to conclude that less than half of the students in the state of Illinois are prepared for college mathematics. In other words, less than a majority of the students in the state of Illinois are prepared for college mathematics.

Now Work Problem 9

EXAMPLE 2   **Testing Hypotheses about a Population Proportion, Two-Tailed Test**

Problem: The drug Prevnar is a vaccine meant to prevent meningitis. (It also helps control ear infections.) It is typically administered to infants. In clinical trials, the vaccine was administered to 710 randomly sampled infants between 12 and 15 months of age. Of the 710 infants, 121 experienced a loss of appetite. Is there significant evidence to conclude that the proportion of infants who receive Prevnar and experience a loss of appetite is different from 0.135, the proportion of children who experience a loss of appetite with competing medications? Use the $\alpha = 0.01$ level of significance.

Approach: We assume that there is no difference between the proportion of infants taking Prevnar who experience a loss of appetite and the proportion of infants taking the competing medication who experience a loss of appetite. That is, we assume that $p = 0.135$.

We must verify the requirements to perform the hypothesis test: the sample must be a simple random sample with $np_0(1 - p_0) \geq 10$, and the sample size cannot be more than 5% of the population. Then we follow Steps 1 through 6, as laid out previously.

Solution: We want to know if the proportion of infants who experience a loss of appetite is different from 0.135; that is, $p \neq 0.135$. The sample is a simple random sample. Also, $np_0(1 - p_0) = (710)(0.135)(1 - 0.135) = 82.9 > 10$. Because there are about 1 million babies between 12 and 15 months of age, the sample size is less than 5% of the population size. The requirements are satisfied, so we now proceed to follow Steps 1 through 6.

Step 1: We want to know whether $p \neq 0.135$. This is a two-tailed test.

$$H_0: p = 0.135 \quad \text{versus} \quad H_1: p \neq 0.135$$

Step 2: The level of significance is $\alpha = 0.01$.

Step 3: The assumed value of the population proportion is $p_0 = 0.135$. The sample proportion is $\hat{p} = \dfrac{x}{n} = \dfrac{121}{710} = 0.170$. Is it likely to obtain a sample proportion of

0.170 from a population whose proportion is 0.135, or is this result unusual? The test statistic is

$$z_0 = \frac{\hat{p} - p_0}{\sqrt{\dfrac{p_0(1 - p_0)}{n}}} = \frac{0.170 - 0.135}{\sqrt{\dfrac{0.135(1 - 0.135)}{710}}} = 2.73$$

Classical Approach	*P-Value Approach*

Classical Approach

Step 4: Because this is a two-tailed test, we determine the critical values at the $\alpha = 0.01$ level of significance to be $-z_{0.01/2} = -z_{0.005} = -2.575$ and $z_{0.01/2} = z_{0.005} = 2.575$. The critical regions are displayed in Figure 22.

Figure 22

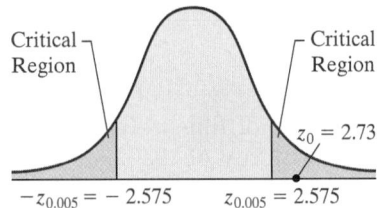

P-Value Approach

Step 4: Because this is a two-tailed test, the *P*-value is the area under the standard normal distribution to the left of $-z_0 = -2.73$ and to the right of $z_0 = 2.73$, as shown in Figure 23. That is, $P\text{-value} = P(Z < -|z_0|) + P(Z > |z_0|) = 2P(Z < -2.73) = 2(0.0032) = 0.0064.$

Figure 23

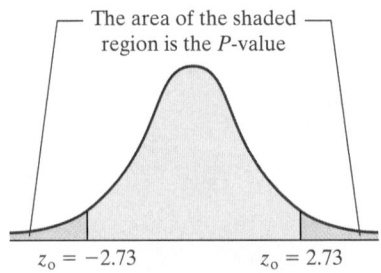

Step 5: The test statistic is $z_0 = 2.73$. We label this point in Figure 22. Because the test statistic is greater than the critical value $(2.73 > 2.575)$, we reject the null hypothesis.

Step 5: Because the *P*-value is less than the level of significance $\alpha = 0.01$ $(0.0064 < 0.01)$, we reject the null hypothesis.

Step 6: There is sufficient evidence to conclude that the proportion of infants who experienced a loss of appetite when receiving Prevnar is different from 0.135 at the $\alpha = 0.01$ level of significance.

Now Work Problem 15

EXAMPLE 3 **Testing Hypotheses Regarding a Population Proportion Using Technology**

Problem: Test the hypotheses presented in Example 2 by obtaining the *P*-value using statistical software or a graphing calculator with advanced statistical features.

Approach: We will use MINITAB to obtain the *P*-value. The steps for testing hypotheses regarding a population proportion using the TI-83/84 Plus graphing calculator, MINITAB, and Excel are given in the Technology Step-by-Step on page 560.

Solution: Figure 24 shows the results using MINITAB. The *P*-value is 0.006. Because the *P*-value is less than the level of significance $(0.006 < 0.01)$, we reject the null hypothesis.

Figure 24 **Test and CI for One Proportion**

```
Test of p = 0.135 vs p not = 0.135

Sample    X    N     Sample          99% CI           Z-Value   P-Value
1        121  710   0.170423   (0.134075, 0.206770)    2.76      0.006
```

Note to Instructor

The purpose of this activity is to give students a hands-on experience with hypothesis testing involving proportions. The activity could be elaborated to include review questions involving binomial or normal probabilities. Time limit: 40 to 45 minutes.

IN CLASS ACTIVITY

(Hypothesis Testing): Taste the Rainbow

The advertising campaign for Skittles® Brand candy in 2005 said to "Taste the Rainbow!". While the original candies do not have all the colors of the rainbow, they do come in red, orange, yellow, green, and purple (violet). But are the proportions of each color the same? If so, the proportion of each color would be $p = 0.2$.

(a) Obtain a 1-pound bag of Skittles (original flavor).

(b) Select one of the five original colors. Count the total number of candies in your bag, as well as the number for the color you selected.

(c) Is $np_0(1 - p_0) \geq 10$? If not, what could you do?

(d) Determine if the proportion of the selected color is different from $p = 0.2$.

(e) Compare your results to others in the class. Did everyone arrive at the same conclusion for the same color? What about different colors?

2 Test Hypotheses about a Population Proportion Using the Binomial Probability Distribution

Note to Instructor

This section is optional and may be skipped without loss of continuity.

For the sampling distribution of $\hat{p}$ to be approximately normal, we require that $np(1 - p)$ be at least 10. What if this requirement is not satisfied? In Section 6.2, we used the binomial probability formula to identify unusual events. We stated that an event was unusual if the probability of observing the event was less than 0.05. This criterion is based on the P-value approach to testing hypotheses; the probability that we computed was the P-value. We use this same approach to test hypotheses regarding a population proportion for small samples.

EXAMPLE 4 **Hypothesis Test for a Population Proportion: Small Sample Size**

Problem: According to the U.S. Department of Agriculture, 48.9% of males between 20 and 39 years of age consume the minimum daily requirement of calcium. After an aggressive "Got Milk" advertising campaign, the USDA conducts a survey of 35 randomly selected males between the ages of 20 and 39 and finds that 21 of them consume the recommended daily allowance of calcium. At the $\alpha = 0.10$ level of significance, is there evidence to conclude that the percentage of males between the ages of 20 and 39 who consume the recommended daily allowance of calcium has increased?

Approach: We use the following steps:

Step 1: Determine the null and alternative hypotheses.

Step 2: Check whether $np_0(1 - p_0)$ is greater than or equal to 10, where p_0 is the proportion stated in the null hypothesis. If it is, then the sampling distribution of $\hat{p}$ is approximately normal and we can use the steps presented on page 553. Otherwise, we use Steps 3 and 4, presented next.

Step 3: Compute the P-value. For right-tailed tests, the P-value is the probability of obtaining x or more successes. For left-tailed tests, the P-value is the probability of obtaining x or fewer successes.* The P-value is always computed with the proportion given in the null hypothesis. Remember, we assume that the null is true until we have evidence to the contrary.

Step 4: If the P-value is less than the level of significance, α, reject the null hypothesis.

---

*We will not address P-values for two-tailed hypothesis tests. For those who are interested, the P-value is 2 times the probability of obtaining x or more successes if $\hat{p} > p$ and 2 times the probability of obtaining x or fewer successes if $\hat{p} < p$.

Solution

Step 1: The status quo or no change proportion of 20- to 39-year-old males who consume the minimum daily requirement of calcium is 0.489. We wish to know whether or not the advertising campaign helped to increase this proportion. Therefore,

$$H_0: p = 0.489 \quad \text{and} \quad H_1: p > 0.489$$

Step 2: From the null hypothesis, we have $p_0 = 0.489$. There were $n = 35$ individuals surveyed, so $np_0(1 - p_0) = 35(0.489)(1 - 0.489) = 8.75$. Because $np_0(1 - p_0) < 10$, the sampling distribution of $\hat{p}$ is not approximately normal.

Step 3: Let the random variable X represent the number of individuals who consume the daily requirement of calcium. We have $x = 21$ successes in $n = 35$ trials, so $\hat{p} = \dfrac{21}{35} = 0.6$. We want to judge whether the larger proportion is due to an increase in the population proportion or to sampling error. We obtained $x = 21$ successes in the survey and this is a right tailed test, so the P-value is $P(X \geq 21)$.

$$\text{P-value} = P(X \geq 21) = 1 - P(X < 21) = 1 - P(X \leq 20)$$

We will compute this P-value using a TI-84 Plus graphing calculator, with $n = 35$ and $p = 0.489$. Figure 25 shows the results.

The P-value is 0.1261. MINITAB will compute exact P-values using this approach as well.

Step 4: The P-value is greater than the level of significance ($0.1261 > 0.10$), so we do not reject H_0. There is insufficient evidence (at the $\alpha = 0.1$ level of significance) to conclude that the proportion of 20- to 39-year-old males who consume the recommended daily allowance of calcium has increased.

Figure 25

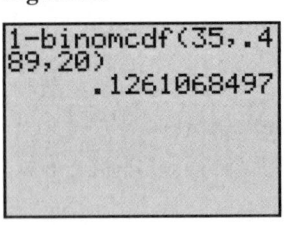

Now Work Problem 21

10.4 ASSESS YOUR UNDERSTANDING

Concepts and Vocabulary

1. State the assumptions required to test a hypothesis about a population proportion.

2. The headline reporting the results of a poll conducted by the Gallup organization stated "Majority of Americans at Personal Best in the Morning." The results indicated that a survey of 1,100 Americans resulted in 55% stating they were at their personal best in the morning. The poll's results were reported with a margin of error of 3%. Explain why the Gallup organization's headline is accurate.

Skill Building

In Problems 3–8, test the hypothesis using (a) the classical approach and (b) the P-value approach. Be sure to verify the requirements of the test.

3. $H_0: p = 0.3$ versus $H_1: p > 0.3$
   $n = 200; x = 75; \alpha = 0.05$ P-value = 0.0104

4. $H_0: p = 0.6$ versus $H_1: p < 0.6$
   $n = 250; x = 124; \alpha = 0.01$ P-value = 0.0004

5. $H_0: p = 0.55$ versus $H_1: p < 0.55$
   $n = 150; x = 78; \alpha = 0.1$ P-value = 0.2296

6. $H_0: p = 0.25$ versus $H_1: p < 0.25$
   $n = 400; x = 96; \alpha = 0.1$ P-value = 0.3228

7. $H_0: p = 0.9$ versus $H_1: p \neq 0.9$
   $n = 500; x = 440; \alpha = 0.05$ P-value = 0.1362

8. $H_0: p = 0.4$ versus $H_1: p \neq 0.4$
   $n = 1000; x = 420; \alpha = 0.01$;   P-value = 0.1970

Applying the Concepts

9. **Lipitor** The drug Lipitor is meant to reduce total cholesterol and LDL cholesterol. In clinical trials, 19 out of 863 patients taking 10 mg of Lipitor daily complained of flulike symptoms. Suppose that it is known that 1.9% of patients taking competing drugs complain of flulike symptoms. Is there evidence to conclude that more than 1.9% of Lipitor users experience flulike symptoms as a side effect at the $\alpha = 0.01$ level of significance?
   $H_0: p = 0.019$ vs. $H_1: p > 0.019$; P-value = 0.2578

10. **Nexium** Nexium is a drug that can be used to reduce the acid produced by the body and heal damage to the esophagus due to acid reflux. The manufacturer of Nexium claims that more than 94% of patients taking Nexium are healed within 8 weeks. In clinical trials, 213 of 224 patients suffering from acid reflux disease were healed after 8 weeks. Test the manufacturer's claim at the $\alpha = 0.01$ level of significance. Do not reject H_0; $H_0: p = 0.94$, $H_1: p > 0.94$, $z_0 = 0.69$, P-value = 0.2451

11. **Worried about Retirement?** In February 2008, the Gallup organization surveyed 1,034 adults between 30 and 64 years of age and found that 548 were worried that they will outlive their money after they retire. Does the sample evidence suggest that a majority of 30- to 64-year-olds in the United States are worried they will outlive their money? Use the $\alpha = 0.05$ level of significance.   Reject H_0

12. **Ready for College?** There are two major college entrance exams that a majority of colleges accept for admission, the SAT and ACT. ACT looked at historical records and

established 21 as the minimum score on the ACT reading portion of the exam for a student to be considered prepared for social science in college.

Note: "Being prepared" means there is a 75% probability of successfully completing a social science in college.

An official with the Illinois State Department of Education wonders whether a majority of the students in her state are prepared to take social science. She obtains a simple random sample of 500 records of students who have taken the ACT and finds that 269 are prepared for social science in college (that is, scored at least 21 on the reading portion of the ACT). Does this represent significant evidence that a majority of the students in the state of Illinois are prepared for social science in college upon graduation? Use the $\alpha = 0.05$ level of significance.

Source: ACT High School Profile Report.   Reject H_0

13. **Eating Together** In December 2001, 38% of adults with children under the age of 18 reported that their family ate dinner together 7 nights a week. In a recent poll, 403 of 1,122 adults with children under the age of 18 reported that their family ate dinner together 7 nights a week. Has the proportion of families with children under the age of 18 who eat dinner together 7 nights a week decreased? Use the $\alpha = 0.05$ significance level.   Do not reject H_0

14. **Critical Job Skills** In August 2003, 56% of employed adults in the United States reported that basic mathematical skills were critical or very important to their job. The supervisor of the job placement office at a 4-year college thinks this percentage has increased due to increased use of technology in the workplace. He takes a random sample of 480 employed adults and finds that 297 of them feel that basic mathematical skills are critical or very important to their job. Is there sufficient evidence to conclude that the percentage of employed adults who feel basic mathematical skills are critical or very important to their job has increased at the $\alpha = 0.05$ level of significance?   Reject H_0

15. **Taught Enough Math?** In 1994, 52% of parents of children in high school felt it was a serious problem that high school students were not being taught enough math and science. A recent survey found that 256 of 800 parents of children in high school felt it was a serious problem that high school students were not being taught enough math and science. Do parents feel differently today than they did in 1994? Use the $\alpha = 0.05$ level of significance.   Reject H_0

Source: Based on "Reality Check: Are Parents and Students Ready for More Math and Science?" *Public Agenda,* 2006.

16. **Living Alone?** In 2000, 58% of females aged 15 years of age and older lived alone, according to the U.S. Census Bureau. A sociologist tests whether this percentage is different today by conducting a random sample of 500 females aged 15 years of age and older and finds that 285 are living alone. Is there sufficient evidence at the $\alpha = 0.1$ level of significance to conclude the proportion has changed since 2000?   Do not reject H_0

17. **Quality of Education** In August 2002, 47% of parents who had children in grades K–12 were satisfied with the quality of education the students receive. In August 2007, the Gallup organization conducted a poll of 1,035 parents who have children in grades K–12 and asked if they were satisfied with the quality of education the students receive. Of the 1,035 surveyed, 476 indicated that they were satisfied. Construct a 95% confidence interval to assess whether this represents evidence that parents' attitudes toward the quality of education in the United States has changed since August, 2002.   (0.430, 0.490); do not reject H_0

18. **Infidelity** According to menstuff.org, 22% of married men have "strayed" at least once during their married lives.

   (a) Describe how you might go about administering a survey to assess they accuracy of this statement.

   (b) A survey of 500 married men results in 122 indicating that they have "strayed" at least once during their married life. Construct a 95% confidence interval for the population proportion of married men who have strayed. Use this interval to assess the accuracy of the statement made by menstuff.org.   (0.206, 0.282); do not reject H_0

19. **Talk to the Animals** In a survey conducted by the American Animal Hospital Association, 37% of respondents stated that they talk to their pets on the answering machine or telephone. A veterinarian found this result hard to believe, so he randomly selected 150 pet owners and discovered that 54 of them spoke to their pet on the answering machine or telephone. Does the veterinarian have the right to be skeptical? Use a 0.05 level of significance.   No

20. **Eating Salad** According to a survey conducted by the Association for Dressings and Sauces (this is an actual association!), 85% of American adults eat salad at least once a week. A nutritionist suspects that the percentage is higher than this. She conducts a survey of 200 American adults and finds that 171 of them eat salad at least once a week. Conduct the appropriate test that addresses the nutritionist's suspicions. Use a 0.1 level of significance. H_0: $p = 0.85$ vs. H_1: $p > 0.85$; P-value = 0.4207

21. **Small-Sample Hypothesis Test** In 1997, 4% of mothers smoked more than 21 cigarettes during their pregnancy. An obstetrician believes that the percentage of mothers who smoke 21 cigarettes or more is less than 4% today. She randomly selects 120 pregnant mothers and finds that 3 of them smoked 21 or more cigarettes during pregnancy. Does the sample data support the obstetrician's belief? Use the $\alpha = 0.05$ level of significance.   P-value = 0.2887

22. **Small-Sample Hypothesis Test** According to the U.S. Census Bureau, in 2000, 3.2% of Americans worked at home. An economist believes that the percentage of Americans working at home has increased since then. He randomly selects 150 working Americans and finds that 8 of them work at home. Do a higher proportion of Americans work at home? Use the $\alpha = 0.05$ level of significance.   P-value = 0.1099

23. **Small-Sample Hypothesis Test** According to the U.S. Census Bureau, in 2000, 9.6% of Californians had a travel time to work of more than 60 minutes. An urban economist believes that the percentage of Californians who have a travel time to work of more than 60 minutes has increased since then. She randomly selects 80 working Californians and finds that 13 of them have a travel time to work that is more than 60 minutes. Test the urban economist's belief at the $\alpha = 0.1$ level of significance.   P-value = 0.0410

24. **Small-Sample Hypothesis Test** According to the U.S. Census Bureau, in 2000, 1.5% of males living in Colorado were teachers. A researcher believes that this percentage has decreased since then. She randomly selects 500 males living in Colorado and finds that 3 of them are teachers. Test the researcher's belief at the $\alpha = 0.1$ level of significance.

25. **Statistics in the Media** One of the more popular statistics reported in the media is the president's job approval rating. The approval rating is reported as the proportion of Americans who approve of the job that the sitting president

24. P-value = 0.0578

is doing and is typically based on a random sample of about 1,100 Americans.

(a) This proportion tends to fluctuate from week to week. Name some reasons for the fluctuation in the statistic.

(b) A recent article had the headline "Bush Ratings Show Decline." This headline was written because a January 2008 poll showed President Bush's approval rating to be 0.45 (45%). A poll the following February based on 1,100 randomly selected Americans showed that 484 approved of the job Bush was doing. Do the results of the February poll indicate that the proportion of Americans who approve of the job Bush is doing is significantly less than January's level? Explain.

26. **Statistics in the Media** In May 2006, 65% (0.65) of Americans favored the death penalty for a person convicted of murder. In October 2006, 1,005 adult Americans were asked by the Gallup organization, "Are you in favor of the death penalty for a person convicted of murder?" Of the 1,005 adults surveyed, 673 responded yes. The headline in the article reporting the survey results stated, "More Americans' Favor the Death Penalty." Use a test of significance to support or refute this headline.   *Refute*

27. **Putting It Together: Lupus** Based on historical birthing records, the proportion of males born worldwide is 0.51. In other words, the commonly held belief that boys are just as likely as girls is false. Systematic lupus erythematosus (SLE), or lupus for short, is a disease in which one's immune system attacks healthy cells and tissue by mistake. It is well known

that lupus tends to exist more in females than in males. Researchers wondered, however, if families with a child who had lupus had a lower ratio of males to females than the general population. If this were true, it would suggest that something happens during conception that causes males to be conceived at a lower rate when the SLE gene is present. To determine if this hypothesis is true, the researchers obtained records of families with a child who had SLE. A total of 23 males and 79 females were found to have SLE. The 23 males with SLE had a total of 23 male siblings and 22 female siblings. The 79 females with SLE had a total of 69 male siblings and 80 female siblings. *Source*: L.N. Moorthy, M.G.E. Peterson, K.B. Onel, and T.J.A. Lehman. "Do Children with Lupus Have Fewer Male Siblings" *Lupus* 2008 17:128–131, 2008.

(a) Explain why this is an observational study.

(b) Is the study retrospective or prospective? Why?

(c) There are a total of $23 + 69 = 92$ male siblings in the study. How many female siblings are in the study?   *102*

(d) Draw a relative frequency bar graph of gender of the siblings.

(e) Find a point estimate for the proportion of male siblings in families where one of the children has SLE.   *0.474*

(f) Does the sample evidence suggest that the proportion of male siblings in families where one of the children has SLE is less than 0.51, the accepted proportion of males born in the general population? Use the $\alpha = 0.05$ level of significance.   *Do not reject H_0*

(g) Construct a 95% confidence interval for the proportion of male siblings in a family where one of the children has SLE.   *(0.404, 0.544)*

TECHNOLOGY STEP-BY-STEP

Hypothesis Tests Regarding a Population Proportion

TI-83/84 Plus

1. Press STAT, highlight TESTS, and select 5:1-PropZTest.
2. For the value of p_0, enter the value of the population proportion stated in the null hypothesis.
3. Enter the number of successes, x, and the sample size, n.
4. Select the direction of the alternative hypothesis.
5. Highlight **Calculate** or **Draw**, and press ENTER. The TI-83 or TI-84 gives the P-value.

MINITAB

1. If you have raw data, enter them in C1, using 0 for failure and 1 for success.
2. Select the **Stat** menu, highlight **Basic Statistics**, then highlight **1-Proportion**.
3. If you have raw data, select the "Samples in columns" radio button and enter C1. If you have summarized statistics, select "Summarized data." Enter the number of trials and the number of successes.
4. Click Options. Enter the value of the proportion stated in the null hypothesis. Enter the direction of the alternative hypothesis. If $np_0(1 - p_0) \geq 10$, check the box marked "Use test and interval based on normal distribution." Click OK twice.

Excel

1. If you have raw data, enter the raw data into column A. If you have summarized data, enter the number of successes in column 1 and the number of trials in column B. Highlight the data.
2. Load the DDXL Add-in, if necessary.
3. Select the **DDXL** menu and highlight **Hypothesis Tests**. From the drop-down menu under Function Type:, select 1 Var Prop Test if you have raw data; select Summ 1 Var Prop Test if you have summarized data.
4. If you have raw data, select the column that contains the raw data from the "Names and Columns" window. Use the ◄ arrow to select the data. Click OK. If you have summarized data, highlight the observation in "Names and Columns" and use the ◄ arrow to select the number of successes; repeat this for the number of trials. Click OK.
5. Fill in the DataDesk window. In Step 1, click "Set hypothesized value of proportion" and enter the value of the hypothesized proportion (this is the value of the proportion stated in the null hypothesis). In Step 2, select the level of significance. In Step 3, select the direction in the alternative hypothesis. Click Compute.

10.5 HYPOTHESIS TESTS FOR A POPULATION STANDARD DEVIATION

Preparing for This Section Before getting started, review the following:

- Confidence intervals for a population standard deviation (Section 9.4, pp. 496–501)

| **Objective** | | Test hypotheses about a population standard deviation |

Note to Instructor
This section is optional and may be skipped without loss of continuity.

Note to Instructor
If you like, you can print out and distribute the Preparing for This Section quiz located in the Instructor's Resource Center. The purpose of the quiz is to verify that the students have the prerequisite knowledge for the section.

In this section, we discuss methods for testing hypotheses regarding a population variance or standard deviation.

Why might we be interested in testing hypotheses regarding σ^2 or σ? Many production processes not only require accuracy on average (the mean), but they also require consistency. Consider a filling machine (such as a coffee machine) that consistently over- and underfills cups, but, on average, fills correctly. Certainly, customers are not happy if the machine underfills their cups, and they might be dissatisfied even if it overfills, because of spilling. A machine that *consistently* delivers the correct amount of liquid is desired. As another example, consider a mutual fund that invests in the stock market. An investor would prefer consistent year-to-year returns near 12%, rather than returns that fluctuate wildly, yet result in a mean return of 12%. Both of these situations illustrate the importance of measuring variability. The main idea is that the standard deviation and the variance are measures of consistency. The less consistent the values of a variable are, the higher the standard deviation of the variable.

We begin by reviewing the chi-square distribution.

> **Chi-Square Distribution**
>
> If a simple random sample of size n is obtained from a normally distributed population with mean μ and standard deviation σ, then
>
> $$\chi^2 = \frac{(n-1)s^2}{\sigma^2}$$
>
> where s^2 is a sample variance has a chi-square distribution with $n-1$ degrees of freedom.

Remember, the symbol χ^2 is pronounced "kigh-square." You can find critical values of the chi-square distribution in Table VII in Appendix A of the text.

Figure 26
Chi-Square Distributions

> **Characteristics of the Chi-Square Distribution**
>
> **1.** It is not symmetric.
> **2.** The shape of the chi-square distribution depends on the degrees of freedom, just as with Student's t-distribution.
> **3.** As the number of degrees of freedom increases, the chi-square distribution becomes more nearly symmetric, as is illustrated in Figure 26.
> **4.** The values of χ^2 are nonnegative: that is, the values of χ^2 are greater than or equal to 0.

Recall that Table VII is structured similarly to Table VI (for the t-distribution). The left column represents the degrees of freedom, and the top row represents the area under the chi-square distribution to the right of the critical value. We use the notation χ_α^2 to denote the critical χ^2-value for which the area under the chi-square distribution to the right of χ_α^2 is α. For example, the area under the chi-square distribution to the right of $\chi_{0.10}^2$ is 0.10.

> **1** **Test Hypotheses about a Population Standard Deviation**
>
> We now present the steps for testing hypotheses for a population variance or standard deviation.

Testing Hypotheses about a Population Variance or Standard Deviation

To test hypotheses about the population variance or standard deviation, we can use the following steps, provided that

1. the sample is obtained using simple random sampling
2. the population is normally distributed.

Step 1: Determine the null and alternative hypotheses. The hypotheses can be structured in one of three ways:

Two-Tailed	Left-Tailed	Right-Tailed
$H_0: \sigma = \sigma_0$	$H_0: \sigma = \sigma_0$	$H_0: \sigma = \sigma_0$
$H_1: \sigma \neq \sigma_0$	$H_1: \sigma < \sigma_0$	$H_1: \sigma > \sigma_0$

Note: σ_0 is the assumed value of the population standard deviation.

Step 2: Select a level of significance, α, based on the seriousness of making a Type I error.

Step 3: Compute the test statistic

$$\chi_0^2 = \frac{(n-1)s^2}{\sigma_0^2}$$

Classical Approach

Step 4: Use Table VII to determine the critical value using $n - 1$ degrees of freedom.

Two-Tailed

$\chi_{1-\frac{\alpha}{2}}^2$ (critical value) $\chi_{\frac{\alpha}{2}}^2$ (critical value)

Left-Tailed

$\chi_{1-\alpha}^2$ (critical value)

Right-Tailed

χ_α^2 (critical value)

Step 5: Compare the critical value with the test statistic.

Two-Tailed	Left-Tailed	Right-Tailed
If $\chi_0^2 < \chi_{1-\alpha/2}^2$ or $\chi_0^2 > \chi_{\alpha/2}^2$, reject the null hypothesis.	If $\chi_0^2 < \chi_{1-\alpha}^2$, reject the null hypothesis.	If $\chi_0^2 > \chi_\alpha^2$, reject the null hypothesis.

P-Value Approach

Step 4: Use Table VII to determine the approximate P-value for a left-tailed or right-tailed test by determining the area under the chi-square distribution with $n - 1$ degrees of freedom to the left (for a left-tailed test) or right (for a right-tailed test) of the test statistic. For two-tailed tests, we recommend the use of technology or confidence intervals.

Left-Tailed

P-value = $P(\chi^2 < \chi_0^2)$

χ_0^2

Right-Tailed

P-value = $P(\chi^2 > \chi_0^2)$

χ_0^2

Step 5: If the P-value $< \alpha$, reject the null hypothesis.

Step 6: State the conclusion.

CAUTION The procedures in this section are not robust.

The methods presented for testing a hypothesis about a population variance or standard deviation are not robust. Therefore, if analysis of the data indicates that the variable does not come from a population that is normally distributed, the procedures presented in this section are not valid. Again, always be sure to verify that the requirements are satisfied before proceeding with the test!

| EXAMPLE 1 | **Testing a Hypothesis about a Population Standard Deviation, Left-Tailed Test** |

Table 4

19.68	20.66	19.56
19.98	20.65	19.61
20.55	20.36	21.02
21.50	19.74	

Source: Michael Carlisle, student at Joliet Junior College

Problem: In Example 3 from Section 10.3, the quality-control engineer for M&M–Mars tested whether or not the mean weight of fun-size Snickers was 20.1 grams. Suppose that the standard deviation of the weight of the candy was 0.75 gram before a machine recalibration. The quality-control engineer wants to know if the recalibration resulted in more consistent weights. Conduct the appropriate test at the $\alpha = 0.05$ level of significance. For convenience, the data are reproduced in Table 4.

Approach: If the recalibration results in more consistent weights, then the standard deviation weight should be less than it was prior to recalibration. We want to test if $\sigma < 0.75$. Before we can perform the hypothesis test, we must verify that the data come from a population that is normally distributed. We will construct a normal probability plot to verify this requirement. We then proceed to follow Steps 1 through 6.

Solution: A normal probability plot was shown for these data in Figure 17. The plot indicates that the weights of the candy could come from a population that is normally distributed.

CAUTION The test statistic requires s^2 and σ^2, so be careful if the problem gives s or σ.

Step 1: We need evidence to conclude that the population standard deviation is less than 0.75 gram. This can be written $\sigma < 0.75$. We have

$$H_0: \sigma = 0.75 \quad \text{versus} \quad H_1: \sigma < 0.75$$

This is a left-tailed test.

Step 2: The level of significance is $\alpha = 0.05$.

Step 3: From the data in Table 4, the sample standard deviation is computed to be $s = 0.6404$. The test statistic is

$$\chi_0^2 = \frac{(n-1)s^2}{\sigma_0^2} = \frac{(11-1)(0.6404)^2}{0.75^2} = 7.291$$

Classical Approach

Step 4: Because this is a left-tailed test, we determine the critical χ^2-value at the $\alpha = 0.05$ level of significance with $n - 1 = 11 - 1 = 10$ degrees of freedom to be $\chi_{1-0.05}^2 = \chi_{0.95}^2 = 3.940$. The critical region is displayed in Figure 27.

Figure 27

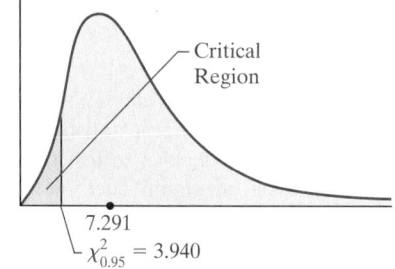

P-value Approach

Step 4: Because this is a left-tailed test, the *P*-value is the area under the χ^2-distribution with $11 - 1 = 10$ degrees of freedom to the left of the test statistic, $\chi_0^2 = 7.291$, as shown in Figure 28. That is, *P*-value $= P(\chi^2 < \chi_0^2) = P(\chi^2 < 7.291)$, with 10 degrees of freedom.

Using Table VII, we find the row that corresponds to 10 degrees of freedom. The value 7.291 is greater than 4.865. The value of 4.865 has an area under the χ^2-distribution of 0.10 to the left. So the *P*-value is greater than 0.10.

Figure 28

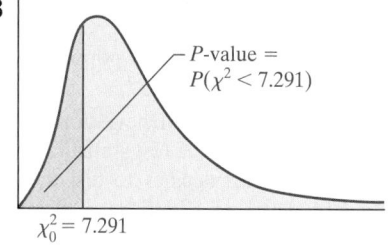

Step 5: Because the test statistic $\chi_0^2 = 7.291$ is greater than the critical value $\chi_{0.95}^2 = 3.940$, the quality-control engineer does not reject the null hypothesis. We label this point in Figure 27.

Step 5: Because the *P*-value is greater than the level of significance $\alpha = 0.05$, we do not reject the null hypothesis.

Step 6: There is not sufficient evidence at the $\alpha = 0.05$ level of significance to conclude the standard deviation of the weight of fun-size Snickers is less than 0.75 gram. It appears that the recalibration did not result in more consistent weights.

EXAMPLE 2 **Testing a Hypothesis for a Population Standard Deviation Using Technology**

Problem: Test the hypothesis from Example 1 by obtaining the *P*-value using statistical software.

Approach: We will use MINITAB to obtain the *P*-value. We could also use the DDXL Add-in that accompanies this text. Currently, the TI-83/84 Plus graphing calculator does not test hypotheses regarding the population standard deviation. The steps for testing hypotheses regarding the population standard deviation using MINITAB or the DDXL plug-in for Excel are given in the Technology Step-by-Step on page 566.

Solution: Figure 29 shows partial output from MINITAB. Notice that MINITAB uses two methods. The standard method assumes that the data come from a population that is normally distributed, while the adjusted method assumes that the data come from a continuous distribution (a less stringent requirement and one not covered in this text). The *P*-value for the standard method is 0.302, which means that, *if* the statement in the null hypothesis were true, we would expect to get the results we got in about 30 samples out of 100. The results we obtained are not unusual, so we do not reject the statement in the null hypothesis

Figure 29 **Test and CI for One Standard Deviation: Weight**

```
Method

Null hypothesis          Sigma = 0.75
Alternative hypothesis   Sigma = < 0.75

The standard method is only for the normal distribution.
The adjusted method is for any continuous distribution.

Tests

Variable   Method     Chi-Square    DF    P-Value
Weight     Standard         7.29   10.00    0.302
           Adjusted        10.87   14.91    0.244
```

Now Work Problem 9

10.5 ASSESS YOUR UNDERSTANDING

Concepts and Vocabulary

1. State the requirements to test hypotheses regarding a population standard deviation.

2. Determine the critical value for a right-tailed test of a population standard deviation with 18 degrees of freedom at the $\alpha = 0.05$ level of significance. $\chi_{0.05}^2 = 28.869$

Skill Building

3. To test $H_0: \sigma = 50$ versus $H_1: \sigma < 50$, a random sample of size $n = 24$ is obtained from a population that is known to be normally distributed.

   (a) If the sample standard deviation is determined to be $s = 47.2$, compute the test statistic. $\chi_0^2 = 20.496$

   (b) If the researcher decides to test this hypothesis at the $\alpha = 0.05$ level of significance, determine the critical value. $\chi_{0.95}^2 = 13.091$

   (c) Draw a chi-square distribution and depict the critical region.

   (d) Will the researcher reject the null hypothesis? Why? No

4. To test $H_0: \sigma = 35$ versus $H_1: \sigma > 35$, a random sample of size $n = 15$ is obtained from a population that is known to be normally distributed.

   (a) If the sample standard deviation is determined to be $s = 37.4$, compute the test statistic. $\chi_0^2 = 15.986$

   (b) If the researcher decides to test this hypothesis at the $\alpha = 0.01$ level of significance, determine the critical value. $\chi_{0.01}^2 = 29.141$

   (c) Draw a chi-square distribution and depict the critical region.

   (d) Will the researcher reject the null hypothesis? Why? No

5. To test $H_0: \sigma = 1.8$ versus $H_1: \sigma > 1.8$, a random sample of size $n = 18$ is obtained from a population that is known to be normally distributed.

(a) If the sample standard deviation is determined to be $s = 2.4$, compute the test statistic. $\chi_0^2 = 30.222$

(b) If the researcher decides to test this hypothesis at the $\alpha = 0.10$ level of significance, determine the critical value. $\chi_{0.1}^2 = 24.769$

(c) Draw a chi-square distribution and depict the critical region.

(d) Will the researcher reject the null hypothesis? Why? Yes

6. To test $H_0: \sigma = 0.35$ versus $H_1: \sigma < 0.35$, a random sample of size $n = 41$ is obtained from a population that is known to be normally distributed.

(a) If the sample standard deviation is determined to be $s = 0.23$, compute the test statistic. $\chi_0^2 = 17.273$

(b) If the researcher decides to test this hypothesis at the $\alpha = 0.01$ level of significance, determine the critical value. $\chi_{0.99}^2 = 22.164$

(c) Draw a chi-square distribution and depict the critical region.

(d) Will the researcher reject the null hypothesis? Why? Yes

7. To test $H_0: \sigma = 4.3$ versus $H_1: \sigma \neq 4.3$, a random sample of size $n = 12$ is obtained from a population that is known to be normally distributed. 7. (b) $\chi_{0.975}^2 = 3.816$, $\chi_{0.025}^2 = 21.920$

(a) If the sample standard deviation is determined to be $s = 4.8$, compute the test statistic. $\chi_0^2 = 13.707$

(b) If the researcher decides to test this hypothesis at the $\alpha = 0.05$ level of significance, determine the critical values.

(c) Draw a chi-square distribution and depict the critical regions.

(d) Will the researcher reject the null hypothesis? Why? No

8. To test $H_0: \sigma = 1.2$ versus $H_1: \sigma \neq 1.2$, a random sample of size $n = 22$ is obtained from a population that is known to be normally distributed. 8. (b) $\chi_{0.95}^2 = 11.591$, $\chi_{0.05}^2 = 32.671$

(a) If the sample standard deviation is determined to be $s = 0.8$, compute the test statistic. $\chi_0^2 = 9.333$

(b) If the researcher decides to test this hypothesis at the $\alpha = 0.10$ level of significance, determine the critical values.

(c) Draw a chi-square distribution and depict the critical regions.

(d) Will the researcher reject the null hypothesis? Why? Yes

Applying the Concepts

9. **Mutual Fund Risk** One measure of the risk of a mutual fund is the standard deviation of its rate of return. Suppose a mutual fund qualifies as having moderate risk if the standard deviation of its monthly rate of return is less than 4%. A mutual-fund manager claims that his fund has moderate risk. A mutual-fund rating agency does not believe this claim and randomly selects 25 months and determines the rate of return for the fund. The standard deviation of the rate of return is computed to be 3.01%. Is there sufficient evidence to conclude that the fund has moderate risk at the $\alpha = 0.05$ level of significance? A normal probability plot indicates that the monthly rates of return are normally distributed. Reject H_0

10. **Filling Machine** A machine fills bottles with 64 fluid ounces of liquid. The quality-control manager determines that the fill levels are normally distributed with a mean of 64 ounces and a standard deviation of 0.42 ounces. He has an engineer recalibrate the machine in an attempt to lower the standard deviation. After the recalibration, the quality-control manager randomly selects 19 bottles from the line and determines that the standard deviation is 0.38 ounces. Is there less

variability in the filling machine? Use the $\alpha = 0.01$ level of significance. Do not reject H_0

11. **Pump Design** The piston diameter of a certain hand pump is 0.5 inch. The quality-control manager determines that the diameters are normally distributed, with a mean of 0.5 inch and a standard deviation of 0.004 inch. The machine that controls the piston diameter is recalibrated in an attempt to lower the standard deviation. After recalibration, the quality-control manager randomly selects 25 pistons from the production line and determines that the standard deviation is 0.0025 inch. Was the recalibration effective? Use the $\alpha = 0.01$ level of significance. Reject H_0

12. **Counting Carbs** The manufacturer of processed deli meats reports that the standard deviation of the number of carbohydrates in its smoked turkey breast is 0.5 gram per 2-ounce serving. A dietician does not believe the manufacturer and randomly selects eighteen 2-ounce servings of the smoked turkey breast and determines the number of carbohydrates per serving. The standard deviation of the number of carbs is computed to be 0.62 gram per serving. Is there sufficient evidence to indicate that the standard deviation is not 0.5 gram per serving at the $\alpha = 0.05$ level of significance? A normal probability plot indicates that the number of carbohydrates per serving is normally distributed. Do not reject H_0

13. **Calcium in Rain Water** In Problem 23 from Section 10.2, we tested a hypothesis regarding the mean concentration of calcium in rainwater in Chautauqua, New York. To test this hypothesis, we verified that the data are normally distributed and assumed that $\sigma = 0.08$. Test this assumption at the $\alpha = 0.05$ level of significance. Do not reject H_0

| 0.065 | 0.087 | 0.070 | 0.262 | 0.126 |
| 0.183 | 0.120 | 0.234 | 0.313 | 0.108 |

Source: National Atmospheric Deposition Program

14. **Acid Rain** In Problem 24 from Section 10.2, we tested a hypothesis regarding the mean amount of acidity in rainwater in the Columbia River Gorge, Washington. To test this hypothesis, we verified that the data are normally distributed and assumed that $\sigma = 0.27$. Test this assumption at the $\alpha = 0.05$ level of significance. Do not reject H_0

5.11	5.70	5.27	5.59
4.98	5.13	5.49	4.81
5.23	5.16	5.58	5.86
5.20	5.54	5.34	5.39

Source: National Atmospheric Deposition Program

15. **Filling Bottles** In Problem 25 from Section 10.2, we tested a hypothesis regarding the mean amount of juice in a bottle. To test this hypothesis, we verified that the data are normally distributed and assumed that $\sigma = 0.06$. Test this assumption at the $\alpha = 0.05$ level of significance. Do not reject H_0

64.05	64.05	64.03	63.97	63.95	64.02
64.01	63.99	64.00	64.01	64.06	63.94
63.98	64.05	63.95	64.01	64.08	64.01
63.95	63.97	64.10	63.98		

16. Fuel Catalyst In Problem 26 from Section 10.2, we conducted a hypothesis test regarding the mean number of miles per gallon for semitrucks. To conduct this test, we verified that the data are normally distributed and assumed that $\sigma = 0.5$ mile per gallon. Test this assumption at the $\alpha = 0.05$ level of significance, given that $s = 0.375$ mile per gallon. $\chi_0^2 = 6.188$; do not reject H_0

5.9	6.7	6.9	6.4	6.6	6.3
6.2	5.9	6.2	6.4	6.6	5.6

17. An Inconsistent Player We often hear sports announcers say, "I wonder which player will show up to play today." This is the announcer's way of saying that the player is inconsistent, that his or her performance varies dramatically from game to game. Suppose that the standard deviation of the number of points scored by shooting guards in the NBA is 8.3. A random sample of 25 games played by Allen Iverson of the Denver Nuggets results in a sample standard deviation of 6.7 points. Assume that a normal probability plot indicates that the points scored are approximately normally distributed. Is Allen Iverson more consistent than other shooting guards in the NBA at the $\alpha = 0.10$ level of significance? Reject H_0

18. Waiting in Line One aspect of queuing theory is to consider waiting time in lines. A fast-food chain is trying to determine whether it should switch from having four cash registers with four separate lines to four cash registers with a single line. It has been determined that the mean wait time in both lines is equal. However, the chain is uncertain about which line has less variability in wait time. From experience, the chain knows that the wait times in the four separate lines are normally distributed with $\sigma = 1.2$ minutes. In a study, the chain reconfigured five restaurants to have a single line and measured the wait times for 50 randomly selected customers. The sample

standard deviation was determined to be $s = 0.84$ minute. Is the variability in wait time less for a single line than for multiple lines at the $\alpha = 0.05$ level of significance? Reject H_0

19. Heights of Baseball Players Data obtained from the National Center for Health Statistics show that men between the ages of 20 and 29 have a mean height of 69.3 inches, with a standard deviation of 2.9 inches. A baseball analyst wonders whether the standard deviation of heights of major-league baseball players is less than 2.9 inches. The heights (in inches) of 20 randomly selected players are shown in the table.

72	74	71	72	76
70	77	75	72	72
77	72	75	70	73
73	75	73	74	74

Source: espn.com

(a) Verify that the data are normally distributed by drawing a normal probability plot.
(b) Compute the sample standard deviation. 2.059 inches
(c) Test the notion at the $\alpha = 0.01$ level of significance. Do not reject H_0

20. NCAA Softball NCAA rules require the circumference of a softball to be 12 ± 0.125 inches. A softball manufacturer bidding on an NCAA contract is shown to meet the requirements for mean circumference. Suppose that the NCAA also requires that the standard deviation of the softball circumferences not exceed 0.05 inch. A representative from the NCAA believes the manufacturer does not meet this requirement. She collects a random sample of 20 softballs from the production line and finds that $s = 0.09$ inch. Is there enough evidence to support the representative's belief at the $\alpha = 0.05$ level of significance? Yes; reject H_0

TECHNOLOGY STEP-BY-STEP
Hypothesis Tests Regarding a Population Standard Deviation

TI-83/84 Plus
The TI-83/84 Plus graphing calculator does not conduct hypothesis tests regarding a population standard deviation.

MINITAB
1. Enter the raw data into column C1, if necessary.
2. Select the **Stat** menu, highlight **Basic Statistics**, then highlight **1 Variance**.
3. Make sure the pull-down menu has "Enter standard deviation" in the window. If you have raw data, enter C1 in the window marked "Samples in columns" and make sure the radio button is selected. If you have summarized data, select the "Summarized data" radio button and enter the sample size and sample standard deviation.
4. Click Options and select the direction of the alternative hypothesis. Click OK.

5. Check the "Perform hypothesis test" box and enter the value of the standard deviation in the null hypothesis. Click OK.

Excel
1. If you have raw data, enter the raw data into column A. Highlight the data.
2. Load the DDXL Add-in, if necessary.
3. Select the **DDXL** menu and highlight **Hypothesis Tests**. From the drop-down menu under "Function Type:", select "Chisquare for SD."
4. Select the column that contains the raw data from the "Names and Columns" window. Use the ◄ arrow to select the data. Click OK.
5. Fill in the DataDesk window. In Step 1, click "Set hypothesized sigma" and enter the value of the standard deviation stated in the null hypothesis and click OK. In Step 2, select the level of significance. In Step 3, select the direction in the alternative hypothesis. Click Compute.

10.6 PUTTING IT TOGETHER: WHICH METHOD DO I USE?

Objective	**1** Determine the appropriate hypothesis test to perform

 ## Determine the Appropriate Hypothesis Test to Perform

Perhaps the most difficult aspect of testing hypotheses is determining which hypothesis test to conduct. To assist in the decision making, we present Figure 30, which shows which approach to take in testing hypotheses for the three parameters discussed in this chapter.

Figure 30

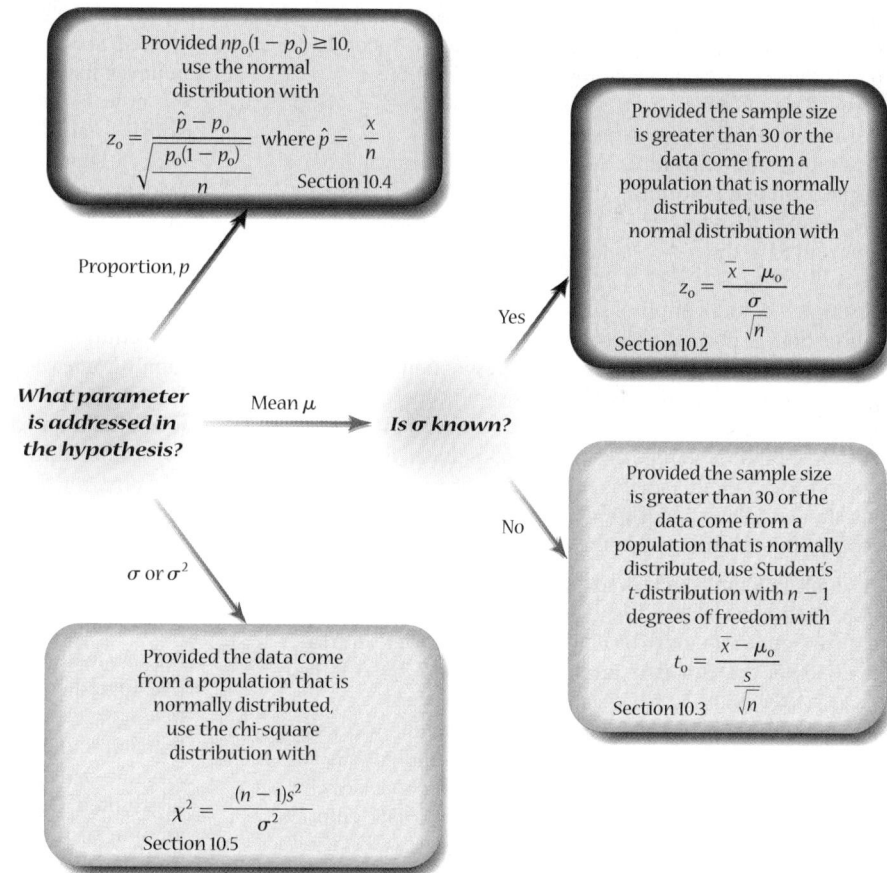

10.6 ASSESS YOUR UNDERSTANDING

Concepts and Vocabulary

1. What requirements must be satisfied to test a hypothesis about a population mean? When do we use the normal model to test a hypothesis about a population mean? When do we use Student's t-distribution to test a hypothesis about a population mean?

2. What are the requirements that must be satisfied before we can test a hypotheses about a population proportion?

Skill Building

In Problems 3–12, test each hypothesis.

3. A simple random sample of size $n = 14$ is drawn from a population that is normally distributed with $\sigma = 20$. The sample mean is found to be 60. Test whether the population mean is less than 70 at the $\alpha = 0.1$ level of significance.

$H_0: \mu = 70$, $H_1: \mu < 70$, $z_0 = -1.87$, P-value $= 0.0307$; reject H_0

10. $H_0: \mu = 600$, $H_1: \mu \neq 600$, $t_0 = -1.186$, P-value = 0.2401; do not reject H_0

4. A simple random sample of size $n = 19$ is drawn from a population that is normally distributed. The sample mean is found to be 0.8, and the sample standard deviation is found to be 0.4. Test whether the population mean is less than 1.0 at the $\alpha = 0.01$ level of significance.
   P-value = 0.0214; do not reject H_0

5. A simple random sample of size $n = 200$ individuals with a valid driver's license is asked if they drive an American-made automobile. Of the 200 individuals surveyed, 115 responded that they drive an American-made automobile. Determine if a majority of those with a valid driver's license drive an American-made automobile at the $\alpha = 0.05$ level of significance. $H_0: p = 0.5$, $H_1: p > 0.5$, $z_0 = 2.12$, P-value = 0.0170; reject H_0

6. A simple random sample of size $n = 20$ is drawn from a population that is normally distributed. The sample variance is found to be 49.3. Determine whether the population variance is less than 95 at the $\alpha = 0.1$ level of significance.
   $H_0: \sigma^2 = 95$, $H_1: \sigma^2 < 95$, $\chi_0^2 = 9.86$, P-value = 0.0437; reject H_0

7. A simple random sample of size $n = 15$ is drawn from a population that is normally distributed. The sample mean is found to be 23.8, and the sample standard deviation is found to be 6.3. Is the population mean different from 25 at the $\alpha = 0.01$ level of significance? $H_0: \mu = 25$, $H_1: \mu \neq 25$, $t_0 = -0.738$, P-value = 0.4729; do not reject H_0

8. A simple random sample of size $n = 25$ is drawn from a population that is normally distributed with $\sigma = 7$. The sample mean is found to be 53.2. Is the population mean different from 55 at the $\alpha = 0.05$ level of significance? $H_0: \mu = 55$, $H_1: \mu \neq 55$, $z_0 = -1.29$, P-value = 0.1970; do not reject H_0

9. A simple random sample of size $n = 16$ is drawn from a population that is normally distributed. The sample variance is found to be 13.7. Test whether the population variance is greater than 10 at the $\alpha = 0.05$ level of significance. $H_0: \sigma^2 = 10$, $H_1: \sigma^2 > 10$, $\chi_0^2 = 20.55$, P-value = 0.1518; do not reject H_0

10. A simple random sample of size $n = 65$ is drawn from a population. The sample mean is found to be 583.1, and the sample standard deviation is found to be 114.9. Is the population mean different from 600 at the $\alpha = 0.1$ level of significance?

11. A simple random sample of size $n = 40$ is drawn from a population. The sample mean is found to be 108.5, and the sample standard deviation is found to be 17.9. Is the population mean greater than 100 at the $\alpha = 0.05$ level of significance? $H_0: \mu = 100$, $H_1: \mu > 100$, $t_0 = 3.003$, P-value = 0.0023; reject H_0

12. A simple random sample of size $n = 320$ adults was asked their favorite ice cream flavor. Of the 320 individuals surveyed, 58 responded that they preferred mint chocolate chip. Do less than 25% of adults prefer mint chocolate chip ice cream? Use the $\alpha = 0.01$ level of significance.
    $H_0: p = 0.25$, $H_1: p < 0.25$, $z_0 = -2.84$, P-value = 0.0023; reject H_0

Applying the Concepts

13. **Smarter Kids?** Does playing Mozart for unborn babies result in children with higher IQs? A psychologist obtains a random sample of 20 mothers in the first trimester of their pregnancy. The mothers are asked to play Mozart in the house at least 30 minutes each day until they give birth. After 5 years, the child is administered an IQ test. We know that IQs are normally distributed with a mean of 100 and standard deviation 15. If the IQs of the 20 children in the study result in a sample mean of 104.2, is there evidence that the children have higher IQs? Use the $\alpha = 0.05$ level of significance.
    $H_0: \mu = 100$, $H_1: \mu > 100$, $z_0 = 1.25$, P-value = 0.1056, do not reject H_0

14. **The Atomic Bomb** In October 1945, the Gallup organization asked 1,487 randomly sampled Americans, "Do you think we can develop a way to protect ourselves from atomic bombs in case other countries tried to use them against us?" with 788 responding yes. Did a majority of Americans feel the United States could develop a way to protect itself from atomic bombs in 1945? Use the $\alpha = 0.05$ level of significance. $H_0: p = 0.5$, $H_1: p > 0.5$, $z_0 = 2.31$, P-value = 0.0104, reject H_0

15. **Yield Strength** A manufacturer of high-strength, low-alloy steel beams requires that the standard deviation of yield strength not exceed 7,000 pounds per square inch (psi). The quality-control manager selected a sample of 20 steel beams and measured their yield strength. The standard deviation of the sample was 7,500 psi. Assume that yield strengths are normally distributed. Does the evidence suggest that the standard deviation of yield strength exceeds 7,000 psi at the $\alpha = 0.01$ level of significance? $H_0: \sigma = 7,000$, $H_1: \sigma > 7,000$, $\chi_0^2 = 21.81$, P-value = 0.2938; do not reject H_0

16. **Auto Insurance** According to the Insurance Information Institute, the mean expenditure for auto insurance in the United States was $774 in 2002. An insurance sales person believes that mean expenditure for auto insurance is different now. He obtains a random sample of 35 auto insurance policies and determines the mean expenditure to be $735 with a standard deviation of $48.31. Is there enough evidence to conclude that the mean expenditure for auto insurance is different from the 2002 amount at the $\alpha = 0.01$ level of significance? $H_0: \mu = \$774$, $H_1: \mu \neq \$774$, $t_0 = -4.776$, P-value < 0.0001; reject H_0

17. **Mortgage Rates** In 2001, the mean contract interest rate for a conventional 30-year first loan for the purchase of a single-family home was 6.3%, according to the U.S. Federal Housing Board. A real estate agent believes that interest rates are lower today and obtains a random sample of 41 recent 30-year conventional loans. The mean interest rate was found to be 6.05%, with a standard deviation of 1.75 percent. Is this enough evidence to conclude that interest rates are lower at the $\alpha = 0.05$ level of significance? $H_0: \mu = 6.3$, $H_1: \mu < 6.3$, $t_0 = -0.95$, P-value = 0.1829; do not reject H_0

18. **Pharmaceuticals** A pharmaceutical company manufactures a 200-milligram (mg) pain reliever. Company specifications require that the standard deviation of the amount of the active ingredient must not exceed 5 mg. The quality-control manager selects a random sample of 30 tablets from a certain batch and finds that the sample standard deviation is 7.3 mg. Assume that the amount of the active ingredient is normally distributed. Determine whether the standard deviation of the amount of the active ingredient is greater than 5 mg at the $\alpha = 0.05$ level of significance. $H_0: \sigma = 5$ mg, $H_1: \sigma > 5$ mg, $\chi_0^2 = 61.82$, P-value = 0.0004; reject H_0

19. **Tattoos** In 2001, 23% of American university undergraduate students had at least one tattoo. A health practitioner suspects that the percent has changed since then. She obtains a random sample of 1,026 university undergraduates and finds that 254 have at least one tattoo. Is this sufficient evidence to conclude that the proportion is different from 0.23 at the $\alpha = 0.1$ level of significance? $H_0: p = 0.23$, $H_1: p \neq 0.23$, $z_0 = 1.37$, P-value = 0.1706; do not reject H_0

20. **Toner Cartridge** The manufacturer of a toner cartridge claims the mean number of printouts is 10,000 for each cartridge. A consumer advocate is concerned that the actual mean number of printouts is lower. He selects a random

sample of 14 such cartridges and obtains the following number of printouts:

9,600	10,300	9,000	10,750	9,490	9,080	9,655
9,520	10,070	9,999	10,470	8,920	9,964	10,330

(a) Because the sample size is small, he must verify that the number of printouts is normally distributed and the sample does not contain any outliers. The normal probability plot and boxplot are shown. Are the conditions for testing the hypothesis satisfied? Yes

Printouts

(b) Are the consumer advocate's concerns founded? Use the $\alpha = 0.05$ level of significance. $H_0: \mu = 10{,}000$, $H_1: \mu < 10{,}000$, $t_0 = -1.343$, P-value = 0.1012, do not reject H_0

21. **Vehicle Emission Inspection** A certain vehicle emission inspection station advertises that the wait time for customers is less than 8 minutes. A local resident is skeptical and collects a random sample of 49 wait times for customers at the testing station. He finds that the sample mean is 7.34 minutes, with a standard deviation of 3.2 minutes. Does the sample evidence support the resident's skepticism? Use the $\alpha = 0.01$ level of significance. $H_0: \mu = 8$ min, $H_1: \mu < 8$ min, $t_0 = -1.444$, P-value = 0.0777; do not reject H_0

22. **Lights Out** With a previous contractor, the mean time to replace a streetlight was 3.2 days. A city councilwoman thinks that the new contractor is not getting the streetlights replaced as quickly. She selects a random sample of 12 streetlight service calls and obtains the following times to replacement (in days).

6.2	7.1	5.4	5.5	7.5	2.6
4.3	2.9	3.7	0.7	5.6	1.7

(a) Because the sample size is small, she must verify that replacement time is normally distributed and the sample does not contain any outliers. The normal probability

22. (b) $H_0: \mu = 3.2$, $H_1: \mu > 3.2$, $t_0 = 1.989$, P-value = 0.0361; reject H_0
plot and boxplot are shown. Are the conditions for testing the hypothesis satisfied? Yes

Replacement Time (days)

(b) Is there enough evidence to support the councilwoman's belief at the $\alpha = 0.05$ level of significance?

23. **Putting It Together: Ideal Number of Children** In June 2007, the Gallup organization conducted a survey and asked, "What do you think is the ideal number of children for a family to have?" The results of the survey are shown in the table.
23. (c) $\bar{x} = 2.47$; $s = 1.02$

Ideal Number of Children	Frequency
0	15
1	31
2	525
3	256
4	66
5	10
6	4
7	3
8	1
9	0
10	3
11	1

(a) Construct a relative frequency histogram for the ideal number of children. Comment on the shape of the distribution. Skewed right
(b) What is the mode ideal number of children? 2
(c) Determine the mean and standard deviation number of children. Round your answers to the nearest hundreth.
(d) Explain why a large sample size is needed to perform any inference regarding this population. Skewed right
(e) In May 1997, the ideal number of children was considered to be 2.64. Do the results of this poll indicate that people's beliefs as to the ideal number of children have changed? Use $\alpha = 0.05$. $H_0: \mu = 2.67$, $H_1: \mu \neq 2.67$, $t_0 = -5.041$; P-value < 0.0001; reject H_0

10.7 THE PROBABILITY OF A TYPE II ERROR AND THE POWER OF THE TEST

Preparing for This Section Before getting started, review the following:

- Computing normal probabilities (Section 7.3, pp. 397–399)

Objectives	**1** Determine the probability of making a Type II error
	2 Compute the power of the test

Note to Instructor
This section is optional and may be skipped without loss of continuity.

 Determine the Probability of Making a Type II Error

Recall, from Section 10.1, that a Type II error is made if we fail to reject the null hypothesis when the alternative hypothesis is true. The probability of making a Type II error is called β. It can be shown that the probability of making a Type II error; the probability of making a Type I error, α; and the sample size, n, are related. Once two of the three values are chosen, the third value can be determined when a specific value of the parameter in the alternative hypothesis is chosen. Usually researchers choose a level of significance α and the sample size n. To minimize the value of β for a given level of α, a researcher should choose n to be as large as time, money, and other resources allow.

In this section we present the procedure for computing the probability of making a Type II error for tests regarding the population mean when the population standard deviation is known. We will not find β for any other hypothesis tests.

In Example 1 from Section 10.2, we tested

$$H_0: \mu = 515 \text{ versus } H_1: \mu > 515$$

at the $\alpha = 0.05$ level of significance by obtaining a random sample of size $n = 40$. The population standard deviation σ was 114. The alternative hypothesis is true if the true population mean is greater than 515, and a Type II error is committed whenever H_0 is not rejected and $\mu > 515$. So

$$\beta = P(\text{Type II error}) = P(\text{do not reject } H_0 \text{ given } H_1 \text{ is true})$$

To compute the probability of making a Type II error, we need to know the criterion for not rejecting H_0. Since in this example $\alpha = 0.05$, we would not reject H_0 if $z_0 < z_{0.05} = 1.645$. We can write the criterion for not rejecting the null hypothesis in terms of a sample mean. Using the Z-score, we will not reject H_0 if

$$z_0 = \frac{\bar{x} - 515}{\frac{114}{\sqrt{40}}} < 1.645$$

Solving the inequality for $\bar{x}$, we would not reject H_0 if

$$\bar{x} < 515 + 1.645\left(\frac{114}{\sqrt{40}}\right) = 545$$

Figure 31

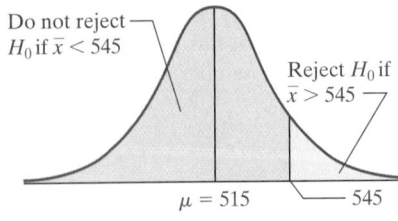

Do not reject H_0 if $\bar{x} < 545$

Reject H_0 if $\bar{x} > 545$

$\mu = 515$ 545

Figure 31 shows the "reject" and "do not reject" regions.

To compute the probability of making a Type II error, we also need a specific value of the population mean that is in the alternative hypothesis. For example, if the true population mean is 530, then

$$P(\text{Type II error}) = P(\text{do not reject } H_0 \text{ given } H_1 \text{ is true})$$

$$= P(\text{sample mean is less than 545 given that } \mu = 530)$$

$$= P\left(Z < \frac{545 - 530}{\frac{114}{\sqrt{40}}}\right)$$

$$= P(Z < 0.83)$$

$$= 0.7967$$

The probability of making a Type II error is 0.7967 if the population mean is 530. Figure 32 helps to illustrate the concept.

Figure 32

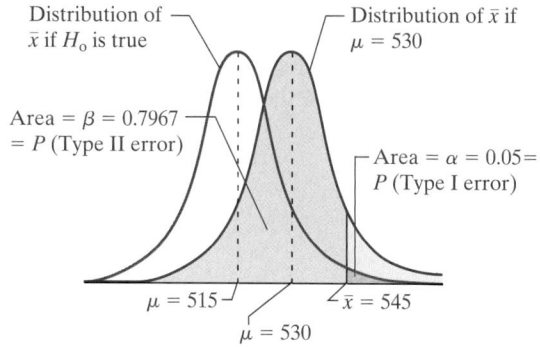

Distribution of $\bar{x}$ if H_o is true

Distribution of $\bar{x}$ if $\mu = 530$

Area $= \beta = 0.7967$ $= P$ (Type II error)

Area $= \alpha = 0.05 =$ P (Type I error)

$\mu = 515$

$\bar{x} = 545$

$\mu = 530$

There are an infinite number of values for the mean that are greater than 515, and each has its own Type II error probability.

We summarize the procedure for computing the probability of making a Type II error with the steps that follow.

Probability of a Type II Error

Step 1: Determine the sample mean that separates the rejection region from the nonrejection region.

Two-Tailed Test (H_1: $\mu \neq \mu_0$)	Right-Tailed Test (H_1: $\mu > \mu_0$)	Left-Tailed Test (H_1: $\mu < \mu_0$)
$\bar{x}_L = \mu_0 - z_{\alpha/2} \cdot \dfrac{\sigma}{\sqrt{n}}$ $\bar{x}_U = \mu_0 + z_{\alpha/2} \cdot \dfrac{\sigma}{\sqrt{n}}$	$\bar{x} = \mu_0 + z_\alpha \cdot \dfrac{\sigma}{\sqrt{n}}$	$\bar{x} = \mu_0 - z_\alpha \cdot \dfrac{\sigma}{\sqrt{n}}$

Note: z_α is the critical value, μ_0 is the value of the population mean stated in the null hypothesis, σ is the population standard deviation, and n is the sample size.

Step 2: Draw a normal curve whose mean is a particular value from the alternative hypothesis, with the sample mean(s) found in Step 1 labeled.

Step 3

Two-Tailed Test (H_1: $\mu \neq \mu_0$)	Right-Tailed Test (H_1: $\mu > \mu_0$)	Left-Tailed Test (H_1: $\mu < \mu_0$)
Find the area under the normal curve drawn in Step 2 between $\bar{x}_L$ and $\bar{x}_U$ found in Step 1. This area represents β, the probability of not rejecting the null hypothesis when the alternative hypothesis is true.	Find the area under the normal curve drawn in Step 2 to the left of the sample mean, $\bar{x}$, found in Step 1. This area represents β, the probability of not rejecting the null hypothesis when the alternative hypothesis is true.	Find the area under the normal curve drawn in Step 2 to the right of the sample mean, $\bar{x}$, found in Step 1. This area represents β, the probability of not rejecting the null hypothesis when the alternative hypothesis is true.

Let's look at an example that uses these steps.

EXAMPLE 1   **Computing the Probability of a Type II Error**

Problem: In Example 1 from Section 10.2, we tested H_0: $\mu = 515$ versus H_1: $\mu > 515$ for a random sample of size $n = 40$, with the population standard deviation equal to 114 at the $\alpha = 0.05$ level of significance. Compute the probability of a Type II error, given that the population mean is $\mu = 535$.

Approach: We follow Steps 1 through 3.

Solution

Step 1: We first determine $z_{0.05}$ to be 1.645. We let $Z = 1.645$, $\mu_0 = 515$, $\sigma = 114$, and $n = 40$ to find the sample mean that separates the rejection region from the nonrejection region:

$$1.645 = \frac{\bar{x} - 515}{\dfrac{114}{\sqrt{40}}}$$

Now solve for the sample mean, $\bar{x}$:

$$1.645 \cdot \frac{114}{\sqrt{40}} = \bar{x} - 515 \qquad \text{Multiply both sides by } \dfrac{114}{\sqrt{40}}.$$

$$\bar{x} = 515 + 1.645 \cdot \frac{114}{\sqrt{40}} \approx 545 \qquad \text{Add 515 to both sides and simplify.}$$

For any sample mean less than 545, we do not reject the null hypothesis.

Step 2: Figure 33 shows the normal curve with $\mu = 535$. The sample mean found in Step 1, $\bar{x} = 545$, is also labeled.

Figure 33

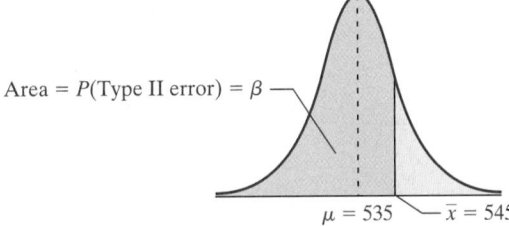

Area $= P(\text{Type II error}) = \beta$

$\mu = 535$ $\bar{x} = 545$

Step 3: Because this is a right-tailed test, the area to the left of $\bar{x} = 545$ represents β, the probability of a Type II error.

$$P(\text{Type II error}) = P(\bar{x} < 545 \text{ given that } \mu = 535)$$

$$= P\left(Z < \frac{545 - 535}{\dfrac{114}{\sqrt{40}}} \right) = P(Z < 0.55) = 0.7088$$

There is a 0.7088 probability of making a Type II error if the true population mean is 535.

Now Work Problem 13

Notice, the further the population mean is from the hypothesized mean, the lower the probability of making a Type II error.

② Compute The Power of the Test

In Other Words
The power of the test is the probability that you will correctly reject H_0.

The probability of rejecting the null hypothesis when the alternative hypothesis is true is $1 - \beta$. The value of $1 - \beta$ is referred to as the **power of the test**. The higher the power of the test is, the more likely the test will reject the null when the alternative hypothesis is true.

EXAMPLE 2   **Computing the Power of the Test**

Problem: Compute the power of the test for the situation in Example 1.

Approach: The power of the test is $1 - \beta$. We computed β in Example 1 to be 0.7088 when the true population mean is 535.

Solution: The power of the test is $1 - 0.7088 = 0.2912$. There is a 0.2912 probability of rejecting the null hypothesis if the true population mean is 535.

In Table 5, we show the probability of making a Type II error and the power of the test for a number of different values of the population mean greater than 515. Notice that the closer the population mean gets to the hypothesized value of 515, the larger the probability of a Type II error becomes. This should not be surprising. When the true population mean is close to the population mean stated in the null hypothesis, there is a high probability that we will not reject the null hypothesis and will make a Type II error.

We can use the values of μ and their corresponding powers to construct a *power curve*. A **power curve** is a graph that shows the power of the test against values of the population mean that make the null hypothesis false. Figure 34 shows the power curve for the values in Table 5.

	Table 5	
Value of μ	Probability of Making a Type II Error, β	Power, $1 - \beta$
516	0.9463	0.0537
520	0.9177	0.0823
525	0.8665	0.1335
530	0.7967	0.2033
535	0.7088	0.2912
540	0.6103	0.3897
550	0.3897	0.6103
560	0.2033	0.7967
570	0.0823	0.9177

Figure 34 shows that, as the true mean gets farther from the hypothesized mean, the power of the test approaches 1.

Figure 34

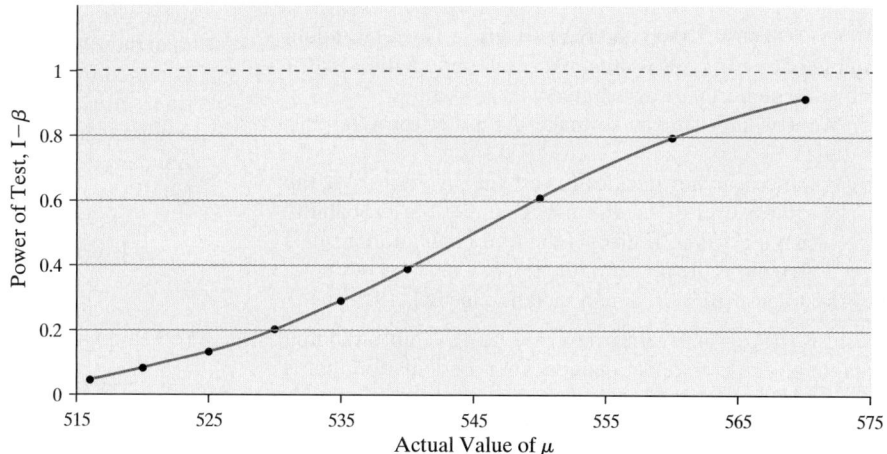

10.7 ASSESS YOUR UNDERSTANDING

Concepts and Vocabulary

1. Explain what it means to make a Type II error.

2. Explain the term *power of the test*.

3. What happens to the power of the test as the true mean gets closer to the hypothesized value of the mean? Why is this result reasonable?   Decreases

4. What effect would increasing the sample size have on the power of the test, assuming that all else remains unchanged?   Increases

Skill Building

5. To test $H_0: \mu = 50$ versus $H_1: \mu < 50$, a simple random sample of size $n = 24$ is obtained from a population that is known to be normally distributed with $\sigma = 12$.
   (a) What would it mean to make a Type II error for this test?
   (b) If the researcher decides to test this hypothesis at the $\alpha = 0.05$ level of significance, compute the probability

of making a Type II error if the true population mean is 48. What is the power of the test? *0.7967; 0.2033*

(c) Redo part (b) if the true population mean is 49.2.

6. To test $H_0: \mu = 40$ versus $H_1: \mu > 40$, a simple random sample of size $n = 25$ is obtained from a population that is known to be normally distributed with $\sigma = 6$.

(a) What would it mean to make a Type II error for this test?

(b) If the researcher decides to test this hypothesis at the $\alpha = 0.05$ level of significance, compute the probability of making a Type II error if the true population mean is 42. What is the power of the test? *0.4920; 0.5080*

(c) Redo part (b) if the true population mean is 40.6.

7. To test $H_0: \mu = 100$ versus $H_1: \mu \neq 100$, a simple random sample of size $n = 23$ is obtained from a population that is known to be normally distributed with $\sigma = 7$.

(a) What would it mean to make a Type II error for this test?

(b) If the researcher decides to test this hypothesis at the $\alpha = 0.01$ level of significance, compute the probability of making a Type II error if the true population mean is 103. What is the power of the test? *0.6985; 0.3015*

(c) Redo part (b) if the true population mean is 101.4.

8. To test $H_0: \mu = 80$ versus $H_1: \mu < 80$, a simple random sample of size $n = 22$ is obtained from a population that is known to be normally distributed with $\sigma = 11$.

(a) What would it mean to make a Type II error for this test?

(b) If the researcher decides to test this hypothesis at the $\alpha = 0.01$ level of significance, compute the probability of making a Type II error if the true population mean is 79. What is the power of the test? *0.9713; 0.0287*

(c) Redo part (b) if the true population mean is 77.5.

9. To test $H_0: \mu = 20$ versus $H_1: \mu < 20$, a simple random sample of size $n = 18$ is obtained from a population that is known to be normally distributed with $\sigma = 3$.

(a) What would it mean to make a Type II error for this test?

(b) If the researcher decides to test this hypothesis at the $\alpha = 0.05$ level of significance, compute the probability of making a Type II error if the true population mean is 17.4. What is the power of the test? *0.0212; 0.9788*

(c) Redo part (b) if the true population mean is 19.2.

10. To test $H_0: \mu = 4.5$ versus $H_1: \mu > 4.5$, a simple random sample of size $n = 13$ is obtained from a population that is known to be normally distributed with $\sigma = 1.2$.

(a) What would it mean to make a Type II error for this test?

(b) If the researcher decides to test this hypothesis at the $\alpha = 0.05$ level of significance, compute the probability of making a Type II error if the true population mean is 4.7. What is the power of the test? *0.8531; 0.1469*

(c) Redo part (b) if the true population mean is 5.4.

11. To test $H_0: \mu = 105$ versus $H_1: \mu \neq 105$, a simple random sample of size $n = 35$ is obtained from a population whose standard deviation is known to be $\sigma = 12$.

(a) What would it mean to make a Type II error for this test?

(b) If the researcher decides to test this hypothesis at the $\alpha = 0.1$ level of significance, compute the probability of

making a Type II error if the true population mean is 101.8. What is the power of the test? *0.5273; 0.4727*

(c) Redo part (b) if the true population mean is 103.1.

12. To test $H_0: \mu = 45$ versus $H_1: \mu \neq 45$, a simple random sample of size $n = 40$ is obtained from a population whose standard deviation is known to be $\sigma = 8$.

(a) What would it mean to make a Type II error for this test?

(b) If the researcher decides to test this hypothesis at the $\alpha = 0.1$ level of significance, compute the probability of making a Type II error if the true population mean is 46.2. What is the power of the test? *0.7532; 0.2468*

(c) Redo part (b) if the true population mean is 48.3. *0.1685; 0.8315*

Applying the Concepts

13. ATM Withdrawals According to the Crown Network, the
NW mean ATM withdrawal is $67. PayEase, Inc., manufactures an ATM that allows one to pay bills (electric, water, parking tickets, and so on), as well as withdraw money. An analyst with PayEase randomly selects 40 transactions to determine if the average withdraw from a PayEase machine is higher. Assume that the population standard deviation withdrawal is $10.

(a) What would it mean to make a Type II error for this test?

(b) If the researcher decides to test this hypothesis at the $\alpha = 0.05$ level of significance, determine the probability of making a Type II error if the true population mean for withdrawals from a PayEase machine is $70. What is the power of the test? *0.4013; 0.5987*

(c) Redo part (b) if the true population mean for withdrawals from a PayEase machine is $72. *0.0643; 0.9357*

14. Are Women Getting Taller? A researcher believes that the average height of a woman aged 20 years or older is greater than the 1994 mean height of 63.7 inches, on the basis of data obtained from the Centers for Disease Control and Prevention's *Advance Data Report*, No. 347. She obtains a simple random sample of 45 women. Assume that the population standard deviation is 6.5 inches.

(a) What would it mean to make a Type II error for this test?

(b) If the researcher decides to test this hypothesis at the $\alpha = 0.05$ level of significance, compute the probability of making a Type II error if the true population mean is 64 inches. What is the power of the test?

(c) Redo part (b) if the true population mean is 66 inches.

15. SAT Exam Scores A school administrator believes that students whose first language learned is not English score worse on the verbal portion of the SAT exam than students whose first language is English. The mean SAT verbal score of students whose first language is English is 515, on the basis of data obtained from the College Board. The administrator obtains a simple random sample of 20 students whose first language learned was not English. SAT verbal scores are normally distributed with a population standard deviation of 112.

(a) What would it mean to make a Type II error for this test?

(b) If the administrator decides to test this hypothesis at the $\alpha = 0.01$ level of significance, compute the probability of making a Type II error if the true population mean is 500. What is the power of the test? *0.9582; 0.0418*

(c) Redo part (b) if the true population mean is 480.

(d) Draw a power curve for this test.

16. **SAT Exam Scores** A school administrator believes that students whose first language learned is not English score differently on the math portion of the SAT exam than students whose first language is English. The mean SAT math score of students whose first language is English is 516, on the basis of data obtained from the College Board. The administrator obtains a simple random sample of 20 students whose first language learned was not English. SAT math scores are normally distributed with a population standard deviation of 114.

    (a) What would it mean to make a Type II error for this test?

    (b) If the administrator decides to test this hypothesis at the $\alpha = 0.05$ level of significance, compute the probability of making a Type II error if the true population mean is 505. What is the power of the test? *0.9286; 0.0714*

    (c) Redo part (b) if the true population mean is 475. *0.6367; 0.3633*

17. **Effect of α** Redo Problem 5(b) with $\alpha = 0.01$. What effect does lowering α have on the power of the test? *0.9345; 0.0655*

18. **Effect of α** Redo Problem 6(b) with $\alpha = 0.1$. What effect does increasing α have on the power of the test? *0.3520; 0.6480*

19. **Probability of a Type II Error in Tests on Proportions** We wish to test H_0: $p = 0.75$ versus H_1: $p < 0.75$. In this problem, we compute the power of the test for proportions.

    (a) The researcher decides to test this hypothesis at the $\alpha = 0.05$ level of significance by conducting a simple random sample of $n = 500$ people. Compute the probability of making a Type II error if the true population proportion is 0.70.

    Hint: The hypothesized mean is $p_0 = 0.75$, and the standard deviation is $\sqrt{\dfrac{p_0(1 - p_0)}{n}}$. *0.1894*

    (b) What is the power of the test? *0.8106*

20. **Probability of a Type II Error in Tests on Proportions** We wish to test H_0: $p = 0.35$ versus H_1: $p > 0.35$. In this problem, we compute the power of the test for proportions.

    (a) The researcher decides to test this hypothesis at the $\alpha = 0.05$ level of significance by conducting a simple random sample of $n = 700$ people. Compute the probability of making a Type II error if the true population proportion is 0.39.

    Hint: The hypothesized mean is $p_0 = 0.35$ and the standard deviation is $\sqrt{\dfrac{p_0(1 - p_0)}{n}}$. *0.2946*

    (b) What is the power of the test? *0.7054*

21. **Hypothesis Tests for the Mean Applet** Load the hypothesis tests for the mean applet. Set the applet so that $n = 40$, distribution is Normal, mean is 515, and standard deviation is 114.

    (a) Let's start by setting the Null mean to 515 and the Alternative is $>$. As we press simulate, we are "pretending" to obtain simple random samples of size 40 from a population whose mean is 515. Each time we press simulate, we obtain 100 simple random samples of size 40. The cumulative results screen tells us the proportion of samples that lead us to reject the statement in the null. Press simulate about 20 times (so you are simulating obtaining a simple random sample of size $n = 40$ about 2,000 times). What do the cumulative results represent?

    (b) Now set the true mean to 535 and simulate obtaining simple random samples of size $n = 40$ by pressing simulate at least 20 times. What proportion of times is the null hypothesis rejected (that $\mu = 515$) when the true population mean is 535? Compare this result to the value of the power of the test in Table 5.

    (c) Now set the true mean to 570 and repeat part (b).

CHAPTER 10 REVIEW

Summary

In this chapter, we discussed hypothesis testing. A statement is made regarding a population parameter, which leads to a null and an alternative hypothesis. The null hypothesis is assumed true. Given sample data, we either reject or do not reject the null hypothesis. In performing a hypothesis test, there is always the possibility of making a Type I error (rejecting the null hypothesis when it is true) or of making a Type II error (not rejecting the null hypothesis when it is false). The probability of making a Type I error is equal to the level of significance, α, of the test.

We discussed four types of hypothesis tests in this chapter. First, we performed tests about a population mean with σ known. Second, we performed tests about a population mean with σ unknown.

In both of these cases, we required that either the sample size be large ($n \geq 30$) or the population be approximately normal with no outliers. For small sample sizes, we verified the normality of the data by using normal probability plots. Boxplots were used to check for outliers.

The third test we performed regarded hypothesis tests for a population proportion. To perform these tests, we required that $np(1 - p) \geq 10$ so we could use the normal model.

Finally, we performed tests regarding a population standard deviation (or variance). These tests require that the population from which the sample is drawn be normally distributed. This test is not robust, so deviation from the requirement of normality was not allowed.

All four hypothesis tests were performed using classical methods and the P-value approach. The P-value approach to testing hypotheses has appeal because the rejection rule is always to reject the null hypothesis if the P-value is less than the level of significance, α.

We concluded the section by learning how to compute the probability of making a Type II error and the power of the test. The power of the test is the probability of rejecting the null hypothesis when the alternative hypothesis is true. The closer the true value of the population mean is to the hypothesized value of the population mean, the lower the power of the test.

Vocabulary

Hypothesis (p. 515)
Hypothesis testing (p. 516)
Null hypothesis (p. 516)
Alternative hypothesis (p. 516)
Two-tailed test (p. 517)
Left-tailed test (p. 517)
Right-tailed test (p. 517)
One-tailed test (p. 517)

Type I error (p. 518)
Type II error (p. 518)
Level of significance (p. 520)
Statistically significant (p. 524)
Test statistic (pp. 526, 542, 553)
Critical value (p. 526)
Critical region (p. 527)
Rejection region (p. 527)

Decision rule (p. 527)
Robust (p. 527)
P-value (p. 529)
Practical significance (p. 535)
Student's t-distribution (p. 541)
Power of the test (p. 572)
Power curve (p. 573)

Formulas

Test Statistics

- $z_0 = \dfrac{\bar{x} - \mu_0}{\dfrac{\sigma}{\sqrt{n}}}$ follows the standard normal distribution if the

  population from which the sample was drawn is normal or if the sample size is large ($n \geq 30$).

- $t_0 = \dfrac{\bar{x} - \mu_0}{\dfrac{s}{\sqrt{n}}}$ follows Student's t-distribution with $n - 1$

  degrees of freedom if the population from which the sample was drawn is normal or if the sample size is large ($n \geq 30$).

- $z_0 = \dfrac{\hat{p} - p_0}{\sqrt{\dfrac{p_0(1 - p_0)}{n}}}$ follows the standard normal distribution

  if $np_0(1 - p_0) \geq 10$ and $n < 0.05N$

- $\chi_0^2 = \dfrac{(n - 1)s^2}{\sigma_0^2}$ follows the χ^2-distribution with $n - 1$

  degrees of freedom if the population from which the sample was drawn is normal.

Type I and Type II Errors

- $\alpha = P(\text{Type I error})$

  $= P(\text{rejecting } H_0 \text{ when } H_0 \text{ is true})$

- $\beta = P(\text{Type II error})$

  $= P(\text{not rejecting } H_0 \text{ when } H_1 \text{ is true})$

Objectives

Section	You should be able to . . .	Examples	Review Exercises
10.1	1 Determine the null and alternative hypotheses (p. 515)	2	1(a), 2(a)
	2 Explain Type I and Type II errors (p. 518)	3	1–4, 15(b), (c)
	3 State conclusions to hypothesis tests (p. 520)	4	1(d) and (e); 2(d) and (e)
10.2	1 Explain the logic of hypothesis testing (p. 523)	pp. 523–526	23
	2 Test hypotheses about a population mean with σ known using the classical approach (p. 526)	1 and 2	5, 6, 14
	3 Test hypotheses about a population mean with σ known using P-values (p. 529)	3–5	5, 6, 14
	4 Test hypotheses about a population mean with σ known using confidence intervals (p. 534)	6	6(f), 16, 18
	5 Distinguish between statistical significance and practical significance (p. 534)	7	22
10.3	1 Test hypotheses about a population mean with σ unknown (p. 541)	1–3	7, 8, 13, 15(a), 16
10.4	1 Test hypotheses about a population proportion (p. 552)	1–3	9, 10, 17, 18
	2 Test hypotheses about a population proportion using the binomial probability distribution (p. 557)	4	21
10.5	1 Test hypotheses about a population standard deviation (p. 562)	1	11, 12, 19
10.6	1 Determine the appropriate hypothesis test to perform (p. 567)		5–19
10.7	1 Determine the probability of making a Type II error (p. 570)	1	20(a)
	2 Compute the power of the test (p. 572)	2	20(b)

Review Exercises

For Problems 1 and 2, (a) determine the null and alternative hypotheses, (b) explain what it would mean to make a Type I error, (c) explain what it would mean to make a Type II error, (d) state the conclusion that would be reached if the null hypothesis is not rejected, and (e) state the conclusion that would be reached if the null hypothesis is rejected.

1. Credit-Card Debt According to the *Statistical Abstract of the United States*, the mean outstanding credit-card debt per cardholder was $4,277 in 2000. A consumer credit counselor suspects that the mean outstanding credit-card debt per cardholder is now more than the amount in 2000.

$H_0: \mu = \$4277$, $H_1: \mu > \$4277$

2. Downloading Music According to a study by Ipsos-Reid, 61% of Internet users aged 18 to 24 years old had downloaded music from the Internet by the end of 2000. A researcher suspects that the percentage is now higher than 61%. $H_0: p = 0.61, H_1: p > 0.61$

3. A test is conducted at the $\alpha = 0.05$ level of significance. What is the probability of a Type I error? 0.05

4. β is computed to be 0.113. What is the probability of a Type II error? What is the power of the test? How would you interpret the power of the test? $0.113; 0.887$

5. To test $H_0: \mu = 30$ versus $H_1: \mu < 30$, a simple random sample of size $n = 12$ is obtained from a population that is known to be normally distributed with $\sigma = 4.5$.
  (a) If the sample mean is determined to be $\bar{x} = 28.6$, compute the test statistic. $z_0 = -1.08$
  (b) If the researcher decides to test this hypothesis at the $\alpha = 0.05$ level of significance, determine the critical value. $-z_{0.05} = -1.645$
  (c) Draw a normal curve that depicts the rejection region.
  (d) Will the researcher reject the null hypothesis? Why?   No
  (e) What is the P-value? 0.1401

6. To test $H_0: \mu = 65$ versus $H_1: \mu \neq 65$, a simple random sample of size $n = 23$ is obtained from a population that is known to be normally distributed with $\sigma = 12.3$.
  (a) If the sample mean is determined to be $\bar{x} = 70.6$, compute the test statistic. $z_0 = 2.18$
  (b) If the researcher decides to test this hypothesis at the $\alpha = 0.1$ level of significance, determine the critical values. $-z_{0.05} = -1.645, z_{0.05} = 1.645$
  (c) Draw a normal curve that depicts the rejection region.
  (d) Will the researcher reject the null hypothesis? Why?   Yes
  (e) What is the P-value? 0.0290
  (f) Test the hypothesis by constructing a 90% confidence interval. $(66.38, 74.82)$; reject H_0

7. To test $H_0: \mu = 8$ versus $H_1: \mu \neq 8$, a simple random sample of size $n = 15$ is obtained from a population that is known to be normally distributed.   7. (a) $t_0 = -1.506$
  (a) If $\bar{x} = 7.3$ and $s = 1.8$, compute the test statistic.
  (b) If the researcher decides to test this hypothesis at the $\alpha = 0.02$ level of significance, determine the critical values. $-t_{0.01} = -2.624, t_{0.01} = 2.624$
  (c) Draw a t-distribution that depicts the rejection region.
  (d) Will the researcher reject the null hypothesis? Why?   No
  (e) Determine the P-value. 0.1543

8. To test $H_0: \mu = 3.9$ versus $H_1: \mu < 3.9$, a simple random sample of size $n = 25$ is obtained from a population that is known to be normally distributed.   8. (a) $t_0 = -2.222$
  (a) If $\bar{x} = 3.5$ and $s = 0.9$, compute the test statistic.
  (b) If the researcher decides to test this hypothesis at the $\alpha = 0.05$ level of significance, determine the critical value. $-t_{0.05} = -1.711$
  (c) Draw a t-distribution that depicts the rejection region.
  (d) Will the researcher reject the null hypothesis? Why?   Yes
  (e) Determine the P-value. 0.0180

In Problems 9 and 10, test the hypothesis at the $\alpha = 0.05$ level of significance, using (a) the classical approach and (b) the P-value approach. Be sure to verify the requirements of the test.

9. $H_0: p = 0.6$ versus $H_1: p > 0.6$
   $n = 250; x = 165; \alpha = 0.05$ reject H_0

10. $H_0: p = 0.35$ versus $H_1: p \neq 0.35$
   $n = 420; x = 138; \alpha = 0.01$ do not reject H_0

11. To test $H_0: \sigma = 5.2$ versus $H_1: \sigma \neq 5.2$, a simple random sample of size $n = 18$ is obtained from a population that is known to be normally distributed.
  (a) If the sample standard deviation is determined to be $s = 4.9$, compute the test statistic. $\chi_0^2 = 15.095$
  (b) If the researcher decides to test this hypothesis at the $\alpha = 0.05$ level of significance, determine the critical values. $\chi_{0.975}^2 = 7.564, \chi_{0.025}^2 = 30.191$
  (c) Draw a chi-square distribution that depicts the rejection region.
  (d) Will the researcher reject the null hypothesis? Why?   No

12. To test $H_0: \sigma = 15.7$ versus $H_1: \sigma > 15.7$, a simple random sample of size $n = 25$ is obtained from a population that is known to be normally distributed.
  (a) If the sample standard deviation is determined to be $s = 16.5$, compute the test statistic. $\chi_0^2 = 26.508$
  (b) If the researcher decides to test this hypothesis at the $\alpha = 0.1$ level of significance, determine the critical value.
  (c) Draw a chi-square distribution that depicts the rejection region.   12. (b) $\chi_{0.1}^2 = 33.196$
  (d) Will the researcher reject the null hypothesis? Why?   No

13. Linear Rotary Bearing A linear rotary bearing is designed so that the distance between the retaining rings is 0.875 inch. The quality-control manager suspects that the manufacturing process needs to be recalibrated because the mean distance between the retaining rings is longer than 0.875 inch. In a random sample of 36 bearings, he finds the sample mean distance between the retaining rings to be 0.876 inch with standard deviation 0.005 inch. Test the quality-control manager's suspicion at the $\alpha = 0.05$ level of significance.   Do not reject H_0

14. Birth Weight An obstetrician wants to determine whether a new diet significantly increases the birth weight of babies. In 2005, birth weights of full-term babies (gestation period of 37 to 41 weeks) were normally distributed, with mean 7.53 pounds and standard deviation 1.15 pounds, according to the *National Vital Statistics Report*. The obstetrician randomly selects 50 recently pregnant mothers and persuades them to partake of this new diet. The obstetrician then records the birth weights of the babies and obtains a mean of 7.79 pounds. Is the new diet effective? Use the $\alpha = 0.01$ level of significance.   Do not reject H_0

15. High Cholesterol Do 20- to 39-year-old males consume too much cholesterol? The USDA-recommended daily allowance of cholesterol is 300 mg. In a survey conducted by the U.S. Department of Agriculture of 404 males 20 to 39 years old, it was determined the mean daily cholesterol intake was 326 milligrams, with standard deviation 342 milligrams.
  (a) Do 20- to 39-year-old males consume too much cholesterol? Use the $\alpha = 0.05$ level of significance.   No
  (b) What would it mean for the nutritionist to make a Type I error? A Type II error?
  (c) What is the probability the nutritionist will make a Type I error? 0.05

16. Boston Apartments According to Boston Rental Exchange, the mean monthly rental cost of a one-bedroom apartment in the Cambridge area of Boston is $1,400 with a standard deviation of $200. A random sample of 12 apartment rentals in Cambridge is shown.

| $1,325 | $1,850 | $1,800 | $1,750 | $1,750 | $1,275 |
| $1,609 | $1,600 | $1,500 | $1,475 | $1,450 | $1,150 |

Source: Google Housing

(a) Because the sample size is small, we must verify that the rental rates are normally distributed with no outliers and the sample does not contain any outliers. The normal probability plot and boxplot are shown. Are the conditions for testing the hypothesis satisfied? *Yes*

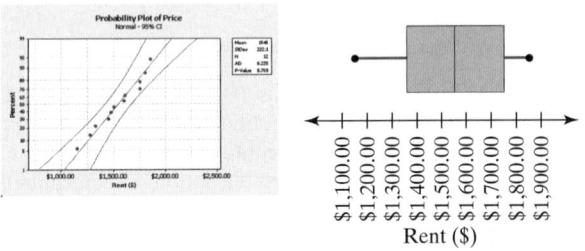

Rent ($)

(b) Judge whether the mean rental may, in fact, be different from the amount suggested by Boston Rental Exchange. Use the $\alpha = 0.10$ level of significance. *Reject H_0*

17. Sleeping Patterns of Pregnant Women A random sample of 150 pregnant women indicated that 81 napped at least twice per week. Do a majority of pregnant women nap at least twice a week? Use the $\alpha = 0.05$ level of significance.

Source: National Sleep Foundation *Do not reject H_0*

18. Trust in Government In 1997, 11% of adult Americans had no faith that the federal government was capable of effectively dealing with domestic problems. In a survey conducted during September 2007 by the Gallup organization of 1,100 adult Americans, 143 had no faith that the federal government was capable of effectively dealing with domestic problems. Judge whether the proportion has changed since 1997. Use the $\alpha = 0.10$ level of significance. *Reject H_0*

19. Birth Weights An obstetrician maintains that preterm babies (gestation period less than 37 weeks) have a higher variability in birth weight than do full-term babies (gestation period 37 to 41 weeks). According to the *National Vital Statistics Report*, the birth weights of full-term babies are normally distributed, with standard deviation 505.6 grams. A random sample of 41 preterm babies results in a standard deviation equal to 840 grams. Test the researcher's hypothesis that the variability in the birth weight of preterm babies is more than the variability in birth weight of full-term babies, at the $\alpha = 0.01$ level of significance. *Reject H_0*

20. Birth Weight Refer to Problem 14. Suppose that the true mean weight of babies whose mothers partake of the new diet is 7.59 pounds.
(a) What is the probability of a Type II error? *0.9750*
(b) What is the power of the test? *0.0250*

21. Teen Prayer In 1995, 40% of adolescents stated they prayed daily. A researcher wanted to know whether this percentage has risen since then. He surveys 40 adolescents and finds that 18 pray on a daily basis. Is this evidence that the proportion of adolescents who pray daily has increased at the $\alpha = 0.05$ level of significance? *No*

22. A New Teaching Method A large university has a college algebra enrollment of 5,000 students each semester. Because of space limitations, the university decides to offer its college algebra courses in a self-study format in which students learn independently, but have access to tutors and other help in a lab setting. Historically, students in traditional college algebra scored 73.2 points on the final exam, and the coordinator of this course is concerned that test scores are going to decrease in the new format. At the end of the first semester using the new delivery system, 3,851 students took the final exams and had a mean score of 72.8 and a standard deviation of 12.3. Treating these students as a simple random sample of all students, determine whether or not the scores decreased significantly at the $\alpha = 0.05$ level of significance. Do you think that the decrease in scores has any practical significance? *Reject H_0; no practical significance*

23. In your own words, explain the procedure for testing a hypothesis about a population mean when assuming that the population standard deviation is known.

CHAPTER TEST

1. According to the American Time Use Survey, adult Americans spent 42.6 minutes per day on phone calls and answering or writing email in 2006.
(a) Suppose that we want to judge whether the amount of daily time spent on phone calls and answering or writing email has increased. Write the appropriate null and alternative hypothesis. *$H_0: \mu = 42.6$; $H_1: \mu > 42.6$*
(b) The sample data indicated that the null hypothesis should be rejected. Write a conclusion.
(c) Explain what it would mean if we made a Type I error in conducting the test from part (a).
(d) Explain what it would mean if we made a Type II error in conducting the test from part (a).

2. The trade magazine *QSR* routinely examines fast-food drive-through service times. Recent research by the magazine indicates that the mean time a car spends in a McDonald's drive-through is 167.1 seconds. A McDonald's manager in

Salt Lake City feels that she has instituted a drive-through policy that results in lower drive-through service times. A random sample of 70 cars results in a mean service time of 163.9 seconds. Assuming that $\sigma = 15.3$ seconds, determine whether the policy is effective in reducing drive-through service times. *2. (a) $H_0: \mu = 167.1$; $H_1: \mu < 167.1$*
(a) State the null and alternative hypotheses.
(b) Because the cost of instituting the policy is quite high, the quality-control researcher at McDonald's chooses to test the hypothesis using an $\alpha = 0.01$ level of significance. Why is this a good idea?
(c) Conduct the appropriate test to determine if the policy is effective. *Do not reject H_0*

3. Perhaps you have been asked this question: "Did you get your 8 hours of sleep last night?" In a recent survey of 151 postpartum women, the folks at the National Sleep Foundation found that the mean sleep time was 7.8 hours, with a standard deviation of 1.4 hours. Does the evidence suggest that postpartum women do not get enough sleep? Use $\alpha = 0.05$ level of significance.   *Reject H_0*

4. The outside diameter of a manufactured part must be 1.3825 inches, according to customer specifications. The data shown represent a random sample of 10 parts. Use a 95% confidence interval to judge whether the part has been manufactured to specifications.

   Note: A normal probability plot and boxplot indicate that the data come from a population that is normally distributed with no outliers.   *(1.3824, 1.3828); do not reject H_0*

1.3821	1.3830	1.3823	1.3829	1.3830
1.3829	1.3826	1.3825	1.3823	1.3824

   Source: Dennis Johnson, student at Joliet Junior College

5. In many parliamentary procedures, a supermajority is defined as an excess of 60% of voting members. In a poll conducted by the Gallup organization on May 10, 1939, 1,561 adult Americans were asked, "Do you think the United States will have to fight Japan within your lifetime?" Of the 1,561 respondents, 954 said no. Does this constitute sufficient evidence that a supermajority of Americans did not feel the United States would have to fight Japan within their lifetimes?   *Do not reject H_0*

6. A Zone diet is one with a 40%–30%–30% distribution of carbohydrate, protein, and fat, respectively, and is based on the book *Enter the Zone*. In a study conducted by researchers Christopher Gardner and associates, 79 subjects were administered the Zone diet. After 12 months, the mean weight loss was 1.6 kg, with a standard deviation of 5.4 kg. Do these results suggest that the weight loss was statistically significantly greater than zero at the 0.05 level of significance? Do you believe the weight loss has any practical significance? Why?   *Reject H_0; not practical*

   Source: Christopher D. Gardner, Alexandre Kiazand, and Sofiya Alhassan, et al. "Comparison of the Atkins, Zone, Ornish, and LEARN Diets for Change in Weight and Related Risk Factors among Overweight Premenopausal Women. The A to Z Weight Loss Study: A Randomized Trial." *Journal of the American Medical Association*, March 2007.

7. According to the Pew Research Center, the proportion of the American population who use only a cellular telephone (no land line) is 0.37. Jason conducts a survey of thirty 20- to 24-year-olds who live on their own and finds that 16 do not have a land line to their home. Does this provide sufficient evidence to conclude that the proportion of 20- to 24-year-olds who live on their own and don't have a land line is greater than 0.37? Use an $\alpha = 0.10$ level of significance.   *Reject H_0*

8. Standard deviation rate of return is a measure of risk in the stock market. An investment manager claims that the standard deviation rate of return for his portfolio is less than the general market, which is known to be 18%. Treating the past 10 years as a random sample, you find the standard deviation rate of return of the manager's portfolio is 16%. Does this represent sufficient evidence to conclude that the investment manager's portfolio has less risk than the general market? Use $\alpha = 0.05$.   *Do not reject H_0*

9. Refer to Problem 2. If the true population mean drive-through time at the McDonald's with the new drive-through policy is 166.5 seconds:
   (a) What is the probability of making a Type II error?   *0.8186*
   (b) What is the power of the test?   *0.1814*

MAKING AN INFORMED DECISION

What Does It Really Weigh?

Many consumer products that we purchase have labels that describe the net weight of the contents. For example, the net weight of a candy bar might be listed as 4 ounces. Choose any consumer product that reports the net weight of the contents on the packaging.

(a) Obtain a random sample of size 8 or more of the consumer product. We will treat the random purchases as a simple random sample. Weigh the contents without the packaging.

(b) If your sample size is less than 30, verify that the population from which the sample was drawn is normal and that the sample does not contain any outliers.

(c) As the consumer, you are concerned only with situations in which you are getting ripped off. Determine the null and alternative hypotheses from the point of view of the consumer.

(d) Test whether the consumer is getting ripped off at the $\alpha = 0.05$ level of significance. Are you getting ripped off? What makes you say so?

(e) Suppose that you are the quality-control manager. How would you structure the alternative hypothesis? Test this hypothesis at the $\alpha = 0.05$ level of significance. Is there anything wrong with the manufacturing process? What makes you say so?

Approximately 8 miles north of Salisbury, Wiltshire, England, stands a large circular stone monument surrounded by an earthwork. This prehistoric structure is known throughout the world as Stonehenge. Its name is derived from the Old English word *hengen*, referring to something hung up. In the case of the monument, this name refers to the large horizontal lintel stones. The monument consists of an outer ring of sarsen stones, surrounding two inner circles of bluestones. The first and third circles are adorned with the familiar stone lintels. The entire structure is surrounded by a ditch and bank. Just inside the bank are 56 pits, named the Aubrey Holes, after their discoverer. These holes appear to have been filled shortly after their excavation.

Recently, it has been discovered that a number of the stone alignments are associated with important solar and lunar risings and settings, suggesting that the site served as some sort of massive astronomical calendar. If this conclusion is accurate, it seems likely that the monument might have been used as a temple for sky worshipers.

Corinn Dillion is interested in dating the construction of the structure. Excavations at the site uncovered a number of unshed antlers, antler tines, and animal bones. Carbon 14 dating methods were used to estimate the ages of the Stonehenge artifacts. Carbon 14 is one of three carbon isotopes found in Earth's atmosphere. Carbon 12 makes up 99% of all the carbon dioxide in the air. Virtually all the remaining 1% is composed of carbon 13. By far, the rarest form of carbon isotope found in the atmosphere is carbon 14.

The ratio of carbon 14 to carbon 12 remains constant in living organisms. However, once the organism dies, the amount of carbon 14 in the remains of the organism begins to decline, because it is radioactive, with a half-life of 5,730 years (the "Cambridge half-life"). So the decay of carbon 14 into ordinary nitrogen makes possible a reliable estimate about the time of death of the organism. The counted carbon 14 decay events can be modeled by the normal distribution.

Dillion's team used two different carbon 14 dating methods to arrive at age estimates for the numerous Stonehenge artifacts. The liquid scintillation counting (LSC) method utilizes benzene, acetylene, ethanol, methanol, or a similar chemical. Unlike the LSC method, the accelerator mass spectrometry (AMS) technique offers direct carbon 14 isotope counting. The AMS method's greatest advantage is that it requires only milligram-sized samples for testing. The AMS method was used only on recovered artifacts that were of extremely small size.

Stonehenge's main ditch was dug in a series of segments. Excavations at the base of the ditch uncovered a number of antlers, which bore signs of heavy use. These antlers could have been used by the builders as picks or rakes. The fact that no primary silt was discovered beneath the antlers suggests that they were buried in the ditch shortly after its completion. Another researcher, Phillip Corbin, using an archeological markings approach, had previously claimed that the mean date for the construction of the ditch was 2950 B.C. A sample of nine age estimates from unshed antlers excavated from the ditch produced a mean of 3033.1 B.C., with standard deviation 66.9 years. Assume that the ages are normally distributed with no obvious outliers. At an $\alpha = 0.05$ significance level, is there any reason to dispute Corbin's claim?

Four animal bone samples were discovered in the ditch terminals. These bones bore signs of attempts at artificial preservation and might have been in use for a substantial period of time before being placed at Stonehenge. When dated, these bones had a mean age of 3187.5 B.C. and standard deviation of 67.4 years. Assume that the ages are normally distributed with no obvious outliers. Use an $\alpha = 0.05$ significance level to test the hypothesis that the population mean age of the site is different from 2950 B.C.

In the center of the monument are two concentric circles of igneous rock pillars, called bluestones. The construction of these circles was never completed. These circles are known as the Bluestone Circle and the Bluestone Horseshoe. The stones in these two formations were transported to the site from the Prescelly Mountains in Pembrokeshire, southwest Wales. Excavation at the center of the monument revealed an antler, an antler tine, and an animal bone. Each artifact was submitted for dating. It was determined that this sample of three artifacts had a mean age of 2193.3 B.C, with a standard deviation of 104.1 years. Assume that the ages are normally distributed with no obvious outliers. Use an $\alpha = 0.05$ significance level to test the hypothesis that the population mean age of the Bluestone formations is different from Corbin's declared mean age of the ditch, that is, 2950 B.C.

Finally, three additional antler samples were uncovered at the Y and Z holes. These holes are part of a formation of concentric circles, 11 meters and 3.7 meters, respectively, outside the Sarsen Circle. The sample mean age of these antlers is 1671.7 B.C. with a standard deviation of 99.7 years. Assume that the ages are normally distributed with no obvious outliers. Use an $\alpha = 0.05$ significance level to test whether the population mean age of the Y and Z holes is different from Corbin's stated mean age of the ditch, that is, 2950 B.C.

From your analysis, does it appear that the mean ages of the artifacts from the ditch, the ditch terminals, the Bluestones, and the Y and Z holes dated by Dillion are consistent with Corbin's claimed mean age of 2950 B.C. for construction of the ditch? Can you use the results from your hypothesis tests to infer the likely construction order of the various Stonehenge structures? Explain.

Using Dillion's data, construct a 95% confidence interval for the population mean ages of the various sites. Do these confidence intervals support Corbin's claim? Can you use these confidence intervals to infer the likely construction order of the various Stonehenge structures? Explain.

Which statistical technique, hypothesis testing or confidence intervals, is more useful in assessing the age and likely construction order of the Stonehenge structures? Explain.

Discuss the limitations and assumptions of your analysis. Is there any additional information that you would like to have before publishing your findings? Would another statistical procedure be more useful in analyzing these data? If so, which one? Explain. Write a report to Corinn Dillion detailing your analysis.

Source: This fictional account is based on information obtained from *Archaeometry and Stonehenge*, (www.eng_h.gov.uk/stoneh). The means and standard deviations used throughout this case study were constructed by calculating the statistics from the midpoint of the calibrated date range supplied for each artifact.

Inferences on Two Samples

Outline

11.1 Inference about Two Means: Dependent Samples

11.2 Inference about Two Means: Independent Samples

11.3 Inference about Two Population Proportions

11.4 Inference about Two Population Standard Deviations

11.5 Putting It Together: Which Method Do I Use?

MAKING AN INFORMED DECISION

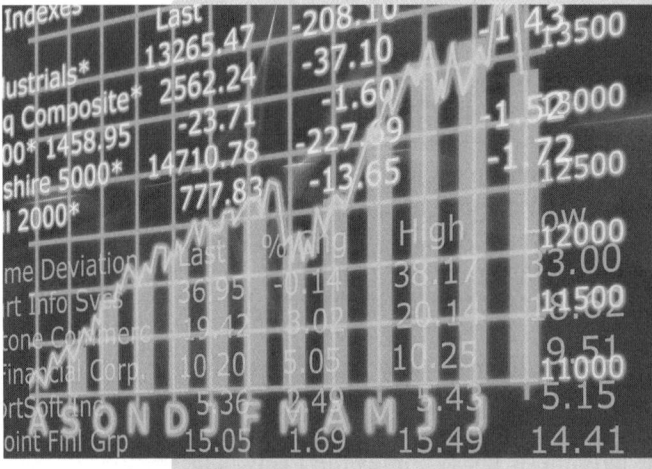

You have just received an inheritance of $10,000 and decide that the money should be invested, rather than blown on frivolous items. You have decided that you will invest the money in one of two types of mutual funds. But which type? See the Decisions project on page 641.

PUTTING IT TOGETHER

In Chapters 9 and 10 we discussed inferences regarding a single population parameter. The inferential methods presented in these chapters will be modified slightly in this chapter so that we can compare two population parameters.

The first two sections of this chapter deal with testing for the difference of two population means. We will discuss how to determine whether a certain treatment results in significantly different sample statistics. From a design-of-experiments point of view, the methods presented in Section 11.1 are used to handle matched-pairs designs (Section 1.6, page 50) with a quantitative response variable. For example, we might want to know whether the reaction time in one's dominant hand is different from reaction time in the nondominant hand. To conduct this test, we might randomly choose the individual's hand to begin with and measure the reaction time in each hand. We could then determine if the difference in reaction time is significant.

Section 11.2 presents inferential methods used to handle completely randomized designs when there are two levels of treatment and the response variable is quantitative (Section 1.6, pages 48–50). For example, we might randomly divide 100 volunteers who have the common cold into two groups, a control group and an experimental group. The control group would receive a placebo and the experimental group would receive a predetermined amount of some experimental drug. The response variable might be the time until the cold symptoms go away.

Section 11.3 discusses the difference between two population proportions. Again, we can use a completely randomized design to compare two population proportions. However, rather than having a quantitative response variable, we would have a binomial response variable; that is, either the experimental unit has a characteristic or it does not.

Finally, Section 11.4 presents a discussion for comparing two population standard deviations.

11.1 INFERENCE ABOUT TWO MEANS: DEPENDENT SAMPLES

Preparing for This Section   Before getting started, review the following:

- Matched-pairs design (Section 1.6, p. 50)
- Confidence intervals about μ, σ unknown (Section 9.2, pp. 479–482)
- Hypothesis tests about μ, σ unknown (Section 10.3, pp. 541–547)
- Type I and Type II errors (Section 10.1, pp. 518–520)

Objectives

 Distinguish between independent and dependent sampling

 Test hypotheses regarding matched-pairs data

 Construct and interpret confidence intervals about the population mean difference of matched-pairs data

---

① Distinguish between Independent and Dependent Sampling

Let's consider two scenarios.

Scenario 1: You might theorize that men and women who marry tend to have similar IQs. To test this theory, you randomly select 30 married individuals and measures the IQ of each spouse. Your goal is to determine whether the difference in their IQs is significantly different from zero.

Scenario 2: Do individuals who make fast-food purchases with a credit card tend to spend more than those who pay with cash? To answer this question, a marketing manager randomly selects 30 credit-card receipts and 30 cash receipts to determine if the credit-card receipts have a significantly higher dollar amount, on average.

Is there a difference in the approach taken to select the individuals in each study? Yes! In scenario 1, once a husband (or wife) is selected to be in the study, we automatically *match* the individual up with his or her spouse. In scenario 2, the receipts selected from the credit-card group have nothing at all to do with the receipts selected from the cash group.

In this regard the husbands selected *depend* on the wives selected (or vice versa), while the credit-card receipts selected are *independent* of the cash receipts.

Definition

A sampling method is **independent** when the individuals selected for one sample do not dictate which individuals are to be in a second sample. A sampling method is **dependent** when the individuals selected to be in one sample are used to determine the individuals in the second sample. Dependent samples are often referred to as **matched-pairs** samples.

So, the sampling method in scenario 1 is dependent (or a matched-pairs sample), while the sampling method in scenario 2 is independent.

EXAMPLE 1   **Distinguishing between Independent and Dependent Sampling**

Problem: For each of the following experiments, determine whether the sampling method is independent or dependent.

(a) Researcher Steven J. Sperber, MD, and his associates wanted to determine the effectiveness of a new medication* in the treatment of discomfort associated with

---

*The medication was a combination of pseudoephedrine and acetaminophen. The study was published in the *Archives of Family Medicine* 9:979–985, 2000.

the common cold. They randomly divided 430 subjects into two groups: Group 1 received the new medication and group 2 received a placebo. The goal of the study was to determine whether the mean of the symptom assessment scores of the individuals receiving the new medication (group 1) was less than that of the placebo group (group 2).

(b) In an experiment conducted in a biology class, Professor Andy Neill measured the time required for 12 students to catch a falling meter stick using their dominant hand and nondominant hand. The goal of the study was to determine whether the reaction time in an individual's dominant hand is different from the reaction time in the nondominant hand.

Approach: We must determine whether the individuals in one group were used to determine the individuals in the other group. If so, the sampling method is dependent. If not, the sampling method is independent.

Solution

(a) The sampling method is independent because the individuals in group 1 were not used to determine which individuals are in group 2.

(b) The sampling method is dependent because the individuals are related. The measurements for the dominant and nondominant hand are on the same individual.

Now Work Problem 5

In this section, we discuss inference on the difference of two means for dependent sampling. We will address inference when the sampling is independent in Section 11.2.

② Test Hypotheses Regarding Matched-Pairs Data

Inference on matched-pairs data is very similar to inference regarding a population mean when the population standard deviation is unknown. Recall that, if the population from which the sample was drawn is normally distributed or the sample size is large ($n \geq 30$), we said that

$$t = \frac{\overline{x} - \mu}{\frac{s}{\sqrt{n}}}$$

In Other Words

Statistical inference methods on matched-pairs data use the same methods as inference on a single population mean with σ unknown, except that the *differences* are analyzed.

follows Student's t-distribution with $n - 1$ degrees of freedom.

When analyzing matched-pairs data, we compute the difference in each matched pair and then perform inference on the differenced data using the methods of Section 9.2 or 10.3.

Testing Hypotheses Regarding the Difference of Two Means Using a Matched-Pairs Design

To test hypotheses regarding the mean difference of matched-pairs data, we can use the following steps, provided that

1. the sample is obtained using simple random sampling,

2. the sample data are matched pairs,

3. the differences are normally distributed with no outliers or the sample size, n, is large ($n \geq 30$).

Step 1: Determine the null and alternative hypotheses. The hypotheses can be structured in one of three ways, where μ_d is the population mean difference of the matched-pairs data.

Two-Tailed	Left-Tailed	Right-Tailed
$H_0: \mu_d = 0$	$H_0: \mu_d = 0$	$H_0: \mu_d = 0$
$H_1: \mu_d \neq 0$	$H_1: \mu_d < 0$	$H_1: \mu_d > 0$

Step 2: Select a level of significance, α, depending on the seriousness of making a Type I error.

Step 3: Compute the test statistic

$$t_0 = \frac{\bar{d} - 0}{\frac{s_d}{\sqrt{n}}} = \frac{\bar{d}}{\frac{s_d}{\sqrt{n}}}$$

which approximately follows Student's t-distribution with $n - 1$ degrees of freedom. The values of $\bar{d}$ and s_d are the mean and standard deviation of the differenced data.

Classical Approach

Step 4: Use Table VI to determine the critical value using $n - 1$ degrees of freedom.

	Two-Tailed	Left-Tailed	Right-Tailed
Critical value(s)	$-t_{\frac{\alpha}{2}}$ and $t_{\frac{\alpha}{2}}$	$-t_\alpha$	t_α
Critical region(s)			

Step 5: Compare the critical value with the test statistic.

Two-Tailed	Left-Tailed	Right-Tailed
If $t_0 < -t_{\frac{\alpha}{2}}$ or $t_0 > t_{\frac{\alpha}{2}}$, reject the null hypothesis.	If $t_0 < -t_\alpha$, reject the null hypothesis.	If $t_0 > t_\alpha$, reject the null hypothesis.

P-Value Approach

Step 4: Use Table VI to estimate the P-value using $n - 1$ degrees of freedom.

Two-Tailed	Left-Tailed	Right-Tailed

Step 5: If P-value $< \alpha$, reject the null hypothesis.

Step 6: State the conclusion.

The procedures just presented are **robust**, which means that minor departures from normality will not adversely affect the results of the test. If the data have outliers, however, the procedure should not be used.

We verify the assumption that the differenced data come from a population that is normally distributed by constructing normal probability plots. We use boxplots to determine whether there are outliers. If the normal probability plot indicates that the differenced data are not normally distributed or the boxplot reveals outliers, nonparametric tests should be performed, as discussed in Section 15.4.

EXAMPLE 2   **Testing Hypotheses Regarding Matched-Pairs Data**

Problem: Professor Andy Neill measured the time (in seconds) required to catch a falling meter stick for 12 randomly selected students' dominant hand and nondominant hand. Professor Neill wants to know if the reaction time in an individual's dominant hand is less than the reaction time in his or her nondominant hand. A coin flip is used to determine whether reaction time is measured using the dominant or nondominant hand first. Conduct the test at the $\alpha = 0.05$ level of significance. The data obtained are presented in Table 1.

Table 1		
Student	**Dominant Hand, X_i**	**Nondominant Hand, Y_i**
1	0.177	0.179
2	0.210	0.202
3	0.186	0.208
4	0.189	0.184
5	0.198	0.215
6	0.194	0.193
7	0.160	0.194
8	0.163	0.160
9	0.166	0.209
10	0.152	0.164
11	0.190	0.210
12	0.172	0.197

Source: Professor Andy Neill, Joliet Junior College

Note to Instructor

Remind students of some of the key phrases in the statement we are gathering evidence for that help them to determine whether the test is right-tailed, left-tailed, or two-tailed. Examples include "less than," "more than," "no different."

Approach: This is a matched-pairs design because the variable is measured on the same subject for both the dominant and nondominant hand, the treatments in this experiment. We compute the difference between the dominant time and the nondominant time. So, for the first student we compute $X_1 - Y_1$, for the second student we compute $X_2 - Y_2$, and so on. If the reaction time in the dominant hand is less than the reaction time in the nondominant hand, we would expect the values of $X_i - Y_i$ to be negative. We assume that there is no difference and seek evidence that leads us to believe that there is a difference.

Before we perform the hypothesis test, we must verify that the differences come from a population that is approximately normally distributed with no outliers because the sample size is small. We will construct a normal probability plot and boxplot of the differenced data to verify these requirements. We then proceed to follow Steps 1 through 6.

Note to Instructor

Emphasize the importance of constructing a table such as Table 2. Not only does it help organize the information, but it can be used to help students see the direction of the alternative hypothesis.

Solution: We compute the differences as $d_i = X_i - Y_i =$ time of dominant hand for ith student minus time of nondominant hand for ith student. We expect these differences to be negative, so we wish to determine if $\mu_d < 0$. Table 2 displays the differences.

CAUTION The way that we define the difference determines the direction of the alternative hypothesis in one-tailed tests. In Example 1, we expect $X_i < Y_i$, so the difference $X_i - Y_i$ is expected to be negative. Therefore, the alternative hypothesis is $H_1: \mu_d < 0$, and we have a left-tailed test. However, if we computed the differences as $Y_i - X_i$, we would expect the differences to be positive, and we have a right-tailed test!

Table 2			
Student	**Dominant Hand, X_i**	**Nondominant Hand, Y_i**	**Difference, d_i**
1	0.177	0.179	$0.177 - 0.179 = -0.002$
2	0.210	0.202	$0.210 - 0.202 = 0.008$
3	0.186	0.208	-0.022
4	0.189	0.184	0.005
5	0.198	0.215	-0.017
6	0.194	0.193	0.001
7	0.160	0.194	-0.034
8	0.163	0.160	0.003
9	0.166	0.209	-0.043
10	0.152	0.164	-0.012
11	0.190	0.210	-0.020
12	0.172	0.197	-0.025

$$\sum d_i = -0.158$$

We compute the mean and standard deviation of the differences and obtain $\bar{d} = -0.0132$ rounded to four decimal places and $s_d = 0.0164$ rounded to four decimal places. We must verify that the data come from a population that is approximately normal with no outliers. Figure 1 shows the normal probability plot and boxplot of the differenced data.

Figure 1

The normal probability plot is roughly linear and the boxplot does not show any outliers. We can proceed with the hypothesis test.

Step 1: Professor Neill wants to know if the reaction time in the dominant hand is less than the reaction time in the nondominant hand. We express this as $\mu_d < 0$. We have

$$H_0\text{: } \mu_d = 0 \quad \text{versus} \quad H_1\text{: } \mu_d < 0$$

This test is left-tailed.

Step 2: The level of significance is $\alpha = 0.05$.

Step 3: The sample mean is $\bar{d} = -0.0132$ second, and the sample deviation is $s_d = 0.0164$ second. The test statistic is

$$t_0 = \frac{\bar{d}}{\frac{s_d}{\sqrt{n}}} = \frac{-0.0132}{\frac{0.0164}{\sqrt{12}}} = -2.788$$

Classical Approach

Step 4: Because this is a left-tailed test, we determine the critical t-value at the $\alpha = 0.05$ level of significance with $n - 1 = 12 - 1 = 11$ degrees of freedom to be $-t_{0.05} = -1.796$. The critical region is displayed in Figure 2.

Figure 2

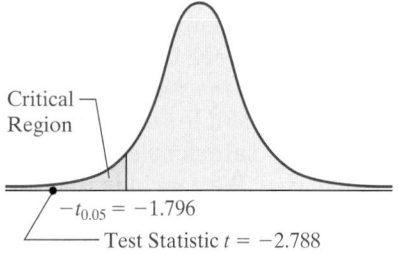

P-Value Approach

Step 4: Because this is a left-tailed test, the P-value is the area under the t-distribution with $12 - 1 = 11$ degrees of freedom to the left of the test statistic, $t_0 = -2.788$, as shown in Figure 3(a). That is, P-value $= P(t < t_0) = P(t < -2.788)$, with 11 degrees of freedom.

Because of the symmetry of the t-distribution, the area under the t-distribution to the left of -2.788 equals the area under the t-distribution to the right of 2.788. So the P-value $= P(t_0 < -2.788) = P(t_0 > 2.788)$. See Figure 3(b).

Figure 3

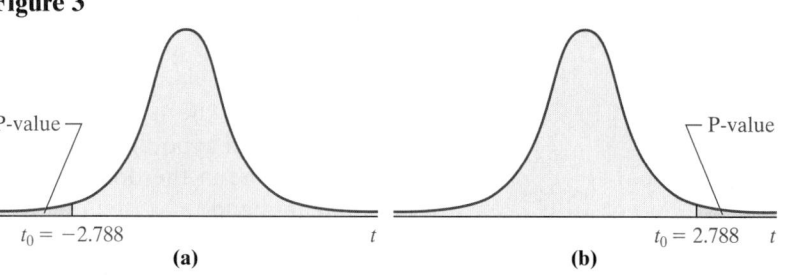

Using Table VI, we find the row that corresponds to 11 degrees of freedom. The value 2.788 lies between 2.718 and 3.106. The value of 2.718 has an area of 0.01 to the right under the *t*-distribution with 11 degrees of freedom. The value of 3.106 has an area of 0.005 to the right under the *t*-distribution with 11 degrees of freedom.

Because 2.788 is between 2.718 and 3.106, the *P*-value is between 0.005 and 0.01. So $0.005 < P\text{-value} < 0.01$. Less than 1 sample in 100 will yield the results we obtained *if* the statement in the null hypothesis is true. The results we obtained are unusual if the null hypothesis is true.

Step 5: Because the test statistic $t_0 = -2.788$ is less than the critical value $-t_{0.05} = -1.796$, Professor Neill rejects the null hypothesis. We show the test statistic in Figure 2.

Step 5: Because the *P*-value is less than the level of significance $\alpha = 0.05$, Professor Neill rejects the null hypothesis.

Step 6: There is sufficient evidence to conclude that the reaction time in the dominant hand is less than the reaction time in the nondominant hand at the $\alpha = 0.05$ level of significance.

EXAMPLE 3 **Testing Hypotheses Regarding Matched-Pairs Data Using Technology**

Problem: Obtain an exact *P*-value for the problem in Example 2 using statistical software or a graphing calculator with advanced statistical features.

Approach: We will use MINITAB to obtain the *P*-value. The steps for testing hypotheses regarding matched-pairs data using the TI-83/84 Plus graphing calculators, MINITAB, and Excel are given in the Technology Step-by-Step on page 595.

Solution: Figure 4 shows the results obtained from MINITAB. Notice that the *P*-value is 0.009.

Figure 4

Paired T-Test and Confidence Interval

Paired T for Dominant − Non-dominant

	N	Mean	StDev	SE Mean
Dominant	12	0.17975	0.01752	0.00506
Non-domi	12	0.19292	0.01799	0.00519
Difference	12	−0.01317	0.01643	0.00474

95% CI for mean difference: (−0.02361, −0.00273)
T-Test of mean difference = 0 (vs < 0): T-Value = −2.78 P-Value = 0.009

Interpretation: There is a 0.009 probability of obtaining a sample mean difference of −0.0132 or less from a population whose mean difference is 0. The results that we obtained would happen about 1 time in 100 samples if the statement in the null hypothesis were true. The results we obtained are unusual if the null hypothesis is true. At the $\alpha = 0.05$ level of significance, there is sufficient evidence to reject the null hypothesis because the *P*-value is less than α. We conclude that the reaction time in the dominant hand is faster than the reaction time in the nondominant hand.

Note to Instructor

The purpose of this activity is to have students experience a situation where a matched comparison is necessary. In addition to discussing why matching is important, it is also useful to discuss how earlier concepts, such as randomization, come into play.

Reaction times tend to be skewed right. You may consider taking three to five measurements on each hand for each student and use the median reaction time for each hand. Ask students to explain why this may be a better approach. Time limit: 45 to 50 minutes.

IN CLASS ACTIVITY

Measuring Reaction Time

We just saw that reaction time is different between your dominant and nondominant hand. Let's try to reproduce the results of Example 2. We can estimate reaction time by measuring reaction distance, in particular, the distance a ruler will fall before being caught. Would you expect this distance to be larger or smaller with your dominant hand?

(a) Pair up with another student in the class.

(b) Randomly determine whether to work first with the dominant hand or the nondominant hand. Why is this step important?

(c) One student holds his or her hand perpendicular to the floor so that the thumb and forefinger are roughly 5 cm apart. The other student holds a ruler (with centimeters) vertically just above the first student's fingers. The second student releases the ruler so that it falls vertically between the first student's thumb and forefinger (without hinting at when it will be dropped), and the first student grasps the ruler as quickly as possible. Record the number of centimeters required to grasp the ruler.

(d) Repeat the process for the other hand of the first student and then for each hand of the second student.

(e) Compute the difference in each student's reaction distances by computing distance$_{\text{dom. hand}}$ − distance$_{\text{nondom. hand}}$.

(f) Combine your team data with the rest of the class and conduct an appropriate hypothesis test to answer the question.

Now Work Problems 13(a) and (b)

---

3 **Construct and Interpret Confidence Intervals for the Population Mean Difference of Matched-Pairs Data**

We can also create a confidence interval for the population mean difference, μ_d, using the sample mean difference, $\bar{d}$, the sample standard deviation difference, s_d, the sample size, and $t_{\frac{\alpha}{2}}$. Remember, a confidence interval about a population mean is given in the following form:

$$\text{Point estimate} \pm \text{margin of error}$$

Based on the preceding formula, we compute the confidence interval for μ_d as follows:

Confidence Interval for Matched-Pairs Data

A $(1 - \alpha) \cdot 100\%$ confidence interval for μ_d is given by

$$\text{Lower bound:}\ \ \bar{d} - t_{\frac{\alpha}{2}} \cdot \frac{s_d}{\sqrt{n}} \qquad \text{Upper bound:}\ \ \bar{d} + t_{\frac{\alpha}{2}} \cdot \frac{s_d}{\sqrt{n}} \qquad \textbf{(1)}$$

The critical value $t_{\alpha/2}$ is determined using $n - 1$ degrees of freedom. The values of $\bar{d}$ and s_d are the mean and standard deviation of the differenced data.

Note: The interval is exact when the population is normally distributed and approximately correct for nonnormal populations, provided that n is large. ◄

| EXAMPLE 4 | **Constructing a Confidence Interval for Matched-Pairs Data** |

Problem: Using the data from Table 2, construct a 95% confidence interval estimate of the mean difference, μ_d.

Approach

Step 1: Compute the differenced data. Because the sample size is small, we must verify that the differenced data come from a population that is approximately normal with no outliers.

Step 2: Compute the sample mean difference, $\bar{d}$, and the sample standard deviation difference, s_d.

Step 3: Determine the critical value, $t_{\frac{\alpha}{2}}$, with $\alpha = 0.05$ and $n - 1$ degrees of freedom.

Step 4: Use Formula (1) to determine the lower and upper bounds.

Step 5: Interpret the results.

Solution

Step 1: We computed the differenced data and verified that they come from a population that is approximately normally distributed with no outliers in Example 2.

Step 2: We computed the sample mean difference, $\bar{d}$, to be -0.0132 and the sample standard deviation of the difference, s_d, to be 0.0164 in Example 2.

Step 3: Using Table VI with $\alpha = 0.05$ and $12 - 1 = 11$ degrees of freedom, we find $t_{\frac{\alpha}{2}} = t_{0.025} = 2.201$.

Step 4: Substituting into Formula (1), we find

$$\text{Lower bound: } \bar{d} - t_{\frac{\alpha}{2}} \cdot \frac{s_d}{\sqrt{n}} = -0.0132 - 2.201 \cdot \frac{0.0164}{\sqrt{12}} = -0.0236$$

$$\text{Upper bound: } \bar{d} + t_{\frac{\alpha}{2}} \cdot \frac{s_d}{\sqrt{n}} = -0.0132 + 2.201 \cdot \frac{0.0164}{\sqrt{12}} = -0.0028$$

Step 5: We are 95% confident that the mean difference between the dominant hand's reaction time and the nondominant hand's reaction time is between -0.0236 and -0.0028 second. In other words, we are 95% confident that the dominant hand has a mean reaction time that is somewhere between 0.0028 second and 0.0236 second faster than the nondominant hand. Notice that the confidence interval does not contain zero. This evidence supports the belief that the reaction time of a person's dominant hand is different from the reaction time of the nondominant hand.

Now Work Problem 13(c)

We can see that the results of Example 4 agree with the 95% confidence interval determined by MINITAB in Figure 4.

11.1 ASSESS YOUR UNDERSTANDING

Concepts and Vocabulary

1. A sampling method is independent when the individuals selected for one sample do not dictate which individuals are in a second sample.

2. A sampling method is dependent when the individuals selected for one sample are used to determine the individuals in the second sample.

3. A researcher wants to gather evidence to show that the mean from population 1 is less than the mean from population 2 in matched-pairs data. How would you define μ_d? How would you determine d_i? How would you determine the alternative hypothesis?

4. What are the requirements to test hypotheses regarding the difference of two means with dependent sampling?

Skill Building

In Problems 5–10, determine whether the sampling is dependent or independent.

5. A sociologist wishes to compare the annual salaries of married couples. She obtains a random sample of 50 married couples in which both spouses work and determines each spouse's annual salary. Dependent

6. A researcher wishes to determine the effects of alcohol on people's reaction times to a stimulus. She randomly divides 100 people aged 21 or older into two groups. Group 1 is asked to drink 3 ounces of alcohol, while group 2 drinks a placebo. Both drinks taste the same, so the individuals in the study do not know which group they belong to. Thirty minutes after consuming the drink, the subjects in each group perform a series of tests meant to measure reaction time. Independent

7. An educator wants to determine whether a new curriculum significantly improves standardized test scores for third grade students. She randomly divides 80 third-graders into two groups. Group 1 is taught using the new curriculum, while group 2 is taught using the traditional curriculum. At the end of the school year, both groups are given the standardized test and the mean scores are compared. Independent

8. A psychologist wants to know whether subjects respond faster to a go/no go stimulus or a choice stimulus. With the go/no go stimulus, subjects must respond to a particular stimulus by pressing a button and disregard other stimuli. In the choice stimulus, the subjects respond differently depending on the stimulus. The psychologist randomly selects 20 subjects, and each subject is presented a series of go/no go stimuli and choice stimuli. The mean reaction time to each stimulus is compared. Dependent

9. A study was conducted by researchers designed "to determine the genetic and nongenetic factors to structural brain abnormalities on schizophrenia." The researchers examined the brains of 29 patients diagnosed with schizophrenia and compared them with 29 healthy patients. The whole-brain volumes of the two groups were compared. Independent

   Source: William F. C. Baare et al., "Volumes of Brain Structures in Twins Discordant for Schizophrenia," *Archives of General Psychiatry* **58**:33–40, 2000

10. An agricultural researcher wanted to determine whether there were any significant differences in the plowing method used on crop yield. He divided a parcel of land that had uniform soil quality into 30 subplots. He then randomly selected 15 of the plots to be chisel plowed and 15 plots to be fall plowed. He recorded the crop yield at the end of the growing season to determine whether there was a significant difference in the mean crop yield. Independent

In Problems 11 and 12, assume that the differences are normally distributed.

11.

Observation	1	2	3	4	5	6	7
X_i	7.6	7.6	7.4	5.7	8.3	6.6	5.6
Y_i	8.1	6.6	10.7	9.4	7.8	9.0	8.5

(a) Determine $d_i = X_i - Y_i$ for each pair of data.
(b) Compute $\bar{d}$ and s_d. $\bar{d} = -1.614$, $s_d = 1.915$
(c) Test if $\mu_d < 0$ at the $\alpha = 0.05$ level of significance. Reject H_0
(d) Compute a 95% confidence interval about the population mean difference $\mu_d = \mu_X - \mu_Y$. $(-3.39, 0.16)$

12.

Observation	1	2	3	4	5	6	7	8
X_i	19.4	18.3	22.1	20.7	19.2	11.8	20.1	18.6
Y_i	19.8	16.8	21.1	22.0	21.5	18.7	15.0	23.9

(a) Determine $d_i = X_i - Y_i$ for each pair of data.
(b) Compute $\bar{d}$ and s_d. $\bar{d} = -1.075$, $s_d = 3.833$
(c) Test if $\mu_d \neq 0$ at the $\alpha = 0.01$ level of significance.
(d) Compute a 99% confidence interval about the population mean difference $\mu_d = \mu_X - \mu_Y$. $(-5.82, 3.67)$

12. (c) Do not reject H_0

Applying the Concepts

13. Muzzle Velocity The following data represent the muzzle
NW   velocity (in feet per second) of rounds fired from a 155-mm
     gun. For each round, two measurements of the velocity were

13. (c) $(-0.31, 0.54)$
recorded using two different measuring devices, with the following data obtained:

Observation	1	2	3	4	5	6
A	793.8	793.1	792.4	794.0	791.4	792.4
B	793.2	793.3	792.6	793.8	791.6	791.6

Observation	7	8	9	10	11	12
A	791.7	792.3	789.6	794.4	790.9	793.5
B	791.6	792.4	788.5	794.7	791.3	793.5

Source: Ronald Christenson and Larry Blackwood. "Tests for Precision and Accuracy of Multiple Measuring Devices." *Technometrics*, 35(4):411–421, 1993.

(a) Why are these matched-pairs data?
(b) Is there a difference in the measurement of the muzzle velocity between device A and device B at the $\alpha = 0.01$ level of significance? Do not reject H_0
    Note: A normal probability plot and boxplot of the data indicate that the differences are approximately normally distributed with no outliers.
(c) Construct a 99% confidence interval about the population mean difference. Interpret your results.
(d) Draw a boxplot of the differenced data. Does this visual evidence support the results obtained in part (b)?

14. Reaction Time In an experiment conducted online at the University of Mississippi, study participants are asked to react to a stimulus. In one experiment, the participant must press a key on seeing a blue screen. Reaction time (in seconds) to press the key is measured. The same person is then asked to press a key on seeing a red screen, again with reaction time measured. The results for six randomly sampled study participants are as follows:

Participant	1	2	3	4	5	6
Blue	0.582	0.481	0.841	0.267	0.685	0.450
Red	0.408	0.407	0.542	0.402	0.456	0.533

Source: PsychExperiments at the University of Mississippi

(a) Why are these matched-pairs data?
(b) In this study, the color that the student was first asked to react to was randomly selected. Why is this a good idea in this experiment?
(c) Is the reaction time to the blue stimulus different from the reaction time to the red stimulus at the $\alpha = 0.01$ level of significance? Do not reject H_0
    Note: A normal probability plot and boxplot of the data indicate that the differences are approximately normally distributed with no outliers.
(d) Construct a 99% confidence interval about the population mean difference. Interpret your results.
(e) Draw a boxplot of the differenced data. Does this visual evidence support the results obtained in part (b)?

15. Secchi Disk A Secchi disk is an 8-inch-diameter weighted disk that is painted black and white and attached to a rope. The disk is lowered into water and the depth (in inches) at which it is no longer visible is recorded. The measurement is an indication of water clarity. An environmental biologist is interested in determining whether the water clarity of the lake at Joliet Junior College is improving. She takes measurements at the same location on eight dates during the course of a year and repeats the measurements on the same dates 5 years later. She obtains the following results:

14. (d) $(-0.3316, 0.1456)$

Observation	1	2	3	4
Date:	5/11	6/7	6/24	7/8
Initial depth, X_i	38	58	65	74
Depth 5 years later, Y_i	52	60	72	72
Observation	5	6	7	8
Date:	7/27	8/31	9/30	10/12
Initial depth, X_i	56	36	56	52
Depth 5 years later, Y_i	54	48	58	60

Source: Virginia Piekarski, Joliet Junior College

(a) Why is it important to take the measurements on the same date?

(b) Does the evidence suggest that the clarity of the lake is improving at the $\alpha = 0.05$ level of significance?

Note: A normal probability plot and boxplot of the data indicate that the differences are approximately normally distributed with no outliers. Reject H_0

(c) Draw a boxplot of the differenced data. Does this visual evidence support the results obtained in part (b)?

16. **Rat's Hemoglobin** Hemoglobin helps the red blood cells transport oxygen and remove carbon dioxide. Researchers at NASA wanted to determine the effects of space flight on a rat's hemoglobin. The following data represent the hemoglobin (in grams per deciliter) at lift-off minus 3 days (H-L3) and immediately upon the return (H-R0) for 12 randomly selected rats sent to space on the Spacelab Sciences 1 flight.

Rat	1	2	3	4	5	6
H-L3, X_i	15.2	16.1	15.3	16.4	15.7	14.7
H-R0, Y_i	15.8	16.5	16.7	15.7	16.9	13.1
Rat	7	8	9	10	11	12
H-L3, X_i	14.3	14.5	15.2	16.1	15.1	15.8
H-R0, Y_i	16.4	16.5	16.0	16.8	17.6	16.9

Source: NASA Life Sciences Data Archive

(a) Does the evidence suggest that the hemoglobin levels at lift-off minus 3 days are less than the hemoglobin levels upon return at the $\alpha = 0.05$ level of significance?

Note: A normal probability plot and boxplot of the data indicate that the differences are approximately normally distributed with no outliers. Reject H_0

(b) Draw a boxplot of the differenced data. Does this visual evidence support the results obtained in part (a)?

17. **Getting Taller?** To test the belief that sons are taller than their fathers, a student randomly selects 13 fathers who have adult male children. She records the height of both the father and son in inches and obtains the following data.

	1	2	3	4	5	6	7
Height of father, X_i	70.3	67.1	70.9	66.8	72.8	70.4	71.8
Height of son, Y_i	74.1	69.2	66.9	69.2	68.9	70.2	70.4
	8	9	10	11	12	13	
Height of father, X_i	70.1	69.9	70.8	70.2	70.4	72.4	
Height of son, Y_i	69.3	75.8	72.3	69.2	68.6	73.9	

Source: Anna Behounek, student at Joliet Junior College

Are sons taller than their fathers? Use the $\alpha = 0.1$ level of significance.

Note: A normal probability plot and boxplot of the data indicate that the differences are approximately normally distributed with no outliers. Do not reject H_0

18. **Waiting in Line** A quality-control manager at an amusement park feels that the amount of time that people spend waiting in line for the American Eagle roller coaster is too long. To determine if a new loading/unloading procedure is effective in reducing wait time in line, he measures the amount of time (in minutes) people are waiting in line on 7 days. After implementing the new procedure, he again measures the amount of time (in minutes) people are waiting in line on 7 days and obtains the following data. To make a reasonable comparison, he chooses days when the weather conditions are similar.

Day:	Mon (2 P.M.)	Tues (2 P.M.)	Wed (2 P.M.)	Thurs (2 P.M.)	Fri (2 P.M.)
Wait time before, X_i	11.6	25.9	20.0	38.2	57.3
Wait time after, Y_i	10.7	28.3	19.2	35.9	59.2

Day:	Sat (11 A.M.)	Sat (4 P.M.)	Sun (12 noon)	Sun (4 P.M.)
Wait time before, X_i	32.1	81.8	57.1	62.8
Wait time after, Y_i	31.8	75.3	54.9	62.0

Is the new loading/unloading procedure is effective in reducing wait time at the $\alpha = 0.05$ level of significance?

Note: A normal probability plot and boxplot of the data indicate that the differences are approximately normally distributed with no outliers. Do not reject H_0

19. **Hardness Testing** The manufacturer of hardness testing equipment uses steel-ball indenters to penetrate metal that is being tested. However, the manufacturer thinks it would be better to use a diamond indenter so that all types of metal can be tested. Because of differences between the two types of indenters, it is suspected that the two methods will produce different hardness readings. The metal specimens to be tested are large enough so that two indentions can be made. Therefore, the manufacturer uses both indenters on each specimen and compares the hardness readings.

Specimen	1	2	3	4	5
Steel ball	50	57	61	71	68
Diamond	52	56	61	74	69

Specimen	6	7	8	9
Steel ball	54	65	51	53
Diamond	55	68	51	56

Construct a 95% confidence interval to judge whether the two indenters result in different measurements.

Note: A normal probability plot and boxplot of the data indicate that the differences are approximately normally distributed with no outliers. (0.1, 2.5); Reject H_0

20. Car Rentals The following data represent the daily rental for a compact automobile charged by two car rental companies, Thrifty and Hertz, in 10 locations.

City	Thrifty	Hertz
Chicago	21.81	18.99
Los Angeles	29.89	48.99
Houston	17.90	19.99
Orlando	27.98	35.99
Boston	24.61	25.60
Seattle	21.96	22.99
Pittsburgh	20.90	19.99
Phoenix	47.75	36.99
New Orleans	33.81	26.99
Minneapolis	33.49	20.99

Source: Yahoo!Travel

Test whether Thrifty is less expensive than Hertz at the $\alpha = 0.1$ level of significance.
Note: A normal probability plot and boxplot of the data indicate that the differences are approximately normally distributed with no outliers. *Do not reject* H_0

21. DUI Simulator To illustrate the effects of driving under the influence (DUI) of alcohol, a police officer brought a DUI simulator to a local high school. Student reaction time in an emergency was measured with unimpaired vision and also while wearing a pair of special goggles to simulate the effects of alcohol on vision. For a random sample of nine teenagers, the time (in seconds) required to bring the vehicle to a stop from a speed of 60 miles per hour was recorded.

Subject	1	2	3	4	5
Normal, X_i	4.47	4.24	4.58	4.65	4.31
Impaired, Y_i	5.77	5.67	5.51	5.32	5.83

Subject	6	7	8	9
Normal, X_i	4.80	4.55	5.00	4.79
Impaired, Y_i	5.49	5.23	5.61	5.63

(a) Whether the student had unimpaired vision or wore goggles first was randomly selected. Why is this a good idea in designing the experiment?
(b) Use a 95% confidence interval to test if there is a difference in braking time with impaired vision and normal vision where the differences are computed as "impaired minus normal."

Note: A normal probability plot and boxplot of the data indicate that the differences are approximately normally distributed with no outliers. *(0.688, 1.238)*

22. Braking Distance An automotive researcher wanted to estimate the difference in distance required to come to a complete stop while traveling 40 miles per hour on wet versus dry pavement. Because car type plays a role, the researcher used eight different cars with the same driver and tires. The braking distance (in feet) on both wet and dry pavement is shown in the following table. Construct a 95% confidence interval for the mean difference in braking distance on wet versus dry pavement where the differences are computed as "wet minus dry." Interpret the interval.

Note: A normal probability plot and boxplot of the data indicate that the differences are approximately normally distributed with no outliers. *(29.55, 35.85)*

Car	1	2	3	4
Wet	106.9	100.9	108.8	111.8
Dry	71.8	68.8	74.1	73.4

Car	5	6	7	8
Wet	105.0	105.6	110.6	107.9
Dry	75.9	75.2	75.7	81.0

23. Does Octane Matter? Octane is a measure of how much the fuel can be compressed before it spontaneously ignites. Some people believe that higher-octane fuels result in better gas mileage for their cars. To test this claim, a researcher randomly selected 11 individuals (and their cars) to participate in the study. Each participant received 10 gallons of gas and drove his or her car on a closed course that simulated both city and highway driving. The number of miles driven until the car ran out of gas was recorded. A coin flip was used to determine whether the car was filled up with 87-octane or 92-octane fuel first, and the driver did not know which type of fuel was in the tank. The results are in the following table:

Driver:	1	2	3	4	5	6
Miles on 87 octane	234	257	243	215	114	287
Miles on 92 octane	237	238	229	224	119	297

Driver:	7	8	9	10	11
Miles on 87 octane	315	229	192	204	547
Miles on 92 octane	351	241	186	209	562

(a) Why is it important that the matching be done by driver and car?
(b) Why is it important to conduct the study on a closed track?
(c) The normal probability plots for miles on 87 octane and miles on 92 octane are shown. Are either of these variables normally distributed? *No*

(d) The differences are computed as 92 octane minus 87 octane. The normal probability plot of the differences is shown. Is there reason to believe that the differences are normally distributed? Conclude that the differences can be normally distributed even though the original data are not. Yes

(e) The researchers used MINITAB to determine whether the mileage from 92 octane is greater than the mileage from 87 octane. The results are as follows:

```
Paired T-Test and CI: 92 Octane, 87 Octane

Paired T for 92 Octane - 87 Octane

              N      Mean      StDev    SE Mean
92 Octane     11   263.000   115.041    34.686
87 Octane     11   257.909   109.138    32.906
Difference    11   5.09091   14.87585    4.48524

95% lower bound for mean difference: -3.03841
T-Test of mean difference = 0 (vs > 0): T-Value = 1.14  P-Value = 0.141
```

What do you conclude? Why?
Fail to reject H_0; P-value is too large.

24. **Putting It Together: Glide Testing** You are a passenger in a single-propeller-driven aircraft that experiences engine failure in the middle of a flight. The pilot wants to maximize the distance that the plane can glide to increase the likelihood of finding a safe place to land. To accomplish this goal, should the pilot allow the propeller to "windmill" or should the pilot force the propeller to stop?

   To obtain the data needed to answer the research question, a pilot climbed to 8,000 feet at a speed of 60 knots and then killed the engine with the propeller either windmilling or stopped. Because the time to descend is directly proportional to glide distance, the time to descend to 7,200 feet was

recorded in seconds and used as a proxy for glide distance. The design called for randomly choosing the order in which the propeller would windmill or be stopped. The data in the table represent the time to descend 800 feet for each of 27 trials.

Note: Visit www.aceaerobaticschool.com to see footage of this scenario.

Trial	Windmilling	Stopped	Trial	Windmilling	Stopped
1	73.4	82.3	15	64.2	82.5
2	68.9	75.8	16	67.5	81.1
3	74.1	75.7	17	71.2	72.3
4	71.7	71.7	18	75.6	77.7
5	74.2	68.8	19	73.1	82.6
6	63.5	74.2	20	77.4	79.5
7	64.4	78.0	21	77.0	82.3
8	60.9	68.5	22	77.8	79.5
9	79.5	90.6	23	77.0	79.7
10	74.5	81.9	24	72.3	73.4
11	76.5	72.9	25	69.2	76.0
12	70.3	75.7	26	63.9	74.2
13	71.3	77.6	27	70.3	79.0
14	72.7	174.3			

Source: Catherine Elizabeth Cavagnaro. "Glide Testing: A Paired Samples Experiment." *Stats 46*, Fall, 2006.

(a) The trials took place over the course of a few days. However, for each trial, the pilot conducted both windmilling and stopped propeller one right after the other to minimize any impact of a change in weather conditions. Knowing this, explain why this is matched-pair data.

(b) Why does the researcher randomly determine whether to windmill or stop the propeller first for each trial?

(c) Explain why blinding is not possible for this experiment.

(d) What is the response variable in the study? What are the treatments?

(e) Compute the difference as "difference = stopped − windmilling." Draw a boxplot of the differenced data. What do you notice? An outlier

(f) From part (b), you should notice that trial 14 results in an outlier. Because our sample size is small, this outlier will have a major effect on any results. The author of the article indicated that it was possibly a situation in which there was an updraft of wind, causing the plane to take quite a bit longer than normal to fall 800 feet. Explain why this explanation makes it reasonable to eliminate trial 14 from the analysis.

(g) Redraw a boxplot of the data with trial 14 eliminated. Based on the shape of the boxplot, do you believe it is reasonable to proceed with a matched-pair *t*-test? Yes

(h) The researchers wanted to determine if stopping the propeller resulted in a longer glide distance. Based on this goal, determine the null and alternative hypotheses. $H_0: \mu_d = 0$ vs. $H_1: \mu_d > 0$

(i) Conduct the appropriate test to answer the researcher's question. Reject H_0

(j) Write a few sentences outlining your recommendations to pilots who experience engine failure.

TECHNOLOGY STEP-BY-STEP
Two-Sample *t*-Tests, Dependent Sampling

TI-83/84 Plus

Hypothesis Tests
1. If necessary, enter raw data in L1 and L2. Let L3 = L1 − L2 (or L2 − L1), depending on how the alternative hypothesis is defined.
2. Press STAT, highlight TESTS, and select `2:T-Test`.
3. If the data are raw, highlight DATA, making sure that List is set to L3 with frequency set to 1. If summary statistics are known, highlight STATS and enter the summary statistics.
4. Highlight the appropriate relation in the alternative hypothesis.
5. Highlight Calculate or Draw and press ENTER. Calculate gives the test statistic and *P*-value. Draw will draw the *t*-distribution with the *P*-value shaded.

Confidence Intervals
Follow the same steps given for hypothesis tests, except select `8: T Interval`. Also, select a confidence level (such as 95% = 0.95).

MINITAB
1. If necessary, enter raw data in columns C1 and C2.
2. Select the **Stat** menu, highlight **Basic Statistics**, and then select **Paired-t . . . .**
3. If you have raw data, enter C1 in the cell marked "First Sample" and enter C2 in the cell marked "Second Sample." If you have summarized data, click the "Summarized data" radio button and enter the summary statistics. Click Options . . ., select the direction of the alternative hypothesis and select a confidence level. Click OK twice.

Excel
1. Enter raw data in columns A and B.
2. Select the **Tools** menu and highlight **Data Analysis . . . .**
3. Select "*t*-test: Paired Two-Sample for Means." With the cursor in the "Variable 1 Range" cell, highlight the data in column A. With the cursor in the "Variable 2 Range" cell, highlight the data in column B. Enter the hypothesized difference in the means (usually 0) and a value for alpha. Click OK.

11.2 INFERENCE ABOUT TWO MEANS: INDEPENDENT SAMPLES

Preparing for This Section Before getting started, review the following:

- The Completely Randomized Design (Section 1.6, pp. 48–50)
- Confidence intervals about μ, σ unknown (Section 9.2, pp. 479–482)
- Hypothesis tests about μ, σ unknown (Section 10.3, pp. 541–547)
- Type I and Type II errors (Section 10.1, pp. 518–520)

> **Objectives**   Test hypotheses regarding the difference of two independent means
>   Construct and interpret confidence intervals regarding the difference of two independent means

We now turn our attention to inferential methods for comparing means from two independent samples. For example, we might wish to know whether a new experimental drug relieves symptoms attributable to the common cold. The response variable might be the time until the cold symptoms go away. If the drug is effective, the mean time until the cold symptoms go away should be less for individuals taking the drug than for those not taking the drug. If we let μ_1 represent the mean time until cold symptoms go away for the individuals taking the drug, and μ_2 represent the mean time until cold symptoms go away for individuals taking a placebo, the null and alternative hypotheses will be

$$H_0: \mu_1 = \mu_2 \quad \text{versus} \quad H_1: \mu_1 < \mu_2$$

or, equivalently,

$$H_0: \mu_1 - \mu_2 = 0 \quad \text{versus} \quad H_1: \mu_1 - \mu_2 < 0$$

To conduct this test, we might randomly divide 500 volunteers who have a common cold into two groups: an experimental group (group 1) and a control group

Note to Instructor

The computations in this section become quite tedious. You might consider emphasizing technology solutions. This allows for more emphasis on the P-value approach to hypothesis testing.

Note to Instructor

We do not discuss comparing the difference between two means using the pooled standard deviation. This is because the test requires that the two independent samples come from populations with the same variance. Verifying the requirement of equal population variances suggests using the F-test. Numerous statisticians (including George Box) have shown that the F-test is extremely sensitive to departures from normality. In fact, Box states, "it would seem logical to replace the usual analysis . . . which uses a pooled estimate . . . by the alternative criterion proposed by Welch."

(Source: "Nonnormality and Tests on Variances." Biometrica 40: 318–340)

Note to Instructor

The actual degrees of freedom is

$$df = \frac{\left(\dfrac{s_1^2}{n_1} + \dfrac{s_2^2}{n_2}\right)^2}{\dfrac{1}{n_1 - 1} \cdot \left(\dfrac{s_1^2}{n_1}\right)^2 + \dfrac{1}{n_2 - 1} \cdot \left(\dfrac{s_2^2}{n_2}\right)^2}$$

This formula is so messy that we recommend using the smaller of $n_1 - 1$ or $n_2 - 1$ degrees of freedom when performing by-hand computation.

(group 2). The control group will receive a placebo and the experimental group will receive a predetermined amount of the experimental drug. Next, determine the time until the cold symptoms go away. Compute $\bar{x}_1$, the sample mean time until cold symptoms go away in the experimental group, and $\bar{x}_2$, the sample mean time until cold symptoms go away in the control group. Now we determine whether the difference in the sample means, $\bar{x}_1 - \bar{x}_2$, is significantly less than 0, the assumed difference stated in the null hypothesis. To do this, we need to know the sampling distribution of $\bar{x}_1 - \bar{x}_2$.

It is unreasonable to expect to know information regarding σ_1 and σ_2 without knowing information regarding the population means. Therefore, we must develop a sampling distribution for the difference of two means when the population standard deviations are unknown.

The comparison of two means with unequal (and unknown) population variances is called the Behrens–Fisher problem. While an exact method for performing inference on the equality of two means with unequal population standard deviations does not exist, an approximate solution is available. The approach that we use is known as **Welch's approximate t**, in honor of English statistician Bernard Lewis Welch (1911–1989).

Sampling Distribution of the Difference of Two Means: Independent Samples with Population Standard Deviations Unknown (Welch's t)

Suppose that a simple random sample of size n_1 is taken from a population with unknown mean μ_1 and unknown standard deviation σ_1. In addition, a simple random sample of size n_2 is taken from a second population with unknown mean μ_2 and unknown standard deviation σ_2. If the two populations are normally distributed or the sample sizes are sufficiently large ($n_1 \geq 30$ and $n_2 \geq 30$), then

$$t = \frac{(\bar{x}_1 - \bar{x}_2) - (\mu_1 - \mu_2)}{\sqrt{\dfrac{s_1^2}{n_1} + \dfrac{s_2^2}{n_2}}} \tag{1}$$

approximately follows Student's t-distribution with the smaller of $n_1 - 1$ or $n_2 - 1$ degrees of freedom, where $\bar{x}_1$ is the sample mean and s_1 is the sample standard deviation from population 1, and $\bar{x}_2$ is the sample mean and s_2 is the sample standard deviation from population 2.

---

1 **Test Hypotheses Regarding the Difference of Two Independent Means**

Now that we know the approximate sampling distribution of $\bar{x}_1 - \bar{x}_2$, we can introduce a procedure that can be used to test hypotheses regarding two population means.

Testing Hypotheses Regarding the Difference of Two Means

To test hypotheses regarding two population means, μ_1 and μ_2, with unknown population standard deviations, we can use the following steps, provided that

1. the samples are obtained using simple random sampling;

2. the samples are independent;

3. the populations from which the samples are drawn are normally distributed or the sample sizes are large ($n_1 \geq 30$ and $n_2 \geq 30$).

Step 1: Determine the null and alternative hypotheses. The hypotheses are structured in one of three ways:

Two-Tailed	Left-Tailed	Right-Tailed
$H_0: \mu_1 = \mu_2$	$H_0: \mu_1 = \mu_2$	$H_0: \mu_1 = \mu_2$
$H_1: \mu_1 \neq \mu_2$	$H_1: \mu_1 < \mu_2$	$H_1: \mu_1 > \mu_2$

Note: μ_1 is the population mean for population 1, and μ_2 is the population mean for population 2.

Step 2: Select a level of significance α, depending on the seriousness of making a Type I error.

Step 3: Compute the test statistic

$$t_0 = \frac{(\bar{x}_1 - \bar{x}_2) - (\mu_1 - \mu_2)}{\sqrt{\dfrac{s_1^2}{n_1} + \dfrac{s_2^2}{n_2}}}$$

which approximately follows Student's t-distribution.

Classical Approach

Step 4: Use Table VI to determine the critical value using the smaller of $n_1 - 1$ or $n_2 - 1$ degrees of freedom.

	Two-Tailed	Left-Tailed	Right-Tailed
Critical Value	$-t_{\frac{\alpha}{2}}$ and $t_{\frac{\alpha}{2}}$	$-t_\alpha$	t_α
Critical Region			

Step 5: Compare the critical value with the test statistic.

Two-Tailed	Left-Tailed	Right-Tailed
If $t_0 < -t_{\frac{\alpha}{2}}$ or $t_0 > t_{\frac{\alpha}{2}}$, reject the null hypothesis.	If $t_0 < -t_\alpha$, reject the null hypothesis.	If $t_0 > t_\alpha$ reject the null hypothesis.

P-Value Approach

Step 4: Use Table VI to estimate the P-value using the smaller of $n_1 - 1$ or $n_2 - 1$ degrees of freedom.

Two-Tailed	Left-Tailed	Right-Tailed

Step 5: If P-value $< \alpha$, reject the null hypothesis.

Step 6: State the conclusion.

The procedure just presented is robust, so minor departures from normality will not adversely affect the results of the test. If the data have outliers, however, the procedure should not be used.

We verify these requirements by constructing normal probability plots (to assess normality) and boxplots (to determine whether there are outliers). If the normal probability plots indicates that the data come from populations that are not normally distributed or the boxplot reveals outliers, then nonparametric tests should be performed, as discussed in Section 15.4.

EXAMPLE 1 **Testing Hypotheses Regarding Two Means**

Problem: In the Spacelab Life Sciences 2 payload, 14 male rats were sent to space. Upon their return, the red blood cell mass (in milliliters) of the rats was determined. A control group of 14 male rats was held under the same conditions (except for space flight) as the space rats, and their red blood cell mass was also determined when the space rats returned. The project, led by Dr. Paul X. Callahan, resulted in the data listed in Table 3. Does the evidence suggest that the flight animals have a different red blood cell mass from the control animals at the $\alpha = 0.05$ level of significance?

Note that this experiment is a completely randomized design with two levels of treatment: flight and control.

Table 3

Flight				Control			
8.59	8.64	7.43	7.21	8.65	6.99	8.40	9.66
6.87	7.89	9.79	6.85	7.62	7.44	8.55	8.70
7.00	8.80	9.30	8.03	7.33	8.58	9.88	9.94
6.39	7.54			7.14	9.14		

Source: NASA Life Sciences Data Archive

Approach: This is a completely randomized design with response variable red blood cell mass. The treatment is space flight, which is set at two levels: space flight or no space flight. The experimental units are the 28 rats. The expectation is that all other variables that may affect red blood cell mass are accounted for by holding both groups of rats in the same condition (other than space flight).

We are attempting to determine if the evidence suggests that space flight affects red blood cell mass. We assume no difference, so we assume the mean red blood cell mass of the flight group equals that of the control group. We want to show that the mean of the flight group is different from the mean of the control group.

We verify that each sample comes from a population that is approximately normal with no outliers by drawing normal probability plots and boxplots. The boxplots will be drawn on the same graph so that we can visually compare the two samples. We then follow Steps 1 through 6, listed on pages 596–597.

Solution: Figure 5 shows normal probability plots of the data, which indicate that the data could come from populations that are normal. On the basis of the boxplots, it seems that there is not much difference in the red blood cell mass of the two samples, although the flight group might have a slightly lower red blood cell mass. We have to determine if this difference is significant or due to random sampling error (chance).

Figure 5

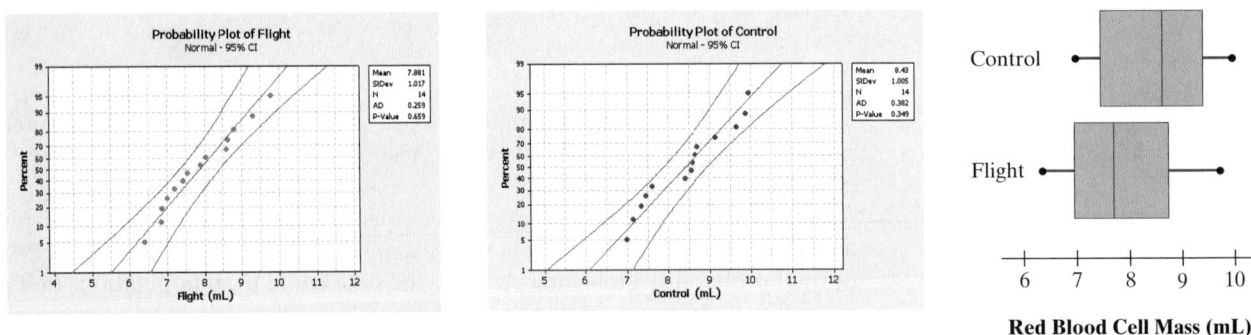

Step 1: We want to know whether the flight animals have a different red blood cell mass from the control animals. Let μ_1 represent the mean red blood cell mass of the flight animals and μ_2 represent the mean red blood cell mass of the control animals. We are attempting to gather evidence that shows $\mu_1 \neq \mu_2$, and we have the hypotheses

$$H_0: \mu_1 = \mu_2 \qquad\qquad H_0: \mu_1 - \mu_2 = 0$$
$$\text{versus} \qquad \text{or} \qquad \text{versus}$$
$$H_1: \mu_1 \neq \mu_2 \qquad\qquad H_1: \mu_1 - \mu_2 \neq 0$$

Step 2: The level of significance $\alpha = 0.05$.

Table 4	Flight Animals	Control Animals
Sample size	$n_1 = 14$	$n_2 = 14$
Sample mean	$\bar{x}_1 = 7.881$	$\bar{x}_2 = 8.430$
Sample standard deviation	$s_1 = 1.017$	$s_2 = 1.005$

Step 3: The sample statistics for the data in Table 3 are shown in Table 4. The test statistic is

$$t_0 = \frac{(\bar{x}_1 - \bar{x}_2) - (\mu_1 - \mu_2)}{\sqrt{\dfrac{s_1^2}{n_1} + \dfrac{s_2^2}{n_2}}} = \frac{(7.881 - 8.430) - 0}{\sqrt{\dfrac{1.017^2}{14} + \dfrac{1.005^2}{14}}}$$

$$= \frac{-0.549}{0.3821288115}$$

$$= -1.437$$

Classical Approach

Step 4: This is a two-tailed test with $\alpha = 0.05$. Since the sample sizes of the experimental group and control group are both 14, we have $n_1 - 1 = 14 - 1 = 13$ degrees of freedom. The critical values are $t_{\frac{\alpha}{2}} = t_{\frac{0.05}{2}} = t_{0.025} = 2.160$ and $-t_{0.025} = -2.160$.

The critical region is displayed in Figure 6.

Figure 6

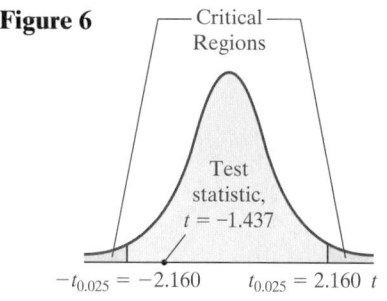

Step 5: Because the test statistic does not lie within a critical region, we do not reject the null hypothesis.

P-Value Approach

Step 4: Because this is a two-tailed test, the *P*-value is the area under the *t*-distribution to the left of $t_0 = -1.437$ plus the area under the *t*-distribution to the right of $t_0 = 1.437$. See Figure 7.

Figure 7 The sum of the area in the tails is the *P*-value

Since the sample size of the experimental group and control group are both 14, we have $n_1 - 1 = 14 - 1 = 13$ degrees of freedom. Because of symmetry, we use Table VI to estimate the area under the *t*-distribution to the right of $t_0 = 1.437$ and double it.

$$P\text{-value} = P(t_0 < -1.437 \text{ or } t_0 > 1.437)$$
$$= 2P(t_0 > 1.437)$$

Using Table VI, we find the row that corresponds to 13 degrees of freedom. The value 1.437 lies between 1.350 and 1.771. The area under the *t*-distribution with 13 degrees of freedom to the right of 1.350 is 0.10. The area under the *t*-distribution with 13 degrees of freedom to the right of 1.771 is 0.05. After doubling these values, we have

$$0.10 < P\text{-value} < 0.20$$

If the statement in the null hypothesis were true, we would expect to get results similar to the ones obtained in about 10 to 20 samples out of 100. The results we obtained are not unusual if the null hypothesis is true.

Step 5: Because *P*-value $> \alpha$, we do not reject the null hypothesis.

Step 6: There is not sufficient evidence to conclude that the flight animals have a different red blood cell mass from the control animals at the $\alpha = 0.05$ level of significance.

The degrees of freedom used to determine the critical value(s) presented in Example 1 are conservative. Results that are more accurate can be obtained by using the following degrees of freedom:

$$\text{df} = \frac{\left(\dfrac{s_1^2}{n_1} + \dfrac{s_2^2}{n_2}\right)^2}{\dfrac{\left(\dfrac{s_1^2}{n_1}\right)^2}{n_1 - 1} + \dfrac{\left(\dfrac{s_2^2}{n_2}\right)^2}{n_2 - 1}} \qquad (2)$$

When using Formula (2) to compute degrees of freedom, round down to the nearest integer to use Table VI. For hand inference, it is recommended that we use the smaller of $n_1 - 1$ or $n_2 - 1$ as the degrees of freedom to ease computation. However, computer software will use Formula (2) when computing the degrees of freedom for increased precision in determining the P-value.

EXAMPLE 2 **Testing Hypotheses Regarding Two Means Using Technology**

Problem: Obtain an exact P-value for the problem in Example 1 using statistical software or a graphing calculator with advanced statistical features.

Approach: We will use Excel to obtain the P-value. The steps for testing hypotheses regarding two means using the TI-83/84 Plus graphing calculator, MINITAB, and Excel are given in the Technology Step-by-Step on pages 607–608.

Solution: Figure 8 shows the results obtained from Excel. The P-value is 0.1627.

Figure 8 t-Test: *Two-Sample Assuming Unequal Variances*

	Flight	Control
Mean	7.880714286	8.43
Variance	1.035207143	1.010969231
Observations	14	14
Hypothesized Mean Difference	0	
df	26	
t Stat	−1.436781704	
P(T<=t) one-tail	0.081352709	
t Critical one-tail	1.705616341	
P(T<=t) two-tail	0.162705419	
t Critical two-tail	2.055530786	

Interpretation: There is a 0.1627 probability of obtaining a sample mean difference that is $|t_0| = |-1.437| = 1.44$ sample standard deviations from the hypothesized mean difference of 0. We would expect to obtained the results obtained, assuming that the statement in the null hypothesis is true, in about 16 samples out of 100 samples. There is not sufficient evidence to conclude that the flight animals have a different red blood cell mass from the control animals at the $\alpha = 0.05$ level of significance.

Notice that the degrees of freedom in the technology solution are 26* versus 13 in the conservative solution done by hand in Example 1. With the lower degrees of freedom, the critical t is larger (2.160 with 13 degrees of freedom versus 2.056 with approximately 26 degrees of freedom). The larger critical value increases the number of standard deviations the difference in the sample means must be from the hypothesized mean difference before the null hypothesis is rejected. Therefore, in using the smaller of $n_1 - 1$ or $n_2 - 1$ degrees of freedom, we need more substantial evidence to reject the null hypothesis. This requirement decreases the probability of a Type I error (rejecting the null hypothesis when the null hypothesis is true) below the actual level of α chosen by the researcher. This is what we mean when we say that the method of using the lesser of $n_1 - 1$ and $n_2 - 1$ as a proxy for degrees of freedom is conservative compared with using Formula (2).

CAUTION The degrees of freedom in by-hand solutions will not equal the degrees of freedom in technology solutions unless you use Formula (2) to compute degrees of freedom.

Now Work Problems 13(a) and (b)

*Actually, the degrees of the freedom are 25.996, but Excel rounded to 26.

Note to Instructor
The purpose of this activity is to give students a hands-on experience with hypothesis testing involving two means. The second rope should be clearly longer or shorter than the first rope. Be sure to tell students the lengths of the ropes only after all estimates have been reported. Time limit: 30 to 45 minutes depending on discussion.

IN CLASS ACTIVITY

Stringing Them Along (Part II)

Do you believe that it is easier to estimate the length of a longer rope or shorter rope by sight?

(a) Look at the piece of rope that your instructor is holding and estimate the length of the rope in inches. Now look at the second piece of rope and estimate its length in inches. After your instructor tells you the actual length of each piece of rope, compute the absolute value of the difference between your estimate and the actual length. That is, compute |actual − estimate| for each student's estimate.

(b) Assuming that estimates are just as good for long ropes as they are for short ropes, the null hypothesis is H_0: $\mu_{\text{longer}} = \mu_{\text{shorter}}$ (where μ represents the population mean absolute difference between the actual length and the estimated length). Based on your answer to the question posed at the beginning of the activity, select an appropriate alternative hypothesis and a level of significance.

(c) Combine your data with the rest of the class. Conduct the hypothesis test you outlined in part (b). What did you conclude?

(d) Could this test have been done as a matched-pairs test? Explain.

Note: Save the class data for use in another activity.

---

② **Construct and Interpret Confidence Intervals Regarding the Difference of Two Independent Means**

Constructing a confidence interval for the difference of two means is an extension of the results presented in Section 9.2.

Constructing a $(1 - \alpha) \cdot 100\%$ Confidence Interval for the Difference of Two Means

A simple random sample of size n_1 is taken from a population with unknown mean μ_1 and unknown standard deviation σ_1. Also, a simple random sample of size n_2 is taken from a population with unknown mean μ_2 and unknown standard deviation σ_2. If the two populations are normally distributed or the sample sizes are sufficiently large ($n_1 \geq 30$ and $n_2 \geq 30$), a $(1 - \alpha) \cdot 100\%$ confidence interval about $\mu_1 - \mu_2$ is given by

$$\text{Lower bound:} \quad (\bar{x}_1 - \bar{x}_2) - t_{\frac{\alpha}{2}} \cdot \sqrt{\frac{s_1^2}{n_1} + \frac{s_2^2}{n_2}}$$

and

(3)

$$\text{Upper bound:} \quad (\bar{x}_1 - \bar{x}_2) + t_{\frac{\alpha}{2}} \cdot \sqrt{\frac{s_1^2}{n_1} + \frac{s_2^2}{n_2}}$$

where $t_{\frac{\alpha}{2}}$ is computed using the smaller of $n_1 - 1$ or $n_2 - 1$ degrees of freedom or Formula (2).

| EXAMPLE 3 | **Constructing a Confidence Interval for the Difference of Two Means** |

Problem: Construct a 95% confidence interval for $\mu_1 - \mu_2$ using the data presented in Table 3.

Approach: The normal probability plots and boxplot (Figure 5) indicate that the data are approximately normal with no outliers. We compute the confidence interval with $\alpha = 0.05$ using Formula (3).

Solution: We have already found the sample statistics in Example 1. In addition, we found $t_{\alpha/2} = t_{0.025}$ with 13 degrees of freedom to be 2.160. Substituting into Formula (3), we obtain the following results:

Lower bound:

$$(\bar{x}_1 - \bar{x}_2) - t_{\frac{\alpha}{2}} \cdot \sqrt{\frac{s_1^2}{n_1} + \frac{s_2^2}{n_2}} = (7.881 - 8.430) - 2.160 \cdot \sqrt{\frac{1.017^2}{14} + \frac{1.005^2}{14}}$$
$$= -0.549 - 0.825$$
$$= -1.374$$

Upper bound:

$$(\bar{x}_1 - \bar{x}_2) + t_{\frac{\alpha}{2}} \cdot \sqrt{\frac{s_1^2}{n_1} + \frac{s_2^2}{n_2}} = (7.881 - 8.430) + 2.160 \cdot \sqrt{\frac{1.017^2}{14} + \frac{1.005^2}{14}}$$
$$= -0.549 + 0.825$$
$$= 0.276$$

Interpretation: We are 95% confident that the mean difference between the red blood cell mass of the flight animals and control animals is between −1.374 and 0.276 mL. Because the confidence interval contains zero, there is not sufficient evidence to conclude that there is a difference in the red blood cell mass of the flight group and the control group.

Now Work Problems 13(c) and (d)

CAUTION We would use the pooled two-sample t-test when the two samples come from populations that have the same variance. *Pooling* refers to finding a weighted average of the two sample variances from the independent samples. It is difficult to verify that two population variances might be equal based on sample data, so we will always use Welch's t when comparing two means.

What about the Pooled Two-Sample t-Tests?

Perhaps you have noticed that statistical software and graphing calculators with advanced statistical features provide an option for two types of two-sample t-tests: one that assumes equal population variances (pooling) and one that does not assume equal population variances. Welch's t-statistic does not assume that the population variances are equal and can be used whether the population variances are equal or not. The test that assumes equal population variances is referred to as the *pooled t-statistic.*

The **pooled t-statistic** is computed by finding a weighted average of the sample variances and uses this average in the computation of the test statistic. The advantage of this test statistic is that it exactly follows Student's t-distribution with $n_1 + n_2 - 2$ degrees of freedom.

The disadvantage of the test statistic is that it requires that the population variances be equal. How is this requirement to be verified? While a test for determining the equality of variances does exist (F-test, Section 11.4), the test *requires* that each population be normally distributed. However, the F-test is not robust. Any minor departures from normality will make the results of the F-test unreliable. It has been recommended by many statisticians* that a preliminary F-test to check the requirement of equality of variance not be performed. In fact, George Box once said, "To make preliminary tests on variances is rather like putting to sea in a rowing boat to find out whether conditions are sufficiently calm for an ocean liner to leave port!"

*Moser and Stevens, "Homogeneity of Variance in the Two-Sample Means Test." *American Statistician* 46(1).

Because the formal *F*-test for testing the equality of variances is so volatile, we are content to use Welch's *t*. Welch's *t*-test is more conservative than the pooled *t*. The price that must be paid for the conservative approach is that the probability of a Type II error is higher with Welch's *t* than with the pooled *t* when the population variances are equal. However, the two tests typically provide the same conclusion, even if the assumption of equal population standard deviations seems reasonable.

11.2 ASSESS YOUR UNDERSTANDING

Concepts and Vocabulary

1. What are the requirements that need to be satisfied to test a hypothesis regarding the difference of two means with σ unknown?

2. Explain why using the smaller of $n_1 - 1$ or $n_2 - 1$ degrees of freedom to determine the critical *t* instead of Formula (2) is conservative.

Skill Building*

In Problems 3–8, assume that the populations are normally distributed.

3. (a) Test whether $\mu_1 \neq \mu_2$ at the $\alpha = 0.05$ level of significance for the given sample data.   Do not reject H_0
   (b) Construct a 95% confidence interval about $\mu_1 - \mu_2$.

	Population 1	Population 2
n	15	15
$\overline{x}$	15.3	14.2
s	3.2	3.5

   3. (b) $(-1.53, 3.73)$

4. (a) Test whether $\mu_1 \neq \mu_2$ at the $\alpha = 0.05$ level of significance for the given sample data.   Reject H_0
   (b) Construct a 95% confidence interval about $\mu_1 - \mu_2$.

	Population 1	Population 2
n	20	20
$\overline{x}$	111	104
s	8.6	9.2

   4. (b) $(1.11, 12.89)$

5. (a) Test whether $\mu_1 > \mu_2$ at the $\alpha = 0.1$ level of significance for the given sample data.   Reject H_0
   (b) Construct a 90% confidence interval about $\mu_1 - \mu_2$.

	Population 1	Population 2
n	25	18
$\overline{x}$	50.2	42.0
s	6.4	9.9

   5. (b) $(3.57, 12.83)$

6. (a) Test whether $\mu_1 < \mu_2$ at the $\alpha = 0.05$ level of significance for the given sample data.   Reject H_0
   (b) Construct a 95% confidence interval about $\mu_1 - \mu_2$.

	Population 1	Population 2
n	40	32
$\overline{x}$	94.2	115.2
s	15.9	23.0

   6. (b) $(-30.75, -11.25)$

7. Test whether $\mu_1 < \mu_2$ at the $\alpha = 0.02$ level of significance for the given sample data.   Reject H_0

	Population 1	Population 2
n	32	25
$\overline{x}$	103.4	114.2
s	12.3	13.2

8. Test whether $\mu_1 > \mu_2$ at the $\alpha = 0.05$ level of significance for the given sample data.   Do not reject H_0

	Population 1	Population 2
n	23	13
$\overline{x}$	43.1	41.0
s	4.5	5.1

Applying the Concepts

9. **Elapsed Time to Earn a Bachelor's Degree** Clifford Adelman, a researcher with the Department of Education, followed a cohort of students who graduated from high school in 1992. He monitored the progress the students made toward completing a bachelor's degree. One aspect of his research was to determine whether students who first attended community college took longer to attain a bachelor's degree than those who immediately attended and remained at a 4-year institution. The data in the table summarize the results of his study.

	Community College to 4-Year Transfer	No Transfer
n	268	1,145
Sample mean time to graduate in years	5.43	4.43
Sample standard deviation time to graduate in years	1.162	1.015

   Source: Clifford Adelman, *The Toolbox Revisited*. United States Department of Education, 2006.

   (a) Does the evidence suggest that community college transfer students take longer to attain a bachelor's degree? Use an $\alpha = 0.01$ level of significance.   Yes; reject H_0
   (b) Construct a 95% confidence interval for $\mu_{\text{community college}} - \mu_{\text{no transfer}}$ to approximate the mean additional time it takes to complete a bachelor's degree if you begin in community college. $(0.818, 1.182)$
   (c) Do the results of parts (a) and (b) imply that community college causes you to take extra time to earn a bachelor's degree? Cite some reasons that you think might contribute to the extra time to graduate.

*The by-hand confidence intervals in the back of the text were computed using the smaller of $n_1 - 1$ or $n_2 - 1$ degrees of freedom.

10. **Treating Bipolar Mania** Researchers conducted a randomized, double-blind study to measure the effects of the drug olanzapine on patients diagnosed with bipolar disorder. A total of 115 patients with a DSM-IV diagnosis of bipolar disorder were randomly divided into two groups. Group 1 ($n_1 = 55$) received 5 to 20 mg per day of olanzapine, while group 2 ($n_2 = 60$) received a placebo. The effectiveness of the drug was measured using the Young–Mania rating scale total score with the net improvement in the score recorded. The results are presented in the table. Does the evidence suggest that the experimental group experienced a larger mean improvement than the control group at the $\alpha = 0.01$ level of significance? *Reject H_0*

	Experimental Group	Control Group
n	55	60
Mean improvement	14.8	8.1
Sample standard deviation	12.5	12.7

Source: "Efficacy of Olanzapine in Acute Bipolar Mania," *Archives of General Psychiatry*, 59(9), pp. 841–848.

11. **Walking in the Airport, Part I** Do people walk faster in the airport when they are departing (getting on a plane) or when they are arriving (getting off a plane)? Researcher Seth B. Young measured the walking speed of travelers in San Francisco International Airport and Cleveland Hopkins International Airport. His findings are summarized in the table.

Direction of Travels	Departure	Arrival
Mean speed (feet per minute)	260	269
Standard deviation (feet per minute)	53	34
Sample size	35	35

Source: Seth B. Young. "Evaluation of Pedestrian Walking Speeds in Airport Terminals," *Transportation Research Record*. Paper 99-0824.

(a) Is this an observational study or a designed experiment? Why? *Observational*
(b) Explain why it is reasonable to use Welch's *t*-test.
(c) Do individuals walk at different speeds depending on whether they are departing or arriving at the $\alpha = 0.05$ level of significance? *Do not reject H_0*
(d) Construct a 95% confidence interval for $\mu_{arrival} - \mu_{departure}$. Interpret the interval. *($-12.6, 30.6$)*

12. **Walking in the Airport, Part II** Do business travelers walk at a different pace than leisure travelers? Researcher Seth B. Young measured the walking speed of business and leisure travelers in San Francisco International Airport and Cleveland Hopkins International Airport. His findings are summarized in the table.

Type of Traveler	Business	Leisure
Mean speed (feet per minute)	272	261
Standard deviation (feet per minute)	43	47
Sample size	20	20

Source: Seth B. Young. "Evaluation of Pedestrian Walking Speeds in Airport Terminals." *Transportation Research Record*, Paper 99-0824.

(a) Is this an observational study or a designed experiment? Why? *Observational*
(b) What must be true regarding the populations to use Welch's *t*-test to compare the means? *Normally distributed*

(c) Assuming that the requirements listed in part (b) are satisfied, determine whether business travelers walk at a different speed from leisure travelers at the $\alpha = 0.05$ level of significance. *Do not reject H_0*
(d) Construct a 95% confidence interval for $\mu_{business} - \mu_{leisure}$. Interpret the interval. *($-18.8, 40.8$)*

13. **Concrete Strength** An engineer wanted to know whether the strength of two different concrete mix designs differed significantly. He randomly selected 9 cylinders, measuring 6 inches in diameter and 12 inches in height, into which mixture 67-0-301 was poured. After 28 days, he measured the strength (in pounds per square inch) of the cylinder. He also randomly selected 10 cylinders of mixture 67-0-400 and performed the same test. The results are as follows:

Mixture 67-0-301			Mixture 67-0-400			
3,960	4,090	3,100	4,070	4,890	5,020	4,330
3,830	3,200	3,780	4,640	5,220	4,190	3,730
4,080	4,040	2,940	4,120	4,620		

(a) Is it reasonable to use Welch's *t*-test? Why? *Yes*
    Note: Normal probability plots indicate that the data are approximately normal and boxplots indicate that there are no outliers.
(b) Determine whether mixture 67-0-400 is stronger than mixture 67-0-301 at the $\alpha = 0.05$ level of significance.
(c) Construct a 90% confidence interval for $\mu_{400} - \mu_{301}$ and interpret the results. *($416, 1212$)*
(d) Draw boxplots of each data set using the same scale. Does this visual evidence support the results obtained in part (b)? *13(b) Reject H_0*

14. **Measuring Reaction Time** Researchers at the University of Mississippi wanted to determine whether the reaction time (in seconds) of males differed from that of females to a go/no go stimulus. The researchers randomly selected 20 females and 15 males to participate in the study. The go/no go stimulus required the student to respond to a particular stimulus and not to respond to other stimuli. The results are as follows:

Female Students				Male Students		
0.588	0.652	0.442	0.293	0.375	0.256	0.427
0.340	0.636	0.391	0.367	0.654	0.563	0.405
0.377	0.646	0.403	0.377	0.374	0.465	0.402
0.380	0.403	0.617	0.434	0.373	0.488	0.337
0.443	0.481	0.613	0.274	0.224	0.477	0.655

Source: PsychExperiments at the University of Mississippi

(a) Is it reasonable to use Welch's *t*-test? Why? *Yes*
    Note: Normal probability plots indicate that the data are approximately normal and boxplots indicate that there are no outliers.
(b) Test whether there is a difference in the reaction times of males and females at the $\alpha = 0.05$ level of significance. *Do not reject H_0*
(c) Construct a 90% confidence interval for $\mu_f - \mu_m$ and interpret the results. *($-0.0482, 0.1006$)*
(d) Draw boxplots of each data set using the same scale. Does this visual evidence support the results obtained in part (b)?

15. Bacteria in Hospital Carpeting Researchers wanted to determine if carpeted rooms contained more bacteria than uncarpeted rooms. To determine the amount of bacteria in a room, researchers pumped the air from the room over a Petri dish at the rate of 1 cubic foot per minute for eight carpeted rooms and eight uncarpeted rooms. Colonies of bacteria were allowed to form in the 16 Petri dishes. The results are presented in the table. A normal probability plot and boxplot indicate that the data are approximately normally distributed with no outliers. Do carpeted rooms have more bacteria than uncarpeted rooms at the $\alpha = 0.05$ level of significance? *Do not reject H_0*

Carpeted Rooms (bacteria/cubic foot)		Uncarpeted Rooms (bacteria/cubic foot)	
11.8	10.8	12.1	12.0
8.2	10.1	8.3	11.1
7.1	14.6	3.8	10.1
13.0	14.0	7.2	13.7

Source: William G. Walter and Angie Stober. "Microbial Air Sampling in a Carpeted Hospital." *Journal of Environmental Health*, 30 (1968), p. 405.

16. Visual versus Textual Learners Researchers wanted to know whether there was a difference in comprehension among students learning a computer program based on the style of the text. They randomly divided 36 students into two groups of 18 each. The researchers verified that the 36 students were similar in terms of educational level, age, and so on. Group 1 individuals learned the software using a visual manual (*multimodal instruction*), while group 2 individuals learned the software using a textual manual (*unimodal instruction*). The following data represent scores that the students received on an exam given to them after they studied from the manuals.

Visual Manual		Textual Manual	
51.08	60.35	64.55	56.54
57.03	76.60	57.60	39.91
44.85	70.77	68.59	65.31
75.21	70.15	50.75	51.95
56.87	47.60	49.63	49.07
75.28	46.59	43.58	48.83
57.07	81.23	57.40	72.40
80.30	67.30	49.48	42.01
52.20	60.82	49.57	61.16

Source: Mark Gellevij et al. "Multimodal versus Unimodal Instruction in a Complex Learning Context." *Journal of Experimental Education* 70(3):215–239, 2002.

16. (a) *Completely randomized design*
(a) What type of experimental design is this?
(b) What are the treatments? *visual vs. textual manual*
(c) A normal probability plot and boxplot indicate it is reasonable to use Welch's *t*-test. Is there a difference in test scores at the $\alpha = 0.05$ level of significance? *Reject H_0*

17. Does the Designated Hitter Help? In baseball, the American League allows a designated hitter (DH) to bat for the pitcher, who is typically a weak hitter. In the National League, the pitcher must bat. The common belief is that this results in

American League teams scoring more runs. In interleague play, when American League teams visit National League teams, the American League pitcher must bat. So, if the DH does result in more runs, we would expect that American League teams will score fewer runs when visiting National League parks. To test this claim, a random sample of runs scored by American League teams with and without their DH is given in the following table. Does the designated hitter result in more runs scored at the $\alpha = 0.05$ level of significance?

Note: $\bar{x}_{NL} = 4.3$, $s_{NL} = 2.6$, $\bar{x}_{AL} = 6.0$, $s_{AL} = 3.5$. *Reject H_0*

National League Park (without DH)				
1	5	5	4	7
2	6	2	9	2
8	8	2	10	4
4	3	4	1	9
3	5	1	3	3
3	5	2	7	2

American League Park (with DH)				
6	2	3	6	8
1	3	7	6	4
4	12	5	6	13
6	9	5	6	7
4	3	2	5	5
6	14	14	7	0

Source: espn.com

18. Rhythm & Blues versus Alternatives A music industry producer wondered whether there is a difference in lengths (in seconds) of rhythm & blues songs versus alternative songs. He obtained a random sample of each music category and documented song lengths. The results are in the following table. Test whether the length of rhythm & blues songs is different from the length of alternative songs at the $\alpha = 0.1$ level of significance.

Note: $\bar{x}_{RB} = 242.7$, $s_{RB} = 26.9$, $\bar{x}_{ALT} = 238.3$, $s_{ALT} = 28.9$.
Do not reject H_0

Rhythm & Blues (in seconds)				
267	244	233	293	231
224	271	246	258	255
281	256	236	231	224
203	258	237	228	217
205	217	227	211	235
241	211	257	321	264

Alternative (in seconds)				
246	279	226	255	249
225	216	197	216	232
256	307	237	216	187
258	253	223	264	255
227	274	192	213	272
226	251	202	278	216

Source: www.yahoo.com/music

19. **Kids and Leisure** Young children require a lot of time. This time commitment cuts into a parent's leisure time. A sociologist wanted to estimate the difference in the amount of daily leisure time (in hours) of adults who do not have children under the age of 18 years and the amount of daily leisure time (in hours) of adults who have children under the age of 18 years. A random sample of 40 adults with no children under the age of 18 years results in a mean daily leisure time of 5.62 hours, with a standard deviation of 2.43 hours. A random sample of 40 adults with children under the age of 18 years results in a mean daily leisure time of 4.10 hours, with a standard deviation of 1.82 hours. Construct and interpret a 90% confidence interval for the mean difference in leisure time between adults with no children and adults with children. (0.71, 2.33)

    Source: American Time Use Survey

20. **Aluminum Bottles** The aluminum bottle, first introduced in 1991 by CCL Container for mainly personal and household items such as lotions, has become popular with beverage manufacturers. Besides being lightweight and requiring less packaging, the aluminum bottle is reported to cool faster and stay cold longer than typical glass bottles. A small brewery tests this claim and obtains the following information regarding the time (in minutes) required to chill a bottle of beer from room temperature (75°F) to serving temperature (45°F). Construct and interpret a 90% confidence interval for the mean difference in cooling time for clear glass versus aluminum. (38.08, 44.72)

	Clear Glass	Aluminum
Sample size	42	35
Mean time to chill	133.8	92.4
Sample standard deviation	9.9	7.3

21. **Comparing Step Pulses** A physical therapist wanted to know whether the mean step pulse of men was less than the mean step pulse of women. She randomly selected 51 men and 70 women to participate in the study. Each subject was required to step up and down onto a 6-inch platform for 3 minutes. The pulse of each subject (in beats per minute) was then recorded. After the data were entered into MINITAB, the following results were obtained.

Two Sample T-Test and Confidence Interval

Two sample T for Men vs Women

	N	Mean	StDev	SE Mean
Men	51	112.3	11.3	1.6
Women	70	118.3	14.2	1.7

95% CI for mu Men $-$ mu Women: (-10.7, -1.5)
T-Test mu Men $=$ mu Women (vs $<$):T $= -2.61$ P $= 0.0051$ DF $= 118$

(a) State the null and alternative hypotheses.
(b) Identify the P-value and state the researcher's conclusion if the level of significance was $\alpha = 0.01$. *0.0051; reject H_0*
(c) What is the 95% confidence interval for the mean difference in pulse rates of men versus women? Interpret this interval. (-10.7, -1.5)

22. **Comparing Flexibility** A physical therapist believes that women are more flexible than men. She measures the flexibility of 31 randomly selected women and 45 randomly selected men by determining the number of inches subjects could reach while sitting on the floor with their legs straight out and back perpendicular to the ground. The more flexible an individual is, the higher the measured flexibility will be. After entering the data into MINITAB, she obtained the following results: 22. (a) $H_0: \mu_{men} = \mu_{women}$ vs. $H_1: \mu_{men} < \mu_{women}$

Two Sample T-Test and Confidence Interval

Two sample T for Men vs Women

	N	Mean	StDev	SE Mean
Men	45	18.64	3.29	0.49
Women	31	20.99	2.07	0.37

95% CI for mu Men $-$ mu Women: (-3.58, -1.12)
T-Test mu Men $=$ mu Women (vs $<$):T $= -3.82$ P $= 0.0001$ DF $= 73$

(a) State the null and alternative hypotheses.
(b) Identify the P-value and state the researcher's conclusion if the level of significance was $\alpha = 0.01$. *0.0001; reject H_0*
(c) What is the 95% confidence interval for the mean difference in flexibility of men versus women? Interpret this interval. (-3.58, -1.12)

23. **Putting It Together: Online Homework** Professor Stephen Zuro of Joliet Junior College wanted to determine whether an online homework system improved scores on a final exam. In the fall semester, he taught a precalculus class using the online homework system (which meant students did their homework online and received instant feedback about their answers along with helpful guidance). In the spring semester, he taught a precalculus class without the homework system (which meant students were responsible for doing their homework the old-fashioned way—paper and pencil). Professor Zuro made sure to teach the two courses identically (same text, syllabus, tests, meeting time, meeting location, and so on). The table summarizes the results of the two classes on their final exam.

	Fall Semester	Spring Semester
Number of students	27	25
Mean final exam score	73.6	67.9
Standard deviation final exam score	10.3	12.4

(a) What type of experimental design is this?
(b) What is the response variable? What are the treatments in the study? *Final exam; homework delivery*
(c) What factors are controlled in the experiment?
(d) In many experiments, the researcher will recruit volunteers and randomly assign the individuals to a treatment group. In what regard was this done for this experiment?
(e) Did the students perform better on the final exam in the fall semester? Use an $\alpha = 0.05$ level of significance. *Yes*
(f) Can you think of any factors that may confound the results? Could Professor Zuro have done anything about these confounding factors? *Quality of students entering class; warm weather in spring*

21. (a) $H_0: \mu_{men} = \mu_{women}$ vs. $H_1: \mu_{men} < \mu_{women}$ 23. (a) Completely randomized design 23. (c) Teacher, location, time, text, syllabus, tests

Consumer Reports The High Cost of Convenience

Consumer Reports was interested in comparing a name-brand paper towel with a new version packaged in a box. The towels in the box, which cost nearly twice as much as the traditional roll, are marketed for their convenience. Given the difference in cost, one might wonder if the boxed version performs better than the traditional roll. To help answer this question, technicians at Consumers Union subjected both types of towels to five physical tests: absorption time in water, absorption time in oil, absorption capacity in water, absorption capacity in oil, and wet strength. For brevity, we will discuss only the results of the absorption time in water test.

The absorption time in water was defined as the amount of time necessary for a single sheet to absorb a predetermined amount of water. To compare the absorption times of the two types of towels, we tested six randomly selected sheets of paper towels. To avoid potential sources of bias, the individual sheets were taken from different samples of the products, and the tests were conducted in a randomly chosen order.

Consumer Reports wanted to determine whether the water absorption time for the boxed version is less than the water absorption time for the traditional roll.

(a) Write the null and alternative hypotheses, letting μ_{box} represent the mean absorption time for the boxed version and μ_{roll} represent the mean absorption time for the roll version.

(b) Normal probability plots of the water absorption times for the two products are shown next. Based on the normal probability plots, is it reasonable to conduct a two-sample hypothesis test?

 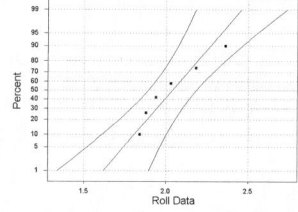

(c) A boxplot of the water absorption times for the two products follows:

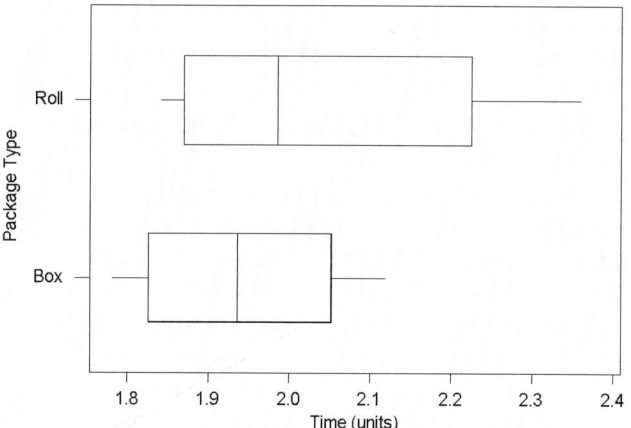

Does the data set have any outliers? Based on the boxplots, do you think that the absorption times for the boxed version are lower than the absorption times for the roll?

(d) To conduct the test, we used MINITAB to perform a two-sample *t*-test. The results are as shown. Using the MINITAB output, determine the value of the test statistic. What is the *P*-value of the test? Although they are not discussed here, the other physical tests provided similar results. Write an article that states your conclusion and any recommendations that you would make regarding the purchase of the two products.

Two-Sample T-Test and CI: Absorption Time In Water, CU

```
Two-sample    T    for Absorption    Time    In Water
CU-Text       N              Mean    StDev    SE Mean
Box           6            0.9717   0.0538      0.022
Roll          6            1.0200   0.0942      0.038

Difference = mu (Box) - mu (Roll)
Estimate for difference: -0.0483
95% upper bound for difference: 0.0320
T-Test of difference = 0 (vs <):
T-Value = -1.09 P-Value = 0.150 DF = 10
Both use Pooled StDev = 0.0767
```

Note to Readers: *In many cases, our test protocol and analytical methods are more complicated than described in these examples. The data and discussions have been modified to make the material more appropriate for the audience.*

Source: © 2001 by Consumers Union of U.S., Inc., Yonkers, NY 10703-1057, a nonprofit organization. Reprinted with permission from the June 2001 issue of CONSUMER REPORTS® for educational purposes only. No commercial use or photocopying permitted. To learn more about Consumers Union, log onto www.ConsumersReports.org.

TECHNOLOGY STEP-BY-STEP   Two-Sample *t*-Tests, Independent Sampling

TI-83/84 Plus

Hypothesis Tests

1. If necessary, enter raw data in L1 and L2.

2. Press STAT, highlight TESTS, and select 4:2-SampTTest . . . .

3. If the data are raw, highlight Data, making sure that List1 is set to L1 and List2 is set to L2, with frequencies set to 1. If summary statistics are

known, highlight STATS and enter the summary statistics.

4. Highlight the appropriate relation between μ_1 and μ_2 in the alternative hypothesis. Set Pooled to NO.

5. Highlight Calculate or Draw and press ENTER. Calculate gives the test statistic and *P*-value. Draw will draw the *t*-distribution with the *P*-value shaded.

Confidence Intervals

Follow the steps given for hypothesis tests, except select Ø: `2-SampTInt`. Also, select a confidence level (such as 95% = 0.95).

MINITAB

1. If necessary, enter raw data in columns C1 and C2.

2. Select the **Stat** menu, highlight **Basic Statistics**, then highlight **2-Sample t . . . .**

3. If you have raw data, select "Samples in different columns." Enter C1 in the cell marked "First" and enter C2 in the cell marked "Second." If you have summarized data, select "Summarized data." Enter the summary statistics in the appropriate cell. Click

Options. . . . Select the direction of the alternative hypothesis, enter the "test difference" (usually zero), and select a confidence level. Click OK twice.

Excel

1. Enter raw data in columns A and B.

2. Select the **Tools** menu and highlight **Data Analysis . . . .**

3. Select "*t*-test: Two-Sample Assuming Unequal Variances." With the cursor in the "Variable 1 Range" cell, highlight the data in column A. With the cursor in the "Variable 2 Range" cell, highlight the data in column B. Enter the hypothesized difference in the means (usually 0) and a value for alpha. Click OK.

11.3 INFERENCE ABOUT TWO POPULATION PROPORTIONS

Preparing for This Section Before getting started, review the following:

• Confidence intervals about a population proportion (Section 9.3, pp. 489–491)

• Hypothesis tests about a population proportion (Section 10.4, pp. 552–557)

Objectives	
1	Test hypotheses regarding two population proportions
2	Construct and interpret confidence intervals for the difference between two population proportions
3	Use McNemar's Test to compare two proportions from matched-pairs data
4	Determine the sample size necessary for estimating the difference between two population proportions within a specified margin of error

In Sections 9.3 and 10.4, we discussed inference regarding a single population proportion. We will now discuss inferential methods for comparing two population proportions. For example, in clinical trials of the drug Nasonex, a drug that is meant to relieve allergy symptoms, 26% of patients receiving 200 micrograms (μg) of Nasonex reported a headache as a side effect, while 22% of patients receiving a placebo reported a headache as a side effect. Researchers want to determine whether the proportion of patients receiving Nasonex and complaining of headaches is significantly higher than the proportion of patients receiving the placebo and complaining of headaches.

To conduct inference about two population proportions, we must first determine the sampling distribution of the difference of two proportions. Recall that the point estimate of a population proportion, p, is given by $\hat{p} = \dfrac{x}{n}$, where x is the number of the n individuals in the sample that have a specific characteristic. In addition, we recall that the sampling distribution of $\hat{p}$ is approximately normal with mean $\mu_{\hat{p}} = p$ and standard deviation $\sigma_{\hat{p}} = \sqrt{\dfrac{p(1-p)}{n}}$, provided that $np(1-p) \geq 10$, so

$$Z = \frac{\hat{p} - p}{\sqrt{\dfrac{p(1-p)}{n}}}$$

is approximately normal with mean 0 and standard deviation 1. Using this information along with the idea of independent sampling from two populations, we obtain the sampling distribution of the difference between two proportions.

Sampling Distribution of the Difference between Two Proportions

Suppose a simple random sample of size n_1 is taken from a population where x_1 of the individuals have a specified characteristic, and a simple random sample of size n_2 is independently taken from a different population where x_2 of the individuals have a specified characteristic. The sampling distribution of $\hat{p}_1 - \hat{p}_2$, where $\hat{p}_1 = \dfrac{x_1}{n_1}$ and $\hat{p}_2 = \dfrac{x_2}{n_2}$, is approximately normal, with mean $\mu_{\hat{p}_1 - \hat{p}_2} = p_1 - p_2$ and standard deviation $\sigma_{\hat{p}_1 - \hat{p}_2} = \sqrt{\dfrac{p_1(1 - p_1)}{n_1} + \dfrac{p_2(1 - p_2)}{n_2}}$, provided that $n_1\hat{p}_1(1 - \hat{p}_1) \geq 10$ and $n_2\hat{p}_2(1 - \hat{p}_2) \geq 10$. The standardized version of $\hat{p}_1 - \hat{p}_2$ is then written as

$$Z = \frac{(\hat{p}_1 - \hat{p}_2) - (p_1 - p_2)}{\sqrt{\dfrac{p_1(1 - p_1)}{n_1} + \dfrac{p_2(1 - p_2)}{n_2}}}$$

which has an approximate standard normal distribution.

---

1 Test Hypotheses Regarding Two Population Proportions

Now that we know the approximate sampling distribution of $\hat{p}_1 - \hat{p}_2$, we can introduce a procedure that can be used to test hypotheses regarding two population proportions. We first consider the test statistic. Following the discussion for comparing two means, it seems reasonable that the test statistic for the difference of two population proportions would be

$$z_0 = \frac{(\hat{p}_1 - \hat{p}_2) - (p_1 - p_2)}{\sqrt{\dfrac{p_1(1 - p_1)}{n_1} + \dfrac{p_2(1 - p_2)}{n_2}}} \qquad (1)$$

When comparing two population proportions, the null hypothesis is a statement of "no difference" (as always), so $H_0\colon p_1 = p_2$. Because the null hypothesis is assumed to be true, the test assumes that $p_1 = p_2$, or $p_1 - p_2 = 0$. We also assume that both p_1 and p_2 equal p, where p is the common population proportion. If we substitute this value of p into Equation (1), we obtain

$$z_0 = \frac{(\hat{p}_1 - \hat{p}_2) - (p_1 - p_2)}{\sqrt{\dfrac{p_1(1 - p_1)}{n_1} + \dfrac{p_2(1 - p_2)}{n_2}}} = \frac{\hat{p}_1 - \hat{p}_2 - 0}{\sqrt{\dfrac{p(1 - p)}{n_1} + \dfrac{p(1 - p)}{n_2}}} = \frac{\hat{p}_1 - \hat{p}_2}{\sqrt{p(1 - p)}\sqrt{\dfrac{1}{n_1} + \dfrac{1}{n_2}}} \qquad (2)$$

In Other Words

The pooled estimate of p is obtained by summing the number of individuals in the sample that have a certain characteristic and dividing this result by the sum of the two sample sizes.

We need a point estimate of p because it is unknown. The best point estimate of p is called the **pooled estimate of p**, denoted $\hat{p}$, where

$$\hat{p} = \frac{x_1 + x_2}{n_1 + n_2}$$

Substituting the pooled estimate of p into Equation (2), we obtain

$$z_0 = \frac{\hat{p}_1 - \hat{p}_2}{\sigma_{\hat{p}_1 - \hat{p}_2}} = \frac{\hat{p}_1 - \hat{p}_2}{\sqrt{\hat{p}(1 - \hat{p})}\sqrt{\dfrac{1}{n_1} + \dfrac{1}{n_2}}}$$

This test statistic will be used to test hypotheses regarding two population proportions.

Hypothesis Test Regarding the Difference between Two Population Proportions

To test hypotheses regarding two population proportions, p_1 and p_2, we can use the steps that follow, provided that

1. the samples are independently obtained using simple random sampling,
2. $n_1\hat{p}_1(1 - \hat{p}_1) \geq 10$ and $n_2\hat{p}_2(1 - \hat{p}_2) \geq 10$, and
3. $n_1 \leq 0.05N_1$ and $n_2 \leq 0.05N_2$ (the sample size is no more than 5% of the population size); this requirement ensures the independence necessary for a binomial experiment.

Step 1: Determine the null and alternative hypotheses. The hypotheses can be structured in one of three ways:

Two-Tailed	Left-Tailed	Right-Tailed
$H_0: p_1 = p_2$	$H_0: p_1 = p_2$	$H_0: p_1 = p_2$
$H_1: p_1 \neq p_2$	$H_1: p_1 < p_2$	$H_1: p_1 > p_2$

Note: p_1 is the population proportion for population 1, and p_2 is the population proportion for population 2.

Step 2: Select a level of significance, α, depending on the seriousness of making a Type I error.

Step 3: Compute the test statistic

$$z_0 = \frac{\hat{p}_1 - \hat{p}_2}{\sqrt{\hat{p}(1 - \hat{p})}\sqrt{\dfrac{1}{n_1} + \dfrac{1}{n_2}}}$$

where $\hat{p} = \dfrac{x_1 + x_2}{n_1 + n_2}$.

Classical Approach

Step 4: Use Table V to determine the critical value.

Step 5: Compare the critical value with the test statistic.

Two-Tailed	Left-Tailed	Right-Tailed
If $z_0 < -z_{\frac{\alpha}{2}}$ or $z_0 > z_{\frac{\alpha}{2}}$, reject the null hypothesis.	If $z_0 < -z_\alpha$, reject the null hypothesis.	If $z_0 > z_\alpha$, reject the null hypothesis.

P-Value Approach

Step 4: Use Table V to estimate the P-value.

Step 5: If P-value $< \alpha$, reject the null hypothesis.

Step 6: State the conclusion.

EXAMPLE 1 | **Testing a Hypothesis Regarding Two Population Proportions**

Problem: In clinical trials of Nasonex, 3774 adult and adolescent allergy patients (patients 12 years and older) were randomly divided into two groups. The patients in group 1 (experimental group) received 200 μg of Nasonex, while the patients in group 2 (control group) received a placebo. Of the 2103 patients in the experimental group, 547 reported headaches as a side effect. Of the 1671 patients in the control group, 368 reported headaches as a side effect. Is there significant evidence to conclude that the proportion of Nasonex users that experienced headaches as a side effect is greater than the proportion in the control group at the $\alpha = 0.05$ level of significance?

Approach: Note that this is a completely randomized design. The response variable is whether or not the patient reports a headache. The treatments are the drugs: Nasonex or a placebo. The subjects are the 3774 adult and adolescent allergy patients.

We are attempting to determine if the evidence suggests that the proportion of patients who report a headache and are receiving Nasonex is greater than the proportion of patients who report a headache and are receiving a placebo. We will call the group that received Nasonex sample 1 and the group that received a placebo sample 2.

We must verify the requirements to perform the hypothesis test. That is, the sample must be a simple random sample and $n_1 \hat{p}_1 (1 - \hat{p}_1) \geq 10$ and $n_2 \hat{p}_2 (1 - \hat{p}_2) \geq 10$. In addition, the sample size cannot be more than 5% of the population size. Then we follow the preceding Steps 1 through 6.

Solution: First we verify that the requirements are satisfied.

1. The samples are independently. The subjects were assigned to the treatment randomly.
2. We have $x_1 = 547$, $n_1 = 2103$, $x_2 = 368$, and $n_2 = 1671$, so
$$\hat{p}_1 = \frac{x_1}{n_1} = \frac{547}{2103} = 0.260 \text{ and } \hat{p}_2 = \frac{x_2}{n_2} = \frac{368}{1671} = 0.220. \text{ Therefore,}$$
$$n_1 \hat{p}_1 (1 - \hat{p}_1) = 2103(0.260)(1 - 0.260) = 404.6172 \geq 10$$
$$n_2 \hat{p}_2 (1 - \hat{p}_2) = 1671(0.220)(1 - 0.220) = 286.7436 \geq 10$$

3. More than 10 million Americans 12 years old or older are allergy sufferers, so both sample sizes are less than 5% of the population size.

All three requirements are satisfied, so we now proceed to follow Steps 1 through 6.

Step 1: We want to know whether the proportion of patients taking Nasonex who experience a headache is greater than the proportion of patients taking the placebo who experience a headache. Letting p_1 represent the population proportion of patients taking Nasonex who experience a headache and p_2 represent the population proportion of patients taking the placebo who experience a headache, we want to know if $p_1 > p_2$. This is a right-tailed hypothesis with

$$H_0: p_1 = p_2 \quad \text{versus} \quad H_1: p_1 > p_2$$

or, equivalently,

$$H_0: p_1 - p_2 = 0 \quad \text{versus} \quad H_1: p_1 - p_2 > 0$$

Step 2: The level of significance is $\alpha = 0.05$.

Step 3: From verifying requirement 2, we have that $\hat{p}_1 = 0.260$ and $\hat{p}_2 = 0.220$. To find the test statistic, we first compute the pooled estimate of $\hat{p}$:

$$\hat{p} = \frac{x_1 + x_2}{n_1 + n_2} = \frac{547 + 368}{2103 + 1671} = 0.242$$

The test statistic is

$$z_0 = \frac{\hat{p}_1 - \hat{p}_2}{\sqrt{\hat{p}(1 - \hat{p})}\sqrt{\frac{1}{n_1} + \frac{1}{n_2}}} = \frac{0.260 - 0.220}{\sqrt{0.242(1 - 0.242)}\sqrt{\frac{1}{2103} + \frac{1}{1671}}} = 2.85$$

Classical Approach

Step 4: This is a right-tailed test with $\alpha = 0.05$. The critical value is $z_{0.05} = 1.645$. The critical region is displayed in Figure 9.

Figure 9

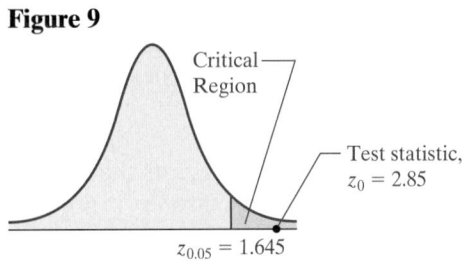

Critical Region

Test statistic, $z_0 = 2.85$

$z_{0.05} = 1.645$

Step 5: Because $z_0 > z_{0.05}$ (the test statistic lies within critical region), we reject the null hypothesis.

P-Value Approach

Step 4: Because this is a right-tailed test, the *P*-value is the area under the standard normal distribution to the right of $z_0 = 2.85$. See Figure 10.

Figure 10

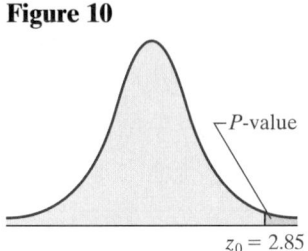

P-value

$z_0 = 2.85$

$$P\text{-value} = P(z_0 > 2.85)$$
$$= 0.0022$$

About 2 samples in 1,000 would yield the results obtained if the statement in the null hypothesis were true.

Step 5: Because *P*-value $< \alpha$ (0.0022 < 0.05), we reject the null hypothesis.

Step 6: There is sufficient evidence at the $\alpha = 0.05$ level of significance to conclude that the proportion of individuals 12 years and older taking 200 μg of Nasonex who experience headaches is greater than the proportion of individuals 12 years and older taking a placebo who experience headaches.

CAUTION In any statistical study, be sure to consider practical significance. Many statistically significant results can be produced simply by increasing the sample size.

Looking back at the results of Example 1, we notice that the proportion of individuals taking 200 μg of Nasonex who experience headaches is *statistically significantly* greater than the proportion of individuals 12 years and older taking a placebo who experience headaches. However, we need to ask ourselves a pressing question. Would you not take an allergy medication because 26% of patients experienced a headache taking the medication versus 22% who experienced a headache taking a placebo? Most people would be willing to accept the additional risk of a headache to relieve their allergy symptoms. While the difference of 4% is statistically significant, it does not have any *practical significance*.

EXAMPLE 2 Testing Hypotheses Regarding the Difference of Two Population Proportions Using Technology

🖥️ **Using Technology**
The *P*-value obtained from MINITAB differs from the *P*-value obtained by hand in Example 1 because of rounding.

Problem: Obtain the exact *P*-value for the problem in Example 1 using statistical software or a graphing calculator with advanced statistical features.

Approach: We will use MINITAB to obtain the *P*-value. The steps for testing hypotheses regarding two proportions using the TI-83/84 Plus graphing calculator, MINITAB, and Excel are given in the Technology Step-by-Step on page 621.

Solution: Figure 11 shows the results obtained from MINITAB. The *P*-value is 0.002.

Figure 11 **Test and CI for Two Proportions**

```
Sample       X       N   Sample p
1          547    2103   0.260105
2          368    1671   0.220227


Difference = p (1) - p (2)
Estimate for difference: 0.0398772
90% CI for difference: (0.0169504, 0.0628040)
Test for difference = 0 (vs > 0): Z = 2.86 P-Value = 0.002
```

Interpretation: We would expect 2 samples in 1,000 to yield the results we obtained if the statement in the null hypothesis were true. The results we obtained while assuming the two proportions are equal are highly unusual. There is sufficient evidence to conclude that the proportion of individuals 12 years and older taking 200 μg of Nasonex who experience headaches is greater than the proportion of individuals 12 years and older taking a placebo who experience headaches at the $\alpha = 0.05$ level of significance.

Now Work Problem 15

2 Construct and Interpret Confidence Intervals for the Difference between Two Population Proportions

The sampling distribution of the difference of two proportions, $\hat{p}_1 - \hat{p}_2$, can also be used to construct confidence intervals for the difference of two proportions.

Constructing a $(1 - \alpha) \cdot 100\%$ Confidence Interval for the Difference between Two Population Proportions

To construct a $(1 - \alpha) \cdot 100\%$ confidence interval for the difference between two population proportions, the following requirements must be satisfied:

1. The samples are obtained independently, using simple random sampling.
2. $n_1\hat{p}_1(1 - \hat{p}_1) \geq 10$ and $n_2\hat{p}_2(1 - \hat{p}_2) \geq 10$.
3. $n_1 \leq 0.05N_1$ and $n_2 \leq 0.05N_2$ (the sample size is no more than 5% of the population size); this ensures the independence necessary for a binomial experiment.

Provided that these requirements are met, a $(1 - \alpha) \cdot 100\%$ confidence interval for $p_1 - p_2$ is given by

$$\text{Lower bound:} \quad (\hat{p}_1 - \hat{p}_2) - z_{\frac{\alpha}{2}} \cdot \sqrt{\frac{\hat{p}_1(1 - \hat{p}_1)}{n_1} + \frac{\hat{p}_2(1 - \hat{p}_2)}{n_2}}$$

$$\text{Upper bound:} \quad (\hat{p}_1 - \hat{p}_2) + z_{\frac{\alpha}{2}} \cdot \sqrt{\frac{\hat{p}_1(1 - \hat{p}_1)}{n_1} + \frac{\hat{p}_2(1 - \hat{p}_2)}{n_2}}$$

(3)

Notice that we do not pool the sample proportions. This is because we are not making any assumptions regarding their equality, as we did in hypothesis testing.

EXAMPLE 3   **Constructing a Confidence Interval for the Difference between Two Population Proportions**

Problem: The Gallup organization surveyed 1100 adult Americans on May 6–9, 2002, and conducted an independent survey of 1100 adult Americans on May 10–13, 2007. In both surveys they asked the following: "Right now, do you think the state of moral values in the country as a whole is getting better or getting worse?" On May 10–13, 2007, 902 of the 1100 surveyed responded that the state of moral values is getting worse; on May 6–9, 2002, 737 of the 1100 surveyed responded that the state of moral values is getting worse. Construct and interpret a 90% confidence interval for the difference between the two population proportions.

Approach: We can compute a 90% confidence interval for the two population proportions provided that the stated requirements are satisfied. We then construct the interval using Formula (3).

Solution

Step 1: We have to verify the requirements for constructing a confidence interval for the difference between two population proportions.

1. The samples were obtained independently.

2. For the May 10–13, 2007, survey (sample 1), we have $n_1 = 1100$ and $x_1 = 902$, so $\hat{p}_1 = \dfrac{x_1}{n_1} = \dfrac{902}{1100} = 0.82$. For the May 6–9, 2002, survey (sample 2), we have $n_2 = 1100$ and $x_2 = 737$, so $\hat{p}_2 = \dfrac{x_2}{n_2} = \dfrac{737}{1100} = 0.67$. Therefore,

$$n_1\hat{p}_1(1 - \hat{p}_1) = 1100(0.82)(1 - 0.82) = 162.36 \geq 10$$

$$n_2\hat{p}_2(1 - \hat{p}_2) = 1100(0.67)(1 - 0.67) = 243.21 \geq 10$$

3. The population of adult Americans exceeded 100 million in 2002 and 2007, so the sample size is definitely less than 5% of the sample size.

Step 2: Substituting into Formula (3) with $\hat{p}_1 = 0.82$, $n_1 = 1100$, $\hat{p}_2 = 0.67$, $n_2 = 737$, and $n_2 = 1100$ we obtain the lower and upper bounds on the confidence interval:

Lower bound: $(\hat{p}_1 - \hat{p}_2) - z_{\frac{\alpha}{2}} \cdot \sqrt{\dfrac{\hat{p}_1(1 - \hat{p}_1)}{n_1} + \dfrac{\hat{p}_2(1 - \hat{p}_2)}{n_2}} = (0.82 - 0.67) - 1.645 \cdot \sqrt{\dfrac{0.82(1 - 0.82)}{1100} + \dfrac{0.67(1 - 0.67)}{1100}}$

$$= 0.15 - 0.03$$

$$= 0.12$$

Upper bound: $(\hat{p}_1 - \hat{p}_2) + z_{\frac{\alpha}{2}} \cdot \sqrt{\dfrac{\hat{p}_1(1 - \hat{p}_1)}{n_1} + \dfrac{\hat{p}_2(1 - \hat{p}_2)}{n_2}} = (0.82 - 0.67) + 1.645 \cdot \sqrt{\dfrac{0.82(1 - 0.82)}{1100} + \dfrac{0.67(1 - 0.67)}{1100}}$

$$= 0.15 + 0.03$$

$$= 0.18$$

Using Technology

Graphing calculators with advanced statistical features and statistical spreadsheets can be used to construct confidence intervals for the difference between two population proportions. Figure 12 shows the results using a TI-84 Plus graphing calculator.

Figure 12

```
2-PropZInt
 (.11989,.18011)
 p̂1=.82
 p̂2=.67
 n1=1100
 n2=1100
```

Now Work Problem 19

We are 90% confident that the difference between the proportion of adult Americans who believed that the state of moral values in the country as a whole was getting worse from 2002 to 2007 is between 0.12 and 0.18. To put this statement into everyday language, we might say that we are 90% confident that the proportion of adult Americans who believe that the state of moral values in the country as a whole was getting worse increased between 12% and 18% from 2002 to 2007. Because this interval does not contain 0, we can say that a higher proportion of the country believed that the state of moral values was getting worse in the United States in 2007 than in 2002.

3 Use McNemar's Test to Compare Two Proportions from Matched-Pairs Data

In Section 11.1, we stated that dependent samples were samples in which the individuals selected to participate in the study were somehow related. We went on to analyze matched-pairs data when the response variable was quantitative. Objectives 1 and 2 in this section compared two proportions obtained from independent samples. But what if we want to compare two proportions with matched-pairs data (i.e. dependent samples)? In this case, we can use **McNemar's Test**.

To understand the idea behind the McNemar's Test, we present a hypothetical situation. Suppose we want to determine whether there is a difference between two ointments meant to treat poison ivy. Rather than randomly divide a group of individuals with poison ivy into two groups, where group 1 gets ointment A and group 2 gets ointment B and compare the proportion of individuals who heal in each group, we might instead apply ointment A on one arm and ointment B on the other arm of each individual and record whether the poison ivy cleared up. The individuals in each group are not independent, since each ointment is applied to the same individual. How might we determine whether the proportion of healed poison ivy sufferers differs between the two treatments? To answer this question, let's say the results of the experiment are as given in Table 5.

Table 5		Ointment A	
		Healed (success)	Did not heal (failure)
Ointment B	**Healed (success)**	293	43
	Did not heal (failure)	31	103

Just as we did when comparing two population proportions from independent samples, we assume that the proportion of subjects healed with ointment A equals the proportion of subjects healed with ointment B (there is no healing difference in the ointments). So, the null hypothesis is H_0: $p_A = p_B$. There are a total of $293 + 43 + 31 + 103 = 470$ subjects in the study. In this experiment, the sample proportion of subjects who healed with ointment A is $\hat{p}_A = \dfrac{293 + 31}{470} = 0.689$, and the sample proportion of subjects who healed with ointment B is $\hat{p}_A = \dfrac{293 + 43}{470} = 0.715$. McNemar's Test will be used to determine if the difference in sample proportions is due to sampling error, or if the differences are significant enough to conclude that the proportions are different, so the alternative hypothesis is H_0: $p_A \neq p_B$.

Testing a Hypothesis Regarding the Difference of Two Proportions: Dependent Samples

To test hypotheses regarding two population proportions, p_1 and p_2, where the samples are dependent, arrange the data in a contingency table as follows:

		Treatment A	
		Success	Failure
Treatment B	**Success**	f_{11}	f_{12}
	Failure	f_{21}	f_{22}

We can use the steps that follow provided that

1. the samples are dependent and are obtained randomly and
2. the total number of observations where the outcomes differ must be greater than or equal to 10. That is, $f_{12} + f_{21} \geq 10$.

Step 1: Determine the null and alternative hypotheses.

H_0: the proportions between the two populations are equal ($p_1 = p_2$)
H_1: the proportions between the two populations differ ($p_1 \neq p_2$)

Step 2: Select a level of significance, α, depending on the seriousness of making a Type I error.
Step 3: Compute the test statistic*

$$z_0 = \frac{|f_{12} - f_{21}| - 1}{\sqrt{f_{12} + f_{21}}}$$

*We will not discuss the underlying theory behind the test statistic as it is beyond the scope of this course.

Classical Approach

Step 4: Use Table V to determine the critical value. This is a two-tailed test. However, z_0 is always positive, so we only need to find the right critical value, $z_{\frac{\alpha}{2}}$.

Critical Region

$z_{\frac{\alpha}{2}}$

Step 5: If $z_0 > z_{\frac{\alpha}{2}}$, reject the null hypothesis.

P-Value Approach

Step 4: Use Table V to determine the *P*-value. Because z_0 is always positive, we find the area right of z_0 and then double this area (since this is a two-tailed test).

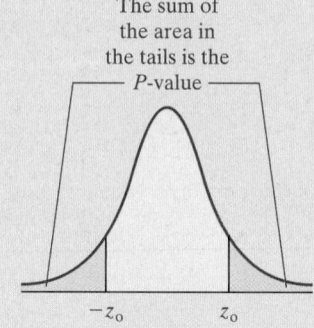

The sum of the area in the tails is the *P*-value

$-z_0$ z_0

Step 5: If the *P*-value $< \alpha$, reject the null hypothesis.

Step 6: State the conclusion.

EXAMPLE 4

Analyzing the Difference of Two Proportions from Matched-Pairs Data

Problem: A recent General Social Survey asked the following two questions of a random sample of 1492 adult Americans under the hypothetical scenario that the government suspected that a terrorist act was about to happen:

• Do you believe the authorities should have the right to tap people's telephone conversations?

• Do you believe the authorities should have the right to stop and search people on the street at random?

The results of the survey are shown in Table 6.

Table 6			
		Random Stop	
		Agree	**Disagree**
Tap Phone	**Agree**	494	335
	Disagree	126	537

Do the proportions who agree with each scenario differ significantly? Use the $\alpha = 0.05$ level of significance.

Approach: The sample proportion of individuals who believe that the authorities should be able to tap phones is $\hat{p}_T = \dfrac{494 + 335}{1492} = 0.556$. The sample proportion of individuals who believe that the authorities should be able to randomly stop and search an individual on the street is $\hat{p}_R = \dfrac{494 + 126}{1492} = 0.416$. We want to determine whether the difference in sample proportions is due to sampling error or to the fact that the population proportions differ.

The samples are dependent and were obtained randomly. The total number of individuals who agree with one scenario, but disagree with the other, is $335 + 126 = 461$, which is greater than 10. We can proceed with McNemar's Test.

Solution

Step 1: The hypotheses are as follows:

H_0: the proportions between the two populations are equal ($p_T = p_R$)

H_1: the proportions between the two populations differ ($p_T \neq p_R$)

Step 2: The level of significance is $\alpha = 0.05$.

Step 3: The test statistic is

$$z_0 = \frac{|f_{12} - f_{21}| - 1}{\sqrt{f_{12} + f_{21}}} = \frac{|335 - 126| - 1}{\sqrt{326 + 126}} = 9.69$$

Classical Approach

Step 4: The critical value with an $\alpha = 0.05$ level of significance is $z_{\frac{\alpha}{2}} = z_{0.025} = 1.96$. The critical region is displayed in Figure 13.

Figure 13

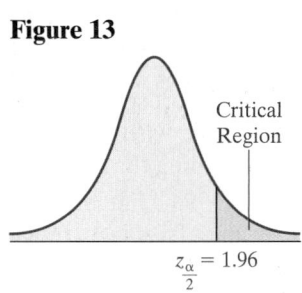

Critical Region

$z_{\frac{\alpha}{2}} = 1.96$

Step 5: Because $z_0 > z_{\frac{\alpha}{2}}$ (the test statistic lies in the critical region), we reject the null hypothesis.

P-Value Approach

Step 4: The *P*-value is two times the area under the standard normal distribution to the right of the test statistic, $z_0 = 9.69$. The test statistic is so large that the *P*-value < 0.0001.

Step 5: Because *P*-value $< \alpha$, we reject the null hypothesis.

Step 6: There is sufficient evidence to conclude that there is a difference in the proportion of adult Americans who believe it is okay to phone tap versus stopping and searching people on the street in the event that the government believed a terrorist plot was about to happen. In fact, looking at the sample proportions, it seems clear that more people are willing to allow phone tapping than they are to allow stopping and searching on the street.

Now Work Problem 25

4 Determine the Sample Size Necessary for Estimating the Difference between Two Population Proportions within a Specified Margin of Error

In Section 9.3, we introduced a method for determining the sample size, n, required to estimate a single population proportion within a specified margin of error, E, with a specified level of confidence. This formula was obtained by solving the margin of error, $E = z_{\frac{\alpha}{2}} \cdot \sqrt{\dfrac{\hat{p}(1 - \hat{p})}{n}}$, for n. We can follow the same approach to determine the sample size when we want to estimate two population proportions. Notice that the margin of error, E, in Formula (3) is given by $E = z_{\frac{\alpha}{2}} \cdot \sqrt{\dfrac{\hat{p}_1(1 - \hat{p}_1)}{n_1} + \dfrac{\hat{p}_2(1 - \hat{p}_2)}{n_2}}$. Assuming that $n_1 = n_2 = n$, we can solve this expression for $n = n_1 = n_2$ and obtain the following result:

> **Sample Size for Estimating $p_1 - p_2$**
>
> The sample size required to obtain a $(1 - \alpha) \cdot 100\%$ confidence interval with a margin of error, E, is given by
>
> $$n = n_1 = n_2 = [\hat{p}_1(1 - \hat{p}_1) + \hat{p}_2(1 - \hat{p}_2)]\left(\frac{z_{\frac{\alpha}{2}}}{E}\right)^2 \qquad (4)$$

 CAUTION When doing sample size calculations, always round up.

rounded up to the next integer, if prior estimates of p_1 and p_2, $\hat{p}_1$ and $\hat{p}_2$, are available. If prior estimates of p_1 and p_2 are unavailable, the sample size is

$$n = n_1 = n_2 = 0.5\left(\frac{z_{\frac{\alpha}{2}}}{E}\right)^2 \tag{5}$$

rounded up to the next integer. The margin of error should always be expressed as a decimal when using Formulas (4) and (5).

Note to Instructor

The 0.5 in Formula (5) results from adding 0.25 and 0.25, the maximum value of $P(1-p)$.

EXAMPLE 5 | **Determining Sample Size**

Problem: A nutritionist wishes to estimate the difference between the proportion of males and females who consume the USDA's recommended daily intake of calcium. What sample size should be obtained if she wishes the estimate to be within 3 percentage points with 95% confidence, assuming that

(a) she uses the results of the USDA's 1994–1996 Diet and Health Knowledge Survey, according to which 51.1% of males and 75.2% of females consume the USDA's recommended daily intake of calcium, and

(b) she does not use any prior estimates?

Approach: We have $E = 0.03$ and $z_{\frac{\alpha}{2}} = z_{\frac{0.05}{2}} = z_{0.025} = 1.96$. To answer part (a), we let $\hat{p}_1 = 0.511$ (for males) and $\hat{p}_2 = 0.752$ (for females) in Formula (4). To answer part (b), we use Formula (5).

Solution

(a) Substituting $E = 0.03$, $z_{0.025} = 1.96$, $\hat{p}_1 = 0.511$, and $\hat{p}_2 = 0.752$ into Formula (4), we obtain

$$n_1 = n_2 = [\hat{p}_1(1 - \hat{p}_1) + \hat{p}_2(1 - \hat{p}_2)]\left(\frac{z_{\frac{\alpha}{2}}}{E}\right)^2$$

$$= [0.511(1 - 0.511) + 0.752(1 - 0.752)]\left(\frac{1.96}{0.03}\right)^2$$

$$= 1862.6$$

We round this value up to 1,863. The nutritionist must survey 1,863 randomly selected males and 1,863 randomly selected females.

(b) Substituting $E = 0.03$ and $z_{0.025} = 1.96$ into Formula (5), we obtain

$$n_1 = n_2 = 0.5\left(\frac{z_{\frac{\alpha}{2}}}{E}\right)^2 = 0.5\left(\frac{1.96}{0.03}\right)^2 = 2{,}134.2$$

We round this value up to 2,135. The nutritionist must survey 2,135 randomly selected males and 2,135 randomly selected females.

Now Work Problem 31

In Other Words
If possible, obtain a prior estimate of $\hat{p}$ when doing sample size computations.

We can see that having prior estimates of the population proportions reduces the number of individuals that need to be surveyed.

11.3 ASSESS YOUR UNDERSTANDING

Concepts and Vocabulary

1. Explain why we determine a pooled estimate of the population proportion when testing hypotheses regarding the difference of two proportions, but do not pool when constructing confidence intervals for the difference of two proportions.

2. What is the difference between an independent and dependent sample?

3. State the requirements that must be satisfied to test hypotheses regarding two population proportions from independent samples.

4. State the requirements that must be satisfied to test hypotheses regarding two population proportions from dependent samples.

9. $(-0.075, 0.015)$ 10. $(-0.090, 0.068)$ 11. $(-0.063, 0.043)$ 12. $(-0.039, 0.009)$ 16. Do not reject H_0; P-value = 0.8414

Skill Building

18. Yes; reject H_0; P-value = 0.0018

In Problems 5–8, conduct each test at the $\alpha = 0.05$ level of significance by determining (a) the null and alternative hypotheses, (b) the test statistic, (c) the critical value, and (d) the P-value. Assume that the samples were obtained independently using simple random sampling.

5. Test whether $p_1 > p_2$. Sample data: $x_1 = 368, n_1 = 541$, $x_2 = 351, n_2 = 593$ Reject H_0

6. Test whether $p_1 < p_2$. Sample data: $x_1 = 109, n_1 = 475$, $x_2 = 78, n_2 = 325$ Do not reject H_0

7. Test whether $p_1 \neq p_2$. Sample data: $x_1 = 28, n_1 = 254$, $x_2 = 36, n_2 = 301$ Do not reject H_0

8. Test whether $p_1 \neq p_2$. Sample data: $x_1 = 804, n_1 = 874$, $x_2 = 902, n_2 = 954$ Reject H_0

In Problems 9–12, construct a confidence interval for $p_1 - p_2$ at the given level of confidence.

9. $x_1 = 368, n_1 = 541, x_2 = 421, n_2 = 593$, 90% confidence

10. $x_1 = 109, n_1 = 475, x_2 = 78, n_2 = 325$, 99% confidence

11. $x_1 = 28, n_1 = 254, x_2 = 36, n_2 = 301$, 95% confidence

12. $x_1 = 804, n_1 = 874, x_2 = 892, n_2 = 954$, 95% confidence

In Problems 13 and 14, test whether the population proportions differ at the $\alpha = 0.05$ level of significance by determining (a) the null and alternative hypotheses, (b) the test statistic, (c) the critical value, and (d) the P-value. Assume that the samples are dependent and were obtained randomly.   13. Do not reject H_0

13.

		Treatment A	
		Success	Failure
Treatment B	Success	45	19
	Failure	14	23

14.

		Treatment A	
		Success	Failure
Treatment B	Success	84	21
	Failure	11	37

14. Do not reject H_0

Applying the Concepts

15. **Prevnar** The drug Prevnar is a vaccine meant to prevent certain types of bacterial meningitis. It is typically administered to infants starting around 2 months of age. In randomized, double-blind clinical trials of Prevnar, infants were randomly divided into two groups. Subjects in group 1 received Prevnar, while subjects in group 2 received a control vaccine. After the first dose, 107 of 710 subjects in the experimental group (group 1) experienced fever as a side effect. After the first dose, 67 of 611 of the subjects in the control group (group 2) experienced fever as a side effect. Does the evidence suggest that a higher proportion of subjects in group 1 experienced fever as a side effect than subjects in group 2 at the $\alpha = 0.05$ level of significance?   Yes; reject H_0; P-value = 0.0139

16. **Prevnar** The drug Prevnar is a vaccine meant to prevent certain types of bacterial meningitis. It is typically administered to infants starting around 2 months of age. In randomized, double-blind clinical trials of Prevnar, infants were randomly divided into two groups. Subjects in group 1 received Prevnar, while subjects in group 2 received a control vaccine. After the

second dose, 137 of 452 subjects in the experimental group (group 1) experienced drowsiness as a side effect. After the second dose, 31 of 99 subjects in the control group (group 2) experienced drowsiness as a side effect. Does the evidence suggest that a lower proportion of subjects in group 1 experienced drowsiness as a side effect than subjects in group 2 at the $\alpha = 0.05$ level of significance?

17. **Abstain from Alcohol** In November 1945, the Gallup organization surveyed 1,100 adult Americans and asked, "Are you a total abstainer from, or do you on occasion consume, alcoholic beverages?" Of the 1,100 adults surveyed, 363 indicated that they were total abstainers. In July 2007, the same question was asked of 1,100 adult Americans and 396 indicated that they were total abstainers. Has the proportion of adult Americans who totally abstain from alcohol changed? Use the $\alpha = 0.05$ level of significance.   No; do not reject H_0; P-value = 0.1388

18. **Views on the Death Penalty** The Pew Research Group conducted a poll in which they asked, "Are you in favor of, or opposed to, executing persons as a general policy when the crime was committed while under the age of 18?" Of the 580 Catholics surveyed, 180 indicated they favored capital punishment; of the 600 seculars (those who do not associate with a religion) surveyed, 238 favored capital punishment. Is there a significant difference in the proportion of individuals in these groups in favor of capital punishment for persons under the age of 18? Use the $\alpha = 0.01$ level of significance.

19. **Tattoos** The Harris Poll conducted a survey in which they asked, "How many tattoos do you currently have on your body?" Of the 1,205 males surveyed, 181 responded that they had at least one tattoo. Of the 1,097 females surveyed, 143 responded that they had at least one tattoo. Construct a 95% confidence interval to judge whether the proportion of males that have at least one tattoo differs significantly from the proportion of females that have at least one tattoo. Interpret the interval. $(-0.008, 0.048)$

20. **Body Mass Index** The body mass index (BMI) of an individual is one measure that is used to judge whether an individual is overweight or not. A BMI between 20 and 25 indicates that one is at a normal weight. In a survey of 750 men and 750 women, the Gallup organization found that 203 men and 270 women were normal weight. Construct a 90% confidence interval to gauge whether there is a difference in the proportion of men and women who are normal weight. Interpret the interval. $(-0.128, -0.050)$

21. **Side Effects** In clinical trials of the allergy medicine Clarinex (5 mg), it was reported that 50 out of 1,655 individuals in the Clarinex group and 31 out of 1,652 individuals in the placebo group experienced dry mouth as a side effect of their respective treatments.

    Source: www.clarinex.com   21. (b) No

    (a) Is the proportion of individuals experiencing dry mouth greater for those taking Clarinex than for those taking a placebo at the $\alpha = 0.05$ level of significance?   Reject H_0
    (b) Is the difference between the groups practically significant?

22. **Practical versus Statistical Significance** In clinical trials for treatment of a skin disorder, 642 of 2,105 patients receiving the current standard treatment were cured of the disorder and 697 of 2,115 patients receiving a new proposed treatment were cured of the disorder.
    (a) Does the new procedure cure a higher percentage of patients at the $\alpha = 0.05$ level of significance?   Reject H_0

(b) Do you think that the difference in success rates is practically significant? What factors might influence your decision?

23. **Iraq War** In March 2003, the Pew Research Group surveyed 1,508 adult Americans and asked, "Do you believe the United States made the right or wrong decision to use military force in Iraq?" Of the 1,508 adult Americans surveyed, 1,086 stated the United States made the right decision. In February 2008, the Pew Research Group asked the same question of 1,508 adult Americans and found that 573 believed the United States made the right decision.

(a) In the survey question, the choices "right" and "wrong" were randomly rotated. Why?

(b) Construct and interpret a 90% confidence interval for the difference between the two population proportions, $p_{2003} - p_{2008}$. *(0.312, 0.368)*

24. **Civil Liberties** In June 2002, the Gallup organization surveyed 1,100 adult Americans and asked, "Do you think the Bush administration [Rotated: has gone too far, has been about right, or has not gone far enough] in restricting people's civil liberties in order to fight terrorism?" Of the 1,100 adult Americans surveyed in June 2002, 121 felt the Bush administration had gone too far. In May 2006, 451 felt the Bush administration had gone too far.

(a) In the survey question, the choices were randomly rotated. Why?

(b) Construct and interpret a 95% confidence interval for the difference between the two population proportions, $p_{2006} - p_{2003}$. *(0.266, 0.334)*

25. **Hazardous Activities** In a survey of 3,029 adult Americans, the Harris Poll asked people whether they smoked cigarettes and NW whether they always wear a seat belt in a car. The table shows the results of the survey. For each activity, we define a success as finding an individual that participates in the hazardous activity.

	No Seat Belt (success)	Seat Belt (failure)
Smoke (success)	67	448
Do not smoke (failure)	327	2,187

(a) Why is this a dependent sample?

(b) Is there a significant difference in the proportion of individuals who smoke and the proportion of individuals that do not wear a seat belt? In other words, is there a significant difference between the proportion of individuals who engage in hazardous activities? Use the $\alpha = 0.05$ level of significance. *Reject H_0*

26. **Income Taxes** The Gallup organization conducted a survey in which they asked 1,020 adult Americans whether they felt low-income people paid their fair share of taxes. Then they asked whehter they felt high-income people paid their fair share of taxes. For each income group, a success is identifying an individual who feels the person pays his or her fair share of taxes. Is there a significant difference in the proportion of adult Americans who feel high-income people pay their fair share of taxes and the proportion who feel low-income people pay their fair share of taxes? Use the $\alpha = 0.05$ level of significance.

		Low-Income	
		Fair Share (success)	Not Fair Share (failure)
High-Income	**Fair share (success)**	73	146
	Not fair share (failure)	274	548

26. Reject H_0

27. **Voice-Recognition Systems** Have you ever been frustrated by computer telephone systems that do not understand your voice commands? Quite a bit of effort goes into designing these systems to minimize voice-recognition errors. Researchers at the Oregon Graduate Institute of Science and Technology developed a new method of voice recognition (called a remapped network) that was thought to be an improvement over an existing neural network. The data shown are based on results of their research. Does the evidence suggest that the remapped network has a different proportion of errors than the neural network? Use the $\alpha = 0.05$ level of significance. *Reject H_0*

		Remapped Network	
		Recognized Word (success)	Did Not Recognize Word (failure)
Neural Network	**Recognized word (success)**	9,326	385
	Did not recognize word (failure)	456	29

Source: Wei, Wei, Leen, Todd, Barnard, and Etienne, "A Fast Histogram-Based Postprocessor That Improves Posterior Probability Estimates." *Neural Computation* 11:1235–1248.

28. **Poison Ivy** Look back at the data in Table 5 comparing the effectiveness of two ointments on page 615. Conduct the appropriate test to determine if one ointment has a different effectiveness than the other. Use the $\alpha = 0.05$ level of significance. *Do not reject H_0*

29. **Own a Gun?** In May 2007, the Gallup organization surveyed 1,134 American adults and found that 340 owned a gun. In October 2004, the Gallup organization had surveyed 1,134 American adults and found that 363 owned a gun. Suppose that a newspaper article has a headline that reads, "Percentage of American Gun Owners on the Decline." Is this an accurate headline? Why? *No*

30. **Accupril** Accupril, a medication supplied by Pfizer Pharmaceuticals, is meant to control hypertension. In clinical trials of Accupril, 2,142 subjects were divided into two groups. The 1,563 subjects in group 1 (the experimental group) received Accupril. The 579 subjects in group 2 (the control group) received a placebo. Of the 1,563 subjects in the experimental group, 61 experienced dizziness as a side effect. Of the 579 subjects in the control group, 15 experienced dizziness as a side effect. To test whether the proportion experiencing dizziness in the experimental group is greater than that in the control group, the researchers entered the data into MINITAB statistical software and obtained the following results:

```
Test and Confidence Interval for Two Proportions
Sample    X      N    Sample p
1        61    1563   0.039028
2        15     579   0.025907

Estimate for p(1) - p(2): 0.0131208
95% CI for p(1) - p(2): (-0.00299150, 0.0292330)
Test for p(1) - p(2) = 0 (vs > 0): Z = 1.46 P-Value = 0.072
```

What conclusion can be drawn from the clinical trials?

31. **Determining Sample Size** A physical therapist wants to determine the difference in the proportion of men and women who participate in regular, sustained physical activity. What sample size should be obtained if she wishes the estimate to be within 3 percentage points with 95% confidence, assuming that

(a) she uses the 1998 estimates of 21.9% male and 19.7% female from the U.S. National Center for Chronic Disease Prevention and Health Promotion? *1,406*

(b) she does not use any prior estimates? *2,135*

32. Determining Sample Size An educator wants to determine the difference between the proportion of males and females who have completed 4 or more years of college. What sample size should be obtained if she wishes the estimate to be within 2 percentage points with 90% confidence, assuming that

(a) she uses the 1999 estimates of 27.5% male and 23.1% female from the U.S. Census Bureau?   2,551

(b) she does not use any prior estimates?   3,383

33. Putting It Together: Salk Vaccine On April 12, 1955, Dr. Jonas Salk released the results of clinical trials for his vaccine to prevent polio. In these clinical trials, 400,000 children were randomly divided in two groups. The subjects in group 1 (the experimental group) were given the vaccine, while the subjects in group 2 (the control group) were given a placebo. Of the 200,000 children in the experimental group, 33 developed polio. Of the 200,000 children in the control group, 115 developed polio.

(a) What type of experimental design is this?

(b) What is the response variable?

(c) What are the treatments?   Placebo or vaccine

(d) What is a placebo?   Innocuous medication

(e) Why is such a large number of subjects needed for this study?   Low incidence rate of polio

(f) Does it appear to be the case that the vaccine was effective?   Yes; reject H_0

TECHNOLOGY STEP-BY-STEP   Inference for Two Population Proportions

TI-83/84 Plus

Hypothesis Tests

1. Press STAT, highlight TESTS, and select 6:2-PropZTest ....

2. Enter the values of x_1, n_1, x_2, and n_2.

3. Highlight the appropriate relation between p_1 and p_2 in the alternative hypothesis.

4. Highlight Calculate or Draw and press ENTER. Calculate gives the test statistic and P-value. Draw will draw the Z-distribution with the P-value shaded.

Confidence Intervals

Follow the same steps given for hypothesis tests, except select B:2-PropZInt .... Also, select a confidence level (such as 95% = 0.95).

MINITAB

1. Enter the raw data into columns C1 and C2, if necessary.

2. Select the **Stat** menu, highlight **Basic Statistics**, then highlight **2 Proportions** ....

3. If you have raw data, click "Samples in different columns" and enter C1 for first sample and C2 for second sample. If you have summary statistics, select "Summarized data." Enter the number of successes in the "events" cell and the number of trials in the "trials" cell for each sample.

4. Click Options ... and enter the level of confidence desired, the "test difference" (usually 0), and the direction of the alternative hypothesis. Click OK twice.

Excel

1. Enter the raw data into columns A and B, using 0 for failure and 1 for success. Highlight the data.

2. Load the DDXL Add-in, if necessary.

3. Select the **DDXL** menu, highlight **Hypothesis Tests**. From the drop-down menu under Function Type:, select 2 Var Prop Test.

4. Select the column that contains the raw data for sample 1 from the "Names and Columns" window. Use the ◄ arrow to select the data for 1 Prop Variable. Select the column that contains the raw data for sample 2 from the "Names and Columns" window. Use the ◄ arrow to select the data for 2 Prop Variable. Click OK.

Note: If the first row contains the name of the variable, check the "first row is variable names" box.

5. Fill in the DataDesk window. In Step 1, click "Set Success 1" so that 1 is a success. Click "Set Success 2" so that 1 is also a success. In Step 2, click "Set p" and enter the value of the difference in the proportions stated in the null hypothesis (usually 0). In Step 3, select the level of significance. In Step 4, select the direction in the alternative hypothesis. Click Compute.

11.4 INFERENCE FOR TWO POPULATION STANDARD DEVIATIONS

Objectives	1	Find critical values of the F-distribution
	2	Test hypotheses regarding two population standard deviations

1 Find Critical Values of the F-distribution

Note to Instructor

This section is optional and may be skipped without loss of continuity.

In this section, we discuss methods for comparing two population standard deviations (or variances). For example, we might be interested in determining whether the rate of return for Cisco Systems stock is more volatile than General Electric (GE) stock. If Cisco Systems stock is more volatile than GE, the standard deviation rate of return on Cisco Systems would be higher than the standard deviation rate of return on GE. To test hypotheses regarding population standard deviations, we use Fisher's **F-distribution**, named in honor of Sir Ronald A. Fisher. Certain requirements must be satisfied to test hypotheses regarding two population standard deviations.

Requirements for Testing Hypotheses Regarding Two Population Standard Deviations

1. The samples are independent simple random samples.

2. The populations from which the samples are drawn are normally distributed.

The second requirement is critical. The procedures introduced in this section are **not robust**, so any departures from normality will adversely affect the results of the test and make them unreliable. One reason for this is that the standard deviation is not a good measure of spread in nonsymmetric distributions because the standard deviation is not resistant to extreme values. Populations that are skewed will have extreme values that inflate the value of the standard deviation. Therefore, whenever performing inference regarding two population standard deviations, we must verify the requirement of the normality of the population using normal probability plots.

We use the following notation when describing the two populations.

CAUTION If the populations from which the samples are drawn are not normal, do not use the inferential procedures discussed in this section.

Notation Used When Comparing Two Population Standard Deviations

σ_1^2: Variance for population 1 σ_2^2: Variance for population 2

s_1^2: Sample variance for population 1 s_2^2: Sample variance for population 2

n_1: Sample size for population 1 n_2: Sample size for population 2

Before we can perform statistical inference regarding two population standard deviations, we want to know the sampling distribution of the test statistic. In comparing two population standard deviations, the test statistic follows Fisher's F-distribution.

Fisher's *F*-distribution

If $\sigma_1^2 = \sigma_2^2$ and s_1^2 and s_2^2 are sample variances from independent simple random samples of size n_1 and n_2, respectively, drawn from normal populations, then

$$F = \frac{s_1^2}{s_2^2}$$

follows the F-distribution with $n_1 - 1$ degrees of freedom in the numerator and $n_2 - 1$ degrees of freedom in the denominator.

We can find critical values of the F-distribution using Table VIII in Appendix A. Before discussing how to read Table VIII, we present characteristics of the F-distribution.

Figure 14
F-distributions

Characteristics of the *F*-distribution

1. The F-distribution is not symmetric. It is skewed right.

2. The shape of the F-distribution depends on the degrees of freedom in the numerator and denominator. See Figure 14. This is similar to the χ^2 distribution and Student's t-distribution, whose shapes depend on their degrees of freedom.

3. The total area under the curve is 1.

4. The values of F are always greater than or equal to zero.

Table VIII is structured differently from those for the t- or χ^2 distributions. The row across the top provides the degrees of freedom in the numerator, while the column on the left provides the degrees of freedom in the denominator. Corresponding to the degrees of freedom in the numerator and denominator, we have various areas (0.1, 0.05, 0.025, 0.01, 0.001) in the right tail of the F-distribution. The body of the table provides the critical F values. We use the notation

$$F_{\alpha, n_1-1, n_2-1}$$

where $n_1 - 1$ is the degrees of freedom in the numerator, $n_2 - 1$ is the degrees of freedom in the denominator, and α is the area to the right of F_{α, n_1-1, n_2-1}. To determine the critical value that has an area of α to the left, we use the following property:

$$F_{1-\alpha, n_1-1, n_2-1} = \frac{1}{F_{\alpha, n_2-1, n_1-1}}$$

So, to find the critical F that has an area of $\alpha = 0.05$ to the left with 12 degrees of freedom in the numerator and 20 degrees of freedom in the denominator, find the critical F that has an area of $\alpha = 0.05$ to the right with 20 degrees of freedom in the numerator and 12 degrees of freedom in the denominator and compute its reciprocal.

EXAMPLE 1   Finding Critical Values for the F-distribution

Problem: Find the critical F-values

(a) for a right-tailed test with $\alpha = 0.05$, degrees of freedom in the numerator = 10, and degrees of freedom in the denominator = 7.

Figure 15

(b) for a two-tailed test with $\alpha = 0.05$, degrees of freedom in the numerator = 15, and degrees of freedom in the denominator = 20.

Approach: We will perform the following steps to obtain the critical values.

Step 1: Draw an F-distribution with the critical value(s) and area labeled.

Step 2: Use Table VIII to find the critical value(s).

Solution

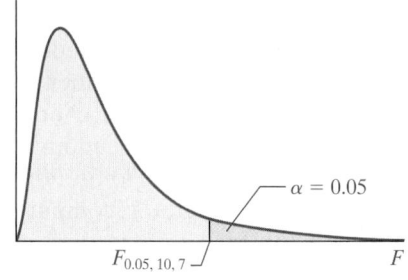

$\alpha = 0.05$

$F_{0.05, 10, 7}$ F

(a) Step 1: Figure 15 shows the F-distribution with 10 degrees of freedom in the numerator and 7 degrees of freedom in the denominator. The area to the right of the unknown critical value is 0.05. We denote this critical value $F_{0.05,10,7}$.

Step 2: Figure 16 shows a partial representation of Table VIII. We box the column corresponding to 10 degrees of freedom (the numerator degrees of freedom) and the row corresponding to 7 degrees of freedom (the denominator degrees of freedom) with $\alpha = 0.05$. The critical value is $F_{0.05,10,7} = 3.64$.

Figure 16

Area to the Right of Critical Value	Degrees of Freedom in the Numerator							
	9	10	15	20	30	60	120	1000
0.100	59.86	60.19	61.22	61.74	62.26	62.79	63.06	63.30
0.050	240.54	241.88	245.95	248.01	250.10	252.20	253.25	254.19
1 0.025	963.28	968.63	984.87	993.10	1001.4	1009.8	1014	1017.7
0.010	6022.5	6055.8	6157.3	6208.7	6260.6	6313	6339.4	6362.7
0.001	602284	605621	615764	620908	626099	631337	633972	636301
0.100	2.72	2.70	2.63	2.59	2.56	2.51	2.49	2.47
0.050	3.68	3.64	3.51	3.44	3.38	3.30	3.27	3.23
7 0.025	4.82	4.76	4.57	4.47	4.36	4.25	4.20	4.15
0.010	6.72	6.62	6.31	6.16	5.99	5.82	5.74	5.66
0.001	14.33	14.08	13.32	12.93	12.53	12.12	11.91	11.72

(b) Step 1: Figure 17 shows the F-distribution with 15 degrees of freedom in the numerator and 20 degrees of freedom in the denominator. The area to the right of the right critical value is $\dfrac{\alpha}{2} = 0.025$. We denote this critical value $F_{0.025,15,20}$. The area to the right of the left critical value is $1 - \dfrac{\alpha}{2} = 0.975$. We denote this critical value $F_{0.975,15,20}$.

Figure 17

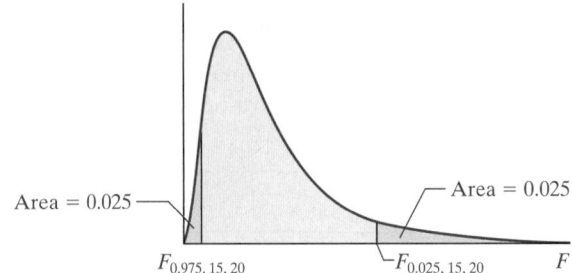

Area = 0.025

Area = 0.025

$F_{0.975,\,15,\,20}$ $F_{0.025,\,15,\,20}$ F

Step 2: We refer to Table VIII. To find the right critical value, identify the column that represents 15 degrees of freedom (the numerator degrees of freedom) and the row that represents 20 degrees of freedom (the denominator degrees of freedom) with $\dfrac{\alpha}{2} = 0.025$. The right critical value is $F_{0.025,15,20} = 2.57$. To find the left critical value, we use the fact that $F_{1-\alpha,n_1-1,n_2-1} = \dfrac{1}{F_{\alpha,n_2-1,n_1-1}}$. Therefore, we use Table VIII and find that $F_{0.025,20,15} = 2.76$. So the left critical value is $F_{0.975,15,20} = \dfrac{1}{F_{0.025,20,15}} = \dfrac{1}{2.76} = 0.36$.

In studying Table VIII, we notice that some values of the degrees of freedom for either the numerator or denominator are not in the table. If the number of degrees of freedom is not found in the table, we follow the practice of choosing the degrees of freedom closest to that desired. If the degrees of freedom is exactly between two values, find the mean of the values. For example, to find the critical value corresponding to 35 degrees of freedom in the numerator, compute the mean of the critical values corresponding to 30 and 40 degrees of freedom in the numerator.

Now Work Problem 3

2 Test Hypotheses Regarding Two Population Standard Deviations

Now that we know the approximate sampling distribution of $\dfrac{s_1^2}{s_2^2}$ and how to find critical values in the F-distribution, we can introduce a procedure that can be used to test hypotheses regarding two population standard deviations (or variances).

Test Hypotheses Regarding Two Population Standard Deviations

To test hypotheses regarding two population standard deviations, σ_1 and σ_2, we can use the following steps, provided that

1. the samples are obtained using simple random sampling,
2. the sample data are independent, and
3. the populations from which the samples are drawn are normally distributed.

Step 1: Determine the null and alternative hypotheses. The hypotheses can be structured in one of three ways:

Two-Tailed	Left-Tailed	Right-Tailed
H_0: $\sigma_1 = \sigma_2$	H_0: $\sigma_1 = \sigma_2$	H_0: $\sigma_1 = \sigma_2$
H_1: $\sigma_1 \neq \sigma_2$	H_1: $\sigma_1 < \sigma_2$	H_1: $\sigma_1 > \sigma_2$

Note: σ_1 is the population standard deviation for population 1; σ_2 is the population standard deviation for population 2.

Step 2: Select a level of significance, α, depending on the seriousness of making a Type I error.

Step 3: Compute the test statistic

$$F_0 = \frac{s_1^2}{s_2^2}$$

which follows Fisher's F-distribution with $n_1 - 1$ degrees of freedom in the numerator and $n_2 - 1$ degrees of freedom in the denominator.

Classical Approach

Step 4: Use Table VIII to determine the critical value(s) using $n_1 - 1$ degrees of freedom in the numerator and $n_2 - 1$ degrees of freedom in the denominator. The shaded regions represent the critical region.

	Two-Tailed	Left-Tailed	Right-Tailed
Critical value(s)	$F_{1-\alpha/2,n_1-1,n_2-1}$ and $F_{\alpha/2,n_1-1,n_2-1}$	$F_{1-\alpha,n_1-1,n_2-1}$	F_{α,n_1-1,n_2-1}

Critical region(s)

Step 5: Compare the critical value with the test statistic.

Two-Tailed	Left-Tailed	Right-Tailed
If $F_0 < F_{1-\alpha/2,n_1-1,n_2-1}$ or $F_0 > F_{\alpha/2,n_1-1,n_2-1}$, reject the null hypothesis.	If $F_0 < F_{1-\alpha,n_1-1,n_2-1}$, reject the null hypothesis.	If $F_0 > F_{\alpha,n_1-1,n_2-1}$, reject the null hypothesis.

P-Value Approach

Step 4: Use technology to determine the P-value.

Step 5: If P-value $< \alpha$, reject the null hypothesis.

Step 6: State the conclusion.

Because the procedures just presented are **not robust**, minor departures from normality will adversely affect the results of the test. Therefore, the test should be used only when the requirement of normality has been verified. We will verify this requirement by constructing normal probability plots.

EXAMPLE 2   **Testing Hypotheses Regarding Two Population Standard Deviations**

⬦ CAUTION   The test for equality of population standard deviations is not robust. Thus, any departures from normality make the results of the inference useless.

Problem: An investor believes that Cisco Systems is a more volatile stock than General Electric. The volatility of a stock is measured by the standard deviation rate of return on the stock. The data in Table 6 represent the monthly rate of return between 1990 and 2007 for 10 randomly selected months for Cisco Systems stock and 14 randomly selected months for General Electric stock.

Table 6							
Monthly Rate of Return for Cisco Systems Stock (%)				**Monthly Rate of Return for General Electric Stock (%)**			
1.93	31.11	−7.60	9.72	1.15	−1.92	−0.55	5.29
11.64	4.87	5.18	8.91	4.68	−2.32	−5.88	9.00
23.13	−5.56			3.23	−5.19	−3.26	−0.60
				0.98	4.80		

Source: Yahoo!Finance

Does the evidence suggest that Cisco Systems stock is more volatile than General Electric stock at the $\alpha = 0.05$ level of significance.

Approach: We want to know if the evidence suggests that Cisco Systems is more volatile than General Electric. Symbolically, this is represented as $\sigma_1 > \sigma_2$, where σ_1 is the standard deviation rate of return of Cisco Systems stock and σ_2 is the standard deviation rate of return of General Electric stock. We assume that there is no difference, or $\sigma_1 = \sigma_2$. We first verify that both variables are normally distributed by constructing normal probability plots. We then follow Steps 1 through 6 to test the claim.

Solution: Figure 18(a) shows the normal probability plot for Cisco Systems, while Figure 18(b) shows the normal probability plot for General Electric.

Figure 18

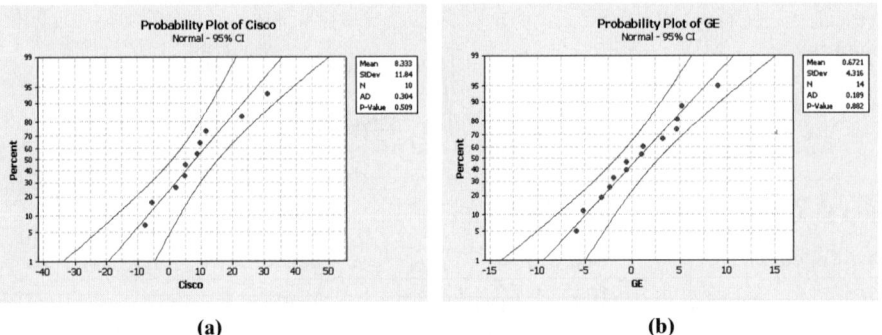

(a)   (b)

Both normal probability plots are linear, so the data come from a population that is normally distributed. We now follow Steps 1 through 6.

Step 1: The investor wants to know if Cisco Systems is a more volatile stock than General Electric. This is written $\sigma_1 > \sigma_2$. The null hypothesis is a statement of no difference, so we have

$$H_0: \sigma_1 = \sigma_2 \quad \text{versus} \quad H_1: \sigma_1 > \sigma_2$$

This is a right-tailed test.

Step 2: The level of significance is $\alpha = 0.05$.

Step 3: We compute the sample standard deviation of the rate of return for Cisco Systems, s_1, to be 11.84% and the sample standard deviation of the rate of return for General Electric, s_2, to be 4.32%. Because the data are normally distributed, the test statistic is

$$F_0 = \frac{s_1^2}{s_2^2} = \frac{11.84^2}{4.32^2} = 7.51$$

Classical Approach

Step 4: Because this is a right-tailed test, we determine the critical value at the $\alpha = 0.05$ level of significance with $n_1 - 1 = 10 - 1 = 9$ degrees of freedom in the numerator and $n_2 - 1 = 14 - 1 = 13$ degrees of freedom in the denominator and find it to be $F_{0.05,9,13} \approx 2.80$ (using 12 degrees of freedom in the denominator, because that is closest). The critical region is displayed in Figure 19.

Figure 19

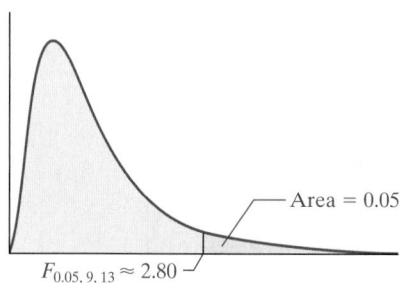

Area = 0.05

$F_{0.05,\,9,\,13} \approx 2.80$

Step 5: Because the test statistic $F_0 = 7.51$ is greater than the critical value $F_{0.05,9,13} \approx 2.80$, we reject the null hypothesis.

Now Work Problem 19

P-Value Approach Using Technology

Step 4: We will use Excel to obtain the P-value. The steps for testing claims comparing two population standard deviations using the TI-83/84 Plus graphing calculators, MINITAB, and Excel are given in the Technology Step-by-Step on page 631. Figure 20 shows the results obtained from Excel.

Figure 20

F-Test Two-Sample for Variances

	Cisco	GE
Mean	8.333	0.67214286
Variance	140.082668	18.6297566
Observations	10	14
df	9	13
F	7.51929673	
P(F<=t) one-tail	0.00069363	
F Critical one-tail	2.71435852	

The P-value is 0.0007. If the statement in the null hypothesis were true we would expect to get the results obtained in about 7 samples out of 10,000. Very unusual results, indeed!

Step 5: Because the P-value is less than the level of significance $\alpha = 0.05$, we reject the null hypothesis.

Step 6: There is sufficient evidence to conclude that Cisco Systems stock is more volatile than General Electric stock at the $\alpha = 0.05$ level of significance. Investors would use this result to demand a higher rate of return on investments in Cisco Systems.

EXAMPLE 3 **Testing Hypotheses Regarding Two Population Standard Deviations**

Table 7

Flight		Control	
8.59	8.64	8.65	6.99
6.87	7.89	7.62	7.44
7.00	8.80	7.33	8.58
6.39	7.54	7.14	9.14
7.43	7.21	8.40	9.66
9.79	6.85	8.55	8.70
9.30	8.03	9.88	9.94

Source: NASA, Life Sciences Data Archive

Problem: In the Spacelab Life Sciences 2 payload, 14 male rats were sent to space. Upon their return, the red blood cell mass (in milliliters) of the rats was determined. A control group of 14 male rats was held under the same conditions (except for spaceflight) as the space rats, and their red blood cell mass was likewise determined when the space rats returned. The project was led by Dr. Paul X. Callahan. The data in Table 7 were obtained.

Is the standard deviation of the red blood cell mass in the flight animals different from the standard deviation of the red blood cell mass in the control animals at the $\alpha = 0.05$ level of significance?

Approach: We verified that the data are normally distributed, in Example 1 from Section 11.2. See Figure 5 on page 598.

Step 1: We want to know whether the standard deviation of the red blood cell mass in the flight animals is different from the standard deviation of the red blood cell mass in the control animals. If we let σ_1 represent the standard deviation of the red blood cell mass for the flight animals and σ_2 represent the standard deviation of the red blood cell mass for the control animals, this can be written $\sigma_1 \neq \sigma_2$. We have

$$H_0: \sigma_1 = \sigma_2 \quad \text{versus} \quad H_1: \sigma_1 \neq \sigma_2$$

This is a two-tailed test.

Step 2: The level of significance is $\alpha = 0.05$.

Step 3: In Example 1 from Section 11.2, we computed the sample standard deviation of the red blood cell mass for the experimental group, s_1, to be 1.017 and the sample standard deviation of the red blood cell mass for the control group, s_2, to be 1.005. Because the data are normally distributed, the test statistic is

$$F_0 = \frac{s_1^2}{s_2^2} = \frac{1.017^2}{1.005^2} = 1.024$$

Classical Approach

Step 4: Because this is a two-tailed test, we determine the critical value at the $\alpha = 0.05$ level of significance with $n_1 - 1 = 14 - 1 = 13$ degrees of freedom in the numerator and $n_2 - 1 = 14 - 1 = 13$ degrees of freedom in the denominator and find them to be $F_{0.025,13,13} \approx 3.28$ (using 12 degrees of freedom in the denominator, because that is closest) and

$$F_{0.975,13,13} = \frac{1}{F_{0.025,13,13}} = \frac{1}{3.28} = 0.30.$$

The critical regions are displayed in Figure 21.

Figure 21

Area = 0.025

Area = 0.025

$F_{0.975, 13, 13} \approx 0.30$ $F_{0.05, 13, 13} \approx 3.28$

Step 5: Because the test statistic $F_0 = 1.024$ lies between the critical values 0.30 and 3.28, we do not reject the null hypothesis.

P-Value Approach Using Technology

Step 4: We will use a TI-84 graphing calculator to obtain the P-value. The steps for testing claims comparing two population standard deviations using the TI-83/84 Plus graphing calculators, MINITAB, and Excel are given in the Technology Step-by-Step on page 631. Figure 22 shows the result obtained from the TI-84 Plus using the DRAW option.

Figure 22

The P-value is 0.9666.

Step 5: Because the P-value is greater than the level of significance $\alpha = 0.05$, we do not reject the null hypothesis.

Step 6: There is not sufficient evidence to conclude that the standard deviation of the red blood cell mass in the experimental group is significantly different from the red blood cell mass in the control group at the $\alpha = 0.05$ level of significance.

IN CLASS ACTIVITY

Stringing Them Along (Part III)

Do you believe there is more variability in the error (estimate minus actual) in the length of a longer rope or shorter rope? Continue the activity from page 601 by doing the following.

(a) Assuming there is no difference in the variability of the errors in the longer and shorter ropes, the null hypothesis is H_0: $\sigma_{longer} = \sigma_{shorter}$ (where σ represents the population standard deviation of absolute differences between the actual length and the estimated length). Based on your answer to the question posed at the beginning of the activity, select an appropriate alternative hypothesis and a level of significance.

(b) Retrieve the class data for Stringing Them Along (Part II) on page 601.

(c) Conduct the hypothesis test you outlined in part (a). What did you conclude?

(d) Are the two sets of data normally distributed? If not, how will that affect your results?

11.4 ASSESS YOUR UNDERSTANDING

Concepts and Vocabulary

1. Is the test for comparing two population standard deviations robust? Why is the assumption of normality so important to perform the test presented in this section?

2. State the assumptions that must be satisfied to compare two population standard deviations.

Skill Building

3. Find the critical value for a right-tailed test with $\alpha = 0.05$, degrees of freedom in the numerator = 9, and degrees of freedom in the denominator = 10.   3.02

4. Find the critical value for a right-tailed test with $\alpha = 0.01$, degrees of freedom in the numerator = 20, and degrees of freedom in the denominator = 25.   2.70

5. Find the critical values for a two-tailed test with $\alpha = 0.05$, degrees of freedom in the numerator = 6, and degrees of freedom in the denominator = 8.   0.18, 4.65

6. Find the critical values for a two-tailed test with $\alpha = 0.02$, degrees of freedom in the numerator = 5, and degrees of freedom in the denominator = 7.   0.10, 7.46

7. Find the critical value for a left-tailed test with $\alpha = 0.10$, degrees of freedom in the numerator = 25, and degrees of freedom in the denominator = 20.   0.58

8. Find the critical value for a left-tailed test with $\alpha = 0.01$, degrees of freedom in the numerator = 15, and degrees of freedom in the denominator = 20.   0.30

9. Find the critical value for a right-tailed test with $\alpha = 0.05$, degrees of freedom in the numerator = 45, and degrees of freedom in the denominator = 15.   2.19

10. Find the critical value for a right-tailed test with $\alpha = 0.01$, degrees of freedom in the numerator = 55, and degrees of freedom in the denominator = 50.   1.93

In Problems 11–16, assume that the populations are normally distributed.

11. Test the hypothesis that $\sigma_1 \neq \sigma_2$ at the $\alpha = 0.05$ level of significance for the given sample data.   Do not reject H_0

	Population 1	Population 2
n	16	16
s	3.2	3.5

12. Test the hypothesis that $\sigma_1 \neq \sigma_2$ at the $\alpha = 0.1$ level of significance for the given sample data.   Do not reject H_0

	Population 1	Population 2
n	21	21
s	8.6	9.2

13. Test the hypothesis that $\sigma_1 > \sigma_2$ at the $\alpha = 0.01$ level of significance for the given sample data.   Do not reject H_0

	Population 1	Population 2
n	26	19
s	9.9	6.4

14. Test the hypothesis that $\sigma_1 < \sigma_2$ at the $\alpha = 0.05$ level of significance for the given sample data.   Reject H_0

	Population 1	Population 2
n	21	26
s	15.9	23.0

15. Test the hypothesis that $\sigma_1 < \sigma_2$ at the $\alpha = 0.1$ level of significance for the given sample data.   Reject H_0

	Population 1	Population 2
n	51	26
s	8.3	13.2

16. Test the hypothesis that $\sigma_1 > \sigma_2$ at the $\alpha = 0.05$ level of significance for the given sample data.   Do not reject H_0

	Population 1	Sample for Population 2
n	23	13
s	7.5	5.1

Applying the Concepts

17. **Treating Bipolar Mania** Researchers conducted a randomized, double-blind study to measure the effects of the drug olanzapine on patients diagnosed with bipolar disorder. One hundred fifteen patients with a DSM-IV diagnosis of bipolar disorder were randomly divided into two groups. Group 1 ($n = 55$) received 5 to 20 mg per day of olanzapine, while group 2 ($n = 60$) received a placebo. The effectiveness of the drug was measured by the Young Mania Rating Scale total score, with the net improvement in the score recorded. The results are presented in the following table:

	Treatment Group	Control Group
n	55	60
Mean improvement	14.8	8.1
Sample standard deviation	12.5	12.7

Source: "Efficacy of Olanzapine in Acute Bipolar Mania" *Archives of General Psychology*, 57(9): 841–849

Assuming that the data are normally distributed, do the data suggest that the standard deviation in the treatment group is different from the standard deviation in the control group at the $\alpha = 0.05$ level of significance.   Do not reject H_0

18. **Treating the Common Cold** Researcher Steven J. Sperber, MD, and his associates wanted to determine the effectiveness of pseudoephedrine and acetaminophen in the treatment of discomfort associated with the common cold. They published their results in the *Archives of Family Medicine 2000* 9:979–985. In their study, they randomly

divided 430 subjects into two groups: group 1 ($n = 216$) received pseudoephedrine and acetaminophen; group 2 ($n = 214$) received a placebo. The goal of the study was to discover whether the mean symptom assessment score of the individuals receiving the treatment (group 1) was less than that of the control group (group 2). In group 1, the mean reduction in the symptom assessment scores was 1.30, with a standard deviation of 0.88; in group 2, participants had a mean reduction in the symptom assessment score of 0.93, with a standard deviation of 0.88. Assuming that the data are normally distributed, determine whether the standard deviation of the symptom assessment score of the subjects in group 1 is different from the standard deviation of the symptom assessment score for the subjects in group 2 at the $\alpha = 0.05$ level of significance.   Do not reject H_0

19. **Vitamin A Supplements in Low-Birth-Weight Babies**
NW Low-birth-weight babies are at increased risk of respiratory infections in the first few months of life and have low liver stores of vitamin A. In a randomized, double-blind experiment, 130 low-birth-weight babies were randomly divided into two groups. Subjects in group 1 (the treatment group, $n_1 = 65$) were given 25,000 IU of vitamin A on study days 1, 4, and 8; study day 1 was between 36 and 60 hours after delivery. Subjects in group 2 (the control group, $n_2 = 65$) were given a placebo. The treatment group had a mean serum retinol concentration of 45.77 micrograms per deciliter ($\mu g/dL$), with a standard deviation of 17.07 $\mu g/dL$. The control group had a mean serum retinol concentration of 12.88 $\mu g/dL$, with a standard deviation of 6.48 $\mu g/dL$. Does the treatment group have a higher standard deviation for serum retinol concentration than the control group at the $\alpha = 0.01$ level of significance? It is known that serum retinol concentration is normally distributed.   Reject H_0

20. **SAT Test Scores** A researcher wants to know if students who do not plan to apply for financial aid had more variability on the SAT I math test than those who plan to do so. She obtains a random sample of 35 students who do not plan to apply for financial aid and a random sample of 38 students who do plan to apply for financial aid and obtains the following results:

Do Not Plan to Apply for Financial Aid	Plan to Apply for Financial Aid
$n_1 = 35$	$n_2 = 38$
$s_1 = 123.1$	$s_2 = 119.4$

Do students who do not plan to apply for financial aid have a higher standard deviation on the SAT I math exam than students who plan to apply for financial aid at the $\alpha = 0.01$ level of significance? SAT I math exam scores are known to be normally distributed.   Do not reject H_0

21. **Waiting Time in Line** McDonald's executives want to experiment with redesigning its restaurants so that the customers form one line leading to four registers to place orders, rather than four lines leading to four separate registers. They redesign 30 randomly selected restaurants with the single line. In addition, they randomly select 30 restaurants with the four-line configuration to participate in the study. At each restaurant, an employee monitors the wait time (in minutes) of randomly selected patrons. The following data are collected.

Single Line				Multiple Lines			
1.2	2.1	1.7	2.8	1.1	1.6	2.9	4.6
1.9	2.1	2.4	3.0	3.8	2.9	2.8	2.9
2.1	2.3	1.9	2.9	4.3	2.3	2.0	2.6
2.7	2.0	2.9	2.3	1.3	1.3	2.0	2.7
2.8	1.1	3.1	1.8	2.0	3.2	2.3	0.9

(a) Is the variability in wait time in the single line less than that for the multiple lines at the $\alpha = 0.05$ level of significance?   Reject H_0

Note: Normal probability plots indicate that the data are normally distributed.

(b) Draw boxplots of each data set to confirm the results of part (a) visually.

22. **Filling Machines** A quality-control engineer wants to find out whether or not a new machine that fills bottles with liquid has less variability than the machine currently in use. The engineer calibrates each machine to fill bottles with 16 ounces of a liquid. After running each machine for 5 hours, she randomly selects 15 filled bottles from each machine and measures their contents. She obtains the following results:

Old Machine			New Machine		
16.01	16.04	15.96	16.02	15.96	16.05
16.00	16.07	15.89	15.95	15.99	16.02
16.04	16.05	15.91	16.00	15.97	16.03
16.10	16.01	16.00	16.06	16.05	15.94
15.92	16.16	15.92	16.08	15.96	15.95

(a) Is the variability in the new machine less than that of the old machine at the $\alpha = 0.05$ level of significance?

Note: Normal probability plots indicate that the data are normally distributed.   Reject H_0

(b) Draw boxplots of each data set to confirm the results of part (a) visually.

23. **Systolic Blood Pressure** A nurse was interested in discovering whether men have more variability in their systolic blood pressure than women. She randomly selects 20 males and 17 females from the surgical floor of her hospital and records their systolic blood pressures. The data are as follows:

Females				Males			
140	124	126	106	112	134	118	112
126	132	126	140	140	105	134	128
136	120	110	122	148	95	124	140
118	130	118	114	120	130	150	112
140				126	116	128	142

Source: Lora McGuire, nursing instructor, Joliet Junior College

(a) Given the following normal probability plots, comment on whether the requirement of normality required for the *F*-test is satisfied and justify your answer.   *Satisfied*

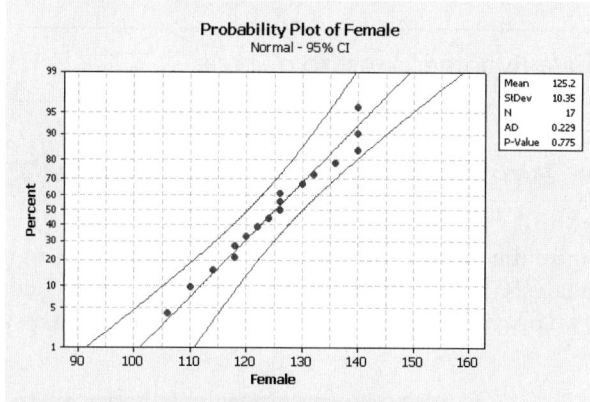

Probability Plot of Female
Normal - 95% CI

Mean	125.2
StDev	10.35
N	17
AD	0.229
P-Value	0.775

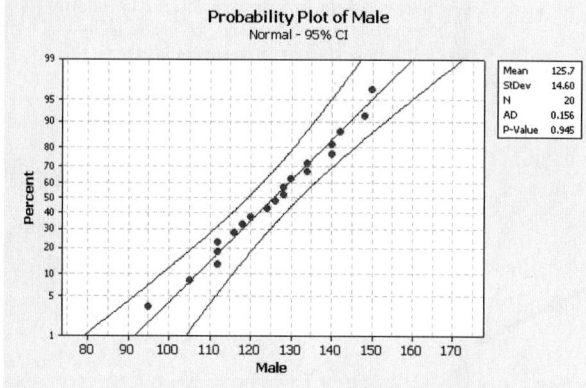

Probability Plot of Male
Normal - 95% CI

Mean	125.7
StDev	14.60
N	20
AD	0.156
P-Value	0.945

(b) The nurse enters the data into MINITAB to determine whether males have a higher standard deviation of systolic blood pressure than females at the $\alpha = 0.05$ level of significance. She obtains a *P*-value of 0.0844. What should the nurse conclude?   *Do not reject H_0*

(c) Compute the test statistic, and use Table VIII to verify that the *P*-value computed is correct. $F_0 = 0.50$

24. Measuring Reaction Time Researchers at the University of Mississippi wanted to discover whether variability for reaction time to a go/no go stimulus of males was different from that of females. The researchers randomly selected 20 females and 15 males to participate in the study. The go/no go stimulus required the student to respond to a particular stimulus and not to respond to other stimuli. The data are as follows:

Female Students						
0.588	0.403	0.293	0.377	0.613	0.377	0.391
0.367	0.442	0.274	0.434	0.403	0.636	0.481
0.652	0.443	0.380	0.646	0.340	0.617	

Male Students						
0.375	0.477	0.374	0.465	0.402	0.337	0.655
0.488	0.427	0.373	0.224	0.654	0.563	0.405
0.256						

Source: PsychExperiments at the University of Mississippi (www.olemiss.edu/psychexps)

Normal probability plots indicate that the requirement of normality is satisfied. The output below is from a TI-84 Plus.

```
2-SampFTest
 σ1≠σ2
 F=.9674532069
 p=.9276177898
 Sx1=.122578986
 Sx2=.124623815
↓x̄1=.45785
```

(a) Use the results to determine whether there is a difference in variability of reaction time in males and females at the $\alpha = 0.05$ level of significance.   *Do not reject H_0*
(b) Draw boxplots of each data set, using the same scale. Does this visual evidence support the results obtained in part (a)?

TECHNOLOGY STEP-BY-STEP   Comparing Two Population Standard Deviations

TI-83/84 Plus
1. If necessary, enter raw data in L1 and L2.
2. Press STAT, highlight TESTS, and select D:2-SampleFTest.
3. If the data are raw, highlight DATA and make sure List1 is set to L1 and List2 is set to L2, with frequencies set to 1. If summary statistics are known, highlight STATS and enter the summary statistics.
4. Highlight the appropriate relation between σ_1 and σ_2 in the alternative hypothesis.
5. Highlight Calculate or Draw and press ENTER. Calculate gives the test statistic and *P*-value. Draw draws the *F*-distribution with the *P*-value shaded.

MINITAB
1. If necessary, enter the raw data in columns C1 and C2.
2. Select the **Stat** menu, highlight **Basic Statistics**, then highlight **2 Variances . . . .**

3. If you have raw data, click "Samples in different columns," and enter C1 in the cell marked "First:" and enter C2 in the cell marked "Second." If you have summarized data, enter them in the appropriate "Summarized data" cells. Be careful to enter sample variances, not sample standard deviations.
4. Click Options . . . . Select a level of confidence. Click OK twice.

Excel
1. Enter raw data in columns A and B.
2. Select the **Tools** menu; highlight **Data Analysis . . . .**
3. Select "*F*-test Two-Sample for Variances." With the cursor in the "Variable 1 Range" cell, highlight the data in column A. With the cursor in the "Variable 2 Range" cell, highlight the data in column B. Enter a value for alpha. Click OK.

11.5 PUTTING IT TOGETHER: WHICH METHOD DO I USE?

Objective	① Determine the appropriate hypothesis test to perform

① Determine the Appropriate Hypothesis Test to Perform

Again, the ability to recognize the type of test to perform is one of the most important aspects of statistical analysis. To help decide which test to use when conducting inference on two samples, we provide the flow chart in Figure 23. Use it to assist you in the problems that follow.

Figure 23

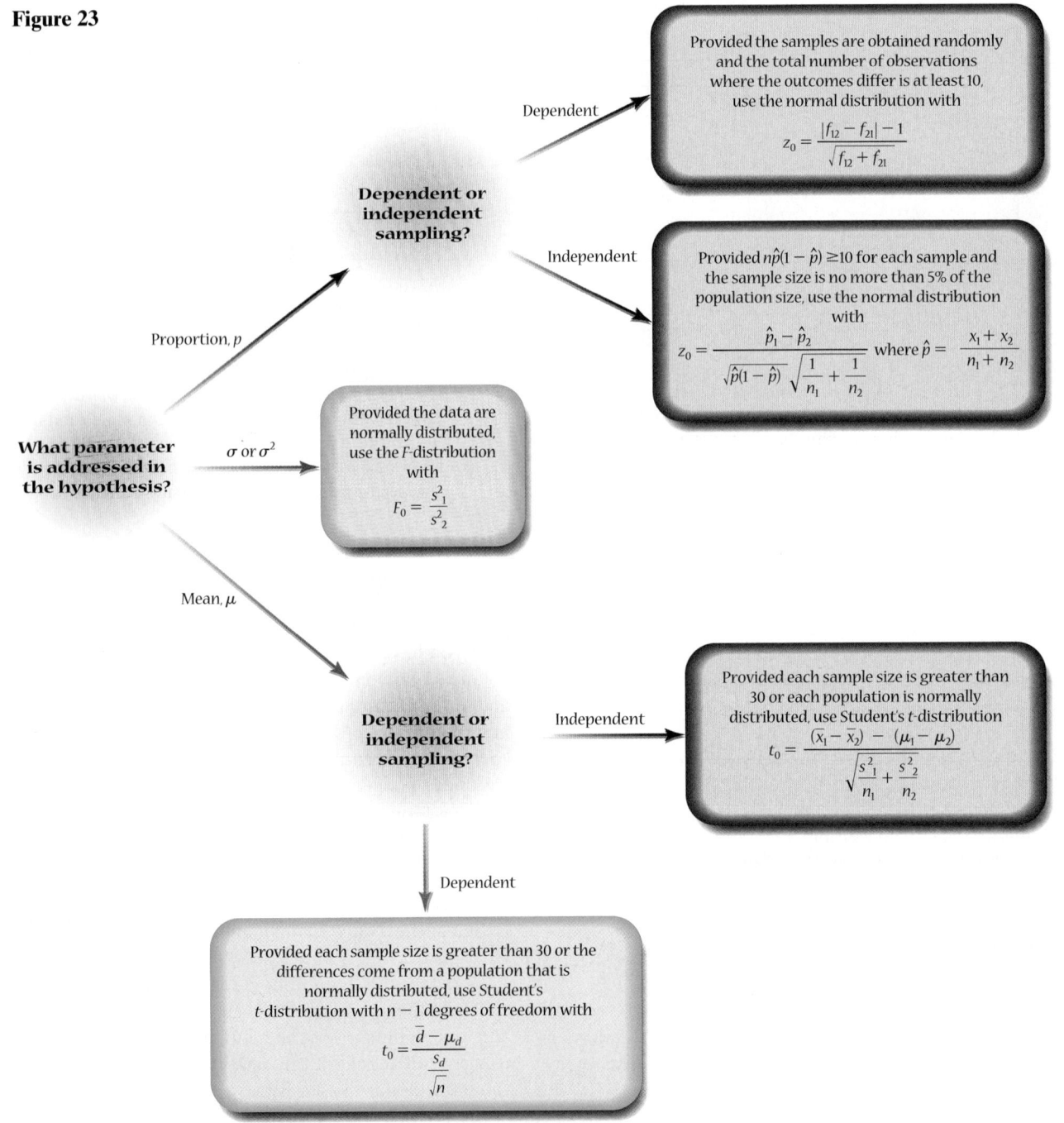

11.5 ASSESS YOUR UNDERSTANDING

Concepts and Vocabulary

1. What type of language should you look for when deciding whether a sample is dependent or independent?

2. What type of language should you look for when deciding whether the inference pertains to means, proportions, or standard deviations?

3. What type of experimental design is analyzed using the inferential techniques for comparing two proportions from independent samples? Is the response variable quantitative or qualitative? How many levels of treatment are there?

4. What type of experimental design is analyzed using the inferential techniques for comparing two means from dependent samples? Is the response variable quantitative or qualitative? How many levels of treatment are there?

Skill Building

In Problems 5–14, perform the appropriate hypothesis test.

5. A researcher wanted to determine the effectiveness of a new cream in the treatment of warts. She identified 138 individuals who had two warts. She applied cream A on one wart and cream B on the second wart. Test whether the proportion of successes with cream A is different from cream B at the $\alpha = 0.05$ level of significance.   *Do not reject H_0*

		Treatment A	
		Success	Failure
Treatment B	Success	63	9
	Failure	13	53

6. A random sample of $n_1 = 120$ individuals results in $x_1 = 43$ successes. An independent sample of $n_2 = 130$ individuals results in $x_2 = 56$ successes. Does this represent sufficient evidence to conclude that $p_1 \neq p_2$ at the $\alpha = 0.01$ level of significance?   *Do not reject H_0*

7. If $n_1 = 31$, $s_1 = 12$, $n_2 = 51$, and $s_2 = 10$, test whether $\sigma_1 > \sigma_2$ at the $\alpha = 0.05$ level of significance.   *Do not reject H_0*

8. A random sample of size $n = 13$ obtained from a population that is normally distributed results in a sample mean of 45.3 and sample standard deviation of 12.4. An independent sample of size $n = 18$ obtained from a population that is normally distributed results in a sample mean of 52.1 and sample standard deviation of 14.7. Does this constitute sufficient evidence to conclude that the population means differ at the $\alpha = 0.05$ level of significance?   *Do not reject H_0*

9. A random sample of $n_1 = 135$ individuals results in $x_1 = 40$ successes. An independent sample of $n_2 = 150$ individuals results in 60 successes. Does this represent sufficient evidence to conclude that $p_1 < p_2$ at the $\alpha = 0.05$ level of significance?   *Reject H_0*

10. If $n_1 = 61$, $s_1 = 18.3$, $n_2 = 57$, and $s_2 = 13.5$, test whether the population standard deviations differ at the $\alpha = 0.05$ level of significance.   *Reject H_0*

11. A random sample of size $n = 41$ results in a sample mean of 125.3 and a sample standard deviation of 8.5. An independent sample of size $n = 50$ results in a sample mean of 130.8 and sample standard deviation of 7.3. Does this constitute sufficient evidence to conclude that the population means differ at the $\alpha = 0.01$ level of significance?   *Reject H_0*

12. The following data represent the measure of a variable before and after a treatment.

Individual	1	2	3	4	5
Before, X_i	93	102	90	112	107
After, Y_i	95	100	95	115	107

Does the sample evidence suggest that the treatment is effective in increasing the value of the response variable? Use the $\alpha = 0.05$ level of significance.

Note: Assume that the differenced data come from a population that is normally distributed with no outliers.
Do not reject H_0

13. The following data represent the measure of a variable before and after a treatment.

Individual	1	2	3	4	5
Before, X_i	40	32	53	48	38
After, Y_i	38	33	49	48	33

Does the sample evidence suggest that the treatment is effective in decreasing the value of the response variable? Use the $\alpha = 0.10$ level of significance.

Note: Assume that the differenced data come from a population that is normally distributed with no outliers.   *Reject H_0*

14. Conduct the appropriate test to determine if the population proportions for the two treatments differ at the $\alpha = 0.05$ level of significance.

Note: The samples are dependent and obtained randomly.
Do not reject H_0

		Treatment A	
		Success	Failure
Treatment B	Success	392	45
	Failure	58	103

Applying the Concepts

15. **Collision Claims** Automobile collision insurance is used to pay for any claims made against the driver in the event of an accident. This type of insurance will typically pay to repair any assets that your vehicle damages.

    (a) Collision claims tend to be skewed right. Why do you think this is the case?

    (b) A random sample of 40 collision claims of 30- to 59-year-old drivers results in a mean claim of $3,669 with a standard deviation of $2,029. An independent random sample of 40 collision claims of 20- to 24-year-old drivers results in a mean claim of $4,586 with a standard deviation of $2,302. Using the concept of hypothesis testing, provide an argument that justifies charging a higher insurance premium to 20- to 24-year-old drivers.   *Reject H_0*

    Source: Based on data obtained from the Insurance Institute for Highway Safety.

16. **TIMMS Report and Kumon** TIMMS is an acronym for the Third International Mathematics and Science Study. Kumon promotes a method of studying mathematics that they claim develops mathematical ability. Do data support this claim? In one particular question on the TIMMS exam, a random sample of 400 non-Kumon students resulted in 73 getting the correct answer. For the same question, a random sample of 400 Kumon students resulted in 130 getting the correct answer. Perform the appropriate test to substantiate Kumon's claims. Are there any confounding factors regarding the claim? Reject H_0

Source: TIMMS and PROM/SE Assessment of Kumon Students: What the Results Indicate, Kumon North America.

17. **Health and Happiness** In a General Social Survey, adult Americans were asked if they were happy or unhappy, and they were asked whether they were healthy or unhealthy. The table shows the results of the survey. Are healthy people also happy people? Use the $\alpha = 0.05$ level of significance. Reject H_0

	Healthy (Success)	Not Healthy (Failure)
Happy (success)	2,499	123
Not happy (failure)	70	59

18. **Cash or Credit?** Do people tend to spend more money on fast-food when they use a credit card? The following data represent a random sample of credit-card and cash purchases.

Credit				
16.78	23.89	13.89	15.54	10.35
12.76	18.32	20.67	18.36	19.16

Cash				
10.76	6.26	18.98	11.36	6.78
21.76	8.90	15.64	13.78	9.21

Source: Brian Ortiz, student at Joliet Junior College

(a) Draw boxplots of each data set using the same scale. What do the boxplots imply for cash versus credit?

(b) Test whether the sample evidence suggests that people spend more when using a credit card. Use the $\alpha = 0.01$ level of significance.

Note: Normal probability plots indicate that each sample could come from a population that is normally distributed. Do not reject H_0

(c) Suppose that you were looking to gather evidence to convince your manager that an effort needs to be made to boost credit-card sales. Would it be legitimate to change the level to $\alpha = 0.05$ after seeing the results from part (b)? Why? No

19. **Walmart versus Target** Is there a difference in the pricing at Walmart versus Target for health and beauty supplies? To answer this question, a student randomly selected 10 identi-cal products at each store and recorded the price. Assuming that the conditions for conducting the test are satisfied, determine if there is a price difference between Walmart and Target for health and beauty supplies. Use the $\alpha = 0.05$ level of significance. Do not reject H_0

Product	Price at Walmart ($)	Price at Target ($)
Herbal Essence	2.94	2.94
Dial body wash	3.16	3.79
Listerine Whitening	4.74	4.74
Colgate White	2.84	2.49
Mens Speed Stick	1.72	1.97
Women Dove deodorant	1.72	1.72
Benadryl Allergy	3.77	3.99
Gillette razors	7.44	7.99
Q-Tips	3.77	3.64
Nice 'n Easy color blend	5.98	5.99

Source: Vicki Wnek, student at Joliet Junior College

20. **Bribe 'em with Chocolate** In a study published in the journal *Teaching of Psychology*, the article "Fudging the Numbers: Distributing Chocolate Influences Student Evaluations of an Undergraduate Course" states that distributing chocolate to students prior to teacher evaluations increases results. The authors randomly divided three sections of a course taught by the same instructor into two groups. Fifty of the students were given chocolate by an individual not associated with the course and 50 of the students were not given chocolate. The mean score from students who received chocolate was 4.2, while the mean score for the nonchocolate group was 3.9. Suppose that the sample standard deviation of both the chocolate and non-chocolate group was 0.8. Does chocolate appear to improve teacher evaluations? Use the $\alpha = 0.1$ level of significance. Yes; reject H_0

21. **Unwed Women Having Children** The Pew Research Group asked the following question of individuals who earned in excess of $100,000 per year and those who earned less than $100,000 per year: "Do you believe that it is morally wrong for unwed women to have children?" Of the 1,205 individuals who earned in excess of $100,000 per year, 710 said yes; of the 1,310 individuals who earned less than $100,000 per year, 695 said yes. Construct a 95% confidence interval to determine if there is a difference in the proportion of individuals who believe it is morally wrong for unwed women to have children. (0.019, 0.097)

22. **Volume of Stock** The daily volume of a stock represents the total number of shares traded in the stock. The following data represent the daily volume (in millions) of General Electric (GE) Corporation stock and Pfizer stock for 13 randomly selected days in 2008.

(a) What conditions must be satisfied to conduct the appropriate test to determine if the daily volume of General Electric Corporation stock is greater than that of Pfizer? Differences normal with no outliers

(b) Assuming that the conditions from part (a) are satisfied, determine if the daily volume of General Electric Corporation stock is greater than that of Pfizer. Use the $\alpha = 0.05$ level of significance. *Do not reject H_0*

Date	Volume of GE (millions)	Volume of Pfizer (millions)
1/2	38.9	45.9
1/7	47.5	48.1
1/28	37.8	37.9
1/31	55.5	52.7
2/1	56.2	52.0
2/19	33.3	34.4
2/22	40.0	32.6
2/26	46.6	47.1
2/27	32.8	26.3
3/3	34.5	32.7
3/4	44.9	36.0
3/5	43.5	46.7
3/7	56.9	42.3

Source: Yahoo!Finance

23. **Comparing Rates of Return** You want to invest some money in a domestic (only U.S. stocks) mutual fund and have narrowed your choice down to value funds or growth funds. Value funds tend to invest in companies that appear to be inexpensive relative to the stock market; growth funds tend to invest in companies that are expected to grow their revenues substantially over time. To help make your decision about which of the two fund types to invest in, you decide to obtain a random sample of 3-year rates of return for 10 different value funds and 10 different growth funds.

Value Funds				
9.54	8.76	12.53	9.52	8.71
6.09	7.63	6.02	6.02	11.71

Growth Funds				
7.57	8.37	8.63	9.02	8.36
7.95	9.33	7.53	6.93	8.37

Source: Morningstar.com

(a) We want to compare two means. Because the sample sizes are small, the sample data must come from populations that are normally distributed with no outliers. The normal probability plots for both sets of data are shown. Do the plots indicate that it is reasonable to believe that the sample data come from a population that is normally distributed? *Yes*

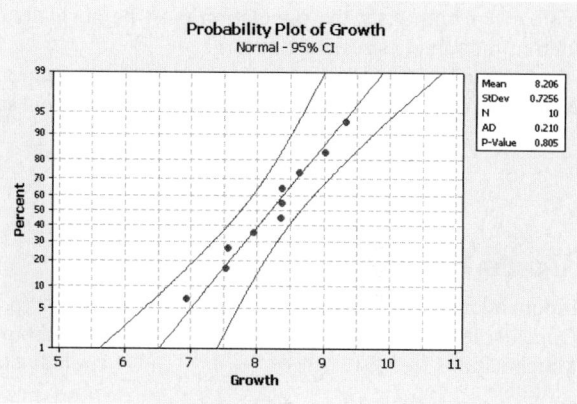

(b) To judge whether the sample data have any outliers and to visualize any differences between the two sample data sets, draw side-by-side boxplots of the data. Are there any outliers? *No*

(c) Conduct the appropriate test to determine if there is any difference in the rate of return between value funds and growth funds. Use the $\alpha = 0.05$ level of significance. *Do not reject H_0*

(d) Another method for evaluating funds is to consider their risk. One measure of risk is the standard deviation rate of return. The higher the standard deviation is, the riskier the fund. Conduct the appropriate test to determine if there is any difference in the risk of each fund. Use the $\alpha = 0.05$ level of significance. *Reject H_0*

(e) Based on the results from parts (c) and (d), write a report detailing which fund type you would recommend.

24. **Which Stock?** You want to invest in a stock and have narrowed your choices down to either Citibank (C) or Wachovia Bank (WB). To help you decide which stock to invest in, you decide to compare weekly rates of return for the two stocks. Which would be a better sampling plan: (a) randomly choose 15 weeks and determine the rate of return of Citibank and then independently randomly choose 15 weeks and determine the rate of return of Wachovia or (b) randomly choose 15 weeks and determine the rate of return of both companies and compare the rate of return. For both scenarios, explain the inferential method you would use and justify your sampling plan. *Matched-pairs design*

CHAPTER 11 REVIEW

Summary

This chapter discussed performing statistical inference by comparing two population parameters. We began with a discussion regarding the comparison of two population means. To determine the method to use, we must know whether the sampling was dependent or independent. A sampling method is independent when the choice of individuals for one sample does not dictate which individuals will be in a second sample. A sampling method is dependent when the individuals selected for one sample are used to determine the individuals in the second sample. For dependent sampling, we use the paired t-test to perform statistical inference. For independent sampling, we use Welch's approximate t. For both tests, the population must be normally distributed or the sample sizes must be large.

Section 11.3 began by considering statistical inference for comparing two population proportions from independent samples.

To perform these tests, $n\hat{p}(1 - \hat{p})$ must be greater than or equal to 10 for each population, and each sample size can be no more than 5% of the population size. The distribution of $\hat{p}_1 - \hat{p}_2$ is approximately normal, with mean $p_1 - p_2$ and standard deviation $\sqrt{\dfrac{p_1(1 - p_1)}{n_1} + \dfrac{p_2(1 - p_2)}{n_2}}$. If the samples are dependent, we use McNemar's Test.

In Section 11.4, we discussed inference for comparing two population standard deviations. We used the F-test, but require that both populations be normally distributed. This test is not robust, so if the data show any departures from normality, the test should not be used.

To help determine which test to use, we included the flow chart in Figure 23.

Vocabulary

Independent (p. 583)
Dependent (p. 583)
Matched pairs (p. 583)

Robust (p. 585)
Welch's approximate t (p. 596)
Pooled t-statistic (p. 602)

Pooled estimate of p (p. 609)
McNemar's Test (p. 614)
F-distribution (p. 622)

Formulas

- Test statistic for matched-pairs data:

$$t_0 = \frac{\bar{d} - \mu_d}{\dfrac{s_d}{\sqrt{n}}}$$

where $\bar{d}$ is the mean and s_d is the standard deviation of the differenced data

- Confidence interval for matched-pairs data:

Lower bound: $\bar{d} - t_{\frac{\alpha}{2}} \cdot \dfrac{s_d}{\sqrt{n}}$

Upper bound: $\bar{d} + t_{\frac{\alpha}{2}} \cdot \dfrac{s_d}{\sqrt{n}}$

- Test statistic comparing two means (independent sampling):

$$t_0 = \frac{(\bar{x}_1 - \bar{x}_2) - (\mu_1 - \mu_2)}{\sqrt{\dfrac{s_1^2}{n_1} + \dfrac{s_2^2}{n_2}}}$$

- Confidence interval for the difference of two means (independent samples):

Lower bound: $(\bar{x}_1 - \bar{x}_2) - t_{\frac{\alpha}{2}} \cdot \sqrt{\dfrac{s_1^2}{n_1} + \dfrac{s_2^2}{n_2}}$

Upper bound: $(\bar{x}_1 - \bar{x}_2) + t_{\frac{\alpha}{2}} \cdot \sqrt{\dfrac{s_1^2}{n_1} + \dfrac{s_2^2}{n_2}}$

- Test statistic comparing two population proportions (independent sampling)

$$z_0 = \frac{\hat{p}_1 - \hat{p}_2 - (p_1 - p_2)}{\sqrt{\hat{p}(1 - \hat{p})}\sqrt{\dfrac{1}{n_1} + \dfrac{1}{n_2}}}$$

where $\hat{p} = \dfrac{x_1 + x_2}{n_1 + n_2}$

- Confidence interval for the difference of two proportions (independent sampling)

Lower bound: $(\hat{p}_1 - \hat{p}_2) - z_{\frac{\alpha}{2}} \cdot \sqrt{\dfrac{\hat{p}_1(1 - \hat{p}_1)}{n_1} + \dfrac{\hat{p}_2(1 - \hat{p}_2)}{n_2}}$

Upper bound: $(\hat{p}_1 - \hat{p}_2) + z_{\frac{\alpha}{2}} \cdot \sqrt{\dfrac{\hat{p}_1(1 - \hat{p}_1)}{n_1} + \dfrac{\hat{p}_2(1 - \hat{p}_2)}{n_2}}$

- Test statistic comparing two population proportions (dependent sampling)

$$z_0 = \frac{|f_{12} - f_{21}| - 1}{\sqrt{f_{12} + f_{21}}}$$

- Sample size for estimating $p_1 - p_2$

$$n = n_1 = n_2 = [\hat{p}_1(1 - \hat{p}_1) + \hat{p}_2(1 - \hat{p}_2)]\left(\frac{z_{\alpha/2}}{E}\right)^2$$

$$n = n_1 = n_2 = 0.5\left(\frac{z_{\alpha/2}}{E}\right)^2$$

- Finding a critical F for the left tail

$$F_{1-\alpha,\, n_1-1,\, n_2-1} = \frac{1}{F_{\alpha,\, n_2-1,\, n_1-1}}$$

- Test statistic for comparing two population standard deviations:

$$F_0 = \frac{s_1^2}{s_2^2}$$

Objectives

Section	You should be able to . . .	Examples	Review Exercises
11.1	1 Distinguish between independent and dependent sampling (p. 583)	1	1, 2, 8(a), 9(a)
	2 Test hypotheses regarding matched-pairs data (p. 584)	2 and 3	4(c), 8(b)
	3 Construct and interpret confidence intervals for the population mean difference of matched-pairs data (p. 589)	4	4(d), 14
11.2	1 Test hypotheses regarding the difference of two independent means (p. 596)	1 and 2	5(a), 6(a), 9(b)
	2 Construct and interpret confidence intervals regarding the difference of two independent means (p. 601)	3	5(b), 15
11.3	1 Test hypotheses regarding two population proportions (p. 609)	1 and 2	7, 10(a)
	2 Construct and interpret confidence intervals for the difference between two population proportions (p. 613)	3	10(b)
	3 Use McNemar's Test to compare two proportions from matched-pairs data (p. 614)	4	11
	4 Determine the sample size necessary for estimating the difference between two population proportions within a specified margin of error (p. 617)	5	12
11.4	1 Find critical values of the F-distribution (p. 621)	1	3
	2 Test hypotheses regarding two population standard deviations (p. 624)	2 and 3	5(c), 6(b), 13
11.5	1 Determine the appropriate hypothesis test to perform (p. 632)		4–11; 13–15

Review Exercises

In Problems 1 and 2, determine if the sampling is dependent or independent.

1. A researcher wants to know if the mean length of stay in for-profit hospitals is different from the mean length of stay in not-for-profit hospitals. He randomly selected 20 individuals in the for-profit hospital and matched them with 20 individuals in the not-for-profit hospital by diagnosis. *Dependent*

2. An urban economist believes that commute times to work in the South are less than commute times to work in the Midwest. He randomly selects 40 employed individuals in the South and 45 employed individuals in the Midwest and determines their commute times. *Independent*

3. (a) Find the critical F-value for a right-tailed test with $\alpha = 0.05$, degrees of freedom in the numerator = 8, and degrees of freedom in the denominator = 9. *3.23*
(b) Find the critical F-value for a two-tailed test with $\alpha = 0.05$, degrees of freedom in the numerator = 10, and degrees of freedom in the denominator = 5. *0.24, 6.62*

In Problem 4, assume that the paired differences come from a population that is normally distributed.

4.

Observation	1	2	3	4	5	6
X_i	34.2	32.1	39.5	41.8	45.1	38.4
Y_i	34.9	31.5	39.5	41.9	45.5	38.8

(a) Compute $d_i = X_i - Y_i$ for each pair of data.
(b) Compute $\bar{d}$ and s_d. *$\bar{d} = -0.167$, $s_d = 0.450$*
(c) Test the hypothesis that $\mu_d < 0$ at the $\alpha = 0.05$ level of significance. *Do not reject H_0*
(d) Compute a 98% confidence interval for the population mean difference μ_d. *$(-0.79, 0.45)$*

In Problems 5 and 6, assume that the populations are normally distributed and that independent sampling occurred.

5.

	Population 1	Population 2
n	13	8
$\bar{x}$	32.4	28.2
s	4.5	3.8

5. (b) (0.73, 7.67)

(a) Test the hypothesis that $\mu_1 \neq \mu_2$ at the $\alpha = 0.1$ level of significance for the given sample data.   Reject H_0
(b) Construct a 90% confidence interval for $\mu_1 - \mu_2$.
(c) Test the hypothesis that $\sigma_1 \neq \sigma_2$ at the $\alpha = 0.05$ level of significance for the given sample data.   Do not reject H_0

6.

	Population 1	Population 2
n	45	41
$\overline{x}$	48.2	45.2
s	8.4	10.3

(a) Test the hypothesis that $\mu_1 > \mu_2$ at the $\alpha = 0.01$ level of significance for the given sample data.   Do not reject H_0
(b) Test the hypothesis that $\sigma_1 < \sigma_2$ at the $\alpha = 0.01$ level of significance for the given sample data.   Do not reject H_0

7. A random sample of $n_1 = 555$ individuals results in $x_1 = 451$ successes. An independent sample of $n_2 = 600$ individuals results in $x_2 = 510$ successes. Does this represent sufficient evidence to conclude that $p_1 \neq p_2$ at the $\alpha = 0.05$ level of significance?   Do not reject H_0

8. **Height versus Arm Span** A statistics student heard that an individual's arm span is equal to the individual's height. To test this hypothesis, the student used a random sample of 10 students and obtained the following data.

Student:	1	2	3	4	5
Height (inches)	59.5	69	77	59.5	74.5
Arm span (inches)	62	65.5	76	63	74
Student:	6	7	8	9	10
Height (inches)	63	61.5	67.5	73	69
Arm span (inches)	66	61	69	70	71

Source: John Climent, Cecil Community College

(a) Is the sampling method dependent or independent? Why?   Dependent
(b) Does the sample evidence contradict the belief that an individual's height and arm span are the same at the $\alpha = 0.05$ level of significance?

Note: A normal probability plot indicates that the data and differenced data are normally distributed. A boxplot indicates that the data and differenced data have no outliers.   Do not reject H_0

9. **McDonald's versus Wendy's** A student wanted to determine whether the wait time in the drive-through at McDonald's differed from that at Wendy's. She used a random sample of 30 cars at McDonald's and 27 cars at Wendy's and obtained these results:

Wait Time at McDonald's Drive-Through (seconds)				
151.09	227.38	111.84	131.21	128.75
191.60	126.91	137.90	195.44	246.59
141.78	127.35	121.21	101.03	95.09
122.06	122.62	100.04	71.37	153.34
140.44	126.62	116.72	131.69	100.94
115.66	147.28	81.43	86.31	156.34

Wait Time at Wendy's Drive-Through (seconds)				
281.90	71.02	204.29	128.59	133.56
187.53	199.86	190.91	110.55	110.64
196.84	233.65	171.01	182.54	183.79
284.48	363.34	270.82	390.50	471.62
123.66	174.43	385.90	386.71	155.53
203.62	119.61			

Source: Catherine M. Simmons, student at Joliet Junior College

9. (a) Independent

Note: The sample size for Wendy's is less than 30. However, the data do not contain any outliers, so the Central Limit Theorem can be used.

(a) Is the sampling method dependent or independent?
(b) Is there a difference in wait times at each restaurant's drive-through? Use the $\alpha = 0.1$ level of significance.   Reject H_0
(c) Draw boxplots of each data set using the same scale. Does this visual evidence support the results obtained in part (b)?   Yes

10. **Treatment for Osteoporosis** Osteoporosis is a condition in which people experience decreased bone mass and an increase in the risk of bone fracture. Actonel is a drug that helps combat osteoporosis in postmenopausal women. In clinical trials, 1,374 postmenopausal women were randomly divided into experimental and control groups. The subjects in the experimental group were administered 5 milligrams (mg) of Actonel, while the subjects in the control group were administered a placebo. The number of women who experienced a bone fracture over the course of 1 year was recorded. Of the 696 women in the experimental group, 27 experienced a fracture during the course of the year. Of the 678 women in the control group, 49 experienced a fracture during the course of the year.

(a) Test the hypothesis that a lower proportion of women in the experimental group experienced a bone fracture than the women in the control group at the $\alpha = 0.01$ level of significance.   Reject H_0
(b) Construct a 95% confidence interval for the difference between the two population proportions, $p_{exp} - p_{control}$.
(c) What type of experimental design is this? What are the treatments?
(d) The experiment was double-blind. What does this mean?

11. **Obligations to Vote and Serve** In the General Social Survey, individuals were asked whether civic duty included voting and whether it included serving on a jury. The results of the survey are shown in the table. Is there a difference in the proportion of individuals who feel jury duty is a civic duty and the proportion of individuals who feel voting is a civic duty? Use the $\alpha = 0.10$ level of significance.   Do not reject H_0

		Jury	
		Duty (success)	Not Duty (failure)
Voting	Duty (success)	1,322	65
	Not duty (failure)	45	17

10. (b) $(-0.06, -0.01)$ 10. (c) Completely randomized design; placebo and Actonel

12. Determining Sample Size A nutritionist wants to estimate the difference between the percentage of men and women who have high cholesterol. What sample size should be obtained if she wishes the estimate to be within 2 percentage points with 90% confidence, assuming that
  (a) she uses the 1994 estimates of 18.8% male and 20.5% female from the National Center for Health Statistics? 2,136
  (b) she does not use any prior estimates? 3,383

13. Wait Time Using the data from Problem 9, test whether the standard deviation of wait time at Wendy's is more than that at McDonald's at the $\alpha = 0.05$ level of significance. Reject H_0

14. Height versus Arm Span Construct and interpret a 95% confidence interval for the population mean difference between height and arm span using the data from Problem 8. What does the interval lead us to conclude regarding any differences between height and arm span? (−1.37, 2.17)

15. McDonald's versus Wendy's Construct and interpret a 95% confidence interval about $\mu_M - \mu_W$ using the data from Problem 9. How might a marketing executive with McDonald's use this information? (−128.868, −42.218)

CHAPTER TEST

In Problems 1 and 2, determine whether the sampling method is independent or dependent.

1. A stock analyst wants to know if there is a difference between the mean rate of return from energy stocks and that from financial stocks. He randomly selects 13 energy stocks and computes the rate of return for the past year. He randomly selects 13 financial stocks and computes the rate of return for the past year. Independent

2. A prison warden wants to know if men receive longer sentences for crimes than women. He randomly samples 30 men and matches them with 30 women by type of crime committed and records their lengths of sentence. Dependent

In Problem 3, assume that the paired differences come from a population that is normally distributed.

3.

Observation	1	2	3	4	5	6	7
X_i	18.5	21.8	19.4	22.9	18.3	20.2	23.1
Y_i	18.3	22.3	19.2	22.3	18.9	20.7	23.9

  (a) Compute $d_i = X_i - Y_i$ for each pair of data.
  (b) Compute $\overline{d}$ and s_d. $\overline{d} = -0.2$, $s_d = 0.526$
  (c) Test the hypothesis that $\mu_d \neq 0$ at the $\alpha = 0.01$ level of significance. Do not reject H_0
  (d) Compute a 95% confidence interval for the population mean difference μ_d. (−0.69, 0.29)

In Problems 4 and 5, assume that the populations are normally distributed and that independent sampling occurred.

4.

	Population 1	Population 2
n	24	27
$\overline{x}$	104.2	110.4
s	12.3	8.7

  (a) Test the hypothesis that $\mu_1 \neq \mu_2$ at the $\alpha = 0.1$ level of significance for the given sample data. Reject H_0
  (b) Construct a 95% confidence interval for $\mu_1 - \mu_2$.
  (c) Test the hypothesis that $\sigma_1 > \sigma_2$ at the $\alpha = 0.1$ level of significance for the given sample data. Reject H_0

4. (b) (−12.44, 0.04)

5.

	Population 1	Population 2
n	13	8
$\overline{x}$	96.6	98.3
s	3.2	2.5

  (a) Test the hypothesis that $\mu_1 < \mu_2$ at the $\alpha = 0.05$ level of significance for the given sample data. Do not reject H_0
  (b) Test the hypothesis that $\sigma_1 \neq \sigma_2$ at the $\alpha = 0.05$ level of significance for the given sample data. Do not reject H_0

6. A random sample of $n_1 = 650$ individuals results in $x_1 = 156$ successes. An independent sample of $n_2 = 550$ individuals results in $x_2 = 143$ successes. Does this represent sufficient evidence to conclude that $p_1 < p_2$ at the $\alpha = 0.05$ level of significance? Do not reject H_0

7. A researcher wants to know whether the acidity of rain (pH) near Houston, Texas, is significantly different from that near Chicago, Illinois. He randomly selects 12 rain dates in Texas and 14 rain dates in Illinois and obtains the following data:

Texas					
4.69	5.10	5.22	4.46	4.93	4.65
5.22	4.76	4.25	5.14	4.11	4.71

Illinois						
4.40	4.69	4.22	4.64	4.54	4.35	4.69
4.40	4.75	4.63	4.45	4.49	4.36	4.52

Source: National Atmospheric Deposition Program

  (a) Is the sampling method dependent or independent? Why? Independent
  (b) Because the sample sizes are small, what must be true regarding the populations from which the samples were drawn? Normal
  (c) Draw side-by-side boxplots of the data. What does the visual evidence imply about the pH of rain in the two states?
  (d) Does the evidence suggest that there is a difference in the pH of rain in Chicago and Houston? Use the $\alpha = 0.05$ level of significance. Yes

8. Laparoscopic gastric bypass surgery reduces the size of the stomach and can cause malabsorption of nutrients, leading to weight loss according to webmd.com. Researchers wanted to determine whether body mass index (BMI) reduction is significantly greater than zero 10 months after surgery. They selected 110 patients who elected to have laparoscopic gastric bypass surgery and measured their BMI prior to surgery. After 10 months, they again measured the BMI. The mean reduction in BMI in the 110 patients was found to be 12.61 with a standard deviation of 4.90.   8. (a) Matched-pairs design

   Source: Shawn D. St. Peter, et al., "Impact of Advanced Age on Weight Loss and Health Benefits after Laparoscopic Gastric Bypass." *Archives of Surgery*, 140(2): 2005

   (a) What type of experimental design is this? Why?
   (b) Does the evidence suggest that the BMI reduction is greater than zero at the $\alpha = 0.05$ level of significance?   Reject H_0
   (c) Construct a 90% confidence interval for the mean BMI reduction after laparoscopic gastric bypass surgery. Write a sentence that a doctor could read to his or her patients that explains the expected BMI reduction 10 months after the surgery.   (11.834, 13.386)

9. Zoloft is a drug used to treat obsessive–compulsive disorder (OCD). In randomized, double-blind clinical trials, 926 patients diagnosed with OCD were randomly divided into two groups. Subjects in group 1 (experimental group) received 200 milligrams per day (mg/day) of Zoloft, while subjects in group 2 (control group) received a placebo. Of the 553 subjects in the experimental group, 77 experienced dry mouth as a side effect. Of the 373 subjects in the control group, 34 experienced dry mouth as a side effect.
   (a) What type of experimental design is this?
   (b) What is the response variable?
   (c) Do a higher proportion of subjects experience dry mouth who are taking Zoloft versus the proportion taking the placebo? Use the $\alpha = 0.05$ level of significance.   Yes

10. Does hypnotism result in a different success rate for men and women who are trying to quit smoking? Researchers at *Science* magazine analyzed studies involving 5,600 male and female smokers. Of the 2,800 females, 644 quit smoking; of the 2,800 males, 840 quit smoking. Construct a 90% confidence interval for the difference in proportion of males and females, $p_M - p_F$, and use the interval to judge whether there is a difference in the proportions.   (0.051, 0.089); reject H_0

11. The General Social Survey asked the following two questions of randomly selected individuals.

- Do you favor or oppose the death penalty for persons convicted of murder?
- Should it be possible for a woman to obtain a legal abortion?

   The results of the survey are given in the table. Is there a difference in the proportion who favor the death penalty and favor abortion? Use $\alpha = 0.01$ level of significance.   Reject H_0

	Favor Death Penalty	Oppose Death Penalty
Favor abortion	7,956	2,549
Oppose abortion	11,685	4,272

12. A researcher wants to estimate the difference between the percentage of individuals without a high school diploma who smoke and the percentage of individuals with bachelor's degrees who smoke. What sample size should be obtained if she wishes the estimate to be within 4 percentage points with 95% confidence, assuming that
   (a) she uses the 1999 estimates of 32.2% of those without a high school diploma and 11.1% of those with a bachelor's degree from the National Center for Health Statistics?   762
   (b) she does not use any prior estimates?   1,201

13. It is commonplace to gain weight after quitting smoking. Does the drug Naltrexone help limit weight gain when individuals quit smoking? To determine the effectiveness of this drug, 147 subjects who smoked 20 or more cigarettes daily were randomly divided into two groups. Everyone received a 21-milligram (mg) transdermal nicotine patch (to curb nicotine cravings while trying to quit smoking). Seventy-two subjects also received a placebo, while 75 received 25 mg of Naltrexone. After 6 weeks, the placebo subjects had a mean weight gain of 1.9 kg, with a standard deviation of 0.22 kg; the Naltrexone subjects had a mean weight gain of 0.8 kg with a standard deviation of 0.21 kg. Construct a 95% confidence interval for the mean difference in weight gain for the two groups. Based on this interval, do you believe that Naltrexone is effective in controlling weight gain following smoking cessation? Do the results have any practical significance.   (1.03, 1.17); reject H_0

   Source: Stephanie O'Malley et al. "A Controlled Trial of Naltrexone Augmentation of Nicotine Replacement Therapy for Smoking Cessation." *Archives of Internal Medicine*, Vol. 166, 667–674

14. Using the data from Problem 7, test whether the standard deviation of acidity in the rain near Houston, Texas, is different from that near Chicago, Illinois, at the $\alpha = 0.05$ level of significance.   Reject H_0

9. (a) Completely randomized design   9. (b) Whether the subject gets dry mouth or not

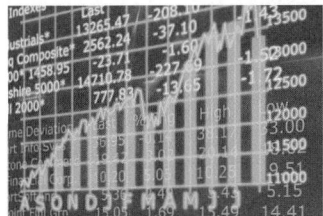

MAKING AN
INFORMED DECISION

Where Should I Invest?

You have just received an inheritance of $10,000 and you decide that you should invest the money rather than blow it on frivolous items. You have decided that you will invest the money in one of two types of mutual funds. The first type that you are considering follows a *large-value* approach to investing. This means that the mutual fund invests only in large, established companies that are considered to be a good bargain. The second type follows a *large-growth* approach to investing. This means that the mutual fund invests in large companies that are experiencing solid revenue growth. To make an informed decision, you decide to research the rate of return for the past 3 years for each type of mutual fund. The mutual fund must have a Morningstar rating of four or five stars.

The Morningstar mutual-fund rating system ranks mutual funds, using one to five stars. The stars divide the mutual-fund performances into quintiles; that is, a mutual fund with a one-star rating is in the bottom 20% of mutual funds in its category, a mutual fund with a two-star rating has an investment performance between the 21st and 40th percentile, and so on. These data can be found at www.morningstar.com or screen.yahoo.com/funds.html.

(a) Obtain a simple random sample of at least 15 mutual funds for each investment category. Determine the 3-year rate of return for each fund.

(b) Verify that the 3-year rates of return come from a population that is normally distributed. Also, verify that the data have no outliers. If the data do not come from a population that is normally distributed, you will have to increase the sample size so that the Central Limit Theorem can be used.

(c) Construct a boxplot for the rate of return for each fund category using the same scale. Which investment category, if any, seems superior?

(d) Obtain a 95% confidence interval for the difference between the mean rates of return. Interpret the interval.

(e) Write a report that details which investment category seems to be superior.

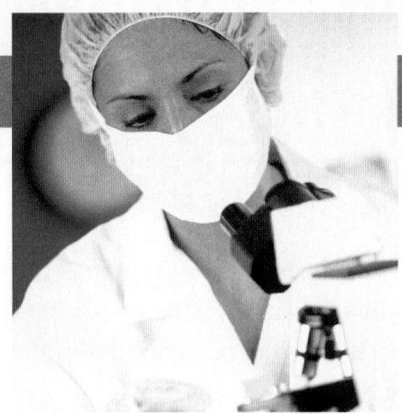

Control in the Design of an Experiment

Dr. Penelope Nicholls is interested in exploring a possible connection between high plasma homocysteine (a toxic amino acid created by the body as it metabolizes protein) levels and cardiac hypertrophy (enlargement of the heart) in humans. Because there are many complex relationships among human characteristics, it will be difficult to answer her research question because there is a significant risk that confounding factors will cloud her inferences. She wants to be sure that any differences in cardiac hypertrophy are due to high plasma homocysteine levels and not to other factors. Consequently, she needs to design her experiment carefully so that she controls lurking variables to the extent possible. Therefore, she decides to design a two-sample experiment with independent sampling: one group will be the experimental group, the other a control group. Knowing that many factors can affect the degree of cardiac hypertrophy (the response variable), Dr. Nicholls controls these factors by randomly assigning the experimental units to the experimental or control group. She hopes the randomization will result in both groups having similar characteristics.

In her preliminary literature review, Dr. Nicholls uncovered an article in which the authors hypothesized that there might be a relationship between high plasma homocysteine levels in patients with end-stage renal disease (ESRD) and cardiac hypertrophy. She has asked you, as her assistant, to review this article.

Upon reading the article, you discover that the authors used a nonrandom process to select a control and an ESRD group. The researchers enlisted 75 stable ESRD patients into their study. All these patients were on hemodialysis for between 6 and 312 months. The control group subjects were chosen so as to eliminate any intergroup differences in terms of mean blood pressure (BP) and gender. In an effort to minimize situational contaminants, all physical and biochemical measurements were made after an overnight fast. The results of the clinical characteristics and the biochemical findings for the control and ESRD groups are reproduced in the following tables:

Clinical Characteristics (Mean ± Standard Deviation)		
Parameters	**Controls ($n = 57$)**	**ESRD Subjects ($n = 75$)**
Age (years)	49.2 ± 14.7	57.3 ± 15.1
Sex (M/F ratio)	1.4 ± 0.50	1.4 ± 0.50
Body surface area (m^2)	1.85 ± 0.25	1.67 ± 0.20
Body mass index (kg/m^2)	26.0 ± 4.70	23.7 ± 3.90
Systolic BP (mmHg)	145.0 ± 15.5	148.8 ± 29.7
Diastolic BP (mmHg)	85.0 ± 14.8	80.2 ± 14.3
Mean BP (mmHg)	104.5 ± 14.2	103.6 ± 17.4
Pulse pressure (mmHg)	59.4 ± 15.5	68.6 ± 24.3
Heart rate (beats/min)	63.0 ± 8.0	70.0 ± 9.0

Biological Findings (Mean ± Standard Deviation)		
Parameters	**Controls ($n = 57$)**	**ESRD Subjects ($n = 75$)**
Total cholesterol (mmol/L)	5.28 ± 1.04	4.91 ± 1.06
HDL cholesterol (mmol/L)	1.38 ± 0.39	1.07 ± 0.38
Triglycerides (mmol/L)	1.39 ± 0.63	1.90 ± 1.02
Serum albumin (g/L)	44.7 ± 2.60	39.9 ± 3.00
Plasma fibrinogen (g/L)	3.21 ± 0.78	4.75 ± 1.04
Plasma creatinine (mmol/L)	0.10 ± 0.01	0.90 ± 0.13
Blood urea (mmol/L)	6.10 ± 1.20	24.3 ± 2.00
Calcium (mmol/L)	2.46 ± 0.08	2.45 ± 0.12
Phosphates (mmol/L)	1.03 ± 0.21	1.88 ± 0.38

Source: Jacques Blacher et al., "Association between Plasma Homocysteine Concentrations and Cardiac Hypertrophy in End-Stage Renal Disease." *Journal of Nephrology* 12(4): 248–255, 1999. Article available at www.sin_italia.org/jnonline/vol12n4/blacher/blacher.htm.

Which type of sampling method, independent or dependent, was used in this experiment? Explain.

Using the appropriate hypothesis-testing procedure, determine whether the control and ESRD groups have equivalent population means for each of the various clinical and biochemical parameters. Dr. Nicholls requires that you indicate those parameters that have P-values less than 0.05 and those less than 0.01.

Detail any assumptions and the rationale behind making them that you made while carrying out your analysis. Is there any additional information that you would like to have? Explain. Are there any additional statistical procedures that you think might be useful for analyzing these data? Explain.

Based on your findings, does it appear that the control and ESRD groups have similar initial clinical characteristics and biochemical findings? Does it appear that the authors of this article were successful in reducing the likelihood that a confounding effect would obscure their results?

Even though Dr. Nicholls does not wish to restrict her research to patients with end-stage renal disease, how might the information presented for this research assist her in designing her own experiment?

Submit a written report to Dr. Nicholls that outlines all your findings and recommendations.

Inference on Categorical Data

Outline

12.1 Goodness-of-Fit Test

12.2 Tests for Independence and the Homogeneity of Proportions

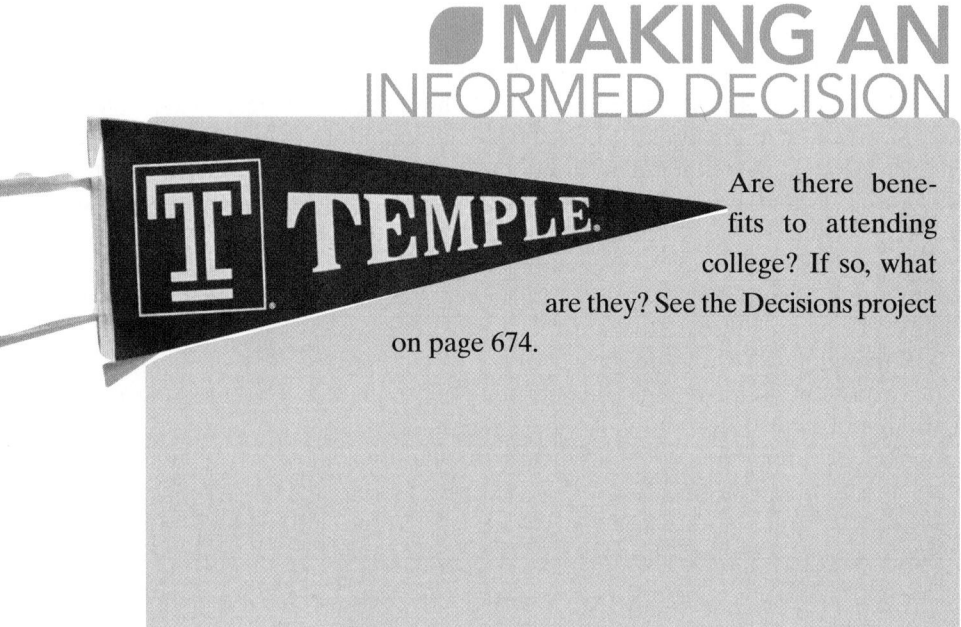

MAKING AN INFORMED DECISION

Are there benefits to attending college? If so, what are they? See the Decisions project on page 674.

PUTTING IT TOGETHER

In Chapters 9 through 11, we introduced statistical methods that can be used to test hypotheses regarding a population parameter such as μ or σ.

Often, however, rather than being interested in testing a hypothesis regarding a parameter of a probability distribution, we are interested in testing a hypothesis regarding the entire probability distribution. For example, we might wish to test if the distribution of colors in a bag of plain M&M candies is 13% brown, 14% yellow, 13% red, 20% orange, 24% blue, and 16% green. We introduce methods for testing hypotheses such as this in Section 12.1.

In Section 12.2, we discuss a method that can be used to determine whether two qualitative variables are independent based on a sample. If they are not independent, the value of one variable affects the value of the other variable, so the variables are somehow related. We conclude Section 12.2 by introducing tests for homogeneity. This procedure is used to compare proportions from two or more populations. It is an extension of the two-sample z-test for proportions from independent samples discussed in Section 11.3.

12.1 GOODNESS-OF-FIT TEST

Preparing for This Section   Before getting started, review the following:

- Mutually exclusive (Section 5.2, p. 274)
- Mean of a binomial random variable (Section 6.2, pp. 334–336)
- Expected value (Section 6.1, pp. 336–337)
- Chi-square distribution (Section 9.4, pp. 496–499)

Objective   **1**   Perform a goodness-of-fit test

---

1   **Perform a Goodness-of-Fit Test**

In this section, we present a procedure that can be used to test hypotheses regarding a probability distribution. For example, we might want to test whether the distribution of plain M&M candies in a bag is 13% brown, 14% yellow, 13% red, 20% orange, 24% blue, and 16% green. Or we might want to test whether the number of hits a player gets in his next four at-bats follows a binomial distribution with $n = 4$ and $p = 0.298$.

The methods for testing these types of hypotheses use the chi-square distribution, introduced in Section 9.4. Recall the following properties of the chi-square distribution.

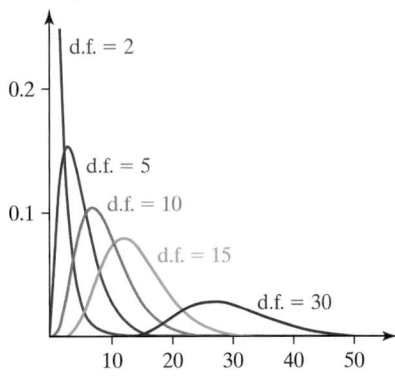

Note to Instructor
If you have not introduced the chi-square distribution, be sure to cover it now.

Note to Instructor
If you like, you can print out and distribute the Preparing for This Section quiz located in the Instructor's Resource Center. The purpose of the quiz is to verify that the students have the prerequisite knowledge for the section.

> **Characteristics of the Chi-Square Distribution**
>
> **1.** It is not symmetric.
> **2.** The shape of the chi-square distribution depends on the degrees of freedom, just like Student's t-distribution.
> **3.** As the number of degrees of freedom increases, the chi-square distribution becomes more symmetric, as illustrated in Figure 1.
> **4.** The values of χ^2 are nonnegative. That is, the values of χ^2 are greater than or equal to 0.

The critical values of the chi-square distribution can be found in Table VII.

Definition   A **goodness-of-fit test** is an inferential procedure used to determine whether a frequency distribution follows a specific distribution.

Figure 1
Chi-square distributions

As an example, we might want to test if a die is fair. This would mean the probability of each outcome is $\dfrac{1}{6}$ when a die is cast. Because we give the die the benefit of the doubt (that is, assume that the die is fair), we express the null hypothesis as:

$$H_0\colon p_1 = p_2 = p_3 = p_4 = p_5 = p_6 = \frac{1}{6}$$

Here's another example: According to the U.S. Census Bureau in 2000, 19.0% of the population of the United States resided in the Northeast, 22.9% resided in the Midwest, 35.6% resided in the South, and 22.5% resided in the West. We might want to test if the distribution of U.S. residents is the same today as it was in 2000. Remember, the null hypothesis is a statement of "no change," so for this situation, the null hypothesis is

H_0: The distribution of residents in the United States is the same today as it was in 2000.

The idea behind testing these types of hypotheses is to compare the actual number of observations for each category of data with the number of observations we would expect if the null hypothesis were true. If a significant difference exists between the observed counts and expected counts, we have evidence against the null hypothesis.

The method for obtaining the **expected counts** is an extension of the expected value of a binomial random variable. Recall that the mean (and therefore expected value) of a binomial random variable with n independent trials and probability of success, p, is given by $E = \mu = np$.

In Other Words

The expected count for each category is the number of trials of the experiment times the probability of success in the category.

Expected Counts

Suppose that there are n independent trials of an experiment with $k \geq 3$ mutually exclusive possible outcomes. Let p_1 represent the probability of observing the first outcome and E_1 represent the expected count of the first outcome; p_2 represent the probability of observing the second outcome and E_2 represent the expected count of the second outcome; and so on. The expected counts for each possible outcome are given by

$$E_i = \mu_i = np_i \quad \text{for} \quad i = 1, 2, \ldots, k$$

EXAMPLE 1 **Finding Expected Counts**

Problem: An urban economist wishes to determine whether the distribution of residents in the United States is the same today as it was in 2000. That year, 19.0% of the population of the United States resided in the Northeast, 22.9% resided in the Midwest, 35.6% resided in the South, and 22.5% resided in the West (based on data obtained from the Census Bureau). If the economist randomly selects 1,500 households in the United States, compute the expected number of households in each region, assuming that the distribution of households did not change from 2000.

Approach

Step 1: Determine the probabilities for each outcome.

Step 2: There are $n = 1,500$ trials (the 1,500 households surveyed) of the experiment. We expect $np_{\text{Northeast}}$ of the households surveyed to reside in the Northeast, np_{Midwest} of the households to reside in the Midwest, and so on.

Solution

Step 1: The probabilities are the relative frequencies from the 2000 distribution: $p_{\text{Northeast}} = 0.190$, $p_{\text{Midwest}} = 0.229$, $p_{\text{South}} = 0.356$, and $p_{\text{West}} = 0.225$.

Step 2: The expected counts for each location within the United States are as follows:

Expected count of Northeast: $np_{\text{Northeast}} = 1,500(0.190) = 285$

Expected count of Midwest: $np_{\text{Midwest}} = 1,500(0.229) = 343.5$

Expected count of South: $np_{\text{South}} = 1,500(0.356) = 534$

Expected count of West: $np_{\text{West}} = 1,500(0.225) = 337.5$

Of the 1,500 households surveyed, the economist expects to have 285 households in the Northeast, 343.5 households in the Midwest, 534 households in the South, and 337.5 households in the West if the distribution of residents of the United States is the same today as it was in 2000.

Historical Note

The goodness-of-fit test was invented by Karl Pearson (the Pearson of correlation coefficient fame). Pearson believed that statistics should be done by determining the distribution of a random variable. Such a determination could be made only by looking at large numbers of data. This philosophy caused Pearson to "butt heads" with Ronald Fisher, because Fisher believed in analyzing small samples.

Now Work Problem 5

To conduct a hypothesis test, we compare the observed counts with the expected counts. If the observed counts are significantly different from the expected counts, we have evidence against the null hypothesis. To perform this test, we need a test statistic and sampling distribution.

CAUTION Goodness-of-fit tests are used to test hypotheses regarding the distribution of a variable based on a single population. If you wish to compare two or more populations, you must use the tests for homogeneity presented in Section 12.2.

Test Statistic for Goodness-of-Fit Tests

Let O_i represent the observed counts of category i, E_i represent the expected counts of category i, k represent the number of categories, and n represent the number of independent trials of an experiment. Then the formula

$$\chi^2 = \sum \frac{(O_i - E_i)^2}{E_i} \qquad i = 1, 2, \ldots, k$$

approximately follows the chi-square distribution with $k - 1$ degrees of freedom, provided that

1. all expected frequencies are greater than or equal to 1 (all $E_i \geq 1$) and

2. no more than 20% of the expected frequencies are less than 5.

Note: $E_i = np_i$ for $i = 1, 2, \ldots, k$.

From Example 1, there were $k = 4$ categories (Northeast, Midwest, South, and West). For the Northeast, the expected frequency, E, is 285.

Now that we know the distribution of goodness-of-fit tests, we can present a method for testing hypotheses regarding the distribution of a random variable.

The Goodness-of-Fit Test

To test hypotheses regarding a distribution, we use the steps that follow.

Step 1: Determine the null and alternative hypotheses:

H_0: The random variable follows a certain distribution.
H_1: The random variable does not follow a certain distribution.

Step 2: Decide on a level of significance, α, depending on the seriousness of making a Type I error.

Step 3

(a) Calculate the expected counts for each of the k categories. The expected counts are $E_i = np_i$ for $i = 1, 2, \ldots, k$, where n is the number of trials and p_i is the probability of the ith category, assuming that the null hypothesis is true.

(b) Verify that the requirements for the goodness-of-fit test are satisfied.

1. All expected counts are greater than or equal to 1 (all $E_i \geq 1$).

2. No more than 20% of the expected counts are less than 5.

CAUTION If the requirements in Step 3(b) are not satisfied, one option is to combine two or more of the low-frequency categories into a single category.

(c) Compute the **test statistic**:

$$\chi_0^2 = \sum \frac{(O_i - E_i)^2}{E_i}$$

Note: O_i is the observed count for the ith category.

Classical Approach

Step 4: Determine the critical value. All goodness-of-fit tests are right-tailed tests, so the critical value is χ_α^2 with $k - 1$ degrees of freedom. See Figure 2.

Figure 2

χ_α^2
(critical value)

Critical Region
Area = α

P-Value Approach

Step 4: Use Table VII to obtain an approximate P-value by determining the area under the chi-square distribution with $k - 1$ degrees of freedom to the right of the test statistic. See Figure 3.

Figure 3

P-value

χ_0^2

Step 5: Compare the critical value to the test statistic. If $\chi_0^2 > \chi_\alpha^2$, reject the null hypothesis.

Step 5: If the *P*-value $< \alpha$, reject the null hypothesis.

Step 6: State the conclusion.

EXAMPLE 2 | **Conducting a Goodness-of-Fit Test**

Table 1	
Region	**Frequency**
Northeast	274
Midwest	303
South	564
West	359

Problem: An urban economist wonders if the distribution of U.S. residents in the United States is different today than it was in 2000. In 2000, 19.0% of the population of the United States resided in the Northeast, 22.9% resided in the Midwest, 35.6% resided in the South, and 22.5% resided in the West (based on data obtained from the Census Bureau). The economist randomly selects 1,500 households in the United States and obtains the frequency distribution shown in Table 1.

Does the evidence suggest that the distribution of residents in the United States is different today from the distribution in 2000 at the $\alpha = 0.05$ level of significance?

Approach: We follow Steps 1 through 6 just listed.

Solution

Step 1: We want to know if the distribution of residents is different today from the distribution in 2000. The null hypothesis is a statement of "no difference." Here, this means no difference between 2000 and today. We need the evidence (sample data) to show that the distribution is different today.

H_0: The distribution of residents of the United States is the same today as it was in 2000.

Table 2		
Region	**Observed Counts**	**Expected Counts**
Northeast	274	285
Midwest	303	343.5
South	564	534
West	359	337.5

H_1: The distribution of residents of the United States is different today from what it was in 2000.

Step 2: The level of significance is $\alpha = 0.05$.

Step 3:

(a) The expected counts were computed in Example 1. For convenience, we show the observed and expected counts in Table 2.

(b) Since all expected counts are greater than or equal to 5, the requirements for the goodness-of-fit test are satisfied.

(c) The test statistic is

$$\chi_0^2 = \sum \frac{(O_i - E_i)^2}{E_i} = \frac{(274 - 285)^2}{285} + \frac{(303 - 343.5)^2}{343.5} + \frac{(564 - 534)^2}{534} + \frac{(359 - 337.5)^2}{337.5}$$
$$= 8.255$$

Classical Approach

Step 4: There are $k = 4$ categories, so we find the critical value using $4 - 1 = 3$ degrees of freedom. The critical value is $\chi_{0.05}^2 = 7.815$. See Figure 4.

Figure 4

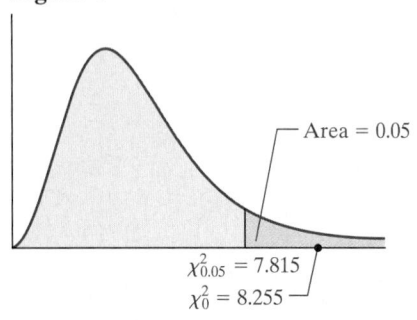

$\chi_{0.05}^2 = 7.815$
$\chi_0^2 = 8.255$

Area = 0.05

P-Value Approach

Step 4: There are $k = 4$ categories. The *P*-value is the area under the chi-square distribution with $4 - 1 = 3$ degrees of freedom to the right of $\chi_0^2 = 8.255$, as shown in Figure 5.

Figure 5

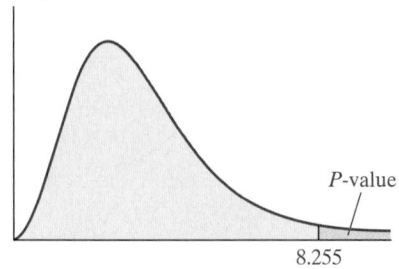

P-value

8.255

Step 5: Because the test statistic, 8.255, is greater than the critical value, 7.815, we reject the null hypothesis.

Using Table VII, we find the row that corresponds to 3 degrees of freedom. The value of 8.255 lies between 7.815 and 9.348. The area under the chi-square distribution (with 3 degrees of freedom) to the right of 7.815 is 0.05. The area under the chi-square distribution to the right of 9.348 is 0.025. Because 8.255 is between 7.815 and 9.348, the P-value is between 0.025 and 0.05. So $0.025 < P\text{-value} < 0.05$.

Step 5: Because the P-value is less than the level of significance, $\alpha = 0.05$, we reject the null hypothesis.

Step 6: There is sufficient evidence at the $\alpha = 0.05$ level of significance to conclude that the distribution of United States residents today is different from the distribution in 2000.

If we compare the observed and expected counts, we notice that the Northeast and Midwest regions of the United States have observed counts lower than expected, while the South and West regions of the United States have observed counts higher than expected. So, we might conclude that residents of the United States are moving to southern and western locations.

EXAMPLE 3 **Conducting a Goodness-of-Fit Test Using Technology**

Problem: Conduct the goodness-of-fit test for the problem described in Example 2.

Approach: We will use MINITAB to perform the goodness-of-fit test. The steps for performing goodness-of-fit tests using the TI-84 Plus graphing calculator, MINITAB, and Excel are given in the Technology Step-by-Step on page 656.

We enter the categories of data in C1, the observed counts in C2, and expected proportions, assuming no change, in C3.

Solution: Figure 6 shows the results from MINITAB.

Figure 6 **Chi-Square Goodness-of-Fit Test for Observed Counts in Variable: C2**

```
Using category names in C1
                           Test                   Contribution
Category   Observed   Proportion   Expected       to Chi-Sq
Northeast       274        0.190      285.0          0.42456
Midwest         303        0.229      343.5          4.77511
South           564        0.356      534.0          1.68539
West            359        0.225      337.5          1.36963

   N   DF   Chi-Sq   P-Value
1500    3  8.25469     0.041
```

Interpretation: The P-value is 0.041. We would only expect to get the results we obtained in about 4 samples in 100 samples if the statement in the null hypothesis were true. The results observed are unusual under the assumption that the distribution has not changed, so we conclude that the distribution did change. Based on the observed and expected counts, we can see that fewer than expected individuals live in the Midwest and Northeast, and more than expected live in the South and West.

Now Work Problem 11

In the next example, each of the k categories is equally likely.

EXAMPLE 4   **Conducting a Goodness-of-Fit Test**

Problem: An obstetrician wants to know whether or not the proportions of children born on each day of the week are the same. She randomly selects 500 birth records and obtains the data shown in Table 3 (based on data obtained from *Vital Statistics of the United States*, 2006).

Is there reason to believe that the day on which a child is born occurs with equal frequency at the $\alpha = 0.01$ level of significance?

Approach: We follow Steps 1 through 6 presented on pages 647–648.

Solution

Step 1: The null hypothesis is a statement of "no difference." So, we assume that the day on which a child is born occurs with equal frequency. If we let 1 represent Sunday, 2 represent Monday, and so on, we can express this as $p_1 = p_2 = \cdots = p_7 = \dfrac{1}{7}$. Thus, we have

$$H_0: p_1 = p_2 = p_3 = p_4 = p_5 = p_6 = p_7 = \frac{1}{7}$$

H_1: At least one of the proportions is different from the others.

Step 2: The level of significance is $\alpha = 0.01$.

Step 3

(a) The expected counts for each category (day of the week), assuming the null hypothesis is true, are shown in Table 4.

Table 3

Day of Week	Frequency
Sunday	57
Monday	78
Tuesday	74
Wednesday	76
Thursday	71
Friday	81
Saturday	63

Table 4

Day of the Week	Frequency (observed count)	Assumed Probability	Expected Count
Sunday	57	$\dfrac{1}{7}$	$500\left(\dfrac{1}{7}\right) = \dfrac{500}{7}$
Monday	78	$\dfrac{1}{7}$	$\dfrac{500}{7}$
Tuesday	74	$\dfrac{1}{7}$	$\dfrac{500}{7}$
Wednesday	76	$\dfrac{1}{7}$	$\dfrac{500}{7}$
Thursday	71	$\dfrac{1}{7}$	$\dfrac{500}{7}$
Friday	81	$\dfrac{1}{7}$	$\dfrac{500}{7}$
Saturday	63	$\dfrac{1}{7}$	$\dfrac{500}{7}$

(b) Since all expected counts are greater than or equal to 5 $\left(\dfrac{500}{7} \approx 71.4\right)$, the requirements for the goodness-of-fit test are satisfied.

(c) The test statistic is

$$\chi_0^2 = \frac{(57 - 500/7)^2}{500/7} + \frac{(78 - 500/7)^2}{500/7} + \frac{(74 - 500/7)^2}{500/7} + \frac{(76 - 500/7)^2}{500/7}$$

$$+ \frac{(71 - 500/7)^2}{500/7} + \frac{(81 - 500/7)^2}{500/7} + \frac{(63 - 500/7)^2}{500/7} = 6.184$$

Classical Approach

Step 4: There are $k = 7$ categories, so we find the critical value using $7 - 1 = 6$ degrees of freedom. The critical value is $\chi^2_{0.01} = 16.812$. See Figure 7.

Figure 7

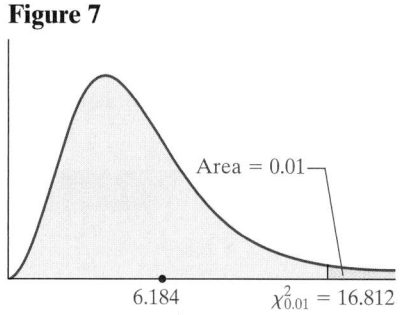

Area = 0.01

6.184 $\chi^2_{0.01} = 16.812$

Step 5: Because the test statistic, 6.184, is less than the critical value, 16.812, we do not reject the null hypothesis.

P-Value Approach

Step 4: There are $k = 7$ categories. The *P*-value is the area under the chi-square distribution with $7 - 1 = 6$ degrees of freedom to the right of $\chi^2_0 = 6.184$, as shown in Figure 8.

Figure 8

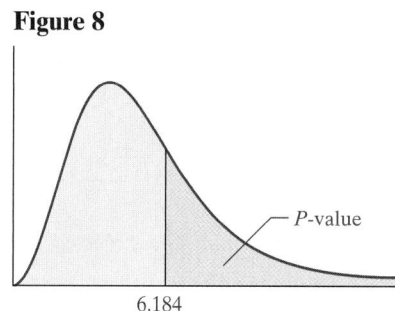

P-value

6.184

Using Table VII, we find the row that corresponds to 6 degrees of freedom. The value of 6.184 is less than 10.645, which has an area under the chi-square distribution of 0.10 to the right, so the *P*-value is greater than 0.1 (*P*-value > 0.10).

Step 5: Because the *P*-value is greater than the level of significance, $\alpha = 0.01$, we do not reject the null hypothesis.

Step 6: There is not sufficient evidence at the $\alpha = 0.01$ level of significance to reject the belief that the day of the week on which a child is born occurs with equal frequency.

Now Work Problem 21

IN CLASS ACTIVITY

If the Candy Fits—Eat It

Researchers can sometimes help determine or refute the authorship of a text or play by looking at the distribution of word lengths and sentence lengths. On a tastier note, could you determine the type of M&M candy (plain, peanut, and so on) just by knowing the distribution of colors in the bag?

(a) Each student should purchase a bag of M&Ms that are either plain, peanut, almond, crispy, or peanut butter. Make sure the bag is large enough to obtain a decent sample size.

(b) At home, record the number of each color from your bag (ignore broken candies).

(c) In class, give your data to your partner and see if he or she can determine which type of candy you purchased while you try to determine his or her type.

(d) Compare your results to the rest of the class. Were there types that were harder to distinguish? Why do you think this was the case?

[**Note:** Actual distributions can be found at us.mms.com/us/about/products].

12.1 ASSESS YOUR UNDERSTANDING

Concepts and Vocabulary

1. Why is goodness of fit a good choice for the title of the procedures used in this section?

2. Explain why chi-square goodness-of-fit tests are always right tailed.

3. State the requirements to perform a goodness-of-fit test.

4. If the expected count of a category is less than 1, what can be done to the categories so that a goodness-of-fit test can still be performed?

Skill Building

In Problems 5 and 6, determine the expected counts for each outcome.

5.

$n = 500$				
p_i	0.2	0.1	0.45	0.25
Expected counts	100	50	225	125

6.

$n = 700$				
p_i	0.15	0.3	0.35	0.20
Expected counts	105	210	245	140

In Problems 7–10, determine (a) the χ^2 test statistic, (b) the degrees of freedom, and (c) the critical value using $\alpha = 0.05$, and (d) test the hypothesis at the $\alpha = 0.05$ level of significance.

7. $H_0: p_A = p_B = p_C = p_D = \dfrac{1}{4}$

H_1: At least one of the proportions is different from the others. Do not reject H_0

Outcome	A	B	C	D
Observed	30	20	28	22
Expected	25	25	25	25

8. $H_0: p_A = p_B = p_C = p_D = p_E = \dfrac{1}{5}$

H_1: At least one of the proportions is different from the others. Do not reject H_0

Outcome	A	B	C	D	E
Observed	38	45	41	33	43
Expected	40	40	40	40	40

9. H_0: The random variable X is binomial with $n = 4$, $p = 0.8$
H_1: The random variable X is not binomial with $n = 4$, $p = 0.8$ Reject H_0

X	0	1	2	3	4
Observed	1	38	132	440	389
Expected	1.6	25.6	153.6	409.6	409.6

10. H_0: The random variable X is binomial with $n = 4$, $p = 0.3$
H_1: The random variable X is not binomial with $n = 4$, $p = 0.3$ Reject H_0

X	0	1	2	3	4
Observed	260	400	280	50	10
Expected	240.1	411.6	264.6	75.6	8.1

Applying the Concepts

11. **Plain M&Ms** According to the manufacturer of M&Ms, 13% of the plain M&Ms in a bag should be brown, 14% yellow, 13% red, 24% blue, 20% orange, and 16% green. A student randomly selected a bag of plain M&Ms. He counted the number of M&Ms that were each color and obtained the results shown in the table. Test whether plain M&Ms follow the distribution stated by M&M/Mars at the $\alpha = 0.05$ level of significance. Reject H_0

Color	Frequency
Brown	61
Yellow	64
Red	54
Blue	61
Orange	96
Green	64

12. **Peanut M&Ms** According to the manufacturer of M&Ms, 12% of the peanut M&Ms in a bag should be brown, 15% yellow, 12% red, 23% blue, 23% orange, and 15% green. A student randomly selected a bag of peanut M&Ms. He counted the number of M&Ms that were each color and obtained the results shown in the table. Test whether peanut M&Ms follow the distribution stated by M&M/Mars at the $\alpha = 0.05$ level of significance. Do not reject H_0

Color	Frequency
Brown	53
Yellow	66
Red	38
Blue	96
Orange	88
Green	59

13. **Benford's Law, Part I** Our number system consists of the digits 0, 1, 2, 3, 4, 5, 6, 7, 8, and 9. The first significant digit in any number must be 1, 2, 3, 4, 5, 6, 7, 8, or 9 because we do not write numbers such as 12 as 012. Although we may think that each digit appears with equal frequency so that each digit has a $\dfrac{1}{9}$ probability of being the first significant digit, this is not true. In 1881, Simon Newcomb discovered that first digits do not occur with equal frequency. This same result was discovered again in 1938 by physicist Frank Benford. After studying much data, he was able to assign probabilities of occurrence to the first digit in a number as shown.

Digit	1	2	3	4	5
Probability	0.301	0.176	0.125	0.097	0.079

Digit	6	7	8	9	
Probability	0.067	0.058	0.051	0.046	

Source: T. P. Hill, "The First Digit Phenomenon," *American Scientist*, July–August, 1998.

The probability distribution is now known as Benford's Law and plays a major role in identifying fraudulent data on tax returns and accounting books. For example, the following distribution represents the first digits in 200 allegedly fraudulent checks written to a bogus company by an employee attempting to embezzle funds from his employer.

First digit	1	2	3	4	5	6	7	8	9
Frequency	36	32	28	26	23	17	15	16	7

Source: State of Arizona vs. Wayne James Nelson

(a) Because these data are meant to prove that someone is guilty of fraud, what would be an appropriate level of significance when performing a goodness-of-fit test?

(b) Using the level of significance chosen in part (a), test whether the first digits in the allegedly fraudulent checks obey Benford's Law. Reject H_0

(c) Based on the results of part (b), do you think that the employee is guilty of embezzlement? Yes

14. Benford's Law, Part II Refer to Problem 13. The following distribution lists the first digit of the surface area (in square miles) of 335 rivers. Is there evidence at the $\alpha = 0.05$ level of significance to support the belief that the distribution follows Benford's Law? Yes

First digit	1	2	3	4	5	6	7	8	9
Frequency	104	55	36	38	24	29	18	14	17

Source: Eric W. Weisstein, Benford's Law, from *MathWorld*—A Wolfram Web Resource.

15. Always Wear a Helmet The National Highway Traffic Safety Administration publishes reports about motorcycle fatalities and helmet use. The distribution shows the proportion of fatalities by location of injury for motorcycle accidents.

Location of injury	Multiple Locations	Head	Neck	Thorax	Abdomen/ Lumbar/ Spine
Proportion	0.57	0.31	0.03	0.06	0.03

The data below show the location of injury and fatalities for 2068 riders not wearing a helmet.

Location of injury	Multiple Locations	Head	Neck	Thorax	Abdomen/ Lumbar/ Spine
Number	1036	864	38	83	47

(a) Does the distribution of fatal injuries for riders not wearing a helmet follow the distribution for all riders? Use the $\alpha = 0.05$ level of significance. No; reject H_0

(b) Compare observed and expected counts for each category. What does this information tell you?

16. Weapon of Choice Nationally, the distribution of weapons used in robberies is as shown in the table.

Weapon	Gun	Knife	Strong-arm	Other
Proportion	0.42	0.09	0.40	0.09

Source: Federal Bureau of Investigation

The following data represent the weapon of choice in 1652 robberies on school property.

Weapon	Gun	Knife	Strong-arm	Other
Proportion	329	122	857	344

(a) Does the distribution of weapon choice in robberies in schools follow the national distribution? Use the $\alpha = 0.05$ level of significance. No; reject H_0

(b) Compare observed and expected counts for each category. What does this information tell you?

17. Does It Matter Where I Sit? Does the location of your seat in a classroom play a role in attendance or grade? To answer this question, Professors Katherine Perkins and Carl Wieman randomly assigned 400 students* in a general education physics course to one of four groups.

Source: Perkins, Katherine K. and Wieman, Carl E, "The Surprising Impact of Seat Location on Student Performance" *The Physics Teacher*, Vol. 43, Jan. 2005.

The 100 students in group 1 sat 0 to 4 meters from the front of the class, the 100 students in group 2 sat 4 to 6.5 meters from the front, the 100 students in group 3 sat 6.5 to 9 meters from the front, and the 100 students in group 4 sat 9 to 12 meters from the front.

(a) For the first half of the semester, the attendance for the whole class averaged 83%. So, if there is no effect due to seat location, we would expect 83% of students in each group to attend. The data show the attendance history for each group. How many students in each group attended, on average? Is there a significant difference among the groups in attendance patterns? Use the $\alpha = 0.05$ level of significance. 84, 84, 84, 81; no

Group	1	2	3	4
Attendance	0.84	0.84	0.84	0.81

(b) For the second half of the semester, the groups were rotated so that group 1 students moved to the back of class and group 4 students moved to the front. The same switch took place between groups 2 and 3. The attendance for the second half of the semester averaged 80%. The data show the attendance records for the original groups (group 1 is now in back, group 2 is 6.5 to 9 meters from the front, and so on). How many students in each group attended, on average? Is there a significant difference in attendance patterns? Use the $\alpha = 0.05$ level of significance. Do you find anything curious about these data? 84, 81, 78, 76; no

Group	1	2	3	4
Attendance	0.84	0.81	0.78	0.76

(c) At the end of the semester, the proportion of students in the top 20% of the class was determined. Of the students in group 1, 25% were in the top 20%; of the students in group 2, 20% were in the top 20%; of the students in group 3, 15% were in the top 20%; of the students in group 4, 19% were in the top 20%. How many students would we expect to be in the top 20% of the class if seat location plays no role in grades? Is there a significant difference in the number of students in the top 20% of the class by group? 20 in each group; no

(d) In earlier sections, we discussed results that were statistically significant, but did not have any practical significance. Discuss the practical significance of these results. In other words, given the choice, would you prefer sitting in the front, or back? Front

18. Racial Profiling On January 1, 2004, it became mandatory for all police departments in Illinois to record data pertaining to race from every traffic stop. The village of Mundelein,

*The number of students was increased so that goodness-of-fit procedures could be used.

Illinois, has been collecting data since 2000. Rather than using census data to determine the racial distribution of the village, they thought it better to use data based on who is using the roads in Mundelein. So, they collected data on at-fault drivers involved in car accidents in the village (the implicit assumption here is that race is independent of fault in a crash) and obtained the following distribution of race for users of roads in Mundelein.

Race	White	African American	Hispanic	Asian
Proportion	0.719	0.028	0.207	0.046

Source: Village of Mundelein, Illinois

The following data represent the races of all 9,868 drivers who were stopped for a moving violation in the village of Mundelein in 2005.

Race	White	African American	Hispanic	Asian
Proportion	7,079	273	2,025	491

Source: Village of Mundelein, Illinois

(a) Does the distribution of race in traffic stops reflect the distribution of drivers in Mundelein? In other words, is there any evidence of racial profiling in Mundelein? Use the $\alpha = 0.05$ level of significance. Yes; no discrimination
(b) Compare observed and expected counts for each category. What does this information tell you?

19. **Are Some Months Busier than Others?** A researcher wants to know whether the distribution of birth month is uniform. The following data, based on results obtained from *Vital Statistics of the United States*, 2005, Volume 1, represent the distribution of months in which 500 randomly selected children were born:

Month	Frequency	Month	Frequency
January	40	July	45
February	38	August	44
March	41	September	44
April	40	October	43
May	42	November	39
June	41	December	43

Is there reason to believe that each birth month occurs with equal frequency at the $\alpha = 0.05$ level of significance?
Do not reject H_0

20. **Bicycle Deaths** A researcher wanted to determine whether bicycle deaths were uniformly distributed over the days of the week. She randomly selected 200 deaths that involved a bicycle, recorded the day of the week on which the death occurred, and obtained the following results (the data are based on information obtained from the Insurance Institute for Highway Safety).

Day of the Week	Frequency	Day of the Week	Frequency
Sunday	16	Thursday	34
Monday	35	Friday	41
Tuesday	16	Saturday	30
Wednesday	28		

Is there reason to believe that bicycle fatalities occur with equal frequency with respect to day of the week at the $\alpha = 0.05$ level of significance? Reject H_0

21. **Pedestrian Deaths** A researcher wanted to determine whether pedestrian deaths were uniformly distributed over the days of the week. She randomly selected 300 pedestrian deaths, recorded the day of the week on which the death occurred, and obtained the following results (the data are based on information obtained from the Insurance Institute for Highway Safety).

Day of the Week	Frequency	Day of the Week	Frequency
Sunday	39	Thursday	41
Monday	40	Friday	49
Tuesday	30	Saturday	61
Wednesday	40		

Test the belief that the day of the week on which a fatality happens involving a pedestrian occurs with equal frequency at the $\alpha = 0.05$ level of significance. Reject H_0

22. **Is the Die Loaded?** A player in a craps game suspects that one of the dice being used in the game is loaded. A loaded die is one in which not all the possibilities (1, 2, 3, 4, 5, and 6) are equally likely. The player throws the die 400 times, records the outcome after each throw, and obtains the following results:

Outcome	Frequency	Outcome	Frequency
1	62	4	62
2	76	5	57
3	76	6	67

(a) Do you think that the die is loaded? Use the $\alpha = 0.01$ level of significance. Do not reject H_0
(b) Why do you think the player might conduct the test at the $\alpha = 0.01$ level of significance rather than, say, the $\alpha = 0.1$ level of significance?

23. **Home Schooling** A school social worker wants to determine if the grade distribution of home-schooled children is different in her district than nationally. The U.S. National Center for Education Statistics provided her with the following data, which represent the relative frequency of home-schooled children by grade level.

Grade	Relative Frequency
K	0.076
1–3	0.253
4–5	0.158
6–8	0.235
9–12	0.278

She obtains a sample of 25 home-schooled children within her district that yields the following data:

Grade	Frequency
K	6
1–3	9
4–5	3
6–8	4
9–12	3

(a) Because of the low cell counts, combine cells into three categories K–3, 4–8, and 9–12.

(b) Is the grade distribution of home-schooled children different in her district from the national grade distribution at the $\alpha = 0.05$ level of significance? *Reject H_0*

24. **Golden Benford** The Fibonacci sequence is a famous sequence of numbers whose elements commonly occur in nature. The terms in the Fibonacci sequence are 1, 1, 2, 3, 5, 8, 13, 21, ... The ratio of consecutive terms approaches the golden ratio, $\Phi = \dfrac{1 + \sqrt{5}}{2}$. For the first digit of the first 85 terms in the Fibonacci sequence, the distribution is as shown in the following table:

Digit	1	2	3	4	5	6	7	8	9
Frequency	25	16	11	7	7	5	4	6	4

Is there evidence to support the belief that the first digit of the Fibonacci numbers follow the Benford distribution (shown in Problem 13) at the $\alpha = 0.05$ level of significance? *Do not reject H_0*

25. **Testing the Random-Number Generator** Statistical software and graphing calculators with advanced statistical features use random-number generators to create random numbers conforming to a specified distribution.

(a) Use a random-number generator to create a list of 500 randomly selected integers numbered 1 to 5.

(b) What proportion of the numbers generated should be 1? 2? 3? 4? 5?

(c) Test whether the random-number generator is generating random integers between 1 and 5 with equal likelihood by performing a chi-square goodness-of-fit test at the $\alpha = 0.01$ level of significance.

26. **Testing the Random-Number Generator** Statistical software and graphing calculators with advanced statistical features use random-number generators to create random numbers conforming to a specified distribution.

(a) Use a random-number generator to create a list of 500 trials of a binomial experiment with $n = 5$ and $p = 0.2$.

(b) What proportion of the numbers generated should be 0? 1? 2? 3? 4? 5?

(c) Test whether the random-number generator is generating random outcomes of a binomial experiment with $n = 5$ and $p = 0.2$ by performing a chi-square goodness-of-fit test at the $\alpha = 0.01$ level of significance.

In Section 10.4, we tested hypotheses regarding a population proportion using a z-test. However, we can also use the chi-square goodness-of-fit test to test hypotheses with $k = 2$ possible outcomes. In Problems 27 and 28, we test hypotheses with the use of both methods.

27. **Low Birth Weight** According to the U.S. Census Bureau, 7.1% of all babies born are of low birth weight (<5 lb, 8 oz). An obstetrician wanted to know whether mothers between the ages of 35 and 39 years give birth to a higher percentage of low-birth-weight babies. She randomly selected 240 births for which the mother was 35 to 39 years old and found 22 low-birth-weight babies.

(a) If the proportion of low-birth-weight babies for mothers in this age group is 0.071, compute the expected number of low-birth-weight births to 35- to 39-year-old mothers. What is the expected number of births to mothers 35 to 39 years old that are not low birth weight? *17.04; 222.96*

(b) Answer the obstetrician's question at the $\alpha = 0.05$ level of significance using the chi-square goodness-of-fit test. *Do not reject H_0*

(c) Answer the question by using the approach presented in Section 10.4. *Do not reject H_0*

28. **Living Alone?** In 2000, 25.8% of Americans 15 years of age or older lived alone, according to the Census Bureau. A sociologist who believes that this percentage is greater today, conducts a random sample of 400 Americans 15 years of age or older, and finds that 164 are living alone.

(a) If the proportion of Americans aged 15 years or older living alone is 0.258, compute the following expected numbers: Americans 15 years of age or older who live alone; Americans 15 years of age or older who do not live alone. *103.2; 296.8*

(b) Test the sociologist's belief at the $\alpha = 0.05$ level of significance using the goodness-of-fit test. *Reject H_0*

(c) Test the belief by using the approach presented in Section 10.4. *Reject H_0*

29. **Putting It Together: The V-2 Rocket in London** In Thomas Pynchon's book *Gravity Rainbow*, the characters discuss whether the Poisson probabilistic model can be used to describe the locations that Germany's feared V-2 rocket would land in. They divided London into 0.25-km^2 regions. They then counted the number of rockets that landed in each region, with the following results:

Number of rockets	0	1	2	3	4	5	6	7
Observed number of hits in each region	229	211	93	35	7	0	0	1

Source: Lawrence Lesser. "Even More Fun Learning Statisitcs." *Stats: The Magazine for Students of Statistics*, Issue 49.

(a) Estimate the mean number of rocket hits in a region by computing $\mu = \sum xP(x)$. Round your answer to four decimal places. *0.9323*

(b) Explain why the requirements for conducting a goodness-of-fit test are not satisfied.

(c) After consolidating the table, we obtain the following distribution for rocket hits. Using the Poisson probability model, $P(x) = \dfrac{\mu^x}{x!} e^{-\mu}$, where μ is the mean from part (a), we can obtain the probability distribution for the number of rocket hits. Find the probability of 0 hits in a region. Then find the probability of 1 hit, 2 hits, 3 hits, and 4 or more hits. *0.3936, 0.3670, 0.1711, 0.0532, 0.0151*

Number of rocket hits	0	1	2	3	4 or more
Observed number of hits in each region	229	211	93	35	8

(d) A total of $n = 576$ rockets was fired. Determine the expected number of hits in a region by computing "expected number of hits" $= np$, where p is the probability of observing that particular number of hits in the region.

(e) Conduct a goodness-of-fit test for the distribution using the $\alpha = 0.05$ level of significance. Do the rockets appear to be modeled by a Poisson random variable? *Yes*

29. (b) *All expected counts should be ≥1*

TECHNOLOGY STEP-BY-STEP   Goodness-of-Fit Test

TI-84 Plus*
1. Enter the observed counts in L1 and enter the expected counts in L2.
2. Press STAT, highlight TESTS, and select D: χ^2-GOF-Test....
3. Enter L1 after Observed:, and enter L2 after Expected: Enter the appropriate degrees of freedom following df:. Highlight either Calculate or Draw and press ENTER.

MINITAB
1. Enter the observed counts in column C1. Enter expected proportions or counts, assuming that the null hypothesis is true, in column C2, if necessary.
2. Select the **Stat** menu, highlight **Tables**, then highlight **Chi-square Goodness-of-Fit Test (One Variable)** . . . .
3. Select the Observed Counts radio button and enter C1 in the cell. If you are testing equal proportions, select this radio button. If you entered expected proportions in C2, select the "Specific

proportions" radio button and enter C2. If you entered expected counts in C2, select the "Proportions specified by historical counts" radio button and enter C2. Click OK.

Excel
1. Load the DDXL Add-in.
2. Enter the category names in column A. Enter the observed counts in column B, and enter the proportions used to formulate expected counts in column C. Highlight all three columns.
3. Select the **DDXL** menu; highlight **Tables**.
4. From the pull-down menu, select Goodness of Fit. Select the column that contains category names and press the ◄ corresponding to Category Names. Select the column that contains the observed counts and press the ◄ corresponding to Observed Counts. Select the column that contains the proportions used to formulate expected counts and press the ◄ corresponding to Test Distribution. Click OK.

*The TI-83 and older TI-84 Plus graphing calculators do not have this capability.

12.2 TESTS FOR INDEPENDENCE AND THE HOMOGENEITY OF PROPORTIONS

Preparing for This Section   Before getting started, review the following:

- The language of hypothesis tests (Section 10.1, pp. 515–521)
- Independent events (Section 5.3, pp. 286–287)
- Contingency Tables and Association (Section 4.4, pp. 238–244)
- Mean of a binomial random variable (Section 6.2, pp. 334–336)
- Testing a hypothesis about two population proportions (Section 11.3, pp. 609–613)

| **Objectives** | **1** | Perform a test for independence |
| | **2** | Perform a test for homogeneity of proportions |

In Section 4.4, we discussed the association between two variables by examining the relative frequency marginal distributions. In this section, we develop methods for performing statistical inference on two categorical variables to determine whether there is any association between the two variables. We call the method the *chi-square test for independence*.

1 Perform a Test for Independence

We begin with a definition.

Definition The **chi-square test for independence** is used to determine whether there is an association between a row variable and column variable in a contingency table constructed from sample data. The null hypothesis is that the variables are not associated; in other words, they are independent. The alternative hypothesis is that the variables are associated, or dependent.

In Other Words
In a chi-square independence test, the null hypothesis is always

   H_0: The variables are independent

The alternative hypothesis is always

   H_1: The variables are not independent

The idea behind testing these types of hypotheses is to compare actual counts to the counts we would expect if the null hypothesis were true (if the variables are independent). If a significant difference between the actual counts and expected counts exists, we take this as evidence against the null hypothesis.

The method for obtaining the expected counts requires that we compute the number of observations expected within each cell under the assumption that the null hypothesis is true. Recall, if two events E and F are independent, then $P(E \text{ and } F) = P(E) \cdot P(F)$. We can use the Multiplication Rule for independent events to obtain the expected proportion of observations within each cell under the assumption of independence. We then multiply this result by n, the sample size, to obtain the expected count within each cell.* We present an example to introduce the method for obtaining expected counts.

EXAMPLE 1   **Determining the Expected Counts in a Test for Independence**

Problem: Is there a relationship between marital status and happiness? The data in Table 5 show the marital status and happiness of individuals who participated in the General Social Survey in 2006. Compute the expected counts within each cell, assuming that marital status and happiness are independent.

Table 5

		Married	Widowed	Divorced/Separated	Never Married
		Marital Status			
Happiness	**Very Happy**	600	63	112	144
	Pretty Happy	720	142	355	459
	Not Too Happy	93	51	119	127

Approach

Step 1: Compute the row and column totals.

Step 2: Compute the relative marginal frequencies for the row variable and column variable.

Step 3: Use the Multiplication Rule for Independent Events to compute the expected proportion of observations within each cell under the assumption of independence.

Step 4: Multiply the proportions by 2985, the sample size, to obtain the expected counts within each cell.

Solution

Step 1: The row totals (blue) and column totals (red) are presented in Table 6.

Table 6

		Married	Widowed	Divorced/Separated	Never Married	Row Totals
		Marital Status				
Happiness	**Very Happy**	600	63	112	144	919
	Pretty Happy	720	142	355	459	1676
	Not Too Happy	93	51	119	127	390
	Column Totals	1413	256	586	730	2985

Step 2: The relative marginal frequencies for the row variable (happiness) and column variable (marital status) are presented in Table 7.

---

*Recall that the expected value of a binomial random variable for n independent trials of a binomial experiment with probability of success p is given by $E = \mu = np$.

Table 7

| | | \multicolumn{5}{c}{**Marital Status**} |
		Married	**Widowed**	**Divorced/Separated**	**Never Married**	**Relative Frequency**
Happiness	**Very Happy**	600	63	112	144	$\frac{919}{2985} \approx 0.308$
	Pretty Happy	720	142	355	459	$\frac{1676}{2985} \approx 0.561$
	Not Too Happy	93	51	119	127	$\frac{390}{2985} \approx 0.131$
	Relative Frequency	$\frac{1413}{2985} \approx 0.473$	$\frac{256}{2985} \approx 0.086$	$\frac{586}{2985} \approx 0.196$	$\frac{730}{2985} \approx 0.245$	1

Step 3: Assuming that happiness and marital status are independent, we use the Multiplication Rule for Independent Events to compute the proportion of observations we would expect in each cell. For example, the proportion of individuals who are "very happy" and "married" would be

$$\binom{\text{Proportion "very happy"}}{\text{and "married"}} = (\text{proportion "very happy"}) \cdot (\text{proportion "married"})$$

$$= \left(\frac{1413}{2985}\right)\left(\frac{919}{2985}\right)$$

$$= 0.145737$$

Table 8 contains the expected proportion in each cell, under the assumption of independence.

Table 8

| | | \multicolumn{4}{c}{**Marital Status**} |
		Married	**Widowed**	**Divorced/Separated**	**Never Married**
Happiness	**Very Happy**	0.145737	0.026404	0.060440	0.075292
	Pretty Happy	0.265783	0.048153	0.110226	0.137312
	Not Too Happy	0.061847	0.011205	0.025649	0.031952

Step 4: We multiply the expected proportions in Table 8 by 2985, the sample size, to obtain the expected counts under the assumption of independence. The results are presented in Table 9.

Table 9

| | | \multicolumn{4}{c}{**Marital Status**} |
		Married	**Widowed**	**Divorced/Separated**	**Never Married**
Happiness	**Very Happy**	2985(0.145737) = 435.025	2985(0.026404) = 78.816	2985(0.060440) = 180.413	2985(0.075292) = 224.747
	Pretty Happy	793.362	143.737	329.025	409.876
	Not Too Happy	184.613	33.447	76.562	95.377

If happiness and marital status are independent, we would expect a random sample of 2985 individuals to contain about 435 who are "very happy" and "married."

The technique used in Example 1 to find the expected counts might seem rather tedious. It certainly would be more pleasant if we could determine a shortcut formula that could be used to obtain the expected counts. Let's consider the expected count for "very happy" and "married." This expected count was obtained by multiplying the proportion of individuals who are "very happy," the proportion of individuals who are "married," and the number of individuals in the sample. That is,

Expected count = (proportion "very happy")(proportion "married")(sample size)

$$= \frac{919}{2985} \cdot \frac{1413}{2985} \cdot 2985$$

$$= \frac{919 \cdot 1413}{2985} \qquad \text{Cancel the 2985s}$$

$$= \frac{(\text{row total for happiness})(\text{column total for marital status})}{\text{table total}}$$

This leads to the following general result:

Expected Frequencies in a Chi-Square Test for Independence

To find the expected frequencies in a cell when performing a chi-square independence test, multiply the row total of the row containing the cell by the column total of the column containing the cell and divide this result by the table total. That is,

$$\text{Expected frequency} = \frac{(\text{row total})(\text{column total})}{\text{table total}} \qquad (1)$$

For example, to calculate the expected frequency for "very happy and married," we compute

$$\text{Expected frequency} = \frac{(\text{row total})(\text{column total})}{\text{table total}} = \frac{(919)(1413)}{2985} = 435.024$$

This result is close to that obtained in Table 9 (the difference exists because of rounding error; in fact, 435.024 is more accurate).

Now Work Problem 7(a)

To test hypotheses regarding the independence of two variables, we compare the actual (observed) counts to those expected. If the observed counts are significantly different from the expected counts, we take this as evidence against the null hypothesis. We need a test statistic and sampling distribution to test the hypotheses.

Test Statistic for the Test of Independence

Let O_i represent the observed number of counts in the ith cell and E_i represent the expected number of counts in the ith cell. Then

$$\chi^2 = \sum \frac{(O_i - E_i)^2}{E_i}$$

approximately follows the chi-square distribution with $(r - 1)(c - 1)$ degrees of freedom, where r is the number of rows and c is the number of columns in the contingency table, provided that (1) all expected frequencies are greater than or equal to 1 and (2) no more than 20% of the expected frequencies are less than 5.

From Example 1, there were $r = 3$ rows and $c = 4$ columns.

We now present a method for testing hypotheses regarding the association between two variables in a contingency table.

Chi-Square Test for Independence

To test the association between (or independence of) two variables in a contingency table, we use the steps that follow:

Step 1: Determine the null and alternative hypotheses.

H_0: The row variable and column variable are independent.
H_1: The row variable and column variable are dependent.

Step 2: Choose a level of significance, α, depending on the seriousness of making a Type I error.

Step 3

(a) Calculate the expected frequencies (counts) for each cell in the contingency table using Formula (1).

(b) Verify that the requirements for the chi-square test for independence are satisfied:

    1. All expected frequencies are greater than or equal to 1 (all $E_i \geq 1$).

    2. No more than 20% of the expected frequencies are less than 5.

(c) Compute the **test statistic**:

$$\chi_0^2 = \sum \frac{(O_i - E_i)^2}{E_i}$$

Note: O_i is the observed frequency for the ith category.

Classical Approach

Step 4: Determine the critical value. All chi-square tests for independence are right-tailed tests, so the critical value is χ_α^2 with $(r-1)(c-1)$ degrees of freedom, where r is the number of rows and c is the number of columns in the contingency table. See Figure 9.

Figure 9

Critical Region Area = α

χ_α^2
(critical value)

Step 5: Compare the critical value to the test statistic. If $\chi_0^2 > \chi_\alpha^2$, reject the null hypothesis.

P-Value Approach

Step 4: Use Table VII to determine an approximate P-value by determining the area under the chi-square distribution with $(r-1)(c-1)$ degrees of freedom to the right of the test statistic, where r is the number of rows and c is the number of columns in the contingency table. See Figure 10.

Figure 10

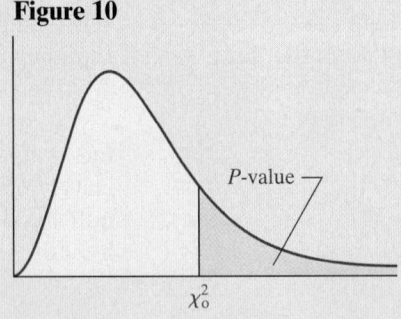

P-value

χ_0^2

Step 5: If the P-value $< \alpha$, reject the null hypothesis.

Step 6: State the conclusion.

EXAMPLE 2   Performing a Chi-Square Test for Independence

Problem: Is there a relationship between marital status and happiness? In the 2006 General Social Survey, 2985 randomly sampled individuals were asked their level of happiness and marital status. The results are shown in Table 10. Does the sample evidence suggest that one's happiness depends on one's marital status? Use the $\alpha = 0.05$ level of significance.

	Table 10			
		Marital Status		
		Married	**Widowed**	**Divorced/Separated**	**Never Married**
Happiness	**Very Happy**	600	63	112	144
	Pretty Happy	720	142	355	459
	Not Too Happy	93	51	119	127

Approach: We follow Steps 1 through 6 just given.

Solution

Step 1: We wish to determine whether happiness and marital status are dependent or independent. The null hypothesis is a statement of "no effect," so we state the hypotheses as follows:

H_0: happiness and marital status are independent (not related)

H_1: happiness and marital status are dependent (related)

Step 2: The level of significance is $\alpha = 0.05$.

Step 3

(a) The expected frequencies were determined in Example 1. Table 11 shows the observed frequencies, with the expected frequencies in parentheses.

	Table 11			
		Marital Status		
		Married	**Widowed**	**Divorced/Separated**	**Never Married**
Happiness	**Very Happy**	600 (435.025)	63 (78.816)	112 (180.413)	144 (224.747)
	Pretty Happy	720 (793.362)	142 (143.737)	355 (329.025)	459 (409.876)
	Not Too Happy	93 (184.613)	51 (33.447)	119 (76.562)	127 (95.377)

(b) Since none of the expected frequencies are less than 5, the requirements for the goodness-of-fit test are satisfied.

(c) The test statistic is

$$\chi_0^2 = \frac{(600 - 435.025)^2}{435.025} + \frac{(63 - 78.816)^2}{78.816} + \frac{(112 - 180.413)^2}{180.413} + \cdots + \frac{(119 - 76.562)^2}{76.562} + \frac{(127 - 95.377)^2}{95.377}$$
$$= 224.116$$

Classical Approach

Step 4: There are $r = 3$ rows and $c = 4$ columns, so we find the critical value using $(r - 1)(c - 1) = (3 - 1)(4 - 1) = 6$ degrees of freedom. The critical value is $\chi_{0.05}^2 = 12.592$. See Figure 11.

Figure 11

$\chi_{0.05}^2 = 12.592$

P-Value Approach

Step 4: There are $r = 3$ rows and $c = 4$ columns, so we find the P-value using $(r - 1)(c - 1) = (3 - 1)(4 - 1) = 6$ degrees of freedom. The P-value is the area under the chi-square distribution with 6 degrees of freedom to the right of $\chi_0^2 = 224.116$.

Using Table VII, we find the row that corresponds to 6 degrees of freedom. The value of 224.116 is greater than 18.548. The area under the chi-square distribution to the right of 18.548 is 0.005. Because 224.116 is greater than 18.548, the P-value is less than 0.005, so we have P-value < 0.005.

The exact P-value using the TI-84 Plus χ^2 cdf command is 1.26×10^{-45}, which is extremely small.

Step 5: Because the test statistic, 224.116, is greater than the critical value, $\chi^2_{0.05} = 12.592$, we reject the null hypothesis.

Step 5: Because the P-value is less than the level of significance, we reject the null hypothesis.

Step 6: There is sufficient evidence, at the $\alpha = 0.05$ level of significance, to conclude that happiness and marital status are dependent. We conclude that happiness and marital status are related to each other.

Now Work Problems 7(b)–(e)

To see the relation between happiness and marital status, we draw bar graphs of the conditional distributions of happiness by marital status. Recall that a conditional distribution lists the relative frequency of each category of a variable, given a specific value of the other variable in a contingency table. For example, we can calculate the relative frequency of "very happy," given that an individual is "married." We repeat this for each remaining category of marital status.

EXAMPLE 3   **Constructing a Conditional Distribution and Bar Graph**

Problem: Find the conditional distribution of happiness by marital status for the data in Table 10. Then draw a bar graph that represents the conditional distribution of happiness by marital status.

Approach: First, compute the relative frequency for happiness, given that the individual is "married." Then compute the relative frequency for happiness, given that the individual is "widowed," and so on. We will draw three bars side by side for each level of happiness. The horizontal axis represents marital status, and the vertical axis represents the relative frequency of happiness for each marital status.

Solution: We start with the individuals who are "married." The relative frequency with which we observe an individual who is "very happy," given that the individual is "married," is $\dfrac{600}{1413} = 0.425$. Therefore, 42.5% of individuals who are "married" are "very happy." The relative frequency with which we observe an individual who is "pretty happy," given that the individual is "married," is $\dfrac{720}{1413} = 0.510$. The relative frequency with which we observe an individual who is "not too happy," given that the individual is "married," is $\dfrac{93}{1413} = 0.066$.

We now proceed to compute the relative frequency for each level of happiness, given that the individual is "widowed." The relative frequency with which we observe an individual who is "very happy," given that the individual is "widowed," is $\dfrac{63}{256} = 0.246$. The relative frequency with which we observe an individual who is "pretty happy," given that the individual is "widowed," is $\dfrac{142}{256} = 0.555$. The relative frequency with which we observe an individual who is "not too happy," given that the individual is "widowed," is $\dfrac{51}{256} = 0.199$.

We repeat the process for "divorced/separated" and "never married" and obtain Table 12.

Table 12					
		Marital Status			
		Married	**Widowed**	**Divorced/Separated**	**Never Married**
Happiness	**Very Happy**	$\dfrac{600}{1413} = 0.425$	$\dfrac{63}{256} = 0.246$	$\dfrac{112}{586} = 0.191$	$\dfrac{144}{730} = 0.197$
	Pretty Happy	$\dfrac{720}{1413} = 0.510$	$\dfrac{142}{256} = 0.555$	$\dfrac{355}{586} = 0.606$	$\dfrac{459}{730} = 0.629$
	Not Too Happy	$\dfrac{93}{1413} = 0.066$	$\dfrac{51}{256} = 0.199$	$\dfrac{119}{586} = 0.203$	$\dfrac{127}{730} = 0.174$

From the conditional distribution by marital status, the association between happiness and marital status should be apparent. The proportion of individuals who are "very happy" is much higher for "married" individuals than any other category of marital status. In addition, the proportion of individuals who are "not too happy" is much lower for those individuals who are "married" compared to any other marital status.

Figure 12 shows the bar graph of the conditional distribution. The blue bars represent the proportion of individuals who are "very happy" for each level of marital status, the green bars represent the proportion of individuals who are "pretty happy" for each level of marital status, and the purple bars represent the proportion of individuals who are "not too happy" for each level of marital status.

Figure 12

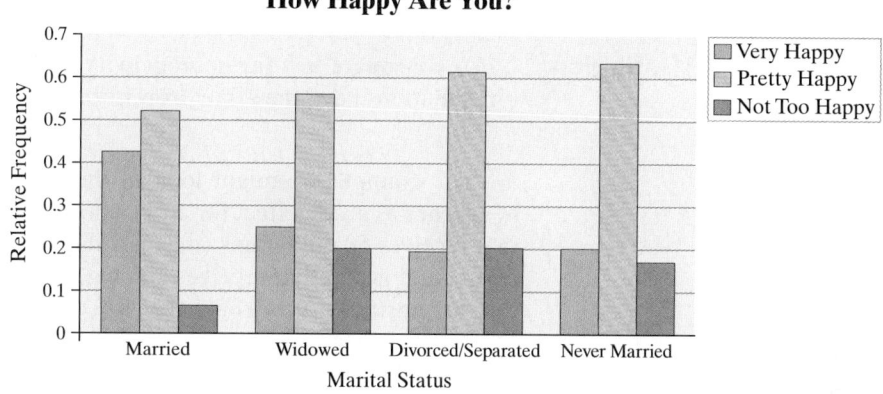

How Happy Are You?

| EXAMPLE 4 | **Chi-Square Test for Independence Using Technology** |

Problem: Using the data presented in Table 10 from Example 2, test whether happiness and marital status are independent at the $\alpha = 0.05$ level of significance using statistical software or a graphing calculator with advanced statistical features.

Approach: We use MINITAB to conduct the hypothesis test. The steps for testing for independence using the TI-83/84 Plus graphing calculators, MINITAB, and Excel are given in the Technology Step-by-Step on page 671.

Solution: Figure 13 shows the results obtained from MINITAB.

Figure 13 **Chi-Square Test: Married, Widowed, Divorced/Separated, Never Married**

```
Expected counts are printed below observed counts
Chi-Square contributions are printed below expected counts
                                      Divorced/     Never
        Married     Widowed     Separated     Married     Total
   1        600          63           112         144       919
          435.02       78.82        180.41      244.75
          62.564        3.174        25.943      29.011

   2        720         142           355         459      1676
          793.36      143.74        329.02      409.88
           6.784        0.021         2.051       5.888

   3         93          51           119         127       390
          184.61       33.45         76.56       95.38
          45.462        9.212        23.522      10.485

Total      1413         256           586         730      2985

Chi-Sq = 224.116, DF = 6, P-Value = 0.000
```

Interpretation: Because the *P*-value is less than 0.001, which is less than the level of significance, 0.05, we reject the null hypothesis. There is sufficient evidence to conclude that happiness and marital status are related.

---

2 Perform a Test for Homogeneity of Proportions

In Other Words

The chi-square test for homogeneity of proportions is used to compare proportions from two or more populations.

We now discuss a second type of chi-square test that can be used to compare the population proportions from two or more independent samples. The test is an extension of the two-sample *Z*-test introduced in Section 11.3, where we compared two population proportions from independent samples.

Definition   In a **chi-square test for homogeneity of proportions**, we test whether different populations have the same proportion of individuals with some characteristic.

For example, we might look at the proportion of individuals who experience headaches as a side effect for a placebo group (group 1), for an experimental group that receives 50 milligrams (mg) per day of a medication (group 2), and for an experimental group that receives 100 mg per day of the medication (group 3). Under this circumstance, we assume that the proportion of individuals in each group who experience a headache as a side effect is the same in each population (because the null hypothesis is always a statement of "no difference"). So our null hypothesis would be

$$H_0: p_1 = p_2 = p_3$$

versus the alternative,

H_1: At least one of the population proportions is different from the others.

The procedures for performing a test of homogeneity are identical to those for a test of independence.

EXAMPLE 5   A Test for Homogeneity of Proportions

Problem: Zocor is a drug manufactured by Merck and Co. that is meant to reduce the level of LDL (bad) cholesterol, while increasing the level of HDL (good) cholesterol. In clinical trials of the drug, patients were randomly divided into three groups. Group 1 received Zocor, group 2 received a placebo, and group 3 received cholestyramine, a cholesterol-lowering drug currently available. Table 13 contains the number of patients in each group who did and did not experience abdominal pain as a side effect.

Table 13			
	Group 1 (Zocor)	Group 2 (placebo)	Group 3 (cholestyramine)
Number of people who experienced abdominal pain	51	5	16
Number of people who did not experience abdominal pain	1532	152	163

Source: Merck and Co.

Is there evidence to indicate that the proportion of subjects in each group who experienced abdominal pain is different at the $\alpha = 0.01$ level of significance?

Approach: We will follow Steps 1 through 6 on page 660.

Solution

Step 1: The null hypothesis is a statement of "no difference," so the proportions of subjects in each group who experienced abdominal pain are equal. We state the hypotheses as follows:

H_0: $p_1 = p_2 = p_3$
H_1: At least one of the proportions is different from the others.

Here, p_1, p_2, and p_3 are the proportions in groups 1, 2, and 3, respectively.

Step 2: The level of significance is $\alpha = 0.01$.

Step 3:

(a) The expected frequency of subjects who experienced abdominal pain in group 1 is computed by multiplying the row total of individuals who experienced abdominal pain by the column total of number of individuals in group 1 and dividing this result by the total number of subjects in the study. There were $51 + 5 + 16 = 72$ subjects who experienced abdominal pain and $51 + 1532 = 1583$ subjects in group 1. There were a total of $51 + 5 + 16 + 1532 + 152 + 163 = 1919$ subjects in the study. The number of subjects expected to experience abdominal pain in group 1 is

$$E = \frac{72 \cdot 1583}{1919} = 59.393$$

Table 14 contains the row and column totals along with the observed frequencies. The expected frequencies are in parentheses.

Table 14				
Observed (and Expected) Frequencies				
	Group 1 (Zocor)	**Group 2 (placebo)**	**Group 3 (cholestyramine)**	**Row Totals**
Number of people who experienced abdominal pain	51 (59.393)	5 (5.891)	16 (6.716)	72
Number of people who did not experience abdominal pain	1532 (1523.607)	152 (151.109)	163 (172.284)	1847
Column totals	1583	157	179	1919

(b) All the expected frequencies are greater than 5. The requirements have been satisfied.

(c) The test statistic is

$$\chi_0^2 = \frac{(51 - 59.393)^2}{59.393} + \frac{(5 - 5.891)^2}{5.891} + \frac{(16 - 6.716)^2}{6.716}$$

$$+ \frac{(1532 - 1523.607)^2}{1523.607} + \frac{(152 - 151.109)^2}{151.109} + \frac{(163 - 172.284)^2}{172.284}$$

$$= 14.707$$

Classical Approach

Step 4: There are $r = 2$ rows and $c = 3$ columns, so we find the critical value using $(2 - 1)(3 - 1) = 2$ degrees of freedom. The critical value is $\chi^2_{0.01} = 9.210$. See Figure 14.

Figure 14

$\chi^2_{0.01} = 9.210$ $\quad$ 14.707

Step 5: Because the test statistic, 14.707, is greater than the critical value, 9.210, we reject the null hypothesis.

P-Value Approach

Step 4: There are $r = 2$ rows and $c = 3$ columns, so we find the P-value using $(2 - 1)(3 - 1) = 2$ degrees of freedom. The P-value is the area under the chi-square distribution with 2 degrees of freedom to the right of $\chi^2_0 = 14.707$, as shown in Figure 15.

Figure 15

P-value

14.707

Using Table VII, we find the row that corresponds to 2 degrees of freedom. The area under the chi-square distribution with 2 degrees of freedom, to the right of 10.597, is 0.005. Because 14.707 is to the right of 10.597, the P-value is less than 0.005. So, P-value < 0.005.

Step 5: Because the P-value is less than the level of significance, $\alpha = 0.01$, we reject the null hypothesis.

⟨CAUTION⟩ If we reject the null hypothesis in a chi-square test for homogeneity, we are saying that there is sufficient evidence for us to believe that at least one proportion is different from the others. However, it does not tell us which proportions differ.

Step 6: There is sufficient evidence at the $\alpha = 0.01$ level of significance to reject the null hypothesis that the proportions of subjects in each group who experience abdominal pain are equal. We conclude that at least one of the three groups experiences abdominal pain at a rate different from the other two groups.

Figure 16 shows the bar graph, with the blue bars representing the proportion of individuals who experienced abdominal pain for each group and the green bars representing the proportion of individuals who did not experience abdominal pain for each group.

Figure 16

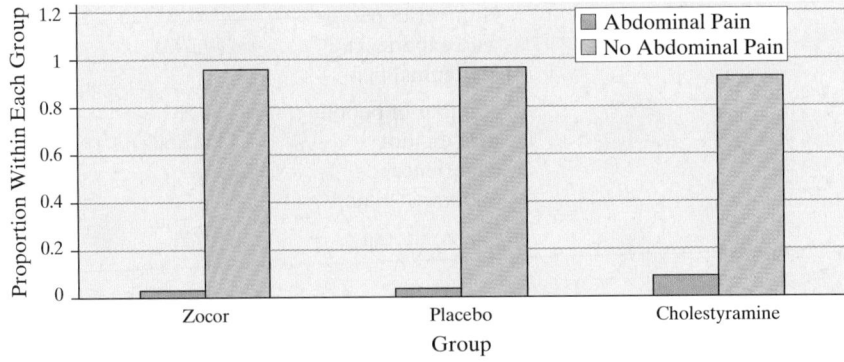

From the graph, it is apparent that a higher proportion of patients taking cholestyramine experience abdominal pain as a side effect.

Now Work Problem 15

Recall that the requirements for performing a chi-square test are that all expected frequencies are greater than 1 and that at most 20% of the expected frequencies can be less than 5. If these requirements are not satisfied, the researcher has one of two options: (1) combine two or more columns (or rows) to increase the expected frequencies or (2) increase the sample size.

12.2 ASSESS YOUR UNDERSTANDING

Concepts and Vocabulary

1. Explain the differences between the chi-square test for independence and the chi-square test for homogeneity. What are the similarities?

2. Why does the test for homogeneity follow the same procedures as the test for independence?

Skill Building

3. The following table contains observed values and expected values in parentheses for two categorical variables, X and Y, where variable X has three categories and variable Y has two categories:

	X_1	X_2	X_3
Y_1	34	43	52
	(36.26)	(44.63)	(48.11)
Y_2	18	21	17
	(15.74)	(19.37)	(20.89)

   (a) Compute the value of the chi-square test statistic. 1.701
   (b) Test the hypothesis that X and Y are independent at the $\alpha = 0.05$ level of significance. Do not reject H_0

4. The following table contains observed values and expected values in parentheses for two categorical variables, X and Y, where variable X has three categories and variable Y has two categories:

	X_1	X_2	X_3
Y_1	87	74	34
	(75.12)	(80.43)	(39.46)
Y_2	12	32	18
	(23.88)	(25.57)	(12.54)

   (a) Compute the value of the chi-square test statistic. 13.053
   (b) Test the hypothesis that X and Y are independent at the $\alpha = 0.05$ level of significance. Reject H_0

5. The following table contains the number of successes and failures for three categories of a variable.

	Category 1	Category 2	Category 3
Success	76	84	69
Failure	44	41	49

   Do not reject H_0; P-value = 0.370
   Test whether the proportions are equal for each category at the $\alpha = 0.01$ level of significance.

6. The following table contains the number of successes and failures for three categories of a variable.

	Category 1	Category 2	Category 3
Success	204	199	214
Failure	96	121	98

   Test whether the proportions are equal for each category at the $\alpha = 0.01$ level of significance.
   Do not reject H_0; P-value = 0.171

Applying the Concepts

7. **Family Structure and Sexual Activity** A sociologist wants to discover whether the sexual activity of females between the ages of 15 and 19 years of age and family structure are associated. She randomly selects 380 females between the ages of 15 and 19 years of age and asks each to disclose her family structure at age 14 and whether she has had sexual intercourse. The results are shown in the table. Data are based on information obtained from the U.S. National Center for Health Statistics.

	Family Structure			
Had Sexual Intercourse	**Both Biological or Adoptive Parents**	**Single Parent**	**Parent and Stepparent**	**Nonparental Guardian**
Yes	64	59	44	32
No	86	41	36	18

   (a) Compute the expected values of each cell under the assumption of independence.
   (b) Verify that the requirements for performing a chi-square test of independence are satisfied.
   (c) Compute the chi-square test statistic. 10.357
   (d) Test whether family structure and sexual activity of 15- to 19-year-old females are independent at the $\alpha = 0.05$ level of significance. Reject H_0
   (e) Compare the observed frequencies with the expected frequencies. Which cell contributed most to the test statistic? Was the expected frequency greater than or less than the observed frequency? What does this information tell you?
   (f) Construct a conditional distribution by family structure and draw a bar graph. Does this evidence support your conclusion in part (d)?

8. **Prenatal Care** An obstetrician wants to learn whether the amount of prenatal care and the wantedness of the pregnancy are associated. He randomly selects 939 women who had recently given birth and asks them to disclose whether their pregnancy was intended, unintended, or mistimed. In addition, they were to disclose when they started receiving prenatal care, if ever. The results of the survey are as follows:

	Months Pregnant before Prenatal Care Began		
Wantedness of Pregnancy	**Less Than 3 Months**	**3 to 5 Months**	**More Than 5 Months (or never)**
Intended	593	26	33
Unintended	64	8	11
Mistimed	169	19	16

   (a) Compute the expected values of each cell under the assumption of independence.

(b) Verify that the requirements for performing a chi-square test of independence are satisfied.

(c) Compute the chi-square test statistic. 21.357

(d) Test whether prenatal care and the wantedness of pregnancy are independent at the $\alpha = 0.05$ level of significance. Reject H_0

(e) Compare the observed frequencies with the expected frequencies. Which cell contributed most to the test statistic? Was the expected frequency greater than or less than the observed frequency? What does this information tell you?

(f) Construct a conditional distribution by wantedness of the pregnancy and draw a bar graph. Does this evidence support your conclusion in part (d)?

9. **Health and Happiness** Are health and happiness related? The following data represent the level of happiness and level of health for a random sample of individuals from the General Social Survey.

9. (a) Yes; they are related

		Health			
		Excellent	**Good**	**Fair**	**Poor**
	Very Happy	271	261	82	20
Happiness	**Pretty Happy**	247	567	231	53
	Not Too Happy	33	103	92	36

Source: General Social Survey

(a) Does the evidence suggest that health and happiness are related? Use the $\alpha = 0.05$ level of significance.

(b) Construct a conditional distribution of happiness by level of health and draw a bar graph.

(c) Write a few sentences that explain the relation, if any, between health and happiness.

10. **Health and Education** Does amount of education play a role in the healthiness of an individual? The following data represent the level of health and the highest degree earned for a random sample of individuals from the General Social Survey.

10. (a) Yes; they are related

		Health			
		Excellent	**Good**	**Fair**	**Poor**
	Less than High School	72	202	199	62
Education	**High School**	465	877	358	108
	Junior College	80	138	49	11
	Bachelor	229	276	64	12
	Graduate	130	147	32	2

Source: General Social Survey

(a) Does the evidence suggest that health and education are related? Use the $\alpha = 0.05$ level of significance.

(b) Construct a conditional distribution of health by level of education and draw a bar graph.

(c) Write a few sentences that explain the relation, if any, between health and education. Can you think of any lurking variables that help to explain the relation between these two variables?

11. **Profile of Smokers** The following data represent the smoking status by level of education for residents of the United States 18 years old or older from a random sample of 1054 residents.

10. (c) Age, since younger folks are less likely to not have a high school diploma

11. (a) Do not reject H_0

Number of Years of Education	Smoking Status		
	Current	**Former**	**Never**
<12	178	88	208
12	137	69	143
13–15	44	25	44
16 or more	34	33	51

Source: National Health Interview Survey

(a) Test whether smoking status and level of education are independent at the $\alpha = 0.05$ level of significance.

(b) Construct a conditional distribution of smoking status by number of years of education, and draw a bar graph. Does this evidence support your conclusion in part (a)?

12. **Pro Life or Pro Choice** A recent Gallup organization poll asked male and female Americans whether they were pro life or pro choice when it comes to abortion issues. The results of the survey are as follows:

Gender	Pro Life/Pro Choice	
	Pro Life	**Pro Choice**
Men	196	199
Women	239	249

(a) Test whether an individual's opinion regarding abortion is independent of gender at the $\alpha = 0.1$ level of significance. Do not reject H_0

(b) Construct a conditional distribution of abortion opinion by gender and draw a bar graph. Does this evidence support your conclusion in part (a)?

13. **Equal Opportunity** Do you believe everyone has an equal opportunity to obtain a quality education in the United States? The results of this General Social Survey question are presented next by level of education.

	Highest Degree				
	Less Than High School	**High School**	**Junior College**	**Bachelor**	**Graduate**
Yes	302	551	29	100	46
No	83	200	24	71	31

Source: General Social Survey

(a) Does the evidence suggest that the proportion of individuals who feel everyone has an equal opportunity to obtain a quality education in the United States is equal for each level of education? Use the $\alpha = 0.05$ level of significance. No; not equal

(b) Construct a conditional distribution of opinion by level of education and draw a bar graph of the conditional distribution. What role does education appear to play in beliefs about access to quality education?

14. **Legalize Marijuana** Do you believe that marijuana should be made legal? The results of this General Social Survey are presented next by political affiliation.

	Democrat	Independent	Republican
Yes	240	292	121
No	326	446	370

Source: General Social Survey

(a) Does the evidence suggest that the proportion of individuals who feel marijuana should be made legal is equal for each political affiliation? Use the $\alpha = 0.05$ level of significance. No; proportions different

(b) Construct a conditional distribution by political affiliation and draw a bar graph of the conditional distribution. What role does political party appear to play in beliefs about the legalization of marijuana?

15. **Celebrex** Celebrex, a drug manufactured by Pfizer, Inc., is used to relieve symptoms associated with osteoarthritis and rheumatoid arthritis in adults. It is considered to be one of the nonsteroidal anti-inflammatory drugs. These types of drugs are known to be associated with gastrointestinal toxicity, such as bleeding, ulceration, and perforation of the stomach, small intestine, or large intestine. In clinical trials, researchers wanted to learn whether the proportion of subjects taking Celebrex who experienced these side effects differed significantly from that in other treatment groups. The following data were collected (Naproxen is a nonsteroidal anti-inflammatory drug that is also used in the treatment of arthritis).

	Treatment				
Side Effect	Placebo	Celebrex (50 mg per day)	Celebrex (100 mg per day)	Celebrex (200 mg per day)	Naproxen (500 mg per day)
Experienced ulcers	5	8	7	13	34
Did not experience ulcers	212	225	220	208	176

Source: Pfizer, Inc.

(a) Test whether the proportion of subjects within each treatment group is the same at the $\alpha = 0.01$ level of significance. Reject H_0

(b) Construct a conditional distribution of side effect by treatment and draw a bar graph. Does this evidence support your conclusion in part (a)?

16. **Celebrex** Celebrex, a drug manufactured by Pfizer, Inc., is used to relieve symptoms associated with osteoarthritis and rheumatoid arthritis in adults. In clinical trials of the medication, some subjects reported dizziness as a side effect. The researchers wanted to discover whether the proportion of subjects taking Celebrex who reported dizziness as a side effect differed significantly from that for other treatment groups. The following data were collected.

	Drug				
Side Effect	Celebrex	Placebo	Naproxen	Diclofenac	Ibuprofen
Dizziness	83	32	36	5	8
No dizziness	4063	1832	1330	382	337

Source: Pfizer, Inc.

(a) Test whether the proportion of subjects within each treatment group who experienced dizziness are the same at the $\alpha = 0.01$ level of significance. Do not reject

(b) Construct a conditional distribution of side effect by treatment and draw a bar graph. Does this evidence support your conclusion in part (a)?

17. **Dropping a Course** A survey of 52 randomly selected students who dropped a course in the current semester was conducted at a community college. The goal of the survey was to learn why students drop courses. The following data were collected: "Personal" drop reasons include financial, transportation, family issues, health issues, and lack of child care. "Course" drop reasons include reducing one's load, being unprepared for the course, the course was not what was expected, dissatisfaction with teaching, and not getting the desired grade. "Work" drop reasons include an increase in hours, a change in shift, and obtaining full-time employment. "Career" drop reasons include not needing the course and a change of plans. The results of the survey are as follows:

Gender	Drop Reason	Gender	Drop Reason
Male	Personal	Male	Work
Female	Personal	Male	Work
Male	Work	Female	Course
Male	Personal	Male	Work
Male	Course	Female	Course
Male	Course	Female	Course
Female	Course	Female	Course
Female	Course	Male	Work
Male	Course	Male	Personal
Female	Course	Male	Course
Male	Personal	Female	Course
Male	Work	Female	Course
Male	Work	Male	Course
Male	Course	Female	Course
Male	Course	Male	Work
Male	Work	Male	Course
Female	Personal	Female	Work
Male	Course	Male	Personal
Female	Work	Male	Work
Male	Work	Female	Course
Male	Work	Male	Course
Female	Course	Male	Personal
Female	Personal	Female	Course
Female	Personal	Female	Work
Female	Personal	Male	Work

(a) Construct a contingency table for the two variables.

(b) Test whether gender is independent of drop reason at the $\alpha = 0.1$ level of significance. Reject H_0

(c) Construct a conditional distribution of gender by drop reason and draw a bar graph. Does this evidence support your conclusion in part (a)?

18. **Political Affiliation** A political scientist wanted to learn whether there is any association between the education level of a registered voter and his or her political party affiliation. He randomly selected 46 registered voters and obtained the following data:

Education	Political Party	Education	Political Party
Grade school	Democrat	High school	Democrat
College	Republican	College	Republican
High school	Democrat	College	Republican
High school	Republican	Grade school	Democrat
High school	Democrat	High school	Republican
Grade school	Democrat	High school	Democrat
College	Republican	High school	Democrat
Grade school	Democrat	College	Republican
High school	Democrat	High school	Republican
High school	Democrat	Grade school	Democrat
Grade school	Democrat	High school	Democrat
College	Republican	College	Democrat
Grade school	Democrat	College	Republican
College	Democrat	High school	Republican
College	Democrat	College	Democrat
Grade school	Republican	College	Democrat
College	Republican	High school	Democrat
Grade school	Republican	College	Republican
College	Republican	College	Democrat
High school	Democrat	High school	Republican
College	Democrat	College	Republican
College	Republican	High school	Republican
College	Democrat	College	Democrat

18. (b) Do not reject H_0

(a) Construct a contingency table for the two variables.
(b) Test whether level of education is independent of political affiliation at the $\alpha = 0.1$ level of significance.
(c) Construct a conditional distribution of political party by level of education and draw a bar graph. Does this evidence support your conclusion in part (a)?

19. **Putting It Together: Women, Aspirin, and Heart Attacks** In a famous study by the Physicians Health Study Group from Harvard University from that late 1980s, 22,000 healthy male

19. (f) Do not reject H_0; $z_0 = -1.44$

physicians were randomly divided into two groups; half the physicians took aspirin every other day, and the others were given a placebo. Of the physicians in the aspirin group, 104 heart attacks occurred; of the physicians in the placebo group, 189 heart attacks occurred. The results were statistically significant, which led to the advice that males should take an aspirin every other day in the interest of reducing the chance of having a heart attack. Does the same advice apply to women?

In a randomized, placebo-controlled study, 39,876 healthy women 45 years of age or older were randomly divided into two groups. The women in group 1 received 100 mg of aspirin every other day; the women in group 2 received a placebo every other day. The women were monitored for 10 years to determine if they experienced a cardiovascular event (such as heart attack or stroke). Of the 19,934 in the aspirin group, 477 experienced a heart attack. Of the 19,942 women in the placebo group, 522 experienced a heart attack.

Source: Paul M. Ridker et al. "A Randomized Trial of Low-Dose Aspirin in the Primary Prevention of Cardiovascular Disease in Women." *New England Journal of Medicine* 352:1293–1304.

(a) What is the population being studied? What is the sample? *Healthy women $\geq$ 45 years old; 39,876 women*
(b) What is the response variable? Is it qualitative or quantitative? *Heart attack or not; qualitative*
(c) What are the treatments? *Aspirin, placebo*
(d) What type of experimental design is this?
(e) How does randomization deal with the explanatory variables that were not controlled in the study?
(f) Determine whether the proportion of cardiovascular events in each treatment group is different using a two-sample Z-test for comparing two proportions. Use the $\alpha = 0.05$ level of significance. What is the test statistic?
(g) Determine whether the proportion of cardiovascular events in each treatment group is different using a chi-square test for homogeneity of proportions. Use the $\alpha = 0.05$ level of significance. What is the test statistic? *$\chi_0^2 = 2.061$; do not reject H_0*
(h) Square the test statistic from part (f) and compare it to the test statistic from part (g). What do you conclude? *$z_0^2 = \chi_0^2$*

19. (d) Completely randomized design

Consumer Reports   Dirty Birds?

Hungry for a cheap, low-fat alternative to beef, Americans are eating more chicken than ever. Although precise figures are impossible to obtain, the U.S. Centers for Disease Control and Prevention reported that the number of cases of outbreaks of illness caused by chicken rose threefold between 1988 and 1992. Salmonella bacteria were the most common cause of these outbreaks.

In a study for *Consumer Reports*, we purchased 1000 fresh, whole broiler chickens at grocery stores in 36 cities across the United States over a 5-week period. Our shoppers packed the birds in coolers and shipped them overnight to the lab. There, tests were conducted to determine the presence of salmonella and campylobacter, another chicken-related bug. The results of the study for salmonella were as follows:

Brand	Salmonella Present	Salmonella Absent	Total
A	8	192	200
B	17	183	200
C	27	173	200
D	14	186	200
E	20	180	200
Total	86	914	1000

Assuming that the chickens represent a random sample from each brand included in the study, use the information presented in the table to answer the following:

(a) Calculate the proportion of incidence for each brand shown in the table.

(b) Compute a 95% confidence interval for the incidence of salmonella for brand C.

(c) Using a chi-square test of homogeneity of proportions, is there evidence that the five brands have the same incidence rate for salmonella?

(d) Brands A and D are major competitors in the same market. The manufacturer of brand A claims to have improved

its cleanliness and claims that it is substantially cleaner than brand D. Is there evidence to support this contention?

(e) Write a paragraph for the readers of *Consumer Reports* magazine that explains your conclusions.

Note to Readers: *In many cases, our test protocol and analytical methods are more complicated than described in these examples. The data and discussions have been modified to make the material more appropriate for the audience.*

Source: © 1998 by Consumers Union of U.S., Inc., Yonkers, NY 10703-1057, a nonprofit organization. Reprinted with permission from the June 2001 issue of CONSUMER REPORTS® for educational purposes only. No commercial use or photocopying permitted. To learn more about Consumers Union, log onto www.ConsumersReports.org.

TECHNOLOGY STEP-BY-STEP   Chi-Square Tests

TI-83/84 Plus
1. Access the MATRX menu. Highlight the EDIT menu, and select 1: [A].
2. Enter the number of rows and columns of the matrix.
3. Enter the cell entries for the observed matrix, and press 2nd QUIT. Repeat Steps 1–3 for the expected values, but enter the expected frequencies in matrix B.
4. Press STAT, highlight the TESTS menu, and select C: χ^2-Test.
5. With the cursor after the Observed:, enter matrix [A] by accessing the MATRX menu, highlighting NAMES, and selecting 1:[A].
6. With the cursor after the Expected:, enter matrix [B] by accessing the MATRX menu, highlighting NAMES, and selecting 2:[B].
7. Highlight Calculate or Draw, and press ENTER.

MINITAB
1. Enter the data into the MINITAB spreadsheet.

2. Select the **Stat** menu, highlight **Tables**, and select **Chi-Square Test (Two-Way Table in Worksheet)** . . . .
3. Select the columns that contain the data, and click OK.

Excel
1. Enter the observed frequencies in the spreadsheet.
2. Compute the expected frequencies and enter them in a different location in the spreadsheet.
3. Select the **Insert** menu and highlight **Function**. Select **Statistical** for the function category and highlight **CHITEST** in the function name. Click OK.
4. With the cursor in the actual cell, highlight the observed data. With the cursor in the expected cell, highlight the expected frequencies. Click OK. The output provided is the *P*-value.

Note: This test can also be performed by using the DDXL add-in. See the Excel Technology Manual.

CHAPTER 12 REVIEW

Summary

In this chapter, we introduced chi-square methods. The first chi-square method involved tests for goodness-of-fit. We used the chi-square distribution to test whether a random variable followed a certain distribution. This is done by comparing the values expected based on the distribution of the random variable to the observed values.

Then we introduced chi-square methods that allowed us to perform tests for independence and homogeneity. In a test for independence, the researcher obtains random data for two variables and tests whether the variables are associated. The null hypothesis in these tests is always that the variables are not associated (independent). The test statistic compares the values expected if the variables were independent to those observed. If

the expected and observed values differ significantly, we reject the null hypothesis and conclude that there is evidence to support the belief that the variables are not independent (they are associated). We draw bar graphs of the marginal distributions to help us see the association, if any.

The last chi-square test was the test for homogeneity of proportions. This test is similar to the test for independence, except we are testing that the proportion of individuals in the study with a certain characteristic are equal ($p_1 = p_2 = \cdots = p_k$). To perform this test, we take random samples of a predetermined size from each group under consideration (a random sample of size n_1 for group 1, a random sample of size n_2 for group 2, and so on).

Vocabulary

Goodness-of-fit test (p. 645)
Expected counts (p. 646)

Test statistic (pp. 647, 660)
Chi-square test for independence (p. 656)

Chi-square test for homogeneity
  of proportions (p. 664)

Formulas

Expected Counts in a Goodness-of-Fit Test

$E_i = \mu_i = np_i$ for $i = 1, 2, \ldots, k$

Chi-Square Test Statistic

$$\chi^2 = \sum \frac{(O_i - E_i)^2}{E_i} \qquad i = 1, 2, \ldots, k$$

Expected Frequencies in a Test for Independence

$$\text{Expected frequency} = \frac{(\text{row total})(\text{column total})}{\text{table total}}$$

Objectives

Section	You should be able to . . .	Examples	Review Exercises
12.1	1 Perform a goodness-of-fit test (p. 645)	1–4	1 and 2
12.2	1 Perform a test for independence (p. 656)	1–4	3 and 4
	2 Perform a test for homogeneity of proportions (p. 664)	5	5

Review Exercises

1. **Roulette Wheel** A pit boss suspects that a roulette wheel is out of balance. A roulette wheel has 18 black slots, 18 red slots, and 2 green slots. The pit boss spins the wheel 500 times and records the following frequencies:

Outcome	Frequency
Black	233
Red	237
Green	30

Is the wheel out of balance? Use the $\alpha = 0.05$ level of significance. *Do not reject H_0*

2. **World Series** Are the teams that play in the World Series evenly matched? To win a World Series, a team must win 4 games. If the teams are evenly matched, we would expect the number of games played in the World Series to follow the distribution shown in the first two columns of the following table. The third column represents the actual number of games played in each World Series from 1930 to 2007. Does the data support the distribution that would exist if the teams are evenly matched and the outcome of each game is independent? Use the $\alpha = 0.05$ level of significance. *Do not reject H_0*

Number of Games	Probability	Observed Frequency
4	0.125	15
5	0.25	15
6	0.3125	17
7	0.3125	30

Source: Major League Baseball

3. **Titanic** With 20% of men, 74% of women, and 52% of children surviving the infamous *Titanic* disaster, it is clear that the saying "women and children first" was followed. But what, if any, role did the class of service play in the survival of passengers? The data shown represent the survival status of passengers by class of service.

		Class		
		First	Second	Third
Survival Status	Survived	203	118	178
	Did Not Survive	122	167	528

(a) Is class of service independent of survival rate? Use the $\alpha = 0.05$ level of significance   No
(b) Construct a conditional distribution of survival status by class of service and draw a bar graph. What does this summary tell you?

4. **Premature Birth and Education** Does the length of term of pregnancy play a role in the level of education of the baby? Researchers in Norway followed over 1 million births between 1967 and 1988 and looked at the educational attainment of the children. The following data are based on the results of their research. Note that a full-term pregnancy is 38 weeks. Is gestational period independent of completing a high school diploma? Use the $\alpha = 0.05$ level of significance. No; dependent

		Gestational Period (weeks)				
		22–27	28–32	33–36	37–42	43+
Less Than High School Degree	Yes	14	34	140	1010	81
	No	26	65	343	3032	208

Source: Chicago Tribune, March 26, 2008.

5. Moral Values of Candidates In a poll conducted by Harris Poll on January 9, 2008, a random sample of adult Americans was asked, "How important are moral values when deciding how to vote?" The results of the survey by disclosed political affiliation are shown in the table.

		Political Affiliation		
		Republican	Independent	Democrat
Morality	Important	644	662	670
	Not Important	56	155	147

(a) Does the sample data suggest that the proportions of adults who feel morality is important differ based on political affiliation? Use the $\alpha = 0.05$ level of significance. *Yes; proportions differ*

(b) Construct a conditional distribution of morality by party affiliation and draw a bar graph. What does this summary tell you?

CHAPTER TEST

1. A pit boss is concerned that a pair of dice being used in a craps game is not fair. The distribution of the expected sum of two fair dice is as follows:

Sum of Two Dice	Probability	Sum of Two Dice	Probability
2	$\frac{1}{36}$	8	$\frac{5}{36}$
3	$\frac{2}{36}$	9	$\frac{4}{36}$
4	$\frac{3}{36}$	10	$\frac{3}{36}$
5	$\frac{4}{36}$	11	$\frac{2}{36}$
6	$\frac{5}{36}$	12	$\frac{1}{36}$
7	$\frac{6}{36}$		

The pit boss rolls the dice 400 times and records the sum of the dice. The table shows the results. Do you think the dice are fair? Use the $\alpha = 0.01$ level of significance. *Do not reject H_0*

Sum of Two Dice	Frequency	Sum of Two Dice	Frequency
2	16	8	59
3	23	9	45
4	31	10	34
5	41	11	19
6	62	12	11
7	59		

2. A researcher wanted to determine if the distribution of educational attainment of Americans today is different from the distribution in 2000. The distribution of educational attainment in 2000 was as follows:

Education	Relative Frequency
Not a high school graduate	0.158
High school graduate	0.331
Some college	0.176
Associate's degree	0.078
Bachelor's degree	0.170
Advanced degree	0.087

Source: Statistical Abstract of the United States

The researcher randomly selects 500 Americans, learns their levels of education, and obtains the data shown in the table. Do the data suggest that the distribution of educational attainment has changed since 2000? Use the $\alpha = 0.1$ level of significance. *Educational attainment has not changed.*

Education	Frequency
Not a high school graduate	72
High school graduate	159
Some college	85
Associate's degree	44
Bachelor's degree	92
Advanced degree	48

3. A sociologist wanted to determine whether the locations in which individuals live are independent of their races. He randomly selects 2712 U.S. residents and asks them to disclose their race and the location in which they live and obtains the following data:

Race	Region			
	Northeast	Midwest	South	West
White	421	520	656	400
Black	56	57	158	28
Asian or Pacific Islander	13	8	11	40
Hispanic	38	17	68	101
Other	19	12	30	59

Source: Statistical Abstract of the United States

(a) Does the evidence suggest that there is a link between race and location in the United States? Use the $\alpha = 0.05$ level of significance. *Yes; reject H_0*

(b) Construct a conditional distribution of race by region and draw a bar graph. How does this evidence support your conclusion in part (a)?

4. Do different proportions of individuals enjoy gambling based on their level of education? The following data represent the results of a survey in which adult Americans were asked to disclose whether they enjoyed making bets and their level of education. Does the evidence suggest that the proportions differ among the different levels of education? Use the $\alpha = 0.05$ level of significance. *Do not reject H_0*

	High School or Less	Some College	College Graduate
Enjoy	143	102	99
Do not Enjoy	407	363	396

5. Many municipalities are passing legislation that forbids smoking in restaurants and bars. Bar owners claim that these laws hurt their business. Are there concerns legitimate? The following data represent the smoking status and frequency of visits to bars from the General Social Survey. Do smokers tend to spend more time in bars? Use the $\alpha = 0.05$ level of significance. *Yes*

	Almost Daily	Several Times a Week	Several Times a Month	Once a Month	Several Times a Year	Once a Year	Never
Smoker	80	409	294	362	433	336	1265
Nonsmoker	57	350	379	471	573	568	3297

▰ MAKING AN INFORMED DECISION

Benefits of College

Are there benefits to attending college? If so, what are they? In this project, we will identify some of the perks that a college education provides. Obtain a random sample of at least 50 people aged 21 years or older and administer the following survey:

Please answer the following questions:

1. What is the highest level of education you have attained?
_____ Have not completed high school
_____ High school graduate
_____ College graduate

2. What is your employment status?
_____ Employed
_____ Unemployed, but actively seeking work
_____ Unemployed, but not actively seeking work

3. If you are employed, what is your annual income?
_____ Less than $20,000
_____ $20,000–$39,999
_____ $40,000–$60,000
_____ More than $60,000

4. If you are employed, which statement best describes the level of satisfaction you have with your career? Answer this question only if you are employed.

_____ Satisfied—I enjoy my job and am happy with my career.

_____ Somewhat satisfied—Work is work, but I am not unhappy with my career.

_____ Somewhat dissatisfied—I do not enjoy my work, but I also have no intention of leaving.

_____ Dissatisfied—Going to work is painful. I would quit tomorrow if I could.

(a) Use the results of the survey to create a contingency table for each of the following categories:
- Level of education/employment status
- Level of education/annual income
- Level of education/job satisfaction
- Annual income/job satisfaction

(b) Perform a chi-square test for independence on each contingency table from part (a).

(c) Draw bar graphs for each contingency table from part (a).

(d) Write a report that details your findings.

Feeling Lucky? Well, Are You?

In fiscal year (FY) 2007–2008 (October 2007–September 2008), the Florida Lottery generated in excess of $4 billion in total sales. Over that period, the state spent $34,869,453 on advertising to promote its various games. Rand Advertising is interested in gaining access to this lucrative market. You have been assigned the task of preparing a report on the lottery sales structure for three of Florida's online (non-scratch-off ticket) games: Fantasy Five, Mega Money, and Lotto. Your findings will become part of a proposal by Rand to the Florida Lottery.

In Fantasy 5, a player picks five numbers from 1 to 36, at $1 per play. Drawings are held 7 days a week. If there is no jackpot winner for a drawing, the money allocated for the top prize rolls down to the next prize tier (4 of 5). The prize structure for this game is as follows:

Prize Structure for Florida's Fantasy 5 Online Game		
Match	Estimated Prize Amount per Winner	Probability
5 of 5	$200,000	$\frac{1}{376,992}$
4 of 5	$100	$\frac{1}{2,432}$
3 of 5	$10	$\frac{1}{81}$
2 of 5	Free ticket	$\frac{1}{8}$

The Mega Money game costs $1 per ticket. Players pick 4 numbers from 1 to 44 and one MEGABALL number from 1 to 22. Drawings are held on Tuesdays and Fridays. If there is no jackpot winner for a drawing, the money allocated for the top prize rolls over to the next drawing, adding to the total of the next jackpot. The following is the prize structure for Mega Money.

Prize Structure for Florida's Mega Money Online Game		
Match	Estimated Prize Amount per Winner	Probability
4 of 4 + MEGABALL	$500,000	$\frac{1}{2,986,522}$
4 of 4	$1,200	$\frac{1}{142,215}$
3 of 4 + MEGABALL	$350	$\frac{1}{18,666}$
3 of 4	$50	$\frac{1}{889}$
2 of 4 + MEGABALL	$25	$\frac{1}{638}$
2 of 4	$2	$\frac{1}{30}$
1 of 4 + MEGABALL	$3	$\frac{1}{76}$

In terms of sales, Lotto is Florida's most lucrative lottery product. Players pick 6 numbers from 1 to 53, at $1 per play. Drawings are held on Wednesdays and Saturdays. Like Mega Money, if there is no jackpot winner, the top prize is rolled over to the next drawing. Because of the game design, it is much more difficult to win the Lotto jackpot. The difficulty in winning the game leads to numerous jackpot rollovers, creating, at times, jackpots exceeding $50,000,000! The propensity to roll over makes it difficult to determine an estimated prize payout per winner. However, the odds structure is shown in the table below.

Odds Structure for Florida's Lotto Online Game	
Match	Probability
6 of 6	$\dfrac{1}{22{,}957{,}480}$
5 of 6	$\dfrac{1}{81{,}410}$
4 of 6	$\dfrac{1}{1{,}416}$
3 of 6	$\dfrac{1}{71}$

To conduct your study, you have obtained the sales figures for each of the three games by district sales office for 1 week. These data are as follows:

Number of Tickets Sold for Florida Lottery Games by Sales District for the Week			
	Florida Lottery Game		
District	Fantasy 5	Mega Money	Lotto
1	87,030	27,221	270,256
3	186,780	56,822	934,451
4	267,955	94,123	1,004,651
5	232,451	61,019	707,934
6	727,390	262,840	2,746,438
8	462,874	135,321	1,563,491
9	353,532	139,421	1,492,549
10	377,627	140,285	1,433,077
11	470,993	153,591	1,743,370
12	588,154	185,946	1,852,986
13	1,283,042	474,067	2,883,453

Are the numbers of tickets sold for each lottery game and sales district independent? Construct a bar graph that represents the conditional distribution of game by sales district. Does this graphical evidence support your conclusion regarding the relationship between the type of game and the sales district? Explain.

Additionally, you are interested in the daily sales structure for the various districts. The following are the numbers of tickets sold each day for a randomly selected week for the three games in District 1.

Number of Tickets Sold for Florida Lottery Games by Day of the Week for District 1			
	Florida Lottery Game		
Day	**Fantasy 5**	**Mega Money**	**Lotto**
Monday	12,794	2,082	13,093
Tuesday	11,564	9,983	18,200
Wednesday	12,562	1,040	60,746
Thursday	11,408	1,677	18,054
Friday	15,299	10,439	38,513
Saturday	15,684	1,502	115,686
Sunday	7,728	498	5,964

Does the evidence suggest that the proportion of Fantasy 5 sales is the same for each day of the week? Perform a similar test for Mega Money and Lotto.

Write a report detailing your assumptions, analyses, findings, and conclusions.

13

Comparing Three or More Means

Outline

13.1 Comparing Three or More Means (One-Way Analysis of Variance)

13.2 Post Hoc Tests on One-Way Analysis of Variance

13.3 The Randomized Complete Block Design

13.4 Two-Way Analysis of Variance

MAKING AN INFORMED DECISION

Remember the inheritance you received in Chapter 11? Suppose you have decided that you now want to try investing in individual stocks rather than mutual funds. Which type of stocks should you invest in to earn the highest rate of return? See the Decisions project on page 733.

PUTTING IT TOGETHER

Do you remember the progression for comparing proportions? Chapters 9 and 10 discussed inference for a single proportion, Chapter 11 discussed inference for two proportions, and Chapter 12 presented a discussion of inference for three or more proportions (homogeneity of proportions).

We have this same progression of topics for inference on means. In Chapters 9 and 10, we discussed inferential techniques for a single population mean. In Chapter 11, we discussed inferential techniques for comparing two means. In this chapter, we continue to expand our horizons by learning inferential techniques for comparing three or more means. Just as we needed to use a different distribution to compare multiple proportions (the chi-square distribution), we use a different distribution for comparing three or more means. Although the choice of distribution initially may seem strange, once the logic of the procedure is understood, the choice of distribution makes sense.

13.1 COMPARING THREE OR MORE MEANS (ONE-WAY ANALYSIS OF VARIANCE)

Preparing for This Section   Before getting started, review the following:

- Completely randomized design (Section 1.6, pp. 45–50)
- The language of hypothesis testing (Section 10.1, pp. 515–521)
- Comparing two population means (Section 11.2, pp. 595–603)

- Normal probability plots (Section 7.4, pp. 405–409)
- *F*-distribution (Section 11.4, pp. 621–624)
- Boxplots (Section 3.5, pp. 177–180)

Objectives **1** Verify the requirements to perform a one-way ANOVA

2 Test a hypothesis regarding three or more means using one-way ANOVA

Note to Instructor

If you like, you can print out and distribute the Preparing for This Section quiz located in the Instructor's Resource Center. The purpose of the quiz is to verify that the students have the prerequisite knowledge for the section.

In Section 11.2, we compared two population means. Just as we extended the concept of comparing two population proportions (Section 11.3) to comparing three or more population proportions (Tests for Homogeneity of Proportions, Section 12.2), we now extend the concept of comparing two population means to comparing three or more population means. The procedure for doing this is called *analysis of variance*, or *ANOVA* for short.

Definition   **Analysis of Variance (ANOVA)** is an inferential method used to test the equality of three or more population means.

In Other Words

In ANOVA, the null hypothesis is always that the means of the different populations are equal. The alternative hypothesis is always that at least one population mean is different from the others.

For example, a family doctor might wonder if the mean HDL (so-called good) levels of cholesterol of males in the age groups 20 to 29, 40 to 49, and 60 to 69 years old is the same or different. To test this, we assume that the mean HDL cholesterol of each age group is the same (remember, the null hypothesis is always a statement of "no difference"). If we call the 20- to 29-year-old group population 1, 40- to 49-year-old group population 2, and 60 to 69-year-old group population 3, our null hypothesis would be

$$H_0: \mu_1 = \mu_2 = \mu_3$$

versus the alternative hypothesis

H_1: At least one of the population means is different from the others

As another example, a medical researcher might want to compare the effect that different levels of an experimental drug have on hair growth. The researcher might randomly divide a group of subjects into three different treatment groups. Group 1 might receive a placebo once a day, group 2 might receive 50 milligrams (mg) of the experimental drug once a day, and group 3 might receive 100 mg of the experimental drug once a day. The researcher then compares the mean number of new hair follicles for each of the three treatment groups. The three different treatment groups correspond to three different populations.

Note to Instructor

It is recommended that hand computations be de-emphasized in this section. Concentrate on the concepts, and let technology do the number crunching.

It is tempting to test the null hypothesis $H_0: \mu_1 = \mu_2 = \mu_3$ by comparing the population means two at a time using the techniques introduced in Section 11.2. If we proceeded this way, we would need to test three different hypotheses:*

$$H_0: \mu_1 = \mu_2 \quad \text{and} \quad H_0: \mu_1 = \mu_3 \quad \text{and} \quad H_0: \mu_2 = \mu_3$$
$$H_1: \mu_1 \neq \mu_2 \qquad\qquad H_1: \mu_1 \neq \mu_3 \qquad\qquad H_1: \mu_2 \neq \mu_3$$

Each test would have a probability of a Type I error (rejecting the null hypothesis when it is true) of α. If we used an $\alpha = 0.05$ level of significance, each test would have

---

*In general, there would be $\binom{k}{2} = kC_2$ pairs to test, where k equals the number of population means to be compared.

CAUTION Do not test $H_0: \mu_1 = \mu_2 = \mu_3$ by conducting three separate hypothesis tests, because the probability of making a Type I error will be much higher than α.

a 95% probability of rejecting the null hypothesis when the alternative hypothesis of no difference is true (i.e., a 95% probability of making a correct decision). The probability that all three tests correctly reject the null hypothesis is $0.95^3 = 0.86$ (assuming that the tests are independent). There is a $1 - 0.95^3 = 1 - 0.86 = 0.14$, or 14%, probability that at least one test will lead to an incorrect rejection of H_0. A 14% probability of a Type I error is much higher than the desired 5% probability. As the number of populations to be compared increases, the probability of making a Type I error using multiple t-tests for a given value of α also increases.

We might try adjusting the individual α-values so that the overall probability of a Type I error is the desired value. For example, we might test three pairs of means using $\alpha = 0.017$. The probability that all three tests correctly reject the null if the alternative hypothesis is true is $0.983^3 \approx 0.95$ (again assuming that the tests are independent). Thus, the overall probability of a Type I error is the desired 5% probability. However, by decreasing the probability of making a Type I error in each test, we increase the probability of making a Type II error for those tests. So, conducting multiple t tests ultimately leads to an increased chance of making a mistake no matter what level of α we use in the individual tests.

To address this problem, Sir Ronald A. Fisher (1890–1962) introduced the method of analysis of variance. The term *analysis of variance* may seem odd since we are conducting a test on means, not variances. However, the name refers to the *approach* we are using, which will involve a comparison of two estimates of the same population variance. The justification for the name will become clear as we develop the test statistic.

The procedure used in this section is called *one-way* analysis of variance because there is only one factor that distinguishes the various populations in the study. For example, in comparing the mean HDL cholesterol levels of males, the only factor that distinguishes the three groups is age. In comparing the effectiveness of the hair growth drug, the only factor that distinguishes the three groups is the amount of the experimental drug received (0 mg, 50 mg, or 100 mg).

In performing one-way analysis of variance, care must be taken so that the subjects are similar in all characteristics except for the level of the treatment. Fisher stated that this is easiest to accomplish through randomization, which neutralizes the effect of the uncontrolled variables. In the hair growth example, the subjects should be similar in terms of eating habits, age, and so on, by randomly assigning the subjects to the three groups.

CAUTION It is vital that individuals be randomly assigned to treatments.

It is worth noting that the methods of one-way ANOVA also apply when comparing only two population means. This, however, does not mean that we should abandon our previous method for comparing two means. First, the ANOVA alternative hypothesis is always nondirectional. That is, we could use ANOVA to test whether two means are different, but we could not use ANOVA to test whether one mean is larger than the other (this would require a t-test). Second, ANOVA requires that the population variances be equal. If they are not, we must use Welch's t-test, which does not assume equal variances. For these reasons, we typically utilize ANOVA only when comparing three or more means.

1 Verify the Requirements to Perform a One-Way ANOVA

To perform a one-way ANOVA test, certain requirements must be satisfied.

> ### Requirements of a One-Way ANOVA Test
>
> **1.** There are k simple random samples; one from each of k populations.
>
> **2.** The k samples are independent of each other; that is, the subjects in one group cannot be related in any way to subjects in a second group.
>
> **3.** The populations are normally distributed.
>
> **4.** The populations have the same variance; that is, each treatment group has population variance σ^2.

Suppose that we are testing a hypothesis regarding $k = 3$ population means so that the null hypothesis is

$$H_0: \mu_1 = \mu_2 = \mu_3$$

and the alternative hypothesis is

$$H_1: \text{at least one of the population means is different from the others}$$

Figure 1(a) shows the distribution of each population if the null hypothesis is true, and Figure 1(b) shows one example of what the distributions of the populations might look like if the alternative hypothesis is true.

Figure 1

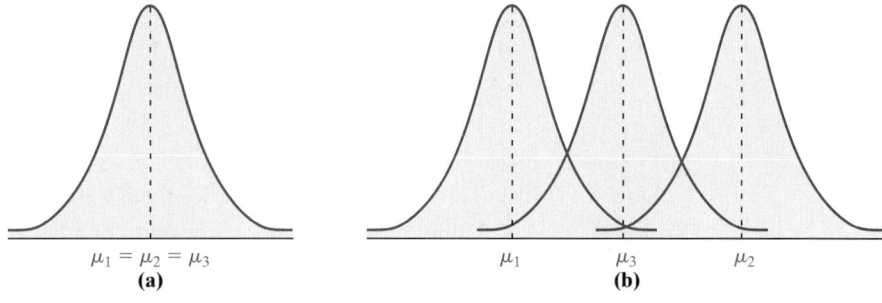

$\mu_1 = \mu_2 = \mu_3$
(a)

μ_1 μ_3 μ_2
(b)

The methods of one-way ANOVA are **robust**, so small departures from the requirement of normality will not significantly affect the results of the procedure. In addition, the requirement of equal population variances does not need to be strictly adhered to, *especially if the sample size for each treatment group is the same.* Therefore, it is worthwhile to design an experiment in which the samples from the populations are roughly equal in size.

We can verify the requirement of normality by constructing normal probability plots. The requirement of equal population variances is more difficult to verify. Recall from Section 11.4 that testing the equality of population variances is discouraged because the test is not robust. In addition, we have seen how multiple paired comparisons increase the chance of making a mistake, so pairwise comparison of population variances is not recommended. However, a general rule of thumb is as follows:

In Other Words

Try to design experiments that use ANOVA so that each treatment group has the same number of experimental units.

Note to Instructor

It may seem contradictory that we require equal population variances in one-way ANOVA, but are unwilling to make this assumption when comparing two means. The reason lies in the fact that there is no parametric alternative to one-way ANOVA. The parametric alternative to pooling is Welch's t.

Verifying the Requirement of Equal Population Variances

The one-way ANOVA procedures may be used provided that the largest sample standard deviation is no more than twice the smallest sample standard deviation.

EXAMPLE 1   **Testing the Requirements of One-Way ANOVA**

Problem: The field of prosthodontics is one of nine specialties recognized by the American Dental Association. Prosthodentists specialize in the restoration of oral function, including the use of dental implants, veneers, dentures, and crowns. Since repairing chipped veneer is less time consuming and less costly than complete restoration, a researcher wanted to determine the effect of different repair kits on shear bond strength for repairs of chipped porcelain veneer in fixed prosthodontics. He randomly divided 20 porcelain specimens into four treatment groups. Group 1 specimens used the Cojet system, group 2 used the Silistor system, group 3 used the Cimara system, and group 4 specimens used the Ceramic Repair system. At the conclusion of the study, shear bond strength (in megapascals, MPa) was measured according to ISO 10477. The results presented in Table 1 are based on the results of the study. Verify that the requirements to perform one-way ANOVA are satisfied.

Table 1			
Cojet	**Silistor**	**Cimara**	**Ceramic Repair**
15.4	17.2	5.5	11.0
12.9	14.3	7.7	12.4
17.2	17.6	12.2	13.5
16.6	21.6	11.4	8.9
19.3	17.5	16.4	8.1

Source: P. Schmage et al. "Shear Bond Strengths of Five Intraoral Porcelain Repair Systems," *Journal of Adhesion Science & Technology* 21(5–6):409–422, 2007

Approach: We verify each of the requirements listed on page 680.

Solution

1. The specimens were randomly assigned to the repair systems.

2. None of the specimens is related in any way, so the samples are independent.

3. Figure 2 shows the normal probability plots for all four treatment groups. All of the normal probability plots are roughly linear, so our normality requirement is satisfied.

Figure 2

4. The sample standard deviations for each sample are computed using MINITAB and presented as part of Figure 3. The largest standard deviation is 4.22 MPa, and the smallest standard deviation is 2.28 MPa. Because the largest standard deviation is not more than twice the smallest standard deviation ($2 \cdot 2.28 = 4.56 > 4.22$), the requirement of equal population variances is considered satisfied.

Figure 3

Descriptive Statistics: Cojet, Silistor, Cimara, Ceramic Repair

```
Variable         Mean StDev Variance Minimum    Q1 Median    Q3 Maximum
Cojet           16.28  2.36     5.57   12.90 14.15  16.60 18.25   19.30
Silistor        17.64  2.60     6.76   14.30 15.75  17.50 19.60   21.60
Cimara          10.64  4.22    17.81    5.50  6.60  11.40 14.30   16.40
Ceramic Repair  10.78  2.28     5.20    8.10  8.50  11.00 12.95   13.50
```

Since all four requirements are satisfied, we can perform a one-way ANOVA.

 Test a Hypothesis Regarding Three or More Means Using One-Way ANOVA

A Conceptual Understanding of One-Way ANOVA

The basic idea in one-way ANOVA is to determine if the sample data could come from populations with the same mean, μ, or if the sample evidence suggests that at least one sample comes from a population whose mean is different from the others.

To help understand the idea behind the ANOVA procedure, consider the data sets in Tables 2(a) and (b). Each set of data represents samples from three populations. If we compute the sample means for each set of data, we find that $\bar{x}_1 = \bar{y}_1 = 5$, $\bar{x}_2 = \bar{y}_2 = 8$, and $\bar{x}_3 = \bar{y}_3 = 11$. Figure 4(a) shows a dot plot for the data in Table 2(a), and Figure 4(b) shows a dot plot for the data in Table 2(b). In Figure 4, we use blue dots to represent sample 1, red squares to represent sample 2, and green diamonds to represent sample 3.

Looking at the dot plot of the data in Table 2(a) in Figure 4(a), it is apparent that the sample data come from populations with different means, because the variability *within* each sample is small relative to the amount of variability between the three sample means (in fact, there is not even any overlap among the samples). However, the difference in the means is not at all apparent from the dot plot for the data in Table 2(b) in Figure 4(b). So, even though the sample means of the data in Table 2(b) vary by the same amount as they do in Table 2(a), the variability within each sample in Table 2(b) makes it difficult to determine whether the means differ enough to conclude that the samples come from populations with different means.

Table 2					
x_1	x_2	x_3	y_1	y_2	y_3
4	7	10	14	10	6
5	8	10	2	3	7
6	9	11	2	15	12
6	7	11	7	7	15
4	9	13	0	5	15
(a)			(b)		

Figure 4

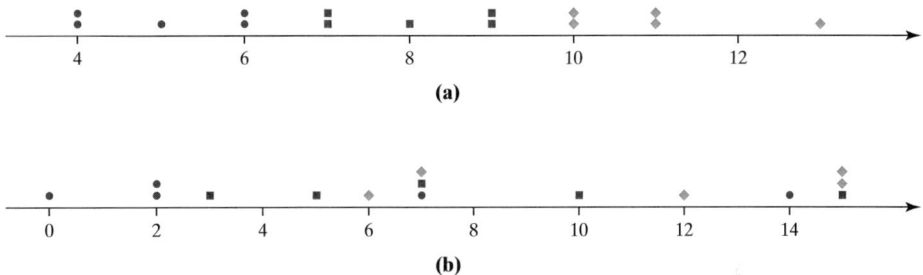

(a)

(b)

In general, we call the variability among the sample means the **between-sample variability**, and we call the variability of each sample the **within-sample variability**. The between-sample variability for the data in Tables 2(a) and (b) is the same (since both sets of data have the same sample means for each sample, the same overall mean, and the same sample size), but the within-sample variability for the data in Table 2(b) is much larger than it is for the data in Table 2(a). So, if the between-sample variability is large relative to the within-sample variability, we have evidence to suggest that the samples come from populations with different means. This is the logic behind *analysis of variance* to test equality of *means*. The test statistic that we use to judge whether the population means might be equal is based on this idea.

ANOVA *F*-Test Statistic

The analysis of variance *F*-test statistic is given by

$$F_0 = \frac{\text{between-sample variability}}{\text{within-sample variability}}$$

How to Compute the *F*-Test Statistic

Remember, in testing any hypothesis, the null hypothesis is assumed to be true until the evidence indicates otherwise. In testing hypotheses regarding k population means, we assume that $\mu_1 = \mu_2 = \cdots = \mu_k = \mu$. That is, we assume that all k samples come from the same normal population whose mean is μ and variance is σ^2. Table 3 shows the statistics that result by sampling from each of the k populations.

Sample	Sample Size	Sample Mean	Sample Standard Deviation
Table 3			
1	n_1	$\overline{x}_1$	s_1
2	n_2	$\overline{x}_2$	s_2
3	n_3	$\overline{x}_3$	s_3
$\vdots$	$\vdots$	$\vdots$	$\vdots$
k	n_k	$\overline{x}_k$	s_k

The computation of the F-test statistic is based on *mean squares*. A **mean square** is an average (mean) of squared values. For example, any variance is a mean square. In Section 3.2, we saw that the population variance, σ^2, is estimated by the sample variance, $s^2 = \dfrac{\sum(x_i - \overline{x})^2}{n-1}$. The numerator of s^2 is called the **sum of squares**. It gives a measure of the variability of the data about the sample mean. The denominator of $s^2, n-1$, represents the *degrees of freedom*. So, in general, a mean square is a sum of squares divided by the corresponding degrees of freedom. The F-test statistic is the ratio of two mean squares, or two estimates of the variance: the between-sample variability and the within-sample variability.

The quantity $\sum(x - \overline{x})^2$ represents the total variability about the mean of the entire set of data, $\overline{x}$, and is called the **total sum of squares** or **SS (Total)**. Within any given set of data, there are two types of variability: variability due to differences in the treatment groups (or samples) and variability within each treatment group (or samples).

The variability within each treatment group, or within-sample variability estimate of σ^2 (or denominator of the F-test statistic), is a weighted average of the sample variances from each treatment (or sample), where the weights are based on the size of each sample. We call this estimate of σ^2 the **mean square due to error**, denoted MSE. To find the MSE, we first compute the **sum of squares due to error**, or SSE. The SSE is the sum of all sample variances weighted by the degrees of freedom. So

$$\text{SSE} = (n_1 - 1)s_1^2 + (n_2 - 1)s_2^2 + \cdots + (n_k - 1)s_k^2$$

For each sample variance in the sum of squares due to error, the degrees of freedom is $n_i - 1$. The total degrees of freedom for the SSE is the sum of the individual degrees of freedom, or

$$(n_1 - 1) + (n_2 - 1) + \cdots + (n_k - 1) = (n_1 + n_2 + \cdots + n_k) - k = n - k$$

where n is the total number of observations. That is, $n = n_1 + n_2 + \cdots + n_k$ and k is the number of treatments (or samples).

The mean square due to error is an unbiased estimator of σ^2 whether the null hypothesis of equal means is true or not. It is computed as follows:

$$\text{MSE} = \frac{\text{SSE}}{\text{degrees of freedom}} = \frac{(n_1 - 1)s_1^2 + (n_2 - 1)s_2^2 + \cdots + (n_k - 1)s_k^2}{n - k}$$

The between-sample variability estimate of σ^2 (or numerator of the F test statistic) is called the **mean square due to treatment**, denoted **MST**, since any differences in the sample means could be attributed to the different levels of the treatment. To find the MST, we first compute the **sum of squares due to treatment** or **SST**. The SST is computed by determining the sum of the squared differences between each treatment (or sample) mean and the overall mean, where each squared difference is weighted by its sample size. That is,

$$\text{SST} = n_1(\overline{x}_1 - \overline{x})^2 + n_2(\overline{x}_2 - \overline{x})^2 + \cdots + n_k(\overline{x}_k - \overline{x})^2$$

Since there are k sample means and SST is measuring how these vary from the overall mean, this sum of squares will have $k - 1$ degrees of freedom. The MST is computed as follows:

$$MST = \frac{SST}{\text{degrees of freedom}} = \frac{n_1(\bar{x}_1 - \bar{x})^2 + n_2(\bar{x}_2 - \bar{x})^2 + \cdots + nk(\bar{x}_k - \bar{x})^2}{k - 1}$$

The mean square due to treatment is an unbiased estimate of σ^2 only if the null hypothesis is true. So, if H_0 is true (that is, if the k populations means are equal), we expect the mean square due to treatment to be close in value to the mean square due to error. However, if H_0 is false (that is, at least one population mean differs from the others), the mean square due to treatment is *not* a good estimate of σ^2. In fact, if the statement in the null hypothesis is false, the MST will overestimate the value of σ^2, because at least one of the sample means in a treatment (or sample) will be "far away" from the overall mean.

The F-test statistic is based on this ratio.

F-Test Statistic

$$F_0 = \frac{\text{mean square due to treatments}}{\text{mean square due to error}} = \frac{MST}{MSE}$$

So, if the F-test statistic is large, the MST is greater than the MSE. We would take this as evidence against the statement in the null hypothesis.

We now present the steps to be used in computing the F-test statistic.

Computing the F-Test Statistic

Step 1: Compute the sample mean of the combined data set by adding up all the observations and dividing by the number of observations. Call this value $\bar{x}$.

Step 2: Find the sample mean for each sample (or treatment). Let $\bar{x}_1$ represent the sample mean of sample 1, $\bar{x}_2$ represent the sample mean of sample 2, and so on.

Step 3: Find the sample variance for each sample (or treatment). Let s_1^2 represent the sample variance for sample 1, s_2^2 represent the sample variance for sample 2, and so on.

Step 4: Compute the sum of squares due to treatments, SST, and the sum of squares due to error, SSE. (See page 684).

Step 5: Divide each sum of squares by its corresponding degrees of freedom ($k - 1$ and $n - k$, respectively) to obtain the mean squares MST and MSE.

Step 6: Compute the F-test statistic:

$$F_0 = \frac{\text{mean square due to treatment}}{\text{mean square due to error}} = \frac{MST}{MSE}$$

EXAMPLE 2 **Computing the F-Test Statistic**

Problem: Compute the F-test statistic for the data in Table 2(a). The data are presented again for convenience.

Approach: We follow Steps 1 through 6, just presented.

Solution

Step 1: We compute the mean of the entire set of data, or the overall mean.

$$\bar{x} = \frac{4 + 5 + 6 + \cdots + 11 + 13}{15} = 8$$

x_1	x_2	x_3
4	7	10
5	8	10
6	9	11
6	7	11
4	9	13

Step 2: Find the sample mean for each treatment (or sample).

$$\bar{x}_1 = 5 \qquad \bar{x}_2 = 8 \qquad \bar{x}_3 = 11$$

Step 3: Find the sample variance for each treatment (or sample).

$$s_1^2 = \frac{(4-5)^2 + (5-5)^2 + (6-5)^2 + (6-5)^2 + (4-5)^2}{5-1} = 1$$

$$s_2^2 = 1 \qquad s_3^2 = 1.5$$

Step 4: Compute the sum of squares due to treatment, SST, and the sum of squares due to error, SSE.

$$\text{SST} = 5(5-8)^2 + 5(8-8)^2 + 5(11-8)^2 = 90$$

$$\text{SSE} = (5-1)1 + (5-1)1 + (5-1)1.5 = 14$$

Step 5: Compute the means square due to treatment, MST, and the mean square due to error, MSE.

$$\text{MST} = \frac{\text{SST}}{k-1} = \frac{90}{3-1} = 45 \qquad \text{MSE} = \frac{\text{SSE}}{n-k} = \frac{14}{15-3} = 1.1667$$

Step 6: Compute the F-test statistic.

$$F_0 = \frac{\text{MST}}{\text{MSE}} = \frac{45}{1.1667} = 38.57$$

Now Work Problem 9

For the data in Table 2(b), MST = 45, MSE = 24.1667, and F = 1.86. You may want to verify these results. Notice that the F-test statistic for the data in Table 2(a) is large, which is evidence that the sample means for each treatment (or sample) differ, whereas the F-test statistic for the data in Table 2(b) is small, which is evidence that the sample means for each treatment do not differ. In addition, notice that MST = 45 for the data in both tables. Do you recall why?

The results of the computations for the data in Table 2(a) that led to the F-test statistic are presented in an **ANOVA table**, the form of which is shown in Table 4.

Table 4				
Source of Variation	**Sum of Squares**	**Degrees of Freedom**	**Mean Squares**	**F-Test Statistic**
Treatment	90	2	45	38.57
Error	14	12	1.1667	
Total	104	14		

Remember, the mean square due to error is an unbiased estimate of σ^2 regardless of whether the null hypothesis is true or not. However, the mean square due to treatment is an unbiased estimate of σ^2 only if the statement in the null hypothesis is true (that is, only if the population means from each treatment, or sample, are the same). If at least one mean for a treatment is significantly different from the others, the mean square due to treatment will substantially overestimate the value of σ^2. Since the F-test statistic is the ratio of MST to MSE, analysis of variance tests are always right-tailed tests.

As you may have realized, the computations in performing any analysis of variance test are tedious, so virtually all researchers use statistical software to conduct the test. When using software, it is easiest to use the P-value approach. The nice thing about P-values is that the decision rule is always the same, regardless of the type of hypothesis being tested.

Decision Rule in the One-Way ANOVA Test

If the P-value is less than the level of significance, α, reject the null hypothesis.

EXAMPLE 3   Performing One-Way ANOVA Using Technology

Problem: The researcher in Example 1 wants to determine if there is a difference in the mean shear bond strength among the four treatment groups at the $\alpha = 0.05$ level of significance.

Approach: We will use MINITAB, Excel, and a TI-84 Plus graphing calculator to conduct the test. If the P-value is less than the level of significance, we reject the null hypothesis. The steps for performing one-way ANOVA using the TI-83/84 Plus graphing calculators, MINITAB, and Excel are given in the Technology Step-by-Step on page 694.

Solution: Remember, the null hypothesis is always a statement of "no difference," so the null hypothesis is that the mean shear bond strength among the four treatment groups is the same, or

$$H_0: \mu_{\text{Cojet}} = \mu_{\text{Silistor}} = \mu_{\text{Cimara}} = \mu_{\text{Ceramic Repair}}$$

versus the alternative hypothesis

H_1: at least one of the population means is different from the others

Figure 5 shows (a) the output from MINITAB, (b) the output from Excel, and (c) the output from a TI-84 Plus graphing calculator.

Figure 5   **One-way ANOVA: Cojet, Silistor, Cimara, Ceramic Repair**

```
Source   DF      SS     MS     F      P
Factor    3  199.99  66.66  7.55  0.002
Error    16  141.36   8.84
Total    19  341.35

s = 2.972  R-Sq = 58.59%  R-Sq(adj) = 50.82%


                                   Individual 95% CIs For Mean Based on
                                   Pooled StDev
Level            N   Mean  StDev  --------+---------+---------+---------+-
Cojet            5 16.280  2.359                     (--------*-------)
Silistor         5 17.640  2.601                       (-------*-------)
Cimara           5 10.640  4.221  (-------*-------)
Ceramic Repair   5 10.780  2.280   (-------*-------)
                                   --------+---------+---------+---------+-
                                       10.5      14.0      17.5      21.0


Pooled StDev = 2.972
```
                            (a) MINITAB Output

Anova: Single Factor

SUMMARY

Groups	Count	Sum	Average	Variance
Cojet	5	81.4	16.28	5.567
Silistor	5	88.2	17.64	6.763
Cimara	5	53.2	10.64	17.813
Ceramic Repair	5	53.9	10.78	5.197

ANOVA

Source of Variation	SS	df	MS	F	P-value	F crit
Between Groups	199.9855	3	66.66183	7.545199	0.002295	3.238872
Within Groups	141.36	16	8.835			
Total	341.3455	19				

(b) Excel Output

Figure 5
Continued

P-value

(c) TI-84 Plus Output

Because the *P*-value, 0.002, is less than the level of significance, α, we reject the null hypothesis. There is sufficient evidence to indicate that at least one population mean shear bond strength is different from the others.

Whenever performing analysis of variance, it is always a good idea to present visual evidence that supports the conclusions of the test. Side-by-side boxplots are a great way to help visually reinforce the results of the ANOVA procedure. Figure 6 shows the side-by-side boxplots of the data presented in Table 1. The boxplots support the ANOVA results from Example 3.

Figure 6

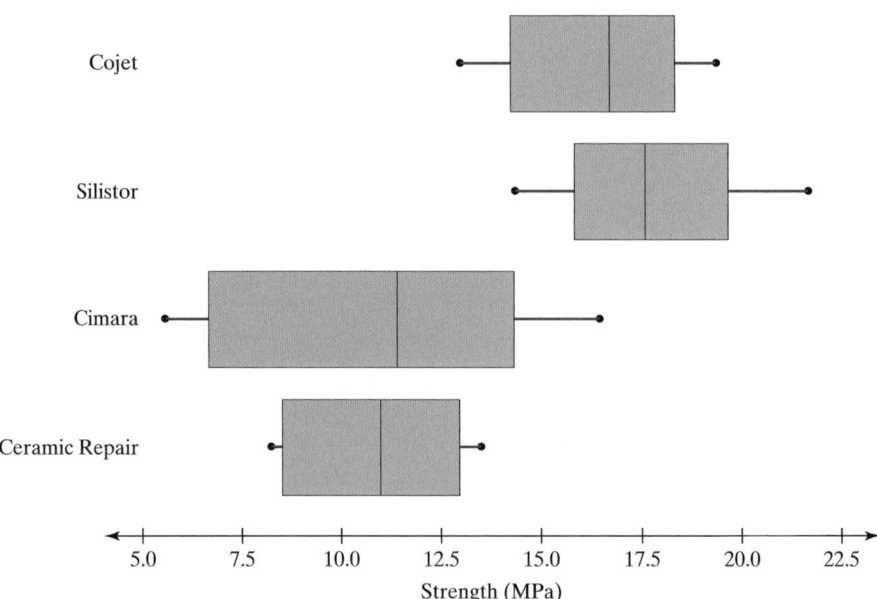

Shear Bond Strengths

Now Work Problem 11

Figure 7

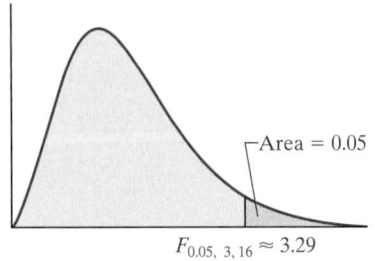

Area = 0.05

$F_{0.05,\ 3,\ 16} \approx 3.29$

In Other Words

If we reject the null hypothesis when doing ANOVA, we are rejecting the null hypothesis that the population means are all equal. However, the test doesn't tell us which means differ.

If we were conducting this ANOVA test by hand, we would compare the *F*-test statistic with a critical *F*-value. The ANOVA test is a right-tailed test, so the **critical F-value** is the *F*-value whose area in the right tail is α with $k - 1$ degrees of freedom in the numerator and $n - k$ degrees of freedom in the denominator. The critical *F*-value for the study in Example 1 at the $\alpha = 0.05$ level of significance is $F_{0.05,3,16} \approx 3.29$ from Table VIII. Note that, because the table is limited, we must use the value for $F_{0.05,3,15}$ as our critical value. In Figure 5(b) we see that the technology gives us a more accurate critical value, $F_{0.05,3,16} \approx 3.239$. Since the *F*-test statistic, 7.55, is greater than the critical *F*, we reject the null hypothesis (see Figure 7).

When we reject the null hypothesis of equal population means, as in this example, this only tells us that at least one population mean differs from the others. The ANOVA test, however, does not tell us which means differ. Side-by-side boxplots or confidence intervals, like those in Figure 6 and Figure 5(a), can give us some idea, but we can more formally answer this question using Tukey's test which will be discussed in the next section.

13.1 ASSESS YOUR UNDERSTANDING

Concepts and Vocabulary

1. The acronym ANOVA stands for <u>analysis of variance</u>.

2. What are the requirements to perform a one-way ANOVA? Is the test robust?

3. What is the mean square due to treatment estimate of σ^2? What is the mean square due to error estimate of σ^2?

4. Why does a large value of the F statistic provide evidence against the null hypothesis $H_0: \mu_1 = \mu_2 = \cdots = \mu_k$?

Skill Building

In Problems 5 and 6, fill in the ANOVA table.

5.

Source of Variation	Sum of Squares	Degrees of Freedom	Mean Squares	F-Test Statistic
Treatment	387	2	193.5	0.650
Error	8,042	27	297.852	
Total	8,429	29		

6.

Source of Variation	Sum of Squares	Degrees of Freedom	Mean Squares	F-Test Statistic
Treatment	2,814	3	938	6.870
Error	4,915	36	136.528	
Total	7,729	39		

In Problems 7 and 8, determine the F-test statistic based on the given summary statistics. [Hint: $\bar{x} = \dfrac{\sum n_i \bar{x}_i}{\sum n_i}$.]

7.

Population	Sample Size	Sample Mean	Sample Variance
1	10	40	48
2	10	42	31
3	10	44	25

$F_0 = 1.154$

8.

Population	Sample Size	Sample Mean	Sample Variance
1	15	105	34
2	15	110	40
3	15	108	30
4	15	90	38

$F_0 = 35.8$

9. The following data represent a simple random sample of NW $n = 4$ from three populations that are known to be normally distributed. Verify that the F-test statistic is 2.04.

Sample 1	Sample 2	Sample 3
28	22	25
23	25	24
30	17	19
27	23	30

10. The following data represent a simple random sample of $n = 5$ from three populations that are known to be normally distributed. Verify that the F-test statistic is 2.599.

Sample 1	Sample 2	Sample 3
73	67	72
82	77	80
82	66	87
81	67	77
97	83	96

Applying the Concepts

11. Corn Production The data in the table represent the number of corn plants in randomly sampled rows (a 17-foot by 5-inch strip) for various types of plot. An agricultural researcher wants to know whether the mean numbers of plants for each plot type are equal.

Plot Type	Number of Plants					
Sludge plot	25	27	33	30	28	27
Spring disk	32	30	33	35	34	34
No till	30	26	29	32	25	29

Source: Andrew Dieter and Brad Schmidgall, Joliet Junior College

11. (a) $H_0: \mu_{SP} = \mu_{SD} = \mu_{NT}$ vs. H_1: at least one mean is different

(a) Write the null and alternative hypotheses.

(b) State the requirements that must be satisfied to use the one-way ANOVA procedure.

(c) Use the following partial MINITAB output to test the hypothesis of equal means at the $\alpha = 0.05$ level of significance.   Reject H_0

One-way ANOVA: Sludge Plot, Spring Disk, No Till

```
Source    DF      SS      MS      F       P
Factor    2    84.11   42.06   7.10   0.007
Error    15    88.83    5.92
Total    17   172.94
```

(d) Shown are side-by-side boxplots of each type of plot. Do these boxplots support the results obtained in part (c)?

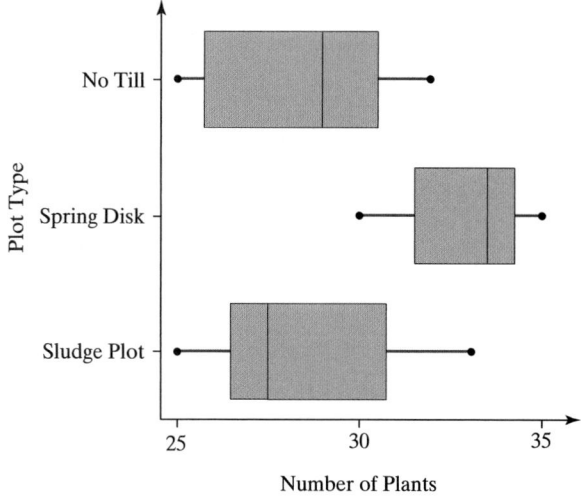

(e) Verify that the F-test statistic is 7.10.

12. (a) $H_0: \mu_L = \mu_{NT} = \mu_{CP}$ vs. H_1: at least one mean is different

12. (c) Reject H_0

12. Soybean Yield The data in the table represent the number of pods on a random sample of soybean plants for various plot types. An agricultural researcher wants to determine if the mean numbers of pods for each plot type are equal.

Plot Type	Pods								
Liberty	32	31	36	35	41	34	39	37	38
No till	34	30	31	27	40	33	37	42	39
Chisel plowed	34	37	24	23	32	33	27	34	30

Source: Andrew Dieter and Brad Schmidgall, Joliet Junior College

(a) Write the null and alternative hypotheses.
(b) State the requirements that must be satisfied to use the one-way ANOVA procedure.
(c) Use the following MINITAB output to test the hypothesis of equal means at the $\alpha = 0.05$ level of significance.

One-way ANOVA: Liberty, No Till Chisel Plowed

```
Source   DF     SS     MS     F      P
Factor    2   149.0   74.5   3.77   0.038
Error    24   474.7   19.8
Total    26   623.6
```

(d) Shown are side-by-side boxplots of each type of plot. Do these boxplots support the results obtained in part (c)?

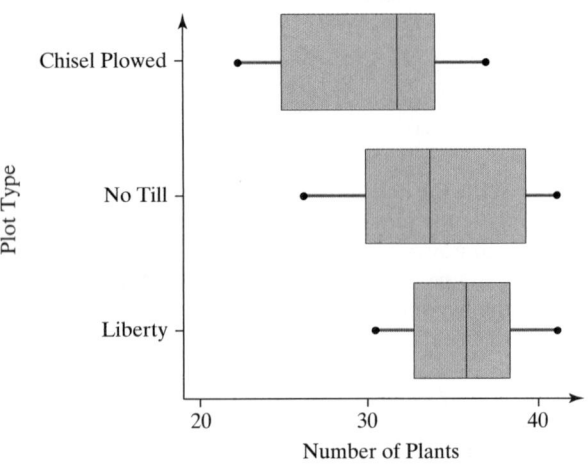

(e) Verify that the F-test statistic is 3.77.
(f) Based on the boxplots, which plot type appears to have a significantly different mean number of plants? *Chisel Plowed*

13. Births by Day of Week An obstetrician knew that there were more live births during the week than on weekends. She wanted to determine whether the mean number of births was the same for each of the five days of the week. She randomly selected eight dates for each of the five days of the week and obtained the following data:

Monday	Tuesday	Wednesday	Thursday	Friday
10,456	11,621	11,084	11,171	11,545
10,023	11,944	11,570	11,745	12,321
10,691	11,045	11,346	12,023	11,749
10,283	12,927	11,875	12,433	12,192
10,265	12,577	12,193	12,132	12,422
11,189	11,753	11,593	11,903	11,627
11,198	12,509	11,216	11,233	11,624
11,465	13,521	11,818	12,543	12,543

Source: National Center for Health Statistics

13. (a) $H_0: \mu_M = \mu_T = \mu_W = \mu_R = \mu_F$ vs. H_1: at least one mean is different

(a) Write the null and alternative hypotheses.
(b) State the requirements that must be satisfied to use the one-way ANOVA procedure.
(c) Use the following MINITAB output to test the hypothesis of equal means at the $\alpha = 0.01$ level of significance.

One-way ANOVA: Mon, Tues, Wed, Thurs, Fri

```
Source   DF      SS        MS        F      P
Factor    4   11507633   2876908   9.80   0.000
Error    35   10270781    293451
Total    39   21778414
```

(d) Shown are side-by-side boxplots of each type of plot. Do these boxplots support the results obtained in part (c)?

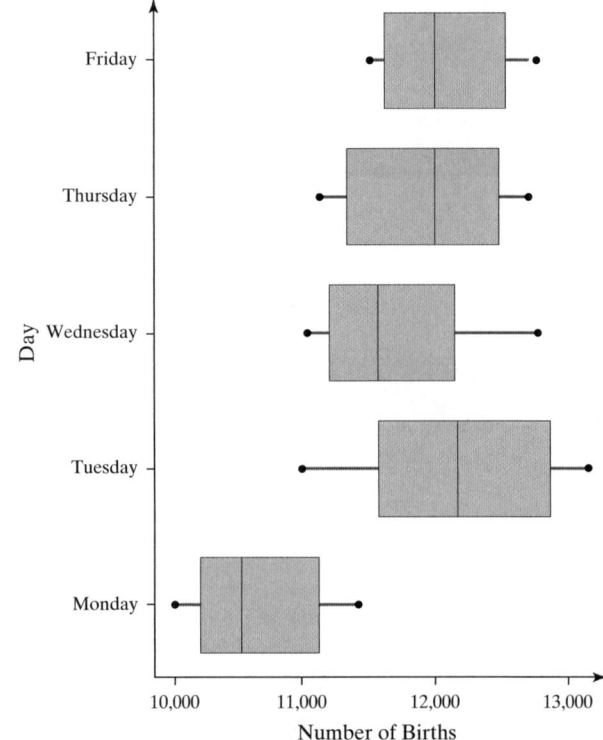

(e) Verify that the F-test statistic is 9.80.
(f) Based on the boxplots, which day of the week appears to have a significantly different number of births? *Monday*

14. Punkin Chunkin The World Championship Punkin Chunkin contest is held every fall in Millsboro, Delaware. Contestants build devices meant to hurl 8- to 10-pound pumpkins across a field. One class of entry is the air cannon, which must use compressed air to fire a pumpkin. The following data represent a simple random sample of distances that pumpkins traveled (in feet) for the years 2004 through 2007. Is there evidence to conclude that the mean distance that a pumpkin travels is different for the various years?

2004	2005	2006	2007
4,224.00	4,331.72	3,870.50	3,489.85
4,065.60	3,633.79	3,579.43	3,416.15
3,967.95	4,267.49	3,623.65	4,211.27
3,596.09	4,237.90	3,275.19	3,238.09
3,970.00	4,211.17	3,022.24	3,579.62
3,877.68	3,034.77	3,632.59	3,552.72

Source: www.punkinchunkin.com

13. (c) Reject H_0

14. (a) $H_0: \mu_{2004} = \mu_{2005} = \mu_{2006} = \mu_{2007}$ vs. H_1: at least one mean is different

    (a) Write the null and alternative hypotheses.

    (b) State the requirements that must be satisfied to use the one-way ANOVA procedure.

    (c) Use the following MINITAB output to conduct the test at the $\alpha = 0.05$ level of significance.   Do not reject H_0

One-way ANOVA: 2004, 2005, 2006, 2007

Source	DF	SS	MS	F	P
Factor	3	1030964	343655	2.68	0.074
Error	20	2561191	128060		
Total	23	3592155			

    (d) Shown are side-by-side boxplots of each type of plot. Do these boxplots support the results obtained in part (c)?

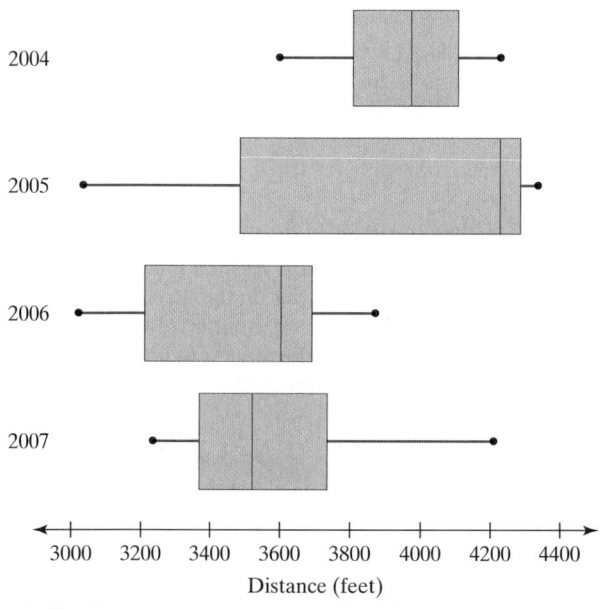

Distance (feet)

    (e) Verify that the F-test statistic is 2.68.

15. **Rates of Return** A stock analyst wondered whether the mean rate of return of financial, energy, and utility stocks differed over the past 5 years. He obtained a simple random sample of eight companies from each of the three sectors and obtained the 5-year rates of return shown in the following table (in percent):

Financial	Energy	Utilities
10.76	12.72	11.88
15.05	13.91	5.86
17.01	6.43	13.46
5.07	11.19	9.90
19.50	18.79	3.95
8.16	20.73	3.44
10.38	9.60	7.11
6.75	17.40	15.70

Source: Morningstar.com

15. (a) $H_0: \mu_F = \mu_E = \mu_U$ vs. H_1: at least one mean is different

    (a) State the null and alternative hypothesis.

    (b) Verify that the requirements to use the one-way ANOVA procedure are satisfied. Normal probability plots indicate that the sample data come from normal populations.

    (c) Are the mean rates of return different at the $\alpha = 0.05$ level of significance?   Do not reject H_0

    (d) Draw boxplots of the three sectors to support the results obtained in part (c).

16. **Reaction Time** In an online psychology experiment sponsored by the University of Mississippi, researchers asked study participants to respond to various stimuli. Participants were randomly assigned to one of three groups. Subjects in group 1 were in the simple group. They were required to respond as quickly as possible after a stimulus was presented. Subjects in group 2 were in the go/no-go group. These subjects were required to respond to a particular stimulus while disregarding other stimuli. Finally, subjects in group 3 were in the choice group. They needed to respond differently, depending on the stimuli presented. Depending on the type of whistle sound, the subject must press a certain button. The reaction time (in seconds) for each stimulus is presented in the table.

Simple	Go/No Go	Choice
0.430	0.588	0.561
0.498	0.375	0.498
0.480	0.409	0.519
0.376	0.613	0.538
0.402	0.481	0.464
0.329	0.355	0.725

Source: PsychExperiments; The University of Mississippi; www.olemiss.edu/psychexps/

16. (a) $H_0: \mu_S = \mu_G = \mu_C$ vs. H_1: at least one mean is different

The researcher wants to determine if the mean reaction times for each stimulus are equal.

    (a) State the null and alternative hypotheses.

    (b) Verify that the requirements to use the one-way ANOVA procedure are satisfied. Normal probability plots indicate that the sample data come from a normal population.

    (c) Test the hypothesis that the mean reaction times to the three stimuli are the same at the $\alpha = 0.05$ level of significance.   Do not reject H_0

    (d) Draw boxplots of the three stimuli to support the analytic results obtained in part (c).

17. **Crash Data** The Insurance Institute for Highway Safety conducts experiments in which cars are crashed into a fixed barrier at 40 mph. In the institute's 40-mph offset test, 40% of the total width of each vehicle strikes a barrier on the driver's side. The barrier's deformable face is made of aluminum honeycomb, which makes the forces in the test similar to those involved in a frontal offset crash between two vehicles of the same weight, each going just less than 40 mph. You are in the market to buy a new family car and you want to know whether the mean chest compression resulting from this offset crash is the same for large family cars, passenger vans, and midsize utility vehicles. The following data were collected from the institute's study.

Large Family Cars	Chest Compression (mm)	Passenger Vans	Chest Compression (mm)	Midsize Utility Vehicles	Chest Compression (mm)
Hyundai XG300	33	Toyota Sienna	29	Honda Pilot	29
Ford Taurus	40	Honda Odyssey	28	Toyota 4Runner	36
Buick LeSabre	28	Ford Freestar	27	Mitsubishi Endeavor	35
Chevrolet Impala	30	Mazda MPV	30	Nissan Murano	32
Chrysler 300	34	Chevrolet Uplander	26	Ford Explorer	34
Pontiac Grand Prix	34	Nissan Quest	33	Jeep Liberty	42
Toyota Avalon	31	Kia Sedona	36	Buick Randezvous	29

Source: Insurance Institute for Highway Safety

The researcher wants to determine if the means for chest compression for each class of vehicle are different.
(a) State the null and alternative hypotheses. $H_0: \mu_L = \mu_P = \mu_M$ vs. H_1: at least one mean is different
(b) Verify that the requirements to use the one-way ANOVA procedure are satisfied. Normal probability plots indicate that the sample data come from normal populations.
(c) Test the hypothesis that the mean chest compression for each vehicle type is the same at the $\alpha = 0.01$ level of significance.
    Do not reject H_0
(d) Draw boxplots of the three types of vehicle to support the analytic results obtained in part (c).

18. **Crash Data** The Insurance Institute for Highway Safety conducts experiments in which cars are crashed into a fixed barrier at 40 mph. In the institute's 40-mph offset test, 40% of the total width of each vehicle strikes a barrier on the driver's side. The barrier's deformable face is made of aluminum honeycomb, which makes the forces in the test similar to those involved in a frontal offset crash between two vehicles of the same weight, each going just less than 40 mph. You are in the market to buy a new family car and you want to know if the mean head injury resulting from this offset crash is the same for large family cars, passenger vans, and midsize utility vehicles. The following data were collected from the institute's study.

Large Family Cars	Head Injury (hic)	Passenger Vans	Head Injury (hic)	Midsize Utility Vehicles	Head Injury (hic)
Hyundai XG300	264	Toyota Sienna	148	Honda Pilot	225
Ford Taurus	134	Honda Odyssey	238	Toyota 4Runner	216
Buick LeSabre	409	Ford Freestar	340	Mitsubishi Endeavor	186
Chevrolet Impala	530	Mazda MPV	693	Nissan Murano	307
Chrysler 300	149	Chevrolet Uplander	550	Ford Explorer	353
Pontiac Grand Prix	627	Nissan Quest	470	Kia Sorento	552
Toyota Avalon	166	Kia Sedona	322	Chevy Trailblazer	397

Source: Insurance Institute for Highway Safety

18. (c) Do not reject H_0

The researcher wants to determine if the means for head injury for each class of vehicle are different.
(a) State the null and alternative hypotheses. $H_0: \mu_L = \mu_P = \mu_M$ vs. H_1: at least one of the means is different
(b) Verify that the requirements to use the one-way ANOVA procedure are satisfied. Normal probability plots indicate that the sample data come from normal populations.
(c) Test the hypothesis that the mean head injury for each vehicle type is the same at the $\alpha = 0.01$ level of significance.
(d) Draw boxplots of the three vehicle types to support the analytic results obtained in part (c).

19. **pH in Rain** An environmentalist wanted to determine if the mean acidity of rain differed among Alaska, Florida, and Texas. He randomly selected six rain dates at each of the three locations and obtained the following data:

Alaska	Florida	Texas
5.41	4.87	5.46
5.39	5.18	6.29
4.90	4.40	5.57
5.14	5.12	5.15
4.80	4.89	5.45
5.24	5.06	5.30

Source: National Atmospheric Deposition Program

19. (a) $H_0: \mu_A = \mu_F = \mu_T$ vs. H_1: at least one of the means is different

(a) State the null and alternative hypothesis.
(b) Verify that the requirements to use the one-way ANOVA procedure are satisfied. Normal probability plots indicate that the sample data come from a normal population.
(c) Test the hypothesis that the mean pHs in the rainwater are the same at the $\alpha = 0.05$ level of significance. Reject H_0
(d) Draw boxplots of the pH in rain for the three states to support the results obtained in part (c).

20. **Lower Your Cholesterol** Researchers Francisco Fuentes and his colleagues wanted to determine the most effective diet for reducing LDL cholesterol, the so-called "bad" cholesterol, among three diets: (1) a saturated-fat diet, (2) the Mediterranean diet, and (3) the U.S. National Cholesterol Education Program or NCEP-1 Diet. The participants in the

20. (a) $H_0: \mu_{SF} = \mu_M = \mu_{NCE}$ vs. H_1: at least one of the means is different

study were shown to have the same levels of LDL cholesterol before the study. Participants were randomly assigned to one of the three treatment groups. Individuals in group 1 received the saturated-fat diet, which is 15% protein, 47% carbohydrates, and 38% fat (20% saturated fat, 12% monounsaturated fat, and 6% polyunsaturated fat). Individuals in group 2 received the Mediterranean diet, which is 47% carbohydrates, and 38% fat (<10% saturated fat, 22% monounsaturated fat, and 6% polyunsaturated fat). Individuals in group 3 received the NCEP-1 Diet (<10% saturated fat, 12% monounsaturated fat, and 6% polyunsaturated fat). After 28 days, their LDL cholesterol levels were recorded. The data in the following table are based on this study.

Saturated Fat		Mediterranean		NCEP-1	
245	218	56	131	125	184
123	173	78	125	100	116
166	223	101	160	140	144
104	177	158	130	151	101
196	193	145	83	138	135
300	224	118	263	268	144
140	149	145	150	75	130
240		211		71	

(a) State the null and alternative hypothesis.
(b) Verify that the requirements to use the one-way ANOVA procedure are satisfied. Normal probability plots indicate that the sample data come from normal populations.
(c) Are the mean LDL cholesterol levels different at the $\alpha = 0.05$ level of significance? Reject H_0
(d) Draw boxplots of the three LDL cholesterol levels for the three groups to support the analytic results obtained in part (c).

21. **Concrete Strength** An engineer wants to know if the mean strengths of three different concrete mix designs differ significantly. He randomly selects 9 cylinders that measure 6 inches in diameter and 12 inches in height in which mixture 67-0-301 is poured, 9 cylinders of mixture 67-0-400, and 9 cylinders of mixture 67-0-353. After 28 days, he measures the strength (in pounds per square inch) of the cylinders. The results are presented in the following table:

Mixture 67-0-301		Mixture 67-0-400		Mixure 67-0-353	
3,960	4,090	4,070	4,120	4,150	3,820
4,040	3,830	4,330	4,640	3,820	3,750
3,780	3,940	4,620	4,190	4,010	3,990
3,890	4,080	3,730	3,850	4,150	4,320
3,990		4,890		4,190	

(a) State the null and alternative hypotheses.
(b) Explain why we cannot use one-way ANOVA to test these hypotheses.

22. **Analyzing Journal Article Results** Researchers (Brian G. Feagan et al., "Erythropoietin with Iron Supplementation to Prevent Allogeneic Blood Transfusion in Total Hip Joint Arthroplasty," *Annals of Internal Medicine*, Vol. 133, No. 11)

wanted to determine whether epoetin alfa was effective in increasing the hemoglobin concentration in patients undergoing hip arthroplasty. The researchers screened patients for eligibility by performing a complete medical history and physical of the patients. Once eligible patients were identified, the researchers used a computer-generated schedule to assign the patients to the high-dose epoetin group, low-dose epoetin group, or placebo group. The study was double-blind. Based on an analysis of variance, it was determined that there were significant differences in the increase in hemoglobin concentration in the three groups with a P-value less than 0.001. The mean increase in hemoglobin in the high-dose epoetin group was 19.5 grams per liter (g/L), the mean increase in hemoglobin in the low-dose epoetin group was 17.2 g/L, and mean increase in hemoglobin in the placebo group was 1.2 g/L.
(a) Why do you think it was necessary to screen patients for eligibility?
(b) Why was a computer-generated schedule used to assign patients to the various treatment groups?
(c) What does it mean for a study to be double-blind? Why do you think the researchers desired a double-blind study?
(d) Interpret the reported P-value.

23. **Putting It Together: Psychological Profiles** Researchers wanted to determine if the psychological profile of healthy children was different than for children suffering from recurrent abdominal pain (RAP) or recurring headaches. A total of 210 children and adolescents were studied and their psychological profiles were graded according to the Child Behaviour Checklist 4–18 (CBCL). Children were stratified in two age groups: 4 to 11 years and 12 to 18 years. The results of the study are summarized in the following table:

	n	Sample Mean	Sample Variance
Control group	70	11.7	21.6
RAP	70	9.0	13.0
Headache	70	12.4	8.4

Source: Galli, et al. "Headache and Recurrent Abdominal Pain: A Controlled Study by Means of the Child Behaviour Checklist (CBCL)." *Cephalalgia* 27, 211–219, 2007

(a) Compute the sample standard deviations for each group. $s_C = 4.6$, $s_R = 3.6$, $s_H = 2.9$
(b) What sampling method was used for each treatment group? Why? Stratified sampling
(c) Use a two sample t-test for independent samples to determine if there is a significant difference in mean CBCL scores between the control group and the RAP group (assume that both samples are simple random samples). Reject H_0
(d) Is it necessary to check the normality assumption to answer part (c)? Explain. No large samples
(e) Use the one-way ANOVA procedure with $\alpha = 0.05$ to determine if the mean CBCL scores are different for the three treatment groups. Reject H_0
(f) Based on your results from parts (c) and (e), can you determine if there is a significant difference between the mean scores of the RAP group and the headache group? Explain. No

21. (a) $H_0: \mu_{67-0-301} = \mu_{67-0-400} = \mu_{67-0-353}$ vs. H_1: at least one of the means is different

TECHNOLOGY STEP-BY-STEP ANOVA

TI-83/84 Plus
1. Enter the raw data into L1, L2, L3, and so on, for each sample or treatment.
2. Press STAT, highlight TESTS, and select F:ANOVA(.
3. Enter the list names for each sample or treatment after ANOVA(. For example, if there are three treatments in L1, L2, and L3, enter

ANOVA(L1,L2,L3)

Press ENTER.

MINITAB
1. Enter the raw data into C1, C2, C3, and so on, for each sample or treatment.
2. Select **Stat**; then highlight **ANOVA** and select **One-way (Unstacked)**.

3. Enter the column names in the cell marked "Responses." Click OK.

Excel
1. Enter the raw data in columns A, B, C, and so on, for each sample or treatment.
2. Be sure the Data Analysis ToolPak is activated. This is done by selecting the **Tools** menu and highlighting **Add-Ins . . . .** Check the box for the Analysis ToolPak and select OK. Select **Tools**, then highlight **Data Analysis**. Select ANOVA: Single Factor and click OK.
3. With the cursor in the "Input Range:" cell, highlight the data. Click OK.

13.2 POST HOC TESTS ON ONE-WAY ANALYSIS OF VARIANCE

Preparing for This Section Before getting started, review the following:

• Using Confidence Intervals to Test Hypotheses (Section 10.2, p. 534)

Objective		Perform the Tukey Test

Note to Instructor
If you like, you can print out and distribute the Preparing for This Section quiz located in the Instructor's Resource Center. The purpose of the quiz is to verify that the students have the prerequisite knowledge for the section.

In Other Words
Post hoc is Latin for after this. Post hoc tests are performed after rejecting the null hypothesis that three or more population means are equal.

Suppose that we perform a one-way ANOVA and the results lead us to conclude that at least one population mean is different from the others. To determine which means differ significantly, we make additional comparisons between means. The procedures for making these comparisons are called **multiple comparison methods**.

Suppose that we used a one-way ANOVA to test the null hypothesis $H_0: \mu_1 = \mu_2 = \mu_3 = \mu_4$ and the sample data led us to reject the null hypothesis. At this point, we probably would want to know which means differ. For example, we might suspect that μ_1 is different from μ_2, which would lead us to test $H_0: \mu_1 = \mu_2$ versus $H_1: \mu_1 \neq \mu_2$. Or we might suspect that μ_1 and μ_2 are equal, but different from μ_3, so we would test $H_0: \mu_1 + \mu_2 = 2\mu_3$ versus the alternative $H_0: \mu_1 + \mu_2 \neq 2\mu_3$.

The researcher typically has some idea as to the type of comparisons that are of interest. In most situations, and in this text, we will only be concerned with comparing pairs of means as in $H_0: \mu_1 = \mu_2$ versus $H_1: \mu_1 \neq \mu_2$. Many different procedures can be used to compare two means. In this text, we present the method introduced by John Tukey (the same Tukey of boxplot fame).

Perform the Tukey Test

The Tukey test is also known as the *Honestly Significant Difference Test* or the *Wholly Significant Difference Test*. It is designed to compare pairs of means after the null hypothesis of equal means has been rejected. That is, it tests $H_0: \mu_i = \mu_j$ versus $H_1: \mu_i \neq \mu_j$ for all means where $i \neq j$. The goal of the test is to determine which population means differ significantly.

The computation of the test statistic for Tukey's test follows the same logic as the test for comparing two means from independent sampling. Suppose that we wish to test $H_0: \mu_1 = \mu_2$ versus $H_1: \mu_1 \neq \mu_2$. This is equivalent to testing $H_0: \mu_2 - \mu_1 = 0$ versus $H_1: \mu_2 - \mu_1 \neq 0$. The test statistic is based on the sample mean difference, $\bar{x}_2 - \bar{x}_1$, and the standard error of the sample mean difference. The standard error is not the same as the standard error used in comparing two means from independent samples. Instead, the standard error is

$$\text{SE} = \sqrt{\frac{s^2}{2} \cdot \left(\frac{1}{n_1} + \frac{1}{n_2} \right)}$$

where s^2 is the mean square error estimate (MSE) of σ^2 from the one-way ANOVA, n_1 is the sample size from population 1, and n_2 is the sample size from population 2.

Test Statistic for Tukey's Test

The test statistic for Tukey's test when testing $H_0: \mu_1 = \mu_2$ versus $H_1: \mu_1 \neq \mu_2$ is given by

$$q_0 = \frac{(\bar{x}_2 - \bar{x}_1) - (\mu_2 - \mu_1)}{\sqrt{\dfrac{s^2}{2} \cdot \left(\dfrac{1}{n_1} + \dfrac{1}{n_2} \right)}} = \frac{\bar{x}_2 - \bar{x}_1}{\sqrt{\dfrac{s^2}{2} \cdot \left(\dfrac{1}{n_1} + \dfrac{1}{n_2} \right)}}$$

where $\bar{x}_2 > \bar{x}_1$

s^2 is the mean square error estimate of σ^2 (MSE) from ANOVA

n_1 is the sample size from population 1

n_2 is the sample size from population 2

Because we assume that the null hypothesis is true, until we have evidence to the contrary, $\mu_2 - \mu_1 = 0$ in the computation of the test statistic.

The question now becomes "What distribution does this test statistic follow?" The q-test statistic follows a distribution called the **Studentized range distribution**. The shape of the distribution depends on the error degrees of freedom, ν, and the total number of means being compared, k. We will compare the test statistic, q_0, to a critical value from this distribution, $q_{\alpha, \nu, k}$, where α is the level of significance of the test and therefore the probability of making a Type I error (rejecting the null hypothesis when the null hypothesis is true). The level of significance α is called the **experimentwise error rate** or the **familywise error rate**.

Critical Value for Tukey's Test

The critical value for Tukey's test using a familywise error rate α is given by

$$q_{\alpha, \nu, k}$$

where

ν is the degrees of freedom due to error (the degrees of freedom due to error is the total number of subjects sampled minus the number of means being compared, or $n - k$)

k is the total number of means being compared

We can determine the critical value from the Studentized range distribution by referring to Table IX. We have provided tables for $\alpha = 0.01$ and $\alpha = 0.05$.

EXAMPLE 1 **Finding the Critical Value from the Studentized Range Distribution**

Problem: Find the critical value from the Studentized range distribution with $\nu = 7$ degrees of freedom and $k = 3$ degrees of freedom, with a familywise error rate $\alpha = 0.05$.

Approach: We look in Table IX with $\alpha = 0.05$ and where the row corresponding to $\nu = 7$ intersects with the column corresponding to $k = 3$. The value in the cell is the critical value.

Solution: See Figure 8. The critical value is $q_{0.05,7,3} = 4.165$.

Figure 8

$\alpha = 0.05$

ν	k(or p):2	3	4	5	6	7	8	9	10
1	17.97	26.98	32.82	37.08	40.41	43.12	45.40	47.36	49.07
2	6.085	8.331	9.798	10.88	11.74	12.44	13.03	13.54	13.99
3	4.501	5.910	6.825	7.502	8.037	8.478	8.853	9.177	9.462
4	3.927	5.040	5.757	6.287	6.707	7.053	7.347	7.602	7.826
5	3.635	4.602	5.218	5.673	6.033	6.330	6.582	6.802	6.995
6	3.461	4.339	4.896	5.305	5.628	5.895	6.122	6.319	6.493
7	3.344	4.165	4.681	5.060	5.359	5.606	5.815	5.998	6.158
8	3.261	4.041	4.529	4.886	5.167	5.399	5.597	5.767	5.918
9	3.199	3.949	4.415	4.756	5.024	5.244	5.432	5.595	5.739
10	3.151	3.877	4.327	4.654	4.912	5.124	5.305	5.461	5.599

Now Work Problem 3

Now that we know the distribution of the test statistic q and how to find the critical value, we introduce a procedure that can be used to make multiple comparisons using Tukey's test.

Tukey's Test

After rejecting the null hypothesis $H_0: \mu_1 = \mu_2 = \cdots = \mu_k$, the following steps can be used to compare pairs of means for significant differences, provided that

1. There are k simple random samples from k populations.
2. The k samples are independent of each other.
3. The populations are normally distributed.
4. The populations have the same variance.

Step 1: Arrange the sample means in ascending order.
Step 2: Compute the pairwise differences, $\bar{x}_i - \bar{x}_j$, where $\bar{x}_i > \bar{x}_j$.

Step 3: Compute the test statistic, $q_0 = \dfrac{\bar{x}_i - \bar{x}_j}{\sqrt{\dfrac{s^2}{2} \cdot \left(\dfrac{1}{n_i} + \dfrac{1}{n_j} \right)}}$, for each pairwise difference.

Step 4: Determine the critical value, $q_{\alpha,\nu,k}$, where α is the level of significance (the familywise error rate).
Step 5: If $q_0 \geq q_{\alpha,\nu,k}$, reject the null hypothesis that $H_0: \mu_i = \mu_j$ and conclude that the means are significantly different.
Step 6: Compare all pairwise differences to identify which means differ.

Let's go through an example to illustrate Tukey's test.

EXAMPLE 2   **Performing Tukey's Test**

Problem: In Example 1 from Section 13.1, we rejected the null hypothesis $H_0: \mu_{\text{Cojet}} = \mu_{\text{Silistor}} = \mu_{\text{Cimara}} = \mu_{\text{Ceramic}}$. Use Tukey's test to determine which pairwise means differ using a familywise error rate of $\alpha = 0.05$.

Approach: We follow Steps 1 through 6 to determine which pairwise means differ.

Solution

Step 1: The means for each category are given in Table 5. The means, in ascending order, are $\bar{x}_{\text{Ci}} = 10.64$, $\bar{x}_{\text{Ce}} = 10.78$, $\bar{x}_{\text{Co}} = 16.28$, and $\bar{x}_{\text{Si}} = 17.64$.

Step 2: We now compute the pairwise differences, $\bar{x}_j - \bar{x}_i$, where $\bar{x}_j > \bar{x}_i$. That is, subtract the smaller sample mean from the larger sample mean, as shown in the second column of Table 6. It is helpful to write the differences in descending order.

Table 5

Cojet	Silistor	Cimara	Ceramic Repair
16.28	17.64	10.64	10.78

Table 6

Comparison	Difference, $\bar{x}_j - \bar{x}_i$	Test statistic, q_0	Critical Value	Decision
Silistor vs. Cimara (Silistor − Cimara)	$17.64 - 10.64 = 7.00$	$q_0 = \dfrac{\bar{x}_{\text{Si}} - \bar{x}_{\text{Ci}}}{\sqrt{\dfrac{s^2}{2} \cdot \left(\dfrac{1}{n_{\text{Si}}} + \dfrac{1}{n_{\text{Ci}}}\right)}} = \dfrac{17.64 - 10.64}{\sqrt{\dfrac{8.835}{2} \cdot \left(\dfrac{1}{5} + \dfrac{1}{5}\right)}} = 5.266$	4.046	Reject $H_0: \mu_{\text{Si}} = \mu_{\text{Ci}}$ since $q_0 > q_{0.05,16,4}$
Silistor vs. Ceramic (Silistor − Ceramic)	$17.64 - 10.78 = 6.86$	$q_0 = \dfrac{\bar{x}_{\text{Si}} - \bar{x}_{\text{Ce}}}{\sqrt{\dfrac{s^2}{2} \cdot \left(\dfrac{1}{n_{\text{Si}}} + \dfrac{1}{n_{\text{Ce}}}\right)}} = \dfrac{17.64 - 10.78}{\sqrt{\dfrac{8.835}{2} \cdot \left(\dfrac{1}{5} + \dfrac{1}{5}\right)}} = 5.161$	4.046	Reject $H_0: \mu_{\text{Si}} = \mu_{\text{Ce}}$ since $q_0 > q_{0.05,16,4}$
Cojet vs. Cimara (Cojet − Cimara)	$16.28 - 10.64 = 5.64$	$q_0 = \dfrac{\bar{x}_{\text{Co}} - \bar{x}_{\text{Ci}}}{\sqrt{\dfrac{s^2}{2} \cdot \left(\dfrac{1}{n_{\text{Co}}} + \dfrac{1}{n_{\text{Ci}}}\right)}} = \dfrac{16.28 - 10.64}{\sqrt{\dfrac{8.835}{2} \cdot \left(\dfrac{1}{5} + \dfrac{1}{5}\right)}} = 4.243$	4.046	Reject $H_0: \mu_{\text{Co}} = \mu_{\text{Ci}}$ since $q_0 > q_{0.05,16,4}$
Cojet vs. Ceramic (Cojet − Ceramic)	$16.28 - 10.78 = 5.50$	$q_0 = \dfrac{\bar{x}_{\text{Co}} - \bar{x}_{\text{Ce}}}{\sqrt{\dfrac{s^2}{2} \cdot \left(\dfrac{1}{n_{\text{Co}}} + \dfrac{1}{n_{\text{Ce}}}\right)}} = \dfrac{16.28 - 10.78}{\sqrt{\dfrac{8.835}{2} \cdot \left(\dfrac{1}{5} + \dfrac{1}{5}\right)}} = 4.138$	4.046	Reject $H_0: \mu_{\text{Co}} = \mu_{\text{Ce}}$ since $q_0 > q_{0.05,16,4}$
Silistor vs. Cojet (Silistor − Cojet)	$17.64 - 16.28 = 1.36$	$q_0 = \dfrac{\bar{x}_{\text{Si}} - \bar{x}_{\text{Co}}}{\sqrt{\dfrac{s^2}{2} \cdot \left(\dfrac{1}{n_{\text{Si}}} + \dfrac{1}{n_{\text{Co}}}\right)}} = \dfrac{17.64 - 16.28}{\sqrt{\dfrac{8.835}{2} \cdot \left(\dfrac{1}{5} + \dfrac{1}{5}\right)}} = 1.023$	4.046	Do Not Reject $H_0: \mu_{\text{Si}} = \mu_{\text{Co}}$ since $q_0 < q_{0.05,16,4}$
Ceramic vs. Cimara (Ceramic − Cimara)	$10.78 - 10.64 = 0.14$	$q_0 = \dfrac{\bar{x}_{\text{Ce}} - \bar{x}_{\text{Ci}}}{\sqrt{\dfrac{s^2}{2} \cdot \left(\dfrac{1}{n_{\text{Ce}}} + \dfrac{1}{n_{\text{Ci}}}\right)}} = \dfrac{10.78 - 10.64}{\sqrt{\dfrac{8.835}{2} \cdot \left(\dfrac{1}{5} + \dfrac{1}{5}\right)}} = 0.105$	4.046	Do Not Reject $H_0: \mu_{\text{Ce}} = \mu_{\text{Ci}}$ since $q_0 < q_{0.05,16,4}$

Step 3: Compute the test statistic q_0 for each pairwise difference. From the ANOVA table in Figure 5, we have the mean square error $= 8.835$. This is the value of s^2 in the computation of the test statistic. The test statistic for each pairwise difference is shown in the third column of Table 6.

Step 4: Find the critical value using an $\alpha = 0.05$ familywise error rate with $\nu = n - k = 20 - 4 = 16$ and $k = 4$. From Table IX, the critical value is $q_{0.05,16,4} = 4.046$. (If the critical value were not in Table IX because of the value for ν, we would use the entry corresponding to the value closest to ν.) The critical value is placed in the fourth column of Table 6.

Step 5: If $q_0 > q_{0.05,16,4}$, we reject the null hypothesis that the pairwise means are equal. We state our conclusion in the fifth column of Table 6. By writing the differences in descending order, once we "do not reject H_0," we can stop, because we won't reject smaller differences either!

Step 6: The conclusions of Tukey's test are

$$\mu_{Co} = \mu_{Si} \neq \mu_{Ci} = \mu_{Ce}$$

It is helpful to use lines to indicate which sample means are not significantly different, as follows:

$$\underline{\mu_{Co}\ \mu_{Si}}\quad \underline{\mu_{Ci}\ \mu_{Ce}}$$

The means listed over a common line are said to be equal. So, we have evidence that indicates that veneer repairs made using the Cojet or Silistor treatment have the highest shear bond strength. The Cimara and Ceramic Repair treatments were not significantly different, but were weaker in terms of shear bond strength than the Cojet or Silistor treatments.

EXAMPLE 3   **Tukey's Test Using Technology**

Problem: Use MINITAB to obtain the results of Tukey's test for the shear bond strength data from Example 1 from Section 13.1.

Approach: The steps for obtaining the results of Tukey's test using MINITAB and Excel are given in the Technology Step-by-Step on page 703.

Solution: The results of Tukey's test using MINITAB are presented in Figure 9. Instead of reporting P-values to test each hypothesis that the pairwise means are equal, MINITAB reports confidence intervals. Recall, we can use confidence intervals to test $H_0: \mu_1 = \mu_2$ versus $H_1: \mu_1 \neq \mu_2$ (or, equivalently, $H_0: \mu_1 - \mu_2 = 0$ versus $H_1: \mu_1 - \mu_2 \neq 0$) by determining whether the interval contains 0. If 0 is contained in the interval, we do not reject the null hypothesis; but if the interval does not contain 0, we reject the null hypothesis at the α level of significance.

Figure 9   **Tukey 95% Simultaneous Confidence Intervals**
All Pairwise Comparisons

```
Individual confidence level = 98.87%

Cojet subtracted from:
                   Lower  Center   Upper  -------+---------+--------+---------+-
Silistor          -4.024   1.360   6.744                (------*------)
Cimara           -11.024  -5.640  -0.256  (------*------)
Ceramic Repair   -10.884  -5.500  -0.116  (------*------)
                                          -------+---------+--------+---------+-
                                             -7.0      0.0      7.0      14.0

Silistor subtracted from:
                   Lower  Center   Upper  -------+---------+--------+---------+-
Cimara           -12.384  -7.000  -1.616  (------*------)
Ceramic Repair   -12.244  -6.860  -1.476  (-----*------)
                                          -------+---------+--------+---------+-
                                             -7.0      0.0      7.0      14.0

Cimara subtracted from:
                   Lower  Center   Upper  -------+---------+--------+---------+-
Ceramic Repair    -5.244   0.140   5.524               (-----*------)
                                          -------+---------+--------+---------+-
                                             -7.0      0.0      7.0      14.0
```

If we reject the null hypothesis, $H_0: \mu_1 = \mu_2$, we can look at the bounds of the confidence interval to determine which mean (μ_1 or μ_2) is higher. For example, if the interval contains only positive numbers, then $\bar{x}_1 - \bar{x}_2$ is positive, so we would conclude that there is evidence that $\mu_1 > \mu_2$. Similarly, if the confidence interval contains only negative numbers, we have evidence that $\mu_1 < \mu_2$.

If we look at the first group of confidence intervals, we are comparing means from the Cojet treatment and the other three treatments. From the output, the lower bound on the confidence interval $\mu_{\text{Silistor}} - \mu_{\text{Cojet}}$ is -4.024 MPa and the upper bound is 6.744 MPa. Because the interval contains 0, we do not reject the null hypothesis that the mean shear strength of the Silistor treatment is the same as the mean shear strength of the Cojet treatment. Next, we compare the Cojet treatment to the Cimara treatment. The lower bound is -11.024 MPa and the upper bound is -0.256 MPa. Because the interval does not contain 0, we reject the null hypothesis that the mean shear strength of the Cojet treatment is the same as the mean shear strength of the Cimara treatment. In addition, because $\mu_{\text{Cimara}} - \mu_{\text{Cojet}}$ is negative, we know that $\mu_{\text{Ci}} < \mu_{\text{Co}}$. Reading the remainder of the output in a similar manner, we have $\mu_{\text{Co}} > \mu_{\text{Ce}}$, $\mu_{\text{Si}} > \mu_{\text{Ci}}$, $\mu_{\text{Si}} > \mu_{\text{Ce}}$, and $\mu_{\text{Ce}} = \mu_{\text{Ci}}$. Summarizing all 6 statements, we have $\mu_{\text{Co}} = \mu_{\text{Si}} > \mu_{\text{Ce}} = \mu_{\text{Ci}}$ which agrees with our results from Example 2.

Now Work Problem 11

Some Cautions Regarding Tukey's Test

Sometimes the results of Tukey's test are ambiguous. Suppose that the null hypothesis $H_0: \mu_1 = \mu_2 = \mu_3 = \mu_4$ is rejected. Also suppose that the results of Tukey's test indicate the following:

$$\underline{\mu_1 \ \mu_2 \ \mu_3} \ \underline{\mu_3 \ \mu_4}$$

It appears that populations 1, 2, and 3 have a population mean that is different from populations 3 and 4. Clearly, this is impossible. Do you see why? The population mean from treatment 3 cannot equal the population mean from treatment 1 and 2, while at the same time equal the population mean from treatment 4, whose mean is different from population 1 and 2! This basically means that at least one Type II error has been committed by Tukey's test.

This result allows us to conclude that $\mu_1 = \mu_2 \neq \mu_4$, but we cannot tell how μ_3 is related to the other population means. A solution to this problem is to increase the sample size so that the test is more powerful.

It can also happen that the one-way ANOVA rejects $H_0: \mu_1 = \mu_2 = \cdots = \mu_k$, but the Tukey test does not detect any pairwise differences. This result occurs because one-way ANOVA is more powerful than Tukey's test. Again, the solution is to increase the sample size.

13.2 ASSESS YOUR UNDERSTANDING

Concepts and Vocabulary

1. Explain the purpose of multiple comparison tests. When do we use them?

2. What is the familywise error rate?

Skill Building

3. (a) Find the critical value from the Studentized range distribution for $\alpha = 0.05, \nu = 10, k = 3$.   3.877
   (b) Find the critical value from the Studentized range distribution for $\alpha = 0.05, \nu = 24, k = 5$.   4.166
   (c) Find the critical value from the Studentized range distribution for $\alpha = 0.05, \nu = 32, k = 8$.   4.602
   (d) Find the critical value from the Studentized range distribution for $H_0: \mu_1 = \mu_2 = \mu_3 = \mu_4 = \mu_5$, with $n = 65$ at $\alpha = 0.05$.   3.977

4. (a) Find the critical value from the Studentized range distribution for $\alpha = 0.05, \nu = 12, k = 3$.   3.773
   (b) Find the critical value from the Studentized range distribution for $\alpha = 0.05, \nu = 20, k = 4$.   3.958
   (c) Find the critical value from the Studentized range distribution for $\alpha = 0.05, \nu = 42, k = 5$.   4.039
   (d) Find the critical value from the Studentized range distribution for $H_0: \mu_1 = \mu_2 = \mu_3 = \mu_4$, with $n = 34$ at $\alpha = 0.05$.   3.845

5. Suppose that there is sufficient evidence to reject $H_0: \mu_1 = \mu_2 = \mu_3$ using a one-way ANOVA. The mean square error from ANOVA is determined to be 26.2. The sample means are $\bar{x}_1 = 9.5, \bar{x}_2 = 9.1, \bar{x}_3 = 18.1$, with $n_1 = n_2 = n_3 = 5$. Use Tukey's test to determine which pairwise means are significantly different using a familywise error rate of $\alpha = 0.05$. $\underline{\mu_2 \ \mu_1} \ \mu_3$; Ambiguous

6. Suppose that there is sufficient evidence to reject $H_0: \mu_1 = \mu_2 = \mu_3 = \mu_4$ using a one-way ANOVA. The mean square error from ANOVA is determined to be 26.2. The sample means are $\bar{x}_1 = 42.6$, $\bar{x}_2 = 49.1$, $\bar{x}_3 = 46.8$, $\bar{x}_4 = 63.7$, with $n_1 = n_2 = n_3 = n_4 = 6$. Use Tukey's test to determine which pairwise means are significantly different using a familywise error rate of $\alpha = 0.05$. _$\mu_1\ \mu_2\ \mu_3\ \mu_4$_

7. The following data are taken from three different populations known to be normally distributed, with equal population variances based on independent simple random samples.

Sample 1	Sample 2	Sample 3
35.4	42.0	43.3
35.0	39.4	48.6
39.2	33.4	42.0
44.8	35.1	53.9
36.9	32.4	46.8
28.9	22.0	51.7

(a) Test the hypothesis that each sample comes from a population with the same mean at the $\alpha = 0.05$ level of significance. That is, test $H_0: \mu_1 = \mu_2 = \mu_3$. _Reject H_0_
(b) If you rejected the null hypothesis in part (a), use Tukey's test to determine which pairwise means differ using a familywise error rate of $\alpha = 0.05$. _$\mu_1\ \mu_2\ \mu_3$_
(c) Draw boxplots of each set of sample data to support your results from parts (a) and (b).

8. The following data are taken from four different populations that are known to be normally distributed, with equal population variances based on independent simple random samples.

Sample 1	Sample 2	Sample 3	Sample 4
110	138	98	130
85	140	100	116
83	130	94	157
95	115	110	137
103	101	104	144
105	130	118	124
107	123	102	139

(a) Test the hypothesis that each sample comes from a population with the same mean at the $\alpha = 0.05$ level of significance. That is, test $H_0: \mu_1 = \mu_2 = \mu_3 = \mu_4$. _Reject H_0_
(b) If you rejected the null hypothesis in part (a), use Tukey's test to determine which pairwise means differ using a familywise error rate of $\alpha = 0.05$. _$\mu_1\ \mu_3\ \ \mu_2\ \mu_4$_
(c) Draw boxplots of each set of sample data to support your results from parts (a) and (b).

9. Corn Production (*See Problem 11 from Section 13.1*) An agricultural researcher wanted to know whether the mean number of plants for each plot type differed. A one-way analysis of variance was performed to test $H_0: \mu_{SP} = \mu_{SD} = \mu_{NT}$. The null hypothesis was rejected with a P-value of 0.007. The researcher proceeded to conduct Tukey's test using MINITAB to determine which means differed. The results are presented next. Which pairwise means differ? Which plot type would you recommend? _$\mu_{SD}\ \mu_{SP}\ \mu_{NT}$; spring disk_

Tukey 95% Simultaneous Confidence Intervals All Pairwise Comparisons:

```
Individual confidence level = 97.97%

Sludge Plot subtracted from:

Spring    Lower  Center  Upper  ------+---------+---------+---------+---
Disk      1.021   4.667  8.313                       (------*-------)
No Till  -3.479   0.167  3.813            (------*-------)
                                 ------+---------+---------+---------+---
                                    -5.0      0.0       5.0      10.0

Spring Disk subtracted from:

          Lower  Center  Upper  ------+---------+---------+---------+---
No Till  -8.146  -4.500 -0.854  (------*------)
                                 ------+---------+---------+---------+---
                                    -5.0      0.0       5.0      10.0
```

10. Soybean Yield (*See Problem 12 from Section 13.1*) An agricultural researcher wanted to determine if the mean soybean yield differed for different plot types. A one-way analysis of variance was performed to test $H_0: \mu_L = \mu_{NT} = \mu_{CP}$. The null hypothesis was rejected with a P-value of 0.038. The researcher proceeded to conduct Tukey's test to determine which pairwise means differed using MINITAB. The results are presented next. Which pairwise means differ? Which plot type would you recommend? _$\mu_{CP}\ \mu_{NT}\ \mu_L$; ambiguous case_

Tukey 95% Simultaneous Confidence Intervals All Pairwise Comparisons

```
Individual confidence level = 98.02%

Liberty subtracted from:

          Lower   Center  Upper  --------+---------+---------+---------+-
No Till  -6.344  -1.111   4.122          (--------*--------)
Chisel                                (--------*--------)
Plowed  -10.677  -5.444  -0.212  --------+---------+---------+---------+-
                                      -6.0      0.0       6.0      12.0

No Till subtracted from:

          Lower  Center  Upper  --------+---------+---------+---------+-
Chisel                                   (--------*-------)
Plowed  -9.566  -4.333   0.900  --------+---------+---------+---------+-
                                     -6.0      0.0       6.0      12.0
```

Applying the Concepts

11. pH in Rain In Problem 19 from Section 13.1, we rejected **NW** $H_0: \mu_{AK} = \mu_{FL} = \mu_{TX}$ and concluded that the mean pHs in rain falling in the three states differ. Use Tukey's test to determine which pairwise means differ using a familywise error rate of $\alpha = 0.05$. _$\mu_{FL}\ \mu_{AK}\ \mu_{TX}$_

12. Lower Your Cholesterol In Problem 20 from Section 13.1, we rejected $H_0: \mu_{SF} = \mu_{MED} = \mu_{NCEP}$ and concluded that there is at least one treatment that results in a mean LDL cholesterol that differs from the rest. Use Tukey's test to determine which pairwise means differ using a familywise error rate of $\alpha = 0.05$. _$\mu_{SF}\ \mu_{MED}\ \mu_{NCEP}$_

13. Attention Deficit Hyperactivity Disorder Researchers William E. Pelham et al. studied the effect that varying levels of Ritalin and Adderall had on a child's ability to follow rules when the child is diagnosed with attention deficit hyperactivity disorder (ADHD). They randomly assigned children to one of five treatment groups: placebo, 10 mg Ritalin, 17.5 mg of Ritalin, 7.5 mg of Adderall, or 12.5 mg of Adderall twice a day. They recorded a score that indicated the child's ability to follow rules, with a higher score indicating a higher ability to follow rules. The following data are based on their study,

"A Comparison of Ritalin and Adderall: Efficacy and Time-Course in Children with Attention Deficit/Hyperactivity Disorder, *Pediatrics*, Vol. 103, No. 4.

Placebo	Ritalin 10 mg	Ritalin 17.5 mg	Adderall 7.5 mg	Adderall 12.5 mg
47	96	37	57	84
20	75	83	71	105
34	57	76	85	83
60	44	43	92	92
28	83	87	75	74
72	69	62	55	92
25	57	99	73	64

(a) Test the null hypothesis that the mean score for each treatment is the same at the $\alpha = 0.05$ level of significance.

Note: The requirements for a one-way ANOVA are satisfied.   Reject H_0

(b) If the null hypothesis is rejected in part (a), use Tukey's test to determine which pairwise means differ using a family-wise error rate of $\alpha = 0.05$. μ_P μ_{R10} $\mu_{R17.5}$ $\mu_{A7.5}$ $\mu_{A12.5}$

(c) Draw boxplots of the five treatment levels to support the analytic results obtained in parts (a) and (b).

14. Nutrition Researchers Sharon Peterson and Madeleine Sigman-Grant wanted to compare the overall nutrient intake of American children (ages 2 to 19) who exclusively use lean meats, mixed meats, or higher-fat meats. The data given represent the daily consumption of calcium (in mg) for a random sample of eight children in each category and are based on the results presented in their article "Impact of Adopting Lower-Fat Food Choices on Nutrient Intake of American Children," *Pediatrics*, Vol. 100, No. 3.

Lean Meats	Mixed Meats	Higher-Fat Meats
844.2	897.7	843.4
745.0	908.1	862.2
773.1	948.8	790.5
823.6	836.6	876.5
812.0	871.6	790.8
758.9	945.9	847.2
810.7	859.4	772.0
790.6	920.2	851.3

(a) Test the null hypothesis that the mean calcium for each category is the same at the $\alpha = 0.05$ level of significance.

Note: The requirements for a one-way ANOVA are satisfied.   Reject H_0

(b) If the null hypothesis is rejected in part (a), use Tukey's test to determine which pairwise means differ using a familywise error rate of $\alpha = 0.05$. μ_{MM} μ_{LM} μ_{HFM}

(c) Draw boxplots of the three treatment levels to support the analytic results obtained in parts (a) and (b).

15. Heart Rate of Smokers A researcher wants to determine the effect that smoking has on resting heart rate. She randomly selects seven individuals from three categories: (1) nonsmokers, (2) light smokers (fewer than 10 cigarettes

per day), and (3) heavy smokers (10 or more cigarettes per day) and obtains the following heart rate data (beats per minute):

Nonsmokers	Light Smokers	Heavy Smokers
56	78	77
53	62	86
53	70	68
65	73	83
70	67	79
58	75	80
51	65	77

(a) Test the null hypothesis that the mean resting heart rate for each category is the same at the $\alpha = 0.05$ level of significance.

Note: The requirements for a one-way ANOVA are satisfied.   Reject H_0

(b) If the null hypothesis is rejected in part (a), use Tukey's test to determine which pairwise means differ using a familywise error rate of $\alpha = 0.05$. μ_{NS} μ_{LS} μ_{HS}

(c) Draw boxplots of the three treatment levels to support the results obtained in parts (a) and (b).

16. Price to Earnings Ratios One measure of the value of a stock is its price to earnings ratio (or P/E ratio). It is the ratio of the price of a stock per share to the earnings per share and can be thought of as the price an investor is willing to pay for $1 of earnings in a company. A stock analyst wants to know whether the P/E ratios for three industry categories differ significantly. The following data represent simple random samples of companies from three categories: (1) financial, (2) food, and (3) leisure goods.

Financial	Food	Leisure Goods
8.83	19.75	14.10
12.75	17.87	10.12
13.48	15.18	15.57
14.42	22.84	13.48
10.06	15.60	11.27

Source: Yahoo!Finance

(a) Test the null hypothesis that the mean P/E ratio for each category is the same at the $\alpha = 0.05$ level of significance.

Note: The requirements for a one-way ANOVA are satisfied.   Reject H_0

(b) If the null hypothesis is rejected in part (a), use Tukey's test to determine which pairwise means differ using a familywise error rate of $\alpha = 0.05$. μ_{Food} μ_{Fin} μ_L

(c) Draw boxplots of the three categories to support the analytic results obtained in parts (a) and (b).

17. Got Milk? Researchers Sharon Peterson and Madeleine Sigman-Grant wanted to compare the overall nutrient intake of American children (ages 2 to 19) who exclusively use skim milk instead of 1%, 2%, or whole milk. The researchers combined children who consumed 1% or 2% milk into a "mixed milk" category. The following data represent the daily calcium intake (in mg) for a random sample of eight children in each category and are based on the results presented in their article "Impact of Adopting Lower-Fat

Food Choices on Nutrient Intake of American Children," *Pediatrics*, Vol. 100, No. 3.

Skim Milk	Mixed Milk	Whole Milk
857	1,006	879
853	991	938
865	1,015	841
904	1,035	818
916	1,024	870
886	1,013	874
854	1,065	881
856	1,002	836

(a) Is there sufficient evidence to support the belief that at least one of the means is different from the others at the $\alpha = 0.05$ level of significance?

Note: The requirements for a one-way ANOVA are satisfied. *Reject H_0*

(b) If the null hypothesis is rejected in part (a), use Tukey's test to determine which pairwise means differ using a familywise error rate of $\alpha = 0.05$. *$\mu_{MM}\ \mu_{SM}\ \mu_{WM}$*

(c) Draw boxplots of the three categories to support the analytic results obtained in parts (a) and (b).

18. The **comparisonwise error rate**, denoted α_c, is the probability of making a Type I error when comparing two means. It is related to the familywise error rate, α, through the formula $1 - \alpha = (1 - \alpha_c)^k$, where k is the number of means being compared.

(a) If the familywise error rate is $\alpha = 0.05$ and there are $k = 3$ means being compared, what is the comparisonwise error rate? *0.017*

(b) If the familywise error rate is $\alpha = 0.05$ and there are $k = 5$ means being compared, what is the comparisonwise error rate? *0.010*

(c) Based on the results of parts (a) and (b), what happens to the comparisonwise error rate as the number of means compared increases? *Decreases*

19. **Putting It Together: Time to Complete a Degree** A researcher wanted to determine if the mean time to complete a bachelor's degree was different depending on the selectivity of the first institution of higher education that was attended. The following

data represent a random sample of 12th-graders in 1992 who earned their degree by December 2000. Probability plots indicate that the data for each treatment level are normally distributed. *19. (b) 4.05, 4.20, 4.21, 5.80, 4.65*

Highly Selective	Selective	Nonselective	Open-door	Not Rated
2.6	3.1	4.7	5.0	4.5
4.1	3.8	4.2	7.3	5.5
3.4	5.2	5.7	5.6	5.5
4.3	4.5	2.3	6.9	4.6
3.9	4.0	4.5	5.1	4.1
2.5	4.6	4.7	5.9	5.1
5.1	4.3	2.3	4.2	4.3
4.3	4.4	4.3	6.4	4.4
4.8	4.0	4.2	5.6	3.8
5.5	4.1	5.1	6.0	4.7

Source: C. Adelman. "The Toolbox Revisited: Paths to Degree Completion from High School Through College," U.S. Department of Education, 2006.

(a) What type of observational study was conducted? *Cohort*
(b) Find the sample mean for each treatment level.
(c) Find the sample standard deviation for each treatment level. Using the general rule presented in this section, does it appear that the population variances are the same? *Yes*
(d) Use the time to degree completion for students first attending highly selective institutions to construct a 95% confidence interval estimate for the population mean.
(e) How many pairwise comparisons are possible among the treatment levels? *10*
(f) Consider the null hypothesis $H_0: \mu_1 = \mu_2 = \mu_3 = \mu_4 = \mu_5$. If we test this hypothesis using t-tests for each pair of treatments, use your answer from part (e) to compute the probability of making a Type I error, assuming that each test uses an $\alpha = 0.05$ level of significance. *0.4013*
(g) Use the one-way ANOVA procedure to determine if there is a difference in the mean time to degree completion for the different types of initial institutions. If the null hypothesis is rejected, use Tukey's test to determine which pairwise differences are significant using a familywise error rate of $\alpha = 0.05$. *Reject H_0; $\mu_{HS}\ \mu_S\ \mu_{NS}\ \mu_{NR}\ \mu_{OD}$*

19. (d) (3.352, 4.743)

Consumer Reports **Tea Antioxidants: An Unexpected Side Benefit to a Cheap and Tasty Beverage**

Antioxidant compounds are thought to be beneficial to human health. In a study for *Consumer Reports*, 15 brands of tea were tested for total antioxidant content. The antioxidant content was measured as oxygen radical absorbance capacity (ORAC) per 8-oz serving at an outside laboratory. Among the 15 brands, 4 were bagged black, 3 were bagged green, 2 were instant, and 6 were ready-to-drink teas.

The data for the 6 ready-to-drink teas are given in the table. To avoid potential sources of bias, measurements were taken from three different lots of each brand, and the tests were conducted in a randomly chosen order. A control was also run repeatedly throughout the test period to determine if there was a time effect, but the data are not included here.

Brand	ORAC	Brand	ORAC
1	427.4	4	484.3
1	481.1	4	617.3
1	428.3	4	624.9
2	667.7	5	664.1
2	737.6	5	623.1
2	630.9	5	647.5
3	715.2	6	606.0
3	724.1	6	793.9
3	686.9	6	668.7

MINITAB was used to perform a one-way analysis of variance of the data. The results are shown next:

Analysis of Variance for ORAC
```
Source DF      SS      MS      F      P
Brand   5  147257   29451   8.80   0.001
Error  12   40180    3348
Total  17  187437
                           Individual 95% CIs For Mean
                           Based on Pooled StDev
Level  N    Mean  StDev  ----------+---------+---------+-------
1      3  445.60  30.75  (-----*-----)
2      3  678.73  54.20                  (-----*-----)
3      3  708.73  19.42                     (-----*-----)
4      3  575.50  79.07           (-----*-----)
5      3  644.90  20.62                (-----*-----)
6      3  689.53  95.67                   (-----*-----)
                           ----------+---------+---------+-------
Pooled StDev = 57.87                480       600       720
```

Using the MINITAB output, answer the following questions:

(a) What are the null and alternative hypotheses?

(b) Do there appear to be any outliers or other unusual observations? What must be true regarding the distribution of the response variable, ORAC, to perform a one-way analysis of variance?

(c) Is there a statistical difference among brands? What is the significance level of the test?

(d) Which brands, if any, appear to have similar amounts of ORAC?

(e) Use Tukey's test to determine which pairwise means differ using a familywise error rate of $\alpha = 0.05$.

(f) Write a paragraph for the readers of *Consumer Reports* magazine that explains your findings. Which brand of tea would you recommend? Why?

Note to Readers: *In many cases, our test protocol and analytical methods are more complicated than described in these examples. The data and discussions have been modified to make the material more appropriate for the audience.*

Source: © 1999 by Consumers Union of U.S., Inc., Yonkers, NY 10703-1057, a nonprofit organization. Reprinted with permission from the June 2001 issue of CONSUMER REPORTS® for educational purposes only. No commercial use or photocopying permitted. To learn more about Consumers Union, log onto www.ConsumersReports.org

TECHNOLOGY STEP-BY-STEP   Tukey's Test

MINITAB
1. Enter the raw data in C1, C2, and so on, for each population or treatment.
2. Select **Stat**; then highlight **A**NOVA and then select **One-Way (Unstacked)**.
3. Enter the column names in the cell marked "Responses". Click "Comparisons . . . ". Check the box labeled "Tukey's, family error rate:". Enter the familywise error rate in the box. For $\alpha = 0.05$, enter 5. Click OK twice.

Excel
1. Load the DDXL Add-in.
2. Enter the measurement values in column A and the category (treatment) names in column B. Highlight the data.

3. Select the **DDXL** menu; then click on **ANOVA**.
4. Use the drop-down menu under Function Type to select **1 Way ANOVA**. Make sure the box labeled *First row is variable names* is checked or unchecked, as appropriate.
5. Select your measurement values from the Names and Columns list; then press the transfer button ◄ under the heading Response Variable. Next, select your factor data from the Names and Columns list; then press the transfer button ◄ under the heading Factor Variable and click OK.
6. At the bottom of the ANOVA screen, in the Tukey Multiple Comparison window, select the desired level of confidence for the pairwise confidence intervals.

13.3 THE RANDOMIZED COMPLETE BLOCK DESIGN

Preparing for This Section Before getting started, review the following:

- Randomized Block Design
  (Section 1.6, pp. 51–53)

- Inference on Two Means: Dependent Samples
  (Section 11.1, pp. 583–590)

Objectives		
		Conduct analysis of variance on the randomized complete block design
		Perform the Tukey test

In Other Words

A block is a method for controlling experimental error. Blocks should form a homogeneous group. For example, if age is thought to explain some of the variability in the response variable, we can remove age from the experimental error by forming blocks of experimental units with the same age. Gender is another common block.

In the completely randomized design, a single **factor** is manipulated and fixed at different levels. The experimental units are then randomly assigned to one of the factor levels, or treatments. If there are only two levels of the factor (or two treatments), we can analyze the data using the methods introduced in Section 11.2. If there are three or more treatments, we analyze the data using the methods of one-way analysis of variance.

Remember, in designing an experiment, the researcher identifies the various factors that may affect the value of the response variable. The researcher can then deal with the factors in one of two ways:

1. Control their levels so that they remain fixed throughout the experiment or allow them to vary with predetermined fixed levels.

2. Randomize so that any effects not identified or uncontrollable are minimized

In the completely randomized design, the researcher manipulates a single factor and fixes it at two or more levels and then randomly assigns experimental units to a treatment. The researcher may have the ability to control certain factors in this design setting so that they remain fixed. The remaining factors are dealt with by randomly assigning the experimental units to treatment groups.

The completely randomized design is not always sufficient, because the researcher may be aware of additional factors that cannot be fixed at a single level throughout the experiment.

One such experimental design that captures more information (and therefore reduces experimental error) is the randomized block design, first introduced in Section 1.6, where we discussed the effect fertilizer might have on crop yield. We designed an experiment in which three levels of fertilizer (the three treatments) were each analyzed on two different plant types (the blocks).

To help further understand the purpose of the completely randomized block design, consider the following example.

EXAMPLE 1	Randomized Complete Block Design

A researcher is interested in determining the tread wear on four different tires after 5,000 miles of highway driving. The researcher has four of each brand of tire and four cars along with four drivers. For simplicity, we call the tire types A, B, C, and D. The researcher wishes to test $H_0: \mu_A = \mu_B = \mu_C = \mu_D$ versus the alternative that at least one of the means differs, where μ_i represents the mean tread loss for each tire type.

The researcher must first determine the variables that affect tire wear. Certainly, the type of car, the driver, tire inflation, and road conditions are a few. For the sake of time, the researcher decides to use all four cars in the experiment rather than one. He decides to set the inflation of each tire at 32 pounds and drive the cars on the same oval track. Each car is assigned one driver.

One possible experimental design in this setting would be to randomly assign the tires to the cars. Tire 1A would be assigned number 1, tire 2A would be assigned number 2, and so on, until we reach tire 4D, which would be assigned number 16. We can then number the cells as shown in Table 7(a). Now use a random-number generator to assign the tires to the cars. If the first number generated is a 15, we would place tire 1A on car 4 on the back-left position. If the next random number is 12, tire 2A is placed on car 3 on the back-right position. We continue until all the tires are assigned to cars. Let X_{1A} represent the tread loss for the first tire A, let X_{2A} represent the tread loss for the second tire A, and so on. Under these circumstances, we might end up with the design shown in Table 7(b).

Table 7				
	Front Left	**Front Right**	**Back Left**	**Back Right**
Car 1	1	2	3	4
Car 2	5	6	7	8
Car 3	9	10	11	12
Car 4	13	14	15	16

(a)

	Front Left	**Front Right**	**Back Left**	**Back Right**
Car 1	X_{4C}	X_{4B}	X_{3D}	X_{4D}
Car 2	X_{2B}	X_{3A}	X_{3B}	X_{2A}
Car 3	X_{4A}	X_{1D}	X_{2C}	X_{1B}
Car 4	X_{2D}	X_{3C}	X_{1A}	X_{1C}

(b)

A quick look at Table 7(b) indicates that tire A is not on car 1, tire C is not on car 2, tire D is not on car 2, and tire B is not on car 4. Therefore, any effect that the car might have on tire wear is not completely accounted for. That is, tire wear variability might be confounded with car variability.

To resolve this issue, we might require that each car must have all four tire types on it. This would result in a randomized complete block design. We use the word *complete* because each block (car) gets every treatment (tire type). We use the word *randomized* because the order in which the treatment is applied within each block is random. To obtain the randomness, we randomly assign one treatment (tire brand) to each block (car). For example, we have four treatments (tire brand), so we randomly select an integer between 1 and 4 for the tire number and a second random integer between 1 and 4 for the tire brand. For example, if a random-number generator results in a 2 and then a 1, we place tire 2 of brand A on car 1. Continuing to place tires on car 1, we repeat the process, but we cannot select brand A again because each brand must be represented on car 1. By randomly assigning each treatment to each block, we might end up with the design shown in Table 8.*

Table 8				
	Front Left	**Front Right**	**Back Left**	**Back Right**
Car 1	X_{2A}	X_{3C}	X_{2D}	X_{3B}
Car 2	X_{1A}	X_{2B}	X_{1D}	X_{2C}
Car 3	X_{4D}	X_{4A}	X_{1B}	X_{4C}
Car 4	X_{1C}	X_{4B}	X_{3A}	X_{3D}

*Table 8 reveals another flaw. Notice that tire B is never in the front-left location. In all likelihood the position of the tire on the car also affects tire wear. We could account for this by rotating the tires every 1,250 miles, or we could require that each treatment (tire) must also be placed in each position on the car, so one car must have tire A in the front left, a second car must have tire A in the front right, and so on. If we impose this second requirement, we would have a **Latin square design**.

In Table 8, you should notice that horizontal lines are used in the table to help the reader see how the blocks are formed. Using this randomized complete block design, the null hypothesis is

$$H_0: \mu_A = \mu_B = \mu_C = \mu_D$$

versus

$$H_1: \text{at least one of the means is different}$$

 When we block, we are not interested in determining whether the block is significant. We only want to remove experimental error to reduce the mean square error.

One specific type of randomized complete block design is the matched-pairs design introduced in Section 1.6. This type of experimental design requires dependent sampling in which the experimental units are somehow related, such as in husband/wife, the same experimental unit, or some other characteristic that relates the individuals. The related experimental units form the blocks in this experimental design. We learned how to analyze data obtained from this experimental design in Section 11.1 using the paired t-test. For example, in Section 11.1, Example 2, we analyzed matched-pairs data where the blocks were the students.

The methods used in this section can also be used when we want to compare the means resulting from an observational study in which there are three or more categories whose means we are interested in comparing (the categories act like the treatment in an experiment) along with blocks. For example, we obtain a simple random sample of individuals and ask them to disclose their number of years of education. We might also wonder if the mean number of years of education differs by age group, where the groups are segmented as 25 to 34, 35 to 49, and 50 years and older. Since gender or ethnicity might be considered factors that contribute to variability in the number of years of education, we might use gender or ethnicity as a block.

1 Conduct Analysis of Variance on the Randomized Complete Block Design

The following requirements must be satisfied to analyze data from a randomized complete block design.

> **Requirements for Analyzing Data from a Randomized Complete Block Design**
>
> **1.** The response variable for each of the k populations is normally distributed.
> **2.** The response variable for each of the k populations has the same variance; that is, each treatment group has population variance σ^2.*

As in one-way ANOVA, we will verify the requirement of equal population variances by comparing the sample standard deviations. The procedures can be used provided the largest sample standard deviation is no more than twice the smallest sample standard deviation.

Because the computations in performing the analysis of the randomized complete block design are tedious, we will use statistical software. We use the P-value approach to test the hypothesis. Again, the decision rule will be to reject the null hypothesis if the P-value is less than the level of significance, α.

---

*There are a number of tests for comparing variances. MINITAB compares variances using two different tests: Bartlett's test and Levene's test. Levene's test will be conducted provided there are no missing observations (we do not cover analysis when there are missing observations because it is beyond the scope of the text). Levene's test is considered to be more robust than Bartlett's test, but neither is very reliable. Therefore, the best approach is to design your experiment so that the sample size for each factor is the same, because analysis of variance is not affected too much when we have equal sample sizes, even if there is inequality in the variances.

EXAMPLE 2	**Analyzing the Randomized Complete Block Design**

Problem: A researcher is interested in the effect of four different diets on the weight gain of newborn rats. To account for genetic differences among the rats, the researcher decides that she should randomly assign rats from the same mother to each treatment so that a set of four rats constitutes a block. The researcher identifies 5 mother rats that had 4 offspring, for a total of 20 rats in the study. For each block (sibling rats), the researcher randomly assigns the experimental units (rats) to a treatment using a random-number generator by generating integers from 1 to 4. After 6 months, she records the weight gain of the 20 rats (in grams) and obtains the data in Table 9. Is there sufficient evidence to conclude that the weight gains of the rats on the four diets differ at the $\alpha = 0.05$ level of significance?

	Table 9			
	Diet 1	**Diet 2**	**Diet 3**	**Diet 4**
Block 1	15	14.6	17.7	10.4
Block 2	17.9	17.4	16.0	12.2
Block 3	17.5	14.8	14.2	14.8
Block 4	16.3	17.3	14.4	12.0
Block 5	15.4	19.3	18.8	14.3

Approach: This is a randomized complete block design. We verify the requirements to analyze data from a randomized complete block design are satisfied and then analyze the results of the experiment using MINITAB. The test procedure we use is called two-way ANOVA (which will be discussed more completely in Section 13.4). The steps for performing two-way ANOVA using MINITAB are given in the Technology Step-by-Step on page 713.

Solution: We wish to test

$$H_0: \mu_1 = \mu_2 = \mu_3 = \mu_4 \quad \text{vs.} \quad H_1: \text{at least one of the means is different}$$

A normal probability plot for the data from each of the four diets indicates that the requirement of normality is satisfied. The highest standard deviation, diet 2 with $s_2 = 2.018$, is not more than twice the lowest standard deviation, diet 1 with $s_1 = 1.268$, so we can proceed with the analysis.

We enter the data into MINITAB in three columns. The first column represents the block, the second column the diet, and the third column the response variable, weight gain. So, for the rat in block 1 that received diet 1, we enter a 1 in column C1, a 1 in C2, and 15 in C3. For the rat in block 1 that received diet 2, we enter 1 in C1, 2 in C2, and 14.6 in C3, and so on.

In Other Words

Remember, the smaller the P-value is, the stronger the evidence against the null hypothesis.

We then analyze the data by selecting two-way ANOVA and choose the row factor to be the block and the column factor to be the treatment, diet. Be sure to check the box marked "Additive Model." We obtain the results in Figure 10.

Figure 10   **Two-way ANOVA: Weight Gain versus Block, Treatment**

```
Analysis of Variance for Weight G
Source      DF      SS      MS      F      P
Block        4   14.71    3.68   1.21   0.359          P-value for treatment
Treatment    3   51.87   17.29   5.67   0.012
Error       12   36.62    3.05
Total       19  103.21
```

We are not interested in whether the weight gains among the blocks are equal, so we will ignore the P-value for blocks. We are interested in knowing whether the treatment appears to have resulted in different weight gains. We take the P-value of 0.012 due to treatment as evidence against the null hypothesis of equal weight gain among treatments. Therefore, we conclude that the treatment, diet, does result in significantly different weight gain. However, we do not know which diets result in different mean weight gains. To determine this, we again rely on the pairwise comparisons of Tukey's test.

Now Work Problem 7(a) and (b)

Perform the Tukey Test

Once the null hypothesis of equal population means is rejected, we proceed to determine which means differ significantly. This is called a *post hoc* (after this) test, and the method that we use to conduct the analysis is Tukey's test. The steps are identical to those presented in Section 13.2. The critical value is $q_{\alpha, \nu, k}$, using a family-wise error rate of α with $\nu = (r - 1)(c - 1) =$ the error degrees of freedom (r is the number of blocks and c is the number of treatments) and k is the number of means being tested.

EXAMPLE 3 **Multiple Comparisons Using Tukey's Test**

Problem: Use Tukey's test to determine which pairwise means differ for the data presented in Example 2, with a familywise error rate of $\alpha = 0.05$, using MINITAB.

Approach: The steps for conducting Tukey's test using MINITAB are given in the Technology Step-by-Step on page 713.

Solution: The results of Tukey's test using MINITAB are presented in Figure 11. MINITAB allows the user to perform pairwise comparisons using either confidence intervals or *P*-values. In the output given next, Figure 11(a) shows the pairwise comparisons using 95% confidence intervals. The first sets of confidence intervals compare diet 1 to diets 2 through 4. We can see that the interval $\mu_{\text{Diet }1} - \mu_{\text{Diet }4}$ does not include 0. Therefore, we reject the null hypothesis that the mean weight gain from diet 1 equals the mean weight gain from diet 4. In addition, the interval contains all negative numbers, so we conclude that the mean weight gain from diet 1 is less than that from diet 4. Continuing the comparisons leads us to conclude that diet 4 results in more weight gain than the other three diets.

If we look at Figure 11(b), we see that the *P*-values comparing diet 4 with the remaining diets are all small (less than 0.05). Therefore, we conclude that the mean weight gain from diet 4 is significantly different from the mean weight gain from the other three diets.

Figure 11

```
Tukey 95.0% Simultaneous Confidence Intervals
Response Variable Gain
All Pairwise Comparisons among Levels of Diet
Diet = 1 subtracted from:

Diet  Lower    Center   Upper    -----+---------+---------+---------+-
2     -3.021   0.260    3.5413                    (----------*----------)
3     -3.481  -0.200    3.0813                 (----------*----------)
4     -6.961  -3.680   -0.3987    (----------*----------)
                                 -----+---------+---------+---------+-
                                   -6.0      -3.0      0.0       3.0


Diet = 2 subtracted from:

Diet  Lower    Center   Upper    -----+---------+---------+---------+-
3     -3.741  -0.460    2.8213                 (---------*----------)
4     -7.221  -3.940   -0.6587    (----------*----------)
                                 -----+---------+---------+---------+-
                                   -6.0      -3.0      0.0       3.0


Diet = 3 subtracted from:

Diet  Lower    Center   Upper    -----+---------+---------+---------+-
4     -6.761  -3.480   -0.1987    (----------*----------)
                                 -----+---------+---------+---------+-
                                   -6.0      -3.0      0.0       3.0
```

(a)

Figure 11
Continued

```
Tukey Sumultaneous Tests
Response Variable Gain
All Pairwise Comparisons among Levels of Diet

Diet = 1 subtracted from:

Level   Difference      SE of                Adjusted
Diet     of Means   Difference   T-Value    P-Value
2           0.260       1.105      0.235      0.9952
3          -0.200       1.105     -0.181      0.9978
4          -3.680       1.105     -3.331      0.0266


Diet = 2 subtracted from:

Level   Difference      SE of                Adjusted
Diet     of Means   Difference   T-Value    P-Value
3          -0.460       1.105     -0.416      0.9746
4          -3.940       1.105     -3.566      0.0176


Diet = 3 subtracted from:

Level   Difference      SE of                Adjusted
Diet     of Means   Difference   T-Value    P-Value
4          -3.480       1.105     -3.150      0.0365
```
(b)

Now Work Problem 7(c)

IN CLASS ACTIVITY

Flight of Fancy: Part I

How does design affect the flight of a paper airplane? Explore this concept by comparing the flight distances of three different designs. Since the type of paper could have an effect, use the same type of paper (for example, newspaper, brown shipping paper, typing paper, or other) and block by gender.

(a) Create a table to record your flight data based on gender (block) and plane design (treatment).

(b) Search the Internet (for example, using the Google search engine) for different designs of paper airplanes.

(c) Discuss the model being used and other variables that might affect flight distance. How can you account for these other variables?

(d) Fly each plane the same number of times and record the flight distances in your table.

(e) Was there a significant difference in flight distances for the different types of designs?

(f) If you answered yes to the previous question, conduct Tukey's test to determine which differences in flight distance are significant using the familywise error rate $\alpha = 0.05$.

13.3 ASSESS YOUR UNDERSTANDING

Concepts and Vocabulary

1. How does the completely randomized design differ from a randomized complete block design?

2. What is blocking? Why might a researcher want to block?

3. What does *randomized* mean in the randomized complete block design? What does *complete* mean in the randomized complete block design?

4. What requirements must be satisfied to analyze a randomized complete block design?

5. Name the two ways that a researcher can deal with explanatory variables in a designed experiment.

6. How is a matched-pairs design related to the randomized complete block design?

Skill Building

7. Given the following ANOVA output, answer the questions
NW that follow:

Source	DF	SS	MS	F	P
Block	4	768.27	192.067	10.96	0.002
Treatment	2	278.53	139.267	7.95	0.013
Error	8	140.13	17.517		
Total	14	1186.93			

(a) The researcher wishes to test $H_0: \mu_1 = \mu_2 = \mu_3$
against H_1: at least one of the means is different.
Based on the ANOVA table, what should the researcher
conclude? *Reject H_0*
(b) What is the mean square due to error? *17.517*
(c) The following output represents the results of Tukey's
test. What should the researcher conclude? *$\mu_1 \mu_2 \mu_3$*

```
Tukey Simultaneous Tests
Response Variable Response
All Pairwise Comparisons among Levels
of Treatment
Treatment = 1 subtracted from:
```

Treat-ment	Difference of Means	SE of Difference	T-Value	Adjusted P-Value
2	−1.000	2.647	−0.3778	0.9251
3	8.600	2.647	3.2489	0.0282

```
Treatment = 2 subtracted from:
```

Treat-ment	Difference of Means	SE of Difference	T-Value	Adjusted P-Value
3	9.600	2.647	3.627	0.0165

8. Given the following ANOVA output, answer the questions
that follow:

Source	DF	SS	MS	F	P
Block	6	1637.81	272.968	7.91	0.001
Treatment	2	707.43	353.714	10.25	0.003
Error	12	413.90	34.492		
Total	20	2759.14			

(a) The researcher wishes to test $H_0: \mu_1 = \mu_2 = \mu_3$
against H_1: at least one of the means is different.
Based on the ANOVA table, what should the researcher
conclude? *Reject H_0*
(b) What is the mean square due to error? *34.492*
(c) The following output represents the results of Tukey's
test. What should the researcher conclude? *$\mu_1 \mu_2 \mu_3$*

```
Tukey 95% Simultaneous Confidence Intervals
Response Variable Response
All Pairwise Comparisons among Levels
of Treatment
Treatment = 1 subtracted from:
Treatment  Lower   Center  Upper  -----+---------+---------+---------+-
2         -3.511   4.857   13.23  (-----------*-----------)
3          5.631  14.000   22.37             (-----------*-----------)
                                  -----+---------+---------+---------+-
                                     0.0      7.0      14.0      21.0

Treatment = 2 subtracted from:
Treatment  Lower   Center  Upper  -----+---------+---------+---------+-
3          0.7743  9.143   17.51        (-----------*-----------)
                                  -----+---------+---------+---------+-
                                     0.0      7.0      14.0      21.0
```

9. Given the following ANOVA output, answer the questions
that follow:

```
Analysis of Variance for Response
```

Source	DF	SS	MS	F	P
Block	8	2105.436	263.179	278.66	0.000
Treatment	3	6.393	2.131	2.26	0.108
Error	24	22.667	0.944		
Total	35	2134.496			

(a) The researcher wishes to test $H_0: \mu_1 = \mu_2 = \mu_3 = \mu_4$
against H_1: at least one of the means is different.
Based on the ANOVA table, what should the researcher
conclude? *Do not reject H_0*
(b) What is the mean square due to error? *0.944*
(c) Explain why it is not necessary to use Tukey's test on
these data. *Did not reject H_0*

10. Given the following ANOVA output, answer the questions
that follow:

```
Analysis of Variance for Response
```

Source	DF	SS	MS	F	P
Block	6	1712.37	285.39	134.20	0.000
Treatment	3	2.27	0.76	0.36	0.786
Error	18	38.28	2.13		
Total	27	1752.91			

(a) The researcher wishes to test $H_0: \mu_1 = \mu_2 = \mu_3 = \mu_4$
against H_1: at least one of the means is different.
Based on the ANOVA table, what should the researcher
conclude? *Do not reject H_0*
(b) What is the mean square due to error? *2.13*
(c) Explain why it is not necessary to use Tukey's test on
these data. *Did not reject H_0*

*In Problems 11 and 12, assume that the data come from popula-
tions that are normally distributed with the same variance.*

11.

Block	Treatment 1	Treatment 2	Treatment 3
1	9.7	8.4	8.8
2	10.4	8.9	8.5
3	10.5	9.3	9.0
4	10.7	10.5	9.3
5	11.1	10.7	10.3

(a) Test $H_0: \mu_1 = \mu_2 = \mu_3$ against H_1: at least one of the
means is different, where μ_1 is the mean for treatment 1,
and so on, at the $\alpha = 0.05$ level of significance. *Reject H_0*
(b) If the null hypothesis from part (a) was rejected, use
Tukey's test to determine which pairwise means differ
using a familywise error rate of $\alpha = 0.05$. *$\mu_1 \mu_2 \mu_3$*
(c) Draw boxplots of the data for each treatment using the
same scale to support the analytical results obtained in
parts (a) and (b).

12.

Block	Treatment 1	Treatment 2	Treatment 3
1	15.8	15.0	15.3
2	16.0	15.8	17.2
3	21.6	18.3	21.5
4	21.6	20.8	21.3
5	22.5	21.5	23.5
6	17.5	16.2	16.8

(a) Test $H_0: \mu_1 = \mu_2 = \mu_3$ against H_1: at least one of the means is different, where μ_1 is the mean for treatment 1, and so on, at the $\alpha = 0.05$ level of significance. Reject H_0

(b) If the null hypothesis from part (a) was rejected, use Tukey's test to determine which pairwise means differ using a familywise error rate of $\alpha = 0.05$. $\underline{\mu_1 \; \mu_3} \; \mu_2$

(c) Draw boxplots of the data for each treatment using the same scale to support the analytical results obtained in parts (a) and (b).

Applying the Concepts

13. Octane An automotive engineer wanted to determine whether the octane of gasoline used in a car increases gas mileage. He recognized that car and driver are variables that affect gas mileage. He selected six different brands of car and assigned a driver to each car, so he blocked by car type and driver. For each car (and driver), the researcher randomly selected a number from 1 to 3, with 1 representing 87-octane gasoline, 2 representing 89-octane gasoline, and 3 representing 92-octane gasoline. Then 5 gallons of the gasoline selected was placed in the car. The car was driven around a closed track at 40 miles per hour until the car ran out of gas. The number of miles driven were recorded and then divided by 5 to obtain the miles per gallon. He obtained the following results:

	87 Octane	89 Octane	92 Octane
Chevrolet Impala	28.3	28.4	28.7
Chrysler 300M	27.1	26.9	27.2
Ford Taurus	26.4	26.1	26.8
Lincoln LS	26.1	26.4	27.3
Toyota Camry	28.4	28.9	29.1
Volvo S60	25.3	25.1	25.8

(a) Normal probability plots for each treatment indicate that the requirement of normality is satisfied. Verify that the requirement of equal population variances for each treatment is satisfied.

(b) Is there sufficient evidence that the mean miles per gallon are different among the three octane levels at the $\alpha = 0.05$ level of significance? Yes

(c) If the null hypothesis from part (b) was rejected, use Tukey's test to determine which pairwise means differ using a familywise error rate of $\alpha = 0.05$. $\underline{\mu_{87} \; \mu_{89}} \; \mu_{92}$

(d) Based on your results for part (c), what do you conclude?

14. Healing Rate A medical researcher wanted to determine the effectiveness of coagulants on the healing rate of a razor cut on lab mice. Because healing rates of mice vary from mouse to mouse, the researcher decided to block by mouse. First, the researcher gave each mouse a local anesthesia and then made a 5-mm incision that was 2 mm deep on each mouse. He randomly selected one of the three treatments and recorded the time it took for the wound to stop bleeding (in minutes). He repeated this process two more times on each mouse and obtained the results shown.

Mouse	No Drug	Experimental Drug 1	Experimental Drug 2
1	3.2	3.4	3.4
2	4.8	4.4	3.4
3	6.6	5.9	5.4
4	6.5	6.3	5.2
5	6.4	6.3	6.1

14. (c) $\underline{\mu_{ND} \; \mu_{D1} \; \mu_{D2}}$; ambiguous

(a) Normal probability plots for each treatment indicate that the requirement of normality is satisfied. Verify that the requirement of equal population variances for each treatment is satisfied.

(b) Is there sufficient evidence that the mean healing time is different among the three treatments at the $\alpha = 0.05$ level of significance? Yes

(c) If the null hypothesis from part (b) was rejected, use Tukey's test to determine which pairwise means differ using a familywise error rate of $\alpha = 0.05$. $\underline{\mu_{ND} \; \mu_{D1} \; \mu_{D2}}$

(d) Based on your results for part (c), what do you conclude?

15. Crash Tests The Insurance Institute for Highway Safety regularly tests cars for various safety factors. In one such test, the institute tests the bumpers in 5-mile per hour (mph) crashes. The following data represent the cost of repairs (in dollars) after four different 5-mph crashes on small utility vehicles. The institute blocks by location of crash, and the treatment is car model.

	Jeep Cherokee	Saturn VUE	Toyota RAV4	Hyundai Santa Fe
Front into flat barrier	652	416	489	539
Rear into flat barrier	824	556	1,897	1,504
Front into angle barrier	1,448	1,179	1,151	1,578
Rear into pole	1,553	1,335	2,377	1,988

Source: Insurance Institute for Highway Safety

(a) Normal probability plots for each treatment indicate that the requirement of normality is satisfied. Verify that the requirement of equal population variances for each treatment is satisfied.

(b) Is there sufficient evidence that the mean cost of repairs is different among the four SUVs at the $\alpha = 0.05$ level of significance? No

(c) If the null hypothesis from part (b) was rejected, use Tukey's test to determine which pairwise means differ using a familywise error rate of $\alpha = 0.05$.

16. Lodging A travel agent wanted to know whether the price (in dollars) of Marriott, Hyatt, and Sheraton Hotels differed significantly. She knew that location of the hotel is a factor in determining price, so she blocked each hotel by location. After randomly selecting six cities and obtaining the room rate for each hotel, she obtained the following data:

	Marriott	Hyatt	Sheraton
Chicago	179	139.40	150
Los Angeles	169	161.50	161
Houston	163	187	189
Boston	189	179.10	169
Denver	179	168	112
Orlando	147	159	147

Source: Expedia.com

(a) Normal probability plots for each treatment indicate that the requirement of normality is satisfied. Verify that the requirement of equal population variances for each treatment is satisfied.

(b) Is there sufficient evidence that the mean cost of the room is different among the three hotel chains at the $\alpha = 0.05$ level of significance?   No

(c) If the null hypothesis from part (b) was rejected, use Tukey's test to determine which pairwise means differ using a familywise error rate of $\alpha = 0.05$.

17. **Rats in Space** Researchers at NASA wanted to determine the effects of space flight on a rat's daily consumption of water. The following data represent the water consumption (in milliliters per day) at lift-off minus 1, return plus 1, and 1 month after return for six rats sent to space on the Spacelab Sciences 1 flight.

Rat	Lift-Off Minus 1	Return Plus 1	Return Plus 1 Month
1	18.5	32	30
2	17.5	18	34
3	28.0	31	39
4	28.5	29	44
5	31.0	48	54
6	22.5	25	32

Source: NASA Life Sciences Data Archive

(a) Normal probability plots for each treatment indicate that the requirement of normality is satisfied. Verify that the requirement of equal population variances for each treatment is satisfied.

(b) Is there sufficient evidence that the water consumption is different for the three days at the $\alpha = 0.05$ level of significance?   Yes

(c) If the null hypothesis from part (b) was rejected, use Tukey's test to determine which pairwise means differ using a familywise error rate of $\alpha = 0.05$.
μ_{LO-1} μ_{R+1} $\mu_{R+1\,Month}$

18. **Concrete Strength** Researchers Olivia Carrillo-Gamboa and Richard Gunst presented the following data in their article, "Measurement-Error-Model Collinearities." The data represent the compressive strength (in pounds per square inch) of a random sample of concrete 2 days, 7 days, and 28 days after pouring.

Concrete	2 Days	7 Days	28 Days
1	2830	3505	4470
2	3295	3430	4740
3	2710	3670	5115
4	2855	3355	4880
5	2980	3985	4445
6	3065	3630	4080
7	3765	4570	5390

Source: "Measurement-Error-Model Collinearities," *Technometrics* 34(454–464).

(a) Normal probability plots for each treatment indicate that the requirement of normality is satisfied. Verify that the requirement of equal population variances for each treatment is satisfied.

(b) Is there sufficient evidence that the mean strength is different among the three days at the $\alpha = 0.05$ level of significance?   Yes

(c) If the null hypothesis from part (b) was rejected, use Tukey's test to determine which pairwise means differ using a familywise error rate of $\alpha = 0.05$. μ_2 μ_7 μ_{28}

19. **Waiting in Line** A quality-control manager at an amusement park feels that the amount of time that people spend waiting in line for the American Eagle roller coaster is too long. To determine if a new loading/unloading procedure is effective in reducing wait time in line, he measures the amount of time (in minutes) people are waiting in line for seven days. After implementing the new procedure, he again measures the amount of time (in minutes) people are waiting in line for seven days and obtains the following data. To make a reasonable comparison, he chooses days when weather conditions are alike.

Day	Mon	Tues	Wed	Thurs	Fri	Sat	Sun
Wait time before new procedure	11.6	25.9	20.0	38.2	57.3	32.1	81.8
Wait time after new procedure	10.7	28.3	19.2	35.9	59.2	31.8	75.3

Treat each day as a block and the wait times before and after the procedure as the treatment.

(a) Using the methods introduced in this section, determine whether there is sufficient evidence to conclude that the two loading procedures are resulting in different measurements of the wait time at the $\alpha = 0.05$ level of significance.   Do not reject H_0

(b) Using the methods introduced in Section 11.1, determine whether there is sufficient evidence to conclude that the two loading procedures are resulting in different measurements of the wait time at the $\alpha = 0.05$ level of significance.   Do not reject H_0

(c) Compare the *P*-values of both approaches. Can you conclude that the method presented in this section is a generalization of the matched-pair *t*-test?
P-value = 0.438 for both approaches

TECHNOLOGY STEP-BY-STEP   Randomized Complete Block Design

MINITAB

Conducting the Analysis of Variance
1. In C1, enter the block of the response variable; in C2, enter the treatment of the response variable; and in C3, enter the value of the response variable.
2. Select the **Stat** menu. Highlight **A**NOVA and select **Two-way** . . . .
3. Enter C3 in the box marked "Response Variable," enter C1 in the box marked "Row factor," and enter C2 in the box marked "Column factor." Check the "Fit additive model" box. Click OK.

Tukey's Test
1. With the data entered into the MINITAB spreadsheet as specified in Step 1 above, select the **Stat** menu. Highlight **A**NOVA and select **General Linear Model** . . . .
2. Enter the name of the response variable in the box marked "Responses." Enter "C1 C2," in the box marked "Model," where C1 is the block of the response variable and C2 is the treatment. Enter C1 in the box marked "Random factors."
3. Click "Comparisons . . . ". Click the "Pairwise comparisons" radio button. In the box marked "Terms," enter C2, the treatment level. Check the box marked "Tukey." Check the box marked "Confidence Interval" if you want confidence intervals. Check the box marked "Test" if you want to conduct hypothesis tests of the pairwise differences.
4. Click OK twice.

13.4 TWO-WAY ANALYSIS OF VARIANCE

Objectives		
	1	Analyze a two-way ANOVA design
	2	Draw interaction plots
	3	Perform the Tukey test

One-way analysis of variance is used to compare k population means. In this design, there is one factor set at k levels. For example, we randomly assign 40 males between the ages of 20 and 29 years to $k = 3$ different treatment groups. Group 1 receives 5 mg per day of an experimental drug, group 2 receives 7.5 mg per day of an experimental drug, and group 3 receives a placebo. The expectation is that the 40 males are alike in all ways except the treatment. The experimental design that allows for this type of analysis is the completely randomized design.

The methods of one-way ANOVA can also be used in analyzing observational data. For example, a researcher might wonder whether the mean of hemoglobin levels varies with age. In this circumstance, the factor is age, such as 20 to 29, 30 to 39, and 40 to 49 years old. In this case, the factor has $k = 3$ levels. Of course, in observational studies, there is never any talk of causation when it comes to the relation between the factor (age) and response variable (hemoglobin). In both the experimental design and the observational study, we should notice that the factor is a categorical (qualitative) variable that classifies an individual into one of k groups. The categorical variable in the treatment experiment is the amount of the drug. The categorical variable in the hemoglobin study is age group.

An improvement on analysis involving one-way ANOVA is the randomized complete block design in which experimental units are organized through a technique called *blocking*. For example, if the researcher attempting to determine the effectiveness of a drug feels that genetics may explain some of the variation in the response variable, he may select families that have three male siblings and block by family. For example, one sibling is randomly assigned to group 1, one sibling is randomly assigned to group 2, and the third sibling to group 3. It is important to recognize that we are still only interested in determining whether the factor, drug, affects the response variable. We block so that we reduce experimental error.

⬦ CAUTION
The randomized complete block design is a design that varies a single factor. We are not interested in determining whether the block is significant! If we want to analyze the effect of fixing two different factors at different levels, we use the methods of two-way ANOVA.

1 Analyze a Two-Way Analysis of Variance Design

We now present analysis in which two factors can be used to explain variability in the response variable. We deal with the two factors by fixing them at different levels. Again, remember that there are two ways to deal with factors: (1) control the factors by fixing them at a single level or by fixing them at different levels, and (2) randomize so that their effect on the response variable is minimized. In both the completely randomized design and the randomized complete block design, we manipulated one factor to see how varying it affected the response variable. In this section, we manipulate two factors.

Throughout the section, we will call the two factors factor A and factor B. If factor A has two levels and factor B has two levels, we have a **2 × 2 factorial design** (read "two by two factorial design"). For example, suppose that we want to determine the effect an experimental drug has on hemoglobin levels in humans. We might have two levels in the first factor (placebo or 5 mg per day of the drug) and two levels in the second factor (male or female). In this way, our design will look like Figure 12.

Figure 12

		Factor B	
		Placebo	**5 mg per day**
Factor A	**Male**	Hemoglobin of males receiving the placebo	Hemoglobin of males receiving 5 mg per day
	Female	Hemoglobin of females receiving the placebo	Hemoglobin of females receiving 5 mg per day

In general, the two-factor design looks as presented in Figure 13, where there are n replications for each combination of factor A and factor B. Factor A has a levels and factor B has b levels. Each combination of factor levels is a treatment.

Figure 13

		Factor B			
		1	**2**	**. . .**	**b**
Factor A	**1**	n observations of the response variable with level 1 of factor A and level 1 of factor B	n observations of the response variable with level 1 of factor A and level 2 of factor B	**. . .**	n observations of the response variable with level 1 of factor A and level b of factor B
	2	n observations of the response variable with level 2 of factor A and level 1 of factor B	n observations of the response variable with level 2 of factor A and level 2 of factor B	**. . .**	n observations of the response variable with level 2 of factor A and level b of factor B
	⋮	⋮	⋮		⋮
	a	n observations of the response variable with level a of factor A and level 1 of Factor B	n observations of the response variable with level a of factor A and level 2 of Factor B	**. . .**	n observations of the response variable with level a of factor A and level b of Factor B

So, if there are three levels of factor A and two levels of factor B, we have a 3×2 factorial design as shown in Figure 14(a). If there are three levels of factor A and three levels of factor B, we have a 3×3 factorial design as shown in Figure 14(b).

Figure 14

		Factor B	
		1	**2**
Factor A	**1**	n observations of the response variable with level 1 of factor A and level 1 of factor B	n observations of the response variable with level 1 of factor A and level 2 of factor B
	2	n observations of the response variable with level 2 of factor A and level 1 of factor B	n observations of the response variable with level 2 of factor A and level 2 of factor B
	3	n observations of the response variable with level 3 of factor A and level 1 of factor B	n observations of the response variable with level 3 of factor A and level 2 of factor B

(a)

Figure 14
Continued

Factor B

		1	2	3
Factor A	1	n observations of the response variable with level 1 of factor A and level 1 of factor B	n observations of the response variable with level 1 of factor A and level 2 of factor B	n observations of the response variable with level 1 of factor A and level 3 of factor B
	2	n observations of the response variable with level 2 of factor A and level 1 of factor B	n observations of the response variable with level 2 of factor A and level 2 of factor B	n observations of the response variable with level 2 of factor A and level 3 of factor B
	3	n observations of the response variable with level 3 of factor A and level 1 of factor B	n observations of the response variable with level 3 of factor A and level 2 of factor B	n observations of the response variable with level 3 of factor A and level 3 of factor B

(b)

Each of the n observations of the response variable for the different levels of the factors exists within a **cell**. In a 2×2 factorial design, there are four cells with n observations within each cell. In a 2×3 factorial design, there are six cells with n observations within each cell. In a 3×3 factorial design, there are nine cells with n observations within each cell. Each cell corresponds to a specific treatment.

EXAMPLE 1 **A 2 × 3 Factorial Design**

High-density lipoprotein (HDL) cholesterol is the so-called good cholesterol because it helps to reduce the amount of bad cholesterol in your system. A pharmaceutical company developed a drug that is meant to increase HDL levels in patients. They obtained volunteers whose HDL cholesterol was roughly the same and randomly assigned them to one of three groups. Group 1 was a placebo group that received a sugar tablet. Group 2 received 5 mg of the experimental drug, and group 3 received 10 mg of the experimental drug. In addition to drug dosage, the researchers considered age to be a factor in the analysis; so they divided patients into an 18- to 39-year-old category and a 40 and older category. The design results in a 2×3 factorial design. Table 10 shows the increase in HDL cholesterol in milligrams per deciliter (mg/dL) for each patient in the study after 10 weeks. Each cell has $n = 3$ replications.

Table 10			
	Drug Dosage		
Age	**Placebo**	**5 mg**	**10 mg**
18 to 39 years	4	9	14
	3	5	12
	−1	6	10
40 or older	3	3	10
	2	6	8
	0	7	7

Now Work Problem 17(a)

In Other Words

An example of interaction is sleeping pills and alcohol. They are usually not fatal when taken alone, but can be fatal when combined.

In the factorial design, all levels of factor A are combined with all levels of factor B, so we say that the factors are **crossed**. The effect of factor A is the change in the response variable that results from changing the level of factor A. The effect of factor B is the change in the response variable that results from changing the level of factor B. Together these two effects are called the **main effects**. If changes in the level of factor A result in different changes in the value of the response variable for the different levels of factor B, we say that there is an **interaction effect** between the factors. An example will help clarify the idea of interaction effect.

EXAMPLE 2 **Main Effects and Interaction Effect**

Suppose that we have two factors, A and B, each fixed at two levels, high and low. The value of the response variable at each level is presented in Table 11. For example, the response variables when both factor A and B are set to low are 5 and 3.

Table 11		
	Factor B	
Factor A	**Low**	**High**
Low	5	8
	3	6
High	8	17
	4	18

The main effect of factor A can be thought of as the difference between the mean value of the response variable when factor A is set at low and the mean value of the response variable when factor A is set at high. That is,

$$\text{Main effect of factor A} = \frac{8+4+17+18}{4} - \frac{5+3+8+6}{4} = 6.25 \text{ units}$$

Increasing factor A from low level to high level causes the value of the response variable to increase by 6.25 units, on average.

The main effect of factor B is

$$\text{Main effect of factor B} = \frac{8+6+17+18}{4} - \frac{5+3+8+4}{4} = 7.25 \text{ units}$$

Increasing factor B from low level to high level causes the value of the response variable to increase by 7.25 units, on average.

To see the interaction effect between the factors, we look at one level of one factor and then see how changing the other factor affects the value of the response variable. For example, if we look only at the low level of factor B, we can see that the effect of changing factor A from low to high is

$$\frac{8+4}{2} - \frac{5+3}{2} = 2 \text{ units}$$

This indicates that, if we are at the low level of factor B, increasing factor A from low to high causes the response variable to increase by 2 units, on average. If we look only at the high level of factor B, we can see the effect of changing factor A from low to high is

$$\frac{17+18}{2} - \frac{8+6}{2} = 10.5 \text{ units}$$

CAUTION

If interaction between two factors exists, interpret the main effects with extreme caution.

This indicates that, if we are at the high level of factor B, increasing factor A from low to high causes the response variable to increase by 10.5, on average.

The main effect of factor A is 6.25 units, but this is really misleading because, if we are at the low level of factor B, the mean increase in the response variable is only 2 units; but if we are at the high level of factor B, the mean increase in the response variable is 10.5 units. So, the increase in the value of the response variable depends on the level of factor B. For this reason, we say there is an interaction effect between factors A and B.

The moral: If interaction between two factors exists, it is extremely dangerous to look at main effects because they are misleading.

Now Work Problem 9(a)

Now let's learn to test hypotheses that involve a factorial design. The requirements for the model are as follows:

> **Requirements for the Two-Way Analysis of Variance**
>
> **1.** The populations from which the samples are drawn must be normal.
> **2.** The samples are independent.
> **3.** The populations all have the same variance.

We can check the normality requirement through a normal probability plot of the data within each cell. The requirement for equal variances can be checked by verifying that the largest sample standard deviation is no more than twice the smallest sample standard deviation.

Although not a requirement to conduct two-way ANOVA, we also assume that there are an equal number of observations for each combination of the factors because the power of the test is increased. That is, it reduces the likelihood of making a Type II error.

In a two-way ANOVA, we will be testing three separate hypotheses. The three hypotheses go with the three types of effects presented earlier. The first hypothesis deals with the significance of any interaction effect. So we have

Hypotheses Regarding Interaction Effect

H_0: there is no interaction between the factors
H_1: there is interaction between the factors

Hypotheses Regarding Main Effects

H_0: there is no effect of factor A on the response variable
H_1: there is an effect of factor A on the response variable

H_0: there is no effect of factor B on the response variable
H_1: there is an effect of factor B on the response variable

> Whenever conducting a two-way ANOVA, we always first test the hypothesis regarding interaction effect. If the null hypothesis of no interaction is rejected, we do not interpret the results of the hypotheses involving the main effects. This is because the interaction clouds the interpretation of the main effects.

The decision rule for each of these hypotheses will be the same as always: if the P-value is less than the level of significance, we reject the null hypothesis in favor of the alternative. We will obtain the P-value from the output of statistical software. Let's look at an example.

EXAMPLE 3   **Examining a Two-Way ANOVA**

Problem: In Example 1, we presented data for an experimental drug that was meant to increase HDL cholesterol. The data are represented in Table 12 for convenience.

Table 12			
		Drug Dosage	
Age	**Placebo**	**5 mg**	**10 mg**
18 to 39 years	4	9	14
	3	5	12
	−1	6	10
40 or older	3	3	10
	2	6	8
	0	7	7

(a) HDL cholesterol levels are known to have a distribution that is approximately normal. Verify that the largest sample standard deviation of a cell is no more than twice the smallest sample standard deviation of a cell.

(b) Use MINITAB to test whether there is an interaction effect between the drug dosage and age.

(c) If the null hypothesis of no interaction is not rejected, determine whether there is sufficient evidence to conclude that the mean increase in HDL cholesterol is different among each drug dosage group. If the null hypothesis of no interaction is not rejected, determine whether there is sufficient evidence to conclude that the mean increase in HDL cholesterol is different for each age group.

Approach: We use MINITAB to obtain the two-way analysis of variance. The steps for performing two-way ANOVA using MINITAB are given in the Technology Step-by-Step on page 727. If the P-value corresponding to each hypothesis is small (say, less than $\alpha = 0.05$), we reject the null hypothesis in favor of the alternative hypothesis.

Solution

(a) We obtain the descriptive statistics from MINITAB shown in Figure 15. The largest sample standard deviation, 2.65 mg/dL, is not twice as large as the smallest sample standard deviation, 1.528 mg/dL, so the requirement of equal population variances is satisfied.

Figure 15   **Descriptive Statistics: P/18–39, 5/18–39, 10/18–39, P/40, 5/40, 10/40**

Variable	N	Mean	Median	TrMean	StDev	SE Mean
P/18–39	3	2.00	3.00	2.00	2.65	1.53
5/18–39	3	6.67	6.00	6.67	2.08	1.20
10/18–39	3	12.00	12.00	12.00	2.00	1.15
P/40	3	1.667	2.000	1.667	1.528	0.882
5/40	3	5.33	6.00	5.33	2.08	1.20
10/40	3	8.333	8.000	8.333	1.528	0.882

Variable	Minimum	Maximum	Q1	Q3
P/18–39	−1.00	4.00	−1.00	4.00
5/18–39	5.00	9.00	5.00	9.00
10/18–39	10.00	14.00	10.00	14.00
P/40	0.000	3.000	0.000	3.000
5/40	3.00	7.00	3.00	7.00
10/40	7.000	10.000	7.000	10.000

(b) We first test the hypotheses

H_0: there is no interaction between drug dosage and age

versus

H_1: there is an interaction between drug dosage and age

Enter the data into MINITAB. Let column 1 represent the drug dosage; so if the observation is from the placebo group, we enter a 1, if the observation is from 5 mg, we enter a 2, and so on. We let column 2 represent the age and enter 1 for 18- to 39-year-olds and enter 2 for 40 or older. Column 3 gets the value of the response variable, increase in HDL cholesterol. The results of the two-way analysis of variance are presented in Figure 16.

Figure 16   **Two-way ANOVA: HDL versus Drug, Age**

Analysis of Variance for HDL

Source	DF	SS	MS	F	P
Drug	2	208.33	104.17	25.68	0.000
Age	1	14.22	14.22	3.51	0.086
Interaction	2	8.78	4.39	1.08	0.370
Error	12	48.67	4.06		
Total	17	280.00			

The P-value for the interaction effect is 0.370. Because the P-value is large, we do not reject the null hypothesis and conclude that there is no interaction effect.

Note to Instructor
Some statisticians recommend rerunning the model without the interaction component when the null hypothesis of no interaction is not rejected. That is, if the null hypothesis of no interaction is not rejected, run the model as an additive model.

CAUTION

Although we do not reject the null hypothesis that the mean increase in HDL is the same at the different age levels, there is some evidence that age plays a role in HDL levels.

Now Work Problems 17(b) and (c)

(c) We now test the hypotheses regarding the main effects. The hypothesis regarding the main effect, drug dosage, is

$$H_0: \mu_{\text{placebo}} = \mu_{5 \text{ mg}} = \mu_{10 \text{ mg}}$$

versus

$$H_1: \text{at least one of the means differs}$$

The hypothesis regarding the main effect, age, is

$$H_0: \mu_{18\text{–}39} = \mu_{40 \text{ or older}} \quad \text{versus} \quad H_1: \text{the means differ}$$

The P-value for the main effect, drug dosage, is given as 0.000. The small value of the P-value is taken as evidence against the null hypothesis. We conclude that at least one of the mean increases in HDL is different for the different levels of drug dosage. Therefore, the level of the drug dosage is a significant contributor to explaining the increase in HDL cholesterol.

The P-value for the main effect, age, is given as 0.086. Because this is greater than the level of significance for the test ($\alpha = 0.05$), we do not reject the null hypothesis and conclude that the mean increase in HDL cholesterol does not change with age.

② Draw Interaction Plots

As is always the case in statistics, we like to support results graphically whenever possible. There is a way to graphically represent the role interaction plays in any factorial design. We call these plots **interaction plots**.

> ### Constructing Interaction Plots
>
> **Step 1:** Compute the mean value of the response variable within each cell. In addition, compute the row mean value of the response variable and the column mean value of the response variable with each level of each factor.
>
> **Step 2:** In a Cartesian plane, label the horizontal axis for each level of factor A. The vertical axis will represent the mean value of the response variable. For each level of factor A, plot the mean value of the response variable for each level of factor B. Draw straight lines connecting the points for the common level of factor B. You should have as many lines as there are levels of factor B. The more difference there is in the slopes of the two lines, the stronger the evidence of interaction.

An example should help to clarify the steps given.

EXAMPLE 4 **Drawing an Interaction Plot**

Problem: Draw an interaction plot for the data from Example 3.

Approach: We will follow Steps 1 and 2.

Solution

Step 1: We compute the mean value of the response variable for each cell as shown in Table 13.

Table 13			
	Drug Dosage		
Age	**Placebo**	**5 mg**	**10 mg**
18 to 39 years	$\dfrac{4 + 3 + (-1)}{3} = 2$	$\dfrac{9 + 5 + 6}{3} = 6.7$	$\dfrac{14 + 12 + 10}{3} = 12$
40 or older	$\dfrac{3 + 2 + 0}{3} = 1.7$	$\dfrac{3 + 6 + 7}{3} = 5.3$	$\dfrac{10 + 8 + 7}{3} = 8.3$

Figure 17

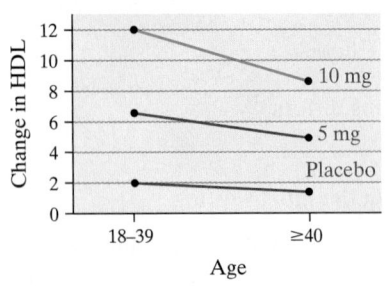

Step 2: We draw a Cartesian plane with the horizontal axis labeled Age with the levels 18 to 39 years and 40 or older indicated. The vertical axis is labeled as the response. For each age group, we plot the corresponding mean values of the response variable for drug. Then connect the points and label each line with its corresponding drug dosage. See Figure 17.

When interpreting interaction plots, we look at the level of parallelism between the lines. The more parallel the lines seem to be, the stronger the visual evidence is of no interaction. From Figure 17, we see that the lines are roughly parallel, so our conclusion of no interaction is verified. Another bit of information that can be learned from the interaction plot is the effect age has on the response variable, change in HDL. Notice that change in HDL is decreasing as age increases. From this, we can see that the decrease in HDL cholesterol is largest for the 10-mg dose and smallest for the placebo.

EXAMPLE 5   Drawing an Interaction Plot Using Technology

Problem: Draw an interaction plot for the data in Example 3 using statistical software.

Approach: We use MINITAB to draw the interaction plot. The steps to follow are given in the Technology Step-by-Step on page 728.

Solution: Figure 18 shows interaction plots from MINITAB using the data in Example 3.

Figure 18

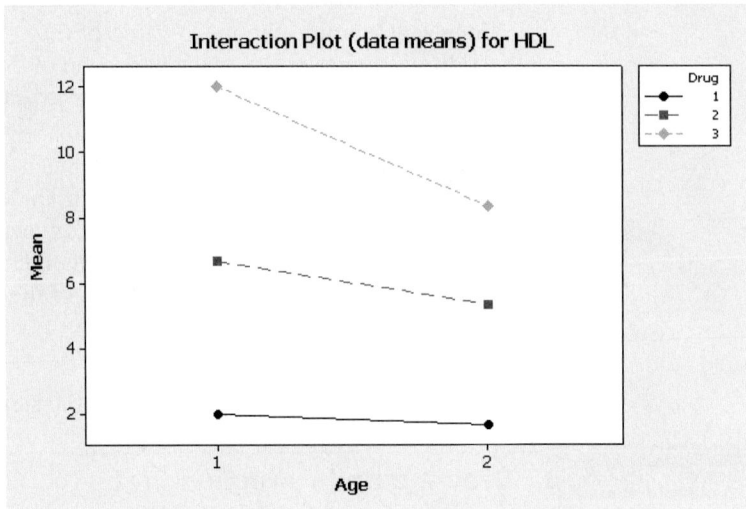

Now Work Problem 17(d)

Figure 19 gives some interaction plots and the level of interaction indicated by the graph. In the graphs, A_1, A_2, and A_3 represent the three levels of factor A, while B_1, B_2, and B_3 represent the three levels of factor B. Remember, though, that the interaction plots are solely meant to help us visualize the interaction (just as boxplots

Figure 19

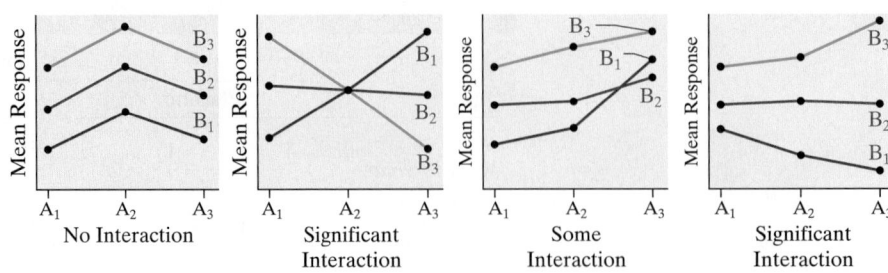

allow us to visualize differences among treatments in one-way ANOVA). They are not meant to be used to test for interaction. We can only test for interaction by looking at the *F*-test statistic and its *P*-value for interaction in the analysis of variance.

EXAMPLE 6

Analyzing a 2 × 2 Factorial Design

Problem: An educational psychologist wants to conduct an experiment to determine whether varying the conditions in which learning and testing take place affects test results. She randomly selects 20 students who are unfamiliar with the Battle at Gettysburg from the Civil War. After presenting the material to the students and allowing them ample time to study, the students are given an exam. Ten of the students receive the lecture in a large lecture hall and 10 receive the lecture in a small classroom (both lectures have the same instructor). Of the students in the large lecture hall, 5 take the exam in the same large lecture hall, while 5 take the exam in a small classroom. Of the students in the small classroom, 5 take the exam in a large lecture hall and 5 take the exam in the same small classroom where they received the lecture. The experimental design is, therefore, a 2 × 2 factorial design with 5 replications in each cell. The scores for each student are presented in Table 14.

Table 14

| Exam Given | Lecture Administered | |
	Large Lecture Hall	Classroom
Large lecture hall	70	63
	63	46
	95	47
	84	71
	72	66
Classroom	51	76
	73	67
	65	80
	72	90
	43	79

Preliminary analysis indicates that the requirements to conduct a two-way ANOVA are satisfied. Test whether there is an interaction effect between the lecture location and exam location. Draw an interaction plot to confirm your results.

Approach: We use MINITAB to perform the two-way analysis of variance and to draw the interaction plot.

Solution: Figure 20 shows the analysis of variance from MINITAB.

Figure 20   **Two-way ANOVA: Score versus Exam, Lecture**

```
Analysis of Variance for Score
Source        DF        SS        MS        F        P
Exam          1         18        18      0.13    0.718
Lecture       1          0         0      0.00    0.954
Interaction   1       1602      1602     11.97    0.003
Error        16       2142       134
```

The *P*-value for the interaction effect is 0.003, indicating that there is a significant interaction effect between lecture location and exam location. Therefore, we will not test the main effects. Figure 21 shows the interaction plot from MINITAB, which confirms the analytic results from the ANOVA.

Figure 21

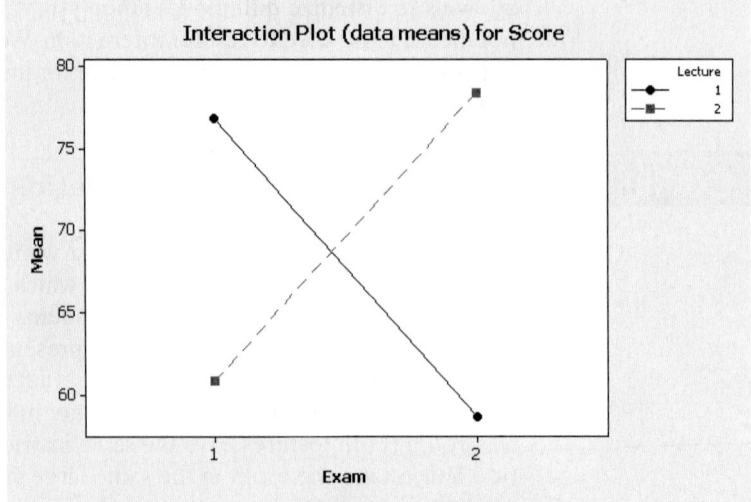

In looking at the interaction plot, it appears that students perform best if they take their exams in the same classroom where their lecture was given. The two high means are the means for (large lecture, large exam) and (classroom lecture, classroom exam). In other words, where a student performs best on the exam seems to depend on where the student attended the lecture.

3 Perform the Tukey Test

Once the null hypothesis of equal population means for either factor is rejected, we proceed to determine which means differ significantly. Again, the method that we use to conduct the analysis is Tukey's test. The steps are identical to those presented for one-way ANOVA. However, the critical value and the estimate of the standard error are a little different. The critical value is $q_{\alpha,\nu,k}$, using a familywise error rate of α with $\nu = N - ab$, where N is the total number of observations (or replications), a is the number of levels for factor A, and b is the number of levels for factor B; k is the number of means being tested for the factor. The standard error is

$$\text{SE} = \sqrt{\frac{\text{MSE}}{m}}$$

where m is the product of the number of levels for the factor and the number of observations within each cell.

| EXAMPLE 7 | **Multiple Comparisons Using Tukey's Test** |

Problem: Use statistical software to perform Tukey's test to determine which pairwise means differ for the data presented in Example 3 using a familywise error rate of $\alpha = 0.05$.

Approach: We will use MINITAB to perform Tukey's test. The steps for performing this test can be found in the Technology Step-by-Step on page 728.

Solution: The results of Tukey's test using MINITAB are presented in Figure 22. MINITAB allows the user to perform pairwise comparisons using either confidence intervals or P-values. In the output shown, Figure 22 gives the pairwise comparisons using 95% confidence intervals. For example, the confidence interval for $\mu_{\text{Drug Level 2}} - \mu_{\text{Drug Level 1}}$ (5 mg–placebo) does not contain 0 and is positive (lower bound: 1.067 mg/dL; upper bound: 7.266 mg/dL). Therefore, the mean increase in HDL cholesterol resulting from 5 mg of the drug is significantly greater than the mean increase due to the placebo. The confidence interval for $\mu_{\text{Drug Level 3}} - \mu_{\text{Drug Level 1}}$ (10 mg–placebo) does not contain 0 and is positive. This indicates that the mean increase in HDL cholesterol resulting from 10 mg of the drug is also greater than the mean increase due to the placebo. Moreover if we look at $\mu_{\text{Drug Level 3}} - \mu_{\text{Drug Level 2}}$, we see that the interval also does not contain 0, so the mean increase in HDL level with the 10-mg drug is higher than the increase with 5 mg of the drug.

Figure 22 **Tukey 95% Simultaneous Confidence Intervals**
Response Variable HDL
All Pairwise Comparisons among Levels of Age

```
Age = 1 subtracted from:

Age      Lower  Center   Upper   --+---------+---------+---------+----
2       -3.846 -1.778  0.2906   (---------------*----------------)
                                 --+---------+---------+---------+----
                                -3.6     -2.4      -1.2       0.0
```

Tukey 95% Simultaneous Confidence Intervals
Response Variable HDL
All Pairwise Comparisons among Levels of Drug

```
Drug = 1 subtracted from:

Drug    Lower  Center   Upper   ------+---------+---------+---------+
2       1.067   4.167   7.266   (---------*---------)
3       5.234   8.333  11.433             (---------*---------)
                                ------+---------+---------+---------+
                                    3.0       6.0       9.0      12.0

Drug = 2 subtracted from:

Drug    Lower  Center   Upper   ------+---------+---------+---------+
3       1.067   4.167   7.266   (---------*---------)
                                ------+---------+---------+---------+
                                    3.0       6.0       9.0      12.0
```

Now Work Problem 17(e)

IN CLASS ACTIVITY

Flight of Fancy: Part II

How does the type of paper affect the flight of a paper airplane? In Part I of this activity, we looked at how the design of the plane affected flight distance while we blocked on gender. Now we also want to know whether type of paper plays a role in paper airplane flight. Use three different types of paper (for example, newspaper, brown shipping paper, typing paper) and perform a two-way ANOVA.

(a) Determine if there is significant interaction between paper type and plane design.

(b) Draw an interaction plot of the data to support the results.

(c) If there is not significant interaction, determine if there is significant difference in the means for the three plane designs. If there is not significant interaction, determine if there is significant difference in the means for the paper types.

(d) If there is significant difference in the means for the three plane designs, use Tukey's test to determine which pairwise means differ using a familywise error rate of $\alpha = 0.05$. If there is significant difference in the means for the paper type, use Tukey's test to determine which pairwise means differ using a familywise error rate of $\alpha = 0.05$.

(e) Check the requirements for the model. Are they all met? If not, how will that affect your conclusions?

13.4 ASSESS YOUR UNDERSTANDING

Concepts and Vocabulary

1. Explain the differences between the completely randomized design, randomized complete block design, and factorial design.

2. Explain what an interaction effect is. Why is it dangerous to analyze main effects if there is an interaction effect?

3. What is an interaction plot? Why are they useful?

4. How many treatments are there in a 2×3 factorial design? How many levels does each factor have?
   6 treatments; 2 levels of factor A, 3 levels of factor B

Skill Building

In Problems 5–8, determine whether the interaction plot suggests that significant interaction exists among the factors.

5. No significant interaction

6. Significant interaction

7. Significant interaction

8. Significant interaction

In Problems 9 and 10, (a) use the same analysis as that presented in Example 2 to conjecture whether interaction exists between factor A and factor B. (b) Draw an interaction plot to verify your conjecture from part (a).

9.
NW

		Factor B	
		Low	High
	Low	12	6
		8	7
Factor A	**High**	20	1
		14	3

Interaction exists

10.

		Factor B	
		Low	High
	Low	104	143
		96	121
Factor A	**High**	84	55
		76	43

Interaction exists

11. Given the following ANOVA output, answer the questions that follow.

Analysis of Variance for Response

Source	DF	SS	MS	F	P
Factor A	1	531.2	531.2	11.73	0.003
Factor B	2	3018.0	1509.0	33.33	0.000
Interaction	2	16.3	8.2	0.18	0.836
Error	18	814.9	45.3		

(a) Is there evidence of an interaction effect? Why or why not? No; P-value is large

(b) Based on the P-value, is there evidence of a difference in the means from factor A? Based on the P-value, is there evidence of a difference in the means from factor B? Yes; yes

(c) What is the mean square error? 45.3

12. Given the following ANOVA output, answer the questions that follow.

Analysis of Variance for Response

Source	DF	SS	MS	F	P
Factor A	2	156	78	0.39	0.679
Factor B	2	132	66	0.33	0.720
Interaction	4	311	78	0.39	0.813
Error	27	5354	198		
Total	35	5952			

(a) Is there evidence of an interaction effect? Why or why not? No; P-value is large

(b) Based on the P-value, is there evidence of a difference in the means from factor A? Based on the P-value, is there evidence of a difference in the means from factor B? No; no

(c) What is the mean square error? 198

13. Given the following ANOVA output, answer the questions that follow.

Analysis of Variance for Response

Source	DF	SS	MS	F	P
Factor A	2	2269.8	1134.9	35.63	0.000
Factor B	2	115.2	57.6	1.81	0.183
Interaction	4	1694.8	423.7	13.30	0.000
Error	27	860.0	31.9		
Total	35	4939.8			

(a) Is there evidence of an interaction effect? Why or why not? Yes; P-value is small

(b) Based on the P-value, is there evidence of a difference in the means from factor A? Based on the P-value, is there evidence of a difference in the means from factor B? Analysis halted

(c) What is the mean square error? 31.9

14. Given the following ANOVA output, answer the questions that follow.

Analysis of Variance for Response

Source	DF	SS	MS	F	P
Factor A	2	1209.7	604.8	8.32	0.002
Factor B	2	577.6	288.8	3.97	0.031
Interaction	4	1474.9	368.7	5.07	0.004
Error	27	1962.2	72.7		
Total	35	5224.3			

(a) Is there evidence of an interaction effect? Why or why not? Yes; P-value is small

(b) Based on the P-value, is there evidence of a difference in the means from factor A? Based on the P-value, is there evidence of a difference in the means from factor B? Analysis halted

(c) What is the mean square error? 72.7

15. (b) Factor A: no significant difference in means; factor B: significant difference in means
15. (d) The means of levels 2 and 3 of factor B are significantly different.

In Problems 15 and 16, assume that the data come from populations that are normally distributed with the same variance.

15.

		Factor B	
	Level 1	Level 2	Level 3
	64.9	53.3	51.9
	59.3	44.2	61.8
Level 1	32.9	46.2	68.5
	59.4	43.3	65.8
	50.7	38.4	53.1
Level 2	59.3	50.7	57.9
	58.1	40.2	55.7
	33.5	52.6	74.4

(Factor A labels levels)

(a) Determine whether or not there is significant interaction between factor A and factor B.   No
(b) If there is no significant interaction, determine if there is a significant difference in the means for the two levels of factor A. If there is no significant interaction, determine if there is a significant difference in the means for the three levels of factor B.
(c) Draw an interaction plot of the data to support the results of parts (a) and (b).
(d) If there is a significant difference in the means for the two levels of factor A, use Tukey's test to determine which pairwise means differ using a familywise error rate of $\alpha = 0.05$. If there is a significant difference in the means for the three levels of factor B, use Tukey's test to determine which pairwise means differ using a familywise error rate of $\alpha = 0.05$.

16.

		Factor B	
	Level 1	Level 2	Level 3
Level 1	104	111	95
	82	104	84
	81	74	104
Level 2	111	109	106
	112	115	110
	82	97	99
Level 3	112	108	92
	108	99	129
	117	104	120

(Factor A)

16. (b) Factor A: no significant difference in means;
factor B: significant difference in means

(a) Determine whether or not there is significant interaction between factor A and factor B.   No
(b) If there is no significant interaction, determine whether there is a significant difference in the means for the three levels of factor A. If there is no significant interaction, determine whether there is a significant difference in the means for the three levels of factor B.
(c) Draw an interaction plot of the data to support the results of parts (a) and (b).
(d) If there is a significant difference in the means for the three levels of factor A, use Tukey's test to determine which pairwise means differ using a familywise error rate of $\alpha = 0.05$. If there is a significant difference in the means for the three levels of factor B, use Tukey's test to determine which pairwise means differ using a family-wise error rate of $\alpha = 0.05$.   The means of levels 1 and 3 of factor A are significantly different.

Applying the Concepts

17. Cholesterol Levels A family physician wanted to know if age and gender were factors that explained levels of serum cholesterol (in mg/dL) in her adult patients. She randomly selects two patients for each category of data and obtains the following results:

Gender	Age (years)		
	18–34	**35–54**	**55 and older**
Female	180, 192	205, 226	218, 231
Male	175, 193	213, 222	203, 185

Source: National Center for Health Statistics

Serum cholesterols are known to be approximately normally distributed and the population variances are equal.

(a) What type of factorial design is this? How many replications are there within each cell? 2×3; $n = 2$ replications
(b) Determine if there is significant interaction between age and gender.   No significant interaction
(c) If there is not significant interaction, determine whether there is significant difference in the means for the three age groups. If there is not significant interaction, determine whether there is significant difference in the means for the genders.
(d) Draw an interaction plot of the data to support the results of parts (b) and (c).
(e) If there is significant difference in the means for the three age groups, use Tukey's test to determine which pairwise means differ using a familywise error rate of $\alpha = 0.05$. If there is significant difference in the means for gender, use Tukey's test to determine which pairwise means differ using a familywise error rate of $\alpha = 0.05$.
The mean of age group 18–34 is significantly different.

18. Reaction Time In an online psychology experiment sponsored by the University of Mississippi, researchers asked study participants to respond to various stimuli. Participants were randomly assigned to one of three treatment groups. Subjects in group 1 were in the simple group. They were required to respond as quickly as possible after a stimulus was presented. Subjects in group 2 were in the go/no-go group. These subjects were required to respond to a particular stimulus while disregarding other stimuli. Finally, subjects in group 3 were in the choice group. They needed to respond differently, depending on the stimuli presented. The researcher felt that age may be a factor in determining reaction time, so she organized the experimental units by age and obtained the following data:

Age	Stimulus		
	Simple	**Go/No-Go**	**Choice**
18–24	0.384	0.338	0.586
	0.248	0.495	0.509
	0.191	0.631	0.364
	0.203	0.485	0.626
25–34	0.331	0.389	0.858
	0.438	0.629	0.529
	0.494	0.585	0.520
35 and older	0.467	0.782	0.854
	0.302	0.529	0.700

Source: PsychExperiments; University of Mississippi; psychexps.olemiss.edu/

17. (c) Significant difference in means for age groups; no significant difference in means for genders

18. (d) Significant difference in means for types of stimulus; no significant difference in means categories for age

(a) What type of factorial design is this? How many replications are there within each cell? 3×3; $n = 3$ replications

(b) Normal probability plots indicate that it is reasonable to believe that the data come from populations that are normally distributed. Verify the requirement of equal population variances.

(c) Determine if there is significant interaction between stimulus and age.   No significant interaction

(d) If there is not significant interaction, determine whether there is significant difference in the means for the three types of stimulus. If there is not significant interaction, determine whether there is significant difference in the means for the three categories of age.

(e) Draw an interaction plot of the data to support the results of parts (c) and (d).

19. **Concrete Strength** An engineer wants to know if the mean strengths of three different concrete mix designs differ significantly. He also suspects that slump may be a predictor of concrete strength. Slump is a measure of the uniformity of the concrete, with a higher slump indicating a less uniform mixture. The following data represent the 28-day strength (in pounds per square inch) of three different mixtures with three different slumps.

Slump	Mixture 67-0-301	Mixture 67-0-400	Mixture 67-0-353
3.75	3,960	4,815	4,595
	4,005	4,595	4,145
	3,445	4,185	4,585
4	4,010	4,070	3,855
	3,415	4,545	3,675
	3,710	4,175	4,010
5	3,290	4,020	3,875
	3,390	4,355	3,700
	3,740	3,935	3,350

(a) Normal probability plots indicate that it is reasonable to believe that the data come from populations that are normally distributed. Verify the requirement of equal population variances.

(b) Determine whether there is significant interaction between mixture type and slump. No significant interaction

(c) If there is not significant interaction, determine whether there is significant difference in the means for the three types of mixture. If there is not significant interaction, determine whether there is significant difference in the means for the slumps.

(d) Draw an interaction plot of the data to support the results of parts (b) and (c).

(e) If there is significant difference in the means for the three mixture types, use Tukey's test to determine which pairwise means differ using a familywise error rate of $\alpha = 0.05$. If there is significant difference in the means for the slumps, use Tukey's test to determine which pairwise means differ using a familywise error rate of $\alpha = 0.05$.

20. **Diet and Birth Weight** An obstetrician wanted to determine the impact that three experimental diets had on the birth weights of pregnant mothers. She randomly selected 27 pregnant mothers in the first trimester of whom 9 were 20 to 29 years old, 9 were 30 to 39 years old, and 9 were 40 or older. For each age group, she randomly assigned the mothers to one of the three diets. After delivery she measured the birth weight (in grams) of the babies and obtained the following data: 20. (e) The mean of diet 1 is significantly different from the means of diets 2 and 3. The mean for age 40 or older is significantly different from the means of the other age groups.

Age	Diet 1	Diet 2	Diet 3
20–29	4,473	3,961	3,667
	3,878	3,557	3,139
	3,936	3,321	3,356
30–39	3,886	3,330	2,762
	4,147	3,644	3,551
	3,693	2,811	3,272
40 or older	3,878	2,937	2,781
	4,002	3,228	3,138
	3,382	2,732	3,435

(a) Birth weights are known to be approximately normally distributed. Verify the requirement of equal population variances.

(b) Determine whether there is significant interaction between age and diet.   No significant interaction

(c) If there is no significant interaction, determine whether there is significant difference in the means for the three age groups. If there is no significant interaction, determine whether there is significant difference in the means for the diets.

(d) Draw an interaction plot of the data to support the results of parts (b) and (c).

(e) If there is significant difference in the means for the three age groups, use Tukey's test to determine which pairwise means differ using a familywise error rate of $\alpha = 0.05$. If there is significant difference in the means for the diets, use Tukey's test to determine which pairwise means differ using a familywise error rate of $\alpha = 0.05$.

21. **Oil Changes** The following data represent the cost of an oil change (in dollars) in three different geographic regions for two types of service centers. A specialty chain is an oil change facility that specializes in oil changes, while a general service station provides a wide array of services in addition to oil changes.

Service Center	Chicago	Bolingbrook	Peoria
Specialty chain	19.95	23.99	24.99
	27.95	29.95	26.99
	23.99	28.99	19.95
General service	21.99	22.45	22.99
	26.95	29.95	24.95
	24.95	28.13	27.99

Source: Anna Paris, student at Joliet Junior College

19. (c) Significant difference in means for types of mixture; significant difference in means for the slumps   19. (e) The mean of mixture 67-0-400 is significantly different from the means of the other two mixtures; the means of slumps 3.75 and 5 differ significantly.
20. (c) No significant difference in means for age groups; significant difference in means for diets

(a) The prices of oil changes are approximately normally distributed. Verify the requirement of equal population variances.

(b) Determine if there is significant interaction between location and service center type. No significant interaction

(c) If there is not significant interaction, determine whether there is significant difference in the means for the three locations. If there is no significant interaction, determine whether there is significant difference in the means for the two service center types.

(d) Draw an interaction plot of the data to support the results of parts (b) and (c).

(e) If there is significant difference in the means for the three locations, use Tukey's test to determine which pairwise means differ using a familywise error rate of $\alpha = 0.05$. If there is significant difference in the means for the service center type, use Tukey's test to determine which pairwise means differ using a familywise error rate of $\alpha = 0.05$. Not applicable

---

22. **Putting It Together: Students at Ease** Do gender and seating arrangement in college classrooms affect student attitude? In a study at a large public university in the United States, researchers surveyed students to measure their level of feeling at ease in the classroom. Participants were shown different classroom layouts and asked questions regarding their attitude toward each layout. The following data represent feeling-at-ease scores for a random sample of 32 students (4 students for each possible treatment).

		Classroom Layout							
		Tablet-Arm Chairs		**U-Shaped**		**Clusters**		**Tables with Chairs**	
Gender	**Female**	19.8	18.4	19.2	19.2	18.1	17.5	17.3	17.1
		18.1	18.5	18.6	18.7	17.8	18.3	17.7	17.6
	Male	18.8	18.2	20.6	19.2	18.4	17.7	17.7	16.9
		18.9	18.9	19.8	19.7	17.1	18.2	17.8	17.5

Source: Brigitte Burgess and Naz Kaya. "Gender Differences in Student Attitude for Seating Layout in College Classrooms," *College Student Journal* 41(4), December 2007.

(a) What is the population of interest? College students

(b) Is this study an experiment or an observational study? Which type? Observational study; cross-sectional

(c) What are the response and explanatory variables? Identify each as qualitative or quantitative.

(d) Compute the mean and standard deviation for the scores in the male/U-shaped cell. $\bar{x} = 19.83$; $s = 0.58$

(e) Assuming that feeling-at-ease scores for males on the U-shaped layout are normally distributed with $\mu = 19.1$ and $\sigma = 0.8$, what is the probability that you would observe a sample mean as large or larger than actually observed? Would this be unusual? 0.035; yes

(f) Determine whether the mean feeling-at-ease score is different for males than females using a two-sample t-test for independent samples. Use the $\alpha = 0.05$ level of significance. Do not reject H_0

(g) Determine whether the mean feeling-at-ease scores for the classroom layouts are different using one-way ANOVA. Use the $\alpha = 0.05$ level of significance. Reject H_0

(h) Determine if there is an interaction effect between the two factors. If not, determine if either main effect is significant.

(i) Draw an interaction plot of the data. Does the plot support your conclusions in part (h)?

(j) In the original study, the researchers sent out e-mails to a random sample of 100 professors at the university asking permission to survey students in their class. Only 32 respondents agreed to allow their students to be surveyed. What type of nonsampling error is this? How might this affect the results of the study? Nonresponse; classes that were allowed to be surveyed may be more relaxed in general, allowing students to feel more at ease.

TECHNOLOGY STEP-BY-STEP Two-Way ANOVA

MINITAB

Obtaining Two-Way ANOVA

1. In C1, enter the level of factor A (that is for level 1 enter a 1, and so on); in C2, enter the level of factor B, and in C3 enter the value of the response variable.

2. Select the **Stat** menu. Highlight **ANOVA** and select **Two-way** . . . .

3. Enter C3 in the box marked "Response Variable." Enter C1 in the box marked "row factor," and enter C2 in the box marked "column factor." Do not check the "Additive Model" box and check the "Display means" box. Click OK. We want to display means so that we can use them for Tukey's test.

Interaction Plots
1. Enter the data as described in Step 1 above. Select the **Stat** menu. Highlight **ANOVA** and select **Interaction Plot . . . .**
2. Enter C3 in the box marked "Response Variable." Enter C1 and C2 in the box marked "Factors." Click OK.

Tukey's Test
1. With the data entered into the MINITAB spreadsheet as specified in Step 1 above, select the **Stat** menu. Highlight **ANOVA** and select **General Linear Model . . . .**
2. Enter the name of the response variable in the box marked "Responses." Enter C1, C2, and C1*C2 in the box marked "Model," where C1 is factor A and C2 is factor B.

3. Click "Comparisons . . . ". Click the "Pairwise comparisons" radio button. In the box marked "Terms," enter C1 and C2. Check the box marked "Tukey." Check the box marked "Confidence interval," if you want confidence intervals. Check the box marked "Test" if you want to conduct hypothesis tests of the pairwise differences.
4. Click OK twice.

Main Effects Plots
1. Enter the data as described in Step 1 above. Select the **Stat** menu. Highlight **ANOVA** and select **Main Effects Plot . . . .**
2. Enter C3 in the box marked "Response Variable." Enter C1 and C2 in the box marked "Factors." Click OK.

CHAPTER 13 REVIEW

Summary

We began the chapter with a discussion of one-way analysis of variance (ANOVA). One-way ANOVA is used to compare k means for equality when there is a single factor that has k levels. To perform any ANOVA test, the sample data must come from a population that is normally distributed. The samples must be obtained independently, and the largest sample standard deviation can be no more than two times the smallest standard deviation. The ANOVA procedures are robust, so minor departures from the normality requirement do not seriously affect the results.

If the null hypothesis, $H_0: \mu_1 = \mu_2 = \cdots = \mu_k$, is rejected in a one-way ANOVA, at least one of the population means is different from the others. To determine which means differ, we use Tukey's test, which compares each pair of sample means for significant differences. That is, it tests $H_0: \mu_i = \mu_j$ versus $H_1: \mu_i \neq \mu_j$ for $i \neq j$.

A different ANOVA procedure is used for analyzing experiments designed as randomized complete block designs. Blocking describes a way of organizing experimental units according to some common characteristic for which the response variable is expected to be similar, such as gender. By blocking, we reduce experimental error.

When data are analyzed from a randomized complete block design, we are not interested in whether the block is significant or not. Once again, if the null hypothesis of equal population means is rejected, we can use Tukey's test to compare each pair of means.

Finally, we analyzed data in which there are two factors. Factor A can be set at a levels and factor B can be set at b levels. When there are two factors, we use a two-way ANOVA procedure to test $H_0: \mu_1 = \mu_2 = \cdots = \mu_k$ versus H_1: at least one of the means differs. When performing a two-way ANOVA, we first look for a significant interaction effect. This means the changes in factor A result in different changes in the value of the response variable for different levels of factor B. If interaction exists, we do not consider main effects.

An example of a main effect would be to see how changes in the levels of factor B affect changes in the response variable. If no interaction exists, we then look for significant main effects. If the main effects indicate that at least one of the means differs, we use Tukey's test to determine which means differ.

Vocabulary

Analysis of variance (p. 679)
Robust (p. 681)
Between-sample variability (p. 683)
Within-sample variability (p. 683)
F-test statistic (pp. 683, 685)
Mean square (p. 684)
Sum of squares (p. 684)
Total sum of squares (p. 684)
Mean square due to error (p. 684)

Sum of squares due to error (p. 684)
Mean square due to treatment (p. 684)
Sum of squares due to treatment (p. 684)
ANOVA table (p. 686)
Critical F-value (p. 688)
Multiple comparison methods (p. 694)
Studentized range distribution (p. 695)
Experimentwise error rate (p. 695)
Familywise error rate (p. 695)

Comparison error rate (p. 702)
Factor (p. 704)
Latin square design (p. 705)
2×2 factorial design (p. 714)
Cell (p. 715)
Crossed (p. 715)
Main effects (p. 715)
Interaction effect (p. 715)
Interaction plots (p. 719)

Formulas

Test Statistic for One-Way ANOVA

$$F_0 = \frac{\text{mean square due to treatment}}{\text{mean square due to error}} = \frac{\text{MST}}{\text{MSE}}, \text{ where}$$

$$\text{MST} = \frac{\text{SST}}{k-1} = \frac{n_1(\bar{x}_1 - \bar{x})^2 + n_2(\bar{x}_2 - \bar{x})^2 + \cdots + n_k(\bar{x}_k - \bar{x})^2}{k-1}$$

$$\text{MSE} = \frac{\text{SSE}}{n-k} = \frac{(n_1 - 1)s_1^2 + (n_2 - 1)s_2^2 + \cdots + (n_k - 1)s_k^2}{n-k}$$

Test Statistic for Tukey's Test after One-Way ANOVA

$$q_0 = \frac{(\bar{x}_2 - \bar{x}_1) - (\mu_2 - \mu_1)}{\sqrt{\frac{s^2}{2} \cdot \left(\frac{1}{n_1} + \frac{1}{n_2}\right)}} = \frac{\bar{x}_2 - \bar{x}_1}{\sqrt{\frac{s^2}{2} \cdot \left(\frac{1}{n_1} + \frac{1}{n_2}\right)}}$$

Objectives

Section	You should be able to . . .	Examples	Review Exercises
13.1	**1** Verify the requirements to perform a one-way ANOVA (p. 680)	1	3(b)
	2 Test a hypothesis regarding three or more means using one-way ANOVA (p. 682)	2 and 3	3(c)
13.2	**1** Perform the Tukey test (p. 694)	1–3	2, 3(f), 4, 5(b)
13.3	**1** Conduct analysis of variance on the randomized complete block design (p. 706)	2	6(a)
	2 Perform the Tukey test (p. 708)	3	6(b)
13.4	**1** Analyze a two-way ANOVA design (p. 714)	1–3 and 6	7(b), (c)
	2 Draw interaction plots (p. 719)	4–6	7(d)
	3 Perform the Tukey test (p. 722)	7	7(e)

Review Exercises

1. (a) Find the critical value from the Studentized range distribution for $\alpha = 0.05$, $\nu = 16$, $k = 7$. *4.741*

   (b) Find the critical value from the Studentized range distribution for $\alpha = 0.05$, $\nu = 30$, $k = 6$. *4.302*

   (c) Find the critical value from the Studentized range distribution for $\alpha = 0.01$, $\nu = 42$, $k = 4$.
   Note: We use $q_{0.05,40,8}$ since $q_{0.05,42,8}$ is not in the table. *4.696*

   (d) Find the critical value from the Studentized range distribution for $H_0: \mu_1 = \mu_2 = \mu_3 = \mu_4 = \mu_5 = \mu_6$, with $n = 46$, $\alpha = 0.05$. *4.232*

2. Suppose that there is sufficient evidence to reject $H_0: \mu_1 = \mu_2 = \mu_3 = \mu_4$ using a one-way ANOVA. The mean square error from ANOVA is determined to be 373. The sample means are $\bar{x}_1 = 78$, $\bar{x}_2 = 64$, $\bar{x}_3 = 70$, $\bar{x}_4 = 47$, with $n_1 = n_2 = n_3 = n_4 = 31$. Use Tukey's test to determine which pairwise means are significantly different using a family-wise error rate of $\alpha = 0.05$. *Ambiguous case*

3. Soil Testing A researcher took water samples from a stream running through a forest. The samples were collected over the course of a year. Each sample was analyzed for the concentration of dissolved organic carbon (mg/L) in it, with the results presented in the following table:

Organic				Mineral					Surface				
22.74	14.90	17.90	11.40	8.50	5.50	3.02	7.31	4.85	10.83	11.94	15.76	15.03	15.77
29.80	14.86	18.30	5.30	3.91	4.71	7.45	16.92	11.97	8.74	12.40	10.96	14.53	6.40
27.10	15.91	5.2	15.72	9.29	7.66	11.33	4.60	7.85	9.20	10.30	19.78	12.04	14.19
16.51	15.35	11.90	20.46	21.00	11.72	7.11	8.50	9.11	8.12	10.48	20.56	16.82	13.89
6.51	9.72	14.00	16.87	10.89	11.80	17.99	4.80	8.79	7.60	12.88	17.93	10.70	8.69
8.81	19.80	7.40	15.42	10.30	8.05	21.40	4.90	9.60	6.30	19.01	14.28	16.00	10.46
5.29	14.86	17.50	22.49	11.56	10.72	8.37	9.10	12.57	6.68	19.19	13.11	20.70	16.23
20.46	8.09	10.30		7.00	21.82	7.92	7.90	12.89	7.34	13.14	12.27	13.70	15.43
				3.99	22.62	17.90	11.72	9.81	9.52	12.51	16.47	16.12	
				3.79	10.74								

Source: Lisa Emili, PhD Candidate, Department of Geography and Wetlands Research Centre, University of Waterloo

Each sample was then categorized according to the type of water collected. Water was collected from streams (surface water), groundwater was collected from organic soil, and groundwater was collected from mineral soil. The researcher wanted to determine if the mean concentration of dissolved organic carbon was the same for each collection area.

(a) State the null and alternative hypotheses. $H_0: \mu_{organic} = \mu_{mineral} = \mu_{surface}$ vs. H_1: At least one mean is different

(b) State the requirements that must be satisfied to use the one-way ANOVA procedure.

(c) Use the following MINITAB output to test if the means are the same at the $\alpha = 0.01$ level of significance.

One-way ANOVA: Organic, Mineral, Surface

Source	DF	SS	MS	F	P
Factor	2	471.4	235.7	9.43	0.000
Error	119	2973.8	25.0		
Total	121	3445.1			

(d) Shown are side-by-side boxplots of each type of plot. Do the boxplots support the analytic results?

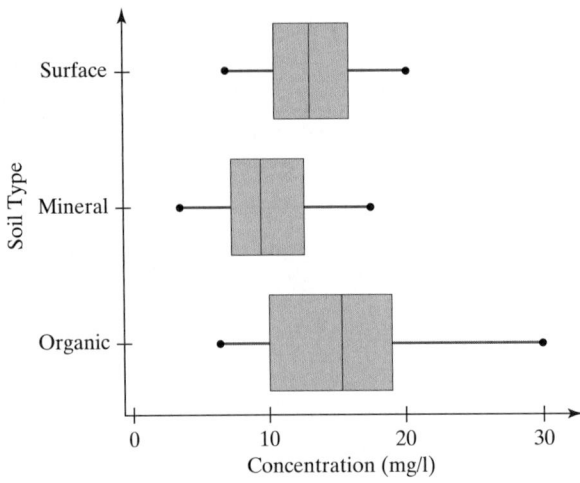

(e) Verify that the F-test statistic is 9.43.

(f) The following display represents the results of Tukey's test obtained from MINITAB. Which pairwise means are different?

$\mu_m \ \mu_s \ \mu_o$

```
Tukey 95% Simultaneous Confidence Intervals
All Pairwise Comparisons

Individual confidence level = 98.09%

Organic subtracted from:

          Lower  Center  Upper  --+---------+---------+---------+-------
Mineral  -7.588  -4.840  -2.092  (-------*-------)
Surface  -4.606  -1.821   0.964             (-------*-------)
                                 --+---------+---------+---------+-------
                                 -7.0      -3.5       0.0       3.5

Mineral subtracted from:

         Lower  Center  Upper  --+---------+---------+---------+-------
Surface  0.527  3.019   5.510                          (-------*------)
                                --+---------+---------+---------+-------
                                -7.0      -3.5       0.0       3.5
```

---

4. **Grading Timber** Desiring to grade timber mechanically, engineers studied the modulus of rupture in lb/in.^{2}, for a sample of untreated green, 7 inch by 9 inch, mixed oak timbers, sorted by grade: select structural, No. 1, No. 2, and below grade. A one-way analysis of variance was performed to test $H_0: \mu_{select} = \mu_{No. 1} = \mu_{No. 2} = \mu_{below\ grade}$. The null hypothesis was rejected with a P-value of 0.018. The engineers proceeded to conduct Tukey's test to determine which pairwise means differed using MINITAB. The results are presented next. Which pairwise means differ? What do you conclude from the test?

Note: 1 = select structural, 2 = No. 1, 3 = No. 2, and 4 = below grade.

Source: "Mechanical Grading of Oak Timbers," *Journal of Materials in Civil Engineering*, 11(2).

$\mu_{select} \ \mu_{No.1} \ \mu_{below\ grade} \ \mu_{No.2}$

```
Tukey's Pairwise Comparison

Family error rate = 0.0500
Individual error rate = 0.0108

Critical value = 3.86

Intervals for (column level mean) - (row level mean)


               1            2            3

   2        -6.914
             13.064

   3         1.936        -1.139
             21.914       18.839

   4        -2.989        -6.064      -14.914
             16.989       13.914        5.064
```

	Mark IV V2	Balloon Ballista	Hydrolaunch	Waterworks II
Peter	92	94	97	100
Shawn	94	93	98	99
Mark	92	94	95	98
Jake	97	96	101	103

(a) Test $H_0: \mu_1 = \mu_2 = \mu_3 = \mu_4$ against H_1: at least one of the means is different, where μ_1 is the mean for the Mark IV V2, μ_2 is the mean for the Balloon Ballista, and so on, at the $\alpha = 0.05$ level of significance. Reject H_0

(b) If the null hypothesis from part (a) was rejected, use Tukey's test to determine which pairwise means differ using a familywise error rate of $\alpha = 0.05$. $\underline{\mu_1\ \mu_2}\ \underline{\mu_3\ \mu_4}$

(c) Draw boxplots of the data for each catapult design using the same scale to support the analytical results obtained in parts (a) and (b).

5. Seating Choice versus GPA In a study of students at Lewis & Clark Community College, a professor compared the chosen seat location of students in mathematics courses to their overall grade point average (GPA). He randomly selected 10 students from each of three seat locations: (1) front, (2) middle, and (3) back. The GPAs follow:

Front	Middle	Back
3.062	2.859	2.583
3.894	2.639	2.653
2.966	3.634	3.090
3.575	3.564	3.060
4.000	2.115	2.463
2.690	3.080	2.598
3.523	2.937	2.879
3.332	3.091	2.926
3.885	2.655	3.221
3.559	2.526	2.646

(a) Test the null hypothesis that the mean score for each location is the same at the $\alpha = 0.05$ level of significance.

Note: The requirements for a one-way ANOVA are satisfied.

(b) If the null hypothesis is rejected in part (a), use Tukey's test to determine which pairwise means differ using a familywise error rate of $\alpha = 0.05$.

(c) Draw boxplots of the three treatment levels to support the analytic results obtained in parts (a) and (b).

6. Catapults Four different catapult designs are being tested for their ability to launch water balloons. Because the person firing the catapult could represent a source of variability, the experimenter decides to use a randomized complete block design and block by person firing. The distances (in feet) achieved for each catapult are given next.

7. Defensive Driving An investigator for the state police wants to determine the effectiveness of three different defensive driving training programs to see if there are gender differences. Five subjects of each gender who recently received speeding tickets are assigned to each program. At the end of the program, each is given a written test on his or her knowledge of defensive driving. The scores (out of 100) are given next.

Gender	Program		
	One 8-hr session	Two 4-hr sessions	Two 2-hr sessions
Male	89	95	77
	96	87	78
	95	90	83
	90	91	78
	96	92	78
Female	88	87	80
	92	92	82
	98	91	79
	99	94	86
	91	93	88

(a) The scores are approximately normally distributed. Verify the requirement of equal population variances.

(b) Determine whether there is significant interaction between program and gender. Not significant

(c) If there is no significant interaction, determine whether there is significant difference in the means for the three programs. Significant

(d) Draw an interaction plot of the data to support the results of parts (a) and (b).

(e) If there is significant difference in the means for the three programs, use Tukey's test to determine which pairwise means differ using a familywise error rate of $\alpha = 0.05$. $\underline{\mu_1 = \mu_2} \neq \mu_3$

5. (a) Reject $H_0: \mu_{front} = \mu_{middle} = \mu_{back}$; at least one mean is different

5. (b) $\mu_{front} \neq \mu_{middle} = \mu_{back}$; there is evidence that the GPAs of students choosing seats in the front are different from those choosing seats in the middle or back.

CHAPTER TEST

1. Many fast-food restaurants use automatic soft-drink dispensing machines that fill cups once an order is placed at a drive-through window. A regional manager for a fast-food chain wants to determine if the machines in his region are dispensing the same amount of product. He samples four different machines and measures a random sample of 16-ounce drinks from each machine.

Machine I	Machine II	Machine III	Machine IV
16.5	15.0	16.0	16.6
16.6	15.4	16.3	15.9
16.5	15.3	16.5	15.5
15.8	15.7	16.4	16.2
15.6	15.2	17.3	17.0
16.4	16.0	16.7	15.5
16.1	15.6	15.7	16.3

(a) Do the data indicate that the mean amount dispensed from the machines is not the same? Use an $\alpha = 0.05$ level of significance.   Reject H_0
(b) Use Tukey's test, if necessary, to determine which pairwise means differ using a familywise error rate of $\alpha = 0.05$.
(c) Draw boxplots of the four treatment levels to support your conclusions in parts (a) and (b).

1. (b) $\mu_1\ \mu_3\ \mu_4\ \mu_2$

2. The Insurance Institute for Highway Safety conducts experiments in which cars are crashed into a fixed barrier at 40 mph. In the Institute's 40-mph offset test, 40% of the total width of each vehicle strikes a barrier on the driver's side. The barrier's deformable face is made of aluminum honeycomb, which makes the forces in the test similar to those involved in a frontal offset crash between two vehicles of the same weight, each going just less than 40 mph. You are in the market to buy a new family car and you want to know if the mean femur force in kilonewtons (kN) on the left leg, resulting from this offset crash, is the same for large family cars, passenger vans, and midsize utility vehicles. The following data were collected from the Institute's study.

Large Family Cars	Femur Force (kN)	Passenger Vans	Femur Force (kN)	Midsize Utility Vehicles	Femur Force (kN)
Chevrolet Lumina	5.8	Toyota Sienna	4.7	Mazda CX-7	1.0
Kia Amanti	4.9	Honda Odyssey	4.3	Toyota 4Runner	0.2
Buick LeSabre	2.8	Ford Windstar	2.1	Mitsubishi Montero	3.6
Hyundai Azera	3.8	Mazda MPV	6.8	Nissan Xterra	1.8
Chrysler LHS	6.2	Chevrolet Astro	8.2	Ford Explorer	0.2
Pontiac Grand Prix	2.4	Nissan Quest	2.6	Jeep Grand Cherokee	2.3
Dodge Intrepid	4.7	Pontiac TransSport	6.7	Nissan Pathfinder	1.9

Source: Insurance Institute for Highway Safety

The researcher wants to test the claim that the mean femur forces for the three classes of vehicle are equal.
(a) State the null and alternative hypotheses. $H_0: \mu_L = \mu_V = \mu_U$ vs. H_1: at least one of the means is different
(b) Verify that the requirements to use the one-way ANOVA procedure are satisfied. Normal probability plots indicate that the sample data come from a population that is normal.
(c) Are the mean femur forces for each vehicle type the same at the $\alpha = 0.05$ level of significance?   Reject H_0
(d) Draw boxplots of the three types of vehicle to support the analytic results obtained in part (c).

3. A rock climber wishes to test the tensile strength of three different types of braided ropes. She knows that the rope thickness can make a difference, so she decides to block by thickness. The tensile strengths for each rope type are given next.

	Nylon Braided	Polyester Braided	Polypropylene Braided
$\frac{1}{4}$ inch	2,500	1,550	1,325
$\frac{3}{8}$ inch	4,900	3,420	2,575
$\frac{1}{2}$ inch	8,400	5,940	4,170
$\frac{5}{8}$ inch	12,300	9,500	6,315

5. (c) Since there is a significant interaction effect, any conclusions about main effects would be confounded.

(a) Test $H_0: \mu_1 = \mu_2 = \mu_3$ against H_1: at least one of the means is different, where μ_1 is the mean for the nylon briaded rope, μ_2 is the mean for the polyester briaded rope, and μ_3 is the mean for the polypropylene braided rope, at the $\alpha = 0.05$ level of significance. Reject H_0

(b) If the null hypothesis from part (a) was rejected, use Tukey's test to determine which pairwise means differ using a familywise error rate of $\alpha = 0.05$. μ_1 μ_2 μ_3

(c) Draw boxplots of the data for each treatment using the same scale to support the analytical results obtained in parts (a) and (b).

4. A manufacturing researcher wants to determine if age or gender significantly affects the time required to learn an assembly line task. He randomly selected 24 adults aged 20 to 65 years old, of whom 8 are 20 to 34 years old (4 male, 4 female), 8 are 35 to 49 years old (4 male, 4 female), and 8 are 50 to 64 years old (4 male, 4 female). He then measured the time (in minutes) required to complete a certain task. The data obtained are shown next.

Gender	Age (years)		
	20–34	**35–49**	**50–64**
Male	5.2, 5.1	4.8, 5.8	5.2, 4.3
	5.7, 6.1	5.0, 4.8	5.5, 4.7
Female	5.3, 5.5	5.0, 5.4	4.9, 5.5
	4.9, 5.6	5.6, 5.1	5.5, 5.0

(a) The learning times are approximately normally distributed. Verify the requirement of equal population variances.

(b) Determine whether there is significant interaction between age and gender.   Not significant

(c) If there is not significant interaction, determine whether or not there is significant difference in the means for the three age groups.   Not significant

(d) Draw an interaction plot of the data to support the results of parts (a) and (b).

(e) If there is significant difference in the means for the three age groups, use Tukey's test to determine which pairwise means differ using a familywise error rate of $\alpha = 0.05$. μ_{20-34} μ_{50-64} μ_{35-49}

5. The following table summarizes the sample mean earnings, in thousands of dollars, of a random sample of year-round, full-time workers by gender and age.

	25–34	**35–44**	**45–54**
Male	42.9	59.5	67
Female	35.2	41.9	43.1

(a) Construct an interaction plot for the data.

(b) Does the interaction plot indicate a significant interaction effect? Explain?   Significant interaction effect

(c) What, if anything, can you conclude about the significance of the main effects?

MAKING AN INFORMED DECISION

Where Should I Invest? Part II

Remember that inheritance you received in Chapter 11? You have now decided that you want to try investing in individual stocks rather than mutual funds. You are told by a friend who is a finance major that there are three broad stock types: large-capitalization stocks, midcapitalization stocks, and small-capitalization stocks. Large-capitalization stocks are companies that have a market value in excess of $10 billion. Small-capitalization stocks are companies with a market value below $2 billion. Midcaps fall in between. Your finance friend also tells you that there are two investment styles: value and growth. Value stocks are companies thought to be undervalued relative to their peers, while growth stocks are companies thought to have a higher growth rate than their peers.

(a) Obtain a random sample of five stocks within each category. Determine the 1- and 5-year rates of return for each stock.

(b) Verify that the rates of return are normally distributed. Also verify that twice the smallest standard deviation is less than the largest standard deviation. If any requirements are not satisfied, increase the sample size until the requirements become satisfied.

(c) Perform a one-way ANOVA with stock type as the factor. Is there any difference in the mean rate of return among the three stock types? If so, perform a Tukey test to determine which mean rates of return differ.

(d) Perform a two-way ANOVA with stock type and investment style as the factors. Is there any interaction between stock type and investment style? If not, do the means of either factor differ? If the means do differ, perform a Tukey test to determine which mean rates of return differ.

(e) Write a report that details which investment category seems to be best.

In the mid-19th century, Paul Broca, a professor of clinical surgery, effectively argued that the degree of a person's intelligence was directly related to the size of the brain. Broca concluded that

> In general, the brain is larger in mature adults than in the elderly, in men than in women, in eminent men than in men of mediocre talent.... Other things equal, there is a remarkable relationship between the development of intelligence and the volume of the brain. (Quoted in Stephen Jay Gould, *The Mismeasure of Man*. W. W. Norton & Company, New York, 1981, p. 83)

During the 20th century, arguments regarding brain size diminished as scientists turned to intelligence tests—a more direct method to measure and compare mental capacities, they claimed. Yet the older argument still manages to creep into modern discussions of intelligence. In a book published in 1978 that was designed to acquaint educators with modern brain research, H. T. Epstein declared,

> First we shall ask if there is any indication of a linkage of any kind between brain and intelligence. It is generally stated that there is no such linkage.... But the one set of data I have found seems to show clearly that there is a substantial connection. Hooton studied the head circumferences of white Bostonians as part of his massive study of criminals. The following table shows that the ordering of people according to head size yields an entirely plausible ordering according to vocational status. It is not at all clear how the impression has been spread that there is no such correlation. (Quoted in Stephen Jay Gould, *The Mismeasure of Man*. W. W. Norton & Company, New York, 1981, p. 109)

Epstein's table is reproduced here:

Mean and Standard Deviation (in mm) of Head Circumference for People of Various Vocational Statuses			
Vocational Status	***n***	**Mean**	**SD**
Professional	25	569.9	1.9
Semiprofessional	61	566.5	1.5
Clerical	107	566.2	1.1
Trades	194	565.7	0.8
Public service	25	564.1	2.5
Skilled trades	351	562.9	0.6
Personal services	262	562.7	0.7
Laborers	647	560.7	0.3

Source: Stephen Jay Gould, *The Mismeasure of Man*. W. W. Norton & Company, New York, 1981, p. 109

At first glance, this table seems to support the assertion that those with more prestigious vocations have a larger head circumference. However, we can examine the alleged relationship more closely through a one-way analysis of variance. Specifically, we test the claim that all the head-circumference population means are equal. We use an $\alpha = 0.05$ significance level and obtain the following ANOVA table, derived from Epstein's statistics:

ANOVA Table for Epstein's Data on Head Circumference by Vocational Status				
Source of Variation	Sum of Squares	Degrees of Freedom	Mean Squares	F-Test Statistic
Treatment	7,865.359	7	1,123.6284	1,998.6275
Error	935.450	1,664	0.5622	
Total	8,800.809	1,671		

From these results, does it appear that at least one of the head-circumference means is different from the others? Explain.

Examine Epstein's table closely. Does it appear that the ANOVA procedure's requirement of equal variances is satisfied? Explain.

Subsequently, it was revealed that there was an error in Epstein's table. The column labeled SD (standard deviation) should have been labeled *standard error*. For each vocational category, calculate the correct standard deviation by multiplying the tabled value by the square root of its sample size, n.

If the ANOVA table was recalculated with the correct standard deviations, predict the effect on the F-test statistic. Would you be more or less likely to reject the null hypothesis? Explain.

Using the formula for MSE, calculate a revised sum of squared errors, mean square due to error, and F-test statistic. Retest the claim that all the head-circumference population means are equal. Use an $\alpha = 0.05$ significance level. From the corrected values for the standard deviation, does it appear that the ANOVA procedure's requirement of equal variances is satisfied? Did any of your conclusions change in light of the new information? Explain.

If the null hypothesis of equal population means was rejected, use Tukey's test to determine which of the pairwise means differ using a familywise error rate of $\alpha = 0.05$. Which of these categories appear to have significantly different means?

Further research revealed that results for three vocational status groups were not presented in Epstein's table. Inexplicably deleted were factory workers (rank 7 out of 11 in status), transportation employees (rank 8), and extractive trades (farming and mining, rank 11). The mean head-circumference sizes for these three groups were 564.7, 564.9, and 564.7 mm, respectively. Also, it was discovered that Epstein's table did not list each group in the order of Hooton's prestige ranking but, rather, listed the groups in order of mean head circumference; this manipulation suggested a perfect correlation where one does not exist. (*Source*: Stephen Jay Gould, *The Mismeasure of Man*. W. W. Norton & Company, New York, 1981, p. 110)

Using all this new information and your previous analyses, write a brief report summarizing your findings and conclusions.

Inference on the Least-Squares Regression Model and Multiple Regression

Outline

14.1 Testing the Significance of the Least-Squares Regression Model

14.2 Confidence and Prediction Intervals

14.3 Multiple Regression

MAKING AN INFORMED DECISION

You continue to find yourself in the market to purchase a new car. You have a pretty good idea as to how much your car will be worth over the years, but you would like to have some measure of confidence in your results. See the Decisions project on page 785.

PUTTING IT TOGETHER

In Chapter 4, we learned methods for describing the relation between two variables—bivariate data. We also learned to perform diagnostic tests, such as determining whether a linear model is appropriate, identifying outliers, and identifying influential observations.

In this chapter, we begin by extending hypothesis testing and confidence intervals to least-squares regression models. In Section 14.1, we test whether a linear relation exists between two quantitative variables using methods based on those presented in Chapter 10. In Section 14.2, we construct confidence intervals about the predicted value of the response variable.

Finally, in Section 14.3 we introduce *multiple regression* in which more than one explanatory variable is used to predict the value of a response variable. We perform the same diagnostic tests for multiple regression that we used for *simple linear regression* (one explanatory variable). We also test whether the relation between the explanatory variables and response variable is significant, and we construct confidence intervals about the predicted value of the response variable. Throughout this section, we use statistical software to do the "heavy lifting" so that we are not bogged down by computations. This approach will allow us to concentrate on analyzing results, rather than calculating results.

14.1 TESTING THE SIGNIFICANCE OF THE LEAST-SQUARES REGRESSION MODEL

Preparing for This Section   Before getting started, review the following:

- Scatter diagrams; correlation (Section 4.1, pp. 193–195)
- Least-squares regression (Section 4.2, pp. 211–216)
- Diagnostics on the least-squares regression line (Section 4.3, pp. 223–232)

- Sampling distribution of the sample mean $\bar{x}$ (Section 8.1, pp. 427–438)
- Testing a hypothesis about μ, σ unknown (Section 10.3, pp. 541–547)
- Confidence intervals about a mean, σ unknown (Section 9.2, pp. 475–482)

Objectives	
1	State the requirements of the least-squares regression model
2	Compute the standard error of the estimate
3	Verify that the residuals are normally distributed
4	Conduct inference on the slope
5	Construct a confidence interval about the slope of the least-squares regression model

As a quick review of the topics discussed in Chapter 4, we present the following example:

EXAMPLE 1   **Least-Squares Regression**

Problem: A family doctor is interested in examining the relationship between a patient's age and total cholesterol. He randomly selects 14 of his female patients and obtains the data presented in Table 1. The data are based on results obtained from the National Center for Health Statistics.

Figure 1

Figure 2

```
LinReg
 y=ax+b
 a=1.399064152
 b=151.3536582
 r²=.5152520915
 r=.7178106237
```

Table 1			
Age, x	**Total Cholesterol, y**	**Age, x**	**Total Cholesterol y**
25	180	42	183
25	195	48	204
28	186	51	221
32	180	51	243
32	210	58	208
32	197	62	228
38	239	65	269

Draw a scatter diagram, compute the correlation coefficient, and find the least-squares regression equation and the coefficient of determination.

Approach: We will use a TI-84 Plus graphing calculator to obtain the information requested.

Solution: Figure 1 displays the scatter diagram. Figure 2 displays the output obtained from the calculator. The linear correlation coefficient is 0.718. The least-squares regression equation for these data is $\hat{y} = 1.3991x + 151.3537$, where $\hat{y}$ represents the predicted total cholesterol for a female whose age is x.

Figure 3

The coefficient of determination, R^2, is 0.515. So, 51.5% of the variation in total cholesterol is explained by the regression line. Figure 3 shows a graph of the least-squares regression equation on the scatter diagram in order to get a feel for the fit.

The information obtained in Example 1 is descriptive in nature. Notice that the descriptions are both graphical (as in the scatter diagram) and numerical (as in the correlation coefficient, the least-squares regression equation, and the coefficient of determination).

① State the Requirements of the Least-Squares Regression Model

In the least-squares regression equation $\hat{y} = b_1 x + b_0$, the values for the slope, b_1, and intercept, b_0, are statistics, just as the sample mean, $\bar{x}$, and sample standard deviation, s, are statistics. The statistics b_0 and b_1 are estimates for the population intercept, β_0, and the population slope, β_1. The true linear relation between the explanatory variable, x, and the response variable, y, is given by $y = \beta_1 x + \beta_0$.

In Other Words

Because b_0 and b_1 are statistics, they have sampling distributions.

Because b_0 and b_1 are statistics, their values vary from sample to sample, so a sampling distribution is associated with each of them. We use this sampling distribution to perform inference on b_0 and b_1. For example, we might want to test whether β_1 is different from 0. If we have sufficient evidence to this effect, we conclude that there is a linear relation between the explanatory variable, x, and response variable, y.

To find the sampling distributions of b_0 and b_1, we have some requirements of the population from which the bivariate data (x_i, y_i) were sampled. Just as in Section 8.1 when we discussed the sampling distribution of $\bar{x}$, we start by asking what would happen if we took many samples for a given value of the explanatory variable, x. For example, in looking back at Table 1, we notice that our sample included three women aged 32 years, so x has the same value, 32, for all three women in our sample, but the corresponding values of y are different: 180, 210, and 197. This means that y varies for a given value of x, so there is a distribution of total cholesterol levels for $x = 32$ years of age. Suppose that we looked at *all* women aged 32 years. From these population data, we could find the population mean total cholesterol for *all* 32-year-old women, denoted $\mu_{y|32}$. The notation $\mu_{y|32}$ is read "the mean value of the response variable y given that the value of the explanatory variable is 32." We could repeat this process for any other age. In general, different ages will have a different population mean total cholesterol. This brings us to our first requirement regarding inference on the least-squares regression model.

> **Requirement 1 for Inference on the Least-Squares Regression Model**
>
> For any particular value of the explanatory variable x (such as 32 in Example 1), the mean of the corresponding responses in the population depends linearly on x. That is,
>
> $$\mu_{y|x} = \beta_1 x + \beta_0$$
>
> for some numbers β_0 and β_1, where $\mu_{y|x}$ represents the population mean response when the value of the explanatory variable is x.

We learned how to check this requirement in Section 4.3. If a plot of the residuals against the explanatory variable shows any discernible pattern (such as a U-shape), then the linear model is not appropriate and requirement 1 is violated.

We also have a requirement regarding the distribution of the response variable for any particular value of the explanatory variable.

In Other Words
When doing inference on the least-squares regression model, we require (1) that for any explanatory variable, x, the mean of the response variable, y, depends on the value of x through a linear equation, and (2) that the response variable, y, is normally distributed with a constant standard deviation, σ. The mean increases/decreases at a constant rate depending on the slope, while the variance remains constant.

Requirement 2 for Inference on the Least-Squares Regression Model

The response variables are normally distributed with mean $\mu_{y|x} = \beta_1 x + \beta_0$ and standard deviation σ.

This requirement states that the mean of the response variable changes linearly, but the variance remains constant, and the distribution of the response variable is normal. For example, if we obtained a sample of many 32-year-old females and measured their total cholesterol, the distribution would be normal with mean $\mu_{y|32} = \beta_1(32) + \beta_0$ and standard deviation σ. If we obtained a sample of many 43-year-old females and measured their total cholesterol, the distribution would be normal with mean $\mu_{y|43} = \beta_1(43) + \beta_0$ and standard deviation σ. See Figure 4.

Figure 4

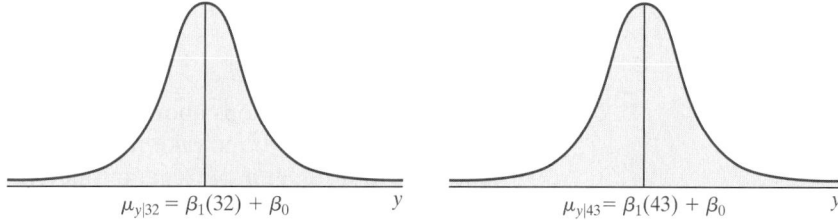

$\mu_{y|32} = \beta_1(32) + \beta_0$ y $\mu_{y|43} = \beta_1(43) + \beta_0$ y

In Other Words
The larger σ is, the more spread out the data are around the regression line.

A large value of σ, the population standard deviation, indicates that the data are widely dispersed about the regression line, and a small value of σ indicates that the data lie fairly close to the regression line. Figure 5 illustrates the ideas just presented. The regression line represents the mean value of each normal distribution at a specified value of x. The standard deviation of each distribution is σ.

Figure 5

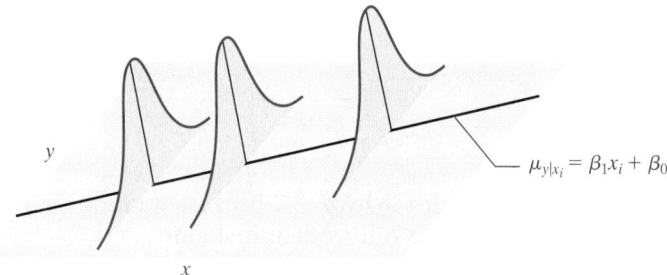

y

$\mu_{y|x_i} = \beta_1 x_i + \beta_0$

x

Of course, not all the observed values of the response variable will lie on the true regression line, $\mu_{y|x} = \beta_1 x + \beta_0$. The difference between the observed and predicted value of the response variable is an error term or residual, ε_i. We now present the least-squares regression model.

Definition

The **least-squares regression model** is given by

$$y_i = \beta_1 x_i + \beta_0 + \varepsilon_i \tag{1}$$

where

> y_i is the value of the response variable for the ith individual
>
> β_0 and β_1 are the parameters to be estimated based on sample data
>
> x_i is the value of the explanatory variable for the ith individual
>
> ε_i is a random error term with mean 0 and variance $\sigma_{\varepsilon_i}^2 = \sigma^2$, the error terms are independent
>
> $i = 1, \ldots, n$, where n is the sample size (number of ordered pairs in the data set)

Now Work Problem 13(a)

Because the expected value, or mean, of y_i is $\beta_1 x_i + \beta_0$ and the expression on the left side of Equation (1) equals the expression on the right side, the expected value, or mean, of the error term, ε_i, is 0.

2 Compute the Standard Error of the Estimate

In Section 4.2, we learned how to obtain estimates for β_0 and β_1. We now present the method for obtaining the estimate of σ, the standard deviation of the response variable y for any given value of x. The unbiased estimator of σ is called the *standard error of the estimate*.

Remember the formula for the sample standard deviation presented in Section 3.2?

$$s = \sqrt{\frac{\sum (x_i - \overline{x})^2}{n - 1}}$$

We compute the deviations about the mean, square them, add up the squared deviations, divide by $n - 1$ and take the square root of the result. We divide by $n - 1$ because we lose 1 degree of freedom since one parameter, $\overline{x}$, is estimated. The same logic is used to compute the standard error of the estimate.

As we mentioned, the predicted values of y, denoted $\hat{y}_i$, represent the mean value of the response variable for any given value of the explanatory variable, x_i. So, $y_i - \hat{y}_i$ = residual represents the difference between the observed value, y_i, and the mean value, $\hat{y}_i$. This calculation is used to compute the standard error of the estimate.

Definition

The **standard error of the estimate**, s_e, is found using the formula

$$s_e = \sqrt{\frac{\sum (y_i - \hat{y}_i)^2}{n - 2}} = \sqrt{\frac{\sum \text{residuals}^2}{n - 2}} \tag{2}$$

We divide by $n - 2$ because we have estimated two parameters, β_0 and β_1. That is, we lose 2 degrees of freedom.

EXAMPLE 2 **Computing the Standard Error**

Problem: Compute the standard error of the estimate for the data in Table 1.

Approach: We use the following steps to compute the standard error of the estimate.
Step 1: Find the least-squares regression line.
Step 2: Obtain predicted values for each observation in the data set.
Step 3: Compute the residuals for each observation in the data set.
Step 4: Compute $\sum \text{residuals}^2$.
Step 5: Compute the standard error of the estimate using Formula (2).

Solution
Step 1: We found the least squares regression line in Example 1 to be $\hat{y} = 1.3991x + 151.3537$.
Step 2: Column 3 of Table 2 represents the predicted values for each of the $n = 14$ observations.
Step 3: Column 4 of Table 2 represents the residuals for each of the 14 observations.

Table 2

Age, x	Total Cholesterol, y	$\hat{y} = 1.3991x + 151.3537$	Residuals, $y - \hat{y}$	Residuals², $(y - \hat{y})^2$
25	180	186.33	−6.33	40.0689
25	195	186.33	8.67	75.1689
28	186	190.53	−4.53	20.5209
32	180	196.12	−16.12	259.8544
32	210	196.12	13.88	192.6544
32	197	196.12	0.88	0.7744
38	239	204.52	34.48	1188.8704
42	183	210.12	−27.12	735.4944
48	204	218.51	−14.51	210.5401
51	221	222.71	−1.71	2.9241
51	243	222.71	20.29	411.6841
58	208	232.50	−24.50	600.2500
62	228	238.10	−10.10	102.0100
65	269	242.30	26.70	712.8900

$$\sum \text{residuals}^2 = 4553.705$$

CAUTION Be sure to divide by $n - 2$ when computing the standard error of the estimate.

Step 4: Column 5 of Table 2 contains the squared residuals. We sum the entries in column 5 to obtain the sum of squared errors. So

$$\sum \text{residuals}^2 = 4553.705$$

Step 5: We use Formula (2) to compute the standard error of the estimate.

$$s_e = \sqrt{\frac{\sum \text{residuals}^2}{n - 2}} = \sqrt{\frac{4553.705}{14 - 2}} = 19.48$$

EXAMPLE 3 **Obtaining the Standard Error of the Estimate Using Technology**

Figure 6

Regression Statistics	
Multiple R	0.7178106
R Square	0.5152521
Adjusted R Square	0.4748564
Standard Error	19.480535
Observations	14

Now Work Problem 13(b)

Problem: Obtain the standard error of the estimate for the data in Table 1 using statistical software.

Approach: We will use Excel to obtain the standard error. The steps for obtaining the standard error of the estimate using TI-83/84 Plus graphing calculators, MINITAB, and Excel are given in the Technology Step-by-Step on page 752.

Solution: Figure 6 shows the partial output obtained from Excel. Notice that the results agree with the by-hand computation.

---

3 **Verify That the Residuals Are Normally Distributed**

CAUTION The residuals must be normally distributed to perform inference on the least-squares regression line.

For the least-squares regression model $y_i = \beta_1 x_i + \beta_0 + \varepsilon_i$, we require that the response variable, y_i, be normally distributed. Because $\beta_1 x_i + \beta_0$ is constant for any x_i, the requirement that y_i be normal means that the residuals, ε_i, must be normal. To perform statistical inference on the regression line, we must verify that the residuals are normally distributed by examining a normal probability plot.

EXAMPLE 4 **Verifying That the Residuals Are Normally Distributed**

Problem: Verify that the residuals obtained in Table 2 from Example 2 are normally distributed.

Approach: We construct a normal probability plot to assess normality. If the normal probability plot is roughly linear, the residuals are said to be normal.

Solution: Figure 7 contains the normal probability plot obtained from MINITAB.

Figure 7

Because the points follow a linear pattern (all the points lie within the bounds created by MINITAB), the residuals are normally distributed. We can perform inference on the least-squares regression equation.

Now Work Problem 13(c)

4 Conduct Inference on the Slope

At this point, we know how to estimate the intercept and slope of the least-squares regression model. In addition, we can compute the standard error of the estimate, s_e, which is an estimate of σ, the standard deviation of the response variable about the true least-squares regression model, and we know how to assess the normality of the residuals. We will now use this information to test whether a linear relation exists between the explanatory and the response variables.

We want to answer the following question: Do the sample data provide sufficient evidence to conclude that a linear relation exists between the two variables? If there is no linear relation between the response and explanatory variables, the slope of the true regression line will be zero. Do you know why? A slope of zero means that information about the explanatory variable, x, does not change our estimate of the value of the response variable, y.

In Other Words

Remember, the null hypothesis is a statement of "no effect." So, the null hypothesis H_0: $\beta_1 = 0$ means there is no linear relation between the explanatory and response variables.

Using the notation of hypothesis testing, we can perform one of three tests:

Two-Tailed	Left-Tailed	Right-Tailed
H_0: $\beta_1 = 0$	H_0: $\beta_1 = 0$	H_0: $\beta_1 = 0$
H_1: $\beta_1 \neq 0$	H_1: $\beta_1 < 0$	H_1: $\beta_1 > 0$

The null hypothesis is $\beta_1 = 0$ since the statement in the null is always a statement of "no effect." We are attempting to find evidence of a relation in the alternative hypothesis. By using the two-tailed test, we are testing whether a linear relation exists between two variables without regard to the sign of the slope. By using the left-tailed test, we are testing whether the slope of the true regression line is

CAUTION Before testing H_0: $\beta_1 = 0$, be sure to draw a residual plot to verify that a linear model is appropriate.

negative. By using the right-tailed test, we are testing whether the slope of the true regression line is positive.

To test any one of these hypotheses, we need to know the sampling distribution of b_1. It turns out that, when the conditions are met,

$$t = \frac{b_1 - \beta_1}{\dfrac{s_e}{\sqrt{\Sigma(x_i - \bar{x})^2}}} = \frac{b_1 - \beta_1}{s_{b_1}}$$

follows Student's t-distribution with $n - 2$ degrees of freedom, where n is the number of observations, b_1 is the estimate of the slope of the regression line β_1, and s_{b_1} is the sample standard deviation of b_1.

Note that

$$s_{b_1} = \frac{s_e}{\sqrt{\Sigma(x_i - \bar{x})^2}}$$

Hypothesis Test Regarding the Slope Coefficient, β_1

To test whether two quantitative variables are linearly related, we use the following steps provided that

1. the sample is obtained using random sampling
2. the residuals are normally distributed with constant error variance.

Step 1: Determine the null and alternative hypotheses. The hypotheses can be structured in one of three ways:

Note to Instructor
Remind students that the procedures presented here are similar to those presented for testing hypotheses about μ with σ unknown.

Two-Tailed	Left-Tailed	Right-Tailed
H_0: $\beta_1 = 0$	H_0: $\beta_1 = 0$	H_0: $\beta_1 = 0$
H_1: $\beta_1 \neq 0$	H_1: $\beta_1 < 0$	H_1: $\beta_1 > 0$

Step 2: Select a level of significance, α, depending on the seriousness of making a Type I error.

Step 3: Compute the test statistic

$$t_0 = \frac{b_1 - \beta_1}{s_{b_1}} = \frac{b_1}{s_{b_1}}$$

which follows Student's t-distribution with $n - 2$ degrees of freedom. Remember, when computing the test statistic, we assume the null hypothesis to be true. So, we assume that $\beta_1 = 0$.

Classical Approach

Step 4: Use Table VI to determine the critical value using $n - 2$ degrees of freedom.

	Two-Tailed	Left-Tailed	Right-Tailed
Critical value	$-t_{\alpha/2}$ and $t_{\alpha/2}$	$-t_\alpha$	t_α
Critical region			

Step 5: Compare the critical value with the test statistic.

Two-Tailed	Left-Tailed	Right-Tailed
If $t_0 < -t_{\alpha/2}$ or $t_0 > t_{\alpha/2}$, reject the null hypothesis	If $t_0 < -t_\alpha$, reject the null hypothesis	If $t_0 > t_\alpha$, reject the null hypothesis

P-value Approach

Step 4: Use Table VI to estimate the P-value using $n - 2$ degrees of freedom.

Two-Tailed	Left-Tailed	Right-Tailed

Step 5: If the P-value $< \alpha$, reject the null hypothesis.

Step 6: State the conclusion.

The procedures just presented are **robust**, so minor departures from normality will not adversely affect the results of the test. In fact, for large samples ($n \geq 30$), inferential procedures regarding b_1 can be used even with significant departures from normality.

EXAMPLE 5	Testing for a Linear Relation

Problem: Test whether a linear relation exists between age and total cholesterol at the $\alpha = 0.05$ level of significance using the data given in Table 1.

Approach: We verify that the requirements to perform the inference are satisfied. We then follow Steps 1 through 6.

Solution: In Example 1, we were told that the individuals were randomly selected. In Example 4, we confirmed that the residuals were normally distributed by constructing a normal probability plot. We can verify the requirement of constant error variance by plotting the residuals against the values of the explanatory variable as shown in Figure 8.

The errors are evenly spread around a horizontal line drawn at 0, so the requirement of constant error variance is satisfied. We can now follow Steps 1 through 6.

⬦ **CAUTION** Use unrounded values of the sample mean in the computation of $\Sigma(x_i - \overline{x})^2$ to avoid round-off error.

Step 1: We want to know if there is a linear relation between age and total cholesterol without regard to the sign of the slope. This is a two-tailed test and we have

$$H_0: \beta_1 = 0 \qquad \text{versus} \qquad H_1: \beta_1 \neq 0$$

Step 2: The level of significance is $\alpha = 0.05$.

Step 3: We obtained an estimate of β_1 in Example 1 to be $b_1 = 1.3991$, and we computed the standard error, $s_e = 19.48$, in Example 2. To determine the standard deviation of b_1, we compute $\Sigma(x_i - \overline{x})^2$, where the x_i are the values of the explanatory variable, age, and $\overline{x}$ is the sample mean. We compute this value in Table 3.

Figure 8

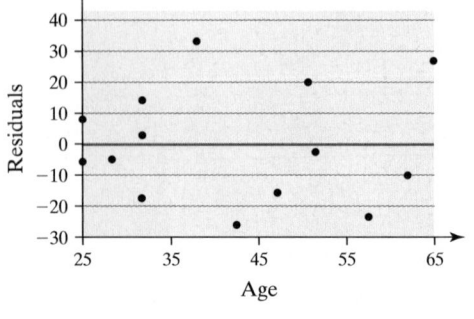

Table 3			
Age, x	$\overline{x}$	$x_i - \overline{x}$	$(x_i - \overline{x})^2$
25	42.07143	−17.07143	291.4337
25	42.07143	−17.07143	291.4337
28	42.07143	−14.07143	198.0051
32	42.07143	−10.07143	101.4337
32	42.07143	−10.07143	101.4337
32	42.07143	−10.07143	101.4337
38	42.07143	−4.07143	16.5765
42	42.07143	−0.07143	0.0051
48	42.07143	5.92857	35.1479
51	42.07143	8.92857	79.7194
51	42.07143	8.92857	79.7194
58	42.07143	15.92857	253.7193
62	42.07143	19.92857	397.1479
65	42.07143	22.92857	525.7193

$$\Sigma(x_i - \overline{x})^2 = 2472.9284$$

Note Because $s_x^2 = \dfrac{\Sigma(x_i - \overline{x})^2}{n - 1}$, the standard deviation of b_1 can be calculated using

$$s_{b_1} = \frac{s_e}{\sqrt{n - 1}\, s_x}$$

◄

We have

$$s_{b_1} = \frac{s_e}{\sqrt{\Sigma(x_i - \overline{x})^2}} = \frac{19.48}{\sqrt{2472.9284}} = 0.3917$$

The test statistic is

$$t_0 = \frac{b_1}{s_{b_1}} = \frac{1.3991}{0.3917} = 3.572$$

Classical Approach

Step 4: Because this is a two-tailed test, we determine the critical t-values at the $\alpha = 0.05$ level of significance with $n - 2 = 14 - 2 = 12$ degrees of freedom to be $-t_{0.05/2} = -t_{0.025} = -2.179$ and $t_{0.05/2} = t_{0.025} = 2.179$ The critical regions are displayed in Figure 9.

Figure 9

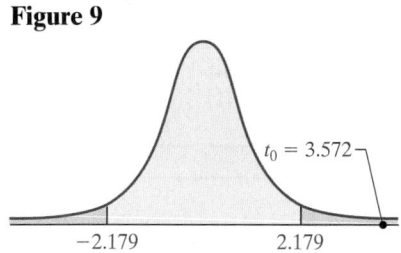

Step 5: The test statistic is $t_0 = 3.572$. We label this point in Figure 9. Because the test statistic is greater than the critical value $t_{0.025} = 2.179$, we reject the null hypothesis.

P-Value Approach

Step 4: Because this is a two-tailed test, the P-value is the sum of the area under the t-distribution with $14 - 2 = 12$ degrees of freedom to the left of $-t_0 = -3.572$, and to the right of $t_0 = 3.572$, as shown in Figure 10. That is, P-value $= P(t < -3.572) + P(t > 3.572) = 2P(t > 3.572)$, with 12 degrees of freedom.

Figure 10

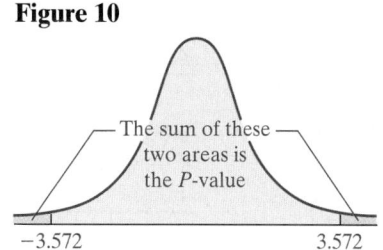

Using Table VI, we find the row that corresponds to 12 degrees of freedom. The value 3.572 lies between 3.428 and 3.930. The area under the t-distribution with 12 degrees of freedom to the right of 3.428 is 0.0025. The area under the t-distribution with 12 degrees of freedom to the right of 3.930 is 0.001.

Because 3.572 is between 3.428 and 3.930, the P-value is between $2(0.001)$ and $2(0.0025)$. So, $0.002 < P$-value < 0.005.

Step 5: Because the P-value is less than the level of significance $\alpha = 0.05$, we reject the null hypothesis.

Step 6: There is sufficient evidence at the $\alpha = 0.05$ level of significance to conclude that a linear relation exists between age and total cholesterol.

EXAMPLE 6   Testing for a Linear Relation Using Technology

Problem: Test whether a linear relation exists between age and total cholesterol at the $\alpha = 0.05$ level of significance using statistical software.

Approach: We will use MINITAB, Excel, and a TI-84 Plus graphing calculator to perform the test. The steps for testing for a linear relation using TI-83/84 Plus graphing calculators, MINITAB, and Excel are given in the Technology Step-by-Step on page 752.

Solution: Figure 11(a) shows the results obtained from MINITAB, Figure 11(b) shows the results obtained from Excel, and Figure 11(c) shows the results obtained from a TI-84 Plus graphing calculator.

Figure 11   Regression Analysis

```
The regression equation is
total cholesterol = 151 + 1.40 age

Predictor        Coef      StDev         T         P
Constant        151.35     17.28      8.76     0.000
Age             1.3991     0.3917     3.57     0.004

S = 19.48         R-Sq = 51.5%      R-Sq(adj)  = 47.5%

Analysis of Variance

Source           Df         SS        MS         F         P
Regression        1       4840.5    4840.5     12.76     0.004
Residual Error   12       4553.9     379.5
Total            13       9394.4
```
(a) MINITAB output

Figure 11
Continued

SUMMARY OUTPUT

Regression Statistics	
Multiple R	0.7178106
R Square	0.5152521
Adjusted R Square	0.4748564
Standard Error	19.480535
Observations	14

ANOVA

	df	SS	MS	F
Regression	1	4840.462	4840.462	12.75514
Residual	12	4553.895	379.4912	
Total	13	9394.357		

	Coefficients	Standard Error	t Stat	P-value
Intercept	151.35366	17.28376	8.756987	1.47E-06
Age	1.3990642	0.391737	3.571433	0.003842

(b) Excel output

P-value S_e

(c) TI-84 Plus output

> **CAUTION** If we do not reject H_0, then we use the sample mean of y to predict the value of the response for any value of the explanatory variable.

Now Work Problems 13(d) and 13(e)

In all three sets of output, the *P*-value for the slope is given as 0.004. About 4 samples in 1000 samples would yield a slope estimate that is as extreme as or more extreme than the one obtained if the null hypothesis of no linear relation were true. Because the *P*-value is less than the level of significance, $\alpha = 0.05$, we reject the null hypothesis of no linear relation and conclude that a linear relation exists between age and total cholesterol.

⑤ Construct a Confidence Interval about the Slope of the Least-Squares Regression Model

We can also obtain confidence intervals for the slope of the least-squares regression line. The procedure is identical to that for obtaining confidence intervals for a mean. As was the case with confidence intervals for a population mean, the confidence interval for the slope of the least-squares regression line is of the form

Point estimate ± margin of error

Confidence Intervals for the Slope of the Regression Line

A $(1 - \alpha) \cdot 100\%$ confidence interval for the slope of the true regression line, β_1, is given by the following formulas:

Lower bound: $b_1 - t_{\alpha/2} \cdot \dfrac{s_e}{\sqrt{\Sigma(x_i - \bar{x})^2}}$

Upper bound: $b_1 + t_{\alpha/2} \cdot \dfrac{s_e}{\sqrt{\Sigma(x_i - \bar{x})^2}}$

(3)

Here, $t_{\alpha/2}$ is computed with $n - 2$ degrees of freedom.

Note: This interval can be computed only if the data are randomly obtained, the residuals are normally distributed, and there is constant error variance.

EXAMPLE 7 **Constructing a Confidence Interval for the Slope of the True Regression Line**

Problem: Compute a 95% confidence interval for the slope of the true regression line for the data presented in Table 1.

Approach

Step 1: Determine the least-squares regression line.

Step 2: Verify that the requirements for inference on the regression line are satisfied.

Step 3: Compute s_e.

Step 4: Determine the critical value $t_{\alpha/2}$ with $n - 2$ degrees of freedom.

Step 5: Compute the bounds on the $(1 - \alpha) \cdot 100\%$ confidence interval for β_1 using Formula (3).

Step 6: Interpret the result by stating, "We are 95% confident that β_1 is somewhere between *lower bound* and *upper bound*."

Solution

Step 1: The least-squares regression line was determined in Example 1 and is $\hat{y} = 1.3991x + 151.3537$.

Step 2: The requirements were verified in Examples 1, 3, and 5.

Step 3: We computed s_e in Example 2, obtaining $s_e = 19.48$.

Step 4: Because we wish to determine a 95% confidence interval, we have $\alpha = 0.05$. Therefore, we need to find $t_{0.05/2} = t_{0.025}$ with $14 - 2 = 12$ degrees of freedom. Referring to Table VI, we find that $t_{0.025} = 2.179$.

Step 5: We use Formula (3) to find the lower and upper bounds.

$$\text{Lower bound:} \quad b_1 - t_{\alpha/2} \cdot \frac{s_e}{\sqrt{\Sigma(x_i - \bar{x})^2}} = 1.3991 - 2.179 \cdot \frac{19.48}{\sqrt{2472.9284}}$$

$$= 1.3991 - 0.8536 = 0.5455$$

$$\text{Upper bound:} \quad b_1 + t_{\alpha/2} \cdot \frac{s_e}{\sqrt{\Sigma(x_i - \bar{x})^2}} = 1.3991 + 2.179 \cdot \frac{19.48}{\sqrt{2472.9284}}$$

$$= 1.3991 + 0.8536 = 2.2527$$

Step 6: We are 95% confident that the mean increase in cholesterol for each additional year of life is somewhere between 0.5455 and 2.2527. Because the 95% confidence interval does not include 0, we reject $H_0: \beta_1 = 0$.

Now Work Problem 13(f)

CAUTION It is best that the explanatory variables be spread out when doing regression analysis.

In looking carefully at the formula for the standard deviation of b_1, we should notice that the larger the value of $\Sigma(x_i - \bar{x})^2$ is, the smaller the value of s_{b_1}. This result implies that whenever we are finding a least-squares regression line we should attempt to make the values of the explanatory variable, x, as evenly spread out as possible so that b_1, our estimate of β_1, is as precise as possible.

Inference on the Linear Correlation Coefficient

Perhaps you are wondering why we have not presented hypothesis tests regarding the linear correlation coefficient in this section. Recall, in Chapter 4 we introduced a quick test for testing the significance of the correlation coefficient, even though we did not have a full appreciation of statistical inference. At this point we intentionally avoid discussion of inference on the correlation coefficient for two basic reasons: (1) The hypothesis test on the slope and a hypothesis test on the linear correlation coefficient will yield the same conclusion, and (2) inferential methods on the linear correlation coefficient, ρ, require that the y's at any given x be normally distributed and that the x's at any given y be normally distributed. That is, testing a hypothesis such as $H_0: \rho = 0$ versus $H_1: \rho \neq 0$ requires that the two variables follow a **bivariate normal distribution** or be **jointly normally distributed**. Verifying this requirement is a difficult task. Although a normal probability plot of the x_i's and a separate normal probability plot of the y_i's generally means that the joint distribution is normal, it is not guaranteed. For these two reasons, we will be content in verifying the linearity of the data by performing inference on the slope coefficient only.

14.1 ASSESS YOUR UNDERSTANDING

Concepts and Vocabulary

1. State the requirements to perform inference on the least-squares regression model. How are these requirements verified?

2. Why is it important to perform graphical as well as analytical analysis when analyzing relations between two quantitative variables?

3. What do the y-coordinates on the least-squares regression line represent?

4. Why is it desirable to have the explanatory variables spread out to test a hypothesis regarding β_1 or construct confidence intervals about β_1?

5. If $H_0: \beta_1 = 0$ is not rejected, what is the best estimate for the value of the response variable for any value of the explanatory variable? $\bar{y}$

6. Why don't we conduct inference on the linear correlation coefficient?

Skill Building

In Problems 7–12, use the results of Problems 11–16, respectively, from Section 4.2 to answer the following questions:

(a) *What are the estimates of β_0 and β_1?*

(b) *Compute the standard error, the point estimate for σ.*

(c) *Assuming that the residuals are normally distributed, determine s_{b_1}.*

(d) *Assuming that the residuals are normally distributed, test $H_0: \beta_1 = 0$ versus $H_1: \beta_1 \neq 0$ at the $\alpha = 0.05$ level of significance.*

7.

x	3	4	5	7	8
y	4	6	7	12	14

8.

x	3	5	7	9	11
y	0	2	3	6	9

9.

x	−2	−1	0	1	2
y	−4	0	1	4	5

10.

x	−2	−1	0	1	2
y	7	6	3	2	0

11.

x	20	30	40	50	60
y	100	95	91	83	70

12.

x	5	10	15	20	25
y	2	4	7	11	18

Applying the Concepts

13. **Height versus Head Circumference** A pediatrician wants to determine the relation that may exist between a child's height and head circumference. She randomly selects 11 children from her practice, measures their heights and head circumferences, and obtains the following data:

Height (inches)	Head Circumference (inches)	Height (inches)	Head Circumference (inches)
27.75	17.5	26.5	17.3
24.5	17.1	27	17.5
25.5	17.1	26.75	17.3
26	17.3	26.75	17.5
25	16.9	27.5	17.5
27.75	17.6		

Source: Denise Slucki, student at Joliet Junior College

Use the results from Problem 21 in Section 4.2 to answer the following questions:

(a) Treating height as the explanatory variable, x, determine the estimates of β_0 and β_1. $b_0 = 12.4932, b_1 = 0.1827$

(b) Compute the standard error of the estimate, s_e. 0.0954

(c) Determine whether the residuals are normally distributed.

(d) If the residuals are normally distributed, determine s_{b_1}.

(e) If the residuals are normally distributed, test whether a linear relation exists between height and head circumference at the $\alpha = 0.01$ level of significance. Reject H_0

(f) If the residuals are normally distributed, construct a 95% confidence interval about the slope of the true least-squares regression line. $(0.1204, 0.2451)$

(g) A child comes in for a physical, and the nurse determines his height to be 26.5 inches. However, the child is being rather uncooperative, so the nurse is unable to measure the head circumference of the child. What would be a good estimate of this child's head circumference? Why is this a good estimate? 17.34 inches

14. **Bone Length** Research performed at NASA and led by Dr. Emily R. Morey-Holton measured the lengths of the right humerus and right tibia in 11 rats that were sent into space on Spacelab Life Sciences 2. The following data were collected:

13. (c) Yes   13. (d) 0.0276

Right Humerus (mm), x	Right Tibia (mm), y	Right Humerus (mm), x	Right Tibia (mm), y
24.80	36.05	25.90	37.38
24.59	35.57	26.11	37.96
24.59	35.57	26.63	37.46
24.29	34.58	26.31	37.75
23.81	34.20	26.84	38.50
24.87	34.73		

Source: NASA Life Sciences Data Archive

14. (c) Yes   14. (d) 0.1501

Use the results from Problem 24 in Section 4.2 to answer the following questions:

(a) Treating the length of the right humerus as the explanatory variable, x, determine the estimates of β_0 and β_1. $b_0 = 1.1140$; $b_1 = 1.3902$

(b) Compute the standard error of the estimate.   0.4944

(c) Determine whether the residuals are normally distributed.

(d) If the residuals are normally distributed, determine s_{b_1}.

(e) If the residuals are normally distributed, test whether a linear relation exists between the length of the right humerus, x, and the length of the right tibia, y, at the $\alpha = 0.01$ level of significance.   Reject H_0

(f) If the residuals are normally distributed, construct a 99% confidence interval for the slope of the true least-squares regression line.   (0.9024, 1.8780)

(g) What is the mean length of the right tibia on a rat whose right humerus is 25.93 mm?   37.162 mm

15. **Concrete** As concrete cures, it gains strength. The following data represent the 7-day and 28-day strength (in pounds per square inch) of a certain type of concrete:

7-Day Strength, x	28-Day Strength, y	7-Day Strength, x	28-Day Strength, y
2,300	4,070	2,480	4,120
3,390	5,220	3,380	5,020
2,430	4,640	2,660	4,890
2,890	4,620	2,620	4,190
3,330	4,850	3,340	4,630

(a) Treating the 7-day strength as the explanatory variable, x, determine the estimates of β_0 and β_1.

(b) Compute the standard error of the estimate.   271.04

(c) Determine whether the residuals are normally distributed.

(d) If the residuals are normally distributed, determine s_{b_1}.

(e) If the residuals are normally distributed, test whether a linear relation exists between 7-day strength and 28-day strength at the $\alpha = 0.05$ level of significance.   Reject H_0

(f) If the residuals are normally distributed, construct a 95% confidence interval for the slope of the true least-squares regression line.   (0.2025, 1.1503)

(g) What is the estimated mean 28-day strength of this concrete if the 7-day strength is 3,000 psi?   4,704.8 psi

16. **Tar and Nicotine** Every year the Federal Trade Commission (FTC) must report tar and nicotine levels in cigarettes to Congress. The FTC obtains the tar and nicotine levels in

15. (a) $b_0 = 2,675.6$, $b_1 = 0.6764$ 15. (c) Yes   15. (d) 0.2055

16. (a) $b_0 = 0.2088$; $b_1 = 0.0575$ 16. (c) Yes

over 1,200 brands of cigarettes. A random sample from those reported to Congress is given in the following table:

Brand	Tar (mg), x	Nicotine (mg), y
Barclay 100	5	0.4
Benson and Hedges King	16	1.1
Camel Regular	24	1.7
Chesterfield King	24	1.4
Doral	8	0.5
Kent Golden Lights	9	0.8
Kool Menthol	9	0.8
Lucky Strike	24	1.5
Marlboro Gold	15	1.2
Newport Menthol	18	1.3
Salem Menthol	17	1.3
Virginia Slims Ultra Light	5	0.5
Winston Light	10	0.8

Source: Federal Trade Commission

(a) Treating the amount of tar as the explanatory variable, x, determine the estimates of β_0 and β_1.

(b) Compute the standard error of the estimate.   0.1121

(c) Determine whether the residuals are normally distributed.

(d) If the residuals are normally distributed, determine s_{b_1}.

(e) If the residuals are normally distributed, test whether a linear relation exists between the amount of tar, x, and the amount of nicotine, y, at the $\alpha = 0.1$ level of significance.

(f) If the residuals are normally distributed, construct a 90% confidence interval for the slope of the true least-squares regression line.   (0.0492, 0.0658)

(g) What is the mean amount of nicotine in a cigarette that has 12 milligrams of tar?   0.90 mg

17. **United Technologies versus the S&P 500** United Technologies is a conglomerate that includes companies such as Otis Elevators and Carrier Heating and Cooling. The ticker symbol of the company is UTX. The following data represent the rate of return of UTX stock for 11 months, compared with the rate of return of the Standard and Poor's Index of 500 stocks. Both are in percent.

Month	Rate of Return of S&P 500, x	Rate of Return in United Technologies, y
Apr-07	4.33	3.28
May-07	3.25	5.09
Jun-07	−1.78	0.54
Jul-07	−3.20	2.88
Aug-07	1.29	2.69
Sept-07	3.58	7.41
Oct-07	1.48	−4.83
Nov-07	−4.40	−2.38
Dec-07	−0.86	2.37
Jan-08	−6.12	−4.27
Feb-08	−3.48	−3.77

Source: TD Ameritrade

(a) Treating the rate of return of the S&P 500 as the explanatory variable, x, determine the estimates of β_0 and β_1. $b_0 = 1.2286$, $b_1 = 0.7622$

16. (d) 0.0046   16. (e) Reject H_0

17. (c) Yes   17. (d) 0.2880   17. (g) 3.706%   19. (a) $b_0 = 163.9988$, $b_1 = 63.1624$ 19. (c) Yes   19. (d) 10.2945

(b) Compute the standard error of the estimate. 3.2309

(c) Determine whether the residuals are normally distributed.

(d) If the residuals are normally distributed, determine s_{b_1}.

(e) If the residuals are normally distributed, test whether a linear relation exists between the rate of return of the S&P 500, x, and the rate of return for United Technologies stock, y, at the $\alpha = 0.1$ level of significance. Reject H_0

(f) If the residuals are normally distributed, construct a 90% confidence interval for the slope of the true least-squares regression line. (0.2343, 1.2900)

(g) What is the mean rate of return for United Technologies stock if the rate of return of the S&P 500 is 3.25%?

18. Fat-free Mass versus Energy Expenditure In an effort to measure the dependence of energy expenditure on body build, researchers used underwater weighing techniques to determine the fat-free body mass in seven men. In addition, they measured the total 24-hour energy expenditure during inactivity. The results are as follows:

Fat-free Mass (kg), x	Energy Expenditure (kcal), y
49.3	1,894
59.3	2,050
68.3	2,353
48.1	1,838
57.6	1,948
78.1	2,528
76.1	2,568

Source: P. Webb "Energy Expenditure and Fat-Free Mass in Men and Women." *American Journal of Clinical Nutrition*, **34**:1816–1826.

(a) What are the estimates of β_0 and β_1?

(b) Compute the standard error of the estimate. 64.8477

(c) Determine whether the residuals are normally distributed.

(d) If the residuals are normally distributed, determine s_{b_1}.

(e) If the residuals are normally distributed, test whether a linear relation exists between fat-free mass, x, and energy expenditure, y, at the $\alpha = 0.01$ level of significance.

(f) If the residuals are normally distributed, construct a 99% confidence interval for the slope of the true least-squares regression line. (16.1862, 33.8370)

(g) What is the mean energy expenditure of a man if his fat-free mass is 57.3 kg? 2,040.9

19. ACT versus SAT A university counselor wants to determine the relation that may exist between ACT and SAT Reasoning Test scores of entering freshmen. She randomly selects 14 entering freshmen who have taken both exams and obtains the following data:

ACT, x	SAT, y	ACT, x	SAT, y
18	1390	19	1470
21	1340	17	1190
27	1910	28	1770
18	1150	30	2290
20	1360	20	1660
25	1780	18	1480
25	1590	22	1370

Source: Based on SAT–ACT score equivalents from the *Princeton Review* for freshmen enrolled in 2006–2007.

18. (a) $b_0 = 607.7034$, $b_1 = 25.0116$ 18. (c) Yes 18. (d) 2.1888 18. (e) Reject H_0

(a) Treating ACT scores as the explanatory variable, x, determine the estimates of β_0 and β_1.

(b) Compute the standard error of the estimate. 157.4752

(c) Determine whether the residuals are normally distributed.

(d) If the residuals are normally distributed, determine s_{b_1}.

(e) If the residuals are normally distributed, test whether a linear relation exists between ACT scores, x, and SAT scores, y, at the $\alpha = 0.01$ level of significance. Reject H_0

(f) If the residuals are normally distributed, construct a 95% confidence interval for the slope of the true least-squares regression line. (40.7307, 85.5941)

(g) What is the mean SAT score for entering freshmen who scores 26 on the ACT? 1806.2

20. American Black Bears The American black bear (*Ursus americanus*) is one of eight bear species in the world. It is the smallest North American bear and the most common bear species on the planet. In 1969, Dr. Michael R. Pelton of the University of Tennessee initiated a long-term study of the population in Great Smoky Mountains National Park. One aspect of the study was to develop a model that could be used to predict a bear's weight (since it is not practical to weigh bears in the field). One variable that is thought to be related to weight is the length of the bear. The following data represent the lengths of 12 American black bears.

Total Length (cm)	Weight (kg)
139.0	110
138.0	60
139.0	90
120.5	60
149.0	85
141.0	100
141.0	95
150.0	85
166.0	155
151.5	140
129.5	105
150.0	110

Source: fieldtripearth.org

20. (a) $b_0 = -142.4700$, $b_1 = 1.6942$ 20. (c) Yes 20. (d) 0.5406

Use the results from Problem 22 in Section 4.2 to answer the following questions:

(a) Treating total length as the explanatory variable, x, determine the estimates of β_0 and β_1.

(b) Compute the standard error of estimate, s_e. 20.8577

(c) Determine whether the residuals are normally distributed.

(d) If the residuals are normally distributed, determine s_{b_1}.

(e) If the residuals are normally distributed, test whether a linear relation exists between total length and weight at the $\alpha = 0.05$ level of significance. Reject H_0

(f) If the residuals are normally distributed, construct a 95% confidence interval for the slope of the true least-squares regression line. (0.4897, 2.8989)

(g) What is the mean weight of American black bears of length 146.0 cm? 104.9 kg

21. Calories versus Sugar The following data represent the number of calories per serving and the number of grams of sugar per serving for a random sample of high-protein and moderate-protein energy bars.

Calories, x	Sugar, y	Calories, x	Sugar, y
180	10	270	20
200	18	320	2
210	14	110	10
220	20	180	12
220	0	200	22
230	28	220	24
240	2	230	24

Source: *Consumer Reports*, June 2003

21. (a) No relation

(a) Draw a scatter diagram of the data, treating calories as the explanatory variable. What type of relation, if any, appears to exist between calories and sugar?
(b) Determine the least-squares regression equation from the sample data. $\hat{y} = 17.8675 - 0.0146x$
(c) Compute the standard error of the estimate. 9.3749
(d) Determine whether the residuals are normally distributed.
(e) Determine s_{b_1}. 0.0549
(f) If the residuals are normally distributed, test whether a linear relation exists between calories and sugar content at the $\alpha = 0.01$ level of significance. Do not reject H_0
(g) If the residuals are normally distributed, construct a 95% confidence interval about the slope of the true least-squares regression line. (−0.1343, 0.1051)
(h) For a randomly selected energy bar, would you recommend using the least-squares regression line obtained in part (b) to predict the sugar content of the energy bar? Why? What would be a good estimate for the sugar content of the energy bar? No; $\bar{y} = 14.7$ grams

22. **Age versus HDL Cholesterol** A doctor wanted to determine whether there is a relation between a male's age and his HDL (so-called good) cholesterol. He randomly selected 17 of his patients and determined their HDL cholesterol. He obtained the following data:

Age, x	HDL Cholesterol, y	Age, x	HDL Cholesterol, y
38	57	38	44
42	54	66	62
46	34	30	53
32	56	51	36
55	35	27	45
52	40	52	38
61	42	49	55
61	38	39	28
26	47		

Source: Data based on information obtained from the National Center for Health Statistics

(a) Draw a scatter diagram of the data, treating age as the explanatory variable. What type of relation, if any, appears to exist between age and HDL cholesterol?
(b) Determine the least-squares regression equation from the sample data. $\hat{y} = 50.7841 - 0.1298x$
(c) Plot the residuals against the explanatory variable, age. Does a linear model seem appropriate on the basis of the residual plot? (*Hint*: See Section 4.3.) Yes
(d) Are there any outliers or influential observations? No
(e) Compute the standard error of the estimate. 9.9534
(f) Determine whether the residuals are normally distributed.
22. (f) Yes

22. (g) 0.2021   22. (j) No; $\bar{y} = 44.9$
(g) If the residuals are normally distributed, determine s_{b_1}.
(h) If the residuals are normally distributed, test whether a linear relation exists between age and HDL cholesterol levels at the $\alpha = 0.01$ level of significance. Do not reject H_0
(i) If the residuals are normally distributed, construct a 95% confidence interval for the slope of the true least-squares regression line. (−0.5605, 0.3008)
(j) For a 42-year-old male patient who visits the doctor's office, would you recommend using the least-squares regression line obtained in part (b) to predict the HDL cholesterol of this patient? Why? What would be a good estimate for the HDL cholesterol of this patient?

23. **The U.S. Population** The following data represent the population of the United States for the years 1900–2000:

Year, x	Population, y	Year, x	Population, y
1900	76,212,168	1960	179,323,175
1910	92,228,496	1970	203,302,031
1920	106,021,537	1980	226,542,203
1930	123,202,624	1990	248,709,873
1940	132,164,569	2000	281,421,906
1950	151,325,798		

Source: U.S. Census Bureau

An ecologist is interested in finding an equation that describes the population of the United States over time.
(a) Determine the least-squares regression equation, treating year as the explanatory variable.
(b) A normal probability plot of the residuals indicates that the residuals are approximately normally distributed. Test whether a linear relation exists between year and population. Reject H_0
(c) Draw a scatter diagram, treating year as the explanatory variable.
(d) Plot the residuals against the explanatory variable, year.
(e) Does a linear model seem appropriate based on the scatter diagram and residual plot? (*Hint*: See Section 4.3.) No
(f) What is the moral?

24. **Kepler's Law of Planetary Motion** The time it takes for a planet to complete its orbit around the sun is called the planet's *sidereal year*. Johann Kepler studied the relation between the sidereal year of a planet and its distance from the sun in 1618. The following data show the distances that the planets are from the sun and their sidereal years.

Planet	Distance from Sun, x (millions of miles)	Sidereal Year, y
Mercury	36	0.24
Venus	67	0.62
Earth	93	1.00
Mars	142	1.88
Jupiter	483	11.9
Saturn	887	29.5
Uranus	1,785	84.0
Neptune	2,797	165.0
Pluto*	3,675	248.0

*Pluto's status was reduced to a dwarf planet in September 2006.
23. (a) $\hat{y} = -3,771,542,830 + 2,018,994.196x$

24. (a) $\hat{y} = -12.4967 + 0.0657x$

(a) Determine the least-squares regression equation, treating distance from the sun as the explanatory variable.

(b) A normal probability plot of the residuals indicates that the residuals are approximately normally distributed. Test whether a linear relation exists between distance from the sun and sidereal year.   Reject H_0

(c) Draw a scatter diagram, treating distance from the sun as the explanatory variable.

(d) Plot the residuals against the explanatory variable, distance from the sun.

(e) Does a linear model seem appropriate based on the scatter diagram and residual plot? (*Hint*: See Section 4.3.)   No

(f) What is the moral?

25. **Influential Observations** The following data represent the heights and weights of a random sample of professional baseball players.

Player	Height (inches)	Weight (pounds)
Alex Rodriguez	75	225
Derek Jeter	75	195
Greg Maddux	72	180
Randy Johnson	82	231
Orlando Cabrera	69	185
Angel Sanchez	74	190
Ken Griffey, Jr.	75	228
Marlon Anderson	71	200
Jason Isringhausen	75	230

Source: Yahoo! Sports, March 2008

25. (b) $\hat{y} = -92.9811 + 4.0432x$; reject H_0

(a) Draw a scatter diagram of the data, treating height as the explanatory variable and weight as the response variable.

(b) Determine the least-squares regression line. Test whether there is a linear relation between height and weight at the $\alpha = 0.05$ level of significance.

(c) Remove the values listed for Randy Johnson. Test whether there is a linear relation between height and weight. What effect does Randy Johnson have on the hypothesis test? Do you think that Randy Johnson is influential? $y = -221.2133 + 5.8067x$; do not reject H_0

26. The output shown was obtained from MINITAB.

```
The regression equation is
y = 12.4 + 1.40 x

Predictor      Coef     StDev       T       P
Constant     12.396     1.381    8.97   0.000
x            1.3962    0.1245   11.21   0.000

S = 2.167     R-Sq = 91.3%   R-Sq(adj) = 90.6%
```

(a) The least-squares regression equation is $\hat{y} = 1.3962x + 12.396$. What is the predicted value of y at $x = 10$?

(b) What is the mean of y at $x = 10$?   26.36

(c) The standard error, s_e, is 2.167. What is an estimate of the standard deviation of y at $x = 10$?   2.167

(d) If the requirements for inference on the least-squares regression model are satisfied, what is the distribution of y at $x = 10$?   Normal; $\mu \approx 26.36$, $\sigma \approx 2.167$

26. (a) 26.36

TECHNOLOGY STEP-BY-STEP   Testing the Least-Squares Regression Model

TI-83/84 Plus

1. Enter the explanatory variable in L1 and the response variable in L2.

2. Press STAT, highlight TESTS, and select E:LinRegTTest....

3. Be sure that Xlist is L1 and Ylist is L2. Make sure that Freq: is set to 1. Select the direction of the alternative hypothesis. Place the cursor on Calculate and press ENTER.

MINITAB

1. With the explanatory variable in C1 and the response variable in C2, select the **Stat** menu and highlight **Regression**. Highlight and select **Regression** ....

2. Select the explanatory variable (MINITAB calls them predictors) and response variable and click OK.

Excel

1. Make sure the Data Analysis Tool Pack is activated by selecting the **Tools** menu and highlighting **Add-Ins** .... Check the box for the Analysis ToolPak and click OK.

2. Enter the explanatory variable in column A and the response variable in column B.

3. Select the **Tools** menu and highlight and select **Data Analysis** ....

4. Select the **Regression** option.

5. With the cursor in the Y-range cell, highlight the range of cells that contains the response variable. With the cursor in the X-range cell, highlight the range of cells that contains the explanatory variable. Click OK.

14.2 CONFIDENCE AND PREDICTION INTERVALS

Preparing for This Section Before getting started, review the following:

- Confidence intervals about μ, σ unknown (Section 9.2, pp. 475–482)

Objectives		
		Construct confidence intervals for a mean response
		Construct prediction intervals for an individual response

We know how to obtain the least-squares regression equation of best fit from data. We also know how to use the least-squares regression equation to obtain a predicted value. For example, the least-squares regression equation for the cholesterol data introduced in Example 1 from Section 14.1 is

$$\hat{y} = 1.3991x + 151.3537$$

where $\hat{y}$ represents the predicted total cholesterol for a female whose age is x. The predicted value of total cholesterol for a given age x actually has two interpretations:

1. It represents the mean total cholesterol for all females whose age is x.

2. It represents the predicted total cholesterol for a randomly selected female whose age is x.

So, if we let $x = 42$ in the least-squares regression equation $\hat{y} = 1.3991x + 151.3537$, we obtain $\hat{y} = 1.3991(42) + 151.3537 = 210.1$. We can interpret this result in one of two ways:

1. The mean total cholesterol for all 42-year-old females is 210.1.

2. Our estimate of the total cholesterol for a randomly selected 42-year-old female is 210.1.

Of course, there is a margin of error in making predictions, so we construct intervals about any predicted value to describe its accuracy. The type of interval constructed will depend on whether we are predicting a mean total cholesterol for all 42-year-old females or the total cholesterol for an individual 42-year-old female. In other words, the margin of error is going to be different for predicting the mean total cholesterol for all females who are 42 years old versus the total cholesterol for one individual. Which prediction (the mean or the individual) do you think will be more accurate? It seems logical that the distribution of means should have less variability (and therefore a lower margin of error) than the distribution of individuals. After all, in the distribution of means, high total cholesterols can be offset by low total cholesterols.

Definitions

Confidence intervals for a mean response are intervals constructed about the predicted value of y, at a given level of x, that are used to measure the accuracy of the mean response of all the individuals in the population.

Prediction intervals for an individual response are intervals constructed about the predicted value of y that are used to measure the accuracy of a single individual's predicted value.

In Other Words

Confidence intervals are intervals for the mean of the population. Prediction intervals are intervals for an individual from the population.

If we use the least-squares regression equation to predict the mean total cholesterol for all 42-year-old females, we construct a confidence interval for a mean response. If we use the least-squares regression equation to predict the total cholesterol for a single 42-year-old female, we construct a prediction interval for an individual response.

Construct Confidence Intervals for a Mean Response

The structure of a confidence interval is the same as it was in Section 9.1. The interval is of the form

$$\text{Point estimate } \pm \text{ margin of error}$$

The following formula can be used to construct a confidence interval about $\hat{y}$.

Confidence Interval for the Mean Response of y, $\hat{y}$

A $(1 - \alpha) \cdot 100\%$ confidence interval for $\hat{y}$, the mean response of y for a specified value of x, is given by

$$\text{Lower bound: } \hat{y} - t_{\alpha/2} \cdot s_e \sqrt{\frac{1}{n} + \frac{(x^* - \overline{x})^2}{\Sigma(x_i - \overline{x})^2}}$$

$$\text{Upper bound: } \hat{y} + t_{\alpha/2} \cdot s_e \sqrt{\frac{1}{n} + \frac{(x^* - \overline{x})^2}{\Sigma(x_i - \overline{x})^2}}$$

$\qquad$ **(1)**

Note The interval may be constructed provided the residuals are normally distributed or the sample size is large. ◄

where x^* is the given value of the explanatory variable, n is the number of observations, and $t_{\alpha/2}$ is the critical value with $n - 2$ degrees of freedom.

EXAMPLE 1 · Constructing a Confidence Interval for a Mean Response

Problem: Construct a 95% confidence interval for the predicted mean total cholesterol of all 42-year-old females using the data in Table 1.

Approach: We wish to determine the predicted mean total cholesterol at $x^* = 42$ using Formula (1) since our estimate is for the mean cholesterol of all 42-year-old females.

Solution: The least-squares regression equation is $\hat{y} = 1.3991x + 151.3537$. To find the predicted mean total cholesterol of all 42-year-olds, let $x^* = 42$ in the regression equation and obtain $\hat{y} = 1.3991(42) + 151.3537 = 210.1$. From Example 2 in Section 14.1, we found that $s_e = 19.48$, and from Example 5 in Section 14.1, we found that $\Sigma(x_i - \overline{x})^2 = 2{,}472.9284$ and $\overline{x} = 42.07143$. The critical t value, $t_{\alpha/2} = t_{0.025}$, with $n - 2 = 14 - 2 = 12$ degrees of freedom is 2.179. The 95% confidence interval for the predicted mean total cholesterol for all 42-year-old females is therefore

$$\text{Lower bound: } \hat{y} - t_{\alpha/2} \cdot s_e \cdot \sqrt{\frac{1}{n} + \frac{(x^* - \overline{x})^2}{\Sigma(x_i - \overline{x})^2}} = 210.1 - 2.179 \cdot 19.48 \cdot \sqrt{\frac{1}{14} + \frac{(42 - 42.07143)^2}{2472.9284}}$$

$$= 198.8$$

$$\text{Upper bound: } \hat{y} + t_{\alpha/2} \cdot s_e \cdot \sqrt{\frac{1}{n} + \frac{(x^* - \overline{x})^2}{\Sigma(x_i - \overline{x})^2}} = 210.1 + 2.179 \cdot 19.48 \cdot \sqrt{\frac{1}{14} + \frac{(42 - 42.07143)^2}{2472.9284}}$$

$$= 221.4$$

We are 95% confident that the mean total cholesterol of all 42-year-old females is between 198.8 and 221.4.

Now Work Problems 3(a) and (b)

2 Construct Prediction Intervals for an Individual Response

In Other Words

Prediction intervals are wider than confidence intervals because it is tougher to guess the value of an individual than the mean of a population.

The procedure for obtaining a prediction interval for an individual response is similar to that for finding a confidence interval for a mean response. The only difference is the standard error. More variability is associated with individuals than with means. Therefore, the computation of the interval must account for this increased variability. Again, the form of the interval is

$$\text{Point estimate} \pm \text{margin of error}$$

The following formula can be used to construct a prediction interval about $\hat{y}$.

Prediction Interval for an Individual Response about $\hat{y}$

A $(1 - \alpha) \cdot 100\%$ prediction interval for $\hat{y}$, the individual response of y, is given by

$$\text{Lower bound: } \hat{y} - t_{\alpha/2} \cdot s_e \sqrt{1 + \frac{1}{n} + \frac{(x^* - \overline{x})^2}{\Sigma(x_i - \overline{x})^2}}$$

$$\text{Upper bound: } \hat{y} + t_{\alpha/2} \cdot s_e \sqrt{1 + \frac{1}{n} + \frac{(x^* - \overline{x})^2}{\Sigma(x_i - \overline{x})^2}}$$ (2)

where x^* is the given value of the explanatory variable, n is the number of observations, and $t_{\alpha/2}$ is the critical value with $n - 2$ degrees of freedom.

Note The interval may be constructed provided the residuals are normally distributed or the sample size is large. ◄

Notice that the only difference between Formula (1) and Formula (2) is the "1 + " under the radical in Formula (2).

EXAMPLE 2 Constructing a Prediction Interval for an Individual Response

Problem: Construct a 95% prediction interval for the predicted total cholesterol of a 42-year-old female.

Approach: We need to determine the predicted total cholesterol at $x^* = 42$ and use Formula (2) since our estimate is for a particular 42-year-old female.

Solution: The least-squares regression equation is $\hat{y} = 1.3991x + 151.3537$. To find the predicted total cholesterol of a 42-year-old, let $x^* = 42$ in the regression equation and obtain $\hat{y} = 1.3991(42) + 151.3537 = 210.1$. From Example 2 in Section 14.1, we found that $s_e = 19.48$; from Example 5 in Section 14.1 we found that $\Sigma(x_i - \overline{x})^2 = 2472.9284$ and $\overline{x} = 42.07143$. We find $t_{\alpha/2} = t_{0.025}$ with $n - 2 = 14 - 2 = 12$ degrees of freedom to be 2.179.

The 95% prediction interval for the predicted total cholesterol for a 42-year-old female is

$$\text{Lower bound: } \hat{y} - t_{\alpha/2} \cdot s_e \sqrt{1 + \frac{1}{n} + \frac{(x^* - \overline{x})^2}{\Sigma(x_i - \overline{x})^2}} = 210.1 - 2.179 \cdot 19.48 \cdot \sqrt{1 + \frac{1}{14} + \frac{(42 - 42.07143)^2}{2472.9284}} = 166.2$$

$$\text{Upper bound: } \hat{y} + t_{\alpha/2} \cdot s_e \sqrt{1 + \frac{1}{n} + \frac{(x^* - \overline{x})^2}{\Sigma(x_i - \overline{x})^2}} = 210.1 + 2.179 \cdot 19.48 \cdot \sqrt{1 + \frac{1}{14} + \frac{(42 - 42.07143)^2}{2472.9284}} = 254.0$$

We are 95% confident that the total cholesterol of a randomly selected 42-year-old female is between 166.2 and 254.0.

Now Work Problems 3(c) and (d)

Notice that the interval about the individual (prediction interval for an individual response) is wider than the interval about the mean (confidence interval for a mean response). The reason for this should be clear: More variability is associated with individuals than with groups of individuals. That is, it is more difficult to predict a single 42-year-old female's total cholesterol than it is to predict the mean total cholesterol for all 42-year-old females.

EXAMPLE 3 **Confidence and Prediction Intervals Using Technology**

 Using Technology

The bounds for confidence and prediction intervals obtained using statistical software may differ from bounds computed by hand due to rounding error.

Problem: Construct a 95% confidence interval for the predicted total cholesterol of all 42-year-old females using statistical software. Construct a 95% prediction interval for the predicted total cholesterol for a 42-year-old female using statistical software.

Approach: We will use MINITAB to obtain the intervals. The steps for obtaining confidence and prediction intervals using MINITAB and Excel are given in the Technology Step-by-Step on page 758.

Solution: Figure 12 shows the results obtained from MINITAB.

Figure 12

Predicted Values

Fit	StDev Fit	95.0% CI	95.0% PI
210.11	5.21	(198.77, 221.46)	(166.18, 254.05)

14.2 ASSESS YOUR UNDERSTANDING

Concepts and Vocabulary

1. Explain the difference between a confidence interval and prediction interval.

2. If a normal probability plot of residuals indicates that the requirement of normally distributed residuals is violated, explain the circumstances under which confidence and prediction intervals could still be constructed.

Skill Building

In Problems 3–6, use the results of Problems 7–10 in Section 14.1.

3. Using the sample data from Problem 7 in Section 14.1,
   NW (a) Predict the mean value of y if x = 7.   11.8
   (b) Construct a 95% confidence interval for the mean value of y if x = 7.   (10.8, 12.8)
   (c) Predict the value of y if x = 7.   11.8
   (d) Construct a 95% prediction interval for the value of y if x = 7.   (9.9, 13.7)
   (e) Explain the difference between the prediction in parts (a) and (c).

4. Using the sample data from Problem 8 in Section 14.1,
   (a) Predict the mean value of y if x = 8.   5.1
   (b) Construct a 95% confidence interval for the mean value of y if x = 8.   (4.0, 6.2)
   (c) Predict the value of y if x = 8.   5.1
   (d) Construct a 95% prediction interval for the value of y if x = 8.   (2.5, 7.7)
   (e) Explain the difference between the prediction in parts (a) and (c).

5. Using the sample data from Problem 9 in Section 14.1,
   (a) Predict the mean value of y if x = 1.4.   4.3

(b) Construct a 95% confidence interval for the mean value of y if x = 1.4.   (2.5, 6.1)
(c) Predict the value of y if x = 1.4.   4.3
(d) Construct a 95% prediction interval for the value of y if x = 1.4.   (0.9, 7.7)

6. Using the sample data from Problem 10 in Section 14.1,
   (a) Predict the mean value of y if x = 1.8.   0.4
   (b) Construct a 90% confidence interval for the mean value of y if x = 1.8.   (−0.8, 1.6)
   (c) Predict the value of y if x = 1.8.   0.4
   (d) Construct a 90% prediction interval for the value of y if x = 1.8.   (−1.6, 2.4)

Applying the Concepts

7. **Height versus Head Circumference** Use the results of Problem 13 from Section 14.1 to answer the following questions:
   (a) Predict the mean head circumference of children who are 25.75 inches tall.   17.20 inches
   (b) Construct a 95% confidence interval for the mean head circumference of children who are 25.75 inches tall.   (17.12, 17.28)
   (c) Predict the head circumference of a randomly selected child who is 25.75 inches tall.   17.20 inches
   (d) Construct a 95% prediction interval for the head circumference of a child who is 25.75 inches tall.   (16.97, 17.43)
   (e) Explain the difference between the predictions in parts (a) and (c).

8. **Bone Length** Use the results of Problem 14 in Section 14.1 to answer the following questions:
   (a) Predict the mean length of the right tibia of all rats whose right humerus is 25.83 mm.   37.023 mm

9. (b) (4,147.8, 4,653.1)   9. (d) (3,726.3, 5,074.6)

(b) Construct a 95% confidence interval for the mean length found in part (a). (36.647, 37.399)

(c) Predict the length of the right tibia of a randomly selected rat whose right humerus is 25.83 mm. 37.023 mm

(d) Construct a 95% prediction interval for the length found in part (c). (35.843, 38.203)

(e) Explain why the predicted lengths found in parts (a) and (c) are the same, yet the intervals constructed in parts (b) and (d) are different.

9. **Concrete** Use the results of Problem 15 from Section 14.1 to answer the following questions:

(a) Predict the mean 28-day strength of concrete whose 7-day strength is 2,550 psi. 4,400.4 psi

(b) Construct a 95% confidence interval for the mean 28-day strength of concrete whose 7-day strength is 2,550 psi.

(c) Predict the 28-day strength of concrete whose 7-day strength is 2,550 psi. 4,400.4 psi

(d) Construct a 95% prediction interval for the 28-day strength of concrete whose 7-day strength is 2,550 psi.

(e) Explain the difference between the predictions in parts (a) and (c).

10. **Tar and Nicotine** Use the results of Problem 16 in Section 14.1 to answer the following questions:

(a) Predict the mean nicotine content of all cigarettes whose tar content is 12 mg. 0.90 mg

(b) Construct a 95% confidence interval for the tar content found in part (a). (0.83, 0.97)

(c) Predict the nicotine content of a randomly selected cigarette whose tar content is 12 mg. 0.90 mg

(d) Construct a 95% prediction interval for the nicotine content found in part (c). (0.64, 1.16)

(e) Explain why the predicted nicotine contents found in parts (a) and (c) are the same, yet the intervals constructed in parts (b) and (d) are different.

11. **United Technologies versus the S&P 500** Use the results of Problem 17 in Section 14.1 to answer the following questions:

(a) What is the mean rate of return for United Technologies stock if the rate of return of the S&P 500 is 4.2%?

(b) Construct a 90% confidence interval for the mean rate of return found in part (a). (1.357, 7.503)

(c) Predict the rate of return on United Technologies stock if the rate of return on the S&P 500 for a randomly selected month is 4.2%. 4.430%

(d) Construct a 90% prediction interval for the rate of return found in part (c). (−2.242, 11.102)

(e) Explain why the predicted rates of return found in parts (a) and (c) are the same, yet the intervals constructed in parts (b) and (d) are different.

12. **Fat-Free Mass versus Energy Expenditure** Use the results of Problem 18 in Section 14.1 to answer the following questions:

(a) What is the mean energy expenditure for individuals whose fat-free mass is 57.3 kg? 2,040.9 kcal

(b) Construct a 99% confidence interval for the mean energy expenditure found in part (a). (1,932.3, 2,149.5)

(c) Predict the energy expenditure of a randomly selected individual whose fat-free mass is 57.3 kg. 2,040.9 kcal

(d) Construct a 99% prediction interval for the energy expenditure found in part (c). (1,757.7, 2,324.0)

(e) Explain why the predicted energy expenditures found in parts (a) and (c) are the same, yet the intervals constructed in parts (b) and (d) are different.

11. (a) 4.430%

13. **ACT versus SAT** Use the results of Problem 19 from Section 14.1 to answer the following questions:

(a) Predict the mean SAT score for entering freshmen who score a 23 on the ACT. 1617

(b) Construct a 95% confidence interval for the mean SAT score for entering freshmen who score a 23 on the ACT. (1522, 1711)

(c) Predict the SAT score of a randomly selected freshman who scores a 23 on the ACT. 1617

(d) Construct a 95% prediction interval for the SAT score for a randomly selected freshman who scores a 23 on the ACT. (1261, 1973)

(e) Explain why the predicted weights in parts (a) and (c) are the same, yet the intervals constructed in parts (b) and (d) are different.

14. **American Black Bears** Use the results of Problem 20 from Section 14.1 to answer the following questions:

(a) Predict the mean weight of American black bears with a total length of 154.5 cm. 119.3 kg

(b) Construct a 95% confidence interval for the mean weight of American black bears with a total length of 154.5 cm. (99.9, 138.7)

(c) Predict the weight of a randomly selected American black bear that is 154.5 cm long. 119.3 kg

(d) Construct a 95% prediction interval for the weight of an American black bear that is 154.5 cm long. (68.9, 169.6)

(e) Explain why the predicted weights in parts (a) and (c) are the same, yet the intervals constructed in parts (b) and (d) are different.

15. **Calories versus Sugar** Use the results of Problem 21 from Section 14.1 to answer the following:

(a) Explain why it does not make sense to construct confidence or prediction intervals based on the least-squares regression equation. Nonlinear relation

(b) Construct a 95% confidence interval for the mean sugar content of energy bars. (9.5, 19.9)

16. **Age versus HDL Cholesterol** Use the results of Problem 22 from Section 14.1 to answer the following:

(a) Explain why it does not make sense to construct confidence or prediction intervals based on the least-squares regression equation. Nonlinear relation

(b) Construct a 95% confidence interval for the mean HDL cholesterol of males. (39.9, 50.0)

17. **Putting It Together: Plasma Television Prices** One factor that influences the cost of a plasma television is its size. The following data represent the size and price for a random sample of plasma televisions of varying brands and models.

Brand/Model	Size (in.)	Price ($)
LG/60PB4D	60	4,000
LG/60PC1D	60	3,600
Panasonic/TH-58PZ750U	58	5,000
Pioneer/PDP-5080HD	50	3,200
Vizio/JV50P	50	1,800
Samsung/HP-T5064	50	1,600
Panasonic/TH-42PZ700U	42	1,900
Hitachi/UltraVision 42HDX99	42	1,700
LG/42PC5D	42	1,300

Source: Consumer Reports, December 2007

17. (h) $b_0 = -4,661.8395$, $b_1 = 145.4990$ 17. (j) Yes

17. (n) $2,613

(a) Draw a scatter diagram of the data using size as the explanatory variable.

(b) Determine the linear correlation coefficient between the size and price.   0.839

(c) Does a linear relation exist between size and price?   Yes

(d) Find the least-squares regression line treating size as the explanatory variable. $\hat{y} = -4,661.8345 + 145.4990x$

(e) Interpret the slope.

(f) Is it reasonable to interpret the intercept? Explain.   No

(g) What proportion of variability in price is explained by the variability in size?   70.4%

(h) Determine extimates for β_0 and β_1.

(i) Compute the standard error of the estimate.   759.6697

(j) Determine whether the residuals are normally distributed.

(k) Determine s_{b_1}.   35.6443

(l) If the residuals are normally distributed, test whether a linear relation exists between size and price at the $\alpha = 0.05$ level of significance.   Reject H_0

(m) If the residuals are normally distributed, construct a 95% confidence interval for the slope of the true least-squares regression line.   (61.200, 229.798)

(n) Predict the mean price of 50-inch plasma televisions.

(o) Construct a 95% confidence interval about the mean price of 50-inch televisions.   ($2,013, $3,213)

(p) Is the price of the 50-inch Samsung/HP-T5064 plasma television above or below the average price for 50-inch plasma televisions? Explain by using the confidence interval found in part (o).   Below

(q) Predict the price of a randomly selected 50-inch plasma television. $2,613

(r) Construct a 95% prediction interval for the price a 50-inch plasma television.   ($718.9, $4507.3)

(s) In part (g), you found the proportion of variability in price that is explained by the variability in size. What lurking variables might also have an effect on price?

TECHNOLOGY STEP-BY-STEP Confidence and Prediction Intervals

TI-83/84 Plus

The TI-83/84 Plus graphing calculators do not compute confidence or prediction intervals.

MINITAB

1. With the predictor variable in C1 and the response variable in C2, select the **Stat** menu and highlight **Regression**. Highlight and select **Regression** . . . .

2. Select the explanatory (predictor) and response variables.

3. Click the Options . . . button.

4. In the cell marked "Prediction intervals for new observations," enter the value of x^*. Select a confidence level. Click OK twice.

Excel

1. Load the DDXL Add-in.

2. Enter the values of the explanatory variable down column A and the corresponding values of the response variable down column B.

3. Enter the value of x^* in the cell below the last explanatory data value in column A, and leave the corresponding cell in column B blank. Highlight the data, including the value of x^* and the corresponding blank cell.

4. Select the **DDXL** menu and click **Regression.**

5. From the drop-down menu under Function type, select **Simple regression.** Select or deselect as appropriate the box labeled "First row is variable names."

6. Select the column that contains the response variable from the "Names and Columns" window.

Use the ◄ arrow in the Response Variable field to select the data. Next, select the column that contains the explanatory variable. Use the ◄ arrow in the Explanatory Variable field to select the data. Click OK.

7. Click on the appropriate button to find 90%, 95%, or 99% Confidence and Prediction Intervals.

14.3 MULTIPLE REGRESSION

Preparing for This Section   Before getting started, review the following:

- Correlation (Section 4.1, pp. 195–201)

- Diagnostics on the Least-Squares Regression Line (Section 4.3, pp. 223–232)

- Least-Squares Regression (Section 4.2, pp. 209–217)

Objectives

1 Obtain the correlation matrix

2 Use technology to find a multiple regression equation

3 Interpret the coefficients of a multiple regression equation

4 Determine R^2 and adjusted R^2

5 Perform an *F*-test for lack of fit

6 Test individual regression coefficients for significance

7 Construct confidence and prediction intervals

8 Build a regression model

① **Obtain the Correlation Matrix**

Note to Instructor
If you like, you can print out and distribute the Preparing for This Section quiz located in the Instructor's Resource Center. The purpose of the quiz is to verify that the students have the prerequisite knowledge for the section.

The least-squares regression model $y_i = \beta_0 + \beta_1 x_i + \varepsilon_i$ introduced in Section 14.1 is a model for describing the linear relation between a single explanatory variable, x, and a response variable, y. However, it is often the case that more than one explanatory variable can be used to predict the value of a response variable. In these circumstances, we use a *multiple regression model*.

Definition

A **multiple regression model** is given by

$$y_i = \beta_0 + \beta_1 x_{1i} + \beta_2 x_{2i} + \cdots + \beta_k x_{ki} + \varepsilon_i \qquad \textbf{(1)}$$

where

y_i is the value of the response variable for the ith individual

$\beta_0, \beta_1, \beta_2, \ldots, \beta_k$ are the parameters to be estimated based on sample data

x_{1i} is the ith observation for the first explanatory variable, x_{2i} is the ith observation for the second explanatory variable, and so on

ε_i is a random error term that is normally distributed with mean 0 and variance $\sigma_{\varepsilon_i}^2 = \sigma^2$

The error terms are independent, and $i = 1, 2, \ldots, n$, where n is the sample size.

If there are two explanatory variables, model (1) reduces to

$$y_i = \beta_0 + \beta_1 x_{1i} + \beta_2 x_{2i} + \varepsilon_i \qquad \textbf{(2)}$$

If there are three explanatory variables, model (1) reduces to

$$y_i = \beta_0 + \beta_1 x_{1i} + \beta_2 x_{2i} + \beta_3 x_{3i} + \varepsilon_i \qquad \textbf{(3)}$$

Because we typically do not have access to population data, the parameters, $\beta_0, \beta_1, \beta_2$, and so on, must be estimated using sample data. We will let b_0 represent the estimate of β_0, b_1 represent the estimate of β_1, and so on. Although formulas do exist for determining the values of $b_0, b_1, \ldots, b_k$, they are beyond the scope of this text. Therefore, we will be content to obtain estimates of the parameters using statistical software, such as MINITAB or Excel.

In obtaining a multiple regression model, we must decide which variables to include in the model and which to exclude. One tool that will aid us in this decision is the *correlation matrix*.

Definition

A **correlation matrix** shows the linear correlation between each pair of variables under consideration in a multiple regression model.

When determining which explanatory variables to include in a multiple regression model, we choose the ones that have a high linear correlation with the response variable. However, some caution is in order. We must guard against including explanatory variables that are highly correlated among themselves. That is, we must guard against *multicollinearity*.

Definition

Multicollinearity exists between two explanatory variables if they have a high linear correlation.

◆ **CAUTION** If two explanatory variables in the regression model are highly correlated with each other, watch out for strange results in the regression output.

To help understand the idea of multicollinearity, consider the following scenario. We are trying to predict sales of lemonade at their corner store. Certainly, one variable that might help to explain lemonade sales is the outside temperature. Another variable that might help explain lemonade sales is air-conditioning bills. If the researcher includes both explanatory variables in the model, he may get results that are a little strange, because the two explanatory variables, temperature and air-conditioning bills, are themselves highly correlated. As temperatures increase, so do air-conditioning bills. It would be silly to include both variables in the model because they are both doing the same job when it comes to explaining lemonade sales. Of course, identifying multicollinearity is not always this obvious.

Multicollinearity does not necessarily cause problems for us, but it can. Some of the problems that result from multicollinearity include getting estimates of slope coefficients that are the opposite sign of what we would expect or obtaining estimates of slope coefficients that are not as large (or small) as we would expect.

There are a few factors, other than a high linear correlation between explanatory variables, that dictate whether multicollinearity is a problem, but the discussion is beyond the scope of this text. For our purposes, we will look at a correlation matrix to determine which, if any, explanatory variables have a high correlation between them. For the sake of having a general rule, we will say that a linear correlation between two explanatory variables less than -0.7 or greater than 0.7 may be cause for concern. If there are two explanatory variables in the regression model that are highly correlated, we will keep an eye out for unexpected results. We will have more to say about this at the end of the section.

EXAMPLE 1 **Constructing a Correlation Matrix**

Problem: A family doctor wishes to further examine the variables that affect his female patients' total cholesterol. He randomly selects 14 of his female patients and asks them to determine their average daily consumption of saturated fat. He then measures their total cholesterol and obtains the data in Table 4.

Table 4		
Age, x_1	Saturated Fat (g), x_2	Total Cholesterol, y
25	19	180
25	28	195
28	19	186
32	16	180
32	24	210
32	20	197
38	31	239
42	20	183
48	26	204
51	24	221
51	32	243
58	21	208
62	21	228
65	30	269

Source: Based on results obtained from the National Center for Health Statistics.

Approach: We enter the data into MINITAB and create the correlation matrix. The steps for creating a correlation matrix using MINITAB and Excel are given in the Technology Step-by-Step on page 780.

Solution: Figure 13 shows the correlation matrix from MINITAB.

Figure 13 **Correlations: Age, Fat, Cholesterol**

```
                  Age       Fat
Fat             0.324
Cholesterol     0.718     0.778

Cell Contents: Pearson correlation
```

The linear correlation between total cholesterol and age is 0.718. The linear correlation between total cholesterol and average daily consumption of saturated fat is 0.778. Because the linear correlation between average daily consumption and age, the two explanatory variables, is only 0.324, we are not concerned with multicollinearity.

Now Work Problem 19(a)

2   Use Technology to Find a Multiple Regression Equation

When obtaining a multiple regression equation, we perform the same diagnostic tests that we performed for the least-squares regression model with one explanatory variable. We should always draw residual plots to verify that the model is appropriate. The residual plots that should be drawn are (1) a plot of residuals against fitted values, $\hat{y}$, to see if the linear model is appropriate and if the errors have constant variance, (2) a plot of residuals against each of the explanatory variables to make sure that the relation between the explanatory and response variables is linear, and (3) a boxplot of the residuals to check for outliers.

EXAMPLE 2   **Multiple Regression**

Problem: A family doctor wishes to further examine the variables that affect his female patients' total cholesterol. He randomly selects 14 of his female patients and asks them to disclose their average daily consumption of saturated fat. He then measures their total cholesterol and obtains the data in Table 4 presented in Example 1.

(a) Find the least-squares regression equation $\hat{y} = b_0 + b_1x_1 + b_2x_2$, where x_1 represents the patient's age, x_2 represents the patient's daily consumption of saturated fat, and y represents the patient's total cholesterol.

(b) Draw residual plots and a boxplot of the residuals to assess the adequacy of the model.

Approach

We will enter the data into MINITAB to obtain the least-squares regression equation and to draw the residual plots and boxplot of the residuals. The steps for determining the multiple regression equation and residual plots using MINITAB and Excel are given in the Technology Step-by-Step on page 780.

Solution

(a) Figure 14 shows the output from MINITAB.

Figure 14   **Regression Analysis: Cholesterol versus Age, Fat**

```
The regression equation is
cholesterol = 90.8 + 1.01 age + 3.24 fat

Predictor        Coef    SE Coef        T        P
Constant        90.84      15.99     5.68    0.000
Age            1.0142     0.2427     4.18    0.002
Fat            3.2443     0.6632     4.89    0.000


S = 11.42        R-Sq = 84.7%       R-Sq(adj) = 82.0%

Analysis of Variance

Source          DF        SS       MS        F        P
Regression       2    7960.3   3980.1    30.53    0.000
Residual Error  11    1434.1    130.4
Total           13    9394.4
```

The least-squares regression equation for these data is $\hat{y} = 90.84 + 1.0142x_1 + 3.2443x_2$.

(b) Figure 15(a) shows a plot of residuals against the predicted values, $\hat{y}$. To obtain this plot by hand, we would first find all the fitted values. For example, the predicted (or fitted) value for the first observation in Table 4 (age = 25, fat consumption = 19) is $\hat{y} = 90.84 + 1.0142(25) + 3.2443(19) = 177.8$. Therefore, residual = observed − predicted = $180 - 177.8 = 2.2$. We would then plot the point (177.8, 2.2) on the graph. We would repeat this for the remaining observations. Figure 15(b) shows a plot of residuals against the explanatory variable, age. Figure 15(c) shows a plot of residuals against the explanatory variable saturated fat. Figure 15(d) shows a boxplot of the residuals. None of the residual plots show any discernible pattern, and the boxplot does not show any outliers. Therefore, the linear model is appropriate.

Figure 15

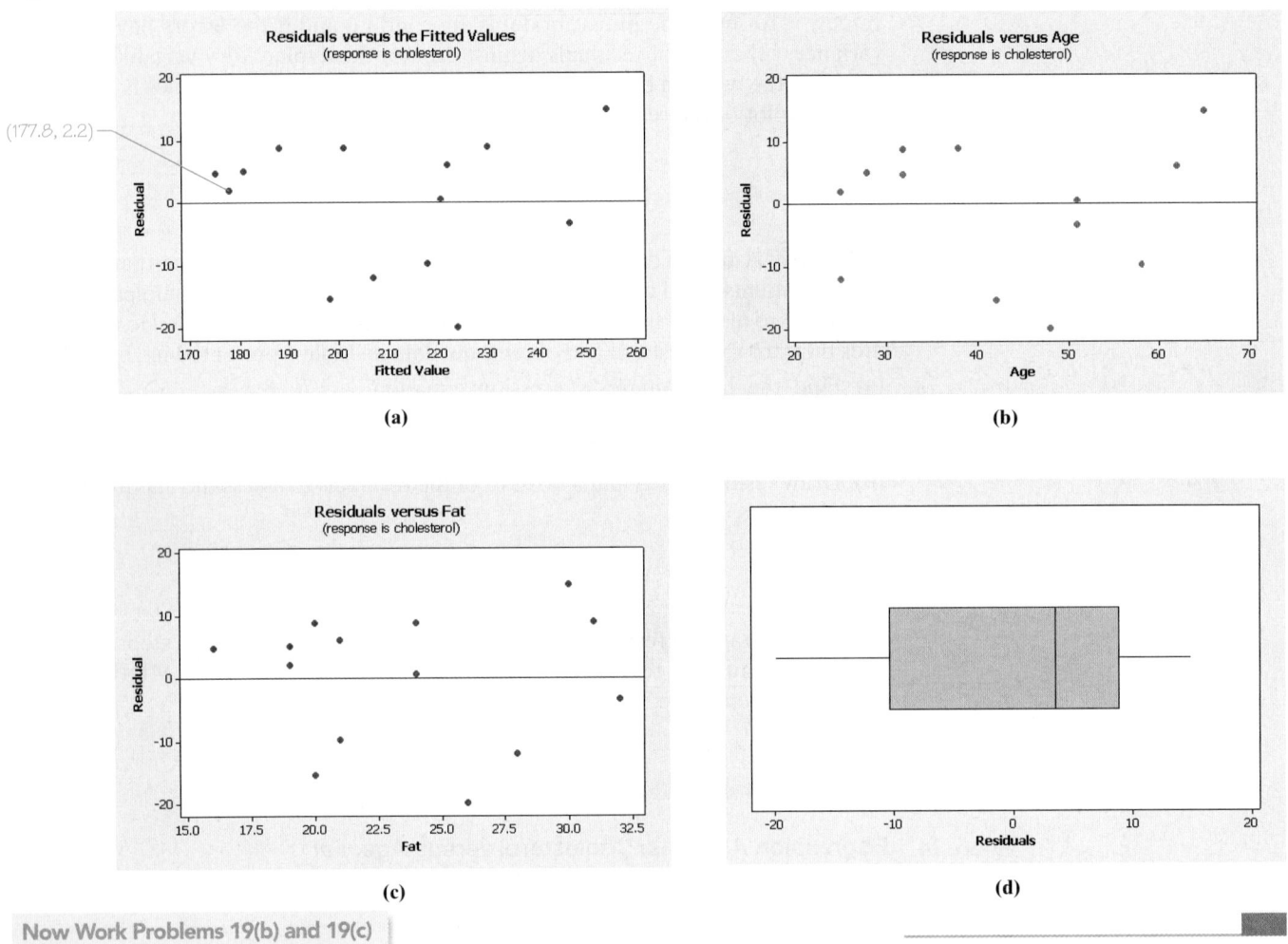

(a)

(b)

(c)

(d)

Now Work Problems 19(b) and 19(c)

③ Interpret the Coefficients of a Multiple Regression Equation

For the simple linear regression model, recall that the slope, β_1, represents the *average* change in the value of the response variable for a 1-unit change in the value of the explanatory variable. For example, if income, y, and years of education, x, are related by the equation $\hat{y} = 17{,}203 + 3{,}423x$, then the slope, 3,423, can be interpreted as follows: If the number of years of education increases by 1 year, income increases by an average of $3,423.

In the multiple regression model, we interpret the regression coefficients similarly. However, because of other variables in the model, we assume that the remaining variables stay constant when interpreting the slope coefficient of a particular variable. If we have three explanatory variables, the multiple regression is $\hat{y} = b_0 + b_1x_1 + b_2x_2 + b_3x_3$. So, the interpretation of the regression coefficient b_1 is that "If x_1 increases by 1 unit, then the response variable y will increase by b_1 units, on average, while x_2 and x_3 are held constant." Likewise, the interpretation of the regression coefficient b_2 is "If x_2 increases by 1 unit, then the response variable y will increase by b_2 units, on average, while x_1 and x_3 are held constant. We could make a similar interpretation for b_3.

EXAMPLE 3   **Interpreting Regression Coefficients**

Problem: Interpret the regression coefficients for the least-squares regression equation found in Example 2.

Approach: We interpret the coefficients the same way as we did for a regression with one explanatory variable. However, we assume that the remaining explanatory variables are constant.

Solution: The least-squares regression equation found in Example 2 was $\hat{y} = 90.84 + 1.0142x_1 + 3.2443x_2$, where x_1 represents the patient's age and x_2 represents the patient's average daily consumption of saturated fat (in grams). The regression coefficient, $b_1 = 1.0142$, means that, if the patient's age increases by 1 year then total cholesterol increases by 1.0142, on average, assuming that the average daily consumption of saturated fat remains unchanged. The regression coefficient, $b_2 = 3.2443$, means that, if the patient's average daily consumption of saturated fat increases by 1 gram, total cholesterol increases by 3.2443, on average, assuming that age remains unchanged.

Now Work Problem 19(d)

For the regression coefficients to be interpreted as described in Example 3, we have the requirement that the effect of x_1 on the value of the response variable does not depend on the value of x_2. Similarly, the effect of x_2 on the value of the response variable does not depend on the value of x_1. This means that the explanatory variables have an **additive effect** or **do not interact**. This is why it is important for the explanatory variables to have a low correlation. A positive correlation between two predictors, x_1 and x_2, implies that, if x_1 changes, then x_2 is likely to change as well. For example, if we are trying to describe the percentage of body fat in an individual, we probably do not want our explanatory variables to be both skinfold thickness on the tricep and skinfold thickness on the thigh. Because they are highly correlated, if skinfold thickness on the tricep increases, so does skinfold thickness on the thigh.

 Determine R^2 and Adjusted R^2

Recall from Section 4.3 that the coefficient of determination, R^2, measures the percentage of total variation in the response variable that is explained by the least-squares regression line. We also said that the computation of R^2 for the least-squares regression model with one explanatory variable was as easy as computing the square of the linear correlation coefficient, r, between the explanatory and response variable. That is, $R^2 = r^2$. While the interpretation of R^2 is the same for the least-squares regression model with two or more explanatory variables, its computation is by no means that straightforward. Once again, we will be content in using software to supply the value of R^2. Although we do not provide detail as to the computation of R^2, it is important to recognize that R^2 is the ratio of variation in the response variable that is explained by the regression equation to the total variation in the response variable. That is,

$$R^2 = \frac{\text{explained variation}}{\text{total variation}} = 1 - \frac{\text{unexplained variation}}{\text{total variation}}$$

In Other Words

The value of R^2 always increases by adding one more explanatory variable.

Remember, the unexplained variation is found by summing the squares of the residuals. The sum of the squared residuals will never increase if more explanatory variables are added. The total variation is constant regardless of the number of explanatory variables. Therefore, the coefficient of determination, R^2, will never decrease with the addition of more explanatory variables, instead, it generally increases. So, R^2 can often be made as large as we like simply by adding more explanatory variables. To compensate for the ability to artificially inflate R^2 by adding more explanatory variables, it is recommended that the *adjusted R^2* be used when working with least-squares regression models with two or more explanatory variables.

Definition

The **adjusted R^2**, denoted R^2_{adj} or $\overline{R}^2$, is the adjusted coefficient of determination. It modifies the value of R^2 based on the sample size, n, and the number of explanatory variables, k. The formula for the adjusted R^2 is

$$R^2_{adj} = 1 - \left(\frac{n-1}{n-k-1}\right)(1 - R^2)$$

The adjusted R^2 will decrease if an explanatory variable is added to the model that does little to explain the variation in the response variable. This is because the decrease in the unexplained variation is offset by the increase in the number of explanatory variables k.

EXAMPLE 4   **Coefficient of Determination**

Problem: For the model obtained in Example 2, determine the coefficient of determination and the adjusted R^2. Compare the R^2 with the two explanatory variables age and daily saturated fat to the R^2 with the single explanatory variable age. Comment on the effect the additional explanatory variable has on the value of the model.

Approach: We will use MINITAB output to determine the values of the coefficient of determination and the adjusted coefficient of determination.

⬥ **CAUTION**

Never use R^2 to compare regression models with a different number of explanatory variables. Rather, use the adjusted R^2.

Solution: Looking back to the output in Figure 14, we see that $R^2 = 0.847 = 84.7\%$. This means that 84.7% of the variation in the response variable is explained by the least-squares regression model. In addition, we find that $R^2_{adj} = 0.820 = 82.0\%$. If we look back to Figure 2 on page 737, we see that $R^2 = 51.5\%$ with age as the only explanatory variable. Based on the adjusted R^2 with the two explanatory variables age and daily saturated fat consumption, we conclude that the additional variable increases the proportion of explained variation.

Now Work Problem 19(e)

---

⑤   **Perform an F-Test for Lack of Fit**

We now wish to determine whether there is a significant linear relation between the explanatory variables and response variables. That is, we want to test

$$H_0: \beta_1 = \beta_2 = \cdots = \beta_k = 0 \quad \text{versus} \quad H_1: \text{at least one } \beta_i \neq 0$$

In Other Words
The null hypothesis states that there is no linear relation between the explanatory variables and the response variable. The alternative hypothesis states that there is a linear relation between at least one explanatory variable and the response variable.

Just as in one-way analysis of variance, the computations in multiple regression can be cumbersome. Therefore, we are content to let statistical software perform the computations.

We use ANOVA to test if there is a significant linear relation between the explanatory variables and response variables. Recall from Section 13.1 that $F_0 = \dfrac{\text{MST}}{\text{MSE}}$ follows Fisher's F-distribution, where MST is the mean square due to treatment and MSE is the mean square error. In the context of regression analysis, the treatment is the regression line itself, and the residuals make up the error, which leads to the F-test statistic.

Test Statistic for Multiple Regression

$$F_0 = \frac{\text{mean square due to regression}}{\text{mean square error}} = \frac{\text{MSR}}{\text{MSE}}$$

with $k - 1$ degrees of freedom in the numerator and $n - k$ degrees of freedom in the denominator, where k is the number of explanatory variables and n is the sample size.

Because the coefficient of determination, R^2, represents the proportion of explained variation in the response variable and $1 - R^2$ represents the proportion of unexplained variation, we can express the F-test statistic using the coefficient of determination.

F-Test Statistic for Multiple Regression Using R^2

$$F_0 = \frac{R^2}{1 - R^2} \cdot \frac{n - (k + 1)}{k}$$

where R^2 is the coefficient of determination

k is the number of explanatory variables

n is the sample size

A large F-test statistic provides evidence against the null hypothesis that all the slope coefficients are zero, because a large F-test statistic implies that the ratio of explained variation to unexplained variation is large. Care must be taken in using this as the sole judge in rejecting the null hypothesis, because a large number of explanatory variables (that is, a large value of k) will cause the ratio $\dfrac{n - (k + 1)}{k}$ to decrease and therefore cause the F-test statistic to decrease.

Rather than comparing the F-test statistic to a critical value, we continue to use the P-value approach to testing hypotheses. We will use the P-value reported in the output of the statistical software package.

Decision Rule for Testing $H_0: \beta_1 = \beta_2 = \cdots = \beta_k = 0$

If the P-value is less than the level of significance, α, reject the null hypothesis. Otherwise, do not reject the null hypothesis.

EXAMPLE 5   **Inference on the Regression Model**

Problem: Test $H_0: \beta_1 = \beta_2 = 0$ versus H_1: at least one $\beta_i \neq 0$ for the regression model found in Example 1.

Approach: To perform this inference, we need to determine whether it is reasonable to believe that the residuals are normally distributed with no outliers. To verify this requirement, we draw a normal probability plot. Once this requirement has been verified, we look at the P-value associated with the F-test statistic. If the P-value is less than the level of significance, α, we reject the null hypothesis.

Solution: Figure 16 shows the normal probability plot.

Figure 16

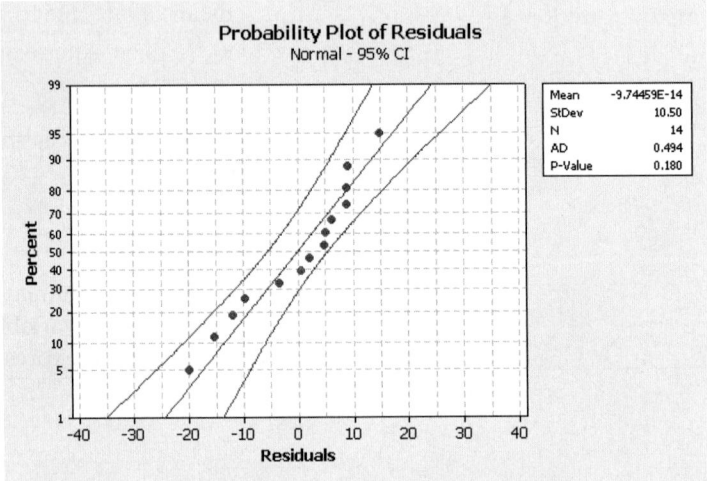

Because the points are roughly linear (or lie within the confidence bounds drawn by MINITAB), it is reasonable to conclude that the residuals are normally distributed. In addition, the boxplot of the residuals drawn in Figure 15(d) indicates that there are no outliers. Therefore, we can continue with the inference.

If we look back at the output in Figure 14, we see that the F-test statistic is 30.53 with a P-value reported as 0.000. This small P-value is sufficient evidence against the null hypothesis. So, we reject the null hypothesis and conclude that at least one of the regression coefficients is different from zero. There is a linear relation between at least one of the explanatory variables and the response variable.

Now Work Problem 19(f)

CAUTION If we reject the null hypothesis that all the slope coefficients are zero, then we are saying that at least one of the slopes is different from zero, *not* that they *all* are different from zero.

By rejecting the null hypothesis in Example 5, we know that *at least* one explanatory variable has a coefficient that is different from zero. Of course, this conclusion leads to this question: Which explanatory variables have a significant linear relation with the response variable?

6 Test Individual Regression Coefficients for Significance

We can use the t-distribution, along with P-values, to determine whether a specific explanatory variable has a significant linear relation with the response variable. Again, if the P-value is sufficiently small (say, less than $\alpha = 0.05$), we conclude that the explanatory variable has a significant linear relation with the response variable.

EXAMPLE 6   **Testing the Significance of Individual Predictor Variables**

Problem: For our model presented in Example 2, test the hypotheses

$$H_0: \beta_1 = 0 \qquad H_0: \beta_2 = 0$$
$$\text{vs.} \qquad \text{vs.}$$
$$H_1: \beta_1 \neq 0 \qquad H_1: \beta_2 \neq 0$$

where β_1 is the slope coefficient for the explanatory variable age, and β_2 is the slope coefficient for the explanatory variable saturated fat.

Approach: We will use MINITAB output to determine the P-values for each explanatory variable. If the P-value is less than the level of significance, we reject the null hypothesis and conclude that the slope coefficient is different from zero.

Solution: Looking again to the output in Figure 14, we see that the test statistic for the explanatory variable age is $t_0 = 4.18$ with a P-value $= 0.002$. We also see that the test statistic for the explanatory variable saturated fat is $t_0 = 4.89$ with a P-value $= 0.000$. Since both P-values are sufficiently small, we reject each null hypothesis. We conclude that both explanatory variables have a significant linear relation with the response variable, total cholesterol.

Now Work Problem 19(g)

If the P-value for a slope coefficient is large, we should consider removing the explanatory variable from the model. If the P-value is small, we should consider keeping the explanatory variable in the model.

7 Construct Confidence and Prediction Intervals

Now that we know that both explanatory variables age and saturated fat have a significant linear relation with the response variable total cholesterol, we can use the model to make predictions. Of course, because our model is based on sample data, we know that variability will be associated with any predictions. Therefore, we will construct intervals about our predicted value and describe the accuracy of our predictions.

Recall from Section 14.2 that there are two interpretations to a predicted value:

1. It represents a mean value of the response variable.
2. It represents a predicted value for a specific individual.

Because of this, we again require two types of intervals. One type, the confidence interval for a mean response, corresponds to an interval about the mean value; the other type, the prediction interval for an individual response, corresponds to an interval for a specific individual. Once again, we will leave the heavy work to MINITAB and let it construct the intervals. Our job will be to interpret the results.

EXAMPLE 7   **Confidence and Prediction Intervals**

Problem: Construct a 95% confidence interval for a mean response and a 95% prediction interval for an individual response for a 32-year-old female who consumes 23 grams of saturated fat daily using the model determined in Example 2. Be sure to interpret the results.

Approach: We will use MINITAB to construct the intervals. The steps for obtaining confidence and prediction intervals using MINITAB are given in the Technology Step-by-Step on page 780.

Solution: Figure 17 shows the partial output from MINITAB.

Figure 17 **Predicted Values for New Observations**

```
New Obs          Fit    SE Fit        95.0% CI           95.0% PI
1              197.91    3.85    (189.45, 206.38)   (171.40, 224.43)

Values of Predictors for New Observations

New Obs        age      fat
1              32.0     23.0
```

Based on the MINITAB output, we are 95% confident that the mean total cholesterol of all 32-year-old females who consume 23 grams of saturated fat daily is between 189.5 and 206.4. We are 95% confident that the total cholesterol of a particular 32-year-old female who consumes 23 grams of saturated fat daily is between 171.4 and 224.4.

Now Work Problems 19(h), (i), and (j)

Multicollinearity Revisited

Suppose that two explanatory variables that have a strong linear association with the response variable are highly correlated with each other. One consequece of this correlation can be that their t-test statistics are small and their P-values are large. The reason for this is that the t-test statistics are *marginal*. The word marginal means incremental. For example, if we had a regression model with three explanatory variables x_1, x_2, and x_3, the t-statistic for x_1 is a measure for how much additional explanation the variable x_1 adds to the model when x_2 and x_3 are already present. Likewise, the t-statistic for x_2 is a measure for how much additional explanation the variable x_2 adds to the model when x_1 and x_3 are already present.

So, a small t-test statistic for an explanatory variable means that a variable does not yield much additional explanation. Suppose that x_1 and x_2 are highly correlated to each other and to the response variable. If we include both explanatory variables in the model, the high correlation may lead to small t-test statistics for x_1 and x_2. This leads us to believe that neither variable is important.

In fact, the model may be "confused." This confusion results because the model believes that not much additional information is learned by adding x_1 to the model when x_2 is already in the model. In addition, x_2 does not provide much additional information when x_1 is already in the model. The model concludes that neither variable is important.

EXAMPLE 8 **Effects of Multicollinearity**

Problem: Using the data presented in Table 5:

(a) Find the correlation matrix among all three variables.

(b) Find the least-squares regression model using both x_1 and x_2 as explanatory variables.

(c) Comment on the effect that including both x_1 and x_2 has on the t-test statistics.

Approach: We will use MINITAB to conduct the analysis.

Solution

(a) Figure 18 shows the correlation matrix. An extremely high correlation exists between x_1 and x_2, so multicollinearity exists between the two variables.

(b) Figure 19 shows the regression output from MINITAB. First, we notice that the P-value for the F-test statistic is 0.018, indicating that at least one of the slope coefficients is different from zero. However, if we look at each individual t-test statistic, we see that each has a very high P-value, indicating that neither is different from zero.

Table 5

x_1	x_2	y
11.4	−9.7	14.7
12.5	−11.5	38.8
16.4	−15.9	42.9
14.4	−13.9	45.7
15.3	−14.2	52.3
18	−18.5	55.9
19.5	−21.2	60.1
25.2	−27.2	72.6

Figure 18

Correlations (Pearson)

```
          x1        x2
x2     -0.996
y       0.891   -0.894
```

Figure 19   **Regression Analysis**

```
The regression equation is
y = 3.2 - 0.02 x1 - 2.72 x2

Predictor          Coef       StDev          T          P
Constant           3.20       35.47       0.09      0.932
x1                -0.015       8.829      -0.00      0.999
x2                -2.721       6.844      -0.40      0.707

S = 9.070        R-Sq = 80.0%     R-Sq(adj) = 72.0%

Analysis of Variance

Source             DF          SS          MS          F          P
Regression          2     1645.85      822.93      10.00      0.018
Residual Error      5      411.32       82.26
Total               7     2057.17
```

(c) The contradictory results of the regression output occur because both x_1 and x_2 are related to the response variable y, as indicated by the correlation matrix. However, x_1 and x_2 are also related to each other. So, with x_1 in the model, x_2 adds little explanation. Likewise, with x_2 in the model, x_1 adds little explanation. The solution is to use only one explanatory variable. Which explanatory variable we choose is up us. We can choose either the explanatory variable with the lower P-value or the explanatory variable that has the higher correlation with the response.

Now Work Problem 21

8   Build a Regression Model

Now that we have all the skills needed to conduct inference on the multiple regression model, we can discuss an approach to determining the "best" model. We put the word best in quotes because there is really no best model. It is up to the researcher to decide which model is best. Of course, we will have to justify the results presented. Nonetheless, we should follow some guidelines when developing a model.

Guidelines in Developing a Multiple Regression Model

1. Construct a correlation matrix to help identify the explanatory variables that have a high correlation with the response variable. In addition, look at the correlation matrix for any indication that the explanatory variables are correlated with each other. Remember, just because two explanatory variables have high correlation, this does not mean that multicollinearity is a problem, but it is a tip-off to watch out for strange results from the regression model.

2. Determine the multiple regression model using all the explanatory variables that have been identified by the researcher.

3. If the null hypothesis that all the slope coefficients are zero has been rejected, we proceed to look at the individual slope coefficients. Identify those slope coefficients that have small t-test statistics (and therefore large P-values). These are candidates for explanatory variables that may be removed from the model. We should only remove one explanatory variable at a time from the model before recomputing the regression model.

4. Repeat Step 3 until all slope coefficients are significantly different from zero.

5. Be sure that the model is appropriate by drawing residual plots.

This procedure is known as **backward stepwise regression**.

| EXAMPLE 9 | **Building a Multiple Regression Model** |

Problem: An engineer wants to develop a model to describe the gas mileage of a sport utility vehicle. He collects the data presented in Table 6. The final drive ratio is the ratio of the gear set that is farthest from the engine. A higher ratio generally means better acceleration and pulling power. Find the best model to describe miles per gallon.

Table 6						
Sport Utility Vehicle (2008 model)	**Curb Weight (pounds)**	**Engine Size (liters)**	**Cylinders**	**Final Drive Ratio ($x : 1$)**	**Ground Clearance (inches)**	**Miles per Gallon**
Mercedes-Benz G500	5,510	5.0	8	4.38	8.3	13
Jeep Wrangler X	3,760	3.8	6	3.21	8.8	16
Mitsubishi Endeavor LS 2WD	3,902	3.8	6	4.01	8.3	18
Toyota Land Cruiser	5,690	5.7	8	3.91	8.9	15
Kia Sorento 4x2	4,068	3.3	6	3.33	8.2	18
Jeep Commander Sport 4x2	4,649	4.7	8	3.73	8.6	15
Dodge Durango SLT 4x2	4,709	4.7	8	3.55	8.7	15
Lincoln Navigator 4x2	5,555	5.4	8	3.73	9.2	15
Chevrolet Tahoe LS 2WD	5,265	4.8	8	3.23	9.1	16
Ford Escape FWD	3,387	3.0	6	2.93	8.5	20
Ford Expedition XLT	5,578	5.4	8	3.31	8.7	14
Buick Enclave CX FWD	4,780	3.6	6	3.16	8.4	19
Cadillac Escalade 2WD	5,459	6.2	8	3.42	9.0	14
Hummer H3 SUV	4,689	3.7	5	4.56	9.1	15
Saab 9-7X	4,720	4.2	6	3.73	7.7	16

Source: www.newcars.org

Approach: We use MINITAB to obtain output and Steps 1 through 5 to guide us in choosing the best model.

Solution

Step 1: Figure 20 shows the correlation matrix.

Figure 20 **Correlations: Weight, Engine, Cylinders, Drive Clearance , MPG**

```
             Weight   Engine  Cylinders   Drive   Clearance
Engine        0.870
Cylinders     0.720    0.851
Drive         0.311    0.184    -0.031
Clearance     0.378    0.450     0.369    0.024
MPG          -0.749   -0.796    -0.636   -0.516     -0.349
```

We notice that high correlations exist between curb weight and engine size (0.870), curb weight and cylinders (0.720), and cylinders and engine size (0.851). The inclusion of these variables in the model may lead to strange results because of multicollinearity.

Step 2: Figure 21 shows the regression model with all explanatory variables included.

Figure 21 **Regression Analysis: MPG versus Weight, Engine, ...**

```
The regression equation is
MPG = 30.4 + 0.000025 Weight - 1.27 Engine - 0.231 Cylinders
      - 1.77 Drive - 0.101 Clearance

Predictor              Coef    SE Coef        T      P
Constant             30.381      7.748     3.92  0.004
Weight            0.0000252  0.0008996     0.03  0.978
Engine              -1.2667     0.9065    -1.40  0.196
Cylinders           -0.2312     0.5607    -0.41  0.690
Drive               -1.7694     0.7759    -2.28  0.049
Clearance           -0.1013     0.8511    -0.12  0.908


S = 1.16167  R-Sq = 77.9%  R-Sq(adj) = 65.6%

Analysis of Variance

Source            DF        SS       MS      F      P
Regression         5    42.788    8.558   6.34  0.009
Residual Error     9    12.145    1.349
Total             14    54.933
```

Step 3: The P-value for the F-test statistic is very low at 0.009. This indicates that our model is reasonable. However, looking at the individual t-test statistics for slope coefficients, we see that some have P-values that are very large. We notice that the P-value for the slope coefficient of the explanatory variable "curb weight" is the largest (0.978). Further, we notice that this slope coefficient is positive, which indicates that SUVs with more weight will get better gas mileage. This contradicts common sense. We will remove the explanatory variable "curb weight" from the model. Note that "curb weight" and "cylinders" have a high correlation. This explains the strange results. Figure 22 shows the new regression model.

Figure 22 **Regression Analysis: MPG versus Engine, Cylinders, Drive, Clearance**

```
The regression equation is
MPG = 30.4 - 1.25 Engine - 0.231 Cylinders - 1.76 Drive - 0.101 Clearance

Predictor         Coef   SE Coef       T      P
Constant        30.404     7.311    4.16  0.002
Engine          -1.2509    0.6738   -1.86  0.093
Cylinders       -0.2306    0.5314   -0.43  0.674
Drive           -1.7628    0.7014   -2.51  0.031
Clearance       -0.1014    0.8075   -0.13  0.903


S = 1.10210  R-Sq = 77.9%  R-Sq(adj) = 69.0%

Analysis of Variance

Source            DF        SS       MS      F      P
Regression         4    42.787   10.697   8.81  0.003
Residual Error    10    12.146    1.215
Total             14    54.933
```

Step 4: The P-value for the F-test decreased to 0.003 which indicates that our model has improved. However, we still have some explanatory variables whose P-values are quite large. We will next remove the explanatory variable "ground clearance" from the model because it has the largest P-value. We notice also that the adjusted R^2 increased from 65.6% to 69.0% when we removed curb weight from the model. This illustrates that the adjusted R^2 punishes a model that is unnecessarily complex. Figure 23 shows the new regression model.

Figure 23 **Regression Analysis: MPG versus Engine, Cylinders, Drive**

```
The regression equation is
MPG = 29.6 − 1.28 Engine − 0.227 Cylinders − 1.76 Drive

Predictor           Coef   SE Coef       T      P
Constant          29.584     3.142    9.42  0.000
Engine           −1.2752    0.6158   −2.07  0.063
Cylinders        −0.2267    0.5063   −0.45  0.663
Drive            −1.7555    0.6670   −2.63  0.023


S = 1.05164   R-Sq = 77.9%   R-Sq(adj) = 71.8%

Analysis of Variance

Source             DF       SS      MS      F      P
Regression          3   42.768  14.256  12.89  0.001
Residual Error     11   12.165   1.106
Total              14   54.933
```

Step 4 (repeated): The P-value for the F-test continues to decline as we eliminate variables! However, we still have explanatory variables with large P-values. Next, we remove the explanatory variable "cylinders" because it has the largest P-value. Figure 24 shows the new regression model.

Figure 24 **Regression Analysis: MPG versus Engine, Drive**

```
The regression equation is
MPG = 28.7 − 1.52 Engine − 1.65 Drive

Predictor           Coef   SE Coef       T      P
Constant          28.683     2.332   12.30  0.000
Engine           −1.5157    0.2915   −5.20  0.000
Drive            −1.6469    0.6002   −2.74  0.018


S = 1.01601   R-Sq = 77.5%   R-Sq(adj) = 73.7%

Analysis of Variance

Source             DF       SS      MS      F      P
Regression          2   42.546  21.273  20.61  0.000
Residual Error     12   12.387   1.032
Total              14   54.933
```

Now the P-value for the F-test is very low at 0.000 (so, P-value < 0.0005), and the P-values for the slope coefficients are also low. In addition, the estimates of the slope coefficients are reasonable. We expect both to be negative because (1) a larger engine should get worse gas mileage and (2) a higher final drive ratio (which indicates better initial acceleration) is likely to get worse gas mileage. We believe that this is the "best" model.

Step 5: Figure 25 shows the residual plots as well as the normal probability plot of the residuals.

Figure 25

Figure 25
Continued

The residual plots do not indicate that there are any problems in the model, and the normal probability plot indicates that the residuals appear to be normally distributed and a boxplot of the residuals indicates there are no outliers, so we accept the model.

Now Work Problem 23

As a final note, it is worthwhile to observe how the *P*-value for the predicted slope of the explanatory variable "engine size" changed as we moved through the backward stepwise regression procedure. In our initial model (Figure 21), the *P*-value for engine size was fairly high at 0.196. When we eliminated the variable "curb weight" (Figure 22), the *P*-value dropped considerably to 0.093. When we later eliminated the variable "cylinders" (see Figure 24), the *P*-value became very small at 0.000. These dramatic changes occurred because engine size is highly correlated with both curb weight and cylinders (Figure 20). Put simply, the model was confused when these three highly correlated variables were included. That is, the model was confused by the multicollinearity.

IN CLASS ACTIVITY

College Success

What variables affect student success in college as determined by college GPA? It is widely accepted that no one single explanatory variable can be used to predict college success. However, several exlanatory variables taken together may yield better results.

(a) As a class, select five variables that might be related to college GPA and for which data can be easily obtained (such as ACT scores or high school GPA).

(b) Write your particular values for the selected variables on a piece of paper and submit the values to your instructor anonymously.

(c) Obtain the aggregate data for the class from your instructor.

(d) Using the data from Step 2, determine a model of best fit to predict college GPA.

(e) Discuss the selected model as a class. Were any of the selected variables removed from the model? Why might this be the case?

(f) How confident are you in the model's ability to predict college GPA? Why?

(g) Use the selected model to predict the college GPA for a student who is not in your class. How well did your model do? Is this surprising?

(h) Check the necessary requirements for your model. If any are not satisfied, how will that affect your previous answers?

14.3 ASSESS YOUR UNDERSTANDING

Concepts and Vocabulary

1. What is a correlation matrix?

2. How do we interpret the coefficients in the multiple regression equation?

3. When testing whether or not there is a linear relation between the response variable and the explanatory variables, we use an F-test. If the P-value indicates that we reject the null hypothesis, $H_0: \beta_1 = \beta_2 = \cdots = \beta_k = 0$, what conclusion should we come to? Is it possible that one of the β_i is zero if we reject the null hypothesis?

4. What does it mean when we say that the explanatory variables have an additive effect or do not interact?

5. Explain the difference between the coefficient of determination, R^2, and the adjusted coefficient of determination, R_{adj}^2. Which is better for determining whether an additional explanatory variable should be added to the regression model?   *Adjusted is better.*

6. What is multicollinearity? How can we check for it? What are the consequences of multicollinearity?

Skill Building

7. You obtain the multiple regression equation $\hat{y} = 5 + 3x_1 - 4x_2$ from a set of sample data.
   (a) Interpret the slope coefficients for x_1 and x_2.
   (b) Determine the regression equation with $x_1 = 10$. Graph the regression equation with $x_1 = 10$. $\hat{y} = 35 - 4x_2$
   (c) Determine the regression equation with $x_1 = 15$. Graph the regression equation with $x_1 = 15$. $\hat{y} = 50 - 4x_2$
   (d) Determine the regression equation with $x_1 = 20$. Graph the regression equation with $x_1 = 20$. $\hat{y} = 65 - 4x_2$
   (e) What is the effect of changing the value x_1 on the graph of the regression equation?   *Changes the y-intercept*

8. You obtain the multiple regression equation $\hat{y} = -5 - 9x_1 + 4x_2$ from a set of sample data.
   (a) Interpret the slope coefficients for x_1 and x_2.
   (b) Determine the regression equation with $x_1 = 10$. Graph the regression equation with $x_1 = 10$. $\hat{y} = -95 + 4x_2$
   (c) Determine the regression equation with $x_1 = 15$. Graph the regression equation with $x_1 = 15$. $\hat{y} = -140 + 4x_2$
   (d) Determine the regression equation with $x_1 = 20$. Graph the regression equation with $x_1 = 20$. $\hat{y} = -185 + 4x_2$
   (e) What is the effect of changing the value x_1 on the graph of the regression equation?   *Changes the y-intercept*

9. A multiple regression model has $k = 3$ explanatory variables. The coefficient of determination, R^2, is found to be 0.653 based on a sample of $n = 25$ observations.
   (a) Compute the adjusted R^2.   *0.603*
   (b) Compute the F-test statistic.   *13.173*
   (c) If one additional explanatory variable is added to the model and R^2 increases to 0.665, compute the adjusted R^2. Would you recommend adding the additional explanatory variable to the model? Why or why not?   *No*

10. A multiple regression model has $k = 4$ explanatory variables. The coefficient of determination, R^2, is found to be 0.542 based on a sample of $n = 40$ observations.
    (a) Compute the adjusted R^2.   *0.490*
    (b) Compute the F-test statistic.   *10.355*

(c) If one additional explanatory variable is added to the model and R^2 increases to 0.579, compute the adjusted R^2. Would you recommend adding the additional explanatory variable to the model? Why or why not?   *Yes*

11. For the data set

x_1	x_2	x_3	y
0.8	2.8	2.5	11.0
3.9	2.6	5.7	10.8
1.8	2.4	7.8	10.6
5.1	2.3	7.1	10.3
4.9	2.5	5.9	10.3
8.4	2.1	8.6	10.3
12.9	2.3	9.2	10.0
6.0	2.0	1.2	9.4
14.6	2.2	3.7	8.7
9.3	1.1	5.5	8.7

11. (b) $\hat{y} = 7.9647 - 0.1035x_1 + 0.9359x_2 + 0.1152x_3$

(a) Construct a correlation matrix between x_1, x_2, x_3, and y. Is there any evidence that multicollinearity exists? Why?   *No*
(b) Determine the multiple regression line with x_1, x_2, and x_3 as the explanatory variables.
(c) Assuming that the requirements of the model are satisfied, test $H_0: \beta_1 = \beta_2 = \beta_3 = 0$ versus H_1: at least one of the β_i is different from zero at the $\alpha = 0.05$ level of significance.   *Reject H_0*
(d) Assuming that the requirements of the model are satisfied, test $H_0: \beta_i = 0$ for $i = 1, 2, 3$ versus $H_1: \beta_i \neq 0$ for $i = 1, 2, 3$ at the $\alpha = 0.05$ level of significance.   *Conclusions: $\beta_1 \neq 0, \beta_2 \neq 0, \beta_3 \neq 0$*

12. For the data set

x_1	x_2	x_3	y
24.9	13.5	3.7	59.8
26.7	15.7	11.4	66.3
30.6	13.8	15.7	76.5
39.6	8.8	8.8	77.1
33.1	10.6	18.3	81.9
41.1	9.7	21.8	84.6
25.4	9.8	16.4	87.3
33.8	6.8	25.9	88.5
23.5	7.5	15.5	90.7
39.8	6.8	30.8	93.4

(a) Construct a correlation matrix between x_1, x_2, x_3, and y. Is there any evidence that multicollinearity exists? Why?   *No*
(b) Determine the multiple regression line with x_1, x_2, and x_3 as the explanatory variables.
(c) Assuming that the requirements of the model are satisfied, test $H_0: \beta_1 = \beta_2 = \beta_3 = 0$ versus H_1: at least one of the β_i is different from zero at the $\alpha = 0.05$ level of significance.   *Reject H_0*
(d) Assuming that the requirements of the model are satisfied, test $H_0: \beta_i = 0$ for $i = 1, 2, 3$ versus $H_1: \beta_i \neq 0$ for $i = 1, 2, 3$ at the $\alpha = 0.05$ level of significance. Should a variable be removed from the model? Why?

12. (b) $\hat{y} = 98.87 - 0.3013x_1 - 2.0456x_2 + 0.7370x_3$ *12. (d) Conclusions: $\beta_1 = 0, \beta_2 \neq 0, \beta_3 \neq 0$; remove x_1; P-value = 0.303*

12. (e) $\hat{y} = 89.995 - 1.9434x_2 + 0.6317x_3$; reject H_0: $\beta_2 = \beta_3 = 0$; conclusion: $\beta_2 \neq 0$, $\beta_1 \neq 0$

(e) Remove the variable identified in part (d) and recompute the regression model. Test whether at least one regression coefficient is different from zero. Then test whether each individual regression coefficient is significantly different from zero.

13. For the data set

x_1	x_2	x_3	x_4	y
43	19.6	7.1	32	200
44	13.1	58.5	37	204
40	24.7	2.1	32	215
35	30.4	41.4	39	229
38	28.2	7.7	30	231
39	24.9	25.0	26	243
39	45.7	28.5	25	266
40	38.4	27.7	24	278
47	36.9	26.2	17	287
35	66.3	4.2	23	298
36	112.8	26.2	21	339
44	108.4	22.3	24	359

(a) Construct a correlation matrix between x_1, x_2, x_3, x_4, and y. Is there any evidence that multicollinearity may be a problem?   No

(b) Determine the multiple regression line using all the explanatory variables listed. Does the F-test indicate that we should reject H_0: $\beta_1 = \beta_2 = \beta_3 = \beta_4 = 0$? Which explanatory variables have slope coefficients that are not significantly different from zero?

(c) Remove the explanatory variable with the highest P-value from the model and recompute the regression model. Does the F-test still indicate that the model is significant? Remove any additional explanatory variables on the basis of the P-value of the slope coefficient. Then compute the model with the variable removed.

(d) Draw residual plots and a boxplot of the residuals to assess the adequacy of the model.   13. (e) 246.7   (f) Yes

(e) Use the model constructed in part (c) to predict the value of y if $x_1 = 34$, $x_2 = 35.6$, $x_3 = 12.4$, and $x_4 = 29$.

(f) Draw a normal probability plot of the residuals. Is it reasonable to construct confidence and prediction intervals?

(g) Construct 95% confidence and prediction intervals if $x_1 = 34$, $x_2 = 35.6$, $x_3 = 12.4$, and $x_4 = 29$.

14. For the data set

x_1	x_2	x_3	x_4	y
47.3	0.9	4	76	105.5
53.1	0.8	6	55	113.8
56.7	0.8	4	65	115.2
48.8	0.5	7	67	118.9
42.7	1.1	7	74	148.9
44.3	1.1	6	76	120.2
44.5	0.7	8	68	121.6
37.7	0.7	7	79	140.0
36.9	1.0	5	73	141.5
28.1	1.8	6	68	141.9
32.0	0.8	8	81	152.8
34.7	0.8	10	68	156.5

(a) Construct a correlation matrix between x_1, x_2, x_3, x_4, and y. Is there any evidence that multicollinearity may be a problem?   No

(b) Determine the multiple regression line using all the explanatory variables listed. Does the F-test indicate that we should reject H_0: $\beta_1 = \beta_2 = \beta_3 = \beta_4 = 0$? Which explanatory variables have slope coefficients that are not significantly different from zero?

(c) Remove the explanatory variable with the highest P-value from the model and recompute the regression model. Does the F-test still indicate that the model is significant? Remove any additional explanatory variables on the basis of the P-value of the slope coefficient. Then compute the model with the variable removed.

(d) Draw residual plots and a boxplot of the residuals to assess the adequacy of the model.   14. (e) 128.04   (f) Yes

(e) Use the model constructed in part (c) to predict the value of y if $x_1 = 44.3$, $x_2 = 1.1$, $x_3 = 7$, and $x_4 = 69$.

(f) Draw a normal probability plot of the residuals. Is it reasonable to construct confidence and prediction intervals?

(g) Construct 95% confidence and prediction intervals if $x_1 = 44.3$, $x_2 = 1.1$, $x_3 = 7$, and $x_4 = 69$.
CI: (120.94, 135.15); PI: (103.13, 152.95)

Applying the Concepts

15. Resisting the Computer Researchers Alfred P. Rovai and Marcus D. Childress asked the following question: "How can resistance to reduction of computer anxiety among teacher education students be explained and predicted?" (*Journal of Research on Technology in Education*, 35(2). To answer this research question, they identified 86 undergraduate teacher education students enrolled in a computer literacy course and administered a series of questionnaires that quantified various predictors of the response variable, computer anxiety, y. For example, computer anxiety was measured by administering each student the Computer Anxiety Scale. This score ranges from 20 to 100, with higher scores indicating higher levels of computer anxiety. The explanatory variables were:

x_1: Computer confidence on a scale from 10 to 40, with higher scores indicating higher confidence

x_2: Computer knowledge on a scale from 0 to 33, with 0 indicating no computer knowledge and 33 indicating superior computer knowledge

x_3: Computer liking on a scale from 10 to 40, with higher scores indicating a greater like of computers

x_4: Trait anxiety on a scale from 20 to 80, with higher scores indicating a higher level of overall anxiety

The multiple regression model was

$$\hat{y} = 84.04 - 0.87x_1 - 0.51x_2 - 0.45x_3 + 0.33x_4$$

(a) The reported P-value of the regression model was less than 0.0001. Would you reject the null hypothesis H_0: $\beta_1 = \beta_2 = \beta_3 = \beta_4 = 0$?   Yes

(b) Interpret the slope coefficients of the model in part (a). Are they all reasonable?

(c) Predict the computer anxiety score of an individual whose computer confidence score was 25, computer knowledge score was 19, computer liking score was 20, and trait anxiety score was 43.   57.79

13. (g) CI: (237.45, 255.91); PI: (214.93, 278.43)

13. (b) $\hat{y} = 279.02 + 0.068x_1 + 1.146x_2 + 0.3897x_3 - 2.9378x_4$; yes; x_1 and x_3

13. (c) $\hat{y} = 282.33 + 1.1426x_2 + 0.3941x_3 - 2.9570x_4$; yes: $\hat{y} = 281.62 + 1.1584x_2 - 2.6267x_4$

14. (b) $\hat{y} = 146.4 - 1.1875x_1 + 1.71x_2 + 3.652x_3 + 0.1387x_4$; yes; all of them

14. (c) $\hat{y} = 154.67 - 1.2554x_1 + 3.431x_3 + 0.1052x_4$; yes; $\hat{y} = 200.00 - 1.6243x_1$

17. (a) $\hat{y} = -12.509 + 1.334x_1 - 0.414x_2$ 18. (a) $\hat{y} = -92.279 + 1.258x_1 + 1.099x_2$ 18. (b) Linear model may not be appropriate.

(d) The coefficient of determination for this model is 0.69. Interpret this value.

(e) The article states that "regression assumptions were tested and found to be tenable." Explain what this means.

16. Pistol Shooting Researchers at Victoria University wanted to determine the factors that affect precision in shooting air pistols "Inter- and Intra-Individual Analysis in Elite Sport: Pistol Shooting," *Journal of Applied Biomechanics*, 28–38, 2003. The explanatory variables were

x_1: Percent of the time the shooter's aim was on target (a measure of accuracy)

x_2: Percent of the time the shooter's aim was within a certain region (a measure of consistency or steadiness)

x_3: Distance (mm) the barrel of the pistol moves horizontally while aiming

x_4: Distance (mm) the barrel of the pistol moves vertically while aiming

(a) One response variable in the study was the score that the individual received on the shot, with a higher score indicating a better shooter. The regression model presented was $\hat{y} = 10.6 + 0.02x_1 - 0.03x_3$. The reported P-value of the regression model was 0.05. Would you reject the null hypothesis $H_0: \beta_1 = \beta_3 = 0$?   No

(b) Interpret the slope coefficients of the model in part (a).

(c) Predict the score of an individual whose aim was on target $x_1 = 20\%$ of the time with a distance the pistol barrel moves horizontally of $x_3 = 12$ mm using the model from part (a).   10.64

(d) A second response variable in the study was the vertical distance that the bullet hole was from the target. The regression model for this response variable was $\hat{y} = -24.6 - 0.13x_1 + 0.21x_2 + 0.13x_3 + 0.22x_4$. The reported P-value of the regression model was 0.04. Would you reject the null hypothesis $H_0: \beta_1 = \beta_2 = \beta_3 = \beta_4 = 0$?   Yes

(e) Interpret the slope coefficients of the model in part (d).

(f) Based on your answer to part (e), do you think that the model is useful in predicting vertical distance from the target? Why?

17. Wind Chill Temperature A researcher wanted to determine if there was a linear relation among wind chill temperature, air temperature, and wind speed. The following data show wind chill temperature, air temperature (in degrees Fahrenheit), and wind speed (in miles per hour) for various days.

Air Temp.	Wind Speed	Wind Chill
15	10	3
15	15	0
15	25	−4
0	5	−11
0	20	−22
−5	10	−22
−5	25	−31
−10	15	−32
−10	20	−35
−15	25	−44
−15	35	−48
−15	50	−52
5	40	−22
10	45	−16

(a) Find the least-squares regression equation $\hat{y} = b_0 + b_1x_1 + b_2x_2$, where x_1 is air temperature, x_2 is wind speed, and y is the response variable "wind chill."

(b) Draw residual plots to assess the adequacy of the model. What might you conclude based on the plot of residuals against wind speed?   Linear model is not appropriate

18. Heat Index A researcher wanted to determine whether there was a linear relation among heat index, air temperature, and dew point. The following data show the heat index, air temperature (in degrees Fahrenheit), and dew point for various days.

Air Temp.	Dew Point	Heat Index
90	64	93
90	68	95
94	66	99
94	70	102
96	70	105
96	76	111
99	68	107
99	72	111
100	74	114
100	80	123
93	72	103
93	78	109
97	80	118
92	82	114
95	66	100
95	82	118

(a) Find the least-squares regression equation $\hat{y} = b_0 + b_1x_1 + b_2x_2$, where x_1 is air temperature, x_2 is dew point, and y is the response variable "heat index."

(b) Draw residual plots to assess the adequacy of the model. What might you conclude based on the residual plots?

19. Concrete A researcher wants to determine a model that can be used to predict the 28-day strength of a concrete mixture. The following data represent the 28-day and 7-day strength (in pounds per square inch) of a certain type of concrete along with the concrete's slump. Slump is a measure of the uniformity of the concrete, with a higher slump indicating a less uniform mixture.

Slump (inches)	7-Day psi	28-Day psi
4.5	2,330	4,025
4.25	2,640	4,535
3	3,360	4,985
4	1,770	3,890
3.75	2,590	3,810
2.5	3,080	4,685
4	2,050	3,765
5	2,220	3,350
4.5	2,240	3,610
5	2,510	3,875
2.5	2,250	4,475

(a) Construct a correlation matrix between slump, 7-day psi, and 28-day psi. Is there any reason to be concerned with multicollinearity based on the correlation matrix?   No

19. (b) $\hat{y} = 3{,}890.5 - 295.9x_1 + 0.552x_2$ 19. (e) $R^2 = 76.0\%$; adjusted $R^2 = 70.1\%$ 20. (h) \$25.56 thousand   20. (i) \$25.56 thousand

(b) Find the least-squares regression equation $\hat{y} = b_0 + b_1x_1 + b_2x_2$, where x_1 is slump, x_2 is 7-day strength, and y is the response variable "28-day strength."

(c) Draw residual plots and a boxplot of the residuals to assess the adequacy of the model.

(d) Interpret the regression coefficients for the least-squares regression equation.

(e) Determine and the interpret R^2 and the adjusted R^2.

(f) Test $H_0: \beta_1 = \beta_2 = 0$ versus H_1: at least one of the $\beta_i \neq 0$ at the $\alpha = 0.05$ level of significance.   Reject H_0

(g) Test the hypotheses $H_0: \beta_1 = 0$ versus $H_1: \beta_1 \neq 0$ and $H_0: \beta_2 = 0$ versus $H_1: \beta_2 \neq 0$ at the $\alpha = 0.05$ level of significance.   Conclusions: $\beta_1 \neq 0$; $\beta_2 \neq 0$

(h) Predict the mean 28-day strength of all concrete for which slump is 3.5 inches and 7-day strength is 2,450 psi.

(i) Predict the 28-day strength of a specific sample of concrete for which slump is 3.5 inches and 7-day strength is 2,450 psi.   4,207.3 psi   19. (h) 4,207.3 psi

(j) Construct 95% confidence and prediction intervals for concrete for which slump is 3.5 inches and 7-day strength is 2,450 psi. Interpret the results.
19. (j) CI: (3,988.6, 4,427.2); PI: (3,533.6, 4,882.2)

20. Income An economist was interested in modeling the relation among annual income, level of education, and work experience. The level of education is the number of years of education beyond eigth grade, so 1 represents completing 1 year of high school, 8 means completing 4 years of college, and so on. Work experience is the number of years employed in the current profession. From a random sample of 12 individuals, he obtained the following data:

Work Experience (years)	Level of Education	Annual Income ($ thousands)
21	6	34.7
14	3	17.9
4	8	22.7
16	8	63.1
12	4	33.0
20	4	41.4
25	1	20.7
8	3	14.6
24	12	97.3
28	9	72.1
4	11	49.1
15	4	52.0

20. (b) $\hat{y} = -15.25 + 1.5449x_1 + 5.568x_2$

(a) Construct a correlation matrix between work experience, level of education, and annual income. Is there any reason to be concerned with multicollinearity based on the correlation matrix?   No

(b) Find the least-squares regression equation $\hat{y} = b_0 + b_1x_1 + b_2x_2$, where x_1 is work experience, x_2 is level of education, and y is the response variable "annual income."

(c) Draw residual plots and a boxplot of the residuals to assess the adequacy of the model.

(d) Interpret the regression coefficients for the least-squares regression equation.

(e) Determine and interpret R^2 and the adjusted R^2.

(f) Test $H_0: \beta_1 = \beta_2 = 0$ versus H_1: at least one of the $\beta_i \neq 0$ at the $\alpha = 0.05$ level of significance.   Reject H_0
20. (e) $R^2 = 81.6\%$; adjusted $R^2 = 77.5\%$

(g) Test the hypotheses $H_0: \beta_1 = 0$ versus $H_1: \beta_1 \neq 0$ and $H_0: \beta_2 = 0$ versus $H_1: \beta_2 \neq 0$ at the $\alpha = 0.05$ level of significance.   Conclusions: $\beta_1 \neq 0$; $\beta_2 \neq 0$

(h) Predict the mean income of all individuals whose experience is 12 years and level of education is 4.

(i) Predict the income of a single individual whose experience is 12 years and level of education is 4.

(j) Construct 95% confidence and prediction intervals for income when experience is 12 years and level of education is 4.   CI: (15.55, 35.58); PI: (-2.99, 54.12)

21. Housing Prices A realtor wanted to find a model that relates the asking price of a house to the square footage, number of bedrooms, and number of baths. The following data are from houses in Greenville, South Carolina.

Square Footage	Bedrooms	Baths	Asking Price ($ thousands)
3,800	4	3.5	498
2,600	4	3	449
2,600	5	3.5	435
2,250	4	4	400
3,300	4	3	379
2,750	3	2.5	375
2,200	3	2.5	356
3,000	4	2.5	350
2,300	3	2	340
2,600	4	2.5	332
2,300	4	2	298
2,000	4	3	280
2,200	3	2.5	260

Source: remax.com

(a) Construct the correlation matrix. Is there any reason to be concerned with multicollinearity?   No

(b) Find the least-squares regression equation $\hat{y} = b_0 + b_1x_1 + b_2x_2 + b_3x_3$, where x_1 is square footage, x_2 is number of bedrooms, x_3 is number of baths, and y is the response variable "asking price."

(c) Test $H_0: \beta_1 = \beta_2 = \beta_3 = 0$ versus H_1: at least one of the $\beta_i \neq 0$ at the $\alpha = 0.05$ level of significance.   Reject H_0

(d) Test the hypotheses $H_0: \beta_1 = 0$ versus $H_1: \beta_1 \neq 0$, $H_0: \beta_2 = 0$ versus $H_1: \beta_2 \neq 0$, and $H_0: \beta_3 = 0$ versus $H_1: \beta_3 \neq 0$ at the $\alpha = 0.05$ level of significance.
Conclusions: $\beta_1 \neq 0$; $\beta_2 = 0$; $\beta_3 = 0$

(e) Remove the explanatory variable with the highest P-value and compute the least-squares regression equation. Are all the slope coefficients significantly different from zero? If not, remove the explanatory variable with the higher P-value and compute the least-squares regression equation. $\hat{y} = 24.09 + 0.0718x_1 + 54.9x_3$; yes

(f) Draw residual plots, a boxplot of the residuals, and a normal probability plot of the residuals to assess the adequacy of the model found in part (e).

(g) Interpret the regression coefficients for the least-squares regression equation found in part (e).

(h) Construct 95% confidence and prediction intervals for the asking price of a 2,900-square-foot house in Greenville, South Carolina, with 4 bedrooms and 3 baths. Interpret the results.   CI: (365.1, 429.1); PI: (294.2, 499.9)

22. Head Circumference A pediatrician wants to determine the relation that may exist between a child's head circumference (in centimeters), height (in inches), and weight (in ounces).

21. (b) $\hat{y} = 25.63 + 0.0719x_1 - 0.81x_2 + 55.3x_3$

22. (b) $\hat{y} = 18.824 + 0.7863x_1 + 0.0128x_2$ 22. (h) $R^2 = 75.8\%$; adjusted $R^2 = 73.8\%$ 23. (b) $\hat{y} = 35.827 + 4.803x_1 - 0.00394x_2 - 0.06583x_3$

She randomly selects 14 three-year-old children from her practice and obtains the following data:

Height	Weight	Head Circumference
30	339	47
26.25	267	42
25	289	43
27	332	44.5
27.5	272	44
24.5	214	40.5
27.75	311	44
25	259	41.5
28	298	46
27.25	288	44
26	277	44
27.25	292	44.5
27	302	42.5
28.25	336	44.5

Source: Denise Slucki, student at Joliet Junior College

(a) Construct a correlation matrix. Is there any reason to be concerned with multicollinearity?   Yes

(b) Find the least-squares regression equation $\hat{y} = b_0 + b_1x_1 + b_2x_2$, where x_1 is height, x_2 is weight, and y is the response variable "head circumference."

(c) Test $H_0: \beta_1 = \beta_2 = 0$ versus H_1: at least one of the $\beta_i \neq 0$ at the $\alpha = 0.05$ level of significance.   Reject H_0

(d) Test the hypotheses $H_0: \beta_1 = 0$ versus $H_1: \beta_1 \neq 0$ and $H_0: \beta_2 = 0$ versus $H_1: \beta_2 \neq 0$ at the $\alpha = 0.05$ level of significance.   Conclusions: $\beta_1 \neq 0$; $\beta_2 = 0$

(e) Compute the regression line after removing any explanatory variable that is not significant from the regression model.   Removing $x_2 =$ weight, $\hat{y} = 16.382 + 1.0157x_1$

(f) Draw residual plots, a boxplot of the residuals, and a normal probability plot of the residuals to assess the adequacy of the model found in part (e).

(g) Interpret the regression coefficients for the least-squares regression equation found in part (e).

(h) Determine and interpret R^2 and the adjusted R^2.

(i) Construct 95% confidence and prediction intervals for the head circumference of a child whose height is 27.5 inches and whose weight is 285 ounces. Interpret the results.
   CI: (43.759, 44.867); PI: (42.320, 46.306)

23. Gas Mileage NW A researcher is interested in developing a model that describes the gas mileage as measured in miles per gallon (mpg) of automobiles. Based on input from an engineer, she decides that the explanatory variables might be engine size (liters), curb weight (pounds), and horsepower. From a random sample of 13 automobiles, she obtains the following data:

Engine Size	Curb Weight	Horsepower	Miles per Gallon
2.4	3,289	177	24
2.4	3,263	158	25
2.5	3,230	170	24
3.5	3,580	272	22
2.8	3,175	255	18
3.5	3,643	263	22
3.5	3,497	306	20
3.0	3,340	230	21
3.6	3,861	263	19
2.4	3,287	173	24
3.3	3,629	234	21
2.5	3,270	170	22
3.5	3,292	270	22

Source: www.newcars.org

(a) Construct a correlation matrix. Is there any reason to be concerned about multicollinearity?   Yes

(b) Find the least-squares regression equation $\hat{y} = b_0 + b_1x_1 + b_2x_2 + b_3x_3$, where x_1 is engine size, x_2 is curb weight, x_3 is horsepower, and y is the response variable "miles per gallon."

(c) Test $H_0: \beta_1 = \beta_2 = \beta_3 = 0$ versus H_1: at least one of the $\beta_i \neq 0$ at the $\alpha = 0.05$ level of significance.   Reject H_0

(d) Test the hypotheses $H_0: \beta_i = 0$ versus $H_1: \beta_i \neq 0$ for $i = 1, 2, 3$ at the $\alpha = 0.05$ level of significance. Should any of the explanatory variables be removed from the model? If so, which one?   Yes; curb weight

(e) Determine the regression model with the explanatory variable identified in part (d) removed. Are both slope coefficients significantly different from zero? If not, remove the appropriate explanatory variable and compute the least-squares regression equation.

(f) Draw residual plots, a boxplot of the residuals, and a normal probability plot of the residuals to assess the adequacy of the model found in part (e).

(g) Interpret the regression coefficients for the least-squares regression equation found in part (e).

(h) Construct 95% confidence and prediction intervals for the gas mileage of an automobile that weights 3,100 pounds and has a 2.5-liter engine and 200 horsepower. Interpret the results.

23. (d) Conclusions: $\beta_1 = 0$, $\beta_2 = 0$, $\beta_3 \neq 0$; yes; curb weight

Problems 24 and 25 use the following definition:

A **dummy variable** or **indicator variable** is a method for including the influence of a qualitative variable in multiple regression analysis. A qualitative variable with k categories is represented by $0, 1, 2, \ldots, k - 1$, corresponding to the k classes of the variable. For example, the variable gender has two classes: male and female; so we might assign $x = 0$ for males and $x = 1$ for females.

24. Using Dummy Variables Researchers wondered whether the size of a person's brain was related to the individual's mental capacity. They selected a sample of right-handed Anglo introductory psychology students who had Scholastic Aptitude Test scores higher than 1,350. The subjects were administered the Wechsler (1981) Adult Intelligence Scale–Revised to obtain their IQ scores. The MRI scans, performed at the same facility, consisted of 18 horizontal MR images. The computer counted all pixels with nonzero gray scale in each of the 18 images, and the total count served as an index for brain size. The resulting data are presented in the following table:

Gender	MRI Count	IQ	Gender	MRI Count	IQ
Female	816,932	133	Male	949,395	140
Female	951,545	137	Male	1,001,121	140
Female	991,305	138	Male	1,038,437	139
Female	833,868	132	Male	965,353	133
Female	856,472	140	Male	955,466	133
Female	852,244	132	Male	1,079,549	141
Female	790,619	135	Male	924,059	135
Female	866,662	130	Male	955,003	139
Female	857,782	133	Male	935,494	141
Female	948,066	133	Male	949,589	144

Source: L. Willerman, R. Schultz, I. N. Rutledge, and E. Bigler. "In Vivo Brain Size and Intelligence." *Intelligence*, 15(223–228), 1991.

23. (e) $\hat{y} = 26.805 + 2.147x_1 - 0.05032x_3$; no; $\hat{y} = 28.723 - 0.0304x_3$
23. (h) CI: (21.622, 23.665); PI: (19.251, 26.036)

24. (a) $\hat{y} = 109.894 + 0.0000286x_1$ 24. (d) $\hat{y} = 121.58 + 0.0000174x_1 - 2.486x_2$ 24. (e) Conclusions: $\beta_1 = 0$; $\beta_2 = 0$

(a) Find the least-squares regression equation $\hat{y} = b_0 + b_1x_1$, where x_1 is MRI count and y is the response variable "IQ."

(b) Test the hypotheses $H_0: \beta_1 = 0$ versus $H_1: \beta_1 \neq 0$. What do you conclude? Reject H_0

(c) Draw a scatter diagram, treating MRI count as the explanatory variable and IQ as the response variable, but use a different plotting symbol for males and females. For example, use a circle for males and a triangle for females.

(d) Find the least-squares regression equation $\hat{y} = b_0 + b_1x_1 + b_2x_2$, where x_1 is MRI count and $x_2 = 0$ for males and $x_2 = 1$ for females.

(e) Test the hypotheses $H_0: \beta_1 = 0$ versus $H_1: \beta_1 \neq 0$ and $H_0: \beta_2 = 0$ versus $H_1: \beta_2 \neq 0$.

(f) What do you conclude from this analysis?

25. **Dummy Variables** The following data represent the time (minutes) it takes to drill an additional 5 feet from the depth indicated for both wet drilling and dry drilling conditions.

Depth	Conditions	Time
5	Wet	8.68
5	Wet	8.61
5	Dry	7.07
10	Wet	7.71
15	Dry	7.43
20	Wet	8.26
20	Dry	6.65
30	Wet	8.27
30	Dry	7.95
40	Wet	9.04
40	Dry	7.80
60	Wet	9.34
60	Dry	7.58
80	Wet	8.96
80	Dry	8.13
105	Wet	8.60
120	Dry	7.47
130	Wet	9.18
130	Dry	8.37
150	Wet	9.54
160	Dry	8.20

Source: American Statistician, 45(1)

(a) Draw a scatter diagram, treating depth as the explanatory variable and time as the response variable, but use a different plotting symbol for wet and dry. For example, use a circle for wet and a triangle for dry.

(b) Find the least-squares regression equation $\hat{y} = b_0 + b_1x_1 + b_2x_2$, where x_1 is depth and $x_2 = 0$ for wet and $x_2 = 1$ for dry. $\hat{y} = 8.351 + 0.006816x_1 - 1.1359x_2$

(c) Test the hypotheses $H_0: \beta_1 = 0$ versus $H_1: \beta_1 \neq 0$ and $H_0: \beta_2 = 0$ versus $H_1: \beta_2 \neq 0$.

(d) Construct 95% confidence and prediction intervals for time to drill an additional 5 feet in dry conditions where drilling starts at 100 feet. Interpret the results.

26. **Putting It Together: Purchasing Diamonds** The value of a diamond is determined by the 4 C's: carat weight, color, clarity, and cut. *Carat weight* is the standard measure for the size of a diamond. Generally, the more a diamond weighs, the more valuable it will be. The Gemological Institute of America (GIA) determines the *color* of diamonds using a 22-grade scale from D (almost clear white) to Z (light yellow). Colorless diamonds are generally considered the most desirable. Diamonds also

exist in other colors such as blue, red and green, but these "fancy colors" will not be considered here.

The clarity of a diamond refers to how "free" the diamond is of imperfections. The GIA determines the *clarity* of diamonds using an 11-grade scale: flawless (FL), internally Flawless (IF), very very slightly imperfect (VVS1, VVS2), very slightly imperfect (VS1, VS2), slightly imperfect (SI1, SI2), and imperfect (I1, I2, I3). The *cut* of a diamond refers to the diamond's proportions and finish. Put simply, the better the diamond's cut is, the better it reflects and refracts light, which makes it more beautiful and thus more valuable. The cut of a diamond is rated using a 5-grade scale: Excellent, Very Good, Good, Fair, and Poor. Finally, the *shape* of a diamond (which is not one of the 4 C's) refers to its basic form—round, oval, pear-shaped, marquis, etc. A novice might confuse shape with cut, so be careful not to confuse the two.

Carat	Color	Clarity	Cut	Price ($)
0.25	D	IF	Excellent	1,060
0.25	E	VVS1	Good	607
0.27	D	VVS1	Excellent	1,105
0.31	E	FL	Good	915
0.48	F	VS2	Very good	1,109
0.39	E	VVS2	Good	1,162
0.39	D	VS1	Excellent	3,043
0.42	E	IF	Excellent	2,790
0.50	D	VVS1	Very good	3,112
0.50	D	IF	Very good	3,557
0.51	E	VVS1	Excellent	2,694
0.55	D	VVS2	Good	2,542
0.56	H	VVS1	Good	2,178
0.61	H	VVS2	Excellent	1,977
0.63	D	FL	Excellent	5,459
0.66	D	IF	Very good	4,816
0.69	D	VS2	Very good	6,625
0.70	E	VVS1	Very good	4,726
0.77	J	SI1	Very good	1,903
0.77	D	VVS1	Excellent	6,121
0.80	D	IF	Excellent	6,680
0.82	E	SI2	Excellent	5,651
0.90	D	IF	Good	9,792
0.91	G	SI2	Excellent	3,266
0.92	J	SI2	Very good	2,512
0.92	D	IF	Excellent	11,095
0.93	H	VVS1	Very good	6,038
0.95	D	VS2	Very good	5,719
1.05	F	SI1	Very good	5,716
1.05	F	VS1	Good	8,203
1.06	E	SI1	Very good	5,877
1.08	G	VS1	Excellent	8,391
1.20	I	IF	Good	8,998
1.21	H	IF	Very good	9,903
1.33	I	SI2	Excellent	5,746
1.52	J	VVS2	Very good	10,098
1.51	I	VVS1	Excellent	13,295
1.24	D	VS2	Excellent	11,013
1.34	F	VS2	Excellent	11,052
1.38	G	VS2	Very good	11,017

Source: diamonds.com

26. (c) $\hat{y} = 266.5 + 11{,}319.2x_1 - 599.47x_2 - 481.26x_3 - 145.6x_4$ 26. (e) Remove cut; $\hat{y} = -36 + 11{,}382x_1 - 613x_2 - 473x_3$

The data on the preceding page provide the 4 C's and the retail price for a random sample of 40 unmounted, round-shaped diamonds. Use the data to answer the questions that follow:

(a) Determine the level of measurement for each variable.
- (i) Carat weight   Ratio
- (ii) Color   Ordinal
- (iii) Clarity   Ordinal
- (iv) Cut   Ordinal
- (v) Price   Ratio
- (vi) Shape   Nominal

(b) Construct a correlation matrix. To do so, first convert the variables color, clarity, and cut to numeric values as follows:

Color: D = 1, E = 2, F = 3, G = 4, H = 5, I = 6, J = 7

Clarity: FL = 1, IF = 2, VVS1 = 3, VVS2 = 4,

VS1 = 5, VS2 = 6, SI1 = 7, SI2 = 8

Cut: Excellent = 1, Very Good = 2, Good = 3

If price is to be the response variable in our model, is there reason to be concerned about multicollinearity? Explain.   No

(c) Find the least-square regression equation $\hat{y} = b_0 + b_1x_1 + b_2x_2 + b_3x_3 + b_4x_4$, where $x_1 =$ carat weight, $x_2 =$ color grade, $x_3 =$ clarity grade, $x_4 =$ cut grade, and y is the price.

(d) Test $H_0: \beta_1 = \beta_2 = \beta_3 = \beta_4$ versus H_1: at least one β_i is different at the $\alpha = 0.05$ level of significance.   Reject H_0

(e) Determine whether any variables should be removed from the model. If necessary, use backward elimination to develop the "best" model.

(f) Draw residual plots, a boxplot of the residuals, and a normal probability plot of the residuals to assess the adequacy of the "best" model.

(g) For the "best" model, interpret each regression coefficient.   26. (h) $R^2 = 92.2\%$; adjusted $R^2 = 91.6\%$

(h) Determine and interpret R^2 and the adjusted R^2.

(i) Predict the mean price of a round-shaped diamond with the following characteristics: 0.85 carats, E, VVS1, Excellent. $6,992

(j) Construct a 95% confidence interval for the mean price found in part (i).   (6,568, 7,415)

(k) Predict the price of an individual round-shaped diamond with the following characteristics: 0.85 carats, E, VVS1 Excellent. $6,992

(l) Construct a 95% prediction interval for the price found in part (k).   (4,870, 9,113)

(m) Explain why the predictions in parts (i) and (k) are the same, yet the intervals in parts (j) and (l) are different.

TECHNOLOGY STEP-BY-STEP

TI-83/84 Plus

The TI-83/84 Plus graphing calculators do not compute multiple regression equations.

MINITAB

Correlation Matrix

1. Enter the explanatory variables and response variable into the spreadsheet.
2. Select the **Stat** menu and highlight **Basic Statistics**. Now select **Correlation** . . . .
3. Highlight all the variables in the list of variables and click Select. Click OK.

Determining the Multiple Regression Equation and Residual Plots

1. Select the **Stat** menu and highlight **Regression**. Highlight and select **Regression** . . . .
2. Select the explanatory variables (MINITAB calls them predictors) and response variable.
3. Click **Graphs** . . . . In the cell that says "Residuals versus the variables" enter the names of the explanatory variables. Select the box that says "Residuals versus fits". Click OK.
4. Click **Storage** . . . . Select the box that says "Residuals". Select OK twice. The residuals are stored in the spreadsheet. Draw a normal probability plot of the residuals as indicated in Section 7.4 and a boxplot of the residuals as indicated in Section 3.5.

Prediction and Confidence Intervals

See the steps given on page 758 in Section 14.2.

Excel

Correlation Matrix

1. Enter the values for the explanatory variables and response variable into the spreadsheet.
2. Be sure the Data Analysis ToolPak is activated. This is done by selecting the **Tools** menu and highlighting **Add-Ins** . . . . Check the box for the Analysis ToolPak and select OK. Select **Tools**; then highlight and select **Data Analysis**. Select Correlation and click OK.
3. With the cursor in the "Input Range:" cell, highlight the data. Click OK.

Determining the Multiple Regression Equation and Residual Plots

1. Select **Tools**; then highlight and select **Data Analysis**. Select Regression and click OK.
2. With the cursor in the "Input Y Range:" cell, highlight the data for the response variable. With the cursor in the "Input X Range:" cell, highlight the data for the explanatory variables. Check the boxes for Residuals, Residual Plots, and Normal Probability Plots. Click OK. The residuals are stored in the spreadsheet. Draw a boxplot of the residuals as indicated in Section 3.5.

Note: We can also use the DDXL add-in to compute the multiple regression equation and to construct some of the related graphs.

Prediction and Confidence Intervals

Excel does not compute prediction and confidence intervals for predictions from multiple regression equations.

CHAPTER 14 REVIEW

Summary

The first two sections of this chapter dealt with inferential techniques that can be used on the least-squares regression model $y_i = \beta_0 + \beta_1 x_i + \varepsilon_i$.

In Section 14.1, we used sample data to obtain estimates of an intercept and slope. The residuals are required to be normally distributed, with mean 0 and constant variance σ^2. The residuals for each observation should be independent. We verified these requirements through residual plots and a normal probability plot of the residuals. Provided that these requirements are satisfied, we can test hypotheses regarding the slope to determine whether or not the relation between the explanatory and response variables is linear.

In Section 14.2, we learned how to construct confidence and prediction intervals for a predicted value. We construct confidence intervals for a mean response and prediction intervals for an individual response.

In Section 14.3, we learned how to build a multiple linear regression model $y_i = \beta_0 + \beta_1 x_{1i} + \beta_2 x_{2i} + \cdots + \beta_k x_{ki} + \varepsilon_i$. We used a correlation matrix to identify the explanatory variables that are linearly related to the response variable, y. We used technology to obtain estimates for the coefficients of each explanatory variable and the intercept.

The multiple linear regression model has the same requirements as the least-squares regression model with one explanatory variable. We used an F-test to test whether at least one coefficient is different from zero. If the null hypothesis that all coefficients are zero is rejected, we then use t-tests on each coefficient to determine which is different from zero.

When building a model, we remove explanatory variables one at a time. The explanatory variable with the highest P-value is removed, and the regression equation is obtained again. This process repeats until all coefficients in the model are significantly different from zero.

Watch out for multicollinearity among explanatory variables. It can easily distort results by giving us coefficients that are opposite in sign to what we would expect or have all coefficients appear to equal zero, even though the F-test leads us to reject the null hypothesis that all coefficients are zero.

Vocabulary

Least-squares regression model (p. 739)
Standard error of the estimate (p. 740)
Robust (p. 744)
Bivariate normal distribution (p. 748)
Jointly normally distributed (p. 748)

Confidence interval for a mean response (p. 753)
Prediction interval for an individual response (p. 753)
Multiple regression model (p. 759)
Correlation matrix (p. 759)

Multicollinearity (p. 759)
Additive effect (p. 763)
Adjusted R^2 (p. 764)
Backwards stepwise regression (p. 769)
Dummy variable (p. 778)
Indicator variable (p. 778)

Formulas

Standard Error of the Estimate

$$s_e = \sqrt{\frac{\sum(y_i - \hat{y}_i)^2}{n-2}} = \sqrt{\frac{\sum \text{residuals}^2}{n-2}}$$

Standard Error of b_1

$$s_{b_1} = \frac{s_e}{\sqrt{\sum(x_i - \bar{x})^2}}$$

Confidence Intervals for the Slope of the Regression Line

A $(1-\alpha)\cdot 100\%$ confidence interval for the slope of the true regression line, β_1, is given by the following formulas:

Lower bound: $\quad b_1 - t_{\alpha/2}\cdot \dfrac{s_e}{\sqrt{\sum(x_i - \bar{x})^2}} = b_1 - t_{\alpha/2}\cdot s_{b_1}$

Upper bound: $\quad b_1 + t_{\alpha/2}\cdot \dfrac{s_e}{\sqrt{\sum(x_i - \bar{x})^2}} = b_1 + t_{\alpha/2}\cdot s_{b_1}$

Here, $t_{\alpha/2}$ is computed with $n-2$ degrees of freedom.

Confidence Interval about the Mean Response of $\hat{y}$

A $(1-\alpha)\cdot 100\%$ confidence interval about the mean response of y, $\hat{y}$, is given by the following formulas:

Lower bound: $\quad \hat{y} - t_{\alpha/2}\cdot s_e\sqrt{\dfrac{1}{n} + \dfrac{(x^* - \bar{x})^2}{\sum(x_i - \bar{x})^2}}$

Upper bound: $\quad \hat{y} + t_{\alpha/2}\cdot s_e\sqrt{\dfrac{1}{n} + \dfrac{(x^* - \bar{x})^2}{\sum(x_i - \bar{x})^2}}$

Here, x^* is the given value of the explanatory variable, and $t_{\alpha/2}$ is the critical value with $n-2$ degrees of freedom.

Prediction Interval about an Individual Response, $\hat{y}$

A $(1-\alpha)\cdot 100\%$ prediction interval for the individual response of y, $\hat{y}$, is given by

Lower bound: $\quad \hat{y} - t_{\alpha/2}\cdot s_e\sqrt{1 + \dfrac{1}{n} + \dfrac{(x^* - \bar{x})^2}{\sum(x_i - \bar{x})^2}}$

Upper bound: $\quad \hat{y} + t_{\alpha/2}\cdot s_e\sqrt{1 + \dfrac{1}{n} + \dfrac{(x^* - \bar{x})^2}{\sum(x_i - \bar{x})^2}}$

where x^* is the given value of the explanatory variable and $t_{\alpha/2}$ is the critical value with $n-2$ degrees of freedom.

Objectives

Section	You should be able to . . .	Examples	Review Exercises
14.1	**1** State the requirements of the least-squares regression model (p. 738)	pp. 738–740	1
	2 Compute the standard error of the estimate (p. 740)	2 and 3	2(b), 3(b)
	3 Verify that the residuals are normally distributed (p. 741)	4	2(c), 3(c)
	4 Conduct inference on the slope (p. 742)	5 and 6	2(e), 3(e), 4(b)
	5 Construct a confidence interval about the slope of the least-squares regression model (p. 746)	7	2(f), 3(f)
14.2	**1** Construct confidence intervals for a mean response (p. 754)	1 and 3	2(g), 3(g)
	2 Construct prediction intervals for an individual response (p. 755)	2 and 3	2(i), 3(i)
14.3	**1** Obtain the correlation matrix (p. 759)	1	5(a), 6(a)
	2 Use technology to find a multiple regression equation (p. 761)	2	5(b), 6(b)
	3 Interpret the coefficients of a multiple regression equation (p. 762)	3	5(d), 6(g)
	4 Determine R^2 and adjusted R^2 (p. 763)	4	5(e), 6(h)
	5 Perform an F-test for lack of fit (p. 764)	5	5(f), 6(c)
	6 Test individual regression coefficients for significance (p. 766)	6	5(g), 6(d)
	7 Construct confidence and prediction intervals (p. 767)	7	5(i), 6(i)
	8 Build a regression model (p. 769)	9	6

Review Exercises

1. What is the simple least-squares regression model? What are the requirements to perform inference on a simple least-squares regression line? How do we verify that these requirements are met?

2. Seat Choice and GPA A biology professor wants to investigate the relation between the seat location chosen by a student on the first day of class and the student's cumulative grade point average. He randomly selected an introductory biology class and obtained the following information for the 38 students in the class.

Row Chosen, x	GPA, y	Row Chosen, x	GPA, y
1	4.00	6	2.63
2	3.35	6	3.15
2	3.50	6	3.69
2	3.67	6	3.71
2	3.75	7	2.88
3	3.37	7	2.93
3	3.62	7	3.00
4	2.35	7	3.21
4	2.71	7	3.53
4	3.75	7	3.74
5	3.10	7	3.75
5	3.22	7	3.90
5	3.36	8	2.30
5	3.58	8	2.54
5	3.67	8	2.61
5	3.69	9	2.71
5	3.72	9	3.74
5	3.84	9	3.75
6	2.35	11	1.71

Source: S. Kalinowski and Taper M. "The Effect of Seat Location on Exam Grades and Student Perceptions in an Introductory Biology Class." *Journal of College Science Teaching*, 36(4):54–57, 2007.

(a) Treating GPA as the explanatory variable, determine the estimates of β_0 and β_1. What is the mean GPA of students who choose to a seat in the fifth row?

(b) Compute the standard error of the estimate, s_e. *0.5102*

(c) Determine whether the residuals are normally distributed.

(d) If the residuals are normally distributed, determine s_{b_1}.

(e) If the residuals are normally distributed, test whether a linear relation exists between the explanatory variable, row choice, and response variable "GPA" at the $\alpha = 0.05$ level of significance. *Reject H_0*

(f) If the residuals are normally distributed, construct a 95% confidence interval for the slope of the true least-squares regression line. *(−0.1791, −0.0307)*

(g) Construct a 95% confidence interval for the mean GPA of students who choose a seat in the fifth row. *(3.159, 3.509)*

(h) Predict the GPA of a randomly selected student who chooses a seat in the fifth row. *3.334*

(i) Construct a 95% prediction interval for the GPA found in part (h). *(2.285, 4.384)*

(j) Explain why the predicted GPAs found in parts (a) and (h) are the same, yet the intervals are different.

3. Apartments The following data represent the square footage and rents for apartments in Queens, New York.

Square Footage, x	Rent per Month (\$), y
500	650
588	1,215
1,000	2,000
688	1,655
825	1,250
1,259	2,700
650	1,200
560	1,250
1,073	2,350
1,452	3,300
1,305	3,100

Source: apartments.com

2. (a) $b_0 = 3.8589$, $b_1 = −0.1049$, 3.334 2. (c) Yes 2. (d) 0.0366

3. (a) $b_0 = -399.2$, $b_1 = 2.5315$; $1879.15   3. (c) Yes   3. (d) 0.2166

(a) What are the estimates of β_0 and β_1? What is the mean rent of a 900-square-foot apartment in Queens?
(b) Compute the standard error of the estimate, s_e.   229.547
(c) Determine whether the residuals are normally distributed.
(d) If the residuals are normally distributed, determine s_{b_1}.
(e) If the residuals are normally distributed, test whether a linear relation exists between the explanatory variable, x, and response variable, y, at the $\alpha = 0.05$ level of significance.   Reject H_0
(f) If the residuals are normally distributed, construct a 95% confidence interval for the slope of the true least-squares regression line.   (2.0416, 3.0214)
(g) Construct a 90% confidence interval for the mean rent of all 900-square-foot apartments in Queens.
(h) Predict the rent of a particular 900-square-foot apartment in Queens. $1879.15
(i) Construct a 90% prediction interval for the rent of a particular 900-square-foot apartment in Queens.
(j) Explain why the predicted rents found in parts (a) and (h) are the same, yet the intervals are different.

4. Depreciation The following data represent the price of a random sample of used Chevy Camaros by age.

Age (years), x	Price ($), y	Age (years), x	Price ($), y
2	15,900	1	20,365
5	10,988	2	16,463
2	16,980	6	10,824
5	9,995	1	19,995
4	11,995	1	18,650
5	10,995	4	10,488

Source: www.onlineauto.com

4. (a) $\hat{y} = 20,976.2 - 2,054.6x$

(a) Determine the least-squares regression equation, treating age as the explanatory variable.
(b) A normal probability plot of the residuals indicates that the residuals are approximately normally distributed. Test whether a linear relation exists between age and price at the $\alpha = 0.05$ level of significance.   Reject H_0
(c) Plot the residuals against the explanatory variable, age.
(d) Does a linear model seem appropriate based on the scatter diagram and residual plot? (*Hint*: See Section 4.3.) What is the moral?   No

5. Course Grade A statistics instructor wishes to investigate the relation between a student's final course grade and grades on a midterm exam and a major project. She selects a random sample of 10 statistics students and obtains the following information:

Midterm	Project	Course Grade
88	90	83
95	80	83
91	90	92
94	93	94
95	90	89
93	58	77
91	90	91
87	74	73
82	92	70
87	74	75

3. (g) ($1752.20, $2006.00)   3. (i) ($1439.60, $2318.60)

(a) Construct a correlation matrix between course grade, midterm grade, and project grade. Is there any reason to be concerned with multicollinearity based on the correlation matrix?   No
(b) Find the least-squares regression equation $\hat{y} = b_0 + b_1x_1 + b_2x_2$, where x_1 is the midterm exam score, x_2 is the project score, and y is the final course grade.
(c) Draw residual plots, a boxplot of residuals, and a normal probability plot of the residuals to assess the adequacy of the model.
(d) Interpret the regression coefficients for the least-squares regression equation.
(e) Determine and interpret R^2 and the adjusted R^2.
(f) Test $H_0: \beta_1 = \beta_2 = 0$ versus H_1: at least one $\beta_i \neq 0$ at the $\alpha = 0.05$ level of significance.   Reject H_0
(g) Test the hypotheses $H_0: \beta_1 = 0$ versus $H_1: \beta_1 \neq 0$ and $H_0: \beta_2 = 0$ versus $H_1: \beta_2 \neq 0$ at the $\alpha = 0.05$ level of significance. Should any of the explanatory variables be removed from the model?   No
(h) Predict the mean final course grade of all statistics students who have an 85 on their midterm and a 75 on their project.   71
(i) Construct and interpret 95% confidence and prediction intervals for statistics students who score an 83 on their midterm and a 92 on their project. Interpret the results.   CI: (69.00, 82.04); PI: (64.04, 87.00)

6. Breakfast Cereal A nutritionist wants to model the relation between calories, protein, fat, and carbohydrates in breakfast cereal. Using a random sample of 12 ready-to-eat breakfast cereals, she obtained the following data per 100 grams (g) of cereal.

Calories	Protein (g)	Fat (g)	Carbohydrates (g)
373	5	1	89
380	7	3.8	83
389	4	3	88
370	9	3.7	81
355	10	3.2	81
381	3.4	3.2	87.1
357	9.1	5.5	73
387	6.4	1.8	89
347	7.9	1.8	78.1
385	3.6	3.9	87.9
386	6.4	3.6	84.9
377	6	1	86

(a) Construct a correlation matrix between calories, protein content, fat content, and carbohydrate content. Is there any reason to be concerned about multicollinearity based on the correlation matrix?   Yes
(b) Find the least-squares regression equation $\hat{y} = b_0 + b_1x_1 + b_2x_2 + b_3x_3$, where x_1 is protein content, x_2 is fat content, x_3 is carbohydrate content, and y is the number of calories. $\hat{y} = 111.24 - 0.239x_1 + 5.388x_2 + 2.9558x_3$
(c) Test $H_0: \beta_1 = \beta_2 = \beta_3 = 0$ versus H_1: at least one $\beta_i \neq 0$ at the $\alpha = 0.05$ level of significance.   Reject H_0
(d) Test the hypotheses $H_0: \beta_i = 0$ versus $H_1: \beta_i \neq 0$ for $i = 1, 2, 3$ at the $\alpha = 0.05$ level of significance. Should any of the explanatory variables be removed from the model? Which one?   Protein

5. (b) $\hat{y} = -91.29 + 1.5211x_1 + 0.441x_2$ 5. (e) $R^2 = 0.833$; adjusted $R^2 = 0.785$

6. (e) $\hat{y} = 101.20 + 5.481x_2 + 3.0536x_3$; yes   6. (h) $R^2 = 0.835$; adjusted $R^2 = 0.798$ 6. (i) CI: (388.08, 407.81) PI: (380.64, 414.25)

(e) Determine the regression model with the explanatory variable identified in part (d) removed. Are each of the slope coefficients significantly different from zero?

(f) Draw residual plots, a boxplot of the residuals, and a normal probability plot of the residuals to assess the adequacy of the model found in part (e).

(g) Interpret the regression coefficients for the least-squares regression equation found in part (e).

(h) Determine and interpret R^2 and adjusted R^2.

(i) Construct and interpret 95% confidence and prediction intervals for calories in 100 g of ready-to-eat cereal with 4 g of fat and 90 g of carbohydrates.

CHAPTER TEST

1. State the requirements to perform inference on a simple least-squares regression line?

2. Crickets make a chirping noise by sliding their wings rapidly over each other. Perhaps you have noticed that the number of chirps seems to increase with the temperature. The following table lists the temperature (in degrees Fahrenheit, °F) and the number of chirps per second for the striped ground cricket.

Temperature, x	Chirps per Second, y	Temperature, x	Chirps per Second, y
88.6	20.0	71.6	16.0
93.3	19.8	84.3	18.4
80.6	17.1	75.2	15.5
69.7	14.7	82.0	17.1
69.4	15.4	83.3	16.2
79.6	15.0	82.6	17.2
80.6	16.0	83.5	17.0
76.3	14.4		

Source: George W. Pierce. *The Songs of Insects*, Cambridge, MA: Harvard University Press, 1949, pp. 12–21.

(a) What are the estimates of β_0 and β_1? What is the mean number of chirps when the temperature is 80.2°F?

(b) Compute the standard error of the estimate, s_e.   0.9715

(c) Determine whether the residuals are normally distributed.

(d) If the residuals are normally distributed, determine s_{b_1}.

(e) If the residuals are normally distributed, test whether a linear relation exists between the explanatory variable, x, and response variable, y, at the $\alpha = 0.05$ level of significance.   Reject H_0

(f) If the residuals are normally distributed, construct a 95% confidence interval for the slope of the true least-squares regression line.   (0.1283, 0.2955)

(g) Construct a 90% confidence interval for the mean number of chirps found in part (a).   (16.24, 17.13)

(h) Predict the number of chirps on a day when the temperature is 80.2°F.   16.69

(i) Construct a 90% prediction interval for the number of chirps found in part (h).   (14.91, 18.46)

(j) Explain why the predicted number of chirps found in parts (a) and (h) are the same, yet the intervals are different.

3. The following data represent the height (inches) of boys between the ages of 2 and 10 years.

Age, x	Boy Height, y	Age, x	Boy Height, y	Age, x	Boy Height, y
2	36.1	5	45.6	8	48.3
2	34.2	5	44.8	8	50.9
2	31.1	5	44.6	9	52.2
3	36.3	6	49.8	9	51.3
3	39.5	7	43.2	10	55.6
4	41.5	7	47.9	10	59.5
4	38.6	8	51.4		

Source: National Center for Health Statistics

3. (c) Yes   3. (d) 0.2067

(a) Treating age as the explanatory variable, determine the estimates of β_0 and β_1. What is the mean height of a 7-year-old boy? $b_0 = 29.705$; $b_1 = 2.6351$; 48.15 inches

(b) Compute the standard error of the estimate, s_e.   2.450

(c) Determine whether the residuals are normally distributed.

(d) If the residuals are normally distributed, determine s_{b_1}.

(e) If the residuals are normally distributed, test whether a linear relation exists between the explanatory variable, age, and response variable, height, at the $\alpha = 0.05$ level of significance.   Reject H_0

(f) If the residuals are normally distributed, construct a 95% confidence interval for the slope of the true least-squares regression line.   (2.2008, 3.0694)

(g) Construct a 90% confidence interval for the mean height found in part (a).   (47.11, 49.19)

(h) Predict the height of a 7-year-old boy.   48.15

(i) Construct a 90% prediction interval for the height found in part (h).   (43.78, 52.52)

(j) Explain why the predicted heights found in parts (a) and (h) are the same, yet the intervals are different.

4. A researcher believes that as age increases the grip strength (pounds per square inch, psi) of an individual's dominant hand decreases. From a random sample of 17 females, he obtains the following data:

Age, x	Grip Strength, y	Age, x	Grip Strength, y
15	65	34	45
16	60	37	58
28	58	41	70
61	60	43	73
53	46	49	45
43	66	53	60
16	56	61	56
25	75	68	30
28	46		

Source: Kevin McCarthy, student at Joliet Junior College

2. (a) $b_0 = -0.309$, $b_1 = 0.2119$; 16.685   2. (c) Yes   2. (d) 0.0387

(a) Treating age as the explanatory variable, determine the estimates of β_0 and β_1. $b_0 = 67.388; b_1 = -0.2632$
(b) Compute the standard error of the estimate, s_e. 11.1859
(c) Determine whether the residuals are normally distributed.
(d) If the residuals are normally distributed, determine s_{b_1}.
(e) If the residuals are normally distributed, test whether a linear relation exists between the explanatory variable, age, and response variable, grip strength, at the $\alpha = 0.05$ level of significance. Do not reject H_0
(f) Based on your answers to (d) and (e), what would be a good estimate of the grip strength of a randomly selected 42-year-old female? 57 psi

4. (c) Yes

4. (d) 0.1680

---

5. A nutritionist wants to develop a model that describes the relation between the calories, total fat content, protein, sugar, and carbohydrates in cheeseburgers at fast-food restaurants. She obtains the following data from the Web sites of the companies. She will use calories as the response variable and the others as explanatory variables.

Restaurant	Fat (g)	Protein (g)	Sugar (g)	Carbs (g)	Calories
1/4-pound single with cheese (Wendy's)	20	25	9	39	430
Whataburger (Whataburger)	32	30	10	61	640
Cheeseburger (In-n-Out)	27	22	10	39	480
Big Mac (McDonald's)	29	25	9	45	540
Whopper with cheese (Burger King)	47	33	11	52	760
Jumbo Jack (Jack in the Box)	42	25	12	54	690
1/4 Pounder with Cheese (McDonald's)	26	29	9	40	510
Cheeseburger (Sonic)	31	29	15	59	630

Source: Each company's Web site

(a) Construct a correlation matrix. Is there any reason to be concerned about multicollinearity? No
(b) Find the least-squares regression equation $\hat{y} = b_0 + b_1x_1 + b_2x_2 + b_3x_3 + b_4x_4$, where x_1 is fat content, x_2 is protein, x_3 is sugar, x_4 is carbohydrates, and y is the response variable, calories.
(c) Test $H_0: \beta_1 = \beta_2 = \beta_3 = 0$ versus H_1: at least one of the $\beta_i \neq 0$ at the $\alpha = 0.05$ level of significance. Reject H_0
(d) Test the hypotheses $H_0: \beta_i = 0$ versus $H_1: \beta_i \neq 0$ for $i = 1, 2, 3$ at the $\alpha = 0.05$ level of significance. Should any of the explanatory variables be removed from the model? If so, which one?
(e) Determine the regression model with the explanatory variable identified in part (d) removed. Are the remaining slope coefficients significantly different from zero? If not, remove the appropriate explanatory variable and compute the least-squares regression equation.
(f) Draw residual plots, a boxplot of the residuals, and a normal probability plot of the residuals to assess the adequacy of the model found in part (e).
(g) Interpret the regression coefficients for the least-squares regression equation found in part (e).
(h) Determine and interpret R^2 and the adjusted R^2.
(i) Construct 95% confidence and prediction intervals for the calories in a fast-food cheeseburger that has 38 g of fat, 29 g of protein, 11 g of sugar, and 52 g of carbohydrates. Interpret the results.

5. (b) $\hat{y} = -11.9 + 9.0765x_1 + 4.4676x_2 + 1.488x_3 + 3.52x_4$ 5. (d) Conclusions: $\beta_1 \neq 0, \beta_2 \neq 0, \beta_3 = 0, \beta_4 \neq 0$; yes; $x_3 =$ sugar

5. (e) $\hat{y} = -4.42 + 9.1099x_1 + 4.2937x_2 + 3.7672x_4$; yes   5. (h) $R^2 = 99.9\%$; adjusted $R^2 = 99.8\%$

5. (i) CI: (656.16, 668.17); PI: (647.53, 676.80)

MAKING AN INFORMED DECISION

Buying a Car

You are still in the market to buy a new car. As we all know, most cars lose value over time. Therefore, another item to consider when purchasing a car is its depreciation rate. The lower the depreciation rate, the less value the car loses each year. Using the same three cars that you used in the Chapter 3 and Chapter 4 Decisions, answer the following questions to determine the depreciation rate. In Chapter 4 we found the exponential equation of best fit $y = ab^x$, where y is the price of the car and x is the age of the car. To do this, we linearized the data by computing the logarithm of the asking price, y, so that the least-squares regression equation was $\log y = \log a + (\log b)x$. We can rewrite this as $Y = A + Bx$, where $Y = \log y$, $A = \log a$, and $B = \log b$.

For each car that you are considering, answer the following:

1. What is the standard error of the estimate of the equation $Y = A + Bx$?

2. Are the residuals normally distributed?

3. If the residuals are normally distributed, test whether a linear relation exists between the explanatory variable, x, and the response variable, Y, at the $\alpha = 0.05$ level of significance.

4. What is the mean price of a 10-year-old car? Construct a 90% confidence interval about the mean price of a 10-year-old car.

5. Predict the price of a 7-year-old car.

6. Construct a 90% prediction interval about the price of a 7-year-old car.

7. Write a report that describes which car you would buy, given the information collected. Be sure to justify your conclusions.

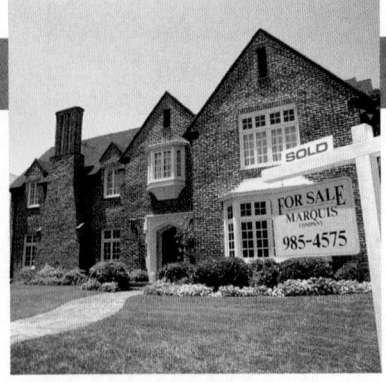

CASE STUDY

Housing Boom

During the early 2000s, the United States experienced a boom in the housing industry. This boom was in large part due to efforts by the government to boost consumer spending. The chairman of the Federal Reserve Board at that time, Alan Greenspan, testified before Congress on the economy (requoted from wallstreetwindow.com):

> The rapid rise in home prices over the past several years has provided households with considerable capital gains. Moreover, a significant increase in the rate of single-family home turnover has meant that many consumers have been able to realize gains from the sale of their homes. To be sure, such capital gains, largely realized through an increase in mortgage debt on the home, do not increase the pool of national savings available to finance new capital investment. But from the perspective of an individual household, cash realized from capital gains has the same spending power as cash from any other source.

For many, the lure of low interest rates put them in the market for a house. When house shopping, a natural question is "How much is the house worth?" This question is difficult to answer because it depends on what the market will bear. That is, the house is worth what someone else is willing to pay for it. So what are others willing to pay? A real estate agent wishes to help answer this question by examining several recent house sales in his territory and developing a formula that could be used to give a rough idea of a house's fair market value.

Articles on how to determine the value of a house often suggest comparing square footage, number of bedrooms, number of bathrooms, and size of the lot. The agent decided to examine these four variables, along with the age of the house and the number of rooms, in an effort to predict the house's selling price. The data in the table on the next page summarize his findings.

(a) Construct a correlation matrix with price, acres, bedrooms, bathrooms, square feet, age, and rooms. Is there any reason to be concerned with multicollinearity based on the correlation matrix?

(b) Find the least-squares regression equation $\hat{y} = b_0 + b_1x_1 + b_2x_2 + b_3x_3 + b_4x_4 + b_5x_5 + b_6x_6$, where x_1 is acres, x_2 is bedrooms, and so on.

(c) Test $H_0: \beta_i = 0$ versus H_1: at least one of the $\beta_i \neq 0$ at the $\alpha = 0.05$ level of significance.

Price ($1,000s)	Acres	Bedrooms	Bathrooms	Sq. ft.	Age (yr)	Rooms
104.9	0.19	3	1.0	900	44	8
109.0	0.15	3	2.0	1,431	34	6
94.9	0.20	3	1.5	1,064	49	6
96.5	0.18	2	1.0	780	52	4
127.9	0.17	3	2.5	1,140	47	6
129.9	0.18	3	1.5	1,140	41	7
145.0	0.18	3	1.5	1,845	45	6
199.9	0.17	4	3.5	1,974	17	8
255.9	0.24	5	3.0	2,460	22	8
310.0	0.23	4	3.5	2,490	14	9
169.0	0.20	4	2.0	1,896	37	8
344.5	0.24	4	4.5	2,709	11	8
123.0	0.13	3	1.0	828	63	5
139.9	0.16	2	2.0	1,131	75	5
169.9	0.15	2	2.0	1,002	96	7
194.9	0.19	3	1.0	1,024	55	6
210.0	0.23	3	1.0	1,694	53	9
275.0	0.17	4	2.0	2,380	10	8
299.5	0.17	4	2.0	1,936	97	8
319.9	0.27	3	2.0	1,648	77	8
397.5	0.30	4	2.5	2,500	106	10
189.9	0.18	2	1.0	1,016	71	6
349.9	0.40	4	2.5	1,816	70	8
454.9	0.96	3	3.0	2,160	37	7
499.9	1.00	5	3.0	3,104	48	10
615.0	0.66	4	3.5	3,205	26	10
635.0	0.44	4	3.5	3,084	27	10
929.0	0.90	5	4.5	4,470	16	14

(d) Test the hypotheses H_0: $\beta_i = 0$ versus H_1: $\beta_i \neq 0$ for $i = 1, 2, \ldots, 6$, at the $\alpha = 0.05$ level of significance.

(e) Examine your regression results and remove any explanatory variable whose coefficient is not significantly different from 0 to obtain the model of best fit.

(f) Once you have obtained your model of best fit, draw residual plots and a box-plot of the residuals to assess the adequacy of the model.

(g) Determine and interpret R^2 and adjusted R^2. How well does your model appear to fit the data?

(h) Use your model to predict the selling price for another house from the agent's territory that has the following characteristics: 0.18 acre, 3 bedrooms, 1 bath, 1,176 square feet, 47 years old, and 6 total rooms. Compare your prediction to the actual selling price: $99,900.

Location, location, location! The agent knows that the location of the house can have a large effect on its selling price. He notes that the first 12 houses listed are from the same zip code, the next 10 houses are from a second zip code, and the last 6 houses listed are from a third zip code.

(i) Construct side-by-side boxplots of selling price for the three zip codes. Is there any reason to believe that selling prices vary from one zip code to the next within the agent's territory?

(j) Introduce a dummy explanatory variable to represent zip code and repeat parts (b)–(g) to find the model of best fit for price.

(k) Repeat part (h) assuming the house comes from the first zip code. Which model did a better job predicting the selling price?

(l) Use the model you obtained in part (k) to predict the selling price of a house in your area. How well did the model work?

(m) Explain the limitations of this model. Which, if any, can be dealt with, and how would you do so?

(n) What other variables might affect the cost of a house? Support your choices; then collect data from your area for the subset of variables you think best predicts house price. Find the model of best fit and test it with additional houses in your area, as well as houses in other areas. How well does your model work?

Appendix A Tables

Table I

Random Numbers
Column Number

Row Number	01–05	06–10	11–15	16–20	21–25	26–30	31–35	36–40	41–45	46–50
01	89392	23212	74483	36590	25956	36544	68518	40805	09980	00467
02	61458	17639	96252	95649	73727	33912	72896	66218	52341	97141
03	11452	74197	81962	48443	90360	26480	73231	37740	26628	44690
04	27575	04429	31308	02241	01698	19191	18948	78871	36030	23980
05	36829	59109	88976	46845	28329	47460	88944	08264	00843	84592
06	81902	93458	42161	26099	09419	89073	82849	09160	61845	40906
07	59761	55212	33360	68751	86737	79743	85262	31887	37879	17525
08	46827	25906	64708	20307	78423	15910	86548	08763	47050	18513
09	24040	66449	32353	83668	13874	86741	81312	54185	78824	00718
10	98144	96372	50277	15571	82261	66628	31457	00377	63423	55141
11	14228	17930	30118	00438	49666	65189	62869	31304	17117	71489
12	55366	51057	90065	14791	62426	02957	85518	28822	30588	32798
13	96101	30646	35526	90389	73634	79304	96635	06626	94683	16696
14	38152	55474	30153	26525	83647	31988	82182	98377	33802	80471
15	85007	18416	24661	95581	45868	15662	28906	36392	07617	50248
16	85544	15890	80011	18160	33468	84106	40603	01315	74664	20553
17	10446	20699	98370	17684	16932	80449	92654	02084	19985	59321
18	67237	45509	17638	65115	29757	80705	82686	48565	72612	61760
19	23026	89817	05403	82209	30573	47501	00135	33955	50250	72592
20	67411	58542	18678	46491	13219	84084	27783	34508	55158	78742

Table II

Critical Values for Correlation Coefficient

n	
3	0.997
4	0.950
5	0.878
6	0.811
7	0.754
8	0.707
9	0.666
10	0.632
11	0.602
12	0.576
13	0.553
14	0.532
15	0.514
16	0.497
17	0.482
18	0.468
19	0.456
20	0.444
21	0.433
22	0.423
23	0.413
24	0.404
25	0.396
26	0.388
27	0.381
28	0.374
29	0.367
30	0.361

Table III

Binomial Probability Distribution

This table computes the probability of obtaining x successes in n trials of a binomial experiment with probability of success p.

n	x	0.01	0.05	0.10	0.15	0.20	0.25	0.30	0.35	0.40	0.45	0.50	0.55	0.60	0.65	0.70	0.75	0.80	0.85	0.90	0.95
2	0	0.9801	0.9025	0.8100	0.7225	0.6400	0.5625	0.4900	0.4225	0.3600	0.3025	0.2500	0.2025	0.1600	0.1225	0.0900	0.0625	0.0400	0.0225	0.0100	0.0025
	1	0.0198	0.0950	0.1800	0.2550	0.3200	0.3750	0.4200	0.4550	0.4800	0.4950	0.5000	0.4950	0.4800	0.4550	0.4200	0.3750	0.3200	0.2550	0.1800	0.0950
	2	0.0001	0.0025	0.0100	0.0225	0.0400	0.0625	0.0900	0.1225	0.1600	0.2025	0.2500	0.3025	0.3600	0.4225	0.4900	0.5625	0.6400	0.7225	0.8100	0.9025
3	0	0.9703	0.8574	0.7290	0.6141	0.5120	0.4219	0.3430	0.2746	0.2160	0.1664	0.1250	0.0911	0.0640	0.0429	0.0270	0.0156	0.0080	0.0034	0.0010	0.0001
	1	0.0294	0.1354	0.2430	0.3251	0.3840	0.4219	0.4410	0.4436	0.4320	0.4084	0.3750	0.3341	0.2880	0.2389	0.1890	0.1406	0.0960	0.0574	0.0270	0.0071
	2	0.0003	0.0071	0.0270	0.0574	0.0960	0.1406	0.1890	0.2389	0.2880	0.3341	0.3750	0.4084	0.4320	0.4436	0.4410	0.4219	0.3840	0.3251	0.2430	0.1354
	3	0.0000+	0.0001	0.0010	0.0034	0.0080	0.0156	0.0270	0.0429	0.0640	0.0911	0.1250	0.1664	0.2160	0.2746	0.3430	0.4219	0.5120	0.6141	0.7290	0.8574
4	0	0.9606	0.8145	0.6561	0.5220	0.4096	0.3164	0.2401	0.1785	0.1296	0.0915	0.0625	0.0410	0.0256	0.0150	0.0081	0.0039	0.0016	0.0005	0.0001	0.0000+
	1	0.0388	0.1715	0.2916	0.3685	0.4096	0.4219	0.4116	0.3845	0.3456	0.2995	0.2500	0.2005	0.1536	0.1115	0.0756	0.0469	0.0256	0.0115	0.0036	0.0005
	2	0.0006	0.0135	0.0486	0.0975	0.1536	0.2109	0.2646	0.3105	0.3456	0.3675	0.3750	0.3675	0.3456	0.3105	0.2646	0.2109	0.1536	0.0975	0.0486	0.0135
	3	0.0000+	0.0005	0.0036	0.0115	0.0256	0.0469	0.0756	0.1115	0.1536	0.2005	0.2500	0.2995	0.3456	0.3845	0.4116	0.4219	0.4096	0.3685	0.2916	0.1715
	4	0.0000+	0.0000+	0.0001	0.0005	0.0016	0.0039	0.0081	0.0150	0.0256	0.0410	0.0625	0.0915	0.1296	0.1785	0.2401	0.3164	0.4096	0.5220	0.6561	0.8145
5	0	0.9510	0.7738	0.5905	0.4437	0.3277	0.2373	0.1681	0.1160	0.0778	0.0503	0.0313	0.0185	0.0102	0.0053	0.0024	0.0010	0.0003	0.0001	0.0000+	0.0000+
	1	0.0480	0.2036	0.3281	0.3915	0.4096	0.3955	0.3602	0.3124	0.2592	0.2059	0.1563	0.1128	0.0768	0.0488	0.0284	0.0146	0.0064	0.0022	0.0005	0.0000+
	2	0.0010	0.0214	0.0729	0.1382	0.2048	0.2637	0.3087	0.3364	0.3456	0.3369	0.3125	0.2757	0.2304	0.1811	0.1323	0.0879	0.0512	0.0244	0.0081	0.0011
	3	0.0000+	0.0011	0.0081	0.0244	0.0512	0.0879	0.1323	0.1811	0.2304	0.2757	0.3125	0.3369	0.3456	0.3364	0.3087	0.2637	0.2048	0.1382	0.0729	0.0214
	4	0.0000+	0.0000+	0.0005	0.0022	0.0064	0.0146	0.0284	0.0488	0.0768	0.1128	0.1563	0.2059	0.2592	0.3124	0.3602	0.3955	0.4096	0.3915	0.3281	0.2036
	5	0.0000+	0.0000+	0.0000+	0.0001	0.0003	0.0010	0.0024	0.0053	0.0102	0.0185	0.0313	0.0503	0.0778	0.1160	0.1681	0.2373	0.3277	0.4437	0.5905	0.7738
6	0	0.9415	0.7351	0.5314	0.3771	0.2621	0.1780	0.1176	0.0754	0.0467	0.0277	0.0156	0.0083	0.0041	0.0018	0.0007	0.0002	0.0001	0.0000+	0.0000+	0.0000+
	1	0.0571	0.2321	0.3543	0.3993	0.3932	0.3560	0.3025	0.2437	0.1866	0.1359	0.0938	0.0609	0.0369	0.0205	0.0102	0.0044	0.0015	0.0004	0.0001	0.0000+
	2	0.0014	0.0305	0.0984	0.1762	0.2458	0.2966	0.3241	0.3280	0.3110	0.2780	0.2344	0.1861	0.1382	0.0951	0.0595	0.0330	0.0154	0.0055	0.0012	0.0001
	3	0.0000+	0.0021	0.0146	0.0415	0.0819	0.1318	0.1852	0.2355	0.2765	0.3032	0.3125	0.3032	0.2765	0.2355	0.1852	0.1318	0.0819	0.0415	0.0146	0.0021
	4	0.0000+	0.0001	0.0012	0.0055	0.0154	0.0330	0.0595	0.0951	0.1382	0.1861	0.2344	0.2780	0.3110	0.3280	0.3241	0.2966	0.2458	0.1762	0.0984	0.0305
	5	0.0000+	0.0000+	0.0001	0.0004	0.0015	0.0044	0.0102	0.0205	0.0369	0.0609	0.0938	0.1359	0.1866	0.2437	0.3025	0.3560	0.3932	0.3993	0.3543	0.2321
	6	0.0000+	0.0000+	0.0000+	0.0000+	0.0001	0.0002	0.0007	0.0018	0.0041	0.0083	0.0156	0.0277	0.0467	0.0754	0.1176	0.1780	0.2621	0.3771	0.5314	0.7351
7	0	0.9321	0.6983	0.4783	0.3206	0.2097	0.1335	0.0824	0.0490	0.0280	0.0152	0.0078	0.0037	0.0016	0.0006	0.0002	0.0001	0.0000+	0.0000+	0.0000+	0.0000+
	1	0.0659	0.2573	0.3720	0.3960	0.3670	0.3115	0.2471	0.1848	0.1306	0.0872	0.0547	0.0320	0.0172	0.0084	0.0036	0.0013	0.0004	0.0001	0.0000+	0.0000+
	2	0.0020	0.0406	0.1240	0.2097	0.2753	0.3115	0.3177	0.2985	0.2613	0.2140	0.1641	0.1172	0.0774	0.0466	0.0250	0.0115	0.0043	0.0012	0.0002	0.0000+
	3	0.0000+	0.0036	0.0230	0.0617	0.1147	0.1730	0.2269	0.2679	0.2903	0.2918	0.2734	0.2388	0.1935	0.1442	0.0972	0.0577	0.0287	0.0109	0.0026	0.0002
	4	0.0000+	0.0002	0.0026	0.0109	0.0287	0.0577	0.0972	0.1442	0.1935	0.2388	0.2734	0.2918	0.2903	0.2679	0.2269	0.1730	0.1147	0.0617	0.0230	0.0036
	5	0.0000+	0.0000+	0.0002	0.0012	0.0043	0.0115	0.0250	0.0466	0.0774	0.1172	0.1641	0.2140	0.2613	0.2985	0.3177	0.3115	0.2753	0.2097	0.1240	0.0406
	6	0.0000+	0.0000+	0.0000+	0.0001	0.0004	0.0013	0.0036	0.0084	0.0172	0.0320	0.0547	0.0872	0.1306	0.1848	0.2471	0.3115	0.3670	0.3960	0.3720	0.2573
	7	0.0000+	0.0000+	0.0000+	0.0000+	0.0000+	0.0001	0.0002	0.0006	0.0016	0.0037	0.0078	0.0152	0.0280	0.0490	0.0824	0.1335	0.2097	0.3206	0.4783	0.6983

Note: 0.0000+ means the probability is 0.0000 rounded to four decimal places. However, the probability is *not* zero.

Table III (continued)

n	x	0.01	0.05	0.10	0.15	0.20	0.25	0.30	0.35	0.40	0.45	0.50	0.55	0.60	0.65	0.70	0.75	0.80	0.85	0.90	0.95
8	0	0.9227	0.6634	0.4305	0.2725	0.1678	0.1001	0.0576	0.0319	0.0168	0.0084	0.0039	0.0017	0.0007	0.0002	0.0001	0.0000+	0.0000+	0.0000+	0.0000+	0.0000+
	1	0.0746	0.2793	0.3826	0.3847	0.3355	0.2670	0.1977	0.1373	0.0896	0.0548	0.0313	0.0164	0.0079	0.0033	0.0012	0.0004	0.0001	0.0000+	0.0000+	0.0000+
	2	0.0026	0.0515	0.1488	0.2376	0.2936	0.3115	0.2965	0.2587	0.2090	0.1569	0.1094	0.0703	0.0413	0.0217	0.0100	0.0038	0.0011	0.0002	0.0000+	0.0000+
	3	0.0001	0.0054	0.0331	0.0839	0.1468	0.2076	0.2541	0.2786	0.2787	0.2568	0.2188	0.1719	0.1239	0.0808	0.0467	0.0231	0.0092	0.0026	0.0004	0.0000+
	4	0.0000+	0.0004	0.0046	0.0185	0.0459	0.0865	0.1361	0.1875	0.2322	0.2627	0.2734	0.2627	0.2322	0.1875	0.1361	0.0865	0.0459	0.0185	0.0046	0.0004
	5	0.0000+	0.0000+	0.0004	0.0026	0.0092	0.0231	0.0467	0.0808	0.1239	0.1719	0.2188	0.2568	0.2787	0.2786	0.2541	0.2076	0.1468	0.0839	0.0331	0.0054
	6	0.0000+	0.0000+	0.0000+	0.0002	0.0011	0.0038	0.0100	0.0217	0.0413	0.0703	0.1094	0.1569	0.2090	0.2587	0.2965	0.3115	0.2936	0.2376	0.1488	0.0515
	7	0.0000+	0.0000+	0.0000+	0.0000+	0.0001	0.0004	0.0012	0.0033	0.0079	0.0164	0.0313	0.0548	0.0896	0.1373	0.1977	0.2670	0.2936	0.3847	0.3826	0.2793
	8	0.0000+	0.0000+	0.0000+	0.0000+	0.0000+	0.0000+	0.0001	0.0002	0.0007	0.0017	0.0039	0.0084	0.0168	0.0319	0.0576	0.1001	0.1678	0.2725	0.4305	0.6634
9	0	0.9135	0.6302	0.3874	0.2316	0.1342	0.0751	0.0404	0.0207	0.0101	0.0046	0.0020	0.0008	0.0003	0.0001	0.0000+	0.0000+	0.0000+	0.0000+	0.0000+	0.0000+
	1	0.0830	0.2985	0.3874	0.3679	0.3020	0.2253	0.1556	0.1004	0.0605	0.0339	0.0176	0.0083	0.0035	0.0013	0.0004	0.0001	0.0000+	0.0000+	0.0000+	0.0000+
	2	0.0034	0.0629	0.1722	0.2597	0.3020	0.3003	0.2668	0.2162	0.1612	0.1110	0.0703	0.0407	0.0212	0.0098	0.0039	0.0012	0.0003	0.0000+	0.0000+	0.0000+
	3	0.0001	0.0077	0.0446	0.1069	0.1762	0.2336	0.2668	0.2716	0.2508	0.2119	0.1641	0.1160	0.0743	0.0424	0.0210	0.0087	0.0028	0.0006	0.0001	0.0000+
	4	0.0000+	0.0006	0.0074	0.0283	0.0661	0.1168	0.1715	0.2194	0.2508	0.2600	0.2461	0.2128	0.1672	0.1181	0.0735	0.0389	0.0165	0.0050	0.0008	0.0000+
	5	0.0000+	0.0000+	0.0008	0.0050	0.0165	0.0389	0.0735	0.1181	0.1672	0.2128	0.2461	0.2600	0.2508	0.2194	0.1715	0.1168	0.0661	0.0283	0.0074	0.0006
	6	0.0000+	0.0000+	0.0001	0.0006	0.0028	0.0087	0.0210	0.0424	0.0743	0.1160	0.1641	0.2119	0.2508	0.2716	0.2668	0.2336	0.1762	0.1069	0.0446	0.0077
	7	0.0000+	0.0000+	0.0000+	0.0000+	0.0003	0.0012	0.0039	0.0098	0.0212	0.0407	0.0703	0.1110	0.1612	0.2162	0.2668	0.3003	0.3020	0.2597	0.1722	0.0629
	8	0.0000+	0.0000+	0.0000+	0.0000+	0.0000+	0.0001	0.0004	0.0013	0.0035	0.0083	0.0176	0.0339	0.0605	0.1004	0.1556	0.2253	0.3020	0.3679	0.3874	0.2985
	9	0.0000+	0.0000+	0.0000+	0.0000+	0.0000+	0.0000+	0.0000+	0.0001	0.0003	0.0008	0.0020	0.0046	0.0101	0.0207	0.0404	0.0751	0.1342	0.2316	0.3874	0.6302
10	0	0.9044	0.5987	0.3487	0.1969	0.1074	0.0563	0.0282	0.0135	0.0060	0.0025	0.0010	0.0003	0.0001	0.0000+	0.0000+	0.0000+	0.0000+	0.0000+	0.0000+	0.0000+
	1	0.0914	0.3151	0.3874	0.3474	0.2684	0.1877	0.1211	0.0725	0.0403	0.0207	0.0098	0.0042	0.0016	0.0005	0.0001	0.0000+	0.0000+	0.0000+	0.0000+	0.0000+
	2	0.0042	0.0746	0.1937	0.2759	0.3020	0.2816	0.2335	0.1757	0.1209	0.0763	0.0439	0.0229	0.0106	0.0043	0.0014	0.0004	0.0001	0.0000+	0.0000+	0.0000+
	3	0.0001	0.0105	0.0574	0.1298	0.2013	0.2503	0.2668	0.2522	0.2150	0.1665	0.1172	0.0746	0.0425	0.0212	0.0090	0.0031	0.0008	0.0001	0.0000+	0.0000+
	4	0.0000+	0.0010	0.0112	0.0401	0.0881	0.1460	0.2001	0.2377	0.2508	0.2384	0.2051	0.1596	0.1115	0.0689	0.0368	0.0162	0.0055	0.0012	0.0001	0.0000+
	5	0.0000+	0.0001	0.0015	0.0085	0.0264	0.0584	0.1029	0.1536	0.2007	0.2340	0.2461	0.2340	0.2007	0.1536	0.1029	0.0584	0.0264	0.0085	0.0015	0.0001
	6	0.0000+	0.0000+	0.0001	0.0012	0.0055	0.0162	0.0368	0.0689	0.1115	0.1596	0.2051	0.2384	0.2508	0.2377	0.2001	0.1460	0.0881	0.0401	0.0112	0.0010
	7	0.0000+	0.0000+	0.0000+	0.0001	0.0008	0.0031	0.0090	0.0212	0.0425	0.0746	0.1172	0.1665	0.2150	0.2522	0.2668	0.2503	0.2013	0.1298	0.0574	0.0105
	8	0.0000+	0.0000+	0.0000+	0.0000+	0.0001	0.0004	0.0014	0.0043	0.0106	0.0229	0.0439	0.0763	0.1209	0.1757	0.2335	0.2816	0.3020	0.2759	0.1937	0.0746
	9	0.0000+	0.0000+	0.0000+	0.0000+	0.0000+	0.0000+	0.0001	0.0005	0.0016	0.0042	0.0098	0.0207	0.0403	0.0725	0.1211	0.1877	0.2684	0.3474	0.3874	0.3151
	10	0.0000+	0.0000+	0.0000+	0.0000+	0.0000+	0.0000+	0.0000+	0.0000+	0.0001	0.0003	0.0010	0.0025	0.0060	0.0135	0.0282	0.0563	0.1074	0.1969	0.3487	0.5987

Note: 0.0000+ means the probability is 0.0000 rounded to four decimal places. However, the probability is *not* zero.

Table III (continued)

n	x	p																			
		0.01	0.05	0.10	0.15	0.20	0.25	0.30	0.35	0.40	0.45	0.50	0.55	0.60	0.65	0.70	0.75	0.80	0.85	0.90	0.95
11	0	0.8953	0.5688	0.3138	0.1673	0.0859	0.0422	0.0198	0.0088	0.0036	0.0014	0.0005	0.0002	0.0000+	0.0000+	0.0000+	0.0000+	0.0000+	0.0000+	0.0000+	0.0000+
	1	0.0995	0.3293	0.3835	0.3248	0.2362	0.1549	0.0932	0.0518	0.0266	0.0125	0.0054	0.0021	0.0007	0.0002	0.0000+	0.0000+	0.0000+	0.0000+	0.0000+	0.0000+
	2	0.0050	0.0867	0.2131	0.2866	0.2953	0.2581	0.1998	0.1395	0.0887	0.0513	0.0269	0.0126	0.0052	0.0018	0.0005	0.0001	0.0000+	0.0000+	0.0000+	0.0000+
	3	0.0002	0.0137	0.0710	0.1517	0.2215	0.2581	0.2568	0.2254	0.1774	0.1259	0.0806	0.0462	0.0234	0.0102	0.0037	0.0011	0.0002	0.0000+	0.0000+	0.0000+
	4	0.0000+	0.0014	0.0158	0.0536	0.1107	0.1721	0.2201	0.2428	0.2365	0.2060	0.1611	0.1128	0.0701	0.0379	0.0173	0.0064	0.0017	0.0003	0.0000+	0.0000+
	5	0.0000+	0.0001	0.0025	0.0132	0.0388	0.0803	0.1321	0.1830	0.2207	0.2360	0.2256	0.1931	0.1471	0.0985	0.0566	0.0268	0.0097	0.0023	0.0003	0.0000+
	6	0.0000+	0.0000+	0.0003	0.0023	0.0097	0.0268	0.0566	0.0985	0.1471	0.1931	0.2256	0.2360	0.2207	0.1830	0.1321	0.0803	0.0388	0.0132	0.0025	0.0001
	7	0.0000+	0.0000+	0.0000+	0.0003	0.0017	0.0064	0.0173	0.0379	0.0701	0.1128	0.1611	0.2060	0.2365	0.2428	0.2201	0.1721	0.1107	0.0536	0.0158	0.0014
	8	0.0000+	0.0000+	0.0000+	0.0000+	0.0002	0.0011	0.0037	0.0102	0.0234	0.0462	0.0806	0.1259	0.1774	0.2254	0.2568	0.2581	0.2215	0.1517	0.0710	0.0137
	9	0.0000+	0.0000+	0.0000+	0.0000+	0.0000+	0.0001	0.0005	0.0018	0.0052	0.0126	0.0269	0.0513	0.0887	0.1395	0.1998	0.2581	0.2953	0.2866	0.2131	0.0867
	10	0.0000+	0.0000+	0.0000+	0.0000+	0.0000+	0.0000+	0.0000+	0.0002	0.0007	0.0021	0.0054	0.0125	0.0266	0.0518	0.0932	0.1549	0.2362	0.3248	0.3835	0.3293
	11	0.0000+	0.0000+	0.0000+	0.0000+	0.0000+	0.0000+	0.0000+	0.0000+	0.0000+	0.0002	0.0005	0.0014	0.0036	0.0088	0.0198	0.0422	0.0859	0.1673	0.3138	0.5688
12	0	0.8864	0.5404	0.2824	0.1422	0.0687	0.0317	0.0138	0.0057	0.0022	0.0008	0.0002	0.0001	0.0000+	0.0000+	0.0000+	0.0000+	0.0000+	0.0000+	0.0000+	0.0000+
	1	0.1074	0.3413	0.3766	0.3012	0.2062	0.1267	0.0712	0.0368	0.0174	0.0075	0.0029	0.0010	0.0003	0.0001	0.0000+	0.0000+	0.0000+	0.0000+	0.0000+	0.0000+
	2	0.0060	0.0988	0.2301	0.2924	0.2835	0.2323	0.1678	0.1088	0.0639	0.0339	0.0161	0.0068	0.0025	0.0008	0.0002	0.0000+	0.0000+	0.0000+	0.0000+	0.0000+
	3	0.0002	0.0173	0.0852	0.1720	0.2362	0.2581	0.2397	0.1954	0.1419	0.0923	0.0537	0.0277	0.0125	0.0048	0.0015	0.0004	0.0001	0.0000+	0.0000+	0.0000+
	4	0.0000+	0.0021	0.0213	0.0683	0.1329	0.1936	0.2311	0.2367	0.2128	0.1700	0.1208	0.0762	0.0420	0.0199	0.0078	0.0024	0.0005	0.0001	0.0000+	0.0000+
	5	0.0000+	0.0002	0.0038	0.0193	0.0532	0.1032	0.1585	0.2039	0.2270	0.2225	0.1934	0.1489	0.1009	0.0591	0.0291	0.0115	0.0033	0.0006	0.0000+	0.0000+
	6	0.0000+	0.0000+	0.0005	0.0040	0.0155	0.0401	0.0792	0.1281	0.1766	0.2124	0.2256	0.2124	0.1766	0.1281	0.0792	0.0401	0.0155	0.0040	0.0005	0.0000+
	7	0.0000+	0.0000+	0.0000+	0.0006	0.0033	0.0115	0.0291	0.0591	0.1009	0.1489	0.1934	0.2225	0.2270	0.2039	0.1585	0.1032	0.0532	0.0193	0.0038	0.0002
	8	0.0000+	0.0000+	0.0000+	0.0001	0.0005	0.0024	0.0078	0.0199	0.0420	0.0762	0.1208	0.1700	0.2128	0.2367	0.2311	0.1936	0.1329	0.0683	0.0213	0.0021
	9	0.0000+	0.0000+	0.0000+	0.0000+	0.0001	0.0004	0.0015	0.0048	0.0125	0.0277	0.0537	0.0923	0.1419	0.1954	0.2397	0.2581	0.2362	0.1720	0.0852	0.0173
	10	0.0000+	0.0000+	0.0000+	0.0000+	0.0000+	0.0000+	0.0002	0.0008	0.0025	0.0068	0.0161	0.0339	0.0639	0.1088	0.1678	0.2323	0.2835	0.2924	0.2301	0.0988
	11	0.0000+	0.0000+	0.0000+	0.0000+	0.0000+	0.0000+	0.0000+	0.0001	0.0003	0.0010	0.0029	0.0075	0.0174	0.0368	0.0712	0.1267	0.2062	0.3012	0.3766	0.3413
	12	0.0000+	0.0000+	0.0000+	0.0000+	0.0000+	0.0000+	0.0000+	0.0000+	0.0000+	0.0001	0.0002	0.0008	0.0022	0.0057	0.0138	0.0317	0.0687	0.1422	0.2824	0.5404

Note: 0.0000+ means the probability is 0.0000 rounded to four decimal places. However, the probability is *not* zero.

Table III (*continued*)

p

n	x	0.01	0.05	0.10	0.15	0.20	0.25	0.30	0.35	0.40	0.45	0.50	0.55	0.60	0.65	0.70	0.75	0.80	0.85	0.90	0.95
15	0	0.8601	0.4633	0.2059	0.0874	0.0352	0.0134	0.0047	0.0016	0.0005	0.0001	0.0000+	0.0000+	0.0000+	0.0000+	0.0000+	0.0000+	0.0000+	0.0000+	0.0000+	0.0000+
	1	0.1303	0.3658	0.3432	0.2312	0.1319	0.0668	0.0305	0.0126	0.0047	0.0016	0.0005	0.0001	0.0000+	0.0000+	0.0000+	0.0000+	0.0000+	0.0000+	0.0000+	0.0000+
	2	0.0092	0.1348	0.2669	0.2856	0.2309	0.1559	0.0916	0.0476	0.0219	0.0090	0.0032	0.0010	0.0003	0.0001	0.0000+	0.0000+	0.0000+	0.0000+	0.0000+	0.0000+
	3	0.0004	0.0307	0.1285	0.2184	0.2501	0.2252	0.1700	0.1110	0.0634	0.0318	0.0139	0.0052	0.0016	0.0004	0.0001	0.0000+	0.0000+	0.0000+	0.0000+	0.0000+
	4	0.0000+	0.0049	0.0428	0.1156	0.1876	0.2252	0.2186	0.1792	0.1268	0.0780	0.0417	0.0191	0.0074	0.0024	0.0006	0.0001	0.0000+	0.0000+	0.0000+	0.0000+
	5	0.0000+	0.0006	0.0105	0.0449	0.1032	0.1651	0.2061	0.2123	0.1859	0.1404	0.0916	0.0515	0.0245	0.0096	0.0030	0.0007	0.0001	0.0000+	0.0000+	0.0000+
	6	0.0000+	0.0000+	0.0019	0.0132	0.0430	0.0917	0.1472	0.1906	0.2066	0.1914	0.1527	0.1048	0.0612	0.0298	0.0116	0.0034	0.0007	0.0001	0.0000+	0.0000+
	7	0.0000+	0.0000+	0.0003	0.0030	0.0138	0.0393	0.0811	0.1319	0.1771	0.2013	0.1964	0.1647	0.1181	0.0710	0.0348	0.0131	0.0035	0.0005	0.0000+	0.0000+
	8	0.0000+	0.0000+	0.0000+	0.0005	0.0035	0.0131	0.0348	0.0710	0.1181	0.1647	0.1964	0.2013	0.1771	0.1319	0.0811	0.0393	0.0138	0.0030	0.0003	0.0000+
	9	0.0000+	0.0000+	0.0000+	0.0001	0.0007	0.0034	0.0116	0.0298	0.0612	0.1048	0.1527	0.1914	0.2066	0.1906	0.1472	0.0917	0.0430	0.0132	0.0019	0.0000+
	10	0.0000+	0.0000+	0.0000+	0.0000+	0.0001	0.0007	0.0030	0.0096	0.0245	0.0515	0.0916	0.1404	0.1859	0.2123	0.2061	0.1651	0.1032	0.0449	0.0105	0.0006
	11	0.0000+	0.0000+	0.0000+	0.0000+	0.0000+	0.0001	0.0006	0.0024	0.0074	0.0191	0.0417	0.0780	0.1268	0.1792	0.2186	0.2252	0.1876	0.1156	0.0428	0.0049
	12	0.0000+	0.0000+	0.0000+	0.0000+	0.0000+	0.0000+	0.0001	0.0004	0.0016	0.0052	0.0139	0.0318	0.0634	0.1110	0.1700	0.2252	0.2501	0.2184	0.1285	0.0307
	13	0.0000+	0.0000+	0.0000+	0.0000+	0.0000+	0.0000+	0.0000+	0.0001	0.0003	0.0010	0.0032	0.0090	0.0219	0.0476	0.0916	0.1559	0.2309	0.2856	0.2669	0.1348
	14	0.0000+	0.0000+	0.0000+	0.0000+	0.0000+	0.0000+	0.0000+	0.0000+	0.0000+	0.0001	0.0005	0.0016	0.0047	0.0126	0.0305	0.0668	0.1319	0.2312	0.3432	0.3658
	15	0.0000+	0.0000+	0.0000+	0.0000+	0.0000+	0.0000+	0.0000+	0.0000+	0.0000+	0.0000+	0.0000+	0.0001	0.0005	0.0016	0.0047	0.0134	0.0352	0.0874	0.2059	0.4633
20	0	0.8179	0.3585	0.1216	0.0388	0.0115	0.0032	0.0008	0.0002	0.0000+	0.0000+	0.0000+	0.0000+	0.0000+	0.0000+	0.0000+	0.0000+	0.0000+	0.0000+	0.0000+	0.0000+
	1	0.1652	0.3774	0.2702	0.1368	0.0576	0.0211	0.0068	0.0020	0.0005	0.0001	0.0000+	0.0000+	0.0000+	0.0000+	0.0000+	0.0000+	0.0000+	0.0000+	0.0000+	0.0000+
	2	0.0159	0.1887	0.2852	0.2293	0.1369	0.0669	0.0278	0.0100	0.0031	0.0008	0.0002	0.0000+	0.0000+	0.0000+	0.0000+	0.0000+	0.0000+	0.0000+	0.0000+	0.0000+
	3	0.0010	0.0596	0.1901	0.2428	0.2054	0.1339	0.0716	0.0323	0.0123	0.0040	0.0011	0.0002	0.0000+	0.0000+	0.0000+	0.0000+	0.0000+	0.0000+	0.0000+	0.0000+
	4	0.0000+	0.0133	0.0898	0.1821	0.2182	0.1897	0.1304	0.0738	0.0350	0.0139	0.0046	0.0013	0.0003	0.0000+	0.0000+	0.0000+	0.0000+	0.0000+	0.0000+	0.0000+
	5	0.0000+	0.0022	0.0319	0.1028	0.1746	0.2023	0.1789	0.1272	0.0746	0.0365	0.0148	0.0049	0.0013	0.0003	0.0000+	0.0000+	0.0000+	0.0000+	0.0000+	0.0000+
	6	0.0000+	0.0003	0.0089	0.0454	0.1091	0.1686	0.1916	0.1712	0.1244	0.0746	0.0370	0.0150	0.0049	0.0012	0.0002	0.0000+	0.0000+	0.0000+	0.0000+	0.0000+
	7	0.0000+	0.0000+	0.0020	0.0160	0.0545	0.1124	0.1643	0.1844	0.1659	0.1221	0.0739	0.0366	0.0146	0.0045	0.0010	0.0002	0.0000+	0.0000+	0.0000+	0.0000+
	8	0.0000+	0.0000+	0.0004	0.0046	0.0222	0.0609	0.1144	0.1614	0.1797	0.1623	0.1201	0.0727	0.0355	0.0136	0.0039	0.0008	0.0001	0.0000+	0.0000+	0.0000+
	9	0.0000+	0.0000+	0.0001	0.0011	0.0074	0.0271	0.0654	0.1158	0.1597	0.1771	0.1602	0.1185	0.0710	0.0336	0.0120	0.0030	0.0005	0.0000+	0.0000+	0.0000+
	10	0.0000+	0.0000+	0.0000+	0.0002	0.0020	0.0099	0.0308	0.0686	0.1171	0.1593	0.1762	0.1593	0.1171	0.0686	0.0308	0.0099	0.0020	0.0002	0.0000+	0.0000+
	11	0.0000+	0.0000+	0.0000+	0.0000+	0.0005	0.0030	0.0120	0.0336	0.0710	0.1185	0.1602	0.1771	0.1597	0.1158	0.0654	0.0271	0.0074	0.0011	0.0001	0.0000+
	12	0.0000+	0.0000+	0.0000+	0.0000+	0.0001	0.0008	0.0039	0.0136	0.0355	0.0727	0.1201	0.1623	0.1797	0.1614	0.1144	0.0609	0.0222	0.0046	0.0004	0.0000+
	13	0.0000+	0.0000+	0.0000+	0.0000+	0.0000+	0.0002	0.0010	0.0045	0.0146	0.0366	0.0739	0.1221	0.1659	0.1844	0.1643	0.1124	0.0545	0.0160	0.0020	0.0000+
	14	0.0000+	0.0000+	0.0000+	0.0000+	0.0000+	0.0000+	0.0002	0.0012	0.0049	0.0150	0.0370	0.0746	0.1244	0.1712	0.1916	0.1686	0.1091	0.0454	0.0089	0.0003
	15	0.0000+	0.0000+	0.0000+	0.0000+	0.0000+	0.0000+	0.0000+	0.0003	0.0013	0.0049	0.0148	0.0365	0.0746	0.1272	0.1789	0.2023	0.1746	0.1028	0.0319	0.0022
	16	0.0000+	0.0000+	0.0000+	0.0000+	0.0000+	0.0000+	0.0000+	0.0000+	0.0003	0.0013	0.0046	0.0139	0.0350	0.0738	0.1304	0.1897	0.2182	0.1821	0.0898	0.0133
	17	0.0000+	0.0000+	0.0000+	0.0000+	0.0000+	0.0000+	0.0000+	0.0000+	0.0000+	0.0002	0.0011	0.0040	0.0123	0.0323	0.0716	0.1339	0.2054	0.2428	0.1901	0.0596
	18	0.0000+	0.0000+	0.0000+	0.0000+	0.0000+	0.0000+	0.0000+	0.0000+	0.0000+	0.0000+	0.0002	0.0008	0.0031	0.0100	0.0278	0.0669	0.1369	0.2293	0.2852	0.1887
	19	0.0000+	0.0000+	0.0000+	0.0000+	0.0000+	0.0000+	0.0000+	0.0000+	0.0000+	0.0000+	0.0000+	0.0001	0.0005	0.0020	0.0068	0.0211	0.0576	0.1368	0.2702	0.3774
	20	0.0000+	0.0000+	0.0000+	0.0000+	0.0000+	0.0000+	0.0000+	0.0000+	0.0000+	0.0000+	0.0000+	0.0000+	0.0000+	0.0002	0.0008	0.0032	0.0115	0.0388	0.1216	0.3585

Note: 0.0000+ means the probability is 0.0000 rounded to four decimal places. However, the probability is *not* zero.

Table IV

Cumulative Binomial Probability Distribution

This table computes the cumulative probability of obtaining x successes in n trials of a binomial experiment with probability of success p.

n	x	0.01	0.05	0.10	0.15	0.20	0.25	0.30	0.35	0.40	0.45	0.50	0.55	0.60	0.65	0.70	0.75	0.80	0.85	0.90	0.95
2	0	0.9801	0.9025	0.8100	0.7225	0.6400	0.5625	0.4900	0.4225	0.3600	0.3025	0.2500	0.2025	0.1600	0.1225	0.0900	0.0625	0.0400	0.0225	0.0100	0.0025
	1	0.9999	0.9975	0.9900	0.9775	0.9600	0.9375	0.9100	0.8775	0.8400	0.7975	0.7500	0.6975	0.6400	0.5775	0.5100	0.4375	0.3600	0.2775	0.1900	0.0975
	2	1	1	1	1	1	1	1	1	1	1	1	1	1	1	1	1	1	1	1	1
3	0	0.9703	0.8574	0.7290	0.6141	0.5120	0.4219	0.3430	0.2746	0.2160	0.1664	0.1250	0.0911	0.0640	0.0429	0.0270	0.0156	0.0080	0.0034	0.0010	0.0001
	1	0.9997	0.9928	0.9720	0.9393	0.8960	0.8438	0.7840	0.7183	0.6480	0.5748	0.5000	0.4253	0.3520	0.2818	0.2160	0.1563	0.1040	0.0608	0.0280	0.0073
	2	1.0000−	0.9999	0.9990	0.9966	0.9920	0.9844	0.9730	0.9571	0.9360	0.9089	0.8750	0.8336	0.7840	0.7254	0.6570	0.5781	0.4880	0.3859	0.2710	0.1426
	3	1	1	1	1	1	1	1	1	1	1	1	1	1	1	1	1	1	1	1	1
4	0	0.9606	0.8145	0.6561	0.5220	0.4096	0.3164	0.2401	0.1785	0.1296	0.0915	0.0625	0.0410	0.0256	0.0150	0.0081	0.0039	0.0016	0.0005	0.0001	0.0000+
	1	0.9994	0.9860	0.9477	0.8905	0.8192	0.7383	0.6517	0.5630	0.4752	0.3910	0.3125	0.2415	0.1792	0.1265	0.0837	0.0508	0.0272	0.0120	0.0037	0.0005
	2	1.0000−	0.9995	0.9963	0.9880	0.9728	0.9492	0.9163	0.8735	0.8208	0.7585	0.6875	0.6090	0.5248	0.4370	0.3483	0.2617	0.1808	0.1095	0.0523	0.0140
	3	1.0000−	1.0000−	0.9999	0.9995	0.9984	0.9961	0.9919	0.9850	0.9744	0.9590	0.9375	0.9085	0.8704	0.8215	0.7599	0.6836	0.5904	0.4780	0.3439	0.1855
	4	1	1	1	1	1	1	1	1	1	1	1	1	1	1	1	1	1	1	1	1
5	0	0.9510	0.7738	0.5905	0.4437	0.3277	0.2373	0.1681	0.1160	0.0778	0.0503	0.0313	0.0185	0.0102	0.0053	0.0024	0.0010	0.0003	0.0001	0.0000+	0.0000+
	1	0.9990	0.9774	0.9185	0.8352	0.7373	0.6328	0.5282	0.4284	0.3370	0.2562	0.1875	0.1312	0.0870	0.0540	0.0308	0.0156	0.0067	0.0022	0.0005	0.0000+
	2	1.0000−	0.9988	0.9914	0.9734	0.9421	0.8965	0.8369	0.7648	0.6826	0.5931	0.5000	0.4069	0.3174	0.2352	0.1631	0.1035	0.0579	0.0266	0.0086	0.0012
	3	1.0000−	1.0000−	0.9995	0.9978	0.9933	0.9844	0.9692	0.9460	0.9130	0.8688	0.8125	0.7438	0.6630	0.5716	0.4718	0.3672	0.2627	0.1648	0.0815	0.0226
	4	1.0000−	1.0000−	1.0000−	0.9999	0.9997	0.9990	0.9976	0.9947	0.9898	0.9815	0.9688	0.9497	0.9222	0.8840	0.8319	0.7627	0.6723	0.5563	0.4095	0.2262
	5	1	1	1	1	1	1	1	1	1	1	1	1	1	1	1	1	1	1	1	1
6	0	0.9415	0.7351	0.5314	0.3771	0.2621	0.1780	0.1176	0.0754	0.0467	0.0277	0.0156	0.0083	0.0041	0.0018	0.0007	0.0002	0.0001	0.0000+	0.0000+	0.0000+
	1	0.9985	0.9672	0.8857	0.7765	0.6554	0.5339	0.4202	0.3191	0.2333	0.1636	0.1094	0.0692	0.0410	0.0223	0.0109	0.0046	0.0016	0.0004	0.0001	0.0000+
	2	1.0000−	0.9978	0.9842	0.9527	0.9011	0.8306	0.7443	0.6471	0.5443	0.4415	0.3438	0.2553	0.1792	0.1174	0.0705	0.0376	0.0170	0.0059	0.0013	0.0001
	3	1.0000−	0.9999	0.9987	0.9941	0.9830	0.9624	0.9295	0.8826	0.8208	0.7447	0.6563	0.5585	0.4557	0.3529	0.2557	0.1694	0.0989	0.0473	0.0159	0.0022
	4	1.0000−	1.0000−	0.9999	0.9996	0.9984	0.9954	0.9891	0.9777	0.9590	0.9308	0.8906	0.8364	0.7667	0.6809	0.5798	0.4661	0.3446	0.2235	0.1143	0.0328
	5	1.0000−	1.0000−	1.0000−	0.9999	0.9999	0.9998	0.9993	0.9982	0.9959	0.9917	0.9844	0.9723	0.9533	0.9246	0.8824	0.8220	0.7379	0.6229	0.4686	0.2649
	6	1	1	1	1	1	1	1	1	1	1	1	1	1	1	1	1	1	1	1	1
7	0	0.9321	0.6983	0.4783	0.3206	0.2097	0.1335	0.0824	0.0490	0.0280	0.0152	0.0078	0.0037	0.0016	0.0006	0.0002	0.0001	0.0000+	0.0000+	0.0000+	0.0000+
	1	0.9980	0.9556	0.8503	0.7166	0.5767	0.4449	0.3294	0.2338	0.1586	0.1024	0.0625	0.0357	0.0188	0.0090	0.0038	0.0013	0.0004	0.0001	0.0000+	0.0000+
	2	1.0000−	0.9962	0.9743	0.9262	0.8520	0.7564	0.6471	0.5323	0.4199	0.3164	0.2266	0.1529	0.0963	0.0556	0.0288	0.0129	0.0047	0.0012	0.0002	0.0000+
	3	1.0000−	0.9998	0.9973	0.9879	0.9667	0.9294	0.8740	0.8002	0.7102	0.6083	0.5000	0.3917	0.2898	0.1998	0.1260	0.0706	0.0333	0.0121	0.0027	0.0002
	4	1.0000−	1.0000−	0.9998	0.9988	0.9953	0.9871	0.9712	0.9444	0.9037	0.8471	0.7734	0.6836	0.5801	0.4677	0.3529	0.2436	0.1480	0.0738	0.0257	0.0038
	5	1.0000−	1.0000−	0.9999	0.9999	0.9996	0.9987	0.9962	0.9910	0.9812	0.9643	0.9375	0.8976	0.8414	0.7662	0.6706	0.5551	0.4233	0.2834	0.1497	0.0444
	6	1.0000−	1.0000−	1.0000−	1.0000−	0.9999	0.9999	0.9998	0.9994	0.9984	0.9963	0.9922	0.9848	0.9720	0.9510	0.9176	0.8665	0.7903	0.6794	0.5217	0.3017
	7	1	1	1	1	1	1	1	1	1	1	1	1	1	1	1	1	1	1	1	1

Note: 0.0000+ means the probability is 0.0000 rounded to four decimal places. However, the probability is *not* zero.
1.0000− means the probability is 1.0000 rounded to four decimal places. However, the probability is *not* one.

Table IV (continued)

										p											
n	x	0.01	0.05	0.10	0.15	0.20	0.25	0.30	0.35	0.40	0.45	0.50	0.55	0.60	0.65	0.70	0.75	0.80	0.85	0.90	0.95
8	0	0.9227	0.6634	0.4305	0.2725	0.1678	0.1001	0.0576	0.0319	0.0168	0.0084	0.0039	0.0017	0.0007	0.0002	0.0001	0.0000+	0.0000+	0.0000+	0.0000+	0.0000+
	1	0.9973	0.9428	0.8131	0.6572	0.5033	0.3671	0.2553	0.1691	0.1064	0.0632	0.0352	0.0181	0.0085	0.0036	0.0013	0.0004	0.0001	0.0000+	0.0000+	0.0000+
	2	0.9999	0.9942	0.9619	0.8948	0.7969	0.6785	0.5518	0.4278	0.3154	0.2201	0.1445	0.0885	0.0498	0.0253	0.0113	0.0042	0.0012	0.0002	0.0000+	0.0000+
	3	1.0000−	0.9996	0.9950	0.9786	0.9437	0.8862	0.8059	0.7064	0.5941	0.4770	0.3633	0.2604	0.1737	0.1061	0.0580	0.0273	0.0104	0.0029	0.0004	0.0000+
	4	1.0000−	1.0000−	0.9996	0.9971	0.9896	0.9727	0.9420	0.8389	0.8263	0.7396	0.6367	0.5230	0.4059	0.2936	0.1941	0.1138	0.0563	0.0214	0.0050	0.0004
	5	1.0000−	1.0000−	1.0000−	0.9998	0.9988	0.9958	0.9887	0.9747	0.9502	0.9115	0.8555	0.7799	0.6846	0.5722	0.4482	0.3215	0.2031	0.1052	0.0381	0.0058
	6	1.0000−	1.0000−	1.0000−	1.0000−	0.9999	0.9996	0.9987	0.9964	0.9915	0.9819	0.9648	0.9368	0.8936	0.8309	0.7447	0.6329	0.4967	0.3428	0.1869	0.0572
	7	1.0000−	1.0000−	1.0000−	1.0000−	1.0000−	1.0000−	0.9999	0.9998	0.9993	0.9983	0.9961	0.9916	0.9832	0.9681	0.9424	0.8999	0.8322	0.7275	0.5695	0.3366
	8	1	1	1	1	1	1	1	1	1	1	1	1	1	1	1	1	1	1	1	1
9	0	0.9135	0.6302	0.3874	0.2316	0.1342	0.0751	0.0404	0.0207	0.0101	0.0046	0.0020	0.0008	0.0003	0.0001	0.0000+	0.0000+	0.0000+	0.0000+	0.0000+	0.0000+
	1	0.9966	0.9288	0.7748	0.5995	0.4362	0.3003	0.1960	0.1211	0.0705	0.0385	0.0195	0.0091	0.0038	0.0014	0.0004	0.0001	0.0000+	0.0000+	0.0000+	0.0000+
	2	0.9999	0.9916	0.9470	0.8591	0.7382	0.6007	0.4628	0.3373	0.2318	0.1495	0.0898	0.0498	0.0250	0.0112	0.0043	0.0013	0.0003	0.0000+	0.0000+	0.0000+
	3	1.0000−	0.9994	0.9917	0.9661	0.9144	0.8343	0.7297	0.6089	0.4826	0.3614	0.2539	0.1658	0.0994	0.0536	0.0253	0.0100	0.0031	0.0006	0.0001	0.0000+
	4	1.0000−	1.0000−	0.9991	0.9944	0.9804	0.9511	0.9012	0.8283	0.7334	0.6214	0.5000	0.3786	0.2666	0.1717	0.0988	0.0489	0.0196	0.0056	0.0009	0.0000+
	5	1.0000−	1.0000−	0.9999	0.9994	0.9969	0.9900	0.9747	0.9464	0.9006	0.8342	0.7461	0.6386	0.5174	0.3911	0.2703	0.1657	0.0856	0.0339	0.0083	0.0006
	6	1.0000−	1.0000−	1.0000−	1.0000−	0.9997	0.9987	0.9957	0.9888	0.9750	0.9502	0.9102	0.8505	0.7682	0.6627	0.5372	0.3993	0.2618	0.1409	0.0530	0.0084
	7	1.0000−	1.0000−	1.0000−	1.0000−	1.0000−	0.9999	0.9996	0.9986	0.9962	0.9909	0.9805	0.9615	0.9295	0.8789	0.8040	0.6997	0.5638	0.4005	0.2252	0.0712
	8	1.0000−	1.0000−	1.0000−	1.0000−	1.0000−	1.0000−	1.0000−	0.9999	0.9997	0.9992	0.9980	0.9954	0.9899	0.9793	0.9596	0.9249	0.8658	0.7684	0.6126	0.3698
	9	1	1	1	1	1	1	1	1	1	1	1	1	1	1	1	1	1	1	1	1
10	0	0.9044	0.5987	0.3487	0.1969	0.1074	0.0563	0.0282	0.0135	0.0060	0.0025	0.0010	0.0003	0.0001	0.0000+	0.0000+	0.0000+	0.0000+	0.0000+	0.0000+	0.0000+
	1	0.9957	0.9139	0.7361	0.5443	0.3758	0.2440	0.1493	0.0860	0.0464	0.0233	0.0107	0.0045	0.0017	0.0005	0.0001	0.0000+	0.0000+	0.0000+	0.0000+	0.0000+
	2	0.9999	0.9885	0.9298	0.8202	0.6778	0.5256	0.3828	0.2616	0.1673	0.0996	0.0547	0.0274	0.0123	0.0048	0.0016	0.0004	0.0001	0.0000+	0.0000+	0.0000+
	3	1.0000−	0.9990	0.9872	0.9500	0.8791	0.7759	0.6496	0.5138	0.3823	0.2660	0.1719	0.1020	0.0548	0.0260	0.0106	0.0035	0.0009	0.0001	0.0000+	0.0000+
	4	1.0000−	0.9999	0.9984	0.9901	0.9672	0.9219	0.8497	0.7515	0.6331	0.5044	0.3770	0.2616	0.1662	0.0949	0.0473	0.0197	0.0064	0.0014	0.0001	0.0000+
	5	1.0000−	1.0000−	0.9999	0.9986	0.9936	0.9803	0.9527	0.9051	0.8338	0.7384	0.6230	0.4956	0.3669	0.2485	0.1503	0.0781	0.0328	0.0099	0.0016	0.0001
	6	1.0000−	1.0000−	1.0000−	0.9999	0.9991	0.9965	0.9894	0.9740	0.9452	0.8980	0.8281	0.7340	0.6177	0.4862	0.3504	0.2241	0.1209	0.0500	0.0128	0.0010
	7	1.0000−	1.0000−	1.0000−	1.0000−	0.9999	0.9996	0.9984	0.9952	0.9877	0.9726	0.9453	0.9004	0.8327	0.7384	0.6172	0.4744	0.3222	0.1798	0.0702	0.0115
	8	1.0000−	1.0000−	1.0000−	1.0000−	1.0000−	1.0000−	0.9999	0.9995	0.9983	0.9955	0.9893	0.9767	0.9536	0.9140	0.8507	0.7560	0.6242	0.4557	0.2639	0.0861
	9	1.0000−	1.0000−	1.0000−	1.0000−	1.0000−	1.0000−	1.0000−	1.0000−	0.9999	0.9997	0.9990	0.9975	0.9940	0.9865	0.9718	0.9437	0.8926	0.8031	0.6513	0.4013
	10	1	1	1	1	1	1	1	1	1	1	1	1	1	1	1	1	1	1	1	1

Note: 0.0000+ means the probability is 0.0000 rounded to four decimal places. However, the probability is *not* zero.
1.0000− means the probability is 1.0000 rounded to four decimal places. However, the probability is *not* one.

Table IV (*continued*)

| | | | | | | | | | | | | *p* | | | | | | | | | |
n	x	0.01	0.05	0.10	0.15	0.20	0.25	0.30	0.35	0.40	0.45	0.50	0.55	0.60	0.65	0.70	0.75	0.80	0.85	0.90	0.95
11	0	0.8953	0.5688	0.3138	0.1673	0.0859	0.0422	0.0198	0.0088	0.0036	0.0014	0.0005	0.0002	0.0000+	0.0000+	0.0000+	0.0000+	0.0000+	0.0000+	0.0000+	0.0000+
	1	0.9948	0.8981	0.6974	0.4922	0.3221	0.1971	0.1130	0.0606	0.0302	0.0139	0.0059	0.0022	0.0007	0.0002	0.0000+	0.0000+	0.0000+	0.0000+	0.0000+	0.0000+
	2	0.9998	0.9848	0.9104	0.7788	0.6174	0.4552	0.3127	0.2001	0.1189	0.0652	0.0327	0.0148	0.0059	0.0020	0.0006	0.0001	0.0000+	0.0000+	0.0000+	0.0000+
	3	1.0000−	0.9984	0.9815	0.9306	0.8389	0.7133	0.5696	0.4256	0.2963	0.1911	0.1133	0.0610	0.0293	0.0122	0.0043	0.0012	0.0002	0.0000+	0.0000+	0.0000+
	4	1.0000−	0.9999	0.9972	0.9841	0.9496	0.8854	0.7897	0.6683	0.5326	0.3971	0.2744	0.1738	0.0994	0.0501	0.0216	0.0076	0.0020	0.0003	0.0000+	0.0000+
	5	1.0000−	1.0000−	0.9997	0.9973	0.9883	0.9657	0.9218	0.8513	0.7535	0.6331	0.5000	0.3669	0.2465	0.1487	0.0782	0.0343	0.0117	0.0027	0.0003	0.0000+
	6	1.0000−	1.0000−	1.0000−	0.9997	0.9980	0.9924	0.9784	0.9499	0.9006	0.8262	0.7256	0.6029	0.4672	0.3317	0.2103	0.1146	0.0504	0.0159	0.0028	0.0001
	7	1.0000−	1.0000−	1.0000−	1.0000−	0.9998	0.9988	0.9957	0.9878	0.9707	0.9390	0.8867	0.8089	0.7037	0.5744	0.4304	0.2867	0.1611	0.0694	0.0185	0.0016
	8	1.0000−	1.0000−	1.0000−	1.0000−	0.9999	0.9999	0.9994	0.9980	0.9941	0.9852	0.9673	0.9348	0.8811	0.7999	0.6873	0.5448	0.3826	0.2212	0.0896	0.0152
	9	1.0000−	1.0000−	1.0000−	1.0000−	1.0000−	1.0000−	1.0000−	0.9998	0.9993	0.9976	0.9941	0.9861	0.9698	0.9394	0.8870	0.8029	0.6779	0.5078	0.3026	0.1019
	10	1.0000−	1.0000−	1.0000−	1.0000−	1.0000−	1.0000−	1.0000−	1.0000−	1.0000−	0.9996	0.9995	0.9986	0.9964	0.9912	0.9802	0.9578	0.9141	0.8327	0.6862	0.4312
	11	1	1	1	1	1	1	1	1	1	1	1	1	1	1	1	1	1	1	1	1
12	0	0.8864	0.5404	0.2824	0.1422	0.0687	0.0317	0.0138	0.0057	0.0022	0.0008	0.0002	0.0001	0.0000+	0.0000+	0.0000+	0.0000+	0.0000+	0.0000+	0.0000+	0.0000+
	1	0.9938	0.8816	0.6590	0.4435	0.2749	0.1584	0.0850	0.0424	0.0196	0.0083	0.0032	0.0011	0.0003	0.0001	0.0000+	0.0000+	0.0000+	0.0000+	0.0000+	0.0000+
	2	0.9998	0.9804	0.8891	0.7358	0.5583	0.3907	0.2528	0.1513	0.0834	0.0421	0.0193	0.0079	0.0028	0.0008	0.0002	0.0001	0.0000+	0.0000+	0.0000+	0.0000+
	3	1.0000−	0.9978	0.9744	0.9078	0.7946	0.6488	0.4925	0.3467	0.2253	0.1345	0.0730	0.0356	0.0153	0.0056	0.0017	0.0004	0.0001	0.0000+	0.0000+	0.0000+
	4	1.0000−	0.9998	0.9957	0.9761	0.9274	0.8424	0.7237	0.5833	0.4382	0.3044	0.1938	0.1117	0.0573	0.0255	0.0095	0.0028	0.0006	0.0001	0.0000+	0.0000+
	5	1.0000−	1.0000−	0.9995	0.9954	0.9806	0.9456	0.8822	0.7873	0.6652	0.5269	0.3872	0.2607	0.1582	0.0846	0.0386	0.0143	0.0039	0.0007	0.0001	0.0000+
	6	1.0000−	1.0000−	0.9999	0.9993	0.9961	0.9857	0.9614	0.9154	0.8418	0.7393	0.6128	0.4731	0.3348	0.2127	0.1178	0.0544	0.0194	0.0046	0.0005	0.0000+
	7	1.0000−	1.0000−	1.0000−	0.9999	0.9994	0.9972	0.9905	0.9745	0.9427	0.8883	0.8062	0.6956	0.5618	0.4167	0.2763	0.1576	0.0726	0.0239	0.0043	0.0002
	8	1.0000−	1.0000−	1.0000−	1.0000−	0.9999	0.9996	0.9983	0.9944	0.9847	0.9644	0.9270	0.8655	0.7747	0.6533	0.5075	0.3512	0.2054	0.0922	0.0256	0.0022
	9	1.0000−	1.0000−	1.0000−	1.0000−	1.0000−	1.0000−	0.9998	0.9992	0.9972	0.9921	0.9807	0.9579	0.9166	0.8487	0.7472	0.6093	0.4417	0.2642	0.1109	0.0196
	10	1.0000−	1.0000−	1.0000−	1.0000−	1.0000−	1.0000−	1.0000−	0.9999	0.9997	0.9989	0.9968	0.9917	0.9804	0.9576	0.9150	0.8416	0.7251	0.5565	0.3410	0.1184
	11	1.0000−	1.0000−	1.0000−	1.0000−	1.0000−	1.0000−	1.0000−	1.0000−	1.0000−	0.9999	0.9998	0.9992	0.9978	0.9943	0.9862	0.9683	0.9313	0.8578	0.7176	0.4596
	12	1	1	1	1	1	1	1	1	1	1	1	1	1	1	1	1	1	1	1	1

Note: 0.0000+ means the probability is 0.0000 rounded to four decimal places. However, the probability is *not* zero.
1.0000− means the probability is 1.0000 rounded to four decimal places. However, the probability is *not* one.

Table IV (continued)

p

n	x	0.01	0.05	0.10	0.15	0.20	0.25	0.30	0.35	0.40	0.45	0.50	0.55	0.60	0.65	0.70	0.75	0.80	0.85	0.90	0.95
15	0	0.8601	0.4633	0.2059	0.0874	0.0352	0.0134	0.0047	0.0016	0.0005	0.0001	0.0000+	0.0000+	0.0000+	0.0000+	0.0000+	0.0000+	0.0000+	0.0000+	0.0000+	0.0000+
	1	0.9904	0.8290	0.5490	0.3186	0.1671	0.0802	0.0353	0.0142	0.0052	0.0017	0.0005	0.0001	0.0000+	0.0000+	0.0000+	0.0000+	0.0000+	0.0000+	0.0000+	0.0000+
	2	0.9996	0.9638	0.8159	0.6042	0.3980	0.2361	0.1268	0.0617	0.0271	0.0107	0.0037	0.0011	0.0003	0.0001	0.0000+	0.0000+	0.0000+	0.0000+	0.0000+	0.0000+
	3	1.0000-	0.9945	0.9444	0.8227	0.6482	0.4613	0.2969	0.1727	0.0905	0.0424	0.0176	0.0063	0.0019	0.0005	0.0001	0.0000+	0.0000+	0.0000+	0.0000+	0.0000+
	4	1.0000-	0.9994	0.9873	0.9383	0.8358	0.6865	0.5155	0.3519	0.2173	0.1204	0.0592	0.0255	0.0093	0.0028	0.0007	0.0001	0.0000+	0.0000+	0.0000+	0.0000+
	5	1.0000-	0.9999	0.9978	0.9832	0.9389	0.8516	0.7216	0.5643	0.4032	0.2608	0.1509	0.0769	0.0338	0.0124	0.0037	0.0008	0.0001	0.0001	0.0000+	0.0000+
	6	1.0000-	1.0000-	0.9997	0.9964	0.9819	0.9434	0.8689	0.7548	0.6098	0.4522	0.3036	0.1818	0.0950	0.0422	0.0152	0.0042	0.0008	0.0001	0.0000+	0.0000+
	7	1.0000-	1.0000-	1.0000-	0.9994	0.9958	0.9827	0.9500	0.8868	0.7869	0.6535	0.5000	0.3465	0.2131	0.1132	0.0500	0.0173	0.0042	0.0006	0.0000+	0.0000+
	8	1.0000-	1.0000-	1.0000-	0.9999	0.9992	0.9958	0.9848	0.9578	0.9050	0.8182	0.6964	0.5478	0.3902	0.2452	0.1311	0.0566	0.0181	0.0036	0.0003	0.0000+
	9	1.0000-	1.0000-	1.0000-	1.0000-	0.9999	0.9992	0.9963	0.9876	0.9662	0.9231	0.8491	0.7392	0.5968	0.4357	0.2784	0.1484	0.0611	0.0168	0.0022	0.0001
	10	1.0000-	1.0000-	1.0000-	1.0000-	1.0000-	0.9999	0.9993	0.9972	0.9907	0.9745	0.9408	0.8796	0.7827	0.6481	0.4845	0.3135	0.1642	0.0617	0.0127	0.0006
	11	1.0000-	1.0000-	1.0000-	1.0000-	1.0000-	1.0000-	0.9999	0.9995	0.9981	0.9937	0.9824	0.9576	0.9095	0.8273	0.7031	0.5387	0.3518	0.1773	0.0556	0.0055
	12	1.0000-	1.0000-	1.0000-	1.0000-	1.0000-	1.0000-	1.0000-	0.9999	0.9997	0.9989	0.9963	0.9893	0.9729	0.9383	0.8732	0.7639	0.6020	0.3958	0.1841	0.0362
	13	1.0000-	1.0000-	1.0000-	1.0000-	1.0000-	1.0000-	1.0000-	1.0000-	1.0000-	0.9999	0.9995	0.9983	0.9948	0.9858	0.9647	0.9198	0.8329	0.6814	0.4510	0.1710
	14	1.0000-	1.0000-	1.0000-	1.0000-	1.0000-	1.0000-	1.0000-	1.0000-	1.0000-	1.0000-	1.0000-	0.9999	0.9995	0.9984	0.9953	0.9866	0.9648	0.9126	0.7941	0.5367
	15	1	1	1	1	1	1	1	1	1	1	1	1	1	1	1	1	1	1	1	1
20	0	0.8179	0.3585	0.1216	0.0388	0.0115	0.0032	0.0008	0.0002	0.0000+	0.0000+	0.0000+	0.0000+	0.0000+	0.0000+	0.0000+	0.0000+	0.0000+	0.0000+	0.0000+	0.0000+
	1	0.9831	0.7358	0.3917	0.1756	0.0692	0.0243	0.0076	0.0021	0.0005	0.0001	0.0000+	0.0000+	0.0000+	0.0000+	0.0000+	0.0000+	0.0000+	0.0000+	0.0000+	0.0000+
	2	0.9990	0.9245	0.6769	0.4049	0.2061	0.0913	0.0355	0.0121	0.0036	0.0009	0.0002	0.0000+	0.0000+	0.0000+	0.0000+	0.0000+	0.0000+	0.0000+	0.0000+	0.0000+
	3	1.0000-	0.9841	0.8670	0.6477	0.4114	0.2252	0.1071	0.0444	0.0160	0.0049	0.0013	0.0003	0.0000+	0.0000+	0.0000+	0.0000+	0.0000+	0.0000+	0.0000+	0.0000+
	4	1.0000-	0.9974	0.9568	0.8298	0.6296	0.4148	0.2375	0.1182	0.0510	0.0189	0.0059	0.0015	0.0003	0.0000+	0.0000+	0.0000+	0.0000+	0.0000+	0.0000+	0.0000+
	5	1.0000-	0.9997	0.9887	0.9327	0.8042	0.6172	0.4164	0.2454	0.1256	0.0553	0.0207	0.0064	0.0016	0.0003	0.0000+	0.0000+	0.0000+	0.0000+	0.0000+	0.0000+
	6	1.0000-	1.0000-	0.9976	0.9781	0.9133	0.7858	0.6080	0.4166	0.2500	0.1299	0.0577	0.0214	0.0065	0.0015	0.0003	0.0000+	0.0000+	0.0000+	0.0000+	0.0000+
	7	1.0000-	1.0000-	0.9996	0.9941	0.9679	0.8982	0.7723	0.6010	0.4159	0.2520	0.1316	0.0580	0.0210	0.0060	0.0013	0.0002	0.0000+	0.0000+	0.0000+	0.0000+
	8	1.0000-	1.0000-	0.9999	0.9987	0.9900	0.9591	0.8867	0.7624	0.5956	0.4143	0.2517	0.1308	0.0565	0.0196	0.0051	0.0009	0.0001	0.0000+	0.0000+	0.0000+
	9	1.0000-	1.0000-	1.0000-	0.9998	0.9974	0.9861	0.9520	0.8782	0.7553	0.5914	0.4119	0.2493	0.1275	0.0532	0.0171	0.0039	0.0006	0.0000+	0.0000+	0.0000+
	10	1.0000-	1.0000-	1.0000-	1.0000-	0.9994	0.9961	0.9829	0.9468	0.8725	0.7507	0.5881	0.4086	0.2447	0.1218	0.0480	0.0139	0.0026	0.0002	0.0000+	0.0000+
	11	1.0000-	1.0000-	1.0000-	1.0000-	0.9999	0.9991	0.9949	0.9804	0.9435	0.8692	0.7483	0.5857	0.4044	0.2376	0.1133	0.0409	0.0100	0.0013	0.0001	0.0000+
	12	1.0000-	1.0000-	1.0000-	1.0000-	1.0000-	0.9998	0.9987	0.9940	0.9790	0.9420	0.8684	0.7480	0.5841	0.3990	0.2277	0.1018	0.0321	0.0059	0.0004	0.0000+
	13	1.0000-	1.0000-	1.0000-	1.0000-	1.0000-	1.0000-	0.9997	0.9985	0.9935	0.9786	0.9423	0.8701	0.7500	0.5834	0.3920	0.2142	0.0867	0.0219	0.0024	0.0000+
	14	1.0000-	1.0000-	1.0000-	1.0000-	1.0000-	1.0000-	1.0000-	0.9997	0.9984	0.9936	0.9793	0.9447	0.8744	0.7546	0.5836	0.3828	0.1958	0.0673	0.0113	0.0003
	15	1.0000-	1.0000-	1.0000-	1.0000-	1.0000-	1.0000-	1.0000-	1.0000-	0.9997	0.9985	0.9941	0.9811	0.9490	0.8818	0.7625	0.5852	0.3704	0.1702	0.0432	0.0026
	16	1.0000-	1.0000-	1.0000-	1.0000-	1.0000-	1.0000-	1.0000-	1.0000-	1.0000-	0.9997	0.9987	0.9951	0.9840	0.9556	0.8929	0.7748	0.5886	0.3523	0.1330	0.0159
	17	1.0000-	1.0000-	1.0000-	1.0000-	1.0000-	1.0000-	1.0000-	1.0000-	1.0000-	1.0000-	0.9998	0.9991	0.9964	0.9879	0.9645	0.9087	0.7939	0.5951	0.3231	0.0755
	18	1.0000-	1.0000-	1.0000-	1.0000-	1.0000-	1.0000-	1.0000-	1.0000-	1.0000-	1.0000-	1.0000-	0.9999	0.9995	0.9979	0.9924	0.9757	0.9308	0.8244	0.6083	0.2642
	19	1.0000-	1.0000-	1.0000-	1.0000-	1.0000-	1.0000-	1.0000-	1.0000-	1.0000-	1.0000-	1.0000-	1.0000-	1.0000-	0.9998	0.9992	0.9968	0.9885	0.9612	0.8784	0.6415
	20	1	1	1	1	1	1	1	1	1	1	1	1	1	1	1	1	1	1	1	1

Note: 0.0000+ means the probability is 0.0000 rounded to four decimal places. However, the probability is *not* zero. 1.0000− means the probability is 1.0000 rounded to four decimal places. However, the probability is *not* one.

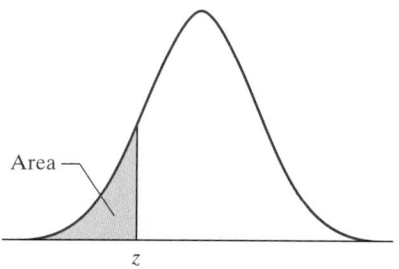

Area

z

Table V

Standard Normal Distribution

z	.00	.01	.02	.03	.04	.05	.06	.07	.08	.09
−3.4	0.0003	0.0003	0.0003	0.0003	0.0003	0.0003	0.0003	0.0003	0.0003	0.0002
−3.3	0.0005	0.0005	0.0005	0.0004	0.0004	0.0004	0.0004	0.0004	0.0004	0.0003
−3.2	0.0007	0.0007	0.0006	0.0006	0.0006	0.0006	0.0006	0.0005	0.0005	0.0005
−3.1	0.0010	0.0009	0.0009	0.0009	0.0008	0.0008	0.0008	0.0008	0.0007	0.0007
−3.0	0.0013	0.0013	0.0013	0.0012	0.0012	0.0011	0.0011	0.0011	0.0010	0.0010
−2.9	0.0019	0.0018	0.0018	0.0017	0.0016	0.0016	0.0015	0.0015	0.0014	0.0014
−2.8	0.0026	0.0025	0.0024	0.0023	0.0023	0.0022	0.0021	0.0021	0.0020	0.0019
−2.7	0.0035	0.0034	0.0033	0.0032	0.0031	0.0030	0.0029	0.0028	0.0027	0.0026
−2.6	0.0047	0.0045	0.0044	0.0043	0.0041	0.0040	0.0039	0.0038	0.0037	0.0036
−2.5	0.0062	0.0060	0.0059	0.0057	0.0055	0.0054	0.0052	0.0051	0.0049	0.0048
−2.4	0.0082	0.0080	0.0078	0.0075	0.0073	0.0071	0.0069	0.0068	0.0066	0.0064
−2.3	0.0107	0.0104	0.0102	0.0099	0.0096	0.0094	0.0091	0.0089	0.0087	0.0084
−2.2	0.0139	0.0136	0.0132	0.0129	0.0125	0.0122	0.0119	0.0116	0.0113	0.0110
−2.1	0.0179	0.0174	0.0170	0.0166	0.0162	0.0158	0.0154	0.0150	0.0146	0.0143
−2.0	0.0228	0.0222	0.0217	0.0212	0.0207	0.0202	0.0197	0.0192	0.0188	0.0183
−1.9	0.0287	0.0281	0.0274	0.0268	0.0262	0.0256	0.0250	0.0244	0.0239	0.0233
−1.8	0.0359	0.0351	0.0344	0.0336	0.0329	0.0322	0.0314	0.0307	0.0301	0.0294
−1.7	0.0446	0.0436	0.0427	0.0418	0.0409	0.0401	0.0392	0.0384	0.0375	0.0367
−1.6	0.0548	0.0537	0.0526	0.0516	0.0505	0.0495	0.0485	0.0475	0.0465	0.0455
−1.5	0.0668	0.0655	0.0643	0.0630	0.0618	0.0606	0.0594	0.0582	0.0571	0.0559
−1.4	0.0808	0.0793	0.0778	0.0764	0.0749	0.0735	0.0721	0.0708	0.0694	0.0681
−1.3	0.0968	0.0951	0.0934	0.0918	0.0901	0.0885	0.0869	0.0853	0.0838	0.0823
−1.2	0.1151	0.1131	0.1112	0.1093	0.1075	0.1056	0.1038	0.1020	0.1003	0.0985
−1.1	0.1357	0.1335	0.1314	0.1292	0.1271	0.1251	0.1230	0.1210	0.1190	0.1170
−1.0	0.1587	0.1562	0.1539	0.1515	0.1492	0.1469	0.1446	0.1423	0.1401	0.1379
−0.9	0.1841	0.1814	0.1788	0.1762	0.1736	0.1711	0.1685	0.1660	0.1635	0.1611
−0.8	0.2119	0.2090	0.2061	0.2033	0.2005	0.1977	0.1949	0.1922	0.1894	0.1867
−0.7	0.2420	0.2389	0.2358	0.2327	0.2296	0.2266	0.2236	0.2206	0.2177	0.2148
−0.6	0.2743	0.2709	0.2676	0.2643	0.2611	0.2578	0.2546	0.2514	0.2483	0.2451
−0.5	0.3085	0.3050	0.3015	0.2981	0.2946	0.2912	0.2877	0.2843	0.2810	0.2776
−0.4	0.3446	0.3409	0.3372	0.3336	0.3300	0.3264	0.3228	0.3192	0.3156	0.3121
−0.3	0.3821	0.3783	0.3745	0.3707	0.3669	0.3632	0.3594	0.3557	0.3520	0.3483
−0.2	0.4207	0.4168	0.4129	0.4090	0.4052	0.4013	0.3974	0.3936	0.3897	0.3859
−0.1	0.4602	0.4562	0.4522	0.4483	0.4443	0.4404	0.4364	0.4325	0.4286	0.4247
−0.0	0.5000	0.4960	0.4920	0.4880	0.4840	0.4801	0.4761	0.4721	0.4681	0.4641

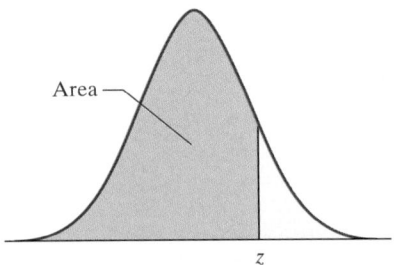

Area — z

Table V (continued)

Standard Normal Distribution

z	.00	.01	.02	.03	.04	.05	.06	.07	.08	.09
0.0	0.5000	0.5040	0.5080	0.5120	0.5160	0.5199	0.5239	0.5279	0.5319	0.5359
0.1	0.5398	0.5438	0.5478	0.5517	0.5557	0.5596	0.5636	0.5675	0.5714	0.5753
0.2	0.5793	0.5832	0.5871	0.5910	0.5948	0.5987	0.6026	0.6064	0.6103	0.6141
0.3	0.6179	0.6217	0.6255	0.6293	0.6331	0.6368	0.6406	0.6443	0.6480	0.6517
0.4	0.6554	0.6591	0.6628	0.6664	0.6700	0.6736	0.6772	0.6808	0.6844	0.6879
0.5	0.6915	0.6950	0.6985	0.7019	0.7054	0.7088	0.7123	0.7157	0.7190	0.7224
0.6	0.7257	0.7291	0.7324	0.7357	0.7389	0.7422	0.7454	0.7486	0.7517	0.7549
0.7	0.7580	0.7611	0.7642	0.7673	0.7704	0.7734	0.7764	0.7794	0.7823	0.7852
0.8	0.7881	0.7910	0.7939	0.7967	0.7995	0.8023	0.8051	0.8078	0.8106	0.8133
0.9	0.8159	0.8186	0.8212	0.8238	0.8264	0.8289	0.8315	0.8340	0.8365	0.8389
1.0	0.8413	0.8438	0.8461	0.8485	0.8508	0.8531	0.8554	0.8577	0.8599	0.8621
1.1	0.8643	0.8665	0.8686	0.8708	0.8729	0.8749	0.8770	0.8790	0.8810	0.8830
1.2	0.8849	0.8869	0.8888	0.8907	0.8925	0.8944	0.8962	0.8980	0.8997	0.9015
1.3	0.9032	0.9049	0.9066	0.9082	0.9099	0.9115	0.9131	0.9147	0.9162	0.9177
1.4	0.9192	0.9207	0.9222	0.9236	0.9251	0.9265	0.9279	0.9292	0.9306	0.9319
1.5	0.9332	0.9345	0.9357	0.9370	0.9382	0.9394	0.9406	0.9418	0.9429	0.9441
1.6	0.9452	0.9463	0.9474	0.9484	0.9495	0.9505	0.9515	0.9525	0.9535	0.9545
1.7	0.9554	0.9564	0.9573	0.9582	0.9591	0.9599	0.9608	0.9616	0.9625	0.9633
1.8	0.9641	0.9649	0.9656	0.9664	0.9671	0.9678	0.9686	0.9693	0.9699	0.9706
1.9	0.9713	0.9719	0.9726	0.9732	0.9738	0.9744	0.9750	0.9756	0.9761	0.9767
2.0	0.9772	0.9778	0.9783	0.9788	0.9793	0.9798	0.9803	0.9808	0.9812	0.9817
2.1	0.9821	0.9826	0.9830	0.9834	0.9838	0.9842	0.9846	0.9850	0.9854	0.9857
2.2	0.9861	0.9864	0.9868	0.9871	0.9875	0.9878	0.9881	0.9884	0.9887	0.9890
2.3	0.9893	0.9896	0.9898	0.9901	0.9904	0.9906	0.9909	0.9911	0.9913	0.9916
2.4	0.9918	0.9920	0.9922	0.9925	0.9927	0.9929	0.9931	0.9932	0.9934	0.9936
2.5	0.9938	0.9940	0.9941	0.9943	0.9945	0.9946	0.9948	0.9949	0.9951	0.9952
2.6	0.9953	0.9955	0.9956	0.9957	0.9959	0.9960	0.9961	0.9962	0.9963	0.9964
2.7	0.9965	0.9966	0.9967	0.9968	0.9969	0.9970	0.9971	0.9972	0.9973	0.9974
2.8	0.9974	0.9975	0.9976	0.9977	0.9977	0.9978	0.9979	0.9979	0.9980	0.9981
2.9	0.9981	0.9982	0.9982	0.9983	0.9984	0.9984	0.9985	0.9985	0.9986	0.9986
3.0	0.9987	0.9987	0.9987	0.9988	0.9988	0.9989	0.9989	0.9989	0.9990	0.9990
3.1	0.9990	0.9991	0.9991	0.9991	0.9992	0.9992	0.9992	0.9992	0.9993	0.9993
3.2	0.9993	0.9993	0.9994	0.9994	0.9994	0.9994	0.9994	0.9995	0.9995	0.9995
3.3	0.9995	0.9995	0.9995	0.9996	0.9996	0.9996	0.9996	0.9996	0.9996	0.9997
3.4	0.9997	0.9997	0.9997	0.9997	0.9997	0.9997	0.9997	0.9997	0.9997	0.9998

(b) Confidence Interval Critical Values, $z_{\alpha/2}$

Level of Confidence	Critical Value, $z_{\alpha/2}$
0.90 or 90%	1.645
0.95 or 95%	1.96
0.98 or 98%	2.33
0.99 or 99%	2.575

(c) Hypothesis Testing Critical Values

Level of Significance, α	Left Tailed	Right Tailed	Two-Tailed
0.10	-1.28	1.28	± 1.645
0.05	-1.645	1.645	± 1.96
0.01	-2.33	2.33	± 2.575

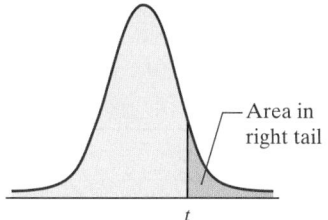
Area in right tail

Table VI

t-Distribution
Area in Right Tail

df	0.25	0.20	0.15	0.10	0.05	0.025	0.02	0.01	0.005	0.0025	0.001	0.0005
1	1.000	1.376	1.963	3.078	6.314	12.706	15.894	31.821	63.657	127.321	318.309	636.619
2	0.816	1.061	1.386	1.886	2.920	4.303	4.849	6.965	9.925	14.089	22.327	31.599
3	0.765	0.978	1.250	1.638	2.353	3.182	3.482	4.541	5.841	7.453	10.215	12.924
4	0.741	0.941	1.190	1.533	2.132	2.776	2.999	3.747	4.604	5.598	7.173	8.610
5	0.727	0.920	1.156	1.476	2.015	2.571	2.757	3.365	4.032	4.773	5.893	6.869
6	0.718	0.906	1.134	1.440	1.943	2.447	2.612	3.143	3.707	4.317	5.208	5.959
7	0.711	0.896	1.119	1.415	1.895	2.365	2.517	2.998	3.499	4.029	4.785	5.408
8	0.706	0.889	1.108	1.397	1.860	2.306	2.449	2.896	3.355	3.833	4.501	5.041
9	0.703	0.883	1.100	1.383	1.833	2.262	2.398	2.821	3.250	3.690	4.297	4.781
10	0.700	0.879	1.093	1.372	1.812	2.228	2.359	2.764	3.169	3.581	4.144	4.587
11	0.697	0.876	1.088	1.363	1.796	2.201	2.328	2.718	3.106	3.497	4.025	4.437
12	0.695	0.873	1.083	1.356	1.782	2.179	2.303	2.681	3.055	3.428	3.930	4.318
13	0.694	0.870	1.079	1.350	1.771	2.160	2.282	2.650	3.012	3.372	3.852	4.221
14	0.692	0.868	1.076	1.345	1.761	2.145	2.264	2.624	2.977	3.326	3.787	4.140
15	0.691	0.866	1.074	1.341	1.753	2.131	2.249	2.602	2.947	3.286	3.733	4.073
16	0.690	0.865	1.071	1.337	1.746	2.120	2.235	2.583	2.921	3.252	3.686	4.015
17	0.689	0.863	1.069	1.333	1.740	2.110	2.224	2.567	2.898	3.222	3.646	3.965
18	0.688	0.862	1.067	1.330	1.734	2.101	2.214	2.552	2.878	3.197	3.610	3.922
19	0.688	0.861	1.066	1.328	1.729	2.093	2.205	2.539	2.861	3.174	3.579	3.883
20	0.687	0.860	1.064	1.325	1.725	2.086	2.197	2.528	2.845	3.153	3.552	3.850
21	0.686	0.859	1.063	1.323	1.721	2.080	2.189	2.518	2.831	3.135	3.527	3.819
22	0.686	0.858	1.061	1.321	1.717	2.074	2.183	2.508	2.819	3.119	3.505	3.792
23	0.685	0.858	1.060	1.319	1.714	2.069	2.177	2.500	2.807	3.104	3.485	3.768
24	0.685	0.857	1.059	1.318	1.711	2.064	2.172	2.492	2.797	3.091	3.467	3.745
25	0.684	0.856	1.058	1.316	1.708	2.060	2.167	2.485	2.787	3.078	3.450	3.725
26	0.684	0.856	1.058	1.315	1.706	2.056	2.162	2.479	2.779	3.067	3.435	3.707
27	0.684	0.855	1.057	1.314	1.703	2.052	2.158	2.473	2.771	3.057	3.421	3.690
28	0.683	0.855	1.056	1.313	1.701	2.048	2.154	2.467	2.763	3.047	3.408	3.674
29	0.683	0.854	1.055	1.311	1.699	2.045	2.150	2.462	2.756	3.038	3.396	3.659
30	0.683	0.854	1.055	1.310	1.697	2.042	2.147	2.457	2.750	3.030	3.385	3.646
31	0.682	0.853	1.054	1.309	1.696	2.040	2.144	2.453	2.744	3.022	3.375	3.633
32	0.682	0.853	1.054	1.309	1.694	2.037	2.141	2.449	2.738	3.015	3.365	3.622
33	0.682	0.853	1.053	1.308	1.692	2.035	2.138	2.445	2.733	3.008	3.356	3.611
34	0.682	0.852	1.052	1.307	1.691	2.032	2.136	2.441	2.728	3.002	3.348	3.601
35	0.682	0.852	1.052	1.306	1.690	2.030	2.133	2.438	2.724	2.996	3.340	3.591
36	0.681	0.852	1.052	1.306	1.688	2.028	2.131	2.434	2.719	2.990	3.333	3.582
37	0.681	0.851	1.051	1.305	1.687	2.026	2.129	2.431	2.715	2.985	3.326	3.574
38	0.681	0.851	1.051	1.304	1.686	2.024	2.127	2.429	2.712	2.980	3.319	3.566
39	0.681	0.851	1.050	1.304	1.685	2.023	2.125	2.426	2.708	2.976	3.313	3.558
40	0.681	0.851	1.050	1.303	1.684	2.021	2.123	2.423	2.704	2.971	3.307	3.551
50	0.679	0.849	1.047	1.299	1.676	2.009	2.109	2.403	2.678	2.937	3.261	3.496
60	0.679	0.848	1.045	1.296	1.671	2.000	2.099	2.390	2.660	2.915	3.232	3.460
70	0.678	0.847	1.044	1.294	1.667	1.994	2.093	2.381	2.648	2.899	3.211	3.435
80	0.678	0.846	1.043	1.292	1.664	1.990	2.088	2.374	2.639	2.887	3.195	3.416
90	0.677	0.846	1.042	1.291	1.662	1.987	2.084	2.368	2.632	2.878	3.183	3.402
100	0.677	0.845	1.042	1.290	1.660	1.984	2.081	2.364	2.626	2.871	3.174	3.390
1000	0.675	0.842	1.037	1.282	1.646	1.962	2.056	2.330	2.581	2.813	3.098	3.300
z	0.674	0.842	1.036	1.282	1.645	1.960	2.054	2.326	2.576	2.807	3.090	3.291

Table VII

Chi-Square (χ^2) Distribution
Area to the Right of Critical Value

Degrees of Freedom	0.995	0.99	0.975	0.95	0.90	0.10	0.05	0.025	0.01	0.005
1	—	—	0.001	0.004	0.016	2.706	3.841	5.024	6.635	7.879
2	0.010	0.020	0.051	0.103	0.211	4.605	5.991	7.378	9.210	10.597
3	0.072	0.115	0.216	0.352	0.584	6.251	7.815	9.348	11.345	12.838
4	0.207	0.297	0.484	0.711	1.064	7.779	9.488	11.143	13.277	14.860
5	0.412	0.554	0.831	1.145	1.610	9.236	11.070	12.833	15.086	16.750
6	0.676	0.872	1.237	1.635	2.204	10.645	12.592	14.449	16.812	18.548
7	0.989	1.239	1.690	2.167	2.833	12.017	14.067	16.013	18.475	20.278
8	1.344	1.646	2.180	2.733	3.490	13.362	15.507	17.535	20.090	21.955
9	1.735	2.088	2.700	3.325	4.168	14.684	16.919	19.023	21.666	23.589
10	2.156	2.558	3.247	3.940	4.865	15.987	18.307	20.483	23.209	25.188
11	2.603	3.053	3.816	4.575	5.578	17.275	19.675	21.920	24.725	26.757
12	3.074	3.571	4.404	5.226	6.304	18.549	21.026	23.337	26.217	28.300
13	3.565	4.107	5.009	5.892	7.042	19.812	22.362	24.736	27.688	29.819
14	4.075	4.660	5.629	6.571	7.790	21.064	23.685	26.119	29.141	31.319
15	4.601	5.229	6.262	7.261	8.547	22.307	24.996	27.488	30.578	32.801
16	5.142	5.812	6.908	7.962	9.312	23.542	26.296	28.845	32.000	34.267
17	5.697	6.408	7.564	8.672	10.085	24.769	27.587	30.191	33.409	35.718
18	6.265	7.015	8.231	9.390	10.865	25.989	28.869	31.526	34.805	37.156
19	6.844	7.633	8.907	10.117	11.651	27.204	30.144	32.852	36.191	38.582
20	7.434	8.260	9.591	10.851	12.443	28.412	31.410	34.170	37.566	39.997
21	8.034	8.897	10.283	11.591	13.240	29.615	32.671	35.479	38.932	41.401
22	8.643	9.542	10.982	12.338	14.041	30.813	33.924	36.781	40.289	42.796
23	9.260	10.196	11.689	13.091	14.848	32.007	35.172	38.076	41.638	44.181
24	9.886	10.856	12.401	13.848	15.659	33.196	36.415	39.364	42.980	45.559
25	10.520	11.524	13.120	14.611	16.473	34.382	37.652	40.646	44.314	46.928
26	11.160	12.198	13.844	15.379	17.292	35.563	38.885	41.923	45.642	48.290
27	11.808	12.879	14.573	16.151	18.114	36.741	40.113	43.195	46.963	49.645
28	12.461	13.565	15.308	16.928	18.939	37.916	41.337	44.461	48.278	50.993
29	13.121	14.256	16.047	17.708	19.768	39.087	42.557	45.722	49.588	52.336
30	13.787	14.953	16.791	18.493	20.599	40.256	43.773	46.979	50.892	53.672
40	20.707	22.164	24.433	26.509	29.051	51.805	55.758	59.342	63.691	66.766
50	27.991	29.707	32.357	34.764	37.689	63.167	67.505	71.420	76.154	79.490
60	35.534	37.485	40.482	43.188	46.459	74.397	79.082	83.298	88.379	91.952
70	43.275	45.442	48.758	51.739	55.329	85.527	90.531	95.023	100.425	104.215
80	51.172	53.540	57.153	60.391	64.278	96.578	101.879	106.629	112.329	116.321
90	59.196	61.754	65.647	69.126	73.291	107.565	113.145	118.136	124.116	128.299
100	67.328	70.065	74.222	77.929	82.358	118.498	124.342	129.561	135.807	140.169

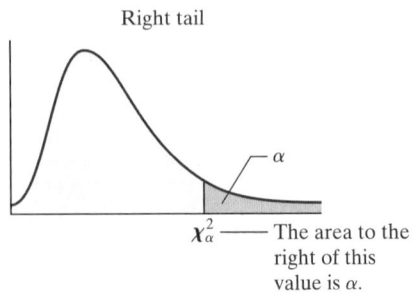

Right tail

χ_α^2 — The area to the right of this value is α.

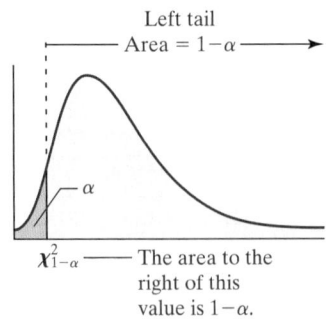

Left tail

Area = $1-\alpha$

$\chi_{1-\alpha}^2$ — The area to the right of this value is $1-\alpha$.

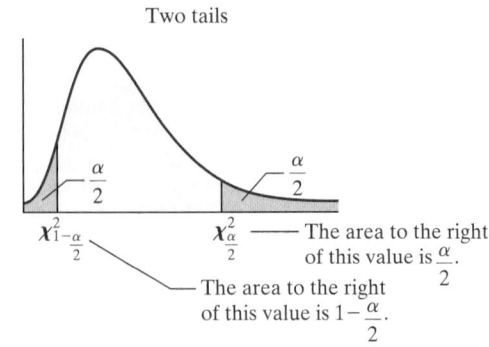

Two tails

$\chi_{1-\frac{\alpha}{2}}^2$

$\chi_{\frac{\alpha}{2}}^2$ — The area to the right of this value is $\frac{\alpha}{2}$.

The area to the right of this value is $1-\frac{\alpha}{2}$.

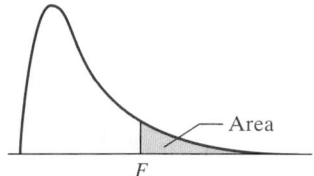
F   Area

Table VIII

F-Distribution Critical Values

Degrees of Freedom in the Numerator

	Area in Right Tail	1	2	3	4	5	6	7	8
1	0.100	39.86	49.59	53.59	55.83	57.24	58.20	58.91	59.44
	0.050	161.45	199.50	215.71	224.58	230.16	233.99	236.77	238.88
	0.025	647.79	799.50	864.16	899.58	921.85	937.11	948.22	956.66
	0.010	4052.20	4999.50	5403.35	5624.58	5763.65	5858.99	5928.36	5981.07
	0.001	405284.07	499999.50	540379.20	562499.58	576404.56	585937.11	592873.29	598144.16
2	0.100	8.53	9.00	9.16	9.24	9.29	9.33	9.35	9.37
	0.050	18.51	19.00	19.16	19.25	19.30	19.33	19.35	19.37
	0.025	38.51	39.00	39.17	39.25	39.30	39.33	39.36	39.37
	0.010	98.50	99.00	99.17	99.25	99.30	99.33	99.36	99.37
	0.001	998.50	999.00	999.17	999.25	999.30	999.33	999.36	999.37
3	0.100	5.54	5.46	5.39	5.34	5.31	5.28	5.27	5.25
	0.050	10.13	9.55	9.28	9.12	9.01	8.94	8.89	8.85
	0.025	17.44	16.04	15.44	15.10	14.88	14.73	14.62	14.54
	0.010	34.12	30.82	29.46	28.71	28.24	27.91	27.67	27.49
	0.001	167.03	148.50	141.11	137.10	134.58	132.85	131.58	130.62
4	0.100	4.54	4.32	4.19	4.11	4.05	4.01	3.98	3.95
	0.050	7.71	6.94	6.59	6.39	6.26	6.16	6.09	6.04
	0.025	12.22	10.65	9.98	9.60	9.36	9.20	9.07	8.98
	0.010	21.20	18.00	16.69	15.98	15.52	15.21	14.98	14.80
	0.001	74.14	61.25	56.18	53.44	51.71	50.53	49.66	49.00
5	0.100	4.06	3.78	3.62	3.52	3.45	3.40	3.37	3.34
	0.050	6.61	5.79	5.41	5.19	5.05	4.95	4.88	4.82
	0.025	10.01	8.43	7.76	7.39	7.15	6.98	6.85	6.76
	0.010	16.26	13.27	12.06	11.39	10.97	10.67	10.46	10.29
	0.001	47.18	37.12	33.20	31.09	29.75	28.83	28.16	27.65
6	0.100	3.78	3.46	3.29	3.18	3.11	3.05	3.01	2.98
	0.050	5.99	5.14	4.76	4.53	4.39	4.28	4.21	4.15
	0.025	8.81	7.26	6.60	6.23	5.99	5.82	5.70	5.60
	0.010	13.75	10.92	9.78	9.15	8.75	8.47	8.26	8.10
	0.001	35.51	27.00	23.70	21.92	20.80	20.03	19.46	19.03
7	0.100	3.59	3.26	3.07	2.96	2.88	2.83	2.78	2.75
	0.050	5.59	4.74	4.35	4.12	3.97	3.87	3.79	3.73
	0.025	8.07	6.54	5.89	5.52	5.29	5.12	4.99	4.90
	0.010	12.25	9.55	8.45	7.85	7.46	7.19	6.99	6.84
	0.001	29.25	21.69	18.77	17.20	16.21	15.52	15.02	14.63
8	0.100	3.46	3.11	2.92	2.81	2.73	2.67	2.62	2.59
	0.050	5.32	4.46	4.07	3.84	3.69	3.58	3.50	3.44
	0.025	7.57	6.06	5.42	5.05	4.82	4.65	4.53	4.43
	0.010	11.26	8.65	7.59	7.01	6.63	6.37	6.18	6.03
	0.001	25.41	18.49	15.83	14.39	13.48	12.86	12.40	12.05

Degrees of Freedom in the Denominator

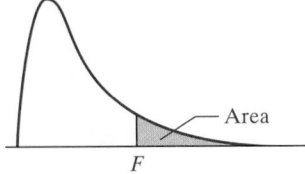
Area

F

Table VIII (continued)

F-Distribution Critical Values
Degrees of Freedom in the Numerator

Degrees of Freedom in the Denominator

	Area in Right Tail	9	10	15	20	30	60	120	1000
1	0.100	59.86	60.19	61.22	61.74	62.26	62.79	63.06	63.30
	0.050	240.54	241.88	245.95	248.01	250.10	252.20	253.25	254.19
	0.025	963.28	968.63	984.87	993.10	1001.41	1009.80	1014.02	1017.75
	0.010	6022.47	6055.85	6157.28	6208.73	6260.65	6313.03	6339.39	6362.68
	0.001	602283.99	605620.97	615763.66	620907.67	626098.96	631336.56	633972.40	636301.21
2	0.100	9.38	9.39	9.42	9.44	9.46	9.47	9.48	9.49
	0.050	19.38	19.40	19.43	19.45	19.46	19.48	19.49	19.49
	0.025	39.39	39.40	39.43	39.45	39.46	39.48	39.49	39.50
	0.010	99.39	99.40	99.43	99.45	99.47	99.48	99.49	99.50
	0.001	999.39	999.40	999.43	999.45	999.47	999.48	999.49	999.50
3	0.100	5.24	5.23	5.20	5.18	5.17	5.15	5.14	5.13
	0.050	8.81	8.79	8.70	8.66	8.62	8.57	8.55	8.53
	0.025	14.47	14.42	14.25	14.17	14.08	13.99	13.95	13.91
	0.010	27.35	27.23	26.87	26.69	26.50	26.32	26.22	26.14
	0.001	129.86	129.25	127.37	126.42	125.45	124.47	123.97	123.53
4	0.100	3.94	3.92	3.87	3.84	3.82	3.79	3.78	3.76
	0.050	6.00	5.96	5.86	5.80	5.75	5.69	5.66	5.63
	0.025	8.90	8.84	8.66	8.56	8.46	8.36	8.31	8.26
	0.010	14.66	14.55	14.20	14.02	13.84	13.65	13.56	13.47
	0.001	48.47	48.05	46.76	46.10	45.43	44.75	44.40	44.09
5	0.100	3.32	3.30	3.24	3.21	3.17	3.14	3.12	3.11
	0.050	4.77	4.74	4.62	4.56	4.50	4.43	4.40	4.37
	0.025	6.68	6.62	6.43	6.33	6.23	6.12	6.07	6.02
	0.010	10.16	10.05	9.72	9.55	9.38	9.20	9.11	9.03
	0.001	27.24	26.92	25.91	25.39	24.87	24.33	24.06	23.82
6	0.100	2.96	2.94	2.87	2.84	2.80	2.76	2.74	2.72
	0.050	4.10	4.06	3.94	3.87	3.81	3.74	3.70	3.67
	0.025	5.52	5.46	5.27	5.17	5.07	4.96	4.90	4.86
	0.010	7.98	7.87	7.56	7.40	7.23	7.06	6.97	6.89
	0.001	18.69	18.41	17.56	17.12	16.67	16.21	15.98	15.77
7	0.100	2.72	2.70	2.63	2.59	2.56	2.51	2.49	2.47
	0.050	3.68	3.64	3.51	3.44	3.38	3.30	3.27	3.23
	0.025	4.82	4.76	4.57	4.47	4.36	4.25	4.20	4.15
	0.010	6.72	6.62	6.31	6.16	5.99	5.82	5.74	5.66
	0.001	14.33	14.08	13.32	12.93	12.53	12.12	11.91	11.72
8	0.100	2.56	2.54	2.46	2.42	2.38	2.34	2.32	2.30
	0.050	3.39	3.35	3.22	3.15	3.08	3.01	2.97	2.93
	0.025	4.36	4.30	4.10	4.00	3.89	3.78	3.73	3.68
	0.010	5.91	5.81	5.52	5.36	5.20	5.03	4.95	4.87
	0.001	11.77	11.54	10.84	10.48	10.11	9.73	9.53	9.36

Table VIII *(continued)*

F-Distribution Critical Values
Degrees of Freedom in the Numerator

	Area in Right Tail	1	2	3	4	5	6	7	8	9	10
9	0.100	3.36	3.01	2.81	2.69	2.61	2.55	2.51	2.47	2.44	2.42
	0.050	5.12	4.26	3.86	3.63	3.48	3.37	3.29	3.23	3.18	3.14
	0.025	7.21	5.71	5.08	4.72	4.48	4.32	4.20	4.10	4.03	3.96
	0.010	10.56	8.02	6.99	6.42	6.06	5.80	5.61	5.47	5.35	5.26
	0.001	22.86	16.39	13.90	12.56	11.71	11.13	10.70	10.37	10.11	9.89
10	0.100	3.29	2.92	2.73	2.61	2.52	2.46	2.41	2.38	2.35	2.32
	0.050	4.96	4.10	3.71	3.48	3.33	3.22	3.14	3.07	3.02	2.98
	0.025	6.94	5.46	4.83	4.47	4.24	4.07	3.95	3.85	3.78	3.72
	0.010	10.04	7.56	6.55	5.99	5.64	5.39	5.20	5.06	4.94	4.85
	0.001	21.04	14.91	12.55	11.28	10.48	9.93	9.52	9.20	8.96	8.75
12	0.100	3.18	2.81	2.61	2.48	2.39	2.33	2.28	2.24	2.21	2.19
	0.050	4.75	3.89	3.49	3.26	3.11	3.00	2.91	2.85	2.80	2.75
	0.025	6.55	5.10	4.47	4.12	3.89	3.73	3.61	3.51	3.44	3.37
	0.010	9.33	6.93	5.95	5.41	5.06	4.82	4.64	4.50	4.39	4.30
	0.001	18.64	12.97	10.80	9.63	8.89	8.38	8.00	7.71	7.48	7.29
15	0.100	3.07	2.70	2.49	2.36	2.27	2.21	2.16	2.12	2.09	2.06
	0.050	4.54	3.68	3.29	3.06	2.90	2.79	2.71	2.64	2.59	2.54
	0.025	6.20	4.77	4.15	3.80	3.58	3.41	3.29	3.20	3.12	3.06
	0.010	8.68	6.36	5.42	4.89	4.56	4.32	4.14	4.00	3.89	3.80
	0.001	16.59	11.34	9.34	8.25	7.57	7.09	6.74	6.47	6.26	6.08
20	0.100	2.97	2.59	2.38	2.25	2.16	2.09	2.04	2.00	1.96	1.94
	0.050	4.35	3.49	3.10	2.87	2.71	2.60	2.51	2.45	2.39	2.35
	0.025	5.87	4.46	3.86	3.51	3.29	3.13	3.01	2.91	2.84	2.77
	0.010	8.10	5.85	4.94	4.43	4.10	3.87	3.70	3.56	3.46	3.37
	0.001	14.82	9.95	8.10	7.10	6.46	6.02	5.69	5.44	5.24	5.08
25	0.100	2.92	2.53	2.32	2.18	2.09	2.02	1.97	1.93	1.89	1.87
	0.050	4.24	3.39	2.99	2.76	2.60	2.49	2.40	2.34	2.28	2.24
	0.025	5.69	4.29	3.69	3.35	3.13	2.97	2.85	2.75	2.68	2.61
	0.010	7.77	5.57	4.68	4.18	3.85	3.63	3.46	3.32	3.22	3.13
	0.001	13.88	9.22	7.45	6.49	5.89	5.46	5.15	4.91	4.71	4.56
50	0.100	2.81	2.41	2.20	2.06	1.97	1.90	1.84	1.80	1.76	1.73
	0.050	4.03	3.18	2.79	2.56	2.40	2.29	2.20	2.13	2.07	2.03
	0.025	5.34	3.97	3.39	3.05	2.83	2.67	2.55	2.46	2.38	2.32
	0.010	7.17	5.06	4.20	3.72	3.41	3.19	3.02	2.89	2.78	2.70
	0.001	12.22	7.96	6.34	5.46	4.90	4.51	4.22	4.00	3.82	3.67
100	0.100	2.76	2.36	2.14	2.00	1.91	1.83	1.78	1.73	1.69	1.66
	0.050	3.94	3.09	2.70	2.46	2.31	2.19	2.10	2.03	1.97	1.93
	0.025	5.18	3.83	3.25	2.92	2.70	2.54	2.42	2.32	2.24	2.18
	0.010	6.90	4.82	3.98	3.51	3.21	2.99	2.82	2.69	2.59	2.50
	0.001	11.50	7.41	5.86	5.02	4.48	4.11	3.83	3.61	3.44	3.30
200	0.100	2.73	2.33	2.11	1.97	1.88	1.80	1.75	1.70	1.66	1.63
	0.050	3.89	3.04	2.65	2.42	2.26	2.14	2.06	1.98	1.93	1.88
	0.025	5.10	3.76	3.18	2.85	2.63	2.47	2.35	2.26	2.18	2.11
	0.010	6.76	4.71	3.88	3.41	3.11	2.89	2.73	2.60	2.50	2.41
	0.001	11.15	7.15	5.63	4.81	4.29	3.92	3.65	3.43	3.26	3.12
1000	0.100	2.71	2.31	2.09	1.95	1.85	1.78	1.72	1.68	1.64	1.61
	0.050	3.85	3.00	2.61	2.38	2.22	2.11	2.02	1.95	1.89	1.84
	0.025	5.04	3.70	3.13	2.80	2.58	2.42	2.30	2.20	2.13	2.06
	0.010	6.66	4.63	3.80	3.34	3.04	2.82	2.66	2.53	2.43	2.34
	0.001	10.89	6.96	5.46	4.65	4.14	3.78	3.51	3.30	3.13	2.99

Degrees of Freedom in the Denominator

Table VIII *(continued)*

F-Distribution Critical Values
Degrees of Freedom in the Numerator

Degrees of Freedom in the Denominator

	Area in Right Tail	12	15	20	25	30	40	50	60	120	1000
9	0.100	2.38	2.34	2.30	2.27	2.25	2.23	2.22	2.21	2.18	2.16
	0.050	3.07	3.01	2.94	2.89	2.86	2.83	2.80	2.79	2.75	2.71
	0.025	3.87	3.77	3.67	3.60	3.56	3.51	3.47	3.45	3.39	3.34
	0.010	5.11	4.96	4.81	4.71	4.65	4.57	4.52	4.48	4.40	4.32
	0.001	9.57	9.24	8.90	8.69	8.55	8.37	8.26	8.19	8.00	7.84
10	0.100	2.28	2.24	2.20	2.17	2.16	2.13	2.12	2.11	2.08	2.06
	0.050	2.91	2.85	2.77	2.73	2.70	2.66	2.64	2.62	2.58	2.54
	0.025	3.62	3.52	3.42	3.35	3.31	3.26	3.22	3.20	3.14	3.09
	0.010	4.71	4.56	4.41	4.31	4.25	4.17	4.12	4.08	4.00	3.92
	0.001	8.45	8.13	7.80	7.60	7.47	7.30	7.19	7.12	6.94	6.78
12	0.100	2.15	2.10	2.06	2.03	2.01	1.99	1.97	1.96	1.93	1.91
	0.050	2.69	2.62	2.54	2.50	2.47	2.43	2.40	2.38	2.34	2.30
	0.025	3.28	3.18	3.07	3.01	2.96	2.91	2.87	2.85	2.79	2.73
	0.010	4.16	4.01	3.86	3.76	3.70	3.62	3.57	3.54	3.45	3.37
	0.001	7.00	6.71	6.40	6.22	6.09	5.93	5.83	5.76	5.59	5.44
15	0.100	2.02	1.97	1.92	1.89	1.87	1.85	1.83	1.82	1.79	1.76
	0.050	2.48	2.40	2.33	2.28	2.25	2.20	2.18	2.16	2.11	2.07
	0.025	2.96	2.86	2.76	2.69	2.64	2.59	2.55	2.52	2.46	2.40
	0.010	3.67	3.52	3.37	3.28	3.21	3.13	3.08	3.05	2.96	2.88
	0.001	5.81	5.54	5.25	5.07	4.95	4.80	4.70	4.64	4.47	4.33
20	0.100	1.89	1.84	1.79	1.76	1.74	1.71	1.69	1.68	1.64	1.61
	0.050	2.28	2.20	2.12	2.07	2.04	1.99	1.97	1.95	1.90	1.85
	0.025	2.68	2.57	2.46	2.40	2.35	2.29	2.25	2.22	2.16	2.09
	0.010	3.23	3.09	2.94	2.84	2.78	2.69	2.64	2.61	2.52	2.43
	0.001	4.82	4.56	4.29	4.12	4.00	3.86	3.77	3.70	3.54	3.40
25	0.100	1.82	1.77	1.72	1.68	1.66	1.63	1.61	1.59	1.56	1.52
	0.050	2.16	2.09	2.01	1.96	1.92	1.87	1.84	1.82	1.77	1.72
	0.025	2.51	2.41	2.30	2.23	2.18	2.12	2.08	2.05	1.98	1.91
	0.010	2.99	2.85	2.70	2.60	2.54	2.45	2.40	2.36	2.27	2.18
	0.001	4.31	4.06	3.79	3.63	3.52	3.37	3.28	3.22	3.06	2.91
50	0.100	1.68	1.63	1.57	1.53	1.50	1.46	1.44	1.42	1.38	1.33
	0.050	1.95	1.87	1.78	1.73	1.69	1.63	1.60	1.58	1.51	1.45
	0.025	2.22	2.11	1.99	1.92	1.87	1.80	1.75	1.72	1.64	1.56
	0.010	2.56	2.42	2.27	2.17	2.10	2.01	1.95	1.91	1.80	1.70
	0.001	3.44	3.20	2.95	2.79	2.68	2.53	2.44	2.38	2.21	2.05
100	0.100	1.61	1.56	1.49	1.45	1.42	1.38	1.35	1.34	1.28	1.22
	0.050	1.85	1.77	1.68	1.62	1.57	1.52	1.48	1.45	1.38	1.30
	0.025	2.08	1.97	1.85	1.77	1.71	1.64	1.59	1.56	1.46	1.36
	0.010	2.37	2.22	2.07	1.97	1.89	1.80	1.74	1.69	1.57	1.45
	0.001	3.07	2.84	2.59	2.43	2.32	2.17	2.08	2.01	1.83	1.64
200	0.100	1.58	1.52	1.46	1.41	1.38	1.34	1.31	1.29	1.23	1.16
	0.050	1.80	1.72	1.62	1.56	1.52	1.46	1.41	1.39	1.30	1.21
	0.025	2.01	1.90	1.78	1.70	1.64	1.56	1.51	1.47	1.37	1.25
	0.010	2.27	2.13	1.97	1.87	1.79	1.69	1.63	1.58	1.45	1.30
	0.001	2.90	2.67	2.42	2.26	2.15	2.00	1.90	1.83	1.64	1.43
1000	0.100	1.55	1.49	1.43	1.38	1.35	1.30	1.27	1.25	1.18	1.08
	0.050	1.76	1.68	1.58	1.52	1.47	1.41	1.36	1.33	1.24	1.11
	0.025	1.96	1.85	1.72	1.64	1.58	1.50	1.45	1.41	1.29	1.13
	0.010	2.20	2.06	1.90	1.79	1.72	1.61	1.54	1.50	1.35	1.16
	0.001	2.77	2.54	2.30	2.14	2.02	1.87	1.77	1.69	1.49	1.22

Table IX

Critical Values for Tukey's Test

$\alpha = 0.05$

ν	k (or p): 2	3	4	5	6	7	8	9	10
1	17.97	26.98	32.82	37.08	40.41	43.12	45.40	47.36	49.07
2	6.085	8.331	9.798	10.88	11.74	12.44	13.03	13.54	13.99
3	4.501	5.910	6.825	7.502	8.037	8.478	8.853	9.177	9.462
4	3.927	5.040	5.757	6.287	6.707	7.053	7.347	7.602	7.826
5	3.635	4.602	5.218	5.673	6.033	6.330	6.582	6.802	6.995
6	3.461	4.339	4.896	5.305	5.628	5.895	6.122	6.319	6.493
7	3.344	4.165	4.681	5.060	5.359	5.606	5.815	5.998	6.158
8	3.261	4.041	4.529	4.886	5.167	5.399	5.597	5.767	5.918
9	3.199	3.949	4.415	4.756	5.024	5.244	5.432	5.595	5.739
10	3.151	3.877	4.327	4.654	4.912	5.124	5.305	5.461	5.599
11	3.113	3.820	4.256	4.574	4.823	5.028	5.202	5.353	5.487
12	3.082	3.773	4.199	4.508	4.751	4.950	5.119	5.265	5.395
13	3.055	3.735	4.151	4.453	4.690	4.885	5.049	5.192	5.318
14	3.033	3.702	4.111	4.407	4.639	4.829	4.990	5.131	5.254
15	3.014	3.674	4.076	4.367	4.595	4.782	4.940	5.077	5.198
16	2.998	3.649	4.046	4.333	4.557	4.741	4.897	5.031	5.150
17	2.984	3.628	4.020	4.303	4.524	4.705	4.858	4.991	5.108
18	2.971	3.609	3.997	4.277	4.495	4.673	4.824	4.956	5.071
19	2.960	3.593	3.977	4.253	4.469	4.645	4.794	4.924	5.038
20	2.950	3.578	3.958	4.232	4.445	4.620	4.768	4.896	5.008
24	2.919	3.532	3.901	4.166	4.373	4.541	4.684	4.807	4.915
30	2.888	3.486	3.845	4.102	4.302	4.464	4.602	4.720	4.824
40	2.858	3.442	3.791	4.039	4.232	4.389	4.521	4.635	4.735
60	2.829	3.399	3.737	3.977	4.163	4.314	4.441	4.550	4.646
120	2.800	3.356	3.685	3.917	4.096	4.241	4.363	4.468	4.560
∞	2.772	3.314	3.633	3.858	4.030	4.170	4.286	4.387	4.474

ν	k (or p): 11	12	13	14	15	16	17	18	19
1	50.59	51.96	53.20	54.33	55.36	56.32	57.22	58.04	58.83
2	14.39	14.75	15.08	15.38	15.65	15.91	16.14	16.37	16.57
3	9.717	9.946	10.15	10.35	10.53	10.69	10.84	10.98	11.11
4	8.027	8.208	8.373	8.525	8.664	8.794	8.914	9.028	9.134
5	7.168	7.324	7.466	7.596	7.717	7.828	7.932	8.030	8.122
6	6.649	6.789	6.917	7.034	7.143	7.244	7.338	7.426	7.508
7	6.302	6.431	6.550	6.658	6.759	6.852	6.939	7.020	7.097
8	6.054	6.175	6.287	6.389	6.483	6.571	6.653	6.729	6.802
9	5.867	5.983	6.089	6.186	6.276	6.359	6.437	6.510	6.579
10	5.722	5.833	5.935	6.028	6.114	6.194	6.269	6.339	6.405
11	5.605	5.713	5.811	5.901	5.984	6.062	6.134	6.202	6.265
12	5.511	5.615	5.710	5.798	5.878	5.953	6.023	6.089	6.151
13	5.431	5.533	5.625	5.711	5.789	5.862	5.931	5.995	6.055
14	5.364	5.463	5.554	5.637	5.714	5.786	5.852	5.915	5.974
15	5.306	5.404	5.493	5.574	5.649	5.720	5.785	5.846	5.904
16	5.256	5.352	5.439	5.520	5.593	5.662	5.727	5.786	5.843
17	5.212	5.307	5.392	5.471	5.544	5.612	5.675	5.734	5.790
18	5.174	5.267	5.352	5.429	5.501	5.568	5.630	5.688	5.743
19	5.140	5.231	5.315	5.391	5.462	5.528	5.589	5.647	5.701
20	5.108	5.199	5.282	5.357	5.427	5.493	5.553	5.610	5.663
24	5.012	5.099	5.179	5.251	5.319	5.381	5.439	5.494	5.545
30	4.917	5.001	5.077	5.147	5.211	5.271	5.327	5.379	5.429
40	4.824	4.904	4.977	5.044	5.106	5.163	5.216	5.266	5.313
60	4.732	4.808	4.878	4.942	5.001	5.056	5.107	5.154	5.199
120	4.641	4.714	4.781	4.842	4.898	4.950	4.998	5.044	5.086
∞	4.552	4.622	4.685	4.743	4.796	4.845	4.891	4.934	4.974

Table IX (continued)

Critical Values for Tukey's Test

α = 0.05

v	k (or p): 20	22	24	26	28	30	32	34	36
1	59.56	60.91	62.12	63.22	64.23	65.15	66.01	66.81	67.56
2	16.77	17.13	17.45	17.75	18.02	18.27	18.50	18.72	18.92
3	11.24	11.47	11.68	11.87	12.05	12.21	12.36	12.50	12.63
4	9.233	9.418	9.584	9.736	9.875	10.00	10.12	10.23	10.34
5	8.208	8.368	8.512	8.643	8.764	8.875	8.979	9.075	9.165
6	7.587	7.730	7.861	7.979	8.088	8.189	8.283	8.370	8.452
7	7.170	7.303	7.423	7.533	7.634	7.728	7.814	7.895	7.972
8	6.870	6.995	7.109	7.212	7.307	7.395	7.477	7.554	7.625
9	6.644	6.763	6.871	6.970	7.061	7.145	7.222	7.295	7.363
10	6.467	6.582	6.686	6.781	6.868	6.948	7.023	7.093	7.159
11	6.326	6.436	6.536	6.628	6.712	6.790	6.863	6.930	6.994
12	6.209	6.317	6.414	6.503	6.585	6.660	6.731	6.796	6.858
13	6.112	6.217	6.312	6.398	6.478	6.551	6.620	6.684	6.744
14	6.029	6.132	6.224	6.309	6.387	6.459	6.526	6.588	6.647
15	5.958	6.059	6.149	6.233	6.309	6.379	6.445	6.506	6.564
16	5.897	5.995	6.084	6.166	6.241	6.310	6.374	6.434	6.491
17	5.842	5.940	6.027	6.107	6.181	6.249	6.313	6.372	6.427
18	5.794	5.890	5.977	6.055	6.128	6.195	6.258	6.316	6.371
19	5.752	5.846	5.932	6.009	6.081	6.147	6.209	6.267	6.321
20	5.714	5.807	5.891	5.968	6.039	6.104	6.165	6.222	6.275
24	5.594	5.683	5.764	5.838	5.906	5.968	6.027	6.081	6.132
30	5.475	5.561	5.638	5.709	5.774	5.833	5.889	5.941	5.990
40	5.358	5.439	5.513	5.581	5.642	5.700	5.753	5.803	5.849
60	5.241	5.319	5.389	5.453	5.512	5.566	5.617	5.664	5.708
120	5.126	5.200	5.266	5.327	5.382	5.434	5.481	5.526	5.568
∞	5.012	5.081	5.144	5.201	5.253	5.301	5.346	5.388	5.427

v	k (or p): 38	40	50	60	70	80	90	100
1	68.26	68.92	71.73	73.97	75.82	77.40	78.77	79.98
2	19.11	19.28	20.05	20.66	21.16	21.59	21.96	22.29
3	12.75	12.87	13.36	13.76	14.08	14.36	14.61	14.82
4	10.44	10.53	10.93	11.24	11.51	11.73	11.92	12.09
5	9.250	9.330	9.674	9.949	10.18	10.38	10.54	10.69
6	8.529	8.601	8.913	9.163	9.370	9.548	9.702	9.839
7	8.043	8.110	8.400	8.632	8.824	8.989	9.133	9.261
8	7.693	7.756	8.029	8.248	8.430	8.586	8.722	8.843
9	7.428	7.488	7.749	7.958	8.132	8.281	8.410	8.526
10	7.220	7.279	7.529	7.730	7.897	8.041	8.166	8.276
11	7.053	7.110	7.352	7.546	7.708	7.847	7.968	8.075
12	6.916	6.970	7.205	7.394	7.552	7.687	7.804	7.909
13	6.800	6.854	7.083	7.267	7.421	7.552	7.667	7.769
14	6.702	6.754	6.979	7.159	7.309	7.438	7.550	7.650
15	6.618	6.669	6.888	7.065	7.212	7.339	7.449	7.546
16	6.544	6.594	6.810	6.984	7.128	7.252	7.360	7.457
17	6.479	6.529	6.741	6.912	7.054	7.176	7.283	7.377
18	6.422	6.471	6.680	6.848	6.989	7.109	7.213	7.307
19	6.371	6.419	6.626	6.792	6.930	7.048	7.152	7.244
20	6.325	6.373	6.576	6.740	6.877	6.994	7.097	7.187
24	6.181	6.226	6.421	6.579	6.710	6.822	6.920	7.008
30	6.037	6.080	6.267	6.417	6.543	6.650	6.744	6.827
40	5.893	5.934	6.112	6.255	6.375	6.477	6.566	6.645
60	5.750	5.789	5.958	6.093	6.206	6.303	6.387	6.462
120	5.607	5.644	5.802	5.929	6.035	6.126	6.205	6.275
∞	5.463	5.498	5.646	5.764	5.863	5.947	6.020	6.085

Table IX (continued)

Critical Values for Tukey's Test

α = 0.01

ν	k (or p): 2	3	4	5	6	7	8	9	10
1	90.03	135.0	164.3	185.6	202.2	215.8	227.2	237.0	245.6
2	14.04	19.02	22.29	24.72	26.63	28.20	29.53	30.68	31.69
3	8.261	10.62	12.17	13.33	14.24	15.00	15.64	16.20	16.69
4	6.512	8.120	9.173	9.958	10.58	11.10	11.55	11.93	12.27
5	5.702	6.976	7.804	8.421	8.913	9.321	9.669	9.972	10.24
6	5.243	6.331	7.033	7.556	7.973	8.318	8.613	8.869	9.097
7	4.949	5.919	6.543	7.005	7.373	7.679	7.939	8.166	8.368
8	4.746	5.635	6.204	6.625	6.960	7.237	7.474	7.681	7.863
9	4.596	5.428	5.957	6.348	6.658	6.915	7.134	7.325	7.495
10	4.482	5.270	5.769	6.136	6.428	6.669	6.875	7.055	7.213
11	4.392	5.146	5.621	5.970	6.247	6.476	6.672	6.842	6.992
12	4.320	5.046	5.502	5.836	6.101	6.321	6.507	6.670	6.814
13	4.260	4.964	5.404	5.727	5.981	6.192	6.372	6.528	6.667
14	4.210	4.895	5.322	5.634	5.881	6.085	6.258	6.409	6.543
15	4.168	4.836	5.252	5.556	5.796	5.994	6.162	6.309	6.439
16	4.131	4.786	5.192	5.489	5.722	5.915	6.079	6.222	6.349
17	4.099	4.742	5.140	5.430	5.659	5.847	6.007	6.147	6.270
18	4.071	4.703	5.094	5.379	5.603	5.788	5.944	6.081	6.201
19	4.046	4.670	5.054	5.334	5.554	5.735	5.889	6.022	6.141
20	4.024	4.639	5.018	5.294	5.510	5.688	5.839	5.970	6.087
24	3.956	4.546	4.907	5.168	5.374	5.542	5.685	5.809	5.919
30	3.889	4.455	4.799	5.048	5.242	5.401	5.536	5.653	5.756
40	3.825	4.367	4.696	4.931	5.114	5.265	5.392	5.502	5.559
60	3.762	4.282	4.595	4.818	4.991	5.133	5.253	5.356	5.447
120	3.702	4.200	4.497	4.709	4.872	5.005	5.118	5.214	5.299
∞	3.643	4.120	4.403	4.603	4.757	4.882	4.987	5.078	5.157

ν	k (or p): 11	12	13	14	15	16	17	18	19
1	253.2	260.0	266.2	271.8	277.0	281.8	286.3	290.4	294.3
2	32.59	33.40	34.13	34.81	35.43	36.00	36.53	37.03	37.50
3	17.13	17.53	17.89	18.22	18.52	18.81	19.07	19.32	19.55
4	12.57	12.84	13.09	13.32	13.53	13.73	13.91	14.08	14.24
5	10.48	10.70	10.89	11.08	11.24	11.40	11.55	11.68	11.81
6	9.301	9.485	9.653	9.808	9.951	10.08	10.21	10.32	10.43
7	8.548	8.711	8.860	8.997	9.124	9.242	9.353	9.456	9.554
8	8.027	8.176	8.312	8.436	8.552	8.659	8.760	8.854	8.943
9	7.647	7.784	7.910	8.025	8.132	8.232	8.325	8.412	8.495
10	7.356	7.485	7.603	7.712	7.812	7.906	7.993	8.076	8.153
11	7.128	7.250	7.362	7.465	7.560	7.649	7.732	7.809	7.883
12	6.943	7.060	7.167	7.265	7.356	7.441	7.520	7.594	7.665
13	6.791	6.903	7.006	7.101	7.188	7.269	7.345	7.417	7.485
14	6.664	6.772	6.871	6.962	7.047	7.126	7.199	7.268	7.333
15	6.555	6.660	6.757	6.845	6.927	7.003	7.074	7.142	7.204
16	6.462	6.564	6.658	6.744	6.823	6.898	6.967	7.032	7.093
17	6.381	6.480	6.572	6.656	6.734	6.806	6.873	6.937	6.997
18	6.310	6.407	6.497	6.579	6.655	6.725	6.792	6.854	6.912
19	6.247	6.342	6.430	6.510	6.585	6.654	6.719	6.780	6.837
20	6.191	6.285	6.371	6.450	6.523	6.591	6.654	6.714	6.771
24	6.017	6.106	6.186	6.261	6.330	6.394	6.453	6.510	6.563
30	5.849	5.932	6.008	6.078	6.143	6.203	6.259	6.311	6.361
40	5.686	5.764	5.835	5.900	5.961	6.017	6.069	6.119	6.165
60	5.528	5.601	5.667	5.728	5.785	5.837	5.886	5.931	5.974
120	5.375	5.443	5.505	5.562	5.614	5.662	5.708	5.750	5.790
∞	5.227	5.290	5.348	5.400	5.448	5.493	5.535	5.574	5.611

Table IX (continued)

Critical Values for Tukey's Test

α = 0.01

v	k (or p): 38	40	50	60	70	80	90	100
1	341.5	344.8	358.9	370.1	379.4	387.3	394.1	400.1
2	43.21	43.61	45.33	46.70	47.83	48.80	49.64	50.38
3	22.39	22.59	23.45	24.13	24.71	25.19	25.62	25.99
4	16.23	16.37	16.98	17.46	17.86	18.02	18.50	18.77
5	13.40	13.52	14.00	14.39	14.72	14.99	15.23	15.45
6	11.80	11.90	12.31	12.65	12.92	13.16	13.37	13.55
7	10.77	10.85	11.23	11.52	11.77	11.99	12.17	12.34
8	10.05	10.13	10.47	10.75	10.97	11.17	11.34	11.49
9	9.521	9.594	9.912	10.17	10.38	10.57	10.73	10.87
10	9.117	9.187	9.486	9.726	9.927	10.10	10.25	10.39
11	8.798	8.864	9.148	9.377	9.568	9.732	9.875	10.00
12	8.539	8.603	8.875	9.094	9.277	9.434	9.571	9.693
13	8.326	8.387	8.648	8.859	9.035	9.187	9.318	9.436
14	8.146	8.204	8.457	8.661	8.832	8.978	9.106	9.219
15	7.992	8.049	8.295	8.492	8.658	8.800	8.924	9.035
16	7.860	7.916	8.154	8.347	8.507	8.646	8.767	8.874
17	7.745	7.799	8.031	8.219	8.377	8.511	8.630	8.735
18	7.643	7.696	7.924	8.107	8.261	8.393	8.508	8.611
19	7.553	7.605	7.828	8.008	8.159	8.288	8.401	8.502
20	7.473	7.523	7.742	7.919	8.067	8.194	8.305	8.404
24	7.223	7.270	7.476	7.642	7.780	7.900	8.004	8.097
30	6.978	7.023	7.215	7.370	7.500	7.611	7.709	7.796
40	6.740	6.782	6.960	7.104	7.225	7.328	7.419	7.500
60	6.507	6.546	6.710	6.843	6.954	7.050	7.133	7.207
120	6.281	6.316	6.467	6.588	6.689	6.776	6.852	6.919
∞	6.060	6.092	6.228	6.338	6.429	6.507	6.575	6.636

v	k (or p): 20	22	24	26	28	30	32	34	36
1	298.0	304.7	310.8	316.3	321.3	326.0	330.3	334.3	338.0
2	37.95	38.76	39.49	40.15	40.76	41.32	41.84	42.33	42.78
3	19.77	20.17	20.53	20.86	21.16	21.44	21.70	21.95	22.17
4	14.40	14.68	14.93	15.16	15.37	15.57	15.75	15.92	16.08
5	11.93	12.16	12.36	12.54	12.71	12.87	13.02	13.15	13.28
6	10.54	10.73	10.91	11.06	11.21	11.34	11.47	11.58	11.69
7	9.646	9.815	9.970	10.11	10.24	10.36	10.47	10.58	10.67
8	9.027	9.182	9.322	9.450	9.569	9.678	9.779	9.874	9.964
9	8.573	8.717	8.847	8.966	9.075	9.177	9.271	9.360	9.443
10	8.226	8.361	8.483	8.595	8.698	8.794	8.883	8.966	9.044
11	7.952	8.080	8.196	8.303	8.400	8.491	8.575	8.654	8.728
12	7.731	7.853	7.964	8.066	8.159	8.246	8.327	8.402	8.473
13	7.548	7.665	7.772	7.870	7.960	8.043	8.121	8.193	8.262
14	7.395	7.508	7.611	7.705	7.792	7.873	7.948	8.018	8.084
15	7.264	7.374	7.474	7.566	7.650	7.728	7.800	7.869	7.932
16	7.152	7.258	7.356	7.445	7.527	7.602	7.673	7.739	7.802
17	7.053	7.158	7.253	7.340	7.420	7.493	7.563	7.627	7.687
18	6.968	7.070	7.163	7.247	7.325	7.398	7.465	7.528	7.587
19	6.891	6.992	7.082	7.166	7.242	7.313	7.379	7.440	7.498
20	6.823	6.922	7.011	7.092	7.168	7.237	7.302	7.362	7.419
24	6.612	6.705	6.789	6.865	6.936	7.001	7.062	7.119	7.173
30	6.407	6.494	6.572	6.644	6.710	6.772	6.828	6.881	6.932
40	6.209	6.289	6.362	6.429	6.490	6.547	6.600	6.650	6.697
60	6.015	6.090	6.158	6.220	6.277	6.330	6.378	6.424	6.467
120	5.827	5.897	5.959	6.016	6.069	6.117	6.162	6.204	6.244
∞	5.645	5.709	5.766	5.818	5.866	5.911	5.952	5.990	6.026

Source: Jerrold Zar, Biostatistical Analysis, Prentice Hall, Inc., 1999.

Photo Credits

Chapter 1   Pages v, 2, 62, Paul Paladin/Shutterstock; Page 8, Page 39, Kari Erik Marttila Photography; Page 46, A. Barrington Brown/Photo Researchers, Inc.; Page 50, www.photos.com/Jupiter Images; Page 55, Sergio Piumatti/Sergio Piumatti; 50, Page 63, Fritz Polking/Bruce Coleman Inc.

Chapter 2   Pages v, 66, 125, Ryan McVay/Getty Images/Getty Images, Inc.-Photodisc; Page 82, PhotoEdit; Page 85, The Granger Collections; Page 126, Gregor Kervina/Shutterstock.

Chapter 3   Pages v, 128, 189, Ryan McVay/Getty Images/Getty Images, Inc.-Photodisc; Page 153, Sovfoto/Eastfoto; Page 159, Consumer Reports; Page 176, Alfred Eisenstaedt/Getty Images/Time Life Pictures; Page 190, Art Resource, N.Y.

Chapter 4   Pages vi, 192, 254, Kelley Blue Book Co., Inc.; Page 196, Photo Researchers, Inc. ; Pages 212, 213, The Granger Collection; Page 255, Mark Leibowitz/Masterfile Stock Image Library.

Chapter 5   Pages vi, 249, 326, Jonathan Nourok/PhotoEdit; Page 265, Mary Evans Picture Library/ Image Works/Mary Evans Picture Library Ltd.; Pages 258, 268, Photo Researchers, Inc.; Page 270 SuperStock, Inc.; Page 297, Sovfoto/Eastfoto; Pages 303, 307, AP Wide World Photos; Page 327, Peter Beck/Corbis/Bettmann; CD page 5–6.

Chapter 6   Pages vi, 330, 369, Steve Gorton/Darling Kindersley Media Library; Page 337, Photo Researchers, Inc.; Page 344, Corbis/Bettmann; Page 345, AP Wide World Photos; Page 360, Photo Researchers, Inc.; Page CD 6–2, EULER; Page 370, Schwenkfelder Library & Heritage Center.

Chapter 7   Pages vi, 372, 421, Bruce Rolff/Shutterstock; Page 375, Photo Researchers, Inc.; Page 376, Northwind Picture Archives; Page 378, Corbis/Bettmann; Page 412, Northwind Picture Archives; Page 412, eStock Photography LLC.

Chapter 8   Pages vii, 426, 453, Juan David Fernando/Shutterstock; Page 437, Corbis/Bettmann; Page 442, SuperStock, Inc.; Page 454, Shutterstock.

Chapter 9   Pages vii, 456, 511, www.indexopen.com; Page 476, The Granger Collection; Page 487, Consumer Reports; Page 511, Rischgitz/Getty Images Editorial.

Chapter 10   Pages vii, 514, 579, Paul Paladin/Shutterstock; Page 519, www.indexopen.com; Page 523, Paul Bishop/University of California—Berkeley; Page 551, Consumer Reports; Page 580, Jan Stromme/Bruce Coleman Inc.

Chapter 11   Pages viii, 582, 641 Sai Young Chan/Shutterstock; Page 642, Comstock Images.

Chapter 12   Pages viii, 644, 674, Kimberly Butler/Getty Images/Time Life Pictures; Page 645, Richard B. Levine/Richard B. Levine/Franco; Page 646, Photo Researchers, Inc.; Page 675, www.indexopen.com.

Chapter 13   Pages viii, 678, 733, EMG Education Management Group; Page 734, Corbis/ Bettmann.

Chapter 14   Pages viii, 736, 785, Burke/Triolo Productions/Getty Images/Getty Images, Inc.-Photodisc; Page 786, Getty Images, Inc.-Stone Allstock.

Chapter 15   Pages ix, CD 15–1, CD 15–57, C Squared Studios/Getty Images/Getty Images, Inc.-Photodisc; CD page 15–12, The Granger Collection; CD page 15–20, Florida State University Department of Statistics; CD page 15–28, Ransom Whitney; CD page 15–40, University College London, Dept. of Psychology; CD page 15–44 University of Rochester Public Relations; CD page 15–58, Bob Thomas/Getty Images Editorial.

Answers

CHAPTER 1 Data Collection

1.1 Assess Your Understanding (page 11)

1. Statistics is the science of collecting, organizing, summarizing, and analyzing information to draw a conclusion and answer questions. In addition, statistics is about providing a measure of confidence in any conclusions.

2. The group to be studied as defined by the research objective is the population. Any subset of the population is a sample.

3. individual
4. Descriptive; inferential
5. statistic parameter
6. Variables

7. Qualitative variables describe characteristics of individuals. Quantitative variables provide numerical measures of individuals.

8. A discrete variable is a quantitative variable that has a finite or countable number of possible values. Continuous variables are also quantitative variables, but there are an infinite number of possible values that are not countable.

9. A variable is at the nominal level of measurement if the values of the variable provide a naming scheme in which the values of the variable cannot be ranked or put in a specific order. A variable is at the ordinal level of measurement if it has the characteristics of the nominal level of measurement and the naming scheme allows the values of the variable to be ranked or placed in a specific order. A variable is at the interval level of measurement if it has the properties of the ordinal level of measurement and the difference in the values of the variable have meaning. A value of zero does not mean the absence of the quantity. Arithmetic operations such as addition and subtraction can be performed on the values of the variable. A variable at the ratio level of measurement has the properties of the interval level and the ratio of the values of the variable has meaning. A value of zero at the ratio level means the absence of the quantity. Arithmetic operations such as multiplication and division can be performed on the values of the variable.

10. This means that the values of the variable change from individual to individual. In addition, certain variables can change over time for certain individuals. Because data vary, two different statistical analyses of the same variable can lead to different results.

11. (1) Identify the research objective, (2) collect the data needed to answer the question(s) posed in the research objective, (3) describe the data, (4) perform inference (extend the results of the sample to the population and report a level of confidence in the results).

12. No. We measure age to as much accuracy as we wish.

13. Parameter
14. Parameter
15. Statistic
16. Statisitc
17. Parameter
18. Parameter
19. Statistic
20. Statistic
21. Qualitative
22. Quantitative
23. Quantitative
24. Qualitative
25. Quantitative
26. Quantitative
27. Qualitative
28. Qualitative
29. Discrete
30. Continuous
31. Continuous
32. Discrete
33. Continuous
34. Continuous
35. Discrete
36. Continuous
37. Nominal
38. Ordinal
39. Ratio
40. Interval
41. Ordinal
42. Nominal
43. Ratio
44. Interval

45. Population: teenagers 13 to 17 years of age who live in the United States. Sample: 1,028 teenagers 13 to 17 years of age who live in the United States

46. Population: all Coca-Cola bottles filled on October 15. Sample: 50 Coca-Cola bottles filled on October 15

47. Population: entire soybean crop. Sample: 100 plants selected

48. Population: all United States households. Sample: 50,000 households surveyed

49. Population: women 27 to 44 years of age with hypertension. Sample: 7,373 women 27 to 44 years of age with hypertension

50. Population: full-time students enrolled at the community college. Sample: the 128 full-time students surveyed

51. Individuals: Hitachi #P50X901, Mitsubishi #WD-73833, Sony #KDF-50E3000, Panasonic #TH-65PZ750U, Phillips #60PP9200D37, Samsung #FP-T5884, LG #52LB5D

    Variables: size, screen type, price
    Data for size: 50, 73, 50, 65, 60, 58, 52 (in.)
    Data for screen type: plasma, projection, projection, plasma, projection, plasma, plasma
    Data for price: $4000, $4300, $1500, $9000, $1600, $4200, $3500
    The variable *size* is continuous; the variable *screen type* is qualitative; the variable *price* is discrete.

52. Individuals: 3 Series, 5 Series, 6 Series, 7 Series, X3, Z4 Roadster

    Variables: body style, weight, number of seats
    Data for body style: coupe, sedan, convertible, sedan, sport utility, coupe
    Data for weight: 3351, 3505, 4277, 4486, 4012, 3087 (lb)
    Data for number of seats: 4, 5, 4, 5, 5, 2
    The variable *body style* is qualitative; the variable *weight* is continuous; the variable *number of seats* is discrete.

53. Individuals: Alabama, Colorado, Indiana, North Carolina, Wisconsin

    Variables: minimum age for driver's license (unrestricted), mandatory belt use seating positions, maximum allowable speed limit on rural interstates in 2007
    Data for minimum age for driver's license: 17, 17, 18, 16, 18
    Data for mandatory belt use seating positions: front, front, all, all, all
    Data for maximum allowable speed limit on rural interstates in 2007: 70, 75, 70, 70, 65 (mph)
    The variable *minimum age for driver's license* is continuous; the variable *mandatory belt use seating positions* is qualitative; the variable *maximum allowable speed limit on rural interstates in 2007* is continuous.

54. Individuals: Samsung YP-U3, SanDisk Sansa c200, Microsoft Zune, SanDisk Sansa Connect, Apple iPod nano, Apple iPod touch, Archos 605

    Variables: memory size, weight, price
    Data for memory size: 2, 2, 4, 4, 4, 8, 30 (GB)
    Data for weight: 0.8, 10.4, 8.3, 1.7, 1.7, 4.2, 6.7 (oz)
    Data for price: $79.99, $74.99, $149.99, $129.99, $149.99, $299.99, $299.99
    The variable *memory size* is continuous; the variable *weight* is continuous; the variable *price* is discrete.

55. (a) To determine if application of duct tape is as effective as cryotherapy in the treatment of common warts
    (b) People with warts; the 51 patients with warts
    (c) 85% of the patients in group 1 and 60% of the patients in group 2 had complete resolution of their warts.
    (d) Duct tape is significantly more effective in treating warts than cryotherapy.

56. (a) To determine if pregnant women in first-time labor could receive low-dose epidurals early without raising their chances of a Caesarean section
    (b) Women in first-time labor; 728 women in first-time labor
    (c) C-section rate in the early epidural group was 18%; C-section rate in the delayed group was 21%.
    (d) Pregnant women in first-time labor can be given a low-dose epidural early without raising their chances of a C-section.

57. (a) To determine the hour of the day adults feel at their best
    (b) Americans aged 18 years or older
    (c) 1,019 adult Americans aged 18 years old or older
    (d) 55% of those surveyed felt they were best in the morning.
    (e) Gallup is 95% certain that the percentage of all Americans aged 18 years or older that feel they are best in the morning is between 52% and 58%.

58. (a) To determine what worries adults most about their personal financial situation in the long term
   (b) Americans aged 18 years or older
   (c) 1,006 adult Americans aged 18 years old or older
   (d) 18% of those surveyed were most worried about having enough money for retirement.
   (e) Gallup is 95% certain that the percentage of all Americans aged 18 years or older that are most worried about having enough money for retirement is between 14% and 22%.

59. Nominal; ordinal. The level of measurement changes because the goal of the research has changed. Rather than the number being used to identify the player, it is now also used to explain the caliber of the player, with a higher number implying a lower caliber of player.

60. (a) Nominal   **(b)** Ordinal   **(c)** Ratio

61. (a) To determine the role that TV-watching by children younger than 3 plays in future attention problems of the children
   (b) All children under 3 years of age
   (c) 967 children
   (d) Every hour that kids under 3 watched violent child-oriented entertainment, their risk doubled for attention problems 5 years later.
   (e) Children under the age of 3 should not watch television, in general. However, if they do watch television, the show should be of the educational variety. Shows that are violent double the risk of attention problems 5 years later for every hour per day the child watches. Even nonviolent (and noneducational) television shows result in a substantial risk for attention problems.

1.2 Assess Your Understanding (page 20)

1. The explanatory variable is the variable that affects the value of the response variable. In research, we want to see how changes in the value of the explanatory variable affect the value of the response variable.

2. An observational study measures the value of the response variable without manipulating or influencing the value of the explanatory variable. A designed experiment attempts to control the values of the explanatory variables and see how varying the value of certain explanatory variables affects the value of the response variable. In a designed experiment, the individuals in the study are typically divided into groups, and each group is given a specific value of the explanatory variable. A designed experiment allows the researcher to claim causation; an observational study only allows the researcher to talk about association.

3. Confounding exists in a study when the effects of two or more explanatory variables are not separated. So any relation that appears to exist between a certain explanatory variable and the response variable may be due to some other variable or variables not accounted for in the study. A lurking variable is a variable not accounted for in a study, but one that affects the value of the response variable.

4. It depends. Sometimes there are ethical reasons why an experiment cannot be conducted. Other times the researcher may want to conduct an observational study first to validate a belief before investing time and money in an experiment. Certainly, a designed experiment is the superior analytical tool if ethics, time, and money are not an issue.

5. Cross-sectional studies collect information at a specific point in time (or over a very short period of time). Case-control studies are retrospective (they look back in time). Also, individuals that have a certain characteristic (such as cancer) in a case-control study are matched with those that do not have the characteristic. Case-control studies are typically superior to cross-sectional studies.

6. A cohort study identifies the individuals to participate and then follows them over a period of time. During this period, information about the individuals is gathered, but there is no attempt to influence the individuals. Cohort studies are superior to case-control studies because cohort studies do not require recall to obtain the data.

7. There is a perceived benefit to obtaining a flu shot, so there are ethical issues in intentionally denying certain seniors access.

8. A retrospective study looks at data from the past either through recall or records. A prospective study gathers data over time by following the individuals in the study and recording data as they occur.

9. Observational study   **10.** Experiment
11. Experiment   **12.** Observational study
13. Observational study   **14.** Experiment
15. Experiment   **16.** Observational study

17. (a) Cross-sectional
   (b) Whether the woman has nonmelanoma skin cancer or not; amount of caffeinated coffee consumed
   (c) The adjustment is necessary to avoid confounding due to lurking variables.

18. (a) Cohort study   **(b)** Presence of CAC; waist girth

19. (a) The researchers administered a questionnaire to obtain their results, so there is no control of the explanatory variable. This is a cross-sectional study.
   (b) Body mass index; whether a TV is in the bedroom or not
   (c) Answers will vary. Some lurking variables might be the amount of exercise per week and eating habits.
   (d) The researchers made an effort to avoid confounding by accounting for potential lurking variables.
   (e) No. This is an observational study, so all we can say is that a television in the bedroom is associated with a higher body mass index.

20. (a) The researchers simply observed the individuals over time. This is a cohort study.
   (b) Weight gain; whether the individual is married/cohabitating or not
   (c) Answers will vary. Some possibilities include having children or the number of times the individual eats out per week.
   (d) No. This is an observational study, so all we can say is that being married or cohabiting is associated with weight gain.

21. Answers will vary. This is a prospective, cohort observational study. Some possible lurking variables include smoking habits, eating habits, exercise, and family history of cancer. The study concluded that there might be an increased risk of certain blood cancers in people with prolonged exposure to electromagnetic fields. The author of the article reminds us that this is an observational study, so there is no control of variables that may affect the likelihood of getting certain cancers. In addition, the author states that we should do things in our lives that promote health.

22. This is a cross-sectional study. Cultural differences, parents' education level

23. (a) To determine whether lung cancer is associated with exposure to tobacco smoke within the household.
   (b) It is case-controlled because there is a group of individuals with lung cancer who never smoked being compared to a group of individuals without lung cancer who never smoked. It is retrospective because the data looked at historical records based on interview.
   (c) Whether the individual has lung cancer or not; qualitative
   (d) Number of smoker-years; quantitative
   (e) Answers will vary. Some possibilities include household income or amount of exposure to tobacco outside the home
   (f) Approximately 17% of lung cancers among nonsmokers can be attributed to high levels of exposure to cigarette smoke during childhood and adolescence. No, we cannot conclude that exposure to smoke causes lung cancer; however, we can conclude that it is associated with lung cancer.
   (g) Yes, but the researcher would need to use lab animals, such as rats, not human subjects.

1.3 Assess Your Understanding (page 27)

1. The frame is necessary because it is the list we use to assign numbers to the individuals in the population.

2. Sampling is used because it is often difficult or impractical to attempt to study each individual in the population under consideration.

3. Once an individual is selected, he or she cannot be selected again.

4. Random sampling is a technique that uses chance to select individuals from a population to be in a sample. It is used because it maximizes the likelihood that the individuals in the sample are representative of the individuals in the population. In convenience sampling, the individuals in the sample likely do not represent the individuals in the population because chance was not used to select the individuals.

5. Answers will vary. One option would be to write each name on a sheet of paper and choose the names out of a hat. A second option would be to number the books from 1 to 9 and randomly select three numbers.

6. Answers will vary. One option would be to write each name of the players on a sheet of paper and choose the names out of a hat. A second option would be to number the players from 1 to 10 and randomly select two numbers.

7. (a) 616, 630; 616, 631; 616, 632; 616, 645; 616, 649; 616, 650; 630, 631; 630, 632; 630, 645; 630, 649; 630, 650; 631, 632; 631, 645; 631, 649; 631, 650; 632, 645; 632, 649; 632, 650; 645, 649; 645, 650; 649, 650

   (b) There is a 1 in 21 chance the pair of courses will be EPR 630 and EPR 645.

8. (a) 1, 2; 1, 3; 1, 4; 1, 5; 1, 6; 1, 7; 2, 3; 2, 4; 2, 5; 2, 6; 2, 7; 3, 4; 3, 5; 3, 6; 3, 7; 4, 5; 4, 6; 4, 7; 5, 6; 5, 7; 6, 7

   (b) There is a 1 in 21 chance the pair *The United Nations* and *Amnesty International* will be selected.

9. (a) 83, 67, 84, 38, 22, 24, 36, 58, 34

   (b) Answers may vary depending on the type of technology used.

10. (a) 2869, 5518, 6635, 2182, 0603, 2654, 2686, 0135, 4080, 6621, 3774, 0826, 0916, 3188, 0876, 5418, 0037, 3130, 2882, 0662

    (b) Answers may vary depending on the type of technology used.

11. (a) Answers will vary.   (b) Answers will vary.

12. (a) Answers will vary.   (b) Answers will vary.

13. (a) This list provided by the administration serve as the frame. Number the students on the list from 1 through 19,935. Using a random-number generator, set a seed (or select a starting point if using Table I in Appendix A). Generate 25 different numbers randomly. The students corresponding to these numbers will be the 25 students in the sample.

    (b) Answers will vary.

14. (a) This list provided by the mayor will serve as the frame. Number the residents on the list from 1 through 5,832. Using a random-number generator, set a seed or select a starting point if using Table I in Appendix A. Generate 20 different numbers randomly. The residents corresponding to these numbers will be the 20 residents in the sample.

    (b) Answers will vary.

15. Answers will vary. However, the members should be numbered from 1 to 32. Then, using the table of random numbers or a random-number generator, four different numbers should be selected. The names corresponding to these numbers will represent the simple random sample.

16. Answers will vary. However, the employees should be numbered from 1 to 29. Then, using the table of random numbers or a random-number generator, five different numbers should be selected. The names corresponding to these numbers will represent the simple random sample.

1.4 Assess Your Understanding (page 36)

1. If the population can be divided into homogeneous, nonoverlapping groups

2. Systematic

3. Convenience samples are not probability samples. Individuals who participate are often self-selected, so the results are not likely to be representative of the population.

4. cluster sample   5. stratified sample   6. False

7. False   8. True   9. True

10. False   11. Systematic   12. Cluster

13. Cluster   14. Stratified   15. Simple random

16. Convenience   17. Cluster   18. Stratified

19. Convenience   20. Systematic   21. Stratified

22. Simple random

23. 16, 41, 66, 91, 116, 141, 166, 191, 216, 241, 266, 291, 316, 341, 366, 391, 416, 441, 466, 491

24. 763, 185, 377, 304, 626, 392, 315, 084, 565, 508

25. Answers will vary. To obtain the sample, number the Democrats 1 to 16 and obtain a simple random sample of size 2. Then number the Republicans 1 to 16 and obtain a simple random sample of size 2. Be sure to use a different starting point in Table I or a different seed for each stratum.

26. Answers will vary.

27. (a) 90

    (b) Randomly select a number between 1 and 90. Suppose that we randomly select 15; then the individuals in the survey will be 15, 105, 195, 285, . . . , 4,425.

28. (a) 7,269

    (b) Randomly select a number between 1 and 7,269. Suppose that we randomly select 2,000; then the individuals in the survey will be 2000, 9269, 16538, . . . , 939701.

29. SRS: number from 1 to 1,280. Randomly select 128 students to survey Stratified: Randomly select four students from each section to survey. Cluster: Randomly select four sections, survey all students in these four sections.
    Answers will vary.

30. No. The "clusters" were not randomly selected.

31. Answers will vary. A good choice might be stratified sampling with the strata being commuters and noncommuters.

32. Answers will vary. One option would be cluster sampling. Each cluster would be a class. Randomly select clusters and then survey all the students in the selected classes.

33. Answers will vary. One option would be cluster sampling. The clusters could be the city blocks. Randomly select clusters and then survey all the households in the selected city blocks.

34. Answers will vary. Probably the most logical choice is systematic sampling.

35. Answers will vary. Simple random sampling will work fine here, especially because a list of 6,600 individuals who meet the needs of our study already exists (the frame).

36. Answers will vary. Simple random sampling will work because a list of all households in the population exists. Just number the households 1 to N and use a random-number generator to obtain the households in the survey.

37. (a) Registered voters who have voted in the past few elections.

    (b) Because each individual has an equally likely chance of being selected, there is a chance that one group may be over- or underrepresented.

    (c) By using a stratified sample, the strategist can obtain a simple random sample within each strata so that the number of individuals in the sample is proportionate to the number of individuals in the population.

38. Random sampling means that the individuals chosen to be in the sample are selected by chance. This approach minimizes the chance that one part of the population is under- or overrepresented in the sample. There is no guarantee, however, that the sample will provide accurate information about the population.

1.5 Assess Your Understanding (page 43)

1. Frames are obtained periodically, whereas populations are constantly changing.

2. Callbacks, incentives

3. A closed question has fixed choices for answers, whereas an open question is a free-response question. Closed questions are easier to analyze, but limit the responses. Open questions allow respondents to state exactly how they feel, but are harder to analyze due to the variety of answers and possible misinterpretation of answers.

4. A certain segment of the population is not represented in the sample proportionally to its size in the population.

5. Better survey results. Trained interviewers can elicit responses to difficult questions.

6. The researcher can learn common answers.

7. Pro: higher chance of making contact with individuals. Con: people upset being interrupted during dinner.

8. Better survey results. A low response rate may mean that some segments of the population are underrepresented or that only individuals with strong opinions have participated.

9. Changing the order helps prevent bias due to previous question answers or situations where respondents are more likely to pick earlier choices.

10. The question is ambiguous since CD could mean compact disc or certificate of deposit. The question could be improved by not using the abbreviation.

11. Bias means that the results of the sample are not representative of the population. Three types of bias: sampling bias, nonresponse bias, response bias. Sampling bias could mean that the sampling was not done using random sampling, but rather through a convenience sample. Nonresponse bias could be the result of an inability to contact an individual selected to be in a sample. Response bias could be the result of misunderstanding a question on a survey.

12. Nonsampling error is the error that results from undercoverage, nonresponse bias, response bias, or data-entry errors. Essentially, it is the error that results from the process of obtaining the data. Sampling error is the error that results because a sample is being used to estimate information about a population.

13. (a) Sampling bias due to undercoverage since the first 60 customers may not be representative of the customer population.
    (b) Since a complete frame is not possible, systematic random sampling could be used to make the sample more representative of the customer population.

14. (a) Sampling bias since only homes in the southwest corner of the village are selected. These households may have different demographics than those in the other parts of the village.
    (b) Perhaps a cluster sample could be used, with the clusters being city blocks.

15. (a) Response bias due to a poorly worded question.
    (b) The survey should begin by stating the current penalty for selling a gun illegally. The question might be rewritten as "Do you approve or disapprove of harsher penalties for individuals who sell guns illegally?" The words *approve* and *disapprove* should be rotated from individual to individual.

16. (a) Response bias due to a poorly worded question
    (b) The question could be rephrased as "On average, how many hours of sleep do you get each night?"

17. (a) Nonresponse bias; if the survey is only written in English, non-English speaking homes will not complete the survey, resulting in undercoverage
    (b) The survey can be improved through face-to-face or telephone interviews.

18. (a) Nonresponse bias; there is a very low response rate.
    (b) It is likely that face-to-face interviews may need to take place, or the survey needs to have an incentive.

19. (a) Sampling bias due to undercoverage, since the readers of the magazine may not be representative of all Australian women, and interviewer error, since advertisements and images in the magazine could affect the women's view of themselves.
    (b) A well-designed sampling plan (not in a magazine), such as a cluster sample, could make the sample more representative of the intended population.

20. (a) Sampling bias due to a bad sampling plan (convenience sampling) and possible response bias due to misrepresented answer
    (b) The teacher could use cluster sampling to obtain students for the sample; then each student would be weighed to get an accurate weight measurement.

21. (a) Response bias due to a poorly worded question
    (b) The question should be reworded so that it doesn't imply the opinion of the editors. One possibility might be "Do you believe that a marriage can be maintained after an extramarital relation?"

22. (a) Sampling bias due to a poor choice of a frame
    (b) The company could use cluster sampling and obtain a list of faculty from the human resources department at selected colleges.

23. (a) Response bias because the students are not likely to be truthful when the teacher is administering the survey
    (b) The survey should be administered by an impartial party so that the students will be more likely to respond truthfully.

24. (a) Response bias because the respondents aren't likely to give truthful responses
    (b) Send a trained interviewer to the houses.

25. No; the survey still suffers from undercoverage (sampling bias), nonresponse bias, and potentially response bias

26. The General Social Survey uses random sampling to obtain the individuals who take the survey, so the results of their survey are more likely to be representative of the population than a Web survey in which individuals typically self-select to be in the survey.

27. The ordering of the questions is likely to affect the survey results. Perhaps question B should be asked first. Another possibility is to rotate the questions randomly.

28. The ordering of the questions is likely to affect the survey results. The questions should be rotated randomly. *Prohibit* is a strong word. People don't like to be prohibited from doing things. If the word must be used, it should be offset by the word *allow*, and the use of the words *prohibit* and *allow* should be rotated within the question.

29. The company is using a reward in the form of the $5.00 payment and an incentive by telling the readers that his or her input will make a difference.

30. The choices need to be rotated so that any response bias due to the ordering of the questions is minimized.

31. The frame is anyone with a phone. Any household without a phone, households on the do-not-call registry, and homeless individuals are excluded. This could result in sampling bias due to undercoverage.

32. Answers will vary. If households that have caller ID have a trait that is not part of those households that do not have caller ID, then the survey would have nonresponse bias.

33. Definitely, especially if households that are on the do-not-call registry have a trait that is not part of those households that are not on the do-not-call registry

34. There is a higher chance that an individual at least 70 years of age will be at home.

35. Poorly trained interviewers; interviewer bias, surveyed too many female voters

36. This has the potential of indicating that responses can be bought. Respondents may attempt to respond the way they think the interviewer wants them to respond as repayment for the reward.

41. Sampling bias: using an incorrect frame led to undercoverage. Nonresponse bias: the low response rate.

43. (a) All cars that travel on the road in question
    (b) Speed   (c) Quantitative   (d) Ratio
    (e) No. It is impossible to get a list of all the cars that travel on the road.
    (f) Yes, systematic sampling makes the most sense.
    (g) Answers will vary. One bias is sampling bias. If the city council wants to use the cars of residents who live in the neighborhood to gauge the prevailing speed, then individuals who are not part of the population were in the sample, so the sample is not representative of the population.

1.6 Assess Your Understanding (page 53)

1. (a) A person, object, or some other well-defined item upon which a treatment is applied
   (b) Any combination of the values of the factors (explanatory variables)
   (c) A quantitative or qualitative variable that represents the variable of interest
   (d) The variable whose effect on the response variable is to be assessed by the experimenter
   (e) An innocuous medication, such as a sugar tablet, that looks, tastes, and smells like the experimental medication
   (f) The effect of two factors (explanatory variables) on the response variable cannot be distinguished.

2. Replication is the application of the treatment to more than one experimental unit.

3. In a single-blind experiment, the subject does not know which treatment is received. In a double-blind experiment, neither the subject nor the researcher in contact with the subject knows which treatment is received.

4. Identify the problem to be solved, determine the factors that affect the response variable, determine the number of experimental units, determine the level of each factor, conduct the experiment, and test the claim.

5. completely randomized; matched pairs

6. blocking   7. True   8. False

9. Control groups are needed to serve as the baseline that other treatments can be compared against.

10. The blocks act like the homogeneous groups in stratified sampling. Blocking is done to reduce the variability in the response variable and to remove potential confounding resulting from the block variable.

11. **(a)** The placebo is the flavored-water drink that looks and tastes like the sports drinks. The placebo serves as the baseline against which to compare the results when the noncaffeinated and caffeinated sports drinks are administered.
    (b) The cyclists and the researcher administering the treatments do not know when the cyclists have been given the caffeinated sports drink, the noncaffeinated sports drink, or the placebo.
    (c) Randomization is used to determine the order of the treatments for each subject.
    (d) Population: all athletes. Sample: 16 highly trained cyclists
    (e) Treatments: caffeinated sports drink, noncaffeinated sports drink, or flavored-water placebo
    (f) Total work
    (g) A repeated-measures design takes measurements on the same subjects using multiple treatments. A matched-pairs design is a special case of the repeated-measures design that uses two treatments.

12. **(a)** The placebo is a drug that looks and tastes like topiramate. The placebo serves as the baseline against which to compare the results when topiramate is administered.
    (b) Neither the subject nor the researcher in contact with the subject knows whether the placebo or topiramate is being administered.
    (c) The subjects were randomly assigned to either the topiramate group or the placebo group.
    (d) Population: all men and women aged 18 to 65 years diagnosed with alcohol dependence. Sample: 371 men and women aged 18 to 65 years diagnosed with alcohol dependence
    (e) Treatments: 300 mg of topiramate or a placebo daily
    (f) Percentage of heavy drinking days

13. **(a)** Score on achievement test
    (b) Method of teaching, grade level, intelligence, school district, teacher. Fixed: grade level, school district, teacher. Set at a predetermined level: method of teaching
    (c) New teaching method and traditional method; 2
    (d) Random assignment
    (e) Group 2
    (f) Completely randomized design
    (g) 500 first-grade students in District 203
    (h)

14. **(a)** Proportion of subjects with a cold
    (b) Gender, age, geographic location, overall health, drug intervention. Fixed: gender, age, location. Set at a predetermined level: drug intervention
    (c) Experimental drug and placebo; 2
    (d) Random assignment
    (e) Completely randomized design
    (f) 300 males
    (g)

15. **(a)** Matched pair
    (b) Whiteness level
    (c) Crest Whitestrips Premium with brushing and flossing versus brushing and flossing alone
    (d) Answers will vary. One possible variable would be diet. Certain foods and tobacco products are more likely to stain teeth. This could affect the whiteness level.
    (e) Answers will vary. One possible answer is that using twins helps control for genetic factors (like weak teeth) that may affect the results of the study.

16. **(a)** Matched pair
    (b) Difference in test scores
    (c) Math course

17. **(a)** Completely randomized design
    (b) Adults with insomnia
    (c) Wake time after sleep onset (WASO)
    (d) CBT, RT, placebo
    (e) 75 adults with insomnia
    (f)

18. **(a)** Completely randomized design
    (b) Adult outpatients diagnosed as having major depression and having a baseline Hamilton Rating Scale for Depression (HAM-D) score of at least 20
    (c) Change in the HAM-D over the treatment period
    (d) Type of drug: St. John's wort extract or placebo
    (e) 200 outpatients diagnosed with depression
    (f) The placebo group
    (g)
    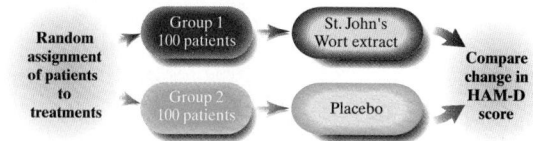

19. **(a)** Completely randomized design
    (b) Adults older than 60 years in good health
    (c) Score on a standardized test of learning and memory
    (d) Drug: 40 mg of ginkgo 3 times per day or a matching placebo
    (e) 98 men and 132 women older than 60 in good health
    (f) The placebo group
    (g)

20. **(a)** Completely randomized design
    (b) Inpatients with a diagnosis of major depression
    (c) Hamilton Rating Scale for Depression score
    (d) Drug: placebo or new drug therapy
    (e) 63 inpatients with a diagnosis of major depression
    (f)

21. **(a)** Matched-pairs design
    (b) Distance yardstick falls
    (c) Dominant versus nondominant hand
    (d) 15 students
    (e) To eliminate bias due to starting on dominant or nondominant first for each trial
    (f)

22. **(a)** Matched-pairs design   **(b)** Distance ball hit
    (c) Shaft type: graphite shaft versus steel shaft
    (d) 10 golfers
    (e) To eliminate bias due to type of shaft used first
    (f)

23. (a) Randomized block design
   (b) Score on recall exam
   (c) Print, radio, or television advertising
   (d) Level of education
   (e)

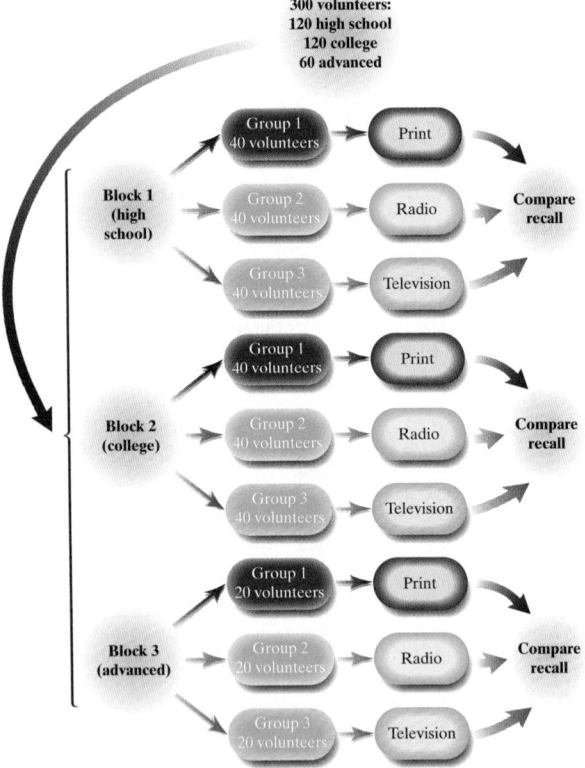

24. (a) Randomized block design
   (b) Total number of truancies
   (c) No intervention, positive reinforcement, or negative reinforcement
   (d) Income
   (e)

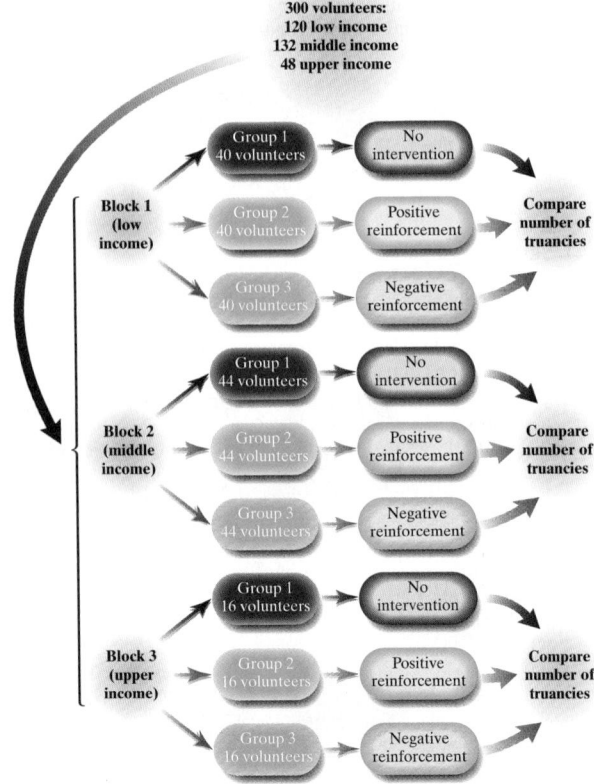

25. Answers will vary.

26. (a) Completely randomized design
   (b) Answers will vary.

27. Answers will vary. Completely randomized design is likely best.

28. Answers will vary. Completely randomized design is likely best.

29. Answers will vary. Matched-pairs design is likely best (match by type of exterior finish).

30. Answers will vary. Matched-pairs design is likely best (match by car model).

31. Answers will vary. Randomized block design is likely best. Block by type of car.

32. Answers will vary. Randomized block design is likely best. Block by gender.

33. (a) Blood pressure
   (b) Daily consumption of salt, daily consumption of fruits and vegetables, body's ability to process salt
   (c) Salt: controlled; fruits/vegetables: controlled, body: cannot be controlled. To deal with variability in body types, randomly assign experimental units to each treatment group.
   (d) Answers will vary. Three might be a good choice; one level below RDA, one equal to RDA, one above RDA.

36. Answers will vary. For the completely randomized design, the researcher would randomly assign each subject to either drink Coke or Pepsi. The response variable would be the proportion of subjects who prefer Coke and the proportion of subjects who prefer Pepsi. The subject would be blinded; however, the researcher would not, so this is a single-blind experiment. For the matched-pairs design, the researcher would randomly determine whether each subject drinks Coke first or Pepsi first. The response variable would be either the proportion of subjects who prefer Coke or the proportion of subjects who prefer Pepsi. This would also be a single-blind experiment. The matched-pairs design is likely superior.

37. (a) To determine if nymphs of *Brachytron pretense* will control mosquitoes
   (b) Completely randomized design
   (c) Mosquito larvae density; quantitative; discrete, since the larvae are counted
   (d) Introduction of nymphs of *Brachytron pretense* into water tanks containing mosquito larvae; nymphs added or no nymphs added
   (e) Temperature, amount of rainfall, fish, other larvae, sunlight
   (f) All mosquito larvae in all breeding places; the mosquito larvae in the ten 300-liter outdoor, open concrete water tanks
   (g) During the study period, mosquito larvae density changed from 7.34 to 0.83 to 6.83 larvae per dip in the treatment tanks, while changing only from 7.12 to 6.83 to 6.79 larvae per dip in the control tanks.
   (h) All 10 tanks were cleaned of all nonmosquito larvae, nymphs, and fish so that only mosquito larvae were left in the tanks. Five tanks were treated with 10 nymphs of *Brachytron pretense*, while five tanks were left untreated, serving as the control. In other words, the contents of the tanks were as identical as possible, except for the treatment.
   (i)

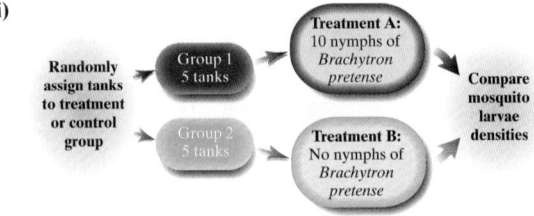

   (j) Nymphs of *Brachytron pretense* can be used effectively as a strong, ecologically friendly control of mosquitoes and mosquito-borne diseases.

Chapter 1 Review Exercises (page 60)

1. The science of collecting, organizing, summarizing, and analyzing data to draw conclusions or answer questions; provides a measure of confidence to conclusions

2. A group of individuals that a researcher wishes to study

3. A subset of the population

4. Measures the value of the response variable without attempting to influence the value of either the response or explanatory variables

5. Applies a treatment to the individuals in the study to isolate the effect of the treatment on the response variable

6. (1) *Cross-sectional studies:* collect information about individuals at a specific point in time or over a very short period of time. (2) *Case-control studies:* look back in time and match individuals possessing certain characteristic with those that do not. (3) *Cohort studies:* collect information about a group of individuals over a period of time.

7. (1) Identify the research objective, (2) collect the data needed to answer the research questions, (3) describe the data, (4) perform inference

8. (1) *Sampling bias* occurs when the techniques used to select individuals to be in the sample favor one part of the population over another. (2) *Nonresponse bias* occurs when the individuals selected to be in the sample that do not respond to the survey have different opinions from those that do respond. (3) *Response bias* exists when the answers on a survey do not reflect the true feelings of the respondent.

9. *Nonsampling errors* are errors that result from undercoverage, non-response bias, response bias, or data-entry errors. *Sampling errors* are errors that result from using a sample to estimate information about a population. They result because samples contain incomplete information regarding a population.

10. (1) Identify the problem to be solved. (2) Determine the factors that affect the response variable. (3) Determine the number of experimental units. (4) Determine the level of each factor. (5) Conduct the experiment. (6) Test the claim.

11. Quantitative; discrete

12. Quantitative; continuous

13. Qualitative

14. Statistic

15. Parameter

16. Interval

17. Nominal

18. Ordinal

19. Ratio

20. Observational study

21. Experiment

22. Cohort study

23. Convenience sample

24. Cluster sample

25. Stratified sample

26. Systematic sample

27. **(a)** Sampling bias; undercoverage or nonrepresentative sample due to poor sampling frame
   (b) Response bias; interviewer error
   (c) Data-entry error

28. Answers will vary.

29. Answers will vary.

30. Answers will vary. Label each goggle with pairs of digits from 00 to 99. Using row 12, column 1 of Table I in Appendix A and reading down, the selected labels would be 55, 96, 38, 85, 10, 67, 23, 39, 45, 57, 82, 90, and 76. The goggles with these labels would be inspected for defects.

31. **(a)** Completely randomized design
   (b) Energy required to light the bulb
   (c) Old ballast and new ballast
   (d) Group 2 (the old ballast)
   (e) 200 fluorescent bulbs
   (f) Randomization is used to deal with the factors that have not been controlled in the study. The idea is that randomization averages out the effects of uncontrolled factors across all treatments.
   (g)

32. **(a)** Randomized block design
   (b) Exam grade
   (c) Notecard use: with notecard or without notecard
   (d) The instructor's statistics students

(e)

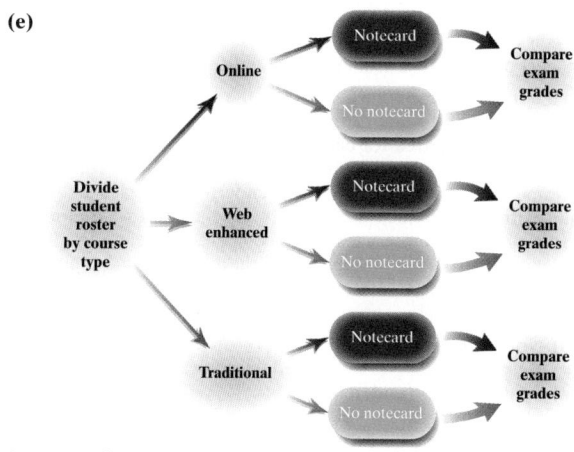

33. Answers will vary.

34. **(a)** Answers will vary;   **(b)** answers will vary.

35. In a completely randomized design, the experimental units are randomly assigned to one of the treatments. The value of the response variable is compared for each treatment. In a matched-pairs design, experimental units are matched up on the basis of some common characteristic (such as husband–wife or twins). The difference in the matched-up experimental units is analyzed.

Chapter 1 Test (page 62)

1. Collect information, organize and summarize the information, analyze the information to draw conclusions, provide a measure of confidence in the conclusions drawn from the information.

2. (1) Identify the research objective, (2) collect the data needed to answer the research questions, (3) describe the data, (4) perform inference

3. Ratio, quantitative, continuous

4. Ordinal, qualitative

5. Ratio, quantitative, discrete

6. Experiment, battery life

7. Observational study; fan opinion on presence of asterisk on record ball

8. A *cross-sectional study* collects data at a specific point in time or over a short period of time; a *cohort study* collects data over a period of time, sometimes over a long period of time; a *case-controlled study* is retrospective, looking back in time to collect data.

9. An experiment involves the researcher actively imposing treatments on experimental units in order to observe any difference between the treatments in terms of effect on the response variable. In an observational study, the researcher observes the individuals in the study without attempting to influence the response variable in any way. Only an experiment will allow a researcher to establish causality.

10. A control group is necessary for a baseline comparison. Comparing other treatments to the control group allows the researcher to identify which, if any, of the other treatments are superior to the current treatment (or no treatment at all). Blinding is important to eliminate bias due to the individual or experimenter knowing which treatment is being applied.

11. (1) Identify the problem to be solved, (2) determine the factors that affect the response variable, (3) determine the number of experimental units, (4) determine the level of each factor, (5) conduct the experiment, (6) test the claim.

12. Number the franchise locations 1 to 15. Use Table 1 in Appendix A or a random-number generator to determine four unique numbers. The franchise locations corresponding to these numbers are the franchises in the sample. Results will vary.

13. Obtain a simple random sample for each stratum. Be sure to use a different starting point in Table 1 in Appendix A or a different seed for each stratum. Results will vary.

14. Number the blocks from 1 to 2,500 and obtain a simple random sample of size 10. The blocks corresponding to these numbers represent the blocks analyzed. Analyze all trees on each of the selected blocks. Results will vary.

15. Ideally, *k* would be 600/14 (rounded down). Select a number between 1 and 42. This represents the first slot machine inspected. Then inspect every 42nd machine thereafter. Results will vary.

16. In a complelely randomized design, the experimental units are randomly assigned to one of the treatments. The value of the response variable is compared for each treatment. In a randomized block design, the experimental units are first divided according to some common characteristic (such as gender). Then each experimental unit within each block is randomly assigned to one treatment. The value of the response variable is compared for each treatment. By blocking, we prevent the effect of the blocked variable from confounding with the treatment.

17. (a) Sampling bias (voluntary response)
(b) Nonresponse bias
(c) Response bias (poorly worded question)
(d) Sampling bias (undercoverage)

18. (a) Lymphocyte count
(b) Space flight
(c) Matched pairs
(d) Four flight members
(e)

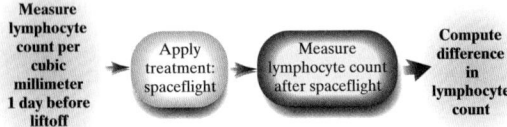

19. (a) Completely randomized design
(b) Improvement in skin irritation
(c) Topical cream; 0.5%, 1.0%, 0%
(d) Neither the subjects, nor the person applying the treatments, were aware of which treatment was being given.
(e) Placebo group (0% cream)
(f) 225 patients with skin irritation
(g)

20. (a) Subjects were observed over a long period of time and certain characteristics were recorded. The response variable was recorded at the end of the study.
(b) Bone mineral density; weekly cola consumption
(c) Quantitative
(d) The researches observed values of variables that could potentially impact bone mineral density (besides cola consumption) so their effect could be isolated from the variable of interest.
(e) Smoking status; alcohol consumption, physical activity, calcium intake.
(f) Women who consumed at least one cola per day (on average) had a bone mineral density that was significantly lower at the femoral neck than those who consumed less than one cola per day. No, they are associated.

CHAPTER 2 Organizing and Summarizing Data

2.1 Assess Your Understanding (page 73)

1. Raw data are data that are not organized.

2. number; proportion (or percent)

3. It is a good idea to make sure that the frequencies add up to the correct number of observations.

4. 1 (although rounding may cause the result to vary slightly)

5. A Pareto chart is a bar graph whose bars are drawn in decreasing order of frequency or relative frequency.

6. Relative frequencies should be used when sample or population sizes are different, because comparisons of frequencies in such cases can be difficult or misleading. When comparing samples with different sample sizes, the sample sizes should also be reported, because the sample size affects the precision of the results.

7. Arrange the ordinal data from least to greatest on either the horizontal or vertical axis. For example, if the possible data values are poor, fair, good, or excellent, then arrange the data in that order. The order of the data in a pie chart cannot be made apparent because pie charts don't have a natural starting point.

8. No; the percentages add to more than 100%

9. (a) Washing your hands; 61%
(b) Drinking orange juice; 2%
(c) 25%

10. (a) 7.7%   (b) 16.2%   (c) 582,000

11. (a) United States has the most Internet users.
(b) There were approximately 50 million Internet users in Germany.
(c) There were approximately 110 million more Internet users in China than in Germany.

12. (a) 22,657,000 whites were living in poverty.
(b) 19.7% of those living in poverty were Hispanic.
(c) The graph could be misleading because it does not account for the different population sizes of each ethnicity.

13. (a) 10.5%   (b) 37.25 million
(c) No; the bars are not arranged in decreasing order.
(d) No; in a relative frequency bar chart, the percents refer to the whole. In this chart, the percents refer to the individual categories.

14. (a) 7%   (b) 1.78 million
(c) No; the percents do not add to 100%. Add another category such as "Someone Else" to cover the remaining cases.

15. (a) 55%; 59%   (b) No effect
(c) No; their opinions could change to "no effect."
(d) Some participants may not have answered the question (nonresponse).

16. (a) 2112   (b) 10.3%; 13.4 %
(c) Education; professional/other
(d) Other sciences   (e) Engineering

17. (a)

Response	Relative Frequency
Never	0.0262
Rarely	0.0678
Sometimes	0.1156
Most of the time	0.2632
Always	0.5272

(b) 52.72%
(c) 9.40%
(d)

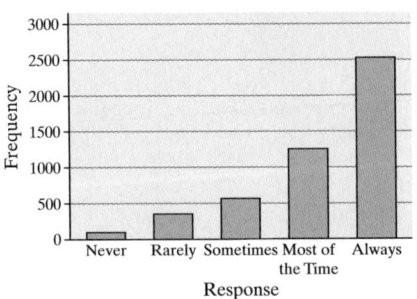

"How Often Do You Wear Your Seat Belt?"

(e)

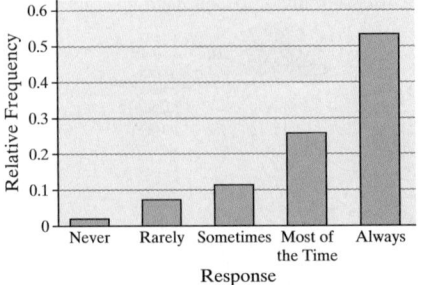

"How Often Do You Wear Your Seat Belt?"

(f)

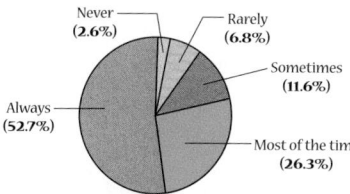

"How Often Do You Wear Your Seat Belt?"

Never (2.6%) · Rarely (6.8%) · Sometimes (11.6%) · Always (52.7%) · Most of the time (26.3%)

(g) This is an inferential statement because it is taking a result of the sample and generalizing it to the population "all college students."

18. (a)

Response	Frequency
I do not drive a car	0.0522
Never	0.0247
Rarely	0.0522
Sometimes	0.0723
Most of the time	0.1501
Always	0.6484

(b) 64.84%
(c) 7.69%
(d)

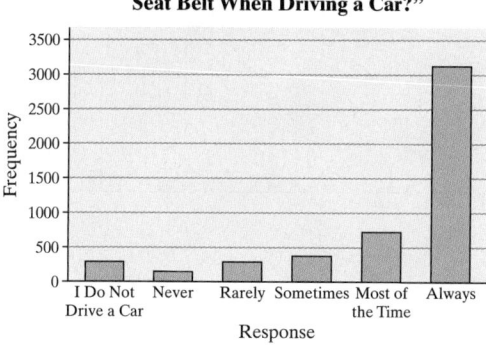

"How Often Do You Wear a Seat Belt When Driving a Car?"

(bar graph, Frequency vs Response: I Do Not Drive a Car, Never, Rarely, Sometimes, Most of the Time, Always)

(e)

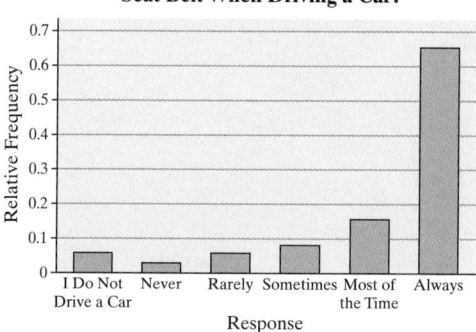

"How Often Do You Wear a Seat Belt When Driving a Car?"

(bar graph, Relative Frequency vs Response)

(f)

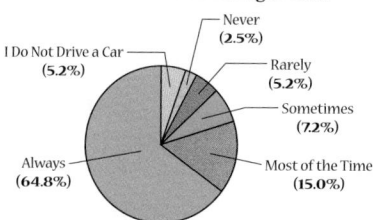

"How Often Do You Wear a Seat Belt When Driving a Car?"

Never (2.5%) · I Do Not Drive a Car (5.2%) · Rarely (5.2%) · Sometimes (7.2%) · Always (64.8%) · Most of the Time (15.0%)

(g)

Response	Relative Frequency
Never	0.0261
Rarely	0.0551
Sometimes	0.0763
Most of the time	0.1584
Always	0.6841

It appears individual's seat belt use does not vary much whether they are a driver or passenger.

(h) This is a descriptive statement since it is a summary of the data collected.

19. (a)

Response	Relative Frequency
More than 1 hour a day	0.3678
Up to 1 hour a day	0.1873
A few times a week	0.1288
A few times a month or less	0.0790
Never	0.2371

(b) 0.2371 (about 24%)
(c)

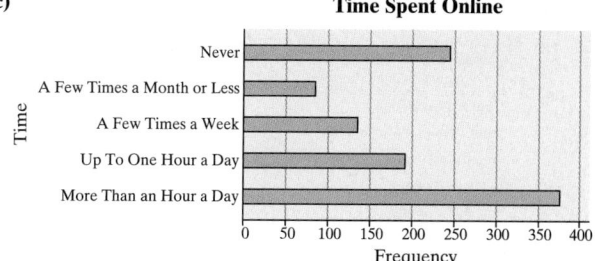

Time Spent Online

(horizontal bar graph, Frequency vs Time)

(d)

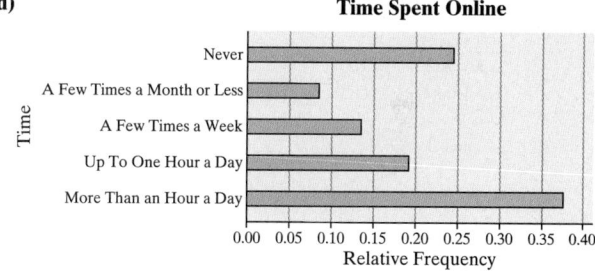

Time Spent Online

(horizontal bar graph, Relative Frequency vs Time)

(e)

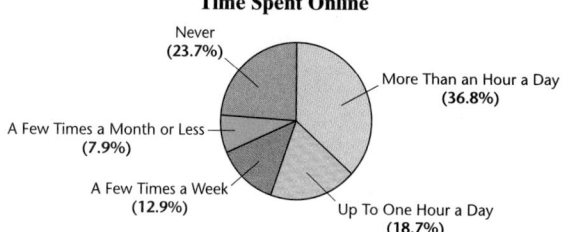

Time Spent Online

Never (23.7%) · More Than an Hour a Day (36.8%) · A Few Times a Month or Less (7.9%) · A Few Times a Week (12.9%) · Up To One Hour a Day (18.7%)

(f) No level of confidence is provided along with the estimate.

20. (a)

Response	Relative Frequency
Frequently	0.0701
Occasionally	0.1597
Rarely	0.1701
Never	0.6000

(b) 0.60, or 60%
(c)

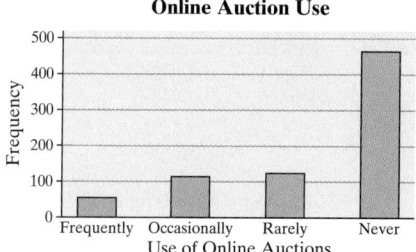

Online Auction Use

(bar graph, Frequency vs Use of Online Auctions)

(d)

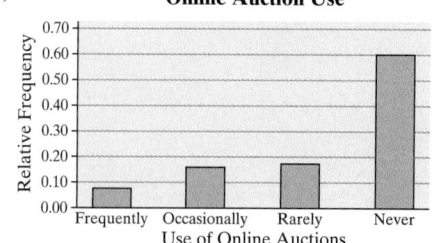

Online Auction Use

(bar graph, Relative Frequency vs Use of Online Auctions)

(e)

Online Auction Use

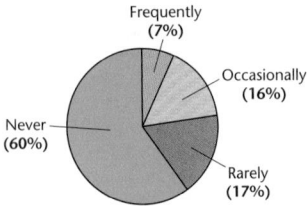

Frequently (7%)
Occasionally (16%)
Never (60%)
Rarely (17%)

(f) Adult Internet users

21. (a)

Educational Attainment	Relative Frequency (males)
Not a high school graduate	0.1497
High school graduate	0.3189
Some college, but no degree	0.1627
Associate's degree	0.0770
Bachelor's degree	0.1855
Advanced degree	0.1063

(b)

Educational Attainment	Relative Frequency (females)
Not a high school graduate	0.1416
High school graduate	0.3163
Some college, but no degree	0.1767
Associate's degree	0.0964
Bachelor's degree	0.1817
Advanced degree	0.0874

(c)

Educational Attainment, 2006

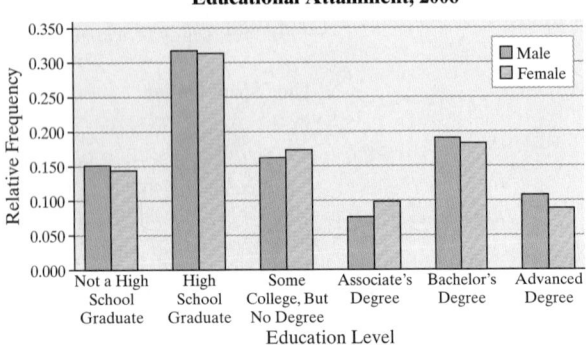

(d) Answers will vary.

22. (a)

Feeling (2003)	Relative Frequency
Big problem	0.2525
Annoying, but not a big problem	0.5755
No problem at all	0.1618
Don't know/Refused	0.0102

(b)

Feeling (2007)	Relative Frequency
Big problem	0.1802
Annoying, but not a big problem	0.5097
No problem at all	0.2800
Don't know/Refused	0.0301

(c)

Feelings Towards Spam

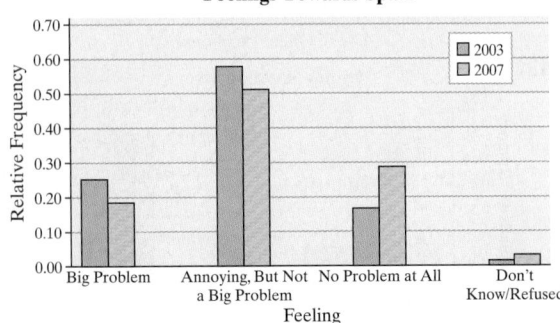

(d) Answers will vary; Internet users may be more aware of spam and are better able to deal with it using email filters.

23. (a)

Age of Victim (male)	Relative Frequency
Less than 17	0.0681
17–24	0.3240
25–35	0.2773
35–54	0.2564
55 or older	0.0741

(b)

Age of Victim (female)	Relative Frequency
Less than 17	0.1208
17–24	0.1781
25–35	0.1939
35–54	0.3567
55 or older	0.1505

(c)

Age of Murder Victims, 2006

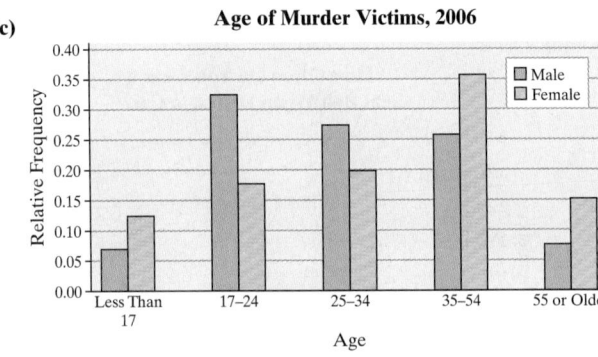

(d) Answers will vary.

24. (a)

Color	Luxury Cars	Sports Cars
White	0.25	0.10
Black	0.22	0.15
Silver	0.16	0.18
Gray	0.12	0.15
Blue	0.07	0.13
Red	0.07	0.15
Gold	0.06	0.05
Green	0.03	0.02
Brown	0.02	0.07

(b)

Car Color

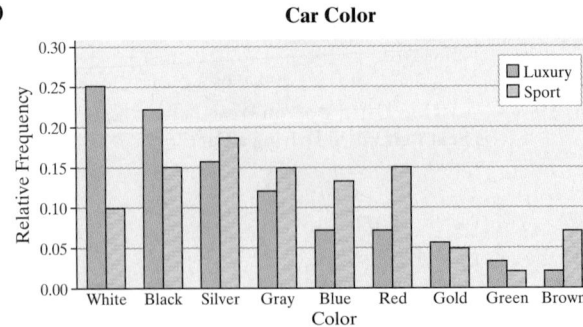

(c) Answers will vary.

25. (a), (b)

Candidate	Frequency	Relative Frequency
Clinton	19	0.475
Obama	8	0.2
Edwards	5	0.125
Kucinich	2	0.05
Biden	2	0.05
No opinion	4	0.10

(c)

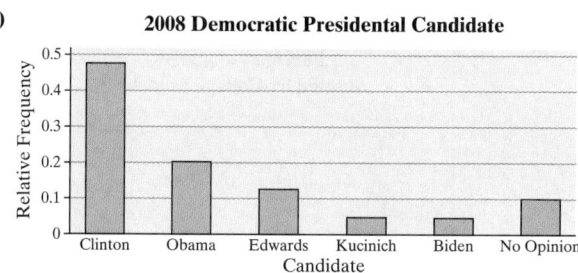
2008 Democratic Presidental Candidate

(d)

2008 Democratic Presidental Candidate

(e) **2008 Democratic Presidental Candidate**

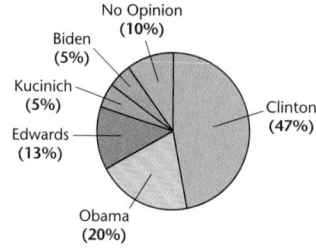

(f) Clinton; inferential; confidence should increase

26. (a), (b)

Diagnosis	Frequency	Relative Frequency
Assault	1	0.05
Cancer	1	0.05
Congestive heart failure	1	0.05
Fall	2	0.10
Gunshot wound	8	0.40
Motor vehicle accident	7	0.35

(c) Gunshot wound   **(d)** 35%

(e)

Hospital Admissions

(f)

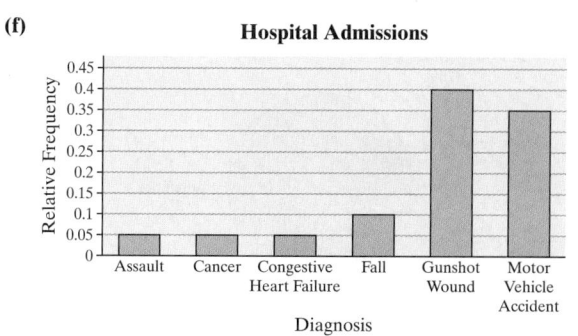
Hospital Admissions

(g) **Hospital Admissions**

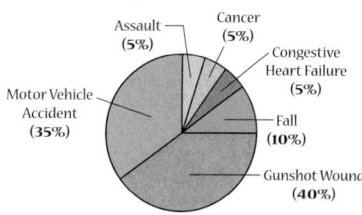

(h) The admissions specialist's comment is inferential, because the results from a sample were generalized and attributed to the population of hospital admissions.

27. (a)

Position	Frequency
First base	5
Second base	0
Third base	1
Shortstop	3
Pitcher	5
Catcher	0
Right field	3
Center field	2
Left field	3
Designated hitter	3

(b)

Position	Relative Frequency
First base	0.20
Second base	0
Third base	0.04
Shortstop	0.12
Pitcher	0.20
Catcher	0
Right field	0.12
Center field	0.08
Left field	0.12
Designated hitter	0.12

(c) Pitcher or first base
(d) Second base or catcher; these positions don't have highly payed players

(e) **Highest Paying Positions, 2007**

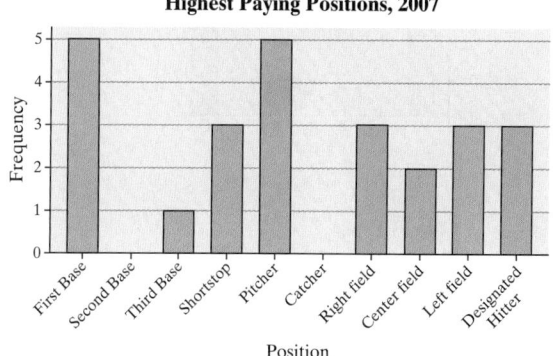

(f) **Highest Paying Positions, 2007**

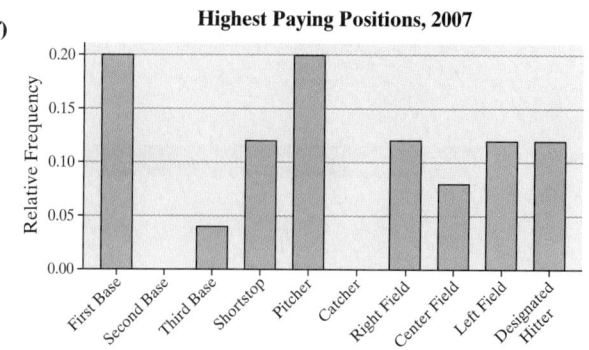

(g)

Highest Paying Positions, 2007

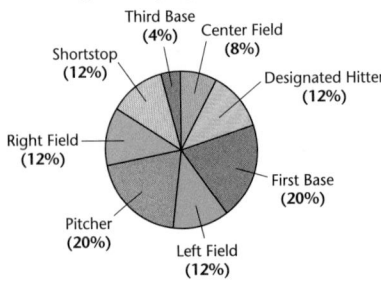

28. (a), (b)

Blood Type	Frequency	Relative Frequency
A	18	0.36
AB	4	0.08
B	6	0.12
O	22	0.44

(c) O
(d) AB
(e) 44%; inferential
(f) Answers will vary.

(g)

Blood Types

(h)

Blood Types

(i)

Blood Types

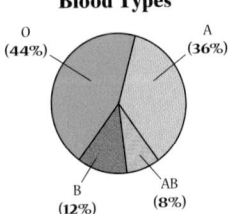

29. (a), (b)

Language Studied	Frequency	Relative Frequency
Chinese	3	0.100
French	3	0.100
German	3	0.100
Italian	2	0.067
Japanese	2	0.067
Latin	2	0.067
Russian	1	0.033
Spanish	14	0.467

(c)

**Foreign Languages
Studied by College Students**

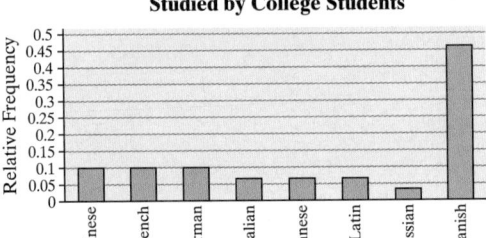

(d)

**Foreign Languages
Studied by College Students**

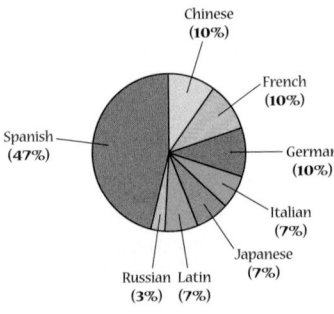

(e)

**Foreign Languages
Studied by College Students**

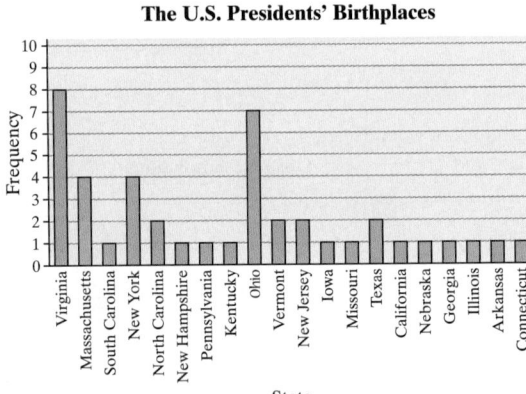

30. (a)

The U.S. Presidents' Birthplaces

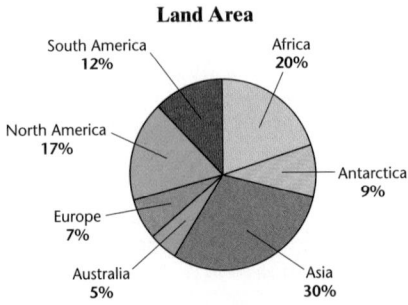

(b) More presidents were born in Virginia than in any other state.
(c) Virginia is one of the original 13 colonies.

31. (a) Yes

Land Area

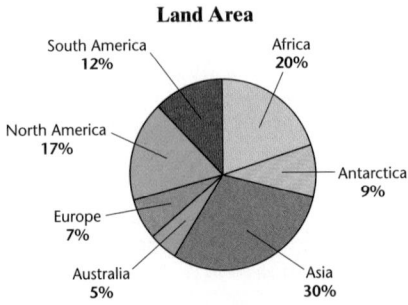

(b) No, because there is no whole to compare the parts to.

32. (a) To determine if online homework improves student learning over traditional pencil-and-paper homework
(b) Experiment
(c) Answers will vary. Some examples are same teacher, same semester, same course.
(d) There could be differences between the classes. The instructor may give more instruction to one class than the other. The instructor is not blinded, so he or she may treat one group differently from the other.
(e) *Number of students*: quantitative, discrete; *average age*: quantitative, continuous; *average exam score*: quantitative, continuous; *type of homework*: qualitative; *college experience*: qualitative
(f) Qualitative; ordinal. Answers will vary. Likely yes because it gives more "weight" to the higher grade and the researcher is attempting to convey that a higher percent of students passed using online homework.
(g) Side-by-side relative frequency bar graph
(h) Yes; the "whole" is the set of students who received a grade for the course for each class type.
(i) The table shows the two groups with no prior college experience had roughly the same average exam grade. From the bar graph, we see that the students using online homework had a lower percent for As, but had a higher percent who passed with a C or better.

2.2 Assess Your Understanding (page 94)

1. Answers will vary.

2. The classes should not overlap so there is no confusion as to which class a data value belongs.

3. An advantage is that the raw data can be retrieved in a stem-and-leaf plot, but they are lost in a histogram. Advantages of histograms over stem-and-leaf plots include more flexibility in choosing class widths in a histogram and the ability of a histogram to represent large data sets.

4. Answers will vary. Some possibilities follow: Histograms represent quantitative data, while bar graphs represent qualitative data. The bars in a histogram touch, but the bars in a bar graph do not touch. The width of the bars of a histogram has meaning, but the width of the bars in a bar graph is meaningless.

5. Classes

6. The class widths are not all the same, and the rectangles in a histogram should touch.

7. True   **8.** False

9. False. The distribution shape shown is skewed right.

10. False. The distribution shape shown is bell shaped.

11. (a) 8   **(b)** 2   **(c)** 15
(d) 4   **(e)** 15%   **(f)** Roughly symmetric

12. (a) 4 cars   **(b)** 9 weeks
(c) 17.3%   **(d)** The distribution is skewed right.

13. (a) 200   **(b)** 10
(c) 60–69, 2; 70–79, 3; 80–89, 13; 90–99, 42; 100–109, 58; 110–119, 40; 120–129, 31; 130–139, 8; 140–149, 2; 150–159, 1
(d) 100–109   **(e)** 150–159

14. (a) Class width is 200.
(b) Classes: 0–199; 200–399; 400–599; 600–799; 800–999; 1000–1199; 1200–1399; 1400–1599; 1600–1799
(c) Highest frequency is in class 0–199.
(d) Distribution is skewed right.
(e) Answers will vary.

15. (a) Likely skewed right. Most household incomes will be to the left (perhaps in the $50,000 to $150,000 range), with fewer higher incomes to the right (in the millions).
(b) Likely bell-shaped. Most scores will occur near the middle range, with scores tapering off equally in both directions.
(c) Likely skewed right. Most households will have, say, 1 to 4 occupants, with fewer households having a higher number of occupants.
(d) Likely skewed left. Most Alzheimer's patients will fall in older-aged categories, with fewer patients being younger.

16. (a) Likely skewed right. More individuals would consume fewer alcoholic drinks per week, while less individuals would consume more alcoholic drinks per week.
(b) Likely uniform. There will be approximately an equal number of students in each age category.
(c) Likely skewed left. Most hearing-aid patients will fall in older-aged categories, with fewer patients being younger.

(d) Likely bell-shaped. Most heights will occur, say, in the 66- to 70-inch range, with heights tapering off equally in both directions.

17. (a)

Number of Children under 5	Relative Frequency
0	0.32
1	0.36
2	0.24
3	0.06
4	0.02

(b) 24%   **(c)** 60%

18. (a)

Number of Free Throws until a Miss	Relative Frequency
1	0.32
2	0.22
3	0.18
4	0.14
5	0.04
6	0.06
7	0
8	0.02
9	0
10	0.02

(b) 14% of the time she first missed on the fourth try.
(c) 2% of the time she first missed on the tenth try.
(d) 10% of the time she made at least five in a row.

19. 10, 11, 14, 21, 24, 24, 27, 29, 33, 35, 35, 35, 37, 37, 38, 40, 40, 41, 42, 46, 46, 48, 49, 49, 53, 53, 55, 58, 61, 62

20. 240, 244, 247, 252, 252, 253, 259, 259, 263, 264, 265, 268, 268, 269, 270, 271, 271, 273, 276, 276, 282, 283, 288

21. 1.2, 1.4, 1.6, 2.1, 2.4, 2.7, 2.7, 2.9, 3.3, 3.3, 3.3, 3.5, 3.7, 3.7, 3.8, 4.0, 4.1, 4.1, 4.3, 4.6, 4.6, 4.8, 4.8, 4.9, 5.3, 5.4, 5.5, 5.8, 6.2, 6.4

22. 12.3, 12.7, 12.9, 12.9, 13.0, 13.4, 13.5, 13.7, 13.8, 13.9, 13.9, 14.2, 14.4, 14.4, 14.7, 14.7, 14.8, 14.9, 15.1, 15.2, 15.2, 15.5, 15.6, 16.0, 16.3

23. (a) Nineteen classes
(b) Lower class limits: 0, 2,000, 4,000, 6,000, 8,000, 10,000, 12,000, 14,000, 16,000, 18,000, 20,000, 22,000, 24,000, 26,000, 28,000, 30,000, 32,000, 34,000, 36,000; upper class limits: 1,999, 3,999, 5,999, 7,999, 9,999, 11,999, 13,999, 15,999, 17,999, 19,999, 21,999, 23,999, 25,999, 27,999, 29,999, 31,999, 33,999, 35,999, 37,999
(c) Class width: 2,000

24. (a) Eight classes
(b) Lower class limits: 0, 1.0, 2.0, 3.0, 4.0, 5.0, 6.0, 7.0; upper class limits: 0.9, 1.9, 2.9, 3.9, 4.9, 5.9, 6.9, 7.9
(c) Class width: 1.0

25. (a) Six classes
(b) Lower class limits: 15, 20, 25, 30, 35, 40; upper class limits: 19, 24, 29, 34, 39, 44
(c) Class width: 5 years

26. (a) Six classes
(b) Lower class limits: 0, 5,000, 10,000, 15,000, 20,000, 25,000; upper class limits: 4999, 9999, 14999, 19999, 24999, 29999
(c) Class width: 5,000

27. (a)

Tuition	Relative Frequency
$0–1,999	0.0106
$2,000–3,999	0.0737
$4,000–5,999	0.1721
$6,000–7,999	0.1006
$8,000–9,999	0.0592
$10,000–11,999	0.0553
$12,000–13,999	0.0497
$14,000–15,999	0.0547
$16,000–17,999	0.0698
$18,000–19,999	0.0648
$20,000–21,999	0.0654
$22,000–23,999	0.0559
$24,000–25,999	0.0464
$26,000–27,999	0.0296
$28,000–29,999	0.0251
$30,000–31,999	0.0201
$32,000–33,999	0.0257
$34,000–35,999	0.0179
$36,000–37,999	0.0034

(b)

Four-Year College Tuition

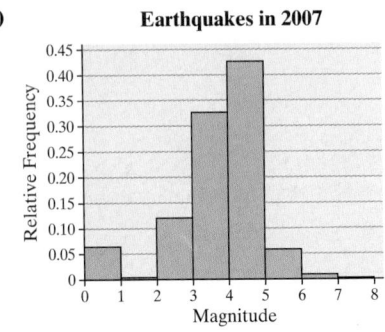

(c)

Four-Year College Tuition

8.44% of 4-year colleges have tuition and fees below $4000; 6.70% of 4-year colleges have tuition and fees of $30,000 or more.

28. (a)

Magnitude	Relative Frequency
0–0.9	0.0647
1.0–1.9	0.0013
2.0–2.9	0.1206
3.0–3.9	0.3245
4.0–4.9	0.4231
5.0–5.9	0.0593
6.0–6.9	0.0061
7.0–7.9	0.0004

(b)

Earthquakes in 2007

(c)

Earthquakes in 2007

42.31% of the earthquakes measured from 4.0 to 4.9 in magnitude; 93.42% of the earthquakes measured 4.9 in magnitude or less.

29. (a)

Age	Relative Frequency
15–19	0.1004
20–24	0.2521
25–29	0.2744
30–34	0.2307
35–39	0.1171
40–44	0.0254

(b)

Live Births

(c)

Live Births

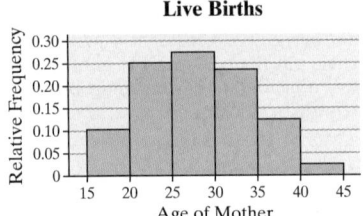

2.54% of births were to women 40 to 44 years of age; 35.25% of births were to women 24 years of age or younger.

30. (a)

Number of Students Enrolled	Relative Frequency
0–4,999	0.3333
5,000–9,999	0.3556
10,000–14,999	0.2
15,000–29,999	0.0889
20,000–24,999	0
25,000–29,999	0.0222

(b)

Illinois Community College Enrollments

(c)

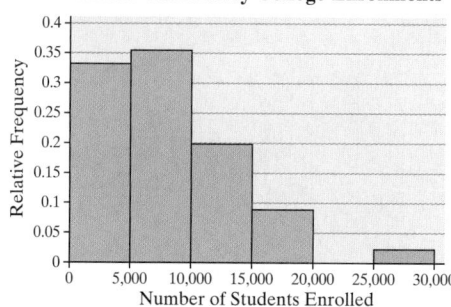

Illinois Community College Enrollments

35.56% of public community colleges in Illinois enrolled between 5,000 and 9,999 students; 11.11% of public community colleges in Illinois enrolled 15,000 or more students.

31. (a) Discrete. The possible values for the number of televisions are countable.

(b), (c)

Number of Televisions	Frequency	Relative Frequency
0	1	0.025
1	14	0.35
2	14	0.35
3	8	0.2
4	2	0.05
5	1	0.025

(d) 20%   **(e)** 7.5%

(f)

Televisions in Household

(g)

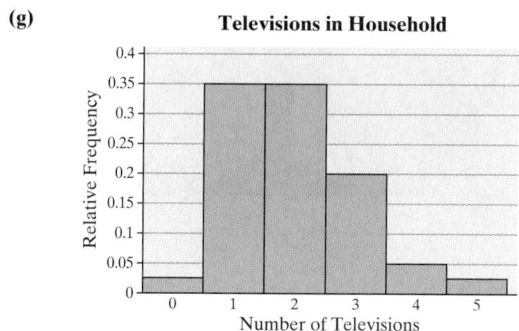

Televisions in Household

(h) Skewed right

32. (a) Discrete. The possible values for the number of customers are countable.

(b), (c)

Number of Customers	Frequency	Relative Frequency	Number of Customers	Frequency	Relative Frequency
3	2	0.05	9	4	0.1
4	3	0.075	10	4	0.1
5	3	0.075	11	4	0.1
6	5	0.125	12	0	0
7	4	0.1	13	2	0.05
8	8	0.2	14	1	0.025

(d) 27.5%   **(e)** 20%

(f)

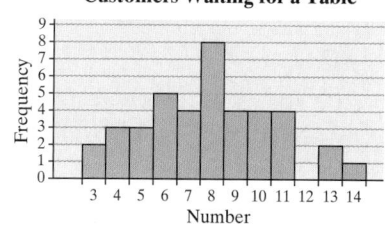

Customers Waiting for a Table

(g)

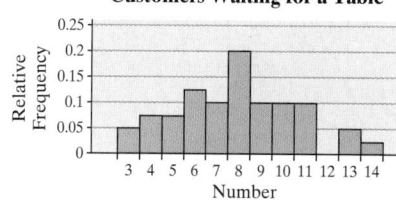

Customers Waiting for a Table

(h) Symmetric

33. (a), (b)

2006 Per Capita Disposable Income by State		
Class Intervals	Frequency	Relative Frequency
24,000–26,999	8	0.1569
27,000–29,999	15	0.2941
30,000–32,999	12	0.2353
33,000–35,999	10	0.1961
36,000–38,999	3	0.0588
39,000–41,999	2	0.0392
42,000–44,999	0	0
45,000–47,999	1	0.0196

(c)

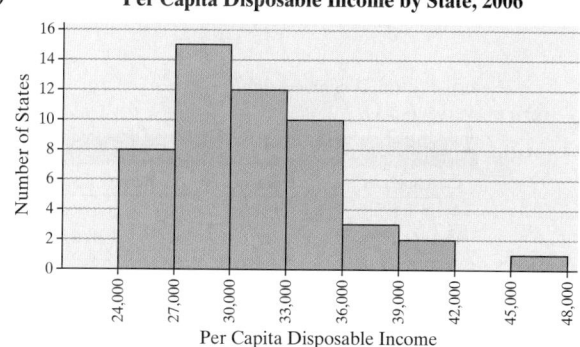

Per Capita Disposable Income by State, 2006

(d)

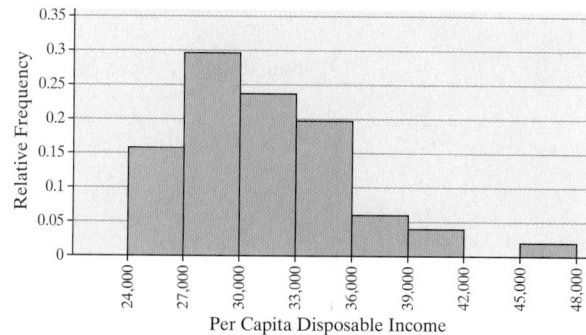

Per Capita Disposable Income by State, 2006

(e) The distribution is skewed right

(f)

2006 Per Capita Disposable Income by State		
Class Intervals	Frequency	Relative Frequency
24,000–27,999	10	0.1961
28,000–31,999	22	0.4314
32,000–35,999	13	0.2549
36,000–39,999	4	0.0784
40,000–43,999	1	0.0196
44,000–47,999	1	0.0196

Per Capita Disposable Income by State, 2006

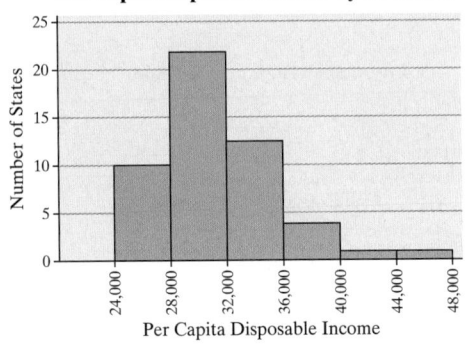

Per Capita Disposable Income by State, 2006

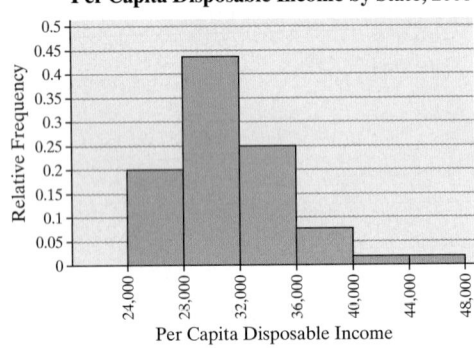

The distribution is skewed right.
(g) Answers will vary.

34. (a), (b)

2006 Uninsured Rates by State		
Class Intervals	Frequency	Relative Frequency
8–9.9	7	0.1373
10–11.9	10	0.1961
12–13.9	11	0.2157
14–15.9	6	0.1176
16–17.9	7	0.1373
18–19.9	4	0.0784
20–21.9	4	0.0784
22–23.9	1	0.0196
24–25.9	1	0.0196

(c)

Uninsured Rates by State, 2006

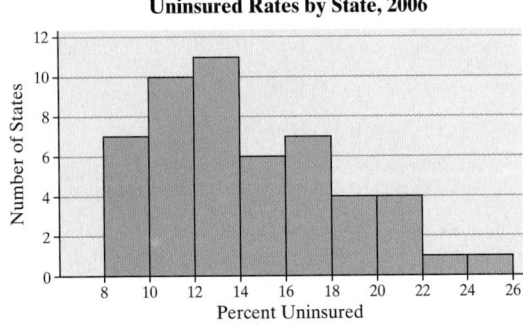

(d)

Uninsured Rates by State, 2006

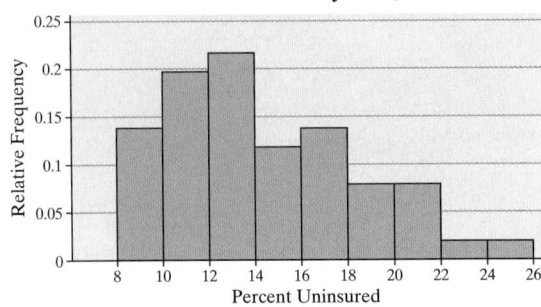

(e) The distribution is skewed right.

(f)

2006 Uninsured Rates by State		
Class Intervals	Frequency	Relative Frequency
8–8.9	3	0.0588
9–9.9	4	0.0784
10–10.9	5	0.0980
11–11.9	5	0.0980
12–12.9	4	0.0784
13–13.9	7	0.1373
14–14.9	1	0.0196
15–15.9	5	0.0980
16–16.9	1	0.0196
17–17.9	6	0.1176
18–18.9	3	0.0588
19–19.9	1	0.0196
20–20.9	2	0.0392
21–21.9	2	0.0392
22–22.9	1	0.0196
23–23.9	0	0
24–24.9	1	0.0196

Uninsured Rates by State, 2006

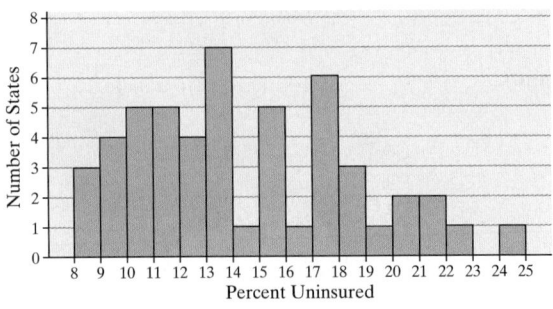

Uninsured Rates by State, 2006

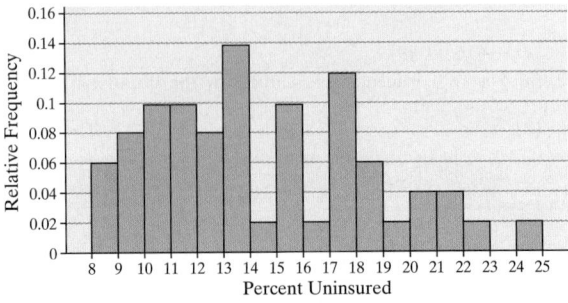

The distribution is skewed right.
(g) Answers will vary.

35. (a), (b)

Class	Frequency	Relative Frequency
20–29	1	0.025
30–39	6	0.15
40–49	10	0.25
50–59	14	0.35
60–69	6	0.15
70–79	3	0.075

(c)

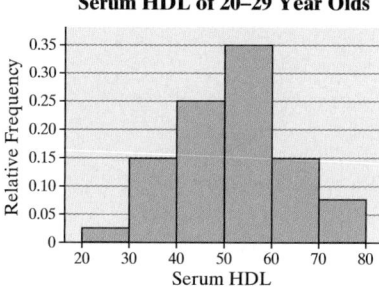

Serum HDL of 20–29 Year Olds

(d)

Serum HDL of 20–29 Year Olds

(e) Bell shaped

(f)

Class	Frequency	Relative Frequency
20–24	0	0
25–29	1	0.025
30–34	2	0.05
35–39	4	0.1
40–44	2	0.05
45–49	8	0.2
50–54	9	0.225
55–59	5	0.125
60–64	4	0.1
65–69	2	0.05
70–74	3	0.075
75–79	0	0

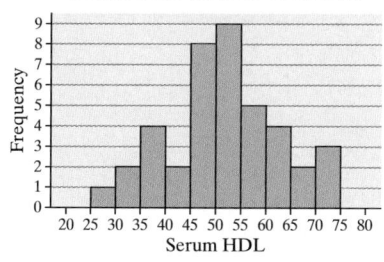

Serum HDL of 20–29 Year Olds

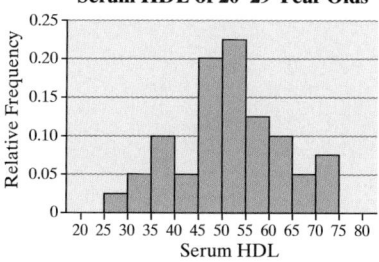

Serum HDL of 20–29 Year Olds

Bell shaped

(g) Answers will vary.

36. (a), (b)

Dividend Yield		
Class Interval	Number of Stocks	Relative Frequency
0–0.39	7	0.2500
0.40–0.79	4	0.1429
0.80–1.19	5	0.1786
1.20–1.59	2	0.0714
1.60–1.99	3	0.1071
2.0–2.39	4	0.1429
2.4–2.79	2	0.0714
2.8–3.19	1	0.0357

(c)

Dividend Yield

(d)

Dividend Yield

(e) The distribution is skewed right.

(f)

Dividend Yield (%)		
Class	Number of Stocks	Relative Frequency
0.0–0.79	11	0.3929
0.8–1.59	7	0.2500
1.6–2.39	7	0.2500
2.4–3.19	3	0.1071

Dividend Yield

Dividend Yield

The distribution is skewed right.

(g) Answers will vary.

37. Answers may vary. One possible answer follows:

(a) Lower class limit of first class: 6; class width: 3

(b), (c)

Daily Volume of Altria Stock (in millions)		
Class Intervals	**Frequency**	**Relative Frequency**
6–8.99	15	0.4286
9–11.99	9	0.2571
12–14.99	4	0.1143
15–17.99	4	0.1143
18–20.99	2	0.0571
21–23.99	1	0.0286

(d)

Daily Volume of Altria Stock

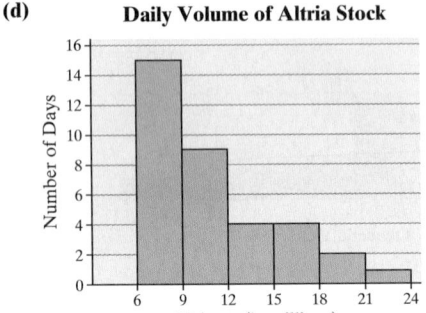

(e)

Daily Volume of Altria Stock

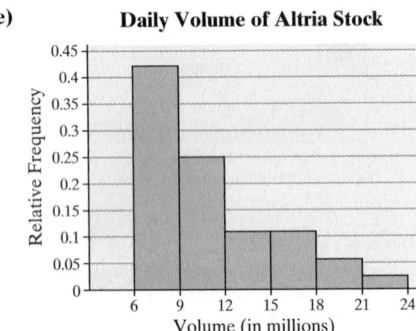

(f) Skewed right.

38. Answers may vary. One possible answer follows:

(a) Lower class limit of first class: 0; class width: 200

(b), (c)

Daily Volume of Altria Stock (in millions)		
Class Intervals	**Frequency**	**Relative Frequency**
0–199	5	0.0980
200–399	22	0.4314
400–599	15	0.2941
600–799	8	0.1569
800–999	0	0
1,000–1,199	0	0
1,200–1,399	0	0
1,400–1,599	1	0.0196

(d)

Violent Crime Rates by State, 2005

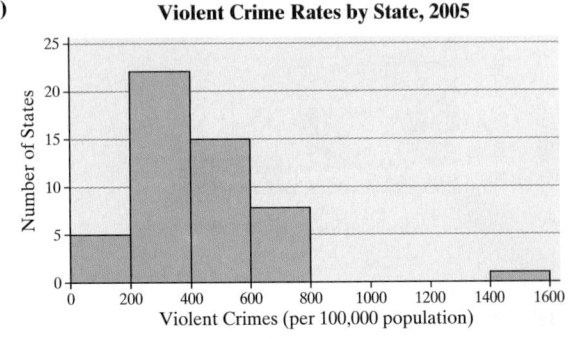

(e)

Violent Crime Rates by State, 2005

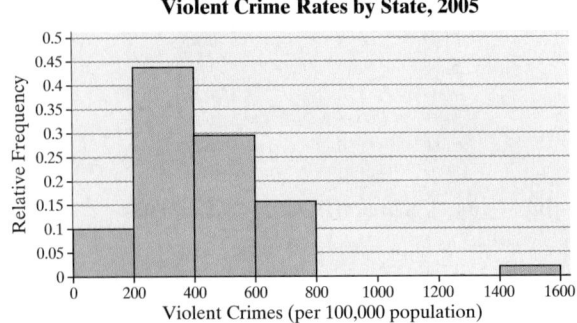

(f) Skewed right.

39. (a)   **President Ages at Inauguration**

```
4 | 23
4 | 667899
5 | 0011112244444
5 | 555566677778
6 | 0111244
6 | 589
```
Legend: 4 | 2 represents 42 years.

(b) Bell shaped

40. (a)   **Divorce Rates by State, 2004**

```
1 | 7
2 | 2
2 | 568889
3 | 00011223
3 | 56667788999
4 | 011244
4 | 5677889
5 | 013
5 |
6 | 34
```
Legend: 1 | 7 represents 1.7 divorces per 1000 population.

(b) Bell shaped

41. (a)   **Fat in McDonald's Breakfast**

```
0 | 39
1 | 1266
2 | 1224577
3 | 0012267
4 | 6
5 | 159
```
Legend: 5 | 1 represents 51 grams of fat.

(b) Bell shaped

42. (a)   **Gasoline Mileages**

```
2 | 34
2 | 56777888899999999
3 | 001111112222222233333333444
3 | 5555667
4 |
4 | 5
```
Legend: 2 | 3 represents 23 miles per gallon.

(b) Slightly skewed right (possibly bell shaped)

43. (a)

7.1	12.8	8.2	7.0	12.8	7.6
14.8	10.1	11.1	10.5	7.6	20.7
4.9	7.1	6.5	7.0	6.9	5.4
8.3	11.8	10.0	15.5	8.1	7.0
8.3	6.3	6.9	6.1	9.6	13.8
11.9	7.4	15.3	7.5	6.2	7.7
7.3	6.5	8.7	14.0	7.0	6.7
7.0	10.3	6.0	11.4	6.9	6.1
5.0	8.1	5.3			

Average Electric Rates by State, 2006

```
 4 | 9
 5 | 034
 6 | 01123557999
 7 | 0000011345667
 8 | 112337
 9 | 6
10 | 0135
11 | 1489
12 | 88
13 | 8
14 | 08
15 | 35
16 |
17 |
18 |
19 |
20 | 7
```

Legend: 4 | 9 represents 4.9 cents/kWh.

(b) Skewed right
(c) 20.72 cents/kW-h; answers will vary.

44. (a)

12	19	14	42	78
40	40	114	56	20
36	87	73	28	42
37	16	24	92	29
14	18	24	41	26
94	63	81	57	41
74	72	29	76	26
19	39	81	19	31

Change in HPI, 2002–2007

```
 1 | 24468999
 2 | 04466899
 3 | 1679
 4 | 001122
 5 | 67
 6 | 3
 7 | 23468
 8 | 117
 9 | 24
10 |
11 | 4
```

Legend: 1 | 2 represents a 12% increase.

(b) Skewed right

45. (a)   **Problems per 100 Vehicles, 2004**

```
16 | 2
17 |
18 | 79
19 | 46
20 | 9
21 | 26
22 | 4
23 |
24 | 0
25 |
26 | 22457
27 | 6
28 | 05589
29 | 578
30 |
31 | 044
32 | 77
33 |
34 | 6
35 |
36 | 5
37 | 5
38 | 6
39 | 3
40 |
41 | 1
42 |
43 | 2
44 |
45 |
46 |
47 | 2
```

Legend: 16 | 2 represents 162 problems.

(b)

Make	Problems per 100 Vehicles	Make	Problems per 100 Vehicles
Lexus	160	Subaru	290
Buick	190	Plymouth	290
Infiniti	190	Audi	300
Lincoln	190	Pontiac	300
Cadillac	200	Dodge	300
Honda	210	Jaguar	310
Acura	210	Jeep	310
Toyota	220	Oldsmobile	310
Mercury	220	Mercedes-Benz	330
Porsche	240	Mitsubishi	330
Chevrolet	260	Volvo	350
GMC	260	Suzuki	370
BMW	260	Hyundai	380
Saab	270	Volkswagen	390
Saturn	270	Isuzu	390
Ford	280	Daewoo	410
Nissan	280	Kia	430
Chrysler	290	Land Rover	470
Mazda	290		

(c)   **Problems per 100 Vehicles, 2004**

```
1 | 6999
2 | 01122466677889999
3 | 0001113357899
4 | 137
```

Legend: 1 | 6 represents 160 problems.

(d)   **Problems per 100 Vehicles, 2004**

```
1 | 6999
2 | 011224
2 | 66677889999
3 | 00011133
3 | 57899
4 | 13
4 | 7
```

Legend: 1 | 6 represents 160 problems.

(e) Answers will vary.

46. (a)

430	710	590	290	350	530
630	450	110	610	510	230
510	260	700	130	290	120
530	260	460	360	430	280
530	550	550	700	250	350
400	320	300	450	760	270
280	290	280	470	180	240
630	390	530	100	750	230
1460	270	280			

(b)   **Violent Crime Rates by State, 2005**

```
 1 | 01238
 2 | 3345667788888999
 3 | 025569
 4 | 0335567
 5 | 113333559
 6 | 133
 7 | 00156
 8 |
 9 |
10 |
11 |
12 |
13 |
14 | 6
```

Legend: 1 | 0 represents 100 violent crimes.

(c)

Violent Crime Rates by State, 2005

```
 1 | 0123
 1 | 8
 2 | 334
 2 | 566778888999
 3 | 02
 3 | 5569
 4 | 033
 4 | 5567
 5 | 113333
 5 | 559
 6 | 133
 6 |
 7 | 001
 7 | 56
 8 |
 8 |
 9 |
 9 |
10 |
10 |
11 |
11 |
12 |
12 |
13 |
13 |
14 |
14 | 6
```

Legend: 1 | 0 represents 100 violent crimes.

(d) Answers will vary.

47. (a)   Ages of Academy   Award Winners

Best Actor   Best Actress

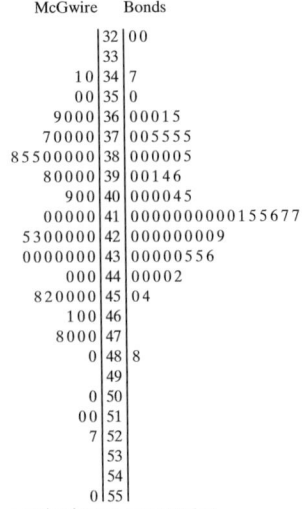

```
           9 | 2 | 1566899
  98877766220 | 3 | 0123333455689
   76555332200 | 4 | 112599
          4321 | 5 |
            20 | 6 | 11
             6 | 7 | 4
               | 8 | 0
```

(b) Answers will vary.

48. (a)   Home Run Distances

McGwire   Bonds

```
          | 32 | 00
          | 33 |
       10 | 34 | 7
       00 | 35 | 0
     9000 | 36 | 00015
    70000 | 37 | 005555
 85500000 | 38 | 000005
    80000 | 39 | 00146
      900 | 40 | 000045
    00000 | 41 | 0000000000155677
  5300000 | 42 | 000000009
  0000000 | 43 | 00000556
      000 | 44 | 00002
   820000 | 45 | 04
      100 | 46 |
     8000 | 47 |
        0 | 48 | 8
          | 49 |
        0 | 50 |
       00 | 51 |
        7 | 52 |
          | 53 |
          | 54 |
        0 | 55 |
```

Legend: 0 | 34 | 7 represents 340 feet

(b) Answers will vary.

49.

Televisions in Household

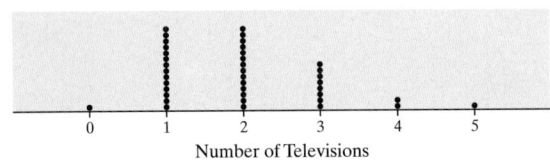

Number of Televisions

50.

Customers Waiting for a Table

Number Waiting

51. Answers will vary.

2.3 Assess Your Understanding (page 106)

1. Answers will vary.

2. Since the cumulative relative frequency displays the proportion (or percentage) of observations less than or equal to the category or class, and all the observations are less than or equal to the last class or category, the cumulative relative frequency for the last class must be 1, or 100%.

3. An ogive is a graph that represents the cumulative frequency or cumulative relative frequency of the class.

4. Time-series data are the values of a variable measured at different points in time.

5. True   6. False

7. **(a)** The class width is 10. There are 10 classes in the graph.
   (b) The midpoint of the first class is 5. The lower limit of the first class is 0; the upper limit is 9.
   (c) The midpoint of the last class is 95. The lower limit of the last class is 90; the upper limit is 99.
   (d) The highest population occurs in the age group 40–49; this population is about 45 million.
   (e) The lowest population occurs in the age group 90–99; this population is about 2 million.
   (f) The total number of U.S. residents below 100 years of age was about 300 million.
   (g) The most extreme change in population occurs between the classes 50–59 and 60–69. The least extreme change occurs between classes 10–19 and 20–29.

8. **(a)** The class width is 10. There are 7 classes in the graph.
   (b) The midpoint of the first class is 20. The lower limit of the first class is 15; the upper limit is 24.
   (c) The midpoint of the last class is 80. The lower limit of the last class is 75; the upper limit is 84.
   (d) The age group with the highest number of deaths from legal intervention is 25–34; this number of deaths is about 106.
   (e) The age group with the lowest number of deaths from legal intervention is 75–84; this number of deaths is about 5.
   (f) The relative frequency for the first class is about 0.215.

9. **(a)** The class width is 4. There are 9 classes in the graph.
   (b) The lower limit of the first class is 1; the upper limit is 4.
   (c) The lower limit of the last class is 33; the upper limit is 36.
   (d) About 76% of students had a composite score of 24 or below.
   (e) About 8% of students had a composite score above 28.
   (f) About 975,449 students had a composite score of 24 or below. About 104,048 students had a composite score above 28.

10. **(a)** The class width is 50. There are 12 classes in the graph.
    (b) The lower limit of the first class is 201; the upper limit is 250.
    (c) The lower limit of the last class is 751; the upper limit is 800.
    (d) About 23 of the students had a writing score of 350 or below.
    (e) About 28 of the students had a writing score above 650.
    (f) The most students fall in the class 501–550; this number of students is about 54.

11. **(a)** The closing price at the end of May 2006 was about $45.
    (b) The closing price at the end of December 2007 was about $215.
    (c) The price of the stock increased by about 378%.
    (d) The price of the stock decreased by about 17%.

12. **(a)** About 8.8 million motor vehicles were produced in the United States in 1991.
    (b) About 13.0 million motor vehicles were produced in the United States in 1999.
    (c) The number of vehicles produced increased by about 47.7%.
    (d) The number of vehicles produced decreased by about 13.1%.

13. **(a)** For 1992, the unemployment rate was about 7.5% and the inflation rate was about 3.0%.

(b) For 2006, the unemployment rate was about 4.6% and the inflation rate was about 3.4%.

(c) For 1992, the misery index was about 10.5%. For 2006, the misery index was about 8.0%.

(d) Answers may vary. One possibility follows: An increase in the inflation rate seems to be followed by an increase in the unemployment rate. Likewise, a decrease in the inflation rate seems to be followed by a decrease in the unemployment rate.

14. (a) In 1990, the men's prize money was £230,000; the ladies' prize money was £207,000.

(b) In 2006, the men's prize money was £655,000; the ladies' prize money was £625,000.

(c) Answers may vary. One possibility follows: Until 2007, the prize money for men's singles is higher than the prize money for ladies' singles. Both prizes increase over time at similar rates.

(d) In 2007, equal prize money was awarded for the first time. The prize money for each was £700,000.

(e) From 2006 to 2007, the men's prize money increased by about 6.9%. The ladies, increased by about 12.0%.

15. (a), (b)

Tuition	Cumulative Frequency	Cumulative Relative Frequency
$0–1,999	19	0.0106
$2,000–3,999	151	0.0844
$4,000–5,999	459	0.2564
$6,000–7,999	639	0.3570
$8,000–9,999	745	0.4162
$10,000–11,999	844	0.4715
$12,000–13,999	933	0.5212
$14,000–15,999	1,031	0.5760
$16,000–17,999	1,156	0.6458
$18,000–19,999	1,272	0.7106
$20,000–21,999	1,389	0.7760
$22,000–23,999	1,489	0.8318
$24,000–25,999	1,572	0.8782
$26,000–27,999	1,625	0.9078
$28,000–29,999	1,670	0.9330
$30,000–31,999	1,706	0.9531
$32,000–33,999	1,752	0.9788
$34,000–35,999	1,784	0.9966
$36,000–37,999	1,790	1

(c)

Four-Year College Tuition

(d)

Four-Year College Tuition

(e)

Four-Year College Tuition

16. (a), (b)

Magnitude	Cumulative Frequency	Cumulative Relative Frequency
0–0.9	1,600	0.0647
1.0–1.9	1,633	0.0660
2.0–2.9	4,616	0.1866
3.0–3.9	12,644	0.5111
4.0–4.9	23,109	0.9342
5.0–5.9	24,575	0.9935
6.0–6.9	24,726	0.9996
7.0–7.9	24,737	1

(c)

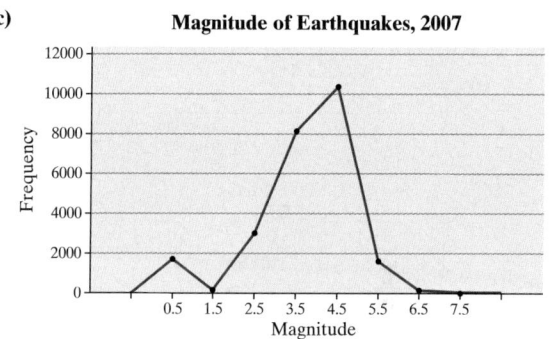

Magnitude of Earthquakes, 2007

(d)

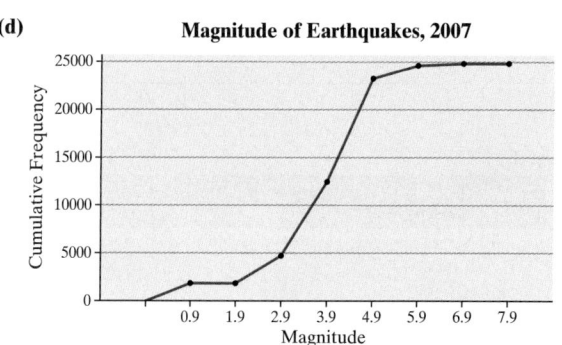

Magnitude of Earthquakes, 2007

(e)

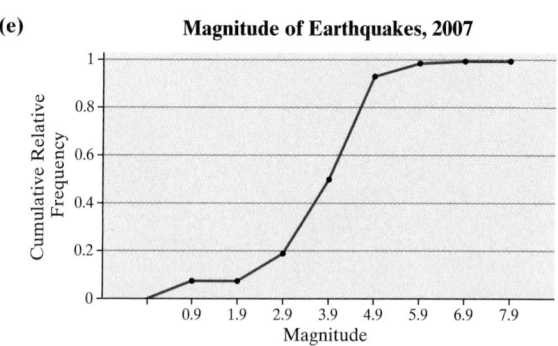

Magnitude of Earthquakes, 2007

17. (a), (b)

Age	Cumulative Frequency	Cumulative Relative Frequency
15–19	414,406	0.1004
20–24	1,454,805	0.3525
25–29	2,587,098	0.6268
30–34	3,539,111	0.8575
35–39	4,022,512	0.9746
40–44	4,127,156	1

(c)

(d)

(e)

18. (a), (b)

Number of Students Enrolled	Cumulative Frequency	Cumulative Relative Frequency
0–4,999	15	0.3333
5,000–9,999	31	0.6889
10,000–14,999	40	0.8889
15,000–19,999	44	0.9778
20,000–24,999	44	0.9778
25,000–29,999	45	1

(c)

(d)

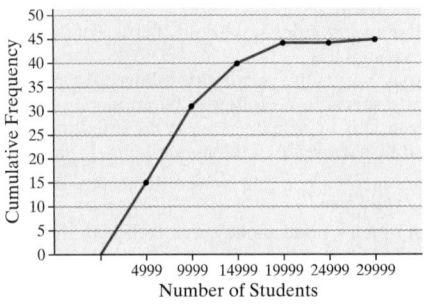

(e)

Illinois Community College Enrollments

19. (a), (b)

Income ($)	Cumulative Frequency	Cumulative Relative Frequency
24,000–26,999	8	0.1569
27,000–29,999	23	0.4510
30,000–32,999	35	0.6863
33,000–35,999	45	0.8824
36,000–38,999	48	0.9412
39,000–41,999	50	0.9804
42,000–44,999	50	0.9804
45,000–47,999	51	1

(c)

(d)

(e)

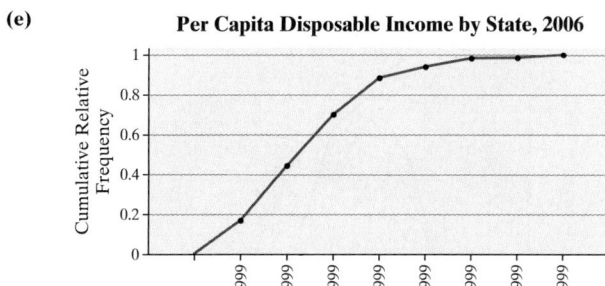

Per Capita Disposable Income by State, 2006

20. (a), (b)

Class Intervals	Cumulative Frequency	Cumulative Relative Frequency
8–9.9	7	0.1373
10–11.9	17	0.3333
12–13.9	28	0.5490
14–15.9	34	0.6667
16–17.9	41	0.8039
18–19.9	45	0.8824
20–21.9	49	0.9608
22–23.9	50	0.9804
24–25.9	51	1

(c)

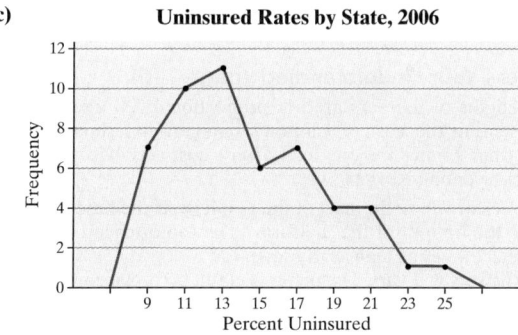

Uninsured Rates by State, 2006

(d)

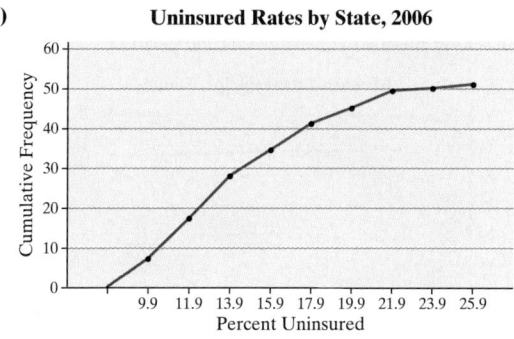

Uninsured Rates by State, 2006

(e)

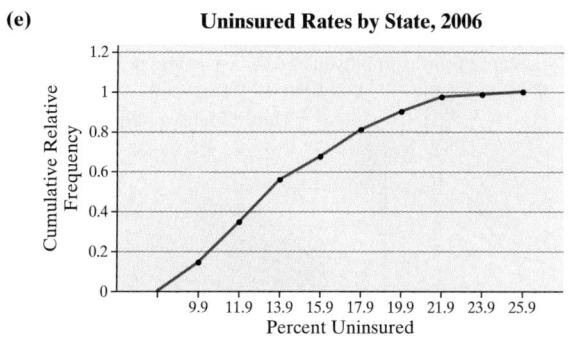

Uninsured Rates by State, 2006

21.

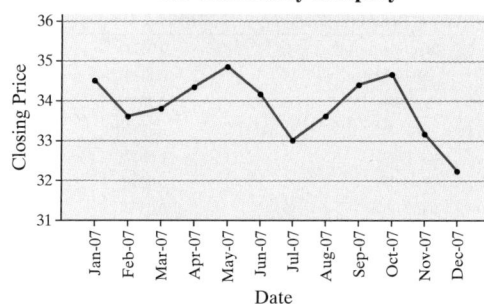

The Walt Disney Company

The price of Disney stock over the year seemed to fluctuate somewhat, with a general downward trend.

22.

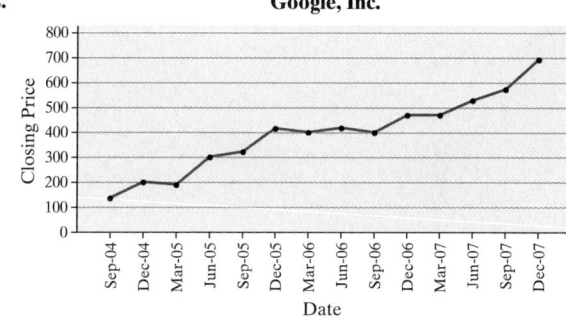

Google, Inc.

Since going public, the price of Google stock has increased steadily and rapidly.

23.

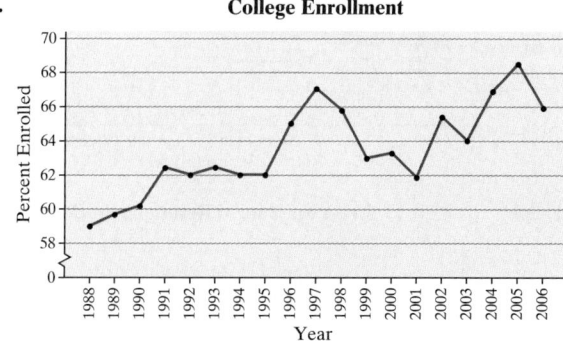

College Enrollment

The percentage of high school graduates who enrolled in college has generally increased, though there have been some down years.

24.

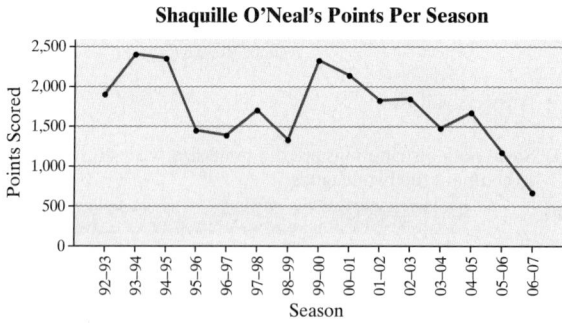

Shaquille O'Neal's Points Per Season

Since the 1999–2000 season, the number of points scored per season by Shaquille O'Neal has decreased steadily.

25. (a), (b)

Financial Stocks		
Rate of Return	**Frequency**	**Relative Frequency**
−20 to −0.01	2	0.0571
0–19.99	5	0.1429
20–39.99	3	0.0857
40–59.99	11	0.3143
60–79.99	3	0.0857
80–99.99	3	0.0857
100–119.99	3	0.0857
120–139.99	1	0.0286
140–159.99	0	0
160–179.99	2	0.0571
180–199.99	2	0.0571

Retail Stocks		
Rate of Return	**Frequency**	**Relative Frequency**
−20 to −0.01	4	0.1143
0–19.99	2	0.0571
20–39.99	10	0.2857
40–59.99	4	0.1143
60–79.99	3	0.0857
80–99.99	3	0.0857
100–119.99	2	0.0571
120–139.99	1	0.0286
140–159.99	2	0.0571
160–179.99	0	0
180–199.99	2	0.0571
200–219.99	0	0
220–239.99	2	0.0571

(c)

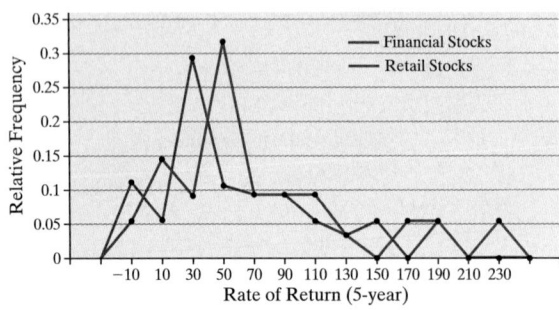

Five-Year Rate of Return on Stocks

(d)

Five-Year Rate of Return on Stocks

(e) Answers will vary.

26. (a) Since both distributions are the same size, we can use frequencies to compare the two leagues.

(b)

Class	American League	National League
2.5–2.99	0	1
3.0–3.49	9	7
3.5–3.99	13	12
4.0–4.49	11	8
4.5–4.99	3	9
5.0–5.49	4	3

(c)

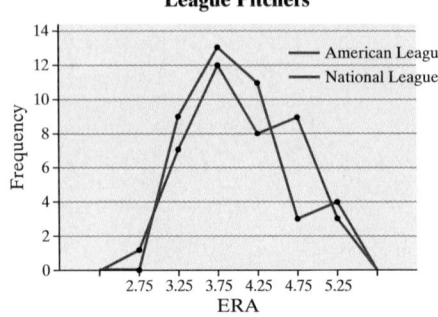

American vs National League Pitchers

(d)

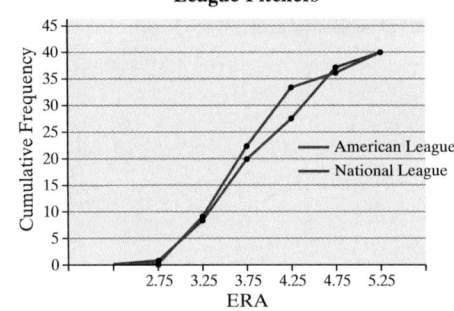

American vs National League Pitchers

(e) Answers will vary.

27. Answers will vary.

2.4 Assess Your Understanding (page 115)

1. The lengths of the bars are not proportional. For example, the bar representing the cost of Clinton's inauguration should be slightly more than 9 times the one for Carter's cost and twice as long as the bar representing Reagan's cost.

2. (a) Unclear where the start of the graph is: At the base of each figure or the bottom of the platform? The top of cheeseburger should be 2.2 times as high as the soda.

(b) Answers will vary. The pictures could be replaced by simple bars that are proportional in area.

3. (a) The vertical axis starts at 31.5 instead of 0. This tends to indicate that the median earnings for females decreased at a faster rate than they actually did.

(b) This graph indicates that the median earnings for females have decreased slightly over the given time period.

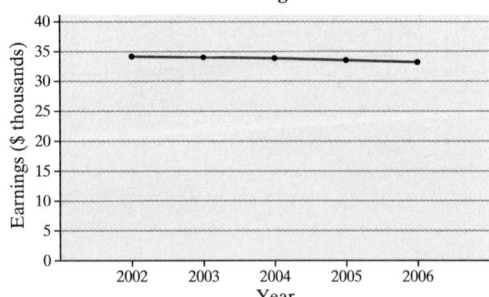

Median Earnings for Females

4. (a) The vertical axis starts at 0.08 instead of 0. Readers may think the percent of those employed aged 45 years and older who are union members is much higher than for those aged 25 to 35 years.

(b)

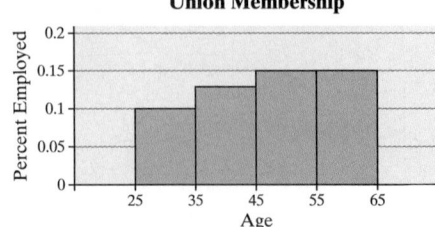

Union Membership

5. The bar for 12p–6p covers twice as many hours as the other bars. By combining two 3-hour periods, this bar looks larger compared to the others, making afternoon hours look more dangerous. When the bar is split into two periods, the graph may give a different impression.

6. The graph is comparing counts for two categories that do not cover the same number of years. A better comparison is the incidence rate (number of accidents per 100,000 licensed drivers).

7. **(a)** The vertical axis starts at 0.1 instead of 0. This might cause the reader to conclude, for example, that the proportion of people aged 25 to 34 who are not covered by health insurance is more than twice the proportion for those aged 45 to 54 years.

(b)

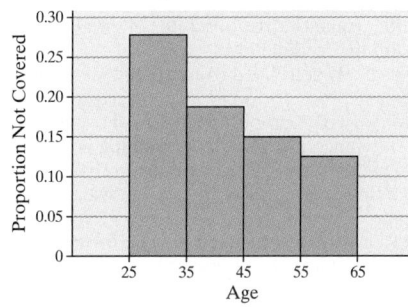

8. **(a)** The vertical axis starts at 150 without indicating a gap.
   (b) It may be trying to convey that new home construction increased significantly in the Midwest between 2000 and 2004, then declined at roughly twice the rate between 2004 and 2006.
   (c) The graph does support this view. The sharp drop in 2006 indicates a market cooling and less demand for new construction.

9. **(a)** The vertical axis starts at 47 without indicating a gap.
   (b) It may convey that the median household income is increasing after a period of decline.

(c)

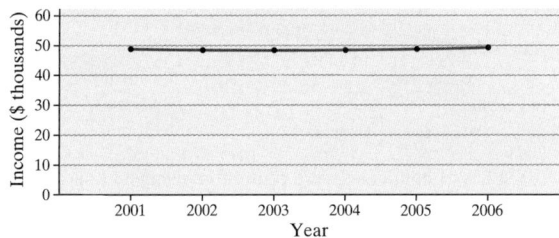

10. **(a)** Roughly 93 times larger
    (b) About 69 days

11. **(a)** The bar for housing should be a little more than twice the length of the bar for transportation, but it is not.
    (b) Adjust the graph so that the lengths of the bars are proportional.

12. **(a)**

(b)

13. **(a)**

(b)

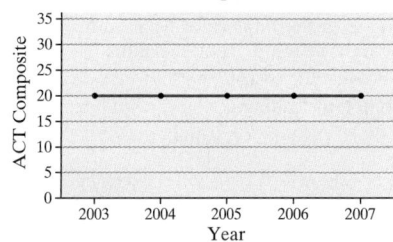

(c) Graph (a) is preferred because the trend can be seen.

14. The graph does not support the safety manager's claim. The vertical scale starts at 0.17 instead of 0, so the difference between the bars is distorted. While there has been a decrease, it appears that the decrease is roughly 10% of the 1992 rate.

15. **(a)** The politician's view:

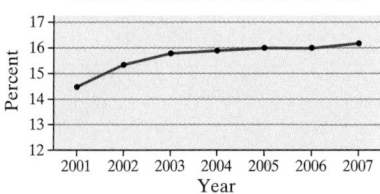

(b) The health care industry's view:

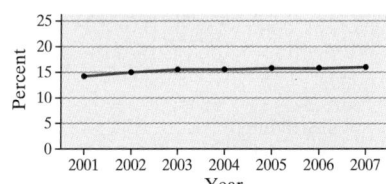

(c) A view that is not misleading:

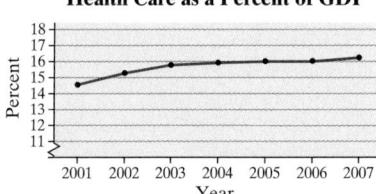

16. **(a)** Roads are less safe view:

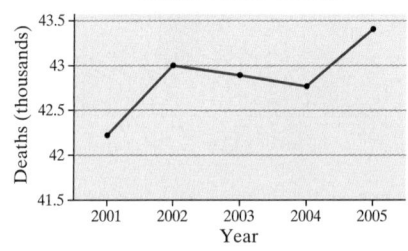

(b) Roads are safer view:

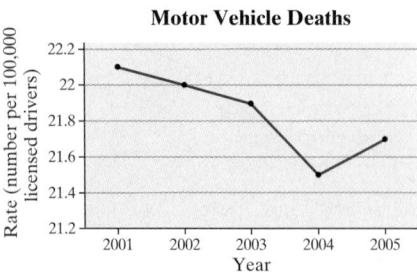

Motor Vehicle Deaths

(c) The graph in part (b) is a better representation. As population grows, an increase in the number of licensed drivers will likely lead to an increase in motor vehicle deaths. The incident rate takes this population growth into account.

17. (a) Graphic that is not misleading:

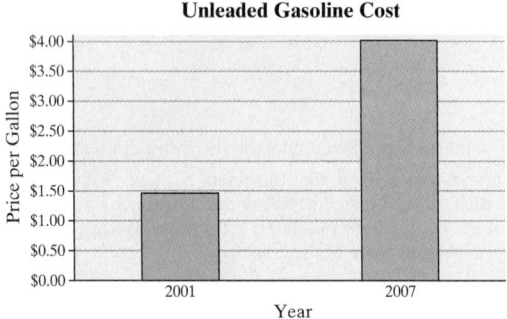

Unleaded Gasoline Cost

(b) Graphic that is misleading (graphics may vary):

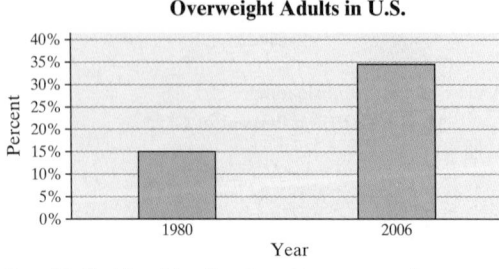

Unleaded Gasoline Cost

18. (a) Graphic that is not misleading:

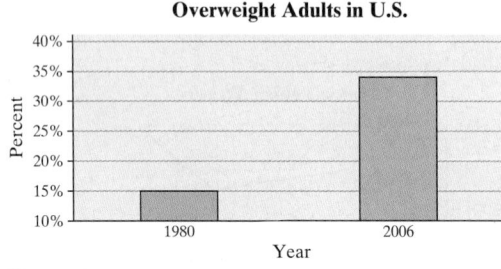

Overweight Adults in U.S.

(b) Graphic that is misleading (graphics may vary):

Overweight Adults in U.S.

19. (a) Time series
(b) The graph is too cluttered; the axes are not labeled; the grid stands out more than the data.

(c) Graph that is not misleading:

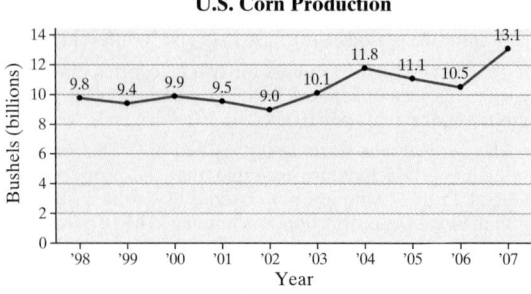

U.S. Corn Production

20. (a) Cornell tuition (quantitative, discrete, interval level); Cornell ranking (qualitative, ordinal level)
(b) The graph was likely generated from existing data sources.
(c) Time series.
(d) Answers may vary. The graph appears to show that the cost to attend Cornell is increasing while its ranking is decreasing. The graph is misleading, because the ranking graph may imply that ranking is getting worse when in fact a lower value means a better ranking.
(e) No horizontal or vertical scale is provided; the horizontal scale is inconsistent; the vertical scale is inconsistent between graphs.

Chapter 2 Review Exercises (page 120)

1. (a) 22.5 quadrillion Btu
(b) 3 quadrillion Btu
(c) 100 quadrillion Btu
(d) Other
(e) No; the data are qualitative.

2. (a)

Type of Weapon	Relative Frequency
Firearms	0.6787
Knives or cutting instruments	0.1281
Blunt objects (clubs, hammers, etc.)	0.0410
Personal weapons (hands, fists, etc.)	0.0601
Strangulation	0.0140
Fire	0.0080
Other weapon or not stated	0.0701

(b) 4.1% of homicides were committed using a blunt object.

(c)

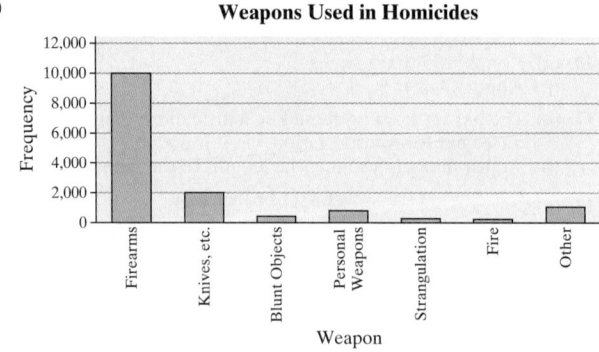

Weapons Used in Homicides

(d)

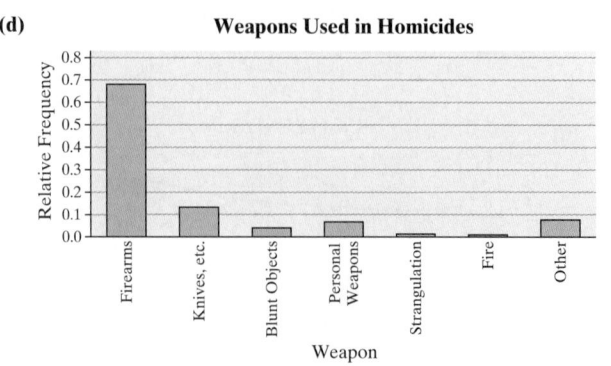

Weapons Used in Homicides

(e)

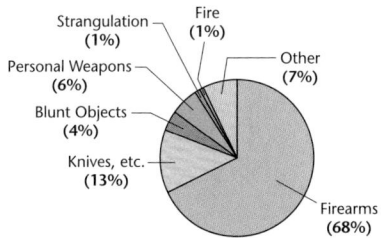

Weapons Used in Homicides

(g)

Live Births in the U.S. by Age of Mother

3. (a), (b), (c)

Age of Mother (years)	Relative Frequency	Cumulative Frequency	Cumulative Relative Frequency
10–14	0.0014	6	0.0014
15–19	0.1022	441	0.1036
20–24	0.2539	1,522	0.3574
25–29	0.2776	2,704	0.6350
30–34	0.2231	3,654	0.8582
35–39	0.1172	4,153	0.9753
40–44	0.0247	4,258	1

(h)

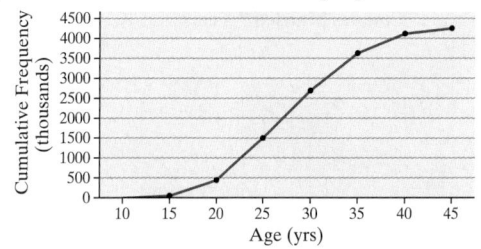

Live Births in the U.S. by Age of Mother

(i)

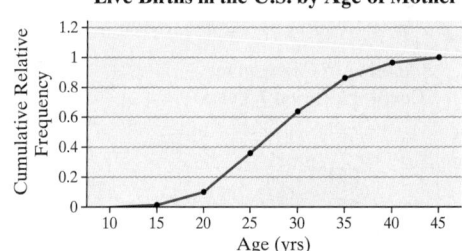

Live Births in the U.S. by Age of Mother

(d)

Live Births in the U.S. by Age of Mother

The distribution is roughly bell shaped.

(j) 25.4% of live births were to mothers aged 20 to 24.

(k) 36.5% of live births were to mothers ages 30 or above.

4. (a), (b)

Affiliation	Frequency	Relative Frequency
Democrat	46	0.46
Independent	16	0.16
Republican	38	0.38

(c)

Political Affiliation

(e)

Live Births in the U.S. by Age of Mother

(d)

Political Affiliation

(f)

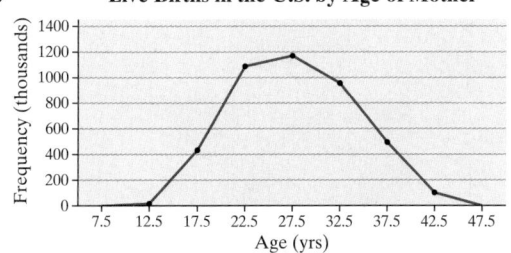

Live Births in the U.S. by Age of Mother

(e) Democrat appears to be the most common affiliation.

5. (a), (b), (c), (d)

Number of Children	Frequency	Relative Frequency	Cumulative Frequency	Cumulative Relative Frequency
0	7	0.1167	7	0.1167
1	7	0.1167	14	0.2333
2	18	0.3000	32	0.5333
3	20	0.3333	52	0.8667
4	7	0.1167	59	0.9833
5	1	0.0167	60	1

(e)

Number of Children for Couples Married 7 Years

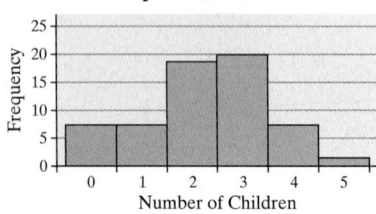

The distribution is symmetric.

(f)

Number of Children for Couples Married 7 Years

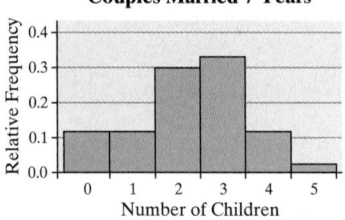

(g) 30% of the couples has two children.
(h) 76.7% of the couples has at least two children.
(i)

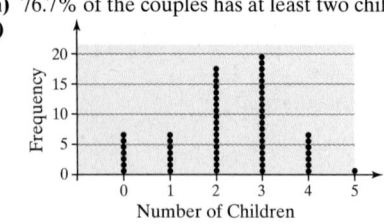

6. (a), (b), (c), (d)

Crime Rate	Frequency	Relative Frequency	Cumulative Frequency	Cumulative Relative Frequency
1,800–2,199	3	0.0588	3	0.0588
2,200–2,599	3	0.0588	6	0.1176
2,600–2,999	10	0.1961	16	0.3137
3,000–3,399	3	0.0588	19	0.3725
3,400–3,799	7	0.1373	26	0.5098
3,800–4,199	4	0.0784	30	0.5882
4,200–4,599	9	0.1765	39	0.7647
4,600–4,999	6	0.1176	45	0.8824
5,000–5,399	5	0.0980	50	0.9804
5,400–5,799	0	0.0000	50	0.9804
5,800–6,199	0	0.0000	50	0.9804
6,200–6,599	1	0.0196	51	1.0000

(e)

Crime Rate by State in 2005

The distribution is roughly symmetric.

(f)

Crime Rate by State in 2005

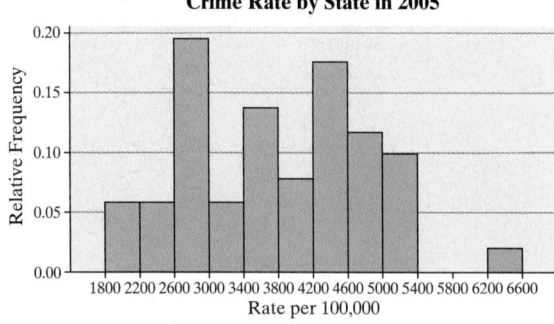

The distribution is skewed right.

(g)

Crime Rate	Frequency	Relative Frequency	Cumulative Frequency	Cumulative Relative Frequency
1,800–2,799	8	0.1569	8	0.1569
2,800–3,799	18	0.3529	26	0.5098
3,800–4,799	16	0.3137	42	0.8236
4,800–5,799	8	0.1569	50	0.9804
5,800–6,799	1	0.0196	51	1

Crime Rate by State in 2005

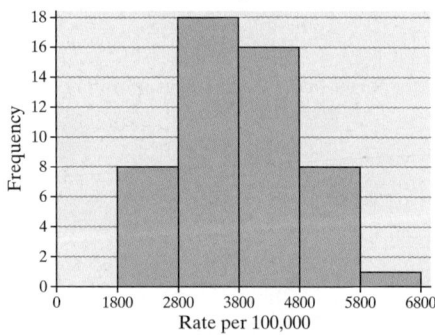

Crime Rate by State in 2005

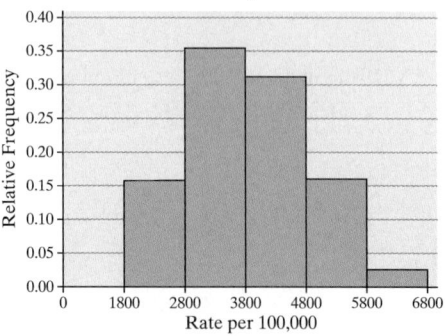

7. (a), (b), (c), (d) Answers will vary. Using 2.2000 as the lower class limit of the first class and 0.0200 as the class width, we obtain the following.

Class	Frequency	Relative Frequency	Cumulative Frequency	Cumulative Relative Frequency
2.2000–2.2199	2	0.0588	2	0.0588
2.2200–2.2399	3	0.0882	5	0.1470
2.2400–2.2599	5	0.1471	10	0.2941
2.2600–2.2799	6	0.1765	16	0.4706
2.2800–2.2999	4	0.1176	20	0.5882
2.3000–2.3199	7	0.2059	27	0.7941
2.3200–2.3399	5	0.1471	32	0.9412
2.3400–2.3599	1	0.0294	33	0.9706
2.3600–2.3799	1	0.0294	34	1

Table title: Diameter of a Cookie

(e)

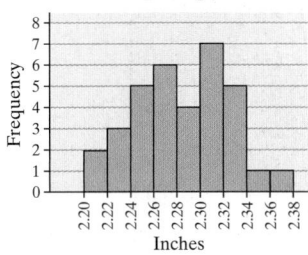

Diameter of Chocolate Chip Cookies

The distribution is roughly symmetric.

(f)

Diameter of Chocolate Chip Cookies

8.

Hours Spent Online

```
12 |
13 | 467
14 | 05578
15 | 1236
16 | 456
17 | 113449
18 | 066889
19 | 2
20 | 168
21 | 119
22 | 29
23 | 48
24 | 4
25 | 7
26 |
```

Legend: 13 | 4 = average 13.4 hours per week.

The distribution is skewed right.

9. (a)

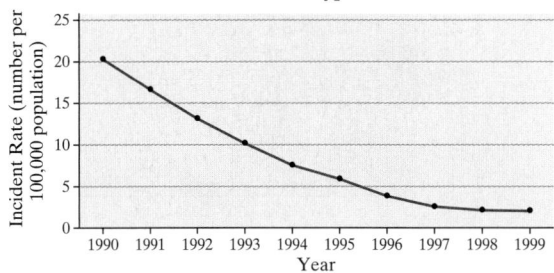

Prevelance of Syphilis in U.S.

The incident rate decreased dramatically over the given time period.

(b)

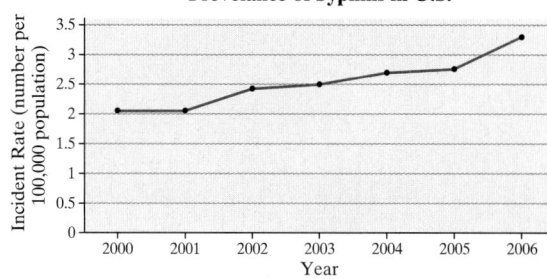

Prevelance of Syphilis in U.S.

(c) Although the incident rate declined between 1990 and 2000, it increases gradually between 2002 and 2006. The plan needed to be adjusted to deal with this increase.

(d) No; a histogram will not allow the observer to see trends over time, only the distribution of yearly incident rates.

10. There is no vertical scale.

11. (a) Answers will vary.

(b) An example of a graph that does not mislead:

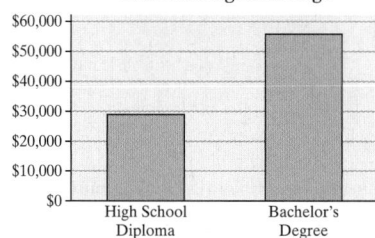

2005 Average Earnings

12. (a) Flats are preferred most; extra-high heels are preferred least.

(b) The bar heights and areas are not proportional.

Chapter 2 Test (page 123)

1. (a) Representatives of the United States have won the most championships. They have won 15 championships.

(b) Representatives of Australia have won 2 more championships than Germany.

(c) Representatives of Sweden won 17.5% of the championships.

(d) It is not appropriate to describe the shape of the distribution as skewed right. The data represented by the graph are qualitative, so the bars in the graph could be placed in any order.

2. (a)

Gas	Relative Frequency
Carbon dioxide	0.8387
Methane	0.0855
Nitrous oxide	0.0535
Hydrofluorocarbons, perfluorocarbons, and sulfur hexafluoride	0.0223

(b) About 83.87% of emissions was due to carbon dioxide.

(c)

U.S. Greenhouse Emissions

(d)

U.S. Greenhouse Emissions

(e)

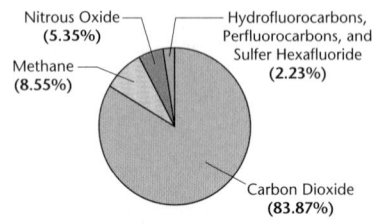

U.S. Greenhouse Emissions

3. (a), (b)

Educational Attainment	Frequency	Relative Frequency
No high school diploma	9	0.18
High school graduate	16	0.32
Some college	9	0.18
Associate's degree	4	0.08
Bachelor's degree	8	0.16
Advanced degree	4	0.08

(c)

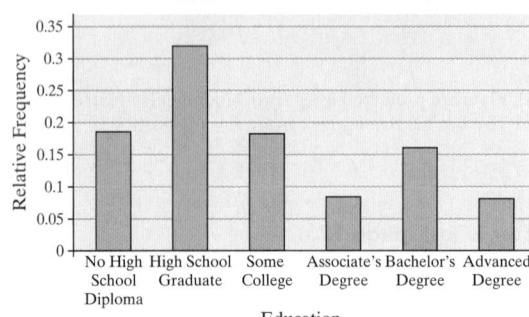

Educational Attainment of Commuters

(d)

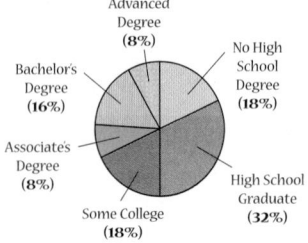

Educational Attainment of Commuters

(e) High school graduate is the most common educational level.

4. (a), (b), (c), (d)

Number of Customers	Frequency	Relative Frequency	Cumulative Frequency	Cumulative Relative Frequency
1	5	0.10	5	0.10
2	7	0.14	12	0.24
3	12	0.24	24	0.48
4	6	0.12	30	0.60
5	8	0.16	38	0.76
6	5	0.10	43	0.86
7	2	0.04	45	0.90
8	4	0.08	49	0.98
9	1	0.02	50	1

(e)

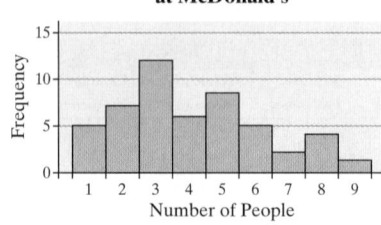

Number of Cars Arriving at McDonald's

The distribution is skewed right.

(f)

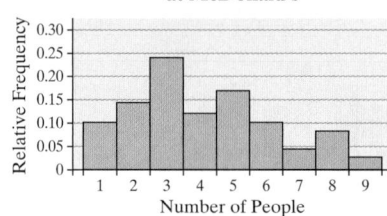

Number of Cars Arriving at McDonald's

(g) 24% of weeks, three cars arrived between 11:50 A.M. and noon.

(h) 76% of weeks, at least three cars arrived between 11:50 A.M. and noon.

(i)

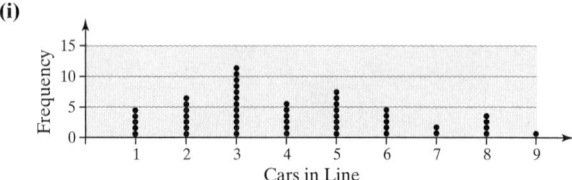

5. Answers may vary. One possibility follows:

(a) The lower class limit of the first class is 100 grams; the class width is 50 grams.

(b), (c)

Serving Size	Frequency	Relative Frequency
100–149	11	0.275
150–199	7	0.175
200–249	9	0.225
250–299	8	0.2
300–349	1	0.025
350–399	2	0.05
400–449	1	0.025
450–499	1	0.025

(d)

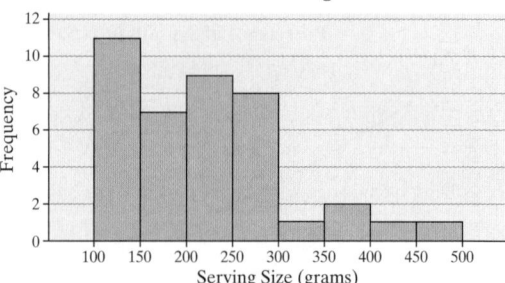

Sandwich Serving Sizes

The distribution is skewed right.

(e)

Sandwich Serving Sizes

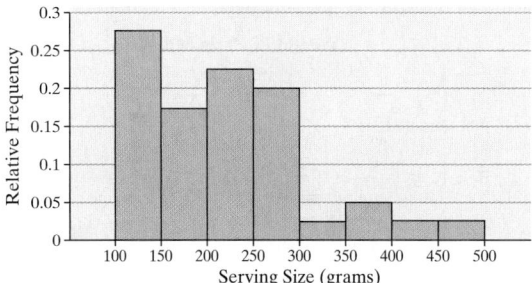

6. (a), (b)

Closing Price	Cumulative Frequency	Cumulative Relative Frequency
50,000–99,999	4	0.08
100,000–149,999	17	0.34
150,000–199,999	36	0.72
200,000–249,999	43	0.86
250,000–299,999	46	0.92
300,000–349,999	48	0.96
350,000–399,999	49	0.98
400,000–449,999	49	0.98
450,000–499,999	50	1

(c) 72% of the homes sold for less than $200,000.

(d)

Closing Price of Homes Sold

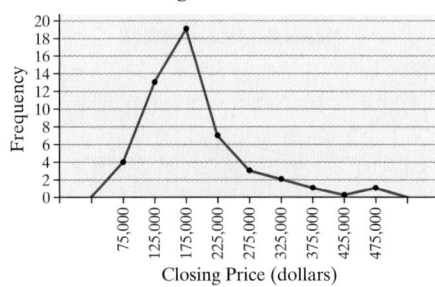

The distribution is skewed right.

(e)

Closing Price of Homes Sold

(f)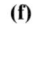

Closing Price of Homes Sold

7. (a)

State	Fertility Rate	State	Fertility Rate
Alabama	67	Montana	70
Alaska	77	Nebraska	75
Arizona	82	Nevada	78
Arkansas	72	New Hampshire	53
California	72	New Jersey	64
Colorado	70	New Mexico	75
Connecticut	59	New York	61
Delaware	67	North Carolina	69
District of Columbia	59	North Dakota	69
Florida	67	Ohio	65
Georgia	72	Oklahoma	75
Hawaii	74	Oregon	66
Idaho	81	Pennsylvania	61
Illinois	67	Rhode Island	57
Indiana	68	South Carolina	70
Iowa	69	South Dakota	78
Kansas	73	Tennessee	68
Kentucky	67	Texas	79
Louisiana	71	Utah	94
Maine	55	Vermont	52
Maryland	64	Virginia	66
Massachusetts	57	Washington	65
Michigan	62	West Virginia	59
Minnesota	69	Wisconsin	64
Mississippi	76	Wyoming	76
Missouri	68		

Fertility Rates by State, 2006

```
5 | 23
5 | 577999
6 | 112444
6 | 5566777778889999
7 | 000122234
7 | 555667889
8 | 12
8 |
9 | 4
```

Legend: 5 | 2 represents 52 births per 1000 women aged 15 to 44.

(b) The distribution is slightly skewed right.

8.

U.S. Average Milk Price

The price of milk decreased slightly from January 2006 to July 2006. It then increased slowly at first, then rapidly.

9. Answers will vary.

CHAPTER 3 Numerically Summarizing Data

3.1 Assess Your Understanding (page 137)

1. A statistic is resistant if it is not sensitive to extreme values. The median is resistant because it is a positional measure of central tendency, and increasing the largest value or decreasing the smallest value does not affect the position of the center. The mean is not resistant because it is a function of the sum of the values of data. Changing the magnitude of one value changes the sum of the values.

2. $55,263 is the mean household income.

3. HUD uses the median because the data are skewed. Explanations will vary.

4. The mean will likely be larger. Explanations will vary.

5. The median is between the 5000th and the 5001st ordered values.

6. False

7. $\bar{x} = 11$ **8.** $\bar{x} = 82$

9. $\mu = 9$ **10.** $\mu = 15$

11. Mean price per ad slot was $2.5 million.

12. The missing value is 32.

13. Mean cost is $1,457.75; median cost is $1,437.50; there is no mode cost.

14. Mean phone bill is $41.41; median phone bill is $40.76; there is no mode phone bill.

15. The mean, median, and mode strengths are 3,670, 3,830, and 4,090 pounds per square inch, respectively.

16. The mean, median, and mode flight times are 266, 266, and 260 minutes, respectively.

17. (a) mean > median   **18. (a)** IV
     (b) mean = median   **(b)** III
     (c) mean < median   **(c)** II
     Justification will vary.   **(d)** I

21. (a) Tap: $\bar{x} = 7.50$; $M = 7.485$; mode = 7.47. Bottled: $\bar{x} = 5.194$; $M = 5.22$; mode = 5.26
     (b) $\bar{x} = 7.05$; $M = 7.485$; the median is resistant.

22. (a) Blue stimulus: $\bar{x} = 0.551$ second, $M = 0.5315$ second; no mode. Red stimulus: $\bar{x} = 0.458$ second, $M = 0.432$ second, no mode.
     (b) Answers will vary.
     (c) $\bar{x} = 1.8125$ seconds; $M = 0.5315$ second; the median is resistant.

23. (a) The mean pulse rate is 72.2 beats per minute.
     (b) Samples and sample means will vary.
     (c) Answers will vary.

24. (a) The mean travel time is 26.4 minutes.
     (b) Samples and sample means will vary.
     (c) Answers will vary.

25. (a) 1,813,654.5 thousand metric tons
     (b) Per capita is better because it adjusts for CO_2 emissions for population. After all, countries with more people will, in general, have higher CO_2 emissions.
     (c) Mean = 2.814 thousand metric tons; median = 2.67 thousand metric tons; mean

26. (a) Mean winning time = 86.572 hours
     Median winning time = 86.251 hours
     (b) Mean winning distance = 3498.7 km
     Median winning distance = 3453 km
     (c) Mean winning margin = 5.667 min
     Median winning margin = 6.317 min
     (d) Mean winning speed: $\bar{x} = 40.420$ km/h

$$\text{Winning speed: } \frac{\sum \text{distance}}{\sum \text{time}} = 40.414 \text{ km/h}$$

$$\text{Winning speed: } \frac{\text{mean distance}}{\text{mean time}} = 40.414 \text{ km/h}$$

27. The distribution is symmetric. The mean is the better measure of central tendency.

28. The distribution is skewed right. The median is the better measure of central tendency of the distribution.

29. $\bar{x} = 0.875$ gram; $M = 0.875$ gram. The distribution is symmetric, so the mean is the better measure of central tendency.

Weight of Plain M&Ms

30. The distributions is symmetric; $\bar{x} = 104.1$ seconds; $M = 104$ seconds. The mean is the better measure of central tendency.

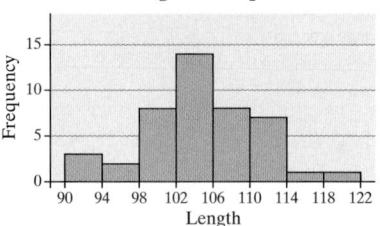

Length of Eruptions

31. The distribution is skewed left; $\bar{x} = 22$ hours; $M = 25$ hours. The median is the better measure of central tendency.

Hours Worked per Week

32. The distribution is skewed right; $\bar{x} = \$1392.83$; $M = \$1177.50$. The median is the better measure of central tendency.

Car Dealer's Profit

33. (a) Moderate   **(b)** Yes, to avoid response bias

34. The mode diagnosis of admission is gunshot wound.

35. Sample of size 5: All data recorded correctly: $\bar{x} = 99.8$; $M = 100$; 106 recorded as 160: $\bar{x} = 110.6$; $M = 100$

Sample of size 12: All data recorded correctly: $\bar{x} = 100.4$; $M = 101$; 106 recorded as 160: $\bar{x} = 104.9$; $M = 101$

Sample of size 30: All data recorded correctly: $\bar{x} = 100.6$; $M = 99$; 106 recorded as 160: $\bar{x} = 102.4$; $M = 99$

For each sample size, the mean becomes larger, but the median remains constant. As the sample size increases, the affect of the misrecorded data on the mean decreases.

36. 67.8 inches

37. No. Each state has a different population size. This must be taken into account.

38. (a) Median   **(b)** Skewed right
(c) There are a few households with very high net worth.

39. The salary distribution is skewed right, so the players' negotiator would want to use the median salary; the owners' negotiator would use the mean salary to refute the players' claim.

40. The distribution is skewed right, so the median amount of money lost is less than the mean amount lost.

41. The unreadable score is 44.

42. (a) Median; the distribution of home prices tends to be skewed.
(b) Mode; the data are qualitative.
(c) Mean; the data are quantitative and symmetric.
(d) Median; the data are quantitative and skewed.
(e) Median; NFL salaries are skewed right.
(f) Mode; the data are qualitative.

43. (a) Mean = \$50,000; median = \$50,000; mode = \$50,000
(b) New data set: 32.5, 32.5, 47.5, 52.5, 52.5, 52.5, 57.5, 57.5, 62.5, 77.5; mean = \$52,500; median = \$52,500; mode = \$52,500. All three measures increased by \$2,500.
(c) New data set: 31.5, 31.5, 47.25, 52.5, 52.5, 52.5, 57.75, 57.75, 63, 78.75; mean = \$52,500; median = \$52,500; mode = \$52,500. All three measures increased by 5%.
(d) New data set: 30, 30, 45, 50, 50, 50, 55, 55, 60, 100; mean = \$52,500; median = \$50,000; mode = \$50,000. The mean increased by \$2,500, but the median and the mode remained at \$50,000.

44. (a) $\bar{x} = 75.2$ **(b)** $M = 71$
(c) The median is the better measure of central tendency since the distribution is skewed right.
(d) $\bar{x} = 79.2$ **(e)** Adding 4 to each score increases the mean by 4.

45. The trimmed mean is 0.875. Explanations will vary.

46. Midrange = 0.87. Midrange is not resistant; it only considers extreme data points.

47. (a) Discrete
(b)

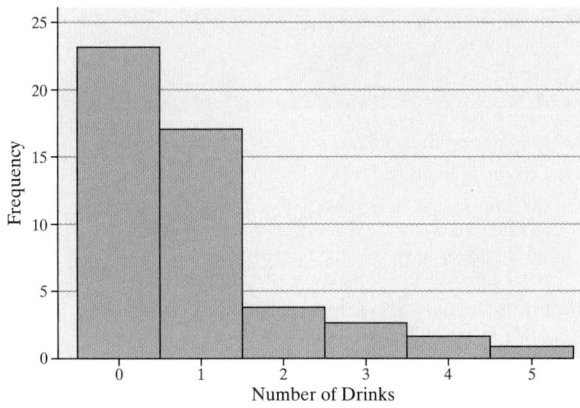

Number of Days High School Students Consume Alcohol Each Week

(c) Since the data are skewed right, we would expect the mean to be greater than the median.
(d) Mean: 0.94; median: 1; the mean can be less than the median in skewed-right data. Therefore, using the rule *mean greater than median implies the data are skewed right* does not always work.
(e) 0
(f) Yes. It is difficult to get truthful responses to this type of question. Carlos would need to ensure that the identity of the respondents is anonymous.

3.2 Assess Your Understanding (page 153)

1. It is not appropriate because the units are different.

2. The degrees of freedom are the number of data values that are free to vary.

3. No, none of the measures of dispersion in this section is resistant.

4. zero

5. A statistic is biased when it consistently overestimates or underestimates the population parameter.

6. The range does not use all the observations.

7. Because male and female heights differ, this leads to a higher standard deviation in the combined group.

8. Mean; mean; spread   **9.** True

10. True   **11.** $s^2 = 36$; $s = 6$

12. $s^2 = 100$; $s = 10$ **13.** $\sigma^2 = 16$; $\sigma = 4$

14. $\sigma^2 = 64$; $\sigma = 8$ **15.** $s^2 = 196$; $s = 14$

16. $\sigma^2 = 25$; $\sigma = 5$

17. $R = \$1,120$; $s^2 = 351,601.6$ dollars^2; $s = \$593.0$

18. $R = \$13.92$; $s^2 = 22.584$ dollars^2; $s = \$4.752$

19. $R = 1,150$ psi; $s^2 = 211,275$ psi^2; $s = 459.6$ psi

20. $R = 25$ minutes; $s^2 = 71$ minutes^2; $s = 8.4$ minutes

21. (b) The data go from 30 to 75; in (a) they are clustered between 40 and 60.

22. (a) III   **(b)** I   **(c)** IV   **(d)** II

23. (a) Tap: $R = 0.59$; bottled: $R = 0.26$; tap water has more dispersion.
(b) Tap: $s = 0.154$; bottled: 0.081; tap water has more dispersion.

24. (a) Blue: $R = 0.574$ second; red: $R = 0.140$ second. The response time to the blue stimulus has more dispersion.
(b) Blue: $s = 0.1994$ second; red: $s = 0.0647$ second. The response time to blue has more dispersion.

25. (a) $\sigma = 7.7$ beats per minutes   **(b), (c)** Answers will vary.

26. (a) $\sigma = 12.8$ minutes   **(b), (c)** Answers will vary.

27. (a) Ethan: $\mu = 10$ fish, $R = 19$ fish; Drew: $\mu = 10$ fish, $R = 19$ fish
(b) Ethan: $\sigma = 4.9$ fish, Drew: $\sigma = 7.9$ fish; Ethan has the more consistent record
(c) Answers will vary.

28. Liberty, since it has a slightly higher median and lower standard deviation.

29. (a) $s = 0.036$ gram
(b) The histogram is approximately symmetric, so the Empirical Rule is applicable.
(c) 95% of the M&Ms should weigh between 0.803 and 0.947 gram.
(d) 96% of the M&Ms actually weigh between 0.803 and 0.947 gram.
(e) 16% of the M&Ms should weigh more than 0.911 gram.
(f) 12% of the M&Ms actually weigh more than 0.911 gram.

30. (a) $s = 6$ seconds
(b) The histogram is approximately symmetric, so the Empirical Rule is applicable.
(c) 95% of the eruptions should last between 92 and 116 seconds.
(d) 93% of the observed eruptions actually lasted between 92 and 116 seconds.
(e) 16% of the eruptions should last less than 98 seconds.
(f) 11% of the observed eruptions actually lasted fewer than 98 seconds.

31.

	Car 1	Car 2
Sample mean	$\bar{x} = 223.5$ mi	$\bar{x} = 237.2$ mi
Median	$M = 223$ mi	$M = 230$ mi
Mode	None	None
Range	$R = 93$ mi	$R = 166$ mi
Sample variance	$s^2 = 475.1$ mi^2	$s^2 = 2406.9$ mi^2
Sample standard deviation	$s = 21.8$ mi	$s = 49.1$ mi

Answers will vary.

32.

	Rates of Return	
	Fund A	Fund B
Sample mean	$\bar{x} = 3.05\%$	$\bar{x} = 3.41\%$
Median	$M = 3.05\%$	$M = 3.65\%$
Mode	None	4.3
Range	$R = 10.9\%$	$R = 19.6\%$
Sample variance	$s^2 = 8.95(\%)^2$	$s^2 = 31.23(\%)^2$
Sample standard deviation	$s = 2.99\%$	$s = 5.59\%$

Answers will vary.

33. (a) Financial stocks: $\bar{x} = 22.357\%$, $M = 16.01\%$; energy stocks: $\bar{x} = 36.254\%$, $M = 34.18\%$. Energy stocks have the higher mean and median rate of return.
(b) Financial stocks: $s = 18.936\%$; energy stocks: $s = 20.080\%$. Energy stocks are riskier, so the investor is paying for the higher return. Probably worth it.

34. Chicago: $R = 35.1°F, \sigma = 8.54°F$; San Diego: $R = 21.9°F, \sigma = 6.14°F$; Chicago has more dispersion.

35. (a) 95% of people have an IQ score between 70 and 130.
(b) 5% of people have an IQ score either less than 70 or greater than 130.
(c) 2.5% of people have an IQ score greater than 130.

36. (a) 68% of SAT Math scores are between 401 and 629.
(b) 32% of SAT Math scores are either less than 401 or greater than 629.
(c) 2.5% of SAT Math scores are greater than 743.

37. (a) 95% of pairs of kidneys weigh between 265 and 385 grams.
(b) 99.7% of pairs of kidneys weigh between 235 and 415 grams.
(c) 0.3% of pairs of kidneys weigh either less than 235 or more than 415 grams.
(d) 81.5% of pairs of kidneys weighs between 295 and 385 grams.

38. (a) 68% of bolts is between 3.993 and 4.007 inches long.
(b) 95% of bolts is between 3.986 and 4.014 inches long.
(c) 5% of the bolts is discarded.
(d) 15.85% of bolts is between 4.007 and 4.021 inches long.

39. (a) 88.9% of gas stations have prices within 3 standard deviations of the mean.
(b) 84% of gas stations have prices within 2.5 standard deviations of the mean. Gasoline priced from $2.91 to $3.21 is within 2.5 standard deviations of the mean.
(c) At least 75% of gas stations have prices between $2.94 and $3.18.

40. (a) At least 75% of commuters in Boston has a commute time within 2 standard deviations of the mean.
(b) At least 55.6% of commuters has a commute time within 1.5 standard deviations of the mean. They commute between 15.15 and 39.45 minutes to work.
(c) At least 88.9% of commuters commute between 3 and 51.6 minutes to work.

41. There is more variation among individuals than among means.

42. (a) $R = \$45, \sigma^2 = 160, \sigma = \$12.6$
(b) Option 1: $R = \$45, \sigma^2 = 160, \sigma = \$12.6$
(c) Option 2: $R = \$47.25, \sigma^2 = 176.4, \sigma = \$13.3$
(d) Option 3: $R = \$70, \sigma^2 = 341.3, \sigma = \$18.5$

43. Sample of size 5: correct $s = 5.3$, incorrect $s = 27.9$
Sample of size 12: correct $s = 14.7$, incorrect $s = 22.7$
Sample of size 30: correct $s = 15.9$, incorrect $s = 19.2$
As the sample size increases, the impact of the misrecorded observation on standard deviation decreases.

44. $s = 0$. If all values in a data set are identical, there is zero variance.

45. (a) 6.11 cm   **(b)** 5.67 cm   **(c)** 5.59 cm
(d) standard deviation is lower for each group than it is for the groups combined.

46. (a) There is more variability in blood pressure after exercise.
(b) There is more variability in calcium concentration in the group with high blood pressure.

47. MAD = $510.75, $s = \$592.96$

48. (a) Skewness = 3; distribution is skewed right.
(b) Skewness = 0; distribution is perfectly symmetric.
(c) Skewness = −2.5; distribution is skewed left.
(d) Skewness = 0; distribution is symmetric.
(e) Skewness = 0.05; distribution is symmetric.

49. (a) Average rate of return = 14.9%, risk level = 14.7%
(b) To minimize risk, invest 30% in foreign stock.
(c) Answers will vary.
(d) At least 75% of returns are between −12.8% and 44.4%. At least 88.9% of returns are between −27.1% and 58.7%.

3.3 Assess Your Understanding (page 164)

1. The class midpoint is meant to represent the average value of all the data points in the class.

2. $\bar{x} = \dfrac{\sum x_i}{n}$ is a weighted average for which the value of each weight is 1.

3. $\mu = 3289.5$ g, $\sigma = 657.2$ g

4. $\bar{x} = 2419$ ft^2, $s = 907.0$ ft^2

5. $\bar{x} = 70.6°F$, $s = 3.5°F$

6. $\mu = 30.5$ years, $\sigma = 20.8$ years

7. (a) $\mu = 32.5$ years, $\sigma = 5.4$ years
(b)

Number of Multiple Births in 2004

(c) 95% of mothers of multiple births are between 21.7 and 43.3 years of age.

8. (a) $\mu = 519.1, \sigma = 114.5$
(b)

SAT Mathematics Score, 2006

(c) 95% of the SAT Math scores are between 290.1 and 748.1.

9. Grouped data: $\bar{x} = 51.8$, $s = 12.1$; raw data: $\bar{x} = 51.1$, $s = 10.9$

10. Grouped data: $\bar{x} \approx 1.214\%$, $s \approx 0.865\%$; raw data: $\bar{x} = 1.129\%$, $s = 0.910\%$

11. GPA = 3.27

12. Course average = 87.15%

13. Cost per pound = $2.97

14. Cost per pound = $3.38

15. (a) Males: $\mu = 35.9$ years, $\sigma = 21.8$ years
(b) Females: $\mu = 38.5$ years, $\sigma = 23.1$ years
(c) Females have the higher mean age.
(d) Females have more dispersion in age.

16. (a) 1980: $\mu = 25.5$ years, $\sigma = 5.4$ years
(b) 2004: $\mu = 27.9$ years, $\sigma = 6.3$ years
(c) 2004 has the higher mean age of new mothers.
(d) 2004 has more dispersion in the age of new mothers.

17. $M = 3367.9$ g

18. $M = 2298.3$ ft^2

19. $M = 32.5$ years

20. $M = 516.2$

21. Modal class: 3,000–3,999 g

22. Modal class: 1,500–1,999 ft^2

3.4 Assess Your Understanding (page 173)

1. Answers will vary. The kth percentile separates the lower k percent of the data from the upper $(100 - k)$ percent of the data.

2. Since the percentile of a score is rounded to the nearest integer, it is possible for two different scores to have the same percentile.

3. A four-star fund is in the 4th *quintile* of the funds. That is, it is above the bottom 60%, but below the top 20% of the ranked funds.

4. No; when an outlier is discovered, it should be investigated to find its cause.

5. One qualifies for Mensa if one's intelligence is in the top 2% of people.

6. Comparing z-scores allows a unitless comparison of the number of standard deviations an observation is from the mean.

7. The interquartile range is preferred when the data are skewed or have outliers. An advantage of standard deviation is that it uses all the observations in its computation.

8. The first quartile is the 25th percentile, which means that 25% of the observations are less than or equal to the value and 75% of the observations are greater than the value. The second quartile is the 50th percentile, which means that 50% of the observations are less than or equal to the value and 50% of the observations are greater than the value. The third quartile is the 75th percentile, which means that 75% of the observations are less than or equal to the value and 25% of the observations are greater than the value.

9. −0.30; −0.43; the 40-week gestation baby weighs less relative to the gestation period.

10. 0.61; 0.85; the 34-week gestation baby weighs less relative to the gestation period.

11. The man is relatively taller.

12. The woman is relatively taller.

13. Peavy had the better year because his ERA was 2.27 standard deviations below the National League mean ERA, while Lackey's ERA was only 1.49 standard deviations below the American League's mean ERA.

14. Williams had the better year relative to his peers, because his batting average was 3.82 standard deviations above the mean 1941 batting average. Ordonez's batting average was only 2.86 standard deviations above the American League's mean.

15. 239

16. Less than 7.9 cm or greater than 8.1 cm

17. **(a)** 15% of 3- to 5-month-old males have a head circumference that is 41.0 cm or less, and 85% of 3- to 5-month-old males have a head circumference that is greater than 41.0 cm.
    (b) 90% of 2-year-old females have a waist circumference that is 52.7 cm or less, and 10% of 2-year-old females have a waist circumference that is more than 52.7 cm.
    (c) The heights at each percentile decrease as the age increases. This implies that adults males are getting taller.

18. **(a)** 5% of 36-month-old males weigh 12.0 kg or less, and 95% of 36-month-old males weighs 12.0 kg or more.
    (b) 95% of newborn females have a length of 53.8 cm or less, and 5% of newborn females has a length that is more than 53.8 cm.

19. **(a)** 25% of the states have a violent crime rate that is 272.8 crimes per 100,000 population or less, and 75% of the states have a violent crime rate more than 272.8. 50% of the states have a violent crime rate that is 387.4 crimes per 100,000 population or less, while 50% of the states have a violent crime rate more than 387.4. 75% of the states have a violent crime rate that is 529.7 crimes per 100,000 population or less, and 25% of the states have a violent crime rate more than 529.7.
    (b) 256.9 crimes per 100,000 population; the middle 50% of all observations have a range of 256.9 crimes per 100,000 population.
    (c) Yes
    (d) Skewed right. The difference between Q_1 and Q_2 is quite a bit less than the difference between Q_2 and Q_3 in addition, the outlier in the right tail of the distribution implies that the distribution is skewed right.

20. **(a)** 25% of the students spend 42 minutes or less on homework for this section, and 75% of the students spend more than 42 minutes. 50% of the students spend 51.5 minutes or less on homework for this section, and 50% of the students spend more than 51.5 minutes. 75% of the students spend 72.5 minutes or less on homework for this section, and 25% of the students spend more than 72.5 minutes.
    (b) 30.5 minutes; the middle 50% of all students has a range of 30.5 minutes of time spent on homework.
    (c) Yes
    (d) Skewed right. The difference between Q_1 and Q_2 is quite a bit less than the difference between Q_2 and Q_3.

21. **(a)** $z = -1.70$. The 1971 rainfall amount was 1.70 standard deviations below the mean April rainfall.
    (b) By hand/TI-83/84: $Q_1 = 2.625$ in., $Q_2 = 3.985$ in., $Q_3 = 5.36$ in.; MINITAB: $Q_1 = 2.548$ in., $Q_2 = 3.985$ in., $Q_3 = 5.430$ in.
    (c) By hand/TI-83/84: IQR = 2.735; MINITAB: IQR = 2.882

(d) By hand/TI-83/84: lower fence = −1.478 in., upper fence = 9.463 in.; MINITAB: lower fence = −1.775 in., upper fence = 9.753 in. No outliers according to this criterion.

22. **(a)** $z = -1.21$. Blackie's hemoglobin level is 1.21 standard deviations below the mean.
    (b) By hand/TI-83/84: $Q_1 = 9.15$ g/dL, $Q_2 = 9.95$ g/dL, $Q_3 = 11.1$ g/dL; MINITAB: $Q_1 = 9.025$ g/dL, $Q_2 = 9.950$ g/dL, $Q_3 = 11.15$ g/dL
    (c) By hand/TI-83/84: IQR = 1.95 g/dL; MINITAB: IQR = 2.125 g/dL
    (d) By hand/TI-83/84: lower fence = 6.225 g/dL, upper fence = 14.025 g/dL; MINITAB: lower fence = 5.8375 g/dL, upper fence = 14.3375 g/dL; the only outlier is 5.7 g/dL.

23. **(a)** By hand/TI-83/84: Q_1: −0.02, Q_2: 0.035, Q_3: 0.095; MINITAB: Q_1: −0.02, Q_2: 0.035, Q_3: 0.0975. Using the by-hand quartiles, 25% of the monthly returns are less than or equal to the first quartile, −0.02, and about 75% of the monthly returns are greater than −0.02; 50% of the monthly returns are less than or equal to the second quartile, 0.035, and about 50% of the monthly returns are greater than 0.035; about 75% of the monthly returns are less than or equal to the third quartile, 0.095, and about 25% of the monthly returns are greater than 0.095.
    (b) 0.47 is an outlier.

24. **(a)** By hand/TI-83/84: Q_1: 1.61, Q_2: 2.165, Q_3: 2.68; MINITAB: Q_1: 1.59, Q_2: 2.165, Q_3: 2.728. Using the by-hand quartiles, 25% of the countries have per capita CO_2 emissions that are less than or equal to 1.61, and about 75% of the countries have per capita CO_2 emissions that exceed 1.61. About 50% of the countries have per capita CO_2 emissions that are less than or equal to the second quartile, 2.165, and about 50% of the countries have per capita CO_2 emissions that exceed 2.165. About 75% of the countries have per capita CO_2 emissions less than or equal to 2.68, and about 25% of the countries have per capita CO_2 emissions that exceed 2.68.
    (b) Yes

25. By hand/TI-83/84: The cutoff point is 574 minutes. MINITAB: The cutoff point is 578 minutes. If more minutes are used, the customer is contacted.

26. By hand/TI-83/84: Daily charges must exceed $219 before the customer is contacted. MINITAB: Daily charges must exceed $229 before the customer is contacted.

27. **(a)** $12,777 is an outlier.
    (b)

Students Weekly Income

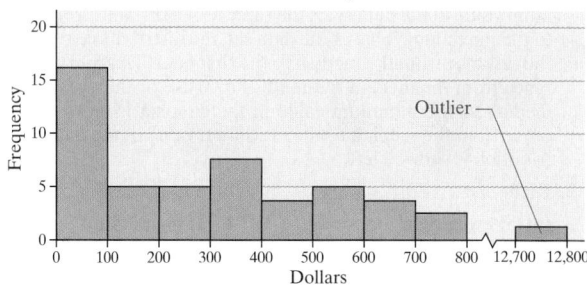

(c) Answers will vary.

28. **(a)** $115 and $1000 are outliers.
    (b)

Students Weekly Expenditures

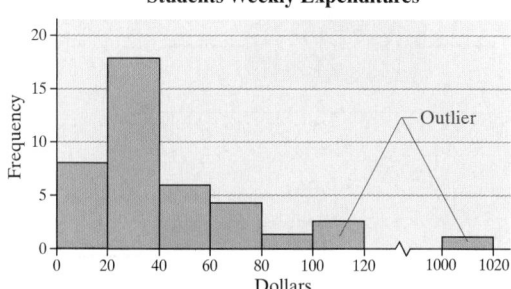

(c) Answers will vary.

29. Mean of the z-scores is 0.0; standard deviation of the z-scores is 1.0.

Student	z-Score
Perpectual Bernpah	0.49
Megan Brooks	−1.58
Jeff Honeycutt	−1.58
Clarice Jefferson	1.14
Crystal Kurtenbach	−0.03
Janette Lantka	1.01
Kevin McCarthy	1.01
Tommy Ohm	−0.55
Kathy Wojdyla	0.10

30. Mean of the z-scores is 0.0; standard deviation of the z-scores is 1.0.

Student	z-Score	Student	z-Score
Amanda	0.98	Scot	1.45
Amber	−0.42	Erica	−1.20
Tim	−1.36	Tiffany	−1.13
Mike	0.44	Glenn	0.98
Nicole	0.28		

31. (a) $s = 58.0$ minutes; by hand/TI-83/84: IQR = 56.5 minutes; MINITAB: IQR = 58.8 minutes
(b) $s = 115.0$ minutes; by hand/TI-83/84: IQR = 56.5 minutes; MINITAB: IQR = 58.8 minutes. The standard deviation almost doubles in value, while the interquartile range is not affected. The standard deviation is not resistant to extreme observations, but the interquartile range is resistant.

3.5 Assess Your Understanding (page 181)

1. Using the boxplot: If the median is left of center in the box, and the right whisker is longer than the left whisker, the distribution is skewed right. If the median is in the center of the box, and the left and right whiskers are roughly the same length, the distribution is symmetric. If the median is right of center in the box, and the left whisker is longer than the right whisker, the distribution is skewed left.
Using the quartiles: If the distance from the median to the first quartile is less than the distance from the median to the third quartile, or the distance from the median to the minimum value in the data set is less than the distance from the median to the maximum value in the data set, then the distribution is skewed right. If the distance from the median to the first quartile is the same as the distance from the median to the third quartile, or the distance from the median to the minimum value in the data set is the same as the distance from the median to the maximum value in the data set, the distribution is symmetric. If the distance from the median to the first quartile is more than the distance from the median to the third quartile, or the distance from the median to the minimum value in the data set is more than the distance from the median to the maximum value in the data set, the distribution is skewed left.

2. Right

3. (a) Skewed right
(b) 0, 1, 3, 6, 16

4. (a) Symmetric
(b) −1, 2, 5, 8, 11

5. (a) 40
(b) 52
(c) y
(d) Symmetric
(e) Skewed right

6. (a) 16
(b) 22
(c) y
(d) Yes; 30
(e) Skewed left

7.
Statistics Exams Scores

8.
Reading Speed

9. (a) 42, 51, 55, 58, 69
(b)
Age of Presidents at Inauguration

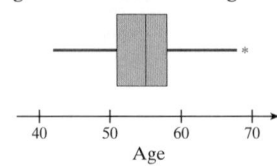

(c) Symmetric with an outlier.

10. (a) 7.2, 9, 10, 11.2, 16.4
(b)
Percentage of Carpoolers for each State

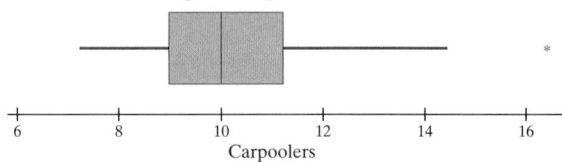

(c) Skewed right since the median is left of center in the box, and the distance from the median to the minimum value is less than the distance from the median to the maximum value.

11. (a)
Weight of Tylenol Tablets

(b) Skewed left

12. (a)
Carbon Dioxide per Capita in Western Europe

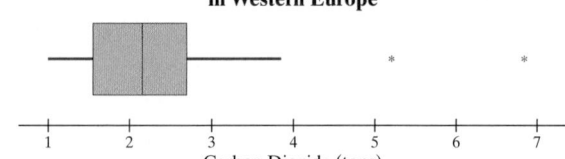

(b) Skewed right

13.
Weight of M&Ms

Since the range of the data between the minimum value and the median is roughly the same as the range between the median and the maximum value, and because the range of the data between the first quartile and median is the same as the range of the data between the median and third quartile, the distribution is symmetric.

14.
Length of Eruption

Since the range of the data between the minimum value and the median is roughly the same as the range between the median and the maximum value, and because the range of the data between the first quartile and median is roughly the same as the range of the data between the median and third quartile, the distribution is symmetric.

15. (a)

Dissolving Time of Vitamins

(b) Generic **(c)** Centrum

16. (a)

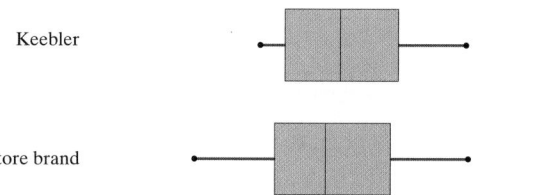

Chips per Cookie

(b) Keebler has a higher median number of chips per cookie based on this sample. In the overall scheme of things, it is not likely the case that we could say that Keebler has more chips per cookie.

(c) Keebler does appear to be more consistent with the number of chips per cookie because the range is lower for Keebler. The interquartile range for both cookie types is close to the same.

17. (a) Observational study

(b) Whether or not the father smoked; birth weight

(c) Eating habits, exercise habits, whether the mother received prenatal care

(d) The researchers attempted to adjust their results for any variables that may also be related to birth weight.

(e) Nonsmokers: mean = 3,665.5 g; median = 3,693.5 g; standard deviation = 356.0 g; quartiles by hand/TI-83/84: first quartile = 3,436.0 g, third quartile = 3,976.0 g; quartiles using MINITAB: first quartile = 3,432.8 g, third quartile = 3,980.5 g. Smokers: mean = 3,460.4 g, median = 3,475.0 g, standard deviation = 452.6 g; quartiles by hand/TI-83/84: first quartile = 3,129.0 g, third quartile = 3,807.0 g; quartiles using MINITAB: first quartile = 3,113.3 g, third quartile = 3,828.3 g

(f) Using the by-hand quartiles: For nonsmoking fathers, 25% of infants has a birth weight that is 3,436.0 g or less, and 75% of infants have a birth weight that is more than 3,436.0 g. For smoking fathers, 25% of infants has a birth weight that is 3,129.0 g or less, and 75% of infants has a birth weight that is more than 3,129.0 g.

(g)

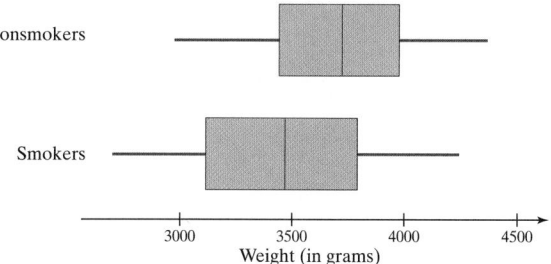

Birthweight

Chapter 3 Review Exercises (page 185)

1. (a) Mean = 792.51 m/sec, median = 792.40 m/sec

(b) Range = 4.8 m/sec, $s^2 = 2.03$, $s = 1.42$ m/sec

2. (a) $\bar{x} = \$10,178.9$, $M = \$9,980$

(b) Range: $R = \$8,550$, $s = \$3,074.9$, IQR = $\$5,954.5$; using MINITAB: IQR = $\$5,954$

(c) $\bar{x} = \$13,178.9$, $M = \$9,980$; range: $R = \$35,550$, $s = \$10,797.5$, IQR = $\$5,954.5$ [using MINITAB: $\$5954$]. The median and interquartile range are resistant.

3. (a) $\mu = 57.8$ years, $M = 58.0$ years, bimodal: 56 and 62

(b) Range = 25 years, $\sigma = 7.0$ years

(c) Answers will vary.

4. (a) Skewed right

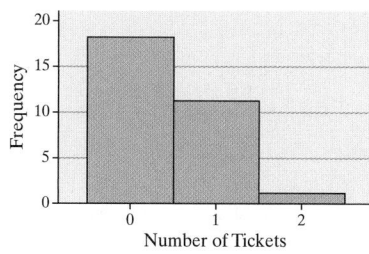

Number of Tickets Issued in a Month

(b) Mean greater than median.

(c) $\bar{x} = 0.4$, $M = 0$.

(d) 0

5. (a) 441; 759

(b) 95% of the light bulbs have a life between 494 and 706 hours.

(c) 81.5% of the light bulbs have a life between 547 and 706 hours.

(d) The firm can expect to replace 0.15% of the light bulbs.

(e) At least 84% of the light bulbs have a life within 2.5 standard deviations of the mean.

(f) At least 75% of the light bulbs have a life between 494 and 706 hours.

6. (a) $\bar{x} = 37.5$ minutes

(b) $s = 19.2$ minutes

7. 3.33

8. Female, since her weight is more standard deviations from the mean

9. (a) The European Union is more densely populated. All three quartiles are higher in the EU.

(b) It depends on which measure of dispersion is used. If the interquartile range is used, then the EU has more dispersion. If the range is used, the dispersion is about the same.

(c) Yes, approximately 490 people per square kilometer.

(d) Both are skewed right.

10. (a) $\mu = 2,363$ words; $M = 2,144$ words

(b) Quartiles by hand/TI-83/84: $Q_1 = 1,355$, $Q_2 = 2,144$, $Q_3 = 2,978$; Quartiles by MINITAB: $Q_1 = 1,351$, $Q_2 = 2,144$, $Q_3 = 3,038$. Using by-hand quartiles: 25% of the inaugural addresses had 1,355 words or less, 75% of the inaugural addresses had more than 1,355 words; 50% of the inaugural addresses had 2,144 words or less, 50% of the inaugural addresses had more than 2,144 words; 75% of the inaugural addresses had 2,978 words or less, 25% of the inaugural addresses had more than 2,978 words.

(c) By hand/TI-83/84: 135, 1355, 2144, 2978, 8445; MINITAB: 135, 1351, 2144, 3038, 8445

(d) $\sigma = 1418$ words; by hand/TI-83/84: IQR = 1,623; MINITAB: IQR = 1,687

(e) Yes; 5433 and 8,445 are outliers

(f)

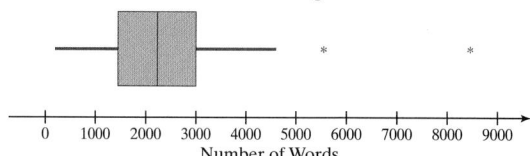

Number of Words in Inaugural Addresses

(g) Skewed right since the median is slightly left of center in the box and the right whisker is longer than the left whisker (even without considering the outlier)

(h) The median is the better measure since the outlier inflates the value of the mean.

(i) The interquartile range is the better measure since the outlier inflates the value of the standard deviation.

11. 85% of 19-year-old females have a height that is 67.1 inches or less, and 15% of 19-year-old females have a height that is more than 67.1 inches.

12. The median is used for three measures since it is likely the case that one of the three measures is extreme relative to the other two, thus substantially affecting the value of the mean. Since the median is resistant to extreme values, it is the better measure of central tendency.

Chapter 3 Test (page 187)

1. (a) $\bar{x} = 441.8$ inches   **(b)** $M = 399.5$ inches
(c) $\bar{x} = 541.8$ inches, $M = 399.5$ inches; the median is resistant.

2. From motor vehicles   **3.** 372 inches

4. (a) 120.4 inches
(b) 184 inches; the middle 50% of all snowfalls have a range of 184 inches.
(c) The interquartile range is resistant; the standard deviation is not resistant.

5. (a) 3,282; 5,322
(b) 95% of the cartridges prints between 3,622 and 4,982 pages.
(c) The firm can expect to replace 2.5% of the cartridges.
(d) At least 55.6% of the cartridges has a page count within 1.5 standard deviations of the mean.
(e) At least 88.9% of the cartridges prints between 3,282 and 5,322 pages.

6. (a) 74.9 minutes   **(b)** 14.7 minutes

7. $2.17

8. (a) Material A: $\bar{x} = 6.404$ million cycles;
Material B: $\bar{x} = 11.332$ million cycles
(b) Material A: $M = 5.785$ million cycles;
Material B: $M = 8.925$ million cycles
(c) Material A: $s = 2.626$ million cycles;
Material B: $s = 5.900$ million cycles
Material B is more dispersed
(d) Material A (in million cycles): 3.17, 4.52, 5.785, 8.01, 11.92
Material B (in million cycles): 5.78, 6.84, 8.925, 14.71, 24.37
(e)

Bearing Failures

Answers will vary.
(f) The distributions are skewed right.

9. Quartiles by hand/TI-83/84 (in grams): $Q_1 = 5.58$, $Q_2 = 5.60$, $Q_3 = 5.67$; quartiles by MINITAB (in grams): $Q_1 = 5.58$, $Q_2 = 5.60$, $Q_3 = 5.6625$. Using the by-hand quartiles: 25% of quarters have a weight that is 5.58 g or less, 75% of the quarters have a weight more than 5.58 g; 50% of the quarters have a weight that is 5.60 g or less, 50% of the quarters have a weight more than 5.60 g; 75% of the quarters have a weight that is 5.67 g or less, 25% of the quarters have a weight that is more than 5.67 g. The quarter whose weight is 5.84 g is an outlier.

10. Armando should report his ACT math score since it is more standard deviations above the mean.

11. 15% of 10-year-old males have a height that is 53.5 inches or less, and 85% of 10-year-old males have a height that is more than 53.5 inches.

12. The median will be less than the mean for income data, so you should report the median.

13. (a) Report the mean since the distribution is symmetric.
(b) Histogram I has more dispersion. The range of classes is larger.

CHAPTER 4 Describing the Relation between Two Variables

4.1 Assess Your Understanding (page 202)

1. Univariate data measure the value of a single variable for each individual in the study. Bivariate data measure values of two variables for each individual.

2. Two variables that are linearly related are positively associated if increases in the explanatory variable tend to be associated with increases in the response variable.

3. If $r = +1$, then a perfect positive linear relation exists between the variables, and the points of the scatter diagram lie exactly on a straight line with a positive slope.

4. If $r = 0$, then no *linear* relationship exists between the variables.

5. The linear correlation coefficient can only be calculated from bivariate *quantitative* data, and the gender of a driver is a qualitative variable.

6. Answers will vary. Answers should include that correlation measures the strength of the linear association between two quantitative variables.

7. A lurking variable is a variable that is related to both the explanatory variable and response variable, but has not been considered in the study.

8. Correlation describes a relation between two variables in an observational study. Causation describes a conditional (if – then) relation in an experimental study.

9. Nonlinear

10. Linear, negative

11. Linear, positive

12. Nonlinear

13. (a) III   **(b)** IV
(c) II   **(d)** I

14. (a) IV   **(b)** III
(c) I   **(d)** II

15. (a) Linear; positive association
(b) The point (48.5, 46000) appears to stick out. Reasons may vary. One possibility is a high concentration of government jobs that require a bachelor's degree but pay less than the private sector in a region with a high cost of living.
(c) The correlation coefficient is not resistant.

16. (a) No linear relation
(b) The point (48000, 21) appears to stick out. One possible reason is the religious beliefs of the residents.
(c) No linear relation

17. (a)

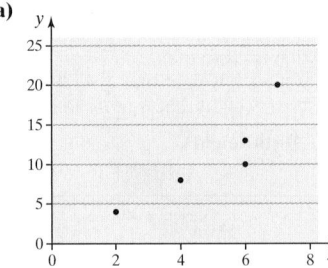

(b) $r = 0.896$ **(c)** Linear relation

18. (a)

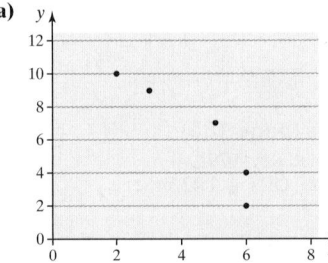

(b) $r = -0.933$ **(c)** Linear relation

19. (a)

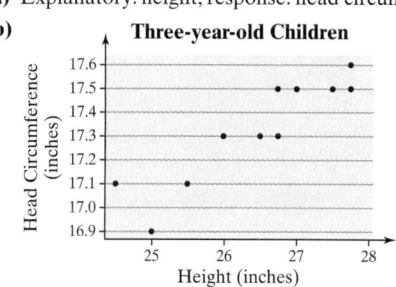

(b) $r = -0.496$ **(c)** No linear relation

20. (a)

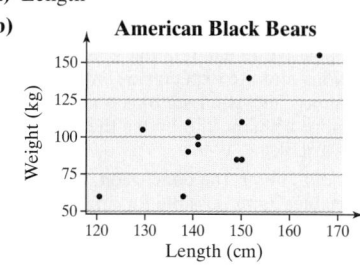

(b) $r = 0.440$ **(c)** No linear relation

21. (a) Positive   **(b)** Negative
(c) Negative   **(d)** Negative
(e) No correlation

22. (a) Negative   **(b)** Positive
(c) Positive   **(d)** No correlation
(e) Negative

23. (a) Explanatory: height; response: head circumference
(b)

Three-year-old Children

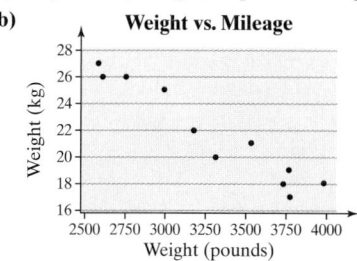

(c) $r = 0.911$ **(d)** Yes; positive association

24. (a) Length
(b)

American Black Bears

(c) $r = 0.704$ **(d)** Yes; positive association

25. (a) Explanatory: weight; response: miles per gallon
(b)

Weight vs. Mileage

(c) $r = -0.964$ **(d)** Yes; negative association

26. (a)

Bone Lengths

(b) $r = 0.951$ **(c)** Yes; positive association
(d) Converting units has no effect on the correlation coefficient.

27. (a)

HDL Cholesterol

No relation appears to exist between age and HDL cholesterol.

(b) -0.164 **(c)** No

28. (a)

Intensity of a Light Bulb

(b) No; the relation between distance and intensity is not linear.

29. (a)

Brain Size vs. IQ

(b) $r = 0.548$. A positive association exists between MRI count and IQ.

(c)

Brain Size vs. IQ

The females have lower MRI counts. Looking at each gender's plot, we see that the relation that appeared to exist between brain size and IQ disappears.
(d) Females: $r = 0.359$; males: $r = 0.236$. No linear relation exists between brain size and IQ.

30. (a)

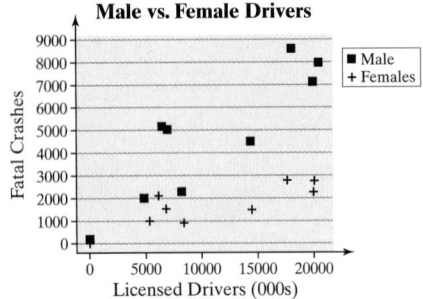

Male vs. Female Drivers

(b) Yes; males tend to have a higher fatal crash rate.
(c) Males: 0.883
(d) Females: 0.836
(e) Males have a slightly stronger linear relation between number of licensed drivers and number of crashes than females. Reasons will vary.

31. (a)

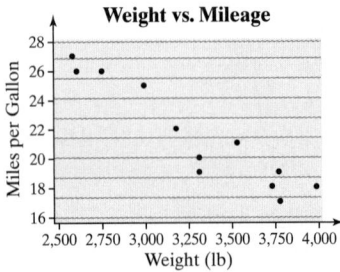

Weight vs. Mileage

(b) Correlation coefficient (with Taurus included): $r = -0.943$
(c) The results are reasonable because the Taurus follows the overall pattern of the data.

(d)

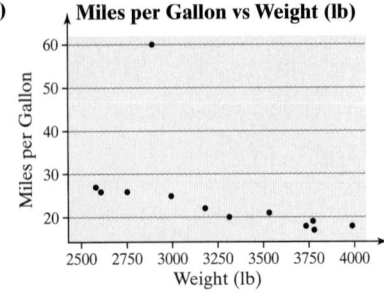

Miles per Gallon vs Weight (lb)

(e) Correlation coefficient (with Prius included): $r = -0.507$
(f) The Prius is a hybrid car; the other cars are not hybrids.

32. (a)

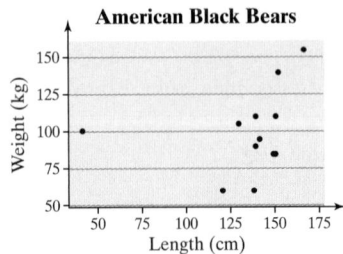

American Black Bears

(b) $r = 0.254$
(c) The incorrectly entered data value is far away from the rest of the points. The incorrectly entered data value decreases the value of the correlation coefficient because the correlation coefficient is not resistant.

33. (a) 1: 0.816; 2: 0.817; 3: 0.816; 4: 0.817

(b)

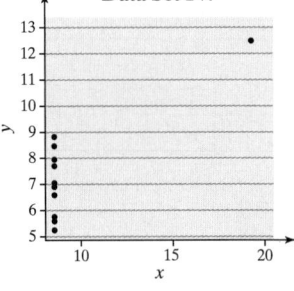

Data Set I: Data Set II: Data Set III: Data Set IV:

34. Answers may vary. Compare correlation coefficients and scatter diagrams to choose the one that appears to have the strongest association. "Batting Average against Team" and "Team Earned Run Average" are good candidates.

35. To have the lowest correlation between the two stocks, invest in General Electric and TECO Energy, $r = -0.009$. If your goal is to have one stock go up when the other goes down, invest in Cisco Systems and TECO Energy: $r = -0.246$.

36. (a)

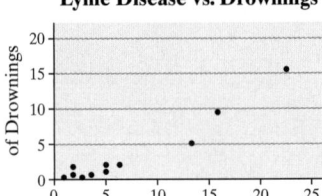

Lyme Disease vs. Drownings

(b) $r = 0.961$
(c) A strong, positive, linear relation exists between cases of Lyme disease and number of drownings. No, Lyme disease is a summer disease. This is an instance of correlation, but not causation. Temperature and time of year are likely lurking variables.

37. $r = 0.599$ implies that a positive linear relation exists between the number of television stations and life expectancy, but this is correlation, not causation. The more television stations a country has, the more affluent it is. The more affluent, the better the health care, so wealth is a likely lurking variable.

38. The investigator is "not clear" about the conclusion, which indicates there may be lurking variables. One possible lurking variable is the health consciousness of the mother.

39. No; a likely lurking variable is the economy. In a strong economy, crime rates tend to decrease, and consumers are better able to afford cell phones.

40. Although no *linear* relation exists between age and median income, the two variables are related.

41. (a)

$r = 0.228$

(b)

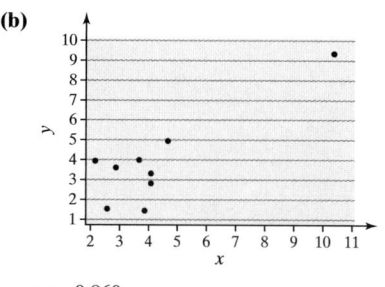

$r = 0.860$

42. (a)

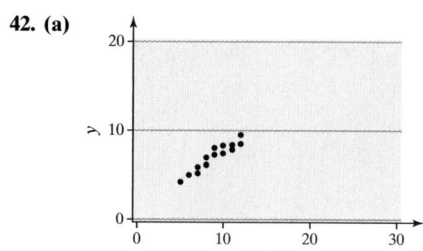

(b) 0.952

(c)

2x	10	12	14	14	16	16	16	16
2y	8.4	10	10.4	11.8	12	12.4	12.2	13.8
2x	18	18	20	20	22	22	24	24
2y	14.4	16	16.6	14.8	16.8	15.6	17	19

(d)

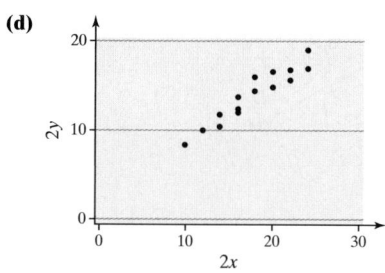

(e) 0.952

(f) By doubling the values of x and y, we double the standard deviations and deviations about the mean. Therefore, the z-scores for each point are unchanged.

43. Answers may vary. For those who feel "in-class" evaluations are meaningful, a correlation of 0.68 would lend some validity, because it indicates that students respond in the same general way on RateMyProfessors.com (high with high, low with low). The correlations between quality and easiness or hotness tend to indicate that evaluations at RateMyProfessors.com are based more on likability rather than actual quality of teaching.

4.2 Assess Your Understanding (page 218)

1. The least-squares regression line is the line that minimizes the sum of the squared errors (residuals).

2. A residual is the difference between the observed value of y and the predicted value of y. If the residual is positive, the observed value is above average for the given value of the explanatory variable.

3. Values of the explanatory variable that are much larger or much smaller than those observed are considered *outside the scope of the model*. It is dangerous to make such predictions because we do not know the behavior of the data for which we have no observations.

4. If the linear correlation between two variables is negative, the slope of the regression line will also be negative.

5. Answers will vary.

6. True.

7. Each point's y-coordinate represents the mean value of the response variable for a given value of the explanatory variable.

8. If $r = 0$, then the slope of the linear regression line will also be zero, and the line will be $\hat{y} = \bar{y}$ since all regression lines contain the point $(\bar{x}, \bar{y})$.

9. (a)

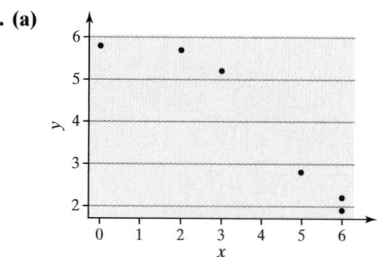

(b) $\hat{y} = -0.7136x + 6.5498$

(c)

10. (a)

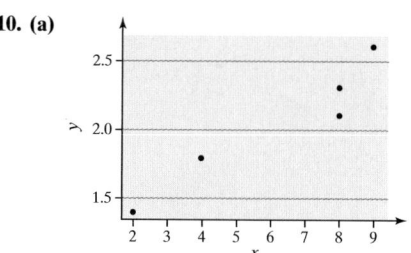

(b) $\hat{y} = 0.1457x + 1.1370$

(c)

11. (a)

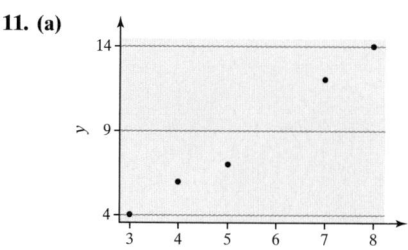

(b) Using points $(3, 4)$ and $(8, 14)$: $\hat{y} = 2x - 2$

(c)

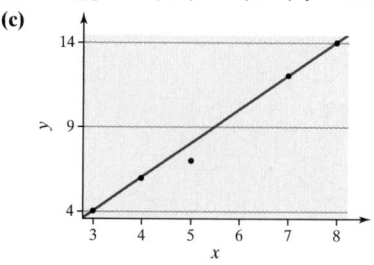

(d) $\hat{y} = 2.0233x - 2.3256$

(e)

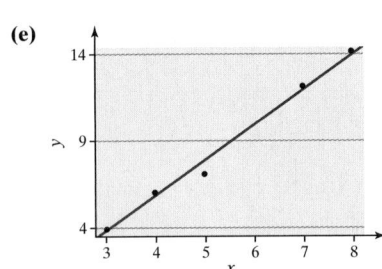

(f) Sum of squared residuals (computed line): 1
(g) Sum of squared residuals (least-squares line): 0.7907
(h) Answers will vary.

12. (a)

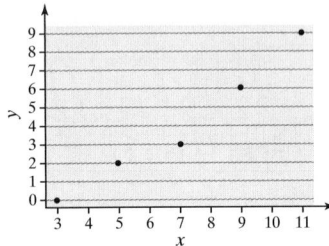

(b) Using points $(3, 0)$ and $(11, 9)$: $\hat{y} = \dfrac{9}{8}x - \dfrac{27}{8}$

(c)

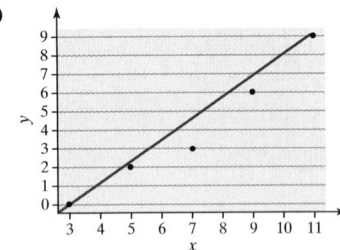

(d) $\hat{y} = 1.1x - 3.7$

(e)

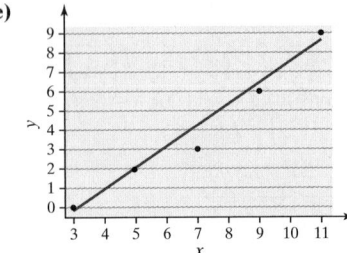

(f) Sum of squared residuals (computed line): 2.875
(g) Sum of squared residuals (least-squares line) : 1.6
(h) Answers will vary.

13. (a)

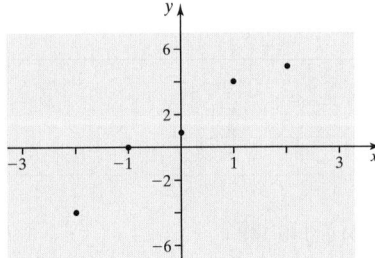

(b) Using points $(-2, -4)$ and $(2, 5)$: $\hat{y} = \dfrac{9}{4}x + \dfrac{1}{2} = 2.25x + 0.5$

(c)

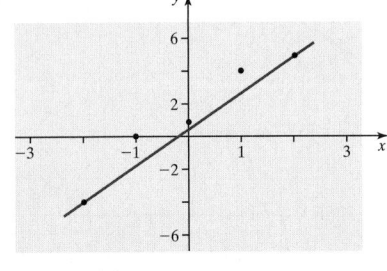

(d) $\hat{y} = 2.2x + 1.2$

(e)

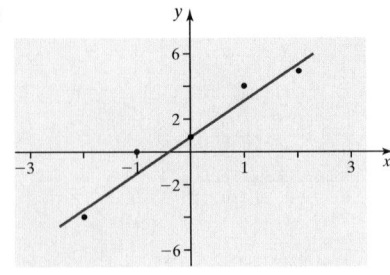

(f) Sum of squared residuals (computed line): 4.875
(g) Sum of squared residuals from least-squares line: 2.4
(h) Answers will vary.

14. (a)

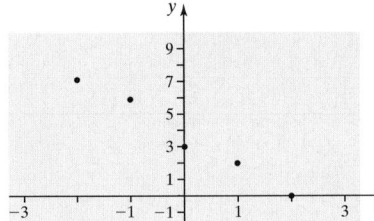

(b) Using the points $(-2, 7)$ and $(2, 0)$: $\hat{y} = -\dfrac{7}{4}x + \dfrac{7}{2} = -1.75x + 3.5$

(c)

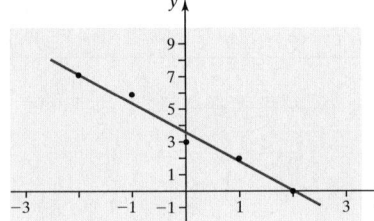

(d) $\hat{y} = -1.8x + 3.6$

(e)

(f) Sum of squared residuals (computed line): 0.875
(g) Sum of squared residuals from least-squares line: 0.8
(h) Answers will vary.

15. (a)

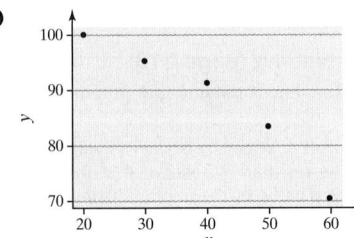

(b) Using points $(30, 95)$ and $(60, 70)$: $\hat{y} = -\dfrac{5}{6}x + 120$

(c)

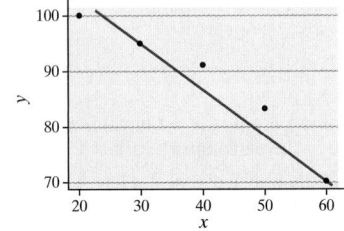

(d) $\hat{y} = -0.72x + 116.6$

(e)

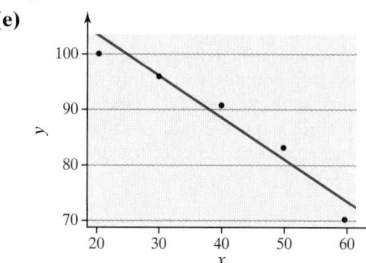

(f) Sum of squared residuals (computed line): 51.6667
(g) Sum of squared residuals from least-squares line: 32.4
(h) Answers will vary.

16. (a)

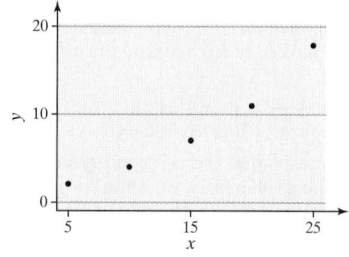

(b) Using points (10, 4) and (25, 18): $\hat{y} = \dfrac{14}{15}x - \dfrac{16}{3}$

(c)

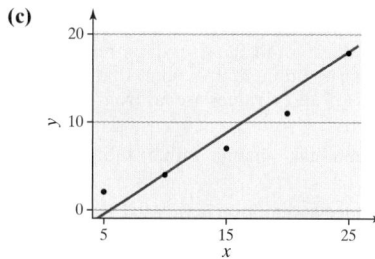

(d) $\hat{y} = 0.78x - 3.3$

(e)

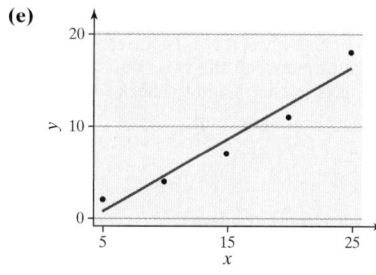

(f) Sum of squares residual (computed line): 15.3333
(g) Sum of squares residual from least-squares line: 9.1
(h) Answers will vary.

17. (a) 2.51
(b) For each additional hour a student spends playing video games in a week, the grade-point average will decrease by 0.0526 points, on average.
(c) The grade-point average for a student who does not play video games is 2.9342.
(d) The grade-point average is above average for those who play video games 7 hours per week.

18. (a) 65.7
(b) For each additional hour spent studying for the exam, the exam score increased by 6.3333 points, on average.
(c) 53.0
(d) The student's score is below average for those who studied for 5 hours.

19. (a) For each percentage point increase in on-base percentage, the winning percentage will increase by 2.94 percentage points, on average.

(b) The y-intercept is outside the scope of the model. An on-base percentage of 0 is not reasonable for this model, since a team cannot win if players do not reach base.
(c) No; 0.250 is outside the scope of the model.
(d) The residual would be 0.0864. This residual indicates that San Diego's winning percentage is above average for teams with an on-base percentage of 0.322.

20. (a) For each thousand megawatts of energy provided, the carbon dioxide emissions will increase by 0.7668 thousand tons, on average.
(b) No; we expect a country to provide at least some energy. We would expect the y-intercept to be 0, since there would be no energy production to generate carbon dioxide emissions.
(c) No; the value is outside the scope of the model.
(d) The residual is 841,023 thousand tons. This indicates that the carbon dioxide emission for China is above average for countries producing 2,410,000 thousand megawatts of energy.

21. (a) $\hat{y} = 0.1827x + 12.4932$
(b) If height increases by 1 inch, head circumference increases by about 0.1827 inch, on average. It is not appropriate to interpret the y-intercept. It is outside the scope of the model.
(c) $\hat{y} = 17.06$ inches
(d) Residual $= -0.16$ inch; below
(e)

Head Circumference vs. Height

Residual $= 16.9 - 17.1 = -0.2$

(f) For children who are 26.75 inches tall, head circumference varies.
(g) No; 32 inches is outside the scope of the model.

22. (a) $\hat{y} = 1.6942x - 142.4709$
(b) For each centimeter increase in length, the weight of the bear will increase by 1.6942 kilograms, on average. It is not appropriate to interpret the y-intercept, because a length of 0 centimeters for a bear does not make sense.
(c) The predicted weight is 110.0 kg.
(d) The residual is -25.0 kg. This bear's weight is below average for 149.0 cm bears.

23. (a) $\hat{y} = -0.0070x + 44.8793$
(b) For every pound added to the weight of the car, gas mileage in the city will decrease by 0.0070 mile per gallon, on average. It is not appropriate to interpret the y-intercept.
(c) Cobalt mileage is below average.
(d) It is not reasonable to use this least-squares regression to predict the miles per gallon of a Toyota Prius because a Prius is a different type of car (hybrid).

24. (a) $\hat{y} = 1.3902x + 1.1140$
(b) If the humerus increases in length by 1 mm, the length of the tibia increases by about 1.3902 mm, on average. It does not make sense to interpret the y-intercept.
(c) Residual $= 0.548$ mm; above
(d)

Bone Lengths

Residual

(e) $\hat{y} = 36.300$ mm

25. (a) $\hat{y} = -0.0029x + 0.8861$
(b) For each additional cola consumed per week, bone mineral density will decrease by 0.0029 g/cm^2, on average.

(c) For a woman who does not drink cola, bone mineral density will be 0.8861 g/cm^2.

(d) The predicted bone mineral density is 0.8745 g/cm^2.

(e) This bone mineral density is below average for women who consume 4 cans of cola per week.

(f) No; 2 cans of cola per day equates to 14 cans per week, which is outside the scope of the model.

26. (a) $\hat{y} = -2.8273x + 88.7327$

(b) For every additional absence, the student's final grade drops 2.8273 points, on average. The average final grade of students who miss no classes is 88.7327.

(c) $\hat{y} = 74.60$; residual is -0.70; the final grade is below average for 5 absences.

(d)

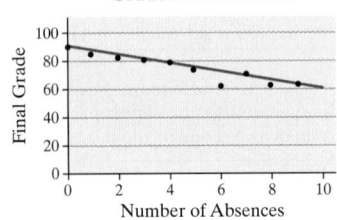

Grades vs. Absences

(e) No; 15 absences is outside the scope of the model.

27. (a) $\hat{y} = 0.00002x + 119.1662$

(b) The slope is close to zero.

(c) MRI count 1,000,000: $\hat{y} = \bar{y} = 134.3$; MRI count 830,000: $\hat{y} = \bar{y} = 134.3$

28. (a) Males: $\hat{y} = 0.3428x + 998.4488$
Females: $\hat{y} = 0.1045x + 514.1520$

(b) Males: If the number of licensed drivers increases by 1 (thousand), then the number of fatal crashes increases by 0.3428, on average. Females: If the number of licensed drivers increases by 1 (thousand), then the number of fatal crashes increases by 0.1045, on average. Since females tend to be involved in fewer fatal crashes, an insurance company may use this information to argue for higher rates for male customers.

(c) Above average; above average; below average. An insurance company may use this information to argue for higher rates for younger drivers and lower rates for older drivers. The same relationship holds for females.

29. Answers may vary. Discussions should involve the scope of the model and the idea of being "outside the scope."

31. (a) Square footage

(b)

Asking Price vs. Square Footage

(c) $r = 0.916$ (d) Yes   (e) $\hat{y} = 0.0686x + 83.2366$

(f) For each square foot added to the area, the asking price of the house will increase by $68.60 (that is, 0.0686 thousand dollars).

(g) It is not reasonable to interpret the intercept.

(h) Above average; factors that could affect the price include location and updates such as thermal windows or new siding.

32. (a) The distribution is bell shaped; class width is 200.

(b) Observational study

(c) A prospective study is one in which subjects are followed forward in time.

(d) Since cotinine leaves the body through fluids, a urinalysis is a less intrusive way to detect cotinine than a blood test. In addition, this provides a means for verifying the statements of the subjects.

(e) The explanatory variable is number of cigarettes smoked during third trimester; the response variable is birth weight.

(f) There appears to be a negative association between the variables.

(g) $r = -0.355$

(h) $\hat{y} = -31.014x + 3456.04$

(i) For each additional cigarette smoked, birth weight decreases by 31.014 grams, on average.

(j) The birth weight of a baby whose mother smokes but does not smoke in the third trimester is 3456.04 grams.

(k) No; 10 cigarettes per day equates to roughly 900 in the third trimester, which is outside the scope of the model.

(l) No; an observational study cannot establish causation.

(m) Some lurking variables could be genetic factors or the general health of the mothers.

4.3 Assess Your Understanding (page 232)

1. 75% of the total variation in the response variable is explained by the regression line.

2. The total deviation of a data point is the difference between the observed value of the response variable, y, and the mean of the response variable, $\bar{y}$. The explained deviation is the difference between the predicted value of the response variable $\hat{y}$ and the mean value, $\bar{y}$. The unexplained deviation is the difference between the observed value y and the predicted value $\hat{y}$.

3. A pattern in the residual plot indicates that the response and explanatory variables may not be linearly related.

4. Constant error variance means that the error of prediction does not depend on the value of the explanatory variable, but is constant for all values of the explanatory variable (within the scope of the model). This is important to guarantee that the reliability of predictions is the same for all values of the explanatory variable.

5. An influential observation is one that significantly affects the correlation coefficient, the slope, or the y-intercept of the least-squares regression line.

6. An outlier is a point that does not fit the overall pattern of the data. An outlier may or may not be influential. A point that is not an outlier may be influential if its x- and y-values are far from the rest of the data.

7. An influential observation can change either the slope or the y-intercept, or both.

8. If the constant error variance assumption is violated, the error of prediction will vary with the value of the predictor variable, making some predictions less reliable than others.

9. If $R^2 = 0.81$, you can determine the magnitude of r, but not the sign of r. To find r, you need to know whether the relation between the variables is positive or negative.

10. We do residual analysis to determine if it is appropriate to use a linear model to describe the relation between the variables, to determine if the variance of the residuals is constant, and to check for outliers.

11. The variance of the residuals is not constant.

12. No conditions are violated.

13. There is an outlier.

14. There is a discernible pattern in the residuals.

15. (a) III   **(b)** II
(c) IV   (d) I

16. (a) $R^2 = 10.24\%$; 10.24% of the variance in the response variable is explained by the least-squares regression line.

(b) $R^2 = 1.69\%$; 1.69% of the variance in the response variable is explained by the least-squares regression line.

(c) $R^2 = 16\%$; 16% of the variance in the response variable is explained by the least-squares regression line.

(d) $R^2 = 86.49\%$; 86.49% of the variance in the response variable is explained by the least-squares regression line.

17. Influential

18. Not influential

19. Not influential

20. Influential

21. (a) Linear; positive association

(b) Yes; the residual plot does not show any violations of the model.

(c) 83.0% of the variation in the length of eruption is explained by the least-squares regression equation.

22. (a) Linear; positive association

(b) Yes; the residuals appear to be randomly distributed, with no obvious departures from the requirements of the model.

(c) 57.5% of the variation in 28-day strength is explained by the least-squares regression equation.

23. (a)

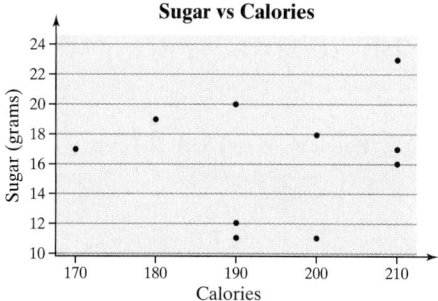

Sugar vs Calories

(b) $r = 0.261$; no, there is no significant linear relation.

(c)

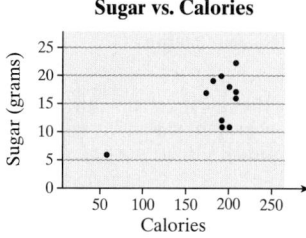

Sugar vs. Calories

$r = 0.649$; yes, there is significant linear relation; All-Bran is an influential observation.

(d) Influential observations can cause the correlation coefficient to increase substantially, thereby increasing the apparent strength of the linear relation between two variables.

24. (a) Yes; the point may be influential because the slope and y-intercept of the regression line changed significantly.

(b) Answers may vary. One possibility is educational and economic division, as well as a high concentration of government jobs. Washington, DC, has an extremely high illiteracy rate, yet it ranks highly in educational attainment with almost half the population having college degrees. The median income in 2006 was about $48,000 (close to the national average), while the median home price was about $440,000 (compared to about $230,000 nationally).

(c) No; while an association may exist, higher levels of education do not *cause* lower teen birth rates. Lurking variables, such as family values, may be present.

25. (a) $R^2 = 83.0\%$

(b)

Residuals vs. Height

(c) 83.0% of the variation in head circumference is explained by the least-squares regression equation. The linear model appears to be appropriate, based on the residual plot.

26. (a) $R^2 = 49.5\%$

(b)

Residuals vs. Length

(c) 49.5% of the variation in weight is explained by the least-squares regression line. The linear model appears to be appropriate, based on the residual plot.

27. (a) $R^2 = 92.9\%$

(b)

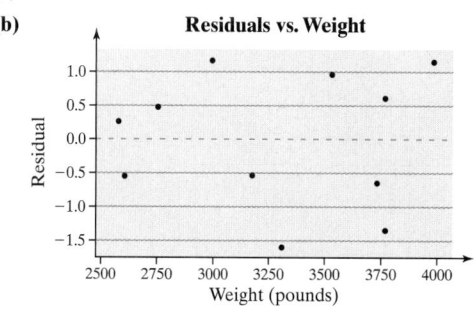

Residuals vs. Weight

(c) 92.9% of the variance in gas mileage is explained by the linear model. The least-squares regression model appears to be appropriate.

28. (a) $R^2 = 90.5\%$

(b)

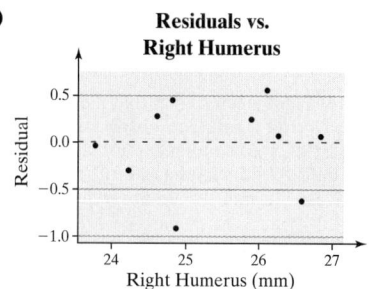

Residuals vs. Right Humerus

(c) 90.5% of the variation in the length of the right tibia is explained by the least-squares regression line. The least-squares regression model appears to be appropriate.

29. (a)

Planetary Motion

(b) $r = 0.989$; yes, there appears to be a linear relation.

(c) $\hat{y} = 0.0657x - 12.4967$

(d)

Residuals vs. Distance

(e) No; the residuals follow a U-shaped pattern.

30. (a)

Wind Chill Factor

(b) $r = -0.952$; yes, there appears to be a linear relation.

(c) $\hat{y} = -1.2286x + 11.2857$

(d)

Residuals vs. Wind Speed

(e) No; the residuals follow a U-shaped pattern.

31. (a) The coefficient of determination with the Viper included is $R^2 = 60.0\%$. Adding the Viper reduces the amount of variability explained by the model by approximately 33%.

(b) The Viper is not influential; neither the slope nor the y-intercept is significantly altered, but the Viper is an outlier.

32. (a) $R^2 = 71.7\%$; the value increases.

(b) The new bear is influential since both the slope and intercept of the regression equation change significantly; the new bear is an outlier, since it lies far outside the rest of the data.

33. The Laramie River Power Plant is unusual in that it emits less carbon than expected from the overall trend. The observation is an outlier and influential. The Jim Bridger power plant is not unusual; it follows the overall trend of the data. Although it has a large residual initially, this effect goes away if the Laramie River observation is removed from the data.

34. Derek Jeter's weight is lower than expected based on the overall trend. His observation is an outlier since it produces a residual that lies away from the general pattern of the other residuals. His observation would also be considered influential since the y-intercept changes significantly if the observation is removed.

35. (a), (d)

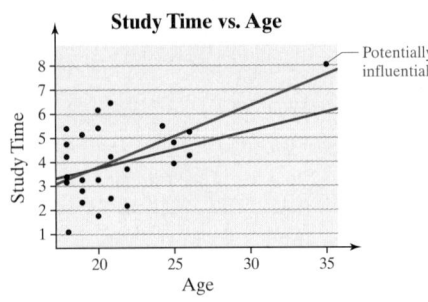

Study Time vs. Age

(b) $\hat{y} = 0.2320x - 0.9204$

(c) $\hat{y} = 0.1549x + 0.6346$

(e) The point $(35, 8.1)$ substantially affects both the slope and the y-intercept of the least-squares regression line.

37. (a)

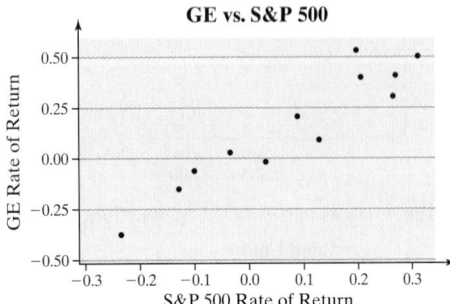

GE vs. S&P 500

(b) $r = 0.942$

(c) Yes

(d) $\hat{y} = 1.5208x + 0.0325$

(e) 0.1846

(f) Below

(g) For each percentage point increase in the rate of return for the S&P 500, the rate of return of GE stock will increase by about 1.52 percentage points, on average.

(h) The y-intercept indicates that the rate of return for GE stock will be 0.0325 when there is no change to the S&P 500.

(i) $R^2 = 88.8\%$

(j)

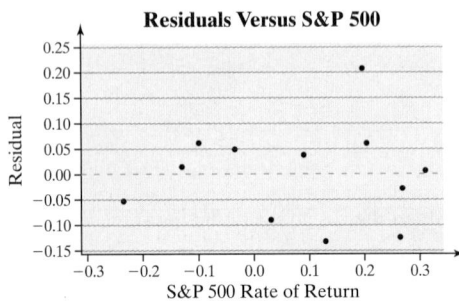

Residuals Versus S&P 500

Overall, the plot supports the linear relation, though there may be a slight concern of a nonconstant variance.

(k) No; a boxplot of the residuals does not show any unusual observations.

4.4 Assess Your Understanding (page 245)

1. A marginal distribution is a frequency or relative frequency distribution of either the row or column variable in a contingency table. A conditional distribution is the relative frequency of each category of one variable, given a specific value of the other variable in a contingency table.

2. Yes; the conditional distribution by level of education is different from the conditional distribution by employment status.

3. Correlation is used with quantitative variables; association is used with categorical variables.

4. Simpson's Paradox represents a situation in which an association between two variables changes directions or goes away when a third variable is introduced.

5. (a)

	x_1	x_2	x_3	Marginal distribution
y_1	20	25	30	75
y_2	30	25	50	105
Marginal distribution	50	50	80	180

(b)

	x_1	x_2	x_3	Relative frequency marginal distribution
y_1	20	25	30	0.417
y_2	30	25	50	0.583
Relative frequency marginal distribution	0.278	0.278	0.444	1

(c)

	x_1	x_2	x_3
y_1	0.400	0.500	0.375
y_2	0.600	0.500	0.625
Total	1	1	1

(d)

Conditional Distribution

6. (a)

	x_1	x_2	x_3	Marginal distribution
y_1	35	25	20	80
y_2	65	75	80	220
Marginal distribution	100	100	100	300

(b)

	x_1	x_2	x_3	Relative frequency marginal distribution
y_1	35	25	20	0.267
y_2	65	75	80	0.733
Relative frequency marginal distribution	0.333	0.333	0.333	1

(c)

	x_1	x_2	x_3
y_1	0.350	0.250	0.200
y_2	0.650	0.750	0.800
Total	1	1	1

(d)

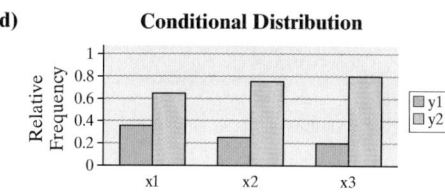

Conditional Distribution

7. (a) 780 adults were surveyed; 195 Hispanics were surveyed.

(b)

Opinion	Ethnicity Non-Hispanic Whites	Blacks	Hispanics	Relative Frequency Marginal Distribution
Good thing	180	154	144	0.613
Bad thing	107	101	33	0.309
Good and bad	9	14	12	0.045
No opinion	9	11	6	0.033
Relative frequency marginal distribution	0.391	0.359	0.250	1

(c) 0.613

(d)

Opinion	Ethnicity Non-Hispanic Whites	Blacks	Hispanics
Good thing	0.590	0.550	0.738
Bad thing	0.351	0.361	0.169
Good and bad	0.030	0.050	0.062
No Opinion	0.030	0.039	0.031
Total	1	1	1

(e)

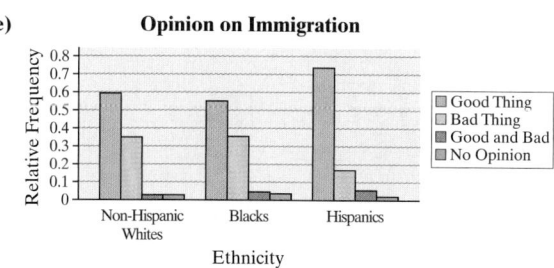

Opinion on Immigration

(f) Yes; Hispanics are more likely to feel that immigration is a good thing for the country and much less likely to feel it is a bad thing.

8. (a) There were 3,834 thousand births in 2005; 983 thousand had Hispanic mothers.

(b)

Delivery Method	Ethnicity Non-Hispanic Whites	Blacks	Hispanics	Relative frequency marginal distribution
Vaginal	1,580	392	698	0.696
Cesarean	690	189	285	0.304
Relative frequency marginal distribution	0.592	0.152	0.256	1

(c) 0.696

(d)

Delivery Method	Ethnicity Non-Hispanic Whites	Blacks	Hispanics
Vaginal	0.696	0.675	0.710
Cesarean	0.304	0.325	0.290
Total	1	1	1

(e)

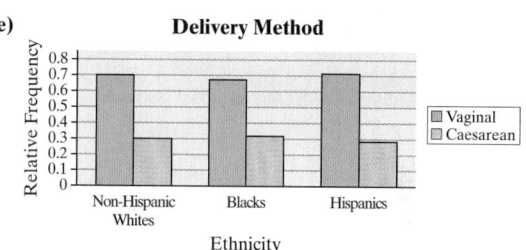

Delivery Method

(f) No; the method of delivery is approximately the same for each group.

9. (a)

Political Party	Gender Female	Male	Frequency Marginal Distribution
Republican	105	115	220
Democrat	150	103	253
Independent	150	179	329
Frequency marginal distribution	405	397	802

(b)

Political Party	Gender Female	Male	Relative Frequency Marginal Distribution
Republican	105	115	0.274
Democrat	150	103	0.315
Independent	150	179	0.410
Relative frequency marginal distribution	0.505	0.495	1

(c) 0.410

(d)

Political Party	Gender Female	Male
Republican	0.259	0.290
Democrat	0.370	0.259
Independent	0.370	0.451
Total	1	1

(e)

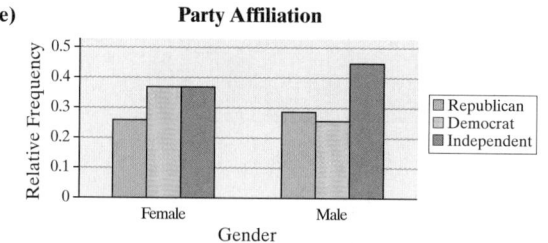

Party Affiliation

(f) Yes; males are more likely to be Independents and less likely to be Democrats.

10. (a)

Opinion on Availability of Abortion	Education Level			Frequency Marginal Distribution
	High School or Less	Some College	College Graduate	
Generally available	90	72	113	275
Allowed, but more limited	51	60	77	188
Illegal, with few exceptions	125	94	69	288
Never permitted	51	14	17	82
Frequency marginal distribution	317	240	276	833

(b)

Opinion on Availability of Abortion	Education Level			Relative Frequency Marginal Distribution
	High School or Less	Some College	College Graduate	
Generally available	90	72	113	0.330
Allowed, but more limited	51	60	77	0.226
Illegal, with few exceptions	125	94	69	0.346
Never permitted	51	14	17	0.098
Relative frequency marginal distribution	0.381	0.288	0.331	1

(c) 0.062

(d)

Opinion on Availability of Abortion	Education Level		
	High School or Less	Some College	College Graduate
Generally available	0.284	0.300	0.409
Allowed, but more limited	0.161	0.250	0.279
Illegal, with few exceptions	0.394	0.392	0.250
Never permitted	0.161	0.058	0.062
Total	1	1	1

(e)

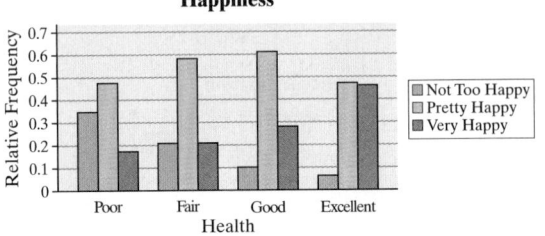

Opinion on Abortion

(f) Yes; as education level increases, respondents are more likely to feel that abortion should be available.

11.

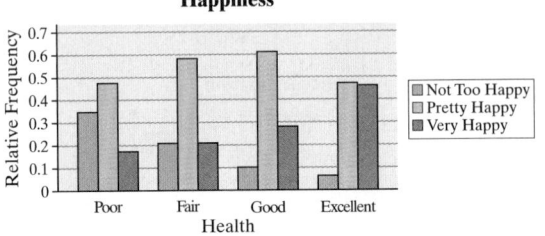

Happiness

Based on the conditional distribution by health, we can see that healthier people tend to be happier. As health increases, the percent who are very happy increases, while the percent who are not happy decreases.

12.

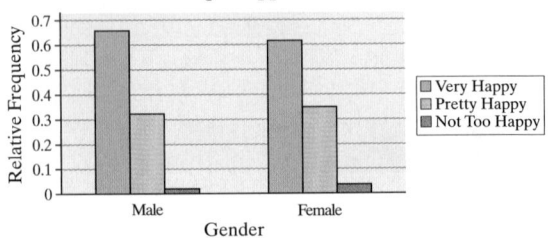

Marriage Happiness

Based on the conditional distribution, there does not appear to be a significant association between gender and marriage happiness.

13. (a) Smokers: 0.239; nonsmokers: 0.314; this implies that it is healthier to smoke.

(b) Smokers: 0.036; Nonsmokers: 0.016

(c) Proportion decreased after 20 years by smoking status and age

	Age						
	18–24	25–34	35–44	45–54	55–64	65–74	75 or older
Smoker	0.036	0.024	0.128	0.208	0.443	0.806	1
Nonsmoker	0.016	0.032	0.058	0.154	0.331	0.783	1

(d)

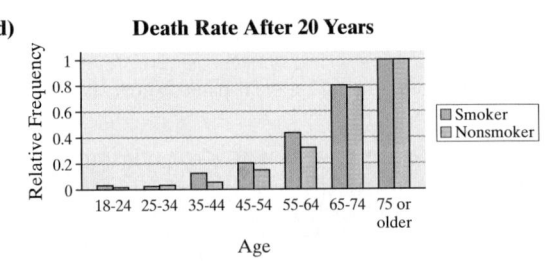

Death Rate After 20 Years

(e) Answers may vary. When taking age into account, the direction of association changed. In almost all age groups, smokers had a higher death rate than nonsmokers. The most notable exception is for the 25 to 34 age group, the largest age group for the non-smokers. A possible explanation could be rigorous physical activity (e.g., rock climbing) that nonsmokers are more likely to participate in than smokers.

14. (a) Treatment B; treatment A was effective 78% of the time, whereas treatment B was effective 82.6% of the time.

(b) Treatment A: 0.931; treatment B: 0.867

(c)

Stone Size	Treatment A	Treatment B
Small	0.931	0.867
Large	0.780	0.688

(d)

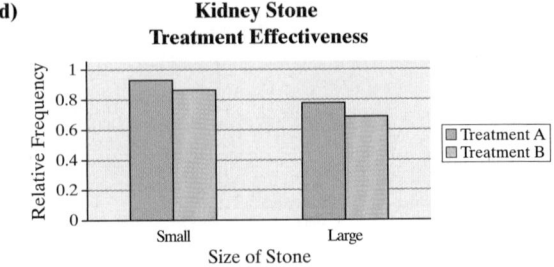

Kidney Stone Treatment Effectiveness

(e) Answers may vary. The direction of the association reversed after taking the size of the stone into account. For each size of stone (small or large), treatment A worked better than treatment B.

Chapter 4 Review Exercises (page 249)

1. (a) Fat content

(b)

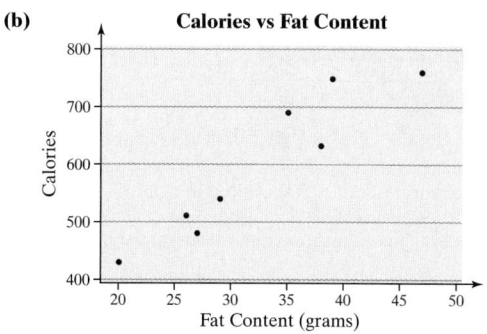

Calories vs Fat Content

(c) $r = 0.944$

(d) Yes; a strong linear relation exists between fat content and calories in fast-food restaurant sandwiches.

2. (a)

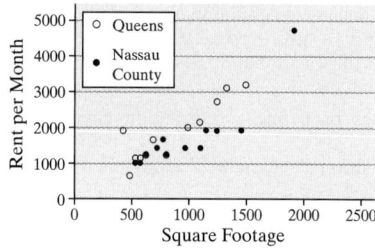

Apartments

(b) Queens: $r = 0.909$; Nassau County: $r = 0.867$

(c) Both locations appear to have a positive linear association between square footage and monthly rent.

(d) For small apartments (those less than 1,000 square feet in area), there seems to be no difference in rent between Queens and Nassau County. In larger apartments, Queens seems to have higher rents than Nassau County.

3. (a) $\hat{y} = 13.7334x + 150.9469$

(b)

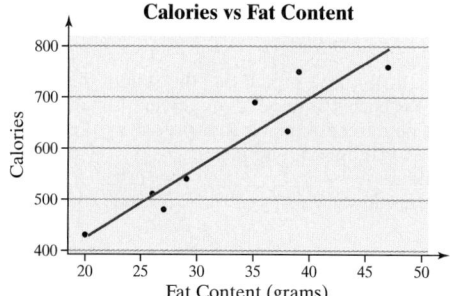

Calories vs Fat Content

(c) The slope indicates that each additional gram of fat in a sandwich adds approximately 13.73 calories, on average. The y-intercept indicates that a sandwich with no fat will contain about 151 calories.

(d) 562.9 calories

(e) Below average (the average value is 727.7 calories)

4. (a) $\hat{y} = 2.2091x - 34.3148$

(b) The slope of the least-squares regression line indicates that, for each additional square foot of floor area, the rent increases by $2.21, on average. It is not appropriate to interpret the y-intercept since it is not possible to have an apartment with 0 square footage.

(c) This apartment's rent is below average.

5. (a)

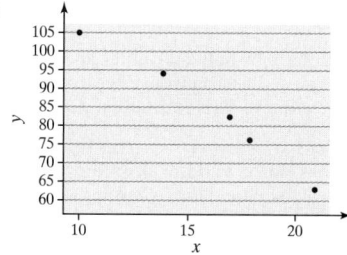

(b) Using points $(10, 105)$ and $(18, 76)$, $\hat{y} = -\dfrac{29}{8}x + \dfrac{565}{4}$.

(c)

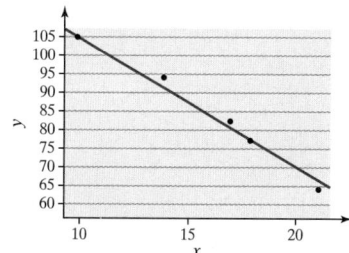

(d) $\hat{y} = -3.8429x + 145.4857$

(e)

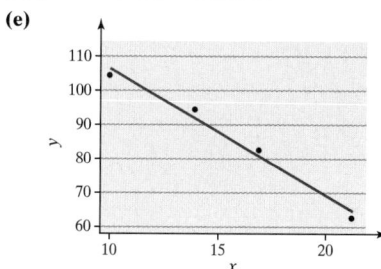

(f) Computed line: sum of squared residuals $= 22.406$

(g) Least-squares line: sum of squared residuals $= 16.271$

(h) Answers will vary.

6. Linear model is appropriate.

7. Linear model is not appropriate; residuals are patterned.

8. Linear model is not appropriate; nonconstant error variance.

9. (a) $R^2 = 89.1\%$; 89.1% of the variation in calories is explained by the least-squares regression line.

(b)

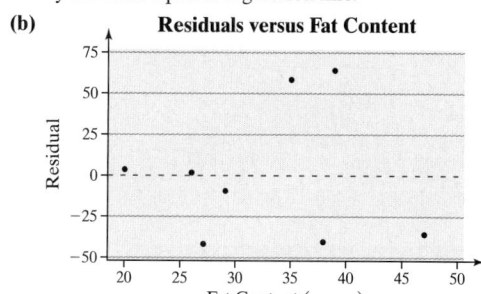

Residuals versus Fat Content

(c) Yes, a linear model is appropriate.

(d) There are no outliers or influential observations.

(e) This observation is an outlier since it lies away from the rest of the data. It is also influential because it significantly changes the slope and y-intercept of the regression line.

10. (a) $R^2 = 82.7\%$; 82.7% of the variance in rent is explained by the least-squares regression model.

(b)

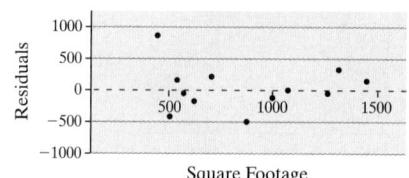

Apartments

(c) The plot of residuals shows no discernible pattern, so a linear model is appropriate.

(d) The observation (460, 1805) is both an outlier and an influential point. The least-squares line omitting the outlier is $\hat{y} = 2.5315x - 399.25$; the y-intercept is substantially different.

11. (a) $\hat{y} = 2.0995x - 347.3641$

(b) The observation (1906, 4625) is both an outlier and an influential point. The least-squares line omitting the outlier is $\hat{y} = 0.8779x + 675.2945$; both the slope and the $\hat{y}$-intercept are substantially different.

12. (a)

Camaro Depreciation

(b) $r = -0.954$; yes

(c) $\hat{y} = -2,054.6460x + 20,976.2124$

(d)

Residuals vs. Age

(e) No; the residuals follow a U-shaped pattern.

13. No; correlation does not imply causation. Florida has a large number of tourists in warmer months, times when more people will be in the water to cool off. The larger number of people in the water splashing around leads to a larger number of shark attacks.

14. (a) 203

(b)

| | Car Type | | Relative Frequency |
Satisfaction	New	Used	Marginal Distribution
Not too satisfied	11	25	0.091
Pretty satisfied	78	79	0.396
Extremely satisfied	118	85	0.513
Relative frequency marginal distribution	0.523	0.477	1

(c) 0.513

(d)

| | Car Type | |
Satisfaction	New	Used
Not too satisfied	0.053	0.132
Pretty satisfied	0.377	0.418
Extremely satisfied	0.570	0.450
Total	1	1

(e)

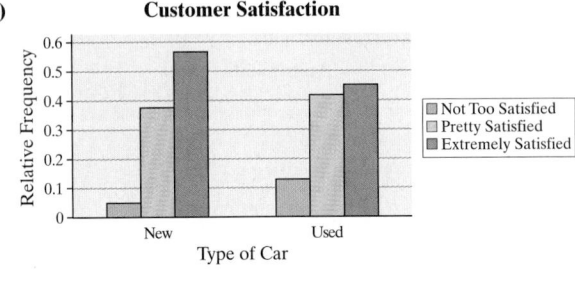

Customer Satisfaction

(f) There appears to be some association. Buyers of used cars are more likely to be dissatisfied and are less likely to be extremely satisfied than buyers of new cars.

15. (a)

	PCH	GH
Survived	0.882	0.807
Died	0.118	0.193
Total	1	1

(b) 0.118 of the surgeries at PCH resulted in death.
0.193 of the surgeries at GH resulted in death.

(c) Conclusion: a higher proportion of surgeries at GH resulted in death.

(d) 0.92 of the planned surgeries at PCH survived.
0.925 of the planned surgeries at GH survived.

(e) 0.60 of the emergency surgeries at PCH survived.
0.625 of the emergency surgeries at GH survived.

(f) Answers will vary.

16. (a) A positive linear relation appears to exist between number of marriages and number unemployed.

(b) Population is highly correlated with both the number of marriages and the number unemployed. The size of the population affects both variables.

(c) No association exists between the two variables.

(d) Answers may vary. A strong correlation between two variables may be due to a third variable that is highly correlated with the two original variables.

17. The eight properties of a linear correlation coefficient are the following:

1. The linear correlation coefficient is always between -1 and 1, inclusive. That is, $-1 \le r \le 1$.

2. If $r = +1$, there is a perfect positive linear relation between the two variables. See Figure 4(a) on page 196.

3. If $r = -1$, there is a perfect negative linear relation between the two variables. See Figure 4(d).

4. The closer r is to $+1$, the stronger is the evidence of positive association between the two variables. See Figure 4(b) and 4(c).

5. The closer r is to -1, the stronger is the evidence of negative association between the two variables. See Figures 4(e) and 4(f).

6. If r is close to 0, there is no evidence of a *linear* relation between the two variables. Because the linear correlation coefficient is a measure of the strength of the linear relation, r close to 0 does not imply no relation, just no linear relation. See Figures 4(g) and 4(h).

7. The linear correlation coefficient is a unitless measure of association. So the unit of measure for x and y plays no role in the interpretation of r.

8. The correlation coefficient is not resistant.

18. (a) Answers will vary.

(b) The slope can be interpreted as "the school day decreases by 0.01 hour for each 1% increase in percent low income, on average." The y-intercept can be interpreted as the length of the school day for those with no income.

(c) $\hat{y} = 6.91$ hours

(d)–(i) Answers will vary.

Chapter 4 Test (page 253)

1. (a) Temperature

(b)

Cricket Chirp Rates

(c) $r = 0.835$

(d) Yes, a positive linear relation exists between temperature and chirps per second.

(e) $\hat{y} = 0.2119x - 0.3091$

(f) If the temperature increases $1°F$, the number of chirps per second increases by 0.2119, on average. Since there are no observations near $0°F$, it does not make sense to interpret the y-intercept.

(g) At $83.3°F$, $\hat{y} = 17.3$ chirps per second.

(h) Below average

(i) No; outside the scope of the model

(j) $R^2 = 69.7\%$; 69.7% of the variation in number of chirps per second is explained by the least-squares regression line.

(k) Yes; the residual plot does not indicate any patterns.

2. Yes; when added, both the slope and y-intercept change substantially.

3. No; although there is a strong correlation, the residual plot is U-shaped, so a linear model is not appropriate.

4. Correlation does not imply causation. It is possible that a lurking variable, such as income level or educational level, is affecting both the explanatory and response variables.

5. (a)

Education Level	Belief Yes, Definitely	Yes, Probably	No, Probably Not	No, Definitely Not	Relative Frequency Marginal Distribution
Less than high school	316	66	21	9	0.173
High school	956	296	122	65	0.606
Bachelor's	267	131	62	64	0.221
Relative frequency marginal distribution	0.648	0.208	0.086	0.058	1

(b) 0.648

(c)

Education Level	Belief Yes, Definitely	Yes, Probably	No, Probably Not	No, Definitely Not	Total
Less than high school	0.767	0.160	0.051	0.022	1
High school	0.664	0.206	0.085	0.045	1
Bachelor's	0.510	0.250	0.118	0.122	1

(d)

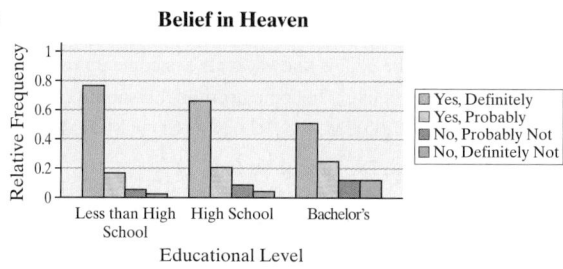

(e) Yes; as education level increases, the percent who definitely believe in Heaven decreases (i.e., doubt in Heaven increases).

6. (a)

College Applicants	Accepted	Denied	Total
Male	0.158	0.842	1
Female	0.310	0.690	1

(b) 0.158 of the males who applied was accepted.
0.310 of the females who applied was accepted.

(c) Conclusion: a higher proportion of females was accepted.

(d) 0.150 of the males applying to the business school was accepted.
0.143 of the females applying to the business school was accepted.

(e) 0.40 of the males applying to the social work school was accepted.
0.364 of the females applying to the social work school was accepted.

(f) Answers will vary. A larger number of males applied to the business school, which has an overall lower acceptance rate than the social work school, so more male applicants were declined.

7. The data would have a perfect negative linear relation. A scatter diagram would show all the observations being collinear (falling on the same line) with a negative slope.

8. If the slope of the least-squares regression line is negative, the correlation between the explanatory and response variables is also negative.

9. If a linear correlation coefficient is close to zero, this means that there is no linear relation between the explanatory and response variable. This does not mean there is no relation, just no *linear* relation.

CHAPTER 5 Probability

5.1 Assess Your Understanding (page 269)

1. Empirical probability is based on the outcomes of a probability experiment and is the relative frequency of the event. Classical probability is based on counting techniques and is equal to the ratio of the number of ways an event can occur to the number of possible outcomes of the experiment.

2. The probability of an impossible event is zero. No; when a probability is based on an empirical experiment, a probability of zero does not mean the event cannot occur.

3. Outcomes are equally likely when each outcome has the same probability of occurring.

4. An event is unusual if it has a low probability of occurring. The choice of a cutoff should consider the context of the problem.

5. True

6. True

7. experiment

8. event

9. From the Law of Large Numbers, as the number of repetitions of a probability experiment increases (long term), the proportion with which a certain outcome is observed (relative frequency) gets closer to the probability of the outcome.

10. A tree diagram is useful for determining sample spaces by systematically listing all possible outcomes of a probability experiment.

11. Rule 1: All probabilities in the model are greater than or equal to zero and less than or equal to one.
Rule 2: The sum of the probabilities in the model is 1.
The outcome "blue" is an impossible event since $P(\text{blue}) = 0$.

12. Rule 1: All probabilities in the model are greater than or equal to zero and less than or equal to one.
Rule 2: The sum of the probabilities in the model is 1.
All the M&M's in the bag are yellow.

13. This is not a probability model because $P(\text{green}) < 0$.

14. This is not a probability model because the sum of the probabilities is not 1.

15. The numbers $0, 0.01, 0.35$, and 1 could be probabilities.

16. The numbers $\frac{1}{2}, \frac{3}{4}, \frac{2}{3}$, and 0 could be probabilities.

17. The probability of 0.42 means that approximately 42 out of every 100 dealt hands will contain two cards of the same value and three cards of different value. No, probability refers to long-term behavior, not short-term.

18. The probability of 0.44 means that approximately 44 out of every 100 dealt hands will contain two cards of the same value and five cards of different value. No, probability refers to long-term behavior, not short-term.

19. The empirical probability is 0.95.

20. The empirical probability is 0.80.

21. $P(2) \neq \frac{1}{11}$ since the outcomes are not equally likely.

22. No; blood types are not equally likely.

23. $S = \{1H, 1T, 2H, 2T, 3H, 3T, 4H, 4T, 5H, 5T, 6H, 6T\}$

24. $S = \{SSS, SSF, SFS, FSS, SFF, FSF, FFS, FFF\}$

25. 0.428   26. 0.372   27. $P(E) = \dfrac{3}{10} = 0.3$

28. $P(F) = \dfrac{2}{5} = 0.4$ 29. $P(E) = \dfrac{2}{5} = 0.4$ 30. $P(F) = \dfrac{1}{2} = 0.5$

31. (a) $P(\text{plays sports}) = \dfrac{288}{500} = 0.576$

 (b) If we sampled a large number of high school students, we would expect that about 57.6% of the students play organized sports.

32. (a) $P(\text{female volunteered}) = \dfrac{341}{1,100} = 0.31$

 (b) If we sampled a large number of adult females (18 years of age or older), we would expect about 31% of the women have volunteered at least once in the past year.

33. (a) $P(\text{red}) = \dfrac{40}{100} = 0.4$ (b) $P(\text{purple}) = \dfrac{25}{100} = 0.25$

 (c) If we sampled a large number of tulip bulbs, we would expect about 40% of the bulbs to be red and about 25% of the bulbs to be purple.

34. (a) $P(\text{Titleist}) = \dfrac{35}{80} = 0.4375$ (b) $P(\text{Top-Flite}) = \dfrac{20}{80} = 0.25$

 (c) If we sampled a large number of golf balls, we would expect about 43.75% of the balls to be Titleist and about 25% to be Top-Flite.

35. (a) $S = \{0, 00, 1, 2, 3, 4, \ldots, 35, 36\}$

 (b) $P(8) = \dfrac{1}{38} = 0.0263$; If we spun the wheel 1,000 times we'd expect about 26 of those times to result in the ball landing in slot 8.

 (c) $P(\text{odd}) = \dfrac{18}{38} = 0.4737$; If we spun the wheel 100 times, we'd expect about 47 of the spins to result in an odd number.

36. (a) $P(\text{1st day of month}) = \dfrac{12}{365}$

 (b) $P(\text{31st day of the month}) = \dfrac{7}{365}$

 (c) $P(\text{born in December}) = \dfrac{31}{365}$

 (d) $P(\text{born on November 8}) = \dfrac{1}{365}$

 (e) No; it is unlikely that you would guess her birthday.
 (f) No; outcomes are not equally likely.

37. (a) $\{SS, Ss, sS, ss\}$

 (b) $P(ss) = \dfrac{1}{4}$; there is a 25% probability that a randomly selected offspring will have sickle-cell anemia.

 (c) $P(Ss \text{ or } sS) = \dfrac{1}{2} = 0.5$; there is 50% probability that a randomly selected offspring will be a carrier of sickle-cell anemia.

38. (a) $\{SS, Ss, sS, ss\}$

 (b) $P(ss) = \dfrac{1}{4} = 0.25$; there is a 25% probability that a randomly selected offspring will not have Huntington's disease.

 (c) $P(SS, Ss, sS) = \dfrac{3}{4} = 0.75$; there is a 75% probability that a randomly selected offspring will have Huntington's disease.

39. (a)

Response	Probability
Never	0.026
Rarely	0.068
Sometimes	0.116
Most of the time	0.263
Always	0.527

 (b) It would be unusual to randomly find a college student who never wears a seatbelt when riding in a car driven by someone else, because $P(\text{never}) < 0.05$.

40. (a)

Response	Probability
Never	0.026
Rarely	0.055
Sometimes	0.076
Most of the time	0.158
Always	0.684

 (b) It would be unusual to randomly find a college student who never wears a seatbelt while driving, because $P(\text{never}) < 0.05$.

41. (a)

Type of Larceny Theft	Probability
Pocket picking	0.006
Purse snatching	0.009
Shoplifting	0.207
From motor vehicles	0.341
Motor vehicle accessories	0.140
Bicycles	0.065
From buildings	0.223
From coin-operated machines	0.008

 (b) Purse snatching larcenies are unusual.
 (c) Bicycle larcenies are not unusual.

42. (a)

Age	Probability
15–19	0.013
20–24	0.071
25–29	0.249
30–34	0.372
35–39	0.244
40–44	0.052

 (b) Multiple births are unusual for 15- to 19-year-old mothers.
 (c) Multiple births are not too unusual for 40- to 44-year-old mothers.

43. A, B, C, and F are consistent with the definition of a probability model.

44. Use model A if the coin is known to be fair.

45. Use model B if the coin is known to always come up tails.

46. If tails are twice as likely to come up, model F should be used.

47. (a) $S = \{JR, JC, JD, JM, RC, RD, RM, CD, CM, DM\}$

 (b) $P(\text{Clarese and Dominique attend}) = \dfrac{1}{10} = 0.10$

 (c) $P(\text{Clarice attends}) = \dfrac{4}{10} = 0.40$

 (d) $P(\text{John stays home}) = \dfrac{6}{10} = 0.60$

48. (a) {Screamin' Eagle–The Boss, Screamin' Eagle–Mine Train, Screamin' Eagle–Batman, Screamin' Eagle – Mr. Freeze, Screamin' Eagle – Ninja, Screamin' Eagle – Big Spin, Screamin' Eagle – Evel Knievel, The Boss – Mine Train, The Boss – Batman, The Boss – Mr. Freeze, The Boss – Ninja, The Boss – Big Spin, The Boss – Evel Knievel, Mine Train – Batman, Mine Train – Mr. Freeze, Mine Train – Ninja, Mine Train – Big Spin, Mine Train – Evel Knievel, Batman – Mr. Freeze, Batman – Ninja, Batman – Big Spin, Batman – Evel Knievel, Mr. Freeze – Ninja, Mr. Freeze – Big Spin, Mr. Freeze – Evel Knievel, Ninja – Big Spin, Ninja – Evel Knievel, Big Spin – Evel Knievel}

 (b) $P(\text{Mr. Freeze and Evel Knievel}) = \dfrac{1}{28} = 0.036$

 (c) $P(\text{Screamin' Eagle}) = \dfrac{7}{28} = 0.25$

 (d) $P(\text{two wooden coasters}) = \dfrac{3}{28} = 0.107$

 (e) $P(\text{no wooden coasters}) = \dfrac{10}{28} = 0.357$

49. (a) $P(\text{right field}) = \dfrac{24}{73} = 0.329$ **(b)** $P(\text{left field}) = \dfrac{2}{73} = 0.027$

   (c) It was unusual for Barry Bonds to hit a home run to left field; the probability is less than 5%.

50. (a) Answers will vary.   **(b)** Answers will vary.

   (c) $P(3) = \dfrac{1}{6}$

51. Answers will vary.

52. (a) Classical method is used.
   (b) Empirical method is used.
   (c) Subjective method is used.
   (d) Empirical method is used.

53. The dice appear to be loaded since the outcomes are not equally likely.

54. Answers will vary.

55. $P(\text{income is greater than } \$58{,}500) = \dfrac{1}{2} = 0.5$

56. $P(\text{SAT math score} \geq 700) = 0.75$

57. Answers will vary.

58. (a) Qualitative
   (b) Because the data are qualitative and multiple responses are possible, a bar chart is the appropriate display.

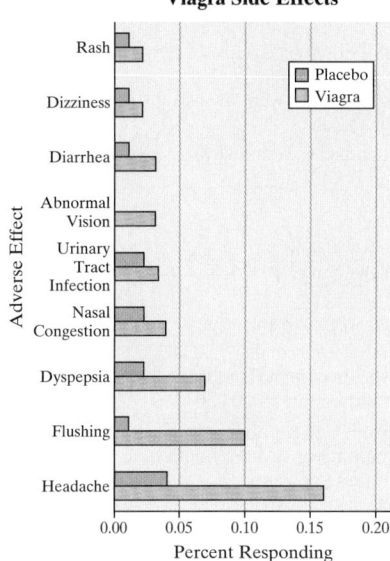

Viagra Side Effects

   (c) For the Viagra group, $P(\text{flushing}) = \dfrac{73}{734} = 0.099$; this is not unusual.

   (d) For the placebo group, $P(\text{flushing}) = \dfrac{7}{725} = 0.010$; this is somewhat unusual.

   (e) Since it is unusual for someone in the placebo group to experience flushing, we would conclude that the individual received the Viagra treatment.

   (f) This is a completely randomized design.

5.2 Assess Your Understanding (page 281)

1. Two events are disjoint (mutually exclusive) if they have no outcomes in common.

2. $P(E) + P(F)$

3. $P(E) + P(F) - P(E \text{ and } F)$

4. Two events E and E^c are complementary if $P(E \text{ and } E^c) = 0$ and if $P(E \text{ or } E^c) = 1$.

5. E and $F = \{5, 6, 7\}$; E and F are not mutually exclusive.

6. F and $G = \{9\}$; F and G are not mutually exclusive.

7. F or $G = \{5, 6, 7, 8, 9, 10, 11, 12\}$; $P(F \text{ or } G) = \dfrac{2}{3}$

8. E or $H = \{2, 3, 4, 5, 6, 7\}$; $P(E \text{ or } H) = \dfrac{1}{2}$

9. There are no outcomes in event "E and G." Events E and G are mutually exclusive.

10. There are no outcomes in event "F and H." Events F and H are mutually exclusive.

11. $E^c = \{1, 8, 9, 10, 11, 12\}$; $P(E^c) = \dfrac{1}{2}$

12. $F^c = \{1, 2, 3, 4, 10, 11, 12\}$; $P(F^c) = \dfrac{7}{12}$

13. $P(E \text{ or } F) = 0.55$ **14.** $P(E \text{ and } F) = 0.10$

15. $P(E \text{ or } F) = 0.70$ **16.** $P(E \text{ and } F) = 0$

17. $P(E^c) = 0.75$ **18.** $P(F^c) = 0.55$

19. $P(F) = 0.30$ **20.** $P(E) = 0.50$

21. $P(\text{Titleist or Maxfli}) = \dfrac{17}{20} = 0.85$

22. $P(\text{Maxfli or Top-Flite}) = \dfrac{11}{20} = 0.55$

23. $P(\text{not a Titleist}) = \dfrac{11}{20} = 0.55$

24. $P(\text{not a Top-Flite}) = \dfrac{17}{20} = 0.85$

25. (a) All the probabilities are nonnegative; the sum of the probabilities equals 1.
   (b) $P(\text{gun or knife}) = 0.797$. There is a 79.7% probability of randomly selecting a murder committed with a gun or a knife.
   (c) $P(\text{knife, blunt object, or strangulation}) = 0.180$. There is an 18.0% probability of randomly selecting a murder committed with a knife, blunt object, or by strangulation.
   (d) $P(\text{not a gun}) = 0.329$. There is a 32.9% chance of randomly selecting a murder that was not committed with a gun.
   (e) A murder by strangulation is unusual.

26. (a) All the probabilities are nonnegative; the sum of the probabilities equals 1.
   (b) $P(\text{earning a physical or life sciences degree}) = 0.271$. There is a 27.1% probability that a randomly selected doctoral candidate received a degree in either the physical or life sciences.
   (c) $P(\text{doctorate in physical, life, or computer sciences or mathematics}) = 0.325$. There is a 32.5% probability that a randomly selected doctoral candidate received a degree in the physical, life, or computer sciences or in mathematics.
   (d) $P(\text{not in mathematics}) = 0.972$. The probability is 97.2% that a randomly selected doctoral candidate did not receive a degree in mathematics.
   (e) It is unusual to earn a doctoral degree in mathematics.

27. No; for example, on one draw of a card from a standard deck, let $E =$ diamond, $F =$ club, and $G =$ red card.

28. $P(A \text{ or } B \text{ or } C) = P(A) + P(B) + P(C) - P(A \text{ and } B) - P(A \text{ and } C) - P(B \text{ and } C) + 2P(A \text{ and } B \text{ and } C)$

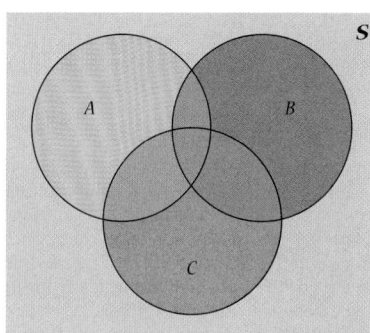

29. (a) $P(\text{30- to 39-year-old mother}) = 0.605$. There is a 60.5% probability that a mother involved in a multiple birth was between 30 and 39 years old.
   (b) $P(\text{not 30 to 39 years old}) = 0.395$. There is a 39.5% probability that a mother involved in a multiple birth was either younger than 30 or older than 39.

(c) $P(\text{younger than 45 years}) = 0.982$. The probability that a randomly selected mother involved in a multiple birth was younger than 45 years old is 98.2%.

(d) $P(\text{at least 20 years old}) = 0.988$. There is a 98.8% probability that a randomly selected mother involved with a multiple birth was at least 20 years old.

30. (a) All the probabilities are nonnegative; the sum of the probabilities equals 1.

(b) $P(4 \text{ or more rooms}) = 0.896$. The probability is 89.6% that a randomly selected house has 4 or more rooms.

(c) $P(\text{fewer than 8 rooms}) = 0.844$. There is an 84.4% probability that a randomly selected house will have fewer than 8 rooms.

(d) $P(\text{from 4 to 6 rooms}) = 0.617$. There is a 61.7% probability that a randomly selected house will have 4, 5, or 6 rooms.

(e) $P(\text{at least 2 rooms}) = 0.995$. The probability is 99.5% that a randomly selected house will have at least 2 rooms.

31. (a) $P(\text{heart or club}) = \dfrac{1}{2} = 0.5$

(b) $P(\text{heart or club or diamond}) = \dfrac{3}{4} = 0.75$

(c) $P(\text{ace or heart}) = \dfrac{4}{13} = 0.308$

32. (a) $P(\text{two or three}) = \dfrac{2}{13} = 0.154$

(b) $P(\text{two or three or four}) = \dfrac{3}{13} = 0.231$

(c) $P(\text{two or club}) = \dfrac{4}{13} = 0.308$

33. (a) $P(\text{birthday is not November 8}) = \dfrac{364}{365} = 0.997$

(b) $P(\text{birthday is not 1st of month}) = \dfrac{353}{365} = 0.967$

(c) $P(\text{birthday is not 31st of month}) = \dfrac{358}{365} = 0.981$

(d) $P(\text{birthday is not in December}) = \dfrac{334}{365} = 0.915$

34. (a) $P(\text{green or red}) = \dfrac{10}{19} = 0.526$

(b) $P(\text{not green}) = \dfrac{18}{19} = 0.947$

35. No; some people have both vision and hearing problems, but we don't know the proportion.

36. No; some people visit the doctor for both a blood pressure check and urine analysis, but we don't know the proportion.

37. (a) $P(\text{between 6 and 10 years old}) = \dfrac{5}{24} = 0.208$; not unusual

(b) $P(\text{more than 5 years old}) = \dfrac{17}{24} = 0.708$

(c) $P(\text{less than 1 year old}) = \dfrac{1}{24} = 0.042$; yes, this is unusual

38. (a) $P(\text{only English or only Spanish is spoken}) = 0.93$

(b) $P(\text{language other than only English or only Spanish}) = 0.07$

(c) $P(\text{not only English is spoken}) = 0.19$

(d) No; the sum of the probabilities would be greater than 1, and there would be no probability model.

39. (a) $P(\text{employee drives or takes public transportation}) = 0.915$. There is a 91.5% probability that a randomly selected employee either drives or takes public transportation to work.

(b) $P(\text{employee neither drives nor takes public transportation}) = 0.085$. There is an 8.5% probability that a randomly selected employee neither drives nor takes public transportation to work.

(c) $P(\text{employee does not drive}) = 0.133$. The probability is 13.3% that a randomly selected employee does not drive to work.

(d) No; the probability a person drives or walks or takes public transportation would be 106.5%, which is greater than 1.

40. (a) $P(\text{both spouses work}) = \dfrac{1,149}{1,700} = 0.676$

(b) $P(1 \text{ child under age 18}) = \dfrac{353}{1,700} = 0.208$

(c) $P(2 \text{ or more children under age 18 and both spouses work}) = \dfrac{37}{170} = 0.218$

(d) $P(\text{no children or only husband works}) = \dfrac{1,041}{1,700} = 0.612$

(e) $P(\text{only wife works}) = \dfrac{63}{850} = 0.074$; no, this would not be unusual

41. (a) $P(\text{died from cancer}) = 0.007$

(b) $P(\text{current smoker}) = 0.057$

(c) $P(\text{died from cancer and was current cigar smoker}) = 0.001$

(d) $P(\text{died from cancer or was current cigar smoker}) = 0.064$

42. (a) $P(\text{employed}) = 0.890$

(b) $P(\text{male}) = 0.518$

(c) $P(\text{employed and male}) = 0.454$

(d) $P(\text{employed or male}) = 0.954$

43. (a) $P(\text{student is satisfied}) = \dfrac{77}{125} = 0.616$

(b) $P(\text{student is a junior}) = \dfrac{94}{375} = 0.251$

(c) $P(\text{student is satisfied and is a junior}) = \dfrac{64}{375} = 0.171$

(d) $P(\text{student is satisfied or is a junior}) = \dfrac{87}{125} = 0.696$

44. (a) $P(\text{placebo}) = \dfrac{2}{5} = 0.40$

(b) $P(\text{headache went away}) = \dfrac{94}{125} = 0.752$

(c) $P(\text{placebo and headache went away}) = \dfrac{28}{125} = 0.224$

(d) $P(\text{placebo or headache went away}) = \dfrac{116}{125} = 0.928$

45. (a) $P(\text{officer}) = 0.163$

(b) $P(\text{Navy}) = 0.243$

(c) $P(\text{Navy officer}) = 0.038$

(d) $P(\text{officer or in the Navy}) = 0.368$

46. (a) $P(\text{male}) = 0.742$

(b) $P(16 \text{ to } 20 \text{ years old}) = 0.126$

(c) $P(16 \text{ to } 20 \text{ years old and male}) = 0.089$

(d) $P(\text{male or } 16 \text{ to } 20 \text{ years old}) = 0.778$

(e) Yes, $P(16\text{–}20 \text{ and female}) = 0.036$

47. (a) Crash type, system, and number of crashes

(b) Crash type: qualitative; system: qualitative; number of crashes: quantitative, discrete

(c)

Crash Type	Current System	Red-Light Cameras
Reported injury	0.26	0.24
Reported property damage only	0.35	0.36
Unreported injury	0.07	0.07
Unreported property damage only	0.32	0.33
Total	1	1

(d)

Crashes at Intersections

(e) Current system: $\dfrac{1121}{13} \approx 86.2$ crashes

With cameras: $\dfrac{922}{13} \approx 70.9$ crashes

(f) Not possible; we would need to know the number of crashes at each intersection.

(g) Since the mean number of crashes is less with the cameras, it appears that the program will be beneficial.

(h) $P(\text{reported injuries}) = \dfrac{289}{1,121} = 0.258$

(i) $P(\text{only property damage}) = \dfrac{641}{922} = 0.695$

(j) When accounting for the cause of the crash (rear-end vs. red-light running), the camera system does not reduce all types of accidents. Under the camera system, red-light running crashes decreased, but rear-end crashes increased.

(k) Recommendations may vary. The benefits of the decrease in red-light running crashes must be weighed against the negative of increased rear-end crashes. Seriousness of injuries and amount of property damage may need to be considered.

5.3 Assess Your Understanding (page 290)

1. independent

2. Multiplication

3. Addition

4. False

5. $P(E) \cdot P(F)$

6. 0

7. (a) Dependent   **(b)** Dependent
(c) Independent

8. (a) Independent   **(b)** Independent
(c) Dependent

9. $P(E \text{ and } F) = 0.18$

10. $P(E \text{ and } F) = 0.63$

11. $P(5 \text{ heads}) = \dfrac{1}{32} = 0.03125$; If we flipped a coin 5 times, one hundred different times, we'd expect to observe 5 heads in a row about 3 times.

12. $P(\text{tossing 4 ones in a row}) = \dfrac{1}{6^4} = 0.0008$. If a die is tossed, 0.08% of the time all 4 tosses will be 1.

13. $P(\text{two left-handed people are chosen}) = 0.0169$
$P(\text{at least one person chosen is right-handed}) = 0.9831$

14. (a) Knowing that Shawn won one of the lotteries would not affect his chance of winning the other.
(b) 0.0000000000000279

15. (a) $P(\text{all five are negative}) = 0.9752$
(b) $P(\text{at least one is positive}) = 0.0248$

16. (a) $P(\text{all 100 last}) = 0.6058$; **(b)** $P(\text{at least one burns out}) = 0.3942$

17. (a) $P(\text{two will live to 41 years}) = 0.99515$
(b) $P(\text{five will live to 41 years}) = 0.98791$
(c) $P(\text{at least one of five dies}) = 0.01209$; it would be unusual that at least one of the five dies before age 41.

18. (a) $P(\text{two will live to 41 years}) = 0.99710$
(b) $P(\text{five will live to 41 years}) = 0.99277$
(c) $P(\text{at least one of five dies}) = 0.00723$; it would be unusual that at least one of the five dies before age 41.

19. (a) $P(\text{two will have Rh}^- \text{ blood}) = 0.9801$
(b) $P(\text{six will have Rh+ blood}) = 0.9415$
(c) $P(\text{at least one of six will have Rh}^- \text{ blood}) = 0.0585$; it would not be unusual to select at least one Chinese person with Rh$^-$ blood.

20. (a) $P(\text{two inspectors do not identify low-quality timber}) = 0.04$
(b) Three inspectors should be hired to keep the probability of failing to identify low-quality timber at less than 1%.
(c) In repeated inspections of timbers, we expect both inspectors will fail to identify a low-quality timber about 4 times out of 100.

21. (a) $P(\text{one failure}) = 0.15$, not unusual; $P(\text{two failure}) = 0.0225$, unusual
(b) $P(\text{succeed}) = 1 - P(\text{fail}) = 1 - 0.0225 = 0.9775$
(c) 5 components

22. (a) $P(12 \text{ positive tests}) = 0.8864$
(b) $P(\text{at least one negative test}) = 0.1136$

23. (a) $P(\text{batter makes 10 consecutive outs}) = 0.02825$
(b) A cold streak would be unusual.
(c) In repeated sets of 10 consecutive at-bats, we expect the hitter to make an out in all 10 at-bats about 28 times out of 1,000.

24. $P(\text{makes eight consecutive free shots}) = 0.032$; it is unusual for the player to make eight consecutive free-throw shots.

25. (a) $P(\text{two strikes in a row}) = 0.09$
(b) $P(\text{turkey}) = 0.027$
(c) $P(\text{strike followed by nonstrike}) = 0.21$

26. (a) $P(\text{four Nascar fans}) = 0.1212$
(b) $P(\text{at least one non-Nascar fan}) = 0.8788$
(c) $P(\text{no one likes Nascar}) = 0.0283$
(d) $P(\text{at least one likes Nascar}) = 0.9717$

27. (a) $P(\text{all three have driven under the influence of alchohol}) = 0.0244$
(b) $P(\text{at least one has not driven under the influence of alcohol}) = 0.9756$
(c) $P(\text{none has driven under the influence of alcohol}) = 0.3579$
(d) $P(\text{at least one has driven under the influence of alcohol}) = 0.6421$

28. $P(\text{at least 1}) = 0.9999$; answers will vary.

29. (a) $P(\text{audit}) = 0.0177$, unusual
(b) $P(\text{both audited}) = 0.000313$
(c) $P(\text{neither audited}) = 0.9649$
(d) $P(\text{at least one audited}) = 1 - P(\text{neither audited}) = 1 - 0.9649 = 0.0351$

30. (a) $P(\text{all 4 visited a casino}) = 0.0033$; this would be unusual.
(b) $P(\text{all 4 not visited a casino}) = 0.3336$; this would not be unusual.

31. (a) No; the two events can happen at the same time. That is, an adult male can bet on professional sports.
(b) $P(\text{male and bets on professional sports}) = 0.0823$
(c) $P(\text{male or bets on professional sports}) = 0.5717$
(d) The independence assumption is not correct.
(e) $P(\text{male or bets on professional sports}) = 0.548$

32. (a) $\left(\dfrac{1}{2}\right)^{24} \approx 5.96 \times 10^{-8}$

(b) $\left(\dfrac{1}{2}\right)^{36} \approx 1.46 \times 10^{-11}$

5.4 Assess Your Understanding (page 298)

1. F occurring; E has occurred

2. No

3. $P(F|E) = 0.75$ **4.** $P(F|E) = 0.525$

5. $P(F|E) = 0.568$ **6.** $P(F|E) = 0.411$

7. $P(E \text{ and } F) = 0.32$ **8.** $P(E \text{ and } F) = 0.24$

9. The events are not independent.

10. The events are not independent.

11. $P(\text{club}) = \dfrac{1}{4}$; $P(\text{club}|\text{black card}) = \dfrac{1}{2}$

12. $P(\text{king}) = \dfrac{1}{13}$; $P(\text{king}|\text{heart}) = \dfrac{1}{13}$; no; independent

13. $P(\text{rainy}|\text{cloudy}) = \dfrac{0.21}{0.37} = 0.568$

14. $P(\text{cancer death}|25 \text{ to } 34 \text{ years old}) = \dfrac{5}{57} = 0.088$

15. $P(\text{white}|16 \text{ to } 17 \text{ years old}) = \dfrac{0.062}{0.084} = 0.738$

16. $P(>\$75,000|\text{live in Northeast}) = \dfrac{0.044}{0.191} = 0.230$

17. (a) $P(\text{no health insurance}|\text{under 18 years of age}) = 0.110$
(b) $P(\text{under 18 years of age}|\text{no health insurance}) = 0.184$

18. (a) $P(\text{former cigar smoker}|\text{died from cancer}) = 0.090$
(b) $P(\text{died from cancer}|\text{former cigar smoker}) = 0.012$

19. (a) $P(\text{passenger}|\text{female}) = \dfrac{2,448}{5,747} = 0.426$

(b) $P(\text{female}|\text{passenger}) = \dfrac{816}{1,681} = 0.485$

(c) Since $P(\text{male}|\text{driving}) = 0.759$ and $P(\text{female}|\text{driving}) = 0.241$, the victim is more likely to be male.

20. (a) $P(\text{HS graduate}|\text{never married}) = 0.303$
(b) $P(\text{never married}|\text{a HS graduate}) = 0.157$

21. $P(\text{both TVs work}) = 0.4$; $P(\text{at least one TV doesn't work}) = 0.6$

22. $P(\text{two women are chosen}) = \dfrac{2}{7} = 0.286$

23. (a) $P(\text{first card is a king and the second card is a king}) = \dfrac{1}{221} = 0.005$

   (b) $P(\text{first card is a king and the second card is a king}) = \dfrac{1}{169} = 0.006$

24. (a) $P(\text{first card is a club and the second card is a club}) = \dfrac{1}{17} = 0.059$

   (b) $P(\text{first card is a club and the second card is a club}) = \dfrac{1}{16} = 0.0625$

25. $P(\text{Dave and then Neta are chosen}) = \dfrac{1}{20} = 0.05$

26. $P(\text{Yolanda hosts, then Lorrie hosts the parties}) = \dfrac{1}{20} = 0.05$

27. (a) $P(\text{like both songs}) = \dfrac{5}{39} = 0.128$; it is not unusual to like both songs.

   (b) $P(\text{like neither song}) = \dfrac{14}{39} = 0.359$

   (c) $P(\text{like exactly one song}) = \dfrac{20}{39} = 0.513$

   (d) $P(\text{like both songs}) = \dfrac{25}{169} = 0.148$;

   $P(\text{like neither song}) = \dfrac{64}{169} = 0.379$;

   $P(\text{like exactly one song}) = \dfrac{80}{169} = 0.473$

28. (a) $P(\text{both are diet soda}) = \dfrac{1}{22} = 0.0455$

   (b) $P(\text{both are regular soda}) = \dfrac{6}{11} = 0.545$; it is not unusual to choose two regular sodas.

   (c) $P(\text{one regular and one diet soda}) = \dfrac{9}{22} = 0.409$.

29.

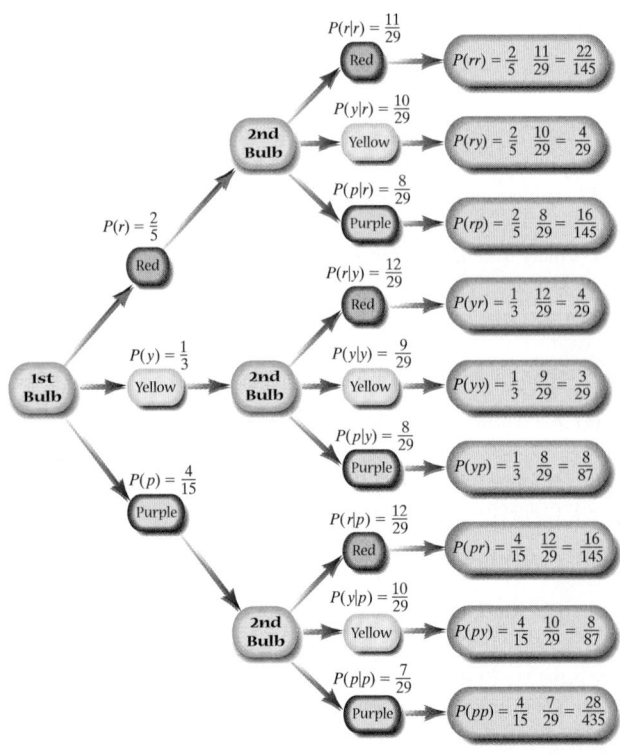

(a) $P(\text{two red bulbs}) = \dfrac{22}{145} = 0.152$

(b) $P(\text{first a red and then a yellow bulb}) = \dfrac{4}{29} = 0.138$

(c) $P(\text{first a yellow and then a red bulb}) = \dfrac{4}{29} = 0.138$

(d) $P(\text{a red bulb and a yellow bulb}) = \dfrac{8}{29} = 0.276$

30.

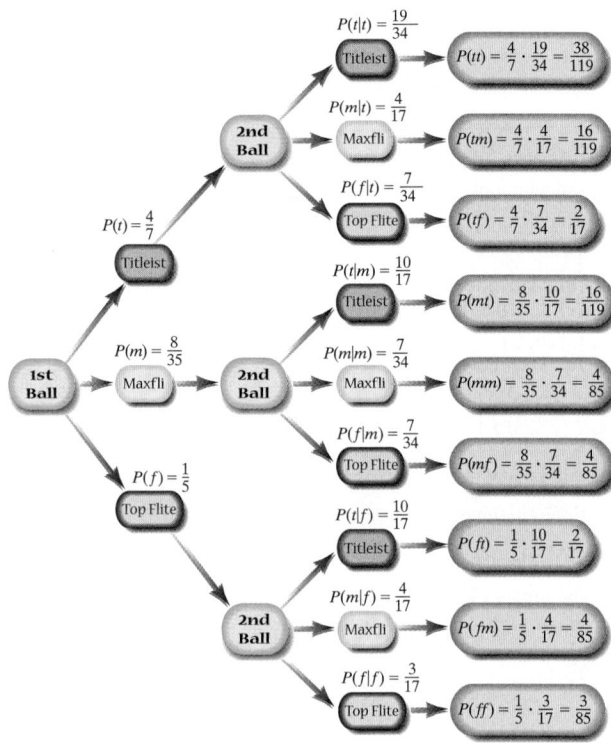

(a) $P(\text{two Titleists}) = \dfrac{38}{119} = 0.319$

(b) $P(\text{first a Titleist and then a Maxfli}) = \dfrac{16}{119} = 0.134$

(c) $P(\text{first a Maxfli and then a Titleist}) = \dfrac{16}{119} = 0.134$

(d) $P(\text{a Maxfli and a Titleist}) = \dfrac{32}{119} = 0.269$

31. $P(\text{female and smokes}) = 0.070$; it would not be unusual to randomly select a female who smokes.

32. $P(\text{male and holds multiple jobs}) = 0.026$; it would be unusual to randomly select an employed male who has more than one job.

33. (a) $P(\text{10 people each have a different birthday}) = 0.883$
   (b) $P(\text{at least two of the ten people have the same birthday}) = 0.117$

34. $P(\text{at least 2 people in a group of 23 share the same birthday}) = 0.507$

35. (a) Yes; $P(\text{male}) = \dfrac{1}{2} = P(\text{male}|0 \text{ activities}) = \dfrac{1}{2}$

   (b) No; $P(\text{female}) = \dfrac{1}{2} \neq P(\text{female}|5{-}7 \text{ activities}) = \dfrac{71}{109} = 0.651$

   (c) Yes; $P(1{-}2 \text{ activities and } 3{-}4 \text{ activities}) = 0$
   (d) No; $P(\text{male and } 1{-}2 \text{ activities}) = 0.2025 \neq 0$

36. (a) No; $P(\text{Republican}) = 0.55 \neq P(\text{Republican}|30{-}44) = 0.470$
   (b) Yes: $P(\text{Democrat}) = 0.45 = P(\text{Democrat}|65+) = 0.45$
   (c) Yes; $P(17{-}29 \text{ and } 45{-}64) = 0$
   (d) No; $P(\text{Republican and } 45{-}64) = 0.269 \neq 0$

37. (a) $P(\text{being dealt five clubs}) = 0.000495$
   (b) $P(\text{being dealt a flush}) = 0.002$

38. P(being dealt a royal flush) $= 0.00000154$

39. (a) P(two defective chips) $= 0.0000245$
  (b) Assuming independence: P(two defective chips) $= 0.000025$

40. (a) P(first is Roger Cummings; second is Rick Whittingham) $= 2.37 \times 10^{-8}$
  (b) P(first is Rick Whittingham; second is Roger Cummings) $= 2.37 \times 10^{-8}$

41. $P(<18$ years old$) = 0.239$; $P(<18$ years old$|$no health insurance$) = 0.184$; the events are not independent.

42. P(died from cancer) $= 0.007$; P(died from cancer$|$current cigar smoker) $= 0.018$; the events "died from cancer" and "smoking cigars" are not independent.

43. P(female) $= 0.307$; P(female$|$driver) $= 0.241$; no, P(female) $\neq P$(female$|$driver)

44. P(divorced) $= 0.117$; P(divorced$|$graduated from college) $= 0.102$; the events "being divorced" and "graduated from college" are not independent.

5.5 Assess Your Understanding (page 312)

1. permutation   **2.** combination   **3.** True

4. In a permutation the order in which the objects are chosen matters; in a combination the order in which the objects are chosen is unimportant.

5. $5! = 120$ **6.** $7! = 5040$ **7.** $10! = 3{,}628{,}800$

8. $12! = 479{,}001{,}600$ **9.** $0! = 1$ **10.** $1! = 1$

11. $_6P_2 = 30$ **12.** $_7P_2 = 42$ **13.** $_4P_4 = 24$

14. $_7P_7 = 5040$ **15.** $_5P_0 = 1$ **16.** $_4P_0 = 1$

17. $_8P_3 = 336$ **18.** $_9P_4 = 3024$ **19.** $_8C_3 = 56$

20. $_9C_2 = 36$ **21.** $_{10}C_2 = 45$ **22.** $_{12}C_3 = 220$

23. $_{52}C_1 = 52$ **24.** $_{40}C_{40} = 1$ **25.** $_{48}C_3 = 17{,}296$

26. $_{30}C_4 = 27{,}405$

27. $ab, ac, ad, ae, ba, bc, bd, be, ca, cb, cd, ce, da, db, dc, de, ea, eb, ec, ed$; $_5P_2 = 20$

28. $ab, ac, ad, ba, bc, bd, ca, cb, cd, da, db, dc$; $_4P_2 = 12$

29. $ab, ac, ad, ae, bc, bd, be, cd, ce, de$; $_5C_2 = 10$

30. ab, ac, ad, bc, bd, cd; $_4C_2 = 6$

31. He can wear 24 different shirt-and-tie combinations.

32. She can wear 15 different outfits.

33. Dan can arrange the songs $12! = 479{,}001{,}600$ ways.

34. Fifteen students can be lined up $15! = 1.30767 \times 10^{12}$ ways.

35. The salesperson can take $8! = 40{,}320$ different routes.

36. The 10 songs can be played $10! = 3{,}628{,}800$ ways.

37. At most 18,278 companies can be listed on the NYSE.

38. At most 12,338,352 companies can be listed on the NASDAQ.

39. (a) 10,000 different codes are possible.
  (b) P(correct code is guessed) $= \dfrac{1}{10{,}000}$

40. (a) 10^9 different Social Security numbers are possible.
  (b) P(guessing the president's Social Security number) $= \dfrac{1}{10^9}$

41. $26^8 = 2.09 \times 10^{11}$ different user names are possible.

42. $10 \cdot 26^7 = 8.03 \times 10^{10}$ additional user names are possible.

43. (a) There are $50^3 = 125{,}000$ lock combinations.
  (b) P(guessing the correct combination) $= \dfrac{1}{50^3} = \dfrac{1}{125{,}000}$

44. There are $26 \cdot 10^5 = 2{,}600{,}000$ different license plates.

45. The top three cars can finish in $_{40}P_3 = 59{,}280$ ways.

46. The top two horses can finish in $_{10}P_2 = 90$ ways.

47. The officers can be chosen in $_{20}P_4 = 116{,}280$ ways.

48. $_{50}P_4 = 5{,}527{,}200$ different leadership structures are possible.

49. There are $_{25}P_4 = 303{,}600$ possible outcomes.

50. There are $_{21}C_9 = 293{,}930$ possible committee structures.

51. There are $_{50}C_5 = 2{,}118{,}760$ possible simple random samples of size 5.

52. There are $_{100}C_7 = 1.60076 \times 10^{10}$ possible simple random samples of size 7.

53. $_6C_2 = 15$ different birth and gender orders are possible.

54. $_8C_3 = 56$ different birth and gender orders are possible.

55. $\dfrac{10!}{3! \cdot 2! \cdot 2! \cdot 3!} = 25{,}200$ different sequences are possible.

56. $\dfrac{12!}{1! \cdot 4! \cdot 3! \cdot 4!} = 138{,}600$ different sequences are possible.

57. The trees can be planted $\dfrac{11!}{4! \cdot 5! \cdot 2!} = 6{,}930$ different ways.

58. $\dfrac{9!}{3! \cdot 4!} = 2{,}520$ different batting orders are possible.

59. P(winning) $= \dfrac{1}{_{39}C_5} = \dfrac{1}{575{,}757}$

60. P(winning) $= \dfrac{1}{_{56}C_5 \cdot 46} = 0.0000000057$

61. (a) P(jury has only students) $= \dfrac{1}{153} = 0.0065$
  (b) P(jury has only faculty) $= \dfrac{1}{34} = 0.0294$
  (c) P(jury has two students and three faculty) $= \dfrac{20}{51} = 0.3922$

62. (a) P(committee is all Democrats) $= 0.0127$
  (b) P(committee is all Republicans) $= 0.0028$
  (c) P(committee has three Democrats and four Republicans) $= 0.2442$

63. P(shipment is rejected) $= 0.1283$

64. P(selecting two 60-watt light bulbs) $= 0.3517$

65. (a) P(you like 2 of 4 songs) $= 0.3916$
  (b) P(you like 3 of 4 songs) $= 0.1119$
  (c) P(you like all 4 songs) $= 0.0070$

66. (a) P(2 of the 3 cans are diet soda) $= 0.1227$
  (b) P(1 of the 3 cans is diet soda) $= 0.4909$
  (c) P(all 3 cans are diet soda) $= 0.0045$

67. (a) Five cards can be selected from a deck $_{52}C_5 = 2{,}598{,}960$ ways.
  (b) Three of the same card can be chosen $13 \cdot {}_4C_3 = 52$ ways.
  (c) The remaining two cards can be chosen $_{12}C_2 \cdot {}_4C_1 \cdot {}_4C_1 = 1{,}056$ ways.
  (d) P(three of a kind) $= \dfrac{52 \cdot 1056}{2{,}598{,}960} = 0.0211$

68. (a) Five cards can be selected from a deck $_{52}C_5 = 2{,}598{,}960$ ways.
  (b) Two of the same card can be chosen $13 \cdot {}_4C_2 = 78$ ways.
  (c) The remaining three cards can be chosen $_{12}C_3 \cdot {}_4C_1 \cdot {}_4C_1 \cdot {}_4C_1 = 14{,}080$ ways.
  (d) P(two of a kind) $= \dfrac{78 \cdot 14{,}080}{2{,}598{,}960} = 0.4226$

69. P(all 4 modems tested worked) $= 0.4912$

70. P(all 5 TVs tested worked) $= 0.7291$

71. (a) $21 \cdot 5 \cdot 21 \cdot 21 \cdot 5 \cdot 21 \cdot 10 \cdot 10 = 486{,}202{,}500$ passwords are possible.
  (b) $42 \cdot 10 \cdot 42 \cdot 42 \cdot 10 \cdot 42 \cdot 10 \cdot 10 = 420^4 \approx 3.11 \times 10^{10}$ passwords are possible.

5.6 Assess Your Understanding (page 319)

1. A permutation is an arrangement in which order matters; a combination is an arrangement in which order does not matter.

2. The empirical method assigns probabilities using relative frequencies.

3. AND is generally associated with multiplication; OR is generally associated with addition.

4. P(seven) $\approx \dfrac{350}{1{,}000} = 0.35$ **5.** $P(E) = \dfrac{4}{10} = 0.4$

6. $P(F) = \dfrac{3}{10} = 0.3$

7. $abc, acb, abd, adb, abe, aeb, acd, adc, ace, aec, ade, aed, bac, bca, bad, bda, bae, bea, bcd, bdc, bce, bec, bde, bed, cde, ced, cab, cba, cad, cda, cae, cea, cbd, cdb, cde, ced, dab, dba, dac, dca, dae, dea, dbc, dcb, dbe, deb, dce, dec, eab, eba, eac, eca, ead, eda, ebc, ecb, ebd, edb, ecd, edc$

8. $P(E$ or $F) = 0.7 + 0.2 = 0.9$

9. $P(E \text{ or } F) = 0.7 + 0.2 - 0.15 = 0.75$

10. $\dfrac{6!2!}{4!} = 60$ **11.** $_7P_3 = 210$ **12.** $_9C_4 = 126$

13. $P(E \text{ and } F) = P(E) \cdot P(F) = 0.4$

14. $P(F|E) = \dfrac{P(E \text{ and } F)}{P(E)} = \dfrac{4}{9} = 0.444$

15. $P(E \text{ and } F) = P(E) \cdot P(F|E) = 0.27$

16. abc, abd, abe, acd, ace, ade, bcd, bce, bde, cde

17. $\dfrac{22}{500} = 0.044$

18. (a)

Duration of Vacancy	Probability
Less than 1 month	0.21
1 to 2 months	0.19
2 to 4 months	0.225
4 to 6 months	0.15
6 to 12 months	0.12
1 to 2 years	0.065
2 years or more	0.04

   (b) It is unusual for an apartment to remain vacant for 2 years or more.
   (c) $P(1 \text{ to } 4 \text{ months}) = 0.19 + 0.225 = 0.415$
   (d) $P(\text{less than 2 years}) = 1 - P(2 \text{ years or more}) = 1 - 0.04 = 0.96$

19. There are $3 \cdot 3 \cdot 2 \cdot 2 \cdot 1 \cdot 1 = 36$ ways to arrange the three men and three women.

20. (a) $_{10}C_5 = 252$ different lineups are possible.
   (b) Select the goalie first, then four fielders from the remaining 9 players (the one not selected as goalie can play on the field). $2 \cdot (_9C_4) = 252$ different lineups are possible.

21. (a) $P(\text{survived}) = \dfrac{711}{2{,}224} = 0.320$

   (b) $P(\text{female}) = \dfrac{425}{2{,}224} = 0.191$

   (c) $P(\text{female or child}) = \dfrac{534}{2{,}224} = 0.240$

   (d) $P(\text{female and survived}) = \dfrac{316}{2{,}224} = 0.142$

   (e) $P(\text{female or survived}) = \dfrac{820}{2{,}224} = 0.369$

   (f) $P(\text{survived}|\text{female}) = \dfrac{316}{425} = 0.744$

   (g) $P(\text{survived}|\text{child}) = \dfrac{57}{109} = 0.523$

   (h) $P(\text{survived}|\text{male}) = \dfrac{338}{1{,}690} = 0.2.$

   (i) Yes, the survival rate was much higher for women and children.
   (j) $P(\text{both females survived}) = \dfrac{316}{425} \cdot \dfrac{315}{424} = 0.552$

22. (a) $P(\text{all 4 users}) = (0.17)^4 = 0.00084$
   (b) $P(\text{at least 1 user}) = 1 - P(\text{no users}) = 1 - (0.83)^4 = 0.525$

23. Shawn can fill out the report in $_{12}C_3 = 220$ different ways.

24. (a) $P(\text{junior}) = \dfrac{112}{449} = 0.249$ **(b)** $P(\text{senior}|\text{NHS}) = \dfrac{37}{87} = 0.425$

25. (a) $P(\text{win both}) = \dfrac{1}{5.2 \times 10^6} \cdot \dfrac{1}{705{,}600} = 0.00000000000027$

   (b) $P(\text{win Jubilee twice}) = \left(\dfrac{1}{705{,}600}\right)^2 = 0.000000000002$

26. (a) $6! = 720$ different arrangements are possible using all 6 letters.
   (b) $_6P_4 = 360$ different arrangements are possible using only 4 letters.

   (c) $P(\text{six-letter word}) = \dfrac{3}{720} = \dfrac{1}{240} = 0.0042$

27. $P(\text{parent owns}|\text{teenager owns}) = \dfrac{0.220}{0.51} = 0.431$

28. Jim is using subjective probability.

29. $_{12}C_8 = 495$ different sets of questions can be answered.

30. Todd could put together $_{12}P_9 = 79{,}833{,}600$ different exercise routines.

31. $2 \cdot 3 \cdot 2 \cdot 8 \cdot 2 = 192$ different Elantras are possible.

32. (a) $P(\text{on Lingo board}) = \dfrac{15}{21} = \dfrac{5}{7} = 0.714$

   (b) $P(\text{stopper}) = \dfrac{3}{21} = \dfrac{1}{7} = 0.143$

   (c) $P(\text{LINGO on first}) = 0$ (there is no way to get 5 in a row with only 1 ball)

   (d) $P(\text{LINGO on 2nd}) = \dfrac{6}{21} \cdot \dfrac{1}{20} = \dfrac{1}{70} = 0.0143$

Chapter 5 Review Exercises (page 322)

1. (a) Possible probabilities are $0, 0.75, 0.41$.
   (b) Possible probabilities are $\dfrac{2}{5}, \dfrac{1}{3}, \dfrac{6}{7}$.

2. $P(E) = \dfrac{1}{5} = 0.2$ **3.** $P(F) = \dfrac{2}{5} = 0.4$

4. $P(E) = \dfrac{3}{5} = 0.6$ **5.** $P(E^c) = \dfrac{4}{5} = 0.8$

6. $P(E \text{ or } F) = 0.89$ **7.** $P(E \text{ or } F) = 0.48$

8. $P(E \text{ and } F) = 0.09$

9. Events E and F are not independent because $P(E \text{ and } F) \neq P(E) \cdot P(F)$.

10. $P(E \text{ and } F) = 0.2655$ **11.** $P(E|F) = 0.5$

12. (a) $7! = 5{,}040$ **(b)** $0! = 1$ **(c)** $_9C_4 = 126$
    (d) $_{10}C_3 = 120$ **(e)** $_9P_2 = 72$ **(f)** $_{12}P_4 = 11{,}880$

13. (a) $P(\text{green}) = \dfrac{1}{19} = 0.0526$; there is a 5.26% probability that the next spin will end with the ball in a green slot.

   (b) $P(\text{green or red}) = \dfrac{10}{19} = 0.5263$; there is a 52.63% probability that the next spin will end with the ball in either a green slot or a red slot.

   (c) $P(00 \text{ or red}) = \dfrac{19}{38} = 0.5$; there is a 50% probability that the next spin will end with the ball either in 00 or in a red slot.

   (d) $P(31 \text{ and black}) = 0$; this is called an impossible event.

14. (a) $P(\text{fatality was alcohol related}) = \dfrac{193}{454} = 0.425$

   (b) $P(\text{fatality was not alcohol related}) = \dfrac{261}{454} = 0.575$

   (c) $P(\text{both fatalities were alcohol related}) = 0.181$
   (d) $P(\text{neither fatality was alcohol related}) = 0.330$
   (e) $P(\text{at least one fatality was alcohol related}) = 0.670$

15. (a)

Class of Worker	Probability
Private wage and salary worker	0.7944
Government worker	0.1422
Self-employed worker	0.0616
Unpaid family worker	0.0018

   (b) It is unusual for a Memphis worker to be an unpaid family worker.
   (c) It is not unusual for a Memphis worker to be self-employed.

16. (a) $P(\text{baby was postterm}) = 0.058$
   (b) $P(\text{baby weighed 3,000 to 3,999 grams}) = 0.656$
   (c) $P(\text{baby weighed 3,000 to 3,999 grams and was postterm}) = 0.042$
   (d) $P(\text{baby weighed 3,000 to 3,999 grams or was postterm}) = 0.672$
   (e) $P(\text{baby weighed} < 1{,}000 \text{ grams and was postterm}) = 0.000004$; this event is not impossible.
   (f) $P(\text{baby weighed 3,000 to 3,999 grams}|\text{baby was postterm}) = 0.722$
   (g) The events "postterm baby" and "weighs 3,000 to 3,999 grams" are not independent.

17. (a) $P(\text{complaint settled}) = 0.722$
   (b) $P(\text{complaint not settled}) = 0.278$
   (c) $P(\text{all five complaints settled}) = 0.196$
   (d) $P(\text{at least one of five complaints not settled}) = 0.804$
   (e) $P(\text{none of five complaints settled}) = 0.002$
   (f) $P(\text{at least one of five complaints settled}) = 0.998$

18. $P(\text{matching the three winning numbers}) = 0.001$

19. $P(\text{matching the four winning numbers}) = 0.0001$

20. $P(\text{drawing three aces}) = 0.00018$

21. $26^2 \cdot 10^4 = 6,760,000$ different license plates can be formed.

22. The students can be seated in $_{10}P_4 = 5,040$ different arrangements.

23. There are $\dfrac{10!}{4! \cdot 3! \cdot 2!} = 12,600$ different vertical arrangements of the flags.

24. There are $_{55}C_8 = 1,217,566,350$ possible simple random samples.

25. $P(\text{winning Pick 5}) = \dfrac{1}{_{35}C_5} = 0.000003$

26. **(a)** $P(\text{three Merlot}) = 0.0455$ **(b)** $P(\text{two Merlot}) = 0.3182$
(c) $P(\text{no Merlot}) = 0.1591$

27. Answers will vary, but should be reasonably close to $\dfrac{1}{38}$ to part (a) and $\dfrac{1}{19}$ for part (b).

28. Answers will vary. Subjective probability, is based on personal experience or intuition (e.g., "There is a 70% chance that the Packers will make it to the NFL playoffs in 2012.")

29. **(a)** There are 13 clubs in the deck.
(b) Thirty-seven cards remain in the deck. Forty-one cards are not known by you. Eight of the unknown cards are clubs.
(c) $P(\text{next card dealt is a club}) = \dfrac{8}{41}$
(d) $P(\text{two clubs in a row}) = 0.0341$
(e) No

30. **(a)** $P(\text{home run to left field}) = \dfrac{34}{70} = 0.486$; there is a 48.6% probability that a randomly selected home run by McGwire went to left field.
(b) $P(\text{home run to right field}) = 0$
(c) No; it was not impossible for McGwire to hit a home run to right field. He just never did it.

31. Someone winning a lottery twice is not that unlikely considering millions of people play lotteries (sometimes more than one) each week, and many lotteries have multiple drawings each week.

32. **(a)** $P(\text{Bryce}) = \dfrac{119}{1,009} = 0.118$; not unusual.
(b) $P(\text{Gourmet}) = \dfrac{264}{1,009} = 0.262$
(c) $P(\text{Mallory}|\text{Single Cup}) = \dfrac{3}{25} = 0.12$
(d) $P(\text{Bryce}|\text{Gourmet}) = \dfrac{3}{88} = 0.034$; yes, this is unusual.
(e) While it is not unusual for Bryce to sell a case, it is unusual for him to sell a Gourmet case.
(f) No; $P(\text{Mallory}) = \dfrac{186}{1,009} \neq P(\text{Mallory}|\text{Filter}) = \dfrac{1}{3}$.
(g) No; $P(\text{Paige and Gourmet}) = \dfrac{42}{1,009} \neq 0$.

Chapter 5 Test (page 324)

1. Possible probabilities are $0.23, 0, \dfrac{3}{4}$.

2. $P(\text{Jason}) = \dfrac{1}{5}$ **3.** $P(\text{Chris or Elaine}) = \dfrac{2}{5}$ **4.** $P(E^c) = \dfrac{4}{5}$

5. **(a)** $P(E \text{ or } F) = P(E) + P(F) = 0.59$
(b) $P(E \text{ and } F) = P(E) \cdot P(F) = 0.0814$

6. **(a)** $P(E \text{ and } F) = P(E) \cdot P(F|E) = 0.105$
(b) $P(E \text{ or } F) = P(E) + P(F) - P(E \text{ and } F) = 0.495$
(c) $P(E|F) = \dfrac{P(E \text{ and } F)}{P(F)} = \dfrac{7}{30} = 0.233$
(d) No; $P(E) = 0.15 \neq P(E|F) = 0.233$.

7. **(a)** $8! = 40,320$ **(b)** $_{12}C_6 = 924$ **(c)** $_{14}P_8 = 121,080,960$

8. **(a)** $P(7 \text{ or } 11) = \dfrac{8}{36} = \dfrac{2}{9} = 0.222$; there is a 22.2% probability that the player will win on the first roll.

(b) $P(2, 3, \text{ or } 12) = \dfrac{4}{36} = \dfrac{1}{9} = 0.111$; there is a 11.1% probability that the player will lose on the first roll.

9. $P(\text{structure}) = 0.32$; $P(\text{not in a structure}) = 1 - P(\text{structure}) = 0.68$

10. **(a)** All the probabilities are greater than or equal to zero and less than or equal to one, and the sum of the probabilities is 1.
(b) $P(\text{a peanut butter cookie}) = 0.24$
(c) $P(\text{next box sold is mint, caramel, or shortbread}) = 0.53$
(d) $P(\text{next box sold is not mint}) = 0.75$

11. **(a)** $P(\text{gold}) = 0.383$
(b) $P(\text{Russia won medal}) = 0.136$
(c) $P(\text{gold and Russia won}) = 0.049$
(d) $P(\text{gold or Russia won}) = 0.469$
(e) $P(\text{Sweden won}|\text{bronze}) = 0.106$
(f) $P(\text{bronze}|\text{Sweden won}) = 0.357$

12. **(a)** $P(\text{win two in a row}) = 0.352$
(b) $P(\text{win seven in a row}) = 0.026$
(c) $P(\text{lose at least one of next seven}) = 1 - P(\text{win seven in a row}) = 0.974$

13. $P(\text{shipment accepted}) = 0.8$

14. There are $6! = 720$ different arrangements of the letters LINCEY.

15. $_{29}C_5 = 118,755$ different subcommittees can be formed.

16. $P(\text{winning Cash 5}) = \dfrac{1}{_{43}C_5} = \dfrac{1}{962,598} = 0.00000104$

17. $26 \cdot 36^7 = 2.04 \times 10^{12}$ different passwords are possible.

18. It would take 679,156 seconds (about 7.9 days) to generate all the passwords.

19. Subjective probability was used. It is not possible to repeat probability experiments to estimate the probability of life on Mars.

20. $\dfrac{15!}{2! \cdot 4! \cdot 4! \cdot 5!} = 9,459,450$ different sequences are possible.

21. $P(\text{guessing correctly}) = \dfrac{9}{40} = 0.225$

CHAPTER 6 Discrete Probability Distributions

6.1 Assess Your Understanding (page 339)

1. A random variable is a numerical measure of the outcome of a probability experiment.

2. A discrete random variable has either a finite number of values or a countable number of values. A continuous random variable has an infinite number of values that can be represented as an interval on a number line.

3. Each probability must be between 0 and 1, inclusive, and the sum of the probabilities must equal 1.

4. Answers will vary. One possibility: The mean of a discrete random variable can be thought of as the mean outcome when a probability experiment is repeated a large number of times.

5. Probability represents long term behavior. A batting average of 0.300 means that the probability of the player's getting a hit at any at-bat is 0.3, despite the results of previous at-bats. No, the player is not due to make an out.

6. In the long run, a player's mean gain (loss) is zero.

7. **(a)** Discrete, $x = 0, 1, 2, \ldots, 20$ **(b)** Continuous, $t > 0$
(c) Discrete, $x = 0, 1, 2, \ldots$ **(d)** Continuous, $s \geq 0$

8. **(a)** Continuous, $t > 0$ **(b)** Continuous, $w > 0$
(c) Discrete, $x = 1, 2, \ldots$ **(d)** Discrete, $x = 0, 1, 2, \ldots, 20$

9. **(a)** Continuous, $r \geq 0$ **(b)** Discrete, $x = 0, 1, 2, 3, \ldots$
(c) Discrete, $x = 0, 1, 2, 3, \ldots$ **(d)** Continuous, $t > 0$

10. **(a)** Discrete, $x = 0, 1, 2, 3, \ldots$ **(b)** Continuous, $d > 0$
(c) Discrete, $x = 0, 1, 2, 3, \ldots$ **(d)** Continuous, $a > 0$

11. Yes, it is a probability distribution.

12. Yes, it is a probability distribution.

13. No, $P(50) < 0$.

14. Yes, it is a probability distribution.

15. No, $\Sigma P(x) \neq 1$ **16.** No, $\Sigma P(x) \neq 1$

17. $P(4) = 0.3$ **18.** $P(2) = 0.15$

19. (a) Each probability is between 0 and 1, inclusive, and the sum of the probabilities equals 1.

(b)

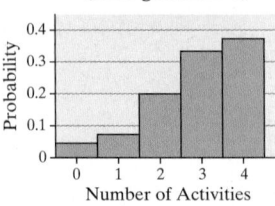

Parental Involvement
in School
(child grades K–5)

(c) $\mu_X = 2.9$ activities; on average, parents of K–5 graders are involved in 2.9 activities.
(d) $\sigma_X^2 = 1.2$ activities^2 **(e)** $\sigma_X = 1.1$ activities
(f) $P(3) = 0.320$ **(g)** $P(3 \text{ or } 4) = 0.694$

20. (a) Each probability is between 0 and 1, inclusive, and the sum of the probabilities equals 1.

(b)

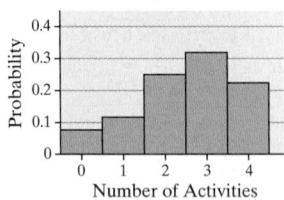

Parental Involvement
in School
(child grades 6–8)

(c) $\mu_X = 2.5$ activities; on average, parents of 6–8 graders are involved in 2.5 activities.
(d) $\sigma_X^2 = 1.4$ activities^2 **(e)** $\sigma_X = 1.2$ activities
(f) $P(3) = 0.322$ **(g)** $P(3 \text{ or } 4) = 0.552$

21. (a) Each probability is between 0 and 1, inclusive, and the sum of the probabilities equals 1.

(b)

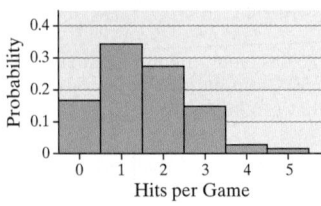

Ichiro's Hit Parade

(c) $\mu_X = 1.6$ hits; over many games, Ichiro is expected to average about 1.6 hits per game.
(d) $\sigma_X = 1.2$ hits   **(e)** $P(2) = 0.2857$
(f) $P(X > 1) = 0.4969$

22. (a) All probabilities are between 0 and 1, inclusive, and the sum of the probabilities is 1.

(b)

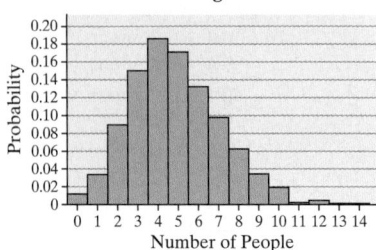

Waiting in Line

(c) $\mu_X = 4.9$ people; In the long run, the average number of people waiting in line during lunch is 4.9.
(d) $\sigma_X^2 = 5.0$ people^2 **(e)** $\sigma_X = 2.2$ people
(f) $P(8) = 0.063$ **(g)** $P(X \geq 10) = 0.029$; yes, this would be unusual

23. (a)

x (games played)	P(x)
4	0.2024
5	0.1905
6	0.2143
7	0.3929

(b)

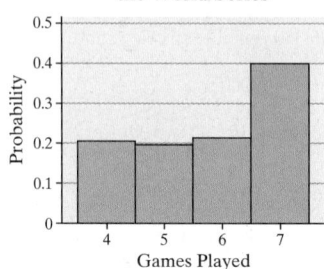

Games Played in
the World Series

(c) $\mu_X = 5.8$ games; the World Series, if played many times, would be expected to last about 5.8 games, on average.
(d) $\sigma_X = 1.2$ games

24. (a)

x (age)	P(x)
11	0.1471
12	0.1765
13	0.2059
14	0.1176
15	0.1471
16	0.0882
17	0.1176

(b)

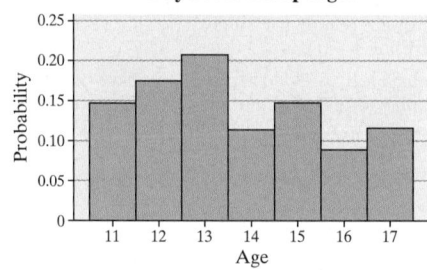

Boy Scout Troup Ages

(c) $\mu_X = 13.7$ years; the average age of the boys scouts in the troup is 13.7 years.
(d) $\sigma_X = 1.9$ years

25. (a)

x (number of children)	P(x)
0	0.0111
1	0.0333
2	0.5778
3	0.2778
4	0.0778
5	0.0189
6	0.0033

(b)

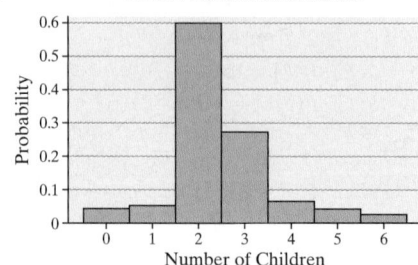

Ideal Number of Children

(c) 2.4; the mean ideal number of children for adult Americans is 2.4.
(d) 0.8

26. (a)

x (grade level)	P(x)
9	0.2481
10	0.2548
11	0.2587
12	0.2384

(b)

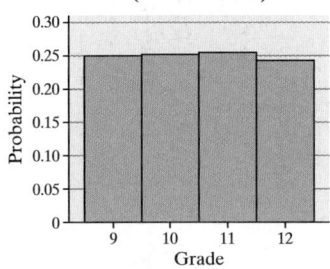

High School Enrollment (October 2005)

(c) $\mu_X = 10.5$; the average grade level for all students enrolled in high school in the United States in October 2005 was 10.5.
(d) $\sigma_X = 1.1$

27. (a) $P(4) = 0.128$
(b) $P(4 \text{ or } 5) = 0.188$
(c) $P(X \geq 6) = 0.102$
(d) $\mu_X = 2.8$ children; we would expect the mother to have had 2.8 children, on average.

28. (a) $P(5) = 0.233$
(b) $P(5 \text{ or } 6) = 0.341$
(c) $P(7, 8, \text{ or } 9) = 0.055$
(d) $\mu_X = 4.3$ rooms; we would expect a rental unit to have 4.3 rooms, on average.

29. $E(X) = \$86.00$; the insurance company expects to make an average profit of $86.00 on every 20-year-old female it insures for 1 year.

30. $E(X) = \$33.50$; the insurance company expects to earn an average profit of $33.50 on every 20-year-old male it insures for 1 year.

31. The expected profit is $12,000.

32. The expected profit is $15,000.

33. $E(X) = -\$0.26$; if you played 1,000 times, you would expect to lose about $260.

34. $E(X) = -\$0.42$; if the lottery is played many times, a player expects to lose $0.42 per ticket.

35. (a) The expected cash prize is $0.30. After paying $1.00 to play, your expected profit is −$0.70.
(b) A grand prize of $118,000,000 has an expected profit greater than zero.
(c) The size of the grand prize does not affect the chance of winning provided the probabilities remain constant.

36. (a) A student who guesses will expect zero points.
(b) Answers will vary.

37. Answers will vary. The simulations illustrate the Law of Large Numbers.

38. Answers will vary. The simulations illustrate the Law of Large Numbers.

6.2 Assess Your Understanding (page 354)

1. An experiment is binomial provided:
   1. The experiment consists of a fixed number, n, of trials.
   2. The trials are independent.
   3. Each trial has two possible mutually exclusive outcomes: success and failure.
   4. The probability of success, p, remains constant for each trial of the experiment.

2. $_nC_x$ represents the number of ways x successes can be obtained from n trials.

3. When the binomial distribution is approximately bell shaped, about 95% of the outcomes are in the interval from $\mu - 2\sigma$ to $\mu + 2\sigma$. The Empirical Rule can be used when $np(1 - p) \geq 10$.

4. As n increases, the binomial distribution becomes more bell shaped.

5. When n is small, the shape of the binomial distribution is determined by p. If p is close to zero, the distribution is skewed right; if p is close to 0.5, the distribution is approximately symmetric; and if p is close to 1, the distribution is skewed left.

6. Success means the outcome you are measuring.

7. Not binomial, because the random variable is continuous

8. Not binomial, because the random variable is continuous

9. Binomial

10. Binomial

11. Not binomial, because the trials are not independent

12. Binomial

13. Not binomial, because the number of trials is not fixed

14. Not binomial, because the number of trials is not fixed

15. Binomial

16. Not binomial, because the trials are not independent

17. $P(3) = 0.2150$ **18.** $P(12) = 0.2184$ **19.** $P(38) = 0.0532$
20. $P(3) = 0.0607$ **21.** $P(3) = 0.2786$ **22.** $P(17) = 0.0123$
23. $P(X \leq 3) = 0.9144$ **24.** $P(X < 5) = 0.0949$
25. $P(X > 3) = 0.5$ **26.** $P(X \geq 12) = 0.8867$
27. $P(X \leq 4) = 0.5833$ **28.** $P(X \geq 8) = 0.7133$

29. (a)

x	P(x)	x	P(x)
0	0.1176	4	0.0595
1	0.3025	5	0.0102
2	0.3241	6	0.0007
3	0.1852		

(b) $\mu_X = 1.8; \sigma_X = 1.1$ **(c)** $\mu_X = 1.8; \sigma_X = 1.1$
(d) $P(x)$

The distribution is skewed right.

30. (a)

x	P(x)	x	P(x)
0	0.0039	5	0.2188
1	0.0313	6	0.1094
2	0.1094	7	0.0313
3	0.2188	8	0.0039
4	0.2734		

(b) $\mu_X = 4; \sigma_X = 1.4$ **(c)** $\mu_X = 4; \sigma_X = 1.4$
(d) $P(x)$

The distribution is symmetric.

31. (a)

x	P(x)	x	P(x)
0	0.0000	5	0.1168
1	0.0001	6	0.2336
2	0.0012	7	0.3003
3	0.0087	8	0.2253
4	0.0389	9	0.0751

(b) $\mu_X = 6.75; \sigma_X = 1.3$ **(c)** $\mu_X = 6.75; \sigma_X = 1.3$

(d) $P(x)$

The distribution is skewed left.

32. (a)

x	P(x)	x	P(x)
0	0.1074	6	0.0055
1	0.2684	7	0.0008
2	0.3020	8	0.0001
3	0.2013	9	0.0000
4	0.0881	10	0.0000
5	0.0264		

(b) $\mu_X = 2; \sigma_X = 1.3$ **(c)** $\mu_X = 2; \sigma_X = 1.3$

(d) $P(x)$

The distribution is skewed right.

33. (a)

x	P(x)	x	P(x)
0	0.0010	6	0.2051
1	0.0098	7	0.1172
2	0.0439	8	0.0439
3	0.1172	9	0.0098
4	0.2051	10	0.0010
5	0.2461		

(b) $\mu_X = 5; \sigma_X = 1.6$ **(c)** $\mu_X = 5; \sigma_X = 1.6$

(d) $P(x)$

The distribution is symmetric.

34. (a)

x	P(x)	x	P(x)
0	0.0000	5	0.0661
1	0.0000	6	0.1762
2	0.0003	7	0.3020
3	0.0028	8	0.3020
4	0.0165	9	0.1342

(b) $\mu_X = 7.2; \sigma_X = 1.2$ **(c)** $\mu_X = 7.2; \sigma_X = 1.2$

(d) $P(x)$

The distribution is skewed left.

35. (a) This is a binomial experiment because:
    1. It is performed a fixed number of times, $n = 15$.
    2. The trials are independent.
    3. For each trial, there are two possible mutually exclusive outcomes: on time and not on time.
    4. The probability of "on time" is fixed at $p = 0.65$.
   (b) $P(10) = 0.2123$ **(c)** $P(X \geq 10) = 0.5643$
   (d) $P(X < 10) = 0.4357$ **(e)** $P(7 \leq X \leq 10) = 0.6059$

36. (a) This is a binomial experiment because:
    1. It is performed a fixed number of times, $n = 10$.
    2. The trials are independent.
    3. For each trial, there are two possible mutually exclusive outcomes: started smoking before turning 21 years old, started smoking at or after 21 years old
    4. The probability of "starting to smoke before 21 years of age" is fixed at $p = 0.90$.
   (b) $P(8) = 0.1937$ **(c)** $P(X \geq 8) = 0.9298$
   (d) $P(X < 8) = 0.0702$ **(e)** $P(7 \leq X \leq 9) = 0.6385$

37. (a) $P(3) = 0.0596$ **(b)** $P(X \leq 3) = 0.9841$
   (c) $P(1 \leq X \leq 4) = 0.6389$
   (d) It would be unusual to find 4 or more patients who experienced insomnia as a side effect because $P(X \geq 4) = 0.0159 < 0.05$.

38. (a) $P(3) = 0.0188$ **(b)** $P(X \leq 3) = 0.9971$
   (c) $P(X \geq 4) = 0.0029$ **(d)** $P(1 \leq X \leq 4) = 0.4542$

39. (a) $P(20) = 0.0244$ **(b)** $P(16 \leq X \leq 18) = 0.3767$
   (c) It would be unusual if fewer than 10 of the murders were cleared because $P(X < 10) = 0.0100 < 0.05$.

40. (a) $P(15) = 0.0376$
   (b) $P(11 \leq X \leq 13) = 0.4027$
   (c) It would be unusual if more than 15 are enrolled in college because $P(X > 15) = 0.0280 < 0.05$.

41. (a) $P(6) = 0.1460$ **(b)** $P(X < 7) = 0.2241$
   (c) $P(X \geq 5) = 0.9803$ **(d)** $P(5 \leq X \leq 8) = 0.7363$
   (e) It would be unusual to find 3 or fewer adult Americans satisfied with the nation's major airlines because $P(X \leq 3) = 0.0035 < 0.05$. We might conclude that airline satisfaction has decreased since 2005.

42. (a) $P(5) = 0.0013$
   (b) $P(X < 8) = 0.0210$; this would be unusual because the probability is below 0.05.
   (c) $P(X \geq 15) = 0.1256$; this would not be unusual because the probability is above 0.05
   (d) $P(8 \leq X \leq 12) = 0.5631$
   (e) It would be unusual for 17 or more adult Internet users to watch video content weekly because $P(X \geq 17) = 0.0160 < 0.05$. We might conclude that the percentage of adult Internet users who watch video content weekly has increased above 60%.

43. (a) 0.85
   (b) $P(X \geq 17) = 0.0029$
   (c) Community college enrollment appears to be a factor that increases the likelihood of living at home.

44. (a) 0.1667
   (b) $P(X \leq 2) = 0.0421$
   (c) The number of Hispanics on the jury is unusually low, given the composition of the population from which it came.

45. (a) $\mu_X = 65$ flights; $\sigma_X = 4.8$ flights
   (b) We expect that, in a random sample of 100 flights from Orlando to Los Angeles, 65 will be on time.
   (c) It would be unusual to have 75 on-time flights because 75 is more than 2 standard deviations above the mean.

46. (a) $\mu_X = 180; \sigma_X = 4.2$
  (b) In a random sample of 200 adult smokers, we expect 180 to report that they started smoking before turning 21 years old.
  (c) No, because 185 is within 2 standard deviations of the mean.

47. (a) $E(X) = 12$ patients with insomnia.
  (b) It would be unusual to observe 20 patients with insomnia, because 20 is more than 2 standard deviations above the mean.

48. It would not be unusual to observe 16 patients who experience weight gain, because 16 is within 2 standard deviations of the mean.

49. (a) $\mu_X = 152.5$ murder clearances; $\sigma_X = 7.7$ murder clearances
  (b) For every 250 murders, we would expect 152.5 of them would be cleared by arrest or exceptional means, on average.
  (c) 137 to 168 murder clearances
  (d) Yes; it would be unusual if more than 170 murders were cleared because 170 is more than 2 standard deviations above the mean.

50. (a) $\mu_X = 215$ women; $\sigma_X = 11.1$ women
  (b) For every 500 women age 18 to 24, we would expect 215 of them to be enrolled in college.
  (c) 193 to 237 women
  (d) No; it would not be unusual if 200 of the 500 women were enrolled in college, because 200 is within 2 standard deviations of the mean.

51. Yes; it would be unusual, because 600 is more than 2 standard deviations above the mean.

52. It would not be unusual to observe 86 patients who experience headaches, because 86 is within 2 standard deviations of the mean.

53. We would expect $500,000(0.56) = 280,000$ of the stops to be pedestrians who are nonwhite. Because $500,000(0.56)(1 - 0.56) = 123,200 \geq 10$, we can use the Empirical Rule to identify cutoff points for unusual results. The standard deviation number of stops is 351. If the number of stops of nonwhite pedestrians exceeds $280,000 + 2(351) = 280,702$, we would say the result is unusual. The actual number of stops is $500,000(0.89) = 445,000$, which is definitely unusual. A potential criticism of this analysis is the use of 0.44 as the proportion of whites, since the actual proportion of whites may be different due to individuals commuting back and forth to the city.

54. (a), (b) Answers will vary.
  (c) $P(10) = 0.1074$ **(d)** Answers will vary.
  (e) $P(X \geq 8) = 0.6778$
  (f) Simulated mean will vary. $E(X) = 8$ free throws

55. (a), (b) Answers will vary.
  (c) $P(29) = 0.3340$ **(d)** Answers will vary.
  (e) $P(X \leq 27) = 0.0217$
  (f) Simulated mean will vary. $E(X) = 29.4$ males.
  (g) Simulated standard deviation will vary. $\sigma_X = 0.8$.
  (h) Answers will vary.

56. (a) You would select 20 high school students.
  (b) You would select 33 high school students.

57. (a) You would select 38 residents 25 years and older.
  (b) You would select 65 residents 25 years and older.

58. (a) $P(3) = 0.1187$
  (b)

x	$P(x)$	x	$P(x)$
1	0.5240	6	0.0128
2	0.2494	7	0.0061
3	0.1187	8	0.0029
4	0.0565	9	0.0014
5	0.0269	10	0.0007

  (c) $\mu_X = 1.9$ free throws
  (d) $\mu_X = 1.9$ free throws; 1.9 free throws

59. (a) $P(1) = 0.0526$
  (b) $P(20) = 0.0199$
  (c) $P(30) = 0.0137$
  (d) $E(X) = 57$

6.3 Assess Your Understanding (page 362)

1. To follow a Poisson process, a random variable X must meet the following:
  1. The probability of two or more successes in a sufficiently small subinterval is 0.
  2. The probability of success is the same for any two intervals of equal length.

3. The number of successes in any interval is independent of the number of successes in any other disjoint interval.

2. λ represents the average number of successes in an interval of length 1. t is the length of the interval under consideration.

3. $\lambda = 10$ per minute; $t = 5$ minutes

4. $\lambda = 5$ per minute; $t = 10$ minutes

5. $\lambda = 0.07$ per linear foot; $t = 20$ linear feet

6. $\lambda = 3.4$ per mile; $t = 10$ miles

7. (a) $P(6) = 0.1462$ **(b)** $P(X < 6) = 0.6160$
  (c) $P(X \geq 6) = 0.3840$ **(d)** $P(2 \leq X \leq 4) = 0.4001$

8. (a) $P(10) = 0.0710$ **(b)** $P(X < 10) = 0.8305$
  (c) $P(X \geq 10) = 0.1695$ **(d)** $P(7 \leq X \leq 9) = 0.3808$

9. (a) $P(4) = 0.0050$ **(b)** $P(X < 4) = 0.9942$
  (c) $P(X \geq 4) = 0.0058$ **(d)** $P(4 \leq X \leq 6) = 0.0057$
  (e) $\mu_X = 0.7; \sigma_X = 0.8$

10. (a) $P(2) = 0.1839$ **(b)** $P(X < 2) = 0.7358$
  (c) $P(X \geq 2) = 0.2642$ **(d)** $P(1 \leq X \leq 3) = 0.6131$
  (e) $\mu_X = 1; \sigma_X = 1$

11. (a) $P(7) = 0.1490$; on about 15 of every 100 days, there will be exactly 7 hits to the website between 7:30 and 7:35 P.M.
  (b) $P(X < 7) = 0.4497$; on about 45 of every 100 days, there will be fewer than 7 hits to the website between 7:30 and 7:35 P.M.
  (c) $P(X \geq 7) = 0.5503$; on about 55 of every 100 days, there will be at least 7 hits to the website between 7:30 and 7:35 P.M.

12. (a) $P(8) = 0.1009$; on about 10 of every 100 days, exactly 8 calls will be received by the help desk between 3:10 and 3:15 P.M.
  (b) $P(X < 8) = 0.1785$; on about 18 of every 100 days, fewer than 8 calls will be received by the help desk between 3:10 and 3:15 P.M.
  (c) $P(X \geq 8) = 0.8215$; on about 82 of every 100 days, at least 8 calls will be received by the help desk between 3:10 and 3:15 P.M.

13. (a) $P(2) = 0.2510$; in about 25 of every 100 five-gram samples of this supply of peanut butter, we would expect to find 2 insect fragments.
  (b) $P(X < 2) = 0.5578$; in about 56 of every 100 five-gram samples of this supply of peanut butter, we would expect to find fewer than 2 insect fragments.
  (c) $P(X \geq 2) = 0.4422$; in about 44 of every 100 five-gram samples of this supply of peanut butter, we would expect to find at least 2 insect fragments.
  (d) $P(X \geq 1) = 0.7769$; in about 78 of every 100 five-gram samples of this supply of peanut butter, we would expect to find at least 1 insect fragment.
  (e) It would not be unusual. About 7 of every 100 five-gram samples of this supply will contain at least 4 insect fragments.

14. (a) $P(7) = 0.0847$; about 8 of every 100 three-mile stretches examined will contain exactly 7 potholes.
  (b) $P(X < 7) = 0.1180$; about 12 of every 100 three-mile stretches examined will contain fewer than 7 potholes.
  (c) $P(X \geq 7) = 0.8820$; about 88 of every 100 three-mile stretches examined will contain at least 7 potholes.
  (d) It would not be unusual. About 6 of every 100 three-mile stretches examined will contain more than 15 potholes.

15. (a) $P(0) = 0.9704$; there will be no deaths in approximately 97 of 100 randomly selected 100 million mile units of flight.
  (b) $P(X \geq 1) = 0.0296$; there will be at least one death in approximately 3 of 100 randomly selected 100 million miles of flight.
  (c) $P(X > 1) = 0.0004$; we expect more than one death in approximately 4 of 10,000 randomly selected 100 million miles of flight.

16. (a) $P(0) = 0.2231$; there will be no deaths in approximately 22 of 100 randomly selected 100 million vehicle miles.
  (b) $P(X \geq 1) = 0.7769$; there will be at least one death in approximately 78 of 100 randomly selected 100 million vehicle miles.
  (c) $P(X > 1) = 0.4422$; we expect more than one death in about 44 of 100 randomly selected 100 million vehicle miles.
  (d) Answers will vary. Flying is statistically safer.

17. (a) $P(0) = 0.7645$
  (b) $P(X \geq 1) = 0.2355$; it is not unusual because the probability is greater than 0.05.
  (c) $P(X \geq 3) = 0.0026$; this is unusual because the probability is less than 0.05.

(d) $P(X \geq 2) = 0.0302$; this is unusual because the probability is less than 0.05.

18. $P(X < 2) = 0.0611$; no, it would not be unusual for him to get fewer than 2 calls.

19. (a), (b)

Number of Cars, x	P(x)	Expected Number of Restaurants	Number of Cars, x	P(x)	Expected Number of Restaurants
0	0.0025	0.50	9	0.0688	13.77
1	0.0149	2.97	10	0.0413	8.26
2	0.0446	8.92	11	0.0225	4.51
3	0.0892	17.85	12	0.0113	2.25
4	0.1339	26.77	13	0.0052	1.04
5	0.1606	32.12	14	0.0022	0.45
6	0.1606	32.12	15	0.0009	0.18
7	0.1377	27.54	16	0.0003	0.07
8	0.1033	20.65			

(c) The observed frequencies are lower for fewer cars (*x* small) and higher for more cars (*x* large), so the advertising campaign appears to be effective.

20. (a), (b)

Imperfections, x	P(x)	Expected Number of Boards
0	0.6703	134.06
1	0.2681	53.63
2	0.0536	10.73
3	0.0072	1.43

(c) Answers will vary.

21. (a)

Number of Deaths, x	Proportion of Years
0	0.545
1	0.325
2	0.110
3	0.015
4	0.005

(b) $\mu_X = 0.61$

(c)

Number of Deaths, x	P(x)
0	0.5434
1	0.3314
2	0.1011
3	0.0206
4	0.0031

(d) Answers will vary.

22. (a) $E(X) = 28$ children
(b), (c), (d) Answers will vary.

23. (a) $E(X) = 118$ colds
(b)–(g) Answers will vary.

24. We would expect to wait about 0.3 minute (18 seconds) for the probability of getting a hit to be 0.95.

Chapter 6 Review Exercises (page 366)

1. (a) Discrete, $s = 0, 1, 2, \ldots$
(b) Continuous, $s \geq 0$
(c) Continuous, $h \geq 0$
(d) Discrete, $x = 0, 1, 2, \ldots$

2. (a) It is not a probability distribution because $\sum P(x) \neq 1$.
(b) It is a probability distribution.

3. (a)

x	P(x)
4	0.2941
5	0.2500
6	0.2500
7	0.2059

(b)

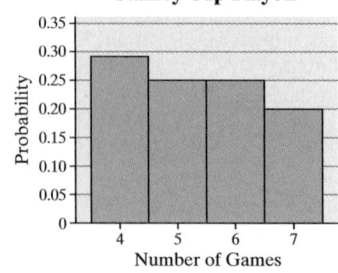

Stanley Cup Playoff

(c) $\mu_X = 5.4$ games; on average, we expect the Stanley Cup playoff to require 5.4 games.
(d) $\sigma_X = 1.1$ games

4. $E(X) = \$0.08$

5. (a) Binomial experiment
(b) Not a binomial experiment because the number of trials is not fixed.

6. (a) $P(0) = 0.4344$
(b) $P(2) = 0.1478$
(c) $P(X \geq 2) = 0.1879$
(d) $P(1) = 0.3777$
(e) $\mu_X = 20$; $\sigma_X = 4.3$
(f) It would not be unusual to have 12 females with high serum cholesterol in a sample of 250 because 12 is within 2 standard deviations of the mean.

7. (a) $P(10) = 0.1859$
(b) $P(X < 5) = 0.0093$
(c) $P(X \geq 5) = 0.9907$
(d) $P(7 \leq X \leq 12) = 0.8779$ (tech: 0.8778)
(e) $\mu_X = 120$ women; $\sigma_X = 6.9$ women
(f) It would not be unusual to have 110 females in a sample of 200 believe that the driving age should be 18, because 110 is within 2 standard deviations of the mean.

8. (a)

x	P(x)	x	P(x)
0	0.00002	5	0.20764
1	0.00037	6	0.31146
2	0.00385	7	0.26697
3	0.02307	8	0.10011
4	0.08652		

(b) $\mu_X = 6$; $\sigma_X = 1.2$

(c)

The distribution is skewed left.

9. As a rule of thumb, if X is binomially distributed, the Empirical Rule can be used when $np(1 - p) \geq 10$.

10. We can sample without replacement and use the binomial probability distribution to approximate probabilities when the sample size is small in relation to the population size. As a rule of thumb, if the sample size is less than 5% of the population size, the trials can be considered nearly independent.

11. To follow a Poisson process, a random variable X must meet the following:
  1. The probability of two or more successes in any sufficiently small subinterval is zero.
  2. The probability of success is the same for any two intervals of equal length.
  3. The number of successes in any interval is independent of the number of successes in any other disjoint interval.

12. (a) $P(2) = 0.2510$ **(b)** $P(X < 2) = 0.5578$
(c) $P(X \geq 2) = 0.4422$ **(d)** $P(1 \leq X \leq 3) = 0.7112$
(e) $\mu_X = 1.5; \sigma_X = 1.2$

13. 1.75% of the rolls are rejected.

14. It would not be unusual to have more than 4 maintenance calls; $P(X > 4) = 0.0527$.

15. $P(X \geq 12) = 0.03$, so the result of the survey is unusual. This suggests that emotional abuse may be a factor that increases the likelihood of self-injurious behavior.

Chapter 6 Test (page 368)

1. (a) Discrete; $r = 0, 1, 2, \ldots, 365$
(b) Continuous; $m > 0$
(c) Discrete; $x = 0, 1, 2, \ldots$
(d) Continuous; $w > 0$

2. (a) It is a probability distribution.
(b) It is not a probability distribution because $P(4) = -0.11$, which is negative.

3. (a)

x	$P(x)$
3	0.45
4	0.25
5	0.30

(b)

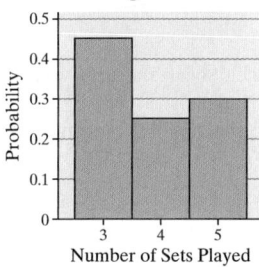

Wimbledon Men's Singles Finals

(c) $\mu_X = 3.9$ sets. On average, we expect the Wimbledon men's singles final match for the championship to require 3.9 sets of play.
(d) $\sigma_X = 0.9$ sets

4. $E(X) = 72.50$; the insurance company expects to earn an average profit of $72.50 for each 35-year-old male it insures for 1 year for $100,000.

5. An experiment is binomial provided:
1. The experiment consists of a fixed number, n, of trials.
2. The trials are independent.
3. Each trial has two possible mutually exclusive outcomes: success and failure.
4. The probability of success, p, remains constant for each trial of the experiment.

6. (a) Not a binomial experiment because the trials are not independent and the number of trials is not fixed
(b) Binomial experiment

7. (a) $P(7) = 0.0545$
(b) $P(X < 5) = 0.6296$
(c) $P(X \geq 3) = 0.7939$
(d) $P(5 \leq X \leq 10) = 0.3698$
(e) $\mu_X = 100$ households; $\sigma_X = 8.9$ households
(f) Yes; it would be unusual if 125 out of 500 households were tuned into the show, because 125 is more than 2 standard deviations above the mean.

8. (a) $P(8) = 0.1607$
(b) $P(X < 4) = 0.0097$
(c) $P(X \geq 5) = 0.9680$
(d) $P(5) = 0.0506$
(e) $\mu_X = 350$ users; $\sigma_X = 15.1$ users
(f) No; it would not be unusual for 330 users in a sample of 1,000 to suffer from insomnia, because 330 is within 2 standard deviation of the mean.

9. (a)

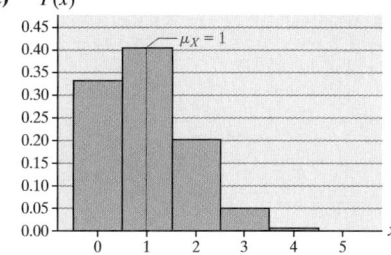

x	$P(x)$	x	$P(x)$
0	0.3277	3	0.0512
1	0.4096	4	0.0064
2	0.2048	5	0.0003

(b) $\mu_X = 1; \sigma_X = 0.9$
(c)

10. (a) $P(3) = 0.0072$
(b) $P(X < 3) = 0.9921$
(c) $P(X \geq 3) = 0.0079$
(d) $P(3 \leq X \leq 5) = 0.0079$
(e) $\mu_X = 0.4; \sigma_X = 0.6$

11. (a) $P(4) = 0.1951$; on about 20 of every 100 randomly chosen days, exactly 4 cars will arrive at the bank's drive-through window between 4:00 P.M. and 4:10 P.M.
(b) $P(X < 4) = 0.4142$; on about 41 of every 100 randomly chosen days, fewer than 4 cars will arrive at the bank's drive-through window between 4:00 P.M. and 4:10 P.M.
(c) $P(X \geq 4) = 0.5858$; on about 59 of every 100 randomly chosen days, at least 4 cars will arrive at the bank's drive-through window between 4:00 P.M. and 4:10 P.M.
(d) $\mu_X = 4.1$ cars
(e) $\sigma_X = 2.0$ cars

CHAPTER 7 The Normal Probability Distribution

7.1 Assess Your Understanding (page 381)

1. For a graph to be that of a probability density function, the area under the graph must equal 1, and the graph must be on or above the horizontal axis for all possible values of the random variable.

2. distribution; density

3. The area under the graph of a probability density function can be interpreted either as the proportion of the population with the characteristic described by the interval or as the probability that a randomly selected individual from the population has the characteristic described by the interval.

4. We standardize normal random variables so that one table can be used to find the area under the curve of any normal density function.

5. $\mu - \sigma; \mu + \sigma$

6. Increasing σ decreases the height of the graph of the normal density function.

7. This graph is not symmetric; it cannot represent a normal density function.

8. The graph can represent a normal density function.

9. This graph is not always greater than or equal to zero; it cannot represent a normal density function.

10. This graph increases as the value of X becomes very large; it cannot represent a normal density function.

11. The graph can represent a normal density function.

12. This graph is not bell-shaped; it cannot represent a normal density function.

13. $P(5 \leq X \leq 10) = \dfrac{1}{6}$ **14.** $P(15 \leq X \leq 25) = \dfrac{1}{3}$

15. $P(X \geq 20) = \dfrac{1}{3}$ **16.** $P(X \leq 5) = \dfrac{1}{6}$

17. (a)

(b) $P(0 \le X \le 0.2) = 0.2$
(c) $P(0.25 \le X \le 0.6) = 0.35$
(d) $P(X > 0.95) = 0.05$
(e) Answers will vary.

18. (a)

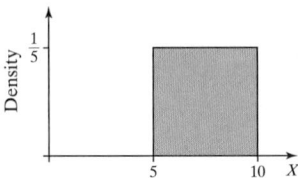

(b) $P(6 \le X \le 8) = \dfrac{2}{5} = 0.4$

(c) $P(5 \le X \le 8) = \dfrac{3}{5} = 0.6$

(d) $P(X \le 6) = \dfrac{1}{5} = 0.2$

19. Normal

20. Not normal

21. Not normal

22. Normal

23. Graph A: $\mu = 10, \sigma = 2$; graph B: $\mu = 10, \sigma = 3$. A larger standard deviation makes the graph lower and more spread out.

24. Graph A: $\mu = 8, \sigma = 2$; graph B: $\mu = 14, \sigma = 2$. A larger mean shifts the graph to the right.

25. $\mu = 2, \sigma = 3$ **26.** $\mu = 5, \sigma = 2$ **27.** $\mu = 100, \sigma = 15$

28. $\mu = 530, \sigma = 100$

29. (a)

(b)

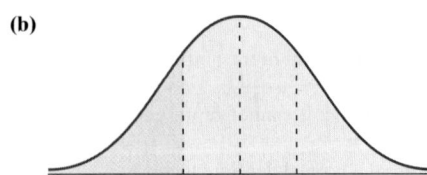

(c) (i) 15.87% of the cell phone plans in the United States are less than $44.00 per month.

(ii) The probability is 0.1587 that a randomly selected cell phone plan in the United States is less than $44.00 per month.

30. (a)

(b)

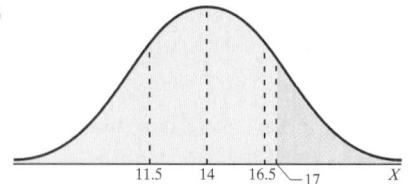

(c) (i) 11.51% of all refrigerators are kept for more than 17 years.

(ii) The probability is 0.1151 that a randomly selected refrigerator is more than 17 years old.

31. (a)

(b)

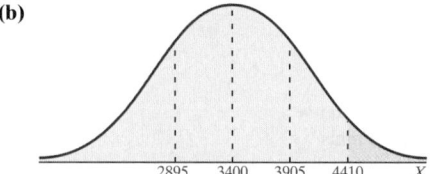

(c) (i) 2.28% of all full-term babies have a birth weight of more than 4,410 grams.

(ii) The probability is 0.0228 that the birth weight of a randomly chosen full-term baby is more than 4410 grams.

32. (a), (b)

(c) (i) The proportion of 10-year-old males who are less than 46.5 inches tall is 0.0496.

(ii) The probability that a randomly selected 10-year-old male is less than 46.5 inches tall is 0.0496.

33. (a) (i) The proportion of human pregnancies that last more than 280 days is 0.1908.

(ii) The probability that a randomly selected human pregnancy lasts more than 280 days is 0.1908.

(b) (i) The proportion of human pregnancies that last between 230 and 260 days is 0.3416.

(ii) The probability that a randomly selected human pregnancy lasts between 230 and 260 days is 0.3416.

34. (a) (i) The proportion of times that Elena gets more than 26 miles per gallon is 0.3309.

(ii) The probability that a randomly selected fill-up yields at least 26 miles per gallon is 0.3309.

(b) (i) The proportion of times that Elena gets between 18 and 21 miles per gallon is 0.1107.

(ii) The probability that a randomly selected fill-up yields between 18 and 21 miles per gallon is 0.1107.

35. (a) $z_1 = -0.67$
(b) $z_2 = 0.67$
(c) The area between z_1 and z_2 is 0.495

36. (a) $z_1 = -1.17$
(b) $z_2 = 0.83$
(c) The area between z_1 and z_2 is 0.6760

37. (c) Answers will vary.

38. (c) Answers will vary.

7.2 Assess Your Understanding (page 394)

1. A standard normal curve has the following properties:
   1. It is symmetric about its mean $\mu = 0$ and has standard deviation $\sigma = 1$.
   2. Its highest point occurs at $\mu = 0$.
   3. It has inflection points at -1 and 1.
   4. The area under the curve is 1.
   5. The area under the curve to the right of $\mu = 0$ equals the area under the curve to the left of $\mu = 0$. Both equal $\frac{1}{2}$.
   6. As Z increases, the graph approaches but never equals zero. When Z decreases, the graph approaches but never equals zero.
   7. The Empirical Rule: Approximately 68% of the area under the standard normal curve is between -1 and 1. Approximately 95% of the area under the standard normal curve is between -2 and 2. Approximately 99.7% of the area under the standard normal curve is between -3 and 3.

2. The area under the curve to the right of $z = 1.20$ is $1 - 0.8849 = 0.1151$

3. False. Explanations will vary.

4. The $P(Z < -1.30) = P(Z \le -1.30)$ because there is no area under the standard normal curve associated with a single value.

5. (a) Area = 0.0071   (b) Area = 0.3336
   (c) Area = 0.9115   (d) Area = 0.9998

6. (a) Area = 0.0002   (b) Area = 0.0233
   (c) Area = 0.8212   (d) Area = 0.9981

7. (a) Area = 0.9987   (b) Area = 0.9441
   (c) Area = 0.0375   (d) Area = 0.0009

8. (a) Area = 0.9998   (b) Area = 0.7088
   (c) Area = 0.0129   (d) Area = 0.0003

9. (a) Area = 0.9586   (b) Area = 0.2088
   (c) Area = 0.8479

10. (a) Area = 0.9892   (b) Area = 0.4525
    (c) Area = 0.9749

11. (a) Area = 0.0456 [Tech: 0.0455]   (b) Area = 0.0646
    (c) Area = 0.5203 [Tech: 0.5202]

12. (a) Area = 0.0032 [Tech: 0.0033]   (b) Area = 0.0476
    (c) Area = 0.2987 [Tech: 0.2988]

13. (a) Area = 0.8877   (b) Area = 0.0500
    (c) Area = 0.9802

14. (a) Area = 0.0198   (b) Area = 0.3686
    (c) Area = 0.9500

15. $z = -1.28$ 16. $z = -0.84$ 17. $z = 2.05$
18. $z = 1.04$ 19. $z = 0.67$ 20. $z = 0.39$
21. $z = -1.23$ 22. $z = -0.67$
23. $z_1 = -1.28$; $z_2 = 1.28$ 24. $z_1 = -1.04$; $z_2 = 1.04$
25. $z_1 = -2.575$; $z_2 = 2.575$ 26. $z_1 = -1.88$; $z_2 = 1.88$
27. $z_{0.05} = 1.645$ 28. $z_{0.35} = 0.39$ 29. $z_{0.01} = 2.33$
30. $z_{0.02} = 2.05$ 31. $z_{0.20} = 0.84$ 32. $z_{0.15} = 1.04$
33. $P(Z < 1.93) = 0.9732$ 34. $P(Z < -0.61) = 0.2709$
35. $P(Z > -2.98) = 0.9986$ 36. $P(Z > 0.92) = 0.1788$
37. $P(-1.20 \le Z < 2.34) = 0.8753$
38. $P(1.23 < Z \le 1.56) = 0.0499$ [Tech: 0.0500]
39. $P(Z \ge 1.84) = 0.0329$ 40. $P(Z \ge -0.92) = 0.8212$
41. $P(Z \le 0.72) = 0.7642$ 42. $P(Z \le -2.69) = 0.0036$
43. $P(Z < -2.56$ or $Z > 1.39) = 0.0875$
44. $P(Z < -0.38$ or $Z > 1.93) = 0.3788$
45. $P(Z < 1) - P(Z < -1) = 0.8413 - 0.1587 = 0.6826$ [Tech: 0.6827]. So about 68% of the data lies within 1 standard deviation of the mean.

   $P(Z < 2) - P(Z < -2) = 0.9772 - 0.0228 = 0.9544$ [Tech: 0.9545]. So about 95% of the data lies within 2 standard deviations of the mean.

   $P(Z < 3) - P(Z < -3) = 0.9987 - 0.0013 = 0.9974$ [Tech: 0.9973]. So about 99.7% of the data lies within 3 standard deviations of the mean.

46. Area = 0.0901 because the graph is symmetric around the mean $\mu = 0$.

47. Area = 0.0054 because the graph is symmetric around the mean $\mu = 0$.

48. Area = 0.4332 because the graph is symmetric around the mean $\mu = 0$.

49. Area = 0.1906 because the graph is symmetric around the mean $\mu = 0$.

50. (a) $a = 2.50$ (b) $a = 0.15$ (c) $b = 1.53$ (d) $b = 2.14$

7.3 Assess Your Understanding (page 402)

1. To find the area under any normal curve:
   1. Draw the normal curve and shade the desired area.
   2. Convert the values of X to z-scores using the formula
      $$z = \frac{x - \mu}{\sigma}.$$
   3. Draw a standard normal curve and shade the desired area.
   4. Find the area under the standard normal curve. This area is equal to the area under the normal curve drawn in Step (1).

2. To find the score that corresponds to a given probability:
   1. Draw a normal curve and shade the area corresponding to the probability that is given.
   2. Use Table V to find the z-score that corresponds to the shaded area.
   3. Obtain the normal value from the formula $x = \mu + z\sigma$.

3.

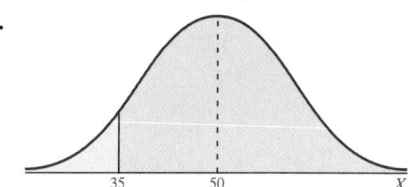

$P(X > 35) = 0.9838$
Tech: $P(X > 35) = 0.9839$

4.

$P(X > 65) = 0.0162$
Tech: $P(X > 65) = 0.0161$

5.

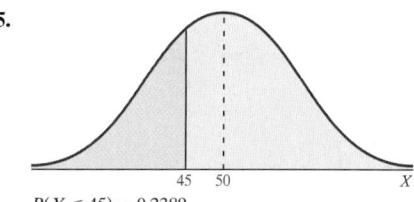

$P(X \le 45) = 0.2389$
Tech: $P(X \le 45) = 0.2375$

6.

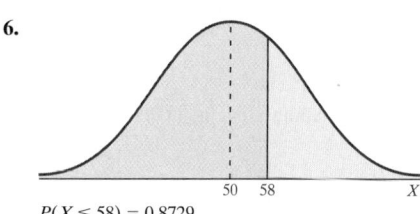

$P(X \le 58) = 0.8729$
Tech: $P(X \le 58) = 0.8735$

7.

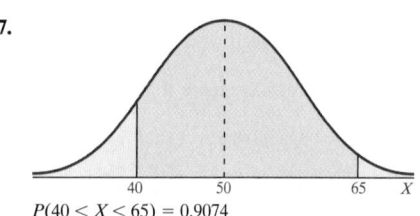

$P(40 < X < 65) = 0.9074$

8.

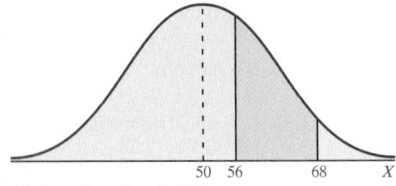

$P(56 < X < 68) = 0.1898$
Tech: $P(56 < X < 68) = 0.1906$

9.

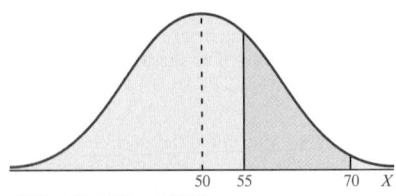

$P(55 \leq X \leq 70) = 0.2368$
Tech: $P(55 \leq X \leq 70) = 0.2354$

10.

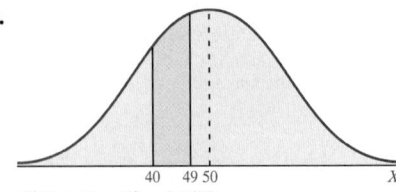

$P(40 \leq X \leq 49) = 0.3679$
Tech: $P(40 \leq X \leq 49) = 0.3666$

11.

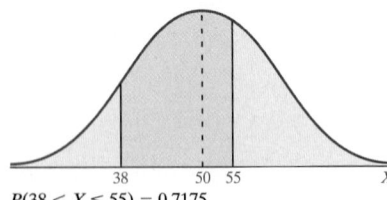

$P(38 < X \leq 55) = 0.7175$
Tech: $P(38 < X \leq 55) = 0.7192$

12.

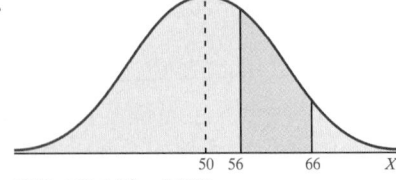

$P(56 \leq X < 66) = 0.1839$
Tech: $P(56 \leq X < 66) = 0.1845$

13. $x = 40.62$ (Tech: 40.61) is at the 9th percentile.
14. $x = 58.96$ (Tech: 58.97) is at the 90th percentile.
15. $x = 56.16$ (Tech: 56.15) is at the 81st percentile.
16. $x = 47.83$ (Tech: 47.86) is at the 38th percentile.
17. (a) $P(X < 20) = 0.1587$
  (b) $P(X > 22) = 0.1587$
  (c) $P(19 \leq X \leq 21) = 0.4772$
  (d) Yes; $P(X < 18) = 0.0013$. About 1 egg in 1,000 hatches in less than 18 days.
18. (a) $P(X < 100) = 0.1492$ (Tech: 0.1488)
  (b) $P(X > 140) = 0.2643$ (Tech: 0.2660)
  (c) $P(110 \leq X \leq 130) = 0.3189$ (Tech: 0.3165)
  (d) Yes; $P(X > 200) = 0.0009$, so less than 1 student in 1,000 can read more than 200 words per minute.
19. (a) $P(1000 \leq X \leq 1400) = 0.8658$ (Tech: 0.8657)
  (b) $P(X < 1000) = 0.0132$
  (c) 0.7019 (Tech: 0.7004) of the bags have more than 1200 chocolate chips.
  (d) 0.1230 (Tech: 0.1228) of the bags have fewer than 1125 chocolate chips.
  (e) A bag that contains 1,475 chocolate chips is at the 96th percentile.
  (f) A bag that contains 1,050 chocolate chips is at the 4th percentile.

20. (a) $P(X < 100) = 0.0918$ (Tech: 0.0922)
  (b) $P(X > 160) = 0.2296$ (Tech: 0.2292)
  (c) $P(120 \leq X \leq 180) = 0.6625$ (Tech: 0.6620)
  (d) $P(X > 180) = 0.0764$ (Tech: 0.0762). No; about 8 cars in 100 will spend more than 3 minutes in the drive-through.
21. (a) 0.4013 of pregnancies last more than 270 days.
  (b) 0.1587 of pregnancies last fewer than 250 days.
  (c) 0.7590 (Tech: 0.7571) of pregnancies last between 240 and 280 days.
  (d) $P(X > 280) = 0.1894$ (Tech: 0.1908)
  (e) $P(X \leq 245) = 0.0951$ (Tech: 0.0947)
  (f) Yes; 0.0043 of births are very preterm. So, about 4 births in 1,000 births are very preterm.
22. (a) 0.1894 (Tech: 0.1902) of the light bulbs last less than the advertised time.
  (b) 0.0401 (Tech: 0.0397) of the light bulbs last more than 1,650 hours.
  (c) $P(1,625 \leq X \leq 1,725) = 0.0923$ (Tech: 0.0931)
  (d) $P(X > 1,400) = 0.9957$ (Tech: 0.9958)
23. (a) 0.0764 (Tech: 0.0766) of the rods have a length of less than 24.9 cm.
  (b) 0.0324 (Tech: 0.0321) of the rods will be discarded.
  (c) The plant manager expects to discard 162 (Tech: 161) of the 5,000 rods manufactured.
  (d) To meet the order, the plant manager should manufacture 11,804 (Tech: 11,808) rods.
24. (a) 0.0668 of the ball bearings have a diameter of more than 5.03 mm.
  (b) 0.0124 of the ball bearings will be discarded.
  (c) Each day the plant manager expects to discard 372 of the 30,000 ball bearings manufactured.
  (d) To meet the order, the plant manufacturer should manufacture 57,711 ball bearings.
25. (a) The 17th percentile for incubation time is 20 days.
  (b) From 19 to 23 days make up the middle 95% of incubation times of the eggs.
26. (a) The 90th percentile reading speed is 156 words per minute.
  (b) The cutoffs for unusual reading times are 78 and 172 words per minute.
27. (a) The 30th percentile for the number of chips in an 18-ounce bag is 1201 (Tech: 1200) chips.
  (b) The middle 99% of the bags contain between 958 and 1,566 chocolate chips.
28. Wendy's should offer a free meal to any customer who must wait more than 206 seconds.
29. (a) 11.51% of customers receive the service for half-price.
  (b) So that no more than 3% receives the discount, the guaranteed time limit should be 22 minutes.
30. (a)

Birth Weight (g)	Relative Frequency
0–499	<0.0001
500–999	0.0001
1,000–1,499	0.0005
1,500–1,999	0.0028
2,000–2,499	0.0276
2,500–2,999	0.1702
3,000–3,499	0.4148
3,500–3,999	0.2954
4,000–4,499	0.0765
4,500–4,999	0.0110
5,000–5,499	0.0012

(b)

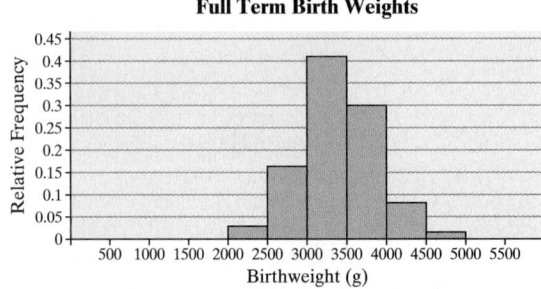

Full Term Birth Weights

The distribution is fairly symmetric and bell shaped.

(c) $\mu = 3375$ g, $\sigma = 493$ g

(d)

Birth Weight (g)	Proportion Using Normal Model (Using Technology)
0–499	<0.0001
500–999	<0.0001
1,000–1,499	0.0001
1,500–1,999	0.0026
2,000–2,499	0.0352
2,500–2,999	0.1849
3,000–3,499	0.3759
3,500–3,999	0.2971
4,000–4,499	0.0911
4,500–4,999	0.0108
5,000–5,499	0.0005

(e) The normal model appears to be effective in describing the birth weights of babies.

7.4 Assess Your Understanding (page 409)

1. Explanations will vary.

2. f_i represents the expected proportion of observations less than or equal to the ith observation.

3. The sample data do not come from a normally distributed population.

4. The sample data come from a normally distributed population.

5. The sample data do not come from a normally distributed population.

6. The sample data do not come from a normally distributed population.

7. The sample data come from a normally distributed population.

8. The sample data come from a normally distributed population.

9. (a) The sample data come from a normally distributed population.
   (b) $\bar{x} = 1{,}247.4$ chips, $s = 101.0$ chips
   (c)

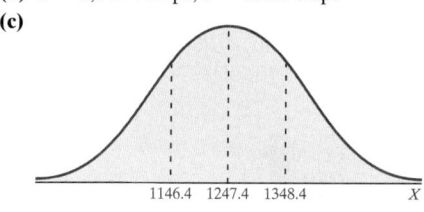

1146.4   1247.4   1348.4   X

   (d) $P(X \geq 1{,}000) = 0.9929$ (Tech: 0.9928)
   (e) $P(1{,}200 \leq X \leq 1{,}400) = 0.6153$ [Tech: 0.6152]

10. (a) The sample data come from a normally distributed population.
   (b) $\bar{x} = 20.90$ hours, $s = 10.52$ hours
   (c)

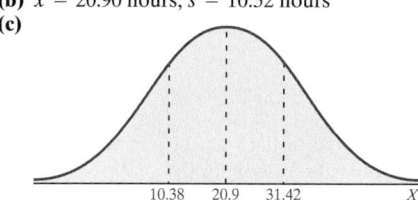

10.38   20.9   31.42   X

   (d) $P(20 \leq X \leq 35) = 0.4457$ (Tech: 0.4440)
   (e) $P(X > 40) = 0.0344$ (Tech: 0.0347)

11. The normal probability plot is approximately linear. So the sample data come from a normally distributed population.

12. The normal probability plot is approximately linear. So the sample data come from a normally distributed population.

13. The normal probability plot is not approximately linear. So the sample data do not come from a normally distributed population.

14. The normal probability plot is not approximately linear. So the sample data do not come from a normally distributed population.

7.5 Assess Your Understanding (page 416)

1. A probability experiment is binomial if:

   1. The experiment is performed n independent times.
   2. For each trial, there are two mutually exclusive outcomes—success and failure.
   3. The probability of success, p, is the same for each trial of the experiment.

2. The normal distribution can be used to approximate binomial probabilities if $np(1 - p) \geq 10$.

3. We use a correction for continuity because we are using a continuous density function to approximate a discrete probability distribution.

4. False

5. Area under the normal curve to the right of $x = 39.5$

6. Area under the normal curve to the left of $x = 20.5$

7. Area under the normal curve between $x = 7.5$ and $x = 8.5$

8. Area under the normal curve between $x = 11.5$ and $x = 12.5$

9. Area under the normal curve between $x = 17.5$ and $x = 24.5$

10. Area under the normal curve between $x = 29.5$ and $x = 40.5$

11. Area under the normal curve to the right of $x = 20.5$

12. Area under the normal curve to the left of $x = 39.5$

13. Area under the normal curve to the right of $x = 500.5$

14. Area under the normal curve to the left of $x = 34.5$

15. Using the binomial formula, $P(20) = 0.0616$; $np(1 - p) = 14.4$, the normal distribution can be used. Approximate probability is 0.0618. (Tech: 0.0603)

16. Using the binomial formula, $P(18) = 0.0221$; $np(1 - p) = 10.2$, the normal distribution can be used. Approximate probability is 0.0220 (Tech: 0.0216).

17. Using the binomial formula, $P(30) < 0.0001$; $np(1 - p) = 7.5$, the normal distribution cannot be used.

18. Using the binomial formula, $P(50) < 0.0001$; $np(1 - p) = 4.75$, the normal distribution cannot be used.

19. Using the binomial formula, $P(60) = 0.0677$; $np(1 - p) = 14.1$, the normal distribution can be used. Approximate probability is 0.0630. (Tech: 0.0645)

20. Using the binomial formula, $P(70) = 0.0970$; $np(1 - p) = 13.6$, the normal distribution can be used. Approximate probability is 0.0926. (Tech: 0.0932)

21. (a) $P(130) \approx 0.0444$ (Tech: 0.0431)
   (b) $P(X \geq 130) \approx 0.9332$ (Tech: 0.9328)
   (c) $P(X < 125) \approx 0.0021$
   (d) $P(125 \leq X \leq 135) \approx 0.5536$ (Tech: 0.5520)

22. (a) $P(80) \approx 0.1034$ (Tech: 0.0995)
   (b) $P(X \geq 80) \approx 0.5517$ (Tech: 0.5497)
   (c) $P(X < 70) \approx 0.0043$
   (d) $P(70 \leq X \leq 90) \approx 0.9914$ (Tech: 0.9913)

23. (a) $P(20) \approx 0.0077$ (Tech: 0.0078)
   (b) $P(X \leq 20) \approx 0.9934$
   (c) $P(X \geq 22) \approx 0.0028$
   (d) $P(20 \leq X \leq 30) \approx 0.0143$ (Tech: 0.0144)

24. (a) $P(40) \approx 0.0227$ (Tech: 0.0222)
   (b) $P(X \geq 35) \approx 0.4286$ (Tech: 0.4279)
   (c) $P(X < 25) \approx 0.0022$
   (d) $P(30 \leq X \leq 35) \approx 0.5926$ (Tech: 0.5944)

25. (a) $P(X \geq 130) \approx 0.0028$
   (b) Yes, the result is unusual. Less than 3 samples in 1000 will result in 130 or more living at home if the true percentage is 55%.

26. (a) $P(X \geq 110) \approx 0.0066$ (Tech: 0.0065)
   (b) Yes, the result is unusual. Less than 7 samples in 1000 will result in 110 or more living at home if the true percentage is 46%.

27. (a) $P(X \geq 75) \approx 0.0007$
   (b) Yes; less than 1 sample in 1,000 will result in 75 or more respondents preferring a male if the true percentage is 37%.

28. (a) $P(X \geq 20) \approx 0.1190$ (Tech: 0.1191)
   (b) No; the result is not unusual.

Chapter 7 Review Exercises (page 418)

1. (a) $\mu = 60$ **(b)** $\sigma = 10$
   (c) (i) The proportion of values for the random variable to the right of $x = 75$ is 0.0668.
   (ii) The probability that a randomly selected value is greater than $x = 75$ is 0.0668.
   (d) (i) The proportion of values for the random variable between $x = 50$ and $x = 75$ is 0.7745.
   (ii) The probability that a randomly selected value is between $x = 50$ and $x = 75$ is 0.7745.

2. (a) $z_1 = -0.5$ **(b)** $z_2 = 0.25$
   (c) The area between z_1 and z_2 is 0.2912.

3.

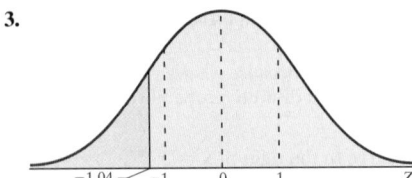

Area under the normal curve to the left of -1.04 is 0.1492.

4.

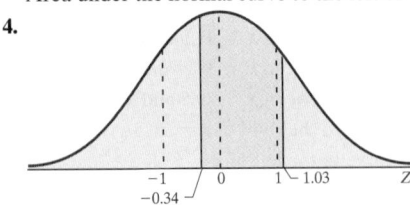

Area under the normal curve between -0.34 and 1.03 is 0.4816.

5. $P(Z < 1.19) = 0.8830$

6. $P(Z \geq 1.61) = 0.0537$

7. $P(-1.21 < Z \leq 2.28) = 0.8756$

8. $z = 0.04$

9. $z_1 = -1.75$ and $z_2 = 1.75$

10. $z_{0.20} = 0.84$

11.

$P(X > 55) = 0.2033$ (Tech: 0.2023)

12.

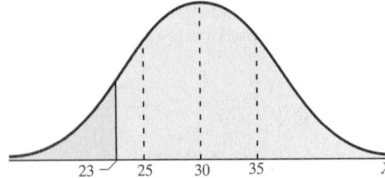

$P(X \leq 23) = 0.0808$

13.

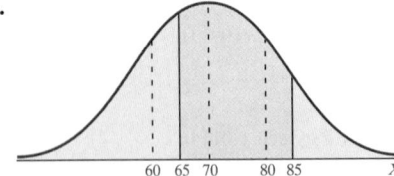

$P(65 < X < 85) = 0.6247$

14. **(a)** 0.1271 (Tech: 0.1279) of the tires last at least 75,000 miles.
(b) 0.0116 (Tech: 0.0115) of the tires last at most 60,000 miles.
(c) $P(65{,}000 \leq X \leq 80{,}000) = 0.8613$ (Tech: 0.8606)
(d) The company should advertise 60,980 (Tech: 60,964) miles as its mileage warranty.

15. **(a)** The probability is 0.0475 (Tech: 0.0478) that the test taker scores above 125.
(b) The probability is 0.2514 (Tech: 0.2525) that the test taker scores below 90.
(c) 0.2476 (Tech: 0.2487) of the test takers score between 110 and 140.
(d) $P(X > 150) = 0.0004$
(e) A score of 131 places a child at the 98th percentile.
(f) Normal children score between 71 and 129 points.

16. **(a)** 0.0119 (Tech: 0.0120) of the baseballs produced are too heavy for use.
(b) 0.0384 (Tech: 0.0380) of the baseballs produced are too light to use.
(c) 0.9497 (Tech: 0.9500) of the baseballs produced are within acceptable weight limits.
(d) 8,424 (Tech: 8,421) should be manufactured.

17. **(a)** $np(1 - p) = 62.1 > 10$, so the normal distribution can be used to approximate the binomial probabilities.
(b) $P(125) \approx 0.0214$ (Tech: 0.0226)

Interpretation: Approximately 2 of every 100 random samples of 250 adult Americans will result in exactly 125 who state that they have read at least 6 books within the past year.

(c) $P(X < 120) \approx 0.7157$ (Tech: 0.7160)
Interpretation: Approximately 72 of every 100 random samples of 250 adult Americans will result in fewer than 120 who state that they have read at least 6 books within the past year.
(d) $P(X \geq 140) \approx 0.0009$
Interpretation: Approximately 1 of every 1000 random samples of 250 adult Americans will result in 140 or more who state that they have read at least 6 books within the past year.
(e) $P(100 \leq X \leq 120) \approx 0.7336$ (Tech: 0.7328)
Interpretation: Approximately 73 of every 100 random samples of 250 adult Americans will result in between 100 and 120, inclusive, who state that they have read at least 6 books within the past year.

18. The sample appears to be from a normally distributed population.

19. The sample is not from a normal population.

20. Not normal

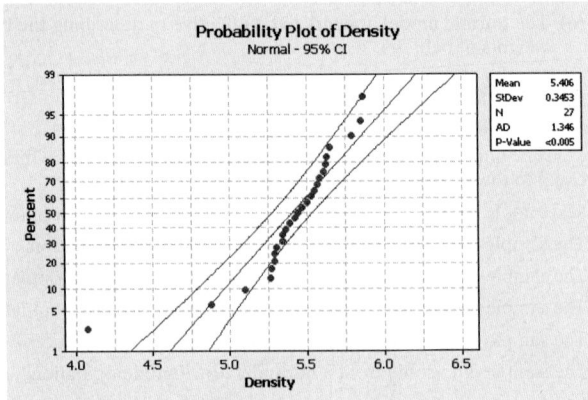

21. **(a)** $P(X \leq 30) = 0.0010$
(b) Yes, this contradicts the *USA Today* "Snapshot." About 1 sample in 1000 will result in 30 or fewer who do their most creative thinking while driving, if the true percentage is 20%.

22. **(a)**

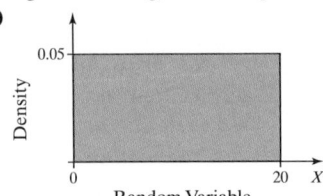

(b) $P(0 \leq X \leq 5) = 0.25$ **(c)** $P(10 \leq X \leq 18) = 0.4$

23. A standard normal curve has the following properties:
 1. It is symmetric about its mean $\mu = 0$ and has standard deviation $\sigma = 1$.
 2. Its highest point occurs at $\mu = 0$.
 3. It has inflection points at -1 and 1.
 4. The area under the curve is 1.
 5. The area under the curve to the right of $\mu = 0$ equals the area under the curve to the left of $\mu = 0$. Both equal $\frac{1}{2}$.
 6. As the value of Z increases, the graph approaches but never equals zero. When the value of Z decreases, the graph approaches but never equals zero.
 7. The Empirical Rule: Approximately 68% of the area under the standard normal curve is between -1 and 1. Approximately 95% of the area under the standard normal curve is between -2 and 2. Approximately 99.7% of the area under the standard normal curve is between -3 and 3.

24. The graph plots actual observations against expected z-scores, assuming that the data are normal. If the plot is not linear, then we have evidence that the data are not normal.

Chapter 7 Test (page 420)

1. **(a)** $\mu = 7$ **(b)** $\sigma = 2$
(c) **(i)** The proportion of values for the random variable to the left of $x = 10$ is 0.9332.
 (ii) The probability that a randomly selected value is less than $x = 10$ is 0.9332.
(d) **(i)** The proportion of values for the random variable between $x = 5$ and $x = 8$ is 0.5328.
 (ii) The probability that a randomly selected value is between $x = 5$ and $x = 8$ is 0.5328.

2. (a) $z_1 = -0.25$ **(b)** $z_2 = 1.25$
(c) The area between z_1 and z_2 is 0.4931.

3.

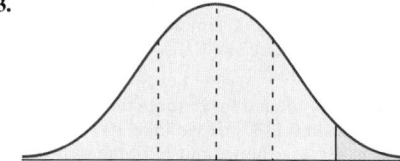

Area under the normal curve to the right of 2.04 is 0.0207.

4. $P(0.21 < Z < 1.69) = 0.3713$ **5.** $z_1 = -1.555$; $z_2 = 1.555$

6. $z_{0.04} = 1.75$

7. (a)

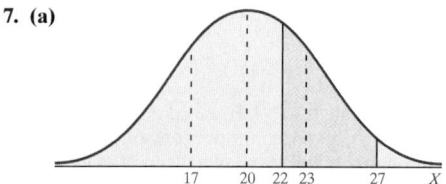

(b) $P(22 \le X \le 27) = 0.2415$ (Tech: 0.2427)

8. (a) 0.8944 of the time, the iPhone will last at least 6 hours.
(b) There is a 0.0062 probability that the iPhone will last less than 5 hours. This is an unusual result.
(c) About 8.3 hours would be the cutoff for the top 5% of all talk times.
(d) Yes; $P(X > 9) = 0.0062$. About 6 out of every 1,000 full charges will result in the iPhone lasting more than 9 hours.

9. (a) The proportion of 20- to 29-year-old males whose waist circumference is less than 100 cm is 0.7088 (Tech: 0.7080).
(b) $P(80 \le X \le 100) = 0.5274$ (Tech: 0.5272)
(c) Waist circumferences between 70 and 115 cm make up the middle 90% of all waist circumferences.
(d) A waist circumference of 75 cm is at the 10th percentile.

10. (a) $P(100) \approx 0.0025$ **(b)** $P(X < 60) \approx 0.0062$

11. The data likely do not come from a population that is normally distributed since one of the observations lies outside the curved bounds.

12. (a)

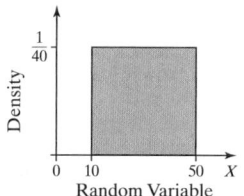

(b) $P(20 \le X \le 30) = 0.25$ **(c)** $P(X < 15) = 0.125$

CHAPTER 8 Sampling Distributions

8.1 Assess Your Understanding (page 438)

1. A sampling distribution is a probability distribution for all possible values of a statistic computed from a sample of size n.

2. The Central Limit Theorem states that, regardless of the distribution of the population, the sampling distribution of the sample mean, $\bar{x}$, becomes approximately normal as the sample size, n, increases.

3. standard error; mean

4. zero

5. $\mu_{\bar{x}} = \mu$, $\sigma_{\bar{x}} = \dfrac{\sigma}{\sqrt{n}}$

6. The population must be normally distributed.

7. four

8. True

9. The sampling distribution of $\bar{x}$ is normal with $\mu_{\bar{x}} = 30$ and $\sigma_{\bar{x}} = \dfrac{8}{\sqrt{10}} \approx 2.530$.

10. The population does not need to be normally distributed because the sample is sufficiently large, $n = 40 \ge 30$. The sampling distribution of $\bar{x}$ is approximately normal with $\mu_{\bar{x}} = 50$, $\sigma_{\bar{x}} = \dfrac{4}{\sqrt{40}} = \dfrac{2}{\sqrt{10}} \approx 0.632$.

11. $\mu_{\bar{x}} = 80, \sigma_{\bar{x}} = 2$

12. $\mu_{\bar{x}} = 64, \sigma_{\bar{x}} = 3$

13. $\mu_{\bar{x}} = 52, \sigma_{\bar{x}} = \dfrac{10}{\sqrt{21}} \approx 2.182$

14. $\mu_{\bar{x}} = 27, \sigma_{\bar{x}} = \dfrac{6}{\sqrt{15}} \approx 1.549$

15. (a) $\mu_{\bar{x}} = 500$ **(b)** $\sigma_{\bar{x}} = 20$
(c) The population must be normally distributed.
(d) $\sigma = 80$

16. (a) $\mu_{\bar{x}} = 12$ **(b)** $\sigma_{\bar{x}} = 0.05$
(c) The population must be normally distributed.
(d) $\sigma = 0.15$

17. (a) $\bar{x}$ is approximately normal with $\mu_{\bar{x}} = 80$, $\sigma_{\bar{x}} = 2$.
(b) $P(\bar{x} > 83) = 0.0668$. If we take 100 simple random samples of size $n = 49$ from a population with $\mu = 80$ and $\sigma = 14$, then about 7 of the samples will result in a mean that is greater than 83.
(c) $P(\bar{x} \le 75.8) = 0.0179$. If we take 100 simple random samples of size $n = 49$ from a population with $\mu = 80$ and $\sigma = 14$, then about 2 of the samples will result in a mean that is less than or equal to 75.8.
(d) $P(78.3 < \bar{x} < 85.1) = 0.7969$ [Tech: 0.7970]. If we take 100 simple random samples of size $n = 49$ from a population with $\mu = 80$ and $\sigma = 14$, then about 80 of the samples will result in a mean that is between 78.3 and 85.1.

18. (a) $\bar{x}$ is approximately normal with $\mu_{\bar{x}} = 64$, $\sigma_{\bar{x}} = 3$.
(b) $P(\bar{x} < 62.6) = 0.3192$ [Tech: 0.3204]. If we take 100 simple random samples of size $n = 36$ from a population with $\mu = 64$ and $\sigma = 18$, then about 32 of the samples will result in a mean that is less than 62.6.
(c) $P(\bar{x} \ge 68.7) = 0.0582$ [Tech: 0.0586]. If we take 100 simple random samples of size $n = 36$ from a population with $\mu = 64$ and $\sigma = 18$, then about 6 of the samples will result in a mean that is greater than or equal to 68.7.
(d) $P(59.8 < \bar{x} < 65.9) = 0.6549$ [Tech: 0.6560]. If we take 100 simple random samples of size $n = 36$ from a population with $\mu = 64$ and $\sigma = 18$, then about 65 of the samples will result in a mean that is between 59.8 and 65.9.

19. (a) The population must be normally distributed to compute probabilities involving the sample mean. If the population is normally distributed, then the sampling distribution of $\bar{x}$ is also normally distributed with $\mu_{\bar{x}} = 64$ and $\sigma_{\bar{x}} = \dfrac{17}{\sqrt{12}} \approx 4.907$.
(b) $P(\bar{x} < 67.3) = 0.7486$ [Tech: 0.7493]. If we take 100 simple random samples of size $n = 12$ from a population that is normally distributed with $\mu = 64$ and $\sigma = 17$, then about 75 of the samples will result in a mean that is less than 67.3.
(c) $P(\bar{x} \ge 65.2) = 0.4052$ [Tech: 0.4034]. If we take 100 simple random samples of size $n = 12$ from a population that is normally distributed with $\mu = 64$ and $\sigma = 17$, then about 41 of the samples will result in a mean that is greater than or equal to 65.2.

20. (a) The population must be normally distributed to compute probabilities involving the sample mean. If the population is normally distributed, then the sampling distribution of $\bar{x}$ is also normally distributed with $\mu_{\bar{x}} = 64$ and $\sigma_{\bar{x}} = \dfrac{17}{\sqrt{20}} \approx 3.801$.
(b) $P(\bar{x} < 67.3) = 0.8078$ [Tech: 0.8073]. If we take 100 simple random samples of size $n = 20$ from a population that is normally distributed with $\mu = 64$ and $\sigma = 17$, then about 81 of the samples will result in a mean that is less than 67.3.
(c) $P(\bar{x} \ge 65.2) = 0.3745$ [Tech: 0.3761]. If we take 100 simple random samples of size $n = 20$ from a population that is normally distributed with $\mu = 64$ and $\sigma = 17$, then about 37 of the samples will result in a mean that is greater than or equal to 65.2.
(d) Increasing the sample size increases $P(\bar{x} < 67.3)$ but decreases $P(\bar{x} > 65.2)$. This happens because $\sigma_{\bar{x}}$ decreases as n increases.

21. (a) $P(X < 260) = 0.3520$ [Tech: 0.3538]. If we randomly select 100 human pregnancies, then about 35 of the pregnancies will last less than 260 days.
(b) The sampling distribution of $\bar{x}$ is normal with $\mu_{\bar{x}} = 266$ and $\sigma_{\bar{x}} = \dfrac{16}{\sqrt{20}} \approx 3.578$.
(c) $P(\bar{x} \le 260) = 0.0465$ [Tech: 0.0468]. If we take 100 simple random samples of size $n = 20$ human pregnancies, then about 5 of

the samples will result in a mean gestation period of 260 days or less.

- **(d)** $P(\bar{x} \le 260) = 0.0040$. If we take 1,000 simple random samples of size $n = 50$ human pregnancies, then about 4 of the samples will result in a mean gestation period of 260 days or less.
- **(e)** This result would be unusual, so the sample likely came from a population whose mean gestation period is less than 266 days.
- **(f)** $P(256 \le \bar{x} \le 276) = 0.9844$ [Tech: 0.9845]. If we take 100 simple random samples of size $n = 15$ human pregnancies, then about 98 of the samples will result in a mean gestation period between 256 and 276 days, inclusive.

22. **(a)** $P(X < 40) = 0.1894$ [Tech: 0.1892]. If we select a simple random sample of $n = 100$ males ages 20 to 29, then about 19 of the males will have an upper leg length that is less than 40 cm.
- **(b)** $P(\bar{x} < 40) = 0.0041$. If we take 1,000 simple random samples of size $n = 9$ males ages 20 to 29, then about 4 of the samples will result in a mean upper leg length that is less than 40 cm.
- **(c)** $P(\bar{x} < 40) = 0.0011$. If we take 1,000 simple random samples of size $n = 12$ males ages 20 to 29, then about 1 of the samples will result in a mean upper leg length that is less than 40 cm.
- **(d)** Increasing the sample size decreases $P(\bar{x} < 40)$. This happens because $\sigma_{\bar{x}}$ decreases as n increases.
- **(e)** Yes; this result is unusual. $P(\bar{x} \ge 46) = 0.0170$.

23. **(a)** $P(X > 95) = 0.3085$. If we select a simple random sample of $n = 100$ second grade students, then about 31 of the students will read more than 95 words per minute.
- **(b)** $P(\bar{x} > 95) = 0.0418$ [Tech: 0.0416]. If we take 100 simple random samples of size $n = 12$ second grade students, then about 4 of the samples will result in a mean reading rate that is more than 95 words per minute.
- **(c)** $P(\bar{x} > 95) = 0.0071$ [Tech: 0.0072]. If we take 1000 simple random samples of size $n = 24$ second grade students, then about 7 of the samples will result in a mean reading rate that is more than 95 words per minute.
- **(d)** Increasing the sample size decreases $P(\bar{x} > 95)$. This happens because $\sigma_{\bar{x}}$ decreases as n increases.
- **(e)** A mean reading rate of 92.8 wpm is not unusual since $P(\bar{x} \ge 92.8) = 0.1056$ [Tech: 0.1052]. This means that the new reading program is not abundantly more effective than the old program.

24. **(a)** $P(X > 95) = 0.3192$ [Tech: 0.3190]. If we select a simple random sample of $n = 100$ time intervals between eruptions, then about 32 of the intervals will be longer than 95 minutes.
- **(b)** $P(\bar{x} > 95) = 0.0179$ [Tech: 0.0177]. If we take 100 simple random samples of size $n = 20$ time intervals between eruptions, then about 2 of the samples will result in a mean longer than 95 minutes.
- **(c)** $P(\bar{x} > 95) = 0.0049$ [Tech: 0.0050]. If we take 1,000 simple random samples of size $n = 30$ time intervals between eruptions, then about 5 of the samples will result in a mean longer than 95 minutes.
- **(d)** Increasing the sample size reduces $P(\bar{x} > 95)$. This happens because $\sigma_{\bar{x}}$ decreases as n increases.
- **(e)** This result would be unusual, so it might indicate that the mean time between eruptions is actually greater than 85 minutes.

25. **(a)** $P(X > 0) = 0.5675$ [Tech: 0.5694]. If we select a simple random sample of $n = 100$ months, then about 57 of the months will have positive rates of return.
- **(b)** $P(\bar{x} > 0) = 0.7291$ [Tech: 0.7277]. If we take 100 simple random samples of size $n = 12$ months, then about 73 of the samples will result in a mean monthly rate of return that is positive.
- **(c)** $P(\bar{x} > 0) = 0.8051$ [Tech: 0.8043]. If we take 100 simple random samples of size $n = 24$ months, then about 81 of the samples will result in a mean monthly rate of return that is positive.
- **(d)** $P(\bar{x} > 0) = 0.8531$ [Tech: 0.8530]. If we take 100 simple random samples of size $n = 36$ months, then about 85 of the samples will result in a mean monthly rate of return that is positive.
- **(e)** The likelihood of earning a positive rate of return increases as the investment time horizon increases.

26. **(a)** $P(X > 34) = 0.2843$ [Tech: 0.2839]. If we select a simple random sample of $n = 100$ Cobalts, then about 28 of the Cobalts will get more than 34 miles per gallon.
- **(b)** $P(\bar{x} > 34) = 0.0351$ [Tech: 0.0354]. If we take 100 simple random samples of size $n = 10$ Cobalts, then about 4 of the samples will result in a mean mileage that exceeds 34 miles per gallon.
- **(c)** $P(\bar{x} > 34) = 0.0052$ [Tech: 0.0053]. If we take 1,000 simple random samples of size $n = 20$ Cobalts, then about 5 of the samples

will result in a mean mileage that exceeds 34 miles per gallon. This result would be unusual.

27. **(a)** A sample size of at least 30 is needed to compute the probabilities.
- **(b)** $P(\bar{x} < 10) = 0.0028$. If we take 1,000 simple random samples of size $n = 40$ oil changes, then about 3 of the samples will result in a mean time of less than 10 minutes.

28. **(a)** A sample size of at least 30 is needed to compute the probabilities.
- **(b)** $P(\bar{x} \le 56.8) = 0.1131$ [Tech: 0.1137]. If we take 100 simple random samples of size $n = 40$ cars, then about 11 of the samples will result in a mean time of 56.8 seconds or less spent at the window. This result is not unusual, so the new system is not abundantly more effective than the old system.

29. **(a)** Since we have a large sample ($n = 50 \ge 30$) the Central Limit Theorem allows us to say that the sampling distribution of the mean is approximately normal.
- **(b)** $\mu_{\bar{x}} = 3, \sigma_{\bar{x}} = \dfrac{\sqrt{3}}{\sqrt{50}} = \sqrt{\dfrac{3}{50}} \approx 0.245$
- **(c)** $P(\bar{x} \ge 3.6) = 0.0071$ [Tech: 0.0072]. If we take 1,000 simple random samples of size $n = 50$ ten-gram portions of peanut butter, then about 7 of the samples will result in a mean of at least 3.6 insect fragments. This result is unusual. We might conclude that the sample comes from a population with a mean higher than 3 insect fragments per ten-gram portion.

30. **(a)** Since we have a large sample ($n = 40 \ge 30$), the Central Limit Theorem allows us to say that the sampling distribution of the mean is approximately normal.
- **(b)** $\mu_{\bar{x}} = 20, \sigma_{\bar{x}} = \dfrac{\sqrt{20}}{\sqrt{40}} = \sqrt{\dfrac{1}{2}} \approx 0.707$
- **(c)** $P(\bar{x} \ge 22.1) = 0.0015$. If we take 1,000 simple random samples of size $n = 40$ one-hour time periods between 12:00 noon and 1:00 P.M., then about 2 of the samples will result in a mean of at least 22.1 cars arriving at the drive-through. This result is unusual. We might conclude that business has increased and that the rate of arrival is now greater than 20 cars per hour between 12:00 noon and 1:00 P.M.

31. **(a)** No; the variable "weekly time spent watching television" is likely skewed right.
- **(b)** $\bar{x}$ is approximately normal with $\mu_{\bar{x}} = 2.35$ and $\sigma_{\bar{x}} = \dfrac{1.93}{\sqrt{40}} \approx 0.305$.
- **(c)** $P(2 \le \bar{x} \le 3) = 0.8583$ [Tech: 0.8577]. If we take 100 simple random samples of size $n = 40$ adult Americans, then about 86 of the samples will result in a mean time between 2 and 3 hours watching television on a weekday.
- **(d)** $P(\bar{x} \le 1.89) = 0.0793$. If we take 100 simple random samples of size $n = 35$ adult Americans, then about 8 of the samples will result in a mean time of 1.89 hours or less watching television on a weekday. This result is not unusual, so this evidence is insufficient to conclude that avid Internet users watch less television.

32. **(a)** No; the variable "ATM withdrawal" is likely skewed right.
- **(b)** $\bar{x}$ is approximately normal with $\mu_{\bar{x}} = 60$ and $\sigma_{\bar{x}} = \dfrac{35}{\sqrt{50}} \approx 4.950$.
- **(c)** $P(70 \le \bar{x} \le 75) = 0.0205$. If we take 100 simple random samples of size $n = 50$ ATM withdrawals, then about 2 of the samples will result in a mean withdrawal amount between \$70 and \$75.

33. **(a)** $\mu = 38.7$ years old
- **(b)** Samples: (37, 43); (37, 29); (37, 47); (37, 36); (37, 40); (43, 29); (43, 47); (43, 36); (43, 40); (29, 47); (29, 36); (29, 40); (47, 36); (47, 40); (36, 40)
- **(c)**

$\bar{x}$	Probability	$\bar{x}$	Probability
32.5	$\frac{1}{15}$	39.5	$\frac{1}{15}$
33	$\frac{1}{15}$	40	$\frac{1}{15}$
34.5	$\frac{1}{15}$	41.5	$\frac{2}{15}$
36	$\frac{1}{15}$	42	$\frac{1}{15}$
36.5	$\frac{1}{15}$	43.5	$\frac{1}{15}$
38	$\frac{2}{15}$	45	$\frac{1}{15}$
38.5	$\frac{1}{15}$		

(d) $\mu_{\bar{x}} = 38.7$ years old   **(e)** $P(35.7 \le \bar{x} \le 41.7) = \dfrac{9}{15} = 0.6$

(f)

Samples	
37, 43, 29	43, 29, 47
37, 43, 47	43, 29, 36
37, 43, 36	43, 29, 40
37, 43, 40	43, 47, 36
37, 29, 47	43, 47, 40
37, 29, 36	43, 36, 40
37, 29, 40	29, 47, 36
37, 47, 36	29, 47, 40
37, 47, 40	29, 36, 40
37, 36, 40	47, 36, 40

Sampling Distribution	
$\bar{x}$	Probability
34	0.05
35	0.05
35.3	0.05
36	0.05
36.3	0.05
37.3	0.10
37.7	0.10
38.7	0.10
39.7	0.10
40	0.10
41	0.05
41.3	0.05
42	0.05
42.3	0.05
43.3	0.05

$\mu_{\bar{x}} = 38.7$ years old; $P(35.7 \le \bar{x} \le 41.7) = 0.7$

As the sample size increases, the probability of obtaining a sample mean age within 3 years of the population mean age increases.

34. (a) $\mu = 142.3$ minutes

(b)

Samples	
132, 201	201, 120
132, 112	112, 134
132, 134	112, 155
132, 155	112, 120
132, 120	134, 155
201, 112	134, 120
201, 134	155, 120
201, 155	

(c)

Sampling Distribution	
$\bar{x}$	Probability
116	0.0667
122	0.0667
123	0.0667
126	0.0667
127	0.0667
133	0.0667
133.5	0.0667
137.5	0.0667
143.5	0.0667
144.5	0.0667
156.5	0.0667
160.5	0.0667
166.5	0.0667
167.5	0.0667
178	0.0667

(d) $\mu_{\bar{x}} = 142.3$ minutes

(e) $P(127.3 \le \bar{x} \le 157.3) = 0.4$

(f)

Samples	
132, 201, 112	201, 112, 134
132, 201, 134	201, 112, 155
132, 201, 155	201, 112, 120
132, 201, 120	201, 134, 155
132, 112, 134	201, 134, 120
132, 112, 155	201, 155, 120
132, 112, 120	112, 134, 155
132, 134, 155	112, 134, 120
132, 134, 120	112, 155, 120
132, 155, 120	134, 155, 120

Sampling Distribution	
$\bar{x}$	Probability
121.3	0.05
122	0.05
126	0.05
128.7	0.05
129	0.05
133	0.05
133.7	0.05
135.7	0.05
136.3	0.05
140.3	0.05
144.3	0.05
148.3	0.05
149	0.05
151	0.05
151.7	0.05
155.7	0.05
156	0.05
158.7	0.05
162.7	0.05
163.3	0.05

$\mu_{\bar{x}} = 142.3$ minutes; $P(127.3 \le \bar{x} \le 157.3) = 0.7$

As the sample size increases, the probability of obtaining a sample mean running time within 15 minutes of the population mean running time increases.

35. (a) Answers will vary.   **(b)** Answers will vary.
(c) Answers will vary.

(d) $\mu_{\bar{x}} = 100$, $\sigma_{\bar{x}} = \dfrac{15}{\sqrt{20}} \approx 3.354$

(e) Answers will vary.
(f) $P(\bar{x} > 108) = 0.0084$ [Tech: 0.0085]
(g) Answers will vary.

36. (a) Answers will vary.
(b) Answers will vary.
(c) Answers will vary.
(d) Answers will vary.

37. (a) Answers will vary.
(b) Answers will vary.
(c) Answers will vary.
(d) Answers will vary.

38. (a) Answers will vary.
(b) Answers will vary.
(c) Answers will vary.
(d) Answers will vary.

39. (a)

x	$P(x)$
35	0.0263
−1	0.9737

(b) $\mu = -\$0.05$, $\sigma = \$5.76$
(c) $\bar{x}$ is approximately normal with $\mu_{\bar{x}} = -\$0.05$ and $\sigma_{\bar{x}} = \dfrac{5.76}{\sqrt{100}} = \$0.576$.

(d) $P(\bar{x} > 0) = 0.4641$ [Tech: 0.4654]
(e) $P(\bar{x} > 0) = 0.4522$ [Tech: 0.4511]
(f) $P(\bar{x} > 0) = 0.3936$ [Tech: 0.3918]
(g) The probability of being ahead decreases as the number of games played increases.

8.2 Assess Your Understanding (page 448)

1. 0.44

2. sample proportion; $\dfrac{x}{n}$

3. False

4. True

5. The sampling distribution of $\hat{p}$ is approximately normal when $n \le 0.05N$ and $np(1 - p) \ge 10$.

6. The standard deviation of $\hat{p}$ decreases as the sample size increases. If the sample size is increased by a factor of 4, the standard deviation is reduced by a factor of 2.

7. The sampling distribution of is approximately normal with $\mu_{\hat{p}} = 0.4$ and $\sigma_{\hat{p}} = \sqrt{\dfrac{0.4(0.6)}{500}} \approx 0.022$.

8. The sampling distribution of $\hat{p}$ is approximately normal with $\mu_{\hat{p}} = 0.7$ and $\sigma_{\hat{p}} = \sqrt{\dfrac{0.7(0.3)}{300}} \approx 0.026$.

9. The sampling distribution of is approximately normal with $\mu_{\hat{p}} = 0.103$ and $\sigma_{\hat{p}} = \sqrt{\dfrac{0.103(0.897)}{1,000}} \approx 0.010$.

10. The sampling distribution of is approximately normal with $\mu_{\hat{p}} = 0.84$ and $\sigma_{\hat{p}} = \sqrt{\dfrac{0.84(0.16)}{1,010}} \approx 0.012$.

11. (a) The sampling distribution of $\hat{p}$ is approximately normal with $\mu_{\hat{p}} = 0.8$ and $\sigma_{\hat{p}} = \sqrt{\dfrac{0.8(0.2)}{75}} \approx 0.046$.

(b) $P(\hat{p} \ge 0.84) = 0.1922$ [Tech: 0.1932]. About 19 out of 100 random samples of size $n = 75$ will result in 63 or more individuals (that is, 84% or more) with the characteristic.
(c) $P(\hat{p} \le 0.68) = 0.0047$. About 5 out of 1,000 random samples of size $n = 75$ will result in 51 or fewer individuals (that is, 68% or less) with the characteristic.

12. (a) The sampling distribution of $\hat{p}$ is approximately normal with
$$\mu_{\hat{p}} = 0.65 \text{ and } \sigma_{\hat{p}} = \sqrt{\frac{0.65(0.35)}{200}} \approx 0.034.$$
(b) $P(\hat{p} \geq 0.68) = 0.1867$ [Tech: 0.1869]. About 19 out of 100 random samples of size $n = 200$ will result in 136 or more individuals (that is, 68% or more) with the characteristic.
(c) $P(\hat{p} \leq 0.59) = 0.0375$ [Tech: 0.0376]. About 4 out of 100 random samples of size $n = 200$ will result in 118 or fewer individuals (that is, 59% or less) with the characteristic.

13. (a) The sampling distribution of $\hat{p}$ is approximately normal with
$$\mu_{\hat{p}} = 0.35 \text{ and } \sigma_{\hat{p}} = \sqrt{\frac{0.35(0.65)}{1000}} \approx 0.015.$$
(b) $P(\hat{p} \geq 0.39) = 0.0040$. About 4 out of 1,000 random samples of size $n = 1,000$ will result in 390 or more individuals (that is, 39% or more) with the characteristic.
(c) $P(\hat{p} \leq 0.32) = 0.0233$ [Tech: 0.0234]. About 2 out of 100 random samples of size $n = 1,000$ will result in 320 or fewer individuals (that is, 32% or less) with the characteristic.

14. (a) The sampling distribution of $\hat{p}$ is approximately normal with
$$\mu_{\hat{p}} = 0.42 \text{ and } \sigma_{\hat{p}} = \sqrt{\frac{0.42(0.58)}{1460}} \approx 0.013.$$
(b) $P(\hat{p} \geq 0.45) = 0.0102$ [Tech: 0.0101]. About 1 out of 100 random samples of size $n = 1,460$ will result in 657 or more individuals (that is, 45% or more) with the characteristic.
(c) $P(\hat{p} \leq 0.4) = 0.0606$ [Tech: 0.0608]. About 6 out of 100 random samples of size $n = 1,460$ will result in 584 or fewer individuals (that is, 40% or less) with the characteristic.

15. (a) The sampling distribution of $\hat{p}$ is approximately normal with
$$\mu_{\hat{p}} = 0.82 \text{ and } \sigma_{\hat{p}} = \sqrt{\frac{0.82(0.18)}{100}} \approx 0.038.$$
(b) $P(\hat{p} \geq 0.85) = 0.2177$ [Tech: 0.2174]. About 22 out of 100 random samples of size $n = 100$ Americans will result in at least 85 (that is, at least 85%) who are satisfied with their lives.
(c) $P(\hat{p} \leq 0.75) = 0.0344$ [Tech: 0.0342]. About 3 out of 100 random samples of size $n = 100$ Americans will result in 75 or fewer individuals (that is, 75% or less) who are satisfied with their lives. This result is unusual.

16. (a) The sampling distribution of $\hat{p}$ is approximately normal with
$$\mu_{\hat{p}} = 0.8 \text{ and } \sigma_{\hat{p}} = \sqrt{\frac{0.8(0.2)}{200}} \approx 0.028.$$
(b) $P(\hat{p} \leq 0.77) = 0.1446$ [Tech: 0.1444]. About 14 out of 100 random samples of size $n = 200$ college students with cell phones will result in 154 or fewer students (that is, 77% or less) who send and receive text messages. This result is not unusual.
(c) $P(\hat{p} \geq 0.86) = 0.0170$ [Tech: 0.0169]. About 2 out of 100 random samples of size $n = 200$ college students with cell phones will result in 172 or more students (that is, 86% or more) who send and receive text messages. This result is unusual.

17. (a) The sampling distribution of $\hat{p}$ is approximately normal with
$$\mu_{\hat{p}} = 0.26 \text{ and } \sigma_{\hat{p}} = \sqrt{\frac{0.26(0.74)}{500}} \approx 0.020.$$
(b) $P(\hat{p} < 0.24) = 0.1539$ [Tech: 0.1540]. About 15 out of 100 random samples of size $n = 500$ adults will result in less than 24% who have no credit cards.
(c) Yes; it would be unusual for 150 of 500 adults to have no credit card. $P(X \geq 150) = P(\hat{p} \geq 0.3) = 0.0207$.

18. (a) The sampling distribution of $\hat{p}$ is approximately normal with
$$\mu_{\hat{p}} = 0.07 \text{ and } \sigma_{\hat{p}} = \sqrt{\frac{0.07(0.93)}{750}} \approx 0.009.$$
(b) $P(\hat{p} > 0.08) = 0.1423$ [Tech: 0.1416]. About 14 out of 100 random samples of size $n = 750$ telephone users will result in more than 8% who are "cell-phone only."
(c) Yes, it would be unusual for 40 or fewer of 750 adults to be "cell-phone only." $P(X \leq 40) = P(\hat{p} \leq 0.053) = 0.0344$ [Tech: 0.0368].

19. $P(X \geq 121) = P(\hat{p} \geq 0.11) = 0.1335$ [Tech: 0.1345]. This result is not unusual, so this evidence is insufficient to conclude that the proportion of Americans who are afraid to fly has increased above 0.10. In

other words, the results obtained could be due to sampling error and the true proportion is still 0.10.

20. $P(X \leq 328) = P(\hat{p} \leq 0.41) = 0.1271$ [Tech: 0.1266]. This result is not unusual, so this evidence is insufficient to conclude that the proportion of adults who have received a "phishing" contact has decreased below 0.43.

21. (a) 62 more adult Americans must be polled to make $np(1 - p) \geq 10$.
(b) 13 more adult Americans must be polled if $p = 0.2$.

22. (a) 12 more teenagers must be sampled if $p = 0.9$.
(b) 111 more teenagers must be sampled if $p = 0.95$.

23. A sample of size $n = 20$ households represents more than 5% of the population size $N = 100$ households in the association. Thus, the results from individuals in the sample are not independent of one another.

24. (a) Answers will vary. **(b)** Answers will vary.
(c) Answers will vary. **(d)** Answers will vary.
(e) Theoretical values: $\mu_{\hat{p}} = 0.3, \sigma_{\hat{p}} = \sqrt{\frac{0.3(0.7)}{25}} \approx 0.092$

25. Answers will vary.

26. (a) $\hat{p} = \frac{410}{500} = 0.82$ **(b)** $\sigma_{\hat{p}} = 0.017$

Chapter 8 Review Exercises (page 451)

1. A sampling distribution is a probability distribution for all possible values of a statistic computed from a sample of size n.

2. The sampling distribution of $\bar{x}$ is exactly normal when the underlying population distribution is normal. The sampling distribution of $\bar{x}$ is approximately normal when the sample size is large, usually greater than 30, regardless of how the population is distributed.

3. The sampling distribution of $\hat{p}$ is approximately normal when $np(1 - p) \geq 10$, provided that $n \leq 0.05N$.

4. $\mu_{\bar{x}} = \mu, \sigma_{\bar{x}} = \frac{\sigma}{\sqrt{n}}$, and $\mu_{\hat{p}} = p, \sigma_{\hat{p}} = \sqrt{\frac{p(1 - p)}{n}}$

5. (a) $P(x > 2,625) = 0.3085$. If we select a simple random sample of $n = 100$ pregnant women, then about 31 will have energy needs of more than 2,625 kcal/day. This result is not unusual.
(b) $\bar{x}$ is normal with $\mu_{\bar{x}} = 2,600$ kcal and $\sigma_{\bar{x}} = \frac{50}{\sqrt{20}} = \frac{25}{\sqrt{5}} \approx 11.180$ kcal.
(c) $P(\bar{x} > 2,625) = 0.0125$ [Tech: 0.0127]. If we take 100 simple random samples of size $n = 20$ pregnant women, then about 1 of the samples will result in a mean energy need of more than 2,625 kcal/day. This result is unusual.

6. (a) $\bar{x}$ is approximately normal with $\mu_{\bar{x}} = 0.75$ inch and $\sigma_{\bar{x}} = \frac{0.004}{\sqrt{30}} \approx 0.001$ inch.
(b) $P(\bar{x} < 0.748) + P(\bar{x} > 0.752) = 0.0062$. There is a 0.0062 probability that the inspector will conclude that the machine needs adjustment when, if fact, it does not need adjustment.

7. (a) No, the variable "number of televisions" is likely skewed right.
(b) $\bar{x} = 2.55$ televisions
(c) $P(\bar{x} \geq 2.55) = 0.0778$ [Tech: 0.0777]. If we take 100 simple random samples of size $n = 40$ households, then about 8 of the samples will result in a mean of 2.55 televisions or more. This result is not unusual, so it does not contradict the results reported by A. C. Nielsen.

8. (a) The sampling distribution of $\hat{p}$ is approximately normal with
$$\mu_{\hat{p}} = 0.72 \text{ and } \sigma_{\hat{p}} = \sqrt{\frac{0.72(0.28)}{600}} \approx 0.018.$$
(b) $P(\hat{p} \leq 0.70) = 0.1379$ [Tech: 0.1376]. About 14 out of 100 random samples of size $n = 600$ 18- to 29-year-olds will result in no more than 70% who would prefer to start their own business.
(c) Yes; it would be a little unusual for 450 of the 600 randomly selected 18- to 20-year-olds to prefer to start their own business. $P(X \geq 450) = P(\hat{p} \geq 0.75) = 0.0505$ [Tech: 0.0509].

9. $P(X \geq 60) = P(\hat{p} \geq 0.12) = 0.0681$ [Tech: 0.0680]. This result is not unusual, so this evidence is insufficient to conclude that the proportion of adults 25 years of age or older with advanced degrees has increased above 10%.

10. (a) $\hat{p} = 0.301$

(b) Since $np(1 - p) = 638(0.273)(1 - 0.273) \approx 126.6 \geq 10$, the distribution of the sample proportion is approximately normal.

(c) The sampling distribution of $\hat{p}$ is approximately normal with

$$\mu_{\hat{p}} = 0.273 \text{ and } \sigma_{\hat{p}} = \sqrt{\frac{0.273(0.727)}{638}} \approx 0.018.$$

(d) No; Cabrera's year was not all that unusual since $P(\hat{p} > 0.301) = 0.0559$ [Tech: 0.0562].

(e) No; it would not be unusual for Cabrera to have a 0.251 batting average in 2008 since $P(\hat{p} < 0.251) = 0.1056$ [Tech: 0.1061].

Chapter 8 Test (page 452)

1. Regardless of the shape of the population, the sampling distribution of $\bar{x}$ becomes approximately normal as the sample size n increases.

2. $\mu_{\bar{x}} = 50$, $\sigma_{\bar{x}} = \dfrac{24}{\sqrt{36}} = 4$

3. (a) $P(X > 100) = 0.3859$ [Tech: 0.3875]. If we select a simple random sample of $n = 100$ batteries of this type, then about 39 batteries would last more than 100 minutes. This result is not unusual.

(b) $\bar{x}$ is normally distributed with $\mu_{\bar{x}} = 90$ minutes and $\sigma_{\bar{x}} = \dfrac{35}{\sqrt{10}} \approx 11.068$ minutes.

(c) $P(\bar{x} > 100) = 0.1841$ [Tech: 0.1831]. If we take 100 simple random samples of size $n = 10$ batteries of this type, then about 18 of the samples will result in a mean charge life of more than 100 minutes. This result is not unusual.

(d) $P(\bar{x} > 100) = 0.0764$ [Tech: 0.0766]. If we take 100 simple random samples of size $n = 25$ batteries of this type, then about 8 of the samples will result in a mean charge life of more than 100 minutes.

(e) The probabilities are different because a change in n causes a change in $\sigma_{\bar{x}}$.

4. (a) $\bar{x}$ is approximately normally distributed with $\mu_{\bar{x}} = 20$ liters and

$$\sigma_{\bar{x}} = \dfrac{0.05}{\sqrt{45}} \approx 0.007 \text{ liter.}$$

(b) $P(\bar{x} < 1.98) + P(\bar{x} > 2.02) = 0.0074$ [Tech: 0.0073]. There is a 0.0074 probability that the quality-control manager will shut down the machine even though it is correctly calibrated.

5. (a) The sampling distribution of $\hat{p}$ is approximately normal with

$$\mu_{\hat{p}} = 0.224 \text{ and } \sigma_{\hat{p}} = \sqrt{\frac{0.224(0.776)}{300}} \approx 0.024.$$

(b) $P(X \geq 50) = P(\hat{p} \geq 0.1667) = 0.9913$ [Tech: 0.9914]. About 99 out of 100 random samples of size $n = 300$ adults will result in at least 50 adults (that is, at least 16.7%) who are smokers.

(c) Yes; it would be unusual for 18% or less of 300 randomly selected adults to be smokers. $P(\hat{p} \leq 0.18) = 0.0336$ [Tech: 0.0338].

6. (a) For the sample proportion to be normal, the sample size must be large enough to meet the condition $np(1 - p) \geq 10$. Since $p = 0.01$, we have

$$n(0.01)(1 - 0.01) \geq 10$$

$$0.0099n \geq 10$$

$$n \geq \frac{10}{0.0099} \approx 1,010.1$$

Thus, the sample size must be at least 1,011 to satisfy the condition.

(b) No; it would not be unusual for a random sample of 1,500 Americans to result in fewer than 10 with peanut or tree nut allergies. $P(X \leq 9) = P(\hat{p} \leq 0.006) = 0.0594$ [Tech: 0.0597].

7. $P(X \geq 82) = P(\hat{p} \geq 0.082) = 0.0681$ [Tech: 0.0685]. This result is not unusual, so this evidence is insufficient to conclude that the proportion of households with a net worth in excess of $1 million has increased above 7%.

CHAPTER 9 Estimating the Value of a Parameter

9.1 Assess Your Understanding (page 468)

1. Level of confidence, sample size, and the standard deviation of the population

2. The margin of error increases because, to be more confident that the interval contains the population mean, we need to make the interval wider.

3. The margin of error decreases as the sample size increases because the Law of Large Numbers states that as the sample size increases the sample mean approaches the value of the population mean.

4. The level of confidence refers to the proportion of samples that result in intervals that capture the unknown parameter.

5. The mean age of the population is a fixed value and so is not probabilistic. The precision of the interval can be increased by increasing the sample size or decreasing the level of confidence.

6. No, the professor should simply calculate the population mean, μ.

7. No; the data are not normal and contain an outlier.

8. No; the data are not normal and contain outliers.

9. No; the data are not normal.

10. No; the data are not normal.

11. Yes; the data appear normal, and there are no outliers.

12. Yes; the data appear normal, and there are no outliers.

13. $z_{\alpha/2} = z_{0.01} = 2.33$

14. $z_{\alpha/2} = z_{0.03} = 1.88$

15. $z_{\alpha/2} = z_{0.075} = 1.44$

16. $z_{\alpha/2} = z_{0.1} = 1.28$

17. $\bar{x} = 21, E = 3$

18. $\bar{x} = 25, E = 5$

19. $\bar{x} = 14, E = 9$

20. $\bar{x} = 25, E = 10$

21. (a) Lower bound: 32.44, upper bound: 35.96

(b) Lower bound: 32.73, upper bound: 35.67; increasing the sample size decreases the margin of error.

(c) Lower bound: 31.89, upper bound: 36.51; the interval in (c) is wider than that in (a). Increasing the confidence level increases the margin of error from 1.76 to 2.31.

(d) No; we have no information about the distribution of the population. If the sample size is 15, the data must come from a normally distributed population.

22. (a) Lower bound: 58.27, upper bound: 60.13

(b) Lower bound: 58.36, upper bound: 60.04; increasing the sample size decreases the margin of error.

(c) Lower bound: 57.88, upper bound: 60.52; the interval in (c) is wider than that in (a). Increasing the confidence level increases the margin of error from 0.93 to 1.32.

(d) No; we have no information about the distribution of the population. If the sample size is 15, the data must come from a normally distributed population.

23. (a) Lower bound: 102.7, upper bound: 113.3

(b) Lower bound: 99.6, upper bound: 116.4 decreasing the sample size increases the margin of error.

(c) Lower bound: 104.0, upper bound: 112.0; decreasing the level of confidence decreases the margin of error.

(d) We could not compute the confidence intervals because the samples are too small for the distribution of $\bar{x}$ to be normal.

(e) The outliers would have increased the mean, shifting the confidence intervals to the right.

24. (a) Lower bound: 115.9, upper bound: 130.1

(b) Lower bound: 113.8, upper bound: 132.2; decreasing the sample size increases the margin of error.

(c) Lower bound: 117.5, upper bound: 128.5; decreasing the level of confidence decreases the margin of error.

(d) We could not compute the confidence intervals because the samples are too small for the distribution of $\bar{x}$ to be normal.

(e) The outlier would have increased the mean, shifting the confidence intervals to the right.

25. (a) Flawed; this interpretation implies that the population mean varies rather than the interval.

(b) Correct

(c) Flawed; this interpretation makes an implication about individuals rather than the mean.

(d) Flawed; the interpretation should be about the mean number of hours worked by adult Americans, not about adults in Idaho.

26. (a) Flawed; this interpretation makes an implication about individuals rather than the mean.

(b) Flawed; the interpretation should be about the mean number of hours of sleep during a weekday, not any day of the week.

(c) Flawed; this interpretation implies that the population mean varies rather than the interval.

(d) Correct

27. We are 90% confident that the mean drive-through service time of Taco Bell restaurants is between 161.5 and 164.7 seconds.

28. We are 95% confident that the mean amount of time spent on MySpace.com per user per month is between 151.4 and 190.6 minutes.

29. (1) Increase the sample size, and (2) decrease the level of confidence to narrow the confidence interval.

30. (1) Increase the sample size, and (2) decrease the level of confidence to narrow the confidence interval.

31. (a) Lower bound: 0.156, upper bound: 0.164; the researcher is 90% confident that the mean BAC of drivers involved in fatal accidents who are found to have positive BAC values is between 0.156 and 0.164 g/dL.

(b) Yes; it is possible that the true mean BAC is not captured in the confidence interval from part (a).

32. (a) Lower bound: 1.198, upper bound: 1.262; the Bureau of Labor Statistics is 90% confident that the mean amount of time that Americans 15 years of age or older spend eating or drinking each day is between 1.198 and 1.262 hours.

(b) Yes; it is possible that the true mean amount of time that Americans spend eating or drinking is not captured in the confidence interval from part (a).

33. (a) Lower bound: \$4.1058, upper bound: \$4.1202; the EIA is 95% confident that the national mean price per gallon for regular-grade gasoline was between \$4.1058 and \$4.1202 on July 14, 2008.

(b) No; the interval from part (a) is about the mean price for gasoline in the entire nation. A different result in a specific town does not make the interval inaccurate.

34. (a) Lower bound: 19.07, upper bound: 29.33; the economist is 95% confident that the mean travel time to work is between 19.07 and 29.33 minutes.

(b) No; the interval from part (a) is about the mean travel time to work nationally. The mean travel time to work in a specific town may differ.

35. (a) $\bar{x} = \$1,204.3$

(b) The conditions are met. The data are approximately normal, and there are no outliers.

(c) Lower bound: \$949.7 [Tech: \$949.6], upper bound: \$1,458.9; the institute is 95% confident that the population "mean cost of repairs" is between \$949.7 and \$1458.9.

(d) Lower bound: \$990.6, upper bound: \$1418.0; the institute is 90% confident that the population "mean cost of repairs" is between \$990.6 and \$1418.0 [Tech: \$1417.9].

(e) When the level of confidence is decreased, the width of the confidence interval is decreased.

36. (a) $\bar{x} = \$3.727$

(b) The conditions are met. The data are approximately normal, and there are no outliers.

(c) Lower bound: \$3.525, upper bound: \$3.929; the economist is 95% confident that the population "mean cost of reduced fat (2%) milk" is between \$3.525 and \$3.929.

(d) Lower bound: \$3.558, upper bound: \$3.896; the economist is 90% confident that the population "mean cost of reduced fat (2%) milk" is between \$3.558 and \$3.896.

(e) When the level of confidence is decreased, the width of the confidence interval is decreased.

37. (a) $\bar{x} = 41.5$ years

(b) The conditions are met. The data are approximately normal, and there are no outliers.

(c) Lower bound: 37.7 [Tech: 37.6], upper bound: 45.3; the agent is 95% confident that the population mean age of investment-home buyers in his area is between 37.7 and 45.3 years.

(d) No; investment-home buyers in the agent's area do not appear to differ in age from those in the general population. The confidence

interval contains the mean from the general population, $\mu = 39$ years.

38. (a) $\bar{x} = 49.2$ years

(b) The conditions are met. The data are approximately normal, and there are no outliers.

(c) Lower bound: 45.1, upper bound: 53.3; the agent is 95% confident that the population mean age of vacation-home buyers in her area is between 45.1 and 53.3 years.

(d) Yes; vacation-home buyers in the agent's area appear to differ in age from those in the general population. The confidence interval does not contain the mean from the general population, $\mu = 44$ years.

39. (a) Since the length of dramas is not normally distributed, the sample must be large.

(b) Lower bound: 125.47, upper bound: 151.13; she is 99% confident that the mean length of a drama is between 125.47 and 151.13 minutes.

40. The mean age of the presidents is known, so it makes no sense to talk about a confidence interval.

41. (a) $\bar{x} = 46,743.6$ miles

(b) The distribution is skewed right.

(c) Since the distribution of number of miles is not normally distributed, the sample must be large so that the $\bar{x}$-distribution will be approximately normal.

(d) Lower bound: 38,353.0, upper bound: 55,134.2 [Tech: (38,350.3, 55,136.9)]; the used-car dealer is 99% confident that the population "mean number of miles on a 4-year-old Hummer H2" is between 38,353.0 and 55,134.2 miles.

(e) Lower bound: 40,357.0, upper bound: 53,130.2 [Tech: (40,357.1, 53,130.1)]; the used-car dealer is 95% confident that the population "mean number of miles on a 4-year-old Hummer H2" is between 40,357.0 and 53,130.2 miles.

(f) Decreasing the level of confidence decreases the width of the interval.

(g) No; because she only sampled Hummers in the Midwest, the results cannot be generalized to the entire United States.

42. (a) $\bar{x} = 133.4$ minutes

(b) The distribution is skewed right.

(c) Since the distribution of the lengths of matches is not normally distributed, the sample must be large so that the $\bar{x}$-distribution will be approximately normal.

(d) Lower bound: 115.1, upper bound: 151.7; the tennis enthusiast is 99% confident that the population "mean length of matches at Wimbledon" is between 115.1 and 151.7 minutes.

(e) Lower bound: 119.5, upper bound: 147.3; the tennis enthusiast is 95% confident that the population "mean length of matches at Wimbledon" is between 119.5 and 147.3 minutes.

(f) Decreasing the level of confidence decreases the width of the interval.

(g) No; because the tennis enthusiast only sampled matches at Wimbledon, the results cannot be generalized to include other professional tennis tournaments.

43. For a 99% confidence level, $n = 298$ patients; for a 95% confidence level, $n = 173$ patients. Decreasing the confidence level decreases the sample size needed.

44. For a 90% confidence level, $n = 188$ subjects are needed; for a 98% confidence level, $n = 378$ subjects are needed. Increasing the confidence level increases the sample size needed.

45. For a 95% confidence level, $n = 1,059$ subjects are needed.

46. For a 95% confidence level, $n = 1,040$ subjects are needed.

47. (a) For an error margin of 2,000 miles, $n = 245$ vehicles are needed.

(b) For an error margin of 1,000 miles, $n = 977$ vehicles are needed.

(c) Doubling the required accuracy approximately quadruples the required sample size. This is expected because $2^2 = 4$.

48. (a) For an error margin of 10 minutes, $n = 110$ matches are needed.

(b) For an error margin of 5 minutes, $n = 440$ matches are needed.

(c) Doubling the required accuracy quadruples the required sample size. This is expected because $2^2 = 4$.

49. (a)–(b) Answers will vary.

(c) Expect 19 intervals to include the population mean; actual number will vary.

50. (a)–(b) Answers will vary.

(c) Expect 27 intervals to include the population mean; actual number will vary.

51. (a)–(b) Answers will vary.
  (c) Expect 95 intervals to include the population mean; actual number will vary.
  (d) It is not true that 95% of the intervals contain μ.

52. (a) Lower bound: 44.6, upper bound: 56.0
  (b) 14 is less than the lower fence; $14 < Q_1 - 1.5(\text{IQR}) = 29.25$
  (c) Lower bound: 42.3; upper bound: 53.7; the outlier shifts the confidence interval to the left.
  (d) $\bar{x} = 50.25$
  (e) Lower bound: 47.0; upper bound: 53.6 [Tech: 53.5]; increasing the sample size reduces the width of the interval.
  (f) 14 is less than the lower fence, $14 < Q_1 - 1.5(\text{IQR}) = 23.5$
  (g) Lower bound: 46.2; upper bound: 52.8; the outlier shifts the confidence interval only slightly to the left.

53. The sample size must be increased by a factor of 4 to decrease the margin of error by one-half.

54. Sample B must be 4 times larger than sample A.

55. (a) Set I: $\bar{x} \approx 99.1$; set II: $\bar{x} = 99.1$; set III: $\bar{x} \approx 99.0$
  (b) Set I: Lower bound: 88.7, upper bound: 109.5. Set II: Lower bound: 92.5, upper bound: 105.7. Set III: Lower bound: 93.6 [Tech: 93.7], upper bound: 104.4.
  (c) As the size of the sample increases, the width of the confidence interval decreases.
  (d) Set I: Lower bound: 77.5, upper bound: 98.3. Set II: Lower bound: 88.0, upper bound: 101.2. Set III: Lower bound: 90.6 [Tech: 90.7]; upper bound: 101.4.
  (e) Each interval except set I, which has an outlier, contains the population mean.

56. (a) Answers will vary. Expect 95% of the intervals to contain the population mean.
  (b) Answers will vary.
  (c) Answers will vary. Expect 99% of the intervals to contain the population mean.

57. (a) Answers will vary. Expect 95% of the intervals to contain the population mean.
  (b) Answers will vary.
  (c) Answers will vary. Expect 95% of the intervals to contain the population mean.
  (d) Confidence intervals with $n = 10$ should be wider than those with $n = 50$.

58. (a) Answers will vary. Expect 95% of the intervals to contain the population mean.
  (b) Answers will vary. Expect less than 95% of the intervals to contain the population mean.
  (c) The true proportion of intervals that contain the population mean is less than what is expected.

59. (a) Completely randomized design
  (b) The treatment is the smoking cessation program. There are 2 levels.
  (c) The response variable is whether or not the smoker quit smoking.
  (d) The statistics reported are 22.3% of participants in the experimental group reported abstinence and 13.1% of participants in the control group reported abstinence.
  (e) $\dfrac{p(1-q)}{q(1-p)} = \dfrac{0.223(1-0.131)}{0.131(1-0.223)} \approx 1.90$; this means that reported abstinence is more likely in the experimental group than in the control group.
  (f) The authors are 95% confident that the population odds ratio is between 1.12 and 3.26.
  (g) Answers will vary. One possibility: Smoking cessation is more likely when the Happy Ending Intervention program is used rather than the control method.

9.2 Assess Your Understanding (page 483)

1. A Z-interval should be constructed if the sample is random, the population from which the sample is drawn is normal or the sample size is large ($n \geq 30$), and if σ is known. A t-interval should be constructed if the sample is random, the population from which the sample is drawn is normal, but if σ is not known. Neither interval can be used if the sample is not random, the population is not normal and the sample size is small, or when there are outliers.

2. t-distribution has less spread as the degrees of freedom increase because as n increases s becomes closer to σ, by the Law of Large Numbers.

3. Robust means that the procedure is still accurate when there are moderate departures from the requirements, such as normality in the distribution of the population.

4. t-values are more dispersed than z-values because the sample standard deviation, s, is a random variable.

5. Similarities: Both are probability density distributions; both have $\mu = 0$; both are symmetric around their means.

Differences: t-distributions vary for different sample sizes, n; there is only one standard normal distribution; t-distributions have longer, thicker tails; the Z-distribution has most of its area between -3 and 3.

6. Answers will vary.

7. (a) $t_{0.10} = 1.316$ **(b)** $t_{0.05} = 1.697$
  (c) $t_{0.99} = -2.552$ **(d)** $t_{0.05} = 1.725$

8. (a) $t_{0.02} = 2.205$ **(b)** $t_{0.10} = 1.309$
  (c) $t_{0.95} = -1.943$ **(d)** $t_{0.025} = 2.120$

9. (a) Lower bound: 103.7, upper bound: 112.3
  (b) Lower bound: 100.4, upper bound: 115.6; decreasing the sample size increases the margin of error.
  (c) Lower bound: 104.6, upper bound: 111.4; decreasing the level of confidence decreases the margin of error.
  (d) No; the sample sizes were too small.

10. (a) Lower bound: 45.5, upper bound: 54.5
  (b) Lower bound: 44.6, upper bound: 55.4; decreasing the sample size increases the margin of error.
  (c) Lower bound: 46.3, upper bound: 53.7; decreasing the level of confidence decreases the margin of error.
  (d) No; the sample sizes were too small.

11. (a) Lower bound: 16.85, upper bound: 19.95
  (b) Lower bound: 17.12, upper bound: 19.68; increasing the sample size decreases the margin of error.
  (c) Lower bound: 16.32, upper bound: 20.48 [Tech: (16.33, 20.48)] increasing the level of confidence increases the margin of error.
  (d) If $n = 15$, the population must be normal.

12. (a) Lower bound: 32.78, upper bound: 37.42
  (b) Lower bound: 33.66, upper bound: 36.54; increasing the sample size decreases the margin of error.
  (c) Lower bound: 31.76, upper bound: 38.44; increasing the level of confidence increases the margin of error.
  (d) If $n = 18$, the population must be normal.

13. Lower bound: 12.05 books, upper bound: 14.75 books; we can be 99% confident that the mean number of books read by Americans during 2004 was between 12.05 and 14.75.

14. (a) Lower bound: 17.19 books, upper bound: 20.41 books; we can be 99% confident that the mean number of books read by Americans during 1978 was between 17.19 and 20.41.
  (b) Americans were reading more in 1978 than in 2005.

15. Lower bound: 1.08 days, upper bound: 8.12 days; we can be 95% confident that the mean incubation period of patients with SARS is between 1.08 and 8.12 days.

16. Lower bound: 228.33 N, upper bound: 256.07 N; researchers are 90% confident that the mean tensile strength of the resin cement is between 228.33 and 256.07 newtons.

17. (a) Lower bound: 43.39 minutes, upper bound: 47.81 minutes
  (b) Yes; it is possible that the mean commute time is less than 40 minutes since it is possible that the true mean is not captured in the confidence interval. It is not likely.

18. (a) Lower bound: 19.52 mpg, upper bound: 20.48 mpg
  (b) Yes; it is possible that the mean gas mileage is greater than 23 miles per gallon since it is possible that the true mean is not captured in the confidence interval. It is not likely.

19. Lower bound: 2.19 days, upper bound: 3.81 days; the researcher can be 95% confident that the mean number of days per week in which adults engage in exercise activities is between 2.19 and 3.81 days.

20. Lower bound: 17.12 [Tech: 17.11], upper bound: 20.30; the server can be 95% confident that the mean tip rate per dinner is between 17.12% and 20.30%.

21. (a) $\bar{x} = 2.337$ million shares
  (b) Lower bound: 2.013, upper bound: 2.661; we are 90% confident that the mean number of shares of Harley-Davidson stock traded per day in 2007 was between 2.013 and 2.661 million shares.
  (c) Lower bound: 1.978, upper bound: 2.412; we are 90% confident that the mean number of shares of Harley-Davidson stock traded per day in 2007 was between 1.978 and 2.412 million shares.

(d) The confidence intervals are different because of variation in sampling. The samples have different means and standard deviations that lead to different confidence intervals.

22. (a) $\bar{x}$ = 5.430 million shares
(b) Lower bound: 4.957 [Tech: 4.956], upper bound: 5.903; we are 95% confident that the mean number of shares of PepsiCo stock traded per day in 2007 was between 4.956 and 5.903 million shares.
(c) Lower bound: 5.298, upper bound: 6.322 [Tech: (5.298, 6.321)]; we are 95% confident that the mean number of shares traded per day in 2007 was between 5.298 and 6.322 million shares.
(d) The confidence intervals are different because of variation in sampling. The samples have different means and standard deviations that lead to different confidence intervals.

23. (a) Yes; the data are approximately normal, and there are no outliers.
(b) Lower bound: 31.9 weeks, upper bound: 44.7 [Tech: 44.6] weeks; we are 95% confident that the mean age at which a baby first crawls is between 31.9 and 44.7 weeks.
(c) To increase the accuracy of the interval, increase the sample size.

24. (a) Yes; the data are approximately normal, and there are no outliers.
(b) Lower bound: 8.23, upper bound: 10.71; we are 90% confident that the mean number of hours that the battery will last on this player is between 8.23 and 10.71 hours.
(c) To increase the accuracy of the interval, increase the sample size.

25. (a) Yes; the data are approximately normal, and there are no outliers.
(b) Lower bound: 151.8 days, upper bound: 183.2 days; we are 95% confident that the mean length of the growing season in the Chicago area is between 151.8 and 183.2 days.
(c) To increase the accuracy of the interval, increase the sample size.

26. (a) Yes; the data are approximately normal, and there are no outliers.
(b) Lower bound: 170.4, upper bound: 173.0 [Tech: 172.9]; we are 95% confident that the mean weight of the discs produced by the manufacturer is between 170.4 and 173.0 grams.

27. (a) $\bar{x}$ = 22.150 years, E = 0.059 years
(b) We are 95% confident that the mean age of people when first married is between 22.091 and 22.209 years.
(c) Lower bound: $22.150 - 1.962 \cdot \dfrac{4.885}{\sqrt{26,540}} \approx 22.091$

upper bound: $22.150 + 1.962 \cdot \dfrac{4.885}{\sqrt{26,540}} \approx 22.209$

28. (a) $\bar{x}$ = 7.678, E = 0.712
(b) We are 95% confident that, of people who engaged in sexual intercourse during the past month, the mean number of times they engaged in intercourse during that month was between 6.966 and 8.390 times.
(c) Lower bound: $7.678 - 1.984 \cdot \dfrac{6.843}{\sqrt{357}} \approx 6.959$

upper bound: $7.678 + 1.984 \cdot \dfrac{6.843}{\sqrt{357}} \approx 8.397$

29. (a)

Home Asking Price, Lexington, KY

(b) Lower bound: $171,599.1, upper bound: $339,167.6 [Tech: ($171,604, $339,162)]
(c) Lower bound: $178,920.8, upper bound: $287,988.2 [Tech: ($178,916, $287,993)]
(d) The outlier widens the interval.

30. (a)

West Nile Virus Victim Ages

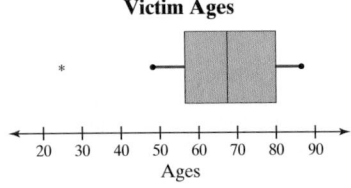

(b) Lower bound: 50.3, upper bound: 80.7
(c) Lower bound: 57.9, upper bound: 80.5 [Tech: 80.4]
(d) The outlier widens the interval.

31. Answers will vary. You would expect 19 of the 20 samples to include the population mean.

32. Answers will vary. You would expect 27 of the 30 samples to include the population mean.

33. Answers will vary.

34. (a)

Number of Drinks

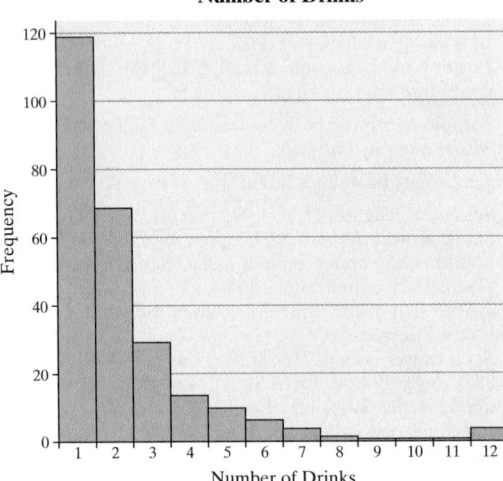

The distribution is skewed right.
(b) $\bar{x}$ = 2.0 drinks, s = 1.6 drinks
(c) Mode = 1 drink
(d) $P(2)$ = 0.2716
(e) Yes; it would be unusual to observe an individual who consumes at least eight drinks. $P(X \geq 8)$ = 0.0082.
(f) The $\bar{x}$-distribution is normal. Since the sample size n = 243 is large, the Central Limit Theorem applies.
(g) Lower bound: 1.8 [Tech: 1.9], upper bound: 2.2; we are 95% confident that the mean number of drinks consumed, when people drink, is between 1.8 and 2.2 drinks.

9.3 Assess Your Understanding (page 493)

1. $\hat{p} = \dfrac{x}{n}$ is the best point estimate of a population proportion.

2. To construct a confidence interval about a population proportion, the sample size n must be less than 5% of the population, and $n\hat{p}(1 - \hat{p}) \geq 10$.

3. Answers will vary.

4. Answers will vary.

5. Lower bound: 0.146, upper bound: 0.254

6. Lower bound: 0.319, upper bound: 0.481

7. Lower bound: 0.191, upper bound: 0.289

8. Lower bound: 0.306 [Tech: 0.307], upper bound: 0.360

9. Lower bound: 0.759 [Tech: 0.758], upper bound: 0.805

10. Lower bound: 0.567 [Tech: 0.566], upper bound: 0.633 [Tech: 0.634]

11. $\hat{p}$ = 0.225, E = 0.024, x = 270

12. $\hat{p}$ = 0.0625, E = 0.0115, x = 70

13. $\hat{p}$ = 0.4855, E = 0.0235, x = 816

14. $\hat{p}$ = 0.862, E = 0.009, x = 9251

15. (a) Flawed; no interval has been provided about the population proportion.
(b) Flawed; this interpretation indicates that the level of confidence is varying.
(c) Correct
(d) Flawed; this interpretation suggests that this interval sets the standard for all the other intervals, which is not true.

16. (a) Correct
(b) Flawed; this interpretation indicates that the level of confidence is varying.

(c) Flawed; this interpretation suggests that this interval sets the standard for all the other intervals, which is not true.

(d) Flawed; no interval has been provided about the population proportion.

17. We are 95% confident that the population proportion of adult Americans who dread Valentine's Day is between 0.135 and 0.225.

18. We are 95% confident that the population proportion of adult Americans who consider their commute to work very or somewhat stressful is between 0.20 and 0.28.

19. (a) $\hat{p} = 0.054$
(b) $n\hat{p}(1 - \hat{p}) = 44.44 \geq 10$, and the sample is less than 5% of the population.
(c) Lower bound: 0.041 [Tech: 0.042], upper bound: 0.067
(d) We are 90% confident that the proportion of Lipitor users who experience a headache as a side effect is between 0.041 and 0.067.

20. (a) $\hat{p} = 0.784$
(b) $n\hat{p}(1 - \hat{p}) = 12.54 \geq 10$, and the sample is less than 5% of the population.
(c) Lower bound: 0.661, upper bound: 0.907
(d) The researchers are 99% confident that the proportion of ulcer patients who receive Pepcid and then have their ulcers heal is between 0.661 and 0.907.

21. (a) $\hat{p} = 0.668$
(b) $n\hat{p}(1 - \hat{p}) = 438.89 \geq 10$, and the sample is less than 5% of the population.
(c) Lower bound: 0.646, upper bound: 0.690
(d) Yes; it is possible that the population proportion is below 60%, because it is possible that the true proportion is not captured in the confidence interval. It is not likely.

22. (a) $\hat{p} = 0.75$
(b) $n\hat{p}(1 - \hat{p}) = 192 \geq 10$, and the sample is less than 5% of the population.
(c) Lower bound: 0.718, upper bound: 0.782 [Tech: (0.719, 0.781)]
(d) Yes; it is possible that the population proportion is below 65%, because it is possible that the true proportion is not captured in the confidence interval. It is not likely.

23. (a) $\hat{p} = 0.140$
(b) $n\hat{p}(1 - \hat{p}) = 277.0 \geq 10$, and the sample is less than 5% of the population.
(c) Lower bound: 0.128, upper bound: 0.152
(d) Lower bound: 0.123, upper bound: 0.157
(e) Increasing the level of confidence widens the interval.

24. (a) $\hat{p} = 0.598$
(b) $n\hat{p}(1 - \hat{p}) = 242.8 \geq 10$, and the sample is less than 5% of the population.
(c) Lower bound: 0.568, upper bound: 0.628
(d) Lower bound: 0.558, upper bound: 0.638
(e) Increasing the level of confidence widens the interval.

25. (a) Using $\hat{p} = 0.69$, $n = 1,576$.
(b) Using $\hat{p} = 0.5$, $n = 1,842$.

26. (a) Using $\hat{p} = 0.681$, $n = 1,470$.
(b) Using $\hat{p} = 0.5$, $n = 1,692$.

27. (a) Using $\hat{p} = 0.15$, $n = 1,731$.
(b) Using $\hat{p} = 0.5$, $n = 3,394$.

28. (a) Using $\hat{p} = 0.34$, $n = 1,269$.
(b) Using $\hat{p} = 0.5$, $n = 1,414$.

29. (a) Using $\hat{p} = 0.48$, $n = 1,066$.
(b) Using $\hat{p} = 0.5$, $n = 1,068$.
(c) The results are close because $0.48(1 - 0.48) = 0.2496$ is very close to 0.25.

30. (a) Using $\hat{p} = 0.55$, $n = 419$.
(b) Using $\hat{p} = 0.5$, $n = 423$.
(c) The results are close because $0.55(1 - 0.55) = 0.2475$ is very close to 0.25.

31. At least $n = 914$ people were surveyed.

32. At least $n = 747$ people were surveyed.

33. Answers will vary.

34. (a) Answers will vary. Expect 95% of the intervals to contain the population proportion.

(b) Answers will vary.
(c) Answers will vary. Expect 99% of the intervals to contain the population proportion.

35. (a) Answers will vary.
(b) Answers will vary.
(c) Answers will vary.
(d) As n increases, the proportion of intervals that captures p approaches the level of confidence.

36. (a) $\hat{p} = 0.920$
(b) $n\hat{p}(1 - \hat{p}) = 73.6 \geq 10$, and the sample is less than 5% of the population.
(c) Lower bound: 0.903, upper bound: 0.937
(d) Yes; it is possible that the proportion is less than 0.85, because it is possible that the true proportion is not captured in the confidence interval. It is not likely.
(e) $\hat{p} = 0.770$
(f) $n\hat{p}(1 - \hat{p}) = 1,075.8 \geq 10$, and the sample is less than 5% of the population.
(g) Lower bound: 0.759, upper bound: 0.781
(h) Yes; it is possible that the proportion is greater than 0.85, because it is possible that the true proportion is not captured in the confidence interval. It is not likely.
(i) The proportion who say that they wash their hands is greater than the proportion who actually do. Explanations why may vary. One possibility is that people lie about their hand washing habits out of embarrassment.

9.4 Assess Your Understanding (page 501)

1. The chi-squared distribution is skewed to the right; its actual shape depends on the degrees of freedom of the distribution. As the degrees of freedom increase, the distribution becomes more symmetric, and the χ^2-values are nonnegative.

2. To construct a confidence interval about a population standard deviation, the sample must come from a normally distributed population.

3. After the population is shown to be normal, a confidence interval for the standard deviation is obtained by completing the following steps.

Step 1: Compute the sample variance.

Step 2: Determine the critical values using the desired confidence level, the correct degrees of freedom, and the χ^2 distribution table.

Step 3: Construct the confidence interval for the population variance by using the formulas

$$\text{Lower bound: } \frac{(n - 1)s^2}{\chi^2_{\alpha/2}} \quad \text{and upper bound: } \frac{(n - 1)s^2}{\chi^2_{1-\alpha/2}}$$

Step 4: Compute the square root of the lower bound and the upper bound to find the confidence interval for the population standard deviation.

4. No. The confidence interval is not symmetric.

5. $\chi^2_{0.95} = 10.117$, $\chi^2_{0.05} = 30.144$

6. $\chi^2_{0.975} = 12.401$, $\chi^2_{0.025} = 39.364$

7. $\chi^2_{0.99} = 9.542$, $\chi^2_{0.01} = 40.289$

8. $\chi^2_{0.995} = 3.565$, $\chi^2_{0.005} = 29.819$

9. (a) Lower bound: 7.94, upper bound: 23.66
(b) Lower bound: 8.59, upper bound: 20.63; the width of the interval decreases.
(c) Lower bound: 6.61, upper bound: 31.36; the width of the interval increases.

10. (a) Lower bound: 9.37, upper bound: 66.00
(b) Lower bound: 12.07, upper bound: 38.32; the width of the interval decreases.
(c) Lower bound: 7.55, upper bound: 102.71; the width of the interval increases.

11. Lower bound: 7.08, upper bound: 16.98; Essential Baby can be 95% confident that the population standard deviation of the time at which babies first crawl is between 7.08 and 16.98 weeks.

12. Lower bound: 1.47, upper bound: 3.91; we can be 95% confident that the population standard deviation of the battery life of a fifth-generation iPod music player is between 1.47 and 3.91 hours.

13. Lower bound: 13.51, upper bound: 49.83; the agricultural researcher can be 99% confident that the population standard deviation of the growing season in the Chicago area is between 13.51 and 49.83 days.

14. Lower bound: 1.26, upper bound: 4.05; we can be 99% confident that the population standard deviation disc weight of the distance drivers produced by this manufacturer is between 1.26 and 4.05 grams.

15. (a)

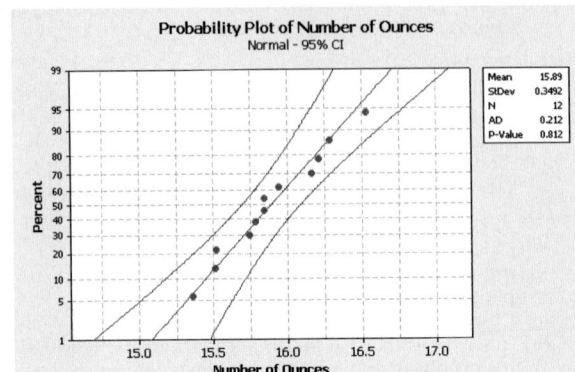

(b) $s = 0.349$ ounce

(c) Lower bound: 0.261, upper bound: 0.541; the quality-control manager can be 90% confident that the population standard deviation of the number of ounces of peanuts is between 0.261 and 0.541 ounce.

(d) No; 0.20 oz is not in the confidence interval.

16. (a)

(b) $s = 2.98\%$

(c) Lower bound: 2.11, upper bound: 5.06; the investment manager can be 95% confident that the population standard deviation of the rate of return is between 2.11% and 5.06%.

(d) Yes; the entire confidence interval is less than 6%.

17. Fisher's approximation: $\chi^2_{0.975} \approx 73.772$, $\chi^2_{0.025} \approx 129.070$

Actual values: $\chi^2_{0.975} = 74.222$, $\chi^2_{0.025} = 129.561$

9.5 Assess Your Understanding (page 505)

1. We construct a t-interval when we are estimating the population mean, we do not know the population standard deviation, and the underlying population is normally distributed. If the underlying population is not normally distributed, we can construct a t-interval to estimate the population mean provided that the sample size is large ($n \geq 30$).

We construct a Z-interval when we are estimating the population mean, we know the population standard deviation, and the underlying population is normally distributed. If the underlying population is not normally distributed, we can construct a Z-interval to estimate the population mean provided that the sample size is large ($n \geq 30$). We also construct a Z-interval when we are estimating the population proportion, provided that the sample size is smaller than 5% of the population and $n\hat{p}(1 - \hat{p}) \geq 10$.

2. To construct a confidence interval about a population proportion, the sample size must be less than 5% of the population size and $n\hat{p}(1 - \hat{p}) \geq 10$.

3. Lower bound: 49.5, upper bound: 70.5

4. Lower bound: 109.52, upper bound: 135.48

5. Lower bound: 0.069, upper bound: 0.165 [Tech: 0.164]

6. Lower bound: 0.317, upper bound: 0.383 [Tech: 0.384]

7. Lower bound: 37.74, upper bound: 52.26

8. Lower bound: 2.65, upper bound: 3.85

9. Lower bound: 114.98, upper bound: 126.02

10. Lower bound: 19.73 [Tech: 19.74], upper bound: 20.47 [Tech: 20.46]

11. Lower bound: 13.25, upper bound: 56.98

12. Lower bound: 1.56, upper bound: 2.77

13. Lower bound: 51.4, upper bound: 56.6; we can be 95% confident that felons convicted of aggravated assault serve a mean sentence between 51.4 and 56.6 months.

14. Lower bound: 0.845, upper bound: 0.895 [Tech: 0.894]; the Harris organization can be 98% confident that the proportion of adults who always wear seat belts is between 0.845 and 0.895.

15. Lower bound: 2,996.1, upper bound: 3845.9; the Internal Revenue Service can be 90% confident that the mean additional tax owed is between $2996.1 and $3845.9.

16. Lower bound: 861.98, upper bound: 864.02; we can be 99% confident that the mean muzzle velocity of the projectile is between 861.98 and 864.02 meters per second.

17. Lower bound: 0.537, upper bound: 0.589 [Tech: 0.588]; the Gallup organization can be 90% confident that the proportion of adult Americans who are worried about having enough money for retirement is between 0.537 and 0.589.

18. Lower bound: 88.78, upper bound: 98.08; we can be 95% confident that the mean amount spent per person in one day at the theme park is between $88.78 and $98.08.

19. Use a Z-interval. The distribution is normal, and we know the population standard deviation. Lower bound: 68.38 [Tech: 68.39], upper bound: 71.32; we are 95% confident that the mean height of 20- to 29-year-old males is between 68.38 and 71.32 inches.

20. Use a Z-interval. The distribution is normal, and we know the population standard deviation. Lower bound: 258.7, upper bound: 276.8; we are 95% confident that the mean gestation period of humans is between 258.7 and 276.8 days.

21. Use neither interval. There is an outlier in the data set.

22. Use a t-interval. The distribution is normal, but we do not know the population standard deviation. Lower bound: 0.851, upper bound: 0.894; we are 95% confident that the mean weight of plain M&Ms is between 0.851 and 0.894 gram.

23. Use a t-interval. The distribution is normal, but we do not know the population standard deviation. Lower bound: 101.3 [Tech: 101.4], upper bound: 117.3; we are 95% confident that the mean pulse rate of women after 3 minutes of exercise is between 101.3 and 117.3 beats per minute.

24. Use neither interval. The data are not normally distributed and the sample size is small.

Chapter 9 Review Exercises (page 508)

1. (a) $t_{0.005} = 2.898$

(b) $t_{0.05} = 1.706$

2. (a) $\chi^2_{0.975} = 10.283$, $\chi^2_{0.025} = 35.479$

(b) $\chi^2_{0.995} = 2.603$, $\chi^2_{0.005} = 26.757$

3. We would expect 95 of the 100 intervals to include the mean 100. Random chance in sampling causes a particular interval to not include the mean 100.

4. In a 90% confidence interval, the 90% represents the proportion of intervals that would contain the parameter (e.g., the population mean, population proportion, or population standard deviation) if a large number of different samples is obtained.

5. If a large number of different samples is obtained, a 90% confidence interval for a population mean will not capture the true population mean 10% of the time.

6. Area to the left of $t = -1.56$ is 0.0681 because the t-distribution is symmetric about zero.

7. There is more area under the t-distribution to the right of $t = 2.32$ than under the standard normal distribution to the right of $z = 2.32$, because the t-distribution uses s to approximate σ, making it more dispersed than the Z-distribution.

8. The properties of Student's *t*-distribution:
   1. It is symmetric around $t = 0$.
   2. It is different for different sample sizes.
   3. The area under the curve is 1; half the area is to the right of 0 and half the area is to the left of 0.
   4. As *t* gets extremely large, the graph approaches, but never equals, zero. Similarly, as *t* gets extremely small (negative), the graph approaches, but never equals, zero.
   5. The area in the tails of the *t*-distribution is greater than the area in the tails of the standard normal distribution.
   6. As the sample size *n* increases, the distribution (and the density curve) of the *t*-distribution becomes more like the standard normal distribution.

9. (a) Lower bound: 50.94, upper bound: 58.66
   (b) Lower bound: 51.65, upper bound: 57.95; increasing the sample size decreases the width of the interval.
   (c) Lower bound: 48.75, upper bound: 60.85; increasing the level of confidence increases the width of the interval.

10. (a) Lower bound: 97.07, upper bound: 111.53
   (b) Lower bound: 98.86, upper bound: 109.74; increasing the sample size decreases the width of the interval.
   (c) Lower bound: 95.49, upper bound: 113.11; increasing the level of confidence increases the width of the interval.
   (d) Lower bound: 12.22, upper bound: 23.21

11. (a) According to the Central Limit Theorem, the sampling distribution of $\bar{x}$ is approximately normal because the sample size is large.
   (b) Lower bound: 99,098, upper bound: 101,490; Michelin can be 90% confident that the mean mileage for its HydroEdge tire is between 99,098 and 101,490 miles.
   (c) Lower bound: 98,868, upper bound: 101,720; Michelin can be 95% confident that the mean mileage for its HydroEdge tire is between 98,868 and 101,720 miles.
   (d) Michelin would need to sample 63 tires to be within 1,500 miles of the mean mileage with 99% confidence.

12. (a) The distribution is skewed right.
   (b) Lower bound: 8.86, upper bound: 11.94; we are 90% confident that the population mean number of e-mails sent per day is between 8.86 and 11.94 e-mails.

13. (a) The sample is probably small because of the difficulty and expense of gathering data.
   (b) Lower bound: 201.5, upper bound: 234.5; the researchers can be 95% confident that the population "mean total work performed" for the sports-drink treatment is between 201.5 and 234.5 kilojoules.
   (c) Yes; it is possible that the population "mean total work performed" for the sports-drink treatment is less than 198 kilojoules, since it is possible that the true mean is not captured in the confidence interval. It is not likely.
   (d) Lower bound: 161.5, upper bound: 194.5; the researchers can be 95% confident that the population "mean total work performed" for the placebo treatment is between 161.5 and 194.5 kilojoules.
   (e) Yes; it is possible that the population "mean total work performed" for the placebo treatment is more than 198 kilojoules, since it is possible that the true mean is not captured in the confidence interval. It is not likely.
   (f) Yes; our findings support the researchers' conclusion. The confidence intervals do not overlap, so we are confident that the mean for the sports-drink treatment is greater than the mean for the placebo treatment.

14. (a) From the Central Limit Theorem, when the sample is large, $\bar{x}$ is approximately normally distributed.
   (b) Lower bound: 1.95, upper bound: 2.59 [Tech: 2.58]; we can be 95% confident that couples who have been married for 7 years have a mean number of children between 1.95 and 2.59.
   (c) Lower bound: 1.85, upper bound: 2.69; we can be 99% confident that couples who have been married for 7 years have a mean number of children between 1.85 and 2.69.

15. (a) $\bar{x} = 147.3$ cm, $s = 28.8$ cm
   (b) The conditions are met. The data are approximately normal, and there are no outliers.
   (c) Lower bound: 129.0, upper bound: 165.6; we are 95% confident that the population mean diameter of a Douglas fir tree in the western Washington Cascades is between 129.0 and 165.6 cm.

   (d) Lower bound: 20.4, upper bound: 48.9; we are 95% confident that the population standard deviation diameter of a Douglas fir tree in the western Washington Cascades is between 20.4 and 48.9 cm.

16. (a) $\hat{p} = 0.086$
   (b) Lower bound: 0.065, upper bound: 0.107 [Tech: (0.064, 0.107)]; the Centers for Disease Control are 95% confident that the proportion of adult males 20 to 34 years old who have hypertension is between 0.065 and 0.107.
   (c) 336 subjects would be needed if we use the point estimate of the proportion found in part (a).
   (d) 1,068 subjects would be needed if no prior estimate is available.

Chapter 9 Test (page 510)

1. The properties of the Student's *t*-distribution:
   1. It is symmetric around $t = 0$.
   2. It is different for different sample sizes.
   3. The area under the curve is 1; half the area is to the right of 0 and half the area is to the left of 0.
   4. As *t* gets extremely large, the graph approaches, but never equals, zero. Similarly, as *t* gets extremely small (negative), the graph approaches, but never equals, zero.
   5. The area in the tails of the *t*-distribution is greater than the area in the tails of the standard normal distribution.
   6. As the sample size *n* increases, the distribution (and the density curve) of the *t*-distribution becomes more like the standard normal distribution.

2. (a) $t_{0.02} = 2.167$ **(b)** $t_{0.01} = 2.567$
3. (a) $\chi^2_{0.99} = 5.229$, $\chi^2_{0.01} = 30.578$
   (b) $\chi^2_{0.95} = 17.708$, $\chi^2_{0.05} = 42.557$
4. $\bar{x} = 139.2$, $E = 13.4$
5. (a) According to the Central Limit Theorem, the sampling distribution of $\bar{x}$ is approximately normal because the sample size is large.
   (b) Lower bound: 315.1, upper bound: 334.9; Motorola can be 94% confident that the mean talk time for its V505 camera phone before the battery must be recharged is between 315.1 and 334.9 minutes.
   (c) Lower bound: 312.8, upper bound: 337.2; Motorola can be 98% confident that the mean talk time for its V505 camera phone before the battery must be recharged is between 312.8 and 337.2 minutes.
   (d) Motorola would need to sample 148 phones to be within 5 minutes of the mean talk time with 95% confidence.

6. (a) The distribution is skewed right.
   (b) Lower bound: 1.151, upper bound: 1.289 [Tech: (1.152, 1.288)]; we are 99% confident that the population "mean number of family members in jail" is between 1.151 and 1.289 members.

7. (a) Lower bound: 4.319, upper bound: 4.841; we are 90% confident that the population "mean time to graduate" is between 4.319 and 4.841 years.
   (b) Yes; our result from part (a) indicates that the mean time to graduate is more than 4 years. The entire interval is above 4.

8. (a) $\bar{x} = 57.8$ inches; $s = 15.4$ inches
   (b) Yes; the conditions are met. The distribution is approximately normal, and there are no outliers.
   (c) Lower bound: 48.0 [Tech: 47.9], upper bound: 67.6; the student is 95% confident that the mean depth of visibility of the Secchi disk is between 48.0 and 67.6 inches.
   (d) Lower bound: 44.0 [Tech: 43.9], upper bound: 71.6; the student is 99% confident that the mean depth of visibility of the Secchi disk is between 44.0 and 71.6 inches.
   (e) Lower bound: 10.9, upper bound: 26.2; the student is 95% confident that the standard deviation of the depth of visibility of the Secchi disk is between 10.9 and 26.2 inches.

9. (a) $\hat{p} = 0.948$
   (b) Lower bound: 0.932, upper bound: 0.964 [Tech: 0.965]; the EPA is 99% confident that the proportion of Americans who live in neighborhoods with acceptable levels of carbon monoxide is between 0.932 and 0.964.
   (c) 593 Americans must be sampled if the prior estimate of *p* is used.
   (d) 3,007 Americans must be sampled for the estimate to be within 1.5 percentage points with 90% confidence if no prior estimate is available.

CHAPTER 10 Hypothesis Tests Regarding a Parameter

10.1 Assess Your Understanding (page 521)

1. Type I error: To reject the null hyothesis when it is true. Type II error: To not reject the null hypothesis when the alternative is true.

2. $\alpha = 0.01$; Choose a small α to make it difficult to reject H_0.

3. As the level of significance, α, decreases, the probability of making a Type II error, β, increases.

4. If the level of significance is $\alpha = 0.05$, the probability of making a Type I error is 0.05.

5. Answers will vary. **6.** Answers will vary.

7. False **8.** False **9.** Right-tailed, μ

10. Left-tailed, p **11.** Two tailed, σ **12.** Right-tailed, p

13. Left-tailed, μ **14.** Two tailed, σ

15. (a) $H_0: p = 0.102$; $H_1: p > 0.102$
(b) The sample evidence led the researcher to believe that the proportion of births to teenage mothers increased, when in fact the proportion had not increased.
(c) The sample evidence did not lead the researcher to believe that the proportion of births to teenage mothers increased, when in fact the proportion did increase.

16. (a) $H_0: \mu = \$1,623$, $H_1: \mu \neq \$1,623$
(b) The researcher rejects the hypothesis that the average charitable contribution per household is $1,623, when in fact it is $1,623.
(c) The researcher fails to reject the hypothesis that the average charitable contribution per household is $1,623, when in fact it is different from $1,623.

17. (a) $H_0: \mu = \$299,800$; $H_1: \mu < \$299,800$
(b) The sample evidence led the real estate broker to conclude that the mean price of a single-family home has decreased, when, in fact the mean price had not decreased.
(c) The sample evidence did not lead the real estate broker to conclude that the mean price of a single-family home increased, when in fact the mean price did increase.

18. (a) $H_0: \mu = 32$ ounces, $H_1: \mu < 32$ ounces
(b) The consumer advocate rejects the hypothesis that the mean net weight of the peanut butter is 32 ounces, when in fact the true mean weight of the peanut butter is 32 ounces.
(c) The consumer advocate fails to reject the hypothesis that the mean net weight of the peanut butter is 32 ounces, when in fact the mean weight of the peanut butter is less than 32 ounces.

19. (a) $H_0: \sigma = 0.7$ psi, $H_1: \sigma < 0.7$ psi
(b) The quality control manager rejects the hypothesis that the variability in the pressure required is 0.7 psi, when the true variability is 0.7 psi.
(c) The quality control manager fails to reject that the variability in the pressure required is 0.7 psi, when the variability is less than 0.7 psi.

20. (a) $H_0: p = 0.16$, $H_1: p > 0.16$
(b) The school nurse rejects that the proportion of children who are overweight is 0.16, when in fact the true proportion of overweight children in her school district is 0.16.
(c) The school nurse fails to reject that the proportion of children who are overweight is 0.16, when the true proportion of overweight children in her school district is more than 0.16.

21. (a) $H_0: \mu = \$49.94$, $H_1: \mu \neq \$49.94$
(b) The sample evidence led the researcher to believe the mean monthly cell phone bill is different from $49.94, when in fact the mean bill is $49.94.
(c) The sample evidence did not lead the researcher to believe the mean monthly cell phone bill is different from $49.94, when in fact the mean bill is different from $49.94.

22. (a) $H_0: \sigma = 113$, $H_1: \sigma < 113$
(b) The sample evidence implies that the standard deviation test score is less than 113, when in fact the standard deviation test score is 113.
(c) The sample evidence did not imply that the standard deviation test score is less than 113, when in fact the standard deviation test score is less than 113.

23. There is sufficient evidence to conclude that the proportion of births to teenage mothers has increased above its 2005 proportion of 0.102.

24. There is not sufficient evidence to conclude that the mean charitable contribution per household has changed from its 2000 level of $1,623.

25. There is not sufficient evidence to conclude that the mean price of a single family home has decreased from its 2005 level of $299,800.

26. There is sufficient evidence to conclude that the mean content in a jar of peanut butter is less than 32 ounces.

27. There is not sufficient evidence to conclude that the variability in pressure has been reduced.

28. There is not sufficient evidence to conclude that the percentage of 6- to 11-year-olds who are overweight is greater than 16%.

29. There is sufficient evidence to conclude that the mean monthly cell phone bill is different from its 2007 level of $49.94.

30. There is not sufficient evidence to conclude that the standard deviation SAT Reasoning test score has decreased from its 2005 value of 113.

31. There is not sufficient evidence to conclude that the proportion of births to teenage mothers has increased from its 2005 level of 0.102.

32. There is sufficient evidence to conclude that the mean charitable contribution has changed from its 2000 level of $1,623.

33. There is sufficient evidence to conclude that the mean price of a single-family home has decreased from its 2005 level of $299,800.

34. There is not sufficient evidence to conclude that the mean content in a jar of peanut butter is less than 32 ounces.

35. (a) $H_0: \mu = 54$ quarts, $H_1: \mu > 54$ quarts
(b) Congratulations to the marketing department at popcorn.org. After a marketing campaign encouraging people to consume more popcorn, our researchers have determined that the mean annual consumption of popcorn is now greater than 54 quarts, the mean consumption prior to the campaign.
(c) A Type I error was made. The probability of making a Type I error is 0.05.

36. (a) $H_0: \mu = 518$, $H_1: \mu > 518$
(b) There is not sufficient evidence to conclude that the mean score on the SAT Math Reasoning exam of students who take the company's course is higher than 518.
(c) A Type II error was committed because the researcher failed to reject a false null hypothesis. When $\alpha = 0.01$, the probability of committing a Type I error is 0.01.
(d) To decrease the probability of making a Type II error, we need to increase the level of significance.

37. (a) $H_0: p = 0.152$, $H_1: p < 0.152$
(b) There is not sufficient evidence to conclude that the changes at DARE have resulted in a decrease in the proportion of tenth graders who have tried marijuana.
(c) A Type II error was committed.

38. (a) $H_0: p = 0.152$, $H_1: p < 0.152$
(b) We are proud to announce a new massage therapy program that is clinically proven to reduce the proportion of individuals who experience migraine headaches.
(c) A Type I error was committed.

39. $H_0: \mu = 0$, $H_1: \mu > 0$, where μ is the mean increase in gas mileage when using the device.

40. (a) $H_0: \mu = 4$ hours, $H_1: \mu < 4$ hours
(b) *Consumer Reports* might reject the null hypothesis and conclude that a car with Prolong will not run 4 hours without oil.

41. If you are going to accuse a company of wrongdoing, you should have fairly convincing evidence. In addition, you likely do not want to find out down the road that your accusations were unfounded. Therefore, it is likely more serious to make a Type I error. For this reason, we should probably make the level of significance $\alpha = 0.01$.

10.2 Assess Your Understanding (page 536)

1. We must have a simple random sample drawn from a normal population to test hypotheses regarding a population mean when we know σ. If the distribution of the population is not normal or if it is unknown, the sample must be large.

2. When $\alpha = 0.01$ and σ is known, the critical value for a right-tailed test is $z_{0.01} = 2.33$.

3. When $\alpha = 0.05$ and σ is known, the critical values for a two-tailed test regarding a population mean are $z_{0.025} = 1.96$ and $-z_{0.025} = -1.96$.

4. Methods for testing hypotheses regarding a population mean if is known are robust means that minor departures from normality will not adversely affect the results of the test.

5. P-value is the probability of observing a sample statistic as extreme or more extreme than the one observed under the assumption that the null hypothesis is true. If the P-value is less than the level of significance, α, the null hypothesis is rejected.

6. $P = 0.23$ is the probability of obtaining a sample mean of $\bar{x}$ or smaller assuming that 100 is the true mean. Since the outcome is not unusual, we do not reject H_0.

7. $P = 0.02$ is the probability of obtaining a sample mean more than $|z_0|$ standard deviations away from the hypothesized mean, 50. Decisions and reasons will vary.

8. Answers will vary.

9. Statistical significance means that the sample statistic likely does not come from the population whose parameter is stated in the null hypothesis. Practical significance represents a situation in which the sample statistic is statistically significantly different from the parameter stated in the null hypothesis, but the difference is not large enough to be considered important.

10. True

11. (a) $z_0 = -1.18$ **(b)** $-z_{0.05} = -1.645$
(c)

(d) No; the test statistic does not lie in the critical region.

12. (a) $z_0 = 1.92$ **(b)** $z_{0.1} = 1.28$
(c)

(d) Yes; the test statistic lies in the critical region.

13. (a) $z_0 = 3.29$ **(b)** $-z_{0.005} = -2.575$, $z_{0.005} = 2.575$
(c)

(d) Yes, the test statistic lies in the critical region.

14. (a) $z_0 = -1.32$ **(b)** $-z_{0.02} = -2.05$
(c)

(d) No; the test statistic does not lie in the critical region.

15. (a) P-value $= P(\bar{x} \leq 18.3) = 0.0082$
(b) Yes; the null hypothesis would be rejected at the $\alpha = 0.05$ level of significance, because the P-value is less than the level of significance ($0.0082 < 0.05$).

16. (a) P-value $= 0.1151$, assuming that $\mu = 4.5$
(b) No; the null hypothesis would not be rejected at the $\alpha = 0.1$ level of significance, because the P-value is greater than the level of significance ($0.1151 > 0.1$).

17. (a) The population does not need to be normally distributed to compute the P-value since the sample size is larger than 30.
(b) P-value $= 0.0614$, assuming that $\mu = 105$; the probability of obtaining a sample mean that is more than 1.87 standard deviations away from the hypothesized mean of 105 is 0.0614.

(c) No; the null hypothesis would not be rejected at the $\alpha = 0.05$ level of significance, because the P-value is greater than the level of significance ($0.0614 > 0.05$).
(d) Lower bound: 97.22; Upper bound: 105.18. Since 105 is contained in this interval, we do not reject the null hypothesis.

18. (a) The population does not need to be normally distributed to compute the P-value since the sample size is larger than 30.
(b) P-value $= 0.0090$, assuming that $\mu = 45$; the probability of obtaining a sample mean that is more than 2.61 standard deviations away from the hypothesized mean of 45 is 0.0090.
(c) Yes; the null hypothesis would be rejected at the $\alpha = 0.05$ level of significance, because the P-value is less than the level of significance ($0.0090 < 0.05$).
(d) Lower bound: 45.82; Upper bound: 50.78. Since 45 is not in the interval, we reject the null hypothesis.

19. (a) $H_0: \mu = \$67$, $H_1: \mu > \$67$
(b) There is a 0.02 probability of obtaining a sample mean of $73 or higher from a population whose mean is $67. So, if we obtained 100 simple random samples of size $n = 40$ from a population whose mean is $67, we would expect about 2 of these samples to result in sample means of $73 or higher.
(c) Because the P-value is low (P-value $= 0.02 < \alpha = 0.05$), we reject the statement in the null hypothesis. There is sufficient evidence to conclude that the mean dollar amount withdrawn from a PayEase ATM is more than the mean amount from a standard ATM (that is, more than $67).

20. (a) $H_0: \mu = 63.7$ inches, $H_1: \mu > 63.7$ inches
(b) There is a 0.35 probability of obtaining a sample mean of 63.9 inches from a population whose mean is 63.7 inches. So, if we obtained 100 simple random samples of size $n = 45$ from a population whose mean is 63.7 inches, we would expect about 35 of these samples to result in a sample mean of 63.9 inches or higher.
(c) Because the P-value is large (P-value $= 0.35 > \alpha = 0.10$), we do not reject the statement in the null hypothesis. There is not sufficient evidence to conclude that the mean height of women 20 years of age or older is greater than it was in 1990.

21. (a) $H_0: \mu = 21.2$, $H_1: \mu > 21.2$
(b) Classical approach: $z_0 = 2.02 > z_{0.05} = 1.645$; reject the null hypothesis. P-value approach: P-value $= 0.0217 < \alpha = 0.05$; reject the null hypothesis.
(c) There is sufficient evidence to conclude that students who take the core mathematics curriculum score better on the ACT.

22. (a) When dealing with small samples ($n < 30$), the population from which the sample is drawn must be normal.
(b) $H_0: \mu = 516$, $H_1: \mu \neq 516$
(c) Classical approach: $z_0 = 0.24$ is between $-z_{0.10/2} = -1.645$ and $z_{0.10/2} = 1.645$; do not reject the null hypothesis. P-value approach: P-value $= 0.8104$ [Tech: 0.8139] $> \alpha = 0.10$; do not reject the null hypothesis.
(d) There is not sufficient evidence to conclude that students whose first language is not English score differently on the math portion of the SAT exam.

23. (a) Yes; all the data lie within the confidence bands of the normal probability plot and the boxplot does not show any outliers.
(b) $H_0: \mu = 0.11$ mg/L, $H_1: \mu \neq 0.11$ mg/L. Classical approach: $z_0 = 1.85$ is between $-z_{0.05/2} = -1.96$ and $z_{0.05/2} = 1.96$; do not reject the null hypothesis. P-value approach: P-value $= 0.0644$ [Tech: 0.0643] $> \alpha = 0.05$; do not reject the null hypothesis. Conclusion: There is not sufficient evidence to indicate that the calcium concentration in rainwater in Chautauqua, New York, has changed since 1990.

24. (a) Yes; all the data lie within the confidence bands of the normal probability plot and the boxplot does not show any outliers.
(b) $H_0: \mu = 5.27$, $H_1: \mu \neq 5.27$. Classical approach: $z_0 = 0.98$ is between $-z_{0.01/2} = -2.575$ and $z_{0.01/2} = 2.575$; do not reject the null hypothesis. P-value approach: P-value $= 0.3270$ [Tech: 0.3264] $> \alpha = 0.01$; do not reject the null hypothesis. Conclusion: There is not sufficient evidence to indicate that the pH in the rain in Columbia River Gorge has changed since 2002.

25. (a) Yes; the conditions are satisfied. The data appear to be normally distributed, and there are no outliers.

(b) Hypotheses: H_0: $\mu = 64.05$ oz, H_1: $\mu \neq 64.05$ oz. Classical approach: $z_0 = -3.36 < -z_{0.005} = -2.575$; reject the null hypothesis. P-value approach: P-value $= 0.0008 < \alpha = 0.01$; reject the null hypothesis. Yes; the machine should be recalibrated.

(c) Remember, α is the probability of making a Type I error. With $\alpha = 0.01$, there is a 1% probability of rejecting the null when the null is true; with $\alpha = 0.1$, there is a 10% probability of rejecting the null when the null is true. Making a Type I error would mean shutting the machine down and recalibrating when the procedure is unnecessary. Quite a bit of revenue would be lost for no reason.

26. (a) Yes; the conditions are satisfied. The data appear to be normally distributed, and there are no outliers.

(b) Hypotheses: H_0: $\mu = 5.6$ mpg, H_1: $\mu > 5.6$ mpg. Classical approach: $z_0 = 4.91 > z_{0.05} = 1.645$; reject the null hypothesis. P-value approach: P-value $< 0.0001 < \alpha = 0.05$; reject the null hypothesis. The fuel catalyst appears to be effective in improving gas mileage.

27. (a) Assessed home values are typically skewed right because there are a few homes with very high assessed values. Because the shape of the distribution of assessed home values is not approximately normal, we need a large sample size so that we can use the Central Limit Theorem, which means that the distribution of the sample mean will be approximately normal.

(b) H_0: $\mu = \$11.38$, H_1: $\mu < \$11.38$. We will use $\alpha = 0.05$. Classical approach: $z_0 = -0.26 > -z_{0.05} = -1.645$; do not reject the null hypothesis. P-value approach: P-value $= 0.3974$ [Tech: 0.3991] $> \alpha = 0.05$; do not reject the null hypothesis. Conclusion: There is not sufficient evidence to indicate that rural households pay less per \$1,000 assessed valuation than all homes in the United States.

28. (a) Birth weights must be approximately normal and the data cannot have any outliers.

(b) H_0: $\mu = 3270$ g, H_1: $\mu < 3270$ g. Classical approach: $z_0 = -1.21 > -z_{0.1} = -1.28$; do not reject the null hypothesis. P-value approach: P-value $= 0.1131$ [Tech: 0.1138] $> \alpha = 0.10$; do not reject the null hypothesis. Conclusion: There is not sufficient evidence to indicate that mothers who are less than 15 years of age have babies with lower birth weights than the general population.

29. (a) The data are not normally distributed and have outliers.

(b) H_0: $\mu = 24.1$ million shares, H_1: $\mu \neq 24.1$ million shares. Classical approach: $z_0 = -1.77$ is between $-z_{0.05/2} = -1.96$ and $z_{0.05/2} = 1.96$; do not reject the null hypothesis. P-value approach: P-value $= 0.0768$ [Tech: 0.0763] $> \alpha = 0.05$; do not reject the null hypothesis. Conclusion: There is not sufficient evidence to indicate that the volume of Dell stock is different from what it was in 2002.

30. (a) The data are not normally distributed and have outliers.

(b) H_0: $\mu = 10.7$ million shares; H_1: $\mu \neq 10.7$ million shares. Classical approach: $z_0 = -4.91 < -z_{0.05/2} = -1.96$; reject the null hypothesis. P-value approach: P-value < 0.0001; reject the null hypothesis. Conclusion: There is sufficient evidence to indicate that the volume of Google stock is different from what it was in 2002. In 2002, there was quite a bit of fanfare surrounding the stock. Clearly, this fanfare has faded.

31. H_0: $\mu = 0.11$ mg/L, H_1: $\mu \neq 0.11$ mg/L; 99% confidence interval. Lower bound: 0.0917 [Tech: 0.0916] mg/L; upper bound: 0.2219 [Tech: 0.2220] mg/L. Because 0.11 is in the 99% confidence interval, we do not reject the statement in the null hypothesis. There is not sufficient evidence to indicate that the calcium concentration in rainwater in Chautauqua, New York, has changed since 1990.

32. H_0: $\mu = 5.27$, H_1: $\mu \neq 5.27$; 95% confidence interval. Lower bound: 5.204, upper bound: 5.468 [Tech: 5.469]. Because 5.27 is not in the 95% confidence interval, we reject the statement in the null hypothesis. There is sufficient evidence to indicate that the pH of the rain in Columbia River Gorge has changed since 2002.

33. H_0: $\mu = 24.1$ million shares, H_1: $\mu \neq 24.1$ million shares; 95% confidence interval. Lower bound: 19.615 million shares, upper bound: 24.325 million shares. Because 24.1 is in the 95% confidence interval, we do not reject the statement in the null hypothesis. Conclusion: There is not sufficient evidence to indicate that the volume of Dell stock is different from what it was in 2002.

34. H_0: $\mu = 10.7$ million shares, H_1: $\mu \neq 10.7$ million shares; 95% confidence interval. Lower bound: 4.082 million shares, upper bound: 7.858 million shares. Because 10.7 is not in the 95% confidence interval, we reject the statement in the null hypothesis. There is sufficient evidence to indicate that the volume of Google stock is different from what it was in 2005.

35. (a) H_0: $\mu = 515$, H_1: $\mu > 515$

(b) Classical approach: $z_0 = 1.49 > z_{0.10} = 1.28$; reject the null hypothesis. P-value approach: P-value $= 0.0681$ [Tech: 0.0683] $< \alpha = 0.10$; reject the null hypothesis.

(c) Answers will vary.

(d) With $n = 400$ students: Classical approach: $z_0 = 0.70 < z_{0.10} = 1.28$; do not reject the null hypothesis. P-value approach: P-value $= 0.2420$ [Tech: 0.2414] $> \alpha = 0.10$; do not reject the null hypothesis.

36. (a) H_0: $\mu = 0$, H_1: $\mu > 0$

(b) Classical approach: $z_0 = 3.85 > z_{0.10} = 1.28$; reject the null hypothesis. P-value approach: P-value $= 0.0001 < \alpha = 0.10$; reject the null hypothesis.

(c) Answers will vary.

(d) With $n = 40$ subject: Classical approach: $z_0 = 0.79 < z_{0.10} = 1.28$; do not reject the null hypothesis. P-value approach: P-value $= 0.2148$ [Tech: 0.2146] $> \alpha = 0.10$; do not reject the null hypothesis.

37. (a), (c), (d) Answers will vary.

(b) Expect 5 samples to result in a Type I error.

38. (a), (c), (d) Answers will vary.

(b) Expect 2 samples to result in a Type I error.

39. Yes; because the head of institutional research has access to the entire population, inference is unnecessary. He can say with 100% confidence that the mean age decreased because the mean age in the current semester is less than the mean age is 1995.

40. (a) *Step 1: Research objective.* To determine whether there is an association between distance of home address at birth from high-voltage power lines and the incidence of leukemia and other cancers in children in England and Wales.

Step 2: Collect information. This is a case-control study, which is an observational study in which two groups are compared. Here the two groups are children who were born near high-voltage lines and those who were not born near high-voltage lines.

Step 3: Organize and summarize the information. The statistics based on the sample are based on relative risk. The relative risk of leukemia for children born within 200 meters (m) of high-voltage power lines was 1.69 (these children were 1.69 times more likely to contract cancer than those who lived more than 600 m from the power lines). The relative risk of leukemia of children who lived between 200 and 600 m from high-voltage lines was 1.23 when compared with children who lived more than 600 m from the power line.

Step 4: Draw conclusions. The 95% confidence interval for relative risk of children who lived within 200 m of the high-voltage power lines compared to those who lived more than 600 m from the power lines was lower bound: 1.13, upper bound: 2.53. The researchers are 95% confident that the relative risk is between 1.13 and 2.53. Because a relative risk of 1 would imply no association, and this interval does not contain 1, we would reject the null hypothesis of no association. The 95% confidence interval for relative risk for children who lived between 200 and 600 m of high-voltage power lines compared to those who lived more than 600 m from the power lines was lower bound: 1.02, upper bound: 1.49. The researchers are 95% confident that the relative risk is between 1.02 and 1.49. Because a relative risk of 1 would imply no association, and this interval does not contain 1, we would reject the null hypothesis of no association. There is a relation between the distance one is from the power lines and the relative risk of contracting leukemia with a P-value < 0.01. The likelihood of observing the relation observed when there is no relation between proximity to the power lines and leukemia is 0.01. There is an association between childhood leukemia and proximity of home address at birth to high-voltage power lines.

(b) It would be highly unethical to conduct this experiment on human subjects. A researcher could try to replicate the results of this experiment with lab rats. We need a case-control to help diminish the likelihood of lurking variables. We must assume that the subjects are similar in all other traits that might affect the likelihood of contracting leukemia.

10.3 Assess Your Understanding (page 547)

1. A hypothesis about a population mean with σ unknown can be tested provided that the sample is obtained using simple random sampling, and the population from which the sample is drawn is either normally distributed with no outliers or the sample size n is larger than 30.

2. The critical value for a right-tailed test at an $\alpha = 0.01$ level of significance when σ is unknown and there are 15 degrees of freedom is $t_{0.01} = 2.602$.

3. The critical values for a two-tailed test at an $\alpha = 0.05$ level of significance when σ is unknown and there are 12 degrees of freedom are $t_{0.025} = 2.179$ and $-t_{0.025} = -2.179$.

4. The critical value for a left-tailed test at an $\alpha = 0.05$ level of significance when σ is unknown and there are 19 degrees of freedom is $-t_{0.05} = -1.729$.

5. (a) $t_0 = -1.379$ (b) $-t_{0.05} = -1.714$
   (c)

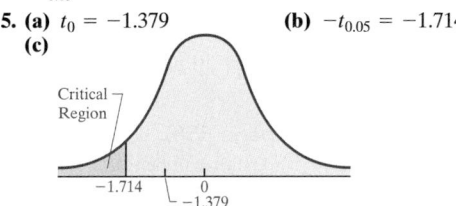

   (d) There is not enough evidence for the researcher to reject the null hypothesis because it is a left-tailed test and the test statistic is greater than the critical value, $(-1.379 > -1.714)$.

6. (a) $t_0 = 2.674$ (b) $t_{0.1} = 1.318$
   (c)

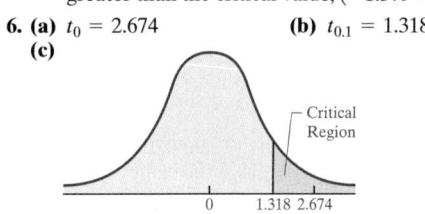

   (d) The researcher will reject the null hypothesis because it is a right-tailed test and the test statistic is greater than the critical value $(2.674 > 1.318)$.

7. (a) $t_0 = 2.502$ (b) $-t_{0.005} = -2.819; t_{0.005} = 2.819$
   (c)

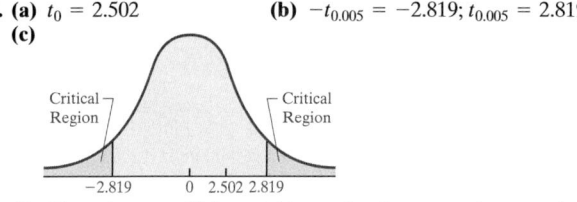

   (d) There is not sufficient evidence for the researcher to reject the null hypothesis, since the test statistic is between the critical values $(-2.819 < 2.502 < 2.819)$.
   (e) Lower bound: 99.39, upper bound: 110.21. Because the 99% confidence interval includes 100, we do not reject the statement in the null hypothesis.

8. (a) $t_0 = -1.711$ (b) $-t_{0.02} = -2.189$
   (c)

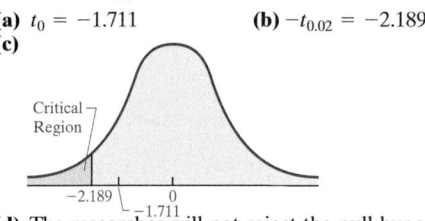

   (d) The researcher will not reject the null hypothesis because it is a left-tailed test and the test statistic is greater than the critical value $(-1.711 > -2.189)$.

9. (a) $t_0 = -1.677$
   (b)

   (c) $0.05 < P$-value < 0.10 [Tech: $P = 0.0559$]; If we take 100 random samples of size 18, we would expect about 6 of the samples to result in a sample mean of 18.3 or less if $\mu = 20$.
   (d) The researcher will not reject the null hypothesis at the $\alpha = 0.05$ level of significance because the P-value is greater than the level of significance $(0.10 > 0.05)$.

10. (a) $t_0 = 1.109$
    (b)

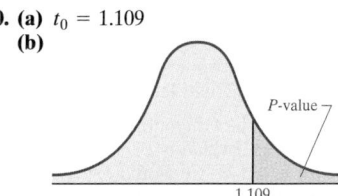

    (c) $0.10 < P$-value < 0.15 [Tech: $P = 0.1445$]; If we obtain 100 random samples of size $n = 35$, we would expect about 15 of the samples to result in a sample mean of 4.9 or higher if $\mu = 4.5$.
    (d) The researcher will not reject the null hypothesis at the $\alpha = 0.10$ level of significance because the P-value is greater than the level of significance $(P$-value $> 0.10)$.

11. (a) No; $n \geq 30$ b) $t = -3.108$
    (c)

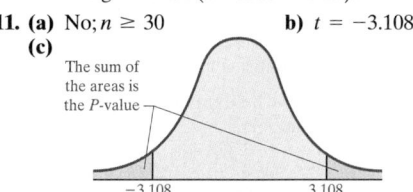

    (d) $0.002 < P$-value < 0.005 [Tech: P-value $= 0.0038$]; If we obtain 1000 random samples of size $n = 35$, we would expect about 4 samples to result in a mean as extreme or more extreme than the one observed if $\mu = 105$.
    (e) The researcher will reject the null hypothesis at the $\alpha = 0.01$ level of significance because the P-value is less than the level of significance $(0.0038 < 0.01)$.

12. (a) No; $n \geq 30$ (b) $t = 2.455$
    (c)

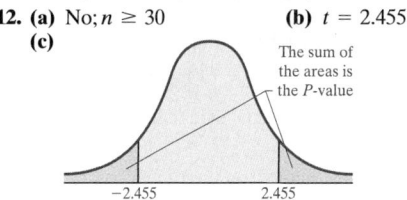

    (d) $0.01 < P$-value < 0.02 [Tech: P-value $= 0.0186$]; If we obtain 100 random samples of size $n = 40$, we'd expect about 2 samples to result in a mean as extreme or more extreme than the one observed if $\mu = 45$.
    (e) The researcher will not reject the null hypothesis at the $\alpha = 0.01$ level of significance because the P-value is greater than the level of significance $(0.0186 > 0.01)$.
    (f) Lower bound: 44.66, upper bound: 51.94. Because the confidence interval includes 45, we do not reject the null hypothesis.

13. Hypotheses: $H_0: \mu = 9.02, H_1: \mu < 9.02$. Classical approach: $t_0 = -4.553 < -t_{0.01} = -2.718$; reject the null hypothesis. P-value approach: P-value < 0.0005 [Tech: P-value $= 0.0004$] $< \alpha = 0.01$; reject the null hypothesis. There is sufficient evidence to conclude that the mean hippocampal volume in alcoholic adolescents is less than the normal mean volume of 9.02 cm³.

14. Assuming that the population of kidney weights is normally distributed, with no outliers: Hypotheses: $H_0: \mu = 355.7, H_1: \mu > 355.7$. Classical approach: $t_0 = 3.144 > t_{0.05} = 1.796$; reject the null hypothesis. P-value approach: $0.0025 < P$-value < 0.005 [Tech: P-value $= 0.0047$] $< \alpha = 0.05$; reject the null hypothesis. There is sufficient evidence to conclude that the mean weight of kidneys of first-generation mice whose both parents were exposed to para-nonylphenol is greater than the mean weight of the kidneys of nonexposed mice.

15. $H_0: \mu = 703.5, H_1: \mu > 703.5$. Classical approach: $t_0 = 0.813 < t_{0.05} = 1.685$ (39 degrees of freedom); do not reject the null hypothesis. P-value approach: $0.25 > P$-value > 0.20 [Tech: P-value $= 0.2105$] $> \alpha = 0.05$; do not reject the null hypothesis. There is not sufficient evidence to conclude that the mean FICO score of high-income individuals is greater than that of the general population. In other words, it is not unlikely to obtain a mean credit score of 714.2 even though the true population mean credit score is 703.5.

16. $H_0: \mu = 154.8$ minutes, $H_1: \mu < 154.8$ minutes. Classical approach: $t_0 = -3.969 < -t_{0.05} = -1.676$ (using 50 degrees of freedom); reject the null hypothesis. P-value approach: P-value < 0.0005 [Tech: P-value $= 0.0001$] $< \alpha = 0.05$; reject the null hypothesis. There is sufficient evidence to conclude that Internet users watch less television per day.

17. (a) $t_0 = -15.119 < -t_{0.01} = -2.330$; reject the null hypothesis.
(b) P-value < 0.0005 [Tech: P-value < 0.0001]; If we take 10,000 random samples of size $n = 700$, we would expect about 1 sample to result in a sample mean of 98.2°F or less if $\mu = 98.6°$F.

18. (a) $t_0 = -3.169 < -t_{0.01} = -2.364$; reject the null hypothesis.
(b) $0.0025 < P$-value < 0.001 [Tech: P-value $= 0.0010$]; If we take 1000 random samples of size $n = 123$, we would expect about 1 sample to result in a sample mean of 98.4°F or less if $\mu = 98.6°$F.

19. $H_0: \mu = 40.7$ years, $H_1: \mu \neq 40.7$ years; 95% confidence interval. Lower bound: 35.44 years, upper bound: 42.36 years. Because the interval includes 40.7 years, there is not significant evidence to conclude that the mean age of a death-row inmate has changed since 2002.

20. $H_0: \mu = \$1,493$, $H_1: \mu \neq \$1,493$; 95% confidence interval. Lower bound: $1,507.7, upper bound: $1,728.3. Because the interval does not include $1,493, there is significant evidence to conclude that the mean energy expenditure (adjusted for inflation) has changed since 2001.

21. (a) Yes; the conditions are satisfied. The data appear to be normally distributed, and there are no outliers.
(b) $H_0: \mu = 1.68$, $H_1: \mu \neq 1.68$; $t_0 = 0.778$ is between $-t_{0.05} = -1.796$ and $t_{0.05} = 1.796$ with 11 degrees of freedom; do not reject the null hypothesis. $0.40 < P$-value < 0.50 [Tech: P-value $= 0.4529$]; Because the P-value is greater than the level of significance, we do not reject the null hypothesis. Conclusion: There is not sufficient evidence to conclude that the golf balls do not conform. Therefore, we will give Maxfli the benefit of the doubt and assume the balls are conforming.

22. (a) Yes; the normal probability plot suggests that the data could come from a population that is normally distributed, and the boxplot does not show any outliers.
(b) $H_0: \mu = 198$, $H_1: \mu > 198$; $t_0 = 3.499$ and $t_{0.10} = 1.383$ with 9 degrees of freedom; Reject the null hypothesis. $0.0025 < P$-value < 0.005 [Tech: P-value $= 0.0033$] $< \alpha = 0.10$; reject the null hypothesis. Conclusion: There is sufficient evidence to conclude that the class was effective.

23. (a) Yes; the conditions are satisfied. The data appear to be normally distributed, and there are no outliers.
(b) Hypotheses: $H_0: \mu = 84.3$ seconds, $H_1: \mu < 84.3$ seconds. Classical approach: $t_0 = -1.310 > -t_{0.10} = -1.383$ with 9 degrees of freedom; do not reject the null hypothesis. P-value approach: $0.15 > P$-value > 0.10 [Tech: P-value $= 0.1113$] $> \alpha = 0.10$; do not reject the null hypothesis. There is not sufficient evidence to conclude that the new system is effective.

24. (a) Yes; the conditions are satisfied. The data appear to be normally distributed, and there are no outliers.
(b) Hypotheses: $H_0: \mu = 7.0$, $H_1: \mu \neq 7.0$. Classical approach: $t_0 = 1.183$ is between $-t_{0.025} = -2.160$ and $t_{0.025} = 2.160$ with 13 degrees of freedom; do not reject the null hypothesis. P-value approach: $0.30 > P$-value > 0.20 [Tech: P-value $= 0.2579$] $> \alpha = 0.05$; do not reject the null hypothesis. There is not sufficient evidence to conclude that there is bias in the pH meter.

25. (a) We assume that there is no difference between actual and predicted earnings, so the null hypothesis is $\mu = 0$. We want to gather evidence that shows that the predictions are off target, but we are not indicating whether the analysts, on average, had predictions that were too high or too low, so the alternative hypothesis is $\mu \neq 0$.
(b) Since P-value $= 0.046 < \alpha = 0.05$, we reject the statement in the null hypothesis. The evidence suggests that the analyst's earnings predictions are not accurate.
(c) The researcher is supposed to select the level of significance and direction of the alternative hypothesis prior to gathering evidence. This removes the possibility of any researcher bias.

26. $H_0: \mu = 0$, $H_1: \mu \neq 0$. The P-value is 0.44, which indicates that we should not reject the null hypothesis (we would expect to get the results we obtained, or more extreme, in about 44 samples out of 100 samples if the null hypothesis were true). There is not sufficient evidence to conclude that the weather forecasts are inaccurate, on average.

27. The analysis conducted by the farmer only applies to his farm, not the entire United States.

28. (a) Answers will vary. Expect 5 samples to result in a rejection of the null hypothesis at $\alpha = 0.05$. The probability of a Type I error is 0.05.
(b) Answers will vary. Expect 5 samples to result in a rejection of the null hypothesis at $\alpha = 0.05$. The probability of a Type I error is 0.05.
(c) Answers will vary.

29. (a) Answers will vary. The experiment does not meet the requirements for hypothesis testing.
(b) Answers will vary. Expect 5 samples to result in a rejection of the null hypothesis at $\alpha = 0.05$.

30. (a), (c) Answers will vary.
(b) Expect 2 samples to result in a Type I error.
(d) Because we know that the population from which we are sampling has a mean equal to 50.

10.4 Assess Your Understanding (page 558)

1. A hypothesis about a population proportion can be tested if the sample is obtained by simple random sampling and $np(1 - p) \geq 10$, with $n \leq 0.05N$ (the sample size is no more than 5% of the population size).

2. If we construct a confidence interval using the margin of error, we obtain *lower bound:* 52% and *upper bound:* 58%. Because a majority would be any percentage greater than 50%, the headline is accurate.

3. $np_0(1 - p_0) = 42 > 10$
(a) Classical approach: $z_0 = 2.31 > z_{0.05} = 1.645$; reject the null hypothesis.
(b) P-value approach: P-value $= 0.0104$ [Tech: 0.0103] $< \alpha = 0.05$; reject the null hypothesis. There is sufficient evidence at the $\alpha = 0.05$ level of significance to reject the null hypothesis.

4. $np_0(1 - p_0) = 60 > 10$
(a) Classical approach: $z_0 = -3.36 < -z_{0.01} = -2.33$; reject the null hypothesis.
(b) P-value approach: P-value $= 0.0004 < \alpha = 0.01$; reject the null hypothesis. There is sufficient evidence at the $\alpha = 0.01$ level of significance to reject the null hypothesis.

5. $np_0(1 - p_0) = 37.1 > 10$
(a) Classical approach: $z_0 = -0.74 > -z_{0.10} = -1.28$; do not reject the null hypothesis.
(b) P-value approach: P-value $= 0.2296$ [Tech: 0.2301] $> \alpha = 0.10$; do not reject the null hypothesis. There is not sufficient evidence at the $\alpha = 0.10$ level of significance to reject the null hypothesis.

6. $np_0(1 - p_0) = 75 > 10$
(a) Classical approach: $z_0 = -0.46 > -z_{0.10} = -1.28$; do not reject the null hypothesis.
(b) P-value approach: P-value $= 0.3228$ [Tech: 0.3221] $> \alpha = 0.10$; do not reject the null hypothesis. There is not sufficient evidence at the $\alpha = 0.10$ level of significance to reject the null hypothesis.

7. $np_0(1 - p_0) = 45 > 10$
(a) Classical approach: $z_0 = -1.49$ is between $-z_{0.025} = -1.96$ and $z_{0.025} = 1.96$; do not reject the null hypothesis.
(b) P-value approach: P-value $= 0.1362$ [Tech: 0.1360] $> \alpha = 0.05$; do not reject the null hypothesis. There is not sufficient evidence at the $\alpha = 0.05$ level of significance to reject the null hypothesis.

8. $np_0(1 - p_0) = 240 > 10$
(a) Classical approach: $z_0 = 1.29$ is between $-z_{0.005} = -2.575$ and $z_{0.005} = 2.575$; do not reject the null hypothesis.
(b) P-value approach: P-value $= 0.1970$ [Tech: 0.1967] $> \alpha = 0.01$; do not reject the null hypothesis. There is not sufficient evidence at the $\alpha = 0.01$ level of significance to reject the null hypothesis.

9. $np_0(1 - p_0) = 16.1 > 10$. Hypotheses: $H_0: p = 0.019$, $H_1: p > 0.019$
(a) Classical approach: $z_0 = 0.65 < z_{0.01} = 2.33$; do not reject the null hypothesis.
(b) P-value approach: P-value $= 0.2578$ [Tech: 0.2582] $> \alpha = 0.01$; do not reject the null hypothesis. There is not sufficient evidence at the $\alpha = 0.01$ level of significance to conclude that more than 1.9% of Lipitor users experience flulike symptoms as a side effect.

10. $np_0(1 - p_0) = 12.6 > 10$. Hypotheses: $H_0: p = 0.94$, $H_1: p > 0.94$
(a) Classical approach: $z_0 = 0.69 < z_{0.01} = 2.33$; do not reject the null hypothesis.

(b) *P*-value approach: *P*-value $= 0.2451$ [Tech: 0.2462] $> \alpha = 0.01$; do not reject the null hypothesis. There is not sufficient evidence at the $\alpha = 0.01$ level of significance to support the manufacturer's claim that more than 94% of patients taking Nexium are healed within 8 weeks.

11. H_0: $p = 0.5, H_1$: $p > 0.5$; $np_0(1 - p_0) = 258.5 > 10$. Classical approach: $z_0 = 1.93 > z_{0.05} = 1.645$; reject the null hypothesis. *P*-value approach: *P*-value $= 0.0268$ [Tech: 0.0269] $< \alpha = 0.05$; reject the null hypothesis. There is sufficient evidence to conclude that a majority of 30- to 64-year-olds in the United States are worried about retirement.

12. H_0: $p = 0.5, H_1$: $p > 0.5$; $np_0(1 - p_0) = 125 > 10$. Classical approach: $z_0 = 1.70 > z_{0.05} = 1.645$; reject the null hypothesis. *P*-value approach: *P*-value $= 0.0446 < \alpha = 0.05$; reject the null hypothesis. There is sufficient evidence to conclude that a majority of students in the state of Illinois are prepared for social science in college upon graduation.

13. H_0: $p = 0.38, H_1$: $p < 0.38$; $np_0(1 - p_0) = 264.3432 > 10$. Classical approach: $z_0 = -1.45 > -z_{0.05} = -1.645$; do not reject the null hypothesis. *P*-value approach: *P*-value $= 0.0735$ [Tech: 0.0754] $> \alpha = 0.05$; do not reject the null hypothesis. There is not sufficient evidence to conclude that the proportion of families with children under the age of 18 years of age who eat dinner together 7 nights a week has decreased since December, 2001.

14. $np_0(1 - p_0) = 118.272 > 10$. Hypotheses: H_0: $p = 0.56, H_1$: $p > 0.56$. Classical approach: $z_0 = 2.59 > z_{0.05} = 1.645$; reject the null hypothesis. *P*-value approach: *P*-value $= 0.0048 < \alpha = 0.05$; reject the null hypothesis. There is sufficient evidence at the $\alpha = 0.05$ level of significance to support the claim that the proportion of employed adults who feel basic mathematical skills are critical or very important to their job is greater than 0.56.

15. H_0: $p = 0.52, H_1$: $p \neq 0.52$; $np_0(1 - p_0) = 199.68 > 10$. Classical approach: $z_0 = -11.32 < -z_{0.05/2} = -1.96$; reject the null hypothesis. *P*-value approach: *P*-value $< 0.0001 < \alpha = 0.05$; reject the null hypothesis. There is sufficient evidence to conclude that the proportion of parents with children in high school who feel it was a serious problem that high school students were not being taught enough math and science has changed since 1994.

16. $np_0(1 - p_0) = 121.8 > 10$. Hypotheses: H_0: $p = 0.58, H_1$: $p \neq 0.58$. Classical approach: $z_0 = -0.45$ is between $-z_{0.05} = -1.645$ and $z_{0.05} = 1.645$; do not reject the null hypothesis. *P*-value approach: *P*-value $= 0.6528$ [Tech: 0.6505] $> \alpha = 0.10$; do not reject the null hypothesis. There is not sufficient evidence at the $\alpha = 0.10$ level of significance to support the claim that the percentage of females aged 15 years or older who live alone has changed.

17. H_0: $p = 0.47, H_1$: $p \neq 0.47$; $\hat{p} = 0.460$; $n\hat{p}(1 - \hat{p}) = 257.094 > 10$. Lower bound: 0.430, upper bound: 0.490. Since 0.47 is contained in the interval, we do not reject the null hypothesis. There is not sufficient evidence to conclude that parents' attitude toward the quality of education in the United States has changed since August 2002.

18. **(a)** Answers will vary. The survey would need to clearly be anonymous and untraceable. In addition, the questions need to be phrased so as to not sound judgmental.
(b) H_0: $p = 0.22, H_1$: $p \neq 0.22$; $\hat{p} = 0.244$; $n\hat{p}(1 - \hat{p}) = 92.232 > 10$. Lower bound: 0.206, upper bound: 0.282. Since 0.22 is contained in the interval, we do not reject the null hypothesis. There is not sufficient evidence to conclude that the proportion of males who have strayed at least once during their married life is different from 0.22.

19. $np_0(1 - p_0) = 35 > 10$. Hypotheses: H_0: $p = 0.37, H_1$: $p < 0.37$. Classical approach: $z_0 = -0.25 > -z_{0.05} = -1.645$; do not reject the null hypothesis. *P*-value approach: *P*-value $= 0.4013$ [Tech: 0.3999] $> \alpha = 0.05$; do not reject the null hypothesis. No; there is not sufficient evidence at the $\alpha = 0.05$ level of significance to conclude that less than 37% of pet owners speaks to their pets on the answering machine or telephone. The sample data do not contradict the results of the Animal Hospital Association.

20. $np_0(1 - p_0) = 25.5 > 10$. Hypotheses: H_0: $p = 0.85, H_1$: $p > 0.85$
(a) Classical approach: $z_0 = 0.20 < z_{0.10} = 1.28$; do not reject the null hypothesis.
(b) *P*-value approach: *P*-value $= 0.4207$ [Tech: 0.4215] $> \alpha = 0.10$; do not reject the null hypothesis. There is not sufficient evidence at the $\alpha = 0.10$ level of significance to conclude that more than 85% of the adult population eats salad at least once a week.

21. Hypotheses: H_0: $p = 0.04, H_1$: $p < 0.04$. $np_0(1 - p_0) = 4.6 < 10$. *P*-value $= 0.2887 > \alpha = 0.05$; do not reject the null hypothesis. There is not sufficient evidence at the $\alpha = 0.05$ level of significance to support the obstetrician's belief that less than 4% of mothers smoke 21 or more cigarettes during pregnancy.

22. Hypotheses: H_0: $p = 0.032, H_1$: $p > 0.032$. $np_0(1 - p_0) = 4.6 < 10$. *P*-value $= 0.1099 > \alpha = 0.05$; do not reject the null hypothesis. There is not sufficient evidence at the $\alpha = 0.05$ level of significance to conclude that more than 3.2% of Americans work at home.

23. Hypotheses: H_0: $p = 0.096, H_1$: $p > 0.096$. $np_0(1 - p_0) = 6.9 < 10$. *P*-value $= 0.0410 < \alpha = 0.10$; reject the null hypothesis. There is sufficient evidence at the $\alpha = 0.10$ level of significance to support the urban economist's belief that the percentage of Californians who spend more than 60 minutes traveling to work has increased since 2000.

24. Hypotheses: H_0: $p = 0.015, H_1$: $p < 0.015$. $np_0(1 - p_0) = 7.4 < 10$. *P*-value $= 0.0578 < \alpha = 0.10$; reject the null hypothesis. There is sufficient evidence at the $\alpha = 0.10$ level of significance to support the researcher's belief that the percentage of males living in Colorado who are teachers has decreased since 2000.

25. **(a)** The proportion could be changing due to sampling error—different people are in the sample. The proportion could also be changing because people's attitudes are changing.
(b) No; the probability of obtaining a sample proportion of $\hat{p} = 0.44$ is 0.45 is 0.25. That is, about 25 samples out of 100 samples will result in a sample proportion of 0.44 or less, if the population proportion is 0.45.

26. H_0: $p = 0.65, H_1$: $p > 0.65$; *P*-value $= 0.0918$ [Tech: 0.0958]. There is a 0.09 probability of obtaining the results we obtain if the null hypothesis is true. That is, about 9 samples in 100 will yield results similar to those found, if the null hypothesis is true. The headline is inaccurate.

27. **(a)** The researchers simply looked at records. There was no treatment imposed on the individuals in the study.
(b) Retrospective
(c) 102 females
(d)

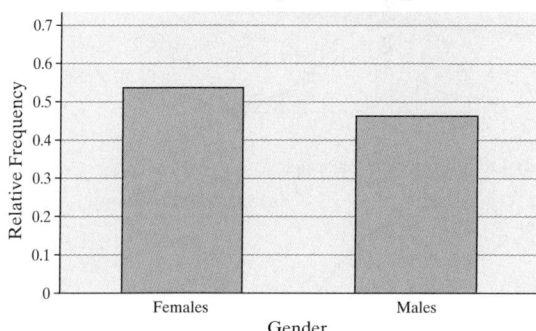

Proportion of Individuals in a Family with a Sibling Who Has Lupus

(e) $\hat{p} = \dfrac{92}{194} = 0.474$

(f) H_0: $p = 0.51, H_1$: $p < 0.51$. Classical approach: $z_0 = -1.00 > -z_{0.05} = -1.645$; do not reject the null hypothesis. *P*-value approach: *P*-value $= 0.1587$ [Tech: 0.1594]; do not reject the null hypothesis. The sample evidence does not indicate that the proportion of males in families where a sibling has lupus is less than 0.51, the accepted proportion of males in the general population at birth.

(g) Lower bound: 0.404, upper bound: 0.544. We are 95% confident that the proportion of males in a family where a sibling has lupus is between 0.404 and 0.544.

10.5 Assess Your Understanding (page 565)

1. To test a claim regarding a population standard deviation, we must have a simple random sample taken from a normally distributed population.

2. $\chi^2_{0.05} = 28.869$

3. (a) $\chi_0^2 = 20.496$ **(b)** $\chi_{0.95}^2 = 13.091$

(c)

13.091 $x_0^2 = 20.496$

(d) Do not reject H_0, because $\chi_0^2 > \chi_{0.95}^2$.

4. (a) $\chi_0^2 = 15.986$ **(b)** $\chi_{0.01}^2 = 29.141$

(c)

$x_0^2 = 15.986$ 29.141

(d) Do not reject H_0, because $\chi_0^2 < \chi_{0.01}^2$.

5. (a) $\chi_0^2 = 30.222$ **(b)** $\chi_{0.1}^2 = 24.769$

(c)

24.769 $x_0^2 = 30.222$

(d) Reject H_0, because $\chi_0^2 > \chi_{0.1}^2$.

6. (a) $\chi_0^2 = 17.273$ **(b)** $\chi_{0.99}^2 = 22.164$

(c)

22.164
$x_0^2 = 17.273$

(d) Reject H_0, because $\chi_0^2 < \chi_{0.99}^2$.

7. (a) $\chi_0^2 = 13.707$ **(b)** $\chi_{0.975}^2 = 3.816, \chi_{0.025}^2 = 21.920$

(c)

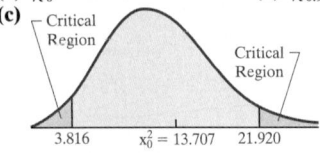

3.816 $x_0^2 = 13.707$ 21.920

(d) Do not reject H_0, because $\chi_{0.975}^2 < \chi_0^2 < \chi_{0.025}^2$.

8. (a) $\chi_0^2 = 9.333$ **(b)** $\chi_{0.95}^2 = 11.591; \chi_{0.05}^2 = 32.671$

(c)

11.591   32.671
$x_0^2 = 9.333$

(d) Reject H_0, because $\chi_0^2 < \chi_{0.95}^2$.

9. Hypotheses: H_0: $\sigma = 0.04$, H_1: $\sigma < 0.04$. $\chi_0^2 = 13.590 < \chi_{0.95}^2 = 13.848$; $0.025 < P$-value < 0.05 [Tech: P-value $= 0.045$] $< \alpha = 0.95$; reject the null hypothesis at the $\alpha = 0.05$ level of significance. There is sufficient evidence to conclude that the mutual fund has moderate risk.

10. Hypotheses: H_0: $\sigma = 0.42$, H_1: $\sigma < 0.42$. $\chi_0^2 = 14.735 > \chi_{0.099}^2 = 7.015$; P-value > 0.10 [Tech: 0.3199] $> \alpha = 0.01$ do not reject the null hypothesis at the $\alpha = 0.05$ level of significance. There is not sufficient evidence at the $\alpha = 0.05$ level of significance to support the engineer's claim that there is less variability in the filling machine.

11. Hypotheses: H_0: $\sigma = 0.004$, H_1: $\sigma < 0.004$. $\chi_0^2 = 9.375 < \chi_{0.099}^2 = 10.856$; P-value < 0.005 [Tech: P-value $= 0.003$] $< \alpha = 0.01$; reject the null hypothesis at the $\alpha = 0.01$ level of significance. There is sufficient evidence at the $\alpha = 0.01$ level of significance for the manager to conclude that the standard deviation has decreased. The recalibration was effective.

12. Hypotheses: H_0: $\sigma = 0.5$, H_1: $\sigma \neq 0.5$. $\chi_0^2 = 26.139$ is between $\chi_{0.975}^2 = 7.564$ and $\chi_{0.025}^2 = 30.191$; do not reject the null hypothesis at

the $\alpha = 0.05$ level of significance. There is not sufficient evidence at the $\alpha = 0.05$ level of significance to support the claim that the standard deviation is not 0.5.

13. H_0: $\sigma = 0.08$, H_1: $\sigma \neq 0.08$; $\chi_0^2 = 10.644$ is between $\chi_{0.975}^2 = 2.700$ and $\chi_{0.025}^2 = 19.023$; do not reject the null hypothesis. The assumption is reasonable.

14. H_0: $\sigma = 0.27$, H_1: $\sigma \neq 0.27$; $\chi_0^2 = 15.902$ is between $\chi_{0.975}^2 = 6.262$ and $\chi_{0.025}^2 = 27.488$; do not reject the null hypothesis. The assumption is reasonable.

15. H_0: $\sigma = 0.06$, H_1: $\sigma \neq 0.06$; $\chi_0^2 = 11.8125$ is between $\chi_{0.975}^2 = 10.283$ and $\chi_{0.025}^2 = 35.479$; do not reject the null hypothesis. The assumption is reasonable.

16. Hypotheses: H_0: $\sigma = 0.5$, H_1: $\sigma \neq 0.5$. $\chi_0^2 = 6.188$ is between $\chi_{0.975}^2 = 3.816$ and $\chi_{0.025}^2 = 21.920$; do not reject the null hypothesis at the $\alpha = 0.05$ level of significance. The assumption is reasonable.

17. Hypotheses: H_0: $\sigma = 8.3$, H_1: $\sigma < 8.3$. $\chi_0^2 = 15.639 < \chi_{0.90}^2 = 15.659$; $0.05 < P$-value < 0.10 [Tech: 0.0993] $< \alpha = 0.10$; reject the null hypothesis at the $\alpha = 0.10$ level of significance. There is sufficient evidence at the $\alpha = 0.10$ level of significance to conclude that Iverson is a more consistent player than other shooting guards in the NBA.

18. Hypotheses: H_0: $\sigma = 1.2$, H_1: $\sigma < 1.2$. $\chi_0^2 = 24.01 < \chi_{0.95}^2 = 34.764$; P-value < 0.005 [Tech: 0.0010] $< \alpha = 0.05$ reject the null hypothesis at the $\alpha = 0.05$ level of significance. There is sufficient evidence at the $\alpha = 0.05$ level of significance to conclude that the standard deviation of the wait time with one line is less than the standard deviation with four lines.

19. (a)

Probability Plot of Heights
Normal - 95% CI

(b) $s = 2.059$ inches

(c) Hypotheses: H_0: $\sigma = 2.9$, H_1: $\sigma < 2.9$. $\chi_0^2 = 9.5779 > \chi_{0.99}^2 = 7.633$; $0.05 > P$-value > 0.025 [Tech: 0.0374] $> \alpha = 0.01$; do not reject the null hypothesis at the $\alpha = 0.01$ level of significance. There is not sufficient evidence at the $\alpha = 0.01$ level of significance to support the claim that the standard deviation of the heights of baseball players is less than 2.9 inches.

20. Hypotheses: H_0: $\sigma = 0.05$, H_1: $\sigma > 0.05$. $\chi_0^2 = 61.56 > \chi_{0.05}^2 = 30.144$; P-value < 0.005 [Tech: < 0.0001] $< \alpha = 0.05$; reject the null hypothesis at the $\alpha = 0.05$ level of significance. There is sufficient evidence at the $\alpha = 0.05$ level of significance to support the representative's claim that the manufacturer does not meet the circumference requirements.

10.6 Assess Your Understanding (page 567)

1. To test a hypothesis about a population mean, we must use a simple random sample that is either drawn from a normally distributed population or the sample must have at least 30 subjects. Assuming that the prerequisites are met, use a normal model to test a hypothesis if the population standard deviation (or variance) is known, and use a Student's t-distribution if the population standard deviation (or variance) is not known.

2. Before testing a hypothesis about a population, proportion, we must be sure that $np(1 - p) \geq 10$ and that the sample size is no larger than 5% of the population ($n \leq 0.05N$).

3. Hypotheses: H_0: $\mu = 70$, H_1: $\mu < 70$. Classical approach: $z_0 = -1.87 < -z_{0.10} = -1.28$; reject the null hypothesis. P-value approach: P-value $= 0.0307 < \alpha = 0.10$; reject the null hypothesis. There is sufficient evidence at the $\alpha = 0.10$ level of significance to conclude that the population mean is less than 70.

4. Hypotheses: H_0: $\mu = 1$, H_1: $\mu < 1$. Classical approach: $t_0 = -2.179 > -t_{0.10} = -2.552$ with 18 degrees of freedom; do not reject the null hypothesis. P-value approach: $0.025 > P$-value > 0.02 [Tech: P-value $= 0.0214$] $> \alpha = 0.01$; do not reject the null hypothesis. There is not sufficient evidence at the level of significance to conclude that the mean is less than 1.

5. Hypotheses: H_0: $p = 0.5$, H_1: $p > 0.5$; $np_0(1 - p_0) = 50 > 10$. Classical approach: $z_0 = 2.12 > z_{0.05} = 1.645$; reject the null hypothesis. P-value approach: P-value $= 0.0170$ [Tech: 0.0169] $< \alpha = 0.05$; reject the null hypothesis. There is sufficient evidence at the $\alpha = 0.05$ level of significance to conclude that more than half of the individuals with valid driver's licenses drive an American-made automobile.

6. Hypotheses: H_0: $\sigma^2 = 95$, H_1: $\sigma^2 < 95$. Classical approach: $\chi_0^2 = 9.86 < \chi_{0.90}^2 = 11.651$; reject the null hypothesis. P-value approach: $0.025 < P$-value < 0.05 [Tech:P-value $= 0.0437$] $< \alpha = 0.10$; reject the null hypothesis. There is sufficient evidence at the $\alpha = 0.10$ level of significance to conclude that the variance is less than 95.

7. Hypotheses: H_0: $\mu = 25$, H_1: $\mu \neq 25$. Classical approach: $t_0 = -0.738$ is between $-t_{0.005} = -2.977$ and $t_{0.005} = 2.977$ with 14 degrees of freedom; do not reject the null hypothesis. P-value approach: P-value > 0.25 [Tech: P-value $= 0.4729$] $> \alpha = 0.01$; do not reject the null hypothesis. There is not sufficient evidence at the $\alpha = 0.01$ level of significance to conclude that the population mean is different from 25.

8. Hypotheses: H_0: $\mu = 55$, H_1: $\mu \neq 55$. Classical approach: $z_0 = -1.29$ is between $-z_{0.025} = -1.96$ and $z_{0.025} = 1.96$; do not reject the null hypothesis. P-value approach: P-value $= 0.1970$ [Tech: 0.1985] $> \alpha = 0.05$; do not reject the null hypothesis. There is not sufficient evidence at the $\alpha = 0.05$ level of significance to conclude that the population mean is different from 55.

9. Hypotheses: H_0: $\sigma^2 = 10$, H_1: $\sigma^2 > 10$. Classical approach: $\chi_0^2 = 20.55 < \chi_{0.05}^2 = 24.996$; do not reject the null hypothesis. P-value approach: P-value > 0.10 [Tech: P-value $= 0.1518$] $> \alpha = 0.05$; do not reject the null hypothesis. There is not sufficient evidence at the $\alpha = 0.05$ level of significance to conclude that the population variance is greater than 10.

10. Hypotheses: H_0: $\mu = 600$, H_1: $\mu \neq 600$. Classical approach: $t_0 = -1.186$ is between $-t_{0.05} = -1.671$ and $t_{0.05} = 1.671$ with 60 degrees of freedom; do not reject the null hypothesis. P-value approach: $0.15 > P$-value > 0.10 [Tech: P-value $= 0.2401$] $> \alpha = 0.10$; do not reject the null hypothesis. There is not sufficient evidence at the $\alpha = 0.10$ level of significance to conclude that the population mean is different from 600.

11. Hypotheses: H_0: $\mu = 100$, H_1: $\mu > 100$. Classical approach: $t_0 = 3.003 > t_{0.05} = 1.685$; reject the null hypothesis. P-value approach: $0.001 < P$-value < 0.0025 [Tech: P-value $= 0.0023$] $< \alpha = 0.05$; reject the null hypothesis. There is sufficient evidence at the $\alpha = 0.05$ level of significance to conclude that the population mean is greater than 100.

12. Hypotheses: H_0: $p = 0.25$, H_1: $p < 0.25$; $np_0(1 - p_0) = 60 > 10$. Classical approach: $z_0 = -2.84 < -z_{0.01} = -2.33$; reject the null hypothesis. P-value approach: P-value $= 0.0023 < \alpha = 0.01$; reject the null hypothesis. There is sufficient evidence at the $\alpha = 0.01$ level of significance to conclude that less than 25% of adults prefers mint chocolate chip ice cream.

13. H_0: $\mu = 100$, H_1: $\mu > 100$. Classical approach: $z_0 = 1.25 < z_{0.05} = 1.645$; do not reject the null hypothesis. P-value approach: P-value $= 0.1056$ [Tech: 0.1052] $> \alpha = 0.05$; do not reject the null hypothesis. There is not sufficient evidence to conclude that mothers who listen to Mozart have children with higher IQs.

14. H_0: $p = 0.5$, H_1: $p > 0.5$. Classical approach: $z_0 = 2.31 > z_{0.05} = 1.645$; reject the null hypothesis. P-value approach: P-value $= 0.0104$ [Tech: 0.0105] $< \alpha = 0.05$; reject the null hypothesis. There is sufficient evidence to conclude that a majority of Americans in 1945 believed that the United States could develop a way to protect itself from atomic bombs.

15. Hypotheses: H_0: $\sigma = 7{,}000$, H_1: $\sigma > 7{,}000$. Classical approach: $\chi_0^2 = 21.81 < \chi_{0.01}^2 = 36.191$; do not reject the null hypothesis. P-value approach: P-value > 0.10 [Tech: P-value $= 0.2938$] $> \alpha = 0.01$; do not reject the null hypothesis. There is not sufficient evidence at the $\alpha = 0.01$ level of significance to conclude that the standard deviation of yield strength is not acceptable. The evidence suggests that the standard deviation yield strength does not exceed 7,000 psi.

16. Hypotheses: H_0: $\mu = 774$, H_1: $\mu \neq 774$. Classical approach: $t_0 = -4.776 < -t_{0.005} = -2.728$; reject the null hypothesis. P-value approach: P-value < 0.0005 [Tech: P-value < 0.0001] $< \alpha = 0.01$; reject the null hypothesis. There is sufficient evidence at the $\alpha = 0.01$ level of significance to conclude that the mean expenditure for auto insurance is different from the 2002 amount.

17. Hypotheses: H_0: $\mu = 6.3$, H_1: $\mu < 6.3$. Classical approach: $t_0 = -0.915 > -t_{0.05} = -1.684$; do not reject the null hypothesis. P-value approach: $0.20 > P$-value > 0.15 [Tech: P-value $= 0.1829$] $> \alpha = 0.05$; do not reject the null hypothesis. There is not sufficient evidence at the $\alpha = 0.05$ level of significance to conclude that interest rates are lower than in 2001.

18. Hypotheses: H_0: $\sigma = 5$, H_1: $\sigma > 5$. Classical approach: $\chi_0^2 = 61.8164 > \chi_{0.05}^2 = 42.557$; reject the null hypothesis. P-value approach: P-value < 0.005 [Tech: P-value $= 0.0004$] $< \alpha = 0.05$; reject the null hypothesis. There is sufficient evidence at the $\alpha = 0.05$ level of significance to conclude that the standard deviation of the amount of the active ingredient is greater than 5 mg.

19. Hypotheses: H_0: $p = 0.23$, H_1: $p \neq 0.23$; $np_0(1 - p_0) = 181.7 > 10$. Classical approach: $z_0 = 1.37$, which is between $-z_{0.05} = -1.645$ and $z_{0.05} = 1.645$; do not reject the null hypothesis. P-value approach: P-value $= 0.1706 > \alpha = 0.10$; do not reject the null hypothesis. There is not sufficient evidence at the $\alpha = 0.10$ level of significance to conclude that the percentage of university undergraduate students who has at least one tattoo has changed since 2001.

20. (a) Yes; the conditions are satisfied. The data appear to be normally distributed, and there are no outliers.
(b) Hypotheses: H_0: $\mu = 10{,}000$, H_1: $\mu < 10{,}000$. Classical approach: $t_0 = -1.343 > -t_{0.05} = -1.771$; do not reject the null hypothesis. P-value approach: $0.15 > P$-value > 0.10 [Tech:P-value $= 0.1012$] $> \alpha = 0.05$; do not reject the null hypothesis. There is not sufficient evidence at the $\alpha = 0.05$ level of significance to conclude that the toner cartridges have a mean of less than 10,000 copies. The consumer advocate's concerns do not appear to be founded.

21. Hypotheses: H_0: $\mu = 8$, H_1: $\mu < 8$. Classical approach: $t_0 = -1.444$, $t_{0.01} = -2.403$; do not reject the null hypothesis. P-value approach: $0.10 > P$-value > 0.05 [Tech: 0.0777] $> \alpha = 0$; do not reject the null hypothesis. There is not sufficient evidence at the $\alpha = 0.01$ level of significance to conclude that the mean wait time is less than 8 minutes. The evidence supports the resident's skepticism.

22. (a) Yes; the conditions are satisfied. The data appear to be normally distributed, and there are no outliers.
(b) Hypotheses: H_0: $\mu = 3.2$, H_1: $\mu > 3.2$. Classical approach: $t_0 = 1.989 > t_{0.05} = 1.796$; reject the null hypothesis. P-value approach: $0.025 < P$-value < 0.05 [Tech: P-value $= 0.0361$] $< \alpha = 0.05$; reject the null hypothesis. There is sufficient evidence at the $\alpha = 0.05$ level of significance to conclude that the new contractor is not getting the streetlights replaced as quickly.

23. (a)

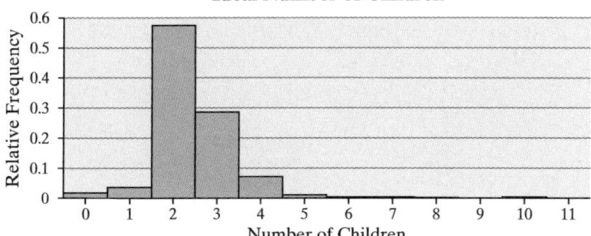

Ideal Number of Children

The distribution is skewed right.
(b) 2
(c) $\bar{x} = 2.47$, $s = 1.02$
(d) The data are clearly skewed to the right, so we need a large sample size to use the Central Limit Theorem.
(e) H_0: $\mu = 2.64$, H_1: $\mu \neq 2.64$; $t_0 = -5.041 < -t_{0.05/2} = -1.962$; reject the null hypothesis. P-value < 0.0001; reject the null hypothesis. The results of the poll indicate that people's beliefs as to the ideal number of children have changed.

10.7 Assess Your Understanding (page 573)

1. A Type II error is made when we fail to reject the null hypothesis and the alternative is true.

2. The power of the test is the probability of rejecting the null hypothesis when the alternative hypothesis is true.

3. As the true mean gets closer to the hypothesized mean, the power of the test decreases.

4. Increasing the sample size increases the power of the test.

5. (a) If the null hypothesis is not rejected and the true mean is less than 50, a Type II error has been made.

(b) $\beta = 0.7967$; power of the test: $1 - \beta = 0.2033$
(c) $\beta = 0.9066$; power of the test: $1 - \beta = 0.0934$

6. (a) If the null hypothesis is not rejected and the true mean is greater than 40, a Type II error has been made.
(b) $\beta = 0.4920$; power of the test: $1 - \beta = 0.5080$
(c) $\beta = 0.8749$; power of the test: $1 - \beta = 0.1251$

7. (a) If the null hypothesis is not rejected and the true mean is different from 100, a Type II error has been made.
(b) $\beta = 0.6985$; power of the test: $1 - \beta = 0.3015$
(c) $\beta = 0.9474$; power of the test: $1 - \beta = 0.0526$

8. (a) If the null hypothesis is not rejected and the true mean is less than 80, a Type II error has been made.
(b) $\beta = 0.9713$; power of the test: $1 - \beta = 0.0287$
(c) $\beta = 0.8962$; power of the test: $1 - \beta = 0.1038$

9. (a) If the null hypothesis is not rejected and the true mean is less than 20, a Type II error has been made.
(b) $\beta = 0.0212$; power of the test: $1 - \beta = 0.9788$
(c) $\beta = 0.6950$; power of the test: $1 - \beta = 0.3050$

10. (a) If the null hypothesis is not rejected and the true mean is greater than 4.5, a Type II error has been made.
(b) $\beta = 0.8531$; power of the test: $1 - \beta = 0.1469$
(c) $\beta = 0.1469$; power of the test: $1 - \beta = 0.8531$

11. (a) If the null hypothesis is not rejected and the true mean is different from 105, a Type II error has been made.
(b) $\beta = 0.5273$; power of the test: $1 - \beta = 0.4727$
(c) $\beta = 0.7562$; power of the test: $1 - \beta = 0.2438$

12. (a) If the null hypothesis is not rejected and the true mean is different from 45, a Type II error has been made.
(b) $\beta = 0.7532$; power of the test: $1 - \beta = 0.2468$
(c) $\beta = 0.1685$; power of the test: $1 - \beta = 0.8315$

13. (a) To not reject the hypothesis that the mean ATM withdrawal is $67, when, in fact, the mean ATM withdrawal is more than $67.
(b) $\beta = 0.4013$; power of the test: $1 - \beta = 0.5987$
(c) $\beta = 0.0643$; power of the test: $1 - \beta = 0.9357$

14. (a) If the null hypothesis is not rejected and the true mean height of a woman is greater than 63.7 inches, a Type II error has been made.
(b) $\beta = 0.9082$; power of the test: $1 - \beta = 0.0918$
(c) $\beta = 0.2327$; power of the test: $1 - \beta = 0.7673$

15. (a) If the null hypothesis is not rejected and the true mean SAT score for students whose first language is not English is less than 515, a Type II error has been made.
(b) $\beta = 0.9582$; power of the test: $1 - \beta = 0.0418$
(c) $\beta = 0.8238$; power of the test: $1 - \beta = 0.1762$
(d)

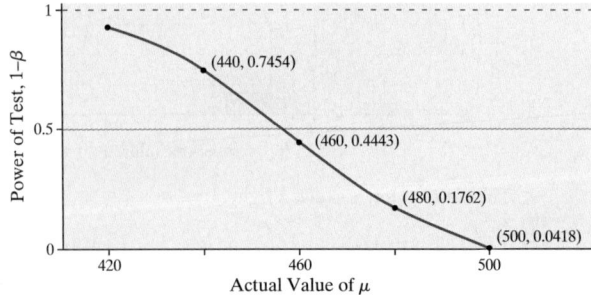

16. (a) If the null hypothesis was not rejected and the true mean SAT math score for students whose first language is not English is different from 516, a Type II error has been made.
(b) $\beta = 0.9286$; power of the test: $1 - \beta = 0.0714$
(c) $\beta = 0.6367$; power of the test: $1 - \beta = 0.3633$

17. $\beta = 0.9345$; power of the test: $1 - \beta = 0.0655$

18. $\beta = 0.3520$; power of the test: $1 - \beta = 0.6480$

19. (a) $\beta = 0.1894$
(b) Power of the test: $1 - \beta = 0.8106$

20. (a) $\beta = 0.2946$
(b) Power of the test: $1 - \beta = 0.7054$

21. Results will vary.

Chapter 10 Review Exercises (page 576)

1. (a) $H_0: \mu = \$4,277$, $H_1: \mu > \$4,277$
(b) If the null hypothesis is rejected, but H_0 is true, a Type I error is made.
(c) A Type II error is made when the null hypothesis is not rejected but H_1 is true.
(d) There is not sufficient evidence at the α level of significance to support the credit counselor's belief that the mean outstanding credit-card debt per cardholder is more than the year 2000 amount.
(e) There is sufficient evidence at the α level of significance to support the credit counselor's belief that the mean outstanding credit-card debt per cardholder is more than the year 2000 amount.

2. (a) $H_0: p = 0.61$, $H_1: p > 0.61$
(b) If the null hypothesis is rejected, but 0.61 is the true population proportion, a Type I error is made.
(c) A Type II error is made when the null hypothesis is not rejected, but the true population proportion is greater than 0.61.
(d) There is not sufficient evidence at the α level of significance to support the researcher's claim that the percentage of Internet users who downloaded music is greater than 61%.
(e) There is sufficient evidence at the α level of significance to support the researcher's claim that the percentage of Internet users who downloaded music is greater than 61%.

3. The probability of a Type I error is 0.05.

4. The probability of a Type II error is 0.113. The power of the test is $1 - \beta = 0.887$. The power of the test is the probability of correctly rejecting the null hypothesis.

5. (a) $z_0 = -1.08$ **(b)** $-z_{0.05} = -1.645$
(c)

(d) No; because $z_0 > -z_{0.05}$.
(e) P-value $= 0.1401$ [Tech: 0.1406]

6. (a) $z_0 = 2.18$ **(b)** $-z_{0.05} = -1.645$; $z_{0.05} = 1.645$
(c)

(d) Yes; because the test statistic lies in the critical region.
(e) P-value $= 0.0292$ [Tech: 0.0290]
(f) Lower bound: 66.38, upper bound: 74.82. We reject the null hypothesis because the confidence interval does not contain $\mu = 65$.

7. (a) $t_0 = -1.506$ **(b)** $-t_{0.01} = -2.624$; $t_{0.01} = 2.624$
(c)

Critical Region / Critical Region, −2.624, 2.624

(d) No; because $-t_{0.01} = -2.624 < t_0 = -1.506 < t_{0.01} = 2.624$.
(e) $0.10 < P$-value < 0.20 [Tech: P-value $= 0.1543$]

8. (a) $t_0 = -2.222$ **(b)** $-t_{0.05} = -1.711$
(c)

Critical Region, −1.711

(d) Yes; because the test statistic lies in the critical region.
(e) $0.01 < P$-value < 0.02 [Tech: P-value $= 0.0180$]

9. Hypotheses: $H_0: p = 0.6$, $H_1: p > 0.6$; $np_0(1 - p_0) = 60 > 10$. Classical approach: $z_0 = 1.94 > z_{0.05} = 1.645$; reject the null hypothesis. P-value approach: P-value $= 0.0262$ [Tech: 0.0264] $< \alpha = 0.05$; reject the null hypothesis. There is sufficient evidence at the $\alpha = 0.05$ level of significance to conclude that $p > 0.6$.

10. Hypotheses: H_0: $p = 0.35$, H_1: $p \neq 0.35$; $np_0(1 - p_0) = 95.6 > 10$. Classical approach: $z_0 = -0.92$ is between $-z_{0.005} = -2.575$ and $z_{0.005} = 2.575$; do not reject the null hypothesis. *P*-value approach: *P*-value $= 0.3576$ [Tech: 0.3572] $> \alpha = 0.01$; do not reject the null hypothesis. There is not sufficient evidence at the $\alpha = 0.01$ level of significance to conclude that $p \neq 0.35$.

11. (a) $\chi_0^2 = 15.095$ **(b)** $\chi_{0.975}^2 = 7.564$; $\chi_{0.025}^2 = 30.191$

(c)

Critical Region

Critical Region

7.564   30.191

(d) Do not reject H_0, because $\chi_{0.975}^2 < \chi_0^2 < \chi_{0.025}^2$.

12. (a) $\chi_0^2 = 26.508$ **(b)** $\chi_{0.1}^2 = 33.196$

(c)

Critical Region

33.196

(d) Do not reject H_0 because $\chi_0^2 < \chi_{0.1}^2$.

13. Hypotheses: H_0: $\mu = 0.875$, H_1: $\mu > 0.875$. Classical approach: $t_0 = 1.2 < t_{0.05} = 1.690$; do not reject the null hypothesis. *P*-value approach: $0.15 > $ *P*-value > 0.10 [Tech: *P*-value $= 0.1191$] $> \alpha = 0.05$; do not reject the null hypothesis. There is not sufficient evidence at the $\alpha = 0.05$ level of significance to conclude that the mean distance between retaining rings is longer than 0.875 inch.

14. Hypotheses: H_0: $\mu = 7.53$, H_1: $\mu > 7.53$. Classical approach: $z_0 = 1.60 < z_{0.01} = 2.33$; do not reject the null hypothesis. *P*-value approach: *P*-value $= 0.0548$ [Tech: 0.0549] $> \alpha = 0.01$; do not reject the null hypothesis. There is not sufficient evidence at the $\alpha = 0.01$ level of significance to conclude that the new diet increases the birth weights of newborns.

15. (a) Hypotheses: H_0: $\mu = 300$, H_1: $\mu > 300$. Classical approach: $t_0 = 1.528 < t_{0.05} = 1.660$; do not reject the null hypothesis. *P*-value approach: $0.15 > $ *P*-value > 0.10 [Tech: *P*-value $= 0.0636$] $> \alpha = 0.05$; do not reject the null hypothesis. There is not sufficient evidence at the $\alpha = 0.05$ level of significance to conclude that mean cholesterol consumption of 20- to 39-year-old males is greater than 300 mg.

(b) Type I error: The nutritionist rejects the null hypothesis that the mean cholesterol consumption is 300 mg when, in fact, the mean consumption is 300 mg. Type II error: The nutritionist does not reject the null hypothesis that the mean cholesterol consumption is 300 mg when, in fact, the mean consumption is more than 300 mg.

(c) The probability of making a Type I error is $\alpha = 0.05$.

16. (a) The conditions for conducting a hypothesis test are satisfied.

(b) H_0: $\mu = \$1,400$, H_1: $\mu \neq \$1,400$. Classical approach: $z_0 = 2.49 > z_{0.10/2} = z_{0.05} = 1.645$; reject the null hypothesis; *P*-value approach: *P*-value $= 0.0128$ [Tech: 0.0123] $< \alpha = 0.10$; reject the null hypothesis; Confidence interval approach: Lower bound: $\$1,449.5$, upper bound: $\$1,639.5$; reject the null hypothesis because the interval does not include $\$1,400$. There is sufficient evidence that the mean price of rent in Cambridge is different from $\$1,400$.

17. H_0: $p = 0.5$, H_1: $p > 0.5$; $np_0(1 - p_0) = 150(0.5)(1 - 0.5) = 37.5 > 10$. Classical approach: $z_0 = 0.98 < z_{0.05} = 1.645$; do not reject the null hypothesis; *P*-value approach: *P*-value $= 0.1635$ [Tech: 0.1636] $> \alpha = 0.05$; do not reject the null hypothesis. There is not sufficient evidence to suggest that a majority of pregnant women nap at least twice each week.

18. H_0: $p = 0.11$, H_1: $p \neq 0.11$; $np_0(1 - p_0) = 1,100(0.11)(1 - 0.11) = 107.69 > 10$. Classical approach: $z_0 = 2.12 > z_{0.10/2} = 1.645$; reject the null hypothesis; *P*-value approach: *P*-value $= 0.0340 < \alpha = 0.10$; reject the null hypothesis. There is sufficient evidence to suggest that the proportion of adult Americans that have no faith that the federal government is capable of dealing effectively with domestic problems has changed since 1997.

19. Hypotheses: H_0: $\sigma = 505.6$, H_1: $\sigma > 505.6$. Classical approach: $\chi_0^2 = 110.409 > \chi_{0.01}^2 = 63.691$; reject the null hypothesis. *P*-value approach: *P*-value < 0.005 [Tech: <0.0001] $< \alpha = 0.01$; reject the null hypothesis. There is sufficient evidence at the $\alpha = 0.01$ level of significance to support the hypothesis that the variance of the birth weight of preterm babies is greater than that of full-term babies.

20. (a) $\beta = 0.9750$
(b) Power of the test: $1 - \beta = 0.0250$

21. Hypotheses: H_0: $p = 0.4$, H_1: $p > 0.4$; $np_0(1 - p_0) = 9.6 < 10$. *P*-value $= 0.3115 > \alpha = 0.05$; do not reject the null hypothesis. There is not sufficient evidence at the $\alpha = 0.05$ level of significance to support the researcher's notion that the proportion of adolescents who prays daily has increased.

22. Hypotheses: H_0: $\mu = 73.2$, H_1: $\mu < 73.2$. Classical approach: $t_0 = -2.018 < -t_{0.05} = -1.645$; reject the null hypothesis. *P*-value approach: *P*-value $= 0.0218 < \alpha = 0.05$; reject the null hypothesis. There is sufficient evidence at the $\alpha = 0.05$ level of significance to support the coordinator's concern that the mean test scores decreased. The results do not illustrate any practical significance. The average score only declined 0.4 point.

23. Answers will vary.

Chapter 10 Test (page 578)

1. (a) H_0: $\mu = 42.6$ minutes, H_1: $\mu > 42.6$ minutes
(b) There is sufficient evidence to conclude that the mean amount of daily time spent on phone calls and answering or writing e-mails has increased since 2006.
(c) We would reject the null hypothesis that the mean is 42.6 minutes, when, in fact, the mean amount of daily time spent on phone calls and answering or writing e-mails is 42.6 minutes.
(d) We would not reject the null hypothesis that the mean is 42.6 minutes, when, in fact, the mean amount of time spent on phone calls and answering or writing emails is greater than 42.6 minutes.

2. (a) H_0: $\mu = 167.1$ seconds, H_1: $\mu < 167.1$ seconds
(b) By choosing a level of significance of 0.01, the probability of rejecting the null hypothesis that the mean is 167.1 seconds in favor of the alternative hypothesis that the mean is less than 167.1 seconds, when, in fact, the mean is 167.1 seconds, is small.
(c) Classical approach: $z_0 = -1.75 > -z_{0.01} = -2.33$; do not reject the null hypothesis. *P*-value approach: *P*-value $= 0.0401 > \alpha = 0.01$; do not reject the null hypothesis. There is not sufficient evidence to conclude that the drive-through service time has decreased.

3. H_0: $\mu = 8$, H_1: $\mu < 8$. Classical approach: $t_0 = -1.755 < -t_{0.05} = -1.660$ (using 100 df); reject the null hypothesis; *P*-value approach: $0.025 < $ *P*-value < 0.05 [Tech: *P*-value $= 0.0406$] $< \alpha = 0.05$; reject the null hypothesis. There is sufficient evidence to conclude that postpartum women get less than 8 hours of sleep each night.

4. H_0: $\mu = 1.3825$ inches, H_1: $\mu \neq 1.3825$ inches. Lower bound: 1.3824 inches; upper bound: 1.3828 inches. Because the interval includes the mean stated in the null hypothesis, we do not reject the null hypothesis. There is not sufficient evidence to conclude that the mean is different from 1.3825 inches. Therefore, we presume that the part has been manufactured to specifications.

5. H_0: $p = 0.6$, H_1: $p > 0.6$; $np_0(1 - p_0) = 1,561(0.6)(0.4) = 374.64 > 10$. We will use an $\alpha = 0.05$ level of significance. Classical approach: $z_0 = 0.89 < z_{0.05} = 1.645$; do not reject the null hypothesis. *P*-value approach: *P*-value $= 0.1867$ [Tech: 0.1843] $> \alpha = 0.05$; do not reject the null hypothesis. There is not sufficient evidence to conclude that a supermajority of Americans did not feel that the United States would need to fight Japan in their lifetimes. It is interesting, however, that significantly fewer than half of all Americans felt the United States would not have to fight Japan in their lifetimes. About 2.5 years after this survey, the Japanese attack on Pearl Harbor thrust the United States into World War II.

6. H_0: $\mu = 0$, H_1: $\mu > 0$. Classical approach: $t_0 = 2.634 > t_{0.05} = 1.664$ (using 80 df); reject the null hypothesis. *P*-value approach: $0.0025 < $ *P*-value < 0.005 [Tech: *P*-value $= 0.0051$] $< \alpha = 0.05$; reject the null hypothesis. There is sufficient evidence to suggest that the diet is effective. However, losing 1.6 kg of weight over the course of a year does not seem to have much practical significance.

7. H_0: $p = 0.37$, H_1: $p > 0.37$, $np_0(1 - p_0) = 6.993 < 10$. *P*-value $= P(\hat{p} \geq 0.37) = P(X \geq 16) = 0.0501 < \alpha = 0.10$; reject the null hypothesis. There is sufficient evidence to conclude that the proportion of 20- to 24-year-olds who live on their own and do not have a land line is greater than 0.37.

8. H_0: $\sigma = 18$, H_1: $\sigma < 18$; $\chi_0^2 = 7.111 > \chi_{0.95}^2 = 3.325$; do not reject the null hypothesis. There is not sufficient evidence to conclude that the investment manager's portfolio is less risky than the market.

9. (a) 0.8186   **(b)** 0.1814

CHAPTER 11 Inferences on Two Samples

11.1 Assess Your Understanding (page 590)

1. Independent   **2.** Dependent

3. $u_d = 0$; $d_j = x_j - y_j$; H_1: $\mu_d < 0$ or H_1: $\mu_d > 0$ if $d_i = Y_i - X_i$

4. To test a claim regarding the difference of two means with dependent sampling, we need a simple random sample for which the differences are normally distributed with no outliers or for which the sample size n is large.

5. Dependent   **6.** Independent

7. Independent   **8.** Dependent

9. Independent   **10.** Independent

11. (a)

Observation	1	2	3	4	5	6	7
d_t	−0.5	1	−3.3	−3.7	0.5	−2.4	−2.9

(b) $\bar{d} = -1.614$; $s_d = 1.915$

(c) Classical approach: $t_0 = -2.230 < -t_{0.05} = -1.943$; reject the null hypothesis. P-value approach: $0.025 < P\text{-value} < 0.05$ [Tech: P-value = 0.0336] $< \alpha = 0.05$; reject the null hypothesis. There is sufficient evidence at the $\alpha = 0.05$ level of significance to reject the null hypothesis that $\mu_d = 0$.

(d) We can be 95% confident that the mean difference is between −3.39 and 0.16.

12. (a)

Observation	1	2	3	4	5	6	7	8
d_t	−0.4	1.5	1	−1.3	−2.3	−6.9	5.1	−5.3

(b) $\bar{d} = -1.075$; $s_d = 3.833$

(c) Classical approach: $t_0 = -0.793$; do not reject the null hypothesis since $-t_{0.005} = -3.499 < -0.793 < t_{0.005} = 3.499$. P-value approach: $0.50 > P\text{-value} > 0.40$ [Tech: P-value = 0.4537] $> \alpha = 0.01$; do not reject the null hypothesis. There is not sufficient evidence at the $\alpha = 0.01$ level of significance to support the claim that $\mu_d \neq 0$.

(d) We can be 99% confident that the mean difference is between −5.82 and 3.67.

13. (a) This is matched-pairs data because two measurements (A and B) are taken on the same round.

(b) Hypotheses: H_0: $\mu_d = 0$, H_1: $\mu_d \neq 0$; $d_i = A_i - B_i$. Classical approach: $t_0 = 0.852$; do not reject the null hypothesis since $-t_{0.005} = -3.106 < 0.852 < t_{0.005} = 3.106$. P-value approach: $0.50 > P\text{-value} > 0.40$ [Tech: P-value = 0.4125] $> \alpha = 0.01$; do not reject the null hypothesis. There is not sufficient evidence at the $\alpha = 0.01$ level of significance to conclude that there is a difference in the measurements of velocity between device A and device B.

(c) Lower bound: −0.309, upper bound: 0.543. We are 99% confident that the mean difference in measurement is between −0.31 and 0.54 feet per second.

(d)

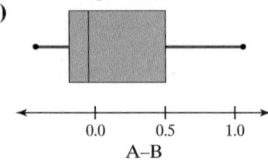

A–B

Yes, the boxplot supports that there is no difference in measurements.

14. (a) These are matched-pairs data because the same person is being timed for both the red and blue stimuli.

(b) To control for any "learning" that may take place in reaction time.

(c) Hypotheses: H_0: $\mu_d = 0$, H_1: $\mu_d \neq 0$; $d_i = \text{red}_i - \text{blue}_i$. Classical approach: $t_0 = -1.312$; do not reject the null hypothesis since $-t_{0.005} = -4.032 < -1.312 < t_{0.005} = 4.032$. P-value approach: $0.30 > P\text{-value} > 0.25$ [Tech: P-value = 0.2466] $> \alpha = 0.01$; do not reject the null hypothesis. There is not sufficient evidence at the $\alpha = 0.01$ level of significance to conclude that there is a difference in the reaction time to the blue and red stimuli.

(d) We can be 99% confident that the mean difference in reaction time between blue and red stimuli is between −0.3789 second and 0.1929 second.

(e)

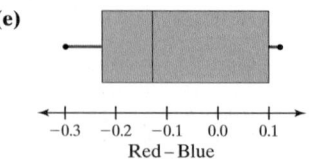

Red − Blue

Yes, the boxplot supports that there is no difference in reaction times.

15. (a) To control for any role that season might have on lake clarity.

(b) Hypotheses: H_0: $\mu_d = 0$, H_1: $\mu_d > 0$; $d_i = Y_i - X_i$. Classical approach: $t_0 = 2.384 > t_{0.05} = 1.895$; reject the null hypothesis. P-value approach: $0.02 < P\text{-value} < 0.025$ [Tech: P-value = 0.0243] $< \alpha = 0.05$; reject the null hypothesis. Yes; there is sufficient evidence at the $\alpha = 0.05$ level of significance to conclude that there has been an improvement in the clarity of the water in the 5-year period.

(c)

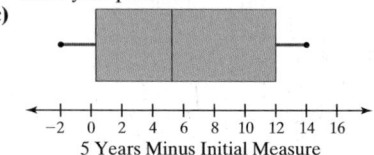

5 Years Minus Initial Measure

Yes, the boxplot supports that the lake is becoming more clear, since most differences are positive.

16. (a) Hypotheses: H_0: $\mu_d = 0$, H_1: $\mu_d > 0$; $d_i = Y_i - X_i$. Classical approach: $t_0 = 2.615 > t_{0.05} = 1.796$; reject the null hypothesis. P-value approach: $0.01 < P\text{-value} < 0.02$ [Tech: P-value = 0.0120] $< \alpha = 0.05$; reject the null hypothesis. Yes; there is sufficient evidence at the $\alpha = 0.05$ level of significance to conclude that the hemoglobin levels at lift-off minus three days are less than the hemoglobin levels upon return.

(b)

R0 − L3

Yes, the boxplot supports that hemoglobin at lift-off minus three days are less, since most differences are positive.

17. Hypotheses: H_0: $\mu_d = 0$, H_1: $\mu_d > 0$; $d_i = Y_i - X_i$. Classical approach: $t_0 = 0.398 < t_{0.10} = 1.356$; do not reject the null hypothesis. P-value approach: $P\text{-value} > 0.25$ [Tech: P-value = 0.3508] $> \alpha = 0.10$; do not reject the null hypothesis. No; there is not sufficient evidence at the $\alpha = 0.10$ level of significance to conclude that sons are taller than their fathers.

18. Hypotheses: H_0: $\mu_d = 0$, H_1: $\mu_d < 0$; $d_i = Y_i - X_i$. Classical approach: $t_0 = -1.220 > -t_{0.05} = -1.860$; do not reject the null hypothesis. P-value approach: $0.15 > P\text{-value} > 0.10$ [Tech: P-value = 0.1286] $> \alpha = 0.05$; do not reject the null hypothesis. No; there is not sufficient evidence at the $\alpha = 0.05$ level of significance to conclude that the new loading procedure reduces wait time.

19. H_0: $\mu_d = 0$; H_1: $\mu_d \neq 0$; $d_i = \text{diamond} - \text{steel}$, $\bar{d} = 1.3$; $s_d = 1.5$, $t_{0.025} = 2.306$. Lower bound: 0.1 [Tech: 0.2]; upper bound: 2.5. We are 95% confident that the difference in hardness reading is between 0.1 and 2.5. Because the interval does not include 0, we reject the null hypothesis. There is sufficient evidence to conclude that the two indenters produce different hardness readings.

20. Hypotheses: H_0: $\mu_d = 0$, H_1: $\mu_d < 0$; $d_i = T_i - H_i$. Classical approach: $t_0 = 0.089 > -t_{0.10} = -1.383$; do not reject the null hypothesis. P-value approach: $P\text{-value} > 0.25$ [Tech: P-value = 0.5345] $> \alpha = 0.10$; do not reject the null hypothesis. There is not sufficient evidence at the $\alpha = 0.10$ level of significance to conclude that *Thrifty* is less expensive than Hertz.

21. (a) To control for any "learning" that may occur in using the simulator

(b) Hypotheses: H_0: $\mu_d = 0$, H_1: $\mu_d \neq 0$. Lower bound: 0.688, upper bound: 1.238. $d_i = Y_i - X_i$. We can be 95% confident that the mean difference in reaction time when teenagers are driving impaired from when driving normally is between 0.688 second and 1.238 seconds. Because the interval does not contain zero, we reject the null hypothesis. There is sufficient evidence to conclude there is a difference in braking time with impared vision and normal vision.

22. Lower bound: 29.55, upper bound: 35.85. We can be 95% confident that the mean difference in braking distance on a wet road from a dry road is between 29.55 and 35.85 feet when driving at 40 miles per hour.

23. (a) Drivers and cars behave differently, so this reduces variability in mpg attributable to the driver's driving style.

(b) Driving conditions also affect mpg. By conducting the experiment on a closed track, driving conditions are constant.

(c) Neither variable is normally distributed.

(d) The difference in mileage appears to be approximately normal.

(e) $H_0: \mu_d = 0$; $H_1: \mu_d > 0$; $d_i = 92 \text{ Oct} - 87 \text{ Oct}_i$. P-value $= 0.141$. We would expect to get the results we obtained in about 14 samples out of 100 samples if the statement in the null hypothesis were true. Our result are not unusual; therefore, do not reject H_0.

24. (a) It is matched-pairs data because the flying conditions are similar for each windmilling/stopped-propeller matching.

(b) The decision to windmill or stop the propeller first was determined randomly to control for any "learning" that may take place while flying without the aid of an engine.

(c) The pilot can see whether the propeller is spinning or not.

(d) Response: time to descend 800 feet; treatments: windmilling or stopped propeller

(e)

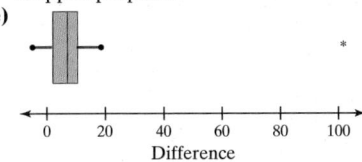

An outlier is present.

(f) The conditions of windmilling and stopped propeller were not the same, so the data are not matched by weather conditions.

(g)

Yes

(h) $H_0: \mu_d = 0$ vs. $H_1: \mu_d > 0$

(i) Classical: $t_0 = 5.49 > t_{0.05} = 1.708$, reject the null hypothesis; P-value < 0.0005 [Tech: < 0.0001], reject the null hypothesis. There is sufficient evidence to conclude that stopping the propeller increases the time to fall 800 feet (thereby increasing the horizontal distance that the plane will travel).

(j) If you experience engine failure, you should stop the propeller from windmilling to increase the distance that the plane will glide.

11.2 Assess Your Understanding (page 603)

1. To test a hypothesis regarding the difference of two means, we need two independent random samples that are drawn from normally distributed populations. If the populations are not normally distributed, each sample must be large ($n_1 \geq 30$ and $n_2 \geq 30$).

2. The degrees of freedom obtained from Formula (2) are larger than the smaller of $n_1 - 1$ or $n_2 - 1$, and t_α decreases as the degrees of freedom increase. The larger the critical value is, the harder it is to reject the null hypothesis.

3. (a) $H_0: \mu_1 = \mu_2$, $H_1: \mu_1 \neq \mu_2$. Classical approach: $t_0 = 0.898$ is between $-t_{0.025} = -2.145$ and $t_{0.025} = 2.145$; do not reject H_0. P-value approach: $0.40 > P$-value > 0.30 [Tech: P-value $= 0.3767$] $> \alpha = 0.05$; do not reject H_0. There is not sufficient evidence at the $\alpha = 0.05$ level of significance to conclude that the population means are different.

(b) Lower bound: -1.53 [Tech: -1.41], upper bound: 3.73 [Tech: 3.61]

4. (a) $H_0: \mu_1 = \mu_2$, $H_0: \mu_1 \neq \mu_2$. Classical approach: $t_0 = 2.486 > t_{0.025} = 2.093$; reject H_0. P-value approach: $0.02 < P$-value < 0.04 [Tech: P-value $= 0.0175$] $< \alpha = 0.05$; reject H_0. There is sufficient evidence at the $\alpha = 0.05$ level of significance to conclude that the population means are different.

(b) Lower bound: 1.11 [Tech: 1.30], upper bound: 12.89 [Tech: 12.70]

5. (a) $H_0: \mu_1 = \mu_2$, $H_1: \mu_1 > \mu_2$. Classical approach: $t_0 = 3.081 > t_{0.10} = 1.333$; reject H_0. P-value approach: $0.0025 < P$-value < 0.005 [Tech: P-value $= 0.0024$] $< \alpha = 0.10$. There is sufficient evidence at the $\alpha = 0.10$ level of significance to conclude that $\mu_1 > \mu_2$.

(b) Lower bound: 3.57 [Tech: 3.67], upper bound: 12.83 [Tech: 12.73]

6. (a) $H_0: \mu_1 = \mu_2$, $H_1: \mu_1 < \mu_2$. Classical approach: $t_0 = -4.393 < -t_{0.05} = -1.696$; reject H_0. P-value approach: P-value < 0.0005

[Tech: P-value < 0.0001] $< \alpha = 0.05$; reject H_0. There is sufficient evidence at the level of significance to conclude that $\mu_1 < \mu_2$.

(b) Lower bound: -30.75 [Tech: -30.59], upper bound: -11.25 [Tech: -11.41]

7. $H_0: \mu_1 = \mu_2$; $H_1: \mu_1 < \mu_2$. Classical approach: $t_0 = -3.158 < -t_{0.02} = -2.172$; reject H_0. P-value approach: $0.001 < P$-value < 0.0025 [Tech: P-value $= 0.0013$] $< \alpha = 0.02$; reject H_0. There is sufficient evidence at the $\alpha = 0.02$ level of significance to conclude that $\mu_1 < \mu_2$.

8. $H_0: \mu_1 = \mu_2$, $H_1: \mu_1 > \mu_2$. Classical approach: $t_0 = 1.237 < t_{0.05} = 1.782$; do not reject H_0. P-value approach: $0.15 > P$-value > 0.10 [Tech: P-value $= 0.1144$] $> \alpha = 0.05$; do not reject H_0. There is not sufficient evidence at the $\alpha = 0.05$ level of significance to conclude that $\mu_1 > \mu_2$.

9. (a) $H_0: \mu_{CC} = \mu_{NT}$ vs. $H_1: \mu_{CC} > \mu_{NT}$. Classical approach: $t_0 = 12.977 > t_{0.01} \approx 2.364$ (using 100 df); reject H_0. P-value approach: P-value < 0.0005 [Tech: P-value < 0.0001]; reject H_0. The evidence suggests that the mean time to graduate for students who first start in community college is longer than the mean time to graduate for those who do not transfer.

(b) Lower bound: 0.818 [Tech: 0.848], upper bound: 1.182 [Tech: 1.152]. We are 95% confident that the mean additional time to graduate for students who start in community college is between 0.818 year and 1.182 years.

(c) No; this is observational data. Community college students may be working more hours, which does not allow them to take additional classes.

10. $H_0: \mu_1 = \mu_2$, $H_1: \mu_1 > \mu_2$. Classical approach: $t_0 = 2.849 > t_{0.01} = 2.403$; reject H_0. P-value approach: $0.0025 < P$-value < 0.005 [Tech: P-value $= 0.0026$] $< \alpha = 0.01$; reject H_0. There is sufficient evidence at the $\alpha = 0.01$ level of significance to conclude that mean improvement in the treatment group was greater than mean improvement in the control group. The drug appears to be effective in improving the Young Mania Rating Scale score.

11. (a) This is an observational study. The researcher did not influence the data.

(b) Large, independent samples

(c) $H_0: \mu_A = \mu_D$, $H_1: \mu_A \neq \mu_D$. Classical approach: $t_0 = 0.846$ is between $-t_{0.025} = -2.032$ and $t_{0.025} = 2.032$; do not reject H_0. P-value approach: $0.50 > P$-value > 0.40 [Tech: P-value $= 0.4013$] $> \alpha = 0.05$; do not reject H_0. There is not sufficient evidence at the $\alpha = 0.05$ level of significance to say that travelers walk at different speeds depending on whether they are arriving or departing an airport.

(d) Lower bound: -12.6 [Tech: -12.3], upper bound: 30.6 [Tech: 30.3]. We can be 95% confident that the mean difference in speed walked between passengers arriving and departing an airport is between -12.6 and 30.6 feet per minute.

12. (a) This is an observational study. The researcher did not influence the data.

(b) Since the samples are small, the populations must be normally distributed, with no outliers.

(c) $H_0: \mu_B = \mu_L$, $H_1: \mu_B \neq \mu_L$. Classical approach: $t_0 = 0.772$ is between $-t_{0.025} = -2.093$ and $t_{0.025} = 2.093$; do not reject H_0. P-value approach: $0.50 > P$-value > 0.40 [Tech: P-value $= 0.4448$] $> \alpha = 0.05$; do not reject H_0. There is not sufficient evidence at the $\alpha = 0.05$ level of significance to say that business travelers walk at different speeds than leisure travelers when walking in an airport.

(d) Lower bound: -18.8 [Tech: -17.8], upper bound: 40.8 [Tech: 39.8]. We can be 95% confident that the mean difference in speed walked between business travelers and leisure travelers in an airport is between -18.8 and 40.8 feet per minute.

13. (a) Yes; we can treat each sample as a simple random sample of all mixtures of each type. The samples were obtained independently. We are told that a normal probability plot indicates that the data could come from a population that is normal, with no outliers.

(b) $H_0: \mu_{301} = \mu_{400}$, $H_1: \mu_{301} < \mu_{400}$. Classical approach: $t_0 = -3.804 < -t_{0.05} = -1.860$; reject H_0. P-value approach: $0.0025 < P$-value < 0.005 [Tech: P-value $= 0.0007$] $< \alpha = 0.05$; reject H_0. There is sufficient evidence at the $\alpha = 0.05$ level of significance to conclude that mixture 67-0-400 is stronger than the mean strength of mixture 67-0-301.

(c) Lower bound: 416 [Tech: 441.7], upper bound: 1212 [Tech: 1187]. We are 90% confident that the mean strength of mixture 67-0-400 is between 416 and 1212 psi stronger than the mean strength of mixture 67-0-301.

(d)

Yes, the boxplots support that the 67-0-400 is stronger.

14. (a) Yes; each sample is a simple random sample. The samples were obtained independently. We are told that a normal probability plot indicates that the data could come from a population that is normal, with no outliers.

(b) $H_0: \mu_F = \mu_M$, $H_1: \mu_F \neq \mu_M$. Classical approach: $t_0 = 0.619$ is between $-t_{0.025} = -2.145$ and $t_{0.025} = 2.145$; do not reject H_0. P-value approach: P-value > 0.50 [Tech: P-value = 0.5403] > $\alpha = 0.05$; do not reject H_0. There is not sufficient evidence at the $\alpha = 0.05$ level of significance to conclude that there is a difference in reaction time between females and males.

(c) Lower bound: -0.0483 [Tech: -0.0456], upper bound: 0.1006 [Tech: 0.0979]. We are 90% confident that the mean difference in reaction time for females and males is between -0.0483 and 0.1006 second.

(d)

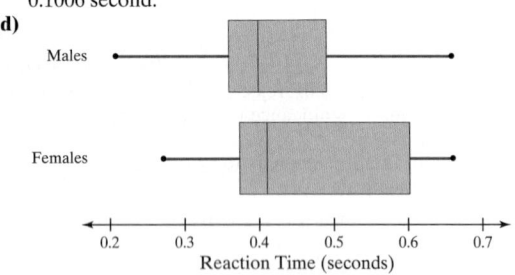

Yes, the boxplots support that there is no difference in reaction times.

15. $H_0: \mu_{carpet} = \mu_{no\ carpet}$, $H_1: \mu_{carpet} > \mu_{no\ carpet}$. Classical approach: $t_0 = 0.956 < t_{0.05} = 1.895$; do not reject H_0. P-value approach: $0.20 > $ P-value > 0.15 [Tech: P-value = 0.1780] > $\alpha = 0.05$; do not reject H_0. There is not sufficient evidence at the $\alpha = 0.05$ level of significance to conclude that carpeted rooms have more bacteria than uncarpeted rooms.

16. (a) This is an experiment using a completely randomized design.

(b) The treatments are multimodal teaching style and unimodal teaching style.

(c) $H_0: \mu_{visual} = \mu_{textual}$, $H_1: \mu_{visual} \neq \mu_{textual}$. Classical approach: $t_0 = 2.378 > t_{0.025} = 2.110$; reject H_0. P-value approach: $0.02 < $ P-value < 0.04 [Tech: P-value = 0.0236] < $\alpha = 0.05$; reject H_0. There is sufficient evidence at the $\alpha = 0.05$ level of significance to conclude that there is a difference in the test scores of people who use the visual manual and those who use the textual manual.

17. $H_0: \mu_{AL} = \mu_{NL}$, $H_1: \mu_{AL} > \mu_{NL}$. Classical approach: $t_0 = 2.136 > t_{0.05} = 1.699$; reject H_0. P-value approach: $0.02 < $ P-value < 0.025 [Tech: P-value = 0.0187] < $\alpha = 0.05$; reject H_0. There is sufficient evidence at the $\alpha = 0.05$ level of significance to conclude that games played with a designated hitter result in more runs.

18. $H_0: \mu_{RB} = \mu_{ALT}$, $H_1: \mu_{RB} \neq \mu_{ALT}$. Classical approach: $t_0 = 0.610$ is between $-t_{0.05} = -1.699$ and $t_{0.05} = 1.699$; do not reject H_0. P-value approach: P-value > 0.50 [Tech: P-value = 0.5440] > $\alpha = 0.10$; do not reject H_0. There is not sufficient evidence at the $\alpha = 0.10$ level of significance to conclude that the lengths of rhythm & blues songs differ from the length of alternative songs.

19. Lower bound: 0.71 [Tech: 0.72], upper bound: 2.33 [Tech: 2.32]. We can be 90% confident that the mean difference in daily leisure time between adults without children and those with children is between 0.71 and 2.33 hours. Since the confidence interval does not include zero, we can conclude that there is a significant difference in the leisure time of adults without children and those with children.

20. Lower bound: 38.08 [Tech: 38.13], upper bound: 44.72 [Tech: 44.67]. We can be 90% confident that the mean difference in cooling time between filled clear glass bottles and filled aluminum bottles is between 38.08 and 44.72 minutes. Since the confidence interval does not include zero, we can conclude that there is a significant difference in the cooling times of glass bottles and aluminum bottles.

21. (a) $H_0: \mu_{men} = \mu_{women}$ versus $H_1: \mu_{men} < \mu_{women}$

(b) P-value = 0.0051. Because P-value < α, we reject the null hypothesis. There is sufficient evidence at the $\alpha = 0.01$ level of significance to conclude that the mean step pulse of men is lower than the mean step pulse of women.

(c) Lower bound: -10.7, upper bound: -1.5. We are 95% confident that the mean step pulse of men is between 1.5 and 10.7 beats per minute lower than the mean step pulse of women.

22. (a) $H_0: \mu_{men} = \mu_{women}$ versus $H_1: \mu_{men} < \mu_{women}$

(b) P-value = 0.0001. Because P-value < α, we reject the null hypothesis. There is sufficient evidence at the $\alpha = 0.01$ level of significance to conclude that the women are more flexible than the men.

(c) Lower bound: -3.58, upper bound: -1.12. We are 95% confident that the mean flexibility of women is between 1.12 and 3.58 inches higher than the mean flexibility of men.

23. (a) Completely randomized design

(b) Final exam; online versus traditional homework

(c) Teacher; location; time; text; syllabus; tests

(d) The assumption is that the students "randomly" enrolled in the course.

(e) $H_0: \mu_F = \mu_S$; $H_1: \mu_F > \mu_S$. Classical: $t_0 = 1.795 > t_{0.05} = 1.711$; reject H_0. $0.025 < $ P-value < 0.05 [Tech: P-value = 0.039] < $\alpha = 0.05$; reject H_0. There is sufficient evidence at the $\alpha = 0.05$ level of significance to conclude that the final exams in the fall semester were higher than the final exams in the spring semester. It would appear to be the case that the online homework system helps in raising final exam scores.

(f) One factor is the fact that the weather is pretty lousy at the end of the fall semester, but pretty nice at the end of the spring semester. If "spring fever" kicked in for the spring semester students, then they probably studied less for the final exam.

11.3 Assess Your Understanding (page 618)

1. A pooled estimate of p is the best point estimate of the common population proportion p. However, when finding a confidence interval, the sample proportions are not pooled because no assumption about their equality is made.

2. In an independent sample, the individuals in sample A are in no way related to the individuals in sample B; in a dependent sample, the individuals in each sample are somehow related.

3. To test a hypothesis regarding two population proportions, we must have two independent random samples, $n_1\hat{p}_1(1 - \hat{p}_1) \geq 10$ and $n_2\hat{p}_2(1 - \hat{p}_2) \geq 10$, and $n_1 \leq 0.05N_1$ and $n_2 \leq 0.05N_2$.

4. The samples must be dependent and obtained randomly. In addition, the total number of observations for which the outcomes differ must be at least 10.

5. (a) $H_0: p_1 = p_2$ versus $H_1: p_1 > p_2$ **(b)** $z_0 = 3.08$

(c) $z_{0.05} = 1.645$

(d) P-value = 0.0010. Because $z_0 > z_{0.05}$ (or P-value < α), we reject the null hypothesis. There is sufficient evidence to support the claim that $p_1 > p_2$.

6. (a) $H_0: p_1 = p_2$ versus $H_1: p_1 < p_2$ **(b)** $z_0 = -0.35$

(c) $-z_{0.05} = -1.645$

(d) P-value = 0.3649. Because $z_0 > -z_{0.05}$ (or P-value > α), we do not reject the null hypothesis. There is not sufficient evidence to support the claim that $p_1 < p_2$.

7. (a) $H_0: p_1 = p_2$ versus $H_1: p_1 \neq p_2$

(b) $z_0 = -0.34$

(c) $-z_{0.025} = -1.96$; $z_{0.025} = 1.96$

(d) P-value = 0.7307. Because $-z_{0.025} < z_0 < z_{0.05}$ (or P-value > α), we do not reject the null hypothesis. There is not sufficient evidence to support the claim that $p_1 \neq p_2$.

8. (a) $H_0: p_1 = p_2$ versus $H_1: p_1 \neq p_2$

(b) $z_0 = -2.19$

(c) $-z_{0.025} = -1.96$; $z_{0.025} = 1.96$

(d) P-value = 0.0286. Because $z_0 < -z_{0.05}$ (or P-value < α), we reject the null hypothesis. There is sufficient evidence to support the claim that $p_1 \neq p_2$.

9. Lower bound: -0.075, upper bound: 0.015

10. Lower bound: -0.090, upper bound: 0.068

11. Lower bound: -0.063, upper bound: 0.043

12. Lower bound: -0.039, upper bound: 0.009

13. (a) H_0: $p_A = p_B$ vs. H_1: $p_A \neq p_B$
(b) $z_0 = 0.70$
(c) $z_{0.025} = 1.96$; do not reject the null hypothesis
(d) P-value $= 0.4840$

14. (a) H_0: $p_A = p_B$ vs. H_1: $p_A \neq p_B$
(b) $z_0 = 1.59$
(c) $z_{0.025} = 1.96$; do not reject the null hypothesis
(d) P-value $= 0.1118$

15. Each sample can be thought of as a simple random sample; $n_1 \hat{p}_1(1 - \hat{p}_1) = 91 \geq 10$ and $n_2 \hat{p}_2(1 - \hat{p}_2) = 60 \geq 10$; and each sample is less than 5% of the population size. H_0: $p_1 = p_2$; H_1: $p_1 > p_2$. Classical approach: $z_0 = 2.20 > z_{0.05} = 1.645$; reject H_0. P-value approach: P-value $= 0.0139 < \alpha = 0.05$; reject H_0. There is sufficient evidence at the $\alpha = 0.05$ level of significance to conclude that a higher proportion of subjects in the treatment group (taking Prevnar) experienced fever as a side effect than in the control (placebo) group.

16. Each sample can be thought of as a simple random sample; $n_1 \hat{p}_1(1 - \hat{p}_1) = 95 \geq 10$ and $n_2 \hat{p}_2(1 - \hat{p}_2) = 21 \geq 10$; and each sample is less than 5% of the population size. H_0: $p_1 = p_2$, H_1: $p_1 \neq p_2$. Classical approach: $z_0 = -0.20 <$ $-z_{0.05} = -1.645$; do not reject H_0. P-value approach: P-value $= 0.4207$ [Tech: 0.4221] $> \alpha = 0.05$; do not reject H_0. There is not sufficient evidence at the $\alpha = 0.05$ level of significance to conclude that a different proportion of subjects taking Prevnar experienced drowsiness as a side effect than in the control (placebo) group.

17. $\hat{p}_{1945} = 0.33$, $\hat{p}_{2007} = 0.36$. Each sample is a simple random sample; $n_{1945}\hat{p}_{1945}(1 - \hat{p}_{1945}) \geq 10$ and $n_{2007}\hat{p}_{2007}(1 - \hat{p}_{2007}) \geq 10$. The sample size is less than 5% of the population for each sample. H_0: $p_{1945} = p_{2007}$ vs. H_1: $p_{1945} \neq p_{2007}$. Classical approach: $z_0 = -1.48$ is between $-z_{0.025} = -1.96$ and $z_{0.025} = 1.96$; do not reject H_0. P-value approach: P-value $= 0.1388$ [Tech: 0.1389] $> \alpha = 0.05$; do not reject H_0. There is not sufficient evidence at the $\alpha = 0.05$ level of significance to conclude that the proportion of adult Americans who were abstainers in 1945 is different from the proportion of abstainers in 2007.

18. $\hat{p}_C = 0.310$; $\hat{p}_S = 0.397$. Each sample is a simple random sample; $n_C\hat{p}_C(1 - \hat{p}_C) \geq 10$ and $n_S\hat{p}_S(1 - \hat{p}_S) \geq 10$. The sample size is less than 5% of the population for each sample. H_0: $p_C = p_S$ vs. H_1: $p_C \neq p_S$. Classical approach: $z_0 = -3.12 < -z_{0.025}$; reject H_0. P-value approach: P-value $= 0.0018$ [Tech: 0.0019] $< \alpha = 0.05$; reject H_0. There is sufficient evidence at the $\alpha = 0.05$ level of significance to conclude that the proportion of Catholics who favor capital punishment for persons under the age of 18 is different from the proportion of seculars who favor capital punishment for persons under the age of 18.

19. H_0: $p_m = p_f$ vs. H_1: $p_m \neq p_f$. Lower bound: -0.008 [Tech: -0.009], upper bound: 0.048. We are 95% confident that the difference in the proportion of males and females that have at least one tattoo is between -0.008 and 0.048. Because the interval includes zero, we do not reject the null hypothesis. There is no significant difference in the proportion of males and females that have tattoos.

20. H_0: $p_m = p_f$ vs. H_1: $p_m \neq p_f$. Lower bound: -0.128 [Tech: -0.129], upper bound: -0.050. We are 90% confident that the difference in the proportion of males and females that are normal weight is between -0.128 and -0.05. Because the interval does not include zero, we have evidence to conclude that there is a difference in the proportion of males and females that are normal weight. It would appear a higher proportion of males are not normal weight.

21. (a) Each sample is a simple random sample, $n_1 \hat{p}_1(1 - \hat{p}_1) = 48 \geq 10$ and $n_2 \hat{p}_2(1 - \hat{p}_2) = 30 \geq 10$, and each sample is less than 5% of the population size. H_0: $p_1 = p_2$, H_1: $p_1 > p_2$. Classical approach: $z_0 = 2.13 > z_{0.05} = 1.645$; reject H_0. P-value $= 0.0166 < \alpha = 0.05$; reject H_0. There is sufficient evidence at the $\alpha = 0.05$ level of significance to conclude that the proportion of individuals taking Clarinex and experiencing dry mouth is greater than that of those taking a placebo.
(b) No

22. (a) Each sample is a simple random sample, $n_1 \hat{p}_1(1 - \hat{p}_1) = 446 \geq 10$ and $n_2 \hat{p}_2(1 - \hat{p}_2) = 468 \geq 10$, and each sample is less than 5% of the population size. H_0: $p_1 = p_2$, H_1: $p_1 < p_2$. Classical approach: $z_0 = -1.71 < -z_{0.05} = -1.645$; reject H_0. P-value $= 0.0432 < \alpha = 0.05$; reject H_0. There is sufficient evidence at the $\alpha = 0.05$ level of significance to conclude that a higher percentage of patients are cured with the new proposed treatment than with the current standard treatment.
(b) Answers will vary.

23. (a) To remove any potential nonsampling error due to the respondent hearing the word "right" or "wrong" first.
(b) Lower bound: 0.312, upper bound: 0.368. We are 90% confident that the difference in the proportion of adult Americans who believe the United States made the right decision to use military force in Iraq from 2003 to 2008 is between 0.312 and 0.368. The attitude regarding the decision to go to war changed substantially.

24. (a) To remove any potential nonsampling error due to respondents hearing one choice first over the others.
(b) Lower bound: 0.266, upper bound: 0.334. We are 95% confident that the difference in the proportion of adult Americans who think the Bush administration went too far in restricting people's civil liberties to fight terrorism from 2002 to 2006 is between 0.266 and 0.334.

25. (a) The same person answered both questions.
(b) H_0: $p_{\text{seat belt}} = p_{\text{smoke}}$ vs. H_1: $p_{\text{seat belt}} \neq p_{\text{smoke}}$. Classical: $z_0 = 4.31 > z_{0.025} = 1.96$; reject the null hypothesis. P-value < 0.0001; reject the null hypothesis. There is sufficient evidence at the $\alpha = 0.05$ level of significance to conclude that there is a difference in the proportion who do not use a seat belt and the proportion who smoke. The sample proportion of smokers is 0.17, while the sample proportion of those who do not wear a seatbelt is 0.13. Smoking appears to be the more popular hazardous activity.

26. H_0: $p_{\text{low}} = p_{\text{high}}$ vs. H_1: $p_{\text{low}} \neq p_{\text{high}}$. Classical: $z_0 = 6.20 > z_{0.025} = 1.96$; reject the null hypothesis. P-value < 0.0001; reject the null hypothesis. There is sufficient evidence at the $\alpha = 0.05$ level of significance to conclude that there is a difference in the proportion who believe low-income and high-income people pay there fair share in taxes.

27. H_0: $p_{\text{NN}} = p_{\text{RN}}$ vs. H_1: $p_{\text{NN}} \neq p_{\text{RN}}$. Classical: $z_0 = 2.41 > z_{0.025} = 1.96$; reject the null hypothesis. P-value $= 0.016$; reject the null hypothesis. There is sufficient evidence at the $\alpha = 0.05$ level of significance to conclude that there is a difference in the proportion of words not recognized by the two systems.

28. H_0: $p_A = p_B$ vs. H_1: $p_A \neq p_B$. Classical: $z_0 = 1.28 < z_{0.025} = 1.96$; do not reject the null hypothesis. P-value $= 0.2006$; do not reject the null hypothesis. There is not sufficient evidence at the $\alpha = 0.05$ level of significance to conclude that there is a difference in the proportion who have their poison ivy healed using ointment A versus ointment B.

29. No. The difference between the two sample proportions is not significant.

30. We are testing H_0: $p_1 = p_2$ versus H_1: $p_1 > p_2$. The P-value is 0.072, which is moderately low, suggesting the Accupril has more dizziness than the placebo.

31. (a) $n = n_1 = n_2 = 1{,}406$ (b) $n = n_1 = n_2 = 2{,}135$

32. (a) $n = n_1 = n_2 = 2{,}551$ (b) $n = n_1 = n_2 = 3{,}383$

33. (a) Completely randomized design
(b) Whether the subject contracted polio or not
(c) The vaccine or placebo
(d) A placebo is an innocuous medication that looks, tastes, and smells like the experimental treatment.
(e) Because the incidence rate of polio is low, a large number of subjects is needed so that we are guaranteed a sufficient number of successes.
(f) H_0: $p_1 = p_2$, H_1: $p_1 < p_2$. Classical approach: $z_0 = -6.74 < -z_{0.01} = -2.33$; reject H_0. P-value approach: P-value $< 0.0001 < \alpha = 0.01$; reject H_0. There is sufficient evidence at the $\alpha = 0.01$ level of significance to conclude that the proportion of children in the experimental group who contracted polio is less than the proportion of children in the control group who contracted polio.

11.4 Assess Your Understanding (page 629)

1. The test is not robust, so even small departures from normality adversely affect the test, making it unreliable. So, in the test for comparing two population standard deviations, the samples must come from populations that are normally distributed.

2. To compare two population standard deviations, the samples are assumed to be independent random samples, and they must be drawn from normally distributed populations.

3. $F_{0.05,9,10} = 3.02$ **4.** $F_{0.01,20,25} = 2.70$

5. $F_{0.975,6,8} = 0.18$, $F_{0.025,6,8} = 4.65$

6. $F_{0.99,5,7} = 0.10$, $F_{0.01,5,7} = 7.46$ **7.** $F_{0.90,25,20} = 0.58$

8. $F_{0.99,15,20} = 0.30$ **9.** $F_{0.05,45,15} = 2.19$ **10.** $F_{0.01,55,50} = 1.93$

11. Classical approach: $F_0 = 0.84$ is between $F_{0.975,15,15} = 0.35$ and $F_{0.025,15,15} = 2.86$; do not reject the null hypothesis. P-value approach: P-value $= 0.7730 > \alpha = 0.05$; do not reject the null hypothesis. There is not sufficient evidence at the $\alpha = 0.05$ level of significance to conclude that $\sigma_1 \neq \sigma_2$.

12. Classical approach: $F_0 = 0.87$ is between $F_{0.95,20,20} = 0.47$ and $F_{0.05,20,20} = 2.12$; do not reject the null hypothesis. P-value approach: P-value $= 0.7659 > \alpha = 0.10$; do not reject the null hypothesis. There is not sufficient evidence at the $\alpha = 0.10$ level of significance to conclude that $\sigma_1 \neq \sigma_2$.

13. Classical approach: $F_0 = 2.39 < F_{0.01,25,18} = 2.84$; do not reject the null hypothesis. P-value approach: P-value $= 0.0303 > \alpha = 0.01$; do not reject the null hypothesis. There is not sufficient evidence at the $\alpha = 0.01$ level of significance to conclude that $\sigma_1 > \sigma_2$.

14. Classical approach: $F_0 = 0.48 < F_{0.95,20,20} = 0.50$; reject the null hypothesis. P-value approach: P-value $= 0.0480 < \alpha = 0.05$; reject the null hypothesis. There is sufficient evidence at the $\alpha = 0.05$ level of significance to conclude that $\sigma_1 < \sigma_2$.

15. Classical approach: $F_0 = 0.40 < F_{0.90,50,25} = 0.65$; reject the null hypothesis. P-value approach: P-value $= 0.0026 < \alpha = 0.10$; reject the null hypothesis. There is sufficient evidence at the $\alpha = 0.10$ level of significance to conclude that $\sigma_1 < \sigma_2$.

16. Classical approach: $F_0 = 2.16 < F_{0.05,22,12} = 2.54$; do not reject the null hypothesis. P-value approach: P-value $= 0.0840 > \alpha = 0.05$; do not reject the null hypothesis. There is not sufficient evidence at the $\alpha = 0.05$ level of significance to conclude that $\sigma_1 > \sigma_2$.

17. Hypotheses: $H_0: \sigma_1 = \sigma_2$, $H_1: \sigma_1 \neq \sigma_2$. Classical approach: $F_0 = 0.97$ is between $F_{0.975,54,59} = 0.58$ and $F_{0.025,54,59} = 1.75$; do not reject the null hypothesis. P-value approach: P-value $= 0.9087 > \alpha = 0.05$; do not reject the null hypothesis. There is not sufficient evidence at the $\alpha = 0.05$ level of significance to conclude that the standard deviation in the treatment group is different from the standard deviation in the control group.

18. Both sample standard deviations are the same, so do not reject H_0.

19. Hypotheses: $H_0: \sigma_1 = \sigma_2$, $H_1: \sigma_1 > \sigma_2$. Classical approach: $F_0 = 6.94 > F_{0.01,64,64} = 1.91$; reject the null hypothesis. P-value approach: P-value $< 0.0001 < \alpha = 0.01$; reject the null hypothesis. There is sufficient evidence at the $\alpha = 0.01$ level of significance to conclude that the treatment group had a higher standard deviation for serum retinal concentration than did the control group.

20. Hypotheses: $H_0: \sigma_1 = \sigma_2$, $H_1: \sigma_1 > \sigma_2$. Classical approach: $F_0 = 1.06 < F_{0.01,34,37} \approx 2.54$; do not reject the null hypothesis. P-value approach: P-value $= 0.3886 > \alpha = 0.01$; do not reject the null hypothesis. There is not sufficient evidence at the $\alpha = 0.01$ level of significance to conclude that students who do not plan to apply for financial aid have a higher standard deviation on the SAT math I exam than do students who plan to apply for financial aid.

21. (a) Hypotheses: $H_0: \sigma_1 = \sigma_2$, $H_1: \sigma_1 < \sigma_2$. Classical approach: $F_0 = 0.32 < F_{0.05,19,19} \approx 0.47$; reject the null hypothesis. P-value approach: P-value $= 0.0087 < \alpha = 0.05$; reject the null hypothesis. There is sufficient evidence at the $\alpha = 0.05$ level of significance to conclude that the standard deviation for wait time in the single line is less than the standard deviation for wait time in the multiple lines. The variability in the single line is less than that of the multiple line.

(b)

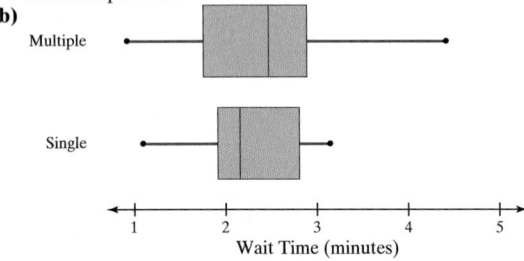

22. (a) Hypotheses: $H_0: \sigma_{\text{old}} = \sigma_{\text{new}}$, $H_1: \sigma_{\text{old}} > \sigma_{\text{new}}$. Classical approach: $F_0 = 2.74 > F_{0.05,14,14} \approx 2.40$; reject the null hypothesis. P-value approach: P-value $= 0.0348 < \alpha = 0.05$; reject the null hypothesis. There is sufficient evidence at the $\alpha = 0.05$ level of significance to conclude that the standard deviation of fill in the new machine is less than the standard deviation of fill in the old machine.

(b)

23. (a) The normal probability plots are roughly linear, so we can conclude that the data are approximately normally distributed.

(b) Since P-value $= 0.0844 > \alpha = 0.05$, which is the level of significance, the nursing student should conclude that there is not sufficient evidence to conclude that men have more variability in their systolic blood pressure than women have.

(c) $F_0 = 0.50 > F_{0.95,19,16} = 0.45$, so do not reject the null hypothesis. The test statistic supports the previous decision.

24. (a) P-value $= 0.9276 > \alpha = 0.05$, so we do not reject the null hypothesis. There is not sufficient evidence to conclude that there is a difference in the variability of reaction time.

(b)

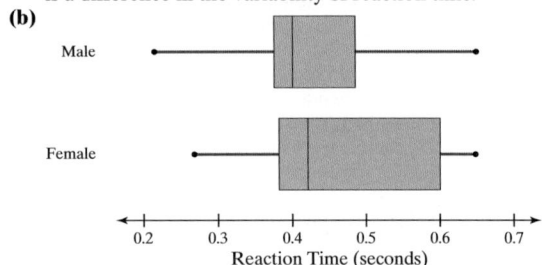

11.5 Assess Your Understanding (page 633)

1. Answers will vary. One word to look for is matched, which indicates that the sampling is dependent. Obviously, if the word independent is in the problem, the sampling method was likely independent. Also, look for language that implies that the two variables are measured on related items, which would mean the sampling is dependent.

2. First, determine whether the response variable is quantitative or qualitative. If qualitative with only two possible outcomes, the inference is likely on proportions. If quantitative, look for words to distinguish whether the inference is on means or standard deviation (such as variability).

3. Completely randomized design; qualitative; 2

4. Matched-pairs design; quantitative; 2

5. $H_0: p_A = p_B$ vs. $H_1: p_A \neq p_B$. Classical: $z_0 = 0.64 < z_{0.025} = 1.96$; do not reject the null hypothesis. P-value $= 0.5222 > \alpha = 0.05$; do not reject the null hypothesis. There is not sufficient evidence at the $\alpha = 0.05$ level of significance to conclude that there is a difference in the proportions.

6. $H_0: p_1 = p_2$ vs. $H_1: p_1 \neq p_2$. All requirements to conduct the test are satisfied. Classical: $z_0 = -1.18$ is between $-z_{0.005} = -2.575$ and $z_{0.005} = 2.575$; do not reject the null hypothesis. P-value $= 0.238$ [Tech: 0.242] $> \alpha = 0.01$; do not reject the null hypothesis. There is not sufficient evidence at the $\alpha = 0.05$ level of significance to conclude that there is a difference in the proportions.

7. $H_0: \sigma_1 = \sigma_2$ vs. $H_1: \sigma_1 > \sigma_2$. Classical: $F = 1.44 < F_{0.05,30,50} = 1.69$; do not reject the null hypothesis. P-value $= 0.1249 > \alpha = 0.05$; do not reject the null hypothesis. There is not sufficient evidence at the $\alpha = 0.05$ level of significance to conclude that $\sigma_1 > \sigma_2$.

8. $H_0: \mu_1 = \mu_2$ vs. $H_1: \mu_1 \neq \mu_2$. All requirements to conduct the test are satisfied. Classical: $t_0 = -1.39$ is between $-t_{0.025} = -2.179$ and $t_{0.025} = 2.179$; do not reject the null hypothesis. $0.20 > $ P-value > 0.10 [Tech: P-value $= 0.1745$] $> \alpha = 0.05$; do not reject the null hypothesis. There is not sufficient evidence at the $\alpha = 0.05$ level of significance to conclude that there is a difference in the means.

9. $H_0: p_1 = p_2$ vs. $H_1: p_1 < p_2$. All requirements to conduct the test are satisfied. Classical: $z_0 = -1.84 < -z_{0.05} = -1.645$; reject the null hypothesis. P-value $= 0.0329$ [Tech: 0.0335] $< \alpha = 0.05$; reject the null hypothesis. There is sufficient evidence at the $\alpha = 0.05$ level of significance to conclude that there is a difference in the proportions.

10. $H_0: \sigma_1 = \sigma_2$ vs. $H_1: \sigma_1 \neq \sigma_2$. Classical: $F = 1.84 > F_{0.025} = 1.72$; reject the null hypothesis. P-value $= 0.0288 < \alpha = 0.05$; reject the null hypothesis. There is sufficient evidence at the $\alpha = 0.05$ level of significance to conclude that $\sigma_1 \neq \sigma_2$.

11. $H_0: \mu_1 = \mu_2$ vs. $H_1: \mu_1 \neq \mu_2$. All requirements to conduct the test are satisfied. Classical: $t_0 = -3.271 < -t_{0.005} = -2.704$; reject the null hypothesis. $0.002 < P$-value < 0.005 [Tech: P-value $= 0.0016$] $< \alpha = 0.01$; reject the null hypothesis. There is sufficient evidence at the $\alpha = 0.05$ level of significance to conclude that there is a difference in the means.

12. $H_0: \mu_d = 0$ vs. $H_1: \mu_d > 0$; $d_i = Y_i - X_i$ Classical: $t_0 = 1.324 < t_{0.05} = 2.132$; do not reject the null hypothesis. $0.15 > P$-value > 0.10 [Tech: P-value $= 0.128$] $> \alpha = 0.05$; do not reject the null hypothesis. There is not sufficient evidence at the $\alpha = 0.05$ level of significance to conclude that the treatment is effective.

13. $H_0: \mu_d = 0$ vs. $H_1: \mu_d < 0$; $d_i = Y_i - X_i$. Classical: $t_0 = -1.754 < -t_{0.1} = -1.533$; reject the null hypothesis. $0.05 < P$-value < 0.10 [Tech: P-value $= 0.0771$] $< \alpha = 0.1$; reject the null hypothesis. There is sufficient evidence at the $\alpha = 0.1$ level of significance to conclude that the treatment is effective.

14. $H_0: p_A = p_B$ vs. $H_1: p_A \neq p_B$. Classical: $z_0 = 1.18 < z_{0.025} = 1.96$; do not reject the null hypothesis. P-value $= 0.238 > \alpha = 0.05$; do not reject the null hypothesis. There is not sufficient evidence at the $\alpha = 0.05$ level of significance to conclude that there is a difference in the proportions.

15. (a) There are a few very large collision claims relative to the majority of claims.
   (b) $H_0: \mu_{30-59} = \mu_{20-24}$ vs. $H_1: \mu_{30-59} < \mu_{20-24}$. All requirements to conduct the test are satisfied; use $\alpha = 0.05$. Classical: $t_0 = -1.890 < -t_{0.05} = -1.685$; reject the null hypothesis. $0.025 < P$-value < 0.05 [Tech: P-value $= 0.0313$] $< \alpha = 0.05$; reject the null hypothesis. There is sufficient evidence at the $\alpha = 0.05$ level of significance to conclude that the mean collision claim of a 30- to 59-year-old is less than the mean claim of a 20- to 24-year-old. Given that 20- to 24-year-olds tend to claim more for each accident, it makes sense to charge them more for coverage.

16. $H_0: p_{nk} = p_k$ vs. $H_1: p_{nk} < p_k$. Independent samples; all requirements to conduct the test are satisfied; use $\alpha = 0.05$. Classical: $z_0 = -4.63 < -z_{0.05} = -1.645$; reject the null hypothesis. P-value $< 0.0001 < \alpha = 0.05$; reject the null hypothesis. There is sufficient evidence at the $\alpha = 0.05$ level of significance to conclude that the proportion of non-Kumon students who answered the question correctly is less than the proportion of Kumon students who answered the question correctly. The Kumon students performed better on the exam question. A confounding factor is that it may be the case that stronger students enroll in Kumon (since it is an after-school program). So, it is not clear what role Kumon plays in the performance of the students compared to their ability.

17. $H_0: p_{HE} = p_{HA}$ vs. $H_1: p_{HE} \neq p_{HA}$. Classical: $z_0 = 3.74 > z_{0.025} = 1.96$; reject the null hypothesis. P-value $= 0.0002 < \alpha = 0.05$; reject the null hypothesis. There is sufficient evidence at the $\alpha = 0.05$ level of significance to conclude that there is a difference in the proportions. It seems that the proportion who are healthy differs from the proportion who are happy. The data imply that more people are happy even though they are unhealthy.

18. (a)

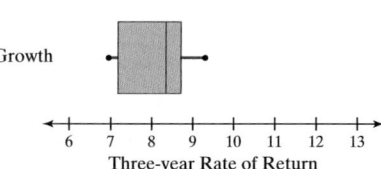

The boxplots indicate that people do spend more on fast food when they use a credit card.

(b) $H_0: \mu_{cr} = \mu_{ca}$ vs. $H_1: \mu_{cr} > \mu_{ca}$. All requirements to conduct the test are satisfied. Classical: $t_0 = 2.247 < t_{0.01} = 2.821$; do not reject the null hypothesis. $0.05 > P$-value > 0.025 [Tech: P-value $= 0.0191$] $> \alpha = 0.01$; do not reject the null hypothesis. There is not sufficient evidence at the $\alpha = 0.01$ level of significance to conclude that the mean amount spent with credit cards is more than the mean amount spent with cash.
   (c) With $\alpha = 0.05$ level of significance, we would reject the null hypothesis. However, once the level of significance is decided on, you should not change it. With that said, the P-value does suggest that the mean amount on credit-card sales is more than the mean amount on cash sales. It would be legitimate to suggest to your manager that further investigation is warranted (such as looking at larger samples).

19. $H_0: \mu_d = 0$ vs. $H_1: \mu_d \neq 0$; $d_i = W_i - T_i$. Classical: $t_0 = -1.244$ is between $-t_{0.025} = -2.262$ and $t_{0.025} = 2.262$; do not reject the null hypothesis. $0.30 > P$-value > 0.20 [Tech: P-value $= 0.2451$] $> \alpha = 0.05$; do not reject the null hypothesis. There is not sufficient evidence at the $\alpha = 0.05$ level of significance to conclude that there is a difference in the pricing of health and beauty products at Walmart and Target.

20. $H_0: \mu_c = \mu_{nc}$ vs. $H_1: \mu_c > \mu_{nc}$. All requirements to conduct the test are satisfied. Classical: $t_0 = 1.875 > t_{0.1} = 1.299$; reject the null hypothesis. $0.025 < P$-value < 0.05 [Tech: P-value $= 0.0319$] $< \alpha = 0.1$; reject the null hypothesis. There is sufficient evidence at the $\alpha = 0.1$ level of significance to conclude that the teacher evaluations were better for the chocolate group than for the nonchocolate group.

21. $H_0: p_{>100K} = p_{<100K}$ vs. $H_1: p_{>100K} \neq p_{<100K}$. Lower bound: 0.019 [Tech: 0.020], upper bound: 0.097. Because the confidence interval does not include 0, there is sufficient evidence at the $\alpha = 0.05$ level of significance to conclude that there is a difference in the proportions. It seems that a higher proportion of individuals who earn over $100,000 per year feel it is morally wrong for unwed women to have children.

22. (a) Since the sample size is small, the distribution of differences must be normal with no outliers.
   (b) $H_0: \mu_d = 0$ vs. $H_1: \mu_d > 0$; $d_i = GE_i - P_i$. Classical: $t_0 = 1.413 < t_{0.05} = 1.782$; do not reject the null hypothesis. $0.10 > P$-value > 0.05 [Tech: P-value $= 0.064$] $> \alpha = 0.05$; do not reject the null hypothesis. There is not sufficient evidence at the $\alpha = 0.05$ level of significance to conclude that the daily volume of General Electric stock is greater than that of Pfizer stock.

23. (a) Yes
   (b)

Value

Growth

6 7 8 9 10 11 12 13
Three-year Rate of Return

There are no outliers in either data set.
   (c) $H_0: \mu_v = \mu_g$ vs. $H_1: \mu_v \neq \mu_g$. Classical: $t_0 = 0.587$ is between $-t_{0.025} = -2.262$ and $t_{0.025} = 2.262$; do not reject the null hypothesis. P-value > 0.50 [Tech: P-value $= 0.5691$] $> \alpha = 0.05$; do not reject the null hypothesis. There is not sufficient evidence at the $\alpha = 0.05$ level of significance to conclude that the rate of return of value funds is different from the rate of return of growth funds.
   (d) $H_0: \sigma_v = \sigma_g$ vs. $H_1: \sigma_v \neq \sigma_g$. Classical: $F = 9.99 > F_{0.025} = 4.03$; reject the null hypothesis. P-value $= 0.002 < \alpha = 0.05$; reject the null hypothesis. The value funds appear to be more volatile than the growth funds.
   (e) Since there does not appear to be a difference in mean rates of return, risk should be used as the determining factor. Using risk as the criteria for investing, the growth fund appears to be the better option.

24. Use matched-pairs design to eliminate variability due to overall market fluctuations.

Chapter 11 Review Exercises (page 637)

1. Dependent   2. Independent

3. (a) $F_{0.05,8,9} = 3.23$ (b) $F_{0.975,10,5} = 0.24$, $F_{0.025,10,5} = 6.62$

4. (a)

Observation	1	2	3	4	5	6
$d_i = X_i - Y_i$	−0.7	0.6	0	−0.1	−0.4	−0.4

(b) $d = -0.167; s_d = 0.450$
(c) Hypotheses: $H_0: \mu_d = 0, H_1: \mu_d < 0$. Classical approach: $t_0 = -0.907 > -t_{0.05} = -2.015$; do not reject the null hypothesis. P-value approach: $0.25 > P$-value > 0.20 [Tech: P-value = 0.2030] $> \alpha = 0.05$; do not reject the null hypothesis. There is not sufficient evidence to conclude that the mean difference is less than zero.
(d) Lower bound: −0.79, upper bound: 0.45

5. (a) Hypotheses: $H_0: \mu_1 = \mu_2, H_1: \mu_1 \neq \mu_2$. Classical approach: $t_0 = 2.290 > t_{0.05} = 1.895$; reject the null hypothesis. P-value approach: $0.05 < P$-value < 0.10 [Tech: P-value = 0.0351] $< \alpha = 0.10$; reject the null hypothesis. There is sufficient evidence at the $\alpha = 0.1$ level of significance to conclude that $\mu_1 \neq \mu_2$.
(b) Lower bound: 0.73 [Tech: 1.01], upper bound: 7.67 [Tech: 7.39]
(c) Hypotheses: $H_0: \sigma_1 = \sigma_2, H_1: \sigma_1 \neq \sigma_2$. Classical approach: $F_0 = 1.40$ is between $F_{0.975,12,7} = 0.28$ and $F_{0.025,12,7} \approx 4.67$; do not reject the null hypothesis. P-value approach: P-value = $0.6734 > \alpha = 0.05$; do not reject the null hypothesis. There is not sufficient evidence at the $\alpha = 0.05$ level of significance to conclude that the standard deviation in population 1 is different from the standard deviation in population 2.

6. (a) Hypotheses: $H_0: \mu_1 = \mu_2, H_1: \mu_1 > \mu_2$. Classical approach: $t_0 = 1.472 < t_{0.01} = 2.423$; do not reject the null hypothesis. P-value approach: $0.10 > P$-value > 0.05 [Tech: P-value = 0.0726] $> \alpha = 0.01$; do not reject the null hypothesis. There is not sufficient evidence at the $\alpha = 0.01$ level of significance to conclude that the mean of population 1 is larger than the mean of population 2.
(b) Hypotheses: $H_0: \sigma_1 = \sigma_2, H_1: \sigma_1 < \sigma_2$. Classical approach: $F_0 = 0.67 > F_{0.99,44,40} \approx 0.50$; do not reject the null hypothesis. P-value approach: P-value = $0.0940 > \alpha = 0.01$; do not reject the null hypothesis. There is not sufficient evidence at the $\alpha = 0.01$ level of significance to conclude that the standard deviation in population 1 is less than the standard deviation in population 2.

7. $H_0: p_1 = p_2, H_1: p_1 \neq p_2$. Classical: $z_0 = -1.70$ is between $-z_{0.025} = -1.96$ and $z_{0.025} = 1.96$; do not reject the null hypothesis. P-value = 0.093 [Tech: 0.0895] $> \alpha = 0.05$; do not reject the null hypothesis. There is not sufficient evidence at the $\alpha = 0.05$ level of significance to conclude that the proportion in population 1 is different from the proportion in population 2.

8. (a) The sampling method is dependent because the same individual is used for both measurements.
(b) Hypotheses: $H_0: \mu_d = 0, H_1: \mu_d \neq 0$. Classical approach: $t_0 = 0.512$ is between $-t_{0.025} = -2.262$ and $t_{0.025} = 2.262$; do not reject the null hypothesis. P-value approach: P-value > 0.50 [Tech: P-value = 0.6209] $> \alpha = 0.05$; do not reject the null hypothesis. There is not sufficient evidence at the $\alpha = 0.05$ level of significance to conclude that arm span is different from height. The sample evidence does not contradict the belief that arm span and height are the same.

9. (a) The testing method is independent since the cars selected for the McDonald's sample had no bearing on the cars chosen for the Wendy's sample.
(b) Hypotheses: $H_0: \mu_{McD} = \mu_W, H_1: \mu_{McD} \neq \mu_W$. Classical approach: $t_0 = -4.059 < -t_{0.05} = -1.706$; reject the null hypothesis. P-value approach: P-value < 0.0005 [Tech: P-value = 0.0003] $< \alpha = 0.10$; reject the null hypothesis. There is sufficient evidence at the $\alpha = 0.05$ level of significance to conclude that the wait times in the drive-throughs of the two restaurants differ.
(c)

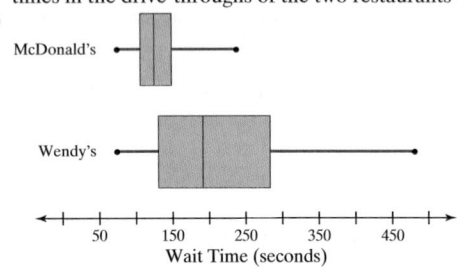

Based on the boxplots, it would appear to be the case that the wait time at McDonalds is less than the wait time at Wendy's.

10. (a) Each sample is a simple random sample; $n_1 \hat{p}_1 (1 - \hat{p}_1) = 26 \geq 10$ and $n_2 \hat{p}_2 (1 - \hat{p}_2) = 45 \geq 10$; and each sample is less than 5% of the population size. Hypotheses: $H_0: p_{exp} = p_{control}, H_1: p_{exp} < p_{control}$. Classical approach: $z_0 = -2.71 < -z_{0.01} = -2.33$; reject the null hypothesis. P-value approach: P-value = $0.0033 < \alpha = 0.01$; reject the null hypothesis. There is sufficient evidence at the $\alpha = 0.01$ level of significance to conclude that a lower proportion of women in the experimental group experienced a bone fracture than in the control group.
(b) Lower bound: −0.06, upper bound: −0.01. We are 95% confident that the difference in the proportion of women who experienced a bone fracture between the experimental and control group is between −0.06 and −0.01.
(c) This is a completely randomized design with two treatments: placebo and 5 mg of Actonel.
(d) A double-blind experiment is one in which neither the subject nor the individual administering the treatment knows which group (experimental or control) the subject is in.

11. $H_0: p_J = p_V, H_1: p_J \neq p_V$. Classical: $z_0 = 1.81 < z_{0.025} = 1.96$; do not reject the null hypothesis. P-value = $0.0702 > \alpha = 0.05$; do not reject the null hypothesis. There is not sufficient evidence at the $\alpha = 0.05$ level of significance to conclude that there is a difference in the proportions. It seems that the proportion who feel serving on a jury is a civic duty is the same as the proportion who feel voting is a civic duty.

12. (a) $n = n_1 = n_2 = 2,136$ **(b)** $n = n_1 = n_2 = 3,383$

13. Hypotheses: $H_0: \sigma_{McD} = \sigma_W, H_1: \sigma_{McD} < \sigma_W$. Classical approach: $F_0 = 0.15 < F_{0.95,29,26} \approx 0.45$; reject the null hypothesis. P-value $< 0.0001 < \alpha = 0.05$; reject the null hypothesis. There is sufficient evidence at the $\alpha = 0.05$ level of significance to conclude that the standard deviation in wait time at Wendy's is more than the standard deviation in wait time at McDonald's.

14. Lower bound: −1.37, upper bound: 2.17. Since the interval includes zero, we conclude that there is not sufficient evidence at the $\alpha = 0.10$ level of significance to reject the claim that arm span and height are equal.

15. Lower bound: −128.868 [Tech: −128.4]; upper bound: −42.218 [Tech: −42.67]. A marketing campaign could be initiated by McDonald's touting the fact that wait times are up to 2 minutes less at McDonald's.

Chapter 11 Test (page 639)

1. Independent   **2.** Dependent

3. (a)

Observation	1	2	3	4	5	6	7
$d_i = X_i - Y_i$	0.2	−0.5	0.2	0.6	−0.6	−0.5	−0.8

(b) $d = -0.2; s_d = 0.526$
(c) Hypotheses: $H_0: \mu_d = 0, H_1: \mu_d \neq 0$. Classical approach: $t_0 = -1.006$ is between $-t_{0.005} = -3.707$ and $t_{0.005} = 3.707$; do not reject the null hypothesis. $0.40 > P$-value > 0.30 [Tech: P-value = 0.3532] $> \alpha = 0.01$; do not reject the null hypothesis. There is not sufficient evidence to conclude that the mean difference is different from zero.
(d) Lower bound: −0.69, upper bound: 0.29

4. (a) Hypotheses: $H_0: \mu_1 = \mu_2, H_1: \mu_1 \neq \mu_2$. Classical approach: $t_0 = -2.054 < -t_{0.05} = -1.714$. Reject the null hypothesis. $0.05 < P$-value < 0.10 [Tech: P-value = 0.0464] $< \alpha = 0.1$; reject the null hypothesis. There is sufficient evidence at the $\alpha = 0.1$ level of significance to conclude that the means are different.
(b) Lower bound: −12.44 [Tech: −12.3], upper bound: 0.04 [Tech: −0.10]
(c) Hypotheses: $H_0: \sigma_1 = \sigma_2, H_1: \sigma_1 > \sigma_2$. Classical approach: $F_0 = 2.0 > F_{0.10,23,26} \approx 1.72$; reject the null hypothesis. P-value = $0.0448 < \alpha = 0.10$; reject the null hypothesis. There is sufficient evidence at the $\alpha = 0.10$ level of significance to conclude that the standard deviation in population 1 is greater than the standard deviation in population 2.

5. (a) Hypotheses: $H_0: \mu_1 = \mu_2, H_1: \mu_1 < \mu_2$. Classical approach: $t_0 = -1.357 > -t_{0.05} = -1.895$; do not reject the null hypothesis. $0.15 > P$-value > 0.10 [Tech: P-value = 0.0959] $> \alpha = 0.05$; do not reject the null hypothesis. There is not sufficient evidence at the $\alpha = 0.05$ level of significance to conclude that the mean of population 1 is less than the mean of population 2.

(b) Hypotheses: $H_0: \sigma_1 = \sigma_2$, $H_1: \sigma_1 \neq \sigma_2$. Classical approach: $F_0 = 1.64$ is between $F_{0.975,12,7} = 0.28$ and $F_{0.025,12,7} \approx 4.76$; do not reject the null hypothesis. P-value $= 0.5243 > \alpha = 0.05$; do not reject the null hypothesis. There is not sufficient evidence at the $\alpha = 0.05$ level of significance to conclude that the standard deviation in population 1 is different from the standard deviation in population 2.

6. $H_0: p_1 = p_2$ vs. $H_1: p_1 < p_2$ Classical: $z_0 = -0.80 > -z_{0.05} = -1.645$; do not reject the null hypothesis. P-value $= 0.2119$ [Tech: 0.2124] $> \alpha = 0.05$; do not reject the null hypothesis. There is not sufficient evidence at the $\alpha = 0.05$ level of significance to conclude that the proportion in population 1 is less than the proportion in population 2.

7. (a) The testing method is independent since the dates selected for the Texas sample have no bearing on the dates chosen for the Illinois sample.
(b) Both samples must come from populations that are normally distributed.
(c)

The boxplots indicate the Chicago rain has a lower pH than Houston rain.
(d) Hypotheses: $H_0: \mu_{\text{Texas}} = \mu_{\text{Illinois}}$, $H_1: \mu_{\text{Texas}} \neq \mu_{\text{Illinois}}$. Classical approach: $t_0 = 2.276 > t_{0.025} = 2.201$; reject the null hypothesis. $0.04 < P$-value < 0.05 [Tech: P-value $= 0.0387$] $< \alpha = 0.05$; reject the null hypothesis. There is sufficient evidence at the $\alpha = 0.05$ level of significance to conclude that the acidity of the rain near Houston is different from its acidity near Chicago.

8. (a) This is a matched-pairs design.
(b) Hypotheses: $H_0: \mu_d = 0$, $H_1: \mu_d > 0$. Classical approach: $t_0 = 26.991 > t_{0.05} = 1.660$; reject the null hypothesis. P-value approach: P-value < 0.0005 [Tech: P-value < 0.0001] $< \alpha = 0.05$; reject the null hypothesis. There is sufficient evidence at the $\alpha = 0.05$ level of significance to conclude that there is a positive BMI reduction 10 months after gastric bypass surgery.
(c) Lower bound: 11.834 [Tech: 11.835], upper bound: 13.386 [Tech: 13.385]. In clinical trails, subjects had a mean weight loss of 12.61 pounds after having this surgery. We are 90% confident that the mean BMI reduction is between 11.8 and 13.4 pounds. This does not mean that each individual will lose between 11.8 and 13.4 pounds!

9. (a) Completely randomized design.
(b) Whether the subject gets dry mouth or not.
(c) Each sample is a sample random sample; $n_1\hat{p}_1(1 - \hat{p}_1) = 66 \geq 10$ and $n_2\hat{p}_2(1 - \hat{p}_2) = 39 \geq 10$; and each sample is less than 5% of the population size. Hypotheses: $H_0: p_{\text{exp}} = p_{\text{control}}$, $H_1: p_{\text{exp}} > p_{\text{control}}$. Classical approach: $z_0 = 2.21 > z_{0.05} = 1.645$; reject the null hypothesis. P-value $= 0.0136 < \alpha = 0.05$; reject the null hypothesis. There is sufficient evidence at the $\alpha = 0.05$ level of significance to conclude that a higher proportion of subjects in the experimental group experienced a dry mouth than in the control group.

10. $H_0: p_M = p_F$, $H_1: p_M \neq p_F$. Lower bound: 0.051, upper bound: 0.089. Because the confidence interval does not include 0, we reject the null hypothesis. There is sufficient evidence at the $\alpha = 0.1$ level of significance to conclude that the proportion of males and females for which hypnotism led to quitting smoking is different.

11. $H_0: p_A = p_{CP}$, $H_1: p_A \neq p_{CP}$. Classical: $z_0 = 76.6 > z_{0.025} = 1.96$; reject the null hypothesis. P-value $< 0.0001 < \alpha = 0.05$; reject the null hypothesis. There is sufficient evidence at the $\alpha = 0.05$ level of significance to conclude that the proportion of individuals who favor the death penalty is different from the proportion who favor abortion.

12. (a) $n = n_1 = n_2 = 762$ **(b)** $n = n_1 = n_2 = 1{,}201$

13. $H_0: \mu_p = \mu_n$; $H_1: \mu_p \neq \mu_n$. Lower bound: 1.03 pounds, upper bound: 1.17 pounds. Because the confidence interval does not contain 0, we

reject the null hypothesis. There is sufficient evidence to conclude that Naltrexone is effective in preventing weight gain among individuals who quit smoking. Answers will vary regarding practical significance, but one must ask, "Do I want to take a drug so that I can keep about 1 pound off?" Probably not.

14. Hypotheses: $H_0: \sigma_{\text{Tex}} = \sigma_{\text{Ill}}$, $H_1: \sigma_{\text{Tex}} \neq \sigma_{\text{Ill}}$. Classical approach: $F_0 = 5.64 > F_{0.025,11,13} \approx 3.325$; reject the null hypothesis. P-value $= 0.0044 < \alpha = 0.05$; reject the null hypothesis. There is sufficient evidence at the $\alpha = 0.05$ level of significance to conclude that the standard deviation in the acidity of rain near Houston is different from the standard deviation in the acidity of rain near Chicago.

CHAPTER 12 Inference on Categorical Data

12.1 Assess Your Understanding (page 652)

1. Answers will vary. One possible answer: *Goodness of fit* is appropriate because we are testing to see if the frequency of outcomes from a sample fits the theoretical distribution.

2. The χ^2 goodness-of-fit tests are always right tailed because the numerator in the test statistic is squared, making every test statistic other than a perfect fit positive. So, we are measuring if $\chi_0^2 > \chi_\alpha^2$.

3. To perform a goodness-of-fit test, all expected frequencies must be greater than or equal to 1, and at least 80% of the expected frequencies must be greater than or equal to 5.

4. If the expected count of a category is less than 1, two (or more) of the categories can be combined so that a goodness-of-fit test can be used. Alternatively, the sample size can be increased.

5.

p_i	0.2	0.1	0.45	0.25
Expected counts	100	50	225	125

6.

p_i	0.15	0.3	0.35	0.20
Expected counts	105	210	245	140

7. (a) $\chi_0^2 = 2.72$
(b) df $= 3$
(c) $\chi_{0.05}^2 = 7.815$
(d) Do not reject H_0, since $\chi^2 < \chi_{0.05}^2$. There is not sufficient evidence at the $\alpha = 0.05$ level of significance to conclude that any one of the proportions is different from the others.

8. (a) $\chi_0^2 = 2.2$
(b) df $= 4$
(c) $\chi_{0.05}^2 = 9.488$
(d) Do not reject H_0, since $\chi^2 < \chi_{0.05}^2$. There is not sufficient evidence at the $\alpha = 0.05$ level of significance to conclude that any one of the proportions is different from the others.

9. (a) $\chi_0^2 = 12.56$
(b) df $= 4$
(c) $\chi_{0.05}^2 = 9.488$
(d) Reject H_0, since $\chi_0^2 > \chi_{0.05}^2$. There is sufficient evidence at the $\alpha = 0.05$ level of significance to conclude that X is not binomial with $n = 4$, $p = 0.8$.

10. (a) $\chi_0^2 = 11.987$
(b) df $= 4$
(c) $\chi_{0.05}^2 = 9.488$
(d) Reject H_0, since $\chi_0^2 > \chi_{0.05}^2$. There is sufficient evidence at the $\alpha = 0.05$ level of significance to conclude that X is not binomial with $n = 4$, $p = 0.3$.

11. Classical approach: $\chi_0^2 = 18.738 > \chi_{0.05}^2 = 11.071$; reject the null hypothesis. P-value approach: P-value $< 0.005 < \alpha = 0.05$ [Tech: P-value $= 0.002$]; reject the null hypothesis. There is sufficient evidence at the $\alpha = 0.05$ level of significance to conclude that the distribution of candies in a bag of M&Ms is not 13% brown, 14% yellow, 13% red, 20% orange, 24% blue, and 16% green.

12. Classical approach: $\chi_0^2 = 3.569 < \chi_{0.05}^2 = 11.071$; do not reject the null hypothesis. P-value approach: P-value $> 0.10 > \alpha = 0.05$ [Tech: P-value $= 0.613$]; do not reject the null hypothesis. There is not sufficient evidence at the $\alpha = 0.05$ level of significance to reject M&M/ Mar's stated distribution of 12% brown, 15% yellow, 12% red, 23% orange, 23% blue, and 15% green candies in a bag of peanut M&Ms.

13. (a) Answers will vary depending on the desired probability of making a Type I error. One possible choice: $\alpha = 0.01$.
(b) Classical approach: $\chi_0^2 = 21.693$; compare χ_0^2 to your chosen χ_α^2. P-value approach: P-value is between 0.01 and 0.005 [Tech: P-value = 0.006].
(c) Answers will vary. One possible answer: Since P-value < 0.01, there is sufficient evident to conclude that Benford's Law is not followed and the employee is guilty of embezzlement.

14. Classical approach: $\chi_0^2 = 5.092 < \chi_{0.05}^2 = 15.507$; do not reject the null hypothesis. P-value approach: P-value $> 0.10 > \alpha = 0.05$ [Tech: P-value = 0.748]; do not reject the null hypothesis. At the $\alpha = 0.05$ level of significance, the evidence supports the belief that the distribution of the surface area of rivers follows Benford's Law.

15. (a) Classical approach: $\chi_0^2 = 121.367 > \chi_{0.05}^2 = 9.488$; reject the null hypothesis. P-value approach: P-value $< 0.005 < \alpha = 0.05$ [Tech: P-value = 0.000]; reject the null hypothesis. There is sufficient evidence at the $\alpha = 0.05$ level of significance to conclude that the distribution of fatal injuries for riders not wearing a helmet does not follow the distribution for all riders.

(b)

Location of Injury	Multiple Locations	Head	Neck	Thorax	Abdomen/ Lumbar/Spine
Observed	1,036	864	38	83	47
Expected	1,178.76	641.08	62.04	124.08	62.04

We notice that the observed count for head injuries is much higher than expected, while the observed counts for all the other categories are lower. We might conclude that motorcycle fatalities from head injuries occur more frequently for riders not wearing a helmet.

16. (a) Classical approach: $\chi_0^2 = 511.475 > \chi_{0.05}^2 = 7.815$; reject the null hypothesis. P-value approach: P-value $< 0.005 < \alpha = 0.05$ [Tech: P-value = 0.000]; reject the null hypothesis. There is sufficient evidence at the $\alpha = 0.05$ level of significance to conclude that the distribution of weapons used in robberies on school property does not follow the national distribution of weapons used in robberies generally.

(b)

Weapon	Gun	Knife	Strong-Arm	Other
Observed	329	122	857	344
Expected	693.84	148.68	660.8	148.68

We notice that the observed counts for gun and knife are lower than expected, while the observed counts for strong-arm and other are higher. We might conclude that guns and knives are used less frequently in robberies on school property than they are used in robberies generally.

17. (a) Group 1: 84; Group 2: 84; Group 3: 84; Group 4: 81. Classical approach: $\chi_0^2 = 0.084$ [Tech: 0.081] $< \chi_{0.05}^2 = 7.815$; do not reject the null hypothesis. P-value approach: P-value $> 0.99 > \alpha = 0.05$ [Tech: P-value = 0.994]; do not reject the null hypothesis. There is not sufficient evidence at the $\alpha = 0.05$ level of significance to conclude that there are differences among the groups in attendance patterns.
(b) Group 1: 84; Group 2: 81; Group 3: 78; Group 4: 76. Classical approach: $\chi_0^2 = 0.463$ [Tech: 0.461] $< \chi_{0.05}^2 = 7.815$; do not reject the null hypothesis. P-value approach: P-value $> 0.90 > \alpha = 0.05$ [Tech: P-value = 0.927]; do not reject the null hypothesis. There is not sufficient evidence at the $\alpha = 0.05$ level of significance to conclude that there are differences among the groups in attendance patterns. It is curious that the farther a group's original position is located from the front of the room, the more the attendance rate for the group decreases.
(c) Group 1: 20; Group 2: 20; Group 3: 20; Group 4: 20. Classical approach: $\chi_0^2 = 2.55$ [Tech: 2.57] $< \chi_{0.05}^2 = 7.815$; do not reject the null hypothesis. P-value approach: P-value $> 0.10 > \alpha = 0.05$ [Tech: P-value = 0.463]; do not reject the null hypothesis. There is not sufficient evidence at the $\alpha = 0.05$ level of significance to conclude that there is a significant difference in the number of students in the top 20% of the class by group.

(d) Though not statistically significant, the group located in the front had both better attendance and a larger number of students in the top 20%. Choose the front.

18. (a) Classical approach: $\chi_0^2 = 3.257 < \chi_{0.05}^2 = 7.815$; do not reject the null hypothesis. P-value approach: P-value $> 0.10 > \alpha = 0.05$ [Tech: P-value = 0.354]; do not reject the null hypothesis. There is not sufficient evidence at the $\alpha = 0.05$ level of significance to conclude that the distribution of races in traffic stops is different from the distribution of drivers in Mundelein. That is, there is not sufficient evidence of racial profiling in Mundelein.

(b)

Race	White	African American	Hispanic	Asian
Observed	7,079	273	2,025	491
Expected	7,095.092	276.304	2,042.676	453.928

We notice that the observed counts for the races are close to the expected counts. Only the Asian traffic stops are higher than expected.

19. Classical approach: $\chi_0^2 = 1.264 < \chi_{0.05}^2 = 19.675$; do not reject the null hypothesis. P-value approach: P-value $> 0.995 > \alpha = 0.05$ [Tech: P-value = 1.000]; do not reject the null hypothesis. There is not sufficient evidence at the $\alpha = 0.05$ level of significance to reject the belief that each birth month occurs with equal frequency.

20. Classical approach: $\chi_0^2 = 19.03 > \chi_{0.05}^2 = 12.592$; reject the null hypothesis. P-value approach: P-value $< 0.005 < \alpha = 0.05$ [Tech: P-value = 0.004]; reject the null hypothesis. There is sufficient evidence at the $\alpha = 0.05$ level of significance to reject the belief that bicycle fatalities occur with equal frequency over the days of the week. We might conclude that fewer bicycle fatalities occur on Sundays and Tuesdays.

21. Classical approach: $\chi_0^2 = 13.227 > \chi_{0.05}^2 = 12.592$; reject the null hypothesis. P-value approach: P-value $< 0.05 = \alpha$ [Tech: P-value = 0.040]; reject the null hypothesis. There is sufficient evidence at the $\alpha = 0.05$ level of significance to reject the belief that pedestrian deaths occur with equal frequency over the days of the week. We might conclude that fewer pedestrian deaths occur on Tuesdays and more occur on Saturdays.

22. (a) Classical approach: $\chi_0^2 = 4.67 < \chi_{0.01}^2 = 15.086$; do not reject the null hypothesis. P-value approach: P-value $> 0.10 > \alpha = 0.01$ [Tech: P-value = 0.457]; do not reject the null hypothesis. There is not sufficient evidence at the $\alpha = 0.01$ level of significance to conclude that the die is loaded.
(b) The player does not want to incorrectly conclude that the die is loaded. That is, the player does not want to make a Type I error.

23. (a)

Grade	Relative Frequency	Observed Frequency	Expected Frequency
K–3	0.329	15	8.225
4–8	0.393	7	9.825
9–12	0.278	3	6.95

(b) Classical approach: $\chi_0^2 = 8.638 > \chi_{0.05}^2 = 5.991$; reject the null hypothesis. P-value approach: P-value $< 0.025 < \alpha = 0.05$ [Tech: P-value = 0.013]; reject the null hypothesis. There is sufficient evidence at the $\alpha = 0.05$ level of significance to conclude that the grade distribution of home-schooled children in her district is different from the national proportions. We might conclude that a greater proportion of students in grades K–3 are home-schooled in this district than nationally.

24. Classical approach: $\chi_0^2 = 1.201 < \chi_{0.05}^2 = 15.507$; do not reject the null hypothesis. P-value approach: P-value $> 0.995 > \alpha = 0.05$ [Tech: P-value = 0.997]; do not reject the null hypothesis. There is not sufficient evidence at the $\alpha = 0.05$ level of significance to reject the belief that the first digit in Fibonacci numbers follows Benford's Law.

25. (a) Answers will vary.
(b) Expect 20% of the numbers to be 1, 20% to be 2, 20% to be 3, 20% to be 4, and 20% to be 5.
(c) Answers will vary.

26. (a) Answers will vary.
(b) Expect 0.3277 of the numbers to be 0, 0.4096 of the numbers to be 1, 0.2048 to be 2, 0.0512 to be 3, 0.0064 to be 4, and 0.0003 to be 5.
(c) Answers will vary.

27. (a) Expected number with low birth weight: 17.04; expected number without low birth weight: 222.96.

(b) H_0: $p = 0.071$ vs. H_1: $p > 0.071$. Classical approach: $\chi_0^2 = 1.554 < \chi_{0.05}^2 = 3.841$; do not reject the null hypothesis. P-value approach: P-value $> 0.10 > \alpha = 0.05$ [Tech: p-value $= 0.213$]; do not reject the null hypothesis. There is not sufficient evidence at the $\alpha = 0.05$ level of significance to conclude that mothers between the ages of 35 and 39 have a higher percentage of low-birth-weight babies.

(c) H_0: $p = 0.71$ vs. H_1: $p > 0.71$; $np_0(1 - p_0) = 15.83 > 10$. Classical approach: $Z_0 = 1.25 < Z_{0.05} = 1.645$; do not reject the null hypothesis. P-value approach: P-value $= 0.1056 > \alpha = 0.05$ [Tech: P-value $= 0.1063$]; do not reject the null hypothesis. There is not sufficient evidence at the $\alpha = 0.05$ level of significance to conclude that mothers between the ages of 35 and 39 have a higher percentage of low-birth-weight babies.

28. (a) We would expect 103.2 of the 400 individuals sampled to live alone and 296.8 to not live alone.

(b) H_0: $p = 0.258$ vs. H_1: $p > 0.258$. Classical approach: $\chi_0^2 = 48.275 > \chi_{0.05}^2 = 3.841$; reject the null hypothesis. P-value approach: P-value $< 0.001 < \alpha = 0.05$ [Tech: P-value $= 0.000$]; reject the null hypothesis. There is sufficient evidence at the $\alpha = 0.05$ level of significance to conclude that the percentage of Americans living alone is more than 25.8%.

(c) H_0: $p = 0.258$ vs. H_1: $p > 0.258$; $np_0(1 - p_0) = 76.5744 > 10$. Classical approach: $Z_0 = 6.948 > Z_{0.05} = 1.645$; reject the null hypothesis. P-value approach: P-value $< 0.0001 < \alpha = 0.05$ [Tech: P-value $= 0.0000$]; reject the null hypothesis. There is sufficient evidence at the $\alpha = 0.05$ level of significance to conclude that the percentage of Americans living alone is more than 25.8%.

29. (a) $\mu = 0.9323$ hits

(b) All expected frequencies will not be greater than or equal to 1. Also, more than 20% (37.5%) of the expected frequencies are less than 5.

(c), (d)

x	$P(x)$	Expected number of hits
0	0.3936	226.741
1	0.3670	211.390
2	0.1711	98.540
3	0.0532	30.623
4 or more	0.0151	8.698

(e) Classical approach: $\chi_0^2 = 1.0116 < \chi_{0.05}^2 = 9.488$; do not reject the null hypothesis. P-value approach: P-value $> 0.90 > \alpha = 0.05$ [Tech: P-value $= 0.907$]; do not reject the null hypothesis. There is not sufficient evidence at the $\alpha = 0.05$ level of significance to conclude that the distribution of rocket hits is different from the Poisson distribution. That is, the rocket hits do appear to be modeled by a Poisson random variable.

12.2 Assess Your Understanding (page 667)

1. Answers may vary, but differences should include: chi-square test for independence compares two characteristics from a single population, whereas the chi-square test for homogeneity compares a single characteristic from two (or more) populations. Similarities should include: the procedures of the two tests and the assumptions of the two tests are the same.

2. Answers may vary.

3. (a) $\chi_0^2 = 1.701$

(b) Classical approach: $\chi_0^2 = 1.701 < \chi_{0.05}^2 = 5.991$; do not reject the null hypothesis. P-value approach: P-value $> 0.10 > \alpha = 0.05$ [Tech: P-value $= 0.427$]; do not reject the null hypothesis. There is evidence at the $\alpha = 0.05$ level of significance to conclude that X and Y are independent. We conclude that X and Y are not related.

4. (a) $\chi_0^2 = 13.053$

(b) Classical approach: $\chi_0^2 = 13.053 > \chi_{0.05}^2 = 5.991$; reject the null hypothesis. P-value approach: P-value $< 0.005 < \alpha = 0.05$ [Tech: P-value $= 0.001$]; reject the null hypothesis. There is sufficient evidence at the $\alpha = 0.05$ level of significance to conclude that X and Y are dependent. We conclude that X and Y are related to each other.

5. Classical approach: $\chi_0^2 = 1.989 < \chi_{0.01}^2 = 9.210$; do not reject the null hypothesis. P-value approach: P-value $> 0.10 > \alpha = 0.01$ [Tech: P-value $= 0.370$]; do not reject the null hypothesis. There is evidence at the $\alpha = 0.01$ level of significance to conclude that the proportions are equal for each category. There is not sufficient evidence to conclude that at least one of the proportions is different from the others.

6. Classical approach: $\chi_0^2 = 3.533 < \chi_{0.01}^2 = 9.210$; do not reject the null hypothesis. P-value approach: P-value $> 0.10 > \alpha = 0.01$ [Tech: P-value $= 0.171$]; do not reject the null hypothesis. There is evidence at the $\alpha = 0.01$ level of significance to conclude that the proportions are equal for each category. There is not sufficient evidence to conclude that at least one of the proportions is different from the others.

7. (a)

Had Sexual Intercourse?	Both Biological/ Adoptive Parents	Single Parent	Parent and Stepparent	Nonparental Guardian
Yes	78.553	52.368	41.895	26.184
No	71.447	47.632	38.105	23.816

(b) (1) All expected frequencies are greater than or equal to 1, and (2) no more than 20% of the expected frequencies are less than 5.

(c) $\chi_0^2 = 10.357$

(d) Classical approach: $\chi_0^2 = 10.357 > \chi_{0.05}^2 = 7.815$; reject the null hypothesis. P-value approach: P-value $< 0.025 < \alpha = 0.05$ [Tech: P-value $= 0.016$]; reject the null hypothesis. There is sufficient evidence at the $\alpha = 0.05$ level of significance to conclude that sexual activity and family structure are associated.

(e) The biggest difference between observed and expected occurs under the family structure in which both parents are present. Fewer females were sexually active than was expected when both parents were present. This means that having both parents present seems to have an effect on whether the child is sexually active.

(f)

Had Sexual Intercourse?	Both Biological/ Adoptive Parents	Single Parent	Parent and Stepparent	Nonparental Guardian
Yes	0.427	0.59	0.55	0.64
No	0.573	0.41	0.45	0.36

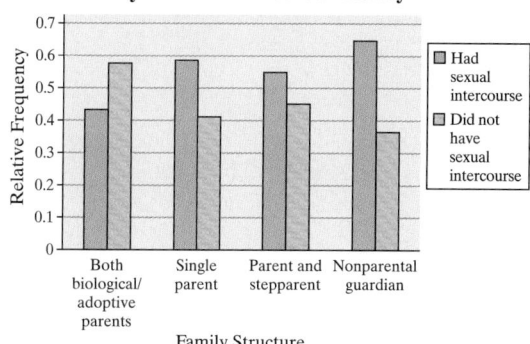

Family Structure and Sexual Activity

8. (a)

	Less Than 3 Months	3–5 Months	More Than 5 Months (or Never)
Intended	573.54	36.80	41.66
Unintended	73.01	4.68	5.3
Mistimed	179.45	11.51	13.04

(b) (1) All expected frequencies are greater than or equal to 1, and (2) no more than 20% of the expected frequencies are less than 5.

(c) $\chi_0^2 = 21.357$.

(d) Classical approach: $\chi_0^2 = 21.357 > \chi_{0.05}^2 = 9.488$; reject the null hypothesis. *P*-value approach: *P*-value < 0.005 < $\alpha = 0.05$ [Tech: *P*-value = 0.000]; reject the null hypothesis. There is sufficient evidence at the $\alpha = 0.05$ level of significance to conclude that wantedness of pregnancy and months pregnant before prenatal care are associated.

(e) The biggest difference between observed and expected occurs between intended and less than 3 months. The observed is greater than the expected, which implies that intended pregnancies are likely to have early prenatal care.

(f)

	Less Than 3 Months	3–5 Months	More Than 5 Months (or Never)
Intended	0.910	0.040	0.051
Unintended	0.771	0.096	0.133
Mistimed	0.828	0.093	0.078

Prenatal Care by Wantedness of the Pregnancy

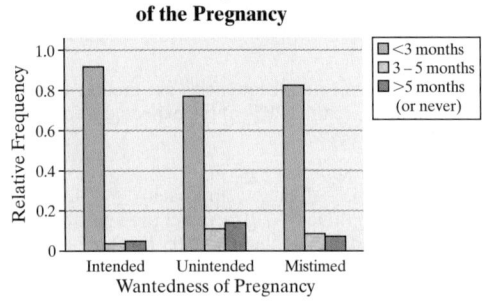

9. (a) Classical approach: $\chi_0^2 = 182.174 > \chi_{0.05}^2 = 12.592$; reject the null hypothesis. *P*-value approach: *P*-value < 0.005 < $\alpha = 0.05$ [Tech: *P*-value = 0.000]; reject the null hypothesis. There is

sufficient evidence at the $\alpha = 0.05$ level of significance to conclude that happiness and health are dependent. That is, happiness and health are related to each other.

(b)

Happiness	Health			
	Excellent	Good	Fair	Poor
Very Happy	0.492	0.280	0.202	0.183
Pretty Happy	0.448	0.609	0.570	0.486
Not Too Happy	0.060	0.111	0.227	0.330

Health and Happiness

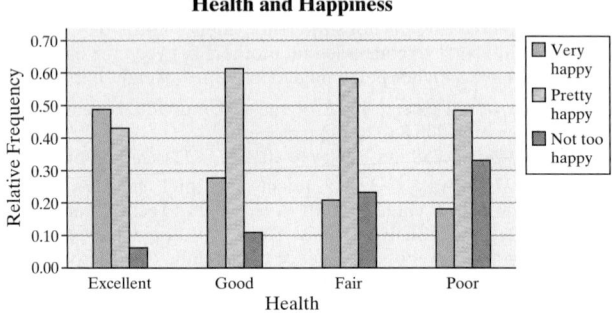

(c) The proportion of individuals who are "very happy" is much higher for individuals in "excellent" health than any other health category. Further, the proportion of individuals who are "not too happy" is much lower for individuals in "excellent" health compared to the other health categories. Put simply, the level of happiness seems to decline as health status declines.

10. (a) Classical approach: $\chi_0^2 = 285.061 > \chi_{0.05}^2 = 21.026$; reject the null hypothesis. *P*-value approach: *P*-value < 0.005 < $\alpha = 0.05$ [Tech: *P*-value = 0.000]; reject the null hypothesis. There is sufficient evidence at the $\alpha = 0.05$ level of significance to conclude that happiness and education are dependent. That is, happiness and education are related to each other.

(b)

Education	Health			
	Excellent	Good	Fair	Poor
Less than High School	0.135	0.378	0.372	0.116
High School	0.257	0.485	0.198	0.060
Junior College	0.288	0.496	0.176	0.040
Bachelor	0.394	0.475	0.110	0.021
Graduate	0.418	0.473	0.103	0.006

Health and Education

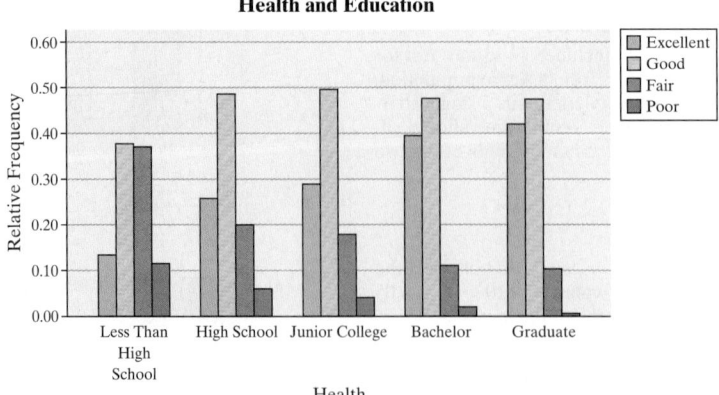

(c) The proportion of individuals with a "less than high school" education is less than the proportions for the other education levels in both the "excellent" and "good" health categories. Further, the proportion of individuals with "less than high school" is greater than the proportions of the other education levels in both the "fair" and "poor" health categories. Similarly, the proportion of individuals with a "graduate" education is higher than the proportions for the other education levels in the "excellent" health category. Likewise, the proportion of individuals with a "graduate" education is lower than the others proportions in the "poor" health category. Generally, a better health category seems to indicate a higher level of education, and a worse health category seems to indicate a lower level of education. Answers for lurking variables will vary. One possible lurking variable is age, since younger individuals are less likely to not have a high school diploma.

11. (a) Classical approach: $\chi_0^2 = 7.803 < \chi_{0.05}^2 = 12.592$; do not reject the null hypothesis. *P*-value approach: *P*-value $> 0.10 > \alpha = 0.05$ [Tech: *P*-value $= 0.253$]; do not reject the null hypothesis. There is not sufficient evidence at the $\alpha = 0.05$ level of significance to conclude that smoking status and number of years of education are associated. It does not appear to be the case that number of years of education plays a role in determining smoking status.

(b)

Years of Education	Current	Former	Never	Total
<12	0.376	0.186	0.439	1
12	0.393	0.198	0.410	1
13–15	0.389	0.221	0.389	1
≥16	0.288	0.280	0.432	1

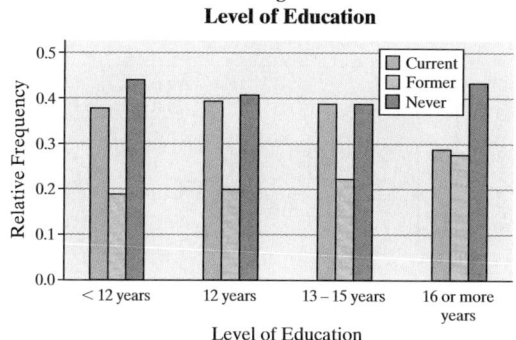

Smoking Status vs. Level of Education

12. (a) Classical approach: $\chi_0^2 = 0.036 < \chi_{0.10}^2 = 2.706$; do not reject the null hypothesis. *P*-value approach: *P*-value $> 0.10 = \alpha$ [Tech: *P*-value $= 0.849$]; do not reject the null hypothesis. There is not sufficient evidence at the $\alpha = 0.10$ level of significance to conclude that gender and opinion are associated. It appears to be the case that gender is not associated with one's opinion regarding choice.

(b)

Gender	Pro-Life	Pro-Choice	Total
Men	0.496	0.504	1
Women	0.490	0.510	1

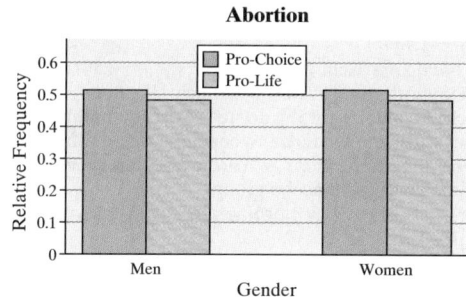

Abortion

13. (a) Classical approach: $\chi_0^2 = 37.198 > \chi_{0.05}^2 = 9.488$; reject the null hypothesis. *P*-value approach: *P*-value $< 0.005 < \alpha = 0.05$ [Tech: *P*-value $= 0.000$]; reject the null hypothesis. There is sufficient evidence at the $\alpha = 0.05$ level of significance to conclude that at least one of the proportions is different from the others. That is, the evidence suggests that the proportion of individuals who feel everyone has an equal opportunity to obtain a quality education in the United States is different for at least one level of education.

(b)

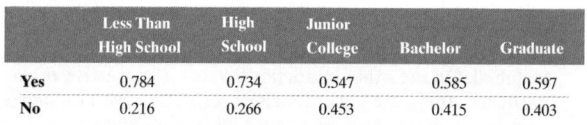

	Less Than High School	High School	Junior College	Bachelor	Graduate
Yes	0.784	0.734	0.547	0.585	0.597
No	0.216	0.266	0.453	0.415	0.403

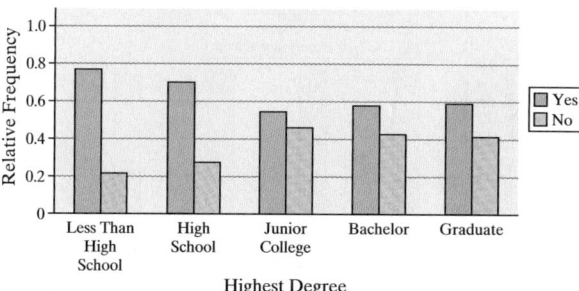

Equal Opportunity for Education

Higher proportions of individuals with a either a "high school" education or "less than a high school" education seem to agree with the statement that everyone has an equal opportunity to obtain a quality education than individuals in the other three education levels. Individuals whose highest degree is from a junior college appear to agree least with the statement.

14. (a) Classical approach: $\chi_0^2 = 41.330 > \chi_{0.05}^2 = 5.991$; reject the null hypothesis. *P*-value approach: *P*-value $< 0.005 < \alpha = 0.05$ [Tech: *P*-value $= 0.000$]; reject the null hypothesis. There is sufficient evidence at the $\alpha = 0.05$ level of significance to conclude that at least one of the proportions is different from the others. That is, the evidence suggests that the proportion of individuals who believe marijuana should be made legal is different for at least one political affiliation.

(b)

	Democrat	Independent	Republican
Yes	0.424	0.396	0.246
No	0.576	0.604	0.754

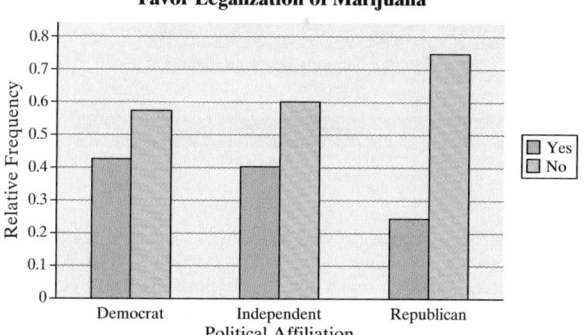

Favor Legalization of Marijuana

A higher proportion of Republicans appears to be against legalizing marijuana than do Democrats or Independents.

15. (a) Classical approach: $\chi_0^2 = 49.703 > \chi_{0.01}^2 = 13.277$; reject the null hypothesis. *P*-value approach: *P*-value $< 0.005 < \alpha = 0.01$ [Tech: *P*-value $= 0.000$]; reject the null hypothesis. There is sufficient evidence at the $\alpha = 0.01$ level of significance to support the belief that at least one proportion is different from the others. The evidence suggests that the subjects taking Naproxen experienced a higher incidence rate of ulcers than the other treatment groups.

(b)

Side Effect		Treatment			
	Placebo	Celebrex (50 mg)	Celebrex (100 mg)	Celebrex (200 mg)	Naproxen (500 mg)
Ulcer	0.023	0.034	0.031	0.059	0.162
No Ulcer	0.977	0.966	0.969	0.941	0.838
Total	1	1	1	1	1

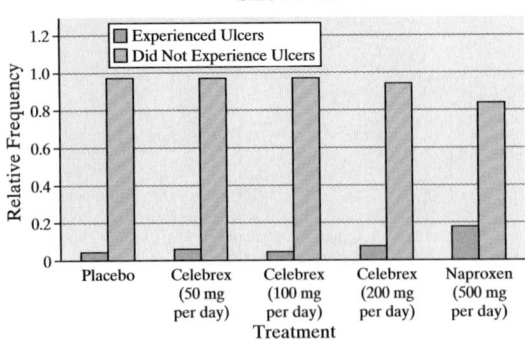

Side Effects

16. **(a)** Classical approach: $\chi_0^2 = 4.673 < \chi_{0.01}^2 = 13.277$; do not reject the null hypothesis. *P*-value approach: *P*-value $> 0.10 > \alpha = 0.01$ [Tech: *P*-value $= 0.323$]; do not reject the null hypothesis. There is not sufficient evidence at the $\alpha = 0.01$ level of significance to conclude that at least one proportion is different from the others. The evidence suggests that the proportions of individuals in each treatment group who experienced dizziness as a side effect are the same.

(b)

	Drug				
Side Effect	Celebrex	Placebo	Naproxen	Diclofenac	Ibuprofen
Dizziness	0.020	0.017	0.026	0.013	0.023
No Dizziness	0.980	0.983	0.974	0.987	0.977
Total	1	1	1	1	1

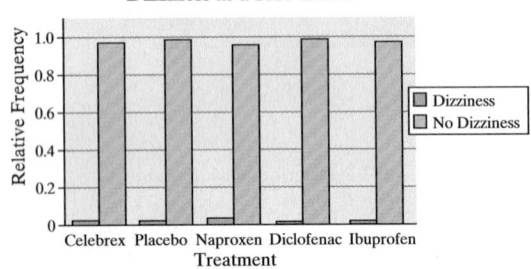

Dizziness as a Side Effect

17. **(a)**

	Course	Personal	Work
Female	13	5	3
Male	10	6	13

(b) Classical approach: $\chi_0^2 = 5.595 > \chi_{0.01}^2 = 4.605$; reject the null hypothesis. *P*-value approach: *P*-value $< 0.10 = \alpha$ [Tech: *P*-value $= 0.061$]; reject the null hypothesis. The evidence suggests a relation between gender and drop reason. Females are more likely to drop because of the course, while males are more likely to drop because of work.

(c)

	Reason		
	Course	Personal	Work
Female	0.565	0.455	0.188
Male	0.435	0.545	0.813
Total	1	1	1

Why Did You Drop?

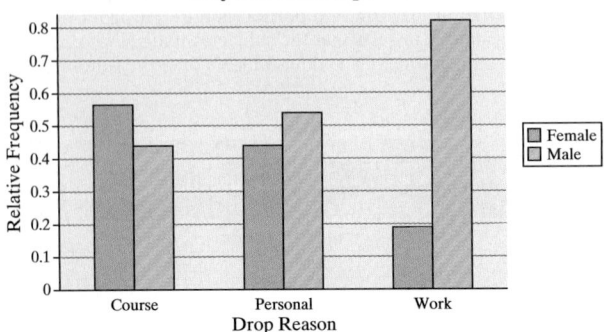

18. **(a)**

	Democrat	Republican
Grade school	7	2
High school	10	6
College	9	12

(b) Classical approach: $\chi_0^2 = 3.483 < \chi_{0.10}^2 = 4.605$; do not reject the null hypothesis. *P*-value approach: *P*-value $> 0.10 = \alpha$ [Tech: *P*-value $= 0.175$]; do not reject the null hypothesis. The evidence suggests that there is no association between level of education and political affiliation.

(c)

	Democrat	Republican	Total
Grade school	0.778	0.222	1
High school	0.625	0.375	1
College	0.429	0.571	1

Political Affiliation by Education

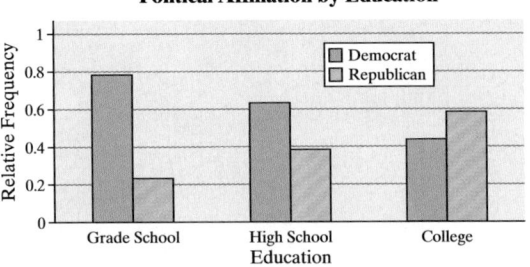

19. **(a)** All healthy women 45 years of age or older
    (b) Whether or not a cardiovascular event (such as heart attach or stroke) occurs; qualitative
    (c) 100-mg aspirin, placebo
    (d) Completely randomized
    (e) The women were randomly assigned into two groups (aspirin versus placebo). This randomization controls for any other explanatory variables, since individuals affected by these lurking variables should be equally dispersed between the two groups.
    (f) Classical approach: $z_0 = -1.44 > z_{0.025} = -1.96$; do not reject the null hypothesis. *P*-value approach: *P*-value $= 0.1498$ [Tech: 0.1511]; do not reject the null hypothesis. There is not sufficient evidence to conclude that a difference exists between the proportions of cardiovascular events in the aspirin group versus the placebo group. The test statistic, rounded to three places, is $z_0 = -1.435$.
    (g) Classical approach: $\chi_0^2 = 2.061 < \chi_{0.05}^2 = 3.841$; do not reject the null hypothesis. *P*-value approach: *P*-value $> 0.10 > \alpha = 0.05$ [Tech: *P*-value $= 0.151$]; do not reject the null hypothesis. There is not sufficient evidence to conclude that a difference exists between the proportions of cardiovascular events in the aspirin group versus the placebo group.
    (h) $(z_0)^2 = (-1.435)^2 = 2.059 \approx \chi_0^2 = 2.061$. Conclusion: $(z_0)^2 = \chi_0^2$.

Chapter 12 Review Exercises (page 672)

1. Classical approach: $\chi_0^2 = 0.578 < \chi_{0.05}^2 = 5.991$; do not reject the null hypothesis. *P*-value approach: *P*-value $> 0.10 > \alpha = 0.05$ [Tech: *P*-value $= 0.749$]; do not reject the null hypothesis. There is not sufficient evidence at the $\alpha = 0.05$ level of significance to conclude that the wheel is out of balance. That is, the evidence suggests that the wheel is in balance.

2. Classical approach: $\chi_0^2 = 7.478 < \chi_{0.05}^2 = 7.815$; do not reject the null hypothesis. *P*-value approach: *P*-value $> 0.05 = \alpha$ [Tech: *P*-value $= 0.058$]; do not reject the null hypothesis. There is not sufficient evidence at the $\alpha = 0.05$ level of significance to conclude that the teams playing in the World Series have not been evenly matched. That is, the evidence suggests that the teams have been evenly matched. On the other hand, the *P*-value is suggestive of an issue. In particular, there are fewer six-game series than we would expect. Perhaps the team that is down "goes all out" in game 6, trying to force game 7.

3. (a) Classical approach: $\chi_0^2 = 133.052 > \chi_{0.05}^2 = 5.991$; reject the null hypothesis. P-value approach: P-value $< 0.005 < \alpha = 0.05$ [Tech: P-value $= 0.000$]; reject the null hypothesis. There is sufficient evidence at the $\alpha = 0.05$ level of significance to conclude that the class of service and survival rates are dependent.

(b)

Titanic	Class		
	First	Second	Third
Survived	0.625	0.414	0.252
Did Not Survive	0.375	0.586	0.748

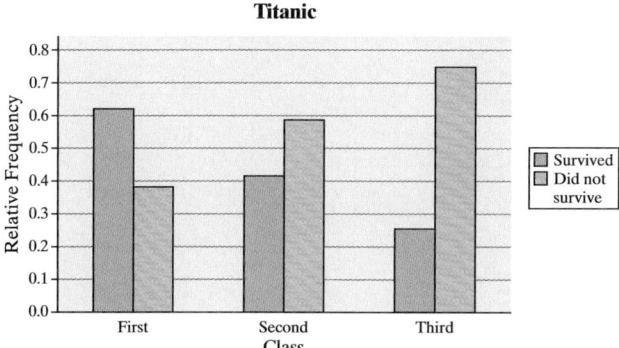

This summary supports the existence of a relationship between class and survival rate. Individuals with higher-class tickets survived in greater proportions than those with lower-class tickets.

4. Classical approach: $\chi_0^2 = 10.239 > \chi_{0.05}^2 = 9.488$; reject the null hypothesis. P-value approach: P-value $< 0.05 = \alpha$ [Tech: P-value $= 0.037$]; reject the null hypothesis. There is sufficient evidence at the $\alpha = 0.05$ level of significance to conclude that length of the gestational period and completion of a high school diploma are dependent.

5. (a) Classical approach: $\chi_0^2 = 41.767 > \chi_{0.05}^2 = 5.991$; reject the null hypothesis. P-value approach: P-value $< 0.005 < \alpha = 0.05$ [Tech: P-value $= 0.000$]; reject the null hypothesis. There is sufficient evidence at the $\alpha = 0.05$ level of significance to conclude that at least one proportion is different from the others. That is, the evidence suggests that the proportion of adults who feel morality is important when deciding how to vote is different for at least one political affiliation.

(b)

	Republican	Independent	Democrat
Important	0.920	0.810	0.820
Not Important	0.080	0.190	0.180

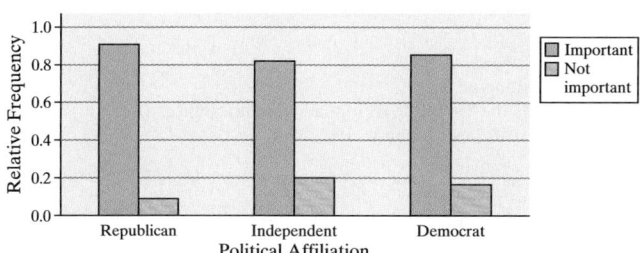

A higher proportion of Republicans appears to feel that morality is important when deciding how to vote than do Democrats or Independents.

Chapter 12 Test (page 673)

1. Classical approach: $\chi_0^2 = 4.940 < \chi_{0.01}^2 = 23.209$; do not reject the null hypothesis. P-value approach: P-value $> 0.10 > \alpha = 0.01$ [Tech: P-value $= 0.895$]; do not reject the null hypothesis. There is not sufficient evidence at the $\alpha = 0.01$ level of significance to conclude that the dice are loaded. That is, the evidence suggests that the dice are fair.

2. Classical approach: $\chi_0^2 = 2.661 < \chi_{0.10}^2 = 9.236$; do not reject the null hypothesis. P-value approach: P-value $> 0.10 = \alpha$ [Tech: P-value $= 0.752$]; do not reject the null hypothesis. There is not sufficient evidence at the $\alpha = 0.10$ level of significance to conclude that the distribution of educational attainment of Americans today is different from the distribution of education attainment in 2000. That is, the evidence suggests that educational attainment has not changed.

3. (a) Classical approach: $\chi_0^2 = 240.873 > \chi_{0.05}^2 = 21.026$; reject the null hypothesis. P-value approach: P-value $< 0.005 < \alpha = 0.05$ [Tech: P-value $= 0.000$]; reject the null hypothesis. There is sufficient evidence at the $\alpha = 0.05$ level of significance to conclude that the race and region are dependent. That is, there is a link between race and region in the United States.

(b)

	Northeast	Midwest	South	West
White	0.770	0.847	0.711	0.637
Black	0.102	0.093	0.171	0.045
Asian or Pacific Islander	0.024	0.013	0.012	0.064
Hispanic	0.069	0.028	0.074	0.161
Other	0.035	0.020	0.033	0.094

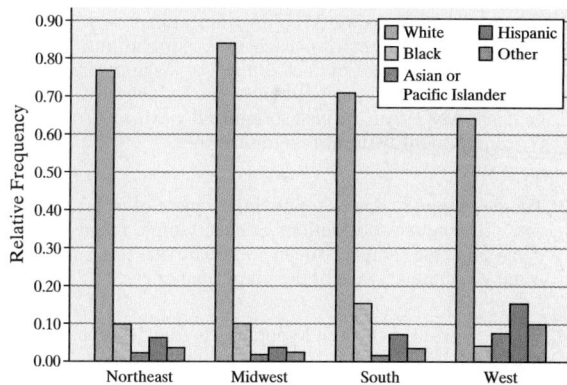

This summary supports the conclusion in part (a) by showing that the proportion for each racial category is not the same within each region of the United States. For example, whites make up a larger proportion in the Midwest than they do in any other region. Blacks make up a larger proportion in the South than they do in any other region. Hispanics make up a larger proportion in the West than they do any other region.

4. Classical approach: $\chi_0^2 = 5.605 < \chi_{0.05}^2 = 5.991$; do not reject the null hypothesis. P-value approach: P-value $> 0.05 = \alpha$ [Tech: P-value $= 0.061$]; do not reject the null hypothesis. There is not sufficient evidence at the $\alpha = 0.05$ level of significance to conclude that the proportions of individuals who enjoy gambling differ among the levels of education.

5. Classical approach: $\chi_0^2 = 330.803 > \chi_{0.05}^2 = 12.592$; reject the null hypothesis. P-value approach: P-value $< 0.005 < \alpha = 0.05$ [Tech: P-value $= 0.000$]; reject the null hypothesis. There is sufficient evidence at the $\alpha = 0.05$ level of significance to conclude that the proportions for the time categories spent in bars differ between smokers and non-smokers.

	Almost Daily	Several Times a Week	Several Times a Month	Once a Month	Several Times a Year	Once a Year	Never
Smoker	0.584	0.539	0.437	0.435	0.430	0.372	0.277
Nonsmoker	0.416	0.461	0.563	0.565	0.570	0.628	0.723

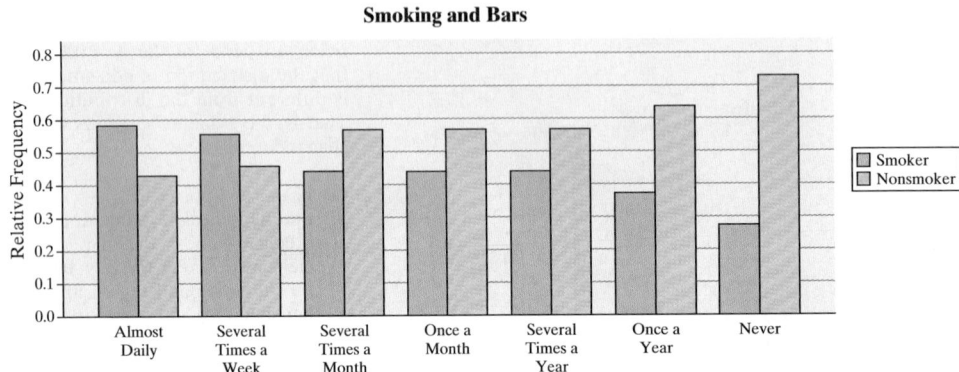

From the conditional distribution and bar graph, it appears that a higher proportion of smokers spends more time in bars than nonsmokers.

CHAPTER 13 Comparing Three or More Means

13.1 Assess Your Understanding (page 689)

1. analysis of variance

2. To perform a one-way ANOVA, there must be k simple random samples drawn; one from each of k populations. The k samples must be independent of each other. The k samples must come from normally distributed populations all of which have the same variance σ^2. ANOVA is robust, so minor departures from the normality requirement will not significantly affect the results of the procedure.

3. The mean square due to treatment estimate of σ^2 is a weighted average of the squared deviations of each sample mean from the grand mean of all the samples. The mean square due to error estimate of σ^2 is the weighted average of the sample variances.

4. $F = \dfrac{\text{MST}}{\text{MSE}} = 1$ if the null hypothesis is true. If the null hypothesis is false, MST is not a good estimate of σ^2 and $F > 1$. So a large value of the F statistic provides evidence against the null hypothesis.

5.

Source of Variation	Sum of Squares	Degrees of Freedom	Mean Squares	F-Test Statistic
Treatment	387	2	193.5	0.650
Error	8,042	27	297.852	
Total	8,429	29		

6.

Source of Variation	Sum of Squares	Degrees of Freedom	Mean Squares	F-Test Statistic
Treatment	2,814	3	938	6.870
Error	4,915	36	136.528	
Total	7,729	39		

7. $F_0 = 1.154$

8. $F_0 = 35.8$

9. $F_0 = \dfrac{\text{MST}}{\text{MSE}} = \dfrac{27.5833}{13.5278} = 2.039$

10. $F_0 = \dfrac{\text{MST}}{\text{MSE}} = \dfrac{191.2667}{73.6} = 2.599$

11. (a) $H_0: \mu_{\text{sludge plot}} = \mu_{\text{spring disk}} = \mu_{\text{no till}}$ versus H_1: at least one of the means is different.
    (b) 1. Each sample is a simple random sample.
        2. The three samples are independent of each other.
        3. The samples are from normally distributed populations.
        4. The populations have equal variances.
    (c) Since the P-value $= 0.007 < \alpha = 0.05$, we reject the null hypothesis and conclude that at least one of the means is different.
    (d) The boxplots support the result obtained in part (c). The boxplots indicate that significantly more plants are growing in the spring disk plot.
    (e) $F_0 = \dfrac{\text{MST}}{\text{MSE}} = \dfrac{42.06}{5.92} = 7.10$

12. (a) $H_0: \mu_{\text{liberty}} = \mu_{\text{chisel plowed}} = \mu_{\text{no till}}$ versus H_1: at least one of the means is different.
    (b) 1. Each sample is a simple random sample.
        2. The three samples are independent of each other.
        3. The samples are from normally distributed populations.
        4. The populations have equal variances.
    (c) Since the P-value $= 0.038 < \alpha = 0.05$, we reject the null hypothesis and conclude that at least one of the means is different.
    (d) Yes; it appears that mean yields for chisel plowed plots are less than yields for liberty plots.
    (e) $F_0 = \dfrac{\text{MST}}{\text{MSE}} = \dfrac{74.5}{19.8} = 3.76$ (The small discrepency is due to rounding error.)
    (f) From the boxplot, it appears that the chisel plowed plot types have different mean yields.

13. (a) $H_0: \mu_M = \mu_T = \mu_W = \mu_R = \mu_F$ versus H_1: at least one of the means is not equal.
    (b) 1. Each sample is a simple random sample.
        2. The five samples are independent.
        3. The populations from which the samples are drawn must be normal.
        4. The populations have the same variance.
    (c) P-value < 0.001, which is less than $\alpha = 0.01$, so we reject the null hypothesis.
    (d) Yes; Monday appears to have fewer births than other weekdays.
    (e) $F_0 = \dfrac{2,876,908}{293,451} = 9.80$
    (f) Monday appears to have significantly fewer births than the other four days.

14. (a) H_0: $\mu_{2004} = \mu_{2005} = \mu_{2006} = \mu_{2007}$ versus H_1: at least one of the means is different.
(b) 1. Each sample is a simple random sample.
  2. The four samples are independent of each other.
  3. The samples are from normally distributed populations.
  4. The populations have equal variances.
(c) Since the P-value $= 0.074 > \alpha = 0.05$, we do not reject the null hypothesis and conclude that there is not enough evidence to support the hypothesis that at least one of the means is different.
(d) Yes, it appears that the distances traveled in 2004 and 2005 are farther than those in 2006 and 2007.
(e) $F = \dfrac{\text{MST}}{\text{MSE}} = \dfrac{343,655}{128,060} = 2.68$

15. (a) H_0: $\mu_{\text{financial}} = \mu_{\text{energy}} = \mu_{\text{utilities}}$ versus H_1: at least one of the means is different.
(b) 1. Each sample is a simple random sample.
  2. The three samples are independent of each other.
  3. The samples are from normally distributed populations.
  4. The largest sample standard deviation is less than twice the smallest sample standard deviation ($5.12 < 2 \cdot 4.53$), so the requirement that the populations have equal variances is satisfied.
(c) $F = 2.077$, P-value $= 0.1502$. Since the P-value is greater than $\alpha = 0.05$, we do not reject the null hypothesis and conclude that there is not enough evidence to support the hypothesis that at least one of the means is different.
(d)

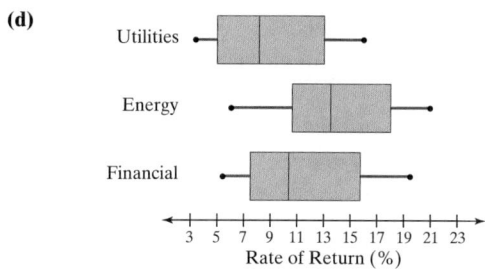

16. (a) H_0: $\mu_{\text{simple}} = \mu_{\text{go/no-go}} = \mu_{\text{choice}}$ versus H_1: at least one of the means is different.
(b) 1. Each sample is a simple random sample.
  2. The three samples are independent.
  3. The samples are from normally distributed populations.
  4. The populations have the same variance.
(c) $F = 3.23$; $F_{0.05,2,15} = 3.68$; P-value $= 0.068$. Do not reject the null hypothesis.
(d)

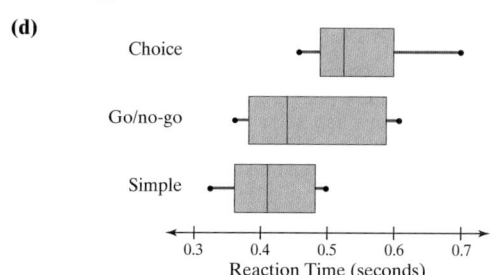

17. (a) H_0: $\mu_{\text{large}} = \mu_{\text{pass van}} = \mu_{\text{mid util veh}}$ versus H_1: at least one of the means is different.
(b) 1. Each sample is a simple random sample.
  2. The three samples are independent of each other.
  3. The samples are from normally distributed populations.
  4. The largest sample standard deviation is less than twice the smallest sample standard deviation ($4.53 < 2 \cdot 3.53$), so the requirement that the populations have equal variances is satisfied.
(c) $F = 1.91 < F_{0.01,2,48} \approx 5.85$; P-value $= 0.178 > \alpha = 0.01$. We do not reject the null hypothesis and conclude that there is not enough evidence to support the hypothesis that at least one of the means is different.

(d)

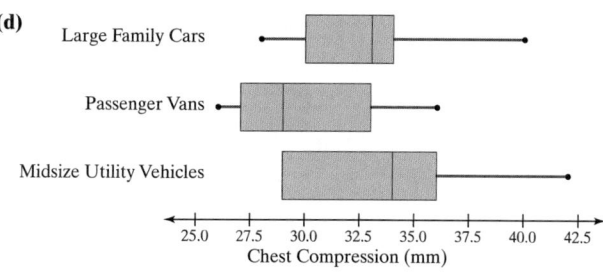

18. (a) H_0: $\mu_{\text{large}} = \mu_{\text{pass van}} = \mu_{\text{mid util veh}}$ versus H_1: at least one of the means is different.
(b) 1. Each sample is a simple random sample.
  2. The three samples are independent of each other.
  3. The samples are from normally distributed populations.
  4. The largest sample standard deviation is less than twice the smallest sample standard deviation ($198.6 < 2 \cdot 128.3$), so the requirement that the populations have equal variances is satisfied.
(c) $F = 0.40 < F_{0.01,2,18} \approx 5.85$; P-value $= 0.677 > \alpha = 0.01$. We do not reject the null hypothesis and conclude that there is not enough evidence to support the hypothesis that at least one of the means is different.

(d)

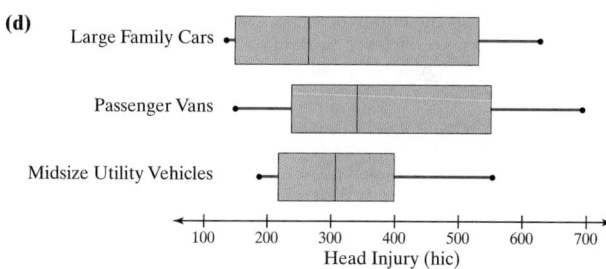

19. (a) H_0: $\mu_{\text{Alaska}} = \mu_{\text{Florida}} = \mu_{\text{Texas}}$ versus H_1: at least one of the means is different.
(b) 1. Each samples is a simple random sample.
  2. The three samples are independent of each other.
  3. The samples are from normally distributed populations.
  4. The largest sample standard deviation is less than twice the smallest sample standard deviation ($0.397 < 2 \cdot 0.252$), so the requirement that the populations have equal variances is satisfied.
(c) $F = 5.811 > F_{0.05,2,15} = 3.68$; P-value $= 0.0135 < \alpha = 0.05$. We reject the null hypothesis and conclude that there is sufficient evidence to support the hypothesis that at least one of the means is different.

(d)

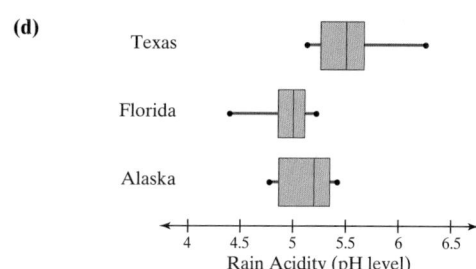

20. (a) H_0: $\mu_{\text{SatFat}} = \mu_{\text{Med}} = \mu_{\text{NCEP-1}}$ versus H_1: at least one of the means is different.
(b) 1. Each sample is a simple random sample.
  2. The three samples are independent of each other.
  3. The samples are from normally distributed populations.
  4. The largest sample standard deviation is less than twice the smallest sample standard deviation ($51.94 < 2 \cdot 47.14$), so the requirement that the populations have equal variances is satisfied.
(c) $F = 6.097 > F_{0.05,2,42} \approx 3.18$; P-value $= 0.004 < \alpha = 0.05$. We reject the null hypothesis and conclude that there is sufficient evidence to support the hypothesis that at least one of the means is different.

(d)

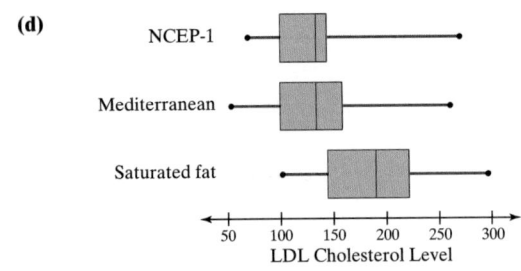

21. (a) H_0: $\mu_{301} = \mu_{400} = \mu_{353}$ versus H_1: at least one of the means is different.
   (b) The standard deviation for mixture 67-0-400 is more than two times larger than the standard deviation for mixture 67-0-301.

22. (a) Answers will vary.
   (b) This is the randomization required for a well-designed experiment. When researchers randomize the individuals to the treatment groups, uncontrolled factors tend to even themselves out.
   (c) Neither the subjects nor the researchers knew which group each subject belonged to. A double-blind study was desired to eliminate bias from the researcher and subjects.
   (d) There is a probability of less than 0.001 of obtaining the sample statistics if the null hypothesis is true. Because this probability is small, we are inclined to believe that the null hypothesis is not true, so we reject the null and conclude that at least one of the means differs from the others.

23. (a) $s_c = 4.6$, $s_R = 3.6$, $s_h = 2.9$
   (b) Stratified sampling; the researchers wanted to be sure that both children and adolescents were represented in the samples.
   (c) $t_0 = 3.87$, P-value $= 0.00017$, reject H_0; there is enough evidence to indicate that the mean CBCL scores are different for the two groups.
   (d) No; since we have large samples, we can assume that the distributions of the sample means are approximately normal.
   (e) $F = 15.74 > F_{0.05,2,207} \approx 3.04$; reject H_0; there is enough evidence to indicate that at least one of the mean scores is different.
   (f) No; the result from part (e) only indicates that *at least one* mean is different. It does not indicate which pairs are different nor even how many. The result from part (c) indicates that the mean scores for the control group and the RAP group are different, but additional pairs could also be significantly different.

13.2 Assess Your Understanding (page 699)

1. Multiple comparison tests help to identify the means that differ after ANOVA results indicate that the null hypothesis should be rejected.

2. The familywise error rate or the experimentwise error rate is the probability of making a Type I error, which is given by the significance level, α.

3. (a) $q_{0.05,10,3} = 3.877$
   (b) $q_{0.05,24,5} = 4.166$
   (c) $q_{0.05,32,8} \approx q_{0.05,30,8} = 4.602$
   (d) $q_{0.05,65,5} \approx q_{0.05,60,5} = 3.977$

4. (a) $q_{0.05,12,3} = 3.773$
   (b) $q_{0.05,20,4} = 3.958$
   (c) $q_{0.05,42,5} \approx q_{0.05,40,5} = 4.039$
   (d) $q_{0.05,34,4} \approx q_{0.05,30,4} = 3.845$

5. $q_{0.05,12,3} = 3.773$;
   $q_{\mu_3,\mu_2} = 3.932 > q_{0.05,12,3} = 3.773$, so reject H_0: $\mu_2 = \mu_3$
   $q_{\mu_3,\mu_1} = 3.757 < q_{0.05,12,3} = 3.773$, so do not reject H_0: $\mu_1 = \mu_3$
   $q_{\mu_1,\mu_2} = 0.175 < q_{0.05,12,3} = 3.773$, so do not reject H_0: $\mu_1 = \mu_2$
   Conclusion: Results are ambiguous, $\underline{\mu_2 \ \mu_1} \ \underline{\mu_1 \ \mu_3}$

6. $q_{0.05,20,4} = 3.958$;
   $q_{\mu_4,\mu_1} = 10.097 > q_{0.05,20,4} = 3.958$, so reject H_0: $\mu_1 = \mu_4$
   $q_{\mu_4,\mu_3} = 8.087 > q_{0.05,20,4} = 3.958$, so reject H_0: $\mu_3 = \mu_4$
   $q_{\mu_4,\mu_2} = 6.987 > q_{0.05,20,4} = 3.958$, so reject H_0: $\mu_2 = \mu_4$
   $q_{\mu_2,\mu_1} = 3.11 < q_{0.05,20,4} = 3.958$, so do not reject H_0: $\mu_1 = \mu_2$
   Conclusion: $\underline{\mu_1 \ \mu_2 \ \mu_3} \ \mu_4$

7. (a) H_0: $\mu_1 = \mu_2 = \mu_3$; H_1: at least one of the means is different.
   $F = 9.72$; P-value $= 0.002 < \alpha = 0.05$. We reject the null hypothesis and conclude that at least one of the means is different.
   (b) The result of Tukey's test indicates that $\mu_1 = \mu_2 \neq \mu_3$ $(\underline{\mu_1 \ \mu_2} \ \mu_3)$.

   (c)

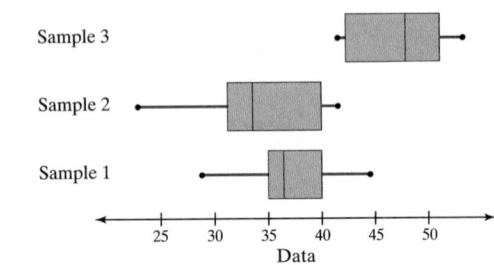

8. (a) H_0: $\mu_1 = \mu_2 = \mu_3 = \mu_4$; H_1: at least one of the means is different.
   $F = 15.64$; P-value $< 0.001 < \alpha = 0.05$. We reject the null hypothesis and conclude that at least one of the means is different.
   (b) The result of Tukey's test indicates that $\mu_1 = \mu_3$ and $\mu_2 = \mu_4$ $(\underline{\mu_1 \ \mu_3} \ \underline{\mu_2 \ \mu_4})$.

   (c)

9. The result of Tukey's test indicates that $\mu_{SP} = \mu_{NT} \neq \mu_{SD}$, $(\underline{\mu_{SP} \ \mu_{NT}} \ \mu_{SD})$. Recommend using the spring-disk method of planting.

10. The result of Tukey's test is ambiguous. It indicates that $\mu_L = \mu_{NT}$ and $\mu_L = \mu_{CP}$, but $\mu_L \neq \mu_{CP}$ $(\underline{\mu_L \ \mu_{NT} \ \mu_{CP}})$. You should not make a recommendation.

11. The result of Tukey's test is ambiguous. It indicates that $\mu_{FL} = \mu_{AK}$ and $\mu_{TX} = \mu_{AK}$, but $\mu_{FL} \neq \mu_{TX}$ $(\underline{\mu_{FL} \ \mu_{AK} \ \mu_{TX}})$.

12. The result of Tukey's test indicates that $\mu_{SF} \neq \mu_{Med} = \mu_{NCEP}$, $(\mu_{SF} \ \underline{\mu_{Med} \ \mu_{NCEP}})$.

13. (a) H_0: $\mu_P = \mu_{R10} = \mu_{R17.5} = \mu_{A7.5} = \mu_{A12.5}$; H_1: at least one of the means is different. $F = 5.75$; P-value $= 0.001 < \alpha = 0.05$. We reject the null hypothesis and conclude that at least one of the mean abilities to follow rules is different.
   (b) The result of Tukey's test indicates that $\mu_P \neq \mu_{R10} = \mu_{R17.5} = \mu_{A7.5} = \mu_{A12.5}$; $(\mu_P \ \underline{\mu_{R10} \ \mu_{R17.5} \ \mu_{A7.5} \ \mu_{A12.5}})$; that is, the mean ability to follow rules of a child taking the placebo is less than the mean ability to follow rules of a child taking any of the four drug treatments.

   (c)

14. (a) H_0: $\mu_{\text{lean}} = \mu_{\text{mixed}} = \mu_{\text{hi fat}}$ versus H_1: at least one of the means is different. $F = 15.599$; P-value $= 0.001 < \alpha = 0.05$. We reject the null hypothesis and conclude that at least one of the mean daily consumptions of calcium is different.

(b) The result of Tukey's test indicates that $\mu_{\text{mixed}} \neq \mu_{\text{lean}} = \mu_{\text{hi fat}}$; $\underline{\mu_{\text{mixed}} \ \mu_{\text{lean}} \ \mu_{\text{hi fat}}}$. We conclude that the mean calcium intake level of children who eat mixed meats is different from the mean calcium intake levels of children who eat lean meats or higher-fat meats.

(c)

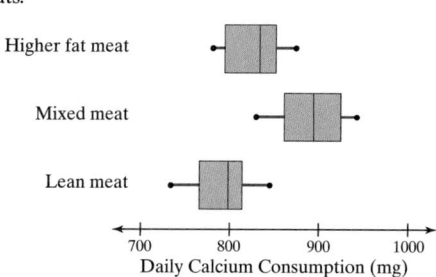

15. (a) H_0: $\mu_{\text{nonsmoker}} = \mu_{\text{light}} = \mu_{\text{heavy}}$ versus H_1: at least one of the means is different. $F = 19.62$; P-value $< 0.001 < \alpha = 0.05$. We reject the null hypothesis and conclude that at least one of the mean heart rates is different.

(b) The result of Tukey's test indicates that $\mu_{\text{nonsmoker}} \neq \mu_{\text{light}} \neq \mu_{\text{heavy}}$; $\underline{\mu_{\text{nonsmoker}} \ \mu_{\text{light}} \ \mu_{\text{heavy}}}$. We conclude that the mean heart rate of nonsmokers is lower than the mean heart rate of light smokers and that the mean heart rate of light smokers is lower than the mean heart rate of heavy smokers.

(c)

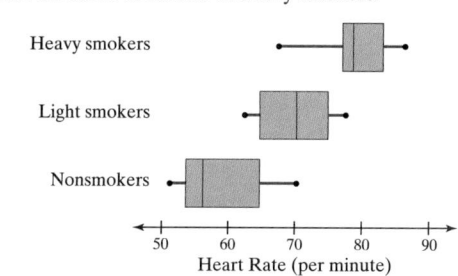

16. (a) H_0: $\mu_{\text{financial}} = \mu_{\text{food}} = \mu_{\text{leisure goods}}$ versus H_1: at least one of the means is different. $F = 8.55$; P-value $= 0.005 < \alpha = 0.05$. We reject the null hypothesis and conclude that at least one of the mean P/E ratios is different.

(b) The result of Tukey's test indicates that $\mu_{\text{food}} \neq \mu_{\text{financial}} = \mu_{\text{leisure goods}}$; $\underline{\mu_{\text{food}} \ \mu_{\text{financial}} \ \mu_{\text{leisure goods}}}$. We conclude that the mean P/E ratio of food stocks is different from the mean P/E ratios of financial and leisure good stocks.

(c)

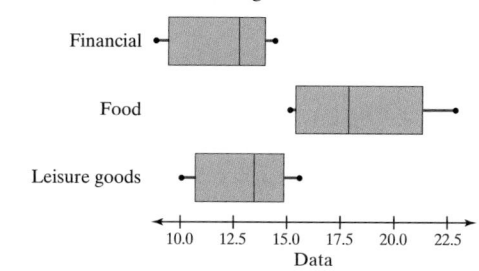

17. (a) H_0: $\mu_{\text{skim milk}} = \mu_{\text{mixed milk}} = \mu_{\text{whole milk}}$ versus H_1: at least one of the means is different. $F = 70.51$; P-value $< 0.001 < \alpha = 0.05$. We reject the null hypothesis and conclude that there is sufficient evidence to support the hypothesis that at least one of the mean calcium intake levels is different.

(b) The result of Tukey's test indicates that $\mu_{\text{skim milk}} = \mu_{\text{whole milk}} \neq \mu_{\text{mixed milk}}$; $\underline{\mu_{\text{skim milk}} \ \mu_{\text{whole milk}} \ \mu_{\text{mixed milk}}}$. We conclude that the mean calcium intake of children who drank mixed milk is different from the mean calcium intakes of children who drank skim or whole milk.

(c)

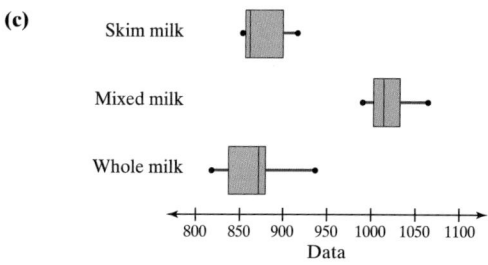

18. (a) $\alpha_c = 0.017$
   (b) $\alpha_c = 0.010$
   (c) As the number of means being compared increases, the comparisonwise error rate decreases.

19. (a) Cohort
   (b) $\mu_{\text{HS}} = 4.05$, $\mu_S = 4.20$, $\mu_{\text{NS}} = 4.21$, $\mu_{\text{OD}} = 5.80$, $\mu_{\text{NR}} = 4.65$; the means do not appear to be equal.
   (c) $1.099 < 2(0.5582) = 1.116$; the population variances can be assumed to be equal.
   (d) $(3.352, 4.743)$
   (e) 10
   (f) 0.4013
   (g) $F = 7.12$, P-value < 0.001, reject H_0; there is enough evidence to indicate that at least one mean time to degree completion is different; the mean time to degree completion appears to be the same for all initial institution types except for those with an open-door policy. It appears that students starting at an institution with an open-door policy take longer to complete their bachelor's degree.

13.3 Assess Your Understanding (page 709)

1. In a completely randomized design, the researcher examines a single factor fixed at k levels and randomly distributes the experimental units among the levels. In a randomized complete block design, there is a factor whose level cannot be fixed. So, the researcher partitions the experimental units according to this factor, forming blocks, which may form homogeneous groups. Within each block the experimental units are assigned to one of the treatments.

2. Blocking is partitioning the experimental units according to some factor whose level cannot be fixed. Blocking removes variability in the response variable due to the blocked variable.

3. Randomized means that the order in which the treatment is applied within each block is random. Complete refers to the fact that each block gets every treatment.

4. The requirements needed to analyze a randomized complete block design are:
   1. The response variable for each of the k populations must be normally distributed.
   2. The population variance of each treatment group must be the same.

5. A researcher can deal with explanatory variables by:
   1. Controlling their levels so that they remain fixed throughout the experiment or setting them at fixed levels.
   2. Randomizing so that any effects that cannot be identified or controlled are minimized.

6. If the experimental units are dependent, the related experimental units form the blocks of the experiment.

7. (a) Since the P-value $= 0.002$, the researcher rejects the null hypothesis that the population means are equal.
   (b) The mean square due to error is MSE $= 17.517$.
   (c) The Tukey test indicates that means 1 and 2 are the same, but mean 3 is different ($\mu_1 = \mu_2 \neq \mu_3$ or $\underline{\mu_1 \ \mu_2 \ \mu_3}$).

8. (a) Since the treatment P-value $= 0.003$, the researcher rejects the null hypothesis that the population means are equal at the $\alpha = 0.05$ level of significance.
   (b) The mean square due to error is MSE $= 34.492$.
   (c) The Tukey test indicates that means 1 and 2 are the same, but mean 3 is different ($\mu_1 = \mu_2 \neq \mu_3$ or $\underline{\mu_1 \ \mu_2 \ \mu_3}$).

9. (a) Since the treatment P-value $= 0.108$, the researcher does not reject the null hypothesis that the population means are equal.

(b) The mean square due to error is MSE = 0.944.

(c) The Tukey test is only used if the null hypothesis is rejected.

10. (a) Since the treatment P-value = 0.786, the researcher does not reject the null hypothesis that the population means are equal.

(b) The mean square due to error is MSE = 2.13.

(c) The Tukey test is only used if the null hypothesis is rejected.

11. (a) Since the treatment P-value = 0.002, we reject the null hypothesis that the population means are equal and conclude at least one of the means is different.

(b) The Tukey test indicates that means of treatment 2 and treatment 3 are equal, but the mean of treatment 1 is different. ($\mu_1 \neq \mu_2 = \mu_3$ or $\underline{\mu_1} \ \underline{\mu_2 \mu_3}$)

(c)

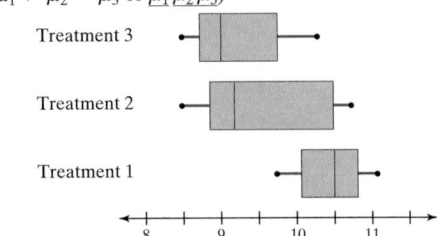

12. (a) Since the treatment P-value = 0.002, we reject the null hypothesis that the population means are equal and conclude at least one of the means is different.

(b) The Tukey test indicates that means of treatment 1 and treatment 3 are equal, but the mean of treatment 2 is different. ($\mu_1 = \mu_3 \neq \mu_2$ or $\underline{\mu_1 \mu_3} \ \underline{\mu_2}$)

(c)

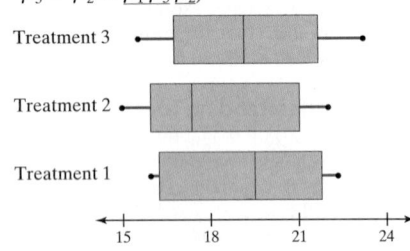

13. (a) The requirement for equal population variances is satisfied since the largest standard deviation is less than twice the smallest standard deviation, $1.439 < 2(1.225)$.

(b) Since the treatment P-value = 0.003, there is evidence that the mean miles per gallon is different among the three octane levels at the $\alpha = 0.05$ level of significance.

(c) The Tukey test indicates that $\mu_{87} = \mu_{89} < \mu_{92}$; $\underline{\mu_{87} \ \mu_{89}} \ \mu_{92}$.

(d) Conclude that the mean gas mileage is equal if 87- or 89-octane gasoline is used, but the mean miles per gallon increases when 92-octane gasoline is used.

14. (a) The requirement for equal population variances is satisfied since the largest standard deviation is less than twice the smallest standard deviation, $1.483 < 2(1.233)$.

(b) Since the treatment P-value = 0.026, there is evidence that the mean healing time is different among the treatment levels at the $\alpha = 0.05$ level of significance.

(c) The Tukey test is ambiguous. It indicates that $\mu_{ND} = \mu_{D1} \neq \mu_{D2}$, but $\mu_{D1} = \mu_{D2}$; $\underline{\mu_{ND} \ \mu_{D1}} \ \underline{\mu_{D2}}$.

(d) Conclude that the mean healing times are not the same; however, we cannot conclude which one(s) differ.

15. (a) The requirement for equal population variances is satisfied since the largest standard deviation is less than twice the smallest standard deviation, $830 < 2(448)$.

(b) Since the treatment P-value = 0.105, there is not sufficient evidence to conclude that the mean cost of repair is different among the car brands at the $\alpha = 0.05$ level of significance.

(c) Since the null hypothesis was not rejected, there is no need to do post hoc analysis.

16. (a) The requirement for equal population variances is satisfied since the largest standard deviation is less than twice the smallest standard deviation, $25.8 < 2(14.81)$.

(b) Since the treatment P-value = 0.329, there is not sufficient evidence to conclude that the mean cost of a room is different among the three hotel chains at the $\alpha = 0.05$ level of significance.

(c) Since the null hypothesis was not rejected, there is no need to do post hoc analysis.

17. (a) The requirement for equal population variances is satisfied since the largest standard deviation is less than twice the smallest standard deviation, $9.97 < 2(5.65)$.

(b) Since the treatment P-value = 0.001, there is sufficient evidence to indicate that the mean water consumption of mice is different among the three experiment levels at the $\alpha = 0.05$ level of significance.

(c) The Tukey test indicates that $\mu_{LO-1} = \mu_{R+1} \neq \mu_{R+1\ \text{Month}}$ ($\underline{\mu_{LO-1} \ \mu_{R+1}} \ \mu_{R+1\ \text{month}}$).

18. (a) The requirement for equal population variances is satisfied since the largest standard deviation is less than twice the smallest standard deviation, $443 < 2(359)$.

(b) Since the treatment P-value < 0.001, there is sufficient evidence to indicate that the mean strength of the concrete is different among the three days at the $\alpha = 0.05$ level of significance.

(c) The Tukey test indicates that all the means are different ($\mu_{2\ \text{days}} \ \mu_{7\ \text{days}} \ \mu_{28\ \text{days}}$).

19. (a) Since the treatment P-value is 0.438, there is not sufficient evidence to conclude that there is a difference in mean wait time between the two loading procedures.

(b) Hypotheses: $H_0: \mu_d = 0$ versus $H_1: \mu_d \neq 0$. Classical approach: $t_0 = 0.83 < t_{0.025,6} = 2.447$, so we do not reject the null hypothesis. P-value approach: P-value = $0.438 > \alpha = 0.05$, so we do not reject the null hypothesis. There is not sufficient evidence at the $\alpha = 0.05$ level of significance to conclude that the new loading procedure changed the mean wait time.

(c) The P-value for both procedures is 0.438, which supports that the method presented in this section is a generalization of the matched-pair t-test.

13.4 Assess Your Understanding (page 724)

1. In a completely randomized design, the researcher examines a single factor fixed at k levels and randomly distributes the experimental units among the levels. In a randomized complete block design, there is a factor whose level cannot be fixed. So the researcher partitions the experimental units according to this factor, forming blocks. The experimental units are then randomly assigned to the blocks, being sure that each block has each treatment. In a factorial design, the researcher has two variables A and B, called factor A and factor B. The factors are fixed, so factor A has a levels and factor B has b levels. The experimental units are then uniformly distributed among the cells formed by the factors, and the response variable is measured at each of the ab cells.

2. An interaction effect occurs if changing the level of one factor results in different changes in the value of the response variable for the different levels of the second factor. A significant interaction effect might cause the main effects to be misleading, and so the main effects should not be analyzed.

3. An interaction plot graphically displays the mean response for each treatment. These plots are useful for illustrating potential interaction between factors.

4. A 2×3 factorial design has six treatments. Factor A has 2 levels, and factor B has 3 levels.

5. The plots are relatively parallel, so there is no significant interaction.

6. The plots cross, so there is significant interaction.

7. The plots cross, so there is significant interaction.

8. The plots are not at all parallel, so there is significant interaction.

9. (a) Main effect of factor A = 1.25; main effect of factor B = −9.25.

Interaction effects: If factor B is fixed at low and factor A changes from low to high, the response variable increases by 3.5 units. On the other hand, if factor B is fixed at high and factor A changes from low to high, the response variable increases by −4.5 (decreases by 4.5) units. So, the change in the response variable for factor A depends on the level of factor B, meaning there is an interaction effect between factors A and B.

If factor A is fixed at low and factor B changes from low to high, the response variable increases by −3.5 (decreases by 3.5) units. On the other hand, if factor A is fixed at high and factor B changes from low to high, the response variable increases by −15 (decreases by 15) units. So, the change in the response variable for factor B depends on the level of factor A, meaning that there is an interaction effect between factors A and B.

(b)

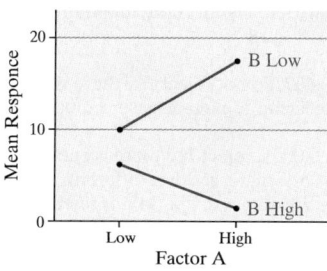

10. **(a)** Main effect of factor A $\neq -51.5$; main effect of factor B $= 0.5$.

   Interaction effects: If factor B is fixed at low and factor A changes from low to high, the response variable decreases by 20 units. On the other hand, if factor B is fixed at high and factor A changes from low to high, the response variable decreases by 83 units. So, the change in the response variable for factor A depends on the level of factor B, meaning there is an interaction effect between factors A and B.

   If factor A is fixed at low and factor B changes from low to high, the response variable increases by 32 units. On the other hand, if factor A is fixed at high and factor B changes from low to high, the response variable decreases by 32.5 units. So, the change in the response variable for factor B depends on the level of factor A, meaning that there is an interaction effect between factors A and B.

(b)

11. **(a)** There is no evidence of an interaction effect since the interaction P-value is 0.836.
   (b) Since the factor A P-value $= 0.003$, there is evidence of difference in means from factor A. The factor B P-value < 0.001, giving evidence that there is also a difference in means from factor B.
   (c) MSE $= 45.3$

12. **(a)** There is no evidence of an interaction effect since the interaction P-value is 0.813.
   (b) Since the factor A P-value $= 0.679$, there is no evidence of difference in means from factor A. The factor B P-value $= 0.720$, giving no evidence that there is a difference in means from factor B.
   (c) MSE $= 198$

13. **(a)** There is evidence of an interaction effect since the interaction P-value < 0.001.
   (b) Whenever there is evidence of an interaction effect, we do not consider main effects because they could be misleading.
   (c) MSE $= 31.9$

14. **(a)** There is evidence of an interaction effect since the interaction P-value $= 0.004$.
   (b) Whenever there is evidence of an interaction effect, we do not consider main effects because they could be misleading.
   (c) MSE $= 72.7$

15. **(a)** There is no evidence of an interaction effect since interaction P-value is 0.965.
   (b) Since the factor A P-value $= 0.579$, there is no evidence of difference in means from factor A. That the factor B P-value $= 0.021$ is evidence that there is a difference in means from factor B.

(c)

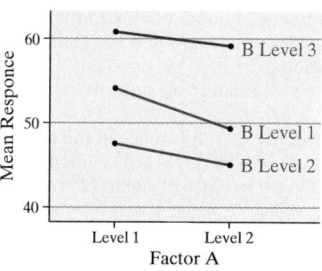

   (d) Tukey's test for factor A is unnecessary. Tukey's test for factor B is ambiguous. It shows $B_1 = B_2$ and $B_1 = B_3$, but $B_2 \neq B_3$; $\underline{B_2\ B_1\ B_3}$.

16. **(a)** There is no evidence of an interaction effect since the interaction P-value is 0.812.
   (b) Since the factor B P-value $= 0.858$, there is no evidence of difference in means from factor B. That the factor A P-value $= 0.037$ is evidence that there is a difference in means from factor A.

(c)

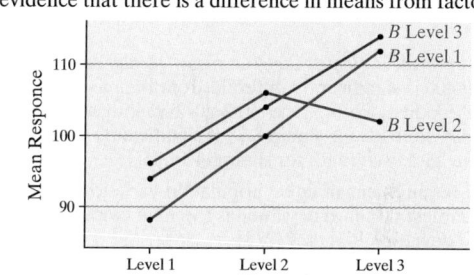

   (d) Tukey's test for factor B is unnecessary. Tukey's test for factor A is ambiguous. It shows $\underline{A_1\ A_2\ A_3}$.

17. **(a)** This is a 2×3 factorial design with two replications per cell.
   (b) There is no evidence of a significant interaction effect since the interaction P-value is 0.159, which is large.
   (c) There is a significant difference in the means for the three age groups; age P-value $= 0.016$. There is no significance difference in the means for the two genders; gender P-value $= 0.164$.

(d)

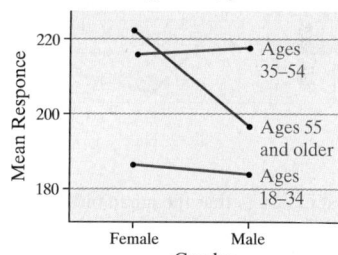

   (e) The mean of age group 18–34 is significantly different. Tukey's test shows $\underline{B_1}\ \underline{B_2\,B_3}$.

18. **(a)** This is a 3×3 factorial design with three replications per cell.
   (b) The largest standard deviation is less than twice the smallest deviation, so the requirement of equal population variances is satisfied [$0.1691 < 2(0.0992)$].
   (c) There is no evidence of an interaction effect since the interaction P-value is 0.834.
   (d) There is a significant difference in the means for the three types of stimuli; stimuli P-value $= 0.001$. There is no evidence of a difference in the means for three categories of age; age P-value $= 0.052$.

(e)

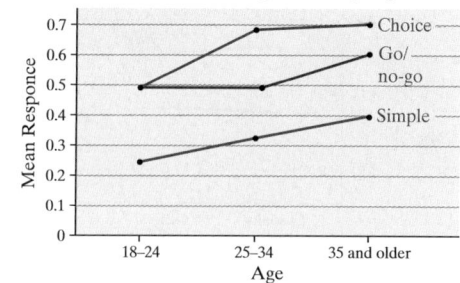

19. (a) The requirement of equal population variances is satisfied since the largest standard deviation is less than twice the smallest standard deviation [320 < 2(168) = 336].

(b) There is no evidence of an interaction effect. Interaction P-value = 0.469.

(c) There is evidence of a difference in the means for the three mixtures (P-value < 0.001). There is evidence of a difference in the means for the three types of slump (P-value = 0.002).

(d)

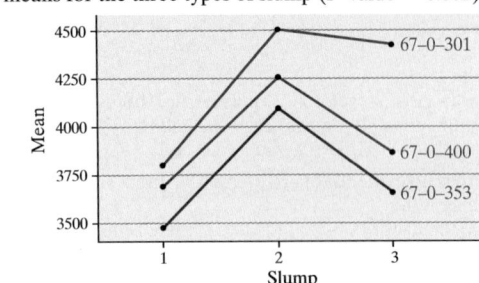

(e) Tukey's test indicates that the mean 28-day strength of mixture 67-0-400 is significantly different from the mean 28-day strength of the other two mixtures. Tukey's test indicates that the mean 28-day strength for slump 3.75 is significantly different from the mean 28-day strength for slumps 4 and 5.

20. (a) The requirement of equal population variances is satisfied since the largest standard deviation is less than twice the smallest standard deviation [421 < 2(228) = 456].

(b) There is no evidence of an interaction effect. Interaction P-value = 0.880.

(c) There is evidence of a difference in the means for the three diets (P-value = 0.042). There is no evidence of a difference in the means for the three ages (P-value < 0.001).

(d)

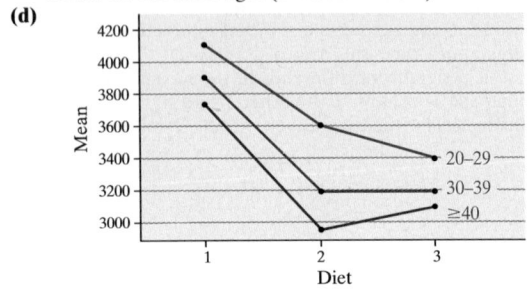

(e) Tukey's test indicates that the mean birth weight for diet 1 is significantly different from the mean birth weight for diets 2 and 3. Tukey's test indicates that the mean birth weight of babies to mothers 40 or older is significantly different from the other age groups.

21. (a) The requirement of equal population variances is satisfied since the largest standard deviation is less than twice the smallest standard deviation [4.00 < 2(2.5) = 5.0].

(b) There is no evidence of an interaction effect. Interaction P-value = 0.854.

(c) There is no evidence of a difference in the means for three locations. Location P-value = 0.287. There is no evidence of a difference in the means for type of service station; type P-value = 0.804.

(d)

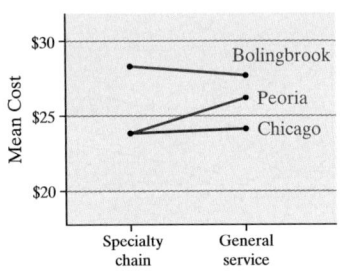

(e) Since there were no significant main effects, there is no need to do Tukey's tests.

22. (a) College students

(b) Observational study; cross-sectional

(c) Response: feeling-at-ease score (quantitative); explanatory; gender and classroom layout (both qualitative)

(d) $\bar{x} = 19.83, s = 0.58$

(e) 0.035; yes

(f) P-value = 0.497, do not reject H_0; there is not enough evidence to indicate the mean feeling-at-ease scores are different for males and females.

(g) P-value < 0.0001, reject H_0; there is enough evidence to indicate that at least one mean score is different.

(h) Interaction: P-value = 0.167, do not reject H_0; there does not appear to be a significant interaction effect. Gender: P-value = 0.206, do not reject H_0; gender does not appear to be significant. Layout: P-value < 0.001, reject H_0; classroom layout appears to be significant.

(i)

Interaction Plot for Feeling at Ease

Data Means

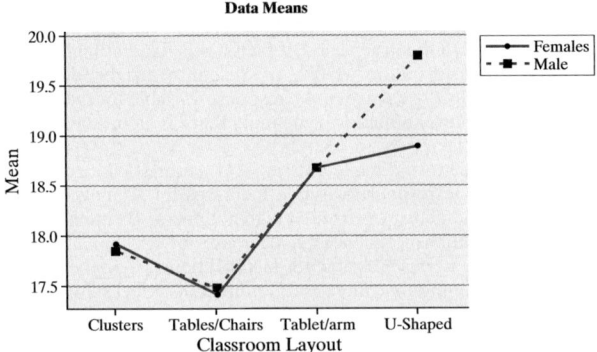

The interaction plot supports our conclusions. *Interaction effect:* The graphs for the two levels of gender are fairly parallel, indicating that there is little interaction between the two factors. *Gender effect:* The graphs for the two levels of gender are almost identical, indicating that gender is not a significant effect. *Classroom layout:* The graphs for the two levels of gender are not horizontal. This indicates that the mean feeling-at-ease score depends on the level of the classroom layout.

(j) Nonresponse; classes that were allowed to be surveyed may be more relaxed in general, allowing students to feel more at ease.

Chapter 13 Review Exercises (page 729)

1. (a) $q_{0.05,16,7} = 4.741$

(b) $q_{0.05,30,6} = 4.302$

(c) $q_{0.01,42,4} \approx q_{0.01,40,4} = 4.696$

(d) $q_{0.05,46,6} \approx q_{0.05,40,6} = 4.232$

2. $q_{0.05,27,4} \approx 3.873$; $q_{x1,x4} = 8.940$; $q_{x1,x2} = 4.036$; $q_{x1,x3} = 2.306$; $q_{x3,x4} = 6.631$; $q_{x3,x2} = 1.730$; $q_{x2,x4} = 4.901$. Conclude that Tukey's test is ambiguous. $\mu_1 \neq \mu_2$, but $\mu_1 = \mu_3 \neq \mu_4$ and $\mu_2 = \mu_3 \neq \mu_4$.

3. (a) H_0: $\mu_{\text{water–organic soil}} = \mu_{\text{water–mineral soil}} = \mu_{\text{surface water}}$ versus H_1: at least one of the means is different.

(b) To perform a one-way ANOVA, there must be k simple random samples drawn from k normally distributed populations all with the same variance. The k samples must be independent of each other.

(c) Since P-value < 0.001, the researcher will reject the null hypothesis and conclude that the mean concentration of dissolved carbon is different in at least one of the collection areas.

(d) Answers will vary.

(e) $F = \dfrac{\text{MST}}{\text{MSE}} = \dfrac{235.7}{25.0} = 9.43$

(f) Tukey's test indicates that the mean dissolved carbon is equal in the surface water and in the ground water taken from organic soil, but it differs from the mean dissolved carbon concentration in ground water taken from mineral soil ($\underline{\mu_{\text{surface water}}\ \mu_{\text{water–organic soil}}}\ \mu_{\text{water–mineral soil}}$).

4. Tukey's test is ambiguous. It indicates that $\mu_{\text{select structural}} \neq \mu_{\text{no. 2}}$, but that the $\mu_{\text{below grade}}$ is equal to all other means ($\underline{\mu_1\ \mu_2\ \mu_4}\ \mu_3$).

5. (a) The P-value = 0.003, so we reject the null hypothesis and conclude that at least one of the means is different.

(b) Tukey's test indicates that $\mu_{\text{middle}} = \mu_{\text{back}} \neq \mu_{\text{front}}$. There is evidence that students who choose seats in the front of the mathematics classroom have a different mean GPA from that of students choosing seats in the middle or back of the classroom.

(c)

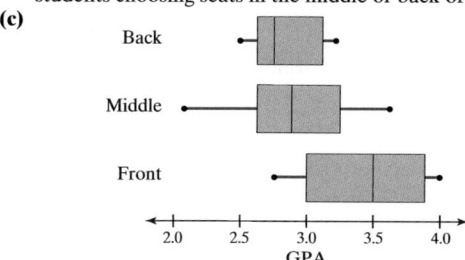

6. (a) The P-value < 0.001, so we reject the null hypothesis and conclude at least one of the means is different.

(b) Tukey's test indicates that $\mu_1 = \mu_2 \neq \mu_3 \neq \mu_4$; $\underline{\mu_1 \ \mu_2} \ \underline{\mu_3} \ \underline{\mu_4}$.

(c)

7. (a) Since the largest standard deviation is less than twice the smallest deviation, the requirement of equal population variances is satisfied $[4.72 < 2(2.39) = 4.78]$.

(b) There is no evidence of an interaction effect. Interaction P-value $= 0.374$.

(c) There is no evidence of a difference in the means for gender; gender P-value $= 0.196$. There is evidence of a difference in the means for type of driving program; program P-value < 0.001. So the null hypothesis $H_0: \mu_{8\text{ hour}} = \mu_{4\text{ hour}} = \mu_{2\text{ hour}}$ is rejected.

(d)

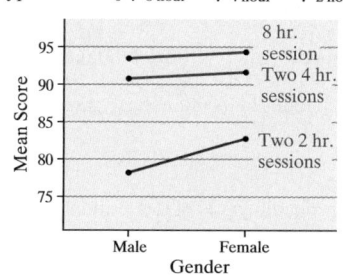

(e) Tukey's test indicates that the mean score after taking one 8-hour defensive driving class is equal to the mean score after taking two 4-hour classes, but that the mean score after taking two 2-hour classes is different. $\mu_{8\text{ hour}} \ \mu_{4\text{ hour}} \ \underline{\mu_{2\text{ hour}}}$

Chapter 13 Test (page 732)

1. (a) Reject H_0; at least one of the means is different.

(b) $\mu_1 = \mu_3 = \mu_4 \neq \mu_2$; it appears that machine II is dispensing less product than the other machines.

(c)

2. (a) $H_0: \mu_L = \mu_V = \mu_U$ vs. H_1: at least one of the means is different

(b) We assume that each sample is a simple random sample. The samples are independent of each other, and the problem statement states that normality is verified. Since the largest standard deviation is less than twice the smallest, our assumption of equal variances is verified $(2.277 < 2(1.218) = 2.436)$.

(c) $F = 8.19$; P-value $= 0.003$; reject the null hypothesis.

(d)

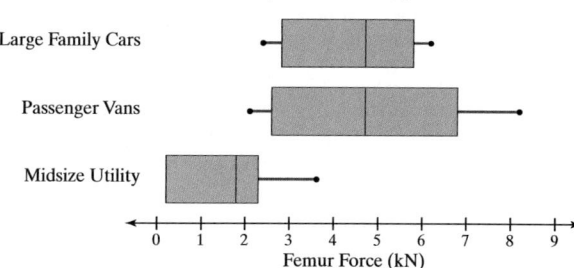

3. (a) The P-value $= 0.011$, so we reject the null hypothesis and conclude at least one of the means is different.

(b) Tukey's test is ambiguous. It indicates that $\mu_3 \neq \mu_1 = \mu_2$, but $\mu_2 = \mu_3$; $\underline{\mu_1 \ \mu_2 \ \mu_3}$.

(c)

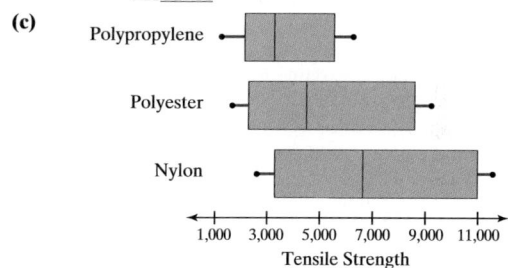

4. (a) Since the largest standard deviation is less than twice the smallest standard deviation, the requirement of equal population variances is satisfied $[0.53 < 2(0.28) = 0.56]$.

(b) There is no evidence of significant interaction. Interaction P-value $= 0.459$.

(c) There is no evidence of a difference in means for gender; gender P-value $= 0.589$. There is no evidence of a difference in the means for age: age P-value $= 0.243$. So the null hypothesis $H_0: \mu_{20-34} = \mu_{35-39} = \mu_{50-64}$ is not rejected.

(d)

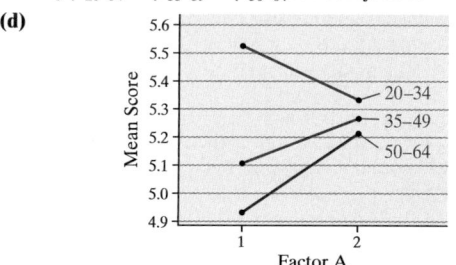

(e) No significant difference in means

5. (a)

(b) The plot indicates a significant interaction effect since the graphs for the two levels of gender are not parallel.

(c) Since there is a significant interaction effect, any conclusions about main effects would be confounded.

CHAPTER 14 Inference on the Least-Squares Regression Model and Multiple Regression

14.1 Assess Your Understanding (page 748)

1. There are two requirements for conducting inference on the least-squares regression model. First, for each particular value of the explanatory variable x, the corresponding responses in the population have a mean that depends linearly on x. Second, the response variables are normally distributed with mean $\mu_{y|x} = \beta_0 + \beta_1 x$ and standard deviation σ.

   The first requirement is tested by examining a plot of the residuals against the explanatory variable. If the plot shows any discernible pattern, the linear model is inappropriate. The normality requirement is checked by examining a normal probability plot of the residuals.

2. It is important to perform both graphical and analytical analysis when analyzing relations between two quantitative variables because the graph describes the type of relation that exists and the analytical description allows for statistical inference to be conducted.

3. The y-coordinates on the least-squares regression line represent the mean value of the response variable for any given value of the explanatory variable.

4. It is desirable to have the explanatory variables be widely dispersed so that the standard deviation of b_1 is smaller.

5. If the null hypothesis, $H_0: \beta_1 = 0$, is not rejected, the best guess for the value of the response variable for any value of the explanatory variable is the sample mean of y.

6. We do not conduct inference on the linear correlation coefficient because a hypothesis test on the slope and a hypothesis test on the linear correlation coefficient yield the same conclusion. Moreover, the requirements for conducting inference on the linear correlation coefficient are very hard to verify.

7. **(a)** $\beta_0 \approx b_0 = -2.3256$, $\beta_1 \approx b_1 = 2.0233$
   (b) $s_e = 0.5134$ is the point estimate for σ.
   (c) $s_{b_1} = 0.1238$
   (d) Because the P-value $< 0.001 < \alpha = 0.05$ (or $t_0 = 16.343$ [Tech: 16.344] $> t_{0.025} = 3.182$), we reject the null hypothesis and conclude that a linear relation exists between x and y.

8. **(a)** $\beta_0 \approx b_0 = -3.700$, $\beta_1 \approx b_1 = 1.100$
   (b) $s_e = 0.7303$ is the point estimate for σ.
   (c) $s_{b_1} = 0.1155$
   (d) Because the P-value $= 0.002 < \alpha = 0.05$ (or $t_0 = 9.524$ [Tech: 9.526] $> t_{0.025} = 3.182$), we reject the null hypothesis and conclude that a linear relation exists between x and y.

9. **(a)** $\beta_0 \approx b_0 = 1.200$, $\beta_1 \approx b_1 = 2.200$
   (b) $s_e = 0.8944$ is the point estimate for σ.
   (c) $s_{b_1} = 0.2828$
   (d) Because the P-value $= 0.004 < \alpha = 0.05$ (or $t_0 = 7.778$ [Tech: 7.779] $> t_{0.025} = 3.182$), we reject the null hypothesis and conclude that a linear relation exists between x and y.

10. **(a)** $\beta_0 \approx b_0 = 3.600$, $\beta_1 \approx b_1 = -1.800$
    (b) $s_e = 0.5164$ is the point estimate for σ.
    (c) $s_{b_1} = 0.1633$
    (d) Because the P-value $= 0.002 < \alpha = 0.05$ (or $t_0 = -11.023 < -t_{0.025} = -3.182$), we reject the null hypothesis and conclude that a linear relation exists between x and y.

11. **(a)** $\beta_0 \approx b_0 = 116.600$, $\beta_1 \approx b_1 = -0.7200$
    (b) $s_e = 3.2863$ is the point estimate for σ.
    (c) $s_{b_1} = 0.1039$
    (d) Because the P-value $= 0.006 < \alpha = 0.05$ (or $t_0 = -6.929$ [Tech: -6.928] $< -t_{0.025} = -3.182$), we reject the null hypothesis and conclude that a linear relation exists between x and y.

12. **(a)** $\beta_0 \approx b_0 = -3.30$, $\beta_1 \approx b_1 = 0.78$
    (b) $s_e = 1.7416$ is the point estimate for σ.
    (c) $s_{b_1} = 0.1102$
    (d) Because the P-value $= 0.006 < \alpha = 0.05$ (or $t_0 = 7.078$ [Tech: 7.081] $> t_{0.025} = 3.182$), we reject the null hypothesis and conclude that a linear relation exists between x and y.

13. **(a)** $\beta_0 \approx b_0 = 12.4932$, $\beta_1 \approx b_1 = 0.1827$
    (b) $s_e = 0.0954$
    (c) A normal probability plot of the residuals shows that they are approximately normally distributed.
    (d) $s_{b_1} = 0.0276$

(e) Because the P-value $< 0.001 < \alpha = 0.01$ (or $t_0 = 6.62$ [Tech: 6.63] $> t_{0.005} = 3.250$), we reject the null hypothesis and conclude that a linear relation exists between a child's height and head circumference.
(f) 95% confidence interval: lower bound: 0.1204; upper bound: 0.2451
(g) A good estimate of the child's head circumference would be 17.34 inches.

14. **(a)** $\beta_0 \approx b_0 = 1.1140$, $\beta_1 \approx b_1 = 1.3902$
    (b) $s_e = 0.4944$
    (c) A normal probability plot of the residuals shows that they are approximately normally distributed.
    (d) $s_{b_1} = 0.1501$
    (e) Because the P-value $< 0.001 < \alpha = 0.01$ (or $t_0 = 9.262$ [Tech: 9.260] $> t_{0.005} = 3.250$), we reject the null hypothesis and conclude that a linear relation exists between the right humerus and the right tibia of rats sent to space.
    (f) 99% confidence interval: lower bound: 0.9024; upper bound: 1.8780
    (g) The mean length of the right tibia on a rat whose right humerus is 25.93 mm is 37.162 mm.

15. **(a)** $\beta_0 \approx b_0 = 2675.6$, $\beta_1 \approx b_1 = 0.6764$
    (b) $s_e = 271.04$
    (c) A normal probability plot of the residuals shows that they are approximately normally distributed.
    (d) $s_{b_1} = 0.2055$
    (e) Because the P-value $= 0.011 < \alpha = 0.05$ (or $t_0 = 3.291 > t_{0.025} = 2.306$), we reject the null hypothesis and conclude that a linear relation exists between the 7-day and 28-day strength of this type of concrete.
    (f) 95% confidence interval: lower bound: 0.2025; upper bound: 1.1503
    (g) The mean 28-day strength of this concrete if the 7-day strength is 3,000 psi is 4,704.8 psi.

16. **(a)** $\beta_0 \approx b_0 = 0.2088$, $\beta_1 \approx b_1 = 0.0575$
    (b) $s_e = 0.1121$
    (c) A normal probability plot of the residuals shows that they are approximately normally distributed.
    (d) $s_{b_1} = 0.0046$
    (e) Because the P-value $< 0.001 < \alpha = 0.10$ (or $t_0 = 12.500$ [Tech: 12.502] $> t_{0.05} = 1.796$), we reject the null hypothesis and conclude that a linear relation exists between the tar and nicotine levels in cigarettes.
    (f) 90% confidence interval: lower bound: 0.0492; upper bound: 0.0658
    (g) The mean amount of nicotine in a cigarette that has 12 mg of tar is 0.90 mg.

17. **(a)** $\beta_0 \approx b_0 = 1.2286$, $\beta_1 \approx b_1 = 0.7622$
    (b) $s_e = 3.2309$
    (c) A normal probability plot of the residuals shows that they are approximately normally distributed.
    (d) $s_{b_1} = 0.2880$
    (e) Because the P-value $= 0.0266 < \alpha = 0.10$ (or $t_0 = 2.647 > t_{0.05} = 1.833$), we reject the null hypothesis and conclude that a linear relation exists between the rate of return of the S&P 500 index and the rate of return of UTX.
    (f) 90% confidence interval: lower bound: 0.2343; upper bound: 1.2901 [Tech: 1.2900]
    (g) When the mean rate of return of the S&P 500 index is 3.25%, the mean rate of return for United Technologies is 3.706%.

18. **(a)** $\beta_0 \approx b_0 = 607.7034$, $\beta_1 \approx b_1 = 25.0116$
    (b) $s_e = 64.8477$
    (c) A normal probability plot of the residuals shows that they are approximately normally distributed.
    (d) $s_{b_1} = 2.1888$
    (e) Because the P-value $< 0.001 < \alpha = 0.01$ (or $t_0 = 11.427 > t_{0.005} = 4.032$), we reject the null hypothesis and conclude that a linear relation exists between men's fat-free body mass and their energy expenditure during inactivity.
    (f) 99% confidence interval: lower bound: 16.187 [Tech: 1.6186]; upper bound: 33.837
    (g) A man with a fat-free body mass of 57.3 kg has a mean inactive energy expenditure level of 2,040.9 kcal per day.

19. **(a)** $\beta_0 \approx b_0 = 163.9988$, $\beta_1 \approx b_1 = 63.1624$
    (b) $s_e = 157.4752$

(c) A normal probability plot of the residuals shows that they are approximately normally distributed.

(d) $s_{b_1} = 10.2945$

(e) Because the P-value = 0.0001 < α = 0.01 (or $t_0 = 6.136 > t_{0.005} = 3.055$), we reject the null hypothesis. We conclude that a linear relation exists between ACT scores and SAT scores.

(f) 95% confidence interval: lower bound: 40.730 [Tech: 40.731]; upper bound: 85.594

(g) Entering freshmen who score 26 on the ACT earn a mean score of 1,806 on the SAT.

20. (a) $\beta_0 \approx b_0 = -142.5$, $\beta_1 \approx b_1 = 1.694$

(b) $s_e = 20.8577$

(c) A normal probability plot of the residuals shows that they are approximately normally distributed.

(d) $s_{b_1} = 0.5406$

(e) Because the P-value = 0.011 < α = 0.05 (or $t_0 = 3.134 > t_{0.025} = 2.228$), we reject the null hypothesis. We conclude that a linear relation exists between the total length and weight of American black bears.

(f) 95% confidence interval: lower bound: 0.490; upper bound: 2.899

(g) American black bears with a total length of 146.0 cm have a mean weight of 104.8 [Tech: 104.9] kg.

21. (a)

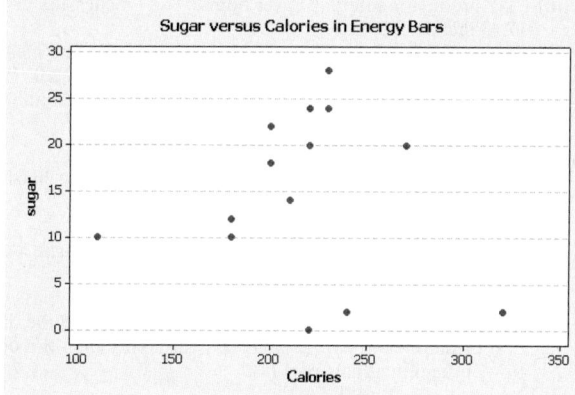

No linear relation appears to exist.

(b) $\hat{y} = 17.8675 - 0.0146x$

(c) $s_e = 9.3749$

(d) A normal probability plot of the residuals shows that they are approximately normally distributed.

(e) $s_{b_1} = 0.0549$

(f) Because the P-value = 0.795 > α = 0.01 (or $t_0 = -0.266$ [Tech: -0.265] > $-t_{0.005} = -3.055$), we do not reject the null hypothesis. We conclude that a linear relation does not exist between the number of calories per serving and the number of grams per serving in high-protein and moderate-protein energy bars.

(g) 95% confidence interval: lower bound: -0.1342 [Tech: -0.1343]; upper bound: 0.1050 [Tech: 0.1051]

(h) Do not recommend using the least-squares regression line to predict the sugar content of the energy bars because we did not reject the null hypothesis. A good estimate for the sugar content would be $\bar{y} = 14.7$ grams.

22. (a)

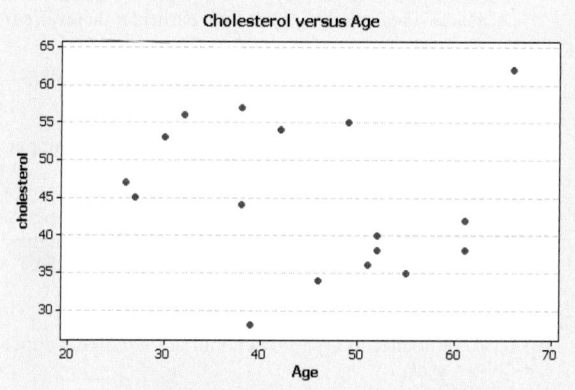

No linear relation appears to exist.

(b) $\hat{y} = 50.784 - 0.1298x$

(c)

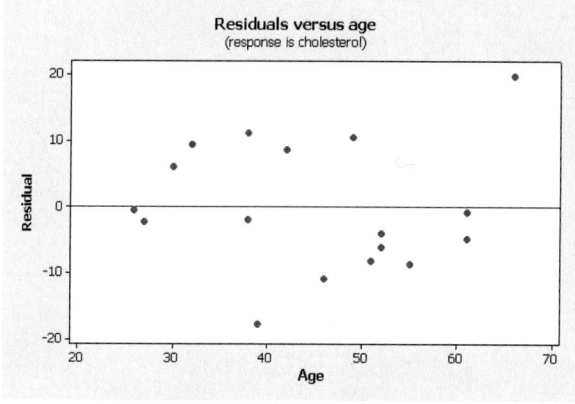

Because the residuals are evenly spread around the horizontal line drawn at 0, the requirement of constant error variance is satisfied, so the linear model seems appropriate.

(d) The lower fence is 7.25, the upper fence is 81.25; so there are no outliers or influential observations.

(e) $s_e = 9.9534$

(f) A normal probability plot of the residuals shows that they are approximately normally distributed.

(g) $s_{b_1} = 0.2021$

(h) Because the P-value = 0.530 > α = 0.01 (or $t_0 = -0.642$ [Tech: -0.643] > $-t_{0.005} = -2.947$), we do not reject the null hypothesis and conclude that a linear relation does not exist between the age and HDL levels.

(i) 95% confidence interval: lower bound: -0.5605; upper bound: 0.3009 [Tech: 0.3008]

(j) Do not recommend using the least-squares regression line to predict the HDL cholesterol levels since we did not reject the null hypothesis. A good estimate for the HDL cholesterol level would be $\bar{y} = 44.9$.

23. (a) $\hat{y} = -3,771,542,830 + 2,018,994x$

(b) $t = 21.81$; P-value < 0.001 < α = 0.05; reject H_0: $\beta_1 = 0$.

(c)

(d)

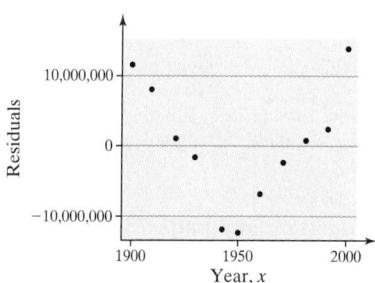

(e) Linear model is not appropriate because there is a pattern in the residual plot.

(f) The moral is that the inferential procedures may lead us to believe that a linear relation between the two variables exists even though diagnostic tools (such as residual plots) indicate that a linear model is inappropriate.

24. (a) $\hat{y} = -12.4967 + 0.0657x$

(b) $t = 17.61$; P-value < 0.001 < α = 0.05; reject H_0: $\beta_1 = 0$.

(c)

Distance from Sun (millions of miles), x

(d)

Distance from Sun (millions of miles), x

(e) Linear model is not appropriate because there is a pattern in the residual plot.

(f) The moral is that the inferential procedures may lead us to believe that a linear relation between the two variables exists even though diagnostic tools (such as residual plots) indicate that a linear model is inappropriate.

25. (a)

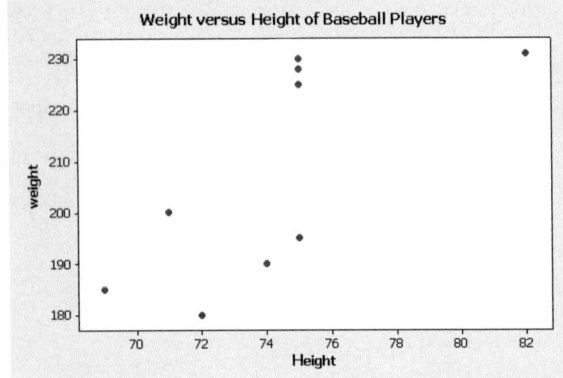

(b) $\hat{y} = -92.9811 + 4.0432x$. Because the P-value $= 0.0374 < \alpha = 0.05$ (or $t_0 = 2.563 > t_{0.025} = 2.365$), we reject the null hypothesis and conclude that a linear relation exists between the height and weight of baseball players.

(c) $\hat{y} = -221.2133 + 5.8067x$. Because the P-value $= 0.0763 > \alpha = 0.05$ (or $t_0 = 2.139 < t_{0.025} = 2.447$), we do not reject the null hypothesis and conclude that a linear relation does not exist between baseball players' height and weight.

26. (a) $\hat{y} = 26.36$ when $x = 10$.

(b) $\mu_{y|10} = 26.36$

(c) An estimate of the standard deviation of y when $x = 10$ is $s = 2.167$

(d) If the requirements for the least-squares regression model are satisfied, y will be normally distributed with $\mu_{y|10} = 26.36$ and $\sigma = 2.167$.

14.2 Assess Your Understanding (page 756)

1. Confidence intervals are used to measure the accuracy of the predicted mean response of all the individuals in the population, whereas prediction intervals are used to measure the accuracy of a single individual's predicted value.

2. If the residuals are not normally distributed, confidence and prediction intervals can still be constructed if the sample is large ($n > 30$).

3. (a) $\hat{y} = 11.8$

(b) Lower bound: 10.8 [Tech: 10.9]; upper bound: 12.8

(c) $\hat{y} = 11.8$

(d) Lower bound: 9.9; upper bound: 13.7

(e) The confidence interval is an interval estimate for the mean value of y at $x = 7$, whereas the prediction interval is an interval estimate for a single value of y at $x = 7$.

4. (a) $\hat{y} = 5.1$

(b) Lower bound: 4.0; upper bound: 6.2

(c) $\hat{y} = 5.1$

(d) Lower bound: 2.5; upper bound: 7.7

(e) The confidence interval is an interval estimate for the mean value of y at $x = 8$, whereas the prediction interval is an interval estimate for a single value of y at $x = 8$.

5. (a) $\hat{y} = 4.3$

(b) Lower bound: 2.5; upper bound: 6.1

(c) $\hat{y} = 4.3$

(d) Lower bound: 0.9; upper bound: 7.7

6. (a) $\hat{y} = 0.4$

(b) Lower bound: -0.8; upper bound: 1.6

(c) $\hat{y} = 0.4$

(d) Lower bound: -1.6 [Tech: -1.7]; upper bound: 2.4

7. (a) $\hat{y} = 17.20$ inches

(b) 95% confidence interval: lower bound: 17.12 inches; upper bound: 17.28 inches

(c) $\hat{y} = 17.20$ inches

(d) 95% prediction interval: lower bound: 16.97 inches; upper bound: 17.43 inches

(e) The confidence interval is an interval estimate for the mean head circumference of all children who are 25.75 inches tall. The prediction interval is an interval estimate for the head circumference of a single child who is 25.75 inches tall.

8. (a) $\hat{y} = 37.023$ [Tech: 37.022] mm

(b) 95% confidence interval: lower bound: 36.647 [Tech: 36.646] mm; upper bound: 37.399 [Tech: 37.398] mm

(c) $\hat{y} = 37.023$ [Tech: 37.022] mm

(d) 95% prediction interval: lower bound: 35.843 [Tech: 35.842] mm; upper bound: 38.203 [Tech: 38.202] mm

(e) Although the predicted lengths of the right tibia in parts (a) and (c) are the same, the intervals are different because the distribution of the means, part (a), has less variability than the distribution of the individuals, part (c).

9. (a) $\hat{y} = 4,400.4$ psi

(b) 95% confidence interval: lower bound: 4,147.8 psi; upper bound: 4,653.1 psi

(c) $\hat{y} = 4,400.4$ psi

(d) 95% prediction interval: lower bound: 3,726.3 psi; upper bound: 5,074.6 psi

(e) The confidence interval is an interval estimate for the mean 28-day strength of all concrete cylinders that have a 7-day strength of 2,550 psi. The prediction interval is an interval estimate for the 28-day strength of a single cylinder whose 7-day strength is 2,550 psi.

10. (a) $\hat{y} = 0.90$ mg

(b) 95% confidence interval: lower bound: 0.83 mg; upper bound: 0.97 mg

(c) $\hat{y} = 0.90$ mg

(d) 95% prediction interval: lower bound: 0.64 mg; upper bound: 1.16 mg

(e) Although the predicted nicotine contents in parts (a) and (c) are the same, the intervals are different because the distribution of the mean nicotine level, part (a), has less variability than the distribution of the individual nicotine levels for a particular tar level, part (c).

11. (a) $\hat{y} = 4.430\%$

(b) 90% confidence interval: lower bound: 1.357%; upper bound: 7.503%

(c) $\hat{y} = 4.430\%$

(d) 90% prediction interval: lower bound: -2.242%; upper bound: 11.102%

(e) Although the predicted rates of return in parts (a) and (c) are the same, the intervals are different because the distribution of the mean rate of return, part (a), has less variability than the distribution of the individual rate of return of a particular S&P 500 rate of return, part (c).

12. (a) $\hat{y} = 2,040.9$ kcal

(b) 99% confidence interval: lower bound: 1,932.3 kcal; upper bound: 2,149.5 kcal

(c) $\hat{y} = 2,040.9$ kcal

(d) 99% prediction interval: lower bound: 1757.8 [Tech: 1757.7] kcal; upper bound: 2324.0 kcal

(e) Although the predicted energy expenditures in parts (a) and (c) are the same, the intervals are different because the distribution of the mean energy expenditure, part (a), has less variability than the distribution of the energy expenditure of a particular individual, part (c).

13. (a) $\hat{y} = 1617$

(b) 95% confidence interval: lower bound: 1523 [Tech: 1522]; upper bound: 1711

(c) $\hat{y} = 1617$

(d) 95% prediction interval: lower bound: 1261; upper bound: 1973

(e) Although the predicted SAT scores in parts (a) and (c) are the same, the intervals are different because the distribution of the mean SAT scores, part (a), has less variability than the distribution of individual SAT scores, part (c).

14. (a) $\hat{y} = 119.2$ [Tech: 119.3] kg

(b) 95% confidence interval: lower bound: 99.8 [Tech: 99.9] kg; upper bound: 138.6 [Tech: 138.7] kg

(c) $\hat{y} = 119.2$ [Tech: 119.3] kg

(d) 95% confidence interval: lower bound: 68.9 kg; upper bound: 169.6 kg

(e) Although the predicted weights in parts (a) and (c) are the same, the intervals are different because the distribution of the mean weights, part (a), has less variability than the distribution of individual weights, part (c).

15. (a) It does not make sense to construct either a confidence interval or prediction interval based on the least-squares regression equation because the evidence indicated that there is no linear relation between calories and sugar.

(b) Since there is no linear relation between x and y, we use the techniques of Section 9.2 on the y-data to construct the confidence interval. 95% confidence interval for the mean sugar content: lower bound: 9.5 grams; upper bound: 19.9 grams.

16. (a) It does not make sense to construct either a confidence interval or prediction interval based on the least-squares regression equation because the evidence indicated that there is no linear relation between age and HDL cholesterol level.

(b) Since there is no linear relation between x and y, we use the techniques of Section 9.2 on the y-data to construct the confidence interval. 95% confidence interval for the mean HDL: lower bound: 39.9; upper bound: 50.0.

17. (a)

(b) $r = 0.839$

(c) Yes, because $0.839 > 0.666$ (Table II)

(d) $\hat{y} = 145.499x - 4661.8395$

(e) For each inch added to the size of the plasma television, the price will increase by about $145.50.

(f) It is not reasonable to interpret the intercept. It would indicate the price of a 0-inch plasma television, which makes no sense.

(g) About 70.4% of variability in price is explained by the variability in size.

(h) $\beta_0 \approx b_0 = -4{,}661.8$, $\beta_1 \approx b_1 = 145.499$

(i) $s_e = 759.6697$

(j) A normal probability plot of the residuals shows that they are approximately normally distributed.

(k) $s_{b_1} = 35.6443$

(l) Because the P-value $= 0.005 < \alpha = 0.05$ (or $t_0 = 4.082 > t_{0.025} = 2.365$), we reject the null hypothesis. We conclude that a linear relation exists between the size and price of plasma televisions.

(m) 95% confidence interval: lower bound: 61.2002; upper bound: 229.7978

(n) $2,613

(o) 95% confidence interval: lower bound: $2,013.1; upper bound: $3,213.1

(p) The price of the Samsung/HP-T5064 is below the average price for 50-inch plasma televisions. Its price, $1,600, is below the low end of the confidence interval found in part (o).

(q) $2,613.1

(r) 95% confidence interval: lower bound: $718.9; upper bound: $4,507.3

(s) Answers will vary. Possible lurking variables: brand name, picture quality, and audio quality.

14.3 Assess Your Understanding (page 774)

1. A correlation matrix shows the linear correlation among all variables under consideration in a multiple linear regression model.

2. The coefficients, b_i, in the multiple regression line represent the average change in the value of the response variable for a 1-unit change in the value of the explanatory variable x_i, when all other explanatory variables are held constant.

3. If the null hypothesis is rejected, we conclude that at least one of the explanatory variables is linearly related to the response variable. It is very possible that all but one of the $\beta_i = 0$ even though the null hypothesis is rejected.

4. When the explanatory variables have an additive effect, or do not interact, it means that the effect of any one explanatory variable on the response variable does not depend on the value of the other explanatory variables.

5. The difference between R^2 and adjusted R^2 is that R^2 becomes larger as more explanatory variables are added to the regression model, regardless of their contribution to the explanation of the response variable. Adjusted R^2 compensates for this ability to artificially increase R^2 by simply adding more explanatory variables. It modifies R^2 based on the sample size, n, and the number of explanatory variables, k. Adjusted R^2 actually decreases if the additional variable does little to explain the variation in the response variable. So, the adjusted R^2 is better for determining whether an additional explanatory variable should be added to the model.

6. Multicollinearity exists when two explanatory variables are highly correlated. We use a correlation matrix to check if multicollinearity exists. A consequence of multicollinearity is that t-test statistics might be small and their P-values large, falsely indicating that neither explanatory variable is significant.

7. (a) The slope coefficient of x_1 is 3. This indicates that $\hat{y}$ will increase 3 units, on average, for every 1-unit increase in x_1, provided that x_2 remains constant. The slope coefficient of x_2 is -4. This indicates that $\hat{y}$ will decrease 4 units, on average, for every 1-unit increase in x_2, provided that x_1 remains constant.

(b) $\hat{y} = 35 - 4x_2$ **(c)** $\hat{y} = 50 - 4x_2$

   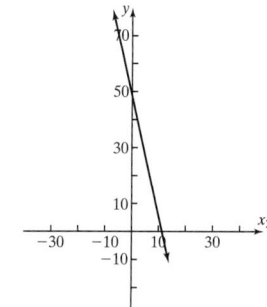

(d) $\hat{y} = 65 - 4x_2$

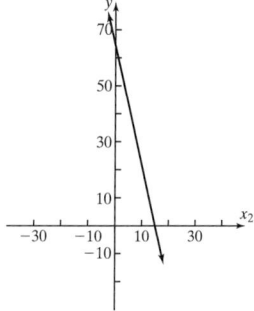

(e) Changing the value of x_1 has the effect of changing the y-intercept of the graph of the regression line.

8. (a) The slope coefficient of x_1 is -9. This indicates that $\hat{y}$ will decrease 9 units, on average, for every 1-unit increase in x_1, provided that x_2 remains constant. The slope coefficient of x_2 is 4. This indicates that $\hat{y}$ will increase 4 units, on average, for every 1-unit increase in x_2, provided that x_1 remains constant.

(b) $\hat{y} = -95 + 4x_2$

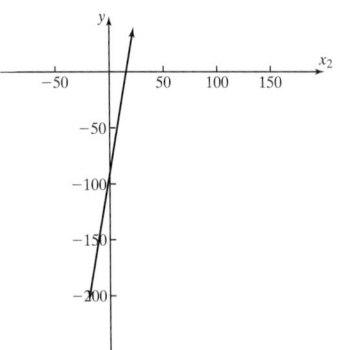

(c) $\hat{y} = -140 + 4x_2$

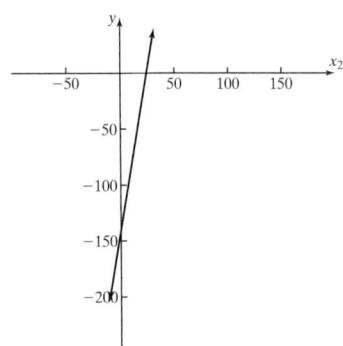

(d) $\hat{y} = -185 + 4x_2$

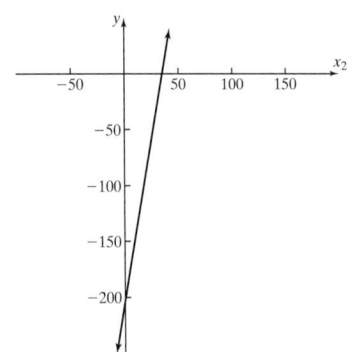

(e) Changing the value of x_1 has the effect of changing the y-intercept of the graph of the regression line.

9. (a) $R^2_{adj} = 0.603$

(b) $F_0 = 13.173$

(c) $R^2_{adj} = 0.598$; do not add the new variable. Its addition reduces the proportion of variance explained by the model.

10. (a) $R^2_{adj} = 0.490$

(b) $F_0 = 10.355$

(c) $R^2_{adj} = 0.517$; add the new variable. Its addition increases the proportion of variance explained by the model.

11. (a) Correlations: x1, x2, x3, y

	x1	x2	x3
x2	−0.460		
x3	0.183	−0.012	
y	−0.748	0.788	0.258

There is no evidence that multicollinearity exists.

(b) $\hat{y} = 7.9647 - 0.1035x_1 + 0.9359x_2 + 0.1152x_3$

(c) $F_0 = 31.33$. Since the P-value $< 0.001 < \alpha = 0.05$, we reject the null hypothesis and conclude that at least one of the explanatory variables is linearly related to the response variable.

(d) Reject H_0: $\beta_1 = 0$ since $t_{\beta 1} = -4.98$ and the P-value $= 0.003 < \alpha = 0.05$
Reject H_0: $\beta_2 = 0$ since $t_{\beta 2} = 4.68$ and the P-value $= 0.003 < \alpha = 0.05$.
Reject H_0: $\beta_3 = 0$ since $t_{\beta 3} = 3.61$ and the P-value $= 0.011 < \alpha = 0.05$.

12. (a) Correlations: x1, x2, x3, y

	x1	x2	x3
x2	−0.424		
x3	0.518	−0.638	
y	0.344	−0.854	0.821

There is no evidence that multicollinearity exists.

(b) $\hat{y} = 98.87 - 0.3013x_1 - 2.0456x_2 + 0.7370x_3$

(c) $F_0 = 15.10$; since the P-value $= 0.003$, we reject the null hypothesis at the $\alpha = 0.05$ level of significance and conclude that at least one of the explanatory variables is linearly related to the response variable.

(d) Do not reject H_0: $\beta_1 = 0$ since $t_{\beta 1} = -1.13$ and the P-value $= 0.303 > \alpha = 0.05$.
Reject H_0: $\beta_2 = 0$ since $t_{\beta 2} = -3.20$ and the P-value $= 0.019 < \alpha = 0.05$.
Reject H_0: $\beta_3 = 0$ since $t_{\beta 3} = 2.80$ and the P-value $= 0.031 < \alpha = 0.05$.
x_1 should be removed from the model.

(e) $\hat{y} = 89.995 - 1.9434x_2 + 0.6317x_3$; $F_0 = 21.19$; since the P-value $= 0.001$, we reject the null hypothesis at the $\alpha = 0.05$ level of significance and conclude that at least one of the explanatory variables is linearly related to the response variable.
Reject H_0: $\beta_2 = 0$ since $t_{\beta 2} = -3.02$ and the P-value $= 0.019 < \alpha = 0.05$.
Reject H_0: $\beta_3 = 0$ since $t_{\beta 3} = 2.52$ and the P-value $= 0.040 < \alpha = 0.05$.

13. (a) Correlations: x1, x2, x3, x4, y

	x1	x2	x3	x4
x2	−0.184			
x3	0.182	−0.106		
x4	−0.166	−0.588	0.291	
y	−0.046	0.932	−0.063	−0.750

There is no evidence that multicollinearity will be a problem.

(b) $\hat{y} = 279.02 + 0.068x_1 + 1.146x_2 + 0.3897x_3 - 2.9378x_4$
$F_0 = 40.90$ and P-value $< 0.001 < \alpha = 0.05$, so we reject the H_0 and conclude that at least one of the explanatory variables is linearly related to the response variable. The variables x_1 and x_3 have slope coefficients that are not significantly different from zero.

(c) $\hat{y} = 282.33 + 1.1426x_2 + 0.3941x_3 - 2.9570x_4$; the F-test still indicates that the model is significant (P-value $< 0.001 < \alpha = 0.05$). Remove x_3; $\hat{y} = 281.62 + 1.1584x_2 - 2.6267x_4$

(d)

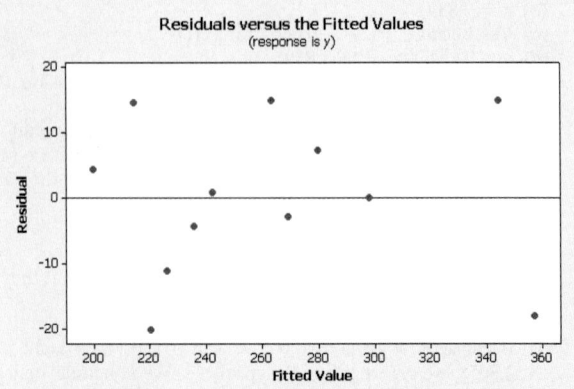

Residuals versus the Fitted Values
(response is y)

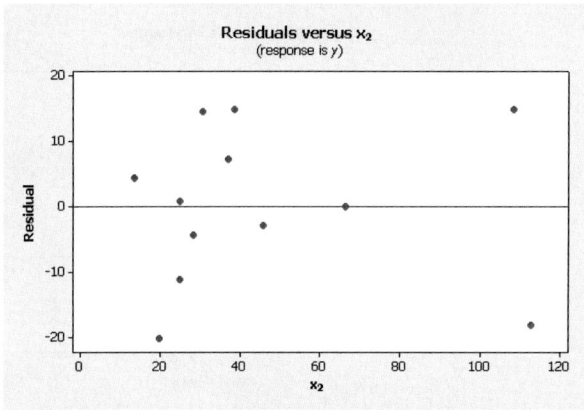

Residuals versus x_2
(response is y)

Residuals versus x_4
(response is y)

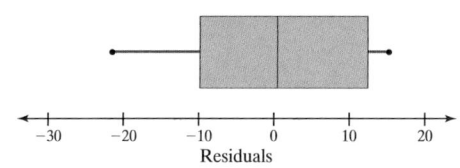

(e) $\hat{y} = 246.7$

(f)

Normal Probability Plot of the Residuals
(response is y)

The residuals are normally distributed, so it is reasonable to construct confidence and prediction intervals.

(g) 95% confidence interval: lower bound: 237.45; upper bound: 255.91
95% prediction interval: lower bound: 214.93; upper bound: 278.43

14. (a)

Correlations: x1, x2, x3, x4, y

	x1	x2	x3	x4
x2	−0.506			
x3	−0.471	−0.225		
x4	−0.504	0.048	0.073	
y	−0.808	0.252	0.640	0.383

There is no evidence that multicollinearity will be a problem.

(b) $\hat{y} = 146.4 - 1.1875x_1 + 1.71x_2 + 3.652x_3 + 0.1387x_4$
$F_0 = 5.00$ and P-value $= 0.032 < 0.05$. We reject H_0 and conclude that at least one of the explanatory variables is linearly related to the response variable.
All four variables, x_1, x_2, x_3, and x_4, have slope coefficients that are not significantly different from zero. The coefficient of x_2 has a P-value of 0.425.

(c) Remove x_2; $\hat{y} = 154.67 - 1.2554x_1 + 3.431x_3 + 0.1052x_4$; the F-test still indicates that the model is significant (P-value $= 0.010$). The coefficient of x_4 has a P-value of 0.844.

Remove x_4; $\hat{y} = 164.94 - 1.3080x_1 + 3.339x_3$; the F-test still indicates that the model is significant (P-value $= 0.002$). The coefficient of x_3 has a P-value of 0.118.

Remove x_3; $\hat{y} = 200.00 - 1.6243x_1$; the F-test still indicates that the model is significant (P-value $= 0.001$).

(d)

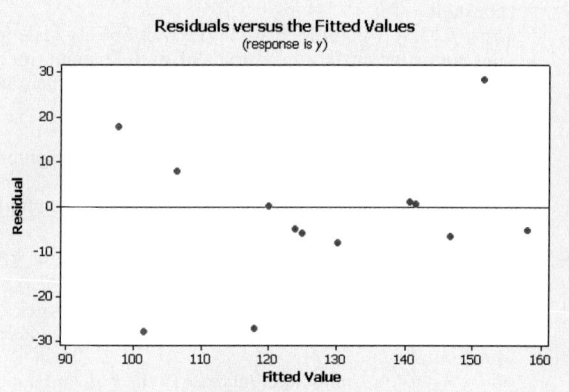

Residuals versus the Fitted Values
(response is y)

Residuals versus x_1
(response is y)

Analysis shows no outliers.

(e) $\hat{y} = 128.04$

(f)

Normal Probability Plot of the Residuals
(response is y)

The residuals are normally distributed, so it is reasonable to construct confidence and prediction intervals.

(g) 95% confidence interval: lower bound: 120.94; upper bound: 135.15
95% prediction interval: lower bound: 103.13; upper bound: 152.95

15. (a) Yes; conclude that at least one of the slope coefficients is linearly related to the response variable, computer anxiety.

(b) $b_1 = -0.87$: A 1-point increase in the computer confidence variable reduces the computer anxiety measurement by 0.87 point, on average, provided that all other explanatory variables remain constant.
$b_2 = -0.51$: A 1-point increase in the computer knowledge variable reduces the computer anxiety measurement by 0.51 point, on average, provided that all other explanatory variables remain constant.
$b_3 = -0.45$: A 1-point increase in the computer liking scale reduces the computer anxiety measurement by 0.45 point, on average, provided that all other explanatory variables remain constant.
$b_4 = 0.33$: A 1-point increase in the trait anxiety scale increases the computer anxiety measurement by 0.33 point, on average, provided that all other explanatory variables remain constant.
They are all reasonable.

(c) $\hat{y} = 57.79$

(d) $R^2 = 0.69$ indicates that 69% of the variance in computer anxiety is explained by this model.

(e) The statement means that the requirements of a multiple linear regression model were checked and were met.

16. (a) Do not reject the null hypothesis since the P-value $= 0.05$.

(b) $b_1 = 0.02$: A 1-percentage-point increase in the time the shooter aim was on target increases the score of the shooter's shot by 0.02 point, on average, provided that the barrel doesn't move horizontally.
$b_3 = -0.03$: A 1-millimeter increase in the horizontal movement of the gun barrel reduces the score of the shooter's shot by 0.03 point, on average, provided that the percent of time the shooter's aim was on target remains constant.

(c) Since the null hypothesis was not rejected, the best prediction of the shooter's score is $\bar{y}$, the mean of the sample responses. Without knowing the sample mean, the model in part (a) predicts a score of 10.64.

(d) Reject the null hypothesis in the second model since the P-value $= 0.04 < 0.05$.

(e) $b_1 = -0.13$: A 1-percentage-point increase in the time the shooter aim was on target reduces the score of the shooter's shot by 0.13 point, on average, provided that the other variables remain constant.
$b_2 = 0.21$: A 1-percentage-point increase in the shooter's region increases the score of the shooter's shot by 0.21 point, on average, provided that the other variables remain constant.
$b_3 = 0.13$: A 1-millimeter increase in the horizontal movement of the gun barrel increases the score of the shooter's shot by 0.13 point, on average, provided that the other variables remain constant.
$b_4 = 0.22$: A 1-millimeter increase in the vertical movement of the gun barrel increases the score of the shooter's shot by 0.22 point, on average, provided that the other variables remain constant.

(f) Answers will vary.

17. (a) $\hat{y} = -12.5091 + 1.3341x_1 - 0.4143x_2$
(b)

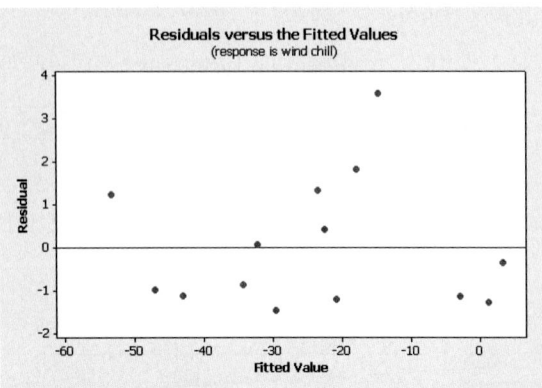

18. (a) $\hat{y} = -92.279 + 1.2575x_1 + 1.0987x_2$
(b)

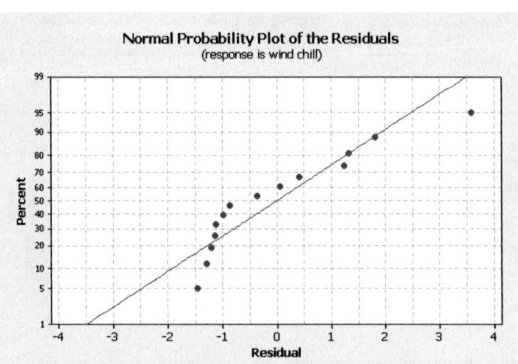

Conclude that the linear model is not appropriate because of the patterned residuals.

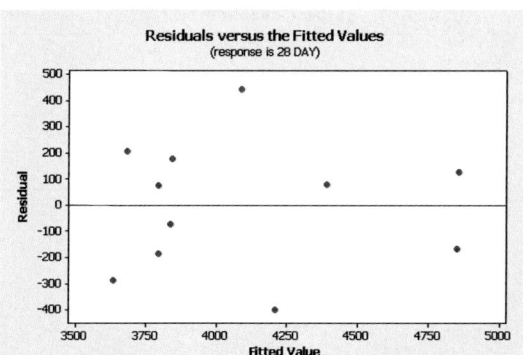

Conclude that a linear model may not be appropriate since the residual plot against fitted values shows some pattern.

19. (a) **Correlations: SLUMP, 7 DAY, 28 DAY**

```
           SLUMP      7 DAY
7 DAY     -0.460
28 DAY    -0.753     0.737
```

There is no reason to be concerned about multicollinearity based on the model.

(b) $\hat{y} = 3{,}890.5 - 295.9x_1 + 0.552x_2$

(c)

(d) $b_1 = -295.9$: A 1-unit increase in slump of the concrete decreases the 28-day strength of the concrete by 295.9 pounds per square inch, on average, provided that the other variable remains constant. $b_2 = 0.5523$: A 1-pound per square inch increase in 7-day strength increases the 28-day strength of the concrete by 0.552 pound per square inch, on average, provided that slump remains constant.

(e) $R^2 = 76.0\%$ represents the variance in 28-day strength explained by the model. $R^2_{\text{adj}} = 70.1\%$ modifies the value of R^2 based on the sample size and the number of explanatory variables in the model.

(f) The F-test has a P-value $= 0.003 < \alpha = 0.05$, so we reject the null hypothesis and conclude that at least one of the slope coefficients is linearly related to the 28-day strength of the concrete.

(g) Reject H_0: $\beta_1 = 0$ since $t_{\beta 1} = -2.69$ and the P-value $= 0.027 < \alpha = 0.05$
Reject H_0: $\beta_2 = 0$ since $t_{\beta 2} = 2.54$ and the P-value $= 0.034 < \alpha = 0.05$.

(h) $\hat{y} = 4207.3$ pounds per square inch.

(i) $\hat{y} = 4207.3$ pounds per square inch.

(j) 95% confidence interval: lower bound: 3,988.6 pounds; upper bound: 4,427.2 pounds per square inch
95% prediction interval: lower bound: 3,533.6 pounds; upper bound: 4,882.2 pounds per square inch

20. (a) Correlations: Work Experience, Level
of Education, Annual Income

	Work Experience	Level of Education
Level of Education	−0.042	
Annual Income	0.463	0.755

There is no concern with multicollinearity.
(b) $\hat{y} = -15.2 + 1.54x_1 + 5.57x_2$
(c)

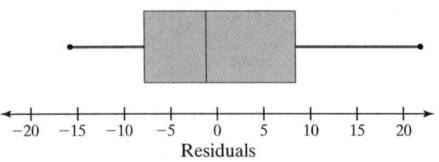

(d) The regression coefficient 1.5449 means that if the person's work experience increases by 1 year then annual income increases, on average, by \$1,540, assuming that education level remains constant. The regression coefficient 5.568 means that if the

person's level of education increases by 1 year then annual income increases, on average, by \$5,570, assuming that work experience remains constant.
(e) $R^2 = 0.816$; $R^2_{adj} = 0.775$
(f) Since the P-value $< 0.001 < \alpha = 0.05$ ($F_0 = 19.96$), we reject the null hypothesis and conclude that at least one of the explanatory variables is linearly associated with annual income.
(g) For the explanatory variable "work experience," $t_0 = 3.46$ with a P-value $= 0.007$.
For the explanatory variable "education level," $t_0 = 5.43$ with a P-value < 0.001. So we reject each null hypothesis and conclude that both explanatory variables have a significant linear relation with the response variable "annual income."
(h) $\hat{y} = 25.56$; the mean income of all individuals whose experience is 12 years and whose level of education is 4 years beyond eighth grade is \$25,560.
(i) $\hat{y} = 25.56$; the income of an individual selected at random whose experience is 12 years and whose level of education is 4 years beyond eighth grade is \$25,560.
(j) 95% confidence interval: lower bound: 15.55, upper bound: 35.58; 95% prediction interval: lower bound: −2.99, upper bound: 54.12

21. (a) Correlations: Sq Ft, Bed, Bath, Price

	Sq Ft	Bed	Bath
Bed	0.267		
Bath	0.274	0.565	
Price	0.665	0.409	0.626

There is no concern with multicollinearity.
(b) $\hat{y} = 25.63 + 0.0719x_1 - 0.81x_2 + 55.35x_3$
(c) Since the P-value is 0.018 ($F_0 = 5.72$), we reject the null hypothesis, and conclude that at least one of the explanatory variables is linearly associated with the asking price for a house.
(d) For the explanatory variable "square footage," $t_0 = 2.61$ and the P-value is 0.028. For the explanatory variable "number of bedrooms," $t_0 = -0.03$ and the P-value is 0.977. For the explanatory variable "number of bathrooms," $t_0 = 2.02$ and the P-value is 0.075. We reject the null hypothesis for square footage and conclude that square footage is linearly related to the asking price for a house.
(e) Remove $x_2 =$ number of bedrooms; $\hat{y} = 24.09 + 0.0718x_1 + 54.92x_3$. Both slope coefficients are significantly different from zero.
(f)

(f)

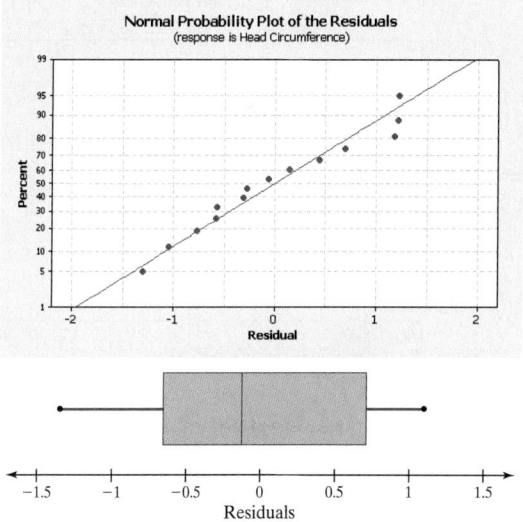

(g) The regression coefficient 0.0718 indicates that, if the house increases by 1 square foot, the asking price will increases by $71.80 on average, assuming that the number of bathrooms remains constant. The coefficient 54.9 indicates that, for each bathroom added to the house, the asking price will increase by $54,900 on average, assuming that the square footage remains constant.

(h) 95% confidence interval: lower bound: 365.1, upper bound: 429.1. We are 95% confident that the mean asking price for all 2,900-square-foot houses with 3 bathrooms is between $365,100 and $429,100. 95% prediction interval: lower bound: 294.2, upper bound: 499.9. We are 95% confident that the asking price for a randomly chosen 2,900-square-foot house with 3 bathrooms is between $294,200 and $499,900.

22. (a) Correlations: Height, Weight, Head Circumference

	Height	Weight
Weight	0.785	
Head Circumference	0.871	0.780

The correlation between height and weight may cause multicollinearity problems.

(b) $\hat{y} = 18.824 + 0.786x_1 + 0.0128x_2$

(c) Since the P-value $< 0.001 < \alpha = 0.05$ ($F_0 = 19.79$), we reject the null hypothesis and conclude that at least one of the explanatory variables is linearly associated with the head circumference of 3-year old children.

(d) For the explanatory variable height, $t_0 = 2.97$ with a P-value $= 0.013$. For the explanatory variable weight, $t_0 = 1.10$ with a P-value $= 0.293$. We reject the first null hypothesis and conclude that height has a significant linear relation with the response variable, head circumference. The hypothesis $\beta_2 = 0$ is not rejected, so we conclude that the explanatory variable, weight, is not linearly related to head circumference, and we remove x_2, weight, from the model.

(e) $\hat{y} = 16.382 + 1.0157x_1$

(g) The regression coefficient 1.0157 indicates that if the child's height increases by 1 inch then the child's head circumference will increase by 1.0157 centimeters, on average.

(h) $R^2 = 0.758$; $R^2_{adj} = 0.738$. R^2 and R^2_{adj} are measures of the proportion of the variance in head circumference that is explained by the model.

(i) 95% confidence interval: lower bound: 43.759, upper bound: 44.867. We are 95% confident that the mean head circumference of all 3-year-old children is between 43.759 and 44.867 cm. 95% prediction interval: lower bound: 42.320, upper bound: 46.306. We are 95% confident that the head circumference of a randomly chosen 3-year-old child is between 42.320 and 46.306 cm.

23. (a) Correlations: Engine, Weight, HP, MPG

	Engine	Weight	HP
Weight	0.764		
HP	0.920	0.558	
MPG	−0.597	−0.390	−0.735

Yes, there is reason to be concerned about multicollinearity.

(b) $\hat{y} = 35.827 + 4.803x_1 - 0.00394x_2 - 0.06583x_3$

(c) Since the P-value is 0.226 ($F_0 = 5.01$), we reject the null hypothesis and conclude that at least one of the explanatory variables is linearly associated with gasoline mileage.

(d) For the explanatory variable "engine size," $t_0 = 1.43$ and the P-value is 0.187. For the explanatory variable "curb weight," $t_0 = -1.03$ and the P-value is 0.332. For the explanatory variable "horsepower," $t_0 = -2.50$ and the P-value is 0.034. We reject the null hypotheses for horsepower and conclude that horsepower is linearly related to gas mileage. We do not reject the null hypotheses for engine size and curb weight.

(e) Remove $x_2 = $ curb weight; $\hat{y} = 26.805 + 2.147x_1 - 0.05032x_3$. The slope coefficient for $x_1 = $ engine size is not significantly different from zero, so we remove it from the model: $\hat{y} = 28.723 - 0.0304x_3$

(f)

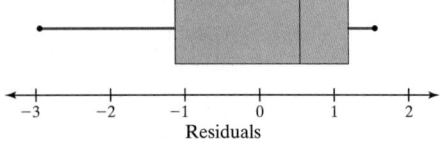

(g) The regression coefficient -0.0304 indicates that, if the horsepower is increased by 1, the gas mileage will decrease by 0.0304 mile per gallon on average.

(h) 95% confidence interval: lower bound: 21.622, upper bound: 23.665. We are 95% confident that the mean gas mileage for all automobiles with 200 horsepower is between 21.622 and 23.665 miles per gallon.
95% prediction interval: lower bound: 19.251, upper bound: 26.036. We are 95% confident that the gas mileage for a randomly chosen automobile with 200 horsepower is between 19.251 and 26.036 miles per gallon.

24. (a) $\hat{y} = 109.894 + 0.0000286x_1$

(b) We reject the null hypothesis that $\beta_1 = 0$ since the P-value $= 0.012$ and conclude that there is a linear relation between MRI count and IQ.

(c)

(d) $\hat{y} = 121.58 + 0.0000174x_1 - 2.486x_2$

(e) For the explanatory variable "gender," $t_0 = -1.23$ and the P-value $= 0.234$ So we do not reject the null hypothesis and conclude that there is not a significant linear relation between gender and intelligence.
For the explanatory MRI count, $t_0 = 1.27$ and the P-value $= 0.221$. So we do not reject the null hypothesis and conclude that there is no significant linear relation between MRI count and intelligence.

(f) The variable x_1, MRI count, originally has a slope coefficient that was significantly different from 0. Adding the variable x_2, gender, caused this relationship to change so that the slope coefficient of both variables are not significantly different from 0. This might lead us to conclude that the two explanatory variables are highly correlated causing the model to become 'confused' when both variables are included.

25. (a)

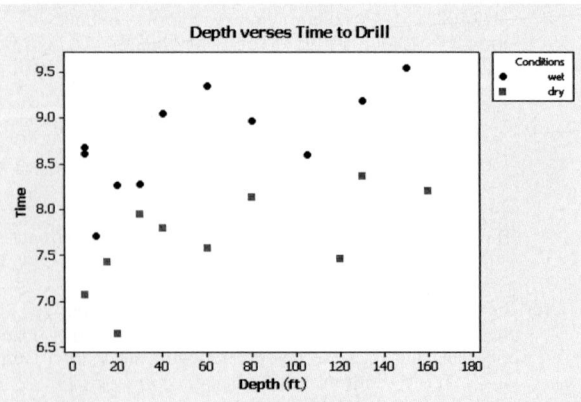

(b) $\hat{y} = 8.3511 + 0.006816x_1 - 1.1359x_2$

(c) For the explanatory variable "depth," $t_0 = 3.86$ and the P-value $= 0.001$. So we reject the null hypothesis and conclude that there is a significant linear relation between depth and time needed to drill another 5 feet.
For the explanatory variable "condition," $t_0 = -6.36$ and the P-value $< 0.001 < \alpha = 0.05$. So we reject the null hypothesis

and conclude that there is a significant linear relation between condition and time needed to drill another 5 feet.

(d) 95% confidence interval: lower bound: 7.598, upper bound: 8.196. We are 95% confident that the mean time it takes to drill an additional 5 feet is between 7.598 and 8.196 minutes. 95% prediction interval: lower bound: 6.990, upper bound: 8.804. We are 95% confident that for a randomly chosen drilling, it will take between 6.990 and 8.804 minutes to drill an additional 5 feet.

26. (a) (i) Ratio   (iv) Ordinal
    (ii) Ordinal   (v) Ratio
    (iii) Ordinal   (vi) Nominal

(b) **Correlations: Carat, Color, Clarity, Cut, Price**

	Carat	Color	Clarity	Cut
Color	0.538			
Clarity	0.368	0.318		
Cut	−0.123	0.093	−0.147	
Price	0.859	0.178	0.025	−0.162

There is no reason to be concerned about multicollinearity.
(c) $\hat{y} = 266.5 + 11{,}319.2x_1 - 599.47x_2 - 481.26x_3 - 145.6x_4$
(d) Since the P-value < 0.001 ($F_0 = 105.31$), we reject the null hypothesis and conclude that at least one of the explanatory variables is linearly associated with price.
(e) Remove $x_4 = $ cut; $\hat{y} = -36 + 11{,}382x_1 - 613x_2 - 473x_3$
(f)

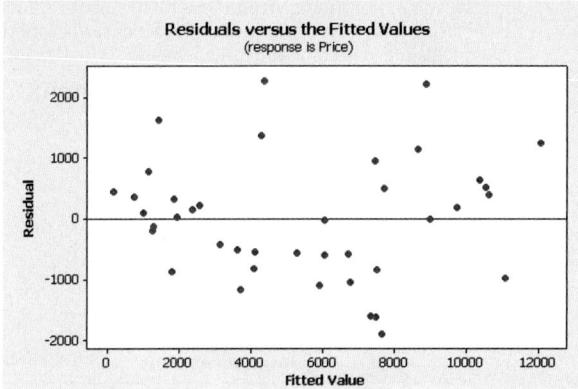

Residuals versus the Fitted Values
(response is Price)

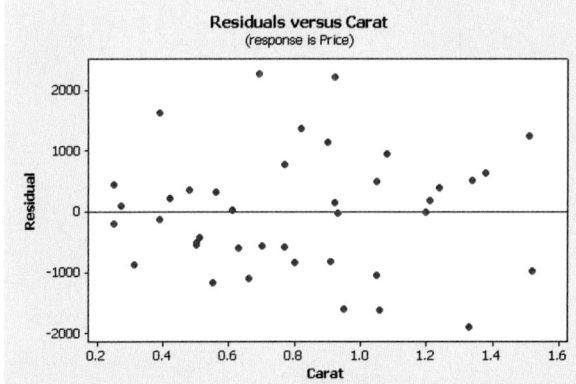

Residuals versus Carat
(response is Price)

Residuals versus Color
(response is Price)

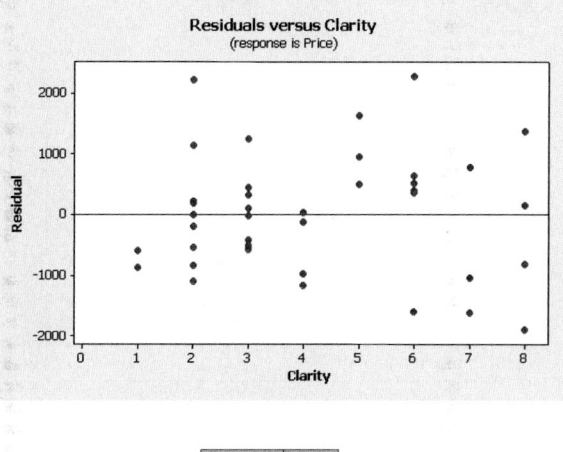

Residuals versus Clarity
(response is Price)

Normal Probability Plot of the Residuals
(response is Price)

(g) $\hat{y} = -36 + 11{,}382x_1 - 613x_2 - 473x_3$. The regression coefficient 11,382 indicates that, if a diamond increases by 1 carat, the price will increase by $11,382 on average, assuming that color and clarity remain constant. The coefficient −613 indicates that, if the color rating increases numerically by 1 (say from D to F, which is actually a decrease in color quality), then the price will decrease by $613 on average, assuming that carat weight and clarity remain constant. The coefficient −473 indicates that, if the clarity rating increases by 1 (say from IF to VVS1, which is actually a decrease in clarity quality), the price will decrease by $473, on average, assuming that carat weight and color remain constant.
(h) $R^2 = 92.2\%$; adjusted $R^2 = 91.6\%$; approximately 92.2% of the variation in price is explained by the least-squares regression model.
(i) $6,992   **(j)** Lower bound: $6,568, upper bound: $7,415
(k) $6,992   **(l)** Lower bound: $4,870, upper bound: $9,113
(m) Although the predicted prices in parts (i) and (k) are the same, the intervals are different because the distribution of the mean price, part (j), has less variability than the distribution of the individual prices of diamonds, part (l).

Chapter 14 Review Exercises (page 782)

1. The least-squares regression model is $y_i = \beta_0 + \beta_1 x_i + \varepsilon_i$. The requirements to perform inference on the least-squares regression line are (1) for any particular values of the explanatory variable x, the mean of the corresponding responses in the population depends linearly on x, and (2) the response variables, y_i, are normally distributed with mean $\mu_{y|x} = \beta_0 + \beta_1 x$ and standard deviation σ. We verify these requirements by checking to see that the residuals are normally distributed, with mean 0 and constant variance σ^2 and that the residuals are independent. We do this by constructing residual plots and a normal probability plot of the residuals.

2. (a) $\beta_0 \approx b_0 = 3.8589$; $\beta_1 \approx b_1 = -0.1049$; $\hat{y} = 3.334$
(b) $s_e = 0.5102$
(c)

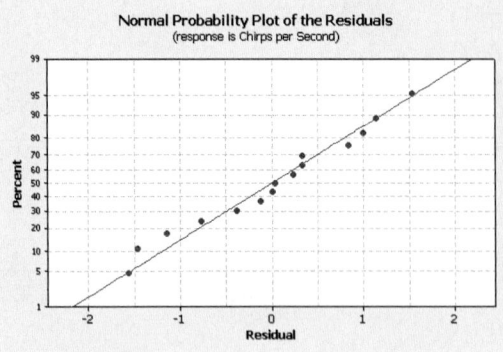

The residuals are normally distributed.
(d) $s_{b_1} = 0.0366$
(e) Because the P-value $= 0.007 < \alpha = 0.05$ (or $t_0 = -2.866$ [Tech: -2.868] $< t_{0.025} = -2.028$), we reject the null hypothesis and conclude that a linear relation exists between the row chosen by students on the first day of class and their cumulative GPAs.
(f) 95% confidence interval: lower bound: -0.1791; upper bound: -0.0307
(g) 95% confidence interval: lower bound: 3.159; upper bound: 3.509
(h) $\hat{y} = 3.334$
(i) 95% prediction interval: lower bound: 2.285; upper bound: 4.383 [Tech: 4.384]
(j) Although the predicted GPAs in parts (a) and (h) are the same, the intervals are different because the distribution of the mean GPAs, part (a), has less variability than the distribution of individual GPAs, part (h).

3. (a) $\beta_0 \approx b_0 = -399.2$; $\beta_1 \approx b_1 = 2.5315$; $\hat{y} = 1879.2$ [Tech: 1879.1], so the mean rent of a 900-square-foot apartment in Queens is $1,879.2.
(b) $s_e = 229.547$
(c)

Normal Probability Plot of the Residuals
(response is Rent per Month)

The residuals are normally distributed.
(d) $s_{b_1} = 0.2166$
(e) There is evidence that a linear relation exists between the square footage of an apartment in Queens, New York, and the monthly rent.
(f) 95% confidence interval about the slope of the true least-squares regression line: lower bound: 2.0416, upper bound: 3.0214.
(g) 90% confidence interval about the mean rent of 900-square-foot apartments: lower bound: $1,752.3 [Tech: 1752.2]; upper bound: $2,006.0.
(h) When an apartment has 900 square feet, $\hat{y} = \$1,879.2$ [Tech: 1879.1].
(i) 90% prediction interval for the rent of a particular 900-square-foot apartment: lower bound: $1,439.7 [Tech: $1439.6]; upper bound: $2,318.6.
(j) Although the predicted rents in parts (a) and (h) are the same, the intervals are different because the distribution of the means, part (a), has less variability than the distribution of the individuals, part (h).

4. (a) $\hat{y} = 20{,}976.2 - 2054.6x$
(b) Reject H_0. There is sufficient evidence at the $\alpha = 0.05$ level of significance that a linear relation exists between the age of used Chevy Camaros and their selling price (P-value < 0.001).
(c)

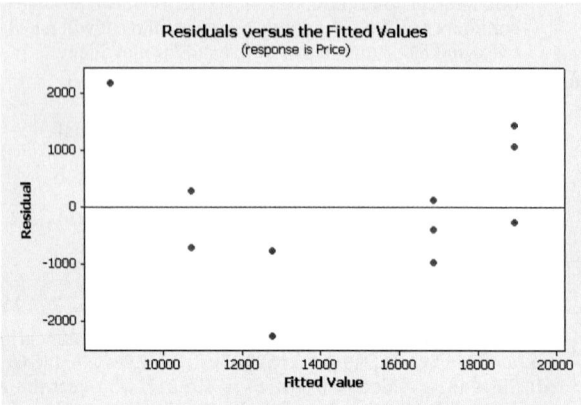

(d) The residual plot shows a pattern which indicates that a linear model is not appropriate. The moral is to perform graphical diagnostic tests along with the inferential procedures before drawing any conclusions regarding the model.

5. (a) **Correlations: Midterm, Project, Course Grade**

	Midterm	Project
Project	-0.076	
Course Grade	0.704	0.526

There is no problem with multicollinearity between the explanatory variables.
(b) $\hat{y} = -91.29 + 1.5211x_1 + 0.4407x_2$
(c)

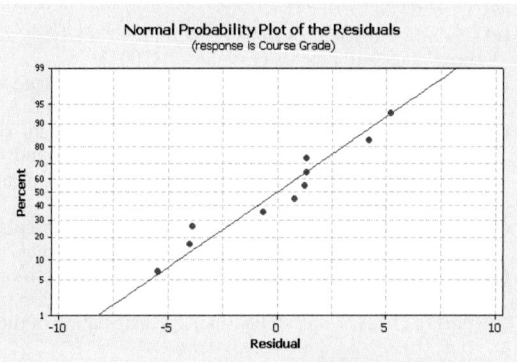

(b) $\hat{y} = 111.24 - 0.239x_1 + 5.388x_2 + 2.9558x_3$

(c) There is sufficient evidence at the $\alpha = 0.05$ level of significance to reject the null hypothesis and conclude that at least one $\beta_i \neq 0$ ($F_0 = 13.5$; P-value = 0.002).

(d) For the explanatory variable "protein," $t_0 = -0.15$ and the P-value = 0.881. So we do not reject $H_0: \beta_1 = 0$. For the explanatory variable "fat," $t_0 = 2.85$ and the P-value = 0.021, so we reject $H_0: \beta_2 = 0$. For the explanatory variable "carbohydrates," $t_0 = 3.72$ and the P-value = 0.006, so we reject $H_0: \beta_3 = 0$. The explanatory variable "protein" should be removed from the model.

(e) $\hat{y} = 101.20 + 5.481x_2 + 3.0536x_3$; each of the slope coefficients is now significantly different from zero.

(f)

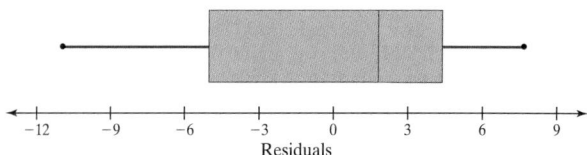

(d) The regression coefficient 1.5211 indicates that, when midterm grade increases by 1 point, the course grade increases by 1.5211 points, on average. The regression coefficient 0.4407 indicates that, when project grade increases by 1 point, the course grade increases by 0.4407 points, on average.

(e) $R^2 = 0.833$; $R^2_{adj} = 0.785$ are measures of the proportion of the variance in the course grade that is explained by the linear regression model.

(f) There is sufficient evidence at the $\alpha = 0.05$ level of significance to reject the null hypothesis and conclude that at least one $\beta_i \neq 0$ ($F_0 = 17.47$; P-value = 0.002).

(g) For the explanatory variable "midterm," $t_0 = 4.83$ and the P-value = 0.002. For the explanatory variable "project," $t_0 = 3.77$ and the P-value = 0.007. We reject both null hypotheses and conclude that both the explanatory variable "midterm" and the explanatory variable "project" are linearly related to course grade.

(h) $\hat{y} = 71.1$

(i) 95% confidence interval: lower bound: 69.00; upper bound: 82.04. We are 95% confident that the mean course grade for students who have an 85 on their midterm and a 75 on their project will be between 69 and 82.

95% prediction interval: lower bound: 64.04; upper bound: 87.00. We are 95% confident that a randomly selected student who has an 85 on the midterm and a 75 on the project will have a course grade between 64 and 87.

6. (a) ## Correlations: Calories, Protein (g), Fat (g), Carbohydrates (g)

	Calories	Protein (g)	Fat (g)
Protein (g)	−0.730		
Fat (g)	−0.064	0.261	
Carbohydrates (g)	0.801	−0.787	−0.541

There is a reason to be concerned about multicollinearity between the variables.

(g) The regression coefficient 5.481 indicates that, when the fat content increases by 1 gram, the calorie content of 100 grams of cereal increases by 5.481 calories, on average, assuming that carbohydrates remain constant. The regression coefficient 3.0536 indicates that, when carbohydrates increase by 1 gram, the calorie content of 100 grams of cereal increases by 3.0536 calories, on average, assuming that fat remains constant.

(h) $R^2 = 0.835$; $R^2_{adj} = 0.798$ are measures of the proportion of the variance in the course grade that is explained by the linear regression model.

(i) 95% confidence interval: lower bound: 388.08; upper bound: 407.81. We are 95% confident that the mean calories in 100 grams of cereal containing 4 grams of fat and 90 grams of carbohydrates will be between 388.1 and 407.8.
95% prediction interval: lower bound: 380.64; upper bound: 415.25. We are 95% confident that 100 grams of a randomly selected cereal containing 4 grams of fat and 90 grams of carbohydrates contains between 380.64 and 415.25 calories.

Chapter 14 Test (page 784)

1. (1) For any particular values of the explanatory variable x, the mean of the corresponding responses in the population depends linearly on x.

(2) The response variables, y_i, are normally distributed with mean $\mu_{y|x_i} = \beta_0 + \beta_1 x$ and standard deviation σ.

2. (a) $\beta_0 \approx b_0 = -0.309$; $\beta_1 \approx b_1 = 0.2119$; $\hat{y} = 16.685$ [Tech: 16.687]; so the mean number of chirps when the temperature is 80.2°F is 16.69.

(b) $s_e = 0.9715$

(c)

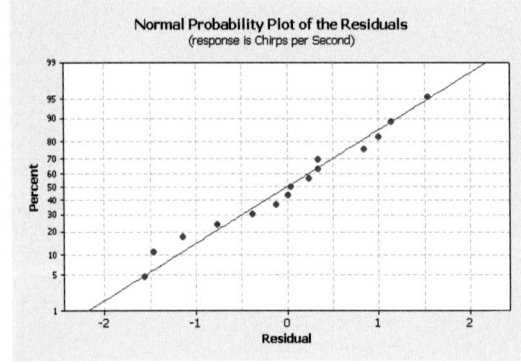

The residuals are normally distributed.

(d) $s_{b_1} = 0.0387$

(e) There is sufficient evidence that a linear relation exists between temperature and the cricket's chirps (P-value < 0.001).

(f) 95% confidence interval about the slope of the true least-squares regression line: lower bound: 0.1283; upper bound: 0.2955.

(g) 90% confidence interval about the mean number of chirps at 80.2°F: lower bound: 16.25 [Tech: 16.24]; upper bound: 17.13.

(h) When the temperature is 80.2°F, $\hat{y} = 16.69$ chirps.

(i) 90% prediction interval for the number of chirps of a particular cricket at 80.2°F: lower bound: 14.91; upper bound: 18.47 [Tech: 18.46].

(j) Although the predicted numbers of chirps in parts (a) and (h) are the same, the intervals are different because the distribution of the means, part (a), has less variability than the distribution of the individuals, part (h).

3. (a) $\beta_0 \approx b_0 = 29.705$; $\beta_1 \approx b_1 = 2.6351$; $\hat{y} = 48.15$; so the mean height of a 7-year-old boy is 48.15 inches.

(b) $s_e = 2.45$

(c)

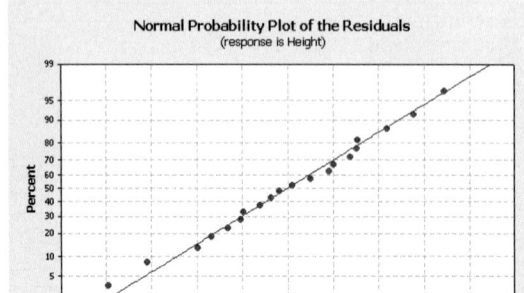

The residuals are normally distributed.

(d) $s_{b_1} = 0.2067$

(e) There is sufficient evidence that a linear relation exists between boys' ages and heights (P-value < 0.001).

(f) 95% confidence interval about the slope of the true least-squares regression line: lower bound: 2.2008; upper bound: 3.0694.

(g) 90% confidence interval about the mean height of 7-year-old boys: lower bound: 47.11 [Tech: 47.12]; upper bound: 49.19 inches.

(h) The predicted height of a randomly chosen 7-year-old boy is 48.15 inches, $\hat{y} = 48.15$.

(i) 90% prediction interval for the height of a particular 7-year-old boy: lower bound: 43.78; upper bound: 52.52 inches.

(j) Although the predicted heights in parts (a) and (h) are the same, the intervals are different because the distribution of the means, part (a), has less variability than the distribution of the individuals, part (h).

4. (a) $\beta_0 \approx b_0 = 67.388$; $\beta_1 \approx b_1 = -0.2632$

(b) $s_e = 11.1859$

(c)

Normal Probability Plot of the Residuals
(response is Grip Strength)

The residuals are normally distributed.

(d) $s_{b_1} = 0.1680$

(e) There is not sufficient evidence at the $\alpha = 0.05$ level of significance to support that a linear relation exists between a woman's age and grip strength (P-value $= 0.138$).

(f) Based on the answers to (d) and (e), a good estimate of the grip strength of a 42-year-old female would be the mean strength of the population, 57 psi.

5. (a) Correlations: Fat, Protein, Sugar, Carbs, Calories

	Fat	Protein	Sugar	Carbs
Protein	0.507			
Sugar	0.412	0.247		
Carbs	0.576	0.550	0.671	
Calories	0.950	0.661	0.542	0.784

There is no reason to be concerned about multicollinearity.

(b) $\hat{y} = -11.9 + 9.0765x_1 + 4.4676x_2 + 1.488x_3 + 3.5202x_4$

(c) Since the P-value < 0.001 ($F_0 = 1,157.97$), we reject the null hypothesis and conclude that at least one of the explanatory variables is linearly associated with calories.

(d) For the explanatory variable "fat content," $t_0 = 37.49$ and the P-value < 0.001. For the explanatory variable "protein," $t_0 = 7.53$ and the P-value is 0.005. For the explanatory variable "sugar," $t_0 = 1.34$ and the P-value is 0.273. For the explanatory variable "carbohydrates," $t_0 = 11.60$ and the P-value is 0.001. We reject the null hypotheses for fat, protein, and carbohydrates and conclude that they are linearly related to calories. We do not reject the null hypothesis for sugar and conclude that sugar is not linearly related to calories.

(e) Remove x_3 = sugar; $\hat{y} = -4.42 + 9.1099x_1 + 4.2937x_2 + 3.7672x_4$. The remaining slope coefficients are significantly different from zero.

(f)

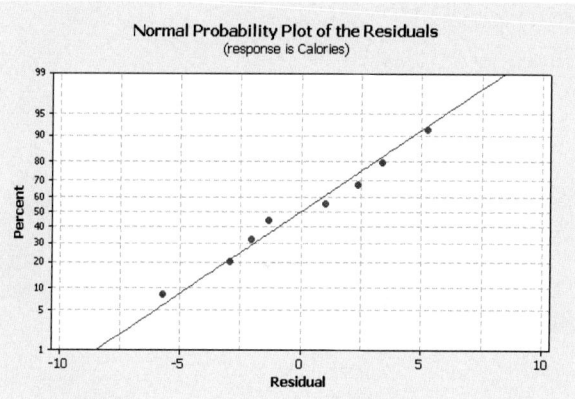

(g) The regression coefficient 9.1099 indicates that, if fat is increased by 1 gram, calories will increase by 9.1099 calories, assuming that protein and carbohydrates remain constant. The coefficient 4.2937 indicates that, if protein is increased by 1 gram, calories will increase by 4.2937 calories, assuming that fat and carbohydrates remain constant. The coefficient 3.7672 indicates that, if carbohydrates are increased by 1 gram, calories will increase by 3.7672 calories, assuming that fat and protein remain constant.

(h) $R^2 = 99.9\%$; adjusted $R^2 = 99.8\%$; virtually all (99.9%) of the variation in calories is explained by the least-squares regression model.

(i) 95% confidence interval: lower bound: 656.16, upper bound: 668.17. We are 95% confident that the mean number of calories for all fast-food cheeseburgers with 38 grams of fat, 29 grams of protein, and 52 grams of carbohydrates is between 656.16 and 668.17 calories. 95% prediction interval: lower bound: 647.53, upper bound: 676.80. We are 95% confident that the number of calories for a randomly selected fast-food cheeseburger with 38 grams of fat, 39 grams of protein, and 52 grams of carbohydrates is between 647.53 and 676.80 calories.

Index

±, 458

A

Absolute deviation, mean, 158
Acceptance sampling, 295–96
Adams, John, 190
Adams, Samuel, 190–91
Addition Rule, 288
  with contingency tables, 277–78
  for Disjoint Events, 273–76, 278
    Benford's Law and, 274–75
    General, 276–78
Additive effect, 763
Adjusted coefficient of determination, 764
Agresti, A., 513
α. See Type I error
Alternative hypothesis, 515–18, 523
  definition of, 516
  structuring, 517, 518
American Academy of Dermatology, 450
American Community Survey, 427
American Medical Association, 450
American Time Use Survey, 426, 440, 453
Analysis of variance (ANOVA), 679–735
  definition of, 679
  F-test statistic, 683–86
  null hypothesis in, 679–80
  one-way, 679–94, 713
    conceptual understanding of, 682–83
    decision rule in, 686
    equal population variances in, 681
    normal distribution in, 681, 682
    post hoc tests on, 694–703
    requirements of, 680–82
    robustness of, 681
    testing hypothesis with, 682–88
    Tukey's test for, 694–703
    using technology, 687–88, 694, 708–9, 713
  on randomized complete block design, 706–7, 713
    analyzing, 707
    illustration of, 704–6
    null hypothesis in, 706
    Tukey's test for, 708–9, 713
    using technology, 708–9, 713
  two-way, 713–28
    crossed factors in, 715
    designs of, analyzing, 714–19
    hypothesis testing using, 717–19
    interaction effect in, 715–16
    interaction plots in, 719–22, 728
    main effects in, 715–16, 728
    requirements for, 717
    Tukey's test for, 722–23, 728
    using technology, 720, 727–28
  Type I error in, 679–80
Anecdotal claims, 3
ANOVA table, 686
Approach to problem solving, 7
Area
  under normal curve, 376–79, 397–99
    finding, 379
    interpreting, 378–79
    as probability, 378–79, 385, 393–94
    as proportion, 378–79, 385
    standard normal curve, 385–89
    as probability, 374
Arithmetic mean. See Mean(s)
Ars Conjectandi (Bernoulli), 259, 344
Ars Magna (Cardano), 264
Associated variables, 194, 198, 201
Association
  among categorical data, conditional
    distribution to identify, 241–44
  Simpson's Paradox and, 245
At-least probability, 288
  for Poisson process, 360
Authorship, questions about, 190–91
Average, 128, 129. See also Mean(s)

B

Bar graph(s), 69–72, 73, 81, 662–63
  of conditional distribution, 243
  frequency and relative frequency, 69–70
  horizontal bars, 72
  side-by-side, 70–72
  technology to draw, 69–70, 81
Bartlett's test, 706n
Before-after (pretest-posttest) experiments, 50
Behrens-Fisher problem, 596
Bell-shaped distribution, 92, 150
  Empirical Rule to describe, 150–52
Benford, Frank, 274, 652
Benford's Law, 274–75, 652–53
Bernoulli, Jacob, 259, 344
Bernoulli trial, 344
β. See Type II error
Between-sample variability, 683
Bias, 38
  in census, 42
  in sampling, 38–45
    frame and, 38–39
    misrepresented answers, 40
    ordering of questions or words, 40–41
    sources of, 38–42
    wording of questions, 40
Biased statistic, 147
Bimodal data set, 136
Binomial experiment
  computing probabilities of, 345–50
  criteria for, 343, 412
  identifying, 343–45
Binomial probability distribution, 343–58,
    426, 557–58
  binomial probability distribution function (pdf),
    346–48
  binomial table to compute binomial
    probabilities, 348–50
  constructing, 345–47
  cumulative, table of, A7–A10
  histograms of, 351–54, 372
  mean and standard deviation of binomial
    random variable, 351, 353–54
  negative, 357
  normal approximation to, 412–17
  notation used in, 343
  table, A3–A6
  using technology, 350, 358
Binomial random variable, 343
  normal approximation to, 414–15
Binomial tables, 348–50
Bivariate data, 192. See also Relation between
    two variables
Bivariate normal distribution, 748
Blinding, 46
Block, 51
  randomized block design, 51–53
Blocking, 51, 157–58, 713
Blood chemistry and health, case study of, 421–23
Bootstrapping, 511–13
Bortkiewicz, Ladislaus von, 363
Boston Gazette and Country Journal, The, 190
Box, George, 602
Boxplots, 177–80
  comparing two distributions using, 180
  constructing, 177–79
  distribution shape based on, 179
  side-by-side, of ANOVA results, 688
  technology to draw, 183
Broca, Paul, 734
Bureau of Labor Statistics, 426, 453

C

Callahan, Paul X., 180
Callbacks, 39
Cardano, Fazio, 264
Cardano, Girolamo, 264
Case-control studies, 18

Categorical data, 644–77
  contingency tables and association, 238–47
    conditional distribution, 241–44, 662–63
    marginal distribution of variable, 239–40
  goodness-of-fit test, 645–56
    characteristics of chi-square
      distribution, 645
    definition of, 645
    expected counts, 646
    technology for, 649, 656
    testing claim using, 647–51
    test statistic for, 647
  tests for homogeneity of proportions, 664–66
  tests for independence, 656–64
Categorical variable, 7–8
Causation, correlation vs., 200–201
Cdf (cumulative distribution function), 350, 387
  inverse, 401
Cells, 239, 277, 715
Census, 19–20, 66
  bias in, 42
  definition of, 19
Census Bureau, 20, 34
Center. See Mean(s)
Centers for Disease Control and Prevention, 19
Central Limit Theorem, 435, 437, 524
Central tendency, measures of, 129–42
  arithmetic mean. See Mean(s)
  from grouped data, 160–61, 166
  mean, 137
  median, 129, 131–33, 137, 166, 171, 179
    approximating from grouped data, 166
    computing, 132–33, 142
    definition of, 131
    IQR and, 179
    shape of distribution identified
      using, 134–35
  mode, 129, 135–37
    bimodality, 136
    computing, 136
    definition of, 135
    multimodality, 136
    of qualitative data, 136–37
    of quantitative data, 136
  trimmed mean, 142
Certainty, 260
Chart(s)
  Pareto, 70
  pie, 72–73, 81
Chebyshev, Pafnuty, 152, 153
Chebyshev's Inequality, 152–53
Chicago Tribune, 252
Chi-square distribution, 645
  characteristics of, 498, 561
  critical values for, 497–99, 502
  definition of, 497
  hypothesis testing about population standard
    deviation and, 561
  table, A14
Chi-square test, 196
  for homogeneity of proportions, 664–66
    definition of, 664
    steps in, 665–66
  for independence, 656–64
    definition of, 656
    expected counts in, 657–59
    expected frequencies in, 659
    steps in, 660–62
    test statistic for, 659
    using technology, 663–64, 671
Chrysalises, 63–64
Claim, 47, 48
Class(es)
  cumulative frequency for, 103–4
  data, 82, 84
  midpoint of, 102–3
  width of, 84
    determining, 86–87

Classical approach to hypothesis testing, 523–25
  in chi-square test
    for homogeneity of proportions, 666
    for independence, 660, 661–62
  of difference between two population proportions, 610, 612
    McNemar's Test for, 616, 617
  of difference between two population standard deviations, 625, 627, 628
  of difference of two means using independent samples, 597, 599
  in goodness-of-fit test, 647–49, 651
  in least-squares regression model, 743, 745
  about population mean
    known population standard deviation, 526–29
    unknown population standard deviation, 542, 544, 546
  about population proportion, 553, 554–55, 556
  about population standard deviation, 562, 563–64
  right-tailed, large sample, 527–28
  to testing claims about matched-pairs data, 585, 587–88
  two-tailed, small sample, 528–29
Classical method, 262–65, 330
  empirical method compared to, 264–65
Classroom survey, 42
Closed question, 41
Cluster sampling, 32–33, 35, 36
Coefficient of determination, 223–27, 763–64
  adjusted, 764
  computing, 225–26
    using technology, 226, 238
  definition of, 224
  F-test in terms of, 765–66
Coefficient of skewness, 158
Coefficient of variation, 158
Coefficients, regression, 762–63
  testing for significance, 766–67
Cohort studies, 19
  prospective, 201
Collaborative Atorvastatin Diabetes Study (CARDS), 46
Column variable, 239, 277
Combinations, 310
  counting problems solved using, 306–8
  definition of, 306
  formula, 307–8
  listing, 307
  of simple random samples, 308
  technology to compute, 308, 314
Comparisonwise error rate, 702
Complement of event, 278
Complement Rule, 278–80, 387
  at-least probabilities and, 288
Completely randomized design, 48–50, 51, 704, 713
Computational formula, 145
Conclusions, stating, 520–21
Conditional distribution, 241–44
  bar graph of, 243
  constructing, 242–43, 662–63
  definition of, 242
Conditional probability, 291–301
  definition of, 291
  independence and, 297
  using the General Multiplication Rule, 294–97
Conditional Probability Rule, 293
Confidence, level of, 5, 458, 459, 462
  margin of error and, 465
Confidence interval(s), 456–513
  definition of, 458, 753
  determining appropriate procedure for constructing, 503–4
  for difference between two population proportions, 613–14
    using technology, 621
  about the difference of two means, 601–3, 608
    hypothesis testing about population mean using, 534
  margin of error of, 459
  for mean response, 753, 754, 758
    using technology, 756, 758
  95%, 460–63, 491
  about a population mean, 589
  about a population mean: known population standard deviation, 457–75
    constructing and interpreting, 458–65, 467
    margin of error in, 465–66

outliers and, 467, 473
point estimate of population mean, 457–58
sample size and, 461, 466–67
using technology, 464–65, 475
about a population mean: unknown population standard deviation, 475–87
  constructing and interpreting, 479–82
  outliers and, 479, 481–82, 486
  Student's t-distribution, 476–78
  t-values, 478–79
  using technology, 481, 487
about the population mean difference of matched-pairs data, 589–90, 595
about a population proportion, 488–96
  constructing and interpreting, 489–91
  point estimate for population proportion, 488–89
  sample size determination, 492–93
  using technology, 490–91, 496
about a population standard deviation, 496–502
  constructing and interpreting, 499–500
  critical values for chi-square distribution, 497–99, 502
  using technology, 502
about the population variance, 499–501
for slope of regression line, 746–48
  constructing, 747
  definition, 746–47
about standard deviation, 499–501
Confounding, 17, 51
Constant error variance, 228–29
Constants, 7
Consumer Reports, 58, 80, 159, 237, 301, 364, 404, 450, 487, 522, 551, 607, 670–71, 702–3
Contingency (two-way) table(s), 238–47, 277.
  See also Chi-square test
  Addition Rule with contingency tables, 277–78
  conditional distribution, 241–44, 662–63
  definition of, 239
  marginal distribution of variable, 239–40
Continuity, correction for, 413
Continuous data, 9
  cumulative frequency and relative frequency for, 103–4
  histograms of, 87–88
  quantitative, mean for, 160–61
  in tables, 84–87
Continuous distributions. See Normal probability distribution; Uniform probability distribution
Continuous random variable, 331–32
  probability density functions to find probabilities for, 373–74
Control
  in experimental design, 642–43
  experiment vs. observational studies and, 16
Control group, 16, 46
Convenience sampling, 6, 23, 34
Correction factor, finite population, 450
Correction for continuity, 413
Correlation, causation vs., 200–201
Correlation coefficient, 646
  critical values for, table of, A2
  linear, 195–99, 747–48
    computing and interpreting, 197–99
    definition of, 195
    properties of, 195–97
    technology to determine, 208–9
Correlation matrix, 199, 759–61, 769
  constructing, 760–61
  definition of, 759
  using technology, 780
Coull, B., 513
Counting problems, 301–14
  appropriate technique to use, determining, 316–18
  combinations for, 306–8, 310–11, 314
  Multiplication Rule for, 301–4
  permutations for, 304–6, 309–11, 314
  without repetition, 303
Counts, expected, 646, 657–59
Critical F-value, 688
Critical region (rejection region), 527
Critical value(s), 462, 526–27
  for chi-square distribution, 497–99, 502
  for correlation coefficient table, A2
  determining linear relation between two variables using, 200
  for F-distribution, 621–24

F-distribution table, A15–A18
  for Tukey's test, 695–96
  table of, A19–A22
Crossed factors, 715
Cross-sectional studies, 18
Cryptosporidium, 237
Cumulative Binomial Probability Distribution table, A7–A10
Cumulative distribution function (cdf), 350, 387
  inverse, 401
Cumulative frequency distribution, 103–4
Cumulative relative frequency distribution, 103–4
Current Population Survey, 34–35, 39
Current Population Survey: Design and Methodology, The, 35
Cutoff point, 260, 261

D

Darwin, Charles, 213
Data, 3–4. See also Qualitative data; Quantitative data
  bivariate, 192. See also Relation between two variables
  categorical. See Categorical data
  classes of, 82, 84
  collection of, 6, 15–22. See also Experiment(s); Observational studies; Sampling
  continuous, 9
    cumulative frequency and relative frequency for, 103–4
    histograms of, 87–88
    quantitative, mean for, 160–61
    in tables, 84–87
  discrete, 9, 82–84
  existing sources of, 19–20
  grouped, 160–66
    mean from, 160–61, 166
    standard deviation from, 162–64, 166
    variance from, 162–64
  misuse of, 3
  polling, 6
  qualitative, 9
  quantitative, 9
  raw, 66, 85
  univariate, 192
  variability in, 4, 11
  variables vs., 9
Data-entry error, 41
Data organization and summary, 66–127. See also Numerically summarizing data
  graphical misrepresentations, 110–19, 125
    by manipulating vertical scale, 111–13
  qualitative data, 67–81
    bar graphs, 69–72, 73, 81
    pie charts, 72–73, 81
    tables, 67–68
  quantitative data, 82–110
    cumulative frequency and relative frequency tables, 103–4
    dot plots, 92, 101
    frequency and relative frequency ogives, 104, 110
    frequency polygons, 102–3, 110
    histograms, 83–84, 87–88, 101
    shape of distribution, 92–93
    split stems, 91–92
    stem-and-leaf plots, 88–92, 101
    tables, 82–83, 84–87
    time-series graphs, 104–5, 110
Data sets, 66
  comparing, 71, 143–44
    standard deviation of two, 150
  small, 405
Decision-making, informed, 62–64
Decision rule, 527, 530
Degrees of freedom, 147, 478–79
  inferences about two means, 596, 599
de Moivre, Abraham, 376, 378, 412
Density function(s)
  exponential, 454–55
  probability, 373–74
  uniform, 375
Department of Justice, 19
Dependent events, 285
Dependent (response) variable, 16, 46, 47, 193–94
Dependent sample(s), 583–95. See also Matched-pairs (dependent) design
  confidence interval for matched-pairs data, 589–90

independent vs. dependent sampling, 583–84
McNemar's Test to compare two proportions
    from, 614–17
testing hypotheses regarding matched-pairs
    data, 584–89
Depreciation rate, 250, 254
Depression, self-treatment for, 58
Descriptive statistics, 5, 6
Designed experiment, 45–58. *See also*
    Experiment(s): design of
completely randomized design, 48–50
defined, 16
matched-pairs design, 50
observational study vs., 16–18, 19
randomized block design, 51–53
steps in designing, 47–48
Determination, coefficient of, 223–27, 763–64
adjusted, 764
computing, 225–26
    using technology, 226, 238
definition of, 224
F-test in terms of, 765–66
Deviation(s), 224–25
explained, 224–25
about the mean, 144–45
total, 224–25
unexplained, 224–25
Dice problem, 267
Die
fair, 259
loaded, 259
Dietary supplements, 58
Diophantus, 265
Discrete data, 9
histograms of, 83–84
in tables, 82–83
Discrete probability distributions, 330–71
binomial, 343–58, 426, 557–58
    binomial probability distribution function
        (pdf), 346–48
    binomial table to compute binomial
        probabilities, 348–50
    constructing, 345–47
    histograms of, 351–54, 372
    identifying binomial experiment, 343–45
    mean and standard deviation of binomial
        random variable, 351, 353–54
    negative, 357
    normal approximation to, 412–17
    notation used in, 343
    using technology, 350, 358
definition of, 332
geometric, 357
identifying, 332–33
Poisson, 359–65, 426
    mean and standard deviation of Poisson
        random variable, 361–62
    Poisson probability distribution function,
        359–60, 361
    probabilities of Poisson random variable,
        359–61
    probability experiment following Poisson
        process, 358
    using technology, 365
probability histograms of, 333–34
rules for, 332
Discrete random variable, 331–42
continuous random variables distinguished
    from, 331–32
mean of, 334–37, 339, 342
    computing, 334–35
    defined, 335
    as an expected value, 336–37
    interpreting, 335–37
    using technology, 339, 342
variance and standard deviation of, 338–39
Disjoint events, 273–76
independent events vs., 285–86
Dispersion, measures of, 143–64
Chebyshev's Inequality, 152–53
Empirical Rule, 150–52
from grouped data, 160–66
range, 144
    computing, 144
    definition of, 144
    interquartile (IQR), 170–71, 178, 179
    technology to determine, 159

standard deviation, 144, 148–50, 196
    of binomial random variable, 351, 353–54
    confidence interval about, 499–501
    of discrete random variables, 338–39
    from grouped data, 162–64, 166
    interpretations of, 150
    outlier distortion of, 172
    of Poisson random variable, 361–62
    population, 148–49, 459, 739
    sample, 148–49, 740
    of sampling distribution of sample mean, 431
    technology to approximate, 164
    technology to determine, 159
    of two data sets, 150
variance, 144–48
    constant error, 228–29
    of discrete random variables, 338–39
    from grouped data, 162–64
    population, 145–46, 162
    of residuals, 228–29
    sample, 144, 146–48, 162
    technology to determine, 149–50, 159
Distribution. *See* Discrete probability distributions;
    Frequency distribution(s); Normal
    probability distribution
Distribution function
binomial probability (pdf), 346–48
cumulative (cdf), 350, 387
    inverse, 401
Poisson probability, 359–60, 361
Doctrine of Chance, The (Leibniz), 376
Dot plots, 92
    using technology, 101
Double-blind experiment, 46, 47
Dummy (indicator) variable, 778

E

EDA (exploratory data analysis), 176
Efron, Brad, 512
Eléments de Géométrie (Legendre), 212
Elements of Sampling Theory and Methods
    (Govindarajulu), 35
Empirical Method, 261–62, 264–65
    classical method compared to, 264–65
Empirical Rule, 150–52, 376, 385, 396
    unusual results in binomial experiment and,
        353–54
Epstein, H. T., 734–35
Equally likely outcomes, 262, 263–64
Error(s)
input (data-entry), 41
margin of, 458, 491
    of confidence interval, 459
    definition of, 465
    level of confidence and, 465
    sample size and, 466–67, 492–93
mean square due to (MSE), 684, 685
nonsampling vs. sampling, 42
residual, 211–12
rounding, 198
round-off, 149
sampling, interviewer error, 40
standard, 476, 740–41
    computing, 740–41
    definition of, 740
    of the mean, 431
    of sample mean difference, 695
    for sampling distribution of population
        proportion, 553
sum of squares due to, 684
Type I, 518–20, 525, 600
    in ANOVA, 679–80
    probability of, 519–20, 525
Type II, 518–20, 569–72
    computing, 570–72
    probability of, 519–20, 569–72
    in Tukey's test, 699
Essay on the Principle of Population, An
    (Malthus), 255
Estimation, 456
Estimator, biased, 147
Event(s), 259
    certain, 260
    complement of, 278
    dependent, 285
    disjoint, 273–76, 285–86
    impossible, 260

independent, 285–87, 297
    Multiplication Rule for, 286–87, 297
    not so unusual, 260–61
    simple, 259
    unusual, 260–61
Excel, 26
area under the normal curve using, 405
    scores corresponding, 405
bar graph using, 70, 81
binomial probabilities using, 350, 358
boxplots using, 183
chi-square tests using, 671
coefficient of determination using, 226, 238
combinations using, 308, 314
confidence intervals using, 758
    for population mean where population standard
        deviation is known, 475
    for population mean where population standard
        deviation is unknown, 487
    for population proportion, 496
    for population standard deviation, 502
correlation coefficient using, 209
difference between two means using, 600
difference between two population standard
    deviations using, 627, 631
difference of two population proportions
    using, 621
factorials on, 314
goodness-of-fit test, 656
histograms using, 101
hypothesis testing using
    about population mean assuming known
        population standard deviation, 540
    about population mean with unknown
        population standard deviation, 552
    about population proportion, 560
    about population standard deviation, 564–65
least-squares regression line using, 214, 223
least-squares regression model using, 745–46, 752
linear correlation coefficient using, 198–99
mean and median using, 142
normal probability plot using, 411
one-way ANOVA using, 687–88, 694
permutations using, 305–6, 314
pie charts using, 81
Poisson probabilities using, 365
prediction intervals using, 758
quartiles using, 175
residual plots using, 238
scatter diagrams using, 198–99, 209
simulation using, 272
standard error using, 741
standard normal distribution using, 396
Tukey's test using, 703
two-sample *t*-tests, dependent sampling using, 595
two-sample *t*-tests, independent sampling
    using, 608
z-score from a specified area to the left using, 390
Expected counts, 646, 657–59
    in chi-square test, 657–59
    in goodness-of-fit test, 646
Expected value, 336–37
Experiment(s), 66, 259, 330
    characteristics of, 46–47
    definition, 46
    design of, 47–58
        completely randomized design, 48–50, 51
        control in, 642–43
        matched-pairs design, 50
        randomized block design, 51–53
        simple random sampling and, 52–53
        steps in, 47–48
    double-blind, 46, 47
    with equally likely outcomes, 262
    following Poisson process, 358
    probability, 261, 262
    single-blind, 46
Experimental units (subjects), 46, 47
    in matched-pairs design, 50
Experimentwise error rate, 695
Explained deviation, 224–25
Explanatory (predictor or independent)
        variable, 193–94
    significance of, 766–67
Explanatory variable, 16, 46
Exploratory data analysis (EDA), 176
Exploratory Data Analysis (Tukey), 176

Exponential density function, 454–55
Exponential probability distribution, 473
Ex post facto studies. *See* Observational studies
Eyeglass lenses, 551

F

Factor(s), 46, 47–48, 704
Factorial Design
  2 × 2, 714, 721–22
  2 × 3, 715
  3 × 2, 714
  3 × 3, 715
Factorial notation, 305
Factorials, technology to compute, 314
Factorial symbol, 304
Fair die, 259
Familywise error rate, 695
F-distribution, 622–24
  characteristics of, 622
  critical values of, 621–24
    table, A15–A18
Federalist papers, 190
Federal Trade Commission, 450
Fences, 172
Fermat, Pierre de, 265, 267, 337
Fermat's Last Theorem, 265
Fibonacci sequence, 655
Finite population correction factor, 450
Fisher, Sir Ronald A., 46, 196, 502, 521, 646, 680
Fisher's *F*-distribution. *See F*-distribution
Five-number summary, 175–77
Food and Drug Administration, 450
Frame, 24, 31, 38–39
Framingham Heart Study, 19
Frequency, relative, 68
Frequency bar graph, 69–70
Frequency distribution(s). *See also* Relative
    frequency distribution
  based on boxplots, 179–80
  bell shaped, 92, 150
    Empirical Rule to describe, 150–52
  center of (average), 128. *See also* Mean(s)
  characteristics of, 128
  chi-square, 645
    characteristics of, 498, 561
    critical values for, 497–99, 502
    definition of, 497
    hypothesis testing about population standard
      deviation and, 561
  comparing, 180
  conditional, 241–44
    bar graph, 243
    constructing, 242–43, 662–63
    definition of, 242
  from continuous data, 84–87
  critical value for, 462
  cumulative, 103–4
  of discrete data, 82–83
  frequency, 67–68
  marginal, 239–40
    relative frequency, 240
  mean of variable from, 160–61
  of qualitative data, 67–68
  relative, 68
  shape of, 92–93, 128, 134–35
  skewed, 134
    mean or median versus skewness, 134–35
  spread of, 128
  Studentized range, 695–96
  symmetric, 150
  variance and standard deviation from, 163
Frequency ogives, 104
  technology to draw, 110
Frequency polygons, 102–3
  technology to draw, 110
F-test, 602–3
  computing, 683–86
  idea behind, 683
  for lack of fit, 764–66

G

Gallup, George, 39
Gallup Organization, 6, 22, 36, 41
Galton, Sir Francis, 213, 292
Gauss, Carl, 378
Gaussian distribution. *See* Normal probability
    distribution

General Addition Rule, 276–78
General Multiplication Rule, conditional probability
    using, 294–97
General Social Survey (GSS), 19
Geometric probability distribution, 357
German immigrants, 370–71
Golden ratio, 655
Goodness-of-fit test, 645–56
  characteristics of chi-square distribution, 645
  definition of, 645
  expected counts, 646
  technology for, 649, 656
  testing claim using, 647–51
  test statistic for, 647
Gosset, William Sealey, 476
Graph(s), 128
  characteristics of good, 115
  cumulative frequency and relative frequency
      tables, 103–4
  dot plots, 92
    using technology, 101
  frequency and relative frequency ogives, 104
    technology to draw, 110
  frequency polygons, 102–3
    technology to draw, 110
  histograms
    binomial probability, 351–54, 372
    of continuous data, 87–88
    of discrete data, 83–84
    probability, 333–34
    technology to draw, 101
  misleading or deceptive, 110–19, 125
  polar area diagram, 85
  stem-and-leaf plots, 88–92
    constructing, 88–91
    split stems, 91–92
    using technology, 101
  tables, 125, 128
    binomial, 348–50
    continuous data in, 84–87
    cumulative frequency and relative
      frequency, 103–4
    discrete data in, 82–83
    open-ended, 84
    qualitative data in, 67–68
  time-series, 104–5
    technology to draw, 110
Greek letters, use of, 129–30
Greenspan, Alan, 786
Grouped data, 160–66
  mean from, 160–61, 166
  standard deviation from, 162–64, 166
  variance from, 162–64
Gun-control laws, 6

H

Hall, Monty, 300–301
Hancock, John, 190, 191
Herbs, 58
Histogram(s), 83
  binomial probability, 351–54, 372
  of continuous data, 87–88
  of discrete data, 83–84
  of discrete probability distributions, 333–34
  relative frequency, 377
  technology to draw, 101
Homogeneity of proportions, chi-square test for,
    664–66
  definition of, 664
  steps in, 665–66
Homoscedasticity, 228
Honestly Significant Difference Test.
    See Tukey's test
How to Lie with Statistics (Huff), 115
Huff, Darrell, 115
Huygens, Christiaan, 337
Hypothesis/hypotheses
  alternative, 515–18, 523
    definition of, 516
    structuring, 517, 518
  definition of, 516
  forming, 517–18
  null, 515–18, 523, 645, 648
    in ANOVA, 679–80
    assumption of trueness of, 524
    definition of, 516
    not rejecting versus acceptance of, 520

in randomized complete block design, 706
    structuring, 518
Hypothesis testing, 456, 514–81. *See also* Inferences;
    One-tailed test(s); Two-tailed tests
  choosing method for, 567–69
  definition of, 516
  illustration of, 515
  language of, 515–22
  large samples, 527–28, 530–32, 535
  logic of, 523–26
    classical approach, 524–25
    P-value approach, 525–26
  outcomes from, 518
  about a population mean assuming known
      population standard deviation, 523–40
    classical approach to, 526–29
    P-values approach to, 529–34
    technology in, 533, 540
    using confidence intervals, 534
  about a population mean in with unknown
      population standard deviation, 541–52
    classical approach to, 542, 544, 546
    outliers and, 543, 545
    P-value approach, 542, 544, 546
    technology in, 545, 552
    using large sample, 543–44
    using small sample, 545–47
  about a population proportion, 552–60
    binomial probability distribution for, 557–58
    classical approach to, 553, 554–55, 556
    normal model for, 552–57
    P-value approach to, 553, 554–55, 556
    right-tailed test, 554–55
    technology in, 556, 560
    two-tailed test, 555–56
  about population standard deviation, 561–66
    chi-square distribution and, 561
    classical approach to, 562, 563–64
    left-tailed test, 563–64
    P-value approach to, 562, 563–64
    technology in, 566
  power of test, 572–73
  probability of Type I error, 519–20, 525
  probability of Type II error, 519–20, 569–72
    computing, 570–72
  small samples, 528–29, 532–33, 545–47, 557–58
  stating conclusions, 520–21
  steps in, 516
  Type I and Type II errors, 518–20
  using one-way ANOVA, 682–88

I

Impossible event, 260
Incentives, nonresponse and, 39
Independence
  chi-square test for, 656–64
    definition of, 656
    expected counts in, 657–59
    expected frequencies in, 659
    steps in, 660–62
    test statistic for, 659
  conditional probability and, 297
Independent events, 285–87, 297
  disjoint events vs., 285–86
  Multiplication Rule for, 286–87, 297
Independent (explanatory or predictor) variable, 193–94
  significance of, 766–67
Independent samples, 583–84
  difference between two means from, 595–608
    confidence intervals regarding, 601–3, 608
    technology for, 600, 607–8
    testing claims regarding, 596–601
Independent trials, 343, 344
Indicator (dummy) variable, 778
Individual, population vs., 5
Inequality, Chebyshev's, 152–53
Inferences, 427, 582–677. *See also* Least-squares
    regression model; Multiple regression
  on categorical data, 644–77
    contingency tables and association, 238–47
    goodness-of-fit test, 645–56
    tests for independence and the homogeneity
        of proportions, 656–71
  determining appropriate test to perform, 632
  about two means
    dependent samples, 583–95
    independent samples, 595–608

about two population proportions, 608–21
  confidence intervals, 613–14
  McNemar's Test to compare two proportions
    from matched-pairs data, 614–17
  sample size requirements for, 617–18
  testing, 609–13
  using technology, 612–13, 621
about two population standard deviations, 621–31
  critical values of F-distribution, 621–24
  notation used for, 622
  robustness of, 622
  testing, 624–28
  using technology, 627, 628, 631
Inferential statistics, 5, 6, 48, 456, 514
Inflection points, 375
Influential observations, 230–32
  removal of, 232
Input errors, 41
Integer distribution, 266
Interaction effect, 715–16
Interaction plots, 719–22
  constructing, 719–20
  two-by-two factorial design analyzed using, 721–22
  using technology, 720
Intercept, 212, 214–16
  of least-squares regression model, inference
    on, 742–46
Internal Revenue Service, 19
Internet surveys, 34
Interquartile range (IQR), 170–71, 176, 178, 179
Interval level of measurement, 10
Interviewer error, 40
Inverse cumulative distribution function, 401

J

Jefferson, Thomas, 20
Jointly normally distributed, 748
Journal of the National Cancer Institute, 15

K

Kepler, Johann, 235, 751
Kepler's Law of Planetary Motion, 235, 751–52
Kolmogorov, Andrei Nikolaevich, 296

L

Lagrange, Joseph-Louis, 360
Landon, Alfred M., 39
Langenscheidt, Hans, 370, 371
Laplace, Pierre Simon, 437
Latin Square design, 705n
Law of Large Numbers, 258–59, 260, 261, 330, 478
Law of Planetary Motion, Kepler's, 235, 751–52
Law of Small Numbers, The (Bortkiewicz), 363
Least-squares regression line, 209–38
  definition of, 211
  diagnostics on, 223–38
    coefficient of determination, 223–27, 238
    influential observations, 230–32
    residual analysis on a regression model, 227–30
  equation of, 212
  finding, 209–14, 223
    using technology, 214, 223
  influential observations and, 230–32
  interpreting the slope and y-intercept of, 214–16
  sum of squared residuals, 216–17
  using technology, 238
Least-squares regression model, 737–58
  confidence interval about slope of, 746–48
    constructing, 747
    definition of, 746–47
  confidence intervals for mean response, 753,
    754, 758
    using technology, 756, 758
  definition of, 739
  example of, 737–38
  inference on the slope and intercept, 742–46
    using technology, 745–46, 752
  normally distributed residuals in, 741–42
  prediction intervals for an individual response,
    755–56, 758
  requirements of, 738–40
  robustness of, 744
  sampling distributions in, 738
  significance of, 737–52
  standard error of the estimate, 740–41
Left-tailed hypothesis testing. *See* One-tailed test(s)
Legendre, Adrien Marie, 211, 212

Leibniz, Gottfried Wilhelm, 376
Level of confidence, 5, 458, 459, 462
  margin of error and, 465
Level of measurement of variable, 10–11
Level of significance, 520
Levene's test, 706n
Levine, Myron, 549
Liber de Ludo Alaea (Cardano), 264
Life on the Mississippi (Twain), 221
Linear correlation coefficient, 195–99, 747–48
  absolute value of, determining linear relation
    between variables from, 200
  computing and interpreting, 197–99
  definition of, 195
  properties of, 195–97
  using technology, 208–9
Linear model, appropriateness of, 227–28
Linear regression
  multiple. *See* Multiple linear regression model
  simple, 736
Linear relation between two variables,
  determining, 200
Linear transformations, 142
Literary Digest, 39
Loaded die, 259
Lower class limit, 84
  of the first class, guidelines for determining, 86
Lurking variable, 4, 17, 200–201, 244, 245

M

Mackowiak, Philip, 549
McNemar's Test, 614–17
Main effects, 715–16, 728
Malthus, Thomas, 255
Marginal distribution
  definition of, 239
  relative frequency, 240
Margin of error, 6, 458, 491
  confidence interval and, 459
  definition of, 465
  level of confidence and, 465
  sample size and, 466–67, 492–93, 617–18
Matched-pairs (dependent) design
  confidence intervals about population mean
    difference of, 589–90, 595
  testing claims about, 584–89
    using technology, 588, 595
Matched-pairs (dependent) samples, 583–95
  McNemar's Test to compare two proportions
    from, 614–17
Matched-pairs design, 50, 706
Mathematics, statistics vs., 4
Matrix, correlation, 199, 759–61, 769
  constructing, 760–61
  definition of, 759
  using technology, 780
Mean(s), 129–31, 137. *See also* Population mean;
    Sample mean
  of binomial random variable, 351, 353–54
  as center of gravity, 131
  comparing median and, 133–35
  comparing three or more. *See* Analysis of
    variance (ANOVA)
  computing, 130–31
    using technology, 133, 142
  definition of, 129
  deviation about the, 144–45
  of discrete random variable, 334–37, 339, 342
    computing, 334–35
    defined, 335
    as an expected value, 336–37
    interpreting, 335–37
    using technology, 339, 342
  from grouped data, 160–61, 166
  least-squares regression model and, 738
  outlier distortion of, 172
  of Poisson random variable, 361–62
  of sampling distribution of sample mean, 431
  shape of distribution from, 134–35
  standard error of the, 431
  technology to approximate, 164
  trimmed, 142
  variability in individuals versus variability in, 431
  weighted, 161–62
Mean absolute deviation, 158
Mean response, confidence intervals for,
    753, 754, 756

Mean squares, 684
  due to error (MSE), 684, 685
  due to treatment (MST), 684–85
Méchanique céleste (Laplace), 437
Median, 129, 131–33, 137, 166, 171, 179
  approximating from grouped data, 166
  comparing mean and, 133–35
  computing, 132–33
    with even number of observations, 132–33
    with odd number of observations, 132
    using technology, 133, 142
  definition of, 131
  IQR and, 179
  sampling distribution of, 454–55
  shape of distribution from, 134–35
Memoryless property of exponential
    distribution, 454
Method of least squares. *See* Least-squares
    regression line
Midpoint, class, 102–3
Midrange, 142
MINITAB, 26, 29
  area under standard normal curve using, 386–87
  area under the normal curve using, 405
    scores corresponding, 405
  bar graph using, 70, 81
  binomial probabilities using, 358
  boxplots using, 183
  chi-square tests using, 663–64, 671
  coefficient of determination using, 238
  comparing mean and median using, 133–34
  comparing standard normal distribution to
    t-distribution using, 477
  confidence intervals using, 756, 758
    for population mean where population
      standard deviation is known, 464–65, 475
    for population mean where population
      standard deviation is unknown, 487
    for population proportion, 491, 496
    for population standard deviation, 502
  constructing 95% confidence intervals, 460–61
  correlation coefficient using, 209
  correlation matrix using, 780
  difference between two population standard
    deviations using, 631
  difference of two population proportions using,
    612–13, 621
  dot plots using, 101
  estimating the population proportion, normality
    requirement not satisfied, 513
  five-number summary using, 177
  goodness-of-fit test, 656
  histograms using, 87–88, 101
  hypothesis testing using
    about population mean assuming known
      population standard deviation, 533, 540
    about population mean with unknown
      population standard deviation, 552
    about population proportion, 556, 560
    about population standard deviation, 566
  interaction plots using, 728
  least-squares regression line using, 214, 223
  least-squares regression model using,
    745–46, 752
  mean and median using, 142
  multiple regression equation using, 761–62
  multiple regression line and residual plots
    using, 780
  normality assessed using, 407–9
  normal probability plot using, 411
  normal random variable using, 401
  one-way ANOVA using, 687–88, 694
  pie charts using, 81
  Poisson probabilities using, 365
  prediction intervals using, 756, 758
  quartiles using, 170
  residual plots using, 238
  sampling distribution of sample mean
    from normal population, 428–29
  sampling from a population that is not
    normal, 433–34
  scatter diagrams using, 208
  simulation using, 266–67, 272
  standard normal distribution using, 396
  stem-and-leaf plot using, 90, 101
  Tally command, 68, 267
  testing claims about matched-pairs data using, 588

MINITAB (*Continued*)
tests for comparing variances, 706n
Tukey's test using, 698–99, 703, 708–9, 713, 722–23, 728
two-sample *t*-tests using
dependent sampling, 595
independent sampling, 608
two-way ANOVA using, 718, 727–28
Misrepresentation of data, graphical, 110–19, 125
Misrepresented answers, 40
Mode, 129, 135–37
bimodality, 136
computing, 136
definition of, 135
multimodality, 136
of qualitative data, 136–37
of quantitative data, 136
Model class of variable, 166
Models, 377
Mood modifiers, herbal, 58
Multicollinearity, 759–60, 768–69
effects of, 768–69
Multimodal data set, 136
Multimodal instruction, 605
Multiple comparison methods, 694
Multiple linear regression model
building, 769–73
guidelines for, 769
coefficient of determination and adjusted coefficient of determination, 763–64
coefficients of multiple regression equation, 762–63
testing for significance, 766–67
construct confidence and prediction intervals, 767–69
correlation matrix, 199, 769
constructing, 760–61
F-test for lack of fit, 764–66
Multiple regression, 736
Multiple regression model, 758–80
correlation matrix, 759–61
definition of, 759
using technology, 780
definition of, 759
using technology, 761–62
Multiplication Rule, 288, 657, 658
for counting, 301–4
General Multiplication Rule, 294–97
for Independent Events, 286–87, 297
Multistage sampling, 34–35
Münchhausen, Baron, 511–12
Murder investigation, case study of, 326–28
Mutually exclusive (disjoint) events, 273–76
independent events vs., 285–86

N

Necomb, Simon, 274
Negative binomial probability distribution, 357
Negatively associated variables, 194
Neuländer, 370–71
Newcomb, Simon, 652
Newton, Isaac, 376
Neyman, Jerzy, 523
Nielsen Media Research, 34
Nightingale, Florence, 85
95% confidence interval, 460–63, 491
Nominal level of measurement, 10
Nonparametric procedures, 482
Nonresponse bias, 39, 42
Nonsampling errors, 42
data-entry errors, 41
nonresponse bias, 39
response bias, 40–41
undercoverage, 38–39
Normal curve, 375
area under, 376–79, 397–99
finding, 379
interpreting, 378–79
as probability, 378, 378–79, 385, 393–94
as proportion, 378–79, 385
standard normal curve, 385–89
inflection points on, 375
Normal distribution, standard, A11–A12
Normal populations, sampling distribution of sample mean from, 428–32
Normal probability density function, 378
Normal probability distribution, 372–423, 426

applications of, 397–405
area under a normal curve, 397–99
value of normal random variable, 400–401
area under, 376–79
finding, 379
interpreting, 378–79
as proportion or probability, 378–79, 385
assessing normality, 405–11
normal probability plots for, 405–11
bivariate, 748
confidence interval construction and, 467
graph of, 375
jointly, 748
least-squares regression model and, 739, 741–42
normal approximation to the binomial probability distribution, 412–17
in one-way ANOVA, 681, 682
properties of, 373–84
statement of, 376
relation between normal random variable and standard normal random variable, 379–80
standard, 379, 385–96
area under the standard normal curve, 385–89, 393–94
notation for probability of standard normal random variable, 393
properties of, 385
t-distribution compared to, 477–78
technology to find, 396
Z-scores for given area, 389–93
technology to find, 404–5
uniform probability distribution, 372, 373–75
definition of, 373
Normal probability plot, 405–11
drawing, 405–9
linearity of, 406, 407
technology to assess, 407–8, 411
Normal random variable, 376–80
probability of, 399
standard, 379–80, 393–94
standardizing, 379–80
value of, 400–401
Normal score, 405
Not so unusual events, 260–61
Nouvelles méthodes pour la determination des orbites des comètes (Legendre), 212
Null hypothesis, 515–18, 523, 645, 648
in ANOVA, 679–80
assumption of trueness of, 524
definition of, 516
not rejecting versus accepting, 520, 528
in randomized complete block design, 706
structuring, 518
Numerically summarizing data, 128–91
boxplots, 177–80
comparing two distributions using, 180
constructing, 177–79
distribution shape based on, 179
technology to draw, 183
five-number summary, 175–77
measures of central tendency, 129–42
arithmetic mean. *See* Mean(s)
from grouped data, 160–61, 166
median, 129, 131–33, 134–35, 142, 166, 176, 179
midrange, 142
mode, 129, 135–37
shape of distribution from mean and median, 134–35
trimmed mean, 142
measures of dispersion, 143–64, 176
Chebyshev's Inequality, 152–53
Empirical Rule, 150–52
from grouped data, 160–66
range, 144, 159, 176, 179
standard deviation. *See* Standard deviation
variance, 144–48, 149, 159, 162–64, 228–29, 338–39
measures of position, 167–75
outliers. *See* Outliers
percentiles, 168–70, 398–99
quartiles, 169–70, 172, 175
z-scores, 167–68, 379–80, 389–93, 405–7, 408, 478
resistant statistic, 133–35

O

Observational studies, 15–19, 66
defined, 16
experiment vs., 16–18, 19
types of, 18–19
Observations, influential, 230–32
removal of, 232
Odds ratio, 474–75
Ogives, frequency and relative frequency, 104
technology to draw, 110
One-tailed test(s), 517, 527–28, 530–32, 542–45, 554–55, 571, 572
of difference between two means, 585
of difference between two means: independent samples, 597
of difference between two population proportions, 610, 611–12
of difference between two population standard deviations, 625
in least-squares regression model, 742–43
about population proportion, 554–55
about population standard deviation, 563–64
One-way ANOVA, 679–94, 713
conceptual understanding of, 682–83
decision rule in, 686
equal population variances in, 681
normal distribution in, 681, 682
post hoc tests on, 694–703
requirements of, 680–82
robustness of, 681
testing hypothesis with, 682–88
Tukey's test for, 694–703
using technology, 687–88, 694, 708–9, 713
Open-ended tables, 84
Open question, 41
Ordinal level of measurement, 10
Otis, James, 190, 191
Outcomes, 258
equally likely, 262, 263–64
Outliers, 128, 171–72, 229–30
confidence intervals and
for population mean where population standard deviation is known, 467, 473
for population mean where population standard deviation is unknown, 479, 481–82, 486
hypothesis testing about population mean and, 543, 545
influential observations and, 231
quartiles to check, 172
Oxygen radical absorbance capacity (ORAC), 702–3

P

Parameter
hypothesis tests regarding. *See* Hypothesis testing
Parameters, 5, 129
Pareto chart, 70
Pascal, Blaise, 265, 267, 337
Pearson, Egon, 523
Pearson, Karl, 158, 196, 375, 476, 523, 646
Pearson product moment correlation coefficient. *See* Linear correlation coefficient
People Meter, 34
Percentile(s), 168–70
interpreting, 168
*k*th, 168
quartiles, 169–70
ranks by, 398–99
value of normal random variable corresponding to, 400–401
Permutations, 304–6, 310
computing, 305–6
using technology, 305–6, 314
definition of, 304
of distinct items, 310
with nondistinct items, 309–11
Pew Internet and American Life Project, 490
Phone-in polling, 34
Pie charts, 72–73
constructing, 72–73
technology to draw, 81
Placebo, 46, 47
Planetary Motion, Kepler's Law of, 235, 751–52
Point estimate
definition of, 457
of population mean, 457–58

of population proportion, 488–89, 608
of two population means, 589
of two population proportions, 609
Points, problem of, 267
Point-slope form of line, 210
Poisson, Siméon Denis, 359, 360
Poisson probability distribution, 358–65, 426
mean and standard deviation of Poisson random variable, 361–62
Poisson probability distribution function, 359–60, 361
probabilities of Poisson random variable, 359–61
probability experiment following Poisson process, 358
using technology, 365
Poisson Process, 358
computing probabilities of, 360
Polar area diagram, 85
Polling, phone-in, 34
Polling data, 6
Polygons, frequency, 102–3
technology to draw, 110
Pooled estimate of p, 609
Pooled t-statistic, 602–3
Pooling, 602
Population, 5
with distribution unknown, 405
finite population correction factor, 450
mean of (μ), 129–31
proportion of, 378
Population growth, 255
Population mean, 129–31, 160
bootstrapping to estimate, 511–13
confidence interval about, 589
confidence interval about, where the population standard deviation is known, 457–75
constructing and interpreting, 458–65, 467
margin of error in, 465–66
outliers and, 467, 473
point estimate of population mean, 457–58
sample size and, 461, 463, 466–67
technology for, 464–65, 475
confidence interval about, where the population standard deviation is unknown, 475–87
constructing and interpreting, 479–82
outliers and, 479, 481–82, 486
Student's t-distribution, 476–78
technology for, 481, 487
t-values, 478–79
forming hypothesis about, 518
hypothesis testing about
known population standard deviation, 523–40
unknown population standard deviation, 541–52
point estimate of, 457–58
Population proportion, 378
confidence intervals about, 488–96
constructing and interpreting, 489–91
point estimate for population proportion, 488–89
sample size determination, 492–93
technology for, 490–91, 496
difference between two, 608–21
confidence intervals, 613–14
McNemar's Test to compare two proportions from matched-pairs data, 614–17
sample size requirements for, 617–18
testing, 609–13
using technology, 612–13, 621
estimating, normality requirement not satisfied, 513
forming hypothesis about, 518
hypothesis testing about, 552–60
binomial probability distribution for, 557–58
classical approach to, 553, 554–55, 556
normal model for, 552–57
P-value approach to, 553, 554–55, 556
right-tailed test, 554–55
technology in, 556, 560
two-tailed test, 555–56
point estimate for, 488–89
sampling distribution of, 489
standard error for, 553
Population size, sample size and, 446
Population standard deviation, 148–49
confidence intervals about, 496–502
constructing and interpreting, 499–501

critical values for chi-square distribution, 497–99, 502
using technology, 502
difference between two, 621–31
critical values of F-distribution, 621–24
notation used for, 622
robustness of, 625
testing, 624–28
using technology, 627, 628, 631
forming hypothesis about, 518
hypothesis testing about, 561–66
chi-square distribution and, 561
classical approach to, 562, 563–64
left-tailed test, 563–64
P-value approach to, 562, 563–64
using technology, 566
least-squares regression model and, 739
margin of error of confidence interval and, 459
Population variance, 145–46, 162
confidence intervals about, 499–501
hypothesis testing about, 562–63
in one-way ANOVA, 681
Population z-score, 167
Position, measures of, 167–75
outliers, 128, 171–72
percentiles, 168–70
quartiles, 169–70
z-scores, 167–68
Positively associated variables, 194, 198
Power curve, 573
Power of test, 572–73
Practical significance, 612
definition of, 535
statistical significance vs., 534–35
Prediction intervals
definition of, 753
for an individual response, 755–56, 758
Predictor (independent or explanatory) variable, 193–94
significance of, 766–67
Pretest-posttest (before-after) experiments, 50
Probability(ies), 257–328
Addition Rule
with contingency tables, 277–78
General, 276–78
Addition Rule for Disjoint Events, 273–76
Benford's Law and, 274–75
area as, 374
area under normal curve as, 378–79, 385, 393–94
at-least, 288
classical, 262–65, 330
Complement Rule, 278–80, 288, 387
conditional, 291–301
definition of, 291
independence and, 297
using the General Multiplication Rule, 294–97
counting problems, 301–14
combinations for, 306–8, 310–11, 314
Multiplication Rule for, 301–4
permutations for, 304–6, 309–11, 314
without repetition, 303
defined, 258
Empirical Method to approximate, 261–62, 264–65
events and the sample space of probability experiment, 259
to identify unusual events, 260–61
Multiplication Rule for Independent Events, 286–87, 297
relative frequency to approximate, 261
rules of, 258–73, 288
determining appropriate, 314–16
simulation to obtain, 265–67
technology in, 272
subjective, 267
value of normal random variable corresponding to, 400–401
Probability density function (pdf), 373–74, 378
normal, 378
Probability distribution, 426. See also Normal probability distribution
binomial, 426, 557–58
cumulative, A7–A10
table, A3–A6
exponential, 473
geometric, 357
negative binomial, 357

Poisson, 426
testing claims regarding. See Contingency (two-way) table(s); Goodness-of-fit test
Probability experiment, 259, 261, 262, 330
binomial. See Binomial experiment, 343
design of, control in, 642–43
following Poisson process, 358
Probability histograms of discrete probability distributions, 333–34
binomial, 351–54
Probability model, 260, 330
for random variables. See Discrete probability distributions
from survey data, 261–62
Proportion(s). See also Population proportion; Sample proportion
area under normal curve as, 378–79, 385
homogeneity of, 664–66
definition of, 664
steps in, 665–66
value of normal random variable corresponding to, 400–401
Prospective cohort studies, 201
Prospective studies, 19
P-value, definition of, 529
P-value approach to hypothesis testing, 525–26
in chi-square test
for homogeneity of proportions, 666
for independence, 660, 661–62
of difference between two means: independent samples, 597, 599
of difference between two population proportions, 610, 612
McNemar's Test for, 616, 617
of difference between two population standard deviations, 625, 627, 628
goodness-of-fit, 647–49, 651
in least-squares regression model, 743, 745
of matched-pairs data, 585, 587–88
in multiple linear regression model, 766–67
in multiple regression model, 765–66
in one-way ANOVA, 686
about population mean
known population standard deviation, 529–34
unknown population standard deviation, 542, 544, 546
about population proportion, 553, 554–55, 556
about population standard deviation, 562, 563–64
right-tailed, large sample, 530–32
two-tailed, 532–33, 557n

Q

Qualitative data, 9, 67–81. See also Categorical data
bar graphs of, 69–72, 73, 81
frequency distribution of, 67–68
relative, 68
mode of, 136–37
pie charts of, 72–73, 81
tables of, 67–68
Qualitative variable, 7–8
nominal or ordinal, 10
Quantitative data, 9, 82–110
cumulative frequency and relative frequency tables of, 103–4
dot plots of, 92, 101
frequency and relative frequency ogives of, 104
technology to draw, 110
frequency polygons of, 102–3
technology to draw, 110
histograms of, 83–84, 87–88, 101
mode of, 136
shape of distribution of, 92–93
stem-and-leaf plots of, 88–92, 101
split stems, 91–92
tables of, 82–83, 84–87
time-series graphs of, 104–5
technology to draw, 110
Quantitative variable, 7–8
interval or ratio, 10
Quartiles, 169–70
checking for outliers using, 172
using technology, 170, 175
Questionnaire, ordering of questions or words in, 40–41
Questions
ordering of, 40–41
type of, 41
wording of, 40

Questions and Answers in Attitude Surveys (Schuman and Presser), 40
Queuing theory, 566

R

Random digit dialing (RDD) telephone surveys, 39
Randomization, 48
Randomized block design, 51–53
Randomized complete block design, 704–13
  analysis of variance on, 706–7, 713
  analyzing, 707
  illustration of, 704–6
  null hypothesis in, 706
  Tukey's test for, 708–9, 713
  using technology, 708–9, 713
Random number generator, 26, 27, 93, 655
Random numbers, table of, 25, A1
Random sampling, 22–29, 30, 31, 35, 36
  combinations of samples, 308
  confidence interval construction and, 467
  definition of, 23
  illustrating, 23, 24
  obtaining sample, 23–29
Random variable(s), 330, 426
  binomial, 343
    normal approximation to, 414–15
  continuous, 331–32
    probability density functions to find probabilities for, 373–74
    definition of, 331
  discrete, 331–42
    continuous random variables distinguished from, 331–32
    definition of, 331
    mean of, 334–37, 339, 342
    variance and standard deviation of, 338–39
  normal, 376–80
    probability of, 399
    standard, 379–80, 393–94
    standardizing, 379–80
    value of, 400–401
  Poisson, 359–61
  probability models for. *See* Discrete probability distributions
  statistics as, 426
Range, 144, 159
  computing, 144
  definition of, 144
  interquartile (IQR), 170–71, 176, 178, 179
  technology to determine, 159
Ratio, golden, 655
Ratio level of measurement, 10
Raw data, 66
  continuous, 85
  mean of variable from, 129–31
  median of a variable from, 131–33
  range of variable from, 144
  standard deviation of variable from, 148–50
  variance of variable from, 144–48
Récherches sur la probabilité des jugements (Poisson), 360
Regression. *See* Least-squares regression model; Multiple regression
Regression analysis, 213
Regression coefficients, 762–63
  testing for significance, 766–67
Rejection region (critical region), 527
Relation between two variables, 192–255
  contingency tables and association, 238–47
    conditional distribution to identify association among categorical data, 241–44
    marginal distribution of a variable, 239–40
    Simpson's Paradox, 244–45
  correlation versus causation, 200–201
  least-squares regression line, 209–38
    coefficient of determination, 223–27, 238
    definition of, 211
    diagnostics on, 223–38
    equation of, 212
    finding, 209–14, 223
    influential observations, 230–32
    interpreting the slope and y-intercept of, 214–16
    residual analysis on a regression model, 227–30
    sum of squared residuals, 216–17, 238
  linear, determining, 200

linear correlation coefficient, 195–99, 747–48
  computing and interpreting, 197–99
  definition of, 195
  properties of, 195–97
  using technology, 208–9
  scatter diagrams, 193–95
    definition of, 193
    drawing, 193–94, 198–99, 208–9
  testing for linear relation, 742–46
Relative frequency(ies)
  association between two categorical variables and, 241
  probability using, 261
  of qualitative data, 68
Relative frequency bar graph, 69–70
  side-by-side, 71, 72
    using horizontal bars, 72
Relative frequency distribution, 68
  from continuous data, 84–87
  cumulative, 103–4
  of discrete data, 82–83
  histogram of, 377
Relative frequency marginal distributions, 240
Relative frequency ogives, 104
Relative risk, 539
Reliability, 11
Replication, 48
Research objective, identification of, 6
Residual(s), 211–12, 227
  normally distributed, 741–42
  sum of squared, 216–17
    using technology, 238
  variance of, 228–29
Residual analysis on regression model, 227–30
  appropriateness of linear model, 227–28
  constant error variance, 228–29
  graphical, 230
  outliers, 229–30
Resistant statistic, 133–35
Response bias, 40–41, 112
Response (dependent) variable, 16, 46, 47, 193–94
Retrospective studies, 18
Rewards, nonresponse and, 39
Right-tailed hypothesis testing. *See* One-tailed test(s)
Risk, 156
  relative, 539
Robustness, 463, 527, 585, 622
  of least-squares regression model, 744
  of one-way ANOVA, 681
  of testing difference between two population standard deviations, 622, 625
Roman letters, use of, 129
Roosevelt, Franklin D., 39
Roti, Joseph L., 16
Rounding, 9
Rounding error, 198
Rounding up vs. rounding off, 466
Round-off error, 149
Row variable, 239, 277

S

St. Andrew (ship), 370–71
Sample(s)
  convenience, 6
  correlation coefficient, 195
  defined, 5
  matched-pairs (dependent), 583–95
    confidence intervals for, 589–90, 595
    McNemar's Test to compare two proportions from, 614–17
    testing claims about, 584–89
  mean of ($\bar{x}$), 129–31
  self-selected (voluntary response), 34
Sample mean, 129–30, 160
  sample size and, 430, 431
  sampling distribution of, 427–42, 456, 459, 460–61
    definition of, 427
    describing, 432
    mean and standard deviation of, 431
    from normal populations, 428–32
    from not-normal populations, 433–38
    shape of, 432
    standard deviation of, 456
Sample proportion
  computing, 443
  definition of, 442

  sampling distribution of, 442–50
    describing, 442–46
    probabilities of, 446–48
    simulation to describe distribution of, 443–45
Sample size, 35
  confidence interval about population mean where population standard deviation is known and, 461, 463, 466–67
  confidence interval about population proportion and, 492–93
  for difference of two population proportions, 617–18
  distribution shape and, 433–37
  hypothesis testing and, 527–33, 535, 542–47, 557–58
  margin of error and, 459, 466–67, 492–93
  population size and, 446
  sampling variability and, 430, 431
  shape of the *t*-distribution and, 476, 478
Sample space, 259
Sample standard deviation, 148–49, 740
Sample variance, 144, 146–48, 162
Sample z-score, 167
Sampling, 22–45
  acceptance, 295–96
  bias in, 38–45
    frame and, 38–39
    misrepresented answers, 40
    nonresponse bias, 39, 42
    ordering of questions or words, 40–41
    response bias, 40–41
    sampling bias, 38–39
    wording of questions, 40
  cluster, 32–33, 35, 36
  convenience, 34
  dependent, 583–84
  errors in
    interviewer error, 40
  goal of, 30, 38
  independent, 583–84
  multistage, 34–35
  with replacement, 24–25
  without replacement, 24, 25
  sample size considerations, 35
  simple random, 22–29, 30, 31, 35, 36
    combinations of, 308
    confidence interval construction and, 467
    definition of, 23
    illustrating, 23, 24
    obtaining sample, 23–29
  stratified, 30–31, 33, 35, 36
  systematic, 31–32, 33, 35, 36
Sampling distribution(s), 426–55
  of difference between two proportions, 609
  of difference of two means, 596
  in least-squares regression model, 738
  of median, 454–55
  of population proportion, 489
    standard error for, 553
  of sample mean, 427–42, 456, 459, 460–61
    definition of, 427
    describing, 432
    mean and standard deviation of, 431
    from normal populations, 428–32
    from not-normal populations, 433–38
    shape of, 432
  of sample proportion, 442–50
    describing, 442–46
    probabilities of, 446–48
Sampling error, 42
Scatter diagrams, 193–95
  definition of, 193
  drawing, 193–94, 198–99, 208–9
Schiavo, Terri, opinion regarding case of, 111–12
Schüz, Joachim, 15
Seed, 26
Self-selected samples, 34
Shape. *See* Normal probability distribution
Side-by-side bar graph, 70–72
  using horizontal bars, 72
Sider, Christopher, 190
Sidereal year, 235, 751
Sigma (Σ), 130
Significance
  of least-squares regression model, 737–52
  level of, 520

practical, 612
definition of, 535
statistical vs., 534–35
of predictor variables, 766–67
of regression coefficients, 766–67
statistical, 612
definition of, 524
practical vs., 534–35
Type I error and, 520
Simple events, 259
Simple linear regression, 736
Simple random sample, 22–29, 30, 31, 35, 36
combinations of, 308
confidence interval construction and, 467
definition of, 23
designed experiment and, 52–53
illustrating, 23, 24
obtaining, 23–29
Simpson's Paradox, 244–45
Simulation, 265–67
using technology, 272
Single-blind experiment, 46
Skewed distributions, 92–93, 134
IQR for, 179
mean or median versus skewness, 134–35
Skewness, 179
coefficient of, 158
Slope, 212, 214–16
of least-squares regression model, inference on, 742–46
SPF (sun-protection factor), 404
Split stems, 91–92
Spread. See Standard deviation; Variance
Spreadsheets. See Statistical spreadsheets
Standard deviation, 144, 148–50, 159, 196
of binomial random variable, 351, 353–54
confidence interval about, 499–501
for known population mean, 457–75
of discrete random variables, 338–39
from grouped data, 162–64, 166
interpretations of, 150
outlier distortion of, 172
of Poisson random variable, 361–62
population, 148–49
confidence intervals about, 496–502
difference between two, 621–31
hypothesis testing about, 561–66
least-squares regression model and, 739
margin of error of confidence interval and, 459
sample, 148–49, 740
of sample mean, 456
of sampling distribution of sample mean, 431
of two data sets, 150
using technology, 159, 164
Standard error, 476, 740–41
computing, 740–41
definition of, 740
of the mean, 431
of sample mean difference, 695
for sampling distribution of population proportion, 553
Standard normal probability distribution, 379, 385–96
area under the standard normal curve, 385–89
to left of z-score, 385–86, 388, 389
as a probability, 393–94
to right of z-score, 387–88, 389, 391
technology to find, 386–87, 390
between two z-scores, 388, 389, 391–92
z-scores for given, 389–93
notation for probability of standard normal random variable, 393
properties of, 385
table, A11–A12
t-distribution compared to, 477–78
technology to find, 396
z-scores for given area, 389–93
Standard normal random variables, 379–80, 393–94
Statistic, 5
biased, 147
defined, 5
parameter versus, 5
as random variable, 426
resistant, 133–35
sample mean as, 129
test, 526, 553
Statistical Abstract of the United States, 266
Statistically significant, defined, 524

Statistical significance, 612
practical significance vs., 534–35
Statistical spreadsheets. See also Excel
area under standard normal curve using, 386–87
ogives on, 104
pie charts on, 73
Tally command, 68
time-series on, 105
Statistical thinking, 3–4
Statistics, 3–15
definition of, 3–4
descriptive, 5
inferential, 5, 6, 48
mathematics vs., 4
process of, 4–6
variables in, 7–9
data vs., 9
discrete vs. continuous, 8–9
qualitative (categorical) vs. quantitative, 7–8
Status quo statement, 516, 517
Stem-and-leaf plots, 88–92
constructing, 88–91
after modifying data, 90–91
using technology, 90
split stems, 91–92
using technology, 101
Stonehenge, age of, 580–81
Strata, 30
Stratified sampling, 30–31, 35, 36
random, 33
Studentized range distribution, 695–96
Student's t. See t-distribution
Subject (experimental unit), 46, 47
in matched-pairs design, 50
Subjective probability, 267
Sum of squared residuals, 216–17
using technology, 238
Sum of squares, 684
due to error, 684
total (SS (Total)), 684
due to treatment (SST), 684–85
Sunscreens, 404
Survey data, probability model from, 261–62
Surveys, 491
American Community Survey, 427
American Time Use Survey, 426, 453
classroom, 42
creating, 511
General Social Survey (GSS), 19
Internet, 34
random digit dialing (RDD) telephone, 39
random sample, 22–29
Suzuki, Ichiro, 340
Symmetric distributions, 92, 150
Systematic sampling, 31–32, 33, 35, 36

T

Tables, 125, 128
binomial, 348–50
continuous data in, 84–87
cumulative frequency and relative frequency, 103–4
discrete data in, 82–83
open-ended, 84
qualitative data in, 67–68
Tanning salons, 450
t-distribution, 476–78, 541
finding values, 478–79
hypothesis testing and, 541, 543
properties of, 477–78, 541
sample size and, 476, 478
standard normal distribution compared to, 477–78
table, A13
Technology. See also Excel; MINITAB; TI-83/84 Plus graphing calculator
ANOVA using
one-way, 687–88, 694, 708–9, 713
two-way, 720, 727–28
area under normal curve using, 398–99
area under standard normal curve using, 386–87, 390
binomial probabilities using, 350, 358
boxplots using, 183
chi-square tests using, 663–64, 671
coefficient of determination using, 226, 238
combinations using, 308, 314

confidence intervals using, 756, 758
for population mean where population standard deviation is known, 464–65, 475
for population mean where population standard deviation is unknown, 481, 487
for population proportion, 490–91, 496
for population standard deviation, 502
correlation matrix using, 780
difference between two means using, 600, 607–8
difference between two population proportions using, 612–13, 621
difference between two population standard deviations using, 627, 628, 631
exact P-values using, 649
factorials using, 314
five-number summary using, 177
goodness-of-fit test using, 649, 656
in hypothesis testing
about population mean assuming known population standard deviation, 533, 540
about population mean with unknown population standard deviation, 545, 552
about population proportion, 556, 560
about population standard deviation, 566
interaction plots using, 720, 728
least-squares regression line using, 214
least-squares regression model using, 745–46, 752
linear correlation coefficient using, 198–99, 208–9
mean and standard deviation using, 164, 339, 342
multiple regression equation using, 761–62
normal probability distribution using, 404–5
standard, 396
normal probability plot using, 411
normal random variable using, 400–401
permutations using, 305–6, 314
Poisson probability distribution using, 365
prediction intervals using, 756, 758
probabilities of a sample proportion using, 447, 448
randomized complete block design using, 708–9, 713
scatter diagram using, 198–99, 208–9
simple random sample using, 26–27, 29
standard error using, 741
sum of squared residuals using, 238
testing claims about matched-pairs data using, 588, 595
Tukey's test using, 698–99, 703, 708–9, 713
two-sample t-tests, independent sampling, 607–8
Test, power of, 572–73
Test statistic, 526, 553
for the test of independence, 659
TI-83/84 Plus graphing calculator, 26–27, 29
area under normal curve using, 398–99, 404
scores corresponding, 404
area under standard normal curve using, 386–87
binomcdf command, 415
binomial probabilities using, 358
boxplots using, 183
chi-square tests using, 671
coefficient of determination using, 238
combinations using, 308, 314
confidence intervals using, 758
for population mean, 481
for population mean where population standard deviation is known, 475
for population mean where population standard deviation is unknown, 487
for population proportion, 496
for population standard deviation, 502
correlation coefficient using, 208
difference between two population proportions using, 621
difference between two population standard deviations using, 628, 631
factorials using, 314
goodness-of-fit test, 656
histograms using, 101
in hypothesis testing
about population mean assuming known population standard deviation, 540
about population mean with unknown population standard deviation, 545, 552
about population proportion, 560
about population standard deviation, 566
invT feature, 479
least-squares regression line using, 214, 223

TI-83/84 Plus graphing calculator (*Continued*)
  least-squares regression model using, 745–46, 752
  mean and median on, 142
  mean and standard deviation using
    approximation, 164
    from grouped data, 166
  normal probability plot using, 411
  one-way ANOVA using, 687–88, 694
  permutations using, 305–6, 314
  Poisson probabilities using, 365
  prediction intervals using, 758
  quartiles using, 170
  residual plots using, 238
  scatter diagrams using, 208
  simulation using, 272
  standard deviation of discrete random variable
    using, 339, 342
  standard normal distribution using, 396
  two-sample *t*-tests using
    dependent sampling, 595
    independent sampling, 607–8
  variance using, 149
  z-score from a specified area to the left using, 390
Time-series graphs, 104–5
  technology to draw, 110
t-interval, 479
Tornadoes, 126–27
Total deviation, 224–25
Total sum of squares (SS (Total)), 684
Transformations, linear, 142
Treatment, 46
Tree diagram, 264
Trials, 343, 412
Trimmed mean, 142
t-statistic, 478–79, 767, 769
  interpretation of, 476
  marginality of, 768
  pooled, 602–3
  two-sample, 601–3, 607–8
  Welch's approximate, 596
Tudor, Abby, 421–23
Tufte, Edward, 115
Tukey, John, 176
Tukey's test, 694–703
  cautions regarding, 699
  critical value for, 695–96
    table of, A19–A22
  goal of, 694
  for one-way ANOVA, 694–703
  for randomized complete block design, 708–9, 713
  steps in performing, 696–98
  test statistic for, 695
  for two-way ANOVA, 722–23, 728
  using technology, 698–99, 703, 708–9, 713
Twain, Mark, 221
2 × 2 factorial design, 714, 721–22
2 × 3 factorial design, 715

Two-tailed tests, 516, 527, 528–29, 530, 532–33, 542,
  555–56, 571
  of difference between two means, 585
  of difference between two population
    proportions, 610, 616
  of difference between two population standard
    deviations, 625
  of difference of two means: independent
    samples, 597
  in least-squares regression model, 742–43
  about population proportion, 555–56
Two-way ANOVA, 713–28
  crossed factors in, 715
  decision rule for, 717
  designs of, analyzing, 714–19
  hypothesis testing using, 717–19
  interaction effect in, 715–16
  interaction plots in, 719–22, 728
  main effects in, 715–16, 728
  requirements for, 717
  Tukey's test for, 722–23, 728
  using technology, 720, 727–28
Two-way table. *See* Contingency (two-way) table(s)
Type I error, 518–20, 525, 600
  in ANOVA, 679–80
  probability of, 519–20, 525
Type II error, 518–20, 569–72
  computing, 570–72
  probability of, 519–20, 569–72
  in Tukey's test, 699

U

Undercoverage, 38–39
Unexplained deviation, 224–25
Uniform density function, 375
Uniform probability distribution, 92, 372, 373–75
  definition of, 373
Unimodal instruction, 605
United States Census, 19–20
Univariate data, 192
Unusual events, 260–61
Upper class limit, 84

V

Validity, 11
Value, expected, 336–37
Variability, 157–58
  between-sample, 683
  within-sample, 683
Variable(s), 7–9. *See also* Random variable(s)
  associated, 194, 198, 201
  column, 239, 277
  data vs., 9
  defined, 7
  dependent (response), 193–94
  discrete vs. continuous, 8–9
  dummy (indicator), 778

explanatory, 16, 46
independent (explanatory or predictor),
  193–94, 766–67
level of measurement of, 10–11
linear relation between two, determining, 200
lurking, 4, 17, 200–201, 244, 245
marginal distribution of, 239–40
model class of, 166
multicollinearity among, 759–60, 768–69
relation between two. *See* Relation between two
  variables
response, 16, 46, 47
row, 239, 277
Variance, 144–48, 149, 159
  constant error, 228–29
  of discrete random variables, 338–39
  from grouped data, 162–64
  population, 145–46, 162
  of residuals, 228–29
  sample, 144, 146–48, 162
  technology to determine, 149, 159
Variation, coefficient of, 158
Venn diagram, 273, 274, 276, 279
VINDEX essay, 190–91
Visual Display of Quantitative Information, The
  (Tufte), 115
Voluntary response samples, 34
Vos Savant, Marilyn, 300–301

W

Wasserman, Steven, 549
Weighted mean, 161–62
Welch, Bernard Lewis, 596
Welch's approximate *t*, 596
Whiskers, 177
Wholly Significant Difference Test.
  See Tukey's test
Wiles, Andrew, 265
Within-sample variability, 683
Wording of questions, 40
Wunderlich, Carl Reinhold August, 548

Y

Yakovlena, Vera, 296
Year, sidereal, 235, 751
y-intercept, 214–16

Z

Z-interval, 463
z-score, 167–68, 478
  area under normal curve using, 379–80
  comparing, 167–68
  expected, 405–7, 408
  for given area under standard normal probability
    distribution, 389–93
  population, 167
  sample, 167